To mother dear
with loads of
love from

Julie

Christmas
1935

SPRING CAME ON FOREVER

By BESS STREETER ALDRICH

SPRING CAME ON FOREVER

by

Bess Streeter Aldrich

D. APPLETON=CENTURY COMPANY
Incorporated

NEW YORK   1935   LONDON

The Author and her Publisher wish to acknowledge the courtesy
of Mrs. Vachel Lindsay and The Macmillan Company in per-
mitting the reprinting of lines from "The Chinese Nightingale,"
from the volume entitled *The Chinese Nightingale and Other
Poems,* by Vachel Lindsay. and the use of the line, "Spring
Came On Forever," as the title for this novel.

SPRING CAME ON FOREVER

"Years on years I but half-remember . . .
Man is a torch, then ashes soon,
May and June, then dead December,
Dead December, then again June.
Who shall end my dream's confusion?
Life is a loom, weaving illusion. . .

One thing, I remember:
Spring came on forever,
Spring came on forever,"
Said the Chinese nightingale.

VACHEL LINDSAY

CHAPTER I

IN the telling of a story the narrator takes a bit from life as definitely and completely as one would cut out a paper doll, trimming away all of the flimsy sheet excepting the figure. A section of real life is not so detached and finished, for the causes and consequences of it reach backward and forward and across the world. For that reason no mere story can ever be complete, no family history contain a beginning or an end.

This is the story of two midwestern families and the strange way in which their paths crossed. It begins in Illinois in the year 1866, and ends in Nebraska in the present one, severed from all that went before and all that will continue beyond—a thing of incompleteness.

Matthias Meier was twenty-one in that year of 1866, tall and stalwart of form, with only a healed red furrow across his upper left arm to show for the last day's fighting of his Illinois regiment.

We find him, now, sitting on a high stool before a sloping desk in the office of his uncle. Office, it may have been called, but the word was something of a misnomer, for it was no separate room, merely the end of a dingy salesroom in connection with the foundry of which his relative was sole owner.

The whole place gave an impression of scowling blackness. Iron coffee-pots, flat-irons, long-legged frying-pans and short-handled spiders occupied several shelves; and the larger utensils, huge kettles and boilers, stood on the floor in disarray, with plowshares shouldering them, as well as rough kegs containing nails of various sizes. At the opposite side of the long room, through an opening, one could see into the blacksmith shop with its anvil and multitudinous horseshoes hanging about on spikes as though this were the luckiest place in all Illinois. Iron was everywhere. Iron was king. One felt there was no other metal or substance in the world.

Matthias, now, was going over an old ledger in which accounts had been kept for a dozen years, and not very accurately either, he was deciding. A master-hand at the molding, his uncle was less punctilious about records of purchases and sales than his more mathematical-minded nephew.

Late morning sunshine filtering through a spattered and cobwebby window fell across the yellow pages of the book.

It was March, and apparently it was going to be an advanced one. The maples were feeling the push of the sap against the dark of their bodies. The hickory and oaks of the virgin timber-land not far away were vaguely responding to the stir of life. In the pulpiness of the bog the trailing arbutus would soon be showing its mauve-colored face,—on the hillside a thousand lavender crocuses spring forth to the call of the sun.

If Matthias Meier, too, vaguely felt the call and the push of the springtime, he was quite unaware of it, and merely checked and figured in the thumb-blackened and well-worn pages of the yellow book.

Up to this time, the room had been quiet save for the bumbling of a single advance guard of bottle-green flies and the sound of some one cutting timber far away. But into the stillness now came the creaking sound of wheels in the yard, the pull of horses' feet from the stickiness of mud and the lusty "whoa" of an unseen driver.

Matthias uncoiled his long legs from their crowded posture under the high table and swung himself off the stool. He even walked over to the opened door, although it went through his mind at the time that it was rather an undignified procedure to hurry out as though customers were so few and far between that they needed a committee of welcome.

A large and sandy-bearded man was swinging himself over the lumber-wagon's wheel preparatory to entering. But it was not at the man Matthias looked. For who, indeed, would look elsewhere with such a flower-like face before one as that of the girl in the green silk bonnet? Her full lips were rosy pink, and in their velvet blueness her wide eyes were like cornflowers. The braid of her soft hair, wound round her head and showing just at the edge of the bonnet, was the color of cornsilk before the summer sun has seared it.

Not that Matthias had time or inclination for any poetic rhapsodies. He merely took in the composite whole with a sensing of the girl's dainty perfection, and the fleeting thought that here was a little Dresden shepherdess.

The girl, in turn, may have been not unpleased at the appearance of the young foundryman, for Matthias was strong-featured and very good to look upon. But so intent was he just now upon the loveliness of the girl that he found himself staring a little stupidly at the man coming toward him.

"Good-morning to you, sir."

"*Guten morgen.*"

When he heard the German tongue, Matthias, too, turned to the language of his ancestors for, although English schooled, he could speak it readily. So in the German he asked politely: "What can I do for you?"

"I'm Wilhelm Stoltz," the man answered much more loudly than the short distance between the two demanded. "I want to look at the large kettles."

"Certainly. I'll be glad to show you." Matthias hesitated, and looked toward the pretty occupant of the wagon sitting rather like a little queen on her high and homely throne. "Perhaps the young lady would like to come and see them, too."

She smiled. "I can give help, Father,"—this, too, in the German tongue,—and began gathering her voluminous skirts in a little mittened hand.

"*Nein,*" the father said brusquely. "It does not take two."

Matthias winced at the domineering tone and felt an embarrassment for the girl who in spite of her youth was apparently no child. So it was with relief and perhaps something more which he had not then analyzed that he heard the man call back over a huge shoulder: "Come, then, if you must." But even so, the father stomped his way on down a path toward the first of the pits, leaving the girl to climb over the high wheel as best she might.

At once Matthias sprang to the wagon and gave her his hand. So daintily small was she that a heady feeling of the strength of his masculinity surged over him as he assisted her to alight in a billowing of skirts.

"It is a nice day," he said a bit inanely in the German.

She nodded gayly: "Meadow larks are singing, and I smell spring."

Quite true. He noticed it for the first time. Meadowlarks *were* singing. You *could* smell spring.

He walked behind her into the dingy room, noting the pretty way she carried her shoulders and held her head. A patrician-looking little thing, not solid and big-boned like so many of the German girls thereabout.

Inside, the two customers moved among the pots and kettles, the nails and plowshares, the man stomping about noisily as though he would tell the business world that no one could pull wool over his eyes, the girl daintily holding back the dark cloth of her skirts and the wide fringe of her flowing shawl.

Each time the man asked the prices in the German tongue and was answered in kind by Matthias, he blustered: "Too much," or "The price . . . it is crazy," until Matthias heartily disliked him, so that if it had not been for the girl he would no doubt have lost a sale by some ill-advised retort.

He could read in the girl's heightened color her embarrassment, and so did his best to make her feel at ease. Once while the blustering parent was squeaking in his cowhide boots at the end of the long room, Matthias pointed out to her a special kettle. "This one I made

5

myself," he said to her very low. "Mostly my uncle does the kettle molding."

The kettle was huge and faultless in its rounded symmetry. Matthias had been painstaking to make the wooden pattern absolutely right,—the inside mold called the core and the outside one called the jacket,—had poured molten metal carefully between them and covered the whole thoroughly with sand to keep every particle of air from it while it cooled.

"It is perfect." She glanced up shyly.

Vollkommen, was it? Matthias, looking down on her daintiness, thought she, too, was perfect. "I wish then, that this should be the one you choose. A perfect kettle for . . ." He wanted to say "a perfect little lady," but that would have been too bold, so he finished "for you." But, after all, he knew the words were synonymous.

She looked up again through long lashes. But this time a little twinkle invaded the blueness that lay behind them and a smile just faintly curled at the edge of her lips: "Do not, then, say to him that this is the one to buy," she suggested demurely.

And Matthias, sharing her little secret of filial disloyalty, grinned sympathetically and said: "That I will not."

"How much is this one? . . . and this? . . . and this?" Wilhelm Stoltz was asking.

And then Matthias Meier did a foolish and unaccountable thing. He priced the kettle which was of his own molding at a lower figure than his uncle had put upon it.

Stoltz looked them all over again, craftily, suspiciously,

thumping their sides for the answering sound of the metal, and then said suddenly and loudly, as though Matthias might discover his mistake: "This one I take."

Matthias looked quickly at the girl and she gave him the ghost of a swiftly mischievous and understanding smile, so that he felt the same headiness of spirit and body which he had experienced before. For with no words she was saying: "I am glad it is your kettle." And Matthias was saying: "I made it for you before I had ever seen you." The messages were as plain as spoken language. No one knows how it can be transmitted,—this Esperanto of Youth. It just is so.

Wilhelm Stoltz took out a leather pouch, counted out the money into the palm of Matthias' hand, lifted the huge iron kettle as though he must get away with his bargain before any attempt to rectify a possible mistake had been made, and said loudly: "Come now, Amalia, we must go." He pronounced it A-moll-ea in the German way.

Coughing and wheezing and blustering, he stalked ahead of the two young people out to the wagon. And Matthias, heady and bold, was saying: "Your name, then, is Amalia?" He, too, pronounced it Amollea, letting his voice linger over the liquid syllables.

"Yes."

"It's . . . like . . . like a bit of music."

And when she smiled up at that, he asked quickly while there was time: "Where do you live?"

"Over the Plum Creek road way . . . on the far side of the Big Woods. But . . ."

But what, Amalia? Say it now before you have taken

7

away with you that which you should not accept. Or have left behind you that which you should not give.

But Amalia did not say it. And when Matthias turned back into the dullness of the room magic gifts had been exchanged.

And so—such is life—had Wilhelm Stoltz driven up to Peter McClure's hardware store, or sent to Chicago, or even to Springfield for an iron kettle, or, for that matter, had Amalia but finished her sentence, the history of future lives and of a state might have been different. Some call it Providence, others Fate. But, Providence or Fate, "life is a loom weaving illusion."

As it was, Matthias stood looking a little bewildered now at the remaining kettles and the plowshares and the spiders, as ugly as ever, but somehow different. How queer that into so gloomy a place should have come something so shining-winged! He set himself again to the task of the book-work and, although the same sand-colored pages of a half-hour before confronted him, they were now strangely illustrated with shadowy half-pictures of blue eyes and rosy lips and hair the color of cornsilks before the summer sun has seared it.

After a time his uncle came in, a quick-moving little man with a bushy graying beard. "Any one here?"

"The Stoltzes . . . a man and daughter." Matthias realized that he was making the simple statement with a certain degree of consciousness.

"Hm! Wilhelm Stoltz, that would be! Up the Plum Creek way . . . one of the several Lutheran families scattered about."

Even now "up Plum Creek way," Amalia and her

father in the high wagon were lumbering along toward their farm which was the first one just out of the Big Woods on the timber road.

The journey had taken much of the afternoon, for it lay over prairie and creek-beds, through muddy roads and timber-land, and the horses which they drove were heavy brood mares, their legs large and clumsy and shaggy with hair.

The two said little as they rode. Sometimes the father made a gruff comment on the stickiness of the mud, the amount of the last rainfall, or the slowness of the horses. Always it pertained to the material world and especially that part of it which lay close at hand. And always when he spoke Amalia agreed with him. For adverse opinions from his daughter or any other human were not welcomed. So, riding beside the bulky form of her father, Amalia lived in her own world, not always the material one and most definitely not that part of it which was close at hand.

Once she volunteered: "The young man . . . he was pleasant."

Her father grunted and said gruffly: "You will do well not to let your thoughts linger on strange young men." Immediately after which he turned toward her so abruptly that she jumped from the sheer fright that, having done this very thing, her thoughts were betraying her.

"You are not doing so?"

"*Nein,*" Amalia said demurely.

But thoughts are acrobats, agile and quite often untrustworthy. So now, with impish disregard of the command, they hopped about quite easily. They asked Amalia innocently why the nice young man wanted to know where she lived. They suggested with subtle art the possibility that he would try to find out. And then when the gruff person at her side questioned their activities they urged her quickly to answer *"Nein."*

It was only in the late afternoon when the heavy horses turned into the barnyard of the Stoltz farm, that the exigency of a quick change of dress, the gathering of the eggs, and the planning of the supper brought all the vagrant thoughts into subjection and made them subservient to matters more practical, that Amalia ceased dwelling on the day's experience.

The Stoltz farm-house was modest but as neat and shining as white paint and green blinds could make it. There were no pigs or chickens boldly running about as there were at many of the neighbors'. Pigs were in their pens and chickens in their yards, both conditions of which were made possible by fences formed of small hickory posts for the pigs and of tall willow saplings set close together for the chickens. That the fence of the chicken yard was now putting forth faint green shoots did not detract from its utility. On a sloping cellar door, scrubbed like a bake-board, sat the milk crocks sweetening in the sunshine. Currant bushes and gooseberry bushes nearby, looking ready to burst their tightly closed buds, held countless freshly washed dish-towels. Lilac bushes which were beginning to feel the stir of sap were near the front door, and a rose vine, brown yet from the winter's sleep, trailed over the doorway.

Amalia coming into the kitchen door now, sighed that there were to be changes so soon. Inside the house, thinking of those changes, she looked about her as with the eye of a stranger. She saw the shining blackness of the cook-stove (the neighbor Kratzes still cooked on an open fire), the scrubbed table with its checkered cloth, the tin brush-and-comb holder on the wall with the mirror above, the clean wooden pail of water with its gourd dipper on the shelf, the rag rugs—Oh, it was a pleasant house. The cellar still held many *schinken* from the butchering, stone jars of *äpfel-butter* and *pflaumen-butter*. No old housewife—not even Mrs. Kratz or Mrs. Rhodenbach—had put by more food last fall than she.

There was soon supper. She and her father and her brother Fritz, fifteen years old, sat down together to the *met-wurst* and the *kartoffel pfannkuchen*. They were Fritz's favorites,—those pork-sausages and potato-pancakes.

Wilhelm Stoltz spoke very little while attending to the primary object of eating. When he did it was about the stock, the shoeing of a horse, and the assignment of Fritz's work for the morrow. The purchase of the iron kettle, too, came in for some explanation to Fritz,—the bargain he had made and the fact that the young man must have made a mistake in the price.

This set all the little acrobatic thoughts somersaulting again in Amalia's pretty head. And, later, if they mischievously put on their tumbling act several times during the ensuing week, who was there to say the performance in that year of 1866 could not be transmitted through Youth's own particular short waves down through the damp, dark timber road and across the prairie?

Spring Came On Forever

For on Sunday, Matthias Meier, with clean-shaven face and in his best suit, mounted his uncle's saddle-horse, Trixie, and turned her head toward Plum Creek and the Big Woods.

CHAPTER II

TO Matthias Meier the ride to the Stoltz farm that Sunday was a long one, but pleasant. The road lay through the straggling town, over the river bridge under which the dark waters of the recently melted snows foamed and charged in wrath at the sturdiness of the timbers, on across the level lands where mud and matted grasses clutched but could not hold Trixie's flying hoofs, and then into the darkness of the Big Woods where it wound sinuously among the maples and oaks and hazelnut underbrush, a leaf-soaked and twig-covered track just wide enough for a single wagon, so that one must turn into the spaces between stumps when meeting another.

As he rode, Matthias tried to analyze what peculiar force in his nature had summoned him on this unbidden call,—what emotional upheaval had urged him to plan this trip all week. He was not accustomed to follow up all his uncle's customers, he admitted, and grinned to himself at the thought.

For the first half of the trip through river bottoms, creek-beds, and on open trails, he rode enthusiastically toward his destination. About the third quarter, on more distant meadow land, he grew a bit apprehensive over his impulsive journey. In the last quarter through the Big Woods, his fervor collapsed so perceptibly that he called himself all kinds of a fool for coming. But it was noticeable that he held doggedly to his way.

At a weather-beaten cabin in a clearing he inquired of a young boy how far it was to the Stoltz farm and was told he was nearly there, that he would find it lying just beyond the third bend of the road and that he would know it from the red barn standing where the timber began to thin for the open land. He thanked the voluble informer and rode on slowly, entirely apprehensive now because of the bold thing he was doing.

The woods were thinning,—the maples and the oaks and the walnuts were not quite so close together,—not quite so thick now, the bare hazel-brush and the sumac. He rounded a clump of undergrowth that tangled with a thicket of wild plum trees, and there in a clearing not twenty feet away was the girl herself. Evidently she had heard the sound of Trixie's padding hoofs for she stood facing the trail, her hand at her throat in an attitude of startled expectancy. To-day she was bareheaded, and the sun shining into the clearing turned the braided coronet of her light yellow hair into a pale golden wreath.

She came forward hesitatingly when Matthias slipped off his horse.

"*Guten nach mittag,*" she said shyly,—and then by way of explaining her presence added, as always, in the German: "I was searching for signs of the first blue-bells."

Bridle-rein over his arm and hat off, Matthias approached and held out his hand.

Even while she put her own little hard hand into it, she flushed and said: "You should not be here."

"Why?" Now that he was here and safely over breaking the ice of the meeting, he felt no fear, but a heady boldness instead.

She raised her eyes to his slowly, and Matthias' heart beat quickly at seeing again the deep blueness of them. "Because . . . I should have told you when you asked where I lived . . . but, of course, I could not know by the asking you meant to come."

Then why were you down in the timber road, watching, Amalia?

Her hand still held in his, Matthias asked: "What is it you meant to have told me . . . Amalia?"

She dropped her eyes away from Matthias' searching ones.

"That I am betrothed." And with that Amalia had completed the unfinished sentence.

"You are betrothed?" . . . he repeated slowly. "I . . . I had not thought of that. I have thought of many things . . . but never that. All week I thought only of you . . . and that I would come to-day."

"I, too, shall be truthful now. Something . . . also . . . some queer thing," she spoke shyly in spite of her honesty, "made me wonder if you might."

"If you are . . . as you say, betrothed, . . who . . . who is he?"

"An old friend of my father's. Oh, not old . . ." she added apologetically, "at least not as old as my father. He is a good man. My father and my brother Fritz are very fond of him. My mother is not living."

"I'm sorry . . . perhaps if your mother . . ."

"I should not be here talking to you," she said, when he seemed not intending to finish his thought. "I don't know why I came. It is not right. I have been promised since I was sixteen. I shall be eighteen soon."

But the hand of Amalia which had been promised for nearly two years still lay trembling in the hand of Matthias Meier. As though just now discovering that member's perfidy, she withdrew it suddenly.

"Where is he now?" Matthias asked quietly.

"Gone with the men to the Nebraska Territory to find suitable holdings for some of our church people. We are to move as soon as they return for us. It is said that sometime before many years it may be a state, too, even as Illinois."

"Yes, I suppose so." He felt definitely disappointed, vaguely sad that this lovely girl of whom he had thought all week was betrothed. A door that had so recently opened a bit seemed suddenly shut in his face.

"You have come a long way. Perhaps you would like to sit down awhile . . ." she smiled, "beside your kettle."

And almost for the first time Matthias gave heed to the fact that the kettle which he had fashioned with such meticulous care hung on three hickory stakes in the clearing with a mound of ashes underneath.

"Already you have used it?"

"Yes . . . we made the soap, using all of our grease from the butchering so we will have a plentiful supply for the long journey and a whole year after."

But the words recalled this disquieting thing he had heard of her betrothal and going away, and he frowned as he seated himself beside her on a log near the kettle.

"But this man . . . you do not love him?" It was as much a statement as a question. She was a mere child and Matthias felt very old.

Amalia pondered. "I respect him . . . and my father says that is the same thing."

"I don't agree with him," Matthias contended boldly, and in the impulsiveness of youth stood up. "Where is your father? I would like to see him."

But Amalia, alarmed, was saying: "Do not go to the house to see him, I beg of you. I am sorry not to be more hospitable. You saw how domineering he was." *Herrscht* was the word she used. "He should not know you are here. He would only anger and hurt you. Always after Sunday dinner he sleeps. Indeed . . ." and the gay little smile which had so captivated Matthias was there again for a flashing moment; "he begins it in the church service."

Matthias laughed at that and sat down again beside her. "What causes you to think of going to that troubled territory?"

"It is no longer troubled. The Pawnees have long been quieted, and my father thinks all is well now to settle there. We are of the Lutheran faith and here our farms are scattered. My father says that by moving there and keeping together we can retain our customs and our language and our church relations."

"But why . . . ?" Matthias wanted to know. "What advantage is there in the people of one church being so close? I can see how the Pilgrims of England—persecuted as they were— But you're not."

"My father says none but the followers of Luther are right, and it is not well to mingle so much with others. Already two of the young people have married out of the church."

If Matthias held his own opinion on the iniquitous depths of that sin, he did not say so. Indeed, when she was speaking so earnestly he found himself far more interested in watching her long lashes sweep a soft cheek.

"Our farm is already sold to the English Dunbar family. All things are as near ready to go as is possible . . . the wagons are kept always in repair—and the harnesses. Already many barrels are packed. When the men arrive, all the families need is a short time for the last of the baking and the loading of the wagons, and the colony can start. My father says it is like the German army, each knowing his part and obeying orders instantly."

For some time sitting there on the sunken log in the clearing the girl told of the plans for the coming journey. Matthias, listening and commenting, was disturbed at his own disturbance over the moving. Once he ventured again: "This man . . . if you do not love him . . . ?"

She glanced away. "I am promised," she said simply.

Very soon, in spite of nature's heralding of the spring, it grew too cool, and when the sun dipped behind the top of the timber, the chilliness of the air made the girl suddenly shiver.

"You must go in," Matthias was all solicitude, but found himself hinting broadly: "You do not wish me to go?"

"*Nein*. It would be too hard to explain to my father. He could not understand that you were—" she put out her hand, "a new friend."

At that, Matthias forgot the coming journey and the faith of Martin Luther, the domineering father and the affianced who was far off beyond the Big Muddy.

"Meet me here again next Sunday afternoon, Amalia. You'll come? It couldn't be otherwise."

When she hesitated, he said, to test her: "Or I shall come boldly to the house to call on my new friend."

"I'll come," she turned away, anxious and hurried now that she had been here such a long time. "But it will be wrong," she called over her shoulder.

"And beautiful," Matthias grinned back at her impudently so that she, too, was smiling a bit mischievously when she went away.

CHAPTER III

ALL week Amalia went about her housework. She cooked and cleaned and scrubbed in her energetic and immaculate way. Everything was as it had been,— save one. And all week Matthias sold his uncle's iron wares, kept the books, and occasionally shod a horse at the blacksmith end of the shop. And everything was as it had been,—save one.

Sunday was milder. The Big Woods gave forth the pungent odor of bursting buds and warming leaf-mold. At the creek-bed fuzzy pussies scratched insistently inside the branches of the willows. Wild gray geese flew honking across the timber-land and disappeared in the distant north. Swallows darted high in their nuptial flight and a meadow-lark sat on a stake-and-rider fence and sang the prairie's love song to the spring.

Amalia had been in the clearing only a short time when Matthias came riding through the damp dark timber road and into the open. At the sight of the gallant figure that had scarce been out of her mind all week, she stopped, frightened at the import of the moment, her hand at her throat as though she must stifle the call of her heart to him.

With no word Matthias dismounted, threw Trixie's bridle-reins over a scrub oak and with open arms walked toward the girl.

With no word Amalia, trembling, waited for him to

come. It was not until his arms closed around her and he had kissed her—and even for a long moment afterward —that a word was spoken.

"I have thought of you every moment." His voice shook with emotion.

"And I of you."

"You must break your betrothal, Amalia."

"At this moment it is broken, Matthias."

"This . . ." said Matthias after a time, "is what love is."

"Yes," said Amalia, "I know now. All week I have known."

"And when the homesteaders go you will stay with me? My uncle is old. In time I shall be able to buy the foundry from him. It is not my choice of businesses. I have been restless in it, but with you to be there with me, I shall settle down and like it better."

"I will stay, Matthias. I fear for the trouble it will make, but I will stay."

"And you do not think it wicked, then, to marry outside the church?" he teased her. "Do I seem now such a heathen . . . such a monster?" But when he saw how troubled it made her, he drew her to him again with comforting words, calling her his *kleine taube*,—"little dove" in the English.

The afternoon slipped away as they talked of this new-old thing that had come to them.

"Spring! It seems that this spring belongs just to us, and to no other," Amalia said once.

"But they will keep coming, little dove. Think of it. They will *all* be ours. All our lives we'll live them over and over together . . . this same feel in the air . . . the odors of the woods . . . the wild geese honking . . ."

"Even when we grow very old . . ."

Matthias laughed at that. How could youth grow old? "I shall hold you close then, just as I do now, and say: 'It's spring again, Amalia! They keep coming.'"

"And I shall say: 'They will go on . . . forever . . . even though we grow old . . . and after.'"

But there were other things besides these sentimental generalities to discuss, so that they must put an end to their first rapturous moments, sit down on the log and speak of the seriousness of the future. Matthias would have gone immediately to the house but Amalia would not hear of it. "Not to-day—" she begged him. "It is so beautiful. For when that time comes, we shall have anger and harsh words. No, Matthias, give me my perfect day."

And because she would have it so, he did not go in to confront her father, but left her there in the clearing until he should come again.

On the next Sunday there came a dash of warm rain as he rode into the clearing, and at once he saw her in the doorway of the sheep-shelter, a hooded gossamer about her shoulders.

He had brought her a gift,—a little work-box covered with shells,—angel-wings and moon shells, Roman snails, and other fragile fan-like shells of a sea they had never seen. On the under side of the cover a mirror fitted into the blue silk lining and in the various compartments were a needle-ball and a pin-cushion and a tiny silver thimble.

Amalia, to whom gifts were rare, was quite beside herself with joy at the daintiness of the treasure. Almost were the strange queer shells symbolic to her of things to come,—unknown journeys with Matthias to far-off seas, hearing the sound of wind in whipping sails and the call of the gulls on the sand.

But when Matthias would have gone in to see her father, she put him off again. She had meant to break the news, she told him, but always when she was about to speak, her courage had failed her. If he would give her but another week, she would prepare him for the announcement which would so anger him. Of one thing she was certain, it must come first from her own lips.

But on the following Sunday when he arrived there was no question about Matthias interviewing the father this time, for Wilhelm Stoltz was away,—gone to one of the church friend's home many miles up the river. It gave Amalia a delicious sense of freedom so that she was as gay as a child.

She had a wonderful piece of news for him,—she had used the thimble and one of the needles. Already she had started a quilt,—the Tree of Life pattern,—*Baum des Lebens.* Even now two finished blocks were in the shell box.

"Ever since I was a tiny girl I have sewed," she said to him. "It comes very easy to me. Many times I have made things for my hope chest"—*hoffnung kiste,* she called it—"knowing I must some day wed but not knowing who the man would be. When I knew it was but my father's friend Herman . . ."

She sighed, so that Matthias' arms went around her

again and he drew her close. "But it will be no Herman now . . ." (*kleine taube*) . . . "little dove."

"No . . . never. And this is so different . . . to think of you as I sew."

But even while she clung to him she told him this: "I wake in the night and think of this which I am doing contrary to my father's wishes. I feel then that I am wicked . . . but when morning comes I know that it is not wicked at all . . . just happiness and right."

And when Matthias said nothing could come between them now, she confessed: "Of that I am sure . . . and yet I am sad to part from my young brother Fritz. That is my greatest sorrow. As for leaving our good people . . . they will all be angry and hurt . . ."

But Matthias turned that away with lover-like speed. "When they know how much we love each other . . . they will see that it could not be otherwise." Of such are the simple rules of youth.

"But my father has so often said only woe comes to those who marry outside the church."

"Love . . . our kind of love . . . is greater than the teachings of a single church."

And now that the afternoon was waning she was anxious and alert about her father's return.

"What was that, Matthias?" she would say, startled.

"Nothing . . . some little wild thing . . . a chipmunk or a squirrel."

And because of her constant watchfulness on this Sunday, Matthias was firm. "You shall cease your worries," calling her *liebes kind*. "It is not good to fear so. It shall not go on longer. Next Sunday I shall tell him,

24

and we will face the consequences. If he is too angry, I shall take you home with me on Trixie with no baggage. My aunt will take you in and we shall be married at once."

He kissed her again and again, held her close to him, could scarcely bear to leave her. Even when he had mounted Trixie and was riding into the timber road he turned back for the last sight of her.

She stood just in front of an alder thicket, and as he looked, she raised her hand high in farewell.

He carried that picture with him all the way home: Amalia, a little blue and pink and golden figure against the green of the new leaves, as though Spring herself had just stepped out of the alder thicket. His *kleine taube,*— little dove!

CHAPTER IV

THE week dragged for Matthias,—seven days that were weighted down with the iron of horseshoes and kettles, plowshares and skillets. The first part of it was all sunshine and mild showers, but on Thursday night a storm broke. The rains came in torrents. All day Friday they lashed and tore at the woods and the prairies. All night and all day Saturday and all that night they beat in a fierce onslaught. A part of the mill-dam went out and a weakened span of the river bridge could not stand the pounding of the flood waters. On Sunday morning the water was roaring and lashing through all the creek-beds and then spreading less turbulently over the valley, inundating all that which had been pasture lands.

Matthias made every attempt to make the trip to Amalia. All day he worked, hoping to find some means whereby he could get through. Many times he rode back and forth seeking some more narrow place where Trixie could make the crossing. But always it was too wide or too turbulent. He tried getting her into a flat boat but she reared and kicked and was completely beside herself with fear. He knew that even if he had been able to manage a boat through the roaring waters for himself the distance for walking was so great that it would have taken into the night to get there.

When he gave up the attempt, he stood for a long time on the bank as the water swept by. In a mental rage he watched a pigeon fly straight for the Big Woods community. How impotent was man. Only the birds could lift wings and soar high over the flood waters. Amalia was waiting for him over there but he was helpless in the face of nature. A winged thing could fly to its mate. Only man and the beasts must cling to the earth and crawl.

But on the next Sunday he could get through. The river was still high and the creek-beds running full, but man's ingenuity had made the river passable with a temporarily trussed-up bridge span.

He took a lantern with him for he knew he might be well into the night getting back. This was the day he was to confront Amalia's father, possibly the day he was to bring her home with him. He had a feeling that there would be a scene, ending, no doubt, in his taking Amalia away without baggage. If it came to that, he was prepared to do so.

Two weeks not to have seen her! The time had been interminable. But he was on his way at last even though the going was formidable. Sometimes Trixie sank in mud so deep she nearly floundered. Sometimes he had to dismount to clear fallen branches away from the wet timber road. Then he would mount and ride on with the air of a conqueror glorying in this journey which was to end by his claiming that which was his own,—the girl who had been his from the moment he first saw her. Occasionally he felt a bit of the winner's sympathy for his fallen adversary. But to have pledged a little sixteen-year-old girl to a mere family friend was unthinkable. Yes, if there was to be a scene, let it come to-day.

These terse thoughts went through his mind like so many pigeons going over, homing always to Amalia. He tied his horse in the dripping woods. This was the end of secretiveness,—on that he was determined.

She was not in the clearing. That would be on account of the dampness. He strode over to the sheep-shed. She might be there hiding mischievously from him. But she was not at that trysting place either. Might she be ill?

With that disquieting thought he started walking over toward the road that led to the house. Suddenly he stopped short. There was no kettle hanging there in the clearing,—only the tipped-over tripod of hickory sticks and the sodden black ashes of the last fire. Something seized him,—a premonition of impending disaster, so that he started on a lope toward the home buildings. A tow-headed young boy, the same who had directed him on his first visit, was coming toward him also with some haste. They met almost at the edge of the timber where the plowed land began.

"You didn't come last Sunday," the boy said in English. "I about give you up to-day, too . . . was just comin' to the clearin' once more. She said to give you this."

And he thrust into Matthias' hands a note directed in the precise and shaded letters of the German script.

As Matthias took the letter and tore hastily into it, the boy stepped away and began pulling bits of bark from the shaggy coat of a soft maple.

Even before he had read a word, Matthias knew it contained nothing but disaster. For a few moments, then, he stood looking at the neat script, frozen to immobility, too fearful of the contents to read.

To speak the language was easy enough,—he had heard it on all sides from boyhood. But the reading was more difficult for he had been to English schools, even to the Princeville Academy for a short time, and the writing of the language had been confined to early copy-book work. So it seemed that he must translate into English as he read.

In his agitation some peculiar instinctive knowledge of what had happened helped him to make the translation. By a labored reading, skipping some of the phrases, he got the gist of it:

> This is news . . . convey to you . . . wagons of church people ready now . . . make long journey . . . new land. Men did not return . . . sent word by letter . . . meet them Nebraska City, Nebraska Territory. There they await us . . . show way to new lands. It is there in Nebraska City I marry.

And something more at the last pertaining to God and forgiveness for which Matthias at that moment was neither interested nor caring.

The words were all swimming together and the earth was falling away from his feet. He felt giddily ill. The boy who had been watching him covertly came up importantly then and Matthias saw him as through a haze. "She said she wanted I should get this one to you, too."

The second note was neither precise nor neat. It was ink-blurred, hurriedly folded, almost it might have been tear stained. In a fever of anxiety to release himself from the shock of the stunning news of the first letter he tried to read it quickly.

In his haste the translation seemed to be:

Matthias, my cruel note under command my father was written. This one I send after. The wishes of my father . . . can no longer hold out. Many times myself I ask why we met when nothing could be. I better could have gone on not knowing you,—indeed, I had not been too unhappy.

One sentence stood out with grim sardonic insistence— "One must not marry outside the church."

Near the last there was a sentence over which he labored to get just what she meant: *"Manchmal sage Ich mir vielleicht ist es besser unsre liebe zu gedenken als es war im frühyahr."* And when he got it, he knew it was: "Sometimes I tell myself perhaps it is better to remember our love as it was in the springtime."

There was something, too, about the quilt blocks: "Unless I can be with you again, I shall never finish. The pieces will lie in my box. I think my heart lies there too."

Matthias looked up through the wavering tree trunks. Dimly he saw the boy walking away. He called to him and gave him a small coin. "Thanks for coming. What day . . ." his throat was so dry the words seemed to crackle ". . . did they go?"

"Two weeks come next Wednesday."

The Wednesday after the Sunday in which he had left her standing so lovely there, in the clearing. Involuntarily he turned his eyes toward the alder thicket not far distant. For a moment he could see her as plainly as though she were there in reality. Then the picture grew dim, and nothing remained but the green dripping boughs of the alders.

Mechanically he turned toward Trixie, stumbling blindly into the protruding roots of a tree stump. When he reached the mare he did not mount her but walked along with the bridle over his arm, taking the right trail only because Trixie led him into it. Occasionally she touched his shoulder with her cold soft nose.

The pungent odor of the loosened moist leaves under them came up to him with every step. A meadow-lark sang its liquid notes at the edge of the clearing. Gone. Amalia was gone,—into the great unsettled west,—to be married there. It was a nightmare from which he would soon waken. No, it was true,—the reality after a short sweet dream.

Shaken to the depths, his thoughts tumbled about uncertainly in a whirling world. One emotion after another went flooding through him as the creek waters had flooded the lowlands. A sickening sense of loss and disappointment. Astonishment,—he had never dreamed of any other turn of events than that the seekers for land would first return home as Amalia had said. Self-remorse that he had been so slow. Self-chastisement that he had not forced some means of crossing the river. And then violent anger at man's feeble efficiencies,—at a God who had sent the water to overflow, at the tyranny of the father, at the narrowness of the church, at the weakness of the girl.

His body seemed drained of blood so there was no strength left in him, and he threw himself down on a wet and matted bed of oak leaves where they had turned to brown pulp.

Over and over in his mind he relived the circumstances of their meeting: the love that seemed to spring between them from that very first day, the trysts in the woods, the softness of her lips and the feel of her body in his arms. His *kleine taube,* little dove.

All these weeks. And now he would not hold her in his arms in another week, nor in another month, nor a year, nor a decade, nor *ever.* Never! It rang in his mind like the brassy sound of a jangling bell. There was hollowness in the spring, mockery in the song of the meadow-lark. Life was empty, drained of its reason for being. He threw an arm across his eyes and turning his face down to the sodden earth, shed wild and angry tears.

For a long time he lay there in the midst of the fallen world in which disappointment and disillusion were the only factors. What matter now that the meadow-lark trilled the prairie's love song to the spring? Of what portent that the sun shone? That the sweet odors of the waxy white May flowers near by were heavy on the air? These were not of his man's mind. Over and over he lived the imaginary scenes of the journey upon which Amalia was being taken,—saw the covered wagons pulled through the stickiness of the mud with the father loudly chiding the lovely girl by his side,—visioned the arriving at the territorial town, the Herman of her betrothal meeting her, the marriage against which she was revolting. At that, in his sick imaginings, he felt himself snatching her away bodily from the outstretched arms of this strange man—

Suddenly a thought struck him with lightning-like effect. Immediately he sat up and brushed a hand across his eyes, a dozen things crowding his mind at once. The colonists were to meet the men in that far-off Nebraska City. Amalia couldn't be married until the wagons reached there. How long would it take them to make the trip? Four weeks, perhaps, if there were no delays. They had been gone twelve days.

The town lay hundreds of miles across the Illinois and Iowa plains on the Missouri River, a long, long journey. It had become a sort of gateway to the new country, the hub of the overland trails which stretched from it and on to the west beyond. It was the beginning of the young man's country, the young man's hope of wealth. Hundreds of them were seeking their fortune out there. Why not do so, too? What matter that his uncle expected him to stay and take over the business eventually? The Unknown Land was calling. This accounted for his restlessness, his vague irritation at everything about the little foundry. He, too, must answer the call.

If he could but get to this Nebraska City in some way before the wagons!

He read the note for the dozenth time. Amalia had told him the father's plans for her. Was it a veiled suggestion that he try to follow? To have said "Unless I can be with you again . . ." Did she hope? Did she have it in mind even as she wrote? Well, then, he would not fail her. He did not know just how or by what way, but he, too, would go. Perhaps by taking the river route he could arrive there ahead of the caravan. Then there

33

would be no marriage to a member of the colony. He would snatch her from them, carry her away.

A wild exuberance seized him. His grief passed into a sense of exaltation, as though the thing were already accomplished. He jumped to his feet, shook the soggy leaves and twigs from his clothes, mounted Trixie and was off, crashing through the narrow dark timber road.

CHAPTER V

TO the Lutheran homesteaders the journey out of Illinois and into the plains of Iowa had been a tedious and apparently endless trip. For weeks now they had lurched over trails which took them through prairie grass and sunflowers, down creek-beds and across gulleys, into tangled clumps of wild growth and past an occasional settlement. It had rained much of the time and the crude wagons drawn by stolid oxen and heavy-footed plow-horses jerked through thick black mud or jounced over the uneven dry ground until some of the women were ill from the torture of the constant shaking.

Day after day the prairie-schooners had crept on to the west,—a winding procession like so many tiny, gray-colored bugs following a twisting line on the wide expanse of a school-room map. The cracking of the blacksnakes, the stentorian calls of the drivers, the creaking of the wagons, were all the sounds heard as the caravan made slow and tortuous progress toward the ever-receding rim of the world.

Night after night they had formed in a wide circle around the fires, their cattle and horses corralled by this human perimeter, more safe from any potential marauder than if left outside of it. There was no danger from the redskins in Iowa, they felt,—but of Nebraska they were not certain. It had been only a few years since the alarm had been spread in the town of Omaha concerning the report of Indian outrages, and the militia had gone out to subdue the Pawnees at Battle Creek. No more Indian troubles had been known in the eastern third of the territory for a half-dozen years, but the men said no one could ever tell when it might break out again. On beyond there were tribes of them always ready to steal cattle and to commit various offenses, but it was scarcely to be supposed that they would attack so large a group.

Today, Amalia, riding beside her brother in one of their two wagons, was shaken almost to the point of illness, for never had the trail seemed so rough. Although the household things had been packed together as solidly as possible, sometimes when the horses forded a creek-bed or lumbered down a rough incline the chairs and walnut bureau knocked together, and the new soap-kettle with its perfect rounded bottom took to rocking back and forth perilously.

The menfolks had said they thought they must be getting near the Nishnabotna River region which lay only a few days' journey this side of the Missouri. All indications seemed to point that way. They were rather excited about a possible sight of the Big Muddy in a few days now.

But Amalia took no great interest in this news. She made no inquiry, commented on nothing,—merely clung to the seat of the lurching wagon and lived over again the days of her leaving,—days whose happenings would be forever burned in her memory.

She had been working on her *Baum des Lebens*—Tree of Life—quilt-block in her bedroom, had hidden it quickly as her father came to the door. She could still see him standing there, big and bustling, filling the doorway, dominating the scene, his sandy beard and thick mustaches almost bristling with importance.

"Well, Amalia, I have news."

"News?" she had said, her body going suddenly cold.

"Yah, the men do not wait to return. Instead they have sent word to us. They have found suitable lands many miles to the west of the town of Nebraska City. We are to go as soon as possible and meet them there in that territorial town."

Sitting here beside her brother now, on this endless, lurching journey, she could feel again the faintness stealing over her at his "We go now."

He had shouted it, excited because of the coming important event. "Fritz brings me the letter just now. You I tell first." He laughed at his joke: "You are the favored,—the one of all honored by me to know first."

"We go?" She had repeated it in a whisper.

"Yah! Fritz at once rides to the homes of our people. It is like the *Paulus Rewere* Fritz told us from school. To-day I give the command. Each knows his part. There shall be no delay. It is, as I have said, like an army under orders,—the army of the Lord. You know your part well. At once the extra baking and roasting of the meat. Then, even as these cool, the last of the packing. The sacks of oats and the seed corn at once Fritz loads in the second wagon. Myself I oversee all. Come Wednesday morning we start . . . Thursday at the latest. That day come the Dunbars to take over the house."

Riding silently by Fritz she was living it all over again,

37

trembling a little now even as she had trembled then. She had tried to tell him.

"Father, I must tell you at once. I do not go."

"Do not go?" The syllables had been lightning bolts.

"No . . . for I cannot now marry Herman Holmsdorfer."

"Have you lost your reason?"

"*Nein.*" At the dear thought of Matthias she had gained a bit of courage. "It is only that the young man at the foundry . . . you recall where we bought the kettle . . . ? Do not be angry, Father . . . he has been here several times since."

"Has he. . . ? He has . . . molested you?"

Amalia flinched again with pain at the memory of the evil thing her father had suggested. How could he have so translated a beautiful thing? How could there ever be evil when two people loved the way she and Matthias did?

"Father! He loves me . . . and I . . ."

"Go on . . . lest in my anger I strike you."

". . . I love him, too, Father . . . so much."

"*Du Narr!*" he had flung at her, calling his Amalia a fool for loving.

Lurching through the sodden wild grass of the Iowa prairie, she closed her eyes now as though she might forever shut out the period that followed, a time as of a great storm which lashed and beat with words, which closed over her in its fury of commands and threats, so that rather than drown in the beating stress of it she had promised obedience.

If only she had acquiesced for once and all at that

time, but she must do something which merely made matters much worse. On the evening before they were to leave she had rolled a few things into a little bundle, slipped out and started down the timber road toward Matthias so many miles away. At the sound of a horse's hoofs thudding behind her she had slipped into the underbrush at the side. But she had not been quick enough, for the lantern's light had focused itself upon her like an evil eye, and her father's cold voice had ordered her to come forth. Well, her spirit was crushed then. There was nothing more to do.

In two things only had she been deceitful,—in writing a second letter to Matthias after the dictated one, and in bringing the shell box with her. She had written her heart out to her lover in a note dictated by no one, and, when ordered to leave the dear gift behind for Mrs. Dunbar, she had pretended to do so. But even now it was in the wagon wrapped in many layers of unbleached muslin sheeting.

"What have you there?" her father had asked as she brought out the yellow-white bundle.

It was then that she had openly lied. "The freshest of the bread," she had answered. And if God would not forgive her, she did not even care.

For the first time after all the tragic days, riding now with Fritz, they spoke of the unhappy situation. The fifteen-year-old brother had something on his mind which had worried him for weeks. He could scarcely speak for the closing of his throat against the words. "I . . . myself I hate, Mollia. This you do not know before. It was I who told Father I saw you go down the timber road.

I did not then know the reason. I would not . . . would not . . . have harmed you."

"Do not worry. Nothing was your fault."

"Are you then so unhappy?"

"I can never know happiness again, Fritz."

The youth shook his head. "It is bad. You should not be unhappy. You are so pretty. We could have managed . . . Father and I. I am a man now."

It broke something in Amalia, some tight-bound band around her heart and throat which had not been loosed for days. She, who had been like a dead woman for all this time, wept wildly. Her young brother needing her,— her lover wanting her. The church pulling her one way, —Matthias another. Obedience asking one thing,—love another. Why did God bring such agony into the world? They taught you God was good. Was it true?

The wagon lurched on through the miles of sodden grass and sunflowers, thickets of sumac, wild plum and Indian currant.

After a while she calmed. "Fritz, I confide in you. You will never tell on Amalia?"

"*Nein,* sister."

"I am praying that I shall see him again," and did not notice that she was turning to the God about whom she had so recently questioned. "Is it too much to ask?"

"How can that be? So far away?"

"Always in the back of my mind, Fritz, I have it that he might come too, that getting my letter on Sunday after the Wednesday we left he would try to overtake us even though so far away and seek me out."

"It is a big thing to hope for."

"He was like that." She spoke proudly. "And his love was like that."

"I wish for you it could be." He glanced shyly sidewise at his sister.

"Perhaps I wish it so much that I make myself think it could be. Do you think it could come true, brother?"

"It could come true," he answered simply. And if he kept to himself the thought that it was not likely, that no one could ever overtake another in this vast ocean of prairie country, it was out of boyish sympathy for Mollia.

Ahead of them lumbered slowly as always through the sodden grass the other wagon belonging to their father and the two of the Schaffers.

Amalia turned now and glanced back across the wide spaces of the prairie. Behind them on the trail came the three wagons of the Kratzes, the two of the Rhodenbachs, the two of the Gebhardts,—four of them oxen-drawn, three with teams of horses. She knew the outfits, every horse and ox as well as their own. As always there were only these same plodding creatures,—no other.

CHAPTER VI

MATTHIAS MEIER was standing on the dock at St. Louis, surveying the scene before him with both impatience and satisfaction.

A wilderness of steamboats confronted his vision. Some were just leaving dock, the hoarse coughing of their exhaust-pipes making discordant notes. Others were coming in, the screeching of their whistles adding to the already deafening din. Small boats slipped in and out and between the larger freighters like busy waterbugs, twisting and turning with insect abandon. The air was charged with the electric-like energy of movement.

As he surveyed the vessel *Missouri Queen,* in which he was to make the rest of his trip up the Big Muddy, he had the complacent feeling of already having accomplished his objective.

He had arrived in St. Louis without mishap and the overland travelers would be moving much more slowly than he,—of that he was sure. The stolid oxen and heavy-footed horses pulling their clumsy prairie-schooners would do scarcely more than sixteen miles per day. There would be the long halts to make camp. Added to that would be the perverseness of the cattle the settlers were driving, their stubborn stops and futile meanderings off the trail. The rains, too, were delaying the caravan, no doubt. Black Illinois and Iowa mud would be an obstacle with which to reckon. Even at this date he would wager anything they had not gone one-third of the way across Iowa.

Rains would not delay the steamboat, he thought exultingly. She would slip up the Big Muddy and land him in Nebraska City before the colonists had arrived. To see Amalia face to face,—to confront her father,—nothing could then keep her from him. He thought rather shamefacedly of his agony there in the woods when all the time the remedy of it was possible.

He surveyed the vessel now with a boyish sense of proprietorship. Never having been on a Missouri River steamer before he eagerly took in the details of this one that was to house him for his long journey.

She was an attractive-looking craft, one deck above the other, the pilot-house and texas still above those. The whiteness of her newly applied coat of paint made her look very aristocratic riding there majestically on the slow rise and dip of the river, a little like the birthday cakes his aunt had made,—the main deck one layer, the boiler deck another, then the texas, containing the suite of rooms for the vessel's officer, topped by the pilot-house high over the river so that the height of the pilot might stress the clarity of his vision in seeing down into the sandy channels. High above all these towered the two lofty smokestacks carrying their sparks away from the roof and giving a strong draft to the furnace,—the candles on the cake, he thought, and grinned to himself at his whimsy.

Two cannon faced bankward in both directions, probably used now only for the purpose of firing salutes, but carrying withal that gesture of authority for any loitering miscreants.

43

She was about two hundred feet long and perhaps thirty-five wide, he decided. The bottom looked flat. His curiosity keen, he asked a Negro crew-hand near how much water she drew and was told with much grotesque flapping of large hands that she was "drawin' thirty inches now, boss," but would be down to fifty when the five hundred tons of cargo were all aboard.

That cargo was now being loaded,—great hogsheads of molasses, household goods, horses, wagons, mules, bales of hay and oats for the stock aboard, these latter supplies to be replenished in St. Joseph.

The vessel was propelled by a steam wheel,—two engines on the respective sides connecting directly with the wheel shaft. The last word in river craft, she had steam capstans in the forecastle and two huge spars for that possible occasion when she would have to be pushed over the tricky shifting sands of the river.

"Dis old ribber . . ." the deck-hand contributed, "she done be onreli'ble as a gal."

It set Matthias' mind to working again, momentarily drawn away by the reference to woman and her caprices. Where was Amalia now? Where the ox-train creeping over the plains? What if it were farther along than his judgment had told him? He grew anxious at the thought.

"There must be no delay," he said. "It's necessary that I get to Nebraska City as soon as possible."

At which the dark boy gave a white, flashing smile and threw out those expressive brown flappers. "Yas sah! Ah'll tell old Missie Ribber about dat."

And then they were leaving,—with the hoarse sound

of whistles, bells, chugging of wheels, Negroes' songs, laughter, sobbing, farewells. It gave Matthias a momentary pang in remembering his recent parting from the good uncle and aunt whose disappointment at his going had been so keen, the latter of whom had given him a needle-book, admonitions, a New Testament, mittens, advice and packages of quinine, calomel and catnip.

Leaning on the railing now, Matthias' blood beat warm within him. This was the real part of the journey. On to a new country,—a new start in life! On to Nebraska City in the raw new territory to be there when the Lutheran settlers came in! His enthusiasm over the future knew no bounds. Some of it was an impassioned emotion over the fact that he would still have Amalia, some the natural reactions after his grief and disappointment, some his forward-looking plans for a new business in a new country, and some of it was merely Hope of Youth.

The gang-plank was up now. They were really under way. Crowds thronged the rails. Almost all were calling out their last farewells. It seemed that Matthias was the only one without friends left behind. No, there was one other,—a sun-burned, leathery-looking sort of young fellow apparently about his own age. They were not far apart, and through some interchange of thought, perhaps, just now their eyes met in a quick appraising look. So friendly did each seem to find the other's expression that almost simultaneously they drew together at the rail.

"First trip?" the young chap asked Matthias.

"Yes. Yours?"

"Nope. First one was ten years ago when I was nine. Mother was a widder woman. Took us up the Muddy to find a home. Landed at Plattsmouth. Just three or four houses there then,—Mother knowed one of the families. Had to sleep on the floor with several other newcomers. Toward mornin' door opened and three old Injun bucks come in and stepped around all over us lookin' down in our faces. Had the hardest time gettin' Ma to stay and settle. She was all for leggin' it back to the steamer still tied up to the post and vamoosin' in favor of returnin' to civilization." And the young fellow laughed long and hilariously.

They told each other their names and destinations.

"Charlie Briggs."

"Matthias Meier."

"Plattsmouth in the main, but stoppin' in Nebraska City, claimin' my team I left there and pushin' on to Plattsmouth 'cross the prairie."

"Nebraska City is where I'm stopping for a time."

There was other information Matthias gleaned from his new-found friend that first afternoon of their acquaintance. Charlie Briggs had learned surveying. He had a homestead not far from Plattsmouth but mostly his younger brothers looked after it while he was off on all sorts of surveying, freighting and scouting missions.

"Volunteered a year ago last October to help put down the Sioux Injuns. Saw the Plum Creek massacre in Phelps County,—got home the very day last April year, the life o' the best president of these here United States got snuffed out."

Both were silent for a few moments,—that wordless reverence of all Union men for the fallen leader.

But not for long could Charlie Briggs remain silent.

He knew—and talked of—the great Platte Valley, had been up the Elkhorn, taken one trip to the Republican Valley. The Platte, he said, was flat and by nature tree-less. It had shallow, muddy water, swarms of mosquitoes and greenhead flies, prairie-dog towns and rattlesnakes,— the country of the Elkhorn was rich and fine with quite a bit of natural timber along the creeks and rivers. He explained the trails, north and south of the Platte River,— the one on the south with its converging trails like the tines of a fork starting from Independence, Missouri, St. Joseph, Leavenworth, and Nebraska City.

He had all the information of the new country at his tongue's end,—the difference of the soil in the Platte, the Elkhorn, the Republican, and the Loup Valleys. He knew where the native trees thrived—the cottonwood, and the oak, the elm and the ash. He knew the Indian tribes, their locale and their habits,—told Matthias about the old Pawnees that had once lived in the Valley of the Republican, the Kitkehahki tribe, and the chief who at the instigation of the young Lieutenant Pike had ordered down the Spanish flag flying in front of the lodge and raised the Stars and Stripes; related the story of the attack on the Arikara Indians by the soldiers from Fort Atkinson who were joined by the Sioux enemies of the Arikaras, how they overpowered them and feasted on the Indians' roasted corn while the peace treaty was being negotiated.

He had at his tongue's end the history of much of the

territory since the days of Coronado and his Spanish horsemen who had once set out to discover the mythical land of Quivira with its silver and precious stones and its king who slept under a great tree with golden bells on its branches, and found instead a vast plain with wild grass and Indians and queer cows with humped backs.

He enjoyed the telling of these tales and not in all the afternoon did he cease from imparting them. "Follow the prairie-dogs and Mormons and you'll find good land," was one of his sage pieces of wisdom.

It rather fascinated Matthias, the young man's ready knowledge of the territory since an earlier day,—and his own more recent adventures.

"Killed buffaloes? Lord, by the dozens. Pick on your animal, shoot, skin the carcass, let it freeze, chop off a hunk with your ax, throw it in a Dutch oven and a couple hours later get busy."

With no recess for his monologue, he went on:

"Buffalo used to be swimmin' along here where we are most any time. They tell a yarn about a greenhorn seein' 'em once for the first time when he was off in a yawl with a passel o' old timers. This fellow could handle a rope right smart, so they got him to set in the bow with a lasso and the first one they should wound could be roped. Some of the crew fired and wounded one but the greenie threw the rope over the head of one that wasn't hit. The crew shouted and backed oars to get old man Buffalo in deeper waters, but his feet touched bottom and he went up the bank with the boat tied to him and would have took it on a cruise all over the prairie if the stem of it hadn't been wrenched off and carried away by the mad animal. Fellows was left shipwrecked far away from their steamboat."

Matthias grinned his skepticism. "Funny how the fellow couldn't have let go of the rope."

Charlie Briggs spat over the railing: "Never spile a good story . . . and besides rope wa'n't so plentiful they wanted to give any away."

"Any hostility along here now from Indians?" Matthias had carried the question in his mind for some time.

"Naw. Only a few years ago they was barricadin' decks and state-rooms,—keepin' up day and night vigilance. Mostly now any hostilities is above the Niobrara from the Sioux tribes on farther west. Pawnees is friendly."

By dusk the boat tied up for the night,—navigation through the treacherous sand-bars was too precarious. If Matthias chafed at the lost hours, he had only to remember that the overland travelers were making camp too.

He and Charlie Briggs sat out on the deck talking until the mosquitoes drove them in, when they joined the other passengers in the too-crowded parlor-like cabin,—for the most part a motley crowd of fussy old ladies with poodle-dogs, anxious mothers with sleeping children, planters, giddy young girls, whole families moving to the new country, many unattached men. Immigration to the territories of Kansas and Nebraska was heavy.

There was some attempt at music that evening in the stuffy cabin,—a group of young fellows volunteering the tear-jerking "Thou Hast Learned to Love Another" and "Meet Me By Moonlight Alone" and the rendition of "Marching Through Georgia" with an aftermath of sullen remarks and a miniature reproduction of the late war on an after-deck.

Matthias' eyes swept the clusters of young girls coldly in spite of the evident admiration for his stalwart figure some of them plainly showed. Not one was little, dainty, fair-haired and blue-eyed. How could a man care for any other type?

In the days that followed, the boat proceeded very slowly on its up-river journey, gliding along smoothly enough over the turbid water. On the seventh day it put in at Weston for repairs. Matthias chafed over the delay until Charlie Briggs hinted broadly: "Ye'd think the' was some *reason* why ye *got* to git there."

Matthias, however, was non-committal. He would never wear his heart on his sleeve, particularly to one he had known no longer than young Briggs. But unlike as the two young men were, there were qualities which drew them together on the whole trip,—a common love of adventure and progress, sincerity of purpose, and some unnamed characteristic which each felt in the other,—a sort of gallant attitude toward humanity.

It was the morning of the ninth day out before they could proceed. The weather turned cold and disagreeable. There was no more promenading on the wind-swept deck by the giggling girls. There were various rumbles of dissatisfaction from the passengers, too, for eatables were getting low and fare was very poor.

They were in Kansas now. One side of the river bank was sheer steep bluffs, the other vast stretches of prairie, dotted with patches of timber. It all looked very wild.

On the eleventh day they docked at St. Joe. A child

died and was taken ashore by a hysterical family. A doctor was called hurriedly from the passengers to attend a woman in childbirth in one of the stuffy state-rooms. A young bride came aboard on her way to California, happy and blithesome, thinking that all California was a paradise. Life is a loom, weaving gay colors indiscriminately with those of somber hue.

And now the long journey was nearing its end. They would get to Brownville on the twelfth day,—the seat of the United States land office in which Daniel Freeman only a little over three years before had obtained the first homestead in the whole territory just after the midnight hour of the day in which the law went into effect,—the place from which the first territorial telegram had been sent six years before. From there to Nebraska City was but a short journey.

Charlie Briggs in his loquacious way was recounting much of this to Matthias now, recalling some of the anecdotes concerning slaves that had been brought through this section by way of the underground railroad.

The two young men were sitting on deck on the Nebraska side looking shoreward, Charlie Briggs pointing out some distant upstream spot.

"Along nigh about a dozen miles over there is the way John Brown brung slaves many's the time from Missouri by way of Falls City, Little Omaha, Camp Creek and Nebraska City to Tabor, Iowa. Can pint out the barn to ye in Falls City they hid in whenever . . ." His high-pitched voice broke off.

There had been a grinding noise, a quivering of the

boat's frame. With a sickening shiver, as a huge animal might shake in the steely mouth of a bear trap, the *Missouri Queen* stopped.

"Sufferin' snakes!" Charlie Briggs jumped up. "We're on a sand-bar."

CHAPTER VII

WHEN the *Missouri Queen* settled grumblingly into the treacherous sand which had shifted since the steamer's last trip, Matthias was a picture of surprise and irritation. "How long will it be?" he wanted to know at once.

Charlie Briggs who had known the river since his childhood days shrugged lean muscular shoulders. "Can't tell. She may be settin' pretty."

And settin' pretty she was.

Now came the work of the two huge spars which like the legs of some gigantic insect swung into position as though the white bug of a steamer intended to walk over the water and be at once on its way. But the bug stupidly lay thrashing impotent legs and could not move.

With every available means the crew and some of the passengers, including Matthias and Charlie Briggs, attempted to get her off. Men in small boats put out to shore and drove stakes into the bank, around which they would wrap the rope attached to the vessel, and pulling this with mighty tugs attempt to entice the vessel from her sandy bed. And every day she seemed lazily to settle farther into the shifting silt of the treacherous river.

Four full days went by filled with exertion on the part of the workers and with irritation over the delay by all hands.

Matthias was beside himself with anger and worry.

Under normal conditions he would have chafed at the delay. Now he was tormented with the thought that after all these days the ox train might have arrived at Nebraska City. Sometimes he tried to comfort himself with the thought that there would be much more delay for the horses and oxen than this unlooked-for delay of the steamer. He reminded himself of all the minute and trying things which would come up to delay their progress. There would be the shoeing of the oxen, tires to be set on more than one wagon, a broken spoke perhaps, the constant delays for rounding up the driven cattle, early twilight stops in order to make camp, none-too-early starts after a cooked breakfast and repacking of the camp utensils and bedding, and always the black Iowa mud after a rain. But once the steamer was off and on its way again nothing would stop it excepting nightfall.

On the fifth day they pulled off. The next day they were caught again by another sand-bar throwing its treacherous arms across a channel which had been traversed easily on the boat's last trip.

This time Matthias slumped into the depths of despair. This time he was moved to confide in Charlie Briggs concerning his love for Amalia, his friendship for the young chap having progressed to this point. Once he even wildly suggested the possible purchase of a horse from some passenger, swim it to shore, there to take to land. Charlie Briggs dissuaded him from this, pointing out his lack of knowledge of his surroundings, called to his distracted mind that when they pulled off, which might be any time now, their progress would be better than Matthias' blind ride through an unknown country. It took all the weight

54

of his argument to make Matthias realize the folly of the plan. Movement was what Matthias wanted,—to feel his legs moving, the motion of a galloping horse under him,—wings.

Charlie Briggs tried to cheer him. "I know that there Iowa gumbo," he would say: "Haint no mud like it any-wheres. As bad any day as a little sand for holdin' you aback. They'll be slowed up fit fer goin' crazy, any the time there comes a rain."

It drew the two young men together,—Matthias' confidences and worry, and Charlie Briggs' sympathy and encouragement because he had nothing more practical to offer. Although they were unaware of it at the time, it was, in truth, the beginning of a long friendship interrupted only by death,—a friendship which was rather unexplainable to the casual observer in the later years of their lives when they appeared to have so little in common.

Charlie Briggs was right. The delay was not so long this time, and the second day they were out of the treacherous sucking sands and into deep water, passing a large Indian encampment on the Nebraska side almost at once.

No more heart-breaking delays! No more anxieties and nervous questioning. The next day—Brownville. A few hours after that—Nebraska City, there to wait for Amalia.

CHAPTER VIII

AND now near the Iowa bluffs the overland travelers had broken camp for the last time before they were to sight the Missouri River.

Slowly the eleven wagons had crawled up and down the last of the unending Iowa trail. Ploddingly men had walked beside the oxen and cracked the long bull whips which circled over the stolid beasts' backs but never touched them. Patiently the women had sat in the covered wagons for all these weeks waiting this day of entering the new territory in which they were to make homes for their men. Most of them had come on the long trek against the desires of their hearts, for always the woman clings longer to the old hearth.

Young Mrs. Henry Gebhardt had given birth to a child on the way. Anna Rhodenbach had become betrothed to Adolph Kratz. Old Grandpa Schaffer, taken with summer complaint, had died and been buried in eastern Iowa.

But now the endless journey lay behind them,—with the worried forebodings of young Mrs. Henry Gebhardt, with the childhood of Anna Rhodenbach and Adolph Kratz, with the unbroken sleep of old Grandpa Schaffer beside the trail in eastern Iowa.

They were soon to see the Big Muddy. And although several days' journey lay beyond it, still it was the gateway to the new home.

Fritz was continually straining his eyes toward the

west hoping to catch the first sight of the river. But Amalia turned often to look back along the trail where the other wagons of the train stretched out like the long lash of a whip.

"Always, Fritz, I foolishly look for the strange wagon or the lone rider. Sometimes I think I see it so plainly that I wonder if I am a little mad."

"There's the river way, too, Mollia. Some one of the men had a paper printed in the big town of Omaha many miles to the north. There it said river crafts come up from the towns to the south and unload their goods."

He unwittingly gave her renewed hope, against which she strove to turn, fearful that it might buoy her up too much and make her suffering more keen when it should come to naught.

And then suddenly from the top of a rise they saw it,— the River! Almost simultaneously some one ahead had shouted back the news. And soon others behind were shouting, too. There it was ahead of them,—the Big Muddy, its waters tawny with the clay of its high banks, —rolling on to its union with the Father of Waters. On the far side,—the Nebraska Territory.

They could see cabins across the wide expanse of water. Nebraska City that was,—cabins and shacks in a sheltering cluster of trees, and a ferry-boat which must be summoned from the far side.

Wilhelm Stoltz, as master, was to go across first with his wagon and the heavy mares whose shaggy legs were like pillars.

There was the long wait, and then: "Come, Amalia," he called loudly. "We go now. You are the first woman of our people to cross. It is good luck for you. Good luck to meet Herman there, too, huh?" He repeated *"Gutes glück"* many times. He was jovial, excited that the Nebraska Territory was in sight,—had almost forgotten his daughter's foolish idea that she had liked the young foundryman. *Verrückt,* she had been.

The ferry came over, so very slowly. But it did not come too slowly for Amalia. Rather she would have waited here on the Iowa side, prolonged the time before she must meet Herman who might even now be among those people over there on the levee.

They were down on the platform-like boat now, Amalia and her father and the one covered wagon with the shaggy-haired team. So many trips it would take to get all the colony across the river. Fritz must stay on the Iowa side with the other wagon, awaiting his turn.

They were crossing the muddy water now with that feeling of being too close to the dark turbulent waves. Amalia looked down at the turbid waters. They were thick, impenetrable. One could not see one inch beyond the muddy surface. Nor one hour into the future of one's life.

The coming of the ferry-boat had brought a scattering group of people down to the dock. From shore came a confused noise of laughter, braying stock, rumbling wagons, and the pounding of hammers far up on the hill. The wind was blowing hard on the river and Amalia with one hand held to her sunbonnet which rattled starchily in the breeze,—with the other she clutched a hard bundle of unbleached muslin.

The ferry-boat docked with a rattle of chains and the crowd idling about the wharf, pressed forward.

"Prettiest gal I've seen yet. She can have me, Pete," Amalia plainly heard an uncouth tobacco-stained individual say.

"Sst! Careful!" his companion idler whispered. "This here fellow comin' is lookin' for her."

CHAPTER IX

THE *Missouri Queen* had passed Brownville. Charlie Briggs in his self-appointed duty of handing out data to any and all who would listen had been regaling several passengers during the afternoon with all the information he possessed concerning Nebraska City, the destination of many. He was still going strong when the town itself was sighted from the steamer's deck.

"The old Nuckolls House burned six years ago. You should a' seen it." As a matter of fact Charlie Briggs had never set foot in its interior, but that did not deter him from his description.

"The night o' the dedicatin' made river history, I guess. All the toniest of the folks on the river from Brownville, Omaha, St. Joe, even as fur away as St. Louis come. They say champagne flowed upstream agin the current from St. Louis,—that many a sedate and long-faced citizen was cuttin' capers agin mornin' come."

"Did you say it burned?"

"To the ground in the big fire that destroyed most all the early buildin's of the town. Raged for hours, but volunteer fire boys couldn't save 'em."

It was sunset when the *Missouri Queen* docked at Nebraska City, greeted with artillery and a self-elected welcoming committee of countless men and boys on the levee. Most of the passengers who were going on to Plattsmouth, Omaha and Sioux City came on shore to bid good-by to these acquaintances of several weeks. Young girls who had not known each other at the beginning of the journey clung together in tearful farewell. Men promised to send for others if ventures proved successful. Women parted with promises of undying friendship and favorite recipes. Two engagements were announced between fellow passengers. Life acquaintances had been formed.

But Matthias had little time for all this display of emotion. He was anxious to get located, to see the town, most of all to ascertain whether the caravan of Lutheran settlers had come in.

The founders of Nebraska City had displayed a good deal of optimism in its baptismal name he decided. It was not much of a city, he could see, although the town proper looked to be on the bluffs back from the river while crude shacks and cabins clustered around the lower village. Twelve years old now, it had a courthouse, several stores and churches, a school and hotels, so Charlie Briggs had told him. But if Matthias' youthful interest in the little city was keen, it was superseded by the important fact that his rival for Amalia was probably somewhere here in the town at this very moment. He might even be one of these many men down at the wharf.

Just where to go for information concerning the Illinois homesteaders he was not sure, so the immediate call for action was to take his valise and seek out the hotel. He said good-by to Charlie Briggs who was to stay with a cousin in a log-cabin in the lower town which he now pointed out to Matthias.

"If you hear any news of these people I'm looking for, you would let me know?" Matthias questioned.

"I'd do that very thing." Charlie Briggs' little blue eyes twinkled under the tumbled forelock of his red hair.

"As for me, I'll clean up and eat and then start out. Maybe I can hear something." And then Matthias was on his way to the hotel.

At the hotel,—a two-story structure with a porch across the front,—Matthias washed and ate his supper alone under the kerosene lamps' glow. The dining-room was well filled. These were the more comfortably fixed travelers eating here he knew,—most of the incoming settlers would be camping just outside the town.

Apparently that was a bride and groom nearby,—he in broadcloth, white-collared and beaming, she in her bridal suit with pale-blue plumed hat,—and the conversation too low for Matthias to catch excepting the fact that they were hiring some one to take them over the Cut-off trail to Otoe County. Matthias wondered how the brave blue plume would face the prairie winds just now so vigorous.

At the other nearby table a group of men discussed the construction of the new Union Pacific Railroad. The names of Durant and General Grenville Dodge were being used freely, but whether they were two of the men present or were merely being discussed he did not know. The conversation included references to General Dodge having come on to Omaha to take charge of the entire construction of the road, and a protracted discussion as to the respective merits of building it out the north Fork Platte toward Fort Laramie, out the south Fork Platte, or due west where the Platte divides at Lodge Pole creek.

He soon knew that General Dodge was not present in the group but rather under discussion.

"He knows more of the possibilities of the country from the Missouri River to Salt Lake than any other American engineer," he heard, and several references to Dodge's former experiences as an engineer among the Indians who had given him the name "Long Eye" after seeing him use his surveying instruments.

The men seemed elated over the fact that the first sixty miles as far as North Bend had been completed, damned the redskins superbly for giving constant trouble, discussed the possibility of the Union Pacific beating the Pacific Central being pushed eastward in California, referred to "The Moving Town," calling it "Hell on wheels," and laughed long and hilariously at the reply some Jack Casement had given General Dodge when he asked if the gamblers were now quiet and behaving,—"You bet they are, General, they're out in the graveyard."

All this overheard talk of large spaces and big projects filled Matthias with a renewed interest in this raw country to which he had come. What his own part in its upbuilding would be he did not even know yet. He must get into something right away,—something important so that his life work would be started early. He was not without a substantial sum of money,—for that he was thankful. Amalia, first,—to see and take Amalia from her people,—that was of primary importance just now. Then to get into the work of this big opportunity-filled territory and make a place in it worthy of them both.

"You're Mr. Meier?"

Matthias looked up to see a waiter addressing him.

"Yes, sir."

"A gentleman outside to see you, sir."

He pushed back his chair and went immediately to the door which opened on the hotel veranda. It gave him an excited feeling of anticipation as though even now he knew there was to be news of Amalia.

He stepped outside where June bugs thumped about clumsily and the sound of voices and a banjo came harshly from one of the saloons across the street.

Charlie Briggs stood there in the pale light which the hotel's lamp cast across the wooden platform. He came up soberly, turned his lean and freckled face away.

"Reckon' I got bad news for ye, Matt."

Even then Matthias knew he would always remember the expression of unspoken sympathy on the young fellow's homely weather-beaten countenance. Twisted, his face looked, as though he might be in physical pain.

With no word Matthias stood tense and expectant.

"The Lutherans got in day afore yistiddy." Charlie Briggs dropped his usual high-pitched voice to a hissing whisper. "Yistiddy they went on west to their land. The girl was married here . . . just afore they pulled out."

Matthias stood with no word, staring at the burned and leathery face of his informant, just as he had stood in the Illinois woods weeks before and stared unseeing at a younger boy, so that it seemed he was living some portion of his life all over again. But it went through him swiftly that this time there was no way out,—no recourse now from a decision which was beyond his changing. He had a distinct sense of finality, as though life were ending here on the porch where Charlie Briggs' weather-beaten face screwed itself into pain and the June bugs thumped on the wooden porch floor.

There was, then, to be no full fruition of any hope for him,—ever.

With a last grasping effort, as a drowning man clutches for something solid, he asked: "You're sure? There's no . . . no mistake?"

"There's no mistake. My cousin's woman's sister saw the ceremony from her cabin. Two couples was married. 'Twas out by the wagons by the side o' the new Nebraska City Cut-off trail . . . Luther'n preacher . . . 'n all kneelin' near the wheel ruts fer the prayin' afterward. One of the brides' faces was whiter'n limestone, my cousin's woman's sister said, and a Luther'n woman standin' by told her it was account o' a team o' horses sudden rarin' nearby . . . but my cousin's woman's sister said it had looked thataway long 'fore ever the horses acted up."

For a time the two men stood with no more words between them. Through Matthias' mind went a kaleido-scopic turning and twisting of parts of pictures, never forming any whole, merely grotesque and fragmentary shapes,—swollen streams—crumpled letters—rushing waters—dripping timber—covered wagons—driven cattle —Amalia's white face, whiter than limestone,—high cliffs —muddy waves—and always a nightmare of clutching hands pulling his body down into a maelstrom of smother-ing quicksands.

Sand! Sucking sand! It always held you back from your heart's desire.

Sand! Moving sand! It ran forever through an hour glass.

Queer he had never realized that about sand before. Some sands held you in their slimy grasp and would not let you go. And while they clutched you tightly, horribly, other sands slipped down, down through the hours, pushing time on until everything was too late.

Too late! Too late . . . too late . . .

"Sorry, Matt. If I can ever do anything more fer you . . ." Pain in Charlie Briggs' leathery red face.

"Thanks, Charlie." Mustn't let Charlie see that no one can ever do anything more.

They were shaking hands. The tight grip of Charlie Briggs' two iron hands couldn't help.

Matthias turned and went back into the hotel and up to his room. For a long time he stood in the middle of the floor looking at the wash-bowl and pitcher and the grayish-white towels on the rack and tried to think just what had happened. He had come too late. On account of sand! Sand! Sand that held you back like the tight grip of two iron hands. So that other sand could run through the hour glass and make you too late . . .

Too late . . .

He dropped on his knees, by the side of the bed, burying his face in his arms.

Oh, *kleine taube,* little dove . . .

CHAPTER X

AMALIA rode quietly at the side of her new husband, Herman Holmsdorfer. She had no spoken reproach for her father, uttered no word of rebellion toward the man who had acquired her body.

Herman possessed her now,—he had a woman to keep his house and cook his food and lie by his side at night. He was secretly proud of her prettiness, too, but it would not have done to tell her so. Far more than the prettiness was the fact that she could cook and sew and scrub, tend chickens and help plant when he needed her. Also she would bear him many sons. Seven,—*ach* in the Fatherland one would get something for that. Here they would give bounty only for coyote skins.

Riding along the Cut-off trail he was fully satisfied with life as he knew it. One-hundred-sixty acres of good rich Nebraska Territorial soil for his portion at the end of the journey, a team, a woman of his own,—one of only two children, too, so that when Wilhelm Stoltz died Amalia would get half of her father's homestead. And Amalia being his, the land would be his. Must discourage any sign of remarrying in Wilhelm,—that would not do.

One-hundred-sixty acres, a good team and a woman,—thus did Herman Holmsdorfer gloat on his good luck and although he did not analyze the statement, thus did he grade them in point of value.

Loudly jovial he was on the trip. Amalia had gone to his head like a drink of *roggen branntwein.*

"The best cabin of all for you I build. Not a house of sod as the people far out on the prairies away from a stream, nor yet dugouts from the earth with only boards and branches and strips of sod over them. What think you? Of good logs from the natural timber along the river and creek-bed where is the fine land we have chosen. Say something, woman." He dug a heavy forefinger playfully into Amalia's pink cheek. "Is it not good?"

"It is good," Amalia said quietly.

Very quiet she had been ever since the day by the Cut-off trail near Nebraska City. Tractable, too, she was, and carefully polite to Herman. But something had frozen in Amalia's being that day, as the roots of the lilac bushes back home freeze in the winter. Outwardly pleasant and obedient, her heart had crept into an inner room, hurt and bleeding, to hide forever from the people about her. The *kleine taube,* little dove, had been wounded,— but only wounded, so she could not die.

Thereafter she lived in two worlds,—the practical one in which all these others moved and had their being, working hard when the wagons stopped, taking her turn at the cooking, washing out the necessary clothing in the streams for her father and Fritz, and now Herman,—and another world in which she existed apart from them, entirely aloof in her thoughts and with nothing in common in her emotions. With characteristic docility she submitted to the rough caresses of the heavy-jowled man be-

side her, but by some cool withdrawal of the spirit found
it possible to remain forever away from him.

For several days the ox train headed west on the trail,
turned from it at the point designated by Herman and
rode miles again across the wild treeless prairie, the long
grass dotted with the white of daisies and the blue of
prairie gentians.

Twice they sighted small bands of Indians and were
frightened, and twice the scare went into nothing.

For a way beyond the Big Muddy the country had
been undulating, a succession of rolling hills and prairie
land. They rode through hills and valleys, uplands and
lowlands, dark sandy loam and black bottom lands, blue
joint verdure, and course slough spikes. And the feet of
the oxen crushed a thousand wild blossoms in the prairie
grass.

Sometimes the way was as level as a floor,—sometimes they went up and down through gullies and creek-
beds. Sometimes the skies opened and the wagons stuck
fast for hours in the black mire. Sometimes the sun shone
and the drying winds blew, and they made fourteen miles
a day. Sometimes they passed greenish sloughs, and occasionally near the streams, a virgin timber,—boxelder,
elm and willow, burr oak, hackberry and ash, and the
tangled vines of undergrowth. A few times they passed
cabins, two or three were occupied, some were abandoned
claim shanties. Once they halted by a pond of muddy
water, warm and brackish, and once by the clear sparkling
water of a spring-fed stream. All this where one day
there would be villages and towns, churches, schools,
countless farms, paved highways, concrete bridges and

searchlights sweeping the night skies for the guidance of the mail planes.

Herman rode proudly all this way at the head of the caravan for it was he who knew the way to the new homesteads. On the sixth day he made a sudden halt, got out of the wagon and waved wildly to those few in his vision. One by one the wagons reached those already assembled, the drivers wondering what had caused the mid-afternoon stop.

"It is here that the lands begin," Herman had been saying to Amalia, ". . . here you shall keep my house for me."

"Yes, Herman," Amalia had said,—little Amalia who was to live in the same house with Herman, but always in Another Room.

It was then that three strange young men on horseback rode out to meet them. And now ensued a protracted argument. The young men had arrived during the absence of the Lutheran scouts, broken sod in a sizable area of prairie, built a shack, and what was to be done about it?

It was nightfall before the Lutheran men had come to the conclusion to buy the squatters off. Loath was a hard-working thrifty German to part with good money to English-speaking squatters, but after an assembled meeting of the heads of the Stoltz, Schaffer, Rhodenbach, Kratz, Gebhardt and Holmsdorfer families, they decided to offer the men one hundred dollars to leave. The young men wanted three hundred. The answer to that mathematical problem was as plain as the nose on every German's face,—two hundred.

So the deal went over and the young men settled on land adjoining that of the colonists,—a small enough business deal at the time, but one to be fraught with far-reaching consequences, for it came to be in time that they and their descendants mixed the English language and customs, English schools, and church services, social events and marriages with those of the Germans,—until no longer could one pick out the descendants of those Lutherans from the children of the English.

The business finished, all the new German settlers gathered around the huge central fire which had been built. Wilhelm Stoltz raised his great hand and a hush fell on them. When the least child had grown quiet he thanked God for leading them into the land which would nourish them and their children after them and their children's children,—told Him that He was closer here to his followers than He had seemed in the land from which they came.

Amalia, looking up at the low-hanging stars shining like so many yellow buttercups in a forest clearing, wondered why He seemed so much farther away.

CHAPTER XI

IMMEDIATELY the settlers went to work to lay out the farms. That all might border the river, they figured out a system whereby they narrowed each holding and allowed it to extend farther back so that every homestead might have its full one-hundred-sixty acres. Thus each family could have access to water, and because of the narrower measurements, be slightly closer to each other for protection from the Indians in case there was trouble. They realized that this homesteading out farther than the Omaha area might bring on Indian depredations any time.

For many days Wilhelm Stoltz and Herman Holmsdorfer, Rudolph Kratz and August Schaffer on horseback, with small pocket compasses and the lines from their horses' harness, laid out the acreage into the eleven farms, for there were that many men in the group over twenty-one. Wilhelm Stoltz nearly shed angry tears that Fritz was only fifteen. It seemed such a waste of years to be but fifteen with all this fine land everywhere.

All camped by the wagons near the river while the farms were being surveyed, with every one anxious for the day to come when that particular phase of the work should be finished so that the building might begin. The women cooked and washed at the river's brink, and gathered for the fires the dead branches of trees along its banks and the dried buffalo chips out on the prairie.

This camp was made in more permanent fashion than those of one-night duration on the way. Now several stoves were set up with quilts hung behind them to lessen the onslaught of the wild winds from across the open country.

Many times the two who had come to pick out the land, Herman Holmsdorfer and Rudolph Kratz, were congratulated for their choice. How terrible, the various members of the company said, not to have had this river with its native timber. Several times they had passed settlers on the way who had chosen land far from trees, claiming it was richer or lay more level. It was because they had not scouted about as Rudolph and Herman had done. There was wide, open prairie land here for the good crops which soon would grow, but there was timber, too, even though not large like the Illinois trees.

On a hot day in July with the wind stilled before the sullen approach of a storm, the work of the surveying was finished. It was a momentous occasion, for now came the choosing of the farms. They gathered about in a close circle. Herman Holmsdorfer placed all the numbers of the tracts on pieces of paper. Young Henry Gebhardt wrote all the names of the families on similar pieces. The numbers were placed in one hat,—the names in another.

"Who shall draw?" they asked.

"The two brides," some one said. "Anna Kratz and Amalia Holmsdorfer."

"The two brides," others chorused. "It is good luck for us all."

"*Gutes glück!*" was heard on all sides.

"Hush!" said Wilhelm Stoltz, Amalia's father. "You

talk of good luck. Ask instead the good God for His
help and protection."

He raised his great hand high above his head and his
loud voice rumbled forth, addressing *Gott im Himmel*. A
similar scene had taken place on a far New England
shore over two hundred years before. "Thou hast led
these Thy chosen people . . ."

Amalia bowed her head. Why were the Lutherans
chosen before all others? Was it true? How were they
sure?

Love,—a very human love for one not of her church,
—made Amalia Holmsdorfer all the years of her life liberal and kind to those who chose to think differently
from her own people. Protestant, Catholic, Jew, and
Gentile, those of Mormon faith and those of no faith at
all found succor at her door until the day of her death.

And now the drawing. Anna Kratz drew a number.
"Eleven . . ." she said in a clear, ringing voice.

Amalia drew a name to match with it. "Herman
Holmsdorfer," she said quietly.

They all shouted and laughed at the joke. "Amalia
is so anxious to get started she draws her own name
first."

She looked down at the paper in her hand stupidly. It
was true. Holmsdorfer was her own name. She had
not remembered for a moment.

In the midst of the laughing and chattering Wilhelm
Stoltz raised his hand high again. *"Stille!"* And there
was immediate silence, for Wilhelm Stoltz, by some force-
fulness of character even more pronounced than the other

74

men also of domineering ways, was their acknowledged leader.

"Of one thing we have not thought. The years will pass. Our children and our children's children will live here on these farmlands. Better they should live side by side those of the same blood. Look you,—if ought happens to any of us,—to be taken in sickness or by death, it should be better that my Fritz and I dwell beside Herman and Amalia that the land may lie together."

"That is good," Herman shouted, and added to himself,—"Three-hundred-twenty acres of land I own instead of one-hundred-sixty should old Wilhelm and Fritz die before me." Almost he was licking his lips at the thought.

It was better so, the men agreed. The women were mere onlookers, consenting readily to whatever satisfied their men.

But one more question came from the lips of young Adolph Kratz. "I am now husband to Anna Rhodenbach. Shall the homestead I own lie then next to my father or her father?"

It was a weighty subject to be settled as the far distant lightning forked in the western sky. Wilhelm decided, this Lutheran Solomon, as he set himself up to be.

"Woman is frailer. It is thought she will die first. It is even so in the English laws. The homesteads of the younger men who have wives of our families shall lie next to the homesteads of the wife's parents. Thus at the deaths of the elderly women the daughter lives next to her father to care for him in his old age."

It was agreeable to all,—this settling so glibly by a

domineering man the entire future of the lives of a dozen families. But this fluent and smooth forecast was by way of being something of a joke,—perhaps the Almighty may have thought so, too,—for it was to be, that years after *Herren* Kratz, Rhodenbach, Gebhardt, and Schaffer had been gathered to their fathers, hardy old *Grossmütter* Kratz, Rhodenbach, Gebhardt and Schaffer met summer afternoons on the porches of their fine farm homes, ate their *kaffee-kuchen,* drank their *kümmel,* and jabbered endlessly in the old tongue, rather to the annoyance of a younger and very American generation.

They now rearranged the drawing, grouping them in clusters as agreed upon, three-hundred and twenty acres to the Rhodenbachs, they to settle between the two families which homestead each should have, three-hundred and twenty to the Stoltz-Holmsdorfers, and finishing the others in the same fashion.

The sky was darker now. The low thunderheads were piling up like a flexible mountain range that constantly changed in depth and height and shadows.

They finished the drawing. Wilhelm and Fritz were to be at one far end of the long line of homesteads, Amalia and Herman next, young Adolph Kratz and his bride, Anna, next, and the others in order.

No roads between these homesteads now: Later, along the side of the vast acreage, a rutty road running as wildly as a vagrant gypsy, dusty or muddy in summer, hard frozen or piled with countless drifts in the winter,—then after a time surveyed and "worked,"—still later straightened and graveled,—then leveled and paved so that cars doing sixty or seventy need not slow down and lose time where the oxen and the shaggy-legged horses of the Kratz, the Schaffer and the Gebhardt, the Stoltz, the Holmsdorfer and the Rhodenbach families once came to a lumbering stop in the midst of the prairie grass at the creek's bend.

CHAPTER XII

IF Matthias Meier drank the bitter dregs of disappointment during those first days in the raw territorial town of Nebraska City on the Big Muddy, there was too much activity going on about him for any continued quaffing at the cup.

It was a time of action, of great physical deeds. Men hewed and dug, sawed and hammered, broke sod and planted. The little town was filled with the sound of pounding, of the crack of the blacksnake, the call to the ferryman, the bawling of tired stock, the creak of wagon wheels.

Scores of wagons, hundreds of horses, mules and oxen still hauled freight from here across the barren plains to Denver. The hot summer winds carried through the town's straggling streets the odors of the river, of alkali dust, of sweating mules and humans, of upturned grass and loam and subsoil. There was the feel in the air of unseen forces,—the push and pull of strange appeals. There was strength and vigor. It was a masculine world, and all men were young.

Matthias, at twenty-one, was stunned and disappointed that his plans for marrying Amalia had gone awry, but found shortly that he was not destroyed. A frustrated life was not necessarily a defeated one. He was too busy to be utterly vanquished by the blow. Whom the gods would destroy they sometimes first make idle rather than mad.

And Matthias Meier was not idle. There was too much to do. It was too good to be a part of the great new country. Out here in all this vast newness one might in time become wealthy, influential, important. Free as the prairie wind itself, he could go anywhere with any of these home-seekers or adventurers. He had only to choose. Or so it seemed to youth.

Strangely enough, then, after those first days of crushing disappointment followed by idealistic dreams of great success, it was something of a deflation of his ego, to find himself again at the humble task of shoeing horses. Even then it was the energetic little Charlie Briggs who suggested it.

Plowshares must be pounded out and edged to turn the virgin prairies. Horseshoes must be forged and shaped. Nails must be made by hand. Much of this was to be done with the thousands of people coming through the Nebraska City gateway to settle westward to the Rocky slope. So blacksmith shops sprang up over night. And Matthias Meier started one.

Charlie Briggs pushed on soon across the prairie to Plattsmouth. Matthias had been sorry to see him leave. Out of the milling throngs he was the one new friend.

"Well, good-by, Matt." He had stood by his wagon loaded with supplies for the homestead which lay between Nebraska City and Plattsmouth.

"Good-by, Charlie."

Neither referred to the intimacy of that hour in which the one had glimpsed the heart of the other and given unspoken sympathy, and yet each knew the other was thinking of it.

"Good luck, Matt."

"Same to you, Charlie."

" 'F ever I can help ye out . . ."

"Thanks, Charlie . . ."

All that year and part of another Matthias Meier worked at his blacksmith shop, shoeing his share of the countless hoofs that came treading through this important gateway to the great plains.

He lived in a man's world, journeying between his boarding-house and the little shop, contacting only the masculine portion of the groups of emigrants stopping there, although many a feminine eye lingered longer than necessary on the young man's stalwart body and fine head set so gallantly on his wide shoulders. But not yet could Matthias see girlish attraction in any one but the shadowy memory of a fair-haired girl standing in front of green alder bushes and waving a farewell that was to last forever.

And now it was 1867 and suddenly Nebraska was no longer a territory. The territorial legislature which had met as usual in Omaha, having drawn up a constitution containing a clause that only white men could vote, found it returned speedily from congress with the rebuke that no one should be kept from voting because of color. Meeting again, it rectified the mistake, and on March 1, 1867, President Andrew Jackson issued his proclamation. Nebraska was a state.

Came now immigration in earnest. Matthias found that he and the settlers of the previous summer had merely come in like the first ripples in the run of the tide.

The great plains of which the newly born state was a part had been dotted by the foot-prints of thousands of people crossing it to the far west. For years settlers had been thinking of it as a great hallway through which they must travel in order to get to those other and more distant rooms where dwelt the Californians or the members of the new Zion in the Great Salt Lake Valley or the Oregon settlements.

Although the soil over which they trod was black and rich and fertile as any beyond, few had lingered. The very vastness of the prairie regions had staggered the mind. So from the days of the earliest fur traders to the year 1867, the great fertile plains beyond the Big Muddy had numbered only a comparative few.

But now they came. Came by the thousands,—especially young soldiers, who having known adventure and having rebelled against the idea of settling down to their old lives in the villages or on the farms of placid New England, turned eyes to the west and let them linger long on thought of the newly formed state with its rolling hills and vast prairies. Many minds decided that the possibilities there were as vast as the green-grown prairie itself.

So the trek began. In they came by boat and by covered wagon,—these strong young men from the northern and eastern states,—American, German, Bohemian, Danish, some of the sturdiest youth of the nation. Some turned to the founding of the villages,—some to the carving of farms out of the raw prairie land, but all to do their part in the building of a great state.

Matthias Meier by instinct clung to the town. Nor

did he intend to shoe horses forever. Already he was thinking that he who would bring in merchandise to sell to these newcomers would make a good profit, or who would loan money out to them for good interest, or set up a lumber business for their homes,—oh, there were many ways to make a good living if one but chose carefully.

Again it was Charlie Briggs who inadvertently helped him decide his course.

The lean-visaged young chap was in Nebraska City en route to Brownville. He sought out Matthias at his shop. It was July and the hot sun beat down on the river town with its dusty streets through which came the never-ceasing procession of ox teams and wagons, with its ferry-boat and its crowded hotels, its steamer in dock from down the river, its bawling cattle in the stockade on the hillside, its unending movement, as though a gigantic gate swung back and forth to let these enthusiastic newcomers through.

Charlie Briggs had news. A committee from the new state's legislature had finally picked the site for the capitol. The news of the decision had just come in. Had Matthias heard?

"No."

"A place on the open prairie out between Salt and Antelope Creeks. Sufferin' snakes, Matt! Open prairie with only three or four log cabins now. Capital of the state! Be a big town some day. 'F I was town-broke . . . But none o' that fer me. I'll take homesteadin' 'n a surveyin' gang 'n a chance to git a gun sighted on a dam' Injun."

Charlie Briggs was right about locating in the newly

chosen capital! Three or four log-cabins on the prairie, was it? How long would that be true,—with a capitol building going up, and the legislature meeting there? Why, in no time at all there would be more houses, a hotel for the legislators, stores, a school, maybe a railroad. No capital city ever stayed a village. Three or four log houses, indeed!

CHAPTER XIII

MATTHIAS MEIER started April first, 1868, for the village of Lincoln, the new Nebraska capitol site, driving his team with a wagon carrying merchandise of the most staple variety,—unbleached muslin, sugar, salt, boots, flour. The wind was strong and cold, and the trail faintly marked over the prairie was deep mud through which the horses struggled with the loaded wagon. By night he had made nine miles.

He had been told he would find a cabin en route and when he sighted it in the late afternoon, a black dot on the bleak prairie, he urged on the team. There he stayed all night with bachelor brothers, graduates of Dartmouth, who had come west to make their fortunes.

The next morning he started out in the rain which soon turned to sleet. All day his team plodded toward the next settler's, never passing a building or traveler. Now and then at the top of a rolling hill he would glimpse another team ahead, always a little fearful that its occupant was making for the same shelter as he was, and from his experience he knew that any house he might reach would be small.

It was after sundown when he drove up to the door of the soddie. A big bearded man stood in the doorway and called out: "Unhitch 'n put the hosses under shelter, friend. Then come in. Always room for one more at Akins'."

84

Matthias unhitched, led the team to the rude shelter, fed and watered them and then entered the house.

He found it contained two rooms, both of which were filled with people, all the men in the front room around a box-stove in which simmered green cottonwood, the women in the back room urging a small and apparently stubborn cook-stove to put forth its best effort in the way of boiling water for coffee.

He went back to his stock of groceries and brought in a sack of cornmeal to add to the gastronomical part of the evening's festivities. After what seemed endless waiting, and during which time the feeble efforts of the little cook-stove almost died on the altar of all vain attempts, there was supper after a fashion.

Later for the simple reason that it made economy of space, the women and children lay down crosswise of the two beds, while the men disported themselves on the floor after the manner of the spokes of a wheel, with the box-stove and its sputtering green wood contents as the lukewarm hub. In the middle of the night, with the wind increasing to the proportions of a gale and rocking the little house, Matthias, almost frozen, picked himself out of the wheel-like effect rather like a spoke which can no longer hold out, and went out into the icy night to run up and down a somewhat limited space of the open prairie and beat his arms.

With the coming of the sun, as though the two could not work well hand in hand, the wind went down. Soon the sparkling ice had gone and all started on their way, with loud and hearty admonitions from the Akins to be sure and come again. Hospitality on the prairie in an early day may have been only figuratively warm, but never did it fail its fellow man.

At Balls Crossing on Stevens Creek, Matthias made a short stop at noon, and then rode into the prairie wind, which was rising again, facing its rough onslaught, his strong young shoulders meeting its buffeting much as a swimmer breasts the current. But its very robustness gave him a feeling of exuberance, that he could meet the obstacles which would confront him in the new town in the same way that he met the wild strength of the prairie.

In the west, clouds were piling on the far horizon, gray and pink-tinged and gold-bordered by the sun slipping now over the rim of the world, forming castles no airier than his own. For as he rode he had dreams as wild as the wind: that plows would one day go up and down all these hills and valleys, leaving behind them broad new furrows; that endless fields of yellow grain would shimmer in the sunlight; that villages and towns would cut the horizon which circled him now in one unbroken ring.

Fantastic as it was, it persisted,—the mirage of the fields and farms, roadways and villages,—and the picture gave him companionship and comfort in the loneliness of his ride.

If he thought of Amalia, it was neither with the sharp pain with which he had first lost her nor the dull heartache which lingered long afterward. Rather it was with a touch of sadness that he was beginning to forget. His memory of the depths of agony to which he had been cast at the time bade him wonder now how it had been possible to live and enter so whole-heartedly into this new venture.

At that, his mind went forward again in its flight to the new town which was to rise there on the prairie and in whose building he was to have a hand. There were those who said the capitol, even if built, would never remain there,—that the absurdity of locating it on the raw prairie with only a few log-cabins about, was so apparent that a short time would see its removal.

Suddenly he found himself defending its retention, thinking of the newly formed town with a distinct air of proprietorship. It made him laugh aloud,—his air of ownership when he had not even arrived.

He admitted to himself that he had developed a distinct pride in the whole raw uncouth state. This new Nebraska with its few straggling frontier towns, its widely scattered soddies and cabins, its countless acres of prairie grass, its undulating hills and vast open spaces was far more something of his own than ever his native state had been. Into the latter he had been born with no volition of his own. Into this he had come of his own determination and here chosen to stay. It belonged to him.

For a long time he had been sighting black dots on the far horizon and then he knew them for the cabins constituting the town.

The sun had almost slipped away. Nothing remained but a last reflection of its gold on the tip of a cloud and in little yellow pools of light on the prairie.

It was almost dark when he drove to the first cabin. It stood isolated and aloof from any other of the small cabins and the blacksmith shop. The burned walls of what had been a school-house constituted the only other building in the vicinity.

Spring Came On Forever

Wide prairie land as far as the eye could see, three or four scattered log houses, a blacksmith shop and the forlorn walls of a little stone seminary! This, then, was the beginning of a midwestern city in which one day there would be countless fine residences and stores, a great University, paved streets and golf courses, parks and libraries, school buildings and churches, and the most beautiful capitol of them all from whose towering top the statue of The Sower overlooks that which Matthias Meier and his kind accomplished for the state,—as though the seed of their early sowing had come to full fruition.

CHAPTER XIV

IN such manner did Matthias Meier and Amalia, the girl he would have married, begin the years of their living in the same new state,—the young man in the village that was to become a city, the girl on a homestead among her church people,—their lives as far apart as the vastness of the wild prairie which separated them.

Amalia now put away her love for Matthias, if indeed one can be said to put away anything which lies always in the next room into whose silences one may slip at any time for surcease from trouble.

Always it lay there before her,—the way of escape. She told no one, could not have pierced the dull stolidity of Lena Schaffer nor the childish cheerfulness of Anna Kratz if she had made the attempt to tell them of The Room which held song and laughter and fragrance. But many times when the body grew weary of the hard work which was the portion of all the women, or when the heart turned sensitively away from the rough ways of the man who claimed them both, she would slip into this Room from whose windows one looked into a dim cool clearing in the woods, and in whose shadowy confines there was love and understanding.

Happily these little journeys into another realm could be performed by some magic means simultaneously with practical work, for otherwise they never could have been taken. Work was indeed the portion of every man, woman and child.

After the homesteads had been drawn, each family drove to its allotted acreage of one-hundred-sixty acres, living thereafter in the wagons until a house could be built. Eleven units of humanity, dotted up and down the river's bank for several miles, a team and wagon for each, a cow and chickens, a plow and a few household goods,—energy, courage, and hope.

Amalia's house went up in record time, for her father and Fritz turned in at once to help Herman build,—to live in it, too, until one for themselves could be finished on the next homestead. Many times as they worked, they boasted of the fact that they could use logs for the houses, and expressed their contempt for the sod houses of many of the settlers who were away from streams and timber-lands, not knowing that the soddies were warmer in winter and cooler in summer than any log house could ever be.

Amalia had something of a fine cabin, rather more elegant than that of Anna Kratz,—for it boasted a partition through it.

In truth, from the moment the initial log was laid for the first of the eleven cabins, there never ceased to be a concealed rivalry in the community over houses and hogs, children and chickens, wagons and windmills. From log houses in 1866 on through frame to the present days of brick and stone and stucco,—from lumber-wagons on through rubber-tired surreys to many-cylindered cars, there lay always under the jovial neighborliness of each family a desire to get ahead of the others. Let a Kratz buy a parlor lamp with a fat round globe and purple pansies on its side, the Gebhardt, Schaffer, and Rhodenbach women could not rest until fat round globes with magenta roses or cerise lilies decked their own parlors. Through all the years, human nature being as it is, two rooms in a log house instead of one, or eight cylinders in a car instead of four was a cause for rivalry.

In Amalia's house, they built the partition of small split logs, not rising to the ceiling but at least above one's head, which would make a good place for hanging washing in bad weather or seed-corn when the big crops should be harvested. When the cabin was finished, Amalia laid her rag rugs over the roughness of the floor, set her walnut bureau against the chinking of the logs and hung her pots and pans on wooden pegs protruding from it. A few household goods, a gun over the door, a willow fishpole beside it, the plow and team, the cow and chickens, —these only with which to conquer the wilderness!

Moving from the wagons into the newness of the little two-roomed house did something for Amalia. It eased the pain which lay always in her heart by giving her a floor to sweep and a hearth to keep clean. An immaculate little *haus frau* to her finger tips, she swept and cleaned and scrubbed her new cabin until even the other women, excellent housekeepers all, began to hold up Amalia Holmsdorfer to their feminine offspring as a shining example of all that a *haus frau* should be, not knowing that her work was an antidote for pain.

For the rest of that summer, hammers and saws were heard all up and down the river until the cabins were finished, one by one. Fritz and his father moved into their own by fall. All broke sod so that a beginning should be made on the land.

If Amalia was known as one of the best of the house-keepers, Herman might have carried the honors of being most adept at breaking the new sod. He seemed to have a knack for it and the others were always calling for him to come and help.

Sometimes when Herman was away at the plowing, Indians came through the prairie grass, in their straggling, single-file way of traveling, and frightened Amalia beyond measure, and often she could see their signal-fires at night on the distant uplands. Sometimes a long loathsome rattlesnake would coil itself in her path when she went to draw water at the spring, and always after sundown she could hear the howl of the coyotes in the timber near the river.

Church services were held at first around the wagons, then in houses. By fall when the last of the cabins had been finished, all turned to the building of a little log church, which would also be the school-house. They chose a site high on a knoll on the Rudolph Kratz place, centrally located, where it would stand like the eye of God overseeing all the valley.

Rock and sand for the foundation were quarried on the land of Henry Gebhardt. The strong capable hands of those who had built the cabins now built solidly and well the house of worship. Ludwig Rhodenbach built the pulpit and benches. But not until fifteen years later was the bell to arrive,—a big one that was to cause the little building to vibrate with its every chime, and whose echoes were to reach far and wide over the fertile fields.

"There will one day be a pastor's house beside the church"—a *pfarr-haus,*—"and when there shall be a grave some day, we shall then build a fence," Wilhelm said solemnly.

And Amalia, hearing him, looked about fearsomely at the assembled group and shuddered. Death,—it could find its way everywhere, even out here on the prairie. Who would it be?

It was young Mrs. Gebhardt's baby. Never strong from the day of its birth on the journey, it sickened and died so suddenly that not even the older women who might have helped with their advice, *flieder tee,* and *pfeffermünz tee* had time to arrive.

Emma Gebhardt was wild with grief. She rocked the little still form and would not let them take it from her. Even when they made a box for it and lined it with a quilt, she clung to the cold little thing and would not let them take it. *Verrückt,* they said she was. And crazy she seemed, until suddenly she broke into sobbing and let them take it away, and they said the crying had saved her.

It was a summer and fall of strange new experiences to Amalia,—of the constant sight of the bend and the dip of the prairie grass, of the loneliness of the cabin, of the fear of marauding Indians and the lurking rattlesnake. And always the hard work and the attempt to please Herman in every way so there would be no loud fault-finding.

Winter came on. The snows came and made of each cabin an isolated island in the vast sea of a snowy prairie. And life became a mere thing of obtaining food. Squir-

rels, prairie chickens, deer, rabbits, wild pigeons, all fell
before the guns of the settlers.

The bearded Herman in his great boots and heavy
clothes came and went, caring for his stock, oiling his
harness, hunting, tramping in with the snow falling from
him and the wild winds rushing in with him. Sometimes
he called loudly and impatiently to Amalia to hurry and
do some task for him,—sometimes he tweaked her ear
jovially or dug his heavy finger into the pinkness of her
cheek. And through both moods Amalia was docile and
very quiet. Had it not been for the stupidity of his
understanding, Herman must have seen that having won
her, he had forever lost her.

She put all her mind to the doing of her share of the
work. Always she went at it vigorously and with deep
responsibility, for it was a fight for their very existence.
Nothing was thrown away,—nothing wasted. Every piece
of dried *korn brot* had its use, every bone its value to the
last moist drop of its marrow. Yes, a good *haus frau*
was Amalia.

Sometimes when she was alone she took out the shell
box from its wrappings of unbleached muslin. All the
time that her father had lived with them while his cabin
was being built she had kept the box hidden in the bottom
drawer of her walnut bureau lest he know of her deception
in bringing it. But even when she was alone in the house
and might have done so without detection, she did not
open the box, merely dusted carefully between the moon
shells and the Roman snails, the angel-wings and the
other fragile fan-like shells of a sea she had never seen.

It was as though, if she opened it, she might see her heart lying there, red and bleeding, or a little dead Amalia.

And then suddenly the strangest of all the experiences was neither Indians nor coyotes, nor yet the long dip and wave of the prairie grass, but the fact that she was to have a child. It gave a new thought to living, a queer concern and responsibility for a life that was not her own and yet a vital part of it.

That second summer was hot and trying and a period of such hard work for all that the tasks were never finished. Everything was to be done at once. Herman worked early and late breaking out raw prairie and planting it and harvesting but a meager crop, lending his huge strength to the neighbors in exchange for help from them at other times. Amalia tried to make garden in a spot near the cabin, but the results were painfully disappointing. She cooked and scrubbed, washed and ironed and bent her pretty yellow-crowned head over tiny stitches for the child's simple wardrobe, making the little garments from a voluminous white petticoat of her own.

News of Indian trouble kept percolating into the settlement. A man by the name of Charlie Briggs camped all night with Adolph Kratz and August Schaffer when they went far to the north to buy two cows. He was on some scouting trip in behalf of the Union Pacific Railroad, told the men that Captain North with four companies of fifty friendly Pawnee Indians in each company was protecting the workmen during the building of the road since so many had been killed by the Sioux and new stations burned.

On a late summer afternoon when Herman was away with Fritz and her father cutting wild hay for winter's storage, Amalia, sitting in the cabin doorway to get any breeze that might come through the blinding heat of the prairie and bending to the tiny stitches of the garment in her hand, looked up to see three Indian bucks appearing before her, so noiselessly had they slipped around the cabin from the other side.

She might have fainted,—indeed, she felt the darkness slipping between her and the red of their ugly faces,—but for the thought of the coming child. It gave her an added bravery, the thought of the unborn child to be protected. Fascinated, she could not take her eyes from the paint and the black plaited hair and the muscles of their brown bodies that glistened in the sunshine. A little bird staring hypnotized at a snake was Amalia that summer afternoon.

They spoke among themselves in their low, guttural tongue, seeming amused at her fright. They stepped inside and filled the space so that Amalia could only shrink against the wall petrified with fear, awaiting the end of the torture.

From that time they began a systematic search of the cabin, handling a dish or pan, uncovering articles at will, drinking from the jug of precious molasses which was the only sweetening Amalia possessed.

From the bedroom one emerged with a pillow which they handed back and forth to examine, tearing a long slit in it to see the inside. Apparently they were highly amused at finding feathers which now floated forth into the room in a fine snowstorm of goose-down. As molasses still lingered on their fingers and lips, they could not rid themselves of the feathers which clung tenaciously to both.

For a long time they entertained themselves childishly

with the combination, paying not the slightest attention to Amalia still staring in a frightened mesmerism at the spectacle. Then, evidently tiring of the whole affair, they appropriated the jug of molasses and without a backward glance departed as suddenly as they had come,—riding their ponies in single file across the prairie, until they were merely outlines against the shimmering summer sky.

When Herman came, he looked sober, but tried to make light of it, explaining the difference between these Pawnees and the Cheyennes who were well worth being feared.

But to Amalia an Indian was an Indian, painted, fearsome, dreadful. And although she tried to comprehend the difference, she knew in her heart that had the friendly battalion of Pawnees appeared at her doorstep even under the command of the white Major North she would have dropped in her tracks. The sight of a painted face framed in two tightly bound braids of coarse black hair always gave her an ill feeling, so much so that when she was middle-aged and attending a wild west show she turned her head away and would not look when the Indians under Buffalo Bill's leadership rode in.

The second fall was upon them. The mad winds blew and the tumble-weeds came charging across the prairie like so many brown Indian bucks riding wild ponies.

It was a cold, windy night in November when Amalia knew her time had come. Herman saddled a horse to go for old Augusta Schaffer across the prairie.

When she heard the sound of the horse's hoofs grow fainter on the frozen ground she grew frantic with pain and fear of the strange new thing which was happening.

97

And then a new fear came upon her, for with the sound of the wind came far-off howls of coyotes on a distant hill. Her blood chilled when she remembered the saying that there were two occasions which brought them near,—times of birth and of death. Each time the little cabin rocked in the onslaught of wind she looked fearfully toward the rattling door to see whether or not it held.

The two of them filled her ears with their howlings,— the coyotes and the wind. When the wind came and threw itself upon the cabin with its wild shrieking, the sounds of the wolves grew fainter. But when the wind ceased for a moment she knew by their blood-curdling calls that the wolves were creeping closer. Once she cried aloud for she thought they were at the window, but it was only tumble-weeds scratching at the glass.

All the time Herman was gone they alternated their eerie calls,—the wind and the wolves,—until Amalia's own voice drowned them both. And when she heard the howl of the coyotes again, the cries of the new-born child mingled with them, and Herman and old Augusta had come.

And then, lying there comfortably after her ordeal, a sturdy man-child by her side, Amalia knew the age-old experience of young mothers,—that nothing in the world mattered but the welfare of that tiny bit of humanity which was flesh of her flesh.

The child, Emil, throve and grew, and sitting in the rocker by the cabin's window with him in her arms, Amalia knew happiness and peace. She told herself that she would never again think of the love for Matthias she had once known, making a sort of childish bargain with God that if He would watch over her baby and protect it she would promise Him this.

But later, when Herman would call her angrily to drop the potatoes faster, or when he would punish little Emil for failing in his baby fashion to mind immediately and unquestioningly in the German way, she would forget her promise and slip away into The Room in which she kept her memories. There she would think of Matthias and all that he might have been to her, and in some queer way which she herself could not fathom, would find a certain surcease from the trials.

CHAPTER XV

ALL the days were filled with hard work for every member of the colony. They were not long enough to accomplish all that the men wanted to do.

To Wilhelm Stoltz, Amalia's father, and to Herman Holmsdorfer, her husband,—to the other heads of all the families, Rudolph Kratz and his son Adolph, to the Gebhardt men, the Schaffers and the Rhodenbachs, the wilderness was a giant with which to wrestle. It must be fought, —more, it must be overcome or it in turn would conquer them.

There were a thousand things to do to make it subservient to their lives, to bring food for the body and safety of living. Daybreak found them at work, darkness only bade them cease from it. New prairie sod was turned, clean-cut with the sharp knife of the plowshare, the planting done slowly and painstakingly by hand. Crops were pitifully meager for all the hard work. Rains held off. In spite of the great snows of the winter, the skies gave only sparingly of moisture. Wood from the river's bank must be cut for fuel. New trees must be planted to replace the inroads being made upon the timberland along the stream. Cottonwood slips were brought to the cabins and planted in long rows to the north for windbreaks. Elm and ash were set near the cabins for potential shade. A shipment of apple and cherry trees was sent out from Illinois and arriving at Omaha was brought on the Union Pacific, completed in 1869. Adolph Kratz and Ludwig Rhodenbach drove an ox team the long miles to a junction to get the saplings for the eleven orchards.

Each man helped the others. Yet this was no communistic colony,—each family fought its own battles, assisted always by the others when occasion arose.

There was eternal vigilance on account of Indians. Sometimes wandering bands came through, begged food and if it were not forthcoming quickly, took it without leave.

There was eternal warfare with the elements,—great snows isolated the cabins so that roads must be broken in order to get through. Cold brought disaster to domestic animals and fowl, so that sheds and barns must be packed tightly with timbers and sod. Heat brought death to priceless horses and spring rains brought floods to the lowlands. It took great physical strength and a knack for careful planning to conquer this Nebraska into which these eleven families of settlers had come. But the German Gebhardts and Kratzes and Schaffers and all the others had them both.

The Annas and the Lenas and the Amalias must do their part,—wash and iron, cook and bake, leach the lye and make the soap, pick the wild fruit,—gooseberry, plum and currant,—patch and sew, work in the gardens, drop the corn, pick up potatoes, and yet bring forth the children who were to carry on the work when these mothers would be gone.

Always the prairie loomed there before them, lonely with silence,—a sullen giant waiting to trap them with blizzard or windstorm, drouth or flood, redskins or red fire.

It was five years now since the wagons, hub-deep in the prairie grass, had stopped at the bend of the river.

Little Emil was nearly four, sturdy and round of face, his hard cheeks apple-red and his hands square and harsh-skinned in the palms as though even now they were fitting themselves for the plow. All Amalia's love was for him.

The world would move from season to season that she and Herman might wrest a living from the soil for this child. The sun would come up each day that little Emil might grow strong in its rays. The night would descend that sleep could restore energy to the tired muscles.

Already Amalia's plans were laid that he was to be a *pastor*. School, confirmation, more schooling, ordination, —she pictured him grown and well known all over this part of the new state. He should be fine and large,—clean and well dressed,—learned and respected.

She pictured him in black suit and snowy white collar going about his pastoral duties,—in fine robe in the high pulpit delivering his sermons robustly after the manner of her church. Long before that time there would be a pastoral house—a *pfarr-haus*,—by the side of the church on the knoll in the Kratzes' pasture. Perhaps Emil would come there for his pastorate. He would marry. But whom? Not Anna Kratz's Elsa nor Lena Schaffer's sturdy little Christine. Some beautiful girl from the cities where he would attend school.

"Lena, I want you should meet Emil's wife." Or: "Little dove" (Emil would call her *"kleine taube"*), "this is my mother's old friend, Mrs. Anna Kratz."

Oh, it was a pleasant picture,—with Emil handsome and finely dressed and so learned, saying: "I am all of this because of my mother."

It was her life now. No longer was it necessary to creep away into a Room for comfort. Her solace was here before her, running about, sturdy and brave, with hard apple cheeks and eyes as blue as her own.

Once she ventured to speak of her dreams to Herman.

He looked at her with but dull understanding. "There are no pastors among the Holmsdorfers. We are all for the land."

Apparently it settled matters in Herman's eyes, but it did not settle them in Amalia's deep blue ones. He spoke of the boy as his, she thought, and felt vaguely that it was not true—that he was hers only.

It was the sixth fall for the settlers,—a mild September afternoon with the air hazy in the distance and a wind from the south.

Herman was over at the Stoltz place helping Wilhelm and Fritz who was twenty now and would soon want to be pushing on to find a suitable homestead of his own.

Amalia was ironing,—hot and ready to drop from fatigue and the heat of the wood-stove into which her irons were set. Always she was sniffing this afternoon, she told herself,—somewhere about her stove there was a faint odor of burning as though a bit of the ash wood was on a griddle. She went all over the top of it with her stove-cloth once more in order to dislodge the piece, but the odor did not stop.

She went to the cabin door, then, with a double purpose,

—to keep an ever watchful eye on little Emil and to see if the faint odor of burning could be located outside.

Once there, she raised her head and drew in a breath from the hot prairie. The smell was outside, somewhere, of that she was sure. The air seemed more hazy, and there was without doubt, now, a far-off telltale odor of smoke.

She had not even time to come to any conclusion concerning it until she could see Herman driving rapidly toward home, the lumber-wagon rattling loudly because of careening about over the rough ground.

Frightened at the combination of the smoke smell and Herman driving home so rapidly, she ran out and called Emil.

There was no answer.

Once he had done so mischievously to frighten her,— made no answer and was hiding behind the oat straw. It had given her such a scare that she had paddled him soundly for his lark. The river, rattlesnakes, Indians,— for these must Emil never leave the immediate ground around the cabin.

But now he was not at the straw stack nor by the log stable nor under the young orchard trees.

Something frightening possessed her,—the smoke odor, the haste of the rattling lumber-wagon, Emil not answering. She was running wildly now, calling here, there, everywhere. On two sides lay the wide open prairie, on one side the dried cornstalks rustling in the hot stiff wind, on the other the timber-land and the river.

Herman was here now, his horses lathering with the heat of their coming.

"Get gunny-sacks," he called. "A prairie-fire."

So there was a prairie-fire coming and little Emil not here.

It took all her strength to say the words and when they came, they seemed not effective: "The baby . . . he is gone."

"Gone?"

"Lost from me."

"Well, then, find him." Herman yelled at her: "Find him before he burns in the prairie-fire."

Fritz was speeding past now across the prairie to the Kratzes'. Years later there would be a bell at the church tower to ring for emergencies, but not yet. To-day must the words be passed by Fritz on horseback.

It did not seem possible that *Gott* would let two catastrophes happen at once,—so did Amalia childishly reason. And so did she call on Him constantly to help her as she ran like a wild woman first toward the corn-field, "Emil . . . baby. Answer mother."

But there was no sound.

Back she sped for another look near the cabin, then down toward the timber and the river: *"Emil . . . liebling! Ach, Gott."*

Up and down the river bank she ran, calling franti-cally, then back to the house, her hair down from its neat braid and flying, her skirt catching on the corner of a wagon-box and tearing its full length.

She could see the low black roll of the smoke now and the air was putrid with the distant burning. Herman was plowing and so was her father. Down in the other direc-tion she could see the Kratz men out too, plowing the strip so that the upturned loam would give the fire nothing upon which to feed and it would die out of hunger for something to consume.

What if the baby were out as far as the plowed strip? Perhaps he had walked even beyond that point and already was between it and the fire. When the blaze rolled in it would bring coyotes running ahead of it and rattlesnakes hissing before it.

And now, calling and running, she had no plan for looking,—was too distracted to hold sane ideas. Fritz was back. The low-running black smoke showed its scarlet flame now like a great black dog, mad and frothing at the mouth, snapping and licking the ground with its slavering scarlet tongue.

She ran toward Fritz and the Kratzes and Herman, calling and shrieking and ready to go out beyond the plowed strip and meet the oncoming red thing if her baby were there too.

Fritz and Herman left the plowing to the Kratzes and came to help hunt. The women were coming up now with wet gunny-sacks ready for beating out any firebrands that might leap the plowed strip when the red menace came near. The thing would not leap the river but it might take all their cabins before reaching the water that was on the north.

Women were hunting now, too,—Lena Schaffer and Anna Kratz, their faces as white as Amalia's chalky one.

"His wagon," Fritz asked, "where is that?"

The wagon was not there. Fritz had made it from timber with round disks cut from a young cottonwood for wheels.

"Where is the wagon, there is the baby." Fritz said and Amalia agreed more sanely.

And it was Fritz who found him. Riding into the cornfield, systematically up and down, so no portion would be missed, he came upon him sleeping by his wagon,—three stubby ears of corn in the little box of it. When Fritz lifted him up, he said sturdily between yawns: "All the corn for winter I husk."

Not even Herman's cross: "See to it you look after him again," could hurt Amalia. She was beyond being hurt when her baby was back in her arms. There was no fear anywhere now but the low sweeping red flame licking closer to the farm land,—as horrible as it was, the finding of Emil had minimized it.

All the rest of the afternoon they worked with plow and wet gunny-sacks. As the firebrands lighted in the dry grass, Amalia beat them like a strong man, for her relief and thankfulness gave her strength.

When the last of the flames died down, the land to the south was a desolate waste, leaving a fear forever branded on the minds of the settlers as marked as the blackness of the scar on the prairie.

Fall came on and the land was mellow with the haze of Indian summer. Amalia cared for little Emil, washed and ironed, baked her *frisches korn brot* and her *kaffee-kuchen,* cleaned and scrubbed, took care of the meat from the hog that Herman butchered, made *met-wurst* and smoked the *schinken* and rendered her lard.

Winter came on and the cabin was isolated in a sea of white so that Herman broke a road to Anna Kratz's and to the church on the knoll against which the drifts packed.

There were Christmas services with the singing of *"Stille Nacht, Heilige Nacht"* and *"Ein Feste Burg Ist Unser Gott,"* and with little Emil big-eyed at the sight of the green *tannen-baum* and the home-made *kerzen* lighted among its branches.

All winter Amalia hoarded every bit of grease from every rind for the making of her soap. She made her own lye for it, too, leaching the alkali from the wood ashes which she saved all winter long.

When the first spring days came over the prairie bringing the scent of wild things growing and the sound of wild things calling to their mates, she would get out the big iron kettle which Matthias had molded so carefully, and prepare for the soap making.

The odor of the grease and lye was not distasteful to her. It smelled good and clean like the wild free winds that blew over the prairie. And though to herself she seemed like another Amalia than the young girl in Illinois, an Amalia who knew nothing but work and responsibility,—and though it was rather like a song that is half remembered,—yet springtime and soap-time and the lilt of the first meadow-lark brought back to her always the poignant memory of lost love.

CHAPTER XVI

MATTHIAS MEIER was now, in 1872, part and
parcel of the new capital town of Lincoln which
like a growing youngster gained in size and importance a
little every day. There had been a vast change since that
April day four years before when he had driven into the
settlement of a few log-cabins. In truth, the village was
no longer isolated and aloof from the older towns. The
Burlington Railroad had arrived in 1870 from Plattsmouth
and the Midland Pacific a year later from Nebraska City.
Stage coaches were passé. And no longer did Charlie
Briggs, through blizzard and scorching heat, freight goods
by team from Council Bluffs and Pacific Junction, Iowa.
In fact, Charlie had nearly lost his life a few years before,
—1869,—with a bunch of frontiersmen and scouts in the
Republican Valley. He had been one of fifty-one men
standing off the Cheyenne, Arapaho, and Sioux Indians
for nine days from a sand-bank in the river. It made
Matthias' blood run cold when Charlie came to the store
one day and told him some of the bloody details.

There were a dozen or more stores dotted here and there
on the straggling streets. Several doctors' shingles swung
in the prairie winds and, while lawyers had not descended
upon the town in hordes quite equal to the grasshopper
scourge, at least a score of them had arrived.

There were a lunatic asylum and a penitentiary and a
cemetery, all appropriated by the state legislature,—the

cemetery called suitably enough *Wyuka* which is the Indian word for "a place to lie down and sleep." The appropriation of this last showed tremendous optimism on the part of the legislature for it contained no less than one hundred acres, and how can enough people to fill one hundred acres ever lie down and sleep there unless they have first been awake nearby?

The capitol itself had been hastily constructed previous to this with lumber brought in from Iowa and stone hauled from Nebraska City and Plattsmouth, by the tedious team or ox-cart method. It was built on high ground to the east of the village, a cumbersome-looking affair, top-heavy with dome. Paths cut diagonally across the meadow toward it where it stood in solitary grandeur, a miniature Rome with all roads leading to it. The grounds surrounding it were treeless virgin prairie on which the cows of the neighborhood munched the early spring grasses.

But there was no doubt about the growth of the village. Almost could one see the added poundage each month which the growing youngster took on.

Meier's and Collins' Emporium was selling high boots and nearly-as-high shoes, New Orleans molasses and sugar, red flannel and cotton batting, coffee berries, pepper, one or two sizes of rope, two or three kinds of nails, shot and powder, tobacco, goods by the yard running largely to calico, eggs and butter, sometimes slightly the worse for their long jolting trips across the prairie,—but who was there to find fault when there were not any better anywhere?

There were two banks now, the State National and the First National. Ten church organizations had been formed, sometimes with but a mere handful of people in one, but as always, the differences of close and open communion, of dipping and sprinkling, of formal ritual or personal testimony, of conversion in one lightning-like stroke or by the slow process of character building, of foreordination or local option, as it were, drove each citizen of the village to seek his own mode of religious expression, however small the group.

There was a University,—a single building,—classrooms on the first floor and a dormitory above, which like the capitol stood in solitary grandeur on the prairie, and toward which the cows also gravitated as though the grass there might benefit from its proximity to an atmosphere of higher education.

Matthias was energetic, purposeful, one with the neighborly spirit of the little town. He wore a beard,—it gave him added dignity and apparently a few extra years. Twenty-seven he was now,—his partner, James Collins, was twenty-five. Young men were the order of the day.

So busy was Matthias with his store, so ambitious, that he worked early and late, living, in the few hours he was away from it, at a Mrs. Smith's boarding-house with several others of the young business men, where came also some of the legislators in season.

He attended church every Sunday morning in a frame and somewhat flimsy building, and if he had two reasons for going,—one to benefit his soul and the other his business, it has been done before.

His association with young women had been as businesslike as he could keep it, for since his love for Amalia had received its blow, he felt no great desire to form another attachment. Already he was being spoken of by the young women in town as an old bachelor, but an eligible one for all that. Nor was he any martyr to a lost love. He merely put his heart and energies into *Meier's and Collin's Emporium*. Business was his mistress, getting ahead his whole desire. If he no longer thought about Amalia, at least he looked upon no other girl with longings.

He found to his own surprise that he was supposed to be the possessor of a very decent voice. The songs in his head which he had often told himself he could hear so plainly, suddenly proved to be quite capable of arriving in the atmosphere with no little degree of accuracy. At the occasional parties he attended his "Drink To Me Only With Thine Eyes" and "Come Where My Love Lies Sleeping" joined in right nobly with those of the Lunds and the McCurdeys who attended the same church.

It did not take long until Mrs. William McCurdey had inveigled Matthias into the choir of which she was both voluntary soprano and self-appointed leader. The rest of the personnel of the choir included Mr. William McCurdey whose "Rocked in the Cradle of the Deep" reached such utter basso profundo depths after its prolonged descension that half the audience, when hearing it at a home-talent concert, inadvertently put hands to their throats in a sort of mesmerized sympathy of aching muscles.

The tenor was Mr. Anton Lund whose tossing head, rapidly winking eyes and mouth gymnastics supplied entertainment for any deficiencies which his voice might lack, and whose whole facial effect was such that little boys and girls otherwise bored with the services looked forward each Sunday to this particular amusement.

Mrs. Anton Lund was a member of the choir merely because she was Mrs. Anton Lund,—it being apparent to all that she neither added to nor took away from the musical output, her faint little voice never attaining to greater volume than that made by a rabbit nibbling grass. The alto was Miss Dolly Thomas, a good, substantial robust alto, who made up for Mrs. Anton Lund's lack of volume by a full, unshaded, monotonously accurate second part as resonant as a bell.

In this fall of 1872, now, Mrs. McCurdey became filled with zeal to add Matthias, some other as yet undiscovered tenor, and another soprano to the choir. Almost in answer to her prayers, a Miss Ida Carter arrived to open a private school, bringing with her a sweet soprano voice which Mrs. McCurdey immediately requisitioned. After some sleuthing she found one Peter Longshore, a drug clerk, fairly capable of following Mr. McCurdey part way down into the cradle of the deep. These then became the double quartette of the church to which they went long and often for practice, the meetings taking upon themselves more and more of the social side as time went on.

Sometimes the Lunds took Ida Carter, the new teacher, home. Sometimes the McCurdeys took her. Sometimes Peter Longshore and Miss Dolly Thomas. And then one night when the Lunds and the McCurdeys were invited to eat oysters at the Atwood House right after choir practice, and Miss Dolly Thomas and Mr. Peter Longshore frankly disappeared while Matthias was gathering up his music, it devolved upon him to take Miss Carter home himself.

Miss Carter was not pretty. She was merely clean and

neat with rather nice frank gray eyes, and having only a level head and a sense of humor instead of any of the feminine appeal which Matthias knew every man required.

He took her arm down the church steps and through the darkness of the streets, realizing it gave him very little headiness of feeling, a fact which genuinely relieved him. In truth, it gave him such a sense of security that he was rather more courteous and gallant all the way to her boarding-house than he would have been otherwise, slipping protectingly to the inside of the walk when they passed the saloon with its swinging doors and sour yeasty smell.

He saw her into her boarding-house, talked for a moment in the dim kerosene-lighted hallway with her landlady who had rushed out to chaperon the two, bade Miss Carter a formal good-night and departed to his own boarding-house.

Upon arriving at his room, for some reason which he could not analyze, he went to the calfskin brass-bound box in which he kept his papers and took out the leather wallet containing the note from Amalia. He had not thought about her for a long time. She was no longer his,—could never be his. But even so, the sight of the note, the precise and shaded script it contained, gave him more genuine stirring of the emotions than the warm human touch of the young woman he had just left.

He read the letter through twice. It stirred him unaccountably. A sudden wave of longing for her and regret swept over him. He had not felt its like for years, and wondered vaguely why he was experiencing it to-night. Dear, lovely little Amalia! And this was all he had of her,—a fragile note. Not a lock of hair nor a picture, not a flower. Just a note and memories.

Almost as though in answer to the wish, for a moment, then, she stepped out of the letter as plainly as anything short of reality could have done.

Vividly he saw the pansy-blueness of her eyes and the pinkness of her mouth, felt again the warm softness of her lips and supple body.

Where was she now? Did she ever think of him? How had the German husband . . . and the years . . . treated her? For the hundredth time he asked himself why he had been late. Other steamers made the trip in regulation time. Not once in two dozen trips, perhaps, was one delayed so long. But the one he chose had been caught and held grimly by the sands. They had proved to be the sands of time. Why had it happened so? Why? For what reason? What right had Fate to intervene between him and his heart's deepest desire?

He looked again at the note, as though from its six years of lying there in the darkness it might speak. And in speaking, answer the unanswered question.

. . . *it is better to remember our love as it was in the springtime.*

CHAPTER XVII

BUT even though Matthias looked upon Ida Carter only as a nice, intelligent young woman with whom he had been thrown in social and vocal contact, at the end of the next choir practice evening, because she very frankly made plans to go home with the McCurdeys to the utter disregard of the previous week's procedure, he found himself really wanting to take her. There was something mentally stimulating about her even though she was so different from Amalia. And she had a sense of humor such as he had never known in any feminine acquaintance,—the humor that could laugh gaily at her own foibles and at his also, but without barbed shafts.

So he took her "home" to the dimly-lighted but resolutely chaperoned boarding-house that night,—and many others.

By Christmas time the walk home with her had grown to be the regular program. By mid-winter he was calling upon her steadily in the late Sunday afternoon and accompanying her to evening church. By February it came to be a rather settled thing in the intimate little social affairs of the growing town,—house warmings, oyster suppers, the McCurdeys' tin wedding,—that Matthias Meier was assigned by the hostess to Miss Ida Carter.

He grew to look forward to their talks. She had such a grasp of human understanding, could turn a subject over in her mind so deftly with such reasonable decisions that she satisfied something in him. He found himself reserving opinions until he had learned her reaction, planning to tell her about problems which came up in his business, even to ask advice outright occasionally. Sometimes he questioned himself closely, tried to analyze just what this type of friendship meant to him,—told himself if this was love, it was a queer kind. There was none of that thunder of blood in his ears he had once felt. He must wait now and see how permanent was the feeling, remembering that when he had loved Amalia there was no question, and no thought of waiting.

So it was that on this Easter Sunday of 1873, a fine one with every one dressed in his best and out on the high wooden sidewalks of the main streets, with many buggies and two-seated carriages tied at the hitching posts in front of the churches, with Mr. Anton Lund's tenor soaring high and Mr. McCurdey's basso profundo rumbling in the opposite direction, that some chemical change took place in Matthias' heart and he warmed toward the young woman sitting in front of him in the choir. He looked at the pretty plum-colored straw hat with its plume hanging over the brim and mingling with her dark hair, at the neat folds of her high collar, and almost before he could question its reason he told himself he was going to marry her.

From that moment on he was lost in a maze of planning. He would build a new house not far from the capitol. He would branch out in other lines of business investments as soon as possible. The town would be twice this size some day. He would never care to live anywhere else. He would always be proud of Ida. His decision sent his mind skyrocketing on an hour of planning far afield from the minister's message.

When the long sermon was over and the congregation poured out on the wooden sidewalks, Matthias slipped his arm through that of Miss Ida Carter, rather to her startled consternation, that gesture being usually reserved for the period following sundown.

With chattering people all about, with buggies pulling up to the edge of the walk near them, and children with Sunday School papers brushing hurriedly past, he said it, as though the saying could not wait, now that he had decided.

"Ida, I want you to be my wife." Now that he had taken the step he found there should never have been any question about it.

No moonlight, no music, no chance for romance. Ida merely saying: "Why, Matt, I am so surprised at . . . How do you do, Mrs. Jamison. Of course I . . . Good morning, Alice. Yes, isn't it nice? . . . If you think you really want me, Matt . . . Hello, Mose."

In such a way did Matthias make his second proposal to a young woman. And in such a way did she accept.

By night there had descended the Easter blizzard of 1873 which still lives on the pages of midwestern diaries and in the annals of its histories. It caught the people of Lincoln unaware as indeed it caught those of the whole state. It caught Matthias Meier at Mrs. Smith's boarding-house sitting on the horse-hair sofa under the unseeing eye of Mrs. Smith's deceased and framed husband but still within the range of Mrs. Smith's own alert, far-sighted one, also framed, but by the crack of the door.

The blizzard gave Matthias a pleasant background for the thought that soon he and this nice girl with her good sense and humor would have a home of their own shut away from all the blizzards of all time. So pleasing were his thoughts that he was almost unaware of what Ida was saying. But now he heard it.

"Matt, I have something I must ask you. I hate myself for thinking about it, but it seems that if I'll face facts and tell you,—get your honest answer I can conquer the feeling I've been working myself into this afternoon. Has there ever been any other girl, Matt, or am I the first and only girl you have loved?"

He sparred for time. "How can I answer? The way you put your question, Ida, calls for both yes, and no." He laughed a bit as though the whole thing were a joke.

Ida laughed, too,—at herself. "I knew it, of course. There has been. It seems that I can almost sense what you're thinking at times, I have learned to know you so well. Well, I brought it on myself and I've nobody but myself to blame. I wonder why I had to torture myself by knowing? I suppose I'd be far happier if I didn't know all the details to mull over in my mind, but tell me, anyway, Matt. I imagine things like a youngster in the dark. Maybe if you'd light the lamp . . . the bogies would turn out to be shadows."

"There's not much to tell, Ida dear." And because seven years is a long time to a young man, he said: "It was years ago. I was only twenty-one and she was not quite eighteen. It was in Illinois that I knew her. Something . . . parted us. I never saw her again. I don't even know just where she lives, although it's somewhere out here in this state . . . away out farther on the prairie. She's married . . . and come to think about it, I don't even know her married name." He was smiling at the nice girl sitting by him on the boarding-house sofa, slipping his arm about her now. "Pretty dangerous rival, isn't she?"

Ida smiled at that, too. It *had* been silly to punch sleeping dogs. But it was a newly engaged girl's prerogative.

Matthias and Ida did not go to church. No one went to church or anywhere else. The storm raged like an infuriated madman. The room grew cold so that Matthias kept feeding chunks of wood into the sheet-iron stove, not knowing that Mrs. Smith was counting every one.

He stayed all evening as the storm continued its fury. Indeed, so terrible was its raging that he stayed all night, a fact that caused Mrs. Smith so much perturbation that after giving him her own room, she made a bed for herself on a couch in the hall in sight of Miss Carter's door.

CHAPTER XVIII

EASTER had come to the valley, too.

In spite of the fact that hitherto the winters had been severe, the seventh one for the settlers, that of 1872 and '73 was unusually fine,—practically an open one with little or no snow. Not once had Amalia missed church, nor had she been forced to stay away from Anna Kratz's for two months at a time as in some of those past seasons.

Almost every other week she had taken Emil to Anna's and spent the afternoon piecing her quilt,—Anna returning the visit the next week. Sometimes she had to walk when Herman was busy or angry about something that had gone wrong with the stock or his tools or the feed. Then he would storm and rage and Amalia would go quietly about her work until he had slammed his way out of the cabin and down to the stable, when she would slip out and trudge the long way over to Anna's.

It would soon be seven years since she and Anna had been married the same day by the side of the Cut-off trail near Nebraska City. Anna had her fourth child this week,—three boys and a girl now.

Only this Easter morning on the way home from Confirmation services in the log church on the knoll Herman had thrown it up to her, saying that Adolph would have help a plenty in a few years and how could one expect to get ahead and have more land with just one son to work it with him.

Amalia, feeling bold, had said: "Emil will not be working the land when a pastor he is to be."

It had set Herman off. Even though it was Easter Sunday and he had sung lustily with the others *"O Du Fröliche, O Du Selige,"* already on the way home he was talking of land,—always talking more land and that Emil should hurry and grow up to help work it, and was now in a rage that she was suggesting otherwise.

"The Holmsdorfers have always been for the land."

"My mother was from a pastor's family," Amalia said. "Her father and her grandfather in Germany were well educated and were pastors."

"Let others do the preaching," Herman struck at the horses in his anger so the wagon bounced over the rutty prairie trail. *"My* son works."

At home Amalia changed her dress to her everyday one, built up her fire and prepared her dinner. Wilhelm and Fritz came as always to have the Sunday meal with them. Sometimes several families took dinner together, —once in a while all eleven of them.

The door of the cabin stood open for the day was almost hot with a strong wind from the south. Amalia had worn her straw bonnet—of the fashion of many years ago—to church, so summer-like had it been. For several weeks men had been working in the fields. Only Saturday Herman had plowed all day in his shirt sleeves. Every indication of winter had vanished.

"Everything is getting green," Herman said to the men when he had finished the *tisch gebet*.

Herman made the table prayer no matter what his

mood. Sometimes when scolding loudly, he would stop suddenly, make the *tisch gebet:*

"Komm Herr Yesu, sei unser Gast und segne was Du uns bescheret hast."

And even though he had said this: "Come, Lord Jesus, be our Guest and bless what Thou hast prepared for us," at the *"Amen"* he would be raising his head and continuing the loud fault-finding as though nothing had intervened, as though he had never prayed the table prayer.

"Yes. Green and pretty," Amalia added. She was glad he was so safely over his anger of the morning.

"Of the pretty we do not care," he snapped. "It is the green for crops we need."

Amalia looked at her plate and said nothing. To Herman there was no need to speak ever of the prettiness of things. Why did she ever do it when she knew he did not care? But to little Emil—that was different. Always she called his attention to the red at the edge of the sunset clouds and the light on the prairie like lakes of gold. He was to be a *pastor* and he must see the beautiful along with the ugly burdens. He must sense the presence of God in every leaf and wild flower. It would help him in his work.

The meal went on, a mere consuming of food and talk of the land and the mares they were buying.

Herman and Wilhelm were leaving right after dinner for one of the Englishmen's homesteads, that of Mr. Lawrence, about seven miles away. "Together we can manage the mares we are to bring," they decided.

"Fritz does not go?"

"*Nein.* If we are late he does the chores for both."

By two o'clock, with the men gone, shifting clouds scudded low across the blue of the spring sky. A little later when surprisingly a slow drizzling sprinkle began, Amalia tied a shawl over her head, put a jacket on Emil and together they went out for eggs.

"So early it is for the eggs," she explained to him, "but later it will rain harder."

Emil was five now, sturdy and strong, his round apple-cheeked face a miniature Herman's. He grasped the basket interwoven with its carpet rags and swung along ahead of Amalia on big stocky legs, calling back German sentences. "I can myself the eggs hunt," and fiercely: "The old hens will I scare."

They gathered the eggs at the straw-stack, Amalia calling out warnings not to go so high, or not go so close to the cow; with Emil, proudly brave, doing the very things of which *Mutter* was fearful.

While they were hunting around the stack down toward the creek-bed where an old hen often stole her nest, the skies grew darker and a chill wind blew in from the northwest. By the time they were in the house rain was falling almost sleet-like in its harshness.

In the midst of the chilling rain, Fritz arrived to do the chores, explaining that he was doing Herman's first and their own later. He wished his father and Herman would get in. "Almost I would say we would have a blizzard if the season was not so late."

When he had finished and gone back home, the clouds grew very black and hung low with a menacing appearance. Amalia watched them from the cabin's small window. The rain turned in truth then to sleet,—then to snow so fine and thick that Amalia could no longer see out of the window. She kept up the fire with the wood from the creek-bed, put Emil to bed very early and sat down close to the stove to wait.

It was a blizzard by now.

She could hear the wild winds of it shrieking about the cabin, feel its blasts shaking the little structure as though the great breath of some insane giant were trying to blow it over. The men folks would not have left the homestead of the Lawrences', of that she was certain. The rain had turned to sleet so early in the afternoon that they would not have started on the long trek across the open prairie.

She crawled into bed beside the sleeping Emil, his rosy face close to hers, and though she said her prayers to the good *Gott* for safety, she shivered with fright whenever the roaring wind shook the cabin. Toward morning she slept,—and because she had been awake so long in the early part of the night, overslept, realizing it when she came to herself with a start.

Sitting up quickly, she had the sensation of a peculiar whiteness about her, as of a strange fantastic light. Everything was white,—the bed blankets were covered with a white powdered snow,—the small window of the cabin was packed solid with it.

Hastily she dressed and leaving Emil sleeping, went out into the coldness of the other room. With freezing fingers she made a fire in the little stove and as its flame tore madly with the wind into the chimney, fearful of setting the cabin on fire, wished she had not done so.

With Herman caught away from home at the Lawrences', she must feed the stock. So she bundled herself in an old coat of his, tied a scarf tightly over her hair and prepared to plunge into the storm.

As she opened the door the fury of the thing was overwhelming. It rushed into the room like a white mad animal. The air itself appeared to be one huge mass of moist and moving snow. The wind howled like so many hungry coyotes.

She stepped out into the welter, scarcely able to pull the door against the fury of the thing, and sank to her hips in a moist and smothering snowbank. Some instinct made her keep one hand tightly clasped to the cabin doorlatch. She held the other mittened one up now to her face and could not see its outline.

For a time she stood there, buffeted, hip deep in the drift, not knowing what to do. But Fritz could not get through this welter from his place she was sure. The stock in the barn needed her,—there were two cows to be milked . . . and the chickens to be fed.

A blast of wind, wilder than the preceding ones, tore the shawl from her head and, unthinking, she let go of the doorlatch to grab for the flying headgear. Immediately she was down in the snowbank gasping for breath like a drowning thing. Frantically she reached back for the door and met only the emptiness of the snow-packed air.

CHAPTER XIX

I AM not four feet from the house," Amalia said to herself, frantic at feeling nothing but the snow-filled air. "It must be here . . . or here . . . or there. . . ."

But it was not there. It was as though the house had vanished, leaving her in a welter of flying, whirling clouds of snow. Arms out, she staggered frantically, her eyes and mouth and nostrils filled with the smothering thing. One thought only possessed her, as it has possessed good mothers always,—her child. She must get to little Emil, alone in the cabin, sleeping there in his bed.

She wallowed, fell, picked herself from the great drifts and staggered about. Frantic, she lunged first in one direction and then another. And then . . . the wall! The good solid wall hitting her suddenly from out a sea of emptiness. *Gott sei dank.* And God be thanked for trees and logs and shelter from the wild elements.

She clung with mittened freezing fingers to the chinks between the logs until she might regain her breath. This way lay the stoop and door. She moved cautiously along, never taking her hands from the wall. When she felt snow piled shoulder-high against the solid thing, she would not remove her hold, but fought the white moist mass with her other hand and shoulders. And it seemed that she would never be able to work herself through the dense mountain. It was so smothering . . . so . . .

She was through. But strangely, here was a corner of the house. How could there be a corner? She must have hit the cabin on the narrow side that first time she had found it in a sea of snow,—shuddered to think she might have missed it entirely.

And now there was this other side to be traversed. It seemed hours that she fought her way through, clinging always to the logs lest for one instant she lose their feel.

And then she stumbled, and the thing that had caused her to stumble was the stoop. With numb hands she clung, worked them slowly up through the hard-packed mass, not seeing, doing all by sense of touch. The latch! With one last exertion of her body she flung herself onto the latch,—into the room,—pushed the door back against the mad white giant, drunk with the power of his strength, trying to follow her into the house.

She must have fainted, for when she knew what was next happening, Emil in his flannel nightgown was bending over her, pulling at her eyelids, calling *"Mutter,"*— and she was down on the floor in a slushy bed of snow that had dropped from her garments.

All day and all night the storm raged. Wild white fingers plucked at the little cabin standing lonely on the prairie, a continent away from the other cabins on the adjoining homesteads, as far away from Fritz in his log house on the next acreage as though a sea separated them. Indeed, it was an ocean that parted them, with snowdrifts for water and Death riding the waves.

All day and all night with the snow blowing under the door and seeping in through every crack, Amalia tried to make her supply of wood last. In the afternoon of the second day she went to bed with Emil clasped in her arms, both fully dressed, and with the quilts wrapped about them. If only they could have foreseen how bad it was to be, Fritz would have stayed here with them for safety and for company. Many times she thought of her father and Herman, thankful that the blizzard must have come on before they started home.

On the third day the storm abated, and the sun came out upon a world devoid of color. White everywhere,— nothing but a sparkling white world and a blue sky, as though an inverted blue china bowl met the rim of a white plate.

Fritz, after nearly a half-day's work through the drifts, managed to get to Amalia. He told her tales she could scarcely believe,—his horses had stamped so much snow under their hoofs that their backs were near the shed roof. Frozen prairie chickens were everywhere and a deer lay dead between the house and the barn. The trees along the river banks were not visible,—only a great solid white wall traced the way of the stream.

Out at the stable he found a horse nearly embedded in snow, frozen chickens, a calf almost lifeless so that he brought it into the house, much to Emil's excited delight.

He agreed verbally with Amalia that the storm would have struck before the menfolks started home, but each knew the other in his heart was not entirely confident.

All day and part of the next Amalia waited to hear from the two men.

And then Ludwick Rhodenbach and August Schaffer

found Wilhelm Stoltz lying against the wagon-box which he had turned on its side to protect himself from the onslaught of the storm. He was unconscious, his feet frozen stiff.

They took him home. When he gained consciousness and could talk, he said he did not know where Herman was,—that he had set out across the prairie for Rudolph Kratz's house. Later a doctor came on horseback across the prairie from the far-away new town of Westville, and amputated Wilhelm's feet,—the feet that had walked with unceasing energy beside the ox-cart all the way from Illinois.

The snows began to melt under the April sun and the river rose. Every hollow and ravine that ran in an easterly or westerly direction was filled with snow from rim to rim. Shacks had been unroofed and people in them frozen. Travelers caught out in the wild onslaught were found when the drifts melted weeks afterward.

The Kratzes out hunting for their horses came across the dead body of Herman. It was at the head of a small canyon pocket, his gun by his side. Evidently he had died on his knees having crawled into the narrow place to get such slight protection from the cold as its walls would afford.

They brought him home to Amalia.

Mrs. Rudolph Kratz and Anna came ahead to tell her. They wanted to break it gently. As though Death is ever gentle.

But when Anna saw Amalia standing at the stove cooking *suppe* for her sick father and thought how the two

couples were married the same day so romantically outdoors by the side of the trail, and how she would feel if
it were Adolph, she threw her apron over her head, burst
into wild weeping, and could not tell.

So the older Mrs. Rudolph Kratz said it bluntly:
"Amalia, you have lost your Herman. They find him
dead."

Amalia stood as one paralyzed and yet wondering
sanely how one can lose something one has never had.

In the days that followed she could not sense what was
happening. It was too strange. She moved in and out of
the cabin and went over to her father's bedside while
Mrs. Rudolph Kratz and old Augusta Schaffer bathed
that which had been Herman and dressed it in its black
suit.

She shed no tears, and for that they whispered among
themselves that she would go crazy if she did not cry.

The neighbors brought *met-wurst* and *kuchen* and all
their children, set the table and ate a great deal and
talked of Herman,—how good he was at turning the new
sod and breaking colts and how mad he would have been
to know the two mares he had already paid good money
for, froze to death on the way home.

Amalia let Mrs. Kratz and Augusta Schaffer swathe a
great black veil around her head that made her feel
suffocated and from which she asked frantically to be
let out at once, for behind its thickness it seemed that
she was in blinding black snow and could not breathe nor
find little Emil.

Herman was buried while Wilhelm still lay hurling
his huge bulk against the wall in the throes of death.

With the prairie soggy from the melting snows and the teams of the settlers hitched all around the log church on the hill, Amalia sat through the long services for Herman, and saw him lowered under the sod that he had known so deftly how to break. And now some one else had broken a little patch of prairie sod for Herman. Who was Herman? A man whose house she had kept and whose bread she had baked and by whose side . . .

And then she thought of little Emil, whose hand she held so tightly, and suddenly burst into wild sobbing.

At that all the women in their black funeral clothes pursed their lips and nodded solemnly to each other across the soggy pile of dirt. She was now all right, having passed the tearless stage. Now she would not go crazy. She had cared so much for her man she had been on the way to going insane. *Verrückt.*

But Amalia was not crying for having thought so much of her man. For herself she was like a stone,—she had no feeling. She was crying because every little boy ought to have a father, and now her little boy had none.

Three days after Herman was buried, Amalia's father died, too.

It was a hard death that old Wilhelm Stoltz had to meet, far harder than Herman's painless sleeping in the snow,—gangrene from the frozen feet, amputation, and after that a lingering and terrible passing.

Never sick a day in his life, always his own master and dictator of those about him, when he realized that he was not to get well,—that, like Herman, he too could never again crack the blacksnake, never break the new sod or plant or reap, never face the wild winds of the prairie or buffet the storms,—he grew hard and bitter and turned on the God whom he had addressed so fervently and for whose worship he had come into the new land. But at the last, with the fever consuming him, when he was worn and spent with his ravings and knew that he must obey the absolute Dictator, he grew meek and muttered humble supplications.

But even then he could not leave his authoritative position without a last strangle-hold upon the lives of his children. He called Fritz to the bedside, bade him bring the big Bible.

"Put . . . your hand on it. A promise make me."

Fritz obeyed. He had always obeyed.

"You will never marry. To look after Amalia and little Emil you will stay single."

Fritz swallowed hard. His bronze face paled. Twenty-two he was, warm-blooded and ready for a wife. Already in the church services he had cast longing eyes toward Minnie Rhodenbach, a young widow with a small child. He could not speak out his mind that it was cruel to expect such a promise. He could scarcely have done so if his father were well. How could he, then, when Death hovered over him?

"Before God . . . you promise?"

Fritz's tall lanky body shook as though he, too, felt the coldness of the grave, and saw its darkness. This looking on at a passing, it was a fearsome thing, at this Death that laid low the two huge frames of his father and brother-in-law. He wet his dry lips. "But if Amalia marries and has protection?" he ventured.

"It releases you. But you will not tell her of your oath. Promise."

Fritz turned frightened eyes toward the log church in the distance as though he might there see the soft round face of Minnie Rhodenbach with dimples at the mouth's corners.

"Promise." Wilhelm heaved himself fearfully on his elbow, his deep-set eyes, glassy in death, piercing those of his son. *"Gleich!"*

"I promise."

They buried old Wilhelm, too,—not old,—but seeming so because of the weatherbeaten countenance and the huge gnarled frame and his long years of hard work beginning in the German mines when he was twelve.

There were four graves now on the high knoll of the church acreage. Sometimes the fierce sun blazed down on them and the hot southwest winds blew. Sometimes the tumble-weeds rolled over them and the crows circled low. And sometimes the great prairie snows piled high between the mounds.

But wind or sun or snows, it was very quiet out there where Herman and old Wilhelm lay.

CHAPTER XX

IN the strange days that followed Herman's death and that of her father, also, in the Easter blizzard, Amalia could not seem to adjust herself to the new way of living. She appreciated the kindness of all the families, knowing how little they had to give from their meager supplies and seeing how generous they were in their giving. For all of them came now bearing gifts to show their sorrow to one who was never anything but kind to them and gentle.

The women brought home-made *käse* and wild *pflau-men-butter*. The men drove in to see about the stock and corn-planting.

She thanked them all, but told them Fritz was going to move over here with her, and bring their father's stock and equipment. She and Fritz would get along fine. She even laughed at a little joke she made that Fritz had always been her favorite brother, when they knew she had only Fritz. Anna Kratz was ashamed for Amalia that she had joked that way before the men, and Herman so recently taken.

"But maybe Fritz wants a wife now and farm his father's place for himself," Elsa Rhodenbach suggested, having been sent as a sort of official spy by her sister Minnie.

But Amalia only laughed aloud at her,—twice to-day she had laughed. "Fritz isn't looking around any yet."

She had a queer feeling of deception; that she was

pretending to be something she was not,—that she was two women, the real Amalia and one who must act a part.

She had shed tears over the passing of Herman and her father, and neither death had touched that which was away down inside her being.

She had been shaken by the shock of both tragedies and the awfulness of the presence of death in the house; but a few days later something inside her had soared as at a release. She would have been ashamed to have any of the women know it. From Anna Kratz who mourned over her constantly because of the double marriage and the closeness of their friendship, she must always keep the knowledge. But it was true. She felt free without Herman's loud orders and his clutching hands upon her, without her father's constant commands and the fear of his opinions. Only for little Emil was she sad. But she and Fritz would teach him to mind them without fear. She and Fritz would be all that Herman had been and more.

In the late summer she unwrapped the shell box which Matthias had given her and left it openly for a few weeks on her walnut bureau, so that all the feminine contingent of the Kratz and Schaffer, the Gebhardt and Rhodenbach women might see and admire and envy, but never know from whence it came.

Fritz, seeing it there with its shining Roman snails and angel-wings, moon shells and fragile fan-shaped ones, said suddenly:

"Amalia . . . you are a young widow. You are . . ." he was embarrassed, ". . . are free."

She had thought of it too. She had known how wicked

it was, but how could she help it,—who had loved Matthias so?

"You would write . . . a letter, Amalia?" If poor Fritz was thinking of Minnie Rhodenbach more than of Amalia,—no one knew it, so who was there to chide?

Amalia shook her head. "Don't speak of it, Fritz. It is not right . . . and seven years is too long. I would only hurt myself to hear of his marriage."

So it came about that Fritz, his mind working a little slowly perhaps, but with stubborn persistence, one day wrote the letter himself, painstakingly, in the German, telling no one, and mailed it to the iron foundry in Illinois.

CHAPTER XXI

BACK in the growing town of Lincoln Ida Carter gave up her private school in June. She and Matthias were to be married on September 20th, the wedding to be at the McCurdeys', for the trip back to her home in Massachusetts would have been long and expensive. The two had now definitely come to another decision, rather a queer one and with Matthias a long time in coming to see it as Ida did,—she was going in the store with him. At first he had thought it all wrong, later came to agree with her that a woman's taste and intuitions might be a good thing in the business.

"When we make our first fifty thousand dollars, I'll stop," she had said laughingly, so that Matthias laughed too at the huge sum.

They were going to live at the boarding-house. "When we get to making money and I stop the store work, we'll have a fine home," she told him.

All summer she was having her new dresses made, the making of a dress taking far longer than the recent making of the new state constitution, the latter not having pleats, panniers, and panels.

The town to a man was interested in the coming event. Plans were secretly under way for a charivari. Matthias had a new horse and high buggy, and the sight of the two fine-looking young people,—Ida with her gray dress and cape and small straw bonnet, Matthias in his dark suit and high hat and with his black beard trimmed in its neat square-cut style,—driving around the dusty streets or through the splashing mud was a sign for much attention from the sidewalk portion of the population.

Mrs. McCurdey was rather beside herself with importance, many cakes to be baked, an elderberry drink to be made and saying often: "Oh, if only there could be such a thing as plenty of ice in the summer."

The invitations were to be mailed out the sixth of September.

On the fifth Matthias received a letter from Fritz Stoltz sent on to him by his uncle in Illinois.

He cut into it at the desk in the back part of the store, not knowing whose stilted German-looking script was before him. When he saw it was from Amalia's brother, he was as surprised as amazed.

It was formally written, the penmanship painstakingly done as by a small boy, although Matthias knew Fritz must be a young man by now.

He read it slowly, carefully, his pulse beating rapidly at this first word in all the seven years concerning the girl he had so loved.

Amalia was a widow, the letter said,—the man she had married because of her father's wishes had been frozen to death in the Easter blizzard of last spring, and their father, too. Matthias shuddered as he read it, remembering the fury of the storm the night he had stayed at Ida's. He had read of many deaths out on the prairie at that time. One of them, then, was Amalia's husband and one her father, and he had not dreamed there was any one frozen to death of whom he had ever heard.

Amalia was free now, Fritz said, but did not know he was writing, would never know that he had done so. He could say that he knew Amalia still loved Matthias although she had never said it in so many words. When he had spoken to her about him, she had said he was no doubt married by this time. If this was true, or if Matthias had forgotten Amalia, he need never take the trouble to answer. But it seemed only right and truthful to let him know that Amalia was free.

Concluding the missive Matthias felt a combination of emotions,—sadness for the cruelty of the girl's mismanaged life, an irritation that the letter had come in just as the invitations for his marriage were to go out, an annoyance that the brother had written at all, but in spite of all this, a revival of love for the little Amalia which would not down. The affair had been as a book that was closed, or a song that was sung,—and now the pages were fluttering open, a strain of the old music was in the air.

All day he went about his business with the letter on his mind and a mixed group of emotions within him. He listened to the merry quips of friends who made bold to speak of the coming event and was provoked that they had taken upon themselves the freedom to do so. He was angry at Fritz for writing and angry that he had not done so sooner.

It weighed so upon him that when he went to Ida's in the evening, he was preoccupied, not himself. Ida, with her quick intuition, caught the mood, asked him about it.

"If there's anything troubling you, Matt,—don't you think it's a better way to begin our married life by talking it over? If I'm wrong for asking, forgive me. It's only . . . that I care . . . and want to help."

How good she was and capable and understanding. Suddenly he wanted to tell her, to go to her as a boy would to his mother, and let her know this upsetting thing which had happened.

He showed her, then, the letter, translating it from the German, for she could not read it. It eased his mind. Already he felt the weight of the burden lifting that she was knowing about the matter.

"I'm glad you have done this, Matt." Ida was cool and poised, keeping from him how it had shaken her to the depths. "I appreciate it. It makes me know how frank you are, and how honest you would have been with me."

" '*Would have been*,' Ida! You can't . . . This doesn't mean anything to me . . . not *anything* now, excepting a bit of sorrow for . . . for her. You must know it. I shouldn't have shown you the letter . . . I was . . ."

"Listen, Matt." She was firm of voice, still poised, but he did not see how her hands were holding each other tightly, each trying to keep the other from its trembling.

"There is something I must know . . . to-night . . . just now . . . before the invitations go out to-morrow. You owe it to me . . . to yourself . . . to her. Answer me this, Matt. Everything depends upon what you say. I can't go on until I know. If we two—this other young woman and I—were side by side in this room. . . . If she . . . just as you knew her . . . and I . . . just as I am . . . were here together. . . . If you walked in here and we were waiting, which one would you choose?"

She was looking bravely at him, her gray eyes steady and unflinching, watching to ascertain how the question affected him, and yet not wanting to see.

Matthias did not hesitate. He looked back steadily into the honest depths of her eyes. "All right," he could even smile now. "You are here . . . and she is here. I am to choose between you. But you have omitted something. What you have forgotten to say is that two Matthias Meiers would walk in here, a twenty-one-year-old one and I. You and I don't care much which one the young cub would choose, now do we? What concerns us is that I . . . the man standing here beside you, would choose *you*."

"Unqualifiedly, Matt?" She searched his face.

"Unqualifiedly. Does it satisfy you?"

"It satisfies me. You're good to put it that way. I think you believe it. I'll never mention her again."

He kissed her,—more tenderly than he had ever done. She cried hard for a few moments so that he comforted her but could not understand the tears. They were the last she shed for any hurt from Matthias, for she was not the crying kind.

In his boarding-house, he went over the queer quality of the question . . . Ida's intensity, the unusualness of her suppressed emotion, his satisfied feeling that the answer he made had been the right one.

But he could not get to sleep. For a long time he lay listening to the early morning sounds of the small town,— a milk wagon going through the street, its cans rattling together, a night watchman's tramp of feet on the high wooden sidewalk.

Just as he was dropping off, dimly between him and the window he saw Amalia, pink and white, infinitely sweet and alluring, heard vaguely for a moment the sound of a meadow-lark and the honk of wild geese flying.

He called to her, his arms seeking her, but she was gone. He woke and lay very still, breathing hard, shaken by the queer thing he had dreamed.

The next day the duties of the store, the meeting with people who spoke of the coming wedding and congratulated him on the young woman he was choosing, Ida's natural talk about her preparation for the wedding, drove into the realm of the unreal the momentary pangs he had felt concerning the girl he once loved so deeply.

In the evening he wrote an answer to Fritz,—several of them. "I am going to be married" was the theme of one,—"I am married," of another. "Remember me kindly to Amalia" and "Give my love to your sister."

Then he wrote one to Amalia herself, trying several ways to express that which he wished to say, realizing his written German was atrocious, and disliking them all; for how could he put into it the delicate touch that would convey to her all that she had once been to him, tell her that he, too, was living in Nebraska now because of her,—that he had tried to get to her but had been caught by sucking sands,—and yet hold her aloof?

He destroyed them all,—and wrote no other.

CHAPTER XXII

LIFE among the German neighbors in the valley went on in much the same way that it had gone on before the deaths of Wilhelm Stoltz and Herman Holmsdorfer in the Easter blizzard.

Wilhelm and Herman both would have said in their arrogant way that the settlers could not get along without their help and advice,—that Fritz and Amalia would not know what to do with no daily commands to guide them in their work, that they would lose the stock and bungle the crops and nothing would be *recht*.

But life closes over the vacancies and goes on. The settlers managed very well without the two, through some of the most trying years of the state. Fritz and Amalia did as well as the others, which is not saying a great deal, for the first few years following the Easter blizzard were lean years.

There were prairie fires and blizzards, grasshoppers and drouths, Indian raids too close for comfort. Prices for farm products were so low that it did not pay to haul the scanty crop to market. So Fritz and Amalia along with the neighbors began burning corn for fuel. In the little shiningly polished four-holed stove of Amalia's neat cabin it would snap and crackle and hold its heat as well as any coal would have done. They burned hard twisted prairie hay, too, at times.

Amalia made the garden, in the good German way, but

she would not go into the field with Fritz as Lena Schaffer and young Mrs. Henry Gebhardt and some of the others did for their menfolks.

In spite of the hardships that confronted them always, the entire colony stayed just a little out of the reach of starvation and failure. The unceasing labors and good management of the homesteads by the men,—the thriftiness of the women,—these brought the settlers safely through a half-dozen years which drove those of less thrift and stamina from the scene.

To Amalia it was pleasant to have Fritz around. Even-tempered, a little jolly at times now that he was his own master, Fritz was a comfortable companion. He took a great deal of pride in Emil too, teaching him masculine chores,—taking him down to the creek for muskrat trapping, allowing him to drive the big team when by his side on the high wagon-seat, letting him husk corn so that his hard little palms grew more calloused. It caused Amalia to say one day to Fritz: "A good father you will be some day, Fritz,—kind and understanding."

But Fritz did not answer, and walked off to the stable hurriedly as though cross at her saying so.

The day that Minnie Rhodenbach was married to Karl Schaffer, Fritz went away to Westville with corn for the grinding, so that Amalia was ashamed he had gone and made excuses why he was not at the wedding festivities which lasted all day, and neither would he later go to the christening of Minnie's baby, little Christina, so stubborn about it he was.

The fall Emil was seven, Amalia got him ready for the Parochial school held now in the log church. She made him a suit out of an old one of her father's, every stitch in it tiny and neat, each one a thought or a wish or a prayer for the sturdy little son.

"You will now learn all there is to know in books," she said to him. "Then you will be a fine pastor."

"Yes . . . a pastor I will like to be . . . I can shout and the pulpit I can pound harder than any."

Amalia laughed at that. "Oh, but there is more to do than shout and pound. You must know books and all that is in the Bible. You much preach wise sermons. You must be kind, and know when to give advice. You must live right and have every act a good one. You must not sing loudly and pray loudly and then after that say and do unkind things. That is not Christianity."

Amalia would not have said: "You must not do this way as your father and your grandfather did." But in her heart she knew she was drawing pictures of them both.

The morning Emil was to start, Fritz brought the team and wagon up to the cabin to take him part of the way. Amalia had his lunch put up in the smallest egg-basket. One would have thought from the contents she expected her small son to stay a week rather than a day. From a larder more meager than usual since the grasshopper siege, she had managed to furnish *speck* and *korn brot* and *äpfelschnitz*, which the English neighbors would have called side meat, corn-bread and dried apples.

Emil was excited, loud and noisy. He ran in and out of the cabin with the slate that had belonged to Fritz under his arm.

Amalia thought she could not stand it, could not bear to see Emil go away from her to the school. But she must be brave, must not let this trouble her, for after his fourteenth year and Confirmation, he must then go on farther away for his learning. Then would it be time to be troubled at his leaving.

But now that the day had come for schooling and he was sturdily climbing high over the big wheel of the wagon, she called to Fritz to wait, ran and got her shawl and her bonnet, set her *korn mehl maus* back on the stove, and went with them.

At the last half-mile, Emil did not want them to go with him farther, told them to stop here, so he could get out and walk the rest of the distance, that the other children might not know he had been brought in a wagon.

"He is a real boy," Fritz said, watching him trudge through the rank prairie grass, brandishing a stick toward a host of imaginary enemies.

But Amalia, sitting in the wagon and gazing after him, could not see what Emil was doing; so blurred a little figure did he look that he seemed swimming in the liquid prairie grass.

Always, these years, Fritz worked constantly. Even when others, far from lazy, were through their work and would congregate in groups to talk over the drouth and the 'hopper damage, the war with the Sioux, the rush into the Black Hills for gold, Fritz must be on the go. The first one in the morning at work and the last one at night must Fritz always be. Often Amalia, looking at him, wondered what was driving him so. Every one worked hard, but he hardest of all.

Sometimes she would say to him: "Fritz, are you never going to get yourself a wife?"

He would laugh at that. "For the girls I do not care," he usually answered, but once when she said it playfully, he turned on her fiercely: "*You* should ask that." And went out to the field, although he had just come in, so that for a long time Amalia tried to think why he said that peculiar thing.

By 1878, times began to be better. When the colonists came together now, there was not so much head shaking, not so much talk of drouth and poor crops and hardships, —more talk of railroads being built,—of the Republican Valley being settled, of the Pawnees all removed to Oklahoma, of the north part of the state being opened to settlers. Crops were better. Fritz was raising enough to eat and even selling a little corn.

There were noticeable changes in the twelve years. A few fences were here and there around door-yards and gardens. Old wagon trails over the prairie had the appearance of real roads. The trees had made unbelievable growth, especially the cottonwoods with their merry leaves, never gloomy, never silent, always dancing in any kind of weather. There was a whole flock of children who had not come in with the wagons,—native-born little Schaffers and Kratzes, Rhodenbachs and Gebhardts. And there were six graves there where the tumble-weeds rolled in the autumn and the sun blazed down in summer and the snows piled in winter.

And Amalia was changed too. Although she still braided her once-golden hair neatly and wound it around her head, it was now rather like sun-burned straw. And the rose-petal of her skin was gone, too, and in its place a redness seared into the delicate flesh by the prairie winds.

So now with times looking up, and Fritz and Amalia such good managers, they built a new house to take the place of the cabin, twelve years old and grown too small and shabby.

Fritz told Amalia to pick out the exact spot of ground she wanted for it, and while she was making her selection she had a swift thought that Herman would not have been so considerate,—that like her father he would have dictated both place and the plans as he wanted them. Amalia was rather happy these days with her brother Fritz and husky Emil, now eleven years old.

Fritz built sturdily and well, even though it took him all through the year, for he must do his regular work first. Amalia drove the team to Westville several times, a day's trip, bringing lumber home.

There was a little cellar this time into which they could put the potatoes and pumpkins, turnips and onions for winter's use and into which they could go if a storm threatened. Amalia was more proud of her cellar than any other part of the house. Fritz built a slanting outside cellar door upon which she could sun her milk crocks, and Amalia set out wild gooseberry and currant bushes close by. Almost was it going to seem like the farm-house in Illinois where she was born. There were four rooms,— a sitting room, a kitchen and two bedrooms. Oh, it was rather grand. Amalia could scarce keep the pride from showing when Anna Kratz and Lena Schaffer and the Gebhardts and the Rhodenbachs all came to see the skeleton of it going up there on the prairie.

On a day in November, an Indian summer day with the

sun shining hazily on the wide brown prairie and the trees over by the river's brink yellow and bronze, and the sumac flaming red, Amalia moved into the shining new four-roomed house.

The wooden floors were scrubbed until one almost saw one's face in them and the new rag rug which she had woven was placed exactly in the center of the sitting-room until such time as they might have carpeting. The walnut table held the Bible and a conch shell, and on the wall were hung the two pictures from the old home,— the *Gute Nacht* and *Guten Morgen,* two chunky semi-nude little girls with daisies in their hair. There was a motto too, which Amalia's mother had worked in the old country in dainty stitches, *Gott Segne Unser Heim,* as though God seeing it there constantly would not fail to bless their home. Two rocking-chairs and a book-shelf that Fritz had made from ends of the lumber for the few German books completed the furnishings.

The kitchen held the table and the cook-stove with the iron hearth, the pots and pans and four straight chairs. Fritz put wooden pegs on the walls for the coats and hats, made a fresh new wood-box, and for Amalia's birthday bought a gay blue mirror with tin comb-box underneath. In Amalia's bedroom was the heavy walnut bureau from her mother, and sometimes she was greatly torn between leaving it there or having it back in the sitting-room where strangers stopping on their trips across the prairie could see it.

It started a perfect disease of unrest among the neighbor women; followed by an orgy of building. "If Amalia Holmsdorfer can have a new home of boughten lumber, so can I," became almost a slogan up and down the river.

Anna Kratz had a new house with five rooms, where-upon Lena Schaffer could not rest until she had six. Oh, but the German colony took upon itself the appearance of more comfortable circumstances.

All of these years Amalia had been very close to her boy. Always she was talking to him of lovely things, of the beauty in nature, of the way God manifested Him-self,—showing him the gentler side of life and the more tender. She walked with him in the timber along the river and talked of the trees as though they were humans,—the ash and the willow, the cottonwood and the wild sumac. She taught him many things for which Fritz had no time or inclination. Together they picked the violets and the ground-plums, the black-eyed Susans and the trillium, bellwort and bloodroot and wild colum-bine, although Amalia's names for them were not always as these. Together they found the meadow-lark's nest in the prairie grass and the place where the owls hooted the night away. She stood with him on the church knoll which looked over the valley and had him repeat with her the Psalm of walking through the valley of the shadow of death and yet fearing no evil.

She had him climb and put back a woodpecker's young one that had fallen from a nest, called him each night to stop work for a moment and see the sunset's after-glow, and bade him note that all things happening now were still like miracles of old.

Sometimes Fritz grew cross at these teachings. *"Du wirst ihm ganz verzärteln,"* he would say disparagingly.

But Amalia knew she would not make him a softie, that it did not make a softie of any one to love beauty in nature. And a *pastor,*—how could a *pastor* better understand humans than to see God in everything?

So time went on and spring came and turned into hot summer with the meadow-larks' songs stilled in the heat. Summer turned into fall with the corn ripe in the shock and the dried tumble-weeds rolling across the prairie like so many brown waves of the sea. And almost before Fritz and Amalia could realize it, Emil was nearly fourteen,—nearly to his Confirmation. After that would come going away to more schooling in preparation for his work.

On this spring day Amalia was thinking how it would seem next fall without him. But to sustain her in the loneliness it would mean she had only to vision him in the pulpit in his black robe, and she knew she must make no outcry about his going. When the other boys of his age were at their farm work, he would be studying away at the Lutheran college, and the thought filled her with an ecstasy of pleasure. She would work her fingers to the bone for Emil's schooling, and Fritz would help her.

Even as Amalia was cherishing these pleasant thoughts, Emil was sitting near the opened window in the little school-house looking out at spring coming over the prairie country, as though it were a person and he could see its tangible form. It was in the call of the crows, in the warmth of the sun, in the odors of the loam.

He fumbled the dog-eared reader, looked at a paragraph which contained no meaning: *"In-zwischen hatte Johann Hus die Schriften von Wycliffe gellesen."*

As though he cared that in the meantime Johann Hus had the writings of Wycliffe read.

Back to the window he turned his lack-luster eyes. Over by Willow Creek there was a faint tinge of green against the gray of the branches. The rolling prairie stretched as far as the eye could see. On the top of a knoll far off, a man and team and plow were silhoueted against the horizon. Maybe it was Uncle Fritz. For a moment they were all poised there as though drawn with pencil,—then they passed out of sight.

Something broke in Emil. Some queer condition arose in his whole being over which he seemed to have no control. He took the two other thumbed old books out of his desk and a cracked slate with red flannel binding, tied them to the reader with a frayed piece of rope, and stood up.

The master rapped sharply on the desk: "What are you doing, Emil?"

"I go home."

"What do you mean? Sit down."

Emil, already on his way to the door, turned and shook his head stolidly.

The teacher advanced toward him, ruler in hand, but he broke into a clumping run, passed the bucket of water and was at once out on the moist prairie grass, from which vantage point he turned and gave a delicate thumb-to-nose gesture of farewell.

He could not have told just what happened,—did not fully sense that he was happily freed from the intricacies of arithmetic and the geography of unknown and undesirable countries, of memorizing hymns and Catechism and

verses. All he knew was that the school-house had caged
him, that spring called,—and the Land.

As he walked over the spongy ground just released from
its frost, he felt rather than thought about the world
around him. There was the first warm sunshine, and the
odors of the prairie ground from which the new grass
would soon shoot. As he looked a long V-shaped line of
wild geese went over. He watched them until they
dropped into the north swampland, then turned on his
heel and broke into a run toward home.

It was nearly noon when he arrived with his lunch still
untouched.

Amalia, seeing him coming across the open field, ran
out to meet him. "What is it?" she called. Nothing but
illness or trouble with the teacher would bring him home.

Now that he was here he did not know quite so well how
to handle it.

Fritz came up from the stable. Emil had not thought
of this contingency. Twice Uncle Fritz had licked him
when his mother told him to. He could feel the last
thrashing yet. Uncle Fritz didn't dare now. If Uncle
Fritz touched him he would light in and thrash too.

"I come home," he said stolidly.

"I see," said Fritz. "But why?"

"I'm through school," he swallowed hard.

Amalia was pale to the lips,—it took schooling and
much of it for the *pastor's* work.

"But why?" Fritz shouted.

Emil turned his head from them. "Never going
again," he muttered. "Going into the field. Going to be
a farmer."

Fritz's face relaxed. The shadow of a grin rested on it.

"There goes your pastor, Mollia," he said gruffly, and to Emil: "The ground is ready to-day . . . get the plow."

But Amalia went into the house and shed bitter tears.

CHAPTER XXIII

SO EMIL decided for himself he was to be a farmer like Uncle Fritz, and Amalia with many a secret sighing over the disappointment put away her dreams of his schooling and a *pastor's* robe and a beautiful girl from some city whom he would one day marry.

But Emil did no sighing,—he was happy and content, and threw his young strength energetically into the work.

To a certain point he was Herman all over again, energetic, loud of speech, noisy with laughter. But at that place where Herman would have been ruthless toward another's feelings, commanding arrogantly, or scolding loudly,—Emil's manner would break into something less formidable as the ice breaks in the springtime, turn gentle with Amalia and end the scene in mere joking. So to Herman's gifts of physical strength and ceaseless energy had been added something of Amalia's own,—a bit of her thoughtfulness and tenderness, a little appreciation of the red tinge on the prairie clouds.

By 1885 the land was largely fenced. Crops were good. Some of the out-buildings were new,—corncribs and a hay barn. Trees were much larger,—the cottonwoods and the elms. Orchards were bearing,—Amalia could make *äpfel-butter* and *pflaumen-butter* every year. There were elderberries, choke-cherries and wild grapes in the woods, and gooseberries and currants in the yard. All the land was taken. Homesteads were now farms. The whole community took on an appearance of prosperity. In addition to Amalia's and Fritz's farm,—up and down the river valley stretched the neat places of all the Gebhardts and the Schaffers, the Rhodenbachs and the Kratzes. If there had been keen rivalry over houses and barns, children and crops, it had made for progress.

There was a road to Westville, clogged with snow in the winter and muddy or dusty in summer, but at that, something better than the unbroken trail of prairie grass over which they had first come.

Trains passed daily through Westville, the western portion of the state was being settled. Every day people going west stopped in their wagons at some one of the farm-houses on the river for water or directions or to stay all night. Some were bound for the Republican Valley, some to the Black Hills of the Dakotas, some to the grassy plateau in the sand-hills.

The German families had grown more friendly with the English ones,—the Kirbys and the Blacks and the Lawrences. The women came sometimes to see Amalia, and every so often she and Anna Kratz would hitch up the spring-wagon, drive to their homes and return the calls.

Amalia had a hard time understanding them, and with some embarrassment and laughter tried to make them know what she was saying. But after all, a sick child or a new design for a quilt or a jar of *gurken* or *kraut* is a common denominator in all feminine language, and they got along very well.

"I bring you apple-jelly," Mrs. Kirby would say.

And Amalia, like a devoted parrot would repeat: "I brin' you äpfel-chelly."

All the weeks she would try to remember this, and when she would arrive at the Kirbys' next time, she would be gay with laughter, jelly, and the surprise of her English for Mrs. Kirby. "I brin' you plom-chelly."

But she could not muster a "w" nor a "th,"—ever, all her life,—nor some of the English words.

"They are water-melon," Mrs. Kirby would say patiently.

"Dey are vater-mel*o*nen." And so far as Amalia was concerned vater-mel*o*nen they stayed.

For several years the old log church on the hillside had been gone and in its place a substantial frame, white-painted, with a spire pointing its long finger to the way all the settlers must look for guidance.

Ludwig Rhodenbach had made the pews and a high pulpit, and all the men had turned in and helped build the *pharr-haus* for the *pastor*.

There was a great bell, too, in the tower of the church, that shook the building and reverberated up and down the valley.

At a passing, it tolled the number of years the dead one had spent on earth, so that when old Rudolph Kratz died it echoed up and down the valley for a long time with its eighty-two strokes, but when Lena Schaffer's little boy died, it gave only a single tap that was heard by scarcely any one but the caretaker who rang it and the prairie-larks and Lena Schaffer many miles away.

Emil worked side by side with Fritz all through his

'teens, strong as a young ox, for he had never known anything but hard work. Amalia was glad the two got along so well. If there was an occasional disagreement, it soon passed. Fritz was always quiet. But Emil, noisy and loud, might rant for a time, start to say ugly unnecessary things as his father before him, and then, looking at the gentle face of his mother—suddenly something would break and his ranting go into nothing. Amalia did not know how this could be. It just was so.

In 1887 Emil was twenty. The two men had cut a great deal of wild hay and stored it and there was to be plenty of corn in the cribs. The combined three hundred and twenty acres were yielding well. No one gave a thought to the ownership,—that there might have been some legal question whose land it was after the death of the two original owners. Fritz and Amalia and Emil thought of it only as "the place," all working long and hard to feed and clothe themselves and "put something by."

And now this year, the biggest change, since Herman's and Wilhelm's deaths, was upon the family. In the late fall or early winter when he would have passed his twenty-first birthday, Emil was going to be married. To Anna Marie Rhodenbach! That was Minnie Rhodenbach's daughter, the child of the Minnie Rhodenbach upon whom Fritz had cast such longing eyes when she was a young widow with this little girl. And curiously enough Anna Marie at eighteen was almost the exact replica of Minnie at the time Fritz had given his solemn oath never to marry.

Fritz and Emil were building the new house in the

very yard with Amalia's house, although over on the next rise of ground beyond the slow-growing lilac bushes.

When they started to plan it, Emil had brought Anna Marie over to talk with Fritz and Amalia about it.

Anna Marie was chubby, her soft round face had dimples at the corners of her mouth, and when she laughed, which she did very often, she looked exactly as her mother had looked at eighteen.

Looking at her sitting there so pretty and soft and demure, Uncle Fritz said suddenly: "Emil, why don't we build this one very grand? The place will all be yours some day. This house, it should be of stone . . . finer than any one's in the valley. You will have a family . . . they will grow up in it. Who knows maybe *their* children too, would live in it. It should be solid and big. I would like to build one so that all the settlers come to see it. I would like the best one in the whole county for you. It would take the year but we could do it fine. What say you, Emil?"

Amalia warmed so to Fritz's kindness. What a good boy he was. And why would he want to put so much labor on something for Emil?

He was thirty-seven now, thin and hard and gnarled, and never had he looked at a girl.

"You should for yourself be making one." Amalia chided him.

But Fritz laughed at that. "What girl would look at a gnarled old bachelor, nearing forty?"

"Oh, there's a plenty," Amalia told him. "I could name as many as fingers on my hand. Shall I name them?"

But Fritz would not stop planning to listen to the naming of them. "The good ones are all married already," he said laconically, so that Amalia pondered it quite awhile.

Fritz and Emil hauled stone from a quarry down the river. It took a day to come and go. Before he was even fifteen, Fritz had learned something of the stone mason's craft from his father so now he built carefully and well.

All the summer and fall of 1887 the two worked on the house every moment between the necessary crop work. The big thing rose slowly on its sturdy foundation, every stone solidly placed, every studding nailed securely.

"It's so sturdy Anna Marie and I will have our golden wedding in it," Emil told them.

"I shall then be ninety years old," Amalia laughed.

"Yah," Fritz said. "You will live, Millia, to see children and grandchildren and (*vielleicht*) great-grandchildren living in it."

But Amalia could not believe that—it seemed so very far in the future. Yet it happened to be true,—Amalia was to live to see Emil and his son and his son's son living in the honestly built stone house.

It was large for the time and for the young state no older than Emil himself. There were a parlor and a sitting-room, a dining-room, a bedroom and a kitchen downstairs, and three more bedrooms upstairs. If not overly artistic it was strong and sturdy and as honest as Fritz Stoltz. People came from miles around to see it. Not in all the days of the settling up of the river valley had there been put up so big and so good a dwelling. It sent Anna Kratz home with a sick headache that her

Frederich was to live for awhile in her own discarded cabin.

Amalia could scarcely get used to the idea that Emil was to be gone from home. But the two houses were only a short distance apart, something like a town block over at Westville. She thought with a warm little feeling of pleasure how nice it would be to have another woman so close. She and Anna Marie could exchange *kaffee kuchen* and *spatzen*. Her twenty-two years here had been only with menfolks about.

She had a dozen quilts ready for the young couple and now every day she sewed carpet rags, great balls of them ready for the loom. If all the carpet rags she sewed that summer had been laid end to end . . . but luckily they never were, but were made instead into much hit-and-miss striped carpeting for the rooms of the big stone house.

Anna Marie made quilts, too, and bleached quantities of tan-colored muslin, sewed petticoats with a great deal of tucking in them and yards of rick-rack and made many pillow-cases with crocheted ends.

Emil bought new things,—the most stylish of all, a walnut bedroom set with marble top to the bureau and a looking-glass built solidly on the back of it. This was called a *dresser* in English, and for all the world as though the dresser had a child, there was a small one just like it called a *commode*. There was a wash-bowl too, and a pitcher, with three fat red roses on the side of each one. It seemed that company washed right there in the very room in which they slept instead of in the kitchen or wash-house. Amalia preened a good deal when she showed these to Anna Kratz. And she bragged sometimes about her brother Fritz. "Nothing is good enough for Emil in Fritz's eyes. The shirt off his back he would take for Emil. Wanting Emil always to have the nicest things in the house." Or so it seemed to Amalia.

Christmas time passed with the church services and the *tannen-baum* set up so prettily at the pulpit and the tallow *kerzen* lighted and twinkling among its branches, with the *"Stille Nacht, Heilige Nacht"* heard everywhere, —at church, in the houses, at the stables, on the prairie road from sleighs.

The wedding was set for January twelfth.

The house was finished. Fritz Stoltz surveyed his handiwork. Emil had worked day and night with him, but he had been the builder. He felt an indescribable pride in the great solid structure. It would stand until long after he was up there on the hill with his father and Herman. He had, after all, something to leave behind him. It wasn't a son, but it was a sort of monument,— for Emil . . . and Minnie's little girl.

The wedding was a big event. It took place in the church on the hill in the morning at ten,—Anna Marie in white India linen and hand-crocheted lace with a veil. When the ceremony was over, all went by buggy and lumber-wagon, spring-wagon and carriage to the new stone house for the wedding feast.

Anna Kratz and Lena Schaffer, young Mrs. Henry Gebhardt, young no longer but going by that name for twenty-five years; and Amalia took charge of the great wedding dinner set out on the boards placed on sawhorses down the length of the combined two new parlors.

There were *schinken* and *gebratene hühner*, which the

English neighbors called ham and fried chicken, and *hühner* pressed into loaves. There was *met-wurst* and *käse*. And there were *bohnen* and *pastete*, which Mrs. Kirby told Amalia were called in the English, beans and pie. There was *kümmel* in which the toasts were openly drunk by all, and there was the strong *roggen branntwein* slipping about surreptitiously among the men who kept their eyes peeled for any approaching and potentially protesting wife.

It was the finest kind of a day. On all sides one heard remarks about it,—January the twelfth and like spring. Yes, it was as soft and mild as Anna Marie's dimpled face.

"It is a sign of your married life," Lena Schaffer said, ". . . the way the day is. Ours was stormy, having thunder and lightning." And she cackled loudly and poked a fat forefinger into August Schaffer's lean ribs.

Through the feasting the doors were all open. The sun shone almost warmly, so that men removed their coats and went out into it that they might boast of it in years to come,—"I remember like yesterday at Emil Holmsdorfer's wedding,—January twelfth and I was out o'doors in my shirt sleeves."

There was moisture on the sides of the elms and the cottonwoods. Hens scratched in the damp steaming ground of manure piles and on the south side of the straw stacks.

The crowd from the gorging of much food grew less noisy, settled for a time into an after-dinner lethargy. The women washed countless dishes. Babies bawled and were put to sleep upstairs on the new beds high with feather ticks and Amalia's intricately-pieced quilts. The men drank more *kümmel* openly for old friendship's sake and a little of the *roggen branntwein* surreptitiously for any fragile reason that presented itself. Then Elsa Rhodenbach came in and started the dancing. "Come! Don't be old. This is a wedding, folks; not a funeral."

It revived the faltering food-stuffed company. August Schaffer and Adolph Kratz got out their *violinen* which the Kirbys called fiddles, tuned them up and activities began.

In the midst of the dancing some of the men came in to say it looked stormy in the north,—maybe they must go and do chores if they were to come back for the evening. Several of the women went out to look, too.

The north sky was the color of burned-out camp-fire ashes. There was a hushed quiet over the whole country-side,—that portentous quiet which is more ominous than noise. Several of the older men began hitching up, but the young folks danced on. Fritz slipped away to his barns for early chores. Amalia called something after him about her chickens. Even as she did so, a single icy blast snarled down from the low-swinging clouds, the wind whipped her new silk dress as though it were a rattling garment of paper.

The storm that followed the initial blast went down into history as the blizzard of '88.

The snow in great packed masses threw itself at the countryside, drove its fury all over a snow-bound land. It lashed at the wedding party, held captive, like a wild thing mad with the knowledge that it could not hurt the great stone house which Fritz and Emil had built so well.

Those who had started home, remembering the fate of

two of their original company of settlers so many years before, sought shelter at the nearest farms, some greatly in danger of losing their lives before they could fight their way to houses and barns.

It threw a pall over the gaiety,—the worry about those who had gone home for the chores. Even Fritz did not come back, could not make it through the storm from so short a distance.

In the big stone house, the dancing took the minds from the mad fury of the elements, the food luckily prepared in such quantities, held out, the *kümmel* sustained the thirsty. Only the drinking of the *roggen branntwein* came to a sudden termination for the simple reason that with Adolph Kratz, it, too, had gone home to do the chores.

So now Amalia was thirty-nine, her son a married man, and never any more did she think of romance for herself or crave it.

Twice during the years had she been asked in marriage. Several times young Fred Gebhardt had come to spend Sunday evening when Emil was small, but Amalia, pretending that she did not know the reason, kept Fritz from leaving and allowed Emil to sit up long beyond his bedtime so they could all make merry together with popping *korn* and making molasses candy, until Fred asked her and she refused him under the noise of the popping *korn*.

And once from beyond the valley Otto Weis had driven in rapidly, explained his matrimonial intentions, given her gratuitously an inventory of his cows, pigs and chickens, and explained a little breathlessly that if she were so minded to take them all on as well as himself, he would appreciate it if she could come before threshing.

Amalia had laughed in his face and told him to go to the fourth homestead down the valley and hire Lizzie Gebhardt for two dollars a week.

No, Amalia craved no more romance for herself. But sometimes when the sun was gone and there was a moment to spare after the supper dishes were done, she sat on the porch of the small frame farm-house and looked across the darkening fields and pastures. From there she would watch the first stars come out, a night hawk dip low and the new moon get caught in the branches of the plum thickets,—would listen to the breeze stirring the leaves of the cottonwoods and to the cicadas and the good-night call of the robins that had come of late years,—would catch the scent of the hay fields and the petunias that bordered the path to her gate. Then she would open the rusty-hinged door and go into The Room.

She could not have explained it to any one,—certainly not to Emil or Fritz, and not even to her daughter-in-law, Anna Marie, or to Anna Kratz or Lena Schaffer. But it was always there,—a little chapel more beautiful than any church, built in a clearing in the woods.

CHAPTER XXIV

FOR SEVEN years after Ida Carter's marriage to Matthias she worked side by side with him in the store, never missing a day nor a chance to help her husband earn a penny. On hot summer mornings she rose with the sun and was ready to go with him through the dusty streets when he left for work. On winter mornings she was up long before daylight, breaking the ice in the pitcher for washing, dressing in her flannels and woolen dress, and was off with him in the dark and the cold.

There were hard times for town people as well as the country folks in those years after the Meier marriage. Every grasshopper cast its tiny reflection into Matthias' store, until the whole became a dark shadow over the counters. Drouth took its toll of the customers and so of Matthias himself. The little town had seen its citizens go out to fight a prairie fire which came rolling in with no apparent regard for the capital's importance. It had seen an uprising among the convicts in the penitentiary several miles away so that Matthias shouldered a gun with other citizens and went out to help quell the riot. It had seen the burning of the Atwood House with its big twenty-thousand-dollar loss.

All these seven years Ida Carter lived in her small suite of rooms in the boarding-house looking forward to the day when she would have a nice home. But the boarding-

168

house was good enough, she insisted, until she could stop work and devote herself to a home.

And then in 1880 her child was coming, so that she must stop her work at the store. They named the boy Carter and he throve and grew even as did the little town into which he had arrived with such welcome.

Even before the baby's coming, the new state had begun to pull out of the hard times, and with these general conditions bettered Matthias' business took on noticeable gains.

Life was very pleasant to Matthias these days. Ida was comrade and friend as well as wife and mother. Any word of hers concerning the business was worth heeding. And then came word of the death of Matthias' uncle, and wholly unlooked for, a fair-sized legacy. Rather suddenly then he sold his share of the store to his partner, bought stock in one of the banks and became an officer of that growing institution.

The town had thirteen thousand inhabitants now,—the University had graduated several small classes. Eight daring young men on the flying trapeze of their enthusiasm had organized the Sigma Chi fraternity and were nearly expelled for their pains. The huge west wing for a new capitol building had gone up.

There were more convicts in the pen, more inmates in the asylum,—and many people had been taken out to the acreage in which to lie down and sleep.

So now Matthias and Ida were to have their new home. It was of red brick and sat far back from the wooden sidewalk of a popular residential street, where it seemed to draw its red skirts away from the splashing of mud all

169

spring and the clouds of fine dust rolling in through the hot midwestern corn-curing weather. It was rather awe-inspiring in its massiveness, dwarfing as it did the modest homes on both sides of it. There were ornate trimmings over the long, narrow windows, and a tower high above the second floor could have served as an excellent Indian lookout if there were need, for from its lofty interior one might gaze over the undulating prairie as far as man's vision could function.

It was one of the town's most showy residences, but scarcely had its final oak balustrade been placed, its last piece of ornate grill-work set in the archway between parlor and library until plans were laid by the William McCurdeys for a new house with more oak grill-work and two towers.

They followed each other like mushrooms after rain,—the huge frame house of a merchant, the red brick one of a banker, the gray stone of an attorney, all dignified and elegant at the time. It was only in the light of after years that they looked fussy, like old ladies bewigged and rouged and loaded with jewelry.

Other town-shaking events were happening. Whereas one had hallooed lustily heretofore from his porch to the neighbor for whom a message was intended, or sent the swiftest-legged member of the family, one might now talk to him through the huge box fastened on the wall. A half-hundred business houses went up, many times that number of homes.

When the Meier house was finished Matthias and Ida gave a housewarming. While scarcely true that half the town came, the impression was there. Young swains and their ladies danced the Virginia reel and the mazurka on the intricately inlaid pattern of the newly polished floors,—a few tackled the schottische. Young Carter, a big healthy boy, was allowed to stay up until nine. Ida had succeeded in making him look almost as effeminate as she desired in his velvet suit with lace collar and cuffs, his hair in curls to his shoulders. Ida herself had a new striped heavy silk dress trimmed with bead passementerie over a huge bustle.

Oyster stew was served in the basement, moist yet from its fresh mortar, the ladies squealing a little and holding up their trailing skirts when descending the long, narrow stairway. Some of the guests had driven to the party in their fringed canopy-topped carriages, those close by had walked, tip-toeing across the puddles on the wooden sidewalks, carrying their party shoes in bags, but a few souls out for adventure and feeling particularly devilish had taken the new street-car to the nearest corner.

Charlie Briggs came, looking a bit incongruous among the other guests with his baggy clothes, his oiled red hair, and his voice rolling out in the same tones he had employed when he snapped the bull-whip at the side of the oxen. But Matthias would have him, and Ida was good-natured about it, laughing heartily with Charlie when they showed him around the new house and he said he'd swum in all sorts o' rivers 'n lakes 'n buffalo wallers, but never swum yet in a big soup-bowl like that there one in the bathroom.

Aside from a *faux pas* or two on the part of Charlie, the whole affair was a huge success.

The newspaper said it was one of the most pleasant

occasions ever known to Lincoln society, that youth and beauty were rampant, that the Meier residence was a model of elegance, its proud owners unexcelled in hospitality and the collation the most appetizing of which ye scribe had ever partaken.

Matthias and Ida were exceedingly pleased over the write-up, felt a curiosity tinged with impatience to see the one which would follow the McCurdeys' housewarming in a few months. When it came out, it said that the party was one of the most pleasant occasions ever known to Lincoln society, that youth and beauty were rampant, that the McCurdey residence was a model of elegance, its proud owners unexcelled in hospitality and the collation the most appetizing of which ye scribe had ever partaken.

Life now to the Meiers took on no small degree of prosperity which in turn gave them their place in the social sun of the little city.

They went to hear Oscar Wilde lecture and Bill Nye,—to the Funk Opera House to see Edwin Booth and Modjeska, Lily Langtry and Fannie Davenport trod the boards. They joined a whist club and kept up their choir work even if somewhat under fire by visiting evangelists for combining the two.

Ida joined with a group of her women friends in receiving calls on New Year's Day to which the gallants of the town in Prince Alberts made yearly pilgrimages by way of a livery hack.

At the turn of the decade came one of the outstanding social events,—the opening of the Lansing Theatre. Matthias was forty-six now, a little pompous looking with his shovel-cut beard and a gray patch above each ear,—quite the picture of a bank vice-president. Ida was forty-three, heavy too, deep bosomed and molded into her stays, wholly the picture of a bank vice-president's wife. Her heavy brown hair was piled high on her head in doughnut formation. In the privacy of her room she pinched her cheeks to bring color to them.

Carter at eleven was to be allowed to go to the great opening. "He can't begin too young to hear and see the best things," Matthias had said, to which Ida assented with reservations that he mustn't expect to go often.

The great building towering all of four stories high was a blaze of light. The boxes were filled with notables. The Governor was there in the dress circle, and the new young congressman, William Jennings Bryan, and his wife. The proscenium was a dazzle of splendor and the audience beautiful and manly if one may take wholeheartedly the newspaper accounts of the day. A painted scenic representation of Thalia, the muse of comedy and bucolic poetry, in an undieted condition, largely covered the sounding board with a languid pose of nonchalant snootiness surrounded by corpulent cupids.

Lillian Lewis and her company played. The orchestra rendered exquisite strains between acts. One would have said it was like a Chicago event. Culture had come to the prairie.

On the way home Matthias and Ida in their carriage, with the man driving who doubled in yard work for them, asked each other what more one could wish for.

Ida said it didn't seem possible all this could have come

to pass in the raw village to which she had come nineteen years before.

Matthias responded with a rather uninspired: "No, it doesn't," . . . thinking, and yet not being able to tell even Ida, of his long journey alone over the cold, wind-swept prairie twenty-three years before, and of his dreaming that one day a city would stand there on the horizon where stood four or five log houses. He felt a little awe-struck to-night,—it seemed too much like sorcery,—as though the magic of his thinking had turned the dreaming into fact.

CHAPTER XXV

THERE were changes again in the German neighborhood in which Amalia Holmsdorfer lived with her brother Fritz. Changes in the farms, certainly, but more among the people. Deaths, births, marriages,—they roll in on a community like the tides of the sea. Most of the marriages had been among the various families which had come into the state together.

But another element was entering in. Lena Schaffer's boy married a Kirby girl who was what they called a *Congregationalist*. Tsk! Tsk! Probably not a Catechism in the house and calling a *pastor* a minister. Young Henry Gebhardt's girl got into trouble with one of the English Brown boys,—the trouble not being so bad as the mixed blood.

And the biggest change of all to Amalia,—she was now fifty years old and a grandmother. Emil and Anna Marie had a little son, Joe, aged ten now. Three times since Joe's birth, Anna Marie had expected a child, but after a few months could not carry it. Anna Marie had now lost her chubbiness to something more substantial. Fat, in no uncertain terms was what she had come to be,—a mound of quivering fat which seemed in no way to detract from her lightness of foot. Looking at her sometimes Amalia wondered how a fat woman could walk so springily. She had all the qualities of a rubber-ball, and even though she had to walk sideways down the porch steps of the big stone house, she seemed to bounce down from step to step.

Emil was a good husband to Anna Marie. Often Amalia talked about it to Fritz, wondering in her mind if he remembered their father's and Herman's harsh ways, but saying nothing about it. When Joe was born and those other times of her illnesses, Emil brought home neighbors' girls to work. He bought a two-seated carriage for her, too, and though Fritz and Amalia rode yet in the spring wagon, Anna Marie never went anywhere excepting in the carriage where she sat alone in her grandeur in the back seat because of her bulk.

Sometimes Amalia would hear Emil telling his wife not to put so much labor on the house, to let up a little in the work, that since the new eighty was all paid for, they would be getting ahead. Four hundred acres in the family now,—that was good. Amalia knew Herman and her father would have been elated at that news.

Only this spring Amalia had seen an example of Emil's thoughtfulness of his wife.

Anna Marie had just pulled the old soap-kettle from the back porch out to the yard, walking sideways up and down the steps in that balloon-like way of hers, when Emil came up from the barn.

"What are you going to do?" he had asked in the German, for although they both could speak some in English they chose the easier way.

"Make soap," Anna Marie had said, "and I'd rather take a licking than stand and stir."

"Why do you then?"

Anna Marie laughed good naturedly, her dimples making large holes in her cheeks. "I think because my mother did before me and her mother before her, and for no other reason, for it is one of the things I do not like to do."

"Don't do it then."

"But, Emil,—I have all the grease saved and the lye is leached."

"Throw it away. You do not have to do it any more. A bushel of corn or two will pay for the soap you would make to-day . . . maybe make yourself sick too!"

So to Amalia's amazement, she saw her daughter-in-law take the pans and waddle lightly down to the edge of the orchard, bury the grease in the ground, throw the cracklings to the chickens, and sit down on the big porch to rock comfortably all the rest of the afternoon. Tsk! Tsk! Such a waste.

At night Emil took the iron kettle down to the hoglot and cooked mash in it for the little pigs.

So, even though large families were the order of the day, because of Anna Marie's inability to bear more children, Joe was to be Emil's only son and Amalia's only grandchild.

It may be for this very reason Amalia centered all her love in him. So devoted was she to little Joe that he seemed her own, that she had borne him herself in some distant year with the pain and the worry now all forgot.

He was less noisy than Emil had been, quiet and uncommunicative. One had to guess what was on his mind, withdrawing it by questioning.

"What is the matter, Joey? What have you on your mind that troubles you?"

"Nothing."

"Is it that you cannot go to town with father?"

"No."

"Is it that the little calf died?"

A long silence,—and Amalia knew it was that the little calf died.

Although he was boyish, full of energy for the farm activities, never a day passed that he did not come down the path between the petunias, to the frame house where Amalia and Fritz lived. She kept cookies in a big stone crock always for Joey. She kept a bed made for him so that when Emil and Anna Marie would want to go somewhere without him, he could stay. She kept a flannel nightgown there for him and a pencil and paper and slate should he want to do his school work.

And that was another change in the community. Joey went to English school and did the German work up on the hill with the *pastor* only for a time in the summer vacation. There was a country school-house on a corner of the Lawrence land called the Evergreen School. It was under a county superintendent, and all the children, both German and English, must attend.

Joey could talk the English just like the Kirbys and the Lawrences, but he could talk the German, too, and usually did with Amalia. But sometimes, in proud boyish way, he wanted to give her an English lesson and although it was tedious and tiring to Amalia, she was patient for the little boy's sake.

"It is a nice day."

"It iss a *schön* day."

"No, Grandma. *Nice.*"

"It iss a nitze day."

"This is soup."

"Dis iss *suppe.*"

"No, Grandma. Soup."

"Sss . . . oop."

And the lesson would go only into laughter and the eating of more cookies.

But in one way, Amalia's association with Joe was identical with that of her own little boy, Emil,—the talking to him of all the lovely things about the farm, of the beauty in nature and the way God manifested Himself. She walked with him in the timber along the river,—a little less buoyantly now because of her fifty years,—and talked of the trees as though they were humans,—the ash, the willow and the cottonwood, and the wild sumac. Together they picked violets and black-eyed Susans and trillium, bellwort and bloodroot and wild columbine, and although Amalia's names for them were not always as these, Joey knew these very words in the English and taught them to her.

Together they found the meadow-lark's nest in the grass and the place where the owls had hooted away the nights in the woods for thirty years. She stood with him on the church knoll which looked over the valley and had him repeat with her in German the Psalm of walking through the valley of the shadow of death and yet fearing no evil.

Fritz did not reprove her as he had done when Emil was small, did not tell her she would make of him a softie. Fritz was nearly fifty now, himself, and someway in the years, he had learned that it is not always softness to be tender.

Sometimes she asked Joey if he would not like to go away to school and study to be a *pastor*. But Joey's answer was always the same, that he would farm all the land and buy more and be the biggest land owner in the county.

So the farm work went on,—a thing of plowing, harrowing, planting, cultivating, laying by the corn, picking it to toss into the wagons, husking it in the big barns,—of wheat planting and harvesting,—of butchering, smoking *speck*, making *met-wurst* and smoked *schinken*, of discouragement over low prices, chuckling pleasure over high ones, of occasional seasons of drouth and short crops, and others of too much moisture followed by rust, of the eternal vigilance over the management of the place which is known only to natural-born farmers. And always one eye on the weather. Rain, dew, sleet, hail, drouth, snow, frost, ice, sunshine, cloudiness, wind,—every morning Emil and Fritz and Joe stepped out of the house with the question on their lips,—which, from the long list of his cohorts had the weather man marshaled for the day? By the small margin of difference in the various combinations would there be success or disaster.

Most amazingly Joe soon went to High School over at Westville. When he had read all the readers and studied all that the country school-teacher had for him, Emil sent him over to the town school.

"Parochial school was good enough for me," Emil said, "but I want Joe to have better."

So with his books tied on the saddle and his lunch in a

tin box, he rode his pony every day to school over the road no longer grass-grown but worn hard and black now from the travel of the thirty-five years. Sometimes he even stayed after school awhile to play baseball and, though Emil needed him badly, he did not swear at him and scold as many of the fathers did, but said: "Get around home a little quicker to-morrow and help with the corn."

It was a great night for the Holmsdorfers when Joe graduated. It was called "the Class of 1907" and four of the graduates were from the families of the old friends in the valley,—Joe, Rose Schaffer, Henry Gebhardt, the third, and Nora Kratz, Anna Kratz's grand-daughter.

Amalia was so proud of Joe one would have thought she was the mother instead of the grandmother. She was fifty-nine now, with not a semblance of the lovely girl she had once been, but an old woman, wrinkled and worn from much hard labor. Fritz was fifty-six and he, too, looked older than his years, gnarled and thin and weather-beaten from his long seasons of battling with the elements.

Joe had something of a time getting ready, what with carrying a wash-tub up to his room for a bath and when almost dressed having to run over to Amalia's for the tie stick-pin he had left there.

But they were all ready in time, although they went in three different rigs. Fritz and Amalia had owned a buggy for several years and they went in that. Joe, excited and not knowing just when he would leave "the bunch" after the exercises, took his own rubber-tired buggy.

Emil and Anna Marie went in the two-seated carriage. From the window Amalia saw them leave a little before she did,—Emil driving up close to the porch and Anna Marie coming sideways down the steps, but lightly like a balloon, and then sitting alone in the grandeur of the back seat as they drove away.

The exercises were very fine, Amalia thought, and although neither she nor Fritz could read a word of the programs, they studied them diligently between speeches.

Rose Schaffer looked as pretty as her namesake, the prairie roses. They called her by a frightfully long name and although Amalia whispered to Fritz to ask if he knew what the word printed there meant . . . that one,— V-a-l-e-d-i-c-t-o-r-i-a-n, Fritz shook his head.

But although there were seventeen in the class, Amalia had eyes only for Joey with his fine shoulders thrown back so proudly, and his nice suit Emil had let him pick from the catalogue. They spoke and sang and received their papers rolled up and tied with ribbons, and last of all they gathered in a group and yelled something which sounded louder and worse than the time the Indians yelled around the molasses jug and the feather pillow.

When Amalia and Fritz went out of the "opera house" to leave for home a fog had fallen over everything. It enveloped the night like a ghostly presence so that Fritz had to let the horses walk and feel their own way. Never had the road seemed so long. They knew when the horses turned the corner on the valley road, and later hearing the grate of the iron tires, knew they were crossing the railroad track, at the curve. Other than that, they scarcely knew their bearings until the faithful team turned in at the farmyard.

Several times Amalia peered out to see whether there was a light in the big house but never seeing one for the fog, she went on to bed.

It was an hour later when the voices sounded outside the door, lanterns flashed, and some one was calling Fritz.

Something terrible seized Amalia, a premonition of impending disaster. As she pulled a dress over her muslin nightgown and lighted a lamp, her hands shook, so that the matches went out twice. She was trembling so she could scarcely get to the door, asking "What's wrong?" in the German.

Fritz was ahead of her, and together they stood, lamp high, in the doorway peering out at Karl Schaffer and young Adolph Kratz and his wife and Anna Kratz, Henry Gebhardt, and back of these old friends two Westville men standing apart, and at Joey coming from beyond them, running, pushing through the fog, pushing through the men and the women, elbowing them aside, white, wild, crying and calling:

"Grandma,—Father and Mother are dead."

"Was ist, Joey?" Amalia was confused and the English words only added to it.

"Vater und Mutter sind todt."

And then Amalia understood.

Emil and Anna Marie, alive and well and proud of their fine boy two hours ago, were not now alive and well, and were quite incapable of further pride in their fine boy.

At the railroad crossing by the curve in the dark of the fog it had happened when the night passenger came through. The men thought Emil must have mistaken a headlight for a light in the Lawrence farm-house. Or so it might have been.

There were details which they were keeping from Joe and Amalia, one gathered. But Amalia was strong. No one knew where or how she could obtain all that reserve strength, nearly sixty as she was, little, too, and almost frail. She went from the small house to the big one and back in the days that followed. She saw the *pastor* and gave directions for the services. She picked out the things for them to put on her boy and his wife, and comforted Minnie Rhodenbach Schaffer, Anna Marie's mother, who came with her other sons and daughters.

She sent Fritz, broken up as he was, out to the horses, knowing that he always found comfort in their sleek hides and their gentle nosing of him. But most of all she helped Joe pull himself together.

"It is happy for them, Joey," she said steadily, although it took effort to say the words. "Always from the time your father was seventeen, there was no one but your mother for him. He loved her, and she loved him and no other. That is a very happy thing. So few people are of that way. They loved each other. They were fine people. They gave you life. It is your gift from them. And now they go where there is nothing but more happiness . . . for them . . . and they go together. That is the nicest way of all . . . no long sickness, no worries about leaving their boy . . . just suddenly . . . and together."

And Joe threw up his head and went bravely through the long ordeal because of what his grandmother had said.

He could do all this because she had put her own

184

strength into him, and because he did not know that in her own bedroom after she had watched him fall asleep these nights, she dropped on her knees and cried aloud in her anguish, finding it hard to walk through the valley of the shadow of death and yet fear no evil.

CHAPTER XXVI

ONLY Amalia, Fritz and Joe were left now of the
family. It was crushing. One could not sense the
thing that had happened so suddenly in the midst of their
ordinary everyday life.

"Im mitte des leben sind wir in tode," the *pastor* had
said that June day when all the countryside came, so that
the road winding up to the old white church was packed
with carriages. *In the midst of life we are in death.*

There had been wild roses that day, tangled everywhere
in the prairie grass on the hill and a pair of thrashers had
flown scolding over the heads of the people for disturbing
their young. The bell had tolled forty long slow strokes
for Emil whom every one respected,—thirty-eight for
Anna Marie whom every one loved,—and then because
this was so strange a service, the caretaker had added
nineteen full, resonant strokes for the years of their
married life together. All over the valley were the solemn
notes heard, so all should remember that in the midst of
life they were also in death.

The fields that had called to Emil were calling yet.
But now it was Joe who answered, who plowed and
planted and harvested.

Fritz and Amalia moved to the big stone house and left
the small one standing vacant and a little forlorn. "Some
day when Joey brings a wife home to the stone house,
we shall come back," Amalia said to Fritz as she moved

her things, carrying in her hands her shell box carefully wrapped in its unbleached muslin.

So in the next few years Amalia and Fritz were mother and father to Joe just as they had been to Emil, his father, before him. But things were quite different now. Emil had stayed so closely on the place, going only to services and to see Anna Marie and sometimes on the wolf hunt or taking part in some other mannish activity. But Joe had his rubber-tired buggy and a pair of slim, fast-stepping horses. He seemed restless. No one worked harder, but always after the work he was cleaning up and leaving. Sometimes he told where he was going,—more often not. Amalia worried about it a little. Such a close-mouthed boy and so hard to understand.

There was new machinery on the place. The old cradle and reaper were falling to pieces in the weeds behind the barn. There was a binder. One might ride now at the plowing. Tsk! Tsk! Like going to town.

Joe was all English now in his talk, would seldom offer to put anything into the German for Amalia and because he did not do so of his own accord, Amalia felt a certain pride in not asking him and would try so very hard both to understand and to express herself. In truth, the whole colony was changing in that respect. A Kratz had married a Lawrence. A Gebhardt had married a Black. Two of the Schaffers were at this moment keeping company with two Kirby sisters. All was changing.

The old white church on the hill was gone this last year and in its place a solid red brick and the *pfarr-haus* for the *pastor* matched it. Only the old bell was not worn out although it had called to worship and tolled and caroled

187

for thirty years. More than these material changes, the services were part English,—there had been almost a rumpus over it, and again over whether to have a short sermon in German and another in English immediately following, or the German every other Sunday. They said they must do it to hold the young folks. Hold them, thought Amalia. How queer! No one could have made her miss church when she was young. What would her father . . . what would Wilhelm Stoltz have said to that, —getting the colony to come out here so they could keep together and retain their customs?

And then rather suddenly Amalia found out where Joe was going this summer of 1910. It was to see Rose Schaffer who had graduated in his class three years before.

It relieved her immensely and pleased her too. Rose Schaffer was everything that Amalia would have wanted for Joey. Pretty, neat and clean, so pleasant to every one. Oh, but that would be *schön,*—no, nice. She could hardly wait to tell Fritz when he came in from the field. They were cutting the new alfalfa which Joe had insisted on sowing. Fritz was all for the old things he understood,—Joe for the new. Fritz was sixty-one, not so young any more, but hardy as a hickory tree. He had given up readily enough about the alfalfa. He was easygoing and, anyway, it would all be Joey's place,—four hundred of the best acres in Nebraska.

"If he wants to plant pepper-nuts," Fritz had said, "nothing will I say."

Amalia had laughed heartily at that, for *pfeffernüsse* were Christmas cookies.

So Amalia was full of excitement over the news that she had just heard from Anna Kratz whose daughter had told her that *her* daughter had told *her* that Joe was keeping steady company with Rose Schaffer.

"Maybe we shall soon move back to the little house, Fritz. See to it that you keep it well painted and repaired and that it always stands ready."

Fritz laughed at that, teasing her whether he should start to pack.

And then others told it about and every one seemed to know it.

Amalia surreptitiously began making a quilt for Joey,— the Jacob's Ladder design. Joe, himself, said nothing. Such a boy,—one never knew what he was thinking. Always doing his work so silently and well. Perhaps she couldn't expect him to confide in his grandmother. But sometimes she wanted so badly to know how things were with him that she hinted, not quite subtly: "What's come of all your old class, Joey,—what's come of Rose Schaffer? Do you never see her any more?"

She would be asking in the German, he replying now in the English.

"Sure I do, Grandma. I saw her last night. We went over to Westville to the band concert."

"And how was she?" as unconcerned as though it were mere conversation, and not the vital thing it was.

"Oh, she's always up and coming."

Amalia was satisfied,—entirely pleased with his choice. If Joe had sent her out on a shopping trip for a wife she believed she would have returned with Rose Schaffer.

Life took on a new interest now. It would be like living over Emil's young days to have Joe bring Rose to the big stone house. She planned every day for it, expected any time now that Joey would tell her the news. She could even anticipate the conversation, so well did she know her Joey.

He would approach it like this:

"Grandma, what would you think if I should bring some one else here to live with us?"

"Oh, Joey,—do you mean it?" She must be surprised.

"Yes . . . I've been thinking of it."

"You mean a wife, Joey?"

"Yes. What would you say to my bringing Rose Schaffer?"

Oh, she would like it,—like it very much indeed. Kind, substantial Rose with a pleasant word for every one,—a girl who would be like a daughter. And it would be nice to live in the little house again and have only the work there to do. Let's see, how old was she now? Almost sixty-two. Time to take it easier. Yes, she would welcome the change,—with Rose nearby for company.

And then the corn was in and the butchering done. The fall winds blew cold across the country bringing a flake of snow or two as though messengers had been sent ahead to remind the countryside of what would soon follow.

Amalia, standing at the kitchen window of the big stone house on a Saturday morning, rubbed away the steam to see out. Across the dark fields and the bare brown stubble she could see the big comfortable white farm-houses and the red barns of two of the neighbors,—the Adolph Kratz place and the Gus Rhodenbachs'. Everywhere the fields were precisely laid out and fenced, square-shaped or long like Joey's dominoes,—not much like the old days of patches of crops here and there with no fences. On the main highway some county commissioner had tried a new-fangled idea of having little stones and gravel hauled for people to drive over. Joe was all for it, Fritz against it. Joey always for the new, Fritz for the old.

What had been wide sweeping prairie was as cut up now as roads and fences could make it,—so much for wheat, so much for corn, this square for pasture and that one for the new alfalfa hay. People scarcely used the word *prairie* itself any more, so subdued and tamed was the wild thing of an earlier day.

As Amalia looked she saw two men with guns crossing the Kratzes' cornfield. That was a part of the wolf hunt to which Joey had gone.

Joe, out on the wolf hunt, swung along over the frozen cornlands, his gun pointing as his father had taught him. He had sighted a coyote once and heard the wild call of others not long before. Far across the field he could see a couple of the hunters, probably young Jim Rhodenbach and his dad taking their cut across the field. Outside the fences down the road, teams were tied and the Kirbys' new automobile was nosed up to the pasture. Noisy things—these automobiles—scare all the horses to death.

The cold bit like a steel trap. Had almost forgotten

what it felt like after the hot summer harvesting and the mild fall corn-picking.

The finish of the hunt would be somewhere near the Schaffers'. He was glad of that,—could drop in and get a cup of hot coffee and see Rose a few minutes. Pretty fine girl,—Rose. Queer how he had never thought very much about her in High School,—merely given her a lift to town occasionally or talked over some lesson a few minutes. But it was different now.

He grinned cheerfully to himself,—she was his girl now all right. Ever since the High School Alumni banquet in June. Something had happened,—he didn't know just what, but things had been different since. He had gone alone, stagging it as usual. She had come with a couple of the other girls from the old class of 1907. Out three years now. Gosh, you couldn't realize it. Seemed as though the class had drifted apart,—Chick Adams and Ray Hostrop and Fat Leaman all going away to college that way. Fraternity fellows now,—with college yarns to spring. Two or three of the girls, too, were back from college or girls' schools. Couldn't blame them for hobnobbing together with a lot of things in common. He'd like to have gone too, but father and mother . . . just then. . . . Not much use in it either, would have just come back to farm anyway and you didn't have to go away to school to learn that. You knew all about that from the time you were a kid.

They had sat side by side at the banquet,—he and Rose. That was when it had happened and for the life of him he didn't yet know *what*. All he knew was that before he went he hadn't thought any more of her than of any other neighbor girl. When it was over and he had taken her home in his new yellow-wheeled rubber-tired buggy he knew she was his girl. And Rose knew it too. He hadn't asked her to marry him yet. Seemed silly to have to put it into words when each one understood, but he supposed he'd have to. Christmas Eve,—that would be the time. Christmas exercises at the church,—ask Rose after those—have the diamond ring in his pocket,— a pretty nice one too,—could use some corn money— seventy-five, or eighty dollars, maybe.

They were closing in now. Men were shouting. The guns opened up. By an almost miraculous watchfulness on the part of a kind providence no human's life was sacrificed, although practically all were in jeopardy, for in the last stages of a coyote round-up shots were as wild as the wolves themselves.

There were seven gray gaunt forms thrown on the pile. There were some drinks and much smoking and whacking of cold hands together to take away their numbness,— then Joe was off through a creek-bed and up a ravine, across a pasture to the Schaffers' house.

He tapped on the kitchen door with a simultaneous opening of it and stepped in. Odors of newly baked cinnamon-rolls and fresh coffee assailed his nostrils as the spices of Araby might have assailed a traveler. Rose was flushed from the baking, but pretty enough to kiss. His heart warmed to her and he was crossing the room, sud- denly inspired to carry out the suggestion when he stopped short, for a young girl came from the Schaffer dining- room and stood in the doorway,—a dainty little thing in a blue kimono held tightly around her cute form. Her eyes swept Joe with a soft pleading expression.

"This is Miss Bates, Joe, the new teacher to take Miss Ray's place. She's going to stay here. Miss Bates, my friend, Joe Holmsdorfer."

The new teacher's name was Myrtie,—Myrtie Bates. She had a delicate flower-shaped face, coming to a sensitive little pointed chin. Her big blue eyes were as soft and innocent as a baby's. She smiled on Joe so gently, with something so vaguely sad in the smile that he felt suddenly sorry for her, but just why he could not have told.

CHAPTER XXVII

NOVEMBER slipped into December. The Christmas exercises this year were partly in English. It disappointed Amalia. The older she got the more she clung to the old ways. Perhaps she should not do so, but it was hard to change. When the young folks sang: "Silent Night . . . Holy Night," Amalia hummed it too under her breath, *"Stille Nacht . . . Heilige Nacht."* It sounded sweeter the old way, and more tender.

Joe was there with Rose and another girl who, Fritz told her, was the new teacher of the Evergreen School. She lived at Schaffers'. Joe had been over to Schaffers' so much lately,—Anna Kratz told her she always watched from behind the curtains to see when he went by in his buggy. Anna said sometimes she could see he had two girls with him. That Anna! *Alte klotsch!* Old gossip, Joe called it in English.

The exercises over, she and Fritz drove home. There was no snow, but the moonlight was so bright it gave the appearance of white everywhere.

When Fritz put the team away and came in, something depressing seized Amalia. It was Christmas Eve and no time for feelings of this sort, but getting home this way from the exercises with Fritz brought it all back, that other night three and a half years ago when they had come home through the fog. And even though she put her packages for Fritz and Joey under the tree and tried to make it seem a happy occasion, she could not do so. Something made her wish constantly that Joe would come, made her listen for the thud of the horses' hoofs on the hard frozen ground.

She could not sleep. Joe had been late before,—dances and candy pulls,—but never like this. She got up. Three o'clock. The weirdness of the moonlight worried her as much as darkness ever had done. She went back to bed. She thought how queer it was that Joey was her grandchild and yet he was her son. It was as though she had borne two sons,—Emil and Joey. You never outgrew that maternal feeling for a child for whom you had cared. That was why people could adopt children and feel the same toward them as toward their own flesh and blood.

Four o'clock and he had not come.

By five the roosters were crowing. She got up and dressed. Something had happened and she could not stand the strain. The agony of all the things that had ever troubled her seemed to return in a great nightmare of foreboding. Always she was losing the people for whom she cared: Fritz and Joe were all that were left, and if anything happened to Joey, there would be no least reason for living.

Six o'clock. The stock was bawling. Fritz was up. Amalia walked the floor, peered from the windows into the gray of the dawn which was coming. Then she heard the team come in. She slipped back into her bedroom and closed the door, sat on the edge of the bed trying to think what could have happened. Some of the thoughts she put from her as unworthy. Whatever it was, she must be kind,—be motherly and patient.

She got breakfast, made a cheerful remark or two and busied herself at another task while Joey ate. They opened their presents, but there was no Christmas feeling among them. Joe went silently about his work during the forenoon. There was Christmas dinner, but though she lighted *kerzen* and put them on the table, the meal was not Christmaslike. After supper Joe hitched the team, came in and dressed up, said shortly as he left: "Don't leave a lamp for me."

Amalia lay in her bed and looked at the black walls of her room. Of all the crosses that she had borne,—of all the hardships that life had brought her,—there was something about this that was the most frightening. She could not have told why she was so shaken. It was as though a strange person had taken the place of her boy,—as though the air about her that was recently so clear was now smoky with gases,—poisonous and stifling.

In the morning she heard the team come in and looked out to see Joey helping a girl out of the buggy. Amalia could have laughed and cried with relief. She saw it all now. He was bringing Rose home just as she had known he would do. That would be Joey's quick way—no fuss, no plans, no talk,—just bring her home when the time came.

Amalia started out to meet them. But when they came up on the porch, she saw it was not Rose. It was a strange girl,—a pretty little girl with a flower-like face and big eyes like a baby's.

"Grandma, this is my wife," Joe said. "Her name is Myrtie."

"How do you do?" the girl said coolly.

Amalia thought she would faint. "Vy . . . vy. . . ." Always she talked more brokenly when under stress. She wiped her hands on her apron and held one out to the girl "Velcome to *unser heim* . . . our home."

But Rose! Rose! What about Rose? Her mind was asking it so loudly that she was afraid it could be heard.

All morning Amalia was confused,—so upset that she had to stop in the kitchen every little while when doing her work and think it all over. Joey had married a girl and brought her home. A strange girl, *not Rose,* not even German. Every time Fritz came into the kitchen with milk pails or to warm the chicken feed, she would look at him with questioning eyes and whisper in German: "Why is it so?"

But poor old Fritz did not know why it was so,—could have no way of knowing that a girl with wide baby blue eyes and cuddling ways and no deep sense of loyalty would deliberately take a man away from her friend,— even though it was a good-looking young man with four hundred acres of the best land in Nebraska. How could Fritz know this,—who had the kind of ethics that would always keep a promise?

Amalia got dinner. She had roast chicken and mashed potatoes and gravy, cole slaw and a pie from her Greening apples in the cellar. And she got out the good pink-flowered dishes and set the table in the dining-room, turning the plates over carefully and putting her stiff new napkins upright in the drinking glasses. She could think only of the queer thing that had happened, but so often had she roasted *hühner* and baked *pastete* that she did it all mechanically.

Myrtie sat in the big sitting-room and looked at the album and the few English books in the corner bookcase while Amalia prepared the dinner. She ate heartily for such a little delicate-looking thing. Joe could scarcely take his eyes from her at the table. He helped her to the white of the chicken and wanted to know if she would rather have peach-sauce than her pie.

After dinner when Joe went to the barn to look after his team and Amalia washed the good pink-flowered dishes, Myrtie went into the cold parlor, wrapped herself in the crocheted afghan and took a nice long nap on the red plush couch.

For a week Amalia did all the work in the big stone house, and always a little worried, kept wondering what was best to do. Then she broached the subject. "Joe, *vielleicht* maybe Fritz and I *besser* over in de old house *geh* . . . go. We can fits it up." Amalia must always talk the English now as best she can for Myrtie does not know the German at all,—not a word. Fritz, too, should speak it always. Amalia must remind him of it. She felt a little cross with Fritz now, sitting and looking at his plate so timidly, as though this new girl could make Fritz feel not at home in the house he himself had built over twenty years before.

Myrtie spoke up immediately and answered for Joe that it would be a good plan to move.

"I vould before go," Amalia said, "but I t'nk maybe I

should de vork do." She spoke slowly and carefully, thinking it out.

"Oh, no, no." Myrtie said pleasantly. "You can go. We won't need you. I'm going to keep a maid,—can't I, Joe?"

"Vass ist . . . a mait, Joey?" Amalia questioned.

"Myrtie means a hired girl, Grandma. Yes, I guess we can manage that . . . all right."

Myrtie turned soft baby blue eyes on Joe and said: "Another thing, we're going to have this house all made over, aren't we, Joe?"

"Sure," Joe said, "any way you want it, Myrtie."

So Amalia moved back to the old house. Myrtie acted gracious and bubbling with good nature the day they left, told Amalia to take anything she wanted; for she and Joe were going to have all new things.

It worried Amalia. Of course everything they had was Joey's and always would be, but farmers were not rich people. And all those things new when Anna Marie and Emil were married,—the red plush parlor set and the dresser, and its child, the commode, and the wash-pitcher and bowl! Tsk! Tsk!

But Myrtie gave them all as graciously to Amalia as though she had owned them the twenty years instead of a week, told her to take all the rag carpet and the sale carpet too, for she was going to have Wilton and Axminster rugs. So Amalia took the walnut corner cupboard and the high-backed bedstead, the dresser and commode, the album and the pictures of the fat semi-nude little girls with daisies in their hair. Fritz backed the wagon up to the side porch and he and Joe put the furniture into it and some of the small things, but Amalia walked down the path, grass choked these last four years, and carried her shell box wrapped in unbleached muslin.

It seemed quite like old times to be settled with Fritz in the little home. Anna Kratz came over and spent whole days, so exciting was it to see all that was going on at the big house.

For, all winter and all spring, repairs and rebuilding went on. There were workmen there for weeks. Myrtie had them put wire all over the fine old gray stones and cover them with little pink sand that glistened in the sunlight. Delivery wagons from Westville came into the driveway nearly every day with furniture which Amalia, pretending that she had always known so, told Anna Kratz was called Mission furniture.

Myrtie had the walls of the two big rooms decorated in large-figured paper that gave the appearance of gilt bamboo-poles slanting across the Aurora Borealis. She had the floors varnished a shining dark red over which Amalia must walk charily on the few occasions of her going over to the big house. She used some of Amalia's beautifully pieced quilts for pads under the mattresses and her hand-woven rugs for wiping feet.

She had Joe paint their own bedroom blue, and because Joe was no artist, either by natural instinct or acquired knowledge, he got too much ultramarine in the mixture so that results gave one a rather nightmarish impression of a storm at sea. But because Myrtie liked it, Joe liked it too. Amalia scarcely knew what she thought about it, excepting to experience a stifled feeling of wanting to get outdoors away from it under the soft blue of the sky and the new green of the elms and maples.

All this change about the house took so much of Joe's time he could scarcely get into the field.

As Myrtie had done none of the work herself, only the planning, she was not especially tired these evenings so she coaxed Joe to clean up to go to dances or band concerts in town every few nights.

When the home was all finished Myrtie would not let Joe come into the main rooms, or for that matter, any farther than the kitchen, explaining to him in her cunning babyish way that it must be kept nice for their friends out from town to see.

Rose Schaffer was holding her head very high these days, going into town with her father and brothers as though nothing had happened. Sometimes she even drove the sleek carriage team herself, their black manes tossing, and the lines pulled taut over their shining dark bodies. People began hearing that Rose had gone to help at a neighbor's where there was sickness,—that she had stayed by old man Rhodenbach all three days that the death noise in his throat sounded louder than a child's rattle,— had nursed a Kirby child through lung fever, saved it too, the doctor said, with the steam from a teakettle and pine resin dropped into the water,—queerest of all, had helped a strange girl through childbirth in the school-house on a stormy Saturday night.

Anna Kratz came waddling up the path between Amalia's petunias one day, out of breath from her efforts, to tell the news. Rose Schaffer had gone to Omaha to learn to be a nurse, although Anna was dubious over what one can learn about it.

"You are a nurse or you are not," she said in German to Amalia. "Augusta Schaffer, Rose's grandmother, was a natural nurse. What can a young upstart like Rose learn that God does not give you?"

"Augusta lost babies sometimes when she helped," Amalia said, also in German.

But Anna Kratz settled that question easily: "It was God's will."

By this time Amalia could see that Myrtie's fragility and her ethereal beauty were misleading, for she began guiding all the destinies of the farm. Whenever the occasion demanded, she could wind Joe around her little finger by any one of the simple processes of wheedling baby-talk or big childish tears or an imitation of hysteria.

One afternoon in the summer when she and Joe had returned from town, she came over to the little house. Amalia saw her picking her way daintily through the bluegrass path under the apple trees past the big lilac bushes, then the petunia-bordered path.

"I've got a big piece of news for you, Grandma." She was excited, sparkling, clapping her hands like a child. Already Amalia had learned that Myrtie was always gracious for a little while after things had gone her way.

Amalia stood in the center of the little sitting-room, a broom-straw and pot holder poised in her hand from testing her *kuchen,* awaiting the news.

"What do you think? Your name isn't Holmsdorfer any more. You'll never have to be saddled with that old German name again. It's just Holms. You're Mrs.

Amalia Holms. We had it changed . . . in the courts. Joe and I. We're Mr. and Mrs. Joseph Rhoden . . . not Rhodenbach but Rhoden. . . . Mr. and Mrs. Joseph Rhoden Holms.

Amalia looked dazed. She called to Fritz to come in and help her interpret this astounding thing. Fritz stood timidly in the background, looking at the floor, as he always did before Myrtie. Amalia asked about it again, as though she could not understand the calamitous thing that had happened. You couldn't change your name like your dress.

When Myrtie explained some more that she had always been ashamed of the big long name and had Joe change it, and that Amalia was Mrs. Holms too, Amalia only stood and shook her head, so that Myrtie lost her graciousness and stamped her foot because of Grandma's stubbornness, and said: "You wouldn't be so dumb as that I hope."

But Amalia was firm. "You . . . *vielleicht* . . . maybe . . . Myrtie, you and Joe. But not me."

CHAPTER XXVIII

THE gay nineties had their good points in the growing city of Lincoln where Matthias Meier lived with Ida and his son Carter. For one thing, the bank in which he was vice-president had blossomed forth in electric lighting. The old horses on the street-cars were turned out to pasture and some of Mr. Edison's discovery took their place. There was a very grand new hotel built called The Lincoln. Matthias helped organize a Board of Trade and Ida a Woman's Club. University registration almost reached the unbelievable figure of two thousand. The first automobile honked its noisy way down "O" Street, a large portion of its inwards immodestly exposed to view.

Matthias, Ida and Carter went to the World's Fair in Chicago, returning with souvenir spoons, much Mexican drawn work, and pictures of Mrs. Potter Palmer and the Ferris wheel.

Upon her return Ida found the salt water pool in the new hospital opened to the public, and having been brought up on the Atlantic shore she took a great deal of pleasure in joining society around the huge affair. She had an entirely new outfit for the occasion,—a navy blue flannel suit gathered becomingly just below the knees with wide ruffles, the waist even cut a bit away from the neck, and the prettiest sort of gathered cap over her large head of hair, also finished in a wide rubber ruffle. With this, naturally, she wore her thigh-high lisle stockings into the water. One in her position had an example to set for the young ladies of the social set who were sometimes in these modern times threatening to leave off their hose when they swam.

At the beginning of the nineties there was drouth, and because nearly all crops were failures, the effect threw its shadow over all business. Settlers out on the prairie lived on what they had saved the year before, and Matthias Meier's bank drew on its reserve,—both rather like camels living on their humps.

There was a panic in 1893 and Matthias and his fellow officers figuratively bailed water night and day to keep the bank afloat. As though that were not enough to bear, the next year a hot seething wind blew across the mid-west and again ruined crops.

By 1896 the state was represented for the first time in a race for the presidency. The platforms created a general upheaval in the country. Gold democrats were bolting and rallying around William McKinley,—silver republicans were bolting and rallying around Matthias' friend, William Jennings Bryan. It gave Nebraska its first but not last political attention. Matthias himself had dipped into politics as far as the state legislature where he was responsible for one or two of the most important bills of the times. Sometimes he cast a speculative eye toward Washington, but "I better stay here and saw wood," he said to Ida,—and then laughed with her that he might not have had any other choice.

Between the years of 1898 and 1902 Carter was in the University,—one of the rather popular young bloods;

when he graduated, he stepped immediately into the bank of which his father was a vice-president and told every one that fellows who said it was hard to find jobs had bats in their belfry.

At twenty-seven he was married to Miss Lucile Bondurant, daughter of one of the other vice-presidents, at an elaborate church wedding. They went to Atlantic City on their honeymoon, and upon their return moved at once to their new home in Cedar City, a nice growing town in another county.

All this was by way of being something of a cataclysm to Matthias and Ida. But Carter, having evinced a great desire to run a bank himself and "run it right," had argued long and volubly before his marriage that he could never have matters his own way in this present job with a group of middle-aged men ahead of him to say nothing of several of their sons.

It had its points, Matthias agreed with him,—helped him purchase the controlling stock in the State Bank of Cedar City, sent him on his way with trepidation successfully concealed, remembering the days of his own ventures in a country that was raw and unsettled.

CHAPTER XXIX

EVERYTHING seemed different to Amalia at the farm since the coming of Myrtie. Sometimes she had a feeling that she and Fritz were visiting here or perhaps living on charity,—a queer enough feeling, too, when you stopped to think that the first two homesteads had belonged to Wilhelm, her father, and to Herman, her husband, and that only the newest eighty had been purchased by Joe's father from the Kratzes.

Life at the big house was so different now that she and Fritz did not go over very often. Myrtie was expecting a child and was so changeable in her moods. Sometimes she grew restless and had Joe take her to town every day. Sometimes she said she was nervous and would shut herself in her bedroom, not answering when Joe tapped on the door to ask what he could do for her. She did no work at all, having May Gebhardt there to keep house.

Amalia tried to smooth it over with Joe. He dropped in at the little house every day now and Amalia would laugh at his worries. Myrtie was all right. That was the way they always acted. But Amalia knew she was fibbing in order to bring oil to troubled waters,—knew that was not the way she had acted long ago, being so busy making garden and cooking and baking, washing and ironing and cleaning. It was not the way Anna Marie had acted, cheerful and laughing good-naturedly at her own shapelessness, pleased that she was bringing life into the world, heart-broken those times she could not carry her babies.

But she would soothe Joe, and feed him cookies from the old stone jar, so that he would leave whistling.

She could see that he was patience itself. Looking at him so eager to please and so willing to do everything Myrtie asked, Amalia wondered sometimes if he would ever tire of that babyish petulance, ever break over the traces and throw patience to the winds. When the time drew near, he paid the trained nurse to come much sooner than necessary so Myrtie would not worry. When she constantly wanted the doctor, too, and the nurse said there was no need, she cried hysterically and would not eat. Joe was quite beside himself with alarm. And Amalia comforted him, but even while she did so, she was remembering the wind and the shaking cabin, the loneliness at the birth of her child, and the sound of the coyotes howling.

The baby was born in September,—a boy, normal and husky, his sturdy little limbs a joy to see. They named him Neal, and Joe was as proud of him as a turkey-cock. Amalia could not comprehend that she was a great-grandmother. Because she and her son and her grandson had all been married at early ages, she was a great-grandmother at sixty-three.

And now, soon, life took on something of its old interest, for by the time Neal was three, Amalia was having much of the care of him. Joe took the little fellow with him on short journeys to the timber or barn or cornfield, and Fritz did likewise, so that it relieved Myrtie of a great deal of responsibility. She had many interests outside her home by that time, belonging as she did to so many organizations in town for the betterment of her mind, and one or two for her soul. It necessitated having a woman for housework and a second girl occasionally, even though Amalia took so much care of Neal. But it was a little hard to run the house as it had always been done, for there were guests out from town so often that the girls seemed never able to accomplish anything excepting to prepare for entertaining. As a consequence, the birds took the cherries, plums rotted on the ground, and apples turned to sour mash. But Myrtie said it didn't matter, now that one could conveniently get canned fruit and jellies in the stores.

She had a discontented droop to her pretty mouth much of the time now. Joe bought an automobile for her,—a fine red four-cylinder affair with top and lamps and windshield included, which materially increased her trips to town, but inasmuch as she never learned to drive it, Joe had to come in from the field almost every day to take her and once more to get her. As she insisted on his clothes being changed each time, this had its disadvantage from the standpoint of the farm work, so that he was obliged to take on another hired man.

When Neal was six, Myrtie was made secretary of a lodge in Westville so she bought a man-sized desk for her clerical work and turned Joe's and her bedroom into a semi-office. The desk just fitted into the corner where Joe's share of the twin beds stood so she retained only her own and put Joe and Neal upstairs. As Myrtie said, it was a very satisfactory arrangement for sometimes she liked to work late at her desk and then sleep late in the morning.

To Amalia, seventy now, fell even more of the care of Neal. But Amalia loved it. Even though she was old and tired, she loved it. What would life have been to her without this lively little boy? It was now as though she had her third son. Emil . . . Joey . . . Neal. Sometimes when he trudged by her side chattering so gaily, she caught herself thinking that which was not right and which she straightway corrected in her mind,—that of all three she loved him most.

Never had she seen so happy a child. Remembering Myrtie's pouting and her nervousness, old Amalia wondered how this had come to pass. One would have expected him to be cross, selfish, discontented. He was none of these. Everything tickled him, the dog running after a jack-rabbit, the martins frightening the sparrows, old Fritz dropping his upper teeth when he was in the corncrib. Neal's smile was always sunny. His laughter rang out at the slightest provocation. How could this be?

Myrtie's love for him took on a queer expression for a mother. Apparently it consisted for the most part in wanting him to be talented and courteous and to show off before her friends. Amalia could not put her finger on the queer quality of it, excepting that whatever he was doing openly and however he was appearing seemed to be of more importance to her than that which lay behind these external qualities.

Sensing this, Amalia bent all the time of her contacts with him to these very things which Myrtie passed over so

casually. She made him go all the way back to old Anna
Kratz's to return a small and unimportant wheel he had
brought from there without asking about it. She labored
a half day with him to get him to tell that he had taken
fruit *kuchen* from her pantry, caring not in the least for
the *kuchen* but only that he should be honest.

Together they walked in the timberland even as she
had walked with the little boy's father and his grandfather,—not buoyantly now, but slowly for her seventy
years. She talked to him of the trees, old now like Amalia
herself,—the hoary old cottonwoods and willow and ash
and the great thickly knotted clumps of wild sumac. Because it was too hard for her to stoop, Neal picked and
brought to her the violets and black-eyed Susans and trillium, the bellwort and bloodroot and wild columbine.
But it was only the English names of these that Neal
knew, for not one word of German could he say but *"Ich
liebe dich"* which Amalia had taught him was "I love
you."

Together they found the meadow-lark's nest in the
grass and the place where the owls had hooted away the
nights in the woods these fifty years. She stood with him
on the church knoll with its fine brick buildings and well-
kept cemetery behind iron gates looking over the valley,
and had him repeat with her,—she in German and he in
the English,—the psalm of walking through the valley of
the shadow of death and yet fearing no evil.

And this time Fritz was not here to make any comment,
either to tell her that she would make a softie of the
little boy as he had when she instructed Emil so, or
to admit that it is not softness to be tender as he had

with Joey.   For old Fritz, himself, was lying back there now behind the wrought-iron gates. Old Fritz, himself, the year before, had walked through the valley of the shadow of death, fearing evil for a time, until Amalia by his bedside, holding his gnarled old hand and thanking him for having been such a good brother to her, made him fear no more.

It was lonely these days without Fritz, but much of the time it seemed to Amalia he had not gone away at all. When she was baking she often forgot and let a pan of *kuchen* get browner because he liked it so, and very often, unthinking, she set the table for two.

But Neal, dashing in then, full of life and laughter and staying to use the other place, would drive the loneliness away and fill her heart with happiness.

CHAPTER XXX

IT was this year of 1917 that strange things came to pass.

The country was at war. Amalia remembered the news of the Civil War when she was twelve, the drafting of several of the men in the neighborhood, the great pride the Illinois people had taken that old Abe was in the presidential chair, the company coming home when she was sixteen.

It had seemed unbelievable that war could touch her again. Even the Spanish-American War of which she had heard had been unreal, for no one from the immediate neighborhood had gone. There were three brave Nebraska regiments, they had told her,—one had gone to the Philippine Islands, wherever they were,—one to Tennessee, and one had crossed to Havana.

But this war was so different. It was coming into the neighborhood. It was asking for the young men. It was making trouble,—was causing bad feelings right here between old neighbors.

There could be no more German in the church on the hill. It must all be English,—not a song, not a sermon, not a psalm could be in the old tongue. Tsk! Tsk! How could one sit through and understand it all? How could it harm the country to say the Psalms in the German?

The *pastor* had been told to leave, had been given a

few days to get out of the neighborhood for making wrong statements. Anna Kratz came over every day now to talk. Almost in a whisper Anna talked to her in the German, looking about furtively as though the walls might have ears. Adolph had been in town, he and Karl Schaffer and Henry Gebhardt had been talking on the corner about the war; some men had come up to them and said to cut it out, meaning, so Adolph said, to speak no more in the German tongue.

Worst of all Myrtie made more trouble. She talked constantly to Joe about the relatives, put strange notions into Neal's little head so that he said: "Grandma, you shall say no more German words to me ever. I am ashamed of them."

"Not even *'Ich liebe dich'?*"

"No, it is not nice."

When the Christmas exercises were held in the church and they sang "Silent Night, Holy Night," Amalia hummed the song below her breath but with no words at all, for the English were too difficult and with the German she did not dare.

Oh, it was a trying time. Sometimes Amalia was wishing with all her might that Fritz were here to talk the queer situation over with her. Then, remembering Fritz's hard time with the English and the things some of the neighbors were saying, she was glad he was not here to be hurt.

Joe was irritable. Not even the high price he was getting for wheat—so much money—could pay him for the mean way he felt, torn by his loyalty to the oldest of the Kratz and Gebhardt and Rhodenbach people and by the harsh things Myrtie and her friends were saying.

And then he was drafted and Amalia and Myrtie were drawn together for a time by their common fright. But the scare went into nothing when the lawyer filled out the answers to the questions that Joe was sole manager of four hundred acres of farm land and must stay home to attend to raising the wheat.

Rose Schaffer was one of the first to go over-seas.

One of Karl Schaffer's boys died of pneumonia in camp. A Gebhardt boy was killed in France. Elsa Rhodenbach, who was a widow living in town now, had two sons leave the same morning together. Elsa got breakfast for them, said good-by, walked out of the house when they did, and never went back. All summer children used to stand on their tiptoes and peek through the woodbine covering the windows, seeing the dishes there on the table, the unmade beds with the boys' shoes under them and their ties and night-clothes thrown across the backs of chairs.

It was over at last,—the war. The whistles blew in town that it was over, and the train coming through, shrieked its way all across the countryside, through the villages and past the fields which had raised so much of the wheat for the armies. The bell in the tower of the big brick church on the knoll, rang, too, for in what language does a bell worship or toll or carol?

It was over for the neighborhood,—all but the scars left by the things that had been said, and for the fact that the Gebhardt boy and Karl Schaffer's boy did not come back, and neither did Elsa Rhodenbach's sanity.

Over, excepting for all of these things and a wild aftermath of economic and moral breakdown that swept into every village and farm.

Joe was making a good deal of money these days. His car was big and new, six cylinders now. The land brought in such good returns that he was anxious to get more. Myrtie was having a great many very nice things; clothes and company and a trip to Chicago with friends. She was back home now but so busy with several social affairs that Neal was still at Amalia's.

To-night while his parents were away, he was making a crude little boat in Amalia's kitchen . . . pound . . . pound . . . with Amalia sitting near looking over *reis* for to-morrow and watching him. Seventy-one she was. Did a woman never outgrow her motherliness? Neal was her little boy just as Emil and Joey had been. Emil . . . Joey . . . Neal! Son . . . grandson . . . great-grandson. The years had all run together so that they seemed three brothers with no great difference in their ages. Three little brothers, and she the mother of them all. How could it be like that?

Neal dropped his hammer now and leaned back against the wall for a time, eyes drooping and hands listless. Even as she was peering questioningly at him, he came languidly over to her. "I don't feel so good, Grandma."

She had him in her lap, was feeling his hot face, his rapid pulse.

"I'll say, *'Ich liebe dich'* Grandma, if you want me to. It is not bad. It is just as good as 'I love you.' "

"Oh, Neal-*liebling*." She pulled him to her, frightened at the premonition of a sickness for him. And he

217

did not even rebel at the endearing word she had said to a big boy of eight.

Old Amalia kept clean night-clothes here in her house for Neal because she had him here so much,—a queer word they called them, pajamas. She never could remember to say it,—"night panties" she called them instead. She got out his night panties now and got him into them, her fingers stiff and slow but tender as always. Already he was dozing, shivering a little, too, and rousing to whimper. She covered him, got drinks for him, sat by the bed, comforting him.

It was late when she heard the automobile come into the yard. Joe would be down in a few minutes. He never failed to come down to see if everything was all right, whether to leave the little boy or carry him up home. Joe was a good father. Sometimes she thought he was father and mother both. In bearing Neal, Myrtie had apparently paid off most of her obligations to motherhood.

When she told him about Neal, he was at the bed in a second bending over his little son. Then out again for the doctor the moment he had seen his flushed face and how he was thrashing about.

Spanish influenza they called it, and it went through the country like the prairie-fires of the old days. People dropped over at their work,—young Mrs. Henry Kratz was frying chicken, fainted, was buried the third day with no one allowed to attend the funeral. A sixteen-year-old boy died, a sixty-year-old woman, a baby,—the whole countryside was panicky.

Myrtie's hired girl took it, then Myrtie.

Joe was beside himself with worry and sleeplessness.

He phoned to Westville for a trained nurse, to Lincoln, to Omaha. None was available. They said they would put him on the list but gave no hope for immediate relief. He plodded between the two houses, staggered almost with loss of sleep.

Old Amalia did everything for Neal the doctor said to do, but with her intuition she sensed he was not confident about his own orders. She carried out his orders fully, adding a few old-fashioned cures of her own, *flieder tee* and *pfeffermünz tee*. She had waged a fight like this many times for Emil and Joey,—now it was for Neal, her third little boy.

It was toward evening of the fourth day when Joe, haggard, unkempt looking, just back to the cottage from caring for Myrtie, was standing by Neal's bed, that the door of Amalia's sitting-room opened. Startled, they both turned to it. Rose Schaffer stood there in a white dress and over-seas cape, a little black satchel in her hand.

"Rose!" Something jumped so plainly from Joe that Amalia, relieved as she was at Rose's coming, turned away from him in embarrassment. As long as she lived Amalia knew she would carry with her the memory of Joe's face when he turned and saw Rose in the doorway. And now Amalia had this secret she must never divulge, must never even remember. And who but old Amalia knew what it meant to have married the wrong person?

"I came to help, Joe." Rose took off her hat. Her clear gray eyes, her serene mouth, her strong capable hands,—how good she looked!

"You're . . . so good, Rose." It was all he said.

Rose went at her work with no other explanation. Joe went out to do his chores.

For two more days and nights Neal was not out of danger and Rose scarcely took her eyes off the child. Then the fever broke and the great sweating sapped his strength.

Joe coming in found Rose crying by the bedside and was almost too frightened to speak: "He's . . . he's worse, Rose?"

"No . . . he's better. He'll get well if you're careful."

"Then why . . . are you crying?"

Amalia saw him start to put his arm around her and then drop it quickly.

"Just . . . a sort of reaction. Silly . . . isn't it?"

But old Amalia, who had lived seventy-one years, knew why Rose Schaffer was crying over Joe's little boy.

CHAPTER XXXI

CARTER MEIER and his wife Lucile had adjusted themselves ably to conditions in the smaller town of Cedar City.

"The smaller the town the more often they tack on the word 'City,'" Lucile had said.

But Carter had called her attention to the fact that when a town gets its baptismal name its sponsors in fancy see it stretched out over half the county.

"Like babies, I suppose," Lucile said with sarcasm, "with the mother always thinking her youngster is to be president or the first lady."

In 1913 Lucile herself had no sarcasm for the situation, but very frankly admitted that her baby was an eligible candidate for the first lady's place. The child had dark red ringlets, creamy petaled skin and hazel eyes. They named her Hazel, but Matthias sometimes facetiously called his only grandchild "Reddie."

He and Ida took their honors solemnly. Because Carter had not been born until they were thirty-five and thirty-two,—and because the child Hazel did not arrive until Carter and Lucile had been married for six years, —it followed that Matthias and Ida were well along in years,—sixty-eight and sixty-five,—before they experienced this ownership of a grandchild. It was almost overwhelming.

They drove out to Cedar City at the least possible excuse, taking advantage of every national holiday, every birthday, and even, so Ida said, April Fool and Columbus Day.

Matthias was out of active business now. He looked after his property, advised Carter on any and all matters that came up in the Cedar City bank of which he owned some stock. Once he and Ida had been abroad, several times to Florida and California.

Ida, at sixty-five, looked the part of an amiable duchess,—snow-white hair in a becoming coiffure, solid pink cheeks, her heavy figure straight and trim in its hard stays. Her word had weight in the Woman's Club,— church organizations asked her to make decisions, every charity included her name.

Matthias, too, was straight as an Indian, his shovel-shaped black beard of the old days white-washed by the years and trimmed down to Scotch-like closeness.

They belonged to the Country Club, ten years old now. Matthias swung a mean club in the newly introduced game of golf, and Ida could hold her own at the card table. Sometimes they laughed at the old days. "Imagine how I used to play croquet in a long trailing skirt!" or "How I ever had the nerve to sing in a choir . . . !" And then quite often the statements would be followed by "Just the same they were the good old days," spoken together like the chorus of a song which they both knew.

The child Hazel could not, if she were able, have chosen more satisfactory grandparents.

Carter's business was good. The State Bank of Cedar City was paying ample dividends spring and fall. Matthias admitted his son had used his head when he went into the smaller bank on his own. His success made Carter Meier rather unsympathetic with failure of any sort. One did with life as one wished. Or so he thought.

Lucile had everything to make life comfortable for her, —sufficient clothes for the exigencies of the small town and for the times when she would go to Lincoln to be entertained by her own people or Father and Mother Meier, —a nice home, plenty of help, her own car, a healthy and attractive little daughter.

Carter worked day and night during the World War, —his own business in the daytime, war work at night,— questionnaires and applications for release from the draft for the farm boys. He was a part and parcel of the smaller town as his father had been of the small Lincoln, grown by this time to fifty thousand people.

To the west twenty million acres of sandy soil held fast to the earth's breast by coarse, tough grasses since the glacial period were being loosened by plows to feed a fighting Europe.

It was easy planting. No forests to fell, few stones to remove. Peel open the top soil with a plow, seed it, scratch it with a harrow, and Mother Nature did the rest. As the crops went in, the soil grew finer, became more powder-like.

A few shook their heads at the unthinking procedure. Once when old Charlie Briggs dropped into Cedar City to see Carter, his old friend's son, and a bit of fine dust was coming through the air on the wings of the west wind, old Charlie lifted his head like a fire-horse and sniffed.

"Dirt from the Panhandle," he said. "Powder, that's what the ground is being pulverized into. It might turn into gunpowder one of these days. A body can't tell. Wheat may get to be scarce. Bread might be a luxury right here in the heart of our own country. Ain't I heard somepin' about a French Revolution startin' over a bread riot?"

Carter Meier laughed a lot about old Charlie Briggs and his ideas.

In 1919 with Spanish influenza sweeping the country, Ida Meier died suddenly in her Lincoln home. Only four days of sickness, and with Matthias employing every means at his command,—doctors, specialists, nurses, oxygen,—she slipped away.

He was too stunned to comprehend. Why, Ida was a part of him. She was one of his hands, one of his feet, one side of his mind, half of his heart. If Ida was dead, that meant half of him was dead.

But he pulled himself together, lived on, imposed his feelings of loss on no one. He sold the old home to the Pi Beta Chis,—when some of the "actives" came in to look it over, closed his ears to their merry quips about the ornate grill-work through which they could hang their neckties, and how they would play checkers on the inlaid woods of the entrance hall. Still, Ida would have laughed merrily if she could hear their humorous sallies. All right, he would laugh too, then.

He moved over to Cedar City to be near Carter and Lucile. They built a larger house so he could have his own suite of rooms. He went down to Carter's bank every day. Carter depended a great deal on his judgment.

Hazel was Matthias' comfort. He watched her grow, —eight—ten—twelve—fourteen. How the years rolled on. She was not quite so pretty now,—her hair was lovely, but she was at the gangling age,—a brace on her teeth, freckles on her nose. The former would come off in time,—it was questionable about the other.

She was athletic,—always on roller skates, ice skates, a bicycle. A tennis racket was her insignia,—"I can beat you" her life's motto. She went hither and yon with the wind. Sometimes he tried to take a hand and tame her down,—tell her that she would soon be a young lady, that ladies should be more demure, that the young men cared more for that kind, and how could she expect to have any young man ever care for her?

"But I don't *want* any young man to care for me," she would respond. "It would just drive me *nuts*. I'm going to be the champion swimmer—or a circus woman—or maybe fly in a plane."

Whatever could you do with a young girl like that? Such times as these were. No modesty, no womanly graces.

Fairly often old Charlie Briggs came to see Matthias. Lucile and Carter laughed a little at the old codger.

"Whatever Father can see in him, with his long-drawn tales of the 'airly days,' " Lucile would say.

"Search me," Carter would respond indifferently. "With all Father's travel and culture, I believe he hangs more on every word that old fellow says than any one I know."

But Hazel always stood up stoutly for him. "I like him. He's a nice old man. He shot an Injun once right in the belly when the Injun was trying to slip up on him."

"Hazel . . . how terrible! Why do you listen to all

that gore? Anyway, it's Indian, not Injun. And do, for pity's sake, say he hit him in the stomach if you *have* to say it at all."

"Charlie Briggs says it's Injun. And your stomach *isn't* your belly. Your belly . . ."

"Hazel. That will do."

". . . is below your stomach."

"Hazel. Do you hear me?"

"Anyway he knows more about our own history than anybody. He knows all about the Vigilantes hanging the horse thieves in summer 'til the crows pecked their eyes out . . . and about sticking them down through ice holes in the winter."

"Oh, Hazel, you have such a delicate sense of the æsthetic."

"And I'm going some day to see where old Charlie Briggs and Grandpa got off the boat at Nebraska City . . . and John Brown's cave where he hid the runaway slaves. And Charlie Briggs can show me yet, he says, where the overland trails all began. He bets he can find ruts some places yet where the wheels of the prairie schooners cut. I can go, can't I, Dad?"

"Sure. Anybody as history-conscious as that ought to be allowed to poke around a bit."

CHAPTER XXXII

TIMES had changed again slowly. The highway was hard packed with gravel. The Evergreen School was closed and a bus came by daily to take Neal and the other pupils into town. When Amalia got out Joe's tin bucket that she had saved carefully and offered to put up Neal's lunch for him every day, thinking how much pleasure it would give her, he rolled on the floor in his mirth.

"Grandma, you are so behind the times. Don't you know I buy a hot lunch in the cafeteria?"

"In de calf . . ."

"Cafeteria . . . where you can buy the food you choose to eat,—soup and hot meat and potatoes and salads,—a balanced meal to keep you healthy."

Tsk! Tsk! And the cold *met-wurst* and the *schinken* and the *korn brot* and *äpfel-butter* she had put up so many times! And who had been more healthy than Emil and Joe?

There were other things about which Neal laughed hilariously.

Once she asked him hesitatingly,—for perhaps, already she knew his answer,—"Neal, vould you . . . vouldn't you like to be a *pastor?*"

Giving it, as she did, the emphasis on the second syllable in the German way, Neal was not sure of her word.

"Pas*tor?* You mean a preacher?"

"So. A preacher."

Neal rolled then on the floor in mirth and shouted. "A preacher! All I would like about that is being invited to all the big dinners in the country."

No, there was no use. No one of her three boys a *pastor* would be.

Myrtie's latest argument with Joe these days was that he should get out of the hog business altogether and depend only on selling his crops.

Joe groaned when she began, for never since their marriage had Myrtie dropped a subject upon which she had once set her mind.

The grain from four hundred acres would bring ample income, she said, and pigs were such dirty things,—you could hear their grunting and squealing away up at the house, too, company or no company.

At first Joe only made joking answers, that he'd have some one in to instruct them at their eating, that the day Mrs. Meredith, the banker's wife, and the lodge ladies came out from town, he would speak to the old porkers himself.

But Myrtie would not joke. She ran instead the full gamut of her little tricks,—teasing, baby-talk, wheedling, tears, hysteria. It was not often that she had to go so far, but Joe set a good deal of store by his Berkshires, and it required her entire bag of tricks before he capitulated.

After the hogs went, she began on Joe about the chickens. She said eggs were so cheap it was foolish to look after those chickens and cackling hens every day, and when they wanted one to eat, Grandma would let them have one of hers.

So they, too, went,—and the farm was exactly like a town home with its nice sloping lawn, no pigs or chickens on the place, and Joe, dressed up, driving the car up to the side porch whenever Myrtie called.

As there were no pigs or chickens to be fed, there was no mash to be cooked. So Myrtie told one of the hired men to scrub up the old soap-kettle, paint it copper-colored, fill it with dirt and bring it onto the front lawn. There she had him cross three stout hickory sticks in camp-fire style and hang the kettle on them by a gilded chain. Then she had the hired girl plant white snow-on-the-mountain in it, and red geraniums under it. And people coming out from town said it looked cute, just as though there were fire under it and steam coming out of it.

Only old Amalia, standing in the doorway of her small house, shading her watery eyes from the sunlight to see the finished article, failed to think it looked cute. She thought the old kettle looked out of place and a little silly.

By the time Neal was through the grammar grades and ready for High School in the fall of 1926, Myrtie's desires took on more radical form. Specifically,—she wanted Joe to retire.

"Retire?" Joe laughed heartily at that one. That one should be in the funny column, he said,—maybe in the department called "Slips That Pass in the Night."

When Myrtie would not laugh, but persisted day after day in referring to a potential retirement, Joe grew irritated. It was too foolish to waste one's breath on it.

"Retire? Say, what do you take me for?"

"Yes . . . retire." Myrtie's little rosebud mouth set in a straight and stubborn line.

"Can you beat it for a cracked idea? Retire when you're thirty-eight."

"Age hasn't anything to do with it,—if you're able financially to retire at thirty-eight."

"But I'm not."

"Oh, you just think you're not. Just that old Holms-*dorfer* idea that you have to hoard." The accent on the *dorfer* which had been dropped and the slur which it implied angered Joe more than Myrtie had ever seen him angry.

"See here, a Holms*dorfer* was good enough for you to want to marry. And you leave the old folks out of this. If you and I are ever half as good as . . ." He caught himself, said more evenly: "I don't call it hoarding to earn your living by hard work so you can have something to depend on in your old age."

"You'll have plenty, never fear."

"Not if I quit while I'm still a young man, I won't. And don't forget that last eighty from the Gebhardts,—costing twenty thousand dollars because the improvements were extra good,—five thousand only paid, only two really which was cash, the bank holding a seven thousand note of mine, Henry Gebhardt an eleven thousand mortgage. That sounds like retirement in a pig's left eye. Oh, excuse me for mentioning pigs."

And when Myrtie's little mouth trembled and she looked misty-eyed, he asked querulously: "Retire . . . *where?*"

"Over to Westville of course, or even to Lincoln."

"In *town?*" Joe was really disturbed.

"Of course."

"But I wouldn't *like* it, Myrtie. I'm a farmer. My father . . . and my father's father and *his* father . . . maybe back to Adam for all I know were *land* people. It's my *work* . . . my *life*."

"There's a lot more to life than a farm."

"I know it. I want to get things running here smoothly so we can take a good trip every year. Canada . . . I'd like to see those real wheat farms, . . . California, maybe, . . . the old Spanish ranchos I've heard about. . . ."

"Farms . . . ranchos." Myrtie said it in the same tone one would speak of tarantulas and scorpions.

"Then there's Neal," he went on. "He's to be thought of."

"How do you mean . . . 'thought of'?"

"Why, that everything shall be in tip-top shape for him."

"Where?"

"'Where?' Why, *here*."

"Neal will have something to say about that."

"Of course, and he'll say the right thing, too. Natural-born farmer . . . look at his 4-H Club work . . . his calf prizes."

At that Myrtie would walk into her own room and close the door.

But a mere walking off by no means closed the argument.

It went on many times after that. Sometimes Myrtie was quietly insistent about it, sometimes she was tearful, and always she kept it over Joe's head. Sometimes she said Joe ought to be generous enough to do it for her after all she'd been through, at which Joe could scarcely restrain himself against asking just what that had been. Sometimes she remarked that he was blind not to see it was for his own good. Often she said it was too bad that he couldn't do that much for his only son.

At that Joe would explode: "My only son's a spoiled kid with everything in the world from his first little velocipede on through town school,—a boy's camp,—asking for his own car at fifteen now,—the promise of one on his sixteenth birthday. At his age I was up at five with my dad, doing my share of chores. . . ."

That would be about the point where Myrtie would cry and take a headache tablet.

Joe, dropping down sometimes on the steps of the old home and looking across the long sloping lawn to the paved highway and his fields beyond, lush with purple alfalfa, to the corn lands and the pastures, and his sleek cattle, tried to think how any one would want to live anywhere else.

He worked hard, of course, but who didn't? Lots of discouraging things,—bad crops, hail, prices slumping, one battle after another with chinch bugs or blight or cutworms. If it wasn't one thing it was another. But wherever you were or whatever you did there was always something. He bet even the banker had his troubles. He'd rather battle his enemies out here in the open.

Sometimes he thought of Rose Schaffer. At first he had put her from his thoughts as disloyal to Myrtie about whom he had once gone off his head. Then, he didn't care whether it was disloyal or not. He liked to think about her. How contented Rose would have been on a fine farm and how efficiently she would have managed. Oh well, she was probably doing just what she was cut out for,—head nurse or some such title in one of the Omaha hospitals.

And now Amalia was seventy-nine, tiny and weather-beaten, her hair in a hard little knob like a walnut, her skin a network of wrinkles, deep rivers on the map of Time.

This was the spring that with Joe, Myrtie, and Neal she took the long drive one Sunday to Nebraska City to visit Arbor Lodge, the beautiful old estate of J. Sterling Morton, now a state park.

All the buds were unfolding under the soft warmth of the sun. There was a smell of burning leaves. Tulips were pushing up through the warm ground. Odors from recently turned earth still lingered in the air. The old grounds were lovely in their new spring growth.

Not once had Amalia ever returned to Nebraska City since the day she stepped from the ferry and found Herman waiting. Sixty-one years.

They were to eat their lunch here under the trees so Myrtie said. Joe said they would drive down toward the town afterward so Grandma could try and find the place where she stood by the overland trail when she was married to Grandpa.

It was the first time Neal had ever been told about it.

He thought that was just about the darnedest thing he'd ever heard. "What do you know about that, Grandma? Married outdoors! And standing by the wagons on an overland trail! Well . . . I'll be . . . Say, you could have sung 'It's a Long, Long Trail A-Winding,' couldn't you?" And he rolled on the pine needles in one of his moments of mirth.

They spread their lunch on a cloth under the pine trees growing on a portion of the grounds. The mansion was visible through the trees, the snowy white pillars of one of its three great rounded porches glistening in the spring sunshine. Here, somewhere, perhaps even where the lunch cloth lay, was held the ceremony in which the Indians made the treaty with the whites, signing away all their rights to Nebraska Territory. Joe said there was a large oil painting of the ceremony in the house, on the landing of the great stairway,—that they could see it when they would go in later.

There were several other groups in the grove. Myrtie was hoping that it was no one she knew, for she was always a little fearful of meeting some of her friends when she was with Grandma who looked so queer these days.

Joe knew who one of the men was in the group nearest, —it was Carter Meier, the banker over at Cedar City. He had seen him the time he went there with Orval Black on that note. That must be his wife and young daughter with him. Myrtie was all interest,—they certainly looked well groomed and as though they *were* some one.

"And I suppose the gentleman with the white beard is old Mr. Matthias Meier, his father," Joe explained.

Amalia trembled a little with the sudden shock of the queer thing Joey had said.

"What did you say his name was, Joey?"

"Matthias Meier. He lived in Lincoln until a few years ago. Now he lives in Cedar City at his son's home."

"Joey, . . . I knew . . . I knew a man in Illinois vonce by de name of Meier."

"Sure you did . . . and you'd known one if you'd lived in Indiana or Michigan or Ohio. Pretty common, Grandma."

When the lunch was finished, Amalia walked over to a bench under the trees and sat down. She wanted to think. Matthias Meier! So often she had wondered about him. Old Amalia Holmsdorfer in her rusty black dress and her little black bonnet with the jet buckle sat and wondered if it could really be the same. After a lifetime!

And then it happened. The tall white-haired and white-bearded old gentleman of the group came walking down the path. Old Amalia who could not see to read could yet see him coming. He was straight and tall and he swung a cane rather pompously. Amalia knew him,—by his walk and the set of his shoulders and the way he held his head,—by her heart and by remembrance.

The years turned back and he was swinging off his horse . . . coming toward her. . . . Yes, old Amalia knew him.

She was suddenly agitated, frightened. Her heart,—it pounded loudly. Should she call to him to stop? Get up and walk toward him? Should she let him know? Should she say something? Or nothing? She sat still and blinked up at him with faded eyes.

If Amalia saw a fine-looking, well-preserved old gentleman, highly groomed and prosperous appearing, Matthias Meier, sauntering down the path, saw a queer little old woman sitting on one of the park benches,—a brown gnome of a woman peering up at him with pale, watery eyes. She looked like one of the peasants of Bavaria he had seen abroad, he was thinking,—or a Breton painting, perhaps. She looked so tiny and ancient, so picturesque in her funny old clothes, so detached from the civilization of to-day, that he nodded courteously to her. Yes, she belonged there under the trees with the squirrels.

"Spring again," he said pleasantly to her.

Amalia twisted her knotted fingers together. "Yes," she said. She tried to wet her shrunken, dry lips over her toothless gums. It all sounded queer and strange,— but familiar, too, like a thing one has learned long ago and never forgotten. "Dey keep comin'."

"Even though we grow old," he added humorously, placing himself humbly in her class.

She clung tightly to the seat, pressing her hands against the wood,—trying to fit it all in,—the puzzle,—nodding acquiescence to the strange thing he had said.

He passed on, leaving the queer-looking little old lady sitting there nodding—nodding agreement that spring was here even though they were old.

For how could young Matthias Meier once have known he was to keep his rendezvous in such a way? And how could old Matthias Meier know that he had not broken his promise,—that he and Amalia had kept their tryst?

CHAPTER XXXIII

IN the fall of Neal's junior High School year, Joe and Myrtie moved to Westville.

Myrtie chose a house on the corner of Fifteenth and Oakland Streets,—a big brown brick and stucco. Joe tried to get her to be satisfied with a smaller one for he reminded her many times that Neal would be away at school in two years' time.

"High School was good enough for me, but Neal is to have college. Even if he goes back to the farm as I hope he will, he'll always have something you can't take away from him. Can't say I ever missed it, but I'd like Neal to go."

Prices were high and the house cost a pretty sum of money. Joe had to do a certain amount of juggling to arrange for its financing, as his lawful limit had been reached at the Westville bank.

He got a personal loan from Henry Kratz for a cash payment and gave a mortgage on the new house to the original owner. When he was going to put a mortgage on the home four hundred, he found it tied up yet in the original owners' names, his grandfather's and his great grandfather's homestead titles, as there had been no settlement of the estate. Not many direct descendants could boast of that, they told him at the courthouse,—there had been so much changing,—but the county recorder said he would bet his last year's hat and the one from the year before, which was the same one, that there were more families on farms which their ancestors homesteaded right there in that valley than in any other section of the state.

It was fairly complicated but not hard to straighten,— Wilhelm Stoltz's one-hundred-sixty acres by the laws of the state were divided equally between Amalia and Fritz. Fritz's half at his death became Amalia's, one-half of Herman's homestead went to Amalia and one-half to Emil, the latter having gone *in toto* to Joe as did also the eighty Emil had purchased later. To sum it all up to Myrtie, Joe told her that after all, out of the land in the farm, Grandma still owned two hundred and forty acres of it and maybe she would have something to say about a mortgage,—all of which seemed especially foolish to Myrtie when Grandma was so old and didn't even care.

"She'd care if she'd lose it," he said grimly.

The town house was eventually financed and Myrtie furnished it newly from top to bottom for she was leaving the furniture in the stone house to the renters.

Whenever Joe grew blue about his finances, knowing that he was going against all the teaching of his people,— all the traditions of the thrifty midwestern pioneers,— reminding himself and Myrtie that Indebtedness was an animal which ate houses for breakfast, farms for dinner, and lunched between times on stock sandwiched between chattel mortgages,—Myrtie would laugh it off and call his attention to the fact that four hundred and eighty acres of the best Nebraska farm land was worth three hundred dollars an acre any day, which according to *her* arithmetic was one hundred and forty-four thousand dollars.

"We *think* it is," Joe would say, "but do we *know* it?"

Another change in Joe's life came now.

At a little bridge party one evening at Banker Meredith's, Myrtie, who was sitting on the davenport with Mr. Meredith before the games started, said in her pretty pouting way that she wished Joe could get in the banking business,—"Oh, maybe not *work* at it but own stock and meet with the directors and feel that he was one of the *business* men of the town."

Mr. Meredith looked at her a moment rather oddly, said she was a bright little woman and he thought maybe it could be arranged. So it came to be that Joe was allowed to buy fifty shares of stock at the bargain price of one-hundred-sixty dollars per share and was made fourth vice-president, which was really the very nicest thing that could have happened to the Holms family.

Myrtie said that it took a woman's ambitions and intuitions together to help a plodder like Joe get anywhere,— and it was not, in fact, until the moratorium of 1933 several years later, when the bank failed to reopen and Joe was assessed for twice the amount of his stock, that Myrtie's intuitions and ambitions appeared not to be puncture-proof.

But that situation had not yet arrived and these years were prosperous ones. Joe's crops brought good prices. They bought a larger car. Neal was to turn his old one in and get a new one the day he would graduate.

So now Mrs. Joseph Rhoden Holms could launch out on what she termed "real living." Neal went in for football and a general good time.

And Joe—?

Joe in his early forties, miserable and uncertain just what life was doing to him, would drive out to the farm nearly every day and look around, "overseeing the tenants," as Myrtie wanted.

But something was happening to the old home place. Spring rains had washed out part of the corn and the renter apologetically said he had thought there wasn't any use to replant when it was so late. Fences were broken here and there. The stucco was dropping off the house in large South-American-shaped chunks. Dandelions and burdock had taken over part of the lawn. A barn door hung by a roller. The old soap-kettle in the yard at the side of the drive hung dejectedly by one chain over the frozen geranium roots and with rotted snow-on-the-mountain spilling out of it.

Sometimes Joe worked all day at these defects, eating his noon meal with old Amalia. Nearly eighty she was, but fairly spry about her house-work and as neat as ever. Her kitchen shone like a child's scrubbed face. No one could make *kaffee kuchen* so well or fry chicken like Grandma.

It always made him feel better to talk to her. He told her many of the things that worried him, but he never complained about Myrtie. It did not seem square to Myrtie to discuss her even with Grandma. Once when he was there Amalia told him Rose Schaffer had been to see her. "In her own car . . . such a fine-looking voman . . . wit' a fur coat."

He started to say something, thought better of it evidently and did not finish.

Together they sat silent and embarrassed.

Sometimes he talked to Grandma about Neal. "Four hundred and eighty acres of the finest Nebraska farmland there is," he said sardonically, ". . . that's what he'll have some day and Myrtie wants him to be a lawyer."

"Vell," old Amalia said cheerfully, "any lawyer can alvays use a goot farm," and laughed at her own joke. Always she was wanting Joe and Myrtie to get along well.

"If there's anything left," Joe said grimly. "I don't like the way my debits and credits look in black and red figures."

Neal graduated from the Westville High School in 1929. One could scarcely contend that it was scholarship which sent him through with more or less flying colors. Football prowess plus a reputation for squareness and a personality that was most likable,—these rather were his assets. Amalia looking at him, sometimes wondered what he had of Myrtie's excepting the cleft in his chin and the gracious manner all the time which she showed only when things went her way. He had something of the noisiness of Emil, his grandfather,—the physical prowess of Herman, his great-grandfather,—perhaps even a little of the arrogance of Wilhelm Stoltz, his great-great-grandfather. From Amalia herself he had several of those traits she had given him when under her care, but that she did not see.

The night of the graduating exercises in the new auditorium Joe drove out to the farm to get Amalia, eighty-one now. She was dressed and waiting for him, and if they were both remembering that other graduating night, neither spoke of it.

She had on her black dress gathered full at the waist-line. Her hair was knotted in its tight little wad on the nape of her neck. She was as shrunken as a tiny brown mummy. There was not a tooth in her head.

Seeing her so, as with newly opened eyes, Joe said suddenly: "Grandma, I'm afraid you're getting along in years. Don't you think you better come to town and live with us?"

"Tsk! Tsk! *Nein*. Besser you come live wid me."

"That's no joke." Joe was solemn.

Myrtie had a new lavender crepe outfit for the occasion, and she loved people telling her it was unbelievable that she was the mother of that strapping big foot-ball player.

Amalia could plainly see that Neal was the finest looking boy in the class of thirty-four young people. And at that, even discounting for prejudice, Amalia was not far wrong, for Neal was big and well-knit and the happy-go-lucky glint in his eyes added something to his charm.

In truth it helped get him into the Pi Beta Chi fraternity at the University that fall, along with the excellent facts that he was a foot-ball player, had a high-powered roadster of his own and a dad well enough off to be retired. That no one inquired into his scholastic standing is not too astounding.

A fraternity bid being, as it is in most midwestern colleges, a ticket to Paradise, a fraternity pin, the receipt of the ticket's purchase, there was no question in Neal's mind but that he would "go frat."

Several of the fraternities looked upon Neal Holms of Westville with covetous eyes, so that there was rather a concerted and noisy fight over him on rush week. And rush week being largely a survival of the fightest, it was hard at one time to tell which of the steam-rolling methods would capture him.

Those methods were varied and telling. Although he did not see it himself, he was told of the fellow taken up in a plane by three Phi Psis, hearing that he was to be wearing a Phi Psi pin en route down or he wouldn't get down, deciding during the third loop to pin it on,—of the fellow who thought his dinner invitation was a bid and arrived with his baggage,—of the mortgage-holding uncle who threatened to foreclose on the house if his nephew didn't qualify.

As for himself and the methods employed to get him— there was the way the Alpha Sigs flashed the magic of Sam Towle in his eyes,—(gosh, *the* Sam Towle who was the All-American half-back). There was the way the Betas dazzled him with the luxury of their palatial house which they spoke of casually as "the dump." There were the Delts trailing across his vision, like a red flag of distress, the plea that he alone could bring back to them the pristine glory that had been theirs when the great Pat Smithson had bled and died for them on the gridiron. (Imagine *that*,—thinking *he* could take Pat Smithson's place.) With fine disregard of laws concerning "sweat shops," the Sig Alphs tried to wear him down in the shower room. The Pi Beta Chis trotted out a Phi Beta Kappa alum as nonchalantly as though he were not the only one of the species that had ever been coralled behind its wrought-iron doors, and who, they said, would be tickled to death to help Neal in any way he could.

"Might be handy to be in a frat with a few walking

encyclopedias dashing in every night or so—what, old boy?"

He attended smokers and dinners at the Cornhusker, was taken for shows and for walks and rides, was called "Pal" and "Buddy" and "Old Chap" and "Kingfish," was slapped on the back, shoulders, knees and in the pit of his stomach, was told he could room with the president of each frat, with every fraternity member of the football team that had licked Pittsburgh, and with every hit in the masculine dramatic Kosmet Klub. He was promised the absolute run of the Theta, Kappa, Delta Gamma and Pi Phi houses, dates with the Junior Prom girl, the Mortar Board president and Nebraska U's Sweetheart.

Small wonder that Neal Holms in tailored suit and high-powered roadster and collegiate spotlight seemed far removed from Herman Holmsdorfer in blue jeans cracking his blacksnake over the backs of oxen on the lonely prairie.

All this time each fraternity house was a womanless Eden,—your college men fight this thing out alone without feminine interference to complicate matters.

Suffice to say, Neal found himself at the end of the battle with five pledge buttons, which under existing conditions were several too many, so that he was compelled to think up four air-tight excuses.

He went Pi Beta Chi,—and sometimes after that the fellows in other fraternities who had nearly wept on his shoulder and tapped him lovingly in the stomach, took time out to speak to him on the campus, but more often they did not.

And life became a geographical thing bounded by a few city blocks and a campus,—a mental affair of no small

effort,—a physical one of hard freshman foot-ball practice,—and an emotional one of rather formidable dimensions caused by the sight of more pulchritude running
around at large than he had been accustomed to see.

CHAPTER XXXIV

IN the last ten years Cedar City had grown accustomed to seeing old Matthias Meier walk up and down the streets of their elm-shaded town, swinging his cane pompously. From his son's home down Washington Street to the corner of Main, turning down Main to the bank, speaking to every one along the way: "Good morning, Miss Smith," "How are you, Boze?", nodding to those whose names he could not recall or did not know.

At the bank he would walk through the lobby into Carter's office. There they would discuss for a time the problems of the day,—to buy the Waterville bonds or not, —whether John Seliger's note could be renewed,—could Tessie Porter, the dressmaker, have a hundred-dollar loan on nothing much but an honest character. Back home toward noon, there to rest and read until about three when he would go down again for the last hour "to see how the day had gone."

Sometimes he went to Lincoln, grown to eighty thousand from the four log-cabins, visiting with old friends here and there for a few moments, always taking one stroll past the Pi Beta Chi house to see how it looked now,—"just as good as ever,—*there* was a house for you, built for the years,"—and always to the new capitol which rose like something of his own he had dreamed.

Uncompleted, but giving promise of perfection, it satisfied his very soul. American, that's what it was,—the broad sweeping base was the fertile prairie,—the tower to rise from this great white spread of stone was to symbolize all the aspirations and dreams and ideals the old builders of the state had held in their hearts but could not express.

No one knew it, but he would rather have been on the capitol commission than anything he could choose. Too old, of course. Lots of grief connected with it. Younger men must serve on that. But he liked to talk with those who had its building on their hearts,—men who were giving it all the loyalty they bore the state. Stop in and see them when he could catch them,—talk over the old days with the State Historian who knew every phase of its beginning and growth.

Once he and Charlie Briggs went up to the capitol together. Matthias, tall and well-tailored, snow-white hair and beard,—Charlie Briggs, little and gnarled, shaggy-whiskered, his navy blue suit hanging sack-like on his thin body,—both in their eighties. Together they walked through the main corridor and rotunda, looking at the tiles and the mosaics. More than one person turned to glance at the two old men, so different in appearance, apparently so engrossed in their own conversation.

"Seems a thousand years ago you advised me to come over here and locate in the prairie grass, Charlie."

"More like yistiddy to me, Matt."

"It's a great old state. Founded by substantial folks. Given the world something, too, besides grain and hogs. Given it artists and writers, singers and actors, big men in educational and business lines, dean of the Harvard law school, a general of all the armies. Something of the strength of the prairie may have been built into her children."

"She was kind of a harsh old mother, Matt,—the prairie,—but sufferin' snakes, I liked her."

There was a long pause, and then:

"I want to live to see it completed, Charlie."

"Me, too, Matt."

But now the trips to Lincoln were all over. Over, too, were the trips down Washington to Main,—down Main to the bank.

Old Matthias was nearly done for. Every day this spring when it was sunshiny enough he sat in the yard for a few hours,—waiting. They didn't need to try to cover it. He knew. Ever since that sudden sick spell. Lucile and Carter in cheerful voices called this convalescing. All right, call it anything they wanted.

Sitting here to-day in the sunshine old Matthias' mind was delving into the past. Until lately he had never been guilty of doing much of that. "Too busy with the crowded hour to fear to live or die,"—Emerson he thought that was. No, he had not succumbed to the habit of retrospection to any great extent as did many men of his age. It was a vicious habit, belonging only to those old people whose mentality could not keep pace with the times.

He had always disliked those who did it too much, making bores of themselves with their ancient reminiscences. Charlie Briggs lived almost entirely in the past with his " 'Long about 1872," or "I recol'ect the winter of '89." But for some reason he had been doing some of it himself lately—going over old memories, suddenly finding how easy it was to recall happenings of years before.

This afternoon with the sun making flickering leaf shadows on the new grass at his feet, he tried to understand this tendency to return to the scenes of youth. Did one go halfway through life, as though to a hilltop, and then start this looking back? No, there was no definite time in which it happened. One seemed always to be looking hopefully and enthusiastically forward,—and then without realizing it, found one's self in these moods of looking back.

On a trip to California, he and Ida, in the Hancock Park section of Los Angeles, had once seen the old La Brea pits where the tar of a score of thousand years bubbles up to the surface of the ground. There had been found the skeleton remains of prehistoric animals,—the saber-tooth tiger and the lion and the sloth,—a bone at a time, the animal skeletons had been found and fitted together for museums.

This afternoon he dug in the past of his life as the workers had dug for bones in the La Brea pits. He took out single scenes, fitting them together with others as the bones were fitted,—a bit of this and a bit of that,—seeing now from his hilltop how events might have been. Some things could have been bettered,—some should have stayed the same. No matter, for good or ill, they had been fitted together, and it was too late now to figure out how productive of good any change would have been. Queer, how things he used to think important, seemed less so now. Little things of minute value at the time, now loomed large in retrospection. Wherein should life have been different? How much of it was Fate? How much his own decision?

Suddenly, with almost no warning thought, he remembered his first sweetheart. She stepped into view out of the past as clear as a picture. He had not thought of her for years, but she came now, white and pink and blue-eyed and lovely. She had been Romance. Ida had never been Romance. She had been steady undying Love. She had been wife, comrade, friend,—but never Romance. That belonged with Amalia. And though desire had long died within him, yet for a moment his blood stirred to the memory of the touch of the pink lips of Amalia and the supple warm body of her.

Yes, some of the things in life we decide for ourselves. In others it is Providence, Luck, or the Spinning Fates. He thought of his youthful hot-headed race to Nebraska City, smiled at the thought of those days on the sand-bar,—of the way such a situation could be handled now. Cars, motor-boats, planes. What the outcome would have been if he had arrived in time, of course he could not know. But to have seen her and to have talked with her, she would no doubt have gone with him. Her father could scarcely have held her against her will.

How different girls were these days. One couldn't imagine a modern girl displaying the weakness with which Amalia must have succumbed to her father's authority and gone obediently with him. She would have been as ready to go with her lover if he could have appeared in time to influence her. But by the hair's breadth of a few hours the thing had been decided. When he arrived, the marriage had been consummated. Now they wouldn't even stop at the marriage vow but would hurdle that too. In those days it constituted a formidable barrier. Well, it was a good thing, perhaps, that some of these decisions did fall into the hands of Providence or Lady Luck or the Spinning Fates. Once he would have chosen Amalia. Probably Ida had made him a better wife,—but even without that in her favor, he could not imagine any one else in her place for the half-century.

Hazel was coming down the terrace toward him with her long athletic stride and her air of freedom from all restraints. She was nearly ready for the University, some of the rough edges toned down, her brace off for several years, the freckles miraculously disappearing into her creamy complexion.

Could one imagine two more opposite young women than Hazel and this little Amalia of whom he had just been thinking? He smiled at the thought, and when she had thrown herself in a chair opposite him, he said suddenly: "Hazel, did you ever stop to think how a person imagines he is carrying out his own decision, doing the thing he planned? But is he? How much is predestined? Except for our higher order of minds we are like the little moles under the earth carrying out blindly the work of digging, thinking our own dark passage-ways constitute all there is to the world. . . ."

Hazel was frankly bored. Restless, energetic, it seemed rather a waste of time to sit here and listen to grandfather's vague generalities. They sounded too much like his pal, the old Indian scout. No longer was old Charlie Briggs a hero to Miss Meier. She twisted about a bit in her chair, as though seeking a more comfortable position,

giving him credit in her mind, though, for one thing,—
he seldom emitted a lot of junk like this.

"A half-dozen people . . ." he went on, "out of all the
hundreds we've contacted stand out in the end as really
and recognizably influencing our lives. A few whom we
have loved or hated or emulated. Why, I've even been
thinking of my first sweetheart," he laughed deprecatingly.

Hazel sat up alertly. Here was no generality, nothing
boresome. Here was interest, concrete and definite. No
longer was she the little girl who had said she would have
none of Romance.

"Oh, I say, Grandad, that *is* something. You mean a
girl . . . *not* Grandmother?"

"Not your grandmother."

"Why, you old flirt . . . tell me about it. She didn't
die?"

"No, . . . much worse." He smiled across at her.
"She married some one else."

"Yes . . . yes . . . go on. Am *I* all *ears?* Tell me.
Tell me everything."

"There's not much to tell. I suppose spring had something to do with it . . . spring and youth and propinquity.
I was working in a foundry in Illinois. She came stepping
out of the sunlight one day into the dark foundry like
a little blue and white and pink figure stepping out of a
miniature,—or a little Dresden china figure."

"Not *really*, Grandpa! Why, you old poet."

"You're the only person in the world I've ever told this
to. She moved out here from Illinois . . . and married.
I came out here, too, to what was then called the new
west . . . following her in a blind sort of way, a young

blade thinking I could pick her up and carry her off, even though good sense told me how foolish it was. But . . . you follow your wild enthusiastic fancies when you're young."

"And you never saw her again?"

"I never saw her."

"Nor heard of her?"

"Nor heard of her specifically . . . but once. I knew in a general way . . . the farming section . . . where her group of people located, but I never saw her again."

"Grandpa . . . tell me this." Hazel leaned forward with wide, dark eyes. "Did you *ever* get over it?"

He laughed aloud. "Oh, yes . . . yes, indeed. The long journey on the boat, the docking at strange towns, the excitement of arriving in the new country, all had their place in the scheme of things. I was young and ambitious. I rather think I was beginning to recover very soon. After awhile there were other young people too . . . your grandmother. Life was very full. And yet. . . ."

"Yet what, Grandfather?"

"Oh, I think one never entirely forgets an emotional experience like that. But after awhile the thing was only half remembered . . . and then almost forgotten . . . then entirely . . . until now."

"Why *now*, Grandpa?"

"You'd laugh."

"No, I won't, Grandpa . . . honestly, I won't laugh."

"I heard a meadow-lark sing."

"It reminded you of her?"

"Yes."

"Oh, how *romantic.*"

"And perhaps because I've had time recently to sit and think . . . and remember times of emotion. In business you have no emotion,—you have only a hard-boiled mental life."

"I think it's a lot sadder that you got over it, Grandpa, than if you hadn't."

"Perhaps it was."

"What was her name?"

"I haven't said it aloud for nearly sixty years. It was . . . Amalia." His voice lingered over it, drawing it out liquidly.

"Amalia. It's kind of musical, isn't it?"

"That's what I used to think."

Old Matthias Meier did not live to see the capitol finished. He died in a few months as he had felt he would. Toward the last he knew it was not going to be so hard to leave as he had always thought. Sometimes during that last month, in his exhaustion and weakness, when the nights were troubled and unnatural and the days no better, he looked forward longingly to that place in Lincoln called *Wyuka,* which is Indian for "a place to lie down and sleep."

Charlie Briggs came as soon as he heard, trudging up the sidewalk to Carter Meier's house, his blue suit hanging baggily on his thin little frame. "Matt knowed I wouldn't fail him."

When it was over,—Matthias' things put away out of

sight, and much of the necessary business attended to, Carter Meier settled down to life without his father.

On a rainy evening when Lucile and Hazel were both there, he brought out and opened his father's small, old-fashioned trunk,—a queer little calf-skin chest bound in brass. He had never seen one just like it anywhere else, with its few red hairs worn by the original animal owner still plainly visible along the sides.

"I wonder if the Historical Society wouldn't like it?" he said to Lucile and to Hazel sitting near.

Lucile had a book and merely said pleasantly but vaguely: "Maybe it would."

Hazel, intent on the opening of the trunk, made no comment for a moment. When she did it was to say: "Do you know, there's something sort of heathenish and unkind about it, Dad. After a death, delving into a dead person's things that way when they can't help it. Don't you feel as though you were trespassing?"

"Oh . . . I might with some people's things. But not Father's. I've had charge of his affairs so much this last year and his life was such an open book."

For a half-hour or more Carter Meier took out and examined the neatly folded papers and account books, a set of income and expense books,—all of ancient vintage and worthless. Anything important was in the lock-box at the bank. There were two or three pictures of his mother,—one in a tight silk dress with panels and enough buttons up and down its length and breadth to start a retail button shop.

There were pictures of himself, too, as a scared-looking baby in a dress cascading to the floor, and as a little boy.

At one he laughed long and loudly and called his family's attention to it. In a velvet suit and lace collar he stood heavily on one foot with the other leg neatly crossed over it, in his hand the end of a long ivy vine wandering down from a flower-pot above him.

"To this day I remember how I was pinching that vine, taking out of my murderous heart all the venom I felt for the photographer and putting it into the death of that innocent plant."

And after his laughter came something more serious,— it seemed such a very short time ago he was that little Fauntleroy-looking boy with an Apache heart,—and now he was fifty-six.

Everything was out now but a dingy, brown wallet. He had not seen it for nearly a half-century, but he could remember his father carrying it in that long gone time. There proved to be nothing in the old thing but a yellowed piece of paper which fell at his touch into six slim oblong sections. It was written in German and almost illegible at that.

"Hazel, how much German do you know?"

"Oh, I can *habe* and *heil* a little. Let me have a try."

She went to the library table and laid the six parts carefully together, bending her fresh loveliness over the musty broken pieces of the yellowed paper.

". . . *'ist es besser.'* That's duck's soup for a starter," she said aloud. *"It is better."*

Her father and mother were both listening, more impressed by their gay young daughter's smartness than with anything the old letter might say.

" *'Zu gedenken'* . . . let's see . . . *'zu gedenken,'* "

her voice slipped into a low murmur as she tried to think of it. "I know . . . *to remember*. How'm I doin', folks?"

They nodded approval. These modern girls!

" *'im frühyahr'* . . . that's 'in springtime.' Now . . . all together . . . pull! *'It is better to remember in springtime.'* "

Suddenly she saw for the first time the word *Amalia*. Something came into her mind,—stole in subtly,—something bringing a faint far-off breath of a long-gone year and the lilt of a meadow-lark singing. This was a note from Grandpa's first sweetheart.

"You're the only person I've ever told . . ." he had said.

She read the remainder of the legible sentence to herself. It was Grandpa's secret and because he was not here to guard the little message as he had evidently done all the years, she would do it for him,—would not drag it out into the open even for Dad and Mother.

Unsre liebe,—our love. Something about the forlorn little note touched her unaccountably. A swift mist came to her eyes and she had to clear her throat to say lightly, "Oh, that's all I can get out of it, folks."

All the rest of the evening it filled her with a vague sadness. She was glad he had married Grandmother, couldn't bear to think of it otherwise. But there was something pathetic about that one legible sentence,—the way life moved on and changed and love went with it, too.

. . . *it is better to remember our love as it was in the springtime.*

CHAPTER XXXV

IN the fall of 1930 Hazel Meier went up to the University too. Lucile had taken her to Omaha to outfit her,—she had purchased sports clothes and silk pajamas, dinner gowns, dresses for afternoon wear, and accessories for everything. Lucile had no trouble in pleasing Hazel with the sports clothes,—it took some effort to get her into long, slinky gowns in which she declared to all and sundry salesladies that she felt like kicking something with every step. But Lucile was firm. Hazel was a young lady now,—no more of this living in tennis outfits all day long. Everything ran to browns and tans and oranges for her,—cream or white or eggshell for evening with that hair and complexion.

When Carter saw the bills he whistled long and loudly. Bonds these days were anæmic,—he was worried. There were more griefs in the banking business now than in all his other years put together. He missed his father every day.

There was no exciting fight over Hazel by the sororities. Lucile had been a Theta. The Delta Gams gave her a half-hearted rush, knowing she had too much Theta blood in her to inoculate with any other virus. The Kappas told her Theta was so badly run down since her mother's time that of course she would put aside that old mother-daughter sentiment, to which she might have given ear

258

if she had not heard a Theta hand out the same line to a Kappa daughter with a mere reversal of Greek letters.

After the usual three days of breakfasts, luncheons, teas, and dinners, with time out to look up her courses, she went Theta. No one was surprised,—it was in the cards. Followed registration,—consternation,—concentration,—amalgamation,—sophistication,—the metamorphosis of a Greek letter girl can be traced as readily as the growth of a tree, by rings of different fibers.

At first she was timid, afraid of the upper classmen, prone to say "Yes, indeed" to any comment from them, deferred to the house mother as to an oracle.

Gradually she began dating. She whose masculine attentions in Westville had consisted heretofore largely of neighbor boys draping themselves at intervals over the front steps and calling to her to get a move on, now learned what collegiate dates were, both of the open-eyed and blind varieties.

By her sophomore year, what with her good clothes and her reputation of being a snappy little number, she was credited at the House with one-hundred per cent dating ability. In her junior year she was sophisticated, svelte, unruffled under any situation, told the house mother in velvet-concealed words where to get off, removed the velvet shield on occasion when some good sister crossed her path in social territory.

It was getting toward spring of that year when she went into the old library, took a casual survey of empty chairs and with apparent superb indifference to her surroundings carefully chose one across from a junior law,—an awfully good-looking Pi Chi by the name of Neal Holms. She gave him a slanting glance several times, but evidently he was occupied with some ponderous volume. All right, —he didn't have to deign to look her way,—suit himself.

In a few moments he was pushing a card toward her. It contained his name engraved thereon, with a penciled caption under it,—so that it now read:

Neal Holms

Pass the tomes.

She frowned,—shoved the two voluminous books near her his way, scribbled underneath:

Hazel Meier

Don't rouse my ire.

Unsmiling, he found his reference, then turned the card over, wrote on it, pushed it back. It questioned:

Why don't I dare?

And was sent back with the laconic answer:

Red hair.

A little later he handed it back. It said:

Date you?

Hazel wrote promptly:

Hate to.

This time he drew a picture,—two toothpick-looking creatures hand in hand, and wrote underneath:

Aw, give in.

Hazel scribbled:

You win.

Neal Holms dated Hazel Meier for a fraternity formal.

From the first he liked her,—liked her tip-tilted nose on which, if the light were right, you could see a freckle or two,—liked her independence and her creamy complexion,—her hazel eyes and her snappy come-backs,—the cocky way she wore a beret on the side of her head.

Two more care-free young people financially and otherwise in the University it would have been hard to find.

He dated her again for another formal, other times for no reason but "a date,"—then for the Junior-Senior prom which ended the winter social season. And for that matter it almost ended everything else for them, too. There was an inauguration of a new president in Washington,—followed by a peculiar phenomenon in banking circles called a moratorium. Carter Meier's bank closed.

Even before this the echoes from the eastern coast financial marts had reverberated to the outskirts of the last little village, to every farm home in every state. But for a time in the small places of the midwestern states, they had been only voices heard afar off. Contrary to geometric equations, the shortest distance between the two given points of Wall Street and Carter Meier's bank was by no means a straight line. It took a multitude of directions, and arrived through various channels,— South American bonds being one of its routes of travel.

Carter Meier had seen the value of his various bonds slipping under par,—skidding, sliding with sickening pace. It was a condition shared in fraternal worry by his colleagues.

All were frightened, bewildered. Not one could share the anxiety with another for fear of giving away his own secret worry.

No, the ocean of catastrophe known as the Wall Street debacle did not sweep at once with full tide into some of the sections of the country. Where its waves crashed with devastating force in many places, in others the back-wash rippled in later. Cedar City seemed secure. It was bounded by agriculture,—its soil rich, its banks secure, its farmers honest. Even though prices were far too low, crops were almost always good these years. A poor wheat year usually found a good corn crop,—when the corn failed, the wheat crop had recompensed for the failure.

But now the back-wash came in,—bonds that had been purchased for one hundred went to eighty, sixty, forty,— defaulted. Two of Carter Meier's corresponding banks stayed closed. Farmers could not pay because they had nothing with which to pay. More, a strange and unbelievable attitude seized a portion of the population, a slipping of morale. "Try and get it" became the manner of some. Carter Meier in noting this insidious change thought often of his father, of old Charlie Briggs, of those others of the old school whose word had been all the legality one needed.

He worked, planned, collected, figured, fought. Sometimes he grew bitter with the injustice of it. Others no smarter or better than he were getting through. The difference of a bond purchase or two,—of a few less notes that had to be charged off,—and they were weathering the storm.

Time,—if he only could have time for things to stage a come-back, he would be all right. Time! That was what a man who was to be hung wanted. He had days of feeling he had won,—followed by days of realizing he had lost,—high moments of hope,—black ones of despair.

The depression won. The bank stayed closed. You could not do with life as you wished.

He paid twice the amount of his stock. It took the last of what his father had left him. The estate, too, had shrunk when Depression, that rough laundryman, had finished with it. Some of the investments had been left as a trust fund for Hazel,—that, of course, could not and should not be touched.

He sold the house for what he could get,—moved to a Lincoln apartment when a receiver job was given him. Lucile was sobered, hurt, still incredulous over what had happened, but game. "For better or for worse" spoken that day in the Lincoln church before an elaborate wedding party of eight bridesmaids attending her, with all the leading families looking on, had meant something to Lucile. The situation was a reversal of her own parents' experiences and that of Father and Mother Meier. The "worse," so far as hard work and getting established, had been their earlier portion, their easy life at the last. Her own was the other way around,—harder, too,—for she and Carter had none of the buoyant hope they had possessed a quarter of a century before.

Farther out in the state Joe Holms wondered every hour of the day and during sleepless nights how any one could get so heavily involved when much of the land had been given him.

Over and over in his mind he pondered the turn of his fortunes. He knew there were great economic forces at work over which he had no control. If things had been as Myrtie always said,—if the land had stayed worth the price they had so blithely put upon it,—if they had not bought so lavishly, had not gone so deeply into debt, had stayed on the first good old half-section without purchasing any more acres,—above all, had *worked* it themselves, earning their living there, content with what it would bring, as his father and grandfather had worked before him for their daily bread, this great indebtedness would not be looming always before him like some fearsome giant.

He went back often in his mind to the first of Myrtie's pleadings to change things. Pasting a cheap stucco over the good old stones of the house had been almost prophetic in its covering up the real issues of life, the things that were vital. Work? Why should he have lessened his activities because there had seemed enough to live on? Work was good. Work was every man's portion in life. He had grown soft,—under fifty yet, and he was flabby. Old Charlie Briggs in his eighties who came visiting through the neighborhood sometimes, wouldn't ride anywhere, wouldn't accept a lift on the highway for fear he'd grow soft.

Yes, that which he had labeled a kindness to Myrtie and which Myrtie had labeled a kindness to Neal had been no kindness at all. But he wouldn't hide behind Myrtie's skirts. He was the head of the house, or should have been. Now he could see he had been no better than the loafers sitting on the sidewalks spitting their contempt at a world which they thought owed them a living.

Other farmers were getting through. All had been

under the same general outside forces,—all under the same weather conditions. But not all had been caught as he was. Young Carl Schaffer was working out,—the Lawrences. But they had used better sense. They had lived on their own butter and eggs, chickens, and small produce. When they sold a crop, it had gone to pay off their principal. He and Myrtie, with their hands in the sack as though there were no end to the income,—they had been caught.

He sat now on the stone-house steps at the farm looking out at the old soap-kettle there in the yard with the dead stems of ancient flowers left in it. There was something symbolic about it, he suddenly decided. His grandmother had made soap in it every spring and fall,—enough to last for a half-year. His mother with her lessening activities had dispensed with it, letting the men take it for hog-feed and chicken-mash. His wife had planted flowers in it,— typical of the way they had grown to look at life,— flowers, no work, but plenty of income. Flowers over all the harsh facts of life. Flowers in the soap-kettle,—and a complacent feeling that the soap would arrive some way.

Well, the flowers in the soap-kettle were dead and rotted now. So were all the fancy notions of life.

He called Neal home from school that week-end for an interview.

He was a long time getting at what he wanted to say, so long that Neal with his more direct way of looking at life said: "What's the racket, Dad? Let's have it out."

"I mean . . . the way things are . . . the town house here is going back to the owner,—the eighty I bought, too,

—the eighty my father bought goes to the bank for notes . . . I have to pay my double indemnity on the Meredith bank. . . ."

"You mean we're sunk?"

"Something like that. Grandma's two hundred and forty is left unencumbered out of the wreckage."

"Here's where I stop school."

"No. Let's figure it out together. I've just one son and he has just one year more. We'll make it some way. You'd disappoint me now not to go that much longer. But for God's sake, don't spend any more than you have to."

"I promise you that."

"And don't tell Mother just yet. It would worry her."

"If you ask me, Dad, there's been an awful lot of that not-telling-mother stuff. I'm going out and tell her."

Joe followed Neal anxiously, protesting, out to the sunroom where Myrtie sat with a book, to hear him tell his mother the bold and bald facts.

Myrtie put her hand over her heart. "Oh . . . oh! I can stand anything but that."

Joe tried to stroke her hair, but she pushed his hand away.

"We'll go back to the stone house, Myrtie. We'll fix it up nice. I'll go into the field again. We'll get some comfort out of life now, not owing any one."

"Oh, Joe . . . how could you . . . how *could* you?"

"He's not done anything disgraceful, Mom. He's just caught like a thousand others. He'll go back and work out, and I'll help."

"Oh . . . oh . . . just the same old thing . . . just

corn and dirt and pigs and chickens." She was gasping, her hand at her throat.

Joe would have called a doctor, but Neal was unmoved. "That's just high-steericks, Mom." He laughed at her. "Tears and wailings and beating your head against the old wall aren't going to do any good." He touseled her hair as though she were a youngster. "You're going to move back to the farm *and like it*. And thank your lucky stars you've got one to go to."

Joe stood looking at him in astonishment, deep respect, and with no small degree of envy.

Joe and Myrtie went back to the big stone house where Myrtie said she just gave up, there was so little to live for.

CHAPTER XXXVI

MOISTURE was below normal all summer even where the lands like Joe's were rich and loamy. But farther west where the season was one of drouth, the powdered top soil was lifted into the air with every high prairie wind. It was as though Mother Nature in disturbed mood was beginning to clean her house, to set to right her disarranged plans. With a giant broom she whisked the dirt from those rooms in which she had intended only grazing lands to be.

But unheeding, the wheat farmers scratched again the pulverized soil and dropped their seed in the looseness of its powder.

Neal and Hazel both went back to school. Life had taken on a more serious aspect, but Youth is hard to keep down. Unless it is cold, hungry, ill, and discouraged, it can find an outlet in its own bubbling vitality,—and they were none of these. To be sure, Hazel, who had walked into the shops and chosen her apparel with little thought to expense, now planned every move with an eye to economy.

"Take a look-see at the dress," she said to Neal who had come for her on a date. "That which used to be the front is now the back, the inside is the outside, the top side is now the bottom side,—proving that all which goes up must come down."

"Huh—that's nothing. I've got a big-time job,—currying Doc Sanders' car. I went over to Prof. Morrison's to see if I could get his yard to mow,—would have gotten it, too, but Bud Merrill, the squirt, took the lawn-mower right out of my mouth, so to speak."

Neal drove home often. "Seems as though my dad has sort of lost his nerve or something. Goes over and over the same old hashing of what he did or didn't do. It isn't that he doesn't work. It isn't physical. He acts bewildered all the time about what's best to do,—all this corn-hog stuff,—anything with a decision to make. And I'll be darned if I know whether he'll ever make any money again or not—what with plowing under the piglets and not letting the big cornstalks have any little corn-stalks. He knows a lot more about the whole thing than I do but is always cornering me and asking my opinion. Makes me feel chesty."

"My poor Dad, too. Says he never wants to be responsible for anything again, content to work for some one else the rest of his life. Queer, isn't it, what a year can bring you?"

And it *was* queer what a year could bring you, for when school ended Neal and Hazel were engaged.

What matter when it was or where it was, or the words that were said. Youth is Youth and the words remain similar. As a matter of fact, perhaps it was at no special time or place. Perhaps too often Neal had said in the jaunty modern unromantic way: "I like your aristo-snooty-looking nose" or "You're some little trick, Red Head," or sung boldly at her in an atrociously frog-like voice: "Stay As Sweet As You Are," to make any proposal necessary.

269

Suffice to say Neal sent the candy to the Theta house, and broke the news to his Pi Beta Chis in the old Meier house where the neckties hung untidily through the grill-work of which Ida had once been so proud, and their owners tried with tragic success to imitate Fred Astaire's dancing on the inlaid mosaic of the great entrance hall.

Mr. and Mrs. Carter Meier announced the engagement of their daughter Hazel to Neal Holms by way of the Sunday papers. Ivy Day arrived. Examinations. Commencement,—in the setting of countless huge buildings with many thousand students swarming over the campus where once the cows snatched at the prairie grass. Hazel had her diploma from the Teachers College of the U,—Neal his law degree, and if "superior scholarship" and "cum laude" were strangely missing from these, the two young people were in the good company of many others of average intelligence.

Hazel was to teach one year at Irving, a small town in the Republican Valley,—Neal was to stay at home with his father for the same length of time, lending his young strength and his unflagging spirits to Joe's discouragement before hanging out his law shingle.

It was a bad summer. Drouth came on like a malignant sore on the breast of nature. Hot belching winds blew in from the southwest. Thin clouds, dry as feathers, slipped across the blue. The grass in the pastures burned as with a prairie-fire. Weeds, devoid of sap, rattled in the hot winds. Leaves, too lifeless to cling, dropped from the dry elms.

"Like in de old days," Amalia said often and shook her head dubiously. Tsk! Tsk!

There was a great deal of talk about legislation and regimentation. Joe snorted: "Legislate the hot winds and regimentate the clouds and we farmers'll get along all right by ourselves."

Neal took Hazel to Irving in September, stayed to cast his eye over her school and her boarding-house, got back to the farm in time to see the rain come. Leaves on the elms dripped clammily. Puddles stood on the graveled highways. Water ran off a hillside that was baked too hard to hold it. And it was not raining anything so sentimental or ornamental as daffodils. It was raining wheat for bread. It was raining forage crops,—sudan grass and rye and sweet clover. It was raining pasturage and wild hay and alfalfa,—next year's apple-buds and cherry-buds and vegetables in gardens. It was raining hope and courage and a renewed morale.

"Stars fell on Alabama," he said jubilantly when he went into the house, "and that's all right with me, but showers fell on Nebraska and that's much more to the point."

Joe worried a good deal now about Grandma down there alone at her little house, but old Amalia was cheerful. "I am goot company for myself," she said. "I vork ven I vish; I sleep ven I vish; I sew my qvilts ven I vish; I do not'ing ven I vish."

Joe and Neal were both good to her,—Myrtie not unkind, merely wrapped in her own troubles.

Toward spring she seemed much more feeble. So little did she walk out now that Neal decided to put in a radio for her. For a while she stood out against it. "For vat should I vant to have de singin' here at all times of de night, Neal?"

When he assured her that no quartette or jazz orchestra had any intention of presuming on her hospitality at times when they were not welcome, she let him put in one.

Her first manipulation of it was under his instruction. "You snap this first. Then turn this until you find what you want, and then this one to get the sound just as you want it. Now try."

Old Amalia snapped the brass knob. Then she turned *this*. Columbus sailing westward, a Wright brother going up in the air,—and old Amalia turning the knob on a radio!

". . . headin' for the last round-up" it blared forth like semi-musical thunder.

"Now tune it down softer."

"Loud I like it," said old Amalia. And loud she kept it.

To the family's surprise it proved to be news that she liked the best. Old Amalia who had lived most of her long years on her Nebraska farm liked best the happenings from far places. She knew when every news period came on, settled herself with her latest quilt, rather appropriately doing the Around-the-World pattern, and listened to the latest happenings in places she had never been, and of whose existence she scarcely knew. Through the waves of the air, across the brown prairie, every day now the mountain came to Mahomet.

CHAPTER XXXVII

SPRING came to the midwest in a cloud of dust. To Carter and Lucile in their modest apartment in Lincoln it was a hazy, disagreeable one, the sunlight sifting through the yellow, dust-laden air from the black blizzard farther to the west.

They had never grown used to Hazel being away,—often in the evening they found themselves sitting idly, listening for the footsteps of a gay young crowd which no longer came. Once in one of these idle moods Lucile caught Carter's eye. "That way lies madness," she laughed, but not quite whole-heartedly. "Let's throw a wild party and go to a movie."

To Hazel in the little town of Irving in the Republican Valley the dust was more severe for she was nearer the source of the storms. It came in clouds, a scourge rolling eastward like reddish-yellow gas across no man's land. Too long in the country farther west had men torn at the earth's vitals,—too many times had the edge of the plow gone into the lands which were meant for grazing. There were sections out beyond Irving and in the neighboring states where schools were closed, traffic paralyzed, business suspended, street lights shining all day through the murky atmosphere.

To Neal and his father on the farm it was a season of worry and discouragement. To what extent were the dust storms affecting them? Were they bringing in enough

273

sandy soil to damage the rich loamy Holms' lands? Was soil erosion to be serious?

Day after day the clouds of dust rolled in from the Panhandle district, northwestern Oklahoma, southeastern Colorado, part of Kansas.

To old Amalia there was no great discouragement,—no deep worry. Too many years had she lived with a Nature that was changeable, as coquettish as a girl.

Too often had she seen rains after drouth, green after the brown of burning, buds after dried stalks, stillness after the strife of storm, life after apparent death. "It vill come all right," she nodded with calm conviction. "It alvays comes right again."

And it came right again. The winds ceased. Snow fell like a white benediction over the wind-torn land. Rains followed,—prolonged soaking rains. The grass grew lush in the pastures. Cattle stood knee-deep in moisture-covered forage. Buds burst forth from the elms, the fruit trees and the lilac hedge. Crocuses bloomed in sheltered spots. The timber-land gave forth the rich, pungent smell of water-soaked undergrowth. Nature's face had the look of a freshly scrubbed child. It was the eighty-sixth miracle Amalia had witnessed.

Neal spent a certain Saturday and part of one Sunday with Hazel at her home in Lincoln, taking her back to her school at Irving in the afternoon.

Carter and Lucile were satisfied with Neal,—liked his energy and his gay humor, his steady blue eyes that looked clean and frank. Of the boys that had ever squired Hazel about, they liked him by far the best they agreed when the two had gone.

It was not until they were well out on the paved highway toward the valley that Neal broached the subject with which he was to confront Hazel to-day, for which he had chosen this very time.

He approached it with a bit of trepidation for he had no idea how she would take it, and because he felt that uncertainty, he was blunt in the telling. Now that his year of helping his father was nearly at an end he had decided to forget law and stay on to manage the farm.

Hazel, assuming for a time that he was joking, was later filled with sudden alarm to discover that he was in deadly earnest.

"I've kidded myself into thinking I was there for just the year. I'm staying. I like the independence of it. I've grown interested in our plans. Besides, I'd have had a heck of a time getting on in the other, what with the thousands of us turned loose and lining the sidewalks waiting for cases."

Because Hazel sat quietly, looking coldly down the highway, he went rambling on rather indefinitely: "You'll like it there . . . not a half bad old place . . . with a little care the lawn looks quite like a park . . . a lot of grand old trees my grandfather planted . . . the house is sturdy and big even if it's old . . . Father and Mother will turn it over to us and live in the small house with Grandma."

He glanced at her but she was stony-faced, so that he went on nervously with his explanations: "This is a business all ready and waiting for me,—not a dub job of looking up references for some older man or starving to death behind my own shingle. And if you don't think it calls

275

for as much of a business head as any other, it's just because you don't know your onions or any of the other crops."

Hazel spoke for the first time. "I just can't *see* myself. That's all there is to it. Just don't speak about it again and kindly drop the whole idea."

"But I *am* speaking about it. And I'm not dropping the whole idea, kindly, benevolently, or otherwise."

"You can't mean that you're in earnest about this crazy notion?"

"I'm in earnest . . . and the notion is so sensible it should take the Pulitzer prize for wisdom. Three hundred and twenty acres of the best and richest land in Nebraska with my Dad ready and willing to turn the management of it to me. To be sure, one of the eighties has a big plaster on it, but we can soak that off. We lost two other eighties in the late lamented depression. I'd be a nut to stick out a shingle in some little burg or run errands for a law firm in a bigger town just as agriculture is going to pull out."

"I don't see it."

"And *I do*."

They were speaking with suppressed heat, firecrackers sputtering under ice.

"And you call this an ambitious idea?"

"About as ambitious a move as I've ever made in my life." His voice dropped to a pleading tone. "I'm terribly in earnest, Hazel. Give me credit for growing up and making my own decisions. You know every one who has any stamina . . . There's another word but not so pretty . . . Drop around some day and I'll tell you what it is . . . Any fellow who hasn't lard in his veins has to map out his own life and his own work. Well, mine's running that big farm and running it *right*. I know it now for sure. I feel energetic about it, enthusiastic, with a hundred plans of things to do. It's my best bet because I *want* to do it. There was a time when I wouldn't have said that I ever would. I know my own mind now."

"And apparently that broad mind of yours doesn't comprehend that I'd have anything to say about it,—that I should be the one to make the decision."

"You can put it that way, of course, to make me feel quite the villain. But I'll have to be more honest than gallant and admit that in this particular thing . . . you shouldn't."

"One could imagine . . . the casual observer maybe . . . that I *would* have the deciding vote."

"I've seen how that works out, Hazel. You don't need to get me wrong,—I think the world of my mother. But she just had her way with my dad in a lot of things he should have decided for them both. Well, it nearly got them."

"I'd make a *scalding*-hot farmer's wife, wouldn't I?"

"Sure you would. You'd . . ."

"I don't know a silo from a centipede . . ."

"A centipede has more legs than a silo, dearie. You can always tell them that way." Now that she was talking he felt easier.

". . . or oats from wheat."

"Wheat has a beard, honey,—whiskers like old man Briggs."

But Hazel would not meet his flippant conversation. "I

tell you, I don't know *anything* about it. I don't know a plow from a harron . . . harrall . . . harrow . . . whatever it is."

"For that matter, would you have known a rejoinder or a summons or a brief if I'd have gone into law?"

"I could learn."

"You can learn this other."

There were icicles in the air now. Hazel stared straight ahead into the diminishing point of the paved highway. Neal, face solemn and jaw set, leaned over and turned on the radio.

"Ah'll call you back in a few minutes, Kingfish. Amos 'n I has got a big business man in here . . ." He snapped it off petulantly.

For a mile they rode in frosty silence.

Hazel broke it with sarcasm. "So you really think I'd move on a farm . . . that I would give in to you about this wild thing?"

"Do I get it that you've not at any time cared for me, myself,—that you've merely liked the smug little idea of marrying a man who sat in a mahogany-furnished office in a downtown business block . . ."

"Maybe I have. Maybe I think that's the sort of environment I'd like to have my husband in."

". . . so that you could have a nice plate-glass window to sit in and see the Shriner's parade go by?"

The car had accelerated in speed with Neal's rising temper. They were passing through Niles Center, such a small village that the general store, the postoffice, and the filling-station flashed by like bits of colored posters. They were both silent, agitated and uncomfortable. It did not add anything, therefore, to the gayety of the nations when the Niles Center constable overtook them. When they stopped, he came over to the car, a big, red-faced man with a curiously small button-like nose set in the full moon of his face.

"Where you think you are—Indianapolis speedway or Ormond Beach or some place?"

"I didn't even see your sissy town," Neal retorted. And for the pleasure he derived from the saying donated unwillingly a five-dollar bill toward the erecting of a new village bandstand.

For the rest of the trip they were silent, excepting for an occasional remark that had neither interest nor entertainment for either one.

The long paved highway passed through fields and orchards of the peaceful Republican River Valley. Acres of green wheat on every side lay shrouded in the soft cool evening. From the alfalfa fields came the fragrance of the budding blossoms,—from the pastures the faint odor of meadow-grass lush with moisture. Only a few weeks before the great billows of dust had enveloped the valley. Wind had blown eerily out of the west. Dirty gray clouds had scudded across yellow skies. Then as though the Caretaker had said: "Thus far shalt thou go and no farther," the winds had ceased and like a benign benediction had come the rains. The Republican Valley was as peaceful now as a lovely lady with emerald pastures and wheatfields for jewels.

They drove into the town of Irving and turned to the street upon which Hazel's boarding-house stood. Neither one knew how the strained interview was to terminate,—both were uncomfortable.

Neal slid up to the curb where a low barberry hedge scraped across the running board. Because they were serious and angry and uncertain what the next move was to be, in the embarrassment of the moment they did nothing,—merely sat, each waiting for the other to speak.

At once three of Hazel's little girl pupils, arm in arm, passed along the street and giggled at the sight of their teacher sitting with a strange young man.

"Hello, Miss Meier."

"Hello, Miss Meier."

"Hello, Miss Meier."

"People all speak the same dialect here." Neal tried to assume his old light way. But because Hazel would not smile, he dropped it immediately. "Well, I guess there's nothing more to say, excepting where do we go from here?"

"I guess that's not going to be hard to interpret."

"You mean . . . ?"

"I most certainly do . . . under the circumstances . . . if they still exist . . . we're through."

"They exist all right. I'll say just one thing more. You've probably had a fond and kiddish notion you were about to marry a member of the United States Supreme Court. Well, you weren't. You were about to marry a young fellow who was going to have a long, slippery climb,—and if you won't do this with him now which is a wise move, you wouldn't have liked the monotony of the other, either,—so it's a good thing for us both you found it out in time. But you can rest assured he will get somewhere a darned sight faster doing the thing he wants to do.

"Become Secretary of Agriculture, maybe." Hazel hated her own sarcasm, even while she gave vent to it.

"Maybe . . . who knows? Stranger things have happened."

"Well . . ." he said again after a strained silence, ". . . let's don't prolong the death pangs."

At that, Hazel was out before he could get around to the door. But he walked along stubbornly by her side to the porch, carrying her small bag, and because he was bursting with hurt and disappointment, he said: "This is the way Emily Post says all engagements should be terminated,—politely and with subtle grace."

But at the door, he broke: "Hazel . . . we're just talking to hear ourselves say words. We're both that way . . . we just enjoy the ragging. Neither one of us meant anything but to bark our heads off. There's no one I could ever love but you,—no one in the world for me but *you*." And would have put his arms around her, but that she said with infinite sarcasm: "Oh, yes, there is. There's *you*." And was gone into the house, shutting the door with infinite pains.

CHAPTER XXXVIII

SPRING rains, heavy, drenching, filling the creek-beds and flooding the lowlands!

They beat upon the Holms' fields and pastures sending moisture down to the grateful sub-soil which had been so long without it, while Neal worked doggedly all day, tight-lipped and serious. So recently life had been such a gay and happy thing,—now so void of interest without funny flippant letters, so dull appearing in the future with no plans involving the constant presence of a merry red-headed girl.

They beat steadily and drowsily upon the little white-painted cottage of old Amalia, piecing her Around-the-World quilt and listening to news from places of which she had never heard. They beat upon the old German country church high on the knoll and the sodden grasses of all the old Kratz and Schaffer graves, and those of the Gebhardts and Rhodenbachs who had come into the prairie together over sixty years before.

They beat upon the apartment building in Lincoln, where Carter and Lucile Meier lived, trying to get along on an absurdly small amount so that they could begin saving again in their fifties for old age. And they beat upon the stone mausoleum covering Matthias Meier and his wife Ida in *Wyuka* which is the Indian word for a place to lie down and sleep.

Out in the Republican Valley in the little town of Irving

the rains beat on Hazel Meier going back and forth in her tan-colored raincoat and cap to school, trying to keep her mind on lesson plans, on hard work, on an interview with the superintendent in which she was to tell him she had changed her mind and was withdrawing her resignation if they would still consider her for next year.

Life was a strange thing now,—all the loveliness of it had vanished, leaving nothing but school work. Beyond the moment she would not look, merely putting her energies and thoughts into the day's teaching.

This morning she took time at recess to scribble a few lines to her parents, making them as gay as though life were still a pleasant thing. They had experienced enough trouble,—she would carry this break with Neal through with head high. She mailed her letter at noon and changed her dress to a fresher one, for she was going out to the Johnson's with Marie, one of her pupils, for supper. They lived out of town, so she was going to have the experience of riding in the school bus. Marie and Katie were both in her room,—Katie had been out sick, was convalescing and wanted "Teacher" to come out for supper. Mr. Johnson would bring her back in the Ford, or if it should rain too hard, she was to stay all night.

As a matter of fact, "Teacher" was going to be distinctly bored and would have preferred going to her own rooming-house where at least she knew what to expect. A pupil's home was always and distinctly X, the unknown quantity. But as she told Miss Evans of the fourth grade, "hers not to question why, hers but to do or die."

When evening came, the school bus occupants were thrilled to death that Miss Meier was entering their chariot for the time being, seven girls wanting to sit by her, and virtually all the boys taking part in voluntary exercises of standing on their heads, cat-calls, and baboon-like climbings up the side of the windows in order to display masculine prowess in front of feminine charm.

Arrived at her destination she found the Johnson's abode was just about what she would have expected from personal appearances made all year by Katie and Marie. The sitting-room had a cheap rug with eye-puncturing red roses which Mrs. Johnson told her Mr. Johnson surprised her with at Christmas, picking it from the catalogue, "hisself," to which the convalescing Katie added the information that to-day in honor of Teacher they took off the newspapers and rag rugs they always kept over it.

While Mrs. Johnson prepared her supper, the intervening time for Hazel was occupied by a protracted sitting on the couch with a girl on either side and the little brother in a state of doubtful stickiness leaning on her knees, all enjoying a never-ending entertainment of stereoscopic views of such titles as "Niagara by Moonlight," "Lake Erie in a Storm" and a side-splitting one of "We Three Donkeys," the big joke being that whoever looked at the picture was *one* of them. "That caught you, didn't it, Teacher?"

Supper was ready. Mrs. Johnson was hot and flurried, forgetting to bring on her biscuits for a time. Mr. Johnson was there, just in from the milking, scrubbed and combed. The hired man was there, a queer crooked-nosed individual with one eye slightly turned.

"Mr. Nils Jensen, Miss Meier."

"Pleased to meetcha."

There was some delay caused by the little boy's insistent demand that he sit by Teacher, too, but the girls were adamant over their personal ownership, and Nils with rare diplomacy put a quietus on the disturbance by reaching for a hot sparerib and bestowing it upon the trouble-maker.

It rained most of the evening. Hazel stayed all night, for which Katie and Marie gave evidence they would eventually lord it over the other girls in their room, for not once had Teacher stayed all night at any of their homes.

Mrs. Johnson loaned Hazel her wedding nightgown,—a high-necked lace-yoked affair with blue ribbons pulled through the holes. Teacher was to have the spare room downstairs,—all the others were to sleep on the second floor. The bed had starched pillow-cases with brown cat-tails and yellow water-lilies embroidered on the ends. Some of the mercury behind the mirror on the dresser was off so one could see the wall-paper through it. The last thing Mrs. Johnson said was: "I do hope you sleep good, Miss Meier. They ain't nobody slep' in here since Grandpa died in this bed."

Hazel got into the erstwhile deathbed, in the ruffled wedding nightgown, laughed a little, thinking of all the funny things she would tell Neal when she saw him,—remembered, and watered the starched cat-tails with a few tears. It did not seem possible that Life could be so miserable and so uninteresting.

She must have been asleep a long time for it seemed near daylight when she heard noises.

"Miss Meier." It resolved itself into her name and some one pounding on her door.

"Yes?" She was sitting up, alarmed: not so much at the disturbance itself as at what it might portend.

"Get up and dress quick." It was Mr. Johnson. "There's water comin' in through the kitchen door,—the whole yard looks under water."

She sprang out of bed in a daze of sleepiness and uncertainty.

Water! Well, what of it? The first of the spring had been dry and dusty. Every one had wanted water. And now they had it. Never satisfied. What was the big commotion about? Water never hurt you,—when you were in a house, it didn't.

She realized her mind was not quite lucid, that her very fear of this unknown thing which had given Mr. Johnson's voice its anxious tone was making her a bit panicky.

She got out of the beribboned wedding nightgown and dressed in a fumbling sort of way, as though in one of those dreams where you couldn't get your clothes on. Her step-ins were wrong side out,—well, no matter. What a ghastly time of morning to get up,—scarcely light.

She could hear a queer swish, swish, a liquid gurgling sound that was not quite right. Some way it just did not seem to belong in a house. There were voices,—Mr. Johnson's,—Mrs. Johnson's. Children crying,—Marie and Katie and the little boy. The hired man was calling, —the hired man with the crossed eye and the crooked nose. A door was banging, too. And through all the other noises that constant swish—swish—swish!

Hose next, never mind the seams. What was the matter with every one? Pumps next. Her brown one-piece dress over her head. Did Mr. Johnson mean they were going away,—going to get out of the house on account of some water? Then she had better put on her beret and jacket, for it was chilly.

She pulled her gay orange beret over her hair, and with scarcely any volition of her own looked at her dim image in the dresser glass from which part of the mercury was missing, gave the beret a pert slant, and reached for her jacket.

Swish, swish—

No! No! Water couldn't do that,—couldn't come slithering under your bedroom door in long creeping lines.

Voices again. Mr. Johnson's. Mrs. Johnson's, this time, calling excitedly: "Miss Meier, are you dressed?" They were anxious for her to come. The children were crying again.

She stared at the long creeping lines under the door—coming—coming—

"Yes, I'm dressed."

Something fearful which ought not to be happening—was happening anyway. Water slipping that way, snake-like, over your bedroom floor.

She tiptoed over the long ribbon-like lines and opened the door. Mr. Johnson had the convalescing Katie in his arms. Mrs. Johnson had Marie and the little boy by the hands. The water snaked and slipped all over the sitting-room, over the fat red and green Axminster roses and under the cheap upright piano. It oozed around the basket of stereopticon views under the center table, and

287

Mrs. Johnson tiptoed through it and set them up on the stand.

The stair door stood open. Mr. Johnson was pushing his wife ahead of him toward it and telling the children to hurry along.

The water ran everywhere now,—bolder and more of it. Tiptoeing didn't do much good,—the red roses were almost obliterated. Some one was pounding or sawing upstairs.

"Shan't we get in the car?" She didn't know whether she whispered or shouted it. "And drive away from this?"

"There's no way," Mr. Johnson said shortly. "It's a regular river . . . everywhere."

"Down the highway?"

"Can't see the highway."

They went up the narrow stairs, the children thumping loudly in their heavy, unlaced shoes.

It seemed good to be up here where everything was dry. It was queer, though, to be in these strange upstairs rooms with a Mr. and Mrs. Johnson whom you did not know well,—the beds not made,—clothes scattered about, —a teddy-bear hanging over the side of a crib.

She knew now what had been making the noise up here. The hired man was cutting a hole in the ceiling of the smallest bedroom. For heaven's sake . . . he didn't think . . . ?

"I'm so sorry . . ." Mrs. Johnson said through her tightly closed teeth. There was a frozen sort of attitude about her, trying to be polite as on the evening before, but frightened to death. "So sorry . . . for this . . .

when you come, Miss Meier. So good to see about Katie
. . . You could be . . . in the dry . . . there in Irving."

Yes, why had she picked to-day . . . no, yesterday, to
come out here? Why do people do queer things . . . on
certain dates? Grandpa used to say no one knew whether
it was Providence or Lady Luck or the Spinning Fates.

Any other previous night on which she might have
chosen to come out here to see her pupil, this water-in-
the-house accident never would have occurred.

But that was always the way,—no matter what happened, people never knew it was *going* to happen, and
so they were always caught doing just the ordinary things
of life. That was why they had found the people of the
Pompeiian ruins in front of ovens and at the bath and
asleep. Heavens, that was a cheerful thought to drag in
just now,—the ruins of Pompeii. Lots of catastrophes in
the world. You read about them in the papers. People
trapped in queer ways. It always seemed so senseless
and stupid when you were reading it. "What were they
doing there?" you always said. Perhaps they couldn't
help it. Perhaps they were sometimes caught. But
nothing could happen here a mile out of Irving, Nebraska,
in the peaceful Republican Valley, in this day and age,
with electricity and radios and telephones and automobiles and . . .

Mr. Johnson came back from the stairway. His eyes
looked frightened and his face above the sandy mustache
was ashy white. "It's a lot higher," he said quietly.

Hazel slipped back to look down the well of the stairway and felt a definite illness at the sight. The dark
water lapped and slapped against the third or fourth stair,

—a chair floated, lightly hitting the door jamb back and forth with little insistent taps, and a fat red pin-cushion bobbed about like a bright-colored floater on an invisible fish-line.

She went back to the Johnsons and the hired man with the cross-eyes and the crooked nose.

"Don't stand, Miss Meier. Sit down." Even yet Mrs. Johnson's hospitality had not forsaken her.

It was queer how quiet every one was. Even the children, sensing something beyond them, stopped crying and only clung to their parents. The little boy wanted his teddy, and Hazel slipped into the tumbled bedroom and brought it to him. She pulled Marie onto her lap, keeping her arms around her. She felt close to these strange Johnsons, closer to them than to most of her friends. When we get out of here, I'll always be their friend, she thought,—I'll come out often to see them.

It was gray daylight now. One could see out of the small bedroom windows,—if one had the temerity to look.

Water! Water rushing through the barnyard. She could tell it was the barnyard for the big barn still stood there, even though a hayrack and a lumber-wagon floated with the current.

The high foundation was stone or cement and the upper part was frame, probably painted the usual barn red. In the gray dawn only a little of the white stone was still showing so that it looked like a fat old lady holding up her skirts from the wet. As she looked, a horse floundered through the water, head up, swimming, thrashing about for solid ground. A chicken-coop whirled crazily about with an old hen and chickens squatted precariously on top.

And now the water seemed rushing harder. There was more of a current. Mr. Johnson went back to the stairway. "My God!" They all heard him. "On the roof!" he called as he ran back.

He helped his wife up on a chair which he placed on the flat-topped bureau. She looked funny trying to squeeze her heavy bulk through the hole that Nils had sawed out. That is, she *would* have looked so if the world hadn't suddenly lost all its fun.

When she was through, Mr. Johnson helped the sick Katie up the same way. Then the little boy. Then Marie. "Hang to Mamma tight," he said each time.

"Now, you . . . Miss Meier." Mr. Johnson took hold of her, and the cross-eyed Nils steadied the chair on the bureau. No one said anything. One couldn't believe that people would stay so quiet under stress.

Hazel pulled herself through the hole and worked her way close to Mrs. Johnson and the children. The roof was wet and sloping and she had to be very careful to keep her footing.

It was frightening out here,—much more so than in the house. The height of the roof, the great puffy clouds billowing so close overhead, the dark rushing water below! It made her feel a distinct nausea, and very chilly. She was shaking uncontrollably. It was noisier here, too. One couldn't know that water would make so much noise, —whirling, sucking, rushing.

Much of the time she felt dazed, as though she were an onlooker at something of which she was not a part. It was a movie on the screen and the suspense would soon be over. Or a bad dream and after awhile she would awaken. But the nightmare persisted. The movie went on, reel after reel.

Mr. Johnson came up through the hole and then Nils, his cross-eyes appearing grotesquely above the aperture, then his crooked nose.

"If it once on its foundation stays yet a'ready," he volunteered.

If it stays . . . ! The house? Whatever put that silly notion in his head? Houses always stayed where they were built. Of course it would stay.

Pigs went by, tumbling along right side up or upside down,—anyway. Chicken-coops. A wagon-box with a dog standing shiveringly in it. A hayrack still partly loaded. And then . . . "Oh, don't look, Mrs. Johnson" —a woman on a house roof, clinging, crying, calling out to them. A woman on a house *that had not stayed on its foundation.*

Helpless, they watched her whirled on through the flood waters.

And now Hazel knew. They, too, might be whirled away with the current.

"Daddy, I'm cold," little Marie was saying. Without a word Mr. Johnson slipped off his coat to put around her.

"How about you, Katie?" Nils wanted to know. "Mebbe you have Nils' coat, huh?" And that came off, too.

Hazel was thinking about people,—homely, uninteresting people, people to whom she had never given a second thought. How different they seemed when you knew them,—when you were on a wet roof with them and the whole world had turned to water.

And now rain fell. The water below whirled by with that peculiar rushing, sucking noise. Water from the skies beat upon them. They cowered under its pommeling force. Mrs. Johnson, clinging to the wetness of the roof, bent her body low over Katie who had been sick, shielding her as best she could from the onslaught. Mr. Johnson held Marie in his arms.

"Don't let go of Jimmie a minute, Nils."

"I won't."

They clung to the roof over which the water ran, while water from the sky pounded them, and water below rushed darkly past. There was no solidity in anything. The world had gone mad, for everything in it was liquid. There was no world at all,—nothing but water.

Then the rain ceased. They could move their stiffened bodies slightly, pull the soaked clothing away from cold beaten flesh, push sodden hair from their eyes, change the position of aching bones.

Mr. Johnson broke the long silence.

"You all right, Mama?" cheerfully.

"Yes, I'm all right?" quietly.

"You all right, Miss Meier?"

"Yes, thank you."

"Too bad . . . by golly . . . when you come to see us so good."

"I want to go back in our house" from the little boy. The girls were crying.

Nils cracked a joke for them. "Don't make more water

wid tears, girls. We got enough water already yet,—huh?"

And now there was some conversation,—all with one import. Some one would get them. There would be people out in boats. Not for long would the neighbors let them stay here.

Neighbors! Mr. Johnson looked up and down the valley. The waters ran darkly as far as he could see. A wagon-box went by,—a horse swimming with the current. Small objects bobbed up and down here and there, —a chicken-coop, boxes, boards.

And then it happened,—the sickening thing which made of Hazel a mad young woman whose eyes would not believe their seeing, nor her ears their hearing, nor any sense function sanely. It all came quickly with crashing, horrible sounds and wrenching movements of the only solid thing in the world. Under them somewhere, solidity moved and dipped and whirled in circular fashion. Mrs. Johnson screamed and clutched the air. Katie was thrown into the gray space. Then Mr. Johnson holding to Marie and grabbing for Katie. Bodies hurtled off the turning building. Staring, uncomprehending, she saw Marie's pink dress for a moment before it sank. Mr. Johnson, his face in the water a dead white mask, came up, swam a way,—and she looked no more.

The roof to which she clung was moving down the current. Nils, too, was clinging near her, his arm still around the little boy who was crying loudly.

"Where did Daddy and Mamma go? I want to go in my house."

"Sh, darling. You're all right. Nils and I will take care of you."

And now the roof under the three went on down the stream, sometimes dipping a little, sometimes whirling in a cross-current. Hazel knew there was no further fear to which she could be subjected than this. She had reached the depths of terror. This was the end of fear, for it was the end of life itself.

But there was one more dread. Nils told her about it, —cautioned her about what to do. The house was making for the top of a grove of trees, or apparently so,—one couldn't tell, for it was subject to so many cross-currents. If it caught in the trees, it might be their salvation. On the other hand, if it struck with force, tree branches could sweep them off into the water. If the house approached it, she was to use all her wits about avoiding that,—was to lie flat, face downward. He would hold Jimmie tightly down by him.

Now, all of life consisted of knowing whether this was to happen or not. They moved, dipped fearfully, swayed, whirled sickeningly. The grove was to the right, no, straight ahead of them,—to the right again. Now it loomed up in front of them. Green dripping foliage and gnarled brown branches were there straight ahead. She pulled her beret down tightly over her ears and lay flat down, face concealed in an arm, clung tightly with one hand, and crooked the other elbow over the roof ridge. The branches swept her, tore at her skirt and jacket and hose. Heavy rain-drops shaken from them pelted her.

When all motion had ceased, she raised her head into the twigs and leaves of a tree top. Protecting her face, she peered through. Nils and Jimmie had withstood the impact, too. Jimmie was beyond the crying stage now, lay supinely on the wet roof, tired out, his teddy-bear in his arms.

"If once it holds together and don't go to crackin' up already yet," Nils volunteered.

Sometimes he climbed carefully from branch to branch trying to see out better, sighting their location. Sometimes he crawled stealthily about the roof top looking over into the dark waters. Often he shouted, his voice, used to hog-calling, echoing across the waters.

She marveled at his patience with Jimmie. There was a place where a stout branch had wedged itself across the roof. Against this he placed the child who slept now on his hard, wet bed.

Time wore on and she did not know whether it was minutes or hours that went by. Whatever it was it had no end. It was eternity. There was no sight but green branches and water,—no human sounds but their own.

Jimmie woke and cried with hunger.

Perhaps it was early afternoon,—they could not tell for the sun was hidden in the gray of the clouds,— that Nils came to his decision to swim,—he would go downstream with the current working gradually toward the right. He knew the gamble of it, but he was assuming it stoically.

"If I get there, I bring help. If I don't, we ain't no worse off anyway, huh?"

"Oh, Nils . . . are you going to? I don't think I can look after Jimmie and hang on, too."

296

"Yah . . . you can all right. You're a strong girl. Betcha you play that there tennis."

He stripped to underwear, felt his way carefully from branch to branch, looked back: "If . . . I don't make it . . . and you're found all right . . . would you get word to my ma on the Missouri mud flats just below Omaha . . . Mrs. Christine Jensen?"

"I would, Nils . . . oh I *would*. But you'll get there."

"Yah . . . I'll get there . . . maybe."

"Good luck, Nils."

Nils was gone into the dark waters. She could hear the steady splash of his strokes and then the sound ceased.

And now there was no such thing as time,—nothing but pain in one's wrists and fingers, and a wet numb body that would soon fail to function.

Now there was nothing but a clinging to the wet roof wedged in the branches that still swayed sickeningly with the current,—watching the orphaned child sleeping there against the heavy limb, ready to grab for him if, as Nils had suggested, the roof might break up with the pounding. Nothing to do but cling and pray,—watch and think.

CHAPTER XXXIX

NEAL was having the experience of a puncture a half-mile from home with the exasperating knowledge that he had taken the jack out to use for his father's car and failed to put it back. With a few choice epithets directed exclusively toward himself, he started down the highway toward home,—a paved highway now. And although he gave no thought to that fact, so used was he to it, if he had done so, he could have called the roll of the various periods through which that highway had progressed. Pathless prairie grass. Grassy road. Dirt road from which all sign of green had vanished. Graveled highway. Pavement. In the valley, the evolution of that road was the history of the people who lived beside it.

He had not gone but a few paces until a roadster drew up and a woman called to him. "Hello, hitch-hiker."

"Oh, hello, Miss Schaffer." The trained nurse from Omaha who came sometimes to the valley to visit her brother.

He rode to the gate with her. She was immaculate, well groomed, exuded freshness.

"So you're going to marry a University girl, Neal?"

" 'So you *were* going to' is a little more appropriate now."

"Oh, Neal . . . I'm sorry I bungled."

298

"That's all right. You can't keep news like that in cold storage,—not in this neck of the woods anyway."

It took such a moment for a half-mile's drive. Rose Schaffer wished that it might have been longer. "Believe me, Neal, I hope . . . with all my heart whatever happens to you, it will be for the best."

"Thanks—for the interest."

He might have shown his surprise at her words more than he intended, for she laughed, then said quickly: "You know how old maids are, incorrigibly romantic. And besides, they say I helped save your life once when you were a small codger, so I've a right to be interested in your welfare."

As he turned into the graveled driveway, old Amalia came to the door of her little house and peered out.

"Evidently laying for me," Neal said to himself.

She looked so tiny standing there just at the stoop's edge, her hands holding to the door jamb to steady herself.

"Joey!" She was calling to him and motioning.

Neal walked up the path toward her cottage to see what she wanted. It made no difference which name she used,—Joe or Neal,—whichever one was nearer to her responded. Sometimes she called them "Emil" or "Fritz," too. No one ever corrected her.

"Der iss news," she called.

She was at it again. Well, he would have to humor her.

Ships in trouble far out at sea and Omaha shoe sales, talk of foreign wars, and the local grain elevator's receipts, deaths of people of whom she had never heard, and the five babies all at one time in Canada,—they were all exciting to her, one of as much consequence as another. It gave her a sense of importance to tell it and have them listen as though interested.

Always when a news period was ended she came to her door to see if there was some one to whom she could call out what she had just heard. Two or three items out of the whole list were all she could remember. Sometimes she garbled those until they were no news at all. Usually she was a bit of a nuisance with any of it. But they tried to be patient,—she was so palpably pleased at the telling.

Neal had to laugh to himself now as he walked toward her. The little news-hound, he thought, her own radio certainly had given her a new lease on life.

"Well, did a man bite a dog, Grandma?"

"No. . . . So long as I am living, Joey, a man biting a dog I never knew. But do not get me off . . . or already I forget. Neal, dere iss trouble by de big rains. Rivers go over. Towns iss swept away. People iss in trees hanging. Railroads iss gone. All iss water where vas de farms."

"Where, Grandma? In Hong-Kong, Czechoslovakia, or Tasmania?"

"No. Close by . . . I remember. It was in de Valley of de Republican River. Some folks ve know in pioneer days by name Weitzal stayed at our house and vent on to de Valley of de Republican. Dey had to sleep on de floor. I remember, dey had dere own bedding . . ."

Neal was not laughing at Grandma now, nor listening to her prattle of a family by the name of Weitzal in pioneer days who had to sleep on the floor on their own bedding.

300

He was standing in the path and scowling at her. "What towns, Grandma? What towns are swept away?"

"I forget vich, Joey. Alvays I forget . . ."

"Was Irving one? Try hard to remember."

"It sounds so, Neal. Irwing? . . . Yes . . . I tink . . ."

Neal turned and went into the big house, still scowling. He felt a curious fright that he could not shake off. It was silly, too, for Grandma was so unreliable. Probably the catastrophe was in Oregon instead of Nebraska,—maybe it was fire instead of water,—and a few other points of misinformation. Maybe she had heard part of a play. Several times she had mistaken one for a real happening. One morning she had come all the way over to the house in her slow way to tell them about a group of people being lost in the desert and it proved to have been one of the Death Valley plays.

But he went to the 'phone and called for information. Yes, it was true. There was a flood of gigantic proportions over a large area of the Republican Valley . . . probably several hundred lives lost . . . millions of property damage.

"How about the town . . ." his throat was dry, ". . . the town of Irving?"

News was meager, but that was one of the places reported in a bad way.

He hung up the receiver, ran to the garage for the jack, went back to fix his car, drove home, had a hurried bath and change of clothes, and came down to tell his mother he was driving to Lincoln and possibly would go on to the flood district.

Myrtie was worried and fearful for him, but he paid no attention to her complaints, went out to see his father for a minute, and was gone down the gravel driveway in his roadster.

In Lincoln he went directly to the Meier apartment. Carter was home with Lucile,—both worried to distraction. All morning they had been trying to get in communication with Irving or some point near there. The town was as isolated as a foreign planet.

A plane carrying a newspaper man had gone over and was not back yet, Carter told Neal.

"A plane,—that's the idea," Neal said. "I'll see if I can go over that way."

Lucile told Neal about a letter from Hazel that had come in that morning. It had been scribbled at the morning recess the day before, mailed at noon, had arrived on the evening train and been delivered that morning. In it she had mentioned going out to one of her pupils in the country.

"That probably took her farther away from the river," Neal said cheerfully. "Or closer," he was thinking.

In the midst of the conversation Hazel's mother suddenly said: "I've just remembered, Neal . . . I thought you and Hazel . . . ? She wrote me . . ."

For the first time during these anxious moments Neal gave his old boyish grin. "I guess I'd forgotten it, too. Officially our engagement wasn't just what it had been previously. This interest on my part is off the record."

It relieved them both immensely to laugh. It seemed to assure each one that Hazel could not help but be all right now.

But they came back to the letter several times. Neal had Hazel's mother read the part again carefully in which she told of her movements—a careless little note written with no thought that a few hours later her family would hang on every word.

Am going out to a Johnson family's home this afternoon in the school bus with my little Marie. (I always think of Booth Tarkington's Little Marie of Kansas City.) Katie Johnson, also my professional property, has been sick for several days,—nothing catching, so don't worry,—and now she's sitting up and Dear Teacher is invited out to supper,—not dinner,—supper, for which I have been informed we are having *spare*-ribs. Papa Johnson will bring me home afterward, or pending another hard rain of which we are having no end, I can stay all night in the *spare* bedroom. Woodman, *spare* that tree.

It was so like her, gay and flippant, that it brought her clearly before them all. The three who had been so worried about her, stood there together, each thinking: "She's all right. Nothing could have happened to her. To other people out there, maybe, but not to Hazel."

When he left them, Neal said: "I'll get to her some way. And I'll get in touch with you as soon as I can. If you don't hear, don't worry. I'll be driving, walking, flying, or swimming."

They followed him out to the lobby door,—anxious, wanting to go with him, sending their hearts along.

"Oh, she's all right."

"Yes, as safe as she can be."

"Of course. But I rather think I'll go see for myself. Good-by."

"Good-by, Neal." It was just a little spat they had, Lucile was thinking.

"Good-by, Neal." Twenty-four, thought Carter, what wouldn't I give to be twenty-four again.

CHAPTER XL

CLINGING—watching—thinking,—life had resolved itself into these three functions for Hazel. Sometimes it seemed the easiest thing in the world just to relax and let go. There would be a few moments of dread, a few moments of swimming with the current, then oblivion, for she could see nothing within her own swimming distances to which to go. Clumps of trees, emerging from the rushing water, another marooned building far in the distance,—nothing better than the roof to which she must still cling.

And there was the child, thrown so strangely in her care, sleeping his troubled, sighing sleep against the wet branch. No matter how painful the clinging nor how dulled her mind she must not forsake him.

There was no sound nor sight of help. Nils, then, had failed. Poor Nils,—so nervy about it all.

In the stillness and the vastness of the flood, then, she grew deathly frightened, panic-stricken.

Up to now something had sustained her in all the horrible experience,—that it would soon be over, that some one would come. But now hope was giving away,—maybe her sanity with it. She cried out, and the little boy cried too at the sound, so that she forgot her own fright and comforted him.

His helplessness steadied her, and under her soothing words he fell again into his troubled slumber.

It seemed late afternoon. Night would soon be coming on. That would mean death, for she could not cling through the night. Her thoughts centered on life as she had known it, as though the thinking could give it back to her. What a glorious thing it was at its very poorest! The hours she had most disliked,—how she would welcome them now! The simplest things would give her pleasure,—the gifts of life we accepted so casually, how beautiful they were.

Three people centered her life,—Mother, Dad, Neal. She saw them all as through a long vista. They were standing there at the end of it waiting for her to come,— were holding out their arms to her, but she couldn't go because she had to cling to this wet roof. They held her,—the wet rotting shingles and the green branches over them, and would not allow her to go where Dad and Mother and Neal were waiting.

Suddenly she remembered a queer thing her grandfather had said the last week of his life. He had been asleep, and half waking, had called out sharply: "Sands! The sucking sands! They hold you back and will not let you go."

She, too, knew the agony of being held back and not allowed to go.

And now she felt only an unselfish sympathy for the three she loved most. She pictured their sorrow until in the torture of it her mind could no longer stand the thought and turned in anguish from it.

She and Neal had quarreled about something, so trivial now she scarcely gave it space in her mind. Dad.

Mother. Neal. She said the names over as a nun says her beads.

She had but those three thoughts, and the thoughts were prayers. Dad. Mother. Neal. Those, and "God, but give me back my everyday living and I will use it to the full."

All the extraneous matters of life were swept away with the flood waters. All the foolish unnecessary things which surrounded it were vanished from her mind as the fields were vanished from the landscape. Life was a simple thing of love and work and courage. Nothing else mattered. To have those, one had everything.

She dropped her head into her arm, tried to still the throbbing and the aching of it with a cramped numb hand. But the pain was sharper,—the throbbing grew loud and louder until it filled—

She jerked her head from her stiff arm, sat up suddenly.

The throbbing was a plane flying low, circling over the flood waters,—a great wide-winged bird throbbing its message of hope. She pulled the now wakened Jimmie to her. She waved, called, cried out. Jimmie added his three-year-old voice to it. They must have seen her for they went around her in one complete circumference of flight, then disappeared rapidly in the distance.

She could not tell how long the time,—it only seemed interminable,—until she saw the two boats. They bobbed about sickeningly at times in the cross-currents. Once it appeared that one would be swamped. Those who were managing them certainly knew their business.

"See, Jimmie, the boats are coming for us."

"I know, it's my Daddy."

Hazel hugged him tightly. "No, Jimmie, it isn't Daddy. Jimmie, have you . . . have you anybody besides Daddy and Mother? Have you any grandma or aunties?"

"I've got my Grandma Johnson and my Grandma Snell and my Aunt Callie and my Aunt . . ."

Wet-eyed, she kissed him.

"I'm glad, Jimmie,—more glad than you can ever know."

The first boat came up, bumping against the trees and the submerged part of a house that had once been a home with a rug of red roses and stereopticon views and a wedding nightgown.

"Oh, Nils, you did make it . . . and you got some dry clothes on and came back. How good you are."

Very soon she was to learn of a hundred incidents like that one, of the reactions of various types of humans under pressure, of the resourcefulness of the rescued and the rescuers, of evidences everywhere of the Nebraska pioneer spirit which had not died out in the third and fourth generations.

She was to know of the rescue of the men marooned for twenty-four hours on a light plant, and of the big gravel-pumping raft floating down the river to them as though Providence had taken a hand in the situation, of the groups clinging to the roofs of houses and trees saved by heroic deeds, and of others which vanished into the boiling current. She was to hear of men rescued from their perilous positions of sixteen hours changing into dry clothing that they in turn might help, of doctors braving the torrents to get to isolated districts to bring new babies into the harassed territory, and of tired women serving coffee until too worn out to go on.

She was to see the shambles of town homes and farms, the washed-out paved highway and the twisted railroad tracks with ties standing as upright as so many fence posts.

It was only later that she was to see the valley peaceful again and new farm homes go up, villages rebuilt and Nature begin to cover her ugly scars with verdure.

It took planning and care to get Jimmie safely down into the first boat. Nils and the man with him pulled away. The second boat came up then.

"Neal."

"Hello, Pink-Hair."

"Neal . . . where did you come from? Was it you in the plane?"

"Yes. What do you mean, Woman, by getting stranded on a desert isle with a cross-eyed man and appearing later with a child?"

And now Hazel was down, too, in a swaying boat which a strange man was helping Neal handle. And absurdly enough, Hazel was crying,—sobbing and crying in the reaction of their coming.

Neal comforted her as best he could with the boat unsteady in the current. She clung to him, a little girl who had looked upon Death and found it awful.

"Neal,—Katie said she hoped I'd finish reading 'Black Beauty' when she got back . . ." and she burst again into loud sobbing.

Hazel snapping come-backs at him as with a rubber sling-shot was nothing new. Hazel a little emotional under a full moon or the spell of an orchestra,—Hazel matter of fact and managerial, giving decided opinions on any subject, ancient or modern,—Hazel as a peppy little tongue-lasher or a gracious social partner,—any and all of these moods were familiar to him. But not this sobbing reaction to a vital experience, nor the anguished tears. It made of her a girl he had never known. She seemed closer to him, tender, more human. He loved her for it.

The two boats navigated the rushing stream back,—in one Neal who had handled oars ever since he could remember, and in the other the cross-eyed Nils Jensen who had spent his boyhood years on the bottoms of the Missouri. It was well for them that they had been water-bugs or they might have been swamped more than once where the ugly water poured heavily around a submerged building or a clump of trees.

As they were coming into the land where people were waiting with blankets and coffee, Hazel said: "Neal, there's one thing I wish you'd promise me,—that if he wants to come, we'll hire this Nils Jensen."

"*We'll* . . . ?" He grinned. "You mean as a law partner?"

And now, life given back to her, Hazel was her old self.

"No,—Muscle-neck,—on our farm."

CHAPTER XLI

IN the early summer Neal took Hazel to his home to meet his people and to see the place where she was to live. She saw the long graveled driveway, the wide sweep of yard under the big trees, the solid old house which Fritz and Emil had built so many years before and which had been modernized with sun-room and furnace and lights in Myrtie's time, and felt a distinct surprise at the lovely old place set so far back from the paved highway.

"In England they'd call it an ancestral home," she admitted when they were circling up the driveway.

A rabbit, bounding across the grass at that moment, Neal said in his light way to cover the emotion he felt: "Ah, the hare! Higgins,—the hounds. We ride at once."

She met Neal's father and mother, warming immediately to his father with his natural dignity and quiet manner. She was not so sure about the mother,—a fluttery little woman whose conversation ran largely to speaking of things she wished she could have or do. She was glad the two were to live over in the small house beyond the lilac hedge.

In the late afternoon Neal took her over to the cottage to meet his great-grandmother.

Hand in hand they sauntered down the old path which led through the bluegrass and the white clover, thick and luxurious again since the great rains.

Neal was a little perturbed as they approached the old house. He wanted in some way to prepare Hazel,—to explain old Amalia to this girl he loved, wished boyishly that he knew how to put her in the best light to this lovely, modern Hazel whose own grandmother had been so different.

"Hazel, you know Grannie is awfully old—eighty-something—I've even lost track of her exact age," he began diffidently. "I guess she's pretty funny looking to strangers,—sort of weather-beaten and toothless and wrinkled as an old walnut. But gosh, she's been awfully good to me . . . you know, cookies in jars, and kiss the bumps and taking care of me when Mother was nervous or away. My dad feels the same way about her. I suppose I can't ever see her the way she must seem to others."

Hazel slipped her arm through Neal's in a sudden tender gesture. For the first time she thought of him as a little boy, felt for a moment much, much older than he. It is eternal Motherhood forever compassionate toward eternal boyhood. "I'll like her, Neal."

To the boy it brought a swift renewed rush of love for her,—he could not have told why. It made him stop in the pathway, suddenly kiss her forehead and her cheek tenderly,—not the kiss of passionate young manhood but a tribute to her friendship and sympathy,—engendered at that moment by a feeling which would be deeper and more lasting than the other.

They went on up the curving path between the petunias toward the little house in which old Amalia had lived for so many years.

They passed the sloping cellar door with the stone crocks in a row, the clump of gooseberries over which the dish-towels dried, and the thick bushes on each side of the steps with their fat cabbage-roses in blossom now.

Old Amalia was just inside the screen door in the sitting-room in which there was all the accumulation of the years,—old blue plates on a shelf and gilded milk-weed pods, a little mirror with blue brush and comb in a tin tray underneath, the sale carpet with its scroll figures tacked tautly over thick oat straw.

Hazel had a feeling that the whole thing was a stage setting or a movie scene,—on the wall the *Guten Morgen* and *Gute Nacht* pictures of the chunky half-nude child with the daisies on her head, the couch with its bright pieced quilt cover, the oval walnut stand on which there were the Bible and some star fish and a blue plush album. There were odors, too, peculiarly fitting to the place,—old clean odors,—soap-suds and mothballs and cinnamon. Whether the latter came from the roses beside the door or the kitchen beyond, she could not tell.

Old Amalia was patching, putting a neat little square in the corner of a table-cloth with small, even stitches. Hazel saw that Neal had described her quite definitely. Her hair, plastered down tightly over the pink spots of her head, was wound in a little hard knob at the nape of her neck. In the big chair she looked as tiny and wrinkled as a little brown gnome.

As the screen door opened she looked at the young people from pale old eyes that had to adjust themselves slowly to the new focus.

"Hello, Grandma. Do you know me to-day?"

313

"Yes. It's Joey," she said with apparent delight at her quickness.

"No . . . guess again. It's Neal . . ."

"Tsk . . . tsk . . . Neal! So big a boy you're gettin' to be."

"No . . . you're fooling, Grannie. I'm only six-feet-one, and one hundred and ninety is all that I weigh."

"And who iss dis?" Old Amalia wanted to know.

"Now this," said Neal, and he slipped an arm around Hazel, and drew her forward, ". . . this needs explaining. *This* . . . is Hazel."

"Hachel?"

"Yes . . . like the other nuts, you know." He grinned, but when he saw old Amalia was not appreciating his little joke, he explained: "She's *my girl,* Grannie. You know I told you about her. We're going to be married."

Old Amalia put out a brown little hand as shrunken as a mummy's. "Excoose me," she said to Hazel with a toothless smile. "Alvays I forget." She spoke apologetically. "Of de long ago I remember . . . but of only yesterday already I forget."

Hazel felt a sudden tenderness toward the little, brown doll of a woman, so shy and so gentle in her broken speech. "Neal has told me about you."

"Neal iss a goot boy. You vill be a goot vife, I hope?" she questioned.

"I hope I'll be."

Old Amalia scanned her closely. "You vill be," she nodded. "A *schön* . . . nice face you have. And your name it is Hachel?"

Neal answered for her. "Yes, Grannie. Hazel Meier, —but not for long."

"Meier?" old Amalia repeated.

"Hazel Meier," he said it louder and more plainly. "Her father, Carter Meier, was a banker at Cedar City. And the old gentleman, Matthias Meier, was Hazel's grandfather."

"Matthias Meier?" Amalia was confused,—was grasping for something,—some queer puzzle which she could not piece together. "Has he come, too? To Nebraska City has he come?"

"He's dead, Grandma. Why, you wanted to go to the services for him yourself. Don't you remember? When we read it in the paper? You wanted to go but Dad thought it was too hot and too far."

"Yes . . . I remember. Alvays I am forgetting . . . and remembering."

"What, Grandma?" Hazel asked. "What are you remembering?"

"Just that . . . *immer* . . . alvays . . . spring . . . comes on . . ."

"That's like a poem I know:

> " 'One thing, I remember:
>   Spring came on forever,
>   Spring came on forever,'
> Said the Chinese nightingale."

"It is so." Old Amalia nodded as though she knew all things, as though her life had embraced all wisdom.

"Perhaps it makes you remember when you were young."

"*Vielleicht* . . . perhaps . . . it does."

But Neal was impatient now.

"Well, how do you like her, Grannie?"

The old woman's eyes still peered up at Hazel's. She reached out a tiny brown hand and stroked the firm white one of the girl. "*Kleine taube*," she murmured.

"Talk United States, Grandma. What's that?"

"Little dove."

"Little dove . . . my eye! Snapping-turtle you mean."

"Hachel Meier," the old woman nodded as though she understood a very wise and very ancient thing. "So it vill be."

"Can't you get up a little more enthusiasm, Grandma? Say something a little more exciting and strong. You surely like her."

"In German I say it, to her, Neal. '*Ich liebe dich.*' "

"That's better. Well, we'll go now, Hazel,—now that Grannie has leeby-dicked you."

They said good-by to the old lady sitting there in her big rocking-chair like a little brown Buddha, and went happily down the path between the fat cabbage roses and the petunias.

Amalia watched them go,—tall, strong, young. For a time she sat there quietly, saying something over to herself as one learns a lesson by rote.

She must think this thing out very carefully and be sure she had it right. She knew she was apt to imagine things that were not true and forget those that were real. It was very hard to know always which ones had happened and which were but dreams.

This was different. This must never get mixed with

the fancies. It belonged here and now among the things that were true. She must not allow it to slip away from her into the shadows,—must hold it as steadily in her mind as she was holding to the chair.

There was something she wanted to do,—something she would do at once while she remembered.

She pulled herself out of her rocker and picking her way carefully from table to chair, went into her bedroom. All the time she held steadily to this queer new thing so that she would not forget any part of it. Sometimes that happened, too,—recalling only a portion of a thing, so that the half-memories worried and distressed her. But this one was still wholly clear.

She opened the bottom drawer of her dresser and removed an unwieldly-looking bundle wrapped in very old muslin, yellowed and worn. This she unwound layer by layer until she had uncovered a long box. It was ornamented with sea shells, angel-wings and moon shells, Roman snails and other fragile, fan-like shells of a sea she had never seen. They were broken and nicked and unglued in places so that ugly brown patches of the wooden frame showed through. Almost were they symbolic of things that had never been,—journeys to far-off seas, hearing the sound of wind in whipping sails and the call of the gulls on the sand.

With hands that trembled with their eighty-six years, she lifted a tray and took out two quilt blocks. Strangely enough in the dark of its shelter, the pink had not faded, —only the white was yellowed. A needle in one of the blocks was brown with rust so that it crumbled to the touch. This she removed and replaced with a bright one from the cushion on her bureau. Then from the box she took a darkly tarnished thimble and fitted it to her tiny finger.

Still holding carefully to the thought in her mind as one might hold lovely fragile china lest it drop, she made her way cautiously back to her rocker and sat down to finish the *Baum des Lebens*—Tree of Life—quilt.

CHAPTER XLII

NEAL and Hazel were married in August with the wheat harvested and the corn maturing for its October husking,—a simple wedding in the rented apartment of the Meiers.

Joe and Myrtie with old Amalia drove down to Lincoln in the big car,—Neal in his own roadster. Myrtie had not been any too gracious about taking Grandma, but when Joe said definitely: "Grandma is going if she is able to take the long ride," Myrtie made no further excuses, but merely went about with a martyred air of having more responsibility on her shoulders than any human could quite bear.

She had a new outfit, too, one of the first of the fall suits with a matching hat of beige and her fox furs: "for no telling what elaborate sort of thing Mrs. Meier will wear" she had said to Joe. So she was somewhat astounded now to be met at the door by Hazel's mother in a simple printed silk.

There were only a few present at the ceremony, three of Hazel's sorority sisters, an old family friend, two of Neal's fraternity brothers, the minister and his wife, Carter and Lucile, Joe and Myrtie, and old Grandma Holmsdorfer who stubbornly would not change her name to Holms.

Carter Meier, looking at Hazel in the traveling dress in which she was to be married, wondered how she felt about this simple affair, whether she was missing the pomp of a

319

big church wedding such as her mother had,—as she might have had if things were different. If she were doing so, she was game about it, giving no intimation of her thoughts.

They were all there now, and some one was whispering that it was time. Neal and Hazel were walking over to the mantel with its garden flowers as informally as though they were playing charades and the members of the little group were to guess what they were portraying. The minister took his place. No ushers, no pipe-organ, no "Promise Me," no bridal-veil,—not a hot-house flower, excepting the bridal bouquet. Hazel, in her soft brown going-away suit with egg-shell blouse, golden-yellow roses in her arms,—Neal, well-tailored, a fine-looking, upstanding figure of a chap with keen, honest eyes. University graduates. And there were people in the world who thought all farmers were bewhiskered gents forever chewing on a succession of straws, and their wives drab creatures always standing forlornly at the doorways of shanties.

The minister was speaking: "Dearly beloved . . ." his voice a mere accompaniment to Carter Meier's thoughts. His little girl was being married. What a short while ago they had watched her first baby step,— she had made one little tottering forward movement, and overcome by her own accomplishment let forth a jubilant crow of delight that lost her the equilibrium she had so recently gained.

And now something was getting in Carter Meier's way so he could not see the bride at all: a little girl skipping up and down the lawn of the Cedar City house in the early morning, arms outstretched like a bird's wings,—

on a single roller-skate propelling herself wildly up and down the sidewalk,—riding her Shetland pony around the streets, her dark red mop of curls blowing in the wind . . . his active, happy little daughter! What would her life be? Hard? He would save her from all the blows it would deal her, if he only could,—from all the hard work of it, if it were possible. But who knew, at that, she might be happier than young women to whom work was a foreign thing. In what direction lay happiness anyway?

Joe Holms was thinking: "That's my boy taking the big step. You won't make mistakes all the time, Neal . . . you're different . . . you'll always be different . . ."

Lucile was thinking: "I mustn't cry . . . if I start I couldn't stop. I left my mother without thinking much about it. I must look straight at Hazel and smile so that when she looks at me she can see how happy I am. I *am* happy . . . I *am*. . . . Oh, no, I'm not, I'm miserable and I want to be young again and have my little girl back."

Myrtie was thinking: "He won't care for me any more. He'll take her places and bring gifts to her and give her all the attention."

Old Amalia Holmsdorfer was not thinking about either Hazel or Neal. She was peering with pale watery eyes across the room at Carter Meier, her thoughts in queer confusion: "So that's your boy, Matthias. He isn't as tall as you, and of course he's gray, and you're not. But he holds his shoulders like you, and you would have looked like that if you had lived to be over twenty-one."

CHAPTER XLIII

THERE are those who would call it the end of the story when Hazel Meier married Neal Holms. To say the story is finished is not true, for no mere story can ever be complete, no family history contain a beginning or an end. One may only cut out a bit from life, trimming away all that went before and all that will come after.

It was early September when Hazel returned from her wedding-trip with Neal and went to live in the old house set in the elms and the maples far back from the paved highway.

Strangely enough, then, she was beginning her married life on the same land where old Amalia had homesteaded so many years before but with two great differences— all the wonderful modern surroundings in contrast to the primitive ones of the pioneer days,—and the fact that where Hazel carried the flame of love burning deep in her heart for her young husband, Amalia had known only gray ashes.

Peculiarly, in spite of the difference in the generations, Hazel approached her task much as the young Amalia had once done, vigorously and with responsibility. With her resourcefulness and her power of accomplishment she put her young shoulder to the wheel, mapping out her day's work just as she had planned her University schedule. She allowed no waste about her. Nothing was thrown away. Every potato peeling had its use, every

322

bone its nutritive value. "So don't try to get up any debate with *me*," she would laugh, "that higher education unfits woman for the home."

It was characteristic of her that one of the first things she did was to ask Neal's parents if the half-hearted pink stucco could be pulled off the honest old gray stones underneath.

"I'm sure I don't care what you do, Hazel," Myrtie said with tired resignation. "There's so little money to do anything with. I wonder how you have the heart to plan a single change."

Joe and Myrtie were living in the small house with Grandma. But on a morning of that September Myrtie came over, stepping daintily through the bluegrass.

Hazel, finishing the last of her dishes, said: "Come on in the living-room, Mother Holms, where you will be more comfortable." Every one always saw to it that Neal's mother was comfortable.

She washed her hands, followed Myrtie into the living-room where she picked up the braided rug she was making. It was apple green and egg-shell. "How do you like it?" she asked. "I'm using all the old green drapes that were worn out. Grandma showed me how and I'm perfectly fascinated with it. I think it tickled her pink to show me. Isn't it funny—this returning to all the old ways? Ever since I knit my dress I'm crazy about the old hand-craft. I've even gone so far as to think I'd like a loom set up in the vacant bedroom. Maybe I'll weave Neal's clothes yet." And she laughed gaily.

Myrtie did not laugh. "I don't see how you can do such homely things cheerfully, Hazel. Well . . ." she broke off abruptly, "I came over to see you about something rather important. Hazel, you know me well enough by this time to realize that I never beat around bushes. I go straight to the point with sincerity and honesty. You know that, don't you, Hazel?"

"Why . . . yes . . . Mother Holms." She was not sure whether it was complimentary to agree or otherwise.

"Hazel . . . my life has been very difficult." Myrtie pressed her little white hands together, as though she must keep herself well under control before this inexperienced girl. Hazel watched their delicate softness, the narrow gold circlet and the flashing of the big diamond solitaire. As always they fascinated her in their fluttering. Katherine Cornell hands they were, she told herself,— they ran the gamut of all her emotions.

"What I have been through . . . no one of your youth, of course, can realize. Childbirth . . . loss of property . . . disappointments . . . nervousness. Oh, well," she sighed, "we won't go into all that. It would only worry you and needlessly torture myself. When one gets cornered in life—in a trap as it were—all one's ambitions frustrated . . . life all inhibitions . . ."

Hazel could have laughed aloud if this had not been Neal's mother. How little like her he was. She was really very sweet and attractive, too, excepting when she mourned and whined.

"But what can one do . . . or say?" Tears came to Myrtie's eyes, but she threw Hazel a brave little smile. "My husband doesn't understand a woman's aspirations . . . her scope of mental vision . . . her emotional reactions. With all your youth and inexperience, Hazel, you are a woman . . . and you can understand . . . this constant beating of your wings against life . . ."

"Oh, I don't know, Mother Holms." Hazel had a swift memory of black water rushing, of bodies hurled into gray space, of the whirling and dipping of wet, rotten shingles. "I guess I'm just too fond of life as it is to do much beating."

"All my life, Hazel, I've been doing things for people . . . and now . . . that I'm in my middle forties . . ."

"Well, life begins at . . ."

"Hazel," Myrtie leaned forward. There were tears on her lashes. "You spoke just now of the vacant bedroom. What I came to see you about is this: Will you take Grandma back here to live with you?"

"You mean for all the time?" It did not seem right. She and Neal were so young . . . so filled with life and energy. Grandma was so old . . . so very old and childish.

"Yes . . . if you will, Hazel, without Neal or his father knowing anything about my speaking to you. Men can misunderstand motives so easily." Her sensitive lip quivered. "I have spoken to Grandma about it . . . sounding her out before I said anything to you."

"What did Grandma say?"

"She said in her broken dialect: 'When you're as old as I am, Myrtie, it won't make much difference what happens.' So you see,—it's immaterial to her."

All noontime and for several hours later Hazel thought about this new thing, how cleverly Neal's mother was manipulating it, pondered on a half-dozen other times in which she had seemed to attain her ends. Sweet, pleasant, babyish,—how she must have wound Neal's father around her finger all these years. Now she was manipulating this about Grandma as sweetly, as adroitly. "And when Grandma dies before long," thought Hazel, "it will be Mother Holms we all must comfort."

By afternoon Hazel was ready to give her answer. The little Grandmother was not to be hurt or made uncomfortable by it, that was sure. So she went down through the grassy path to the small house. "Wouldn't you like to move over to the big house with us for awhile, Grannie?"

Old Amalia looked up, her faded blue eyes filling. "It's not so goot, Hachel, to live too long."

"*You* haven't lived too long, Grannie. Neal and I want you to come. We've been asking Mother Holms for you. We don't like the vacant bedroom shut up. It just needs a little old German grandma and all her things in there to make it look home-like."

The old woman nodded. "I see. To old German grandmas second sight sometimes Gott gives. You're a goot girl, Hachel."

So old Amalia, always shuttled back and forth, went again to the stone house,—a little old lady who had lived too long, clinging to the flotsam left by the tides of life,— old quilts and scrap-books, albums and tintypes, and a work-box from which the shells were broken.

There is one other thing you will want to know,—did Hazel ever discover that the old grandmother over whom she watched for the short time remaining was the girl of her grandfather's youth? And the answer is yes, she and Neal found it out. Else how could they have pieced together the broken fragments of this story and the strange crossing of paths by their two families?

A certain morning dawned with velvet-pink and lace-lavender and satin-yellow lights in the eastern sky, like so many gay bridesmaids stretching gauzy ribbons for the sun down the aisle of the world. Hazel had been up in time to see this bridal procession of the dawn for there was much work to do.

There was the first feeling of fall in the air. The elms, tawny as lions, lazily dropped a leaf or two. The maples held high their ruby-crowned heads. Over by the creek-bed scarlet-flamed sumac shouldered the silver-green of the willows, and orange-colored bittersweet crept through the tangle of wild plums. Winter wheat was faintly green against the brown of newly plowed earth and the tan of the cornfields. Over all was that haze which clings to the midwest landscape in the autumn,—the soft blue far-away haze which dissipates as one rides into it. It seems always to lie softly over the low rolling hills and the valleys in the fall of the year, this faint ghostly smoke from the Indian camp-fires of long ago.

Hazel, on her way out to the mailbox at the roadside, stopped to look at the picture which lay before her,—the low rolling hills swelled and dipped, black with newly turned earth from the fall plowing, tawny brown with their cornfields, green with the faint shoots of winter wheat.

There was something about the new crispness of the air that was energy-creating. She felt a capacity for

327

turning off work this morning that made her think of a dozen tasks she wanted to do,—clean house, bake, sew. However did some people enjoy being idle? She placed her letters in the box and returned to the house, regretting the fact that she could not stay out here in the open in the crisp early fall air.

Mother Holms was out on the porch of the other house sitting in the morning sun, a knitted lavender jacket around her shoulders. Hazel waved to her and called out some little foolish greeting. At that moment she passed the iron kettle hanging on its two chains and stopped abruptly. Why not try her hand at soap? She had promised herself to experiment with it sometime and what better day than the present one which was so enticing in its call to the out-of-doors?

In anticipation of tackling the job before her, she went into the house and put on an old green turtle-necked sweater, a short brown skirt, and a brown beret which with feminine concern she arranged over her dark red hair as jauntily as though she were to be in the pep chorus on the bleachers. Then she was back in the yard bending over the old iron soap-kettle hanging tipsily on two of its three chains with dirt spilling out from its slanting side, unloosing the snaps, and scraping out the hard clods.

Grandma came to the dining-room door and peered out under a gnarled hand,—old Amalia, short and shrunken and toothless, her little knot of colorless hair twisted as hard as a walnut.

"What be doin', Hachel?" she called in her high, cracked voice.

"I'm going to make soap, Grandma," Hazel said loudly,

and when first the old woman did not understand, repeated it patiently.

"Soap?" old Amalia called back tremulously. "Iss spring comin'?"

"No, Grandma, it's fall."

The old woman came out on the porch then, stepping cautiously, taking careful hold of the pillar to assist herself. For a few moments she stood blinking, adjusting her old eyes to the brightness of the day, the pools of light on the meadow, and the hills beyond. Then her face became all wrinkled eagerness. "I smell spring," she said in her high-pitched voice.

"Do you, Grandma?"

Old Amalia standing there with her head thrown back looked at that moment like a painting by an old master,—as though the girl in Breton's *Song of The Lark* had grown wrinkled and feeble after eighty-six years of listening.

"Iss meadow-larks singin'?" she quavered.

"No, Grandma. It's too late for meadow-larks."

Old Amalia cupped her ear with knotted, trembling fingers, then broke into a toothless smile. "I *hear* meadow-larks singin'."

"Oh, all right, have it your own way," Hazel said to herself. But she knew that old Amalia was hearing only the songs of long-silenced meadow-larks.

At that moment Neal came bounding up from the lower lots, chasing a hog that had worked its grunting way through a broken fence. The young man's strong legs, encased in their puttees, covered the ground with such twinkling speed that Hazel's laughter rang out. "Still after the pig-skin?" she called gaily.

Neal tossed her a grin over his shoulder and shouted back: "Score at the end of the hind quarter is nothing to nothing in favor of the pig." And they both laughed at the foolishness, young untroubled laughter.

"What's he say?" Amalia quavered.

"He says he'll get it all right," Hazel called up to the old woman. It took so little to make her cheerful, such small effort to bring childish joy to her.

The hard clods with their decayed flower roots loosened from the kettle's sides now, Hazel went into the kitchen, emerging in a moment with hot water and a short mop-stick. As she passed Grandma, the old woman piped: "No soap iss made here for many's de long year."

Hazel, who was saying to herself: "I can believe *that*," smiled back at Grandma when she questioned: "Hachel, iss you knowin' the soap-kettle come across country from Illinois wid me?"

"Yes, I know."

As a matter of fact, she knew nothing about it, for it was the first time the old kettle had ever been mentioned since her marriage, but the answer would keep Grandma from prattling on indefinitely. In that hope Hazel was mistaken, however, for old Amalia was not to be squelched with such ease. "Dere's more about de kettle dan you know," she called childishly, nodding her head.

Unheeding, Hazel went on with her preparations. Never having made any soap in her life she went into the venture with gay energy.

And so there was to be soap again in old Amalia's kettle that so many years before had rocked tipsily on its rounded bottom in the covered wagon crossing the creek-

330

beds and the hummocky prairie lands. But how could Hazel know this about the old iron kettle? How could she comprehend the fact that in its varied uses . . . soap . . . hog mash . . . geraniums . . . and soap again . . . it had gone through the whole cycle of the changing economic problems of the midwest? And how could she understand that the fate of both,—the humans in two families and the ugly inanimate black thing at her feet,— had been so inextricably bound together for several generations? That the story, perforce, of the old iron kettle was the story of the people themselves?

So she only scrubbed away at the blackness of the old thing with its dangling chain, knowing that she could make good use of the grease from past butcherings. And old Amalia stood on the porch shading her watery eyes from the hazy fall sunshine, and because she was confused in her mind, kept calling out odd, inconsequential things.

Neal, having performed the difficult task of getting his animated pig-skin across the goal line of the hog-lot, came around the corner of the house then, a hammer in his hand from the task of mending the fence.

A little hammer began to tap in Hazel's heart, too,—a happy little trip-hammer as she watched him come up the path in the morning sunshine. She and Neal, together . . . night and day . . . day and night! A bridal procession across the sky in the morning dawn,—and a bridal procession in Hazel's heart!

"What're you doing, Red-top?" He came up to the scene of activities.

"Making soap, Pig-chaser."

"Well, s'ope springs eternal in the human breast," was his cheerful rejoinder.

And then, suddenly, old Amalia, who lately could never recall a thing that occurred the day before, but who would clutch at and grasp the happenings of long ago, like small bits of floatage from the past, said loudly: "Matthias Meier! Matthias Meier was his name."

Hazel raised her head. "What was that you said, Grandma?"

"Matthias Meier. My kettle for me in Illinois he made." And now Amalia was not old and toothless and wrinkled but young and pink-cheeked with hair the color of cornsilk before the summer sun has seared it. "Come here, Hachel. You want I should tell you somet'ing? Sunday afternoons I slip out and by de soap-kettle in de voods I meet him." She chuckled slyly. "Vile my fader sleeps."

Hazel, standing motionless, stared at the ancient woman. "Neal," she said in so queer a tone of voice that startled, he, too, turned and gazed questioningly at the old woman. "Do you hear what she's saying?"

"Yes . . . but don't pay any attention . . . she's like that a lot lately."

"Neal . . . my grandfather came from Illinois. He worked there in a foundry. He made kettles. And he told me once . . ." her voice was low, tense, every statement crisp with fact, ". . . that he came west because of a broken romance . . . that his first sweetheart married some one else. He said that she was a beautiful girl . . ." she finished in a whisper, ". . . named *Amalia*."

She reached out her hand gropingly to Neal so that he

took it quickly. Without moving, the two stared across at the little old woman, brown as a mummy, clutching the porch pillar and shading her eyes with a bird-claw hand.

Then, although Neal had not the slightest idea what his young wife meant when she said brokenly: "It is better to remember our love as it was in the springtime," he saw the mist of tears in her eyes,—something vaguely sad, too, and infinitely tender in her sensitive face,—so that he slipped his arm about her and drew her close, as though by so doing he could forever keep Love from growing old and shrunken and bleary-eyed.

For a time they were all poised there motionless in one of those unusual moments when ordinary life is brushed by the wings of drama,—the young lovers, an old, old woman and a rusted iron kettle whose history was the history of them all.

But already old Amalia was moving and speaking,—already she had forgotten that which so recently she had remembered.

"Meadow-larks iss singin'," she called out in her high cracked voice, "and I smell spring."

(1)

Contemporary Authors

Contemporary Authors

A BIO-BIBLIOGRAPHICAL GUIDE TO
CURRENT AUTHORS AND THEIR WORKS

ANN EVORY

Editor

volumes 41-44

first revision

GALE RESEARCH COMPANY • BOOK TOWER • DETROIT, MICHIGAN 48226

CONTEMPORARY AUTHORS

Published by
Gale Research Company, Book Tower, Detroit, Michigan 48226
Each Year's Volumes Are Revised About Five Years Later

Frederick G. Ruffner, *Publisher*   James M. Ethridge, *Editorial Director*

Christine Nasso, *General Editor, Contemporary Authors*

Ann Evory, *Editor, Revision Volumes*
Linda Metzger, *Associate Editor*
Peter M. Gareffa, Penelope S. Gordon, Margaret Mazurkiewicz,
Ed McKenna, Catherine Stadelman, Deborah Straub,
and Thomas Wiloch, *Assistant Editors*
Ellen Koral, *Editorial Assistant*

Michaeline Nowinski, *Production Director*

Copyright © 1974, 1979 by
GALE RESEARCH COMPANY

Library of Congress Catalog Card Number 62-52046
ISBN 0-8103-0041-9

Preface

This volume represents a complete revision of bio-bibliographical material which originally appeared in *Contemporary Authors,* Volumes 41-44, published in 1974. The material is up-to-date, in most cases, through early 1979.

Questions and Answers About Revised Volumes
of
Contemporary Authors

How much change is undertaken when past volumes of *Contemporary Authors* are revised? Every part of every sketch is changed, if necessary. Present production techniques provide for fast, economical typesetting of all material used in revised volumes, and no attempt is made to minimize changes.

About 80-85% of all sketches in revised volumes have one or more changes from the original volume. The nature and extent of the revisions can be seen by comparing original listings with revised sketches. Notable people in this volume whose entries have undergone extensive revision include Joseph Brodsky, Julia Child, Bob Dylan, Carl Foreman, Barry Goldwater, Diane Johnson, Stanley Kunitz, Sharon Bell Mathis, Rod McKuen, Joan Adams Mondale, Oral Roberts, Jean Thomas ("Tomi") Ungerer, Alan Wilson Watts, and Jose Yglesias.

How are revised volumes prepared? Clippings of previously published sketches are sent to authors at their last-known addresses. Authors mark material to be deleted or changed, and insert any new personal data, new affiliations, new books, new work in progress, new sidelights, and new biographical/critical sources. Gale makes great efforts to encourage responses from all authors, and has a toll-free telephone number so authors can conveniently reply by phone without personal expense.

How do you revise previously published sketches if the authors do not return marked clippings? First, every attempt is made to reach authors through previous home addresses, business affiliations, publishers, organizations, or other practicable means either by mail or telephone. When necessary, searches are made to determine whether the authors have died. A number of sources are checked for obituaries, including newspaper and magazine indexes.

If living authors fail to reply, or if authors are now deceased, work proceeds on verifying and updating the previously published information. Biographical dictionaries are checked (a task made easier through the use of Gale's *Biographical Dictionaries Master Index* and *Author Biographies Master Index*), as are bibliographical sources, such as *Cumulative Book Index, The National Union Catalog,* etc. In other words, all steps are taken which can reasonably be expected to confirm or invalidate previous information, or to provide additional information. Sketches not personally verified by the authors are marked as follows:

       † Research has yielded new information which has been added to the sketch
     † † Research has yielded no new information

Do all sketches in a revised volume undergo some change? No, they do not. In a sense, however, *all* sketches in a revised volume are "revised" sketches, in that the authors have examined them and indicated that the information they furnished for the previous edition is currently correct, or a revision editor has checked as many facts as possible and made the same determination. Obviously, previously published information which is verified as still accurate is just as helpful to the reference user as information newly added.

How much revision takes place in an average volume? It is difficult to measure. Revised Volumes

1-4, for example, showed a net increase of about 70 pages, and Revised Volumes 5-8 an increase of 200 pages. These increases represented only the *net* change in the number of pages, however; they did not measure the total amount of change, since things like new addresses do not affect sketch length, and deletions of memberships or transfers of items from "Work in Progress" to the bibliography of published works usually result in decreases in space used. Even when a substantial number of sketches were transferred from volumes 9-36 to the *Contemporary Authors—Permanent Series,* the resulting revised volumes were larger than the corresponding original volumes.

What is the *Contemporary Authors—Permanent Series*? The two *Permanent Series* volumes contain entries of deceased authors and authors past normal retirement age who were either known or presumed to be no longer actively writing. These sketches were removed from volumes 9-36 during the revision cycle. Because this practice had unsuspected disadvantages, the *Permanent Series* was discontinued with the publication of Volume 2. Now, all entries appearing in original volumes of *Contemporary Authors* remain in those volumes when they are revised. The *Permanent Series* volumes are, of course, an integral part of the entire *Contemporary Authors* series, and they will be kept in print along with all other volumes.

Can any volumes of *Contemporary Authors* safely be discarded because they are obsolete? Users who have all the revised volumes through 33-36 *and* the two *Permanent Series* volumes can discard the superseded volumes. Beginning with Volumes 37-40, each original volume may be discarded after a corresponding revised volume is published.

An unusual number of biographical publications have been appearing recently, and the question is now often asked whether a charge is made for listings in such publications. Do authors listed in *Contemporary Authors* make any payment or incur any other obligation for their listings? Some publishers charge for listings or require purchase of a book by biographees. There is, however, absolutely no charge or obligation of any kind attached to being included in *CA*.

Cumulative Index Should Always Be Consulted

Since *CA* is a multi-volume series which does not repeat author entries from volume to volume, the cumulative index published in alternate new volumes of *CA* will continue to be the user's guide to the location of an individual author's listing. An "R" after a *CA* volume number designates a revised sketch. For example, authors whose revised sketches appear in this volume are listed in the index with the citation "41-44R" following their names. Authors transferred to the *Contemporary Authors—Permanent Series* are indicated in the cumulative index as having appeared in specific original volumes of *CA* (for the benefit of those who do not hold *Permanent Series* volumes), *and* as having their finally revised sketches listed in a specific *Permanent Series* volume.

For the convenience of *CA* users, the *CA* cumulative index also includes references to all entries in two related Gale series—*Contemporary Literary Criticism,* which is devoted entirely to current criticism of major authors, poets, and playwrights, and *Something About the Author,* a series of heavily illustrated sketches on juvenile authors and illustrators.

As always, suggestions from users about any aspect of *CA* will be welcomed.

CONTEMPORARY AUTHORS

† Research has yielded new information which has been added to the sketch, but the author has not personally verified the entry in this edition.

† † Research has yielded no new information, but the author has not personally verified the entry in this edition.

A

ABBOTT, Sidney 1937-

PERSONAL: Born July 11, 1937, in Washington, D.C.; daughter of Ward Terry (a college professor) and Helen (Lindsay) Abbott. *Education:* Attended Smith College, 1955-59; University of New Mexico, B.A., 1962; Columbia University, M.S., 1970. *Politics:* "Democrat—but depressed at all present choices." *Religion:* Episcopalian. *Home:* 43 Fifth Ave., New York, N.Y. 10003. *Agent:* Anita Diamant, 51 East 42nd St., New York, N.Y. *Office:* Department of Mental Health and Mental Retardation Services, City of New York, 93 Worth St., New York, N.Y. 10013.

CAREER: Employee, Department of Mental Health and Mental Retardation Services, City of New York, New York, N.Y. Founder of Identity House (a homosexual and bisexual counseling center). *Member:* National Organization for Women (founder of national task force on sexuality and lesbianism; member of advisory board of New York chapter).

WRITINGS: (Contributor) Vivian Gornick and Barbara K. Moran, editors, *Woman in Sexist Society: Studies in Power and Powerlessness,* Basic Books, 1971; (with Barbara Love) *Sappho Was a Right-On Woman,* Stein & Day, 1972. Contributor to feminist journals.

WORK IN PROGRESS: A book on social policy in America; research on the renaissance of women in New York and related topics.

SIDELIGHTS: Sidney Abbott has appeared on some forty television and radio shows on which she talked about her life and goals and those of other gay women.

BIOGRAPHICAL/CRITICAL SOURCES: Life, December, 1971.

* * *

ABEL, Ernest L(awrence) 1943-

PERSONAL: Born February 10, 1943, in Toronto, Ontario, Canada; son of Jack (a dressmaker) and Rose (Tarshes) Abel; married Barbara Ellen Buckley (a teacher), September 20, 1971; children: Jason Robert, Rebecca Rosanne. *Education:* University of Toronto, B.A., 1965, M.A., 1967, Ph.D., 1971. *Home:* 106 Ranch Trail W., Williamsville, N.Y. 14221. *Office:* Research Institute on Alcoholism, 1021 Main St., Buffalo, N.Y. 14203.

CAREER: University of North Carolina at Chapel Hill, research associate of drug action program, beginning 1971; Research Institute on Alcoholism, Buffalo, N.Y., currently behavioral teratologist. *Awards, honors:* Research fellowship from Medical Research Council of Canada, 1971-73.

WRITINGS: Ancient Views on the Origins of Life, Fairleigh Dickinson University Press, 1973; *Drugs and Behavior,* Wiley, 1974; *The Roots of Anti-Semitism,* Fairleigh Dickinson University Press, 1975; (editor) *The Scientific Study of Marijuana,* Nelson-Hall, 1975; *Moon Madness,* Fawcett, 1976; *The Handwriting on the Wall,* Greenwood Press, 1977; *A Comprehensive Guide to the Cannabis Literature,* Greenwood Press, in press.

WORK IN PROGRESS: Marijuana: The First Twelve Thousand Years; Comic Bonds; Breast-fed Is Best Fed.

* * *

ABELSON, Robert P(aul) 1928-

PERSONAL: Born September 12, 1928, in New York, N.Y.; son of Miles Arthur (a statistician) and Margaret (Coble) Abelson; married Willa Dinwoodie (a psychologist), June 11, 1955; children: John, William. *Education:* Massachusetts Institute of Technology, B.S., 1948, M.S., 1950; Princeton University, Ph.D., 1953. *Home:* 827 Whitney Ave., New Haven, Conn. 06511. *Office:* Department of Psychology, Yale University, 2 Hillhouse Ave., New Haven, Conn. 06520.

CAREER: Yale University, New Haven, Conn., research assistant, 1952-54, assistant professor, 1954-60, associate professor, 1960-63, professor, 1963-71, Eugene Higgins Professor of Psychology, 1971—. Fellow, Center for the Advanced Study of the Behavioral Sciences, 1957-58, 1965-66. Member of board of directors, Simulmatics Corp., 1963-70. *Member:* American Psychological Association (fellow), American Statistical Association (fellow), American Academy of Arts and Sciences (fellow), Psychometric Society.

WRITINGS: (With Ithiel DeSola Pool and Samuel Popkin) *Candidates, Issues and Strategies: A Computer Simulation of the 1960 Presidential Election,* M.I.T. Press, 1962; (editor with Elliot Aronson, W. J. McGuire, T. M. Newcomb, M. J. Rosenberg, and P. H. Tannenbaum) *Theories of Cognitive Consistency: A Sourcebook,* Rand McNally, 1968; (with Philip Zimbardo) *Canvassing for Peace,* Society for the Psychological Study of Social Issues, 1970; (with Roger Schank) *Scripts, Plans, Goals and Understanding,* Erlbaum, 1977. Contributor to psychology journals. Associate editor, *Journal of Personality and Social Psychology,* 1966-69.

WORK IN PROGRESS: Research on the structure of belief systems.

* * *

ACKERMAN, Edward A. 1911-1973

December 5, 1911—March 8, 1973; American geographer, science administrator, writer, and authority on water resources and environmental systems. Obituaries: *Washington Post,* March 10, 1973; *New York Times,* March 12, 1973.

* * *

ACKLEY, Charles Walton 1913-1975

PERSONAL: Born November 23, 1913, in Dexter City, Ohio; son of George Francis (a coal miner) and Mona Azilda (Tabler) Ackley; married Dorothea Laurine Deyo (a kindergarten teacher), September 2, 1938; children: Sylvia Laurine (Mrs. Richard Pritzos), Mary Melodie (Mrs. David Smart), George Walton. *Education:* Spring Arbor Junior College, A.A., 1934; Seattle Pacific College, A.B. (cum laude), 1936; New York Theological Seminary, S.T.B., 1940; University of Southern California, graduate study, 1946-47, 1950; Harvard University, S.T.M. (cum laude), 1953; Claremont University Center (now Claremont Graduate School), Ph.D. (cum laude), 1968. *Office:* Department of Social Science, California State Polytechnic University, Pomona, Calif. 91768.

CAREER: Clergyman of United Methodist Church; pastor in Syosset, N.Y., 1938-42, and in Wichita, Kan., 1942-43; assistant pastor in Los Angeles, Calif., 1946-47; member of Chaplain Corps, U.S. Navy, 1947-64, retired as lieutenant commander; Los Angeles Pacific College, Los Angeles, Calif., field representative, 1964-65; California State Polytechnic University, Pomona, 1965-75, began as lecturer, became professor of philosophy, 1965; visiting fellow, Mansfield College, Oxford University, 1973. Chairman, United Ministries in Higher Education, 1967-71, 1974-75. *Military service:* U.S. Naval Reserve, 1943-46; served in Pacific and European theatres. *Member:* American Philosophical Association, Alpha Kappa Sigma.

WRITINGS: The Modern Military in American Society: A Study in the Nature of Military Power, Westminster, 1972. Contributor to religious, philosophy, and military journals.

WORK IN PROGRESS: Philosophy of Justice, a textbook.†

(Died, 1975)

* * *

ACKOFF, Russell L(incoln) 1919-

PERSONAL: Born February 12, 1919, in Philadelphia, Pa.; son of Jack (a factory representative) and Fannie (Weitz) Ackoff; married Alexandra Makar, July 17, 1949; children: Alan Walter, Karen Beth, Karla Stephanie. *Education:* University of Pennsylvania, B. Architecture, 1941, Ph.D., 1947. *Office:* Wharton School of Finance and Commerce, University of Pennsylvania, Philadelphia, Pa. 19104.

CAREER: Wayne University (now Wayne State University), Detroit, Mich., assistant professor of philosophy and

mathematics, 1947-51; Case Institute of Technology (now Case Western Reserve University), Cleveland, Ohio, associate professor, 1951-55, professor of operations research, 1955-64; University of Pennsylvania, Wharton School of Finance and Commerce, Philadelphia, professor of statistics and operations research, 1964-71, Daniel H. Silverberg Professor of Systems Sciences, 1971—, chairman of department of statistics and operations research, 1964-66, director of Management Science Center, 1964-67, 1969-70, chairman, Graduate Program in Social Sciences and director of Busch Center. Advisory editor in management sciences, John Wiley & Sons, 1964—. Consultant to National Academy of Sciences, Scientific and Technical Research Council (Turkey), U.S. Bureau of the Census, and to prominent corporations. *Military service:* U.S. Army, 1942-46; became first lieutenant.

MEMBER: Operations Research Society (charter member; former president), Institute of Management Sciences (charter member; former vice-president), American Statistical Association (fellow), Society for General Systems Research, Operational Research Society (Great Britain), Operational Research Society of India, Sigma Xi, Tau Sigma Delta. *Awards, honors:* D.Sc., University of Lancaster, 1967; silver medal from Operational Research Society (Great Britain), 1971.

WRITINGS: (With C. W. Churchman and Murray Wax) *Measurement of Consumer Interest,* University of Pennsylvania Press, 1947; (with Churchman) *Methods of Inquiry,* Educational Publishers, 1950; *The Design of Social Research,* University of Chicago Press, 1953; (contributor) J. F. McCloskey and F. N. Trefethen, editors, *Operations Research for Management,* Johns Hopkins Press, 1954; (contributor) *Case Studies in Operations Research: A Cross Section of Business and Industry,* Case Institute of Technology, 1956; (contributor) J. H. Shera, Allen Kent, and J. W. Perry, editors, *Documentation in Action,* Reinhold, 1956; (with Churchman and E. L. Arnoff) *Introduction to Operations Research,* Wiley, 1957; (contributor) *International Conference on Scientific Information,* National Academy of Science, National Research Council, 1958.

(Contributor) D. P. Eckman, editor, *Systems Research and Design,* Wiley, 1961; (with J. S. Minas and S. K. Gupta) *Scientific Method: Optimizing Applied Research Decision,* Wiley, 1962; (with B.H.P. Rivett) *A Manager's Guide to Operations Research,* Wiley, 1963; (contributor) H. G. Shaller, editor, *Public Expenditure Decisions in the Urban Community,* Resources for the Future, 1963; (contributor) C. R. Rao, editor, *Essays on Econometrics and Planning,* Pergamon, 1964; (contributor) M. C. Youitzetal, editor, *Research Program Effectiveness,* Gordon & Breach, 1966; (contributor) Stuart Mudd, editor, *Conflict Resolution and World Education,* Indiana University Press, 1966; (contributor) J. R. Lawrence, editor, *Operational Research and the Social Sciences,* Tavistock, 1966; (with M. W. Sasieni) *Fundamentals of Operations Research,* Wiley, 1968; (contributor) Anthony de Reuck, Maurice Goldsmith, and others, editors, *Decision Making in National Science Policy,* Little, Brown, 1968; (contributor) *Efficiency of Resource Allocation in Education,* Organization for Economic Cooperation and Development, 1969; (contributor) J. S. Aronofsky, editor, *Progress in Operations Research: Relations between Operations Research and the Computer,* Volume III, Wiley, 1969.

A Concept of Corporate Planning, Wiley, 1970; (contributor) *The Place of Research in Social Choice,* Tavistock Institute of Human Relations, 1970; *The Management of*

Change and How It Changes Management, University of Lancaster, 1970; (with F. E. Emery) *On Purposeful Systems,* Aldine-Atherton, 1972; *Redesigning the Future,* Wiley, 1974. Contributor to *American People's Encyclopedia* and *International Encyclopedia of the Social Sciences;* contributor of more than a hundred scientific articles to professional journals. Book review editor, *Philosophy of Science,* 1947-53; member of abstracting staff, *Biological Abstracts,* 1950-51; associate editor, *Operations Research,* 1953-65; associate editor, *Conflict Resolution,* 1964-70; editor, *Management Science,* 1965-70; member of advisory board, *Mathematical Spectrum,* 1968—; member of editorial board, *Management Decision,* 1968—; editor, *Systems and Management Annual,* 1974—.

WORK IN PROGRESS: On Development Planning, a book on planning for development of less developed nations, regions, and communities.

* * *

ACLAND, James H. 1917-1976

PERSONAL: Born November 6, 1917, in Toronto, Ontario, Canada; son of Edward Headley and Dorothea (Chalmers) Acland; married Virginia Conklin (a university administrator), February 3, 1942; children: Laurence. *Education:* Studied at Ecole des Beaux Arts, Montreal, 1933-35, and McGill University, 1935-37; Syracuse University, B.Arch., 1942; graduate study with Architectural Association, London, 1945; Harvard University, M.A., 1948. *Politics:* New Democratic Party. *Home:* 223 Cottingham St., Toronto, Ontario, Canada M4V IC7. *Office:* Department of Architecture, University of Toronto, Toronto, Ontario, Canada M5S 1A1.

CAREER: Worked on factory designs with firms in Montreal and Quebec City, Quebec, 1940-42; Architectural Association, London, England, design critic, 1945-46; worked on school, university, and hospital designs with firms in Boston, Mass., London, England, and Montreal, Quebec, 1946-49; University of Utah, Salt Lake City, associate professor of architectural design and theory, 1949-53; University of British Columbia, School of Architecture, Vancouver, associate professor of design and planning, 1954-56; University of Toronto, Faculty of Architecture, Urban and Regional Planning, and Landscape Architecture, Toronto, Ontario, associate professor of history of architecture, 1956-76. Visiting associate professor, University of California, Berkeley, 1962; Mathews Lecturer, Columbia University, 1966; Canadian Centennial Lecturer, National Gallery, Ottawa, 1967. Planning consultant, Canadian Inventory of Historic Building, Ottawa, 1969-71. Presented television series on architecture, Canadian Broadcasting Corp., 1962, 1966. *Military service:* Canadian Army, Royal Canadian Engineers, photo interpreter, 1942-45; became captain.

MEMBER: Royal Architectural Institute of Canada, Architectural Association (London), Architectural Conservancy of Ontario (president, 1969-72), Ontario Association of Architects, Friends of Old City Hall (chairman, 1966-73). *Awards, honors:* Ford Foundation fellowship for study in England, France, and Germany, 1953-54; University of Toronto humanities fellowships, 1959, 1964; Canada Council grant, 1962.

WRITINGS: Building by the Sea (photographic study of architecture of maritime provinces), limited edition, University of Toronto Press, 1962; *Medieval Structure: The Gothic Vault,* University of Toronto Press, 1972. Contributor to architectural journals, *Scientific American, Arts Canada,* and Toronto newspapers.

WORK IN PROGRESS: Evolution of the House; Mediterranean Building.†

(Died June 22, 1976)

* * *

ADAMS, Anne H(utchinson) 1935-

PERSONAL: Born August 25, 1935, in Hamilton, Miss.; daughter of James Perry and Lois (Wright) Hutchinson; married Charles Floyd Adams, June 28, 1959 (divorced); children: Charles Floyd, Jr. *Education:* Attended Mississippi State University, 1952-53; Mississippi State College for Women (now Mississippi University for Women), B.S., 1956; Duke University, M.Ed., 1957; University of Mississippi, Ed.D., 1966; University of Georgia, postdoctoral study, 1967-68. *Religion:* Presbyterian. *Home:* 2500 Woodrow St., Durham, N.C. 27705. *Office:* Department of Education, Duke University, Durham, N.C. 27708.

CAREER: Elementary teacher in Atlanta, Ga., 1957-59, Tampa, Fla., 1959-60, Hattiesburg, Miss., 1960-61, and Oxford, Miss., 1961-63; Muscogee County School District, Columbus, Ga., director of education, 1965-67; Leflore County School District, Greenwood, Miss., director of education, 1967-68; University of Mississippi, Oxford, inservice education specialist, 1968, curriculum and research specialist at Special Education Service Center, 1969; University of Texas at Austin, assistant professor of special education and associate director of training, Exemplary Early Childhood Education Centers for Handicapped Children, 1969-71; Duke University, Durham, N.C., associate professor, 1970-73, professor of education, 1973—, director of Reading Center, 1971—, director of Writing Institute and of Leadership Institute on Improvement of Preservice and Inservice Education in Reading and Language Arts, member of advisory board of preschool. Visiting professor at University of Mississippi, 1964, and University of Georgia, 1966. Member of President of the United States Committee on Mental Retardation. Member of national advisory board, J. B. Lippincott Co. and International Book Co. Consultant on special education to universities and school systems in a number of states.

MEMBER: National Education Association, Council for Exceptional Children, International Reading Association, American Association for Higher Education, American Association of University Women, American Association of University Professors, Association of College Professors of Reading (president, 1971-73; member of board of directors, 1973—), Association for Children with Learning Disabilities (member of advisory board of Durham chapter), Pi Gamma Mu, Delta Kappa Pi, Delta Kappa Epsilon, Alpha Delta Kappa, Chi Omega. *Awards, honors:* Outstanding Professor, Duke University, 1971-72.

WRITINGS: (With S. Alan Cohen) *The Random House Reading Program,* Random House, 1969; *Plan Readiness Experience Program* (multi-media), Programmed Learning Aids National, 1970; *The Reading Clinic,* Macmillan, 1970; *Sounds for Me,* Leswing Communications, 1971; *Learning Abilities,* Macmillan, 1972; *Threshold Learning Abilities for Children with Handicaps,* Macmillan, 1972; (author of introduction) Richard Greene, *Forgotten Children: Techniques in Teaching the Mentally Retarded,* Leswing Communications, 1972; *Pre- and Post-Instructional Development Audits: An Evaluation Prototype for Early Education,* Programmed Learning Aids National, 1972; *Prep Progress Audits: An Evaluation Prototype for Early Education,* Programmed Learning Aids National, 1972; *The Clock Struck*

One, Leswing Communications, 1973; (contributor) Philip D. Vairo and Robert J. Knajewski, editors, *Learning and Teaching in the Elementary School,* Scarecrow, 1974; (with Susanne A. Goldberg) *Practical Mathematics Program,* Benefic, Volume I: *Addition,* 1975, Volume II: *Subtraction,* 1976, Volume III: *Multiplication,* 1976, Volume IV: *Division,* 1977; (with Charles R. Coble and Paul B. Hounshell) *Mainstreaming Language Arts and Social Studies,* Goodyear Publishing, 1977; (with Coble and Hounshell) *Mainstreaming Science and Mathematics,* Goodyear Publishing, 1977; *Success in Beginning Reading and Writing: The Basal Concept of the Future,* Goodyear Publishing, 1977; *A Book for Parents and Other Important People,* Leswing Communications, 1977; (with Anne Flowers and Elsa E. Woods) *Reading for Survival in Today's Society,* two volumes, Goodyear Publishing, 1978; (with Judith Connors) *Success in Kindergarten Reading and Writing,* Goodyear Publishing, 1978; (with Helen Cappleman) *Success in Reading and Writing, Grade Two,* Goodyear Publishing, 1978; *Success in Beginning Reading and Writing,* Goodyear Publishing, 1978; *Success in Reading and Writing, Grade Three,* Goodyear Publishing, 1978.

Audio-visual materials; all produced by Educational Communications: "A Look at You," four films and teacher's guide, 1970; "Your Self-Image," 1971; "Are You Listening?," 1971; "Litter, Litter Everywhere," 1971. Other materials include video tapes, audio cassette tapes, transparencies, and spirit duplicator masters. Also author of two skills reinforcement books to accompany *Exploring Lands in the Sea,* Leswing Communications, 1971. Contributor of numerous articles to professional journals. Member of advisory board, *Mini-Page,* Universal Press Syndicate, 1977—; member of editorial advisory board, *Reading Teacher,* 1978—; manuscript consultant to several journals, dictionaries, and books, including *American Educational Research Journal, Webster's New World Dictionary,* and *Helping Students Cope with the Language of Every Subject.*

WORK IN PROGRESS: A first grade evaluation program, for Leswing Communications.

*   *   *

ADAMS, George Worthington   1905-

PERSONAL: Born November 22, 1905, in Jacksonville, Ill.; son of Albyn Lincoln (a surgeon) and Minna (Worthington) Adams; married Mabel Rogers, December 29, 1927; children: Pamela (Mrs. Charles Jarvis Meyers). *Education:* Illinois College, B.A., 1927; Harvard University, M.A., 1928, Ph.D., 1946. *Home:* 904 Taylor Dr., Carbondale, Ill. 62901. *Office:* Department of History, Southern Illinois University, Carbondale, Ill. 62901.

CAREER: Massachusetts Institute of Technology, Cambridge, instructor in English and history, 1928-30; Harvard University and Radcliffe College, Cambridge, Mass., assistant in history, 1930-33; MacMurray College, Jacksonville, Ill., associate professor of history and social sciences, 1933-37, head of department, 1933-37; Lake Forest College, Lake Forest, Ill., associate professor of history, 1937-42, head of department, 1937-42; Harvard University, dean of University Extension and dean of special students, 1945-49, secretary of Graduate School of Arts and Sciences, 1945-49, director of summer school, 1946-49; Colorado College, Colorado Springs, professor of history, 1949-54, academic dean, 1949-54; European director of Salzburg Seminar in American Studies, Salzburg, Austria, 1954-58; Southern Illinois University at Carbondale, professor of history, 1958-61;

University of Alaska, College, academic vice-president, 1961-62; Southern Illinois University at Carbondale, professor of history, 1962-73, professor emeritus, 1973—, head of department, 1958-61, 1962-67. *Military service:* U.S. Naval Reserve, 1942-45; became lieutenant commander. *Member:* American Historical Association, Organization of American Historians, American Association of University Professors, Austro-American Society, Southern Historical Association, Illinois State Historical Society (board member, 1958-61). *Awards, honors:* Huntington Library Research Award, 1967.

WRITINGS: Doctors in Blue: The Medical History of the Union Army in the Civil War, Henry Schuman, 1952; (editor) Mary Logan, *Reminiscences of the Civil War and Reconstruction,* Southern Illinois University Press, 1970.

WORK IN PROGRESS: A study of the National Democratic Party, 1861-77.

*   *   *

ADAMS, James Luther   1901-

PERSONAL: Born November 12, 1901, in Ritzville, Wash.; son of James Carey and Lella May (Barnett) Adams; married Margaret Ann Young, 1927; children: Eloise, Elaine (Mrs. Carroll Edward Miller, Jr.), Barbara (Mrs. Bruce Zachary Kraig). *Education:* University of Minnesota, A.B., 1924; Harvard University, S.T.B., 1927, A.M., 1930; University of Chicago, Ph.D., 1945. *Politics:* Independent. *Home:* 5700 Woodlawn Ave., Chicago, Ill. 60637. *Office:* 5701 Woodlawn Ave., Chicago, Ill. 60637.

CAREER: Unitarian Universalist minister; professor of religious ethics at Meadville Theological School and University of Chicago, Chicago, Ill., 1936-56; Harvard University, Cambridge, Mass., professor of Christian ethics, 1958-68; Andover Newton Theological School, Newton Centre, Mass., Distinguished Professor of Social Ethics, 1968-72; Meadville Theological School, Chicago, Lombard Scholar-in-Residence, 1972-73; University of Chicago, Divinity School, professor of theology and religious ethics, 1972-73. Minister of adult education, Arlington Street Church, Boston, Mass., 1971—. Lecturer, Albert Schweitzer College, 1952, and International Association for the History of Religion (Tokyo), 1958; Fulbright research scholar, University of Marburg, 1962-63.

MEMBER: Society for the Scientific Study of Religion (president, 1957-59), American Society of Christian Ethics (president, 1967-68), American Theological Society (president, 1972-73), Unitarian Universalist Association (chairman of advisory committee, department of social responsibility, 1965-69), Fellowship of Racial and Economic Equality (chairman of the board of directors, 1972—), Americans for Democratic Action (member of board of directors), Center for Applied Ethics (member of board of directors), Association of Voluntary Action Scholars (vice-president, 1971—), Center for a Voluntary Society (member of board of directors), Society for the Arts, Religion, and Contemporary Culture (chairman of board of directors, 1972-73), Societe Europeenne de Culture (member of international council), Americans United for Separation of Church and State (member of advisory board), American Sociological Association, American Civil Liberties Union (member of board of directors of Massachusetts chapter). *Awards, honors:* Noble Lecturer, Harvard University, 1953; D.D., Meadville Theological School, 1958; Theol. D., University of Marburg, 1960; Hibbert Lecturer, England, 1963; fellow, Manchester College, Oxford, 1972—.

WRITINGS: (Translator) Paul Tillich, *The Protestant Era*, University of Chicago Press, 1948; *Taking Time Seriously*, Free Press, 1956; *Paul Tillich's "Philosophy of Culture, Science, and Religion,"* Harper, 1965; (translator) Paul Tillich, *What Is Religion?*, Harper, 1969; (editor with Seward Hiltner) *Pastoral Care in the Liberal Churches*, Abingdon, 1970; (translator) Paul Tillich, *Political Expectation*, Harper, 1971; *On Being Human, Religiously: Selected Essays in Religion and Society*, edited by Max L. Stackhouse, Beacon Press, 1976; (editor with Walter F. Bense) *What Did Luther Understand by Religion?*, Fortress, 1977. Editor, "Phoenix" series, Beacon Press; co-editor, *Journal of Religion;* editor, *Journal of Liberal Religion.* Member of editorial board, *Journal of the Liberal Ministry;* consulting editor, *Colloquy.*

WORK IN PROGRESS: By Their Groups Shall You Know Them, the Hibbert lectures; editing and translating collected essays of Ernst Troeltsch and collected essays of Karl Holl.

BIOGRAPHICAL/CRITICAL SOURCES: Hibbert Journal, 1956; D. B. Robertson, editor, *Voluntary Associations: Essays in Honor of James Luther Adams*, John Knox, 1966; *Perkins Theological Journal*, October, 1972; *Colloquy*, October, 1972; John R. Wilcox, *Taking Time Seriously: James Luther Adams*, University Press of America, 1978.

*   *   *

ADAMS, James R(owe) 1934-

PERSONAL: Born June 30, 1934, in Lincoln, Neb.; son of Charles Forehand (a lawyer) and Grace Gertrude (Rowe) Adams; married Virginia Marie Mann, July 24, 1956; children: Lesley Margaret, Gretchen Gail, Nancy Barbara. *Education:* Attended University of Nebraska, 1951-52; George Washington University, B.A., 1955; Episcopal Theological School, S.T.B., 1958. *Home:* 139 12th St. S.E., Washington, D.C. 20003. *Office:* St. Mark's Episcopal Church, 301 A St. S.E., Washington, D.C. 20003.

CAREER: Boston State Hospital, Boston, Mass., trainee in clinical pastoral training, 1957; ordained Episcopal priest, 1958; curate in Episcopal church in Washington, D.C., 1958-60; rector of Episcopal church in Lanham, Md., 1960-66; St. Mark's Episcopal Church, Washington, D.C., rector, 1966—. Academy of Parish Clergy, vice-president, 1972-73, president, 1973-74; member of board of directors, Inter-Faith Metropolitan Theological Education, Inc., 1970-72; Capitol Hiss Group Ministry, president, 1968, 1969, and member of board of directors. Virginia Theological Seminary, colloquy mentor, 1968-70, supervisor of field education, 1968—. Research fellow, Pastoral Institute, 1963-64; visiting fellow, Episcopal Theological Seminary of the Southwest, 1967; president, United Christian Ministries (Prince George's County, Md.), 1966. Guest lecturer at Virginia Theological Seminary, Episcopal Theological School, and Lutheran Theological Seminary; guest tutor, Salisbury and Wells Theological College (England), 1972. *Member:* American Association of Theological Schools, Washington Episcopal Clergy Association.

WRITINGS: The Sting of Death, Seabury, 1971; (with Celia A. Hahn) *Learning to Share the Ministry*, Alban Institute, 1975; (with Hahn) *A Way to Belong*, Alban Institute, 1979. Contributor to theology and social science journals.

*   *   *

ADAMS, Marion 1932-

PERSONAL: Born January 24, 1932, in Sydney, New South

Wales, Australia; daughter of John and Marion (Lindsay) Heatley; married David Adams (an engineer), April, 1958. *Education:* University of Melbourne, B.A. (honors), 1954, Ph.D., 1967; Harvard University, A.M., 1956. *Home and office:* University of Melbourne, Parkville 3052, Victoria, Australia.

CAREER: High school teacher in Ontario, Canada, 1958-62; University of Melbourne, Parkville, Victoria, Australia, part-time tutor, 1964-65, senior tutor, 1965-71, principal tutor, 1971-74, lecturer, 1974-75, senior lecturer in German, 1975—. *Member:* Internationale Vereinigung fuer germanische Sprachund Literaturwissenschaft, Australian Universities Language and Literature Association, Goethe Society (Australia).

WRITINGS: Gottfried Benn's Critique of Substance, Van Gorcum, 1969; (editor) *The German Tradition: Aspects of Art and Thought in the German-Speaking Countries*, Wiley, 1971; (editor with Inge Kirchhoff) *Zeitgeschehen: 1900-1970 in Deutschsprachiger Literatur*, Harrap, 1975. Editor, *Babel*, 1966-72.

WORK IN PROGRESS: Writing *German Expressionist Authors.*

AVOCATIONAL INTERESTS: European art of all periods.

*   *   *

ADAMS, Sally Pepper d. 197(?)

PERSONAL: Born in Philadelphia, Pa.; daughter of Harry Crowell (a lawyer) and Elizabeth (Hughes) Pepper; married Max Peter Haas, September 26, 1942 (divorced, 1959); married Wayne D. Adams (a public relations consultant), May 6, 1959; children: (first marriage) Peter Wayne, Bruce Davidson. *Education:* Attended Western Reserve University (now Case Western Reserve University), 1932-33; University of Pennsylvania, A.B. (honors), 1935; Pratt Institute, B.S. (honors), 1951.

CAREER: John C. Winston Co., Philadelphia, Pa., textbook editor, 1935-37; *Friday*, New York City, photo editor, 1940-41; *P.M.* (later *New York Star*), New York City, photo assignment editor and photo manager, 1942-47; *Family Circle*, New York City, associate food editor, 1951-55, home equipment editor, 1955-71. Active in local liberal political party. *Member:* American Home Economics Association, Electrical Women's Round Table, Home Economists in Business, American Institute of Interior Designers, National Home Fashions League, Silurians.

WRITINGS—All published by Family Circle, except as indicated: (Contributor) *New Standard Dictionary of Folklore*, Funk, 1949; *The Cake and Cookie Cookbook*, 1953; *The Dessert and Fruit Cookbook*, 1954; *The Meat Cookbook*, 1955; *The Fish and Poultry Cookbook*, 1955. Regular contributor of articles to *Family Circle.*

WORK IN PROGRESS: Juvenile folk tale collections; writing for an appliance manufacturer.†

(Deceased)

*   *   *

ADELMAN, Clifford 1942-

PERSONAL: Born September 29, 1942, in Boston, Mass.; son of Samuel Myron (a salesman) and Estaire (Weissman) Adelman; married Nancy E. Kilpatrick (a teacher), December 27, 1965; children: Jonathan Blake, Nicholas Benjamin. *Education:* Brown University, A.B., 1964; University of Chicago, M.A., 1965, Ph.D., 1976. *Politics:* Reform Social Democrat. *Home and office:* 235 Lakeview Ave., Ringwood, N.J. 07456. *Agent:* Scott Meredith Literary Agency, Inc., 845 Third Ave., New York, N.Y. 10022.

CAREER: Worked as a govenment bureaucrat, carpenter, production line worker, manager, political campaign writer, and educational consultant. City College of the City University of New York, New York, N.Y., instructor in English, 1968-71; Yale University, New Haven, Conn., visiting lecturer, 1972-73; William Patterson College of New Jersey, Wayne, assistant dean, 1974-76, associate dean, 1976—.

WRITINGS: Generations: A Collage on Youthcult, Praeger, 1972; *No Loaves, No Parables: Liberal Politics and the American Language*, Harper Magazine Press, 1974. Contributor of articles to *Village Voice, New York Times, San Francisco Book Review, Cambridge Review, Chicago Review*, and others.

WORK IN PROGRESS: Saving the Baby: The New Reform of General Education, for Harper; *Coleridge's Great Chain of Meaning*.

*   *   *

ADOFF, Arnold 1935-

PERSONAL: Born July 16, 1935, in New York, N.Y.; son of Aaron Jacob (a pharmacist) and Rebecca (Stein) Adoff; married Virginia Hamilton (a writer), March 19, 1960; children: Leigh (daughter), Jaime (son). *Education:* City College of New York (now City College of the City University of New York), B.A., 1956; Columbia University, further study, 1956-58; New School for Social Research, poetry workshops, 1965-67. *Politics:* "Committed to change for full freedom for all Americans." *Religion:* "Freethinking Pragmatist." *Office address:* Arnold Adoff Agency, P.O. Box 293, Yellow Springs, Ohio 45387.

CAREER: Board of Education, New York, N.Y., teacher in Harlem and upper west side of Manhattan, 1957-69, teaching in most subject areas in most grades, with the latter years spent in working with teenagers with reading difficulties ("it was a great time with great kids"); Arnold Adoff Agency, Yellow Springs, Ohio, literary agent, 1977—. Instructor in federal projects at New York University, Connecticut College, and other institutions. Lecturer at colleges throughout the country; consultant in children's literature, poetry, and creative writing. Member of Planning Commission, Yellow Springs; "general agitator" for full equality in education, jobs, housing. *Military service:* New York National Guard. *Awards, honors:* American Library Association Notable Book awards, 1968, for *I Am the Darker Brother*, 1970, for *Black Out Loud* and *Malcolm X*, 1971, for *MA nDA LA*, 1972, for *The Poetry of Black America*, and 1979, for *Celebrations*.

WRITINGS—Juvenile: Malcolm X, Crowell, 1970; *MA nDA LA* (picture book; illustrated by Emily McCully), Harper, 1971; *Black Is Brown Is Tan* (poetry; illustrated by McCully), Harper, 1973; *Make a Circle Keep Us In: Poems for a Good Day*, Delacorte, 1975; *Big Sister Tells Me That I'm Black* (poetry), Holt, 1976; *Tornado! Poems*, Delacorte, 1977; *Under the Early Morning Trees* (poetry; illustrated by Himler), Dutton, 1978; *Where Wild Willie* (poetry), Harper, 1978; *Eats: Poems*, Lothrop, 1979; *I Am the Running Girl* (poetry; illustrated by Himler), Harper, 1979.

Editor; anthologies for young adults and adults, except as noted: *I Am the Darker Brother: An Anthology of Modern Poems by Negro Americans*, Macmillan, 1968; *Black on Black: Commentaries by Negro Americans*, Macmillan, 1968; *City in All Directions: An Anthology of Modern Poems*, Macmillan, 1969; *Black Out Loud: An Anthology of Modern Poems by Black Americans* (juvenile), Macmillan, 1970; *Brothers and Sisters: Modern Stories by Black Americans*, Macmillan, 1970; *It Is the Poem Singing into Your Eyes: An Anthology of New Young Poets*, Harper, 1971; *The Poetry of Black America: An Anthology of the 20th Century*, Harper, 1973; *My Black Me: A Beginning Book of Black Poetry* (juvenile), Dutton, 1974; *Celebrations: A New Anthology of Black American Poetry*, Follett, 1978.

Contributor of articles and reviews to periodicals.

WORK IN PROGRESS: Poetry; picture books; anthology of women's poetry; anthology of American Indian poetry.

BIOGRAPHICAL/CRITICAL SOURCES: Horn Book, April, 1970, June, 1970, February, 1972, December, 1972; *Publishers' Weekly*, July 13, 1970; *New York Times Book Review*, January 23, 1972; *Top of the News*, January, 1972.

*   *   *

ADORJAN, Carol (Madden) 1934-

PERSONAL: Surname is pronounced A-*dor*-ian; born August 17, 1934, in Chicago, Ill.; daughter of Roland Aloysius (a salesman) and Marie (Toomey) Madden; married William W. Adorjan (an industrial representative), August 17, 1957; children: Elizabeth Marie, John Martin and Katherine Therese (twins), Matthew Christian. *Education:* Mundelein College, B.A. (magna cum laude), 1956.

CAREER: High school English teacher, St. Scholastica High School, Chicago, Ill., 1956-59. Corresponding secretary, Off Campus Writers' Workshop, 1967-69. *Awards, honors:* Josephine Lusk Prize from Mundelein College, 1956, for short story, "Coin of Decision"; first prize from *Earplay 1972*, University of Wisconsin, for "The Telephone"; Midwest Professional Playwrights fellowship, 1977; Illinois Arts Council completion grant, 1977-78; first prize, Dubuque Fine Arts Society's National One-Act Playwriting Contest, 1978.

WRITINGS—Juveniles: Someone I Know, Random House, 1968; *Jonathan Bloom's Room*, J. Philip O'Hara, 1972; (contributor) N. Gretchen Greiner, editor, *Like It Is*, Broadman, 1972; *The Cat Sitter Mystery*, J. Philip O'Hara, 1976. Author of radio plays including "The Telephone," "Friends," "A Safe Place," All Things Even Frisky," and "The Outcasts of Poker Flat." Contributor of short stories and articles to national magazines, including *Today, Woman's Day, North American Review, American Girl, Ingenue*, and *Redbook*, and to newspapers.

WORK IN PROGRESS: A full length and one-act play; short stories.

SIDELIGHTS: Carol Adorjan told *CA:* "I have been writing for as long as I can remember. It was only about ten years ago, however, that I began to think of myself as 'a writer' rather than as 'someone who wrote.' Once I realized that writing defined who I am and not merely what I do, commitment followed. Now I perceive writing as both art and business, and I spend time and energy on both aspects." Adorjan continues: "I am interested in reality and illusion as they affect our individual lives and our relationships with others. My themes grow out of this concern. My continuing goal is to treat my material with compassion and humor."

AVOCATIONAL INTERESTS: Photography.

AGASSI, Joseph 1927-

PERSONAL: Born May 5, 1927, in Jerusalem; son of Samuel M. and Fruma (Reichmann) Birnbaum; married Judith Buber (a university teacher), 1948; children: Tirzah, Aaron. *Education:* Hebrew University, Jerusalem, M.Sc., 1951; University of London, Ph.D., 1956. *Religion:* Jewish. *Home:* 18 Clark Lane, Sudbury, Mass. 01776; and 161, Hakedmah St., Herzlia, Israel. *Office:* Department of Philosophy, Boston University, Boston, Mass. 02215; and Tel Aviv University, Tel Aviv, Israel.

CAREER: University of London, London School of Economics and Political Science, London, England, lecturer in philosophy, 1957-60; Hong Kong University, Hong Kong, reader in philosophy and head of department, 1960-63; University of Illinois at Urbana-Champaign, associate professor of philosophy, 1963-65; Boston University, Boston, Mass., professor of philosophy, 1965—; Tel Aviv University, Tel Aviv, Israel, professor of philosophy, 1971—. Research associate, Center for Advanced Study in the Behavioral Sciences, 1956-57. *Military service:* Israeli Defense Army, parachutist, 1948-49. *Member:* American Philosophical Association, Philosophy of Science Association, American Association of University Professors.

WRITINGS: Towards an Historiography of Science, Mouton, 1963; *The Continuing Revolution,* McGraw, 1969; (editor with I. C. Jarvie) *Hong Kong: A Society in Transition,* Praeger, 1969; *Faraday as a Natural Philosopher,* Chicago University Press, 1971; *Science in Flux,* D. Reidel, 1975; (with Y. Fried) *Paranoia: A Study in Diagnosis,* D. Reidel, 1976; *Towards a Rational Philosophical Anthropology,* Nijhoff, 1977. Also editor with Jarvie, *Selected Papers of Ernest Gellner,* Routledge & Kegan Paul. Contributor of about a hundred articles to philosophy journals. Consulting editor, *Philosophical Forum,* 1968, and *Studies in the History and Philosophy of Science,* 1970.

WORK IN PROGRESS: The Sociology of Science: A Collection of Essays; Radiation Theory: The Background to Quantum Theory; Academic Agonies and How to Avoid Them; Advice to Young People on Their Way to Academic Careers.

BIOGRAPHICAL/CRITICAL SOURCES: Best Sellers, February 1, 1969.

* * *

AGINSKY, Ethel G(oldberg) 1910-

PERSONAL: Born September 24, 1910, in Scranton, Pa.; daughter of Aaron D. (a wholesale jobber) and Miriam (Sperling) Goldberg; married Bernard W. Aginsky (an anthropologist5, April 7, 1929. *Education:* New York University, B.A., 1932; Columbia University, M.A., 1933, Ph.D., 1935. *Religion:* Jewish. *Office:* Institute for World Understanding of Peoples, Cultures and Languages, 939 Coast Blvd., La Jolla, Calif. 92037.

CAREER: Columbia University, New York City, research associate in linguistics, 1934-36, 1938-39; Hunter College of the City University of New York, New York City, instructor, 1939-47, assistant professor, 1948-53, associate professor, 1953-61, professor of anthropology, 1961-65; Institute for World Understanding of Peoples, Cultures and Languages, La Jolla, Calif., associate director, 1965—. Associate director of social science field laboratory, New York University, summers, 1939-41; associate professor, Maxwell Graduate School of Citizenship, Syracuse University, 1947-48; visiting professor of anthropology, University of Buenos Aires, 1958. Supervisor of study of diet and nutrition, National Committee on Nutrition, 1940. Has conducted field work in North China, South America, the Caribbean, and Europe; has studied California Indians, Puyallup Indians, the Mende, and the Dolphins. Consultant on Japan and Burma, 1942-45.

MEMBER: American Anthropological Association (fellow; member of council, 1947—), American Ethnological Society, American Association for the Advancement of Science (fellow), American Association of University Professors, International Linguistic Association, New York Academy of Science (fellow), Linguistic Circle of New York (member of executive board, 1948-49). *Awards, honors:* Social Science Research Council grant for field work on Mende, 1933, grant for field work on Puyallup and Chehalis, 1936; Institute for Pacific Relations grant, 1939; Viking Fund grants from Wenner-Gren Foundation, for field research on Pomo Indians 1947, 1948, 1949; Research Institute for the Study of Man grant for research on language and culture of the Dolphins, 1964-65.

WRITINGS: (With husband, Bernard W. Aginsky) *Selected Papers of B. W. and E. G. Aginsky,* privately printed, 1955; (with B. W. Aginsky) *Deep Valley: A Presentation of the Pomo Indians,* Stein & Day, 1967. Contributors of many articles to linguistic, anthropology, and social science journals.

WORK IN PROGRESS: Anthropotentialism.

* * *

AHERN, James F. 1932-

PERSONAL: Born January 24, 1932, in New Haven, Conn.; son of James Patrick and Mary (Walsh) Ahern; married Janet Wyatt, February 14, 1952; children: Susan Eileen, Mary Elizabeth. *Education:* Attended St. Thomas Seminary, Bloomfield, Conn., 1949-50, and Gonzaga University, 1950-52; New Haven College (now University of New Haven), A.A., 1962, B.B.A., 1964. *Politics:* Democrat. *Religion:* Roman Catholic. *Home:* 223 Canner St., New Haven, Conn. 06511. *Office:* Insurance Crime Prevention Institute, 15 Franklin St., Westport, Conn. 06880.

CAREER: Department of Police Service, New Haven, Conn., patrolman in traffic and patrol divisions, 1954-62, sergeant and assistant to commander of traffic division, 1962-67, lieutenant, 1967-68, chief of police, 1968-71; Insurance Crime Prevention Institute, Westport, Conn., director, 1971—. Lecturer, Yale University. Member, Presidential Commission on Campus Unrest (Scranton Commission), 1970; consultant, Knapp Commission (investigated charges of corruption in New York City Police Department); member, Connecticut Governor's Planning Committee on Criminal Administration, 1968-71; volunteer executive director, Institute for Effective Criminal Justice. Assistant director, Police Relations Planning Study Committee (funded by U.S. Department of Justice), 1967; member of board of directors, Lower East Side Action Project, 1971—; consultant to U.S. Department of Labor, U.S. Department of Justice, Ford Foundation, University Research Corp., and other organizations. Member of Democratic National Policy Council, 1971-72, and Security Advisory Committee of the Democratic National Committee, 1972. *Member:* International Association of Chiefs of Police.

WRITINGS: Police in Trouble: Our Frightening Crisis in Law Enforcement, foreword by John V. Lindsay, Hawthorn, 1972.

AISTIS, Jonas 1908(?)-1973

1908(?)—June 13, 1973; Lithuanian-born American poet and essayist. Obituaries: *New York Times,* June 15, 1973.

* * *

AITKEN, W(illiam) R(ussell) 1913-
(Stuart Scott)

PERSONAL: Born February 7, 1913, in Calderbank, Lanarkshire, Scotland; son of David Macrae (a minister) and Mary Parlane (Baird) Aitken; married Betsy Mary Murison, September 7, 1939; children: Christine (Mrs. Robin John Davis). *Education:* University of Edinburgh, M.A., 1935, Ph.D., 1956. *Religion:* Society of Friends (Quakers). *Home:* 6 Tannahill Ter., Dunblane FK15 OAX, Perthshire, Scotland. *Office:* Department of Librarianship, University of Strathclyde, Glasgow G1 1XH, Scotland.

CAREER: Clackmannan County Library, Alloa, Scotland, librarian, 1946-49; Perth and Kinross County Library, Perth, Scotland, librarian, 1949-58; Ayr County Library, Ayr, Scotland, librarian, 1958-62; University of Strathclyde, Glasgow, Scotland, 1962—, began as senior lecturer, currently reader in bibl ographical studies. Visiting professor at University of Western Ontario, 1971. *Military service:* Royal Air Force, 1941-46. *Member:* Library Association (fellow), Scottish Library Association (president, 1965), Association for Scottish Literary Studies.

WRITINGS: (Editor) William Soutar, *Poems in Scots and English,* Oliver & Boyd, 1961, 2nd edition, Scottish Academic Press, 1975; (contributor) K. D. Duval and S. G. Smith, editors, *Hugh MacDiarmid: A Festschrift,* K. D. Duval (Scotland), 1962; *A History of the Public Library Movement in Scotland to 1955,* Scottish Library Association, 1971; (contributor) D. Glen, editor, *Hugh Mac-Diarmid: A Critical Survey,* Scottish Academic Press, 1972; (contributor) Alexander Scott and Douglas Gifford, editors, *Neil M. Gunn: The Man and the Writer,* Blackwood, 1973. Contributor to *Cassell's Encyclopaedia of World Literature* and *Encyclopedia of Library and Information Science.* Contributor of check lists of modern Scottish writers to *Bibliotheck* and other publications. Author of book reviews under pseudonym Stuart Scott. Editor of *Library Review,* 1964-77.

WORK IN PROGRESS: A book, *Scottish Literature in English,* for Gale.

BIOGRAPHICAL/CRITICAL SOURCES: Scottish Library Association News, January/February, 1965.

* * *

AKER, George F(rederick) 1927-

PERSONAL: Born June 2, 1927, in Fort Wayne, Ind.; son of George Mosier (an automotive engineer) and Vera (Marten) Aker; married Patricia Lou Lawson, November 16, 1946; children: Linda Lou (Mrs. Michael Midkiff), Kathy Ann (Mrs. John Ackelson), Jon Kent, Susan Nanette. *Education:* Purdue University, B.S. (with highest distinction), 1950; University of Wisconsin, M.S., 1958, Ph.D., 1962; University of Chicago, graduate study, 1958-59. *Home:* 3333 Lakeshore Dr., Tallahassee, Fla. 32303. *Office:* Department of Educational Management, Florida State University, Tallahassee, Fla. 32306.

CAREER: University of Missouri—Columbia, instructor in biochemistry, 1950-51; Purdue University, Lafayette, Ind., extension agent in rural development, 1951-57, extension agent in urban development, 1958-59; University of Chicago, Chicago, Ill., assistant professor of education and director of research on continuing education, 1962-63; Florida State University, Tallahassee, associate professor, 1963-66, professor of adult education and head of department, 1966—. Chairman, National Institute for Adult Education Research, 1967-68; member of board of directors, Multi-Racial Corp., 1968—; chairman of board of directors, Action Research Corp., 1970; adviser, President's Council on Adult Education; member of Joint Commission on Training of Correctional Manpower. Member of Tallahassee Community Educational Television Council; volunteer teacher for Churchwomen United; consultant to National Corporation for Public Broadcasting. *Military service:* U.S. Naval Reserve, active duty, 1945-47. U.S. Army Reserve, 1947-50.

MEMBER: Adult Education Association (president, 1969-70), Association of Public Continuing Adult Education (member of board of directors, 1963-70), National Association of Community Schools, American Educational Research Association, American Vocational Research Association, National University Extension Association, Smithsonian Institute, Venezuelan National Association for Adult Education (honorary president), Phi Delta Kappa. *Awards, honors:* Citation of outstanding service, Florida Law Enforcement Academy.

WRITINGS: (Editor) *Adult Education Procedures: Methods and Techniques: A Classified and Annotated Bibliography, 1953-63,* Syracuse University Press, 1965; *Public School Adult Education Almanac,* National Association of Public School Adult Educators, 1967; (with Irwin R. Jahns and Wayne L. Schroeder) *Evaluation of an Adult Basic Education Program in a Southern Rural Community,* Florida State University Press, 1968; (contributor) Nathan C. Shaw, editor, *Administration of Continuing Education,* National Association of Public School Adult Educators, 1969; (editor with Robert Smith and R. J. Kidd) *1970 Handbook of Adult Education,* Macmillan, 1970; (editor with others) *Materials and Methods in Adult Education,* Klevins Publishing, 1972. Contributor to *Dictionary of Education.* Author of "Lifelong Learning," a television series, and "Community Development," a radio series, and a career opportunity film; also author of a column appearing in *Adult Leadership.* Contributor to social science research journals. Editor, *Adult Education.*

WORK IN PROGRESS: Developing educational technologies for older persons; studying factors associated with motivation and achievement among low income, disadvantaged adults; designing new systems for coordination with community services.

* * *

ALEXANDER, David 1907-1973

April 21, 1907—March 21, 1973; American horse-racing and mystery writer. Obituaries: *New York Times,* March 23, 1973; *Washington Post,* March 24, 1973. (See index for *CA* sketch)

* * *

ALEXANDER, Herbert E(phraim) 1927-

PERSONAL: Born December 21, 1927, in Waterbury, Conn.; son of Nathan and Pearl (Shub) Alexander; married Nancy Greenfield, December 5, 1953; children: Michael, Andrew, Kenneth. *Education:* University of North Carolina, B.S., 1949; University of Connecticut, M.A., 1951; Yale University, Ph.D., 1958. *Politics:* Independent. *Reli-*

gion: Jewish. *Home:* 152 Clover Lane, Princeton, N.J. 08540. *Office:* Citizens' Research Foundation, 245 Nassau St., Princeton, N.J. 08540.

CAREER: University of North Carolina at Chapel Hill, Institute for Research in Social Science, administrative assistant in political finance, 1954-55; Princeton University, Princeton, N.J., instructor, 1956-58; Citizens' Research Foundation, Princeton, director, 1958—. Visiting lecturer, Princeton University, 1965-66, Wharton School, University of Pennsylvania, 1967-68. Executive director of Presidential Commission on Campaign Costs, 1961-62; consultant to U.S. President, 1962-64, Twentieth Century Fund, 1969-70, U.S. Comptroller General, 1972—, and Office of Federal Elections. *Military service:* U.S. Army, 1946-47. *Member:* International Political Science Association, American Political Science Association, American Association of Political Consultants.

WRITINGS—All published by Citizens' Research Foundation, except as indicated: *Money, Politics, and Public Reporting,* 1960; *Tax Incentives for Political Contributions,* 1961; (contributor) Paul T. David, editor, *The Presidential Election and Transition: 1960-1961,* Brookings Institution, 1961; *Financing the 1960 Election,* 1962; (editor) *Money for Politics: A Miscellany of Ideas,* 1963; *Responsibility in Party Finance,* 1963; (editor) *Studies in Money in Politics,* Volume I, 1965, Volume II, 1970; *Financing the 1964 Election,* 1966; (with Laura L. Denny) *Regulation of Political Finance,* Institute of Governmental Studies, University of California, Berkeley, 1966; (contributor) M. Kent Jennings and L. Harmon Zeigler, editors, *The Electoral Process,* Prentice-Hall, 1966; (contributor) Demetrios Caraley, editor, *Party Politics and National Elections,* Little, Brown, 1966; (with John F. Bibby) *The Politics of National Convention Finances and Arrangements,* 1968; (contributor) Bernard Cosman and Robert H. Huckshorn, editors, *Republican Politics: The 1964 Campaign and Its Aftermath for the Party,* Praeger, 1968; (contributor) Cornelius P. Cotter, editor, *Practical Politics in the United States,* Allyn & Bacon, 1969.

(With Kevin L. McKeough) *Financing Campaigns for Governor: New Jersey, 1965,* 1970; *Campaign Expenditures in Virginia,* Tayloe Murphy Institute, University of Virginia, 1970; (contributor) Arnold J. Keidenheimer, editor, *Comparative Political Finance,* Heath, 1970; (contributor) Arthur Schlesinger, Jr., editor, *History of American Presidential Elections,* Chelsea House, 1970; *A Survey of State Statutes Regulating Political Finance,* 1971; (editor with Caroline D. Jones) *Political Contributors of Five Hundred Dollars or More in 1968,* 1971; (editor with Jones) *Political Contributors of Five Hundred Dollars or More in 1969,* 1971; (editor with Jones) *Contributions of National-Level Political Committees to Incumbents and Candidates for Public Offices, 1968,* 1971; (editor with Jones) *Contributions of National-Level Political Committees to Incumbents and Candidates for Public Offices, 1969,* 1971; *Financing the 1968 Election,* Heath, 1971; *Money in Politics,* Public Affairs Press, 1972; (editor with Katharine C. Fischer) *Political Contributors of Five Hundred Dollars or More in 1970,* 1973; (editor with Jones) *Contributions of National-Level Political Committees to Incumbents and Candidates for Public Offices, 1970,* 1973; (editor with Jones) *Political Contributors of Five Hundred Dollars or More in 1971 and January-February, 1972,* 1973; (editor with Jones) *Contributions of National-Level Political Committees to Incumbents and Candidates for Public Offices, 1971 and January-February, 1972,* 1973; *Political Financing,* Burgess, 1973.

(With J. Paul Malloy) *Model State Statute: Politics, Elections, and Public Office,* 1974; (editor) *Political Contributions of Five Hundred Dollars or More in 1972 to Candidates and Committees in Twelve States,* 1974; *Financing Politics: Money, Elections and Political Reform,* Congressional Quarterly, 1976; *Campaign Money: Reform and Reality in the States,* Free Press, 1976; (editor with Richard D. Lambert) *Political Finance: Reform and Reality,* American Academy of Political and Social Science, 1976; (with others) *Financing the 1972 Election,* Lexington Books, 1976; (contributor) Judith H. Parris, editor, *The Costs of Conventions and How They Are Met,* Center for Information on America, 1976.

Contributor to *Encyclopaedia Britannica* and *Grolier's Encyclopedia.* Contributor to professional journals, including *National Civic Review, Fortune, Television Quarterly, Educational Television,* and *Law and Contemporary Problems.*

WORK IN PROGRESS: Further writing and research on political finance.†

* * *

ALEXANDRE, Philippe 1932-

PERSONAL: Born March 14, 1932, in Paris, France; son of Robert and Jeannine (De George) Alexandre; married Celina Cattan, July 26, 1966; children: Nathalie, Agnes. *Education:* Attended secondary school and British Institute, Paris, France. *Home:* 5 Passage Olivier de Serres, Paris 75015, France. *Office:* RTL, 22 rue Bayard, Paris 75008, France.

CAREER: *L'Oise Liberee,* Beauvais, France, editorial secretary, 1957-60; *Jours de France,* Paris, France, editor, 1960-62; *Le Nouveau Candide,* Paris, chief reporter, 1962-65; *Vingt Quatre Heures,* Paris, editor-in-chief, 1965-66; *Le Figaro Litteraire,* Paris, editor, 1968-70; RTL, Paris, editorial writer, 1970—. *Military service:* Served in Algeria, 1956.

WRITINGS: *Gaston Deffere,* Solar, 1963; *Le president est mort,* Solar, 1965, translation by Robert Baldick published as *The President Is Dead,* Hutchinson, 1966; *L'Elysee en Peril,* Fayard, 1969; *Chronique des jours moroses,* Solar, 1971; *Le duel de Gaulle Pompidou,* Grasset, 1970, translation by Elaine P. Halperin published as *The Duel: De Gaulle and Pompidou,* Houghton, 1972; *Execution d'un homme politique,* Grasset, 1972; *Le roman de la gauche,* Plon, 1977.

* * *

ALFORD, Robert R(oss) 1928-

PERSONAL: Born April 18, 1928, in Stockton, Calif.; married, 1949; children: three. *Education:* University of California, Berkeley, A.B., 1950, M.A., 1952, Ph.D., 1961. *Office:* Board of Studies in Sociology, University of California, Santa Cruz, Calif. 95064.

CAREER: University of California, Berkeley, lecturer in sociology, 1959-61; University of Wisconsin—Madison, assistant professor, 1961-63, associate professor, 1963-66, professor of sociology, 1966-74, associate director of Wisconsin Survey Research Laboratory, 1961-63, member of research staff, Institute for Research on Poverty, 1968-70, director of Social Organization Training Program, 1971-74; University of California, Santa Cruz, professor of sociology, 1974—, director of Interdisciplinary Graduate Program in Sociology, 1974-78. Visiting professor at University of Essex, 1966-67, and Columbia University, 1970-71; senior research associate, Center for Policy Research, New York, N.Y., 1970-71. Member of executive committee, Council of Social Science Data Archives, 1967-70. *Member:* International Sociological Association, American Sociological Association, American Political Science Association, American Federation of Teachers, Law and Society Association. *Awards, honors:* Russell Sage Foundation fellow in sociology and law, 1963-68; received honorable mention, C. Wright Mills Award, 1976.

WRITINGS: Party and Society: The Anglo-American Democracies, Rand McNally, 1963; (with Harry M. Scoble) *Bureaucracy and Participation: Political Cultures in Four Wisconsin Cities,* Rand McNally, 1969; *Health Care Politics: Ideological and Interest Group Barriers to Reform,* University of Chicago Press, 1975; (editor with Colin Crough and Claus Offe) *Stress and Contradiction in Modern Capitalism: Public Policy and the Theory of the State,* Lexington Books, 1975.

Contributor: John Meisel, editor, *Papers on the 1962 Canadian General Election,* University of Toronto, 1964; S. M. Lipset and Stein Rokkan, editor, *Party Systems and Voter Alignments: An Approach to Comparative Politics,* Free Press, 1967; Henry Fagin and Leo F. Schnore, editors, *Urban Research and Policy Planning,* Sage Publications, Inc., 1967; Frank Lindenfeld, editor, *Readings in Political Sociology,* Funk, 1968; Robert T. Daland, editor, *Comparative Urban Research: The Administration and Politics of Cities,* Sage Publications, Inc., 1969; Brian J. L. Berry, editor, *City Classification Handbook: Methods and Applications,* Wiley, 1972. Contributor of about thirty articles to education, sociology, public opinion, political science, public administration, and urban affairs journals, and to *New Atlantis.* Member of editorial advisory boards, *Law and Society Review, British Journal of Political Science, American Behavioral Scientist, Comparative Urban Research, International Journal of Health Services, Journal of Health Politics, Policy and Law, International Journal of Urban and Regional Research,* and *American Politics Quarterly.*

WORK IN PROGRESS: With Roger Friedland, *Political Sociology.*

*   *   *

ALLAIRE, Joseph L(eo)   1929-

PERSONAL: Born February 23, 1929, in Detroit, Mich.; son of Leonel Joseph (a production worker) and Stella Marie (Latour) Allaire; married Andrea Woodruff Jensen, June 19, 1974; children: Joseph L., Jr. (adopted). *Education:* Attended Sacred Heart Seminary, Detroit, Mich., 1947-50; University of Detroit, A.B., 1952; Wayne State University, M.A., 1958, Ph.D., 1966. *Politics:* Independent. *Religion:* Roman Catholic. *Home:* 1004 Shalimar, Tallahassee, Fla. 32312. *Office:* Department of Modern Languages, Florida State University, Tallahassee, Fla. 32306.

CAREER: Hi-Park Electric, Detroit, Mich., electrical apprentice, 1950; Ano-Color Engineers, Detroit, laboratory technician, 1950; high school French teacher in Detroit, 1952, teacher of French, Latin, and Spanish, 1953-66; Wayne State University, Detroit, instructor in French, 1962-67; Florida State University, Tallahassee, assistant professor, 1967-72, associate professor of French, 1972—. *Member:* Modern Language Association of America, American Association of Teachers of French (vice-president of Detroit chapter, 1958-62; president, 1963-65), Renaissance Society of America, American Association of University Professors, South Atlantic Modern Language Association

(vice-president, 1975; president, 1976; member of executive board, 1975-77), South Central Modern Language Association.

WRITINGS: (Editor and author of introduction and notes) Marguerite D'Angouleme, Reine de Navarre, *Le Miroir de l'ame pecheresse: Discord etant en l'homme par contrariete de l'esprit et de la chair, Oraison a nostre Seigneur Jesus Christ* (critical edition), Wilhelm Fink (Munich), 1972. Book reviewer, *French Review* and *Renaissance Quarterly.* Member of editorial board, *South Atlantic Bulletin,* 1977-78.

WORK IN PROGRESS: Research on French Renaissance literature, particularly on Marguerite de Navarre.

AVOCATIONAL INTERESTS: Duplicate contract bridge (former president of American Contract Bridge League— Northwest Florida unit), travel.

*   *   *

ALLAN, J(ohn) David   1945-

PERSONAL: Born February 5, 1945, in London, Ontario, Canada; son of Frederick J. (a businessman) and Isabel (Marchant) Allan; married Susan Demirsky, August 25, 1968. *Education:* University of British Columbia, B.Sc., 1966; University of Michigan, Ph.D., 1972. *Home:* 104 Stonegate, Silver Spring, Md. 20904. *Office:* Department of Zoology, University of Maryland, College Park, Md. 20742.

CAREER: University of Maryland, College Park, associate professor of zoology, 1972—. *Member:* American Association for the Advancement of Science, Ecological Society of America, Societas International Linnol.

WRITINGS: (Editor with A. J. Hanson) *Recycle This Book,* Wadsworth, 1972. Contributor of articles to *Ecology, American Naturalist,* and *Limnology and Oceanography.*

WORK IN PROGRESS: Field studies of populations; research on community ecology.

*   *   *

ALLEN, Durward L(eon)   1910-

PERSONAL: Born October 11, 1910, in Uniondale, Ind.; son of Harley J. (a salesman) and Jennie M. (LaTurner) Allen; married Dorothy Ellen Helling, September 23, 1935; children: Stephen R., Harley W., Susan E. *Education:* University of Michigan, A.B., 1932; Michigan State College (now Michigan State University), Ph.D., 1937. *Home:* 1010 Windwood Lane, West Lafayette, Ind. 47906. *Agent:* Mrs. Frances Collin, 141 East 55th St., New York, N.Y. 10022. *Office:* Department of Forestry and Natural Resources, Purdue University, Lafayette, Ind. 47907.

CAREER: Michigan Department of Conservation, Game Division, Lansing, game research biologist, 1935-46, biologist in charge of Swan Creek Wildlife Experiment Station, 1937-39, biologist in charge of Rose Lake Wildlife Experiment Station, 1939-46; U.S. Fish & Wildlife Service, Washington, D.C., biologist in charge of wildlife investigations on agricultural lands (Laurel, Md.), 1946-50, assistant chief of Branch of Wildlife Research, 1951-53, acting chief of branch, 1953-54; Purdue University, Lafayette, Ind., associate professor, 1954-57, professor of wildlife ecology, 1957—. Assistant secretary-general of Inter-American Conference on Renewable Natural Resources, 1948; member of Indiana Water Resources Study Committee, 1957-59; member of Committee on Conservation of National Council of Boy Scouts of America, 1948-72. Member of Secretarial Advisory Board on National Parks, Monuments, and Historic

Sites of U.S. Department of the Interior, 1966-72, chairman of board, 1971-72; member of Committee on Wildlife and Land-use Relationships of National Academy of Sciences; member of Advisory Committee on Predator Control of Council on Environmental Quality and U.S. Department of the Interior, 1971; member of Indiana Pesticide Review Board, 1971—; member of Wolf Specialist Group of Survival Service Commission for International Union for the Conservation of Nature and Natural Resources; chairman of International Committee on American Wildlife Policy of Wildlife Management Institute, 1972-73. *Military service:* U.S. Army, Medical Corps, 1943-45.

MEMBER: International Association of Game, Fish, and Conservation Commissioners, American Association for the Advancement of Science (fellow), American Institute of Biological Sciences, Ecological Society of America, American Society of Mammalogists, American Forestry Association (member of board of directors, 1965-67; honorary vice-president, 1968-69), Wildlife Society (honorary member; president, 1956-57), National Parks and Conservation Association (member of board of trustees), Population Reference Bureau, Wilderness Society, Defenders of Wildlife, Nature Conservancy, National Audubon Society, Izaak Walton League of America, Washington Biologists Field Club, Indiana Academy of Science, Sierra Club, Boone and Crockett Club, Sigma Xi, Phi Sigma, Xi Sigma Pi, Seminarium Botanicum, Explorers Club, Cosmos Club. *Awards, honors:* Annual technical publication award from Wildlife Society, 1945, for *Michigan Fox Squirrel Management;* annual conservation education award from Wildlife Society, 1955, for *Our Wildlife Legacy* and *Pheasants Afield;* medal of honor from Anglers' Club of New York, 1956, for service to wildlife conservation; named Indiana's "Conservation Educator of the Year," 1965; Jade of Chiefs Award from Outdoor Writers Association of America, 1968; Leopold Memorial Medal from Wildlife Society, 1969; L.H.D., Northern Michigan University, 1971.

WRITINGS: Michigan Fox Squirrel Management, Michigan Department of Conservation, 1943; *Pheasants Afield,* Stackpole, 1953; *Our Wildlife Legacy,* Funk, 1954, revised edition, 1962; (editor) *Pheasants in North America,* Stackpole, 1956; *The Life of Prairies and Plains,* McGraw, 1967; (editor) *Land Use and Wildlife Resources,* National Academy of Science, 1970; *Wolves of Minong,* Houghton, 1979. Science editor, "Our Nature World Series," for Reader's Digest Books. Author of conservation education bulletins and contributor to conference transactions. Contributor of over two hundred articles and scientific papers to professional journals and national magazines, including *Field and Stream, Boys' Life, Sports Afield, Outdoor Life, National Wildlife, Sports Illustrated, Ford Times, Family Circle, Science Digest, Audubon,* and *National Geographic.*

SIDELIGHTS: Durward L. Allen told *CA:* "I regard writing as a primary means of making my professional work a lasting benefit to mankind. Work with animal populations has impressed upon me that my own species can survive and prosper only as the life-support systems of the earth—atmosphere, soils, waters, living things—are preserved in something approaching their original integrity.... Unlimited population growth and unlimited technological demand are destroying our finite resources and degrading the environment in which future generations must live. It should be a feature of our mores and our concept of human destiny that every person born has a right to certain endowments and opportunities: a secure and stimulating childhood; education to the extent of his (or her) capacities and inclina-

tion; unlimited horizons in intellectual, creative, and spiritual development. It is the essence of civilization that man can, if he will, plan for a better future. The social, environmental, and economic evils that beset our time could be vastly mitigated by public policies that would reduce our present state of overpopulation and the accelerating 'needs' that it produces."

AVOCATIONAL INTERESTS: Photography, fishing, hunting, camping, canoeing, woodworking.

*   *   *

ALLEN, Louis 1922-

PERSONAL: Born December 22, 1922, in Redcar, England. *Education:* University of Manchester, B.A., 1949, M.A., 1949; also studied at University of London and University of Paris. *Religion:* Roman Catholic. *Home:* Dun Cow Cottage, Durham, England. *Office:* Department of French, University of Durham, Durham, England.

CAREER: University of Durham, Durham, England, senior lecturer in French, 1948—. Chairman of northeast regional advisory council, British Broadcasting Corp. *Military service:* British Army, 1942-46; served in Burma and Southeast Asia; mentioned in dispatches. *Member:* Association Internationale des Etudes Francaises, British Association of Orientalists, Japan Society of London.

WRITINGS: (Editor) Beaumarchais, *Le Barbier de Seville,* Harrap, 1951; (editor) Beaumarchais, *Le Mariage de Figaro,* Harrap, 1952; (translator with Hide Ishiguro) Yuji Aida, *Prisoner of the British,* Cresset, 1967; *Japan: The Years of Triumph,* Macdonald & Co., 1971; *Sittang: The Last Battle,* Macdonald & Co., 1973; (contributor) Hawes and White, editors, *Resistance in Europe, 1939-1945,* Allen Lane, 1975; (contributor) *Decisive Battles of the Twentieth Century,* Sidgwick & Jackson, 1976; *John Henry Newman and the Abbe Jager,* Oxford University Press, 1976; *The End of the War in Asia,* Hart-Davis, 1976; *Singapore, 1941-1942,* Davis-Poynter, 1977. Contributor to *Forum, Tablet, New Blackfriars, Commonweal, Sunday Times,* and other publications.

WORK IN PROGRESS: A book on French Catholics and the Oxford Movement; a book on the Burma campaign.

SIDELIGHTS: Louis Allen has traveled throughout Europe and in Alaska, West Africa, the South Pacific, Japan, Israel, and in Central and Southeast Asia. He speaks Spanish, Portuguese, Italian, German, and Japanese, in addition to French.

*   *   *

ALLOWAY, Lawrence 1926-

PERSONAL: Born September 17, 1926, in London, England; son of Francis Lawrence and Nora (Hatton) Alloway; married Sylvia Sleigh (a painter), June 28, 1954. *Home:* 330 West 20th St., New York, N.Y. 10011. *Office:* Department of Art, State University of New York, Stony Brook, N.Y. 11790.

CAREER: National Gallery, London, England, assistant lecturer, 1948-54; Tate Gallery, London, lecturer, 1952-55; *Art News,* New York City, British correspondent, 1954-57; Institute of Contemporary Arts, London, deputy director, 1957-60; Bennington College, Bennington, Vt., instructor in art history, 1961-62; Guggenheim Museum, New York City, curator, 1962-66; State University of New York at Stony Brook, visiting professor, 1968-69, professor of art, 1969—. *Awards, honors:* Second Foreign Critics Award, 1961, for art criticism of the Venice Biennale; Frank Jewett Mather Award, 1971, for distinction in art criticism.

WRITINGS: Nine Abstract Artists, Alec Tiranti (London), 1954; *Ettore Colla,* Grafica (Rome), 1960; *Metallisation of the Dream,* Lion & Unicorn (London), 1963; *The Venice Biennale, 1895-1968,* New York Graphic Society, 1968; *Violent America: The Movies, 1948-1964,* Museum of Modern Art, 1971; *Mechanismus der Bedeutung,* Bruckmann, 1972; *American Pop Art,* Macmillan and the Whitney Museum of American Art, 1974; *Topics in American Art since 1945,* Norton, 1975. Contributor to art journals. Contributing editor of *Art International,* 1957-60, and *Art Forum,* 1971-75; art critic for *Nation,* 1968—.

WORK IN PROGRESS: A collection of his own art criticism, for Norton; *A History of Pop Art,* for Macmillan.

BIOGRAPHICAL/CRITICAL SOURCES: Book World, December 8, 1968.

* * *

ALLSWANG, John M(yers) 1937-

PERSONAL: Born January 16, 1937, in Chicago, Ill.; son of Eugene A. (a businessman) and Katherine (Myers) Allswang; married Suzanne Menzel, December 19, 1964; children: Eden, Yael. *Education:* University of Illinois, A.B., 1959; University of Iowa, A.M., 1960; University of Pittsburgh, Ph.D., 1967. *Politics:* Democrat. *Religion:* Jewish. *Home:* 2438 La Condesa Dr., Los Angeles, Calif. 90049. *Office:* Department of History, California State University, 5151 State University Dr., Los Angeles, Calif. 90032.

CAREER: Northern Illinois University, DeKalb, instructor in history, 1965-66; Northern Michigan University, Marquette, assistant professor of history, 1966-68; California State University, Los Angeles, associate professor, 1968-73, professor of history, 1973—. Visiting professor of history at Hebrew University of Jerusalem, 1971-72, and University of Leiden, 1977-78. *Member:* American Historical Association, Organization of American Historians, American Professors for Peace in the Middle East, Social Science History Association, Immigration History Group. *Awards, honors:* Fulbright-Hays fellow in Israel, 1971-72, and in the Netherlands, 1977-78.

WRITINGS: (Editor and annotator with Patrick Bova) *NORC Social Research: An Inventory of Studies and Publications in Social Research,* National Opinion Research Center, University of Chicago, 1964; *A House for All Peoples: Ethnic Politics in Chicago, 1890-1936,* University Press of Kentucky, 1971; *Bosses, Machines and Urban Voters: An American Symbiosis,* Kennikat, 1977; *The New Deal and American Politics: A Study in Political Change,* Wiley, 1978.

WORK IN PROGRESS: A study of the effect of the G.I. Bill on the American social structure.

* * *

ALPERT, Paul 1907-

PERSONAL: Born June 2, 1907, in St. Petersburg, Russia (now Leningrad, U.S.S.R.); son of Alexandre and Sophie (Kamber) Alpert; married Sophie Jaszunska (a teacher of French), March 23, 1937; children: Sylvie (Mrs. Stafford Bryant, Jr.), Laurent. *Education:* University of Paris, Dr. Law and Economics, 1930; also attended Ecole des Hautes Etudes Commerciales. *Home:* 12 Welwyn Rd., Great Neck, N.Y. 11021.

CAREER: Le Capital Financial (daily newspaper), Paris, France, foreign editor, 1932-39; Government of France, Paris, chief of section of economic information in Foreign Office, 1944-46; United Nations, New York, N.Y., chief of training program in technical cooperation, 1946-71, currently representative of United Towns Organisation. Adjunct professor of economics, New York University, 1947-71. *Military service:* French Navy, 1939-40. *Member:* Society for International Development. *Awards, honors:* Chevalier de la Legion d'Honneur.

WRITINGS: Economie Organisee, Editions N.R.F., 1933; *L'Amerique de Roosevelt,* Editions Latines, 1939; *Demain la Democratie,* Editions de la Fleche, 1939; *Economie Humaniste,* Desclees de Brouwer, 1945; *Twentieth-Century European Economic History,* Henry Schuman, 1951; *Economic Development: Objectives and Methods,* Free Press, 1963; *Partnership or Confrontation?: Poor Lands and Rich,* Free Press, 1973.

WORK IN PROGRESS: An autobiography, tentatively entitled, *Memories of Two Continents and Three Civilizations.*

SIDELIGHTS: Paul Alpert was imprisoned in a Nazi concentration camp during World War II; he later became a member of the French delegation at the Nuremberg trials of Nazi war criminals.

At the United Nations, Alpert represents a group known as the United Towns Organisation. An international, non-governmental body, it deals with "town twinning," mainly between cities in rich and poor countries.

* * *

AlROY, Gil Carl 1924-

PERSONAL: Born November 7, 1924, in Cernauti, Romania; son of Samuel and Esther (Bley) AlRoy; married Phyllis Delson, December 26, 1954; children: Carolyn Simone, Iris Jeanne, Aileen Bley. *Education:* College of the City of New York (now City College of the City University of New York), B.A., 1959; Princeton University, Ph.D., 1963. *Home:* 798 Kingston Rd., Princeton, N.J. 08540. *Office:* Department of Political Science, Hunter College of the City University of New York, 695 Park Ave., New York, N.Y. 10021.

CAREER: Hunter College of the City University of New York, New York, N.Y., instructor, 1964-65, assistant professor, 1966-67, associate professor, 1968-71, professor of political science, 1972—. Senior information assistant, U.S. Diplomatic Mission in Israel, 1950-54; research associate, Center of International Studies, Princeton, N.J., 1963-68. *Member:* Middle East Studies Association (fellow), National Honor Society in Economics (president, 1960-61).

WRITINGS: The Involvement of Peasants in Internal Wars (monograph), Princeton University, 1966; (editor) *Attitudes toward Jewish Statehood in the Arab World,* American Academic Association for Peace in the Middle East, 1971; *The Kissinger Experience,* Horizon Press, 1975; *Behind the Middle East Conflict,* Putnam, 1975.

WORK IN PROGRESS: Middle East War and Military Science.

* * *

ALT, (Arthur) Tilo 1931-

PERSONAL: Surname is pronounced Ault; born October 14, 1931, in Batavia, Java; U.S. citizen; son of Gustave Karl

Arthur and Edith (Puhlmann) Alt; married Elizabeth Blankenship, June 20, 1958; children: Sharon. *Education:* Attended Free University of Berlin, West Germany, 1952-56, and University of Tennessee, 1956-57; University of Texas, Ph.D., 1964. *Home:* 3 Scott Pl., Durham, N.C. 27707. *Office:* Department of German, Duke University, Durham, N.C. 27706.

CAREER: Duke University, Durham, N.C., instructor, 1961-65; Mount Holyoke College, South Hadley, Mass., assistant professor of German, 1965-67; Duke University, assistant professor, 1967-78, associate professor of German, 1978—, director of undergraduate studies in German department, 1967-68. Visiting assistant professor at Columbia University, summers, 1967, 1968. *Member:* Modern Language Association of America, American Association of Teachers of German, American Association of University Professors, American Association of Professors of Yiddish, American Lessing Society, Theodor-Storm-Gesellschaft (Germany), Hebbel-Gesellschaft.

WRITINGS: Theodor Storm, Twayne, 1973; *Theodor Storm Ernst Esmarch: Briefwechsel,* [Berlin], 1978; *Creative Encounter: Festschrift for Herman Salinger,* University of North Carolina Press, 1978. Contributor of articles to *Schriften der Theodor-Storm-Gesellschaft* and *Hebbel Jahrbuch.* Contributor of book reviews to *German Quarterly, Germanic Review, Monatshefte.*

WORK IN PROGRESS: The Emergence of Modern German Drama; Dialogue in Friedrich Hebbel's Dramas.

AVOCATIONAL INTERESTS: Classical music, political events.

* * *

ALTH, Max O(ctavious) 1927-
(Harry C. Collins)

PERSONAL: Original surname Becker; name legally changed in 1937; born June 17, 1927, in Paterson, N.J.; son of Jake and Anna (Klupavouch) Becker; married Charlotte Annete Liberman (sales manager at Saks Fifth Avenue); children: Simon, Michel, Arabella, Archie. *Education:* Columbia University, B.A., 1950. *Politics:* "Freedom Party." *Religion:* Jewish. *Home:* 6 Tamarack Rd., Port Chester, N.Y. *Agent:* Richard Curtis Literary Agency, 156 East 52nd St., New York, N.Y. 10022.

CAREER: Free-lance writer, editor, and publicist, 1950-58; *Electronics World,* New York City, associate editor, 1958-60; Kollsman Instrument Corp., Elmhurst, N.Y., proposal writer in Research & Development Division, 1960-63; associate editor, *Fleet International* and *Auto International,* 1963-67; *Diesel Equipment Superintendent,* Stamford, Conn., acting managing editor, 1967-68; Aluminum Association, New York City, writer and editor of technical and popular books, brochures, articles, and pamphlets, 1968—. Instructor at Westchester Community College; water works inspector in Port Chester, N.Y.; technical communications consultant. *Military service:* U.S. Army Air Forces, 1943-46; served in European theater of operations; became staff sergeant; received twelve battle stars.

MEMBER: Society of Automotive Engineers, Literary Club of America (vice-president), Eastern Writers Union (president, 1960-67). *Awards, honors:* First prize for nonfiction from New York chapter of Technical Writer's Association, 1959.

WRITINGS: Wicked and Warped, Woodford, 1951; (under pseudonym Harry C. Collins) *Fur Lined G-String,* Midnite,

1952; (under pseudonym Harry C. Collins) *Burlesque Doll,* Midnite, 1953; *Soldering Aluminum,* Aluminum Association, 1969; *Brazing Aluminum,* Aluminum Association, 1969; *Aluminum Cryogenic Engineering,* Aluminum Association, 1972; *All About Bikes and Bicycling,* Hawthorn, 1972, revised edition, 1975; *All About Locks and Locksmithing,* Hawthorn, 1972; *Bicycling and Hiking,* Award Books, 1973; *How to Make Cheese and Yogurt,* Crowell, 1973; *Do-It-Yourself Plumbing,* Harper, 1975; *All About Keeping Your Car Alive,* Hawthorn, 1975; *Antique Radios and Crystal Sets,* Wallace-Homested, 1976; *How to Farm Your Backyard the Mulch Organic Way,* McGraw, 1977; *All About Mopeds,* Franklin Watts, 1977; *Do-It-Yourself Masonry,* Popular Science, 1978; *Home Emergency Repairs,* Popular Science, 1978; *Roofing and Siding,* Hawthorn, 1978; *Wood Stoves and Fireplaces,* Grosset, 1979; *Rattan and Wicker Furniture Making,* Hawthorn, 1979. Contributor to a variety of popular magazines and newspapers, including *Woman's Day, Popular Science, American Home, American Photography, Radio-Electronics, Everywoman, Popular Mechanics, Radio News,* and *New York Times.*

WORK IN PROGRESS: The Life and Times of Boris Tomasheffsky; The Growth of Pornography in America; Thirteen Men and a Boy, Or How We Almost Lost World War II.

AVOCATIONAL INTERESTS: Science and invention (holds ten patents).

* * *

ALTMAN, Richard Charles 1932-

PERSONAL: Born March 3, 1932, in Los Angeles, Calif.; son of Harry I. (a retailer) and Ida (Hirschhorn) Altman. *Education:* University of California, Los Angeles, B.A., 1953. *Home and office:* 8491 Fountain Ave., Los Angeles, Calif. 90069. *Agent:* Robert Hussong, 8271 Melrose Ave., Los Angeles, Calif. 90046.

CAREER: Actor in Los Angeles and Hollywood, 1951 and 1953; director of summer theatre in Colon, Mich. and Warsaw, Ind., 1957; American Academy of Dramatic Arts, New York City, director and instructor, 1957-62; assistant to director, Jerome Robbins, for musical play, "Fiddler on the Roof," New York City, 1963-64, director of same play in London, Paris, Amsterdam, and Tel Aviv, 1965-70, casting consultant for film version of the musical, 1970; director of other stage and television productions, including Tennessee Williams' "Small Craft Warnings," in New York City, 1972; Duke University, Durham, N.C., artist-in-residence in drama, 1974-75; University of North Carolina at Greensboro, artist-in-residence in drama, 1976-77. *Military service:* U.S. Army, 1953-55. *Member:* Society of Stage Directors and Choreographers, Actors Studio, Actors' Equity Association, American Guild of Musical Artists, Zeta Beta Tau.

WRITINGS: (With Mervyn Kaufman) *The Making of a Musical: "Fiddler on the Roof,"* Crown, 1971, revised edition, 1972; *And the Envelope Please: A Quiz Book about the Academy Awards,* Lippincott, 1978.

* * *

AMANN, Victor F(rancis) 1927-

PERSONAL: Born August 29, 1927, in Richardton, N.D.; son of Phillipp (a farmer) and Julia (Thomas) Amann; married Charlotte Swanson, July 5, 1952; children: Stuart. *Education:* University of Minnesota, B.S., 1956, Ph.D., 1962. *Office:* Ministry of Agriculture, Private Bag 003, Gaborone, Botswana.

CAREER: University of Minnesota, St. Paul, instructor in agricultural economics, 1957-62; Haile Sellassie I University, Dire Dawa, Ethiopia, assistant professor of agricultural economics, 1962-66; West Virginia University, Morgantown, assistant professor, 1966-69, associate professor of agricultural economics, 1969-75; Makerere University, Kampala, Uganda, senior lecturer, 1969-73, associate professor of agricultural economics, 1973-75; Ministry of Agriculture, Gaborone, Botswana, chief agricultural economist, 1975—. Executive director of Makerere Institute of Social Research, 1971-75; adjunct professor of agricultural economics, West Virginia University, beginning 1975. *Member:* International Society of Agricultural Economists, American Agricultural Economics Society, East African Agricultural Economics Society (secretary, 1970-71; treasurer, 1971-75).

WRITINGS: Organization and Operation of a Marketing Cooperative in Ethiopia, Oklahoma State University Press, 1965; *Nutrition and Food in an African Economy,* Makerere University Press, 1972; *Agricultural Policy for East Africa,* Makerere University Press, 1973; (editor) *Agricultural Employment and Labour Migration,* Makerere University Press, 1974; (editor with P. Raikes) *Project Appraisal and Evaluation in Agriculture,* Makerere University Press, 1974; (editor with Frank Wilson) *Financing Rural Development,* Makerere University Press, 1975; *Essentials of Food Production and Farm Management Economics,* Makerere University Press, 1975. Editor of *Eastern Africa Journal of Rural Development,* 1971-75.

WORK IN PROGRESS: Editing with Frank Bofoe, *Political and Socio-Economic Development of Uganda, 1961-1971,* for East African Literature Bureau.

*   *   *

AMBROZ, Oton 1905-

PERSONAL: Born September 3, 1905, in the Austro-Hungarian Empire; came to United States in 1959, naturalized citizen in 1964; son of Gabrijel (an agricultural expert) and Jelka (Petz) Ambroz; married Emma Kovsca, October 17, 1953; children: Alexander. *Education:* Zagreb State Real-Gymnasium, Baccalaureat, equivalent to B.A., 1924; Zagreb University, Diploma, equivalent to M.A., 1934, Dr. Iuris, 1935; attended School of Modern Languages, 1935-38. *Home:* 925 West End Ave., New York, N.Y. 10025; and Via S. Pasquale 39, Trieste, Italy.

CAREER: Journalist, correspondent, columnist, and magazine writer in Ljubljana and Zagreb, 1924-38, in Paris, 1939, in Rome, 1940, and again in Zagreb up to 1945. Translator and adaptor from English in information service, Allied Military Government of Trieste Free Territory, 1951-54; Indiana University at Bloomington, Russian and East European Institute, field research assistant, 1951-53; translator and adaptor from Italian for the commissioner general of Italy, 1955; correspondent for *Die Presse* (Vienna) and other Central European dailies, and script writer for Radio Trieste, 1956-59; Free Europe, Inc., New York City, staff assistant and consultant, 1959-70; *East Europe* (magazine), New York City, associate editor, 1970-75. Political research analyst, specializing in comparative communism *ex privata diligentia.* Lecturer in New York City, 1961-63, at Fairleigh-Dickinson University, 1962, in Colombia, 1964, and at the University of Kingston, 1967. *Military service:* Royal Yugoslav Army, 1929-30, 1940-41 (until the collapse of Yugoslavia); became first lieutenant. *Member:* Liberal International (exile group; London), Delta Tau Kappa, New York Hiking Club, and several other hiking clubs.

WRITINGS: Realignment of World Power: The Russo-Chinese Schism under the Impact of Mao Tse-Tung's Last Revolution, two volumes, Speller, 1972. Contributor to specialized magazines, including *Nova Evropa* (Zagreb), *East Europe, Assembly of Captive European News, China Quarterly, East-Central European Papers,* and numerous American periodicals; also contributor to the newspaper syndicates, North American Newspaper Alliance and Foreign News Service.

WORK IN PROGRESS: Preparing "an anthology on William J. Hoeferlin, a leading trail blazer and first hiker region map maker in the metropolitan area of New York."

SIDELIGHTS: Referring to himself, Oton Ambroz told *CA:* "[I] was born at a castle in the Trieste area where [my] father managed the estate. [I] spent two years in prison in Ljubljana under the communist regime, having been indicted as a 'Western' intelligence agent and a member of nationalist resistance movement.... [I] escaped to Trieste, and continued [my] career as a journalist." Ambroz speaks French, German, Italian, Serbian-Croatian, and Slovene, and reads Russian. His writings have been published in Chile, Monaco, and Brazil. A nature lover and mountain hiker, he has hiked in the Eastern Yugoslav-Italian Alps. He has continued to hike in the metropolitan area of New York City as a member of several clubs.

*   *   *

AMERINE, Maynard A(ndrew) 1911-

PERSONAL: Born October 30, 1911, in San Jose, Calif.; son of Roy Reagan (a farmer) and Tennie (Davis) Amerine. *Education:* University of California, Berkeley, B.S., 1932, Ph.D., 1936. *Politics:* Republican. *Religion:* Baptist. *Home address:* P.O. Box 208, St. Helena, Calif. 94574. *Office:* Department of Viticulture and Enology, University of California, Davis, Calif. 95616.

CAREER: University of California, Davis, Experiment Station, instructor and junior enologist, 1936-38, assistant professor and assistant enologist, 1938-46, associate professor and associate enologist, 1946-52, professor of enology and enologist, 1952—, chairman of department of viticulture and enology, 1957-62. All-university lecturer at San Diego, Berkeley, Riverside, and Santa Barbara campuses of University of California, 1962, at San Francisco campus, 1964. Consultant to wine industry in Venezuela, 1960, Japan, 1967, Chile, 1969, Algeria, 1972; judge at International Wine Fair in Yugoslavia, 1964-65, 1976; opened Wine Show in Capetown, South Africa, 1968; member, Concours Mondial de Vins, Budapest, 1972; chairman of wine judging at California State Fair for many years. *Military service:* U.S. Army, Chemical Warfare, 1942-46; served in Algeria and India; became major. U.S. Army Reserve, 1947-64; became lieutenant colonel.

MEMBER: International Wine and Food Society, American Society of Enologists (vice-president, 1957-58; president, 1958-59), American Chemical Society, American Association for the Advancement of Science, Institute of Food Technology, Accademia Italiana de la Vite e del Vino (foreign honorary member), Medical Friends of Wine, Lawyer Friends of Wine, California Vintage Wine Society, Chevaliers du Tastevin (San Francisco; officier commandeur), Wine and Food Society of San Francisco, Sigma Xi, Alpha Zeta, Bohemian Club (San Francisco).

AWARDS, HONORS: Chevalier de Merite Agricole (France), 1947; Diplome d'Honneur of Office International du Vin for *Table Wines,* 1952, and *Dessert, Appetizer and*

Related Flavored Wines, 1965; second prize in Eunice Rockwell Oberly Memorial Award of American Library Association, 1953; Guggenheim fellowship for study in Spain and Germany, 1954-55; medal of Comite National de Propaganda en Faveur du Vin (France), 1962; American Society of Enologists merit award, 1962; Andre Simon Literary Prize of Wine and Food Society (London), 1966, for *Wine: An Introduction for Americans;* officier, Ordre National du Merite, 1977.

WRITINGS: (With L. B. Wheeler) *A Check List of Books and Pamphlets on Grapes and Wine and Related Subjects, 1938-48,* University of California Press, 1951; (with M. A. Joslyn) *Table Wines: The Technology of Their Production in California,* University of California Press, 1951, 2nd edition, 1970; (with W. V. Cruess) *The Technology of Wine Making,* Avi, 1960, 2nd edition (with Cruess and H. W. Berg), 1967, 3rd edition (with Berg), 1972; (with G. L. Marsh) *Wine Making at Home,* Wine Publications, 1962; (with Joslyn) *Dessert, Appetizer and Related Flavored Wines: The Technology of Their Production,* Division of Agricultural Sciences, University of California, 1964; (with R. M. Pangborn and E.B. Roessler) *Principles of Sensory Evaluation of Food,* Academic Press, 1965; (with V. L. Singleton) *Wine: An Introduction for Americans,* University of California Press, 1965, 2nd edition, 1977; *A Check List on Grapes and Wines, 1960-68,* with supplement for 1949-1959, Associated Student Book Store, University of California, Davis, 1969; (with Singleton) *A List of Bibliographies and a Selected List of Publications that Contain Bibliographies on Grapes, Wines, and Related Subjects,* Agricultural Publications, University of California, Berkeley, 1971; (with G. F. Stewart) *Introduction to Food Science and Technology,* Academic Press, 1973; (with Roessler) *Wines: Their Sensory Evaluation,* W. H. Freeman, 1976.

Contributor to *Kirk-Othmer Encyclopedia of Chemical Technology, Encyclopedia Americana, Encyclopaedia Britannica,* and *Encyclopedia of Industrial Chemical Analysis,* and of more than three hundred technical, semi-technical, and popular articles to professional journals and magazines. Member of editorial board, *Food Research* (journal of Institute of Food Technology), 1959-60.

WORK IN PROGRESS: Research covering vermouth, wine analysis, sensory evaluation of foods and health values of wine.

SIDELIGHTS: Maynard Amerine's studies and consultant work on wines have taken him to more than thirty countries, most frequently to France, Portugal, Spain, Italy, Soviet Union, and Greece. In 1977, the Gallo Foundation established the Maynard A. Amerine Professor of Enology and Viticulture Chair at the University of California, Davis.

* * *

AMUZEGAR, Jahangir 1920-

PERSONAL: Born January 13, 1920, in Tehran, Iran; son of Habibollah and Turan (Azemudeh) Amuzegar; married Eleanor R. Horn, September 27, 1958. *Education:* University of Tehran, B.A. (law), 1941, B.A. (political science), 1942; University of Washington, Seattle, M.A., 1948; University of California, Los Angeles, Ph.D., 1955. *Office:* Iranian Economic Mission, 5530 Wisconsin Ave. N.W., Washington, D.C. 20015.

CAREER: Government of Iran, Tehran, economic adviser to plan organization, 1956-57, minister of commerce, ex-officio member of Council of Money and Credit and High Economic Council, and member of board of directors of Bank Melli Iran, all 1961-62, minister of finance and ex-officio chairman of High Council of National Iranian Oil Co., 1962, chief of Iranian Economic Mission in Washington, D.C., 1963-77, ambassador-at-large, 1966—, principal resident representative to the World Bank, 1977—. Distinguished adjunct professor, American University. Lecturer in economics, Whittier College, 1953, and University of Michigan, 1953-55; assistant professor at Pomona College, 1955-56, and Michigan State University, 1956-58; associate professor at Occidental College and University of California, Los Angeles, 1958-60; research professor, Brookings Institution, 1960-61; part-time lecturer in economics at University of Maryland, 1963-74. *Member:* American Economic Association, Iranian Statistics Society, Pi Gamma Mu.

WRITINGS: Technical Assistant in Theory and Practice: The Case of Iran, Praeger, 1966; (contributor) Ehsan Yar-Shater, editor, *Iran Faces the Seventies,* Praegar, 1971; (with M. A. Fekrat)́ *Iran: Economic Development under Dualistic Conditions,* University of Chicago Press, 1971; *Iran,* University of Delaware, 1975; *Iran: An Economic Profile,* Middle East Institute, 1977; (contributor) A. Amirie, editor, *Iran in the 1980's,* Institute for Political and Economic Research, 1978. Contributor of articles and reviews to American and foreign professional journals, including *School and Society, Middle East Economic Papers, Business Topics, Political Science Quarterly, Social Research, Journal of Higher Education, Foreign Affairs, Indian Economic Review,* and *Economia Internazionale.*

* * *

ANDERSON, Carl L(ennart) 1919-

PERSONAL: Born December 3, 1919, in Philadelphia, Pa.; son of Carl A. and Selma (Johnson) Anderson; married Jean Bradley, June 30, 1951; children: William Bradley, Julian Augusta. *Education:* University of Pennsylvania, A.B., 1948, M.A., 1951, Ph.D., 1955. *Office:* Department of English, Duke University, Durham, N.C. 27706.

CAREER: Norwich University, Northfield, Vt., instructor, 1951-54, assistant professor of English, 1954-55; Duke University, Durham, N.C., instructor, 1955-57, assistant professor, 1958-64, associate professor, 1964-71, professor of English, 1971—. Fulbright lecturer at University of Oslo, 1961-62. *Military service:* U.S. Naval Reserve, 1944-46. *Member:* Modern Language Association of America, American Association of University Professors, American Studies Association, Society for the Advancement of Scandinavian Study, South Atlantic Modern Language Association, Phi Beta Kappa. *Awards, honors:* Bernadotte fellowship, Sweden, 1949-50; American Philosophical Society research grant, Scandinavia, 1963.

WRITINGS: The Swedish Acceptance of American Literature, University of Pennsylvania Press, 1957; (editor with G. W. Williams) *British and American Essays,* Holt, 1959; (translator) Knut Hamsun, *On Overgrown Paths,* Ericksson, 1967; (contributor) H. Naess and S. Skard, editors, *Studies in Scandinavian-American Interrelations,* American Institute, University of Oslo, 1971; *Poe in Northlight,* Duke University Press, 1973. Contributor of articles and reviews to learned journals.

WORK IN PROGRESS: American Literature in Scandinavia.

* * *

ANDERSON, Freeman B(urket) 1922-

PERSONAL: Born May 30, 1922, in Washington, D.C.; son

of Andrew Freeman (a clergyman) and Lulu Mabel (a dean of women and teacher; maiden name, Burket) Anderson; married Janet Ballinger Leach, June 29, 1946 (divorced February 14, 1950); married Phyllis Ann Compton, January 3, 1955 (divorced May 18, 1972); children: (second marriage) Charles Compton, Allison Ashby. *Education:* Bucknell University, B.A. (with honors), 1948; Stanford University, Ph.D., 1952. *Politics:* Democratic. *Religion:* Protestant. *Home:* 3109 Southeast Claybourne, Portland, Ore. 97202.

CAREER: G. & C. Merriam Co., Springfield, Mass., assistant editor of etymology, 1952-53, 1957; New Mexico Highlands University, Las Vegas, visiting professor of English, 1954; College of Puget Sound (now University of Puget Sound), Tacoma, Wash., assistant professor of English, 1955-56; Portland State University, Portland, Ore., instructor, 1956-59, assistant professor, 1959-63, associate professor, 1963-69, professor of English, beginning 1969, currently professor emeritus. Visiting professor, Reed College, Portland, 1963-66; instructor in linguistics, National Defense Education Act Summer Institute in English, La Grande, Ore., 1965. Oregon Teacher Standards and Practices Commission, member, 1966-69, chairman, 1968; member, Educational Policies Commission of Oregon Education Association, 1967-70; member, Metropolitan Youth Commission, Portland, 1962-71. *Military service:* U.S. Army Air Forces, 1941-45; became sergeant.

WRITINGS—Editor with others, except as indicated; all published by Harper, except as indicated: (Assistant editor) *Webster's Third New International Unabridged Dictionary,* Merriam, 1961; (author with David Armington, John Dennis, William Dusel, George Rosato, and Richard Sanders) *New Directions in English,* 1970; *All About You,* 1973; *Backgrounds and Beginnings,* 1973; *Codes and Classifications,* 1973; *Differences and Discoveries,* 1973; *Evidence and Evaluation,* 1973; *Facts and Flights of Fancy,* 1973.

*　　*　　*

ANDERSON, Godfrey Tryggve 1909-

PERSONAL: Born September 4, 1909, in Chicago, Ill.; son of Andrew Gideon and Lottie (Bornes) Anderson; married Idalene Skillern, September 6, 1930; children: Dennis Kent, Marilyn Kay (Mrs. Daniel M. Patchin), Donald Lee, Constance Faye (Mrs. Douglas F. Welebir). *Education:* Broadview College, B.A., 1931; Northwestern University, M.S., 1934; University of Chicago, Ph.D., 1944. *Politics:* Democrat. *Religion:* Seventh-day Adventist. *Home:* 24783 Lawton Ave., Loma Linda, Calif. 92354. *Office:* Department of History, Loma Linda University, Loma Linda, Calif. 92354.

CAREER: Kingsway College, Oshawa, Ontario, instructor in history and dean of men, 1937-39; Atlantic Union College, South Lancaster, Mass., professor of history, 1939-46, head of department, 1939-44, academic dean, 1944-46; La Sierra College, Riverside, Calif., president, 1946-54; Loma Linda University, Loma Linda, Calif., president, 1954-67, professor of history, beginning 1967, currently research professor of history and university archivist. Secretary of board of trustees, Loma Linda Community Hospital. *Member:* American Historical Association, Organization of American Historians (past president), World Affairs Council of Inland Southern California (past president), Association of Western Adventist Historians. *Awards, honors:* L.L.D., Walla Walla College, 1961.

WRITINGS: Walk God's Battlefield (inspirational essays), Southern Publishing, 1969; *Outrider of the Apocalypse: Life and Times of Captain Joseph Bates,* Pacific Press Publishing Association, 1972; *The Past Is Always Present,* Review & Herald, 1977. Contributor of articles to *New England Quarterly* and other publications.

WORK IN PROGRESS: Editing *Studies in Adventist History;* research on the life and activities of Edward Bancroft, British spy during American Revolution, with son Dennis K. Anderson; research on imprisonment for debt in colonial America; *Mental Disorders of the Military in the American Civil War,* with son Donald L. Anderson.

*　　*　　*

ANDERSON, James F(rancis) 1910-

PERSONAL: Born June 29, 1910, in Dover, Del.; married Lois M. Gamash, December 21, 1941; children: Mary Lois, Elizabeth, Mark, John, Thomas, David, Margaret. *Education:* University of Virginia, B.A., 1933; University of Toronto, M.A., 1938, Ph.D., 1940; also studied at University of Grenoble, 1932, and took special courses at Harvard University, Columbia University, and other universities. *Home:* 45 Park Ave., Rehoboth Beach, Del. 19971.

CAREER: Instructor in philosophy at St. Anselm's College, Manchester, N.H., 1940-41, and Xavier University, New Orleans, La., 1941-42; Loyola University of Chicago, Chicago, Ill., assistant professor of philosophy, 1946-48; University of Notre Dame, Notre Dame, Ind., associate professor of philosophy, 1948-54; Marquette University, Milwaukee, Wis., associate professor of philosophy, 1954-57; University of Notre Dame, associate professor of philosophy, 1957-59; Villanova University, Villanova, Pa., professor of philosophy, 1959-67; Louisiana State University, Baton Rouge, professor of philosophy, 1967-73. *Military service:* U.S. Army Air Forces, 1942-46; served in England at Headquarters, 8th Air Force; became captain.

MEMBER: American Philosophical Association, American Catholic Philosophical Association, Metaphysical Society of America, Association for Realistic Philosophy, Fellowship of Reconciliation, American Civil Liberties Union.

WRITINGS: The Bond of Being: An Essay on Analogy and Existence, B. Herder, 1949; *The Cause of Being: The Philosophy of Creation in St. Thomas,* B. Herder, 1952; *Natural Theology: The Metaphysics of God,* Bruce, 1962; *St. Augustine and Being,* Nijhoff, 1965; *Reflections on the Analogy of Being,* Nijhoff, 1967; *Tillich: Basics in His Thought,* Magi Books, 1972.

Translator: Charles Journet, *The Dark Knowledge of God,* Sheed (London), 1948; (and editor) *An Introduction to Metaphysics of St. Thomas Aquinas* (selected texts), Regnery, 1953; (and author of introduction and notes) St. Thomas Aquinas, *On the Truth of the Catholic Faith,* Book II: *Creation,* Doubleday, 1955; (and editor) St. Thomas Aquinas, *Treatise on Man,* Prentice-Hall, 1962; (and editor) St. Thomas Aquinas, *Treatise on God,* Prentice-Hall, 1963. Contributor of articles on metaphysics and natural theology to journals.

*　　*　　*

ANDERSON, (Helen) Jean 1930-

PERSONAL: Born October 12, 1930, in Raleigh, N.C.; daughter of Donald Benton (a university vice-president) and Marian (Johnson) Anderson. *Education:* Attended Miami University, Oxford, Ohio, 1947-49; Cornell University, B.S., 1951; Columbia University, M.S., 1957. *Politics:* Independent. *Home:* 1 Lexington Ave., New York, N.Y. 10010.

Agent: McIntosh & Otis, Inc., 475 Fifth Ave., New York, N.Y. 10017.

CAREER: Iredell County, N.C., assistant home demonstration agent, 1951-52; North Carolina Agricultural Extension Service, Raleigh, woman's editor, 1952-55; *Raleigh Times,* Raleigh, N.C., woman's editor, 1955-56; *Ladies' Home Journal,* Philadelphia, Pa., assistant editor, 1957-61, editorial associate, 1961-63, managing editor, 1963; *Venture* (magazine), senior editor, 1964-68, contributing editor, 1968-71. Free-lance writer, 1968—. *Member:* American Home Economics Association, Home Economists in Business, Les Dames D'Escoffier, New York Travel Writers, Gamma Phi Beta, Phi Kappa Phi, Omicron Nu. *Awards, honors:* Pulitzer traveling scholarship, 1957; Southern Women's Achievement Award, 1962; George Hedman Memorial Award, 1971; R. T. French Taskmaker Award for best cookbook of the year, 1975, for *The Doubleday Cookbook.*

WRITINGS: Henry the Navigator: Prince of Portugal, Westminster Press, 1969; *The Haunting of America: Ghost Stories from Our Past,* Houghton, 1973.

Cookbooks: (With Yeffe Kimball) *The Art of American Indian Cooking,* Doubleday, 1965; *Food Is More than Cooking: A Basic Guide for Young Cooks,* Westminster; 1968; (editor) *Family Circle Illustrated Library of Cooking: Your Ready Reference for a Lifetime of Good Eating,* twelve volumes, Rockville House, 1972; *The Family Circle Cookbook,* Quadrangle, 1974; (with Elaine Hanna) *The Doubleday Cookbook,* Doubleday, 1975; *Recipes from America's Restored Villages,* Doubleday, 1975; *The Green Thumb Preserving Guide: The Best and Safest Way to Can and Freeze, Dry and Store, Pickle, Preserve and Relish Home-Grown Vegetables and Fruits,* Morrow, 1976; *The Grass Roots Cookbook,* Quadrangle, 1977; *Jean Anderson's Professional Cooking,* Morrow, 1979. Contributor of articles to *Ladies' Home Journal, Venture, Holiday, Better Homes and Gardens, Family Circle, Travel and Leisure,* and other periodicals.

WORK IN PROGRESS: Two cookbooks.

* * *

ANDERSON, Jerry M(aynard) 1933-

PERSONAL: Born September 16, 1933, in Deronda, Wis.; son of Jens B. and Mamie P. (Hanson) Anderson; married Betty Lou Schultz, February 7, 1959; children: Gregory, Jens, Timothy Benjamin. *Education:* Wisconsin State University (now University of Wisconsin—River Falls), B.S., 1958; Northern Illinois University, M.S., 1959; Michigan State University, Ph.D., 1964. *Politics:* Democrat. *Religion:* Lutheran. *Home:* 1245 Westhaven Dr., Oshkosh, Wis. 54901. *Office:* 335 H Dempsey Hall, University of Wisconsin, Oshkosh, Wis. 54901.

CAREER: University of Maine at Orono, instructor in speech, 1959-61; Michigan State University, East Lansing, assistant professor of speech, 1962-68; Central Michigan University, Mount Pleasant, professor of speech and chairman of department of speech and dramatic arts, 1968-72, vice-provost, 1972-73; Western Washington University, Bellingham, provost, 1973-75; University of Wisconsin—Oshkosh, vice-chancellor, 1975—. Democratic chairman of Michigan's Sixth Congressional District, 1966-67; member of Ingham County, Mich., executive committee. *Military service:* U.S. Naval Reserve, active duty, 1952-54.

MEMBER: International Communication Association, Speech Communication Association (member of executive council, 1968), American Forensic Association (president, 1972-74), American Association of Higher Education, American Council on Education, American Association of University Professors, American Civil Liberties Union, Central State Speech Association (president, 1973-74), Midwest Forensic Association (president, 1969-72), Michigan Speech Association (president, 1967-68), Michigan Academy of Science, Arts and Letters, Delta Sigma Rho-Tau Kappa Alpha, Pi Kappa Delta, Alpha Psi Omega (honorary member), Rotary International. *Awards, honors:* Harry S Truman Library Foundation research fellowship, 1965; American Council on Education fellowship, 1971-72; Phi Delta Kappa education award, 1973.

WRITINGS: (Editor with Paul J Dovre) *Readings in Argumentation,* Allyn & Bacon, 1968; (contributor) William Todd, editor, *Discussion and Debate,* Michigan High School Forensic Association, 1969; (member of editorial board) James McBath, editor, *Essays in Forensics,* American Forensic Association, 1970; (contributor) David Zarefsky, editor, *The Comparative Advantages Case,* privately printed (Evanston), 1970. Contributor of about thirty articles and reviews to higher education administration and other journals, including *Speech Teacher, Issues, Speaker and Gavel, Journal of the American Forensic Association,* and *Quarterly Journal of Speech.*

WORK IN PROGRESS: Research on interpersonal and organizational communication; studies in higher education administration.

AVOCATIONAL INTERESTS: Travel (Canada, Mexico, the Caribbean, Europe, Scandinavia), camping, woodworking, youth projects, sports.

* * *

ANDERSON, Lucia (Lewis) 1922-
(Lucia Z. Lewis)

PERSONAL: Born August 9, 1922, in Pittsburgh, Pa.; daughter of Constanty and Maryanna (Kulwicki) Zylack; married second husband, Allan G. Anderson (a professor of mathematics), April 30, 1955; children: (first marriage) Jeff, Kristina; (second marriage) Patricia Lynn. *Education:* University of Pittsburgh, B.S., 1943, M.S., 1944, Ph.D., 1946, additional study at Graduate School of Public Health, 1950; also studied at University of Pennsylvania Medical School, 1945. *Home:* 41 Bourndale Rd. N., Manhasset, N.Y. 11030. *Office:* Department of Microbiology, Queensborough Community College of the City University of New York, Bayside, N.Y. 11364.

CAREER: Duquesne University, Pittsburgh, Pa., assistant professor of biology, 1953-55; Western Kentucky State College (now Western Kentucky University), Bowling Green, 1958-65, began as associate professor, became professor of biology; E. R. Squibb, New Brunswick, N.J., 1965-66, senior research scientist; Parsons College, Fairfield, Iowa, associate professor of biology, 1966-68; Queensborough Community College of the City University of New York, Bayside, N.Y., associate professor, 1968-70, professor of microbiology, 1970—. *Member:* American Society for Microbiology, American Association for the Advancement of Science, New York Academy of Science, Kentucky Academy of Science.

WRITINGS—Under name Lucia Z. Lewis: (With Anna M. Fisher) *Laboraotry Excercises and Outlines in Microbiology for Nurses,* Lippincott, 1951; *The First Book of Microbes,* F. Watts, 1955, 2nd edition, 1972; *Microbiology for Nurses,* Kendall/Hunt, 1972; *Microbiology for Allied Health and*

Nurses, Kendall/Hunt, 1977; *The Smallest Life around Us,* Crown, 1978. Contributor of Scientific articles to *American Biology Teacher* and *A.S.M. News.*

WORK IN PROGRESS: Audio-visual material for microbiology.

* * *

ANDERSON, Marvin Walter 1933-

PERSONAL: Born January 12, 1933, in Montevideo, Minn.; son of Walter Roy (a minister) and Faith (Benett) Anderson; married Anne Marie Welin, June 11, 1962; children: Stuart, Chad. *Education:* University of Washington, Seattle, B.A., 1955; Bethel Seminary, St. Paul, Minn., B.D., 1959; University of Aberdeen, Ph.D., 1964. *Religion:* Baptist. *Office:* Department of History, Bethel Seminary, 3949 Bethel Dr., St. Paul, Minn. 55112.

CAREER: University of Washington, Seattle, teaching fellow in history, 1959-60; Bethel College, St. Paul, Minn., instructor in history, 1960-61; Northwestern College, Minneapolis, Minn., assistant professor of European history, 1961-62; Bethel Seminary, St. Paul, assistant professor, 1964-68, associate professor, 1968-72, professor of history of theology, 1973—. *Member:* Renaissance Society of America, American Society of Church History, American Society for Reformation Research, Ecclesiastical History Society (England), Phi Delta Theta. *Awards, honors:* American Council of Learned Societies grant-in-aid of research, 1969; American Association of Theological Schools Faculty fellowship, 1970-71, 1977-78.

WRITINGS: (Editor) *Gospel and Authority: A.P.T. Forsyth Reader,* Augsburg, 1971; *Reformer in Exile: Peter Martyr Vermigli 1542-1562,* DeGraaf, 1975; *Battle for the Bible: Bible and Reformation, 1444-1583,* Baker, 1978. Contributor of articles to *Church History, Scottish Journal of Theology, Theologische Zeitschrift, Journal of Ecclesiastical History,* and other theology journals.

* * *

ANDERSON, Randall C. 1934-

PERSONAL: Born August 7, 1934, in Minden, Neb.; son of Carl A. and Margaret (Kelley) Anderson. *Education:* Hastings College, A.B., 1956; University of Nebraska, M.A., 1960, Ed.D., 1963. *Home:* 1219 Merchant St., Emporia, Kan. 66801. *Office:* Division of Social Sciences, Emporia State University, 1200 Commercial St., Emporia, Kan. 66801.

CAREER: Teacher of social sciences, Spanish, and mathematics in secondary schools, Lincoln, Neb., 1957-61; Emporia State University, Emporia, Kan., professor of social sciences and social studies education, 1963—, Division of Social Sciences, acting chairperson, 1975-76, associate chairperson, 1976. Visiting professor, University of Nebraska, summer, 1965; lecturer at University of Moscow, Moscow Scientific-Technological Institute, and University of Riga, 1969-70. Member of national advisory panel, National Science Foundation, 1977—. Member of editorial board, Universities Regents Press of Kansas, 1977—. *Member:* National Council for the Social Studies, Kansas Council for the Social Studies, Pi Gamma Mu, Phi Delta Kappa. *Awards, honors:* Outstanding Educator Award, Phi Delta Theta, 1975-76.

WRITINGS: A Handbook for Developing Map and Globe Skills, Department of Secondary Education, University of Nebraska, 1963; (contributor) J. W. Morris, editor, *Methods*

of Geographic Instruction, Blaisdell, 1968; *A Journey through World Communities: Social Studies Curriculum Guide for Grades K-6,* Kansas Unified District 379, 1969; *American Studies; Social Studies Curriculum Guide for Grades 7 and 8,* Kansas Unified District 379, 1969; *Curriculum Guide for World Cultures: Social Studies Curriculum Guide for Grades 9 and 10,* Kansas Unified District 379, 1969; *American History: Social Studies Curriculum Guide for Grades 11 and 12,* Kansas Unified District 379, 1969; *American Government: Social Studies Curriculum Guide for Grades 11 and 12,* Kansas Unified District 379, 1969; *An Inquiry-Orient Instructional Strategy for Teaching the Changing Nature of Communism.* Teachers College Press, 1969; *Current Trends in Secondary School Social Studies,* Professional Educators Publications, 1972; *Introducing the Behavioral Sciences in Secondary Social Studies: An Interdisciplinary Approach,* Professional Educators Publications, 1975. Contributor of articles to social studies and education journals.

WORK IN PROGRESS: Modern Social Studies Instruction in Secondary Education; Citizenship Education and the American School: A Modern Perspective; Teaching Modern Geography in Social Studies; Citizenship Education in Global Perspective.

* * *

ANDERSON, Scarvia (Bateman) 1926-

PERSONAL: Born August 12, 1926, in Baltimore, Md. *Education:* Mississippi State University, B.S., 1945; George Peabody College for Teachers, M.A., 1951; University of Maryland, Ph.D., 1955; Oxford University, additional study, 1955-56. *Politics:* "Usually Republican." *Religion:* Protestant. *Home:* 145 15th St. N.E., Atlanta, Ga. 30309. *Office:* Educational Testing Service, 3445 Peachtree Rd. N.E., Atlanta, Ga. 30326.

CAREER: Worked as a teacher in public schools of Nashville, Tenn., 1945-50; Naval Research Laboratory, Washington, D.C., research psychologist, 1951-55; Educational Testing Service, executive in Princeton, N.J., 1956-73, executive in Atlanta, Ga., 1973—. *Member:* International Council of Psychologists, American Psychological Association (fellow), American Educational Research Association, National Council on Measurement in Education, Evaluation Research Society, Sigma Xi. *Awards, honors:* Outstanding performance award from Department of the Navy, 1955; Fulbright scholar, 1955-56.

WRITINGS: (With Martin Katz and Benjamin Shimberg) *Meeting the Test,* Scholastic Book Services, 1963; (editor) *Sex Differences and Discrimination in Education,* Charles A. Jones Publishing, 1972; (with Samuel Ball) *The Profession and Practice of Program Evaluation,* Jossey-Bass, 1978. Editor with Ball and Richard Murphy, *Encyclopedia of Educational Evaluation,* Jossey-Bass, 1978. Editor-in-chief, *New Directions for Program Evaluation,* 1978—.

SIDELIGHTS: Scarvia Anderson told *CA:* "The challenge for any writer from a technical background is to communicate to those who don't necessarily have that background—without talking down to them."

* * *

ANDERSON, Theodore R(obert) 1927-

PERSONAL: Born November 3, 1927, in Minneapolis, Minn.; son of John Edward (a professor) and Dorothea (Lynde) Anderson; married Beverly Simpson (a biologist),

August 30, 1952; children: O. Craig, Theodore L., Lincoln E. *Education:* University of Minnesota, B.S., 1948; University of Wisconsin, M.S., 1951, Ph.D., 1953. *Home:* 4816 Aldrich Ave. S., Minneapolis, Minn. 55409. *Office:* Department of Sociology, University of Minnesota, Minneapolis, Minn. 55455.

CAREER: University of Wisconsin—Madison, instructor in sociology, 1951-53; Yale University, New Haven, Conn., instructor, 1953-55, assistant professor of sociology, 1955-59; University of Iowa, Iowa City, associate professor of sociology, 1959-66; University of Oregon, Eugene, professor of sociology, 1966-69; University of Minnesota, Minneapolis, professor of sociology, 1969—. *Military service:* U.S. Naval Reserve, 1944-46. *Member:* American Sociological Association, American Statistical Association, Population Association of America. *Awards, honors:* National Science Foundation grant, 1965-69.

WRITINGS: A Basic Text in Statistics, Holt, 1968, 3rd edition, 1975.

WORK IN PROGRESS: Research in urban population distributions; a general urban text.

* * *

ANDREWS, Frank M(eredith) 1935-

PERSONAL: Born April 2, 1935, in New York, N.Y.; son of F. Emerson and Edith (Severance) Andrews; married Ann Skilling, July 6, 1962; children: Kenneth, Steven. *Education:* Dartmouth College, B.A. (magna cum laude), 1957; graduate study at University of Sydney, 1958, and New School for Social Research, 1959; University of Michigan, Ph.D., 1962. *Office:* Survey Research Center, Institute for Social Research, University of Michigan, Ann Arbor, Mich. 48106.

CAREER: Russell Sage Foundation, New York, N.Y., study director, 1959; University of Michigan, Ann Arbor, assistant study director of Survey Research Center, Institute for Social Research, 1959-61, study director, 1962-68, senior study director, 1968-71, program director, 1971—, assistant chief of party for Peru project, 1966-68 (established Peruvian Sample Survey Center), lecturer, 1963-67, assistant professor, 1967-71, associate professor, 1971-76, professor of psychology, 1976—. Consultant to Republic of Panama, Pan-American Health Organization, UNESCO, U.S. Agency for International Development, National Science Foundation, Korea Development Institute, and other agencies. *Member:* International Sociological Association, American Psychological Association, American Sociological Association, Society for International Development, Society for Social Studies of Science, American Statistical Association, Phi Beta Kappa, Sigma Xi.

WRITINGS: A Study of Company-Sponsored Foundations, Russell Sage Foundation, 1960; (with Donald C. Pelz) *Scientists in Organizations: Productive Climates for Research and Development,* Wiley, 1966, revised edition, Institute for Social Research, University of Michigan, 1976; (with James N. Morgan, John A. Sonquist and Laura Klem) *Multiple Classification Analysis: A Computer Program for Multiple Regression Using Categorical Predictors,* Institute for Social Research, University of Michigan, 1967, 2nd edition, 1973; (with Godofredo Aranda, Maria Aranda, Abel Centurion, and Edgar Flores) *Barriades de Lima: Dwellers' Attitudes Toward Public and Private Services,* Centro de Investigaciones Sociales por Muestro, Ministerio de Trabajo, Lima, Peru, 1967; (contributor) D. Allison, editor, *The R & D Game,* M.I.T. Press, 1969.

(Contributor) N. K. Denzin, editor, *Sociological Methods: A Sourcebook,* Aldine, 1970; (contributor) B. T. Eiduson and L. Beckman, editors, *Career Choice and Development in Scientists,* Russell Sage Foundation, 1972; (with Monica D. Blumenthal, Robert L. Kahn, and Kendra B. Head) *Justifying Violence: Attitudes of American Men,* Institute for Social Research, University of Michigan, 1972; (with Robert C. Messenger) *Multivariate Nominal Scale Analysis: A Report on a New Analysis Technique and a Computer Program,* Institute for Social Research, University of Michigan, 1973; (with others) *A Guide for Analyzing Social Science Data,* Institute for Social Research, University of Michigan, 1974; (contributor) I. A. Taylor and J. Getzels, editors, *Perspectives in Creativity,* Aldine, 1975; (with Stephen B. Withy) *Social Indicators of Well-Being: Americans' Perceptions of Life Quality,* Plenum, 1976; (editor and contributor) *Scientific Productivity: The Effectiveness of Research Groups in Six Countries,* Cambridge University Press and UNESCO, in press. Contributor to professional journals, including *Ekistics, Journal of Developing Areas, Personnel Psychology, Journal of Creative Behavior, Behavioral Science,* and *Journal of Personality.*

* * *

ANSCHEL, Kurt R. 1936-

PERSONAL: Born May 22, 1936, in Cadiz, Spain; son of Eugene Anschel (retired vice-president of pharmaceutical company) and Ada (Heilbrunn) Kozier; married Sara-Ellen Sommers, August 4, 1958; children: Laura, Mark (deceased), Paul. *Education:* Oberlin College, A.B., 1958; Michigan State University, B.S., 1959, M.S., 1961, Ph.D., 1965. *Home:* 3492 Castleton Way N., Lexington, Ky. 40502. *Office:* Agricultural Science Center, University of Kentucky, Lexington, Ky. 40506.

CAREER: University of Kentucky, Lexington, assistant professor, 1965-69, associate professor, 1969-74, professor of agricultural economics, 1974—. Agricultural economist, Agency for International Development, 1974-76. *Member:* American Economic Association, American Agricultural Economics Association, Society for International Development, International Association of Agricultural Economists, Southern Agricultural Economics Association. *Awards, honors:* Travel grant to Sydney, Australia, International Association of Agricultural Economists, 1967; travel grant from Agricultural Development Council, 1967, to observe rural development in Taiwan and Malaysia.

WRITINGS: (With Russell H. Brannon and Eldon D. Smith) *Agricultural Cooperatives and Markets in Developing Countries,* Praeger, 1969. Contributor to *Southern Journal of Agricultural Economics, American Journal of Agricultural Economics,* and *Nigerian Journal of Economic and Social Studies.* Book review editor, *International Development Review.*

WORK IN PROGRESS: Research on economic aspects of migration from Eastern Kentucky to selected urban centers; alternative public policies and institutions for facilitating economic growth in Appalachia.

* * *

ANTON, Frank Robert 1920-

PERSONAL: Born July 22, 1920, in County Leix, Ireland; son of Norman James (a farmer) and Teresa (Baker) Anton. *Education:* London School of Economics, B.Sc., 1950; University of California, Los Angeles, M.A., 1956; University of London, Ph.D., 1961. *Office:* Department of Economics, University of Calgary, Calgary, Alberta, Canada.

CAREER: Export Credit Insurance Corp., Ottawa, Ontario, economist in market research, 1950-51; University of New Brunswick, Fredericton, assistant professor of economics, 1951-53; University of Calgary, Calgary, Alberta, assistant professor, 1956-62, associate professor, 1962-65, professor of economics, 1965—. Has served as chairman of many arbitration and conciliation boards in Canada. *Military service:* Royal Air Force, 1940-46. Royal Canadian Air Force Reserve, 1951—; present rank, squadron leader. *Member:* American Economic Association, Canadian Economics Association (member of executive council, 1971—), Industrial Relations Research Association. *Awards, honors:* Canada Council fellow, 1968-69, 1971-72.

WRITINGS: *Government Supervised Strike Voting,* Commerce Clearing House, Canadian Ltd., 1961; *The Role of Government in the Settlement of Industrial Disputes in Canada,* Commerce Clearing House, Canadian Ltd., 1962; (with M. K. Inman) *Economics in a Canadian Setting,* Copp Clark, 1964; *Wages and Productivity: The New Equation,* Copp Clark, 1969. Contributor of articles and reviews to management and labor journals in Canada and the United States.

WORK IN PROGRESS: Research on a new approach in employer and employee relations within the framework of productivity bargaining and worker participation.

*   *   *

APPIAH, Peggy 1921-

PERSONAL: Born May 21, 1921, in England; daughter of Stafford (a British cabinet minister) and Isobel (Swithenbank) Cripps; married Joe E. Appiah (a barrister and solicitor), July 18, 1954; children: Anthony, Isobel, Adwoa, Abena. *Education:* Attended Whitehall Secretarial College. *Religion:* Christian. *Home address:* P.O. Box 829, Kumasi, Ashanti, Ghana. *Agent:* David Higham Associates, 5-8 Lower John St., London W1R 4HA, England.

CAREER: Worked as research assistant in British Ministry of Information, London, England, as secretary for Racial Unity, London, and as youth representative for the British Council of Churches, London; Kumasi Children's Home, Kumasi, Ashanti, Ghana, chairman of advisory committee, 1968—. *Member:* Zonta International (Kumasi unit), Ghana Historical Society.

WRITINGS: *Ananse the Spider* (folk tale), Pantheon, 1966; *Tales of an Ashanti Father* (folk tales), Deutsch, 1967; *The Pineapple Child and Other Tales from Ashanti,* Deutsch, 1969; *Children of Ananse* (juvenile), Evans Brothers, 1969; *A Smell of Onions,* Longmans, Green, 1971; *Why Are There So Many Roads?,* Pilgrim Books (Nigeria), 1972; *Gift of the Mmoatia* (children's book), Ghana Publishing Corp., 1973; *A Dirge Too Soon,* Ghana Publishing Corp., 1976; *Ring of Gold,* Deutsch, 1976; *Why the Hyena Does Not Care for Fish,* Deutsch, 1977; *Poems of Three Generations,* University of Science and Technology (Kumasi), 1978.

WORK IN PROGRESS: *Asante Goldweights: Proverbs and Folklore,* for Ghana Publishing Corp.

AVOCATIONAL INTERESTS: Arts and crafts, history and social anthropology.

BIOGRAPHICAL/CRITICAL SOURCES: *Christian Science Monitor,* May 4, 1967; *Times Literary Supplement,* October 16, 1969.

*   *   *

ARANOW, Edward Ross 1909-

PERSONAL: Born April 30, 1909, in New York, N.Y.; son of Harry and Sarah (Rosenfield) Aranow; married Rita Abrons, July 11, 1941; children: Vicki (Mrs. Donald Klein), Judith, Robert L. *Education:* Columbia University, A.B., 1929, J.D., 1932. *Home:* 47 Colby Lane, Scarsdale, N.Y. *Office:* Aranow, Brodsky, Bohlinger, Benetar & Einhorn, 469 Fifth Ave., New York, N.Y.

CAREER: Admitted to New York Bar, 1933; Colby, Brown & Pollack, New York City, attorney, 1932-34; Szold & Brandwen, New York City, attorney, 1934-39; private practice in law in New York City 1939-42; Aranow, Brodsky, Bohlinger, Benetar & Einhorn, New York City, founder and senior partner, 1946—. Lecturer at Practising Law Institute; member of board of visitors of Columbia University School of Law, 1957—. Director of Cejwin Camps, Inc., 1946—. Trustee of Scarsdale Adult School, 1967-71; member of Columbia University Senate, 1973-75. *Military service:* U.S. Army, Judge Advocate General's Department, 1942-46; became major.

MEMBER: International Bar Association, American Bar Association, Judge Advocate General's Bar Association, Federal Bar Council, New York Bar Association, New York County Bar Association, New York City Bar Association, Columbia Law School Alumni Association (president, 1965-67), Phi Beta Kappa, Zeta Beta Tau. *Awards, honors:* Columbia Alumni medal for distinguished service, 1962; Royal Order of Vasa (Sweden), 1967, for meritorious services in commerce and industry.

WRITINGS: (With Herbert A. Einhorn) *Proxy Contests for Corporate Control,* Columbia University Press, 1957, 2nd edition, 1968; (with Einhorn) *Tender Offers for Corporate Control,* Columbia University Press, 1973; (with others) *Developments in Tender Offers for Corporate Control, 1973-76,* Columbia University Press, 1977. Contributor to law reviews and other professional journals.

*   *   *

ARBUCKLE, Wanda Rector 1910-

PERSONAL: Born April 18, 1910, in Lewes, Iowa; daughter of James V. (a mason) and Mary (Sprouse) Samson; married John D. Rector, March 21, 1928 (died December 23, 1960); married Tacitus C. Arbuckle, November 22, 1964; children: (first marriage) John D., Peggy J. (Mrs. Warren F. Frederick). *Education:* San Francisco State University, B.Ed., 1954; Chico State College (now California State University, Chico), M.A., 1958. *Politics:* Democrat. *Religion:* Protestant. *Home:* 992 Deschutes Rd., Palo Cedro, Calif. 96073.

CAREER: Elementary school teacher in California, 1943-62; Pupil Personnel Services, Redding, Calif., psychometrist in special education, 1962-75. Member of Women's Parole Advisory Board, 1965-66, County Mental Health Advisory Board, 1966—, County Council for Prevention of Crime and Delinquency, Anti-Poverty Program, Prevention/Intervention for Infants, and Area II Developmental Disabilities Board, 1977—. Consultant to federal Project for the Gifted and Talented. *Member:* International Reading Association, National Congress of Parents and Teachers (honorary life member), American Association of University Women, National Retired Teachers Association, Delta Kappa Gamma, Order of Eastern Star. *Awards, honors:* Ph.D., Colorado State Christian College, 1972.

WRITINGS: (With Eleanor Hill Ball and George C. Cornwell) *Learning to Move and Moving to Learn,* C. E. Merrill, Book I, 1969, Book II, 1971, Book III, 1973; *Moving and Making Believe,* illustrations by Cornwell, Academic

Therapy Publications, 1975. Contributor to *Delta Kappa Gamma Bulletin.*

WORK IN PROGRESS: The Bells of 1776, a historical novel for children; *Fantasy, Fun and Feelings,* an adventure book to help children develop appropriate behaviors or alternatives that could prevent inappropriate behavior; *The Travels of Treadwell the Turtle,* an imaginary story for primary children.

SIDELIGHTS: Wanda Rector Arbuckle explained to *CA* that she began her writing career "to help learning disabled children. . . , to bring history alive for children. . . , [and] to help develop understanding of self and other's behavior."

* * *

AREY, James A. 1936-

PERSONAL: Born September 23, 1936, in Brookline, Mass.; son of Harold L. (a sales engineer) and Ruth (Ross) Arey; married Elizabeth Ann Harvey, September 29, 1961; children: Scott Q., Justin T. *Education:* Boston University, B.S., 1958. *Home:* 11 Montgomery Rd., Scarsdale, N.Y. 10583. *Agent:* Daniel M. O'Shea, 330 West 58th St., New York, N.Y. 10019.

CAREER: United Press International, Boston, Mass., assistant night editor, 1961-66; Pan American World Airways, New York, N.Y., director of corporate public relations, 1966—. *Military Service:* U.S. Army, 1958-61. *Member:* Aviation Space Writers Association, Author's Guild, Sigma Delta Chi.

WRITINGS: The Sky Pirates, Scribner, 1972; (contributing editor) *Dictionary of American History,* Scribner, 1973.

* * *

ARMATAS, James P. 1931-

PERSONAL: Born February 14, 1931, in Joliet, Ill.; son of Peter M. (a businessman) and Mary (Furman) Armatas; married Rena J. Hartzler, June 1, 1956; children: J. Bret, Libby Ann. *Education:* University of Colorado, B.A., 1953, M.S., 1954; University of Kansas, Ph.D., 1959. *Home:* 5424 West 86th St., Prairie Village, Kan. 66207. *Office:* J. P. Armatas & Associates, Inc., Shawnee-Mission, Kan.

CAREER: University of Kansas, Lawrence, lecturer in psychology, 1964-69; Veterans Administration Center, Leavenworth, Kan., psychologist, 1959—; J. P. Armatas & Associates, Inc., Shawnee-Mission, Kan., psychologist, 1959—. *Military service:* U.S. Air Force, 1951-52. *Member:* American Psychological Association, Southwestern Psychological Association, Kansas Psychological Association, Missouri Psychological Association.

WRITINGS: (With Donald E. Lundberg) *The Management of People in Hotels, Restaurants and Clubs,* W. C. Brown, 1964, 4th edition, 1978; (with J. L. Hewitt, L. Lohrenz, and H. P. Remple) *Rehabilitation of the Chronically Institutionalized,* University of Kansas, 1971. Contributor to professional journals.

* * *

ARMSTRONG, Hamilton Fish 1893-1973

April 7, 1893—April 24, 1973; American editor, journalist, and authority on international politics. Obituaries: *New York Times,* April 25, 1973; *Time,* May 7, 1973; *Newsweek,* May 7, 1973.

ARMSTRONG, Robert Plant 1919-

PERSONAL: Born May 19, 1919, in Wheeling, W.Va.; son of Clarence Warren and Dorothy Johanna (Green) Armstrong. *Education:* University of Arizona, B.A., 1944; State University of Iowa, M.A., 1946; Northwestern University, Ph.D., 1957. *Home:* 4119 Rock Creek Dr., Dallas, Tex. 75204. *Office:* Aesthetic Studies, University of Texas at Dallas, Richardson, Tex. 75080.

CAREER: Montana State University, Bozeman, instructor in English, 1946-50; Balai Bahasa Inggeris, Jogjakarta, Indonesia, instructor in English, 1955-56; University of Michigan, Ann Arbor, lecturer in English, summers, 1956-57; Alfred A. Knopf, Inc., New York, N.Y., editor, 1958-59; University of Arizona Press, Tucson, director of publications, 1959-60; Northwestern University Press, Evanston, Ill., director, 1960-73; Northwestern University, Evanston, professor of arts and sciences, 1967-73; University of Texas at Dallas, Richardson, professor of anthropology, 1974—. Visiting professor of art history, State University of New York at Buffalo, summer, 1970; visiting curator of African art, Buffalo Museum of Science, summer, 1970; visiting director, University of Ibadan (Nigeria) Press, 1972-73. Book traveler for Houghton, Mifflin & Co. 1945-46; field editor, Harper & Bros., 1956-58. Attended first African writers workshop in Kampala, Uganda. *Military service:* U.S. Navy, 1940-43.

MEMBER: American Anthropological Association (fellow), African Studies Association (fellow), American Folklore Society (fellow), American Council of Learned Societies (advanced graduate fellow), American Association of University Professors, Mbari Writers and Artists Guild (Ibadan, Nigeria), Sigma Xi. *Awards, honors:* Phoebe M. Bogan Poetry Prize of University of Arizona, 1944.

WRITINGS: (Contributor) De Sola Pool, editor, *Trends in Content Analysis,* University of Illinois Press, 1959; (editor with Jack Berry and John Povey, and contributor) *Proceedings of the Conference on African Languages and Literatures,* Department of Linguistics, Northwestern University, 1966; (with Povey and Michael Crowder), *Three Essays on African Art and Literature,* Northwestern University Press, 1966; (contributor) Gwendolen Carter, editor, *Expanding Horizons in African Studies,* Northwestern University Press, 1969; (contributor) John Paden and Edward Soja, editors, *African Experience: Bibliography,* Northwestern University Press, 1970; *Forms and Processes of African Sculpture,* African and Afro-American Research Institute, University of Texas, 1970; *The Affecting Presence: An Essay in Humanistic Anthropology,* University of Illinois Press, 1971; *Wellspring: On the Myth and Source of Culture,* University of California Press, 1975. Contributor of articles and reviews to *Triquarterly, Scholarly Publishing,* and to folklore and African studies journals. *Book Forum,* columnist, 1975—, editorial director.

WORK IN PROGRESS: From Dissertation to Book: A Publisher's View; The Powers of Presence: Consciousness, Myth, and the Affecting Presence.

* * *

ARONSON, Marvin L. 1925-

PERSONAL: Born May 3, 1925, in New York, N.Y.; son of Moses Leonard (a businessman) and Frances (Diamondston) Aronson; married Helen Chance Fortgang (owner of interior decorating and rocks and minerals business), June 22, 1948; children: David Michael, Ruth Rachel. *Education:* Columbia University, B.A., 1946, M.A., 1947;

University of Michigan, Ph.D., 1950. *Home:* 32 Pasadena Place, Mount Vernon, N.Y. 10552. *Office:* 124 East 28th St., New York, N.Y. 10016.

CAREER: Psychologist in private practice, 1954—; Postgraduate Center for Mental Health, New York, N.Y., associate director, 1962-70, director of group therapy department, training analyst, and senior supervisor, 1970—. Diplomate, American Board of Examiners in Professional Psychology, 1955. Director of psychological services, New Jersey Center for Psychotherapy, Englewood, N.J., 1961-76. *Member:* American Psychological Association (fellow), American Group Therapy Association (fellow), New York Society of Clinical Psychologists, Westchester County Psychological Association.

WRITINGS: How to Overcome Your Fear of Flying, Hawthorn, 1971. Co-editor of "Group Therapy: An Overview" series, Stratton Intercontinental Medical Book Corp., 1974—. Also contributor of numerous articles on group and individual psychotherapy in professional journals.

*   *   *

ARUNDEL, Honor (Morfydd) 1919-1973

August 15, 1919—June 8, 1973; British poet, playwright, and author of teenage fiction. Obituaries: *Publishers Weekly,* July 2, 1973. (See index for *CA* sketch)

*   *   *

ARY, Donald E(ugene) 1930-

PERSONAL: Born July 2, 1930, in Jamestown, Ohio; son of Jesse R. (a housepainter) and Nora E. (King) Ary; married Sheila M. Littleboy, December 21, 1957; children: Richard C., E. Grace, Rachel M. *Education:* Wilmington College, Wilmington, Ohio, B.S.Ed., 1952; Syracuse University, M.S.Ed., 1953; Columbia University, additional study, 1956-57, 1963; University of Iowa, Ph.D., 1966. *Religion:* Society of Friends. *Home:* 526 Russell Rd., DeKalb, Ill. 60115. *Office:* College of Education, Northern Illinois University, DeKalb, Ill. 60115.

CAREER: Worked as an elementary school teacher in Ohio, 1955-57, and in Alconbury, England, 1957-64; Indiana University at Bloomington, assistant professor of education, 1966-69; Northern Illinois University, DeKalb, associate professor, 1969-72, professor of education, 1972—. *Military service:* U.S. Army, 1953-55. *Member:* American Educational Research Association, Phi Delta Kappa.

WRITINGS: (With Lucy Chesses Jacobs and Asghar Razavieh) *Introduction to Research in Education,* Holt, 1972, 2nd edition, in press; *Examination Questions for Introduction to Research in Education,* Holt, 1972; (with Richard J. Mueller and Charles McCormick) *Examination Questions for Classroom Learning and Perception,* Praeger, 1974; (with Mueller and McCormick) *Readings in Classroom Learning and Perception,* Praeger, 1974; (with Jacobs) *Introduction to Statistics: Purposes and Procedures,* Holt, 1976. Contributor to various U.S. Office of Education documents.

*   *   *

ASCH, Frank 1946-

PERSONAL: Born August 6, 1946, in Somerville, N.J.; son of John (a truck driver) and Margaret (Giasullo) Asch. *Education:* Cooper Union, B.A., 1968. *Home:* Route 169, Brooklyn, Conn.

CAREER: Writer and illustrator of children's books.

*WRITINGS—*Most self-illustrated: *George's Store,* McGraw, 1969; *Linda,* McGraw, 1969; *Elvira Everything,* Harper, 1970; *The Blue Balloon,* McGraw, 1971; *Yellow, Yellow,* McGraw, 1971; *Rebecka,* Harper, 1971; *I Met a Penguin,* McGraw, 1972; *In the Eye of the Teddy,* Harper, 1973; *Gia and the Hundred Dollars' Worth of Bubble Gum,* McGraw, 1974; *Good Lemonade,* F. Watts, 1975; *Monkey Face,* Parents' Magazine Press, 1977; *MacGoose's Grocery,* Dial, 1978; *City Sandwich* (poems), Greenwillow, 1978; *Turtle Tale,* Dial, 1978; *Moon Bear,* Scribner, 1978; *Country Pie* (poems), Greenwillow, 1978.

WORK IN PROGRESS: The Little Devil's Dictionary, for Scribner; *Sand Cake,* for Parents' Magazine Press; *Running with Rachel,* for Dial.

SIDELIGHTS: Frank Asch says, "I do kid's books because I like to draw and make up stories which express my feelings and kids' feelings, and because it enables me to put my artistic ability and training to some tangible use."

BIOGRAPHICAL/CRITICAL SOURCES: New York Times Book Review, March 2, 1969, February 1, 1970; *Life,* December 17, 1971; *Washington Post Children's Book World,* November 5, 1972.

*   *   *

ASHFORD, Gerald 1907-

PERSONAL: Born March 24, 1907, in St. Paul, Minn.; son of Nicholas and Amanda Ashford; married Carol Lillo, May 14, 1942; children: James Lillo. *Education:* Attended University of Illinois. *Home:* 341 Laurelwood Dr., San Antonio, Tex.

CAREER: San Antonio Express and News, San Antonio, Tex., former fine arts editor, columnist, and theater critic. *Military service:* U.S. Army, 1942-46; became captain.

WRITINGS: Everyday Publicity: A Practical Guide, Law-Arts Publishers, 1970; *Spanish Texas: Yesterday and Today,* Jenkins Publishing, 1971. Also author of "The Cave of the Wombats," a play.

*   *   *

ASHLEY, Maurice (Percy) 1907-

PERSONAL: Born September 4, 1907, in London, England; son of Percy and Doris (Hayman) Ashley; married Phyllis Mary Griffiths, 1935; children: Philip, Joan. *Education:* Attended St. Paul's School, London; New College, Oxford, B.A. (first class honors), 1929, D. Phil., 1933. *Politics:* Labour. *Religion:* Church of England. *Home:* 34 Wood Lane, Ruislip, Middlesex HA4 6EX, England.

CAREER: Historical research assistant to Winston Churchill, 1929-33; *Manchester Guardian* (now *Guardian*), London, England, member of editorial staff, 1933-37; *Times,* London, member of editorial staff, 1937-39; *Britain Today,* London, editor, 1939-40; *Listener,* London, deputy editor, 1946-58, editor, 1958-67; Loughborough University of Technology, Loughborough, England, research fellow, 1967-69. *Military service:* British Army, Intelligence Corps, 1940-45; became major. *Member:* Cromwell Association (president, 1961), Reform Club (London). *Awards, honors:* Awarded Commander of the British Empire, 1978.

WRITINGS: (With Christopher T. Saunders) *Red Oxford: A History of the Growth of Socialism in the University of Oxford* (booklet), Oxford University Labour Club, 1930, 2nd edition, 1933; *Financial and Commercial Policy Under the Cromwellian Protectorate,* Oxford University Press,

1934, revised edition, 1962; *Louis XIV and the Greatness of France,* Hodder & Stoughton, for English Universities Press, 1946, Macmillan (New York), 1948, reprinted, English Universities Press, 1967; *John Wildman, Plotter and Postmaster: A Study of the English Republican Movement in the Seventeenth Century,* J. Cape, 1947; *Mr. President: An Introduction to American History,* J. Cape, 1948.

England in the Seventeenth Century, Penguin, 1952, 4th edition, Hutchinson, 1978; *Cromwell's Generals,* J. Cape, 1954, St. Martin's, 1955; (author of introduction) Arthur J. L. Fremantle, *The Fremantle Diary,* Deutsch, 1956; *The Greatness of Oliver Cromwell,* Hodder & Stoughton, 1957, Macmillan (New York), 1958; *Is History Bunk?* (pamphlet), Newman Neame, 1958; *Oliver Cromwell and the Puritan Revolution,* Macmillan (New York), 1958.

Great Britain to 1688: A Modern History, University of Michigan Press, 1961; *The Stuarts in Love: With Some Reflections on Love and Marriage in the Sixteenth and Seventeenth Centuries,* Hodder & Stoughton, 1963, Macmillan (New York), 1964; *Life in Stuart England,* Putnam, 1964; *Magna Carta in the Seventeenth Century,* University Press of Virginia, for Magna Carta Commission of Virginia, 1965; *The Glorious Revolution of 1688,* Hodder & Stoughton, 1966, Scribner, 1967, revised edition, Panther, 1968; *Churchill as Historian* (personal memoir), Secker & Warburg, 1968, Scribner, 1969; (editor) *Cromwell,* Prentice-Hall, 1969; *The Golden Century: Europe 1598-1715,* Praeger, 1969, revised edition, Panther, 1973.

Charles II: The Man and the Statesman, Praeger, 1971; *King John and His Times,* Weidenfeld & Nicolson, 1972; *A History of Europe, 1648-1815,* Prentice-Hall, 1973; *William I and His Times,* Weidenfeld & Nicolson, 1973; *The English Civil War: A Concise History,* Thames & Hudson, 1974; *Rupert of the Rhine,* Hart-Davis, 1976; *General Monck,* J. Cape, 1977; *James II,* Dent, 1978.

WORK IN PROGRESS: The Rise and Fall of the House of Stewart.

* * *

ASHWORTH, Kenneth H(ayden) 1932-

PERSONAL: Born February 24, 1932, in Abilene, Tex.; son of Harold L. and Mae B. (Grote) Ashworth; married Sonia Olander, September 12, 1959; children: Rodney Brian, Karen Grace. *Education:* Attended University of the Americas, 1955-56; University of Texas, B.A., 1958, Ph.D., 1969; Syracuse University, M.A., 1959. *Politics:* Democrat. *Religion:* Unitarian-Universalist. *Home:* 4507 Balcones Dr., Austin, Tex. 78731. *Office:* Commissioner's Office, Coordinating Board, Texas College and University System, Lyndon Baines Johnson Building, Austin, Tex. 78711.

CAREER: U.S. Treasury Department, Washington, D.C., management analyst, 1959-60; Urban Renewal Administration, Washington, D.C., regional coordinator, 1960-61; National Association of Housing and Redevelopment Officials, Washington, D.C., assistant director for urban renewal, 1961-63; San Francisco Redevelopment Agency, San Francisco, Calif., assistant executive director, 1963-65; U.S. Office of Education, Bureau of Higher Education, Washington, D.C., chief of college construction grants section, 1965-66; Texas College and University System, Coordinating Board, Austin, assistant commissioner for federal programs and facilities planning, 1966-69; University of Texas System, Austin, assistant to vice-chancellor for academic programs, 1969-70, vice-chancellor for academic affairs, 1970-73; University of Texas at San Antonio, executive vice-president,

1973-76; Texas College and University System, Coordinating Board, commissioner, 1976—. *Military service:* U.S. Navy, 1951-55.

MEMBER: American Educational Research Association, American Educational Studies Association, Association for Institutional Research, American Society for Public Administration, Philosophy of Education Society, History of Education Society, Southern Association of Colleges and Schools, Association of Texas Colleges and Universities, Phi Beta Kappa, Pi Sigma Alpha, Phi Kappa Phi, Phi Delta Kappa.

WRITINGS: Scholars and Statesmen: Higher Education and Government Policy, Jossey-Bass, 1972; *American Higher Education in Decline,* Texas A & M University Press, 1979. Contributor to *Educational Record, Texas Outlook, Journal of Higher Education, Change, Peabody Journal of Education,* and *Phi Delta Kappan.*

* * *

ASSAEL, Henry 1935-

PERSONAL: Born September 12, 1935, in Sofia, Bulgaria; came to United States in 1940, naturalized in 1946; son of Stanley and Anna (Behar) Assael; married Alyce Friedman, August 19, 1961; children: Shaun, Brenda. *Education:* Harvard University, B.A. (cum laude), 1957; University of Pennsylvania, M.B.A., 1959; Columbia University, Ph.D., 1965. *Home:* 110-45 Queens Blvd., Forest Hills, N.Y. 11375. *Office:* Graduate School of Business Administration, New York University, 100 Trinity Pl., New York, N.Y. 10006.

CAREER: Batten, Barton, Durstine & Osborne (advertising firm), New York City, advertising researcher, 1959-62; St. John's University, Jamaica, N.Y., instructor, 1962-63, assistant professor of marketing, 1963-65; Hofstra University, Hempstead, N.Y., assistant professor of marketing, 1965-66; New York University, New York City, assistant professor, 1966-68, associate professor, 1968-73, professor of marketing, 1973—. Consultant to AT&T, 1972—, New York Stock Exchange, 1973—, General Electric, Remington, Pepsico International, and National Academy of Sciences. *Military service:* U.S. Army Reserves, Adjutant General Corps, 1959-64; became second lieutenant. *Member:* American Marketing Association, American Association of University Professors, Academy of Political Science.

WRITINGS: Educational Preparations for Positions in Advertising Management, Association of National Advertisers, 1966; *The Politics of Distributive Trade Associations: A Study in Conflict Resolution,* Hofstra University Press, 1967; (with Robert K. McMillan) *National Survey of Transportation Attitudes and Behavior, Summary Report,* Highway Research Board, National Academy of Sciences, 1968.

Contributor: F. Bennett, editor, *Marketing and Economic Development,* American Marketing Association, 1965; Lee Adler and Irving Crespi, editors, *Attitude Research on the Rocks,* American Marketing Association, 1968; L. W. Stern, editor, *Distribution Channels,* Houghton, 1969; Harold J. Leavitt and Louis R. Pondy, editors, *Readings in Managerial Psychology,* University of Chicago Press, 1971; Perry Bliss, editor, *Readings in the Behavioral Sciences and Marketing,* Allyn & Bacon, 1972. Contributor to *Journal of Marketing, Journal of Advertising Research, Journal of Marketing Research,* and *Administrative Science Quarterly.*

WORK IN PROGRESS: A book on market segmentation and perceptual mapping.

ATWOOD, Ann (Margaret) 1913-

PERSONAL: Born February 12, 1913, in Heber, Calif.; daughter of Howard Catlin (a doctor of osteopathy) and Marie (Jones) Atwood. Education: University of Redlands, B.A., 1934; attended Art Center School, Los Angeles, Calif., summer, 1935. Politics: Republican. Home address: 32013 Point Pl., South Laguna, Calif. 92677.

CAREER: Owner and manager of Ann Atwood Studio of Children's Portraiture in Riverside, Calif., 1937-40, San Marino, Calif., 1940-60, and South Laguna, Calif., 1960-67. Founder and director of adult education class in poetry reading in Riverside, Calif., 1938-40; high school poetry teacher in Hollywood, Calif., 1943-44. Member: Sierra Club, Wilderness Society.

AWARDS, HONORS—For books: University of California at Irvine annual book award, 1967, for The Little Circle; New Moon Cove was named one of Best Books of the Year by the School Library Journal, 1969, won Horn Book Award for illustration from Boston Globe, 1969, the Southern California Council on Literature for Children and Young People award for illustration, 1970, and the University of California at Irvine special award, 1970; The Wild Young Desert was named one of Best Books of the Year by the School Library Journal, 1970; Haiku: The Mood of Earth appeared on the Horn Book Honor List, 1971, the Best Books of the Year list of the School Library Journal, 1972, won Southern California Council on Literature for Children and Young People award, 1972, and the University of California at Irvine Annual Book Award, 1972.

Awards for filmstrips: "The Little Circle" won silver medal at International Film and Television Festival of New York, 1970, and media award of Southern California Social Science Association, 1972; "Haiku: The Mood of Earth" won Chris Award from Columbus Film Festival and silver medal from International Film and Television Festival of New York in 1971, award for distinguished contribution for fusion of poetry and photography from Southern California Council on Literature for Children and Young Peopl ϵ, and Ann Corneille Award from National Educational Film Festival (Oakland, Calif.) in 1972; silver medal from International Film and Television Festival of New York, 1972, for "The Gods Were Tall and Green"; "Haiku: The Hidden Glimmering" won Jack London Award from National Educational Film Festival (Oakland, Calif.), 1973, and gold medal from Atlanta Film Festival; "Inscape: The Realm of Haiku" won Gold Cindy Award from the Informational Film Producers Association.

WRITINGS—All books for children; all with photographs by author; all published by Scribner: Being Made of Earth, 1940; The Little Circle, 1967; New Moon Cove, 1969; The Wild Young Desert, 1970; Haiku: The Mood of Earth, 1971; The Kingdom of the Forest, 1972; My Own Rhythm, 1973; (with Erica Anderson) For All That Lives: With the Words of Albert Schweitzer, 1975; Haiku–Vision in Poetry and Photography, 1977.

Author and photographer of film strips; all produced by Lyceum Productions: "Sea, Sand and Shore," in three parts, 1969; "The Little Circle," 1970; "The Wild Young Desert," in two parts, 1970; "Haiku: The Mood of Earth," in two parts, 1971; "The Gods Were Tall and Green," in two parts, 1972; "Haiku: The Hidden Glimmering," 1973; "Inscape: The Realm of Haiku," 1976. Photographer for filmstrips written by Elizabeth Baldwin Hazelton and produced by Lyceum Productions: "Tahiti Is My Island," 1969; "Sammy the Crow," 1970; "Teeka the Otter," 1971;

"My Forty Years with Beavers," 1974; "For All That Lives," 1975. Also translator of Drifting with the Moon, Tuttle, 1978. Also illustrator with photographs, Sammy: The Crow Who Remembered, Scribner, 1969.

WORK IN PROGRESS: Another book and film on haiku; two filmstrips on wild beavers; two filmstrips on Ireland.†

                    *   *   *

AUMANN, Francis R(obert) 1901-

PERSONAL: Born January 21, 1901, in Delaware, Ohio; son of Frederick A. and Ellen (Maloney) Aumann; married Katherine O. McCarthy, April 4, 1945. Education: Ohio Wesleyan University, A.B., 1921; Western Reserve University (now Case Western Reserve University), graduate study, 1923-24; Ohio State University, A.M., 1925; University of Iowa, Ph.D., 1928. Home: 112 East Como Ave., Columbus, Ohio 43202. Office: Department of Political Science, Ohio State University, Columbus, Ohio 43210.

CAREER: Teacher of history and government in high school in Marietta, Ohio, 1921-23; public school teacher in Cleveland, Ohio, 1925-26; Iowa State Teachers College (now University of Northern Iowa), Cedar Falls, instructor in history and political science, 1926; University of Iowa, Iowa City, assistant in political science, 1926-28; Ohio State University, Columbus, instructor, 1928-32, assistant professor, 1932-37, associate professor, 1937-40, professor of political science, 1940-71, professor emeritus, 1971—. Visiting professor at Ohio Wesleyan University, 1946, 1953, Wayne University (now Wayne State University), summer, 1947, University of Iowa, 1951, 1952, and Southern Illinois University, 1958-60. Military service: U.S. Naval Reserve, 1942-63, active duty, 1942-45; retired as commander.

MEMBER: American Political Science Association, American Judicature Society, U.S. Naval Institute, National Municipal League, Midwest Political Science Association, State Historical Society of Iowa, Ohio Historical Society, Ohio Association of Economists and Political Scientists, Ohioana Library Association, Alpha Tau Omega, Pi Sigma Alpha.

WRITINGS: Municipal Administration of Justice in Iowa, State Historical Society of Iowa, 1929; Through Fifty Years: A Short History of the Beta Eta Chapter of Alpha Tau Omega Fraternity, [Cleveland, Ohio], 1937; The Changing American Legal System: Some Selected Aspects, Ohio State University Press, 1940, reprinted, DaCapo Press, 1972; (with Carl Wittke and others) History of the State of Ohio, Volume VI, Ohio State Historical Society, 1941; Ohio Government and Conservation: Legislation, Program and Administration (monograph), Ohio State University Studies, 1954; Transportation System of Ohio: Organization, Administration, and Regulation (monograph), Ohio State University Studies, 1955; The Instrumentalities of Justice: Their Forms, Functions and Limitations, Ohio State University Press, 1956; (with Harvey Walker) The Government and Administration of Ohio, Crowell, 1956; (with W. Brooke Graves and others) State Constitutional Revision, Public Administrative Service (Chicago, Ill.), 1960. Contributor to Dictionary of American History, Collier's Encyclopedia, Encyclopaedia Britannica, and "Social Science Abstracts." Contributor of about eighty-five articles and reviews to law and education journals, and to Palimpsest.

WORK IN PROGRESS: Research on technological innovation and constitutional change.

AVOCATIONAL INTERESTS: Travel in Great Britain, Australia, and Southeast Asia.

AURAND, Harold Wilson 1940-

PERSONAL: Born June 25, 1940, in Danville, Pa.; son of James Wilson and Esther (Weissinger) Aurand; married Frances Scisly, December 29, 1962; children: Harold, Jr., Michele Renee. Education: Franklin and Marshall College, A.B., 1962; Pennsylvania State University, M.A., 1963, Ph.D., 1969. Home address: R.D. 2, Drums, Pa. 18222. Office: Department of History, Pennsylvania State University, Hazleton, Pa. 18201.

CAREER: Pennsylvania State University, Hazleton, instructor, 1964-70, assistant professor, 1970-72, associate professor of history, 1972—. Member of board of directors, United Charities of Hazleton, 1969-72; member of Lattimer Labor Memorial Committee, 1971-72. Member: American Historical Association, Organization of American Historians, History Teachers Association, Pennsylvania Historical Association, Pennsylvania Labor History Society.

WRITINGS: From the Molly Maguires to the United Mine Workers: The Social Ecology of an Industrial Union, 1869-97, Temple University Press, 1971. Contributor of articles to Labor History, Pennsylvania History, Pennsylvania Magazine of History and Biography, and other history journals.

WORK IN PROGRESS: Research on social, economic, and institutional history of anthracite mine workers, 1900-1950.

*   *   *

AUTEN, James H(udson) 1938-

PERSONAL: Born August 2, 1938, in Washington, D.C.; son of Hudson W. (a bank officer) and Marjorie (Muschaney) Auten; married Anne E. Palko, April 20, 1963; children: Elizabeth, Michael, Susan. Education: Michigan State University, B.S., 1967; University of Illinois at Urbana-Champaign, M.Ed., 1972. Home: 1011 West Union, Champaign, Ill. 61820. Office: Police Training Institute, University of Illinois, 359 Armory Bldg., Champaign, Ill. 61801.

CAREER: Michigan State University, Department of Public Safety, East Lansing, police sergeant, 1961-69; University of Illinois at Urbana-Champaign, Police Training Institute, instructor, 1969—. Military service: U.S. Army, 1956-59.

WRITINGS: Traffic Crash Investigation, with workbook, C. C Thomas, 1972; (with D. G. Webb) The Crash Speed Calculator, C. C Thomas, 1972; Training in the Small Department, C. C Thomas, 1973. Contributor of articles to Police, Police Chief, and Law and Order.

*   *   *

AVAKUMOVIC, Ivan 1926-

PERSONAL: Born August 22, 1926, in Belgrade, Yugoslavia. Education: Cambridge University, B.A., 1947; University of London, M.A., 1954; Oxford University, D.Phil., 1958. Office: Department of History, University of British Columbia, Vancouver 8, British Columbia, Canada.

CAREER: University of Aberdeen, Aberdeen, Scotland, assistant lecturer, 1957-58; University of Manitoba, Winnipeg, assistant professor, 1958-62, associate professor of political science and international relations, 1962-63; University of British Columbia, Vancouver, associate professor, 1963-67, professor of political science, 1967-69, professor of history, 1969—.

WRITINGS: (With George Woodcock) The Anarchist Prince, Boardman, 1950; History of the Communist Party of Yugoslavia, Aberdeen University Press, 1964; (with George Woodcock) The Doukhobors, Oxford University Press, 1968; Mihailovic Prema Nemackim Dokumentima, Nase Delo, 1969; The Communist Party in Canada: A History, McClelland & Stewart, 1975; Socialism in Canada: A Study of the CCF-NDP in Federal and Provincial Politics, McClelland & Stewart, 1978.

*   *   *

AVRAMOVIC, Dragoslav 1919-

PERSONAL: Born October 14, 1919, in Skoplje, Yugoslavia; son of Nikola and Jelena (Sahovic) Avramovic; married Marija Jovanovic, May 23, 1943; children: Zoran, Mila, Dora. Education: University of Belgrade, Ph.D., 1956. Home: 18 Chemin de la Gradelle, 1224 Chene Bougeries, Geneva, Switzerland. Office: Independent Commission on International Development Issues, Rue de Moillebeau 56, Geneva, Switzerland.

CAREER: Yugoslav Monetary Reform Commission, Belgrade, Yugoslavia, secretary, 1945-46; National Bank of Yugoslavia, Belgrade, deputy secretary, 1946-47, secretary, 1948-50; University of Belgrade, Belgrade, lecturer in economics, 1947-53; International Bank for Reconstruction and Development, Washington, D.C., staff member, 1953-77, General Studies Division, chief of economic staff, 1959-63, assistant director of economics department, 1964, director of special economic studies, 1965-67, director of commodity stabilization studies, 1968, director of industrialization studies, South Asia, 1969, Latin American Department, economic advisor, 1970-72, Latin American and the Caribbean Regional Office, chief economist, 1973-74, senior advisor to development policy staff, 1975-76, director of development economics department, 1976-77; Independent Commission on International Development Issues, Geneva, Switzerland, director of the secretariat, 1978—. Headed economic mission to Philippines, 1961-62, Nigeria, 1965-66, Algeria, 1966, Brazil, 1967, Iran, 1969, Pakistan, 1969, and Columbia, 1970. Advisor, Yugoslav Ministry of Finance and National Bank of Yugoslavia, 1950-53; special advisor on international commodity stabilization, United Nations Conference on Trade and Development, 1974-75.

WRITINGS: Postwar Economic Growth in Southeast Asia, International Bank for Reconstruction and Development, 1955; Debt Servicing Capacity and Postwar Growth in International Indebtedness, Johns Hopkins Press, 1958; The Coffee Problem, International Bank for Reconstruction and Development, 1958, 2nd edition, 1960; Debt Servicing Problems of Low-Income Countries, Johns Hopkins Press, 1960; The Commodity Problem, International Bank for Reconstruction and Development, 1964; Economic Growth and External Debt, Johns Hopkins Press, 1965; International Trade, Industrialization, and Growth, International Bank for Reconstruction and Development, 1968; (editor and coordinating author) Economic Growth of Colombia: Problems and Prospects, Johns Hopkins Press, 1972; Stabilization, Adjustment, and Diversification: A Study of the Weakest Commodities Produced by the Poorest Regions, International Bank for Reconstruction and Development, 1976. Also author of papers and monographs on international banking issues.

SIDELIGHTS: Dragoslav Avramovic is an expert on international finance and development. In 1974, he and three other members of the International Bank for Reconstruction and Development took part in a New York Times discussion concerning food production problems in the developing countries. Avramovic asserted that "despite a continuance of enormous problems, there have been substantial advances in a large part of the developing world in the building of skills, technical capacity and capabilities for using resources." Speaking of South America's more developed regions, Avramovic said that "the situation is likely to be considerably better than in the past. Prospects are that [the production of] both foodgrains and livestock will expand...." His optimism was tempered, however, by the anticipation of rising fuel costs. "Developing countries that import oil ... will not have an easy situation." He explained that those countries with a growing export trade will be able to meet rising fuel costs whereas those with little trade will be able to purchase even less as prices rise.

Some of Dragoslav Avramovic's writings have been translated into Spanish.

BIOGRAPHICAL/CRITICAL SOURCES: Choice, Volume IX, December, 1972; *New York Times,* January 27, 1974.

B

BABITZ, Sol 1911-

PERSONAL: Born October 11, 1911, in Brooklyn, N.Y.; son of Abraham (a union organizer) and Luba (Pogorelsky) Babitz; married Mae LaViolette (an artist), 1942; children: Eve, Miriam. Education: Attended Berlin Hochschule fuer Musik, 1930-31, Paris Ecole Normale, 1931, and University of Southern California, 1951. Politics: Radical. Home and office: 1955 North Wilton Pl., Hollywood, Calif. 90068.

CAREER: Los Angeles Philharmonic Orchestra, Los Angeles, Calif., first violinist, 1933-37; free-lance violinist for Hollywood studios, 1933-61; Early Music Laboratory, Hollywood, Calif., founder and director, 1948—. Fulbright lecturer in Germany, 1961-63. Editor of string parts of Igor Stravinsky scores, 1942—. Member: American Musicological Society (honorary president, 1952-57). Awards, honors: Ford Foundation grant, 1961-62; American Council of Learned Societies award, 1967.

WRITINGS: Problems of Rhythm in Baroque Music, Early Music Laboratory, 1967; Modern Errors in Mozart Performance, Early Music Laboratory, 1970; On Using Early Keyboard Fingering, Early Music Laboratory, 1971; (translator) Giuseppe Tartini, Treatise on Ornaments of Music, Early Music Laboratory, 1971; (editor and compiler) J. S. Bach's Six Violin Solos, Early Music Laboratory, 1972. Also author of numerous articles on musicology, published by Early Music Laboratory. Editor, Violin Department, International Musician, 1941-61.

* * *

BACHMAN, Jerald G(raybill) 1936-

PERSONAL: Born October 20, 1936, in Harrisburg, Pa.; son of J. Clarence (a physician) and Harriet (Mathias) Bachman; married Virginia Arlene Ludy, November 28, 1957; children: Terri Lynne, Steven Jerald, Jon Andrew. Education: Lebanon Valley College, A.B., 1958; University of Pennsylvania, M.A., 1961, Ph.D., 1962. Home: 2124 Stephen Ter., Ann Arbor, Mich. 48103. Office: Survey Research Center, Institute for Social Research, University of Michigan, Ann Arbor, Mich. 48106.

CAREER: Franklin Institute, Philadelphia, Pa., research assistant in engineering psychology, 1961; University of Michigan, Ann Arbor, study director at Survey Research Center of Institute for Social Research, 1962-67, senior study director, 1967-72, program director, 1972—, lecturer in psychology, 1963-72, assistant professor of education, 1964-65. Member: American Psychological Association, Society for the Psychological Study of Social Issues, American Association for the Advancement of Science, Sigma Xi.

WRITINGS: Youth in Transition, Institute for Social Research, University of Michigan, Volume I (with R. L. Kahn, M. T. Mednick, T. N. Davidson, and L. D. Johnston): Blueprint for a Longitudinal Study of Adolescent Boys, 1967, Volume II: The Impact of Family Background and Intelligence on Tenth-Grade Boys, 1970, Volume III (with S. Green and I. D. Wirtanen): Dropping Out: Problem or Symptom?, 1971, Volume V (with Jerome Johnston): Young Men and Military Service, 1972, Volume VI (with Patrick O'Malley and Jerome Johnston): Adolescence to Adulthood: Change and Stability in the Lives of Young Men, 1978; (contributor) A. S. Tannenbaum, editor, Control and Organizations, McGraw, 1968; (contributor) H. C. Lindgren, editor, Contemporary Research in Social Psychology, Wiley, 1969.

(Contributor) W. K. Graham and K. Roberts, editor, Comparative Studies in Organizational Behavior, Holt, 1970; (with Jerome Johnston) Young Men Look at Military Service: A Preliminary Report, Institute for Social Research, University of Michigan, 1970; (with E. vanDuinen) Youth Looks at National Problems, Institute for Social Research, University of Michigan, 1971; (contributor) G. A. Comstock and E. A. Rubenstein, editors, Television and Social Behavior, Volume III: Television and Adolescent Aggressiveness, U.S. Government Printing Office, 1971; (contributor) David Gottlieb, editor, Youth in Contemporary Society, Sage Publications, 1971; (contributor) James F. Adams, editor, Understanding Adolescence, Allyn & Bacon, 2nd edition (Bachman was not connected with 1st edition), 1972, 3rd edition, 1976; (contributor) N. Goldman and D. Segal, editors, Social Psychology and Military Service, Sage Publications, Inc., 1976; (with John Blair and Segal) The All-Volunteer Force: A Study of Ideology in the Military, University of Michigan Press, 1977.

Also author of monographs. Contributor of over twenty-five articles and reviews to psychology, sociology, and education journals, including Transaction: Social Science and Modern Society, Journal of Applied Psychology, Human Relations, Journal of Personality and Social Psychology, American Journal of Sociology, Journal of Abnormal and Social Psychology, Armed Forces and Society, and Youth and Society.

WORK IN PROGRESS: Continuing research on the life-styles and values of American youth.

SIDELIGHTS: Jerald G. Bachman told *CA:* "Since 1965 my writing has been based largely on my survey research work dealing with youth and youth-related social issues—including education, military service, and (most recently) drug use. The 'Youth in Transition' project, begun in 1966, has provided nationally representative data on all these topics plus others."

* * *

BACON, Edmund N(orwood) 1910-

PERSONAL: Born May 2, 1910, in Philadelphia, Pa.; son of Ellis Williams (a publisher) and Helen (Comly) Bacon; married Ruth Holmes (a teacher), September 16, 1938; children: Karin, Elinor, Michael, Hilda, Kira, Kevin. *Education:* Cornell University, B.Arch., 1932. *Home and office:* 2117 Locust St., Philadelphia, Pa. 19103.

CAREER: Architectural designer in Shanghai, China, 1934, and Philadelphia, Pa., 1935; Institute of Research and Planning, Flint, Mich., supervisor of city planning, 1937-39; managing director of Philadelphia Housing Association, 1940-43; Philadelphia City Planning Commission, Philadelphia, senior land planner, 1946-47, executive director, 1949-70, development coordinator, 1968-70; Mondev International Ltd. (real estate developers), Montreal, Quebec, vice-president of design, 1971—. Visiting lecturer at University of Pennsylvania, 1950—; member of board of trustees of First Pennsylvania Mortgage Trust, 1970—, and American Academy in Rome, 1965-75. *Member:* American Institute of Architects (fellow), American Institute of Planners. *Awards, honors:* Ford Foundation travel fellow, 1959; Art Alliance of Philadelphia medal of achievement, 1961; Brown medal award from the Franklin Institute, 1962; Rockfeller fellow, 1963; distinguished service award from American Institute of Planners, 1971; medal from American Institute of Architects, 1976.

WRITINGS: Design of Cities, Viking, 1967, revised edition, 1974; (contributor) Daniel J. Boorstin, editor, *American Civilization,* McGraw, 1972.

WORK IN PROGRESS: American Cities and Their Antecedents.

* * *

BACON, Phillip 1922-

PERSONAL: Born July 10, 1922, in Cleveland, Ohio; son of Hollis Phillip (an engineer) and Emma Jean (Schneider) Bacon; married Dorothy Willey; children: Laura Jane (Mrs. Robert C. Fraser), Phillip Everett. *Education:* University of Miami, Coral Gables, Fla., A.B., 1946; George Peabody College for Teachers, M.A., 1951, Ed.D., 1955. *Religion:* Presbyterian. *Home:* 2627 Amherst St., West University Pl., Houston, Tex. 77005. *Office:* Department of Geography, University of Houston, Houston, Tex. 77004.

CAREER: Teacher of social studies at Castle Heights Military Academy, Lebanon, Tenn., 1946-47, and Army and Navy Academy, Carlsbad, Calif., 1948-53; University of Pittsburgh, Pittsburgh, Pa., assistant professor of geography, 1955-57; Columbia University, Teachers College, New York, N.Y., visiting assistant professor, 1956-57, associate professor, 1957-60, professor of geography, 1960-63; George Peabody College for Teachers, Nashville, Tenn., professor of geography and dean of Graduate School, 1963-64; Columbia University, Teachers College, professor of geogra-

phy, 1964-66; University of Washington, Seattle, professor of geography and social studies education, 1966-71, co-director of tri-university project in elementary education, 1967-71; University of Houston, Houston, Tex., professor of geography, 1971—, chairman of department of geography, 1973-78, chairman of department of anthropology, 1973-75. Visiting professor, University of Colorado, 1962, North Carolina Central University, 1966, University of Texas, 1966, Seattle Pacific University, 1977-79; visiting geography scholar, National Science Foundation-Association of American Geographers program, 1969-71. Consultant to U.S. Office of Education, Field Educational Publications, Inc., book division of Time, Inc., and Educational Research Council of America social science project; consulting editor, Golden Press, 1958-61; educational director, Golden Book Institute of Knowledge, 1960-61; member of advisory board, high school geography project, Macmillan Publishing Co., 1970. *Military service:* U.S. Naval Reserve, 1942-45.

MEMBER: National Council for Geographic Education (life member; president, 1966), Association of American Geographers (chairman of Commission on Education, 1970; member of council, 1976—), National Council for the Social Studies, American Geographical Society (fellow), Royal Geographical Society (fellow), National Education Association (life member), Geographic Educators of Texas (founder), Kappa Phi Kappa, Omicron Delta Kappa, Gamma Theta Upsilon, Phi Delta Kappa, Kappa Delta Pi, Pi Gamma Mu, Sigma Xi, Sigma Alpha Epsilon, Mercer Island Country Club, Bay Area Racket Club. *Awards, honors:* Award for distinguished undergraduate teaching, University of Washington, Seattle, 1971; Distinguished Service Award, National Council for Geographic Education, 1974; Teaching Excellence Award, University of Houston, 1975.

WRITINGS: (Editor-in-chief) *The Golden Book Picture Atlas of the World,* six books, author of Book I: *North America* and Book VI: *Australia, Oceania, and the Polar Lands,* Golden Press, 1960, revised series published as *The Children's Picture Atlas of the World,* 1966 (published in England as *The Children's Picture Atlas in Colour,* Hamlyn, 1966); (editor) *Life Pictorial Atlas of the World,* Time-Life, 1961; (with Norman Carls and Frank E. Sorenson) *Knowing Our Neighbors in the United States,* Holt, 1966; (with Carls and Sorenson) *Knowing Our Neighbors in the United States and Canada,* Holt, 1966; (with Lorrin Kennamer) *Research Needs in Geographic Education,* National Council for Geographic Education, 1967; (with Ronald R. Boyce) *Towns and Cities,* Field Educational Publications, 1970; (with Boyce and William B. Conroy) *The United States and Canada,* Field Educational Publications, 1970, teacher's edition, 1972; (with Peter V. Greco) *The Story of Latin America,* Field Educational Publications, 1970; *Regions around the World,* Field Educational Publications, 1970, revised edition, 1972.

Contributor: Preston E. James, editor, *New Viewpoints in Geography,* National Council for the Social Studies, 1959; Wilhelmina Hill, editor, *Curriculum Guide for Geographic Education,* National Council for Geographic Education, 1963; Preston E. James and Lorrin Kennamer, editors, *Geography as a Professional Field,* U.S. Department of Health, Education, and Welfare, 1966; John W. Morris, editor, *Methods of Geographic Instruction,* Blaisdell, 1968; John Jarolimek and Huber M. Walsh, editors, *Readings for Social Studies in Elementary Education,* 2nd edition, Macmillan, 1969; Jonathan C. McLendon, William W. Joyce, and John R. Lee, editors, *Readings on Elementary Social Studies: Emerging Changes,* Allyn & Bacon, 1970; John M.

Ball, John E. Steinbrink, and Joseph P. Stoltman, editors, *The Social Sciences and Geographic Education*, Wiley, 1971; Huber M. Welsh, editor, *An Anthology of Readings in Elementary Social Studies*, National Council for the Social Studies, 1971; Bryan Strong, *America: In Space and Time*, Addison-Wesley, 1976.

Publications include map and globe skills casette program, A. J. Nystrom, 1972, and more than eighty articles in professional journals. Editor with Lorrin Kennamer, "Foundations of World Regional Geography" series, Prentice-Hall, 1970—; co-director, "Elementary Social Studies" series, Addison-Wesley, 1975; member of editorial advisory board, *World Book Encyclopedia*, 1965—, and board of consultants, *World Book Atlas*, 1965-70. Associate editor, *Journal of Geography*, 1967-71; editor of yearbook, *Focus on Geography*, National Council for the Social Studies, 1970; consulting editor, *Social Education*, 1976-79.

WORK IN PROGRESS: Atlas materials for children; revision of social studies textbooks; a world regional geography book.

*   *   *

BAER, Rosemary   1913-

PERSONAL: Born September 6, 1913, in Tsing Tau, China; daughter of Paul Patton and Helena (Alexander) Faris; married John Merle Baer (an electrical tester), January 27, 1951; children: Alexander John, Veloma Helene. *Education:* Middlebury College, A.B., 1934; graduate study at University of Pennsylvania and University of Besancon, 1936, Middlebury College, 1938, 1940, University of California, Los Angeles and Berkeley (extensions), 1963-65, Immaculate Heart College, 1963-65, and Pacific Oaks College, 1969. *Religion:* Christian.

CAREER: High school teacher of French, Latin, English, and sports, in Champlain, N.Y., 1934-36, and New Milford, Conn., 1937-43; American Airlines, Inc., Los Angeles, Calif., sales representative, 1943-51; Los Angeles Department of Recreation and Parks, Los Angeles, assistant in recreation of senior citizens, 1962-63; high school teacher of French, Latin, and Spanish in Los Angeles, 1963-67; United Presbyterian Churches in the U.S.A., Los Angeles, director of Christian education, 1967-72.

WRITINGS: Reflections on the Manson Trial: Journal of a Pseudo-Juror, Word Books, 1972.††

*   *   *

BAHLKE, Valerie Worth   1933-
(Valerie Worth)

PERSONAL: Born October 29, 1933, in Philadelphia, Pa.; daughter of Charles Brooke (a biologist) and Merida (Grey) Worth; married George W. Bahlke (a professor of English literature), December 28, 1955; children: Conrad, Catherine, Margaret. *Education:* Swarthmore College, B.A., 1955. *Residence:* Clinton, N.Y.

CAREER: Poet. Yale University Press, New Haven, Conn., secretary/assistant in promotion department, 1956-58.

WRITINGS—Under name Valerie Worth: *The Crone's Book of Words*, Llewellyn, 1971; *Small Poems*, Farrar, Straus, 1972; *More Small Poems*, Farrar, Straus, 1976; *La Pierre ensevelie* (novel), Editions Entente, 1977; *Still More Small Poems*, Farrar, Straus, 1978. Work is anthologized in *New World Writing, No. 7*, New American Library, 1955, and *Best Poems of 1961-1963* (Borestone Mountain Poetry

Awards, 1962-64), edited by Lionel Stevenson and others, three volumes, Pacific Books, 1962-64. Contributor of poems to *Harper's, Burning Deck, Gnostica*, and *New Letters*.

WORK IN PROGRESS: A novel, *Dethwin;* a novel for young people, *The Fortunes of Two Pugs*.

SIDELIGHTS: Valerie Worth Bahlke wrote to *CA:* "That which changes slowly (the earth's crust, the stars, the diverse species of living things, those aspects of Man which are constant in his progress from embryo to bone to dust) has always seemed to me the stuff of poetry *par excellence;* perhaps because poetry itself does not change, once it is written, and therefore asks its concerns to be as durable as possible." Her many interests have provided subject matter for her poetry—astronomy, gardening, and meditation, among others.

*   *   *

BAILEY, Alfred M(arshall)   1894-1978

PERSONAL: Born February 18, 1894, in Iowa City, Iowa; son of William H. (an attorney) and Mollie (Jellie) Bailey; married Muriel Etta Eggenberg, June 16, 1917; children: Beth Elaine (Mrs. Joseph Clark), Patricia Jean (Mrs. James Witherspoon). *Education:* University of Iowa, B.A., 1916. *Home:* 4340 Montview Blvd., Denver, Colo. 80207. *Office:* Denver Museum of Natural History, City Park, Denver, Colo. 80205.

CAREER: Louisiana State Museum, New Orleans, curator of birds and mammals, 1916-19; U.S. Biological Survey, representative in Juneau, Alaska, 1919-21; Denver Museum of Natural History, Denver, Colo., representative in Arctic Alaska, 1921-22, curator of birds and mammals, 1922-26; Chicago Academy of Sciences, Chicago, Ill., director, 1926-36; Denver Museum of Natural History, director, 1936-70, director emeritus, 1970-78. Member of U.S. Biological Survey expedition to Hawaiian Islands, 1912-13, and Field Museum expedition to Abyssinia, 1926-27; leader of Denver Museum of Natural History expeditions to Mexico, 1941, Alaska, 1945, Labrador, 1946, Mid-Pacific, Australia, New Zealand, and Fiji, 1949, 1952-54, 1957-58, Ecuador and Galapagos Islands, 1960, Botswana and South Africa, 1969. Lecurer, showing his own color films, for more than thirty years, including seventeen consecutive years as National Geographic Society lecturer in Constitution Hall.

MEMBER: American Association for the Advancement of Science (fellow), American Ornithologists' Union (fellow), Cooper Ornithological Society, Wilson Ornithological Society, and other ornithological and conservation organizations. *Awards, honors:* D.Sc., Norwich University, 1944; D.P.S., University of Denver, 1954; C.P.C., Regis College, 1967.

WRITINGS: Birds of Arctic Alaska, Denver Museum of Natural History, 1948; (with J. H. Sorenson) *Subantarctic Campbell Island*, Proceedings of Denver Museum of Natural History, Number 10, 1962; (with Robert J. Niedrach) *Birds of Colorado*, two volumes, Denver Museum of Natural History, 1965, condensation published as *Pictorial Checklist of Colorado Birds*, 1967.

Books in "Museum Pictorial" series, published by Denver Museum of Natural History: *Nature Photography with Miniature Cameras*, 1951; (with Niedrach) *Stepping Stones Across the Pacific*, 1951; *Laysan and Black Footed Albatrosses*, 1952; (with Niedrach and A. Lang Baily) *The Red Crossbills of Colorado*, 1953; (with Niedrach and Robert

Cushman Murphy) *Canton Island,* 1954; *Birds of New Zealand,* 1955; *Birds of Midway and Laysan Islands,* 1956; *Galapagos Island* (account of 1960 field trip), 1970; *Field Work of a Museum Naturalist, 1919-1922,* 1971. Also author of two booklets in "Museum Pictorial" series, *The Hawaiian Monk Seal,* 1952, and *Dusky and Swallow-Tailed Gulls of the Galapagos Islands,* 1961.

Contributor of more than two hundred articles covering expeditions on six continents to *Auk, National Geographic, Natural History, Country Life, Nature, Frontier, Journal of Mammalogy, American Forests,* and other periodicals.†

(Died February 25, 1978)

*   *   *

BAINES, John M. 1935-

PERSONAL: Born December 25, 1935, in Philadelphia, Pa.; son of Matthew J. and Mary (McCammitt) Baines; married Lois A. Rome, November 8, 1958; children: Andrew J., Eileen M. *Education:* Washburn University, A.B., 1962; University of Wisconsin, M.A., 1964, Ph.D., 1968. *Home:* 6611 Rosecroft Pl., Falls Church, Va. 22040.

CAREER: Wittenberg University, Springfield, Ohio, assistant professor of political science and acting chairman of department, 1967-68; University of Wyoming, Laramie, associate professor of political science and director of international studies program, 1968-72; Law Enforcement and Assistance Administration, Washington, D.C., project director, beginning 1972. Has done field work in South and Central America, 1966, 1969. Consultant to Wyoming governor's office, 1968, 1970, to National Sheriffs' Association, 1972. *Military service:* U.S. Air Force, 1955-59. U.S. Air Force Reserve, 1959-62. *Member:* American Political Science Association, Latin American Studies Association, Mid-West Political Science Association, Western Political Science Association. *Awards, honors:* Ford Foundation fellow, 1966-67; Social Science Foundation and University of Denver grant, 1969; Urban Affairs Institute summer fellow, 1971.

WRITINGS: Revolution in Peru: Mariategui and the Myth, University of Alabama Press, 1972; (with others) *Mutual Aid Planning,* National Sheriffs' Association, 1973. Contributor to political science and police journals.†

*   *   *

BAIRD, Jay Warren 1936-

PERSONAL: Born July 1, 1936, in Toledo, Ohio; son of Warren A. and Helen (Siddall) Baird; married Sally Eshelman, 1958; children: Lisa, Bryan, Stanford. *Education:* Denison University, B.A. (with honors), 1958; Free University of Berlin, graduate study, 1958-59; Columbia University, M.A., 1960, Ph.D., 1966. *Home:* 11 Bull Run, Oxford, Ohio 45056. *Office:* Irvin Hall, Miami University, Oxford, Ohio 45056.

CAREER: Stanford University, Stanford, Calif., instructor in history, 1963-65; Pomona College, Claremont, Calif., 1965-67, began as instructor, became assistant professor of history; Miami University, Oxford, Ohio, assistant professor, 1967-71, associate professor, 1971-74, professor of history, 1974—. *Member:* American Philosophical Society, Phi Beta Kappa. *Awards, honors:* Rotary Foundation fellow, Free University of Berlin, 1958-59; Thyssen Fellow, Cologne, Germany, 1966; National Endowment for the Humanities fellow, 1969; Alexander von Humboldt Foundation fellow, Bonn, Germany, 1969-70; American Philosophical Society grant, 1971.

WRITINGS: (Contributor) Ernst Nolte, editor, *Three Faces of Fascism,* Kent State University Press, 1968; (editor) *From Nuremburg to My Lai,* Heath, 1972; *The Mythical World of Nazi War Propaganda, 1939-1945,* University of Minnesota Press, 1974. Contributor of articles to history journals in the United States and abroad. Editorial consultant, *Canadian Review of Historical Nationalism,* 1973—.

*   *   *

BAIRD, W(illiam) David 1939-

PERSONAL: Born July 8, 1939, in Oklahoma City, Okla.; son of Everette W. and Faye (Shinn) Baird; married B. Jane Tacker, November 23, 1962; children: Angela Jane, William Anthony. *Education:* Central State University, Edmond, Okla., B.A., 1962; University of Oklahoma, M.A., 1965, Ph.D., 1969. *Politics:* Democrat. *Religion:* Church of Christ. *Home:* 4902 Country Club Dr., Stillwater, Okla. 74074. *Office:* Department of History, Oklahoma State University, Stillwater, Okla. 74074.

CAREER: Assistant to John Jarman, member of Congress, Washington, D.C., 1957-64; University of Arkansas, Fayetteville, assistant professor, 1968-72, associate professor, 1972-77, professor of history, 1978; Oklahoma State University, Stillwater, professor of history and chairman of department, 1978—. *Member:* Organization of American Historians, Western History Association, Arkansas Historical Association, Rotary Club. *Awards, honors:* American Philosophical Society research grant, 1971.

WRITINGS: Peter Pitchlynn, Chief of the Choctaws, University of Oklahoma Press, 1972; *The Osage People,* Indian Tribal Series, 1972; *The Choctaw People,* Indian Tribal Series, 1973; *The Chickasaw People,* Indian Tribal Series, 1974; *The Quapaw People,* Indian Tribal Series, 1976; *Years of Discontent: Dr. Frank L. James in Arkansas, 1876-1877,* Memphis State University Press, 1977; *The Downstream People: A History of the Quapaw Indians,* University of Delaware Press, in press; *Medical Education in Arkansas, 1879-1978,* Memphis State University Press, in press. Contributor of articles to *Chronicles of Oklahoma, Arkansas Historical Quarterly,* and *Maryland Historical Magazine.*

WORK IN PROGRESS: Research on Oklahoma Indians in the twentieth century.

AVOCATIONAL INTERESTS: Vegetable gardening.

*   *   *

BAKER, Elizabeth Faulkner 1886(?)-1973

1886(?)—January 28, 1973; American writer and professor of economics. Obituaries: *New York Times,* February 1, 1973. (See index for *CA* sketch)

*   *   *

BAKER, Gladys L(ucille) 1910-

PERSONAL: Born April 29, 1910, in Beaconsfield, Iowa; daughter of Horace Kyle (a farmer) and Nell (Doubet) Baker. *Education:* Stephens College, A.A., 1930; University of Michigan, B.A., 1933; University of Chicago, Ph.D., 1939. *Home:* Apt. W908, Van Ness South, 3003 Van Ness St. N.W., Washington, D.C. 20008. *Office:* U.S. Department of Agriculture, Washington, D.C. 20250.

CAREER: U.S. Department of Agriculture, Washington, D.C., agricultural economist, 1938-39, social science analyst for National Defense Advisory Commission, Office of Price Administration, 1940-41, economist, Office of Price Administration, 1941-42, agricultural historian, 1942—, head of historical research section, Agricultural History Branch, 1962—. *Member:* American Agricultural Economic Association, Agricultural History Society (president, 1970-71), Organization of American Historians, Phi Beta Kappa, Delta Sigma Rho. *Awards, honors:* U.S. Dairy Association Superior Service Award.

WRITINGS: The County Agent, University of Chicago Press, 1939; (with Wayne D. Rasmussen, Vivian Wiser, and Jane M. Porter) *Century of Service: The First 100 Years of the U.S. Department of Agriculture,* U.S. Government Printing Office, 1963; (with Rasmussen) *Department of Agriculture,* Praeger, 1972. Contributor of articles to *Agricultural History, Journal of Farm Economics, Wallace Farmer,* and *Courier.*

WORK IN PROGRESS: The Great Plains Council.

* * *

BAKER, Herbert G(eorge) 1920-

PERSONAL: Born February 23, 1920, in Brighton, England; son of Herbert Reginald (a teacher) and Alice (Bambridge) Baker; married Irene Williams (a biologist), April 4, 1945; children: Ruth Elaine (Mrs. Charles Grimes). *Education:* University of London, B.Sc. (honors), 1941, Ph.D., 1945. *Residence:* Berkeley, Calif. 94708. *Office:* Department of Botany, University of California, Berkeley, Calif. 94720.

CAREER: Hosa Research Laboratories, Sunbury-on-Thames, England, research chemist and assistant plant physiologist, 1940-45; University of Leeds, Leeds, England, lecturer in botany, 1945-54; University of Ghana, Legon, senior lecturer, 1954-55, professor of botany, 1955-57, head of department, 1955-57; University of California, Berkeley, professor of botany, 1957—, director of botanical garden, 1957-69. *Military service:* British Civil Defence, 1940-45. *Member:* Society for the Study of Evolution (president, 1969), International Association of Botanical Gardens (vice-president, 1964-69), Organization for Tropical Studies (member of board of directors), American Association for the Advancement of Science (fellow), American Institute of Biological Science (member of governing board), International Organization of Plant Biosystematists (member of executive council), Ecological Society of America, Botanical Society of America (president), Association for Tropical Biology, British Ecological Society, Botanical Society of the British Isles, California Botanical Society, Sigma Xi. *Awards, honors:* Carnegie Institution of Washington, research fellow, 1948-49; Rixford award from California Horticultural Society, 1966, for distinguished contributions to horticulture.

WRITINGS: Plants and Civilization, Wadsworth, 1964, 3rd edition, 1978; (editor with G. L. Stebbins) *The Genetics of Colonizing Species,* Academic Press, 1965.

Contributor: J. B. Wills, editor, *Agriculture and Land Use in Ghana,* Oxford University Press, 1962; D. Brokensha, editor, *Ecology and Economic Development in Tropical Africa,* Institute of International Studies, University of California (Berkeley), 1965; O. H. Frankel and E. Bennett, editors, *Genetic Resources in Plants: Their Exploration and Conservation,* Blackwell Scientific Publications, 1970; C. L. Riley, J. C. Kelley, C. W. Pennington, and R. L. Rands, editors, *Man across the Sea,* University of Texas Press, 1971; D. H. Valentine, editor, *Taxonomy, Phytogeography and Evolution,* Academic Press, 1972; B. J. Meggers, E. S. Ayensu, and W. D. Duckworth, *Tropical Forest Ecosys-*

tems in Africa and South America: A Comparative Review, Smithsonian Institution Press, 1973; L. E. Gilbert and P. H. Raven, *Co-evolution of Animals and Plants,* University of Texas Press, 1975; J. Burley and B. H. Styles, *Tropical Trees,* Academic Press, 1976; P. B. Tomlinson and M. H. Zimmerman, *Tropical Trees as Living Systems,* Cambridge University Press, 1978; J. R. Wilson, *Plant Relations in Pastures,* C.S.I.R.O., 1978. Contributor of more than 130 articles to journals in his field.

Editor of Blackwell Scientific Publications' "Botanical Monographs," 1971—. Associate editor of *Evolution,* 1956-59, 1962-65, of *Ecology,* 1963-66; botanical editor of *Pacific Horticulture* (formerly *California Horticultural Journal*), 1960—.

WORK IN PROGRESS: Books and articles on tropical plants and those of importance to man.

* * *

BAKER, Houston A., Jr. 1943-

PERSONAL: Born March 22, 1943, in Louisville, Ky.; married Charlotte Pierce; children: Mark Frederick. *Education:* Howard University, B.A. (magna cum laude), 1965; University of California, Los Angeles, M.A., 1966, Ph.D., 1968; graduate study at University of Edinburgh, 1967-68. *Office:* Department of Afro-American Studies, University of Pennsylvania, Philadelphia, Pa. 19104.

CAREER: Howard University, Washington, D.C., instructor in English, summer, 1966; Yale University, New Haven, Conn., instructor, 1968-69, assistant professor of English, 1969-70; University of Virginia, Charlottesville, associate professor, 1970-73, professor of English, 1973-74, member of Center for Advanced Studies, 1970-73; University of Pennsylvania, Philadelphia, professor of English, 1974—, director of Afro-American Studies Program, 1974-77. Distinguished visiting professor, Cornell University, 1977. Member of Fulbright-Hays literature screening committee, 1973-74; member of committee on scholarly worth, Howard University Press, 1973—; fellow, Center for Advanced Study in the Behavioral Sciences, 1977-78. *Member:* Modern Language Association of America, College Language Association, Phi Beta Kappa, Kappa Delta Pi. *Awards, honors:* Alfred Longueil Poetry Award from University of California at Los Angeles, 1966; National Phi Beta Kappa visiting scholar, 1975-76; Guggenheim Fellow, 1978-79.

WRITINGS: (Contributor) John Morton Blum, general editor, *Key Issues in the Afro-American Experience,* Harcourt, 1971; (editor) *Black Literature in America,* McGraw, 1971; *Long Black Song: Essays in Black American Literature and Culture,* University Press of Virginia, 1972; (editor) *Twentieth-Century Interpretations of Native Son,* Prentice-Hall, 1972; *Singers of Daybreak: Studies in Black American Literature,* Howard University Press, 1974; *A Many-Colored Coat of Dreams: The Poetry of Countee Cullen,* Broadside Press, 1974; (contributor) *Contemporary Poets,* St. Martin's, 1975; (editor) *Reading Black: Essays in the Criticism of African, Caribbean, and Black American Literature,* Africana Studies and Research Center, Cornell University, 1976; (editor with wife, Charlotte Pierce-Baker) *Renewal: A Volume of Black Poems,* Afro-American Studies Program, University of Pennsylvania, 1977; (editor) *A Dark and Sudden Beauty: Two Essays in Black American Poetry by George Kent and Stephen Henderson,* Afro-American Studies Program, University of Pennsylvania, 1977.

Contributor of about twenty articles and reviews to literature and black studies journals, including *Victorian Poetry*, *Nineteenth Century Fiction*, *Phylon*, *Liberator*, *Black American Literature Forum*, *Black World*, *Afro-American Studies*, *Virginia Quarterly Review*, *Maji*, *Obsidian*, *Yale Review*, *Journal of Popular Culture*, and *Journal of African-Afro-American Affairs*. Member of advisory boards, *Maji*, 1974-76, *Black American Literature Forum*, 1976—, and *Minority Voices*, 1977—.

WORK IN PROGRESS: The Journey Back: Issues in Black Literature and Criticism, for University of North Carolina Press; a book of poems, *No Matter Where You Travel, You Still Be Black*, for Lotus Press; editing *Three American Literatures: Essays in Chicano, Native American and Asian-American Literature for Teachers of "American" Literature*, for Modern Language Association; contributing to *Research in African Literatures*, edited by Marion Berghahn.

*   *   *

BAKER, Jean Hogarth H(arvey)   1933-

PERSONAL: Born February 9, 1933, in Baltimore, Md.; daughter of F. Barton (an insurance agent) and Rose (Hopkins) Harvey; married Ralph Robinson Baker (a physician), September 12, 1953; children: Susan Dixon, Robinson Scott, Robert Walker, Jean H. *Education:* Goucher College, A.B., 1961; Johns Hopkins University, M.A., 1964, Ph.D., 1973. *Politics:* Democrat. *Home:* 807 St. George's Rd., Baltimore, Md. 21210. *Office:* Department of History, Goucher College, Towson, Md. 21204.

CAREER: Goucher College, Towson, Md., assistant professor, 1967-73, associate professor of history, 1973—.

WRITINGS: The Politics of Continuity, Johns Hopkins Press, 1973; *Ambivalent Americans*, Johns Hopkins Press, 1976.

WORK IN PROGRESS: "The Corps of Engineers during the Civil War," a contribution to a book on the U.S. Army Corps of Engineers; a study of nineteenth-century political culture.

*   *   *

BALAWYDER, Aloysius   1924-

PERSONAL: Born March 15, 1924, in Rama, Saskatchewan, Canada; son of Isidore and Catherine (Terleski) Balawyder; married Martha M. Deveau (a guidance teacher), June 27, 1970; children: Bernard. *Education:* University of Western Ontario, B.A., 1949; University of Manitoba, M.Ed., 1956; University of Notre Dame, M.A., 1963; McGill University, Ph.D., 1966. *Religion:* Roman Catholic. *Home address:* Greening Dr., Antigonish, Nova Scotia, Canada. *Office:* Department of History, Box 47, St. Francis Xavier University, Antigonish, Nova Scotia, Canada.

CAREER: St. Francis Xavier University, Antigonish, Nova Scotia, assistant professor, 1966-69, associate professor, 1969-76, professor of history, 1976—, head of department, 1969-70, 1971—. *Member:* Canadian Historical Association, Canadian Association of Slavists, Association of Atlantic Historians (president, 1971-72), Knights of Columbus. *Awards, honors:* Quebec scholarship for research on Russia, 1964-66; Canada Council research grant for research in Poland, 1970, 1971, for research in the Soviet Union, Poland and Great Britain, 1974-75; Canadian-Soviet Cultural Exchange Fellowship, 1974.

WRITINGS: The Winnipeg General Strike, Copp Clark,

1967; *Canadian-Soviet Relations between the Wars*, University of Toronto Press, 1972; *The Odyssey of Polish Treasures*, St. Francis Xavier University Press, 1978. Contributor to *Canadian Slavonic Papers* and *East European Quarterly*.

WORK IN PROGRESS: A book, *The Maple Leaf and the White Eagle: Canadian-Polish Relations, 1919-1978;* editing a volume on *Canadian-Soviet Relations, 1939-1975;* articles on Poles in Canada.

*   *   *

BALDWIN, Leland D(ewitt)   1897-

PERSONAL: Born November 23, 1897, in Fairchance, Pa.; son of Harmon Allen (a minister) and Etta (Weatherly) Baldwin; married Ruth J. Glosser (a social worker), October 8, 1927. *Education:* Greenville College, A.B., 1921; University of Michigan, M.A., 1923, Ph.D., 1932. *Religion:* Protestant. *Home:* Valle Verde, Apt. D-102, 900 Calle de Los Amigos, Santa Barbara, Calif. 93105. *Office:* Department of History, University of Pittsburgh, Pittsburgh, Pa. 15213.

CAREER: History teacher in Kansas, 1922-24, and Pennsylvania, 1924-31; Western Pennsylvania Historical Survey, librarian and research associate, 1932-35, assistant director in charge of research, 1935-36; University of Pittsburgh Press, Pittsburgh, Pa., editor, 1936-39; University of Pittsburgh, Pittsburgh, university librarian, 1940-42, associate professor, 1945-55, professor of history, 1955-61, professor emeritus, 1961—. Visiting professor, University of Southern California, 1950, University of California, Los Angeles, 1955, at Santa Barbara, 1961-62, 1964-65, and University of Natal, 1962-63; Fulbright lecturer, University of Leeds, 1952-53; U.S. State Department lecturer in Pakistan, India, and Ceylon, 1952-54. *Military service:* U.S. Army Air Forces, 1942-46; served in England, North Africa, and Italy; became lieutenant colonel.

WRITINGS: Pittsburgh: The Story of a City, University of Pittsburgh Press, 1937, reprinted, 1970; *Whiskey Rebels: The Story of a Frontier Uprising*, University of Pittsburgh Press, 1938, revised edition, 1969; *The Delectable Country* (novel), Lee Furman, 1939; *The Keelboat Age on Western Waters*, University of Pittsburgh Press, 1941; *The Story of the Americas*, Simon & Schuster, 1943; *God's Englishmen: The Evolution of the Anglo-Saxon Spirit*, J. Cape, 1943, Little, Brown, 1944; *Best Hope of Earth: A Grammar of Democracy*, University of Pittsburgh Press, 1948, revised edition, 1956.

The Stream of American History, two volumes, American Book Co., 1952, 3rd edition (with Robert Kelley), 1965; *Recent American History*, American Book Co., 1954; *Survey of American History*, Van Nostrand, 1955, 2nd edition (with Kelley), 1967; *The Meaning of America: Essays Toward an Understanding of the American Spirit*, University of Pittsburgh Press, 1955.

(With M. S. Warring) *History of Our Republic*, Van Nostrand, 1965; (editor) *Ideas in Action: Documentary and Interpretive Readings in America History*, two volumes, American Book Co., 1969; (editor) *The Flavor of the Past: Readings in American Social and Political Portraiture*, two volumes, American Book Co., 1969; *Reframing the Constitution: An Imperative for Modern America*, Clio Press, 1972; (with E. A. Erickson) *The American Quest*, two volumes, Wadsworth, 1973.

SIDELIGHTS: Leland Baldwin has traveled all over the world. Some of his books have been published in French, Portuguese, and Arabic.

BALDWIN, Robert E(dward) 1924-

PERSONAL: Born July 12, 1924, in Niagara Falls, N.Y.; son of Gilbert E. and Margaret (Ostman) Baldwin; married Janice Murphy (a lawyer), July 31, 1954; children: Jean, Robert, Richard, Nancy. *Education:* University of Buffalo, A.B., 1945; Harvard University, Ph.D., 1950. *Home:* 125 Nautilus Dr., Madison, Wis. *Office:* Department of Economics, 1180 Observatory Dr., University of Wisconsin, Madison, Wis. 53706.

CAREER: University of Buffalo, Buffalo, N.Y., instructor in economics, 1945-46; Harvard University, Cambridge, Mass., instructor, 1950-52, assistant professor of economics, 1952-57; University of California, Los Angeles, associate professor, 1957-62, professor of economics, 1962-64; University of Wisconsin—Madison, professor of economics, 1964—, F. W. Taussig Professor, 1974—, chairman of department, 1975-78. Chief economist, Executive Office of the President, Washington, D.C., 1963-64; research professor, Brookings Institution, Washington, D.C., 1967-68. Consultant to World Bank, 1978-79. *Member:* American Economic Association. *Awards, honors:* Ford Foundation, training fellowship in Rhodesia and Nyassaland, 1960-61, and research fellowship, 1969-70; also received grants from National Science Foundation and U.S. Labor Department.

WRITINGS: (Contributor) W. Glenn Campbell, editor, *Economics of Mobilization and War,* Irwin, 1952; (with G. M. Meier) *Economic Development: Theory, History, Policy,* Wiley, 1957; (contributor) B. F. Jackson, editor, *Economic Development of Africa,* Basil Blackwell, 1965; (contributor) Richard E. Caves, Harry G. Johnson, and Peter B. Kenen, editors, *Trade, Growth, and the Balance of Payments,* Rand McNally, 1965; *Economic Development and Growth,* Wiley, 1966, 2nd edition, 1972; *Economic Development and Export Growth: A Study of Northern Rhodesia, 1920-60,* University of California Press, Berkeley, 1966; *Nontariff Distortions to International Trade,* Brookings Institution, 1970; (editor with J. David Richardson, and contributor) *International Trade and Finance: Readings,* Little, Brown, 1974; *Foreign Trade Regimes and Economic Development: Philippines,* Columbia University Press, 1975. Contributor of articles to *American Economic Review, Journal of Political Economy, Geneva Essays, Review of Economics and Statistics, Quarterly Journal of Economics, Revista Brasiliera de Economia, Explorations in Entrepreneurial History, Europa archiv, Review of Economic Studies, Journal of Economic History, Economics in Action, International Influences on the American Economy, Economic Development and Cultural Change, Race, Economic Journal, Economia Internazionale, Farm Policy Forum, Indian Economic Journal, Review of Social Economy, International Trade and Central Planning, Issues and Objectives of U.S. Foreign Trade Policy, Review of U.S. Trade Policy,* and *United States International Economic Policy in an Interdependent World.* Associate editor of *Journal of International Economics* and *Review of Economics and Statistics.* Member of editorial board, *World Economy.*

WORK IN PROGRESS: Research into the political economy of U.S. trade policy.

* . * . *

BALLANTINE, Joseph W. 1890(?)-1973

1890(?)—January 29, 1973; American diplomat, foreign service administrator, author, and teacher. Obituaries: *Washington Post,* January 30, 1973; *New York Times,* January 30, 1973.

BAMFORD, Paul W(alden) 1921-

PERSONAL: Born April 18, 1921, in Denver, Colo.; son of Paul and Gertrude Helen (Wiard) Bamford; married Pauline Homa, August 4, 1948; children: Anastasia, Philip, Thomas Patrick. *Education:* University of Denver, B.A., 1943; Columbia University, M.A., 1947, Ph.D., 1951. *Office:* Department of History, University of Minnesota, Minneapolis, Minn. 55455.

CAREER: Wells College, Aurora, N.Y., member of faculty, 1952-53; Ohio State University, Columbus, instructor, 1953-57, assistant professor of history, 1957-58; University of Minnesota, Minneapolis, assistant professor, 1958-59, associate professor, 1959-69, professor of European history, 1970—. Fulbright research professor in France, 1960-61; member of Institute for Advanced Study, Princeton, 1966-67. *Military service:* U.S. Army, Military Police, 1943-45. *Member:* Economic History Society, Societe d'histoire moderne, American Historical Association, Economic History Association, Society for French Historical Studies. *Awards, honors:* Fulbright scholar, Columbia University, 1949-50; Ford Foundation research fellow, 1951-52; Howald faculty fellow, Ohio State University, 1955-56; Koren prize from Society for French Historical Studies, 1959; Guggenheim fellow, 1960-61.

WRITINGS: Forests and French Sea Power, University of Toronto Press, 1956; *Fighting Ships and Prisons: The Mediterranean Galleys of France in the Age of Louis XIV,* University of Minnesota Press, 1973. Contributor of articles to *Journal of Modern History, American Historical Review, Agricultural History,* and *Journal of Economic History.*

WORK IN PROGRESS: Research on European history, French history, maritime history, and the history of prisons and penology.

* . * . *

BANCROFT, Peter 1916-

PERSONAL: Born May 5, 1916, in Tucson, Ariz.; son of Roy Francis (an architect) and Lillian (Walker) Bancroft; married Virginia Pomeroy (a teacher), October 21, 1940; children: Martha, Edward, Robert, Barbara, Sumiati. *Education:* University of California, Santa Barbara, A.B., 1940; University of Southern California, M.S., 1948; University of Northern Colorado, Ed.D., 1958. *Home and office:* 3538 Oak Cliff Dr., Fallbrook, Calif. 92028.

CAREER: Vineland School District, Bakersfield, Calif., superintendent of schools, 1943-55; U.S. Department of State, Bolivia, director of education, 1956-58; Cajon Valley School District, San Diego, Calif., superintendent of schools, 1960-66; Hanna-Barbera, Hollywood, Calif., photographer and writer, 1970; Pala Properties, Inc., Fallbrook, Calif., gem and mineral dealer, 1973-75; currently a full-time writer. Football and basketball official. Lecturer for mineral societies and conventions in Tasmania, Bolivia, Brazil, New Zealand, Australia, and the United States; member of White House Conference on Education; vice-president of Livermore Chamber of Commerce; director of El Cajon Chamber of Commerce; president of El Cajon Girl's Club; chairman of Alameda County Community Chest. *Military service:* U.S. Marine Corps. *Member:* California Administrator's Association, University of California Alumni Association (president), Blue Key, Rotary Club (president). *Awards, honors:* Bolivian Educator of the Year Award; Cajon Valley Outstanding Service Award; National Award for Outstanding Minerals, 1967, 1972; Vineland School District Devoted Service Award, 1977.

WRITINGS: What an American Should Know about Brazil, University of Colorado Press, 1958; The World's Finest Minerals and Crystals, Viking, 1973. Contributor of articles to Lapidary Journal, Mojave Record, Rock and Gem, Le Monde et Mineraux, Stern, Mineralogical Record, Australian Gems, and Mineralien.

WORK IN PROGRESS: A book, Great Gem and Mineral Mines of the World, for Mineralogical Record.

SIDELIGHTS: Peter Bancroft told CA: "My family was established in the Old West mining business, with a great-uncle being the superintendent of the Hale Norcross Mine, and a great-grandfather chief carpenter of the Sutro Tunnel, both in Virginia City, Nevada during the 1860's to 1890's. My father's childhood was spent in the Adolf Sutro mansion near Virginia City. As a boy, countless sessions around campfires and before the family fireplace left deep impressions of life as it was on the western frontier and in the mines. I became quite proud of my family's heritage. Then I married a girl whose great-grandfather was a baker and mayor of the mining camp Nevada City, California during the 1870's. But then it was necessary to rear a family, so I suppressed a growing interest and passion for mining adventures and trained for and served in the public schools of California as a teacher and administrator. Upon retirement from education, I immediately returned to my original love, first working for a gem and mineral company, and now devoting full time to writing mineral and mining books and short stories, collecting gem crystals, minerals and Old West antiques, and getting in plenty of travelling."

BIOGRAPHICAL/CRITICAL SOURCES: American Magazine, November, 1947; Flying Sportsman, March, 1948; National Education Association Journal, October, 1948.

*   *   *

BANISTER, Manly (Miles) 1914-

PERSONAL: Born March 9, 1914, in McCormick, Wash.; son of Charles Edwin (a logger) and Marion Isobell (Flowers) Banister; married Eleanor Hammond, 1933 (divorced, 1935); married Edna Reynolds, 1936 (divorced, 1953); married Marjorie Grace Houston (an office manager), August, 1953; children: (second marriage) Nikki Loa Banister, Zoe Banister Stewart. Education: Attended Reed College, 1933-34. Home and office: 6610 Southeast 77th St., Portland, Ore. 97206.

CAREER: Busboy, dishwasher, general restaurant worker in Oregon and California, 1930-36; messboy, wiper, fireman, oiler on various ships of the Union Oil fleet, sailing out of Los Angeles, Calif., 1936-37; employed by Works Progress Administration (WPA), Portland, Ore., 1937-40; radio station KCKN, Kansas City, Kan., continuity writer, 1940-42, 1945-46; advertising copywriter for Western Auto Supply Co., Kansas City, Mo., 1946-53, and for Pacific National Agency, Portland, 1953-54; Hugh Dwight Advertising, Portland, copywriter and copy chief, 1954-60; free-lance writer and translator, 1961—. Military service: U.S. Marine Corps, 1942-45, became sergeant.

WRITINGS: Conquest of Earth (science fiction; first appeared serially under title "The Scarlet Saint" in Amazing Stories), Avalon, 1957; Manual of Bookbinding, Ronald, 1958; Wenn Welten Sich Begegnen (first appeared serially under title "Magnanthropus" in an American science fiction magazine), Moewig Verlag, 1965; Flucht Zur Erde (first appeared in an American science fiction magazine under title "Escape to Earth"), Moewig Verlag, 1966; Prints from Li-noblocks and Wood Cuts, Sterling, 1969; Etching and Other Intaglio Techniques, Sterling, 1969; Lithographic Prints from Stone and Plate, Sterling, 1972; Making Picture Frames, Sterling, 1973; (self-illustrated) Bookbinding as a Handcraft, Sterling, 1975; Wood Block Cutting and Printing, Sterling, 1976.

Translator; all published by Sterling: Ab De Brouwer, Creating with Flexible Foam, 1971; Jo Konijnenberg-DeGroot, Cellophane Creations, 1971; J. Van Ingen, Aquarelle and Watercolor Complete, 1971; Marianne Seitz, Creating Silver Jewelry with Beads, 1971; Hanny Nussbaumer, Lacquer and Crackle, 1971; Alfred Faeustle, Drafting Techniques for the Artist, 1971; Joseph H. Eppens-Van Veen, Colorful Glasscrafting, 1971; R. Boulay, Make Your Own Elegant Jewelry, 1971; Helmut Bechtel, House Plant Identifier, 1973; Walter Lauppi, Mosaics with Natural Stones, 1974; J. J. Hoedeman, Encyclopedia of Freshwater Aquarium Fish, six volumes in one, 1974; Jurgen Kemmler, Skiing on the Level, 1974; Wilbert Neugebauer, Marine Aquarium Fish Identifier, 1975; Ingrid Gabriel, Herb Identifier and Handbook, 1975; Tom Okker, Tennis in Pictures, 1975; A Book of Games, 1976; Gilbert Obermaier, Matchstick Puzzles, Tricks and Games, 1977; A. Pluger, Karate Kiai! Perfecting Your Power, 1977. Contributor of numerous articles to Popular Mechanics, 1960-67, and to juvenile publications and science fiction magazines.

WORK IN PROGRESS: A biography of his father, Charles Edwin Banister, tentatively titled A Man Called Charlie.

SIDELIGHTS: "The only motivating factor behind my writing," Manly Banister wrote CA, "was a desire to make a living without having to punch a time clock. . . . I wrote for Weird Tales Magazine, until it succumbed to reader apathy and suffered the ultimate fate of every magazine—extinction. I also contributed to a number of science fiction magazines—short stories, novelettes, and continued-story book-lengths. Some of the book-lengths were picked up and translated into German; at least one was translated into Spanish. There may have been others I never heard about. In the earliest years of my writing, I contributed poetry, articles, and short stories to juvenile publications. These are doubtless still a good place for the beginning writer to get a start." Banister added: "If I had any advice for aspiring writers, it would be to tell them to write—for fun. Don't eat your heart out waiting for that first acceptance, or afterward, for the big money to come in. Chances are you will wait a long time for acceptance and the big money never will come in. As in the theological industry, many are called but few are chosen."

*   *   *

BANK, Theodore P(aul) II 1923-
(Ted Bank, Ted Kirk)

PERSONAL: Born August 31, 1923, in Patterson, La.; son of Theodore Paul (a colonel in the armed forces) and Madlyn (Huber) Bank; married Janet Fowler, September, 1948 (divorced October, 1953); married Shirley Waterman, April 4, 1954 (divorced December, 1962); married Trina Paula Lindenstein (an elementary school teacher), April 20, 1963; children: (first marriage) Theodore Paul; (third marriage) Kristin Kara. Education: Attended Harvard University, 1941-43; University of Michigan, B.A., 1946, M.S., 1950, graduate study, 1950-54. Politics: "Normally a Republican." Religion: None. Home: 1809 Nichols Rd., Kalamazoo, Mich. 49007. Agent: Emile Jacobson, Curtis Brown Ltd., 60 East 56th St., New York, N.Y. 10022. Office: College of General

Studies, Department of Social Science, Western Michigan University, Kalamazoo, Mich. 49001.

CAREER: Village teacher in Atka, Aleutian Islands, Alaska, 1948-49; American Institute for Exploration, Inc., Ann Arbor, Mich. (other offices in Chicago, Ill. and San Francisco, Calif.), executive director, 1954—; University of Michigan, Museum of Anthropology, Ann Arbor, research associate, 1956-57; assistant professor of anthropology, Chicago Teachers College—North, 1961-63; assistant professor of anthropology, Chapman College, Seven Seas Division, 1967; Western Michigan University, Kalamazoo, assistant professor, 1967-72, associate professor of social science, 1973—, director of World Explorations program, 1972—. Visiting lecturer, Hokkaido University, 1955-56, College of San Mateo, 1965-66. Chairman of U.S. committee, Clark Memorial Student Center Fund (Hokkaido), 1957-60; research anthropologist, Agnews State Hospital (San Jose, Calif.), 1965-66. Director of Aleutian-Bering Sea Expeditions (for University of Michigan and U.S. Office of Naval Research), 1948-49, archaeological expedition to Sea of Okhotsk (for Hokkaido University), 1956; has led or participated in more than thirty expeditions in Argentina, West Africa, Upper Michigan, American Arctic, Aleutians, Mexico, Asia, and the South Pacific. Executive producer of an educational television series on the non-Western world, 1968-69. *Military service:* U.S. Naval Reserve, aerographer's mate, and U.S. Naval Air Corps, Fleet Weather Central (Aleutians), 1944-46.

MEMBER: American Anthropological Association (fellow), Society for American Archaeology, Current Anthropology (associate), American Association for the Advancement of Science (fellow), Polar Society, Asia Society, Japan Society, Japan-American Society, International Platform Association, American Ecological Society, Explorers Club (fellow), Pacific Science Association, Sigma Xi, Phi Sigma. *Awards, honors:* Grant from U.S. Office of Naval Research, Aleutian Islands, 1948-49; grants from Michigan Phoenix Project, 1950, 1951, 1954, for Aleutian research; Wenner-Gren Foundation grant, 1953-54, for research on Aleut-Eskimo prehistory and ethnobiology; Explorers Club grants, 1954, 1955, 1962, 1969, 1971, 1973, 1975, for Japan and Aleutian research. Fulbright research scholarship in anthropology, 1955-56, for research on the Ainu, Hokkaido University; National Research Council travel grant, Asia, 1957; American Academy of Arts and Science grant, 1957-58, for research on Aconitum; Upjohn Pharmaceutical Co. grant, 1957-58, to study Asian and European soil samples; Mellon Fund grant, 1966-67, for research on Alaska; Kalamazoo Civic Fund grants, 1969-78; Sigma Xi grant, 1971.

WRITINGS: A Brochure of Research Projects, Institute for Regional Exploration, 1955; *Birthplace of the Winds*, Crowell, 1956, 2nd edition, Thomas Hale, 1957; *A Bibliography of Anthropology: Contributions Number Three*, Institute for Exploration, Inc., 1962; *Manual for Cultural Anthropology*, Quest Productions, 1966; *Report of the Aleutian-Bering Sea Institutes*, Western Michigan University, 1969; (contributor) Luther Douglas and Conda Douglas, editors, *The Explorers Cookbook*, Caxton, 1971; *People of the Bering Sea*, MSS Educational Publishing, 1971; (contributor) Lidia Selkregg, editor, *Alaska Regional Profiles: Southwest Region*, State of Alaska, 1976; (contributor) Charles Cleland, editor, *For the Director: Essays in Honor of James Griffin*, Museum of Anthropology, University of Michigan, 1977.

Films—photographer and producer: "Our Bering Sea Frontier" and "Ascent of Great Sitkin," both for Dallas Jones

Productions, 1949. Television programs—co-producer and narrator: "Expedition," 1950, "Knowing Our World: Alaska," a four-part series, 1955, "Alaska: The Great Land," 1958, "The Explorers: Quest and Discovery," a two-part series, 1961, "Exploring Today," 1960, "Comparative World Cultures," a series, 1961-63, "World Exploration," 1973, and "Kayaking at the Birthplace of the Winds," 1978.

Contributor to field and research reports and proceedings. Contributor of stories and articles to national magazines, including *Nature, Mariah, Adventure, Natural History, Think,* and *Alaska Sportsman;* contributor of scientific papers to professional journals, including *Science, Scientific American, American Antiquity, R.N. Journal of Nurses, Ecology, Explorers Journal,* and foreign publications. Photography editor, *Harvard Crimson,* 1942-43; editor, *Michigan Forester,* 1946-47; *Explorers Journal,* contributing editor, 1960—, member of editorial board, 1976—; editor, *New Island Research* and American Institute for Exploration, 1962—; member of editorial board, *Mariah,* 1976—.

WORK IN PROGRESS: Aleut-Eskimo!, a sequel to *Birthplace of the Winds;* a monograph on the archaeology and ecology of the Aleutian Islands of Alaska; research on prehistory of northern Japan; *Backdoor to Siberia: A Pictorial Essay.*

SIDELIGHTS: Theodore Bank told *CA:* "When people ask me, as they often do, how I became an explorer, I tell them truthfully that I was born to it naturally. The only decision I ever made about it was, simply, to continue being one—from my earliest childhood when I wandered through the swamps near my Louisiana home, into my adolescent years among the mountains and forests of Idaho, to my present occupation as a scientist, professor and expedition leader.

"As for writing, I also turned to that naturally, just as I did with teaching. I discovered at an early age that the adventures and thrills in exploring become mere memories dimmed by time unless they are told and retold to others, shared and thereby constantly relived with each retelling.

"Some explore and write to discover new truths which they want to share primarily for the benefit of mankind. I hasten to disavow such noble motives. I explore because I love it, and because I know that if I tried to do anything else I would probably be a miserable failure. And I write mainly because it pleases me to do so. It tickles my fancy. It satisfies my ego. And, furthermore, it seems the right thing to do, a natural accompaniment to exploring, just as I think teaching is. I agree with Thoreau: 'I came into this world, not chiefly to make it a good place to live in, but to live in it, be it good or bad. A man has not everything to do, but something; and because he cannot do *everything,* it is not necessary that he should do *something* wrong.'

"In my own case, I have a special fondness for the North and most particularly for Alaska's stormy Aleutian Islands. Wildness is there, untamed elements, violent winds, fog, rugged volcanic coasts, a demanding environment that often is awesome and frightening. Yet there is also delicate beauty—as when tiny scarlet rhododendrons are seen bathing their petals in the mists of mountain waterfalls.

"There is a strange, almost eerie, compelling force about such regions which calls me back to them repeatedly. While there I cannot help but be an explorer. I become exhilarated by the vast unknown surrounding me, and renewed by the challenges I face. When I return to the more mundane existence of a college campus, I find myself drawn equally to the typewriter and the lectern. There is an eagerness to put into words the sights and sounds, the smells, and the excitement of all that I have just done. And once more I am exhilarated and renewed as new dimensions, just discovered, begin to emerge within me.

"Of course there is more than selfish pleasure in what I do. At least I hope I am more admirable than that. My childhood dreams of exploring have become reality, and I am in love with the life I lead. But I realize that this is largely thanks to the encouragement and support I have received along the way—from a special set of parents who refused to shackle me to our home, and, instead, allowed me to explore unleashed; from a kind and much-loved teacher named Professor Harley H. Bartlett at the University of Michigan.

"When Professor Bartlett died, an unfillable void saddened my life, and I cried, but at the same time an illuminating torch passed from his hands to mine. I went on to become a teacher, an explorer and a writer. Through the years, just as Bartlett had done for me, I have introduced new generations of students to the high adventure and challenge of exploration, while at the same time showing them the joy that comes with telling it to others. Some, as I do, discover new dimensions within themselves, and, hopefully with great flair, they will someday share it with the world."

AVOCATIONAL INTERESTS: Mountain climbing, scuba diving, sketching.

BIOGRAPHICAL/CRITICAL SOURCES: Newsweek, December 25, 1950; *New York Times,* April 22, 1956, June 10, 1973; *New York Herald Tribune,* April 29, 1956; *Seattle Times,* September 4, 1969; *Talent,* April, 1970; *Mariah,* March, 1977; *Profiles,* 1978; *Photographer's Market,* 1979.

* * *

BANNICK, Nancy (Meredith) 1926-

PERSONAL: Born December 7, 1926, in Rochester, Minn.; daughter of Edwin George (a physician) and Vesta (Meredith) Bannick. *Education:* Stanford University, B.A. (with great distinction), 1948. *Politics:* Republican. *Religion:* United Church of Christ. *Home:* 2943 Kalakaua Ave., Honolulu, Hawaii 96815.

CAREER: Yakima Daily Republic, Yakima, Wash., society editor and news reporter, 1948-50; *Honolulu Star-Bulletin,* Honolulu, Hawaii, editor of company newsletter, *Family News,* 1950; *Hawaii Farm and Home,* Honolulu, associate editor, 1950-51; Lane Magazine & Book Co., Menlo Park, Calif., member of staff, 1952-74, Hawaii editor of *Sunset* (magazine), 1955-74; free-lance writer. Member of citizens' advisory committee for Honolulu Civic Center Master Plan, 1968-74; chairman of Historic Buildings Task Force for city and county of Honolulu, 1965-75; delegate to Hawaii state Republican conventions, 1964—. Executive secretary, Hawaii Environmental Awareness Resources Council, 1975-76.

MEMBER: Society of Architectural Historians, National League of American Pen Women, Victorian Society of America, National Trust for Historic Preservation, Women in Communications, Pacific Tropical Botanical Garden Foundation, Hawaii Foundation for History and the Humanities, Hawaiian Historical Society, Hawaii Chinese History Center, Hawaiian Trail and Mountain Club, Hawaii Opera Theatre, Oahu Development Conference, Outdoor Circle, Friends of Foster Garden, Friends of the Lahaina Restoration Foundation, Friends of the East-West Center, Bishop Museum Association, Ensemble Players Guild, Friends of Iolani Palace, Outrigger Canoe Club, Save Diamond Head Association (member of board of directors,

1968—), Honolulu Academy of Arts, Honolulu Press Club, Honolulu Community Theatre, Honolulu Symphony Society, Honolulu Chamber Music Series, Stanford Alumni Association, Diamond Head Tennis Club, Punahou Tennis Club, Seattle Tennis Club. *Awards, honors:* First prize from Pacific Area Travel Association, 1966, for magazine articles; award of merit from American Association for State and Local History, 1970, and from Conservation Council for Hawaii, 1971, both for work in historic preservation.

WRITINGS: Hawaii: A Guide to All the Islands, Lane, 1956, 4th edition, 1969; (editor and photographer) *Old Honolulu: A Guide to Oahu's Historic Buildings,* Historic Buildings Task Force, 1969; (editor with Dorothy Kell) *Beautiful Hawaii,* Lane, 1972. Author of special reports for Hawaii Chamber of Commerce and city and county of Honolulu. Contributor of articles to *Honolulu* magazine, *Hawaii Tourist News,* and other periodicals. Managing editor of *Stanford Daily,* at Stanford University, 1946-47; editor, *Thrum's Annual,* 1950, *Mason Bee,* 1976—, and *Historic Hawaii News,* 1976-77.

AVOCATIONAL INTERESTS: Urban planning, historic preservation, tennis, swimming, bicycling, photography, and music—especially playing the piano.

* * *

BARANET, Nancy Neiman 1933-

PERSONAL: Born January 1, 1933, in Detroit, Mich.; daughter of Allen (a teacher) and Mayme (Buch) Nieman; married Nicholas Baranet (a hospital transportation specialist), March 29, 1957; children: Nicholas, Michael, Matthew, Holly. *Education:* Attended Detroit Business University, 1949-50. *Politics:* Republican. *Religion:* Presbyterian. *Home:* 5762 Southwest 1st St., Plantation, Fla. 33317.

CAREER: Secretary for contractors Shaw-Winkler, Inc., 1954-57, and Palmer Smith, Inc., 1957-60, both Detroit, Mich.; Don Gant Associates (manufacturer's representatives), Plantation, Fla., office manager, 1976—. Delegate, United States Olympic Committee. *Member:* United States Cycling Federation (formerly Amateur Bicycle League of America; director, 1956—; secretary, 1957-63, 1977-79), Broward Wheelmen. *Awards, honors:* National bicycle racing champion, 1953, 1954, 1956, 1957; world record holder for 200 meters, 1955; Testimonial Resolution, City of Detroit, 1955; Stayfree Service to Women Sports Award, 1978.

WRITINGS: The Turned Down Bar, Dorrance, 1964; *Bicycling,* A. S. Barnes, 1972. Contributor to *World Book Encyclopedia.* Regular contributor to *Bicycling* and *Bike World;* racing editor, *American Bicyclist and Motorcyclist.*

SIDELIGHTS: Nancy Baranet has led tours, cycle camped, raced, organized school activities, and organized touring and racing organizations, and is a recognized authority on bicycle racing. She is a delegate to Olympic House for Cycling. *Avocational interests:* Oil painting.

* * *

BARBER, T(heodore) X(enophon) 1927-

PERSONAL: Born January 29, 1927, in Martin's Ferry, Ohio; married, 1957; children: three. *Education:* American University, B.A., 1954, Ph.D., 1956. *Office:* Medfield Foundation, Medfield, Mass. 02052.

CAREER: Worcester Foundation, Worcester, Mass., research associate, 1959-61; Medfield State Hospital, Medfield, Mass., research associate, 1961—, director of psychological research, 1965—. Research instructor, Boston University, School of Medicine, 1960—. *Member:* American Psychological Association, Society for Clinical and Experimental Hypnosis. *Awards, honors:* National Institute of Mental Health fellow in social relations at Harvard University, 1956-59.

WRITINGS: Hypnosis: A Scientific Approach, Van Nostrand, 1969; *LSD, Marihuana, Yoga, and Hypnosis,* Aldine, 1970; *Hypnosis, Imagination, and Human Potentialities,* Pergamon, 1974; *Hypnotic Phenomena,* General Learning Press, 1974; *Pitfalls in Human Research: Ten Pivotal Points,* Pergamon, 1976; (editor) *Advances in Altered States of Consciousness and Human Potentialities,* Volume 1, Psychological Dimensions, 1976. Editor with others, *Biofeedback and Self Control: An Aldine Annual on the Regulation of Bodily Processes and Consciousness,* Aldine, 1971-78. Contributor to psychology journals.

* * *

BARCHEK, James Robert 1935-

PERSONAL: Born May 24, 1935, in Norwalk, Conn.; son of John Daniel and Helen I. (Pesti) Barchek; married Ardyce Jean Patchin, September 6, 1956; children: Douglas Allen, Julie Marie. *Education:* Portland State University, B.S., 1959; University of Oregon, M.Ed., 1962, D.Art., 1969. *Home:* 28206 112th S.E., Kent, Wash. 98031. *Office:* Kent School District, 12033 Southeast 256th St., Kent, Wash. 98031.

CAREER: English teacher and chairman of department in Portland, Ore., 1958-65; University of Oregon, Eugene, research associate and instructor in English, 1965-68; Western Washington State College (now University), Bellingham, lecturer, 1968-69, assistant professor of English, 1969-71; Kent School District, Kent, Wash., coordinator of language arts, 1971-76, director of instruction, 1976—. *Member:* International Arthurian Society, National Council of Teachers of English, Mediaeval Academy of America, Washington Council of Teachers of English (president, 1974-75).

WRITINGS: (With Glen A. Love and Lucille Aly) *Language/Rhetoric,* Books I and II, Holt, 1968; (with Gaynor Petreguin and others) *Individualizing Instruction through Modular Flexible Scheduling,* McGraw, 1968; (with Love and Aly) *The Private I,* Holt, 1974; (with Love and Aly) *On Purpose,* Holt, 1974; (with Lee Odell) *Fantasy,* Scholastic, 1978. Contributor to professional journals.

WORK IN PROGRESS: With Joanne Nelson and others, a reading series, "Starbase Five," for Lippincott.

* * *

BARDACH, John E(ugene) 1915-

PERSONAL: Born March 6, 1915, in Vienna, Austria; came to United States in 1946, naturalized in 1953; son of Frederick and Anna (Jerusalem) Bardach; married Josephine Handler, October 7, 1947. *Education:* Queen's University, Kingston, Ontario, B.A., 1946; University of Wisconsin, M.Sc., 1948, Ph.D., 1949. *Home:* 2979 Kalakaua Ave., Honolulu, Hawaii 96815. *Office:* Resource Systems Institute, East-West Center, University of Hawaii, Honolulu, Hawaii 96822.

CAREER: Iowa State Teachers College (now University of Northern Iowa), Cedar Falls, instructor, 1949-51, assistant professor of zoology, 1951-53; University of Michigan, Ann Arbor, assistant professor, 1953-55, associate professor, 1955-61, professor of natural resources zoology, 1961-71;

University of Hawaii, Honolulu, professor of zoology and oceanography, 1971—, director of Hawaii Institute of Marine Biology, 1971-77, research associate, East-West Center, 1977—. *Member:* International Society of Theoretical and Applied Limnology, International Academy of Zoology, American Association for the Advancement of Science (fellow), American Institute of Fishery Research Biologists (fellow), American Society of Zoologists, American Fisheries Society, Ecological Society of America, American Society of Limnology and Oceanography, Bermuda Biological Station for Research, Sigma Xi.

WRITINGS: (With K. F. Lagler and R. R. Miller) *Ichthyology,* Wiley, 1962; *Downstream,* Harper, 1964; *Harvest of the Sea,* Harper, 1968; (with J. H. Ryther and W. McLarney) *Aquaculture: The Farming and Husbandry of Freshwater and Marine Organisms,* Wiley, 1972; *Das Gross Geschaft,* Benziger, 1972. Member of editorial board of *BioScience,* 1973, *Aquaculture* (journal), 1973, *Chemical Ecology,* 1975, and *Geo-Journal,* 1978.

BIOGRAPHICAL/CRITICAL SOURCES: New York Times Book Review, March 17, 1968; *New Republic,* March 30, 1968; *Natural History,* August/September, 1968; *Science Books,* September, 1968.

* * *

BARING, Arnulf Martin 1932-

PERSONAL: Born May 8, 1932, in Dresden, East Germany; son of Martin (presiding judge at the Supreme Administrative Court of the Federal Republic of Germany) and Gertrud (Stolze) Baring; married Heidrun Dietrich (an artist), March 25, 1962; children: Susanne, Juliane. *Education:* Studied at University of Hamburg, 1951-52; Free University of Berlin, 1952-53, University of Freiburg, 1953, and Fondation Nationale des Sciences Politiques, 1960-62; Columbia University, M.A., 1957; Free University of Berlin, LL.D., 1958. *Politics:* Social Democrat. *Religion:* Protestant. *Home:* Ahrenshooper Zeile 64, 1000 Berlin 38, West Germany. *Office:* Fachbereich Geschichtswissenschaften, Habelschwerdter Allee 45, Berlin 33, West Germany.

CAREER: West German Broadcasting Corp., Cologne, West Germany, political editor, 1962-64; German Association for Foreign Policy, Bonn, West Germany, research associate, 1964-65; Freie Universitat Berlin, Berlin, West Germany, lecturer in political science, 1966-68; Harvard University, Center for International Affairs, Cambridge, Mass., research associate, 1968-69; Freie Universitat Berlin, Berlin, professor of comparative politics, 1969-76, professor of contemporary history, 1976—. Researcher, Bundesprasidialamt, 1976-79. *Member:* Deutscher Historikerverband, Conference Group on German Politics, Goethe-Gesellschaft, P.E.N.

WRITINGS: Charles de Gaulle, Kiepenheuer & Witsch, 1963; *Der 17. Juni 1953,* Kiepenheuer & Witsch, 3rd edition, 1966, published as *Uprising in East Germany,* Cornell University Press, 1972; *Aussenpolitik in Adenauers Kanzlerdemokratie* (title means "Foreign Policy in Chancellor Adenauer's Democracy"), Oldenbourg, 1969; *Sehr verehrter Herr Bundeskanzler!* (title means "Dear Mr. Chancellor!"), Hoffmann & Campe, 1974; *Zwei zaghafte Riesen? Japan und Deutschland seit 1945* (title means "Two Timid Giants? Japan and Germany since 1945"), Belser, 1977. Co-editor of *Vierteljahreshefte fur Zeitgeschichte,* 1972—.

WORK IN PROGRESS: A book on the economic, social, and political changes in the Federal Republic during the late sixties and early seventies, especially on the social-liberal coalition of 1969; another book on the writers' association "Group 47" and its role in German politics, 1947-1967.

* * *

BARKER, Eric 1905-1973

July 9, 1905—February 8, 1973; British-born American poet. Obituaries: *New York Times,* February 9, 1973; *Washington Post,* February 10, 1973. (See index for *CA* sketch)

* * *

BARKIN, Kenneth D(avid) 1939-

PERSONAL: Born July 16, 1939, in Brooklyn, N.Y.; son of Julius (a clerk) and Mary (Ratner) Barkin; married Elizabeth Waddell (a potter), January 14, 1964; children: Noah, Gareth. *Education:* Brooklyn College (now Brooklyn College of the City University of New York), B.A., 1960; Brown University, Ph.D., 1966. *Home:* 151 Broadbent Dr., Riverside, Calif. 92507. *Office:* Department of History, University of California, Riverside, Calif. 92502.

CAREER: Brandeis University, Waltham, Mass., 1965-68, began as instructor, became assistant professor of European history; University of California, Riverside, assistant professor, 1968-71, associate professor of European history, 1971—. *Member:* American Historical Association, Central European Historical Association, Phi Beta Kappa. *Awards, honors:* National Endowment for Humanities fellow, summer, 1972.

WRITINGS: The Controversy over German Industrialization: 1890-1902, University of Chicago Press, 1970; (contributor) H. Bass, editor, *The State of American History,* Quadrangle, 1970. Contributor to *Journal of Modern History* and *Central European History.*

WORK IN PROGRESS: Research on the relationship between autobiographies and history; studying comparative history.

* * *

BARLOW, J(ames) Stanley (Jr.) 1924-

PERSONAL: Born August 25, 1924, in Johnson City, Tenn.; son of James Stanley (a lawyer) and Emily Taylor (Miller) Barlow; married Nella Still (a teacher), November 27, 1951; children: Susan Morrison Barlow DuBois, James Stanley III, David Matthew, Ann Elizabeth. *Education:* Vanderbilt University, pre-meteorology certificate, 1944; Wheaton College, Wheaton, Ill., A.B., 1947; Princeton Theological Seminary, B.D., 1950; Harvard University, graduate study, 1959-60; University of St. Andrews, Ph.D., 1961; University of Michigan, post-doctoral study, 1962-64. *Home:* 107 Gladwin Ave., Leonia, N.J. 07605. *Office:* 1-832, St. George Campus, College of Staten Island, City University of New York, New York, N.Y. 10301.

CAREER: Ordained minister of Presbyterian Church; minister in Alabama, Tennessee, and New York, 1948-52; director of Westminster Foundation, University of Oregon, 1954-60, and Pittsburgh, 1961-62; director, Ad Hoc Commission on Theological Education, Detroit Council of Churches, 1962-64; University of Minnesota, Minneapolis, assistant dean for summer session, 1964-66; Columbia University, New York, N.Y., assistant professor of religion, 1966-72, associate dean of summer session, 1966-71; College of Staten Island of the City University of New York, St. George Campus, Staten Island, N.Y., associate dean of faculty, 1972—, associate professor of philosophy, 1972—. Member of Columbia University Seminar on Higher Educa-

tion. Member of council, Borough of Leonia. *Military service:* U.S. Army Air Forces, 1943-46. *Member:* American Philosophical Association. *Awards, honors:* Danforth grant, 1959-60; Michigan Scholar, 1962-63, 1963-64.

WRITINGS: (Editor) *Toward a Center for Theological Studies,* privately printed by Michigan Commission on Theological Education, 1964; *The Fall into Consciousness,* Fortress, 1973. Contributor of articles and book reviews to journals in his field.

WORK IN PROGRESS: Studying perspectives in philosophy, religion, and economics.

AVOCATIONAL INTERESTS: Writing poetry, creative writing, general reading, camping, swimming, and various community activities.

* * *

BARLOW, James 1921-1973

December 1, 1921—January 30, 1973; British novelist. Obituaries: *New York Times,* February 2, 1973. (See index for *CA* sketch)

* * *

BARNEY, William L(esko) 1943-

PERSONAL: Born February 2, 1943, in Kingston, Pa.; son of William (a farmer) and Mary (Siegal) Barney; married Elaine E. Friedmann (a nurse), June 10, 1967; children: Kristina, Jeremy. *Education:* Cornell University, B.A., 1964; Columbia University, M.A., 1965, Ph.D., 1971. *Home:* 329 Burlage Circ., Chapel Hill, N.C. 27514. *Office:* Department of History, University of North Carolina, Chapel Hill, N.C. 27514.

CAREER: Trenton State College, Trenton, N.J., assistant professor of American history, 1972-75; University of North Carolina at Chapel Hill, assistant professor, 1975-76, associate professor, 1976—. *Member:* American Historical Association, Organization of American Historians, Southern Historical Association. *Awards, honors:* National Endowment for the Humanities fellowship, 1977.

WRITINGS: Road to Secession: A New Perspective on the Old South, Praeger, 1972; *The Secessionist Impulse: Alabama and Mississippi in 1860,* Princeton University Press, 1974; *Flawed Victory: A New Perspective on the Civil War,* Praeger, 1975.

WORK IN PROGRESS: A study of the impact of the Civil War on a plantation county in the deep South.

* * *

BARNHART, Joe Edward 1931-

PERSONAL: Born November 1, 1931, in Knoxville, Tenn.; son of Clifford Edward (an independent businessman) and Irene (Snyder) Barnhart; married Mary Ann Shropshire, December 27, 1953; children: Ritschl Edward, Linda Jane. *Education:* Carson-Newman College, B.A., 1953; Southern Baptist Theological Seminary, B.D., 1956; Boston University, Ph.D., 1964. *Home:* 606 Headlee Lane, Denton, Tex. 76201. *Office:* Department of Philosophy, North Texas State University, Denton, Tex. 76203.

CAREER: Western Carolina University, Cullowhee, N.C., instructor in philosophy, 1961-64; University of Redlands, Redlands, Calif., assistant professor of philosophy, 1964-66, coordinator of department, 1965-66; Parsons College, Fairfield, Iowa, associate professor of philosophy, 1966-67; North Texas State University, Denton, associate professor,

1967-74, professor of philosophy, 1974—. Lecturer, University of California, Riverside, 1965-66. *Member:* American Philosophical Association, American Association of University Professors (president of local chapter, 1963-64; vice-president of local chapter, 1965-66), American Academy of Religion, Society for Scientific Study of Religion, Southern Society for Philosophy and Psychology, Southwestern Philosophical Society.

WRITINGS: The Billy Graham Religion, United Church Press, 1972; *Religion and the Challenge of Philosophy,* Littlefield, Adams, 1975; *The Study of Religion and Its Meaning: New Explorations in Light of Karl Popper and Emile Durkheim,* Mouton, 1977. Also author of several dramas for radio and television. Contributor of articles and reviews to *Journal of Social Philosophy, Journal of Value Inquiry, Harvard Theological Review, Idealistic Studies, Southwestern Journal of Philosophy, Gordon Review, American Philosophical Quarterly, Southern Journal of Philosophy, Journal of the History of Philosophy, Religious Studies, Process Studies, Personalist, Portal,* and *Philosophy Today.* Associate editor of *Southwestern Journal of Social Education,* 1970—.

* * *

BARNOON, Shlomo 1940-

PERSONAL: Born January 13, 1940, in Jerusalem, Israel; son of Moshe and Henny (Heinemann) Barnoon; married Ethel L. Joseph (a physician), June 28, 1968; children: Barak Israel. *Education:* Georgia Institute of Technology, B.S.I.E., 1965; University of Pittsburgh, M.S.I.E., 1967, Ph.D., 1970. *Home:* 15 Juno Rd., Tiburon, Calif. 94920. *Office:* American Society of Internal Medicine, 525 Hearst Building, Third and Market Sts., San Francisco, Calif. 94103.

CAREER: Blue Cross of Western Pennsylvania, Pittsburgh, research associate, 1967-70; American Society of Internal Medicine, San Francisco, Calif., project director, 1970-72, director of research, 1972—. Lecturer, San Francisco Medical Center; consultant to St. Mary's Medical Center and Teknekron, Inc. *Military service:* Israel Military Service, 1957-60. *Member:* Operations Research Society of America, Institute of Management Sciences, San Francisco Alliance for Health Care, Alpha Pi Mu.

WRITINGS: (With Harvey Wolfe) *Measuring the Effectiveness of Medical Decisions,* C. C Thomas, 1972. Writer of research reports; contributor to journals.

WORK IN PROGRESS: Design of a drug distribution system for a hospital; evaluation of quality in medical and health care, of nurse practitioner training programs, and of new health care delivery systems.††

* * *

BARON, Robert Alex 1920-

PERSONAL: Born September 2, 1920, in Chicago, Ill.; son of Morris and Emma (Bagus) Baron; married Joan De-Keyser (a theater manager), December 2, 1956 (divorced, 1976); children: Stacy. *Education:* University of Illinois, B.S. (cum laude), 1943; Smith College, M.A., 1949. *Residence:* New York, N.Y. *Agent:* Roberta Pryor, International Famous Agency, Inc., 1301 Avenue of the Americas, New York, N.Y. 10019.

CAREER: Illinois Department of Public Health, milk sanitarian, 1942-44; Smith College, Northampton, Mass., business manager, department of theater, 1947-49; Cinavision,

Inc., New York City, vice-president and feature actor, 1949-50; theatrical work as actor on stage and network radio and television shows, press agent, stage manager, advance man, and other branches of show business, on Broadway, in stock, and summer theaters, 1950-66; Citizens for a Quieter City, Inc., New York City, executive vice-president, 1966—. Member of New York Council on the Environment; panelist at national hearings, Office of Noise Abatement and Control, U.S. Environmental Protection Agency, 1971; chairman or member of various environmental workshops and committees. *Military service:* U.S. Army, surgical technician and actor, 1944-46. *Member:* American Public Health Association, Scientists Committee for Public Information. *Awards, honors:* Annual Award of Merit, Woman's Press Club of New York, 1971.

WRITINGS: The Tyranny of Noise, St. Martin's, 1970. Compiler of "Actor in Search of a Contract," annual survey of employment in the theater for Actors' Equity Association, 1952. Contributor to *Theatre Arts, American Journal of Public Health, Designer,* and other periodicals.

WORK IN PROGRESS: The Tyranny of Noise Continues, to be published as *Proceedings* of Symposium on Community Noise, by American Society of Testing and Materials; assembling a noise abatement library for Citizens for a Quieter City; fiction.

BIOGRAPHICAL/CRITICAL SOURCES: Time, December 5, 1969; *Washington Post,* December 11, 1970; *World,* December 19, 1972.

* * *

BARON, (Ora) Wendy 1937-
(Wendy Dimson)

PERSONAL: Born March 20, 1937, in London, England; daughter of Samuel Barnet (a pediatrician) and Gladys Felicia (a Greater London Council member; maiden name, Sieve) Dimson; married Jeremy Hugh Baron (a gastroenterologist), September 8, 1960; children: Richard Jon, Susannah Eve. *Education:* Courtauld Institute of Art, London, B.A. (honors), 1958, Ph.D., 1967. *Residence:* London, England.

CAREER: Art historian; curator of pictures, Department of the Environment. *Member:* British Museum Society, National Trust, National Art Collections Fund, Friends of the Tate Gallery, Society of Authors, Friends of the Courtauld Institute, Friends of the Royal Academy. *Awards, honors:* Leverhulme research fellowship, 1972-74.

WRITINGS: Sickert, Phaidon, 1973; *Miss Ethel Sands and Her Circle,* Peter Owen, 1976. Contributor to *Burlington* and *Apollo.*

WORK IN PROGRESS: The Camden Town Group.

* * *

BARRACLOUGH, Solon L(ovett) 1922-

PERSONAL: Born August 17, 1922, in Beverly, Mass.; son of Kenneth E. and Esther (Lovett) Barraclough; married Frances Horning, July 18, 1952; children: Ann Marie, Esther, Kenneth. *Education:* University of New Hampshire, B.S., 1944; Harvard University, M.A., 1949, Ph.D., 1950. *Home address:* Mast Rd., Durham, N.H. *Office:* Graduate School of Medical Economy and Health Sciences Center, Ben Gurion University of Negev, Ber Sheva, Israel.

CAREER: Economist, U.S. Forest Service, 1951-53; University of Tennessee, Knoxville, assistant forester at agricultural experimental station, 1954-58; United Service Organizations, agricultural economics adviser in Beirut, Lebanon, 1958-59; Food and Agriculture Organization of the United Nations, Santiago, Chile, regional officer in land tenure and colonization, 1960-63, project manager of Agrarian Reform Institute, 1964-73; currently professor, Ben Gurion University of Negev, Ber Sheva, Israel. Visiting professor, University of Chile, 1962—; adjunct professor of agricultural economics, Cornell University, beginning 1963. Has directed studies in land tenure and agricultural development in Argentina, Brazil, Colombia, Chile, Ecuador, Guatemala, and Peru for Inter-American Committee for Agricultural Development, 1962-67. *Military service:* U.S. Army, 1942-46; served in Pacific Theatre. *Member:* International Association of Agricultural Economists, American Farm Economics Association, Society of American Foresters, American Association for the Advancement of Science.

WRITINGS: (With E. M. Gould) *Economic Analysis for Farm Forest Operating Units,* Harvard University Press, 1952; (contributor) Oscar Delgado, editor, *Reformas Agrarias en la America Latina,* Fondo de Cultura Economica, 1965; (editor) *Land Tenure Studies,* seven volumes, Inter-American Committee for Agricultural Development, 1966; *Notas Sobre Tenencia de la Tierra en America Latina,* I.C.I.R.A. (Santiago, Chile), 1968, translation published as *Notes on Land Tenure,* 1970; (with Juan Carlos Collarte) *El hombre y la tierra en America Latina,* Editorial Universitaria (Santiago), 1972; (with Collarte) *Agrarian Structure in Latin America,* Lexington-Heath, 1973. Contributor to journals in his field.†

*   *   *

BARRAGA, Natalie Carter   1915-

PERSONAL: Born October 10, 1915, in Troy, Tex.; daughter of Bascom Debo (a banker) and Grovie (Harrison) Carter; married John Thomas Barraga, August 9, 1943 (divorced, 1952); children: Karen Jeanne. *Education:* Attended Texas Christian University, 1933-34, and Temple Junior College, 1934-35; North Texas University, B.S., 1938; University of Texas at Austin, M.Ed., 1957; George Peabody College for Teachers, Ed.D., 1963. *Religion:* Disciples of Christ. *Home:* 1215 Larkwood Dr., Austin, Tex. 78723. *Office:* Department of Special Education, University of Texas, 213 Suttin Hall, Austin, Tex. 78712.

CAREER: Teacher of homemaking in public schools in Liberty, Tex., 1939-42; New York Institute for Education of the Blind, New York, N.Y., kindergarten teacher, 1949-51; Texas School for the Blind, Austin, homemaking teacher, 1952-61; University of Texas at Austin, assistant professor, 1963-66, associate professor, 1966-70, professor of special education and coordinator of program for the visually handicapped, 1970—. *Member:* Association for the Education of the Visually Handicapped (member of board of directors, 1966-70), Council for Exceptional Children, American Academy of Optometry (fellow), International Council for Education of Visually Handicapped, University Cooperative Society (member of board of directors, 1968—), Pi Lambda Theta, Delta Kappa Gamma, Kappa Delta Pi. *Awards, honors:* Citation from Texas Association of Mental Health, 1966.

WRITINGS: Increased Visual Behavior in Low Vision Children, American Foundation for the Blind, 1964; (with Barbara Dorward) *Teaching Aids for Blind and Visually Limited Children* (monograph), American Foundation for

the Blind, 1968; (editor) *Teacher's Guide: Utilization of Low Vision* (monograph), American Printing House for the Blind, 1970; (contributor) Berthold Lowenfeld, editor, *Visually Handicapped Children in the Schools,* John Day & Sons, 1973; (with Dorward and P. Ford) *Aids For Teaching Basic Concepts of Sensory Development,* American Printing House, 1973; *Visual Handicaps and Learning: A Developmental Approach,* Wadsworth, 1976. Contributor to proceedings. Contributor of articles and reviews to professional journals, including *Journal of American Optometric Association, Journal of Texas Optometric Association, Exceptional Children, American Journal of Optometry, New Outlook for the Blind,* and *International Journal for the Education of the Blind.* Editor of *Education of the Visually Handicapped,* 1969-72.

WORK IN PROGRESS: Program to Develop Efficiency in Visual Functioning, for American Printing House for the Blind.

*   *   *

BARRETT, C(lifton) Waller   1901-

PERSONAL: Born June 1, 1901, in Alexandria, Va.; son of Robert South (a newspaper publisher, diplomat, and philanthropist) and Annie Viola (a poet; maiden name, Tupper) Barrett; married Cornelia C. Hughes, April 6, 1924; children: Clifton Waller, Jr., William Hughes, Jon Sherwood, Richard Topper, Robert Paul, Kate (Mrs. Robert W. Rennie). *Education:* Attended University of Virginia, 1917-20. *Politics:* Independent. *Religion:* Episcopalian. *Home:* Arcadia, Farmington, Charlottesville, Va. 22901.

CAREER: Munson Steamship Line, New York City, assistant to vice-president, 1930-32; North Atlantic & Gulf Steamship Co., Inc., New York City, founder, vice-president, and director, 1932-52, president, 1952-54; book collector, 1939—. Transportation expert, U.S. Maritime Commission, 1942-45; director of sugar transportation, War Shipping Administration, 1942-45. President of board of education, Henry Holt & Co., 1945-46; president and chairman of board of directors, Norgulf Corp.; chairman of fellows, Pierpont Morgan Library; member of New York City Art Commission; member of advisory board, Mount Vernon; chairman of board of regents, James Monroe Memorial Library; chairman, Friends of Columbia Libraries; founder, Clifton Waller Barrett Library of American Literature (University of Virginia). Regent's Lecturer in American Literature, University of California, Berkeley, 1959; has also lectured at University of Virginia, Yale University, Columbia University, Fairleigh Dickinson University, Princeton University, Mary Baldwin College, Sweet Briar College, and Bryn Mawr College. Member of board of directors of Eastern Broadcasting Corp., Alexandria Improvement Corp., 620 Park Avenue Corp., Barrett Foundation, and Downtown Hospital; member of board of trustees of Lake Placid Educational Foundation (also president and member of executive committee), McGregor Library (University of Virginia), University of Virginia Alumni Fund, New York Public Library, Sweet Briar College, Clark University, Thomas Jefferson Foundation, John Carter Brown Library, and Mount Vernon Junior College.

MEMBER: Modern Language Association of America (financial trustee), American Antiquarian Association (president of Worcester, Mass. chapter, 1964-70), Bibliographical Society of America (president, 1962-64), Grolier Club (honorary member; president, 1958-62), Century Association, Virginia Historical Society, Rowfant Club, Cosmos Club,

Club Odd Volumes, Roxburghe Club, Princeton Library Associates (member of council). *Awards, honors:* Commander Cross of Carlos Miguel Cespedes, Government of Cuba, 1958; Litt.D., Clark University, 1969; L.H.D., Brown University, 1969; Sir Thomas Moore Award, University of San Francisco, 1971; Donald F. Hyde Award, Princeton University, 1972.

WRITINGS: Bibliographical Adventures in Americana, Bibliographical Society of America, 1950; *American Fiction: The First Seventy-Five Years,* American Antiquarian Society, 1954; *John Greenleaf Whittier: Poet, Politician, Antiquarian,* American Antiquarian Society, 1958; *Henry Adams and the Making of a History,* Massachusetts Historical Society, 1959; (editor) Harold Medina, *The Anatomy of Freedom,* Holt, 1959; *Italian Influence on American Literature,* Grolier Club, 1962; *The American Writer in England,* University Press of Virginia, 1969. Also author of monographs for U.S. Government on sugar transportation. Contributor of articles to history, literature, and bookmen's journals.

WORK IN PROGRESS: The American Writer in Spain.

AVOCATIONAL INTERESTS: Golfing, sailing, gardening.

* * *

BARROW, Terence 1923-

PERSONAL: Born January 30, 1923, in Wellington, New Zealand; son of Arthur Thomas (an engineer) and Olive Constance Barrow; married Hisako Sato, September 10, 1967; children: Ken Richard, Leonard James. *Education:* Attended University of Otago, 1950, and University of Auckland, 1953; Victoria University of Wellington, B.A., 1953, M.A., 1954; Cambridge University, Ph.D., 1957. *Office:* P.O. Box 3119, Honolulu, Hawaii 96802.

CAREER: Diplomate in museology of Museums Association, London, England; Dominion Museum, Wellington, New Zealand, ethnologist, 1949-65; Bernice P. Bishop Museum, Honolulu, Hawaii, ethnologist in charge of Pacific collections, 1966-69; Charles E. Tuttle Co., Inc., Rutland, Vt., and Tokyo, Japan, representative for Hawaii and editor, 1970—. Officer of New Zealand Public Service (attached to Dominion Museum, Wellington), 1949-65. UNESCO consultant to Government of Thailand, 1966. *Wartime service:* Radio Officer, special service on New Zealand merchant ships and troop carriers, 1941-45; received Pacific Star and other service decorations.

MEMBER: American Anthropological Association (fellow), Museums Association (London; fellow), New Zealand Art Galleries and Museums Association (fellow), New Zealand Archaeological Association, Polynesian Society (Wellington; life member), Hawaii Museums Association, Hawaiian Historical Society, Bishop Museum Association (life member). *Awards, honors:* Percy Smith Medal for Research in Anthropology, Otago University, 1965.

WRITINGS: Decorative Arts of the New Zealand Maori, A. H. and A. W. Reed, 1964; *Music of the Maori,* Seven Seas Publishing, 1965; *Women of Polynesia,* Seven Seas Publishing, 1967; *Maori Wood Sculpture of New Zealand,* A. H. and A. W. Reed, 1969, Tuttle, 1970; *Art and Life in Polynesia,* A. H. and A. W. Reed, 1972, Tuttle, 1973.

WORK IN PROGRESS: A book on Hawaiian traditional art; introductory prefaces for reprints published by Tuttle; research on Hawaiian traditional culture and the K. A. Webster Maori artifact collection.

AVOCATIONAL INTERESTS: Photography, ships and the sea, travel and exploration.

* * *

BARSACQ, Andre 1909-1973

January 24, 1909—February 3, 1973; Russian-born French playwright, director, and designer. Obituaries: *New York Times,* February 5, 1973; *L'Express,* February 12-18, 1973.

* * *

BARSIS, Max 1894(?)-1973

1894(?)—May 28, 1973; Viennese-born American author and illustrator. Obituaries: *Publishers Weekly,* July 2, 1973.

* * *

BARTH, Edna 1914-
(Edna Weiss)

PERSONAL: Born March 13, 1914, in Marbelhead, Mass.; daughter of Charlton Lyman (a writer) and Elizabeth (Bateman) Smith; married Julius Weiss, August 22, 1938 (divorced, 1965); married George Francis Barth (a writer and lecturer), November 19, 1966; children: (first marriage) Elizabeth Weiss Fein, Peter J., Paul J. *Education:* Radcliffe College, B.A., 1936; Simmons College, B.S. (library science), 1937. *Politics:* Independent. *Religion:* Nonsectarian. *Home:* 85 Fourth Ave., New York, N.Y. 10003. *Agent:* Craig Virdin, Curtis Brown, Ltd., 575 Madison Ave., New York, N.Y. 10022. *Office:* Lothrop, Lee & Shepard Co., 105 Madison Ave., New York, N.Y. 10016.

CAREER: Jones Library, Amherst, Mass., librarian, 1937-39; New York Public Library, New York City, assistant children's librarian, 1939-41; teacher, Hillsboro Center School, 1947-49; McGraw-Hill Book Co., New York City, associate editor of children's books, 1961-63; Thomas Y. Crowell Co., New York City, editor, 1963-66; Lothrop, Lee & Shepard Co., New York City, editor, 1966-68, editor-in-chief, 1968—; William Morrow & Co., New York City, vice-president, 1971—. *Member:* Children's Book Council (member of board of directors), Authors Guild, National Organization of Women, Radcliffe Club of New York.

WRITINGS—Under name Edna Weiss; all juveniles: *Sally Saucer,* Houghton, 1956; *Truly Elizabeth,* Houghton, 1957; *The Rainbow,* Nelson, 1960.

Under name Edna Barth; all published by Seabury, except as indicated: *Lilies, Rabbits, and Painted Eggs: The Story of Easter Symbols,* 1970; *The Day Luis Was Lost,* Little, Brown, 1971; *I'm Nobody, Who Are You?,: The Story of Emily Dickinson,* 1971; *Holly, Reindeer, and Colored Lights,* 1971; *Witches, Pumpkins, and Grinning Ghosts: The Story of the Halloween Symbols,* 1972; *Hearts, Cupids, and Red Roses,* 1973; *Jack O'Lantern,* 1974; *Turkeys, Pilgrims, and Indians Corn: The Story of the Thanksgiving Symbols,* 1975; *Cupid and Psyche: A Love Story,* 1976; *Shamrocks, Harps, and Shillelaghs: The Story of the St. Patrick's Day Symbols,* 1977; *Balder and the Mistletoe: A Story for the Winter Holidays,* 1978.

SIDELIGHTS: Edna Barth told *CA:* "Since childhood I have wanted to be an author and/or editor, but was past forty and the mother of three before realizing either ambition.

"My stories always seem to come from experiences I have had with people within a year or two of the writing. Whether children or adults, they had made a deep impression, and from this impression a story would begin to grow. The settings, too, are always one I have visited or lived in fairly recently."

*   *   *

BARTLETT, Nancy W(hite) 1913-1972

September 14, 1913—December 27, 1972; American educator and novelist. Obituaries: *Publishers Weekly,* February 5, 1973. (See index for *CA* sketch)

*   *   *

BARTLETT, Phyllis 1908(?)-1973

1908(?)—April 17, 1973; American educator, writer, and authority on George Meredith and on Elizabethan literature. Obituaries: *New York Times,* April 19, 1973.

*   *   *

BARTSCHT, Waltraud 1924-

PERSONAL: Surname is pronounced Barch; born October 16, 1924, in Munich, Germany; daughter of Bruno (a painter and graphic artist) and Edith (Snell) Gutensohn; married Heri Bert Bartscht (a professor of sculpture), March 31, 1950; children: Martin Donald. *Education:* Deutsche Meisterschule fuer Mode, Munich, Germany, Diploma, 1949; Southern Methodist University, M.A., 1966. *Religion:* Lutheran. *Home:* 1125 Canterbury Ct., Dallas, Tex. 75208. *Office:* Department of German, University of Dallas, Irving, Tex. 75060.

CAREER: Fashion designer, 1949-65, designing for fashion firms in Dallas, Tex., 1954-65; University of Dallas, Irving, Tex., instructor, 1966-69, assistant professor of German, 1969—. Designer of theatrical costumes for Knox Street Theater, Dallas, and for University of Dallas drama department; has had textile compositions exhibited, 1961—, in Dallas galleries, at Purdue University, and at other locations; commissions for textile designs include vestments for St. Mark's School for Boys, Dallas, and chancel appointments for St. Paul's Lutheran Church, Brenham, Tex. *Member:* Modern Language Association of America, American Association of Teachers of German, South Central Modern Language Association, Texas Foreign Language Association.

WRITINGS: (Translator and author of analysis) Goethe, *Das Maerchen,* University Press of Kentucky, 1972. Contributor of translations of German poetry and of articles on the history of costumes to periodicals.

WORK IN PROGRESS: Gustav Meyrink: Madman, Satirist, or Prophet?

*   *   *

BASIL, Douglas C. 1923-

PERSONAL: Born May 30, 1923, in Vancouver, British Columbia, Canada; son of William (a manager) and Christina (Findley) Basil; married Evelyn Margaret Pitcairn, 1951; children: Wendy Patricia. *Education:* University of British Columbia, B.Com. (first class honors), 1949, B.A., 1950; London School of Economics and Political Science, London, D.B.A., 1951; Northwestern University, Ph.D., 1954. *Religion:* Protestant. *Home:* 2215 Warmouth St., San Pedro, Calif. 90732. *Office:* Graduate School of Business Administration, University of Southern California, Los Angeles, Calif. 90007.

CAREER: Marquette University, Milwaukee, Wis., instructor in management, 1951-54; Northwestern University,

Evanston, Ill., assistant professor of management, 1954-57; University of Minnesota, Minneapolis, associate professor of management, 1957-61; University of Southern California, Los Angeles, professor of management, 1961—. Has lectured in the United States and abroad. Vice-president of Pallisades Home Owner Association. Consultant to businesses, including Pepsi-Cola, Union Carbide, American Can, Remington-Rand Univac, and Transcon Lines. *Military service:* Canadian Army; became captain.

MEMBER: International Management Association, Alpha Kappa Psi, Beta Gamma Sigma. *Awards, honors:* Ford Foundation fellowship.

WRITINGS: Organization and Control of Smaller Enterprise, University of Minnesota Press, 1959; (contributor) Jim McCord and Nicholas S. Vazzana, editors, *Small Business Source Book,* Practising Law Institute, 1970; (contributor) McCord, editor, *Franchising Source Book,* Practising Law Institute, 1970; *Managerial Skills for Executive Action,* American Management Association, 1970; *Leadership Skills for Executive Action,* American Management Association, 1971; (with Paul Cone and others) *Executive Decision Making Through Simulation,* C. E. Merrill, 1971; *Women in Management: Performance, Prejudice, Promotion,* foreword by Edith Head, Cambridge University Press, 1972; *L'Enterprise Effective,* L'Enterprise Moderne Press, 1972; *Corporate Strategies and Managerial Objectives* (monograph), Management Centre Europe, 1972; *The Growing Enterprise* (monograph), Management Centre Europe, 1972; (with Curtis W. Cook) *The Management of Change,* McGraw, 1973; *Conduccion y Liderazgo,* Ateneo, 1973; (editor with others) *Purchasing Information Sources,* Gale, 1977. Also author with Nicholas Glaskowski, *Corporate Strategies and Policy Formulation.* Contributor to professional journals.

WORK IN PROGRESS: Developing Tomorrow's Managers; Organizational Realities and the Executive, for Fundo de Cultura of Rio de Janeiro; *The Effective Leader,* for Fundo de Cultura; *The Effective Organization and the Management Process;* research on the managed economy, on the strategy gap, organizations in the year 2000, the executive chameleon, decision matrix management, and on management of the firm.†

*   *   *

BASS, William M(arvin III) 1928-

PERSONAL: Born August 30, 1928, in Staunton, Va.; married Mary Anna Owen (a nutritionist), August 8, 1953; children: Charles E., William Marvin IV, James O. *Education:* University of Virginia, B.A., 1951; University of Kentucky, M.S., 1956; University of Pennsylvania, Ph.D., 1961. *Home:* 8201 Bennington Dr., Knoxville, Tenn. 37919. *Office:* Department of Anthropology, 252 South Stadium Hall, University of Tennessee, Knoxville, Tenn. 37916.

CAREER: University of Kentucky, Lexington, administrative assistant in counseling office, 1954-55, acting director of counseling office, 1955-56; University of Pennsylvania, School of Medicine, Philadelphia, instructor in physical anthropology, 1956-60; University of Nebraska, Lincoln, instructor in anthropology, 1960; University of Kansas, Lawrence, instructor, 1960-61, assistant professor, 1961-64, associate professor, 1964-67, professor of anthropology, 1967-71; University of Tennessee, Knoxville, professor of anthropology and head of department, 1971—. Physical anthropologist on river basin surveys, Smithsonian Institution, summers, 1956-62, 1964-70. *Military service:* U.S. Army, 1951-53.

MEMBER: American Association of Physical Anthropologists (fellow), American Anthropological Association (fellow), Current Anthropology (associate), Society for American Archaeology, Plains Conference for Anthropology, Missouri Archaeological Society, Kansas Anthropological Association, Kansas Academy of Science, Anthropological Society of Washington, D.C., Sigma Xi. *Awards, honors:* Grants from National Science Foundation, 1962, 1963, 1965, 1967, 1969, National Park Service, 1963, 1966, Wenner-Gren Foundation (for travel to Iran), 1964, and National Geographic Society, 1968; H. Bernard Fink Award for excellence in teaching, 1965; University of Tennessee, Alumni Public Distinguished Professor Award, 1978.

WRITINGS: (Contributor) R.F.G. Spier, *Field Handbook of the Human Skeleton,* Missouri Archaeological Society, 1962; (with David R. Evans, Richard L. Jantz, and Douglas H. Ubelaker) *The Leavenworth Site Cemetery: Archaeology and Physical Anthropology,* University of Kansas Publications in Anthropology, 1971; *Human Osteology,* Missouri Archaeological Society, 1971; *A Review of Human Origins,* University of Tennessee Press, 1972. Writer of course materials in anthropology for University of Kansas; author or co-author of about seventy reports and articles based on archaeological and anthropological investigations, including series published by Smithsonian Institution, 1969. Contributor of about fifteen reviews to professional journals.

* * *

BATEMAN, Barbara Dee 1933-

PERSONAL: Born June 15, 1933, in Medford, Ore.; daughter of Charles (a restaurant owner) and Vivian (Coss) Bateman. *Education:* Attended Reed College, 1950-51, and University of Oregon, 1951-52; University of Washington, Seattle, B.S., 1954; San Francisco State College (now University), M.A., 1958; University of Illinois, Ph.D., 1962. *Politics:* "Either a philosopher-king or an educated electorate would be fine with me." *Religion:* "Mountains, lakes, trees, children." *Home:* 1042 Rio Glen, Eugene, Ore. 97401. *Office:* Department of Special Education, University of Oregon, Eugene, Ore. 97403.

CAREER: Washington State School for Blind, Vancouver, teacher of mentally retarded and emotionally disturbed children, 1956; Sonoma State Hospital for Mental Defectives, Eldridge, Calif., educational intern, 1957; special education teacher in public schools of Ashland, Ore., 1958-60; University of Illinois at Urbana-Champaign, research associate, Institute for Research on Exceptional Children, 1960-64, assistant professor of special education, 1964-65; De Paul University, Chicago, Ill., associate professor of language disorders, 1965-66; University of Oregon, Eugene, associate professor, 1966-69, professor of education, 1969—, associate director, Early Childhood Research and Development Center, 1969-70. Staff consultant on language disorders, Michael Reese Hospital, Chicago, 1965-66. Consultant in early childhood education, Follett Publishing Co.; consultant to hospitals, clinics, schools, universities, and state departments of education in more than forty states. Lecturer and conductor of workshops on special education.

MEMBER: International Reading Association, American Psychological Association, Council on Exceptional Children (member of board of governors, 1969-70), American Association on Mental Deficiency, Association for Children with Learning Disorders, National Rehabilitation Association, Orton Society.

WRITINGS: (With S. A. Kirk) *Ten Years of Research,*

Institute for Research on Exceptional Children, University of Illinois, 1964; *Clinical Interpretation of the ITPA,* Special Child, 1968; *Temporal Learning,* Dimensions Publishing (San Rafael), 1968; (editor) *Learning Disorders,* Volume IV, Special Child, 1971; *Essentials of Teaching,* Dimensions Publishing, 1971; (editor) *Reading Performance,* Special Child, 1973; (with Norris G. Haring) *Learning Disabilities,* Prentice-Hall, 1977.

Contributor: Jerome Hellmuth, editor, *Learning Disorders,* Volume I, Special Child, 1965; David Bilovsky and others, editors, *Readings in Learning Disability,* Selected Academic Readings, 1966; Haring and Richard L. Schiefelbush, editors, *Methods in Special Education,* McGraw, 1967; Mary Meeker and James McGary, editors, *A Curriculum Framework for Mentally Gifted Minors,* California State Department of Public Instruction, 1970.

Contributor of about sixty articles and reviews to professional journals. Associate editor, *Exceptional Children,* 1962—; education editor, *Journal of Learning Disabilities,* 1964—; consulting editor, "Dimensions in Early Learning" monograph series, 1965—.

WORK IN PROGRESS: A short trade book on statistics for the non-mathematician and a textbook in special education.

* * *

BATESON, Gregory 1904-

PERSONAL: Born May 9, 1904, in Cambridge, England; naturalized U.S. citizen; son of William (a geneticist) and Beatrice (Durham) Bateson; married Margaret Mead (the anthropologist), 1936 (divorced, 1950); married Elizabeth Sumner, 1951 (divorced, 1958); married Lois Cammack, 1961; children: (first marriage) Mary Catherine Bateson Kassarjian; (second marriage) John; (third marriage) Nora. *Education:* St. John's College, Cambridge, B.A., 1925, M.A., 1930. *Home:* 1000 Alba Rd., Ben Lomond, Calif. 95005.

CAREER: University of Sydney, Sydney, Australia, lecturer in linguistics, 1928; anthropological field work in New Guinea and Bali; Cambridge University, St. John's College, Cambridge, England, fellow, 1933-38; Museum of Modern Art, New York City, anthropological film analyst, 1942-43; Columbia University, New York City, lecturer in naval school of government and administration, 1943-44; U.S. Office of Strategic Services, regional specialist, 1944-47; Harvard University, Cambridge, Mass., visiting professor of anthropology, 1947-48; Langley Porter Clinic, San Francisco, Calif., research associate, 1949-51; Veterans Administration Hospital, Palo Alto, Calif., ethnologist, 1951-62; research director in ethnology, Communication Research Institute, 1962-64; Oceanic Institute, Waimanalo, Hawaii, chief of Biological Relations Division, 1964-72; presently regent of University of California. *Member:* American Association for the Advancement of Science (fellow). *Awards, honors:* Guggenheim fellow, 1946-47; Frieda Fromm-Reichmann Award for research on schizophrenia, 1962; D.Sc., Northwestern University, 1972.

WRITINGS: Naven, Cambridge University Press, 1936, 2nd enlarged edition, 1958; (with former wife, Margaret Mead) *Balinese Character,* New York Academy of Sciences, 1943; (with J. Ruesch) *Communication,* Norton, 1950; *Steps to an Ecology of Mind,* Chandler Publishing, 1972. Contributor to journals.

WORK IN PROGRESS: Research on epistemology and

the formal resemblance between epistemology and biological evolution.

SIDELIGHTS: Gregory Bateson has been described by the *New Yorker* as "the distinguished ethnologist, biologist, and anthropologist, and the first man to apply cybernetic and communications theory to such problems as cultural instability, schizophrenia, learning theory, evolution, and aesthetics—also the first man to name and define the 'double bind,' a verbal weapon often employed in families with schizophrenic children, and in other places, which consists of issuing a command and implying at the same time that you will hate forever anyone who obeys the command." Bateson told *CA* that he regards the double bind hypothesis as his most important contribution. He is also known for his work on the formation of moral character.

Bateson was appointed to the Board of Regents of the University of California by Governor Jerry Brown. In that capacity, according to *Newsweek,* the "brilliant, peevish Gregory Bateson ... has let fly with stinging opinions on every aspect of university life, from the quality of students to the competence of the regents themselves. ... He admits that his views on education are 'frankly elitist.'" The governor told *Newsweek* that Bateson "is doing just exactly what he was appointed to do: shaking up a board of regents that Jerry Brown complains has been a mere rubber stamp for university administrators."

BIOGRAPHICAL/CRITICAL SOURCES: Margaret Mead, *Blackberry Winter,* Morrow, 1972; *New York Review of Books,* October 19, 1972; *New Statesman,* July 6, 1973; *Harper's,* November, 1973; *New Yorker,* May 27, 1974; *Newsweek,* November 21, 1977.

*   *   *

BATTEN, Mary   1937-

PERSONAL: Born January 19, 1937, in Smithfield, Va.; daughter of H. Taylor and Mary Louise (Jones) Batten. *Education:* Attended University of North Carolina, 1955-57; New School for Social Research, B.A., 1959; Columbia University, M.A., 1962. *Residence:* New York, N.Y.

CAREER: New York Public Library, New York City, library clerk, 1957-59; New York Cancer Research Institute, New York City, secretary, 1961-62; Manhattan Vocational-Technical High School, New York City, English teacher, 1962-63; NBC News, New York City, 1963-67, began as production assistant, became a researcher; Ford Foundation, New York City, information analyst, 1967-69; writer. *Awards, honors:* Fulbright fellowship in Paris, 1959-60; American Film Festival Blue Ribbon, 1972, for documentary, "The Not So Solid Earth."

WRITINGS: Discovery by Chance (nonfiction), Funk, 1968; *The Tropical Forest: Ants, Ants, Animals and Plants,* Crowell, 1973.

Film documentaries; all produced by Time-Life Films for television series: "Life Around Us"; (with Bert Shapiro) "Other Planets: No Place Like Earth," 1970; "The Not-So-Solid Earth," 1971; (also researcher) "Life in a Tropical Forest," 1971; (with Jerry Alden) "More Than Meets the Eye," 1971; (also producer) "Should Oceans Meet?," 1971; "Animal Communication," 1971. Writer of documentary, "Stars, Galaxies and the Southern Skies," produced by Kitt Peak National Observatory, 1971.

Filmstrips: "Oceanography," 1971; "Spanish-American Heroes" series, 1971; "Consumer Education," 1971. Adaptor of two films in British Broadcasting Corp. "Civilis-

ation" series, 1971. Also author of three filmstrips on the U.S. Constitution, 1972, two filmstrips on Africa and Southeast Asia, 1972, and three filmstrip adaptations of films in the Alistair Cooke "America" series.

Short story included in *Bank Street Readers,* Macmillan, 1966. Contributor of interviews, articles, and reviews to *Film Comment,* 1963-66.

WORK IN PROGRESS: A work of fiction.

SIDELIGHTS: "Ecology has become a deep concern," Mary Batten writes, "not simply from the point of view of combating pollution but on the more serious level of the interrelationships that bind together all life on this planet. I think my travel to the tropical forest reserve maintained for scientific research by the Smithsonian Tropical Research Institute on Barro Colorado Island, Panama, really opened my eyes to the subtle interactions which are the heart of any natural system. I now have also a deep love for the tropics and I go there whenever I can. ... The power of words to create characters, to bring them alive and, hopefully, to enlarge the visions of my readers, fascinates me. ... My ideas come from anyplace—a chance remark, an unexpected experience, a crisis, a dream, the newspaper, a subway rider."

*   *   *

BATTERSBY, James L(yons)   1936-

PERSONAL: Born August 24, 1936, in Pawtucket, R.I.; son of James Lyons (an accountant) and Hazel (Deuel) Battersby; married Beverly McClure (an elementary school teacher), August 24, 1957; children: Julie Ann. *Education:* University of Vermont, B.S., 1961; Cornell University, M.A., 1962, Ph.D., 1965. *Home:* 2700 Brandon Rd., Columbus, Ohio 43221. *Office:* Ohio State University, 164 West 17th Ave., Columbus, Ohio 43210.

CAREER: University of California, Berkeley, assistant professor of English, 1965-70; Ohio State University, Columbus, associate professor of English, 1970—. *Military service:* U.S. Army, Security Agency, 1954-57. *Member:* Modern Language Association of America, American Society for Eighteenth Century Studies, Phi Beta Kappa, Kappa Delta Pi, Phi Kappa Phi. *Awards, honors:* Woodrow Wilson fellowship, 1961-62, 1964-65; Samuel S. Fels fellowship, 1964-65.

WRITINGS: Typical Folly: Evaluating Student Performance in Higher Education, National Council of Teachers of English, 1972; *Rational Praise and Natural Lamentation: Johnson, Lycidas, and of Criticism,* Fairleigh Dickinson University Press, 1979. Contributor to *Studies in English Literature, Genre, Studies in Bibliography, Papers of the Bibliographical Society of America, Chicago Review,* and *Modern Philology.*

WORK IN PROGRESS: Editing life of Addison for the Yale edition of Samuel Johnson's *Lives of the Poets;* also a critical study of the *Lives.*

*   *   *

BATTLE, Allen Overton   1927-

PERSONAL: Born November 19, 1927, in Memphis, Tenn.; son of Allen Overton (a pharmacist) and Florence (Castelvecchi) Battle; married Mary Madeline Vroman (a college instructor), June 14, 1952; children: Allen Overton III. *Education:* Siena College, Memphis, Tenn., B.S., 1949; Catholic University of America, M.A., 1953, Ph.D., 1961. *Politics:* No affiliation. *Religion:* No affiliation. *Home:* 2220 Washington Ave., Memphis, Tenn. 38104. *Office:* Department of Psychiatry, University of Tennessee, 42 North Dunlap, Memphis, Tenn. 38103.

CAREER: University of Tennessee Medical Units, Memphis, intern in clinical psychology at School of Medicine, 1952-53, instructor, 1956-61, assistant professor, 1961-66, associate professor, 1966-73, professor of psychiatry, 1973—, clinical psychologist at Mental Health Clinic, 1956—. Visiting lecturer in psychology at Southwestern at Memphis, 1961—. Co-director of Suicide Prevention Service of Memphis; member of board of directors of Memphis House (for drug abuse treatment). *Member:* American Psychological Association, American Anthropological Association, American Association for the Advancement of Science, British Society for Projective Techniques, New York Academy of Science, Sigma Xi. *Awards, honors:* Distinguished service award from Tennessee Mental Health Association, 1971.

WRITINGS: Status Personality in a Negro Holiness Sect, Catholic University of America Press, 1961; *The Health Sciences: A Humanistic Approach,* University of Tennessee Press, 1973; "Suicide Intervention for Pharmacists" (filmscript), College of Pharmacy, University of Tennessee, 1977.

WORK IN PROGRESS: Research on a new scoring technique for the Thematic Apperception Test; *Crisis Intervention and Suicide Prevention for Lay Volunteers.*

AVOCATIONAL INTERESTS: Oriental art, romantic and impressionist music, European travel.

* * *

BATTLES, (Roxy) Edith 1921-

PERSONAL: Born March 29, 1921, in Spokane, Wash.; daughter of Rosco Jiriah (a caterer) and Lucile Zilpha (Jacques) Baker; married Willis Ralph Dawe Battles (a petroleum chemist); children: Margaret Elizabeth, Ralph Willis, Laura Lucile. *Education:* Bakersfield College, A.A., 1940; Long Beach State College (now California State University, Long Beach), B.A., 1959; Pepperdine University, M.A., 1976. *Home:* 560 South Helberta Ave., Redondo Beach, Calif. 90277. *Office:* Arlington Elementary School, Torrance Unified School District, Torrance, Calif.

CAREER: Free-lance writer. Elementary school teacher in Torrance, Calif., 1959—, at Meadow Park School, 1963-69, and Arlington School, 1969—. Teacher of adult education course in writing to sell; instructor in writing, Pepperdine University, 1974—. Member of delegation "U.S. Teachers to Japan," 1975. *Member:* National Education Association, Author's League of America, Southwest Manuscripters (charter member), California Teacher's Association, Southern California Council of Literature for Children and Young People, Torrance Teachers Association, Society of Childrens Book Writers.

WRITINGS—Juvenile: Over the Rickety Fence, with teacher's manual, Fearon, 1967; (illustrated) *The Terrible Trick or Treat,* W. R. Scott, 1970; (illustrated with photographs) *501 Balloons Sail East,* W. R. Scott, 1971; (illustrated) *The Terrible Terrier* (Junior Literary Guild selection), W. R. Scott, 1972; *One to Teeter-Totter,* Whitman, 1973; *Eddie Couldn't Find the Elephants,* Whitman, 1974; *What Does the Rooster Say, Shingo?,* Whitman, 1978. Also author of an as yet unpublished Gothic novel, "The Master of Castle Drai." Author of column appearing in *Manhattan Tide.* Contributor of humor, research articles, short stories, and verse to national magazines, including *Saturday Eve-ning Post, Highlights for Children, American Girl, Outdoor World, Reader's Digest,* and education journals.

WORK IN PROGRESS: Preparing two educational television series, one on reading for grade school use, the other, "How to Write for Publication," for area community colleges; a second Gothic novel.

SIDELIGHTS: "I've always known I would be a writer," Edith Battles told *CA.* "But I have found that I am also hooked on teaching." Having enjoyed reading Gothic novels, she decided to "hack out a book in a summer vacation period, completely to formula. . . . [But] I grew absorbed in the background of my formula novel. . . . "The Master of Castle Drai" is a far better piece of work than I had any intention of doing."

* * *

BATTS, Michael S. 1929-

PERSONAL: Born August 2, 1929, in Mitcham, England; son of Stanley George (a teacher) and Alixe (Watson) Batts; married Miriam Yoshida, March 19, 1959; children: Anna. *Education:* King's College, London, B.A., 1952, B.A. (honors), 1953; University of Freiburg, Dr.Phil., 1957; University of London, D.Litt., 1973. *Politics:* None. *Religion:* None. *Residence:* Vancouver, British Columbia, Canada. *Office:* Department of Germanic Studies, University of British Columbia, 2075 Wesbrook Pl., Vancouver, British Columbia, Canada V6T 1W5.

CAREER: Lecturer in English at University of Mainz, Germersheim, Germany, 1953-54, University of Basel, Basel, Switzerland, 1954-56, and University of Wuerzburg, Wuerzburg, Germany, 1956-58; University of California, Berkeley, instructor in German, 1958-60; University of British Columbia, Vancouver, assistant professor, 1960-64, associate professor, 1964-67, professor of German, 1967—, head of Department of Germanic Studies, 1968—. *Military service:* British Army, 1947-49.

MEMBER: Canadian Association of University Teachers of German, Modern Humanities Research Association, Modern Language Association of America, Mediaeval Academy of America, Humanities Association of Canada (member-at-large of executive committee, 1971-75), Philological Association of the Pacific Coast (chairman of Germanic section, 1962), Alcuin Society (executive vice-president). *Awards, honors:* American Council of Learned Societies grant for computer work, 1964; Alexander von Humboldt Foundation senior fellowship, 1964-65; Canada Council senior fellowship, 1964-65, 1971-72, and grants, 1966, 1967.

WRITINGS: Die Form der Aventiuren im Nibelungenlied, Schmitz Verlag, 1961; (with others) *Geschichte des Sweiten Weltkrieges,* Ploetz Verlag, 1961; (editor) *Bruder Hansens Marienlieder* (critical edition), Max Niemeyer Verlag, 1963; *Studien zu Bruder Hansens Marienliedern,* de Gruyter, 1964; (editor) *Essays on German Literature in Honour of G. Joyce Hallamore,* University of Toronto Press, 1968; *Das hohe Mittelalter,* Francke Verlag, 1969; *Gottfried von Strassburg,* Twayne, 1971; *Das Nibelungenlied: Paralleldruck der Hss A, B und C. nebst Lesarten der uebrigen Handschriften,* Max Niemeyer Verlag, 1971; (editor) Ebenezer Johnson, *A Short Account of a Northwest Voyage Performed in the Years 1796, 1797, and 1798,* Alcuin Society, 1974; (editor) *The History of Bibliography: An Historical and Critical Survey,* Lang, 1978.

Contributor: F. A. Raven, editor, *Germanic Studies in*

Honor of Edward Henry Sehrt, University of Miami Press, 1968; Stanley Werbow, editor, *Formal Aspects of Medieval German Poetry*, University of Texas Press, 1969. Contributor of articles and reviews to professional journals. Member of editorial board, *Bulletin* of Humanities Association of Canada, 1970—. Editor, *Seminar* (journal of Germanic studies), 1971—.

WORK IN PROGRESS: Research in the history of German literary criticism.

*   *   *

BAUGHMAN, M(illard) Dale   1919-

PERSONAL: Surname is pronounced Boff-man; born December 28, 1919, in Helmsburg, Ind.; son of Bert O. (a merchant) and Josephine (Browning) Baughman; married D'Lema Louise Smith (an auditor), August 26, 1950; children: Dala Lee, Dlynn Lea, Brad Dale. *Education:* Indiana University, B.S., 1946, M.S., 1948, Ed.D., 1956. *Home:* 30 Circle Dr., Terre Haute, Ind. 47803. *Office:* Indiana State University, 1000 Statesman Towers West, Terre Haute, Ind. 47809.

CAREER: Teacher in Indiana schools, 1939-52, and junior-senior high school principal, 1952-56; University of Illinois at Urbana-Champaign, assistant professor, 1956-59, associate professor of education and head of administrative placement, 1959-66; Indiana State University, Terre Haute, professor of education and editor of *Contemporary Education*, 1966—. Visiting summer professor at University of Denver, 1960, Utah State University, 1961, University of Colorado, 1962, Oklahoma State University, 1964; visiting professor at Kansas State University and University of North Carolina, 1965. Consultant to Ford Foundation, National Council of Churches, and school systems in four states. Speaker (more than one thousand addresses) in thirty-nine states, Germany, France, and Italy. *Military service:* U.S. Naval Reserve, active duty, 1942-45; became petty officer first class.

MEMBER: Association for Supervision and Curriculum Development, Educational Press Association, International Comparative Education Society, International Council on Education for Teaching, National Association of Secondary School Principals, International Platform Association, Indiana Association for Supervision and Curriculum Development, Phi Delta Kappa, Terre Haute Rotary (president, 1971-72). *Awards, honors:* Distinguished Service Awards from Illinois Junior High School Principals Association and Junior High School Association of Illinois; Presidential citation from Illinois Association of School Administrators.

WRITINGS: (Compiler) *Teachers' Treasury of Stories for Every Occasion*, Prentice-Hall, 1958; (compiler) *Educators Handbook of Stories: Quotes and Humor*, Prentice-Hall, 1963; (with Wendell Anderson, Mark Smith, and Earl Wiltse) *Administration and Supervision of the Modern Secondary School*, Parker Publishing, 1969; (contributor) Ralph H. Jones and Benjamin F. Walker, editors, *Educational Perspectives of the Elementary School*, W. C. Brown, 1969; *Baughman's Handbook of Humor in Education*, Parker Publishing, 1974.

Book-length monographs published by Junior High School Association of Illinois include: *Extra-Class Activities in the Junior High School Grades*, 1957; *School-Community Patterns for Developing Better Citizenship in Junior High School Pupils*, 1958; *Challenging the Talented*, 1959; *Foreign Language Instruction in Illinois Junior High Schools*, 1960.

Editor of and contributor to book-length monographs published by Interstate: *Junior High School Curriculum*, 1961; *Pupil Evaluation*, 1963; *One-Hundred-One Examples of Creative Teaching*, 1962; *The Climate for Learning*, 1964; *Junior High School Staff Personnel: Their Preparation and Professional Growth*, 1966; *Teaching Adolescents to Think*, 1966.

Contributor of about one hundred articles to professional journals and bulletins, and to *Quote*. Columnist, "Mostly Miscellany," in *Contemporary Education*.

SIDELIGHTS: M. Dale Baughman, known as "The Hurryin' Hoosier Humorist," finds a dearth of humor among educators, and says he has "tried to inject some through writing and lecturing." *Avocational interests:* Golf, spectator sports, reading.

*   *   *

BAYH, Birch E(vans), Jr.   1928-

PERSONAL: Surname sounds like "bye"; born January 22, 1928, in Terre Haute, Ind.; son of Birch E. and Leah Ward (Hollingsworth) Bayh; married Marvella Hern, August 24, 1952 (died April 24, 1979); children: Birch Evans III. *Education:* Purdue University, B.S., 1951; Indiana University, J.D., 1960. *Religion:* Methodist. *Home address:* R.R. 1, West Terre Haute, Ind. *Agent:* Sterling Lord Agency, 660 Madison Ave., New York, N.Y. 10021. *Office:* 363 Old Senate Building, Washington, D.C. 20510.

CAREER: Farmer in Terre Haute, Ind., 1952-57; admitted to Indiana Bar, 1961, attorney, 1961—. Indiana House of Representatives, Democratic member from Vigo County, 1954-62, minority leader, 1957-58, 1961-62, speaker, 1959-60; U.S. Senate, Washington, D.C., Democratic senator from Indiana, 1962—, chairman of Senate Intelligence Committee, Judiciary Subcommittee on the Constitution, and Senate Transportation Appropriations Subcommittee, member of Senate Judiciary Committee and Senate Appropriations Committee, member of subcommittees on juvenile delinquency, anti-trust and monopoly, and labor, and of subcommittees for the Departments of Interior, Health, Education, and Welfare, Housing and Urban Development, and Agriculture, member of Senate Steel Caucus. Member of board of visitors of U.S. Merchant Marine Academy. Member of policy council of Democratic National Committee. Member of national advisory committee, Society for Crippled Children and Adults. *Military service:* U.S. Army, 1946-48; served in Europe. *Awards, honors:* LL.D. from Purdue University and Anderson College; L.H.D., Salem College, Salem, W.Va.; named by U.S. Junior Chamber of Commerce as one of America's ten outstanding young men, 1963.

WRITINGS: The Making of an Amendment, Bobbs-Merrill, 1966; *One Heartbeat Away: President Disability and Succession*, Bobbs-Merrill, 1968.

SIDELIGHTS: As a junior senator from Indiana, Birch Bayh has participated in the drafting of three major amendments to the United States Constitution. He was the principal author of the Twenty-Fifth Amendment, which allows for an orderly succession if the president dies, is disabled, or is removed from office (Gerald Ford was the first to take office under its provisions). Bayh was also prominent in the drafting of the Twenty-Sixth Amendment, which lowered the voting age to eighteen, and the controversial Twenty-Seventh (or Equal Rights) Amendment, which, if ratified, would prohibit discrimination on the basis of sex.

In his second book, *One Heartbeat Away*, Bayh fully explains the difficulties involved in preparing the Twenty-Fifth Amendment. His efforts first began in December, 1963, shortly after President John F. Kennedy's assassination. Kennedy had been the eighth president to die in office and be succeeded by his vice-president. Historically speaking, this meant that the United States had been without a vice-president for a total of more than 36 years in its 174-year existence as a government (prior to Bayh's amendment, there was no constitutional way of filling the office of the former vice-president once he had assumed the presidency). Furthermore, there was no provision allowing for the determination of presidential disability—in other words, the vice-president was not free to serve in the president's place, regardless of the circumstances, as long as the president was still alive.

To avoid the inevitable problems which would surface if this situation were to occur again, Bayh introduced an amendment which would insure that the country has a vice-president as well as a president at all times. More importantly, it would also provide the means whereby a president who was too seriously incapacitated to adequately serve as chief executive could be removed from office. After a seemingly endless round of meetings and open hearings, the Twenty-Fifth Amendment was finally ratified in early 1967.

Bayh charts the progress of his efforts "interestingly and in detail," according to Paul Kiniery. "Senator Bayh writes very well," he continues. "You must read this very interesting book to appreciate fully the many obstacles that had to be overcome in preparing the amendment."

In 1976, Birch Bayh ran unsuccessfully for the Democratic presidential nomination.

BIOGRAPHICAL/CRITICAL SOURCES: Best Sellers, September 1, 1968; *Time,* November 3, 1975.

* * *

BAYM, Max I. 1895-

PERSONAL: Born July 19, 1895, in Kovno, Lithuania; son of Isaac (a contractor) and Ida (Karnis) Baym; married Ida Rose Lieberman, December 26, 1916 (died, 1974); married Ida Handler, October 13, 1975. *Education:* University of Michigan, B.A., 1920, M.A., 1922; Yale University, further graduate study, 1932-34; Columbia University, Ph.D., 1948. *Home:* 1560 East 18th St., Brooklyn, N.Y. 11230.

CAREER: Instructor in English and modern languages at Milford School, Colby Academy, and high schools in New York City, 1925-40; Hunter College (now Hunter College of the City University of New York), New York City, lecturer in English and comparative literature, 1929-48; Polytechnic Institute of Brooklyn, Brooklyn, N.Y., 1948-63, began as assistant professor, professor of humanities, 1960-63, chairman of Humanities Forum, 1957-63, professor emeritus, 1963—. Professorial lecturer in aesthetics, New School for Social Research, 1963-69; visiting professor of comparative literature, Emory University, 1965-66. *Member:* Modern Language Association of America, Sigma Xi.

WRITINGS: Symbols and I: Poems and Sonnets, Carranza & Co., 1927; *In Quest of Moody Food* (essay in poetics), Hilding Carlson, 1934; *The French Education of Henry Adams,* Columbia University Press, 1951, reprinted, Kraus Reprint Co., 1969; *A History of Literary Aesthetics in America,* Ungar, 1973; *Let These Symbols Speak,* North Central Publishing, 1974. Contributor to *Encyclopedia of World Literature in the 20th Century, Encyclopedia of Poetry and Poetics, Yearbook of Comparative and General Literature,*

and to *Books Abroad, L'Esprit Createur, Bulletin of the New York Public Library,* and other journals.

WORK IN PROGRESS: A book on the French poet and philosopher, Rene Sully Prudhomme; a book on French literary aesthetics.

SIDELIGHTS: "I am essentially a historian of ideas," Max Baym writes, "with interdisciplinary orientation. My work in literary aesthetics has been done in the context of general aesthetics and has aimed to emphasize a monism which regards knowledge and sensibility as correlative aspects of the human spirit. My writing on the poetry-science tension reflects this. I am particularly indebted to Robert Frost and DeWitt H. Parker, with both of whom I studied at Ann Arbor."

* * *

BAYNE, David C(owan) 1918-

PERSONAL: Born January 11, 1918, in Detroit, Mich.; son of David Cowan and Myrtle (Murray) Bayne. *Education:* University of Detroit, A.B., 1939; Xavier University, graduate study, 1941-44; Georgetown University, LL.B., 1947, LL.M., 1948; Yale University, S.J.D., 1949; Loyola University, S.T.L., 1953. *Office:* College of Law, University of Iowa, Iowa City, Iowa 52242.

CAREER: Ordained Roman Catholic priest of the Society of Jesus (Jesuits), 1952; admitted to practice before Bar in Washington, D.C., 1948, Michigan, 1960, Missouri, 1963, and Iowa, 1973. University of Detroit, Detroit, Mich., assistant professor of law, 1954-60, acting dean of School of Law, 1955-59, dean, 1959-60; St. Louis University, St. Louis, Mo., visiting lecturer, 1960-63, professor of law, 1963-67; University of Iowa, Iowa City, professor of law, 1967—. Visiting professor of law at University of Michigan, 1967, Institut fuer Auslandisches und Internationales Wirtschaftrecht (Frankfurt), 1967, and University of Cologne, 1970, 1974. *Member:* American Bar Association, Federal Bar Association, Michigan Bar Association, Iowa Bar Association, Washington, D.C. Bar Association, Delta Theta Phi.

WRITINGS: Conscience, Obligation, and the Law, Loyola University Press, 1966. Also author of an annual, *Practitioner's Corporations Casebook,* 1976—. Contributor to *America, Commonweal, Social Order,* and law journals.

WORK IN PROGRESS: A Philosophy of Corporate Control.

* * *

BAZIN, Nancy Topping 1934-

PERSONAL: Surname is pronounced Ba-*zan;* born November 5, 1934, in Pittsburgh, Pa.; daughter of Frank W. (a tool designer) and Helen (a school board official; maiden name, Wilson) Topping; married Maurice Jacques Bazin (a physics professor), December 21, 1958 (divorced, 1978); children: Michel (son), Christine Nicole. *Education:* Ohio Wesleyan University, B.A., 1956; graduate study in Paris, 1956-57; Middlebury College, M.A., 1958; Stanford University, Ph.D., 1969. *Home:* 4005 Gosnold Ave., Norfolk, Va. 23508. *Office:* English/Women's Studies, Old Dominion University, Norfolk, Va. 23508.

CAREER: Rutgers University, New Brunswick, N.J., assistant professor of English, 1971-77; University of Pittsburgh, Pittsburgh, Pa., director of women's studies, 1977-78; Old Dominion University, Norfolk, Va., associate professor of English and director of women's studies, 1978—. *Member:* Modern Language Association of America, Phi Beta Kappa.

WRITINGS: Virginia Woolf and the Androgynous Vision, Rutgers University Press, 1973. Contributor to *Modern Language Quarterly, Women's Studies, Contemporary Literature,* and other journals.

WORK IN PROGRESS: A book with Susan Stanford Friedman, *Androgyny as Living Myth: Feminist Theory and Application.*

*   *   *

BEAN, Constance A(ustin)

PERSONAL: Born in Providence, R.I.; daughter of Joel D. (an investment broker) and Ruth (Richardson) Austin; married Orville E. Bean (an electronics engineer); children: David, Carolyn. *Education:* Mount Holyoke College, B.A., 1949; Yale University, M.S., 1950. *Home:* 15 Timber Lane, Wayland, Mass. 01778. *Office:* Department of Medicine, Massachusetts Institute of Technology, Cambridge, Mass. 02139.

CAREER: Northeastern University, Boston, Mass., lecturer in health sciences, 1971-76; Norfolk County-Newton Tuberculosis and Respiratory Disease Association, Newton, Mass., health educator, 1971-74; Massachusetts Institute of Technology, Cambridge, currently coordinator of health education and information for medical department, organizer of preventive health care programs in areas of weight control and smoking. Lecturer and small-group instructor in childbirth education. *Member:* Society of Public Health Education, Massachusetts Public Health Association, Boston Association for Childbirth Education, Inc. (founder; president, 1961-63; member of the board). *Awards, honors:* Ella Lyman Cabot Foundation grant, 1969, to write *Methods of Childbirth.*

WRITINGS: Methods of Childbirth: A Complete Guide to Childbirth Classes and Maternity Care, Doubleday, 1972; *Labor and Delivery: An Observer's Diary,* Doubleday, 1977. Contributor to journals.

*   *   *

BEAN, Lowell John   1931-

PERSONAL: Born April 26, 1931, in St. James, Minn.; son of Edward John and Agnes (Swanson) Bean. *Education:* University of California, Los Angeles, B.A., 1957, M.A., 1961, Ph.D., 1970. *Home:* 1555 Lakeside Dr., No. 64, Oakland, Calif. 94612. *Office:* Department of Anthropology, California State University, Hayward, Calif. 94542.

CAREER: Palm Springs Desert Museum, Palm Springs, Calif., curator of ethnology, 1960-61; Pasadena City College, Pasadena, Calif., instructor, 1961-62, assistant professor of anthropology, 1963-65; California State University, Hayward, assistant professor, 1966-70, associate professor, 1971-76, professor of anthropology, 1976—, chairman of department, 1974-77. Research fellow, Lowie Museum of Anthropology, 1971, 1972; curator, Clarence E. Smith Museum of Anthropology, 1974-78. Has done field work among Cahuilla, Luiseno, Cupeno, Diegueno, Pomo, and urban Indians in Los Angeles, and among Miwok, Wintun, Tubatulabal, Yokut, Majove, Yavapai, Yuma, Cocopa, Wappo, Yurok, Tolowa, Costonoan, Karok, Paiute, Washo, Serrano, Gabrieleno, and Chemehuevi Indians throughout California and the Southwest. Guest lecturer at University of California (Irvine, Berkeley, Riverside, and La Jolla campuses and Medical School), Oakland Continuing Education Center, California State University, Pomona, Fort Ross Historical Society, College of the Desert, University of San

Diego, De Young Museum, and Oakland Museum. Member of advisory Indian committee, American Friends Service, 1961-65; founding member and member of board of directors, Malki Museum, Inc., Morongo Indian Reservation, 1966—; professional participant, Convocation of American Indian Scholars, 1970; member of planning committee, Gabrieleno Cultural Center; president and director of ethnographic research, Cultural Systems Research, Inc., 1978. Consultant to ethics committee, Society of California Archaeologists, 1978; legislative consultant for Native American Heritage Commission, California State Legislative Hearings, 1978. *Military service:* U.S. Marine Corps, 1951-53.

MEMBER: American Anthropological Association (fellow), Current Anthropology (associate), Council for Museum Anthropology, Southwestern Anthropological Association (vice-president, 1974-75; president, 1975-76), Society for California Archaeologists, Bay Area Archaeological Cooperative, Bay Area Teachers of Anthropology. *Awards, honors:* Postdoctoral museum research fellowship from Wenner-Gren Foundation, 1971; Smithsonian Institution grant to research history of economic development at Morongo Indian Reservation, 1972; American Philosophical Society grant-in-aid, 1972, 1973; Outstanding Educators of America Award, 1972; small grant award, 1972, urgent anthropology grant-in-aid, 1974, mini-grant award, 1977, all from California State University, Hayward; National Geographical Society grant-in-aid, 1975.

WRITINGS: (With William Mason) *The Romero Expeditions, 1823-1826,* Palm Springs Desert Museum, 1962; *A Reader in Cultural Ecology,* Academic Readings, 1965; (author of foreword) Florence Shipek, *The Autobiography of Dalphino Cuero,* 2nd edition (Bean was not associated with first edition), Dawson's Bookshelf, 1969; (with Katherine Siva Saubel) *Temalpakh: Cahuilla Knowledge and Uses of Plants,* Malki Museum Press, 1972; *Mukat's People: The Cahuilla Indians of Southern California,* University of California Press, 1972; (editor with Thomas F. King, and contributor) *?Antap: California Indian Political and Economic Organization,* Ballena Press, 1974; (author of foreword) King, Stephen Hammond, Harry W. Lawton, and Philip J. Wilke, *The Cahuilla Indians of the Colorado Desert: Ethnohistory and Prehistory,* Ballena Press, 1975; (editor with Thomas C. Blackburn, and contributor) *Native Californians: A Theoretical Perspective,* Ballena Press, 1975; (author of foreword) Jane MacLaren Walsh, *John Peabody Harrington: The Man and His California Indian Fieldnotes,* Ballena Press, 1976; (author of foreword) Blackburn, editor, *Flowers in the Wind,* Ballena Press, 1977; (with Sylvia Brakke Vane) *California Indians: Primary Resources,* Ballena Press, 1977; (author of foreword) Travis Hudson, Janice Timbrook, and Melissa Rempe, editors, *Tomol: Chumash Watercraft as Described in the Ethnographic Notes of John P. Harrington,* Ballena Press, 1978; (with others) *Persistence and Power: A Study of Native American Peoples in the Sonoran Desert and the Devers-Palo Verde High Voltage Transmission Line,* Cultural System Research, 1978; (editor with Vane) *The Coolwater Coal Project: An Archaeological Assessment,* Cultural Systems Research, 1978.

Contributor: David Barrows, editor, *The Ethnobotany of the Cahuilla Indians of Southern California,* Malki Museum Press, 1967; Roger Daniels and Spencer C. Olin, Jr., editors, *Racism in California: A Reader in the History of Oppression,* Macmillan, 1972; Henry T. Lewis, *Patterns of Indian Burning in California: Ecology and Ethnohistory,*

Ballena Press, 1973; Wayland Hand, editor, *American Folk Medicine,* University of California Press, 1974; *American Indian Economic Development,* Mouton, 1978; Robert F. Heizer, editor, *Handbook of North American Indians,* Volume VIII, Smithsonian Institution, 1978; *Nai Chang,* Abrams, in press.

Editor of "Anthropological Papers" series, Ballena Press, 1973—. Contributor to *Encyclopaedia Britannica;* contributor to numerous articles and reviews to anthropology journals. Member of editorial and publication committee, Malke Museum Press, 1966-78; contributing editor, *Indian Historian,* 1968-78; associate editor, *Journal of California Anthropology,* 1974-78; member of planning committee, *Handbook of North American Indians,* California Volume, Smithsonian Institution.

WORK IN PROGRESS: Ethnography and Culture History of the Southwestern Kashia Pomo Indians; with Sylvia Brakke Vane, *The Ethnology of Native California;* with Charles Smith, *A Comparative Ethnobotany of Twelve Southern California Tribes;* editing with Rex Jones, *Madman or Philosopher: Essays on Shamanism.*

*　　*　　*

BEATTY, William K(aye) 1926-

PERSONAL: Born February 5, 1926, in Toronto, Ontario, Canada; son of E. W. (a business executive) and Muriel K. (Swan) Beatty; married Virginia L. Lewis (a consultant), June 14, 1952; children: Margaret, William, Carol. *Education:* Attended Harvard University, 1946-49; Columbia University, B.A., 1951, M.S.L.S., 1952. *Religion:* Episcopalian. *Home:* 1509 Forest Ave., Evanston, Ill. 60201. *Agent:* Barthold Fles Literary Agency, 507 Fifth Ave., New York, N.Y. 10017. *Office:* Medical School, Northwestern University, 303 East Chicago Ave., Chicago, Ill. 60611.

CAREER: College of Physicians of Philadelphia, Philadelphia, Pa., circulation assistant, 1952-53, assistant librarian, readers' service, 1954-56; University of Missouri—Columbia, medical librarian, 1956-62, assistant professor, 1956-57, associate professor of medical bibliography, 1957-62; Northwestern University, School of Medicine, Chicago, Ill., professor of medical bibliography, 1962—, librarian, 1962-74. Member of Evanston Citizens' Commission on Educational Communication, 1967-68, and Human Relations Commission, 1970-77. *Military service:* U.S. Army, 1944-46.

MEMBER: American Association for the History of Medicine (member of council, 1965-68), American Library Association, Association of Hospital and Institution Libraries (president, 1965-66), American Osler Society (charter member; member of board of governors, 1976-79), Medical Library Association (member of board of directors, 1966-69), Special Libraries Association (member of board of directors, 1964-67), Library Association (Great Britain), Chicago Literary Club (corresponding secretary, 1971-78; vice-president, 1978-79), Institute of Medicine of Chicago (fellow), Society of Medical History of Chicago (member of council, 1963-71), Phi Beta Pi. *Awards, honors:* Ida and George Eliot Prize, 1973; *The Story of Medicine in America* chosen as one of the outstanding science-technology books of 1974 by *Library Journal; Epidemics* chosen as one of the outstanding science-technology books of 1976 by *Library Journal.*

WRITINGS: (Contributor) John P. McGovern and Charles G. Roland, editors, *William Osler: The Continuing Education,* C. C Thomas, 1969; (contributor) Gertrude L. Annan and Jacqueline W. Felter, editors, *Handbook of Medical Library Practice,* Medical Library Association, 3rd edition, 1970; (with Geoffrey Marks) *The Medical Garden,* Scribner, 1971; (with Marks) *Women in White: Their Role as Doctors through the Ages,* Scribner, 1972; (with Marks) *The Story of Medicine in America,* Scribner, 1973; (with Marks) *The Precious Metals of Medicine,* Scribner, 1975; (with Marks) *Epidemics,* Scribner, 1976.

Contributor of articles and reviews to professional journals, including *Bulletin of the Medical Library Association, College and Research Libraries, Nursing Outlook, Special Libraries, Journal of the American Medical Association, New Physician, Hospital Progress, Library Trends, Journal of Medical Education,* and *Hospitals.* Editor, *Transactions and Studies of the College of Physicians of Philadelphia,* 1955-56, and *Vital Notes on Medical Periodicals,* 1955-76; member of editorial board, *Familiar Medical Quotations,* Little, Brown, 1968, Institute of Medicine of Chicago, 1970—, *Bulletin of the Medical Library Association,* 1975—, and *Serials Librarian,* 1976—; editor of special issue, *Association of Hospital and Institution Libraries Quarterly,* summer, 1964; book review editor, *Journal of Medical Education,* 1965-70.

AVOCATIONAL INTERESTS: Gilbert and Sullivan musicals.

*　　*　　*

BEDELL, George C(hester) 1928-

PERSONAL: Born May 13, 1928, in Jacksonville, Fla.; son of Chester (an attorney-at-law) and Edmonia (Hair) Bedell; married Bettie Moor, September 5, 1952; children: George C. III, Frank Moor, Nathan Gale. *Education:* University of the South, B.A., 1950; Virginia Theological Seminary, M.Div., 1953; University of North Carolina, M.A., 1966; Duke University, Ph.D., 1969. *Politics:* Democrat. *Religion:* Episcopal. *Home:* 709 North Ride, Tallahassee, Fla. 32303. *Office:* B.O.R., 107 West Gaines St., Tallahassee, Fla. 32304.

CAREER: Florida State University, Tallahassee, assistant professor of religion, 1967-71; State University System of Florida, Tallahassee, director of humanities and fine arts, 1971—, director of personnel and faculty relations, 1973-76, associate vice-chancellor, 1976-77, executive assistant to the chancellor and director of public affairs, 1977—. *Member:* American Academy of Religion, Modern Language Association of America, Society for the Scientific Study of Religion, South Atlantic Modern Language Association. *Awards, honors:* Danforth fellow at Duke University.

WRITINGS: Kierkegaard and Faulkner: Modalities of Existence, Louisiana State University Press, 1972; (with others) *Introduction to Religion in America,* Macmillan, 1975. Contributor of articles to *Journal of the American Academy of Religion, Anglican Theological Review.*

*　　*　　*

BEEBE, (Ida) Ann 1919-

PERSONAL: Born October 18, 1919, in Yakima, Wash.; daughter of Hulbert (a farmer and trapper) and Jennie (Folkersen) Beebe. *Education:* University of Washington, Seattle, B.A., 1941, B.A. in librarianship, 1942; Berkeley Baptist Divinity School, M.A., 1947; graduate study at Columbia University. *Politics:* "Liberal: unaffiliated with any group." *Religion:* Baptist. *Home:* 711 South 13th Ave., Yakima, Wash. 98902.

CAREER: Children's librarian in Washington, California,

and New Jersey, 1942-56; Northern Illinois University, DeKalb, assistant professor of library science, 1956-58; Monmouth County Library, West Long Branch, N.J., principal children's librarian, 1958-60; Bloomfield Board of Education, Bloomfield, N.J., school library consultant, 1960-70; Cedar Grove Public Library, Cedar Grove, N.J., part-time children's librarian, 1973-77; affiliated with Yakima Greeting Service, Yakima, Wash., 1977—. Lecturer at University of Saskatchewan, summers, 1961-64, Prince of Wales College, summer, 1968, and University of Alberta, summers, 1975, 1976. Consultant for publishers of juvenile books, Scribner, Walck, Grosset & Dunlap, Messner, and Morrow. *Member:* American Library Association, Altrusa International, International Platform Association.

WRITINGS: How to Use the Library, privately printed, 1965; *Easy Cooking,* Morrow, 1972; (contributor) Allan Angoff, editor, *Public Relations for Libraries,* Greenwood Press, 1973.

WORK IN PROGRESS: Fiction for middle-grade children.

AVOCATIONAL INTERESTS: Photography, dramatics, children's theater, music, leatherwork, hand weaving, crewel embroidery, rug hooking.

*   *   *

BEEBE, Frederick S(essions) 1914-1973

February 20, 1914—May 1, 1973; American lawyer and media corporation officer. Obituaries: *New York Times,* May 2, 1973; *Washington Post,* May 5, 1973; *Newsweek,* May 14, 1973; *Time,* May 14, 1973.

*   *   *

BEHARA, Devendra Nath 1940-

PERSONAL: Born September 10, 1940, in Jamshedpur, India; son of Bhabagraphi and Pramila (Dalai) Behara; married Therese Tardif, September 10, 1969. *Education:* University of North Carolina, B.S., 1962; Columbia University, M.S., 1968; attended University of Heidelberg. *Address:* Lehrstuhl fuer Okonometrie, Bergheimer Strasse 147, 69 Heidelberg, West Germany.

CAREER: National Metallurgical Laboratory, Jamshedpur, India, metallurgist, 1963-65; Ryerson Polytechnical Institute, Toronto, Ontario, lecturer in mathematics, 1965-66; Mohawk College, Hamilton, Ontario, lecturer in mathematics, 1968-72.

WRITINGS: Mathematical Methods for Industrial Management, University Press of Canada, 1972.

WORK IN PROGRESS: Input-Output Analysis for Industrial Management; a research monograph, *Markovian Prediction of Speculative Prices and Decision Processes for Optimal Return.*††

*   *   *

BEHLER, Ernst 1928-

PERSONAL: Born September 4, 1928, in Essen, West Germany; son of Philipp and Elisabeth (Lammerskoetter) Behler; married Ursula Carola Volkmuth, November 15, 1955 (divorced, 1967); married Diana Elizabeth Ipsen (an assistant professor), November 24, 1967; children: (first marriage) Constantine; (second marriage) Sophia Elizabeth, Caroline Marie. *Education:* University of Munich, Ph.D., 1951; attended University of Paris, 1953-54; University of Bonn, Habilitation, 1961. *Home:* 5525 Penrith Rd. N.E., Seattle, Wash. 98105. *Office:* Department of Comparative Literature, University of Washington, Seattle, Wash. 98105.

CAREER: University of Bonn, Bonn, West Germany, assistant professor of philosophy, 1961-63; Washington University, St. Louis, Mo., associate professor, 1963-64, professor of Germanic and comparative literature, 1964-65; University of Washington, Seattle, professor of Germanic and comparative literature, 1965—. *Member:* Modern Language Association of America. *Awards, honors:* Guggenheim fellow, 1967, 1975; American Council of Learned Societies fellow, 1969.

WRITINGS: (Editor) *Friedrich von Schlegel, 1772-1829,* thirty-five volumes, F. Schoeningh, 1958-69; *Die Ewigkeit der Welt,* F. Schoeningh, 1965; *Klassische Ironie, Romantische Ironie, Tragische Ironie,* Darmstadt, 1972. Also author of *Madame de Stael and Benjamin Constant in Weimar,* F. Schoeningh.

*   *   *

BEKKER, Hugo 1925-

PERSONAL: Born February 12, 1925, in Burgh, Netherlands; naturalized U.S. citizen; son of Hugo and Adriana (Broekhuizen) Bekker; married Elizabeth K. Meeter, May 14, 1952; children: Stephanie, Anne Sarah. *Education:* Calvin College, B.A., 1954; University of Michigan, M.A., 1956, Ph.D., 1958. *Home:* 85 East Southington Ave., Worthington, Ohio 43085. *Office:* 310 Cunz Hall, Ohio State University, Columbus, Ohio 43022.

CAREER: University of Oregon, Eugene, assistant professor of German, 1958-61; Ohio State University, Columbus, associate professor, 1961-65, professor of German, 1965—. *Member:* Modern Language Association of America, American Association of Teachers of German, American Renaissance Society.

WRITINGS: The Nibelungenlied: A Literary Analysis, University of Toronto Press, 1971; *Andreas Gryphius: Poet Between Epochs,* Lang (Bern), 1974; *Friedrich von Hausen: Inquiries into His Poetry,* University of North Carolina Press, 1977. Contributor to language journals.

WORK IN PROGRESS: Joost van den Vondel: His Life and Works; The Poetry of Albrecht von Johansdorf, for University of California Press; *Gottfried von Strassburg's "Tristan": The Stages of Eros.*

*   *   *

BELL, Gail Winther 1936-

PERSONAL: Born December 6, 1936, in Milwaukee, Wis.; daughter of Carl Anton and Evangeline Ruth (Krueger) Winther; married Val Dee Bell, 1953 (divorced); married Evan Peterson; children: Michael, Cristi Shan, Loren, Valerie. *Education:* Attended Idaho State University, 1963; Brigham Young University, B.A., 1968, M.A., 1970. *Religion:* Church of Jesus Christ of Latter-day Saints. *Residence:* Pleasant Grove, Utah.

CAREER: Brigham Young University, Provo, Utah, instructor in English, 1968-70; St. Francis High School, Provo, Utah, English teacher, 1970-71; Brigham Young University Press, Provo, Utah, senior editor, 1970-73, editorial director, beginning 1973. *Member:* Phi Kappa Phi.

WRITINGS: (With Ralph Britsch and Todd Britsch) *Literature as Art: A Reader,* Brigham Young University Press, 1972; *In the Strange, Strange Wood,* Brigham Young University Press, 1972. Contributor to *New Era, Instructor,* and *Wild Dog.*

WORK IN PROGRESS: Two novels with Evan T. Peterson, *David Barren* and *Across the Bridge;* a children's book, *The Feeper Sings;* "The Singles Issue: Encounter with Reality"; research on adolescent word study.†

* * *

BELL, Sidney 1929-

PERSONAL: Born July 14, 1929, in Brooklyn, N.Y.; son of Edward (a leather cutter) and Minnie (Iskowitz) Bell; married Edith Labowsky, January 15, 1955; children: Alice, Daniel. *Education:* Attended College of the City of New York (now City College of the City University of New York), 1946-50; Brooklyn College (now Brooklyn College of the City University of New York), B.A., 1952; University of Wisconsin, M.A., 1957, Ph.D., 1969. *Home:* 202 Plymouth St., Athens, W.Va. 24712. *Office:* Department of History, Concord College, Athens, W.Va. 24712.

CAREER: University of Wisconsin Extension, Racine and Kenosha, instructor in history, 1959-61; Concord College, Athens, W.Va., 1962—, began as assistant professor, currently professor of history. Danforth Foundation associate, 1977-83; board member, West Virginia Humanities Foundation, 1978—. *Military service:* U.S. Army, 1954-55. *Member:* Organization of American Historians, American Association of University Professors (treasurer, West Virginia Conference, 1973), West Virginia Historical Association.

WRITINGS: Righteous Conquest: Woodrow Wilson and the Evolution of the New Diplomacy, Kennikat, 1972. Contributor to *Appalachian South.* Contributing editor of *Appalachian South,* 1967-68; member of editorial board of *West Virginia History,* 1972—.

WORK IN PROGRESS: Woodrow Wilson and the Paris Peace Conference.

* * *

BELLAMY, Joe David 1941-

PERSONAL: Born December 29, 1941, in Norwood, Ohio; son of Orin Ross (a business executive) and Beulah Pearl (Zutavern) Bellamy; married Connie Sue Arendsee, September 16, 1964; children: Lael Elizabeth, Samuel Ross Carlos. *Education:* Attended Duke University, 1959-61; Antioch College, B.A., 1964; University of Iowa, M.F.A., 1969. *Office:* Department of English, St. Lawrence University, Canton, N.Y. 13617.

CAREER: Antioch College, Yellow Springs, Ohio, assistant college editor and editor of alumni publications, 1965-67; Mansfield State College, Mansfield, Pa., assistant professor of English, 1969-72; St. Lawrence University, Canton, N.Y., assistant professor, 1972-74, associate professor of English, 1974—. Director, *Fiction International*/St. Lawrence University Writers' Conference, 1974—. Consulting editor, University of Illinois Press Short Fiction series, 1974—, Harper & Row Publishers, 1976—, University Press of Kentucky, 1978—. Program consultant in American literature, Division of Public Programs, National Endowment for the Humanities, 1976. Member of board of directors, Coordinating Council of Literary Magazines, 1976—. *Member:* College English Association, Modern Language Association of America, American Association of University Professors, Associated Writing Programs, Committee of Small Magazine Editors and Publishers.

WRITINGS: (Editor) *Apocalypse: Dominant Contemporary Forms,* Lippincott, 1972; (contributor) Jerome Klinkowitz, editor, *The Vonnegut Statement,* Delacorte, 1973;

The New Fiction: Interviews with Innovative American Writers, University of Illinois Press, 1974; (editor) *Super Fiction; or, The American Story Transformed,* Random House, 1975; (editor) *American Poetry Now: Interviews with Contemporary Poets,* University of Illinois Press, in press; *Olympic Gold Medalist* (poems), North American Review, in press. Contributor of fiction, poetry, reviews, interviews, and articles to *Atlantic Monthly, New American Review, Chicago Review, Partisan Review, Wisconsin Review, Saturday Review, New York Times Book Review, Paris Review, Prairie Schooner, Poetry Northwest, Harper's Bookletter, Iowa Review, Ploughshares, Playboy, Quartet, Novel, Chicago Sun-Times, Book Week, Poetry Now,* and other periodicals. Editor of *Falcon,* 1970-73; editor and publisher of *Fiction International,* 1973—.

WORK IN PROGRESS: A novel and other fiction projects; poetry; various articles on the nature of imagination.

* * *

BELMONT, Herman S. 1920-

PERSONAL: Born March 13, 1920, in Philadelphia, Pa.; son of Max and Rose (Saletsky) Belmont; married Lorraine Sobel, April 7, 1946; children: Eileen, Janet, Donald. *Education:* University of Pennsylvania, A.B., 1940, M.D., 1943; graduate training at Pennsylvania Hospital for Mental and Nervous Diseases and Institute of Pennsylvania Hospital, 1944, and Philadelphia Psychoanalytic Society and Philadelphia Association for Psychoanalysis, 1947-50. *Office:* Department of Mental Health Sciences, Hahnemann Medical College and Hospital, 245 North Broad St., Philadelphia, Pa. 19107.

CAREER: University of Pennsylvania, School of Medicine, Philadelphia, instructor, 1947-48, associate in psychiatry, 1948-52; Hahnemann Medical College and Hospital, Philadelphia, Pa., associate professor and senior attendant in child psychiatry, 1952-60, clinical professor of child psychiatry, 1960-63, professor and head of section of child psychiatry, 1963-72, professor and deputy chairman of department of mental health sciences, 1972—. American Board of Psychiatry, certificate in psychiatry, 1948, in child psychiatry, 1960. Institute of Philadelphia Association for Psychoanalysis, supervisor and training analyst in child psychoanalysis, 1952—, in adult psychoanalysis, 1956—, director of child analysis training, 1957-63. Pennsylvania State Commissioner of Mental Health, member of advisory committee on child psychiatry planning, 1964—, member of task force on child mental health, 1971—; member of task force, Joint Commission on Mental Health of Children, 1967—; member, Pennsylvania Governor's Human Services Task Force, 1971—. Member of board of trustees, Parkway Day School, 1967—; member of advisory board, Delaware Valley Association for Children with Learning Disabilities, member of advisory board, 1970—. Co-chairman, Eighth International Congress of Child Psychiatry and Allied Professions, 1974.

MEMBER: International Psychoanalytic Association, American Psychoanalytic Association (member of National Conference on Psychoanalytic Education and Research, 1972—), American Medical Association, American Orthopsychiatric Association, American Psychiatric Association (fellow), American Academy of Child Psychiatry (fellow), American Association for Child Psychoanalysis (charter member), Society for Research in Child Development, Society of Professors of Child Psychiatry, American Association of University Professors, Regional Council of Child Psychiatry (charter member; president, 1963-64),

Pennsylvania Psychiatric Society (fellow), Philadelphia County Medical Society, College of Physicians of Philadelphia (fellow), Philadelphia Psychiatric Society, Philadelphia Association for Psychoanalysis (president, 1946-66), Phi Beta Kappa, Alpha Omega Alpha. *Awards, honors:* Rockefeller fellow in psychiatry, 1944; Lindback Foundation award for distinguished teaching, 1966.

WRITINGS: (Co-author) *Handbook of Child Psychoanalysis,* Basic Books, 1968; (contributor) Paul Jay Fink and Van Buren O. Hammett, editors, *Sex Education of the Child and Adolescent,* F. A. Davis, 1969. Contributor of about fifteen articles and reviews to psychiatry and medical journals.

*   *   *

BENDAVID, Avrom 1942-

PERSONAL: Born June 4, 1942, in Washington, D.C.; son of Hagi (a businessman) and Sylvia (Hurwitz) Bendavid; married Leah Val, May 22, 1962; children: Naftali, Ronnit, Oren. *Education:* University of Maryland, B.Sc., 1965, M.A., 1968.

CAREER: EBS Consultants, Washington, D.C., regional development consultant, 1966-68; Settlement Study Centre, Rehovot, Israel, staff regional economist, 1968-71; United Nations Institute for Planning and Development Team in Northern Thailand, Chiang Mai, Thailand, regional economist, 1971-72; Institute of Social Studies, The Hague, Netherlands, lecturer in regional development planning, beginning 1972. *Military service:* U.S. Army Reserve, 1962-68; became sergeant. *Member:* American Economic Association, Society for International Development, Regional Science Association.

WRITINGS: (Coordinator and editor with Raanan Weitz) *The Lakhish Region,* Settlement Study Centre, 1970; *Regional Economic Analysis for Practitioners: An Introduction to Common Descriptive Methods,* Praeger, 1972, revised edition, 1974. Contributor to journals in his field.

WORK IN PROGRESS: Research on "Primacy, Domination, and Time-Phased Vertical and Horizontal Integration for Regional and National Development," "A Reconsideration of the Role of the West in the Underdeveloped Countries," "The Concepts-Strategy-Projects Approach: Further Elaboration."†

*   *   *

BENEDEK, Therese 1892-1977

PERSONAL: Born November 8, 1892, in Eger, Hungary; came to United States in 1936, naturalized in 1942; daughter of Ignatzius and Charlotte (Link) Friedmann; married Tibor Benedek (a dermatologist), May 18, 1919; children: Thomas G., Judith (Mrs. George Daskal, Jr.). *Education:* University of Budapest, M.D., 1916. *Home:* 5825 Dorchester, Chicago, Ill. 60637. *Office:* Institute for Psychoanalysis, 180 North Michigan Ave., Chicago, Ill. 60601.

CAREER: Budapest City General Hospital, Budapest, Hungary, intern in pediatrics, 1916-17; Epidemic Hospital, Budapest, resident in pediatrics, 1917-18; University Clinic for Pediatrics, Pozsony, Hungary, instructor, 1918-19; University of Leipzig, Leipzig, Germany, assistant in psychiatry clinic, 1920-25; Institute for Psychoanalysis, Chicago, Ill., member of training and research staff, 1936-77, senior staff member, 1948-77. Certified by American Board of Psychiatry, 1943. Lecturer and training analyst, German Psychoanalytic Society, 1925-32; chairman, Psychoanalytic Study Group (Leipzig), 1925-32; instructor, Erikson Institute for Early Childhood Education, beginning 1968.

MEMBER: American Medical Association, American Medical Women's Association, American Psychoanalytic Association, International Psychoanalytic Association, Society for Research in Psychosomatic Medicine, American Orthopsychiatric Association, Illinois Psychiatric Society, Chicago Psychoanalytic Society (president, 1958-59). *Awards, honors:* Immigrants' Service League Award (Chicago), 1962.

WRITINGS: Insight and Personality Adjustment, Ronald, 1946; *Psychosexual Functions in Women,* Ronald, 1952; (with Joan Fleming) *Psychoanalytic Education,* Grune, 1966; (editor with E. J. Anthony) *Parenthood: Its Psychology and Psychopathology,* Little, Brown, 1970; *Psychoanalytic Investigations: Selected Papers,* Quadrangle, 1973; (editor with Anthony) *Depression and Human Existence,* Little, Brown, 1975. Contributor of articles to professional journals.†

(Died October 27, 1977)

*   *   *

BENEDICT, Robert P(hilip) 1924-

PERSONAL: Born May 2, 1924, in Philadelphia, Pa.; name legally changed, 1950; son of Domonic (a printer) and Avis (Smith) deBenedictis; married Ruth Jean Rambo, June 16, 1951; children: Mark Robert, John Howard, James Eric. *Education:* Rensselaer Polytechnic Institute, B.M.E., 1951; Cornell University, M.S., 1954; University of Pennsylvania, graduate study, 1956-60. *Politics:* Republican. *Religion:* Protestant. *Home:* 15 Lakewood Dr., Media, Pa. 19063. *Office:* Steam Turbine Division, Westinghouse Electric Corp., Lester, Pa. 19113.

CAREER: Westinghouse Electric Corp., Steam Turbine Division, Lester, Pa., 1951—, began as engineer, currently manager of instrumentation development. Drexel University, 1958—, began as adjunct associate professor, currently adjunct professor of mechanical engineering. *Military service:* U.S. Army Air Forces, pilot, 1942-46; became first lieutenant. *Member:* American Society of Mechanical Engineers (fellow), American Society for Testing Materials (fellow). *Awards, honors:* Award of Merit, American Society for Testing Materials, 1971.

WRITINGS: (With W. G. Steltz) *Generalized Gas Dynamics,* Plenum, 1966; (with N. A. Carlucci) *Specific Losses in Flow Systems,* Plenum, 1967; *Fundamentals of Temperature, Pressure, and Flow Measurements,* Wiley, 1969, 2nd edition, 1977; (editor) *Use of Thermocouples,* American Society for Testing Materials, 1970, 2nd edition, 1974; *Journey away from God,* Revell, 1972; *Fundamentals of Pipe Flow,* Wiley, in press. Contributor of articles to *ASME Transactions.*

WORK IN PROGRESS: The Jesus Myth (100 B.C. to 100 A.D.).

*   *   *

BENJAMIN, Anna Shaw 1925-

PERSONAL: Born August 6, 1925, in Philadelphia, Pa.; daughter of Charles Dow (a clergyman) and Grace (Shaw) Benjamin. *Education:* University of Pennsylvania, B.A., 1946, M.A., 1947, Ph.D., 1955; American School of Classical Studies, Athens, fellow, 1948-50, 1968. *Home:* 208 Cedar Ave., Highland Park, N.J. 08904. *Office:* Department of Classics, Rutgers University, New Brunswick, N.J., 08903.

CAREER: Juniata College, Huntington, Pa., instructor in

classics, 1952-54; University of Missouri—Columbia, assistant professor, 1955-58, associate professor, 1958-61, professor of classics, 1961-65; Rutgers University, New Brunswick, N.J., professor of classics, 1965—. *Member:* American Association of Field Archaeologists, Archaeological Institute of America, American Philological Association, Modern Language Association of America, Phi Beta Kappa.

WRITINGS: (Translator) St. Augustine, *On Free Choice of the Will,* Bobbs-Merrill, 1965; (translator) *Xenephon's Recollections of Socrates,* Bobbs-Merrill, 1968. Editor of *Archaeology,* 1967-72.

* * *

BENNETT, Daphne Nicholson

PERSONAL: Born in Herne Bay, Kent, England; daughter of Thomas and Ingaborg (Sande) Nicholson; married William Ernest Bennett, December 22, 1945 (died March 21, 1967). *Education:* University of London, B.A., 1942, Diploma in Dramatic Art, 1948; University of Southern California, M.A., 1953, Ph.D., 1955. *Home:* 306 California St., Arcadia, Calif. 91006. *Office:* Department of Speech, East Los Angeles College, Monterey Park, Calif. 91754.

CAREER: Dudley College of Education, Dudley, England, lecturer in speech and drama, 1948-50; University of Southern California, Los Angeles, clinical assistant, 1952-55; private practice in psychology, Los Angeles, Calif., 1955-60; Mount St. Mary's College, Los Angeles, assistant professor, 1961-64, associate professor, 1964-68, professor of English and speech, 1968-73; East Los Angeles College, Monterey Park, Calif., professor of speech, 1973—. Fulbright lecturer at Kansas State University, 1950-51; lecturer in Ceylon, 1970, and in England. *Member:* American Psychological Association, American Speech and Hearing Association.

WRITINGS: Parents Should Be Heard, Hutchinson, 1972. Contributor to *Exceptional Children, Quarterly Journal of Speech, Journal of Speech and Hearing Disorders, New Era,* and *Speech.*

WORK IN PROGRESS: Research in communication and on Shakespeare.

* * *

BENNETT, Harold (Zina) 1936-

PERSONAL: Born September 29, 1936, in Detroit, Mich.; son of Merle F. (a furniture manufacturer) and Martha (a teacher; maiden name, Evenson) Bennett; married Linda (a book illustrator), November 30, 1969; children: Aaron Mathew, Nathanael Aaron. *Education:* San Francisco State College (now University), B.A., 1964. *Residence:* Point Richmond, Calif.

CAREER: Writer.

WRITINGS: Behind the Scenes, Century Communications, 1967; *The Vanishing Pirate* (juvenile), Leswing Communications, 1967; *Battle of Wits,* Leswing Communications, 1968; *Brave the Dragon* (juvenile), Century Communications, 1969; *No More Public School,* Random House, 1972; (editor) *The Tooth Trip,* Random House, 1972; (with Michael Samuels) *The Well Body Book,* Random House, 1973; (with Samuels) *Spirit Guides: Access to Secret Worlds,* Random House, 1974; (with Samuels) *Be Well,* Random House, 1974.†

BENNETT, Robert L. 1931-

PERSONAL: Born March 3, 1931, in Medicine Lodge, Kan.; son of Robert E. Lee (a minister) and Abilene (Fields) Bennett; married Carol Ann Hornsby (a teacher of emotionally-disturbed children), January 21, 1956; children: William Robert, Ann Patrice. *Education:* Attended Southern Bible Institute (now Southwestern Assemblies of God College), Waxahachie, Tex., 1947-48; University of Texas, B.A., 1951, M.A., 1955, Ph.D., 1963. *Religion:* Atheist. *Home:* 6908 Carleton Ter., College Park, Md. 20740. *Office:* Department of Economics, University of Maryland, College Park, Md. 20742.

CAREER: West Texas State College (now University), Canyon, instructor in economics, 1955-56; Texas Western College (now University of Texas at El Paso), assistant professor of economics, 1956-59; University of Maryland, College Park, associate professor of economics, 1963—. *Military service:* U.S. Army, 1953-55. *Member:* American Economic Association, Association for Evolutionary Economics, Latin American Studies Association, American Association of University Professors. *Awards, honors:* Ford Foundation faculty research fellowship, 1966-67.

WRITINGS: The Financial Sector and Economic Development, Johns Hopkins Press, 1965. Contributor to *American Economic Review, Journal of Finance,* and *Journal of Economic Issues.* Contributing editor of *Handbook of Latin American Studies,* 1973.

WORK IN PROGRESS: Research on the role of financial intermediaries and of ideology in economic development of less developed countries.

* * *

BENOIT, Pierre Maurice 1906-

PERSONAL: Born August 3, 1906, in Nancy, France; son of Auguste and Elizabeth (Geny) Benoit. *Education:* College Saint-Sigisbert, Nancy, Bacc. Sciences, 1923; Lycee Henri Poincare, Nancy, Bacc. Philosophy, 1924; College Dominicain du Saulchoir, Lectorat en Theologie, 1932; Ecole Biblique et Archeologique Francaise, Licence en Sciences Bibliques, 1934, Maitre en Theologie, 1958. *Home and office:* Ecole Biblique et Archeologique Francaise, Nablus Rd. 6, P.O. Box 19053, Jerusalem, Israel.

CAREER: Roman Catholic priest of the Order of Preachers (Dominican); Ecole Biblique et Archeologique Francaise, Jerusalem, Israel, professor of New Testament, Exegesis, and Greek New Testament, 1933—, teacher of the topography of Jerusalem, 1960—, director of *Revue Biblique,* 1953-68, pro-director of *Ecole Biblique,* 1964-65, director, 1965-72. Expert consultant, Vatican Council II; Consultor of the Pontifical Biblican Commission, 1977. *Member:* Studiorum Novi Testamenti Societas, Institut Oecumenique de Recherches Theologiques (Jerusalem; member of academic council), Society of Biblical Literature (honorary member), Catholic Biblical Association (honorary member). *Awards, honors:* Officier de la Legion d'Honneur; Doctor honoris causa of the Evangelical Faculty of Theology of Muenchen, 1972, and of the University of Durham (England) Department of Theology, 1977.

WRITINGS: (With Paul Synave) *Traite de la prophetie,* Desclee & Cie (Paris), 1947, translation by Avery R. Dulles and Thomas L. Sheridan, with some revisions, published as *Prophecy and Inspiration: A Commentary on the Summa Theologica II-II, Questions 171-178,* Desclee (New York), 1961; (translator and author of introductions and notes with

Roland de Vaux and others) *Le Bible de Jerusalem,* Editions du Cerf, 1956, 2nd edition, 1973, translation of 1st edition published as *The Jerusalem Bible,* Doubleday, 1966; (with J. T. Milik and de Vaux) *Discoveries in the Judaean Desert,* Volume II: *Les Grottes de Murabba'at,* two parts, Clarendon Press, 1961; *Exegese et theologie* (collection), Editions du Cerf, Volume I-II, 1961, Volume III, 1968; *Aspects of Biblical Inspiration,* French manuscript translated by Jerome Murphy-O'Connor and S. K. Ashe for initial publication in English, Priory, 1965 (published in England as *Inspiration and the Bible,* Sheed, 1965); *Passion et resurrection du Seigneur,* Editions du Cerf, 1966, translation by Benet Weatherhead published as *The Passion and Resurrection of Jesus Christ,* Herder & Herder, 1969; (contributor) Murphy-O'Connor, editor, *Paul and Qumran: Studies in New Testament Exegesis,* Priory, 1968. Also author of *Times and Places of the Passion* (Winslow lectures, 1968).

Editor: (With M. E. Boismard) *Synopse des quatre Evangiles en francais avec paralleles des apocryphes et des Peres,* Editions du Cerf, Volume I, 1965, Volume II, 1972; (and co-author of preface) *The Dynamism of Biblical Tradition,* Paulist Press, 1967; *Le Pere Lagrange: Au Service de la Bible, souvenirs personnels,* Editions du Cerf, 1967; (with Roland E. Murphy and Bastiaan van Iersel) *How Does the Christian Confront the Old Testament?,* Paulist Press, 1968; (with Murphy and van Iersel) *The Breaking of Bread,* Paulist/Newman, 1969; (with others) *The Presence of God,* Paulist/Newman, 1969; (with Konrad Leube and others) *Christmas: A Pictorial Pilgrimage,* Abingdon, 1969; (with others) *Easter: A Pictorial Pilgrimage,* Abingdon, 1969; (with Murphy) *Immortality and Resurrection,* Herder & Herder, 1970; (with Murphy) *Theology, Exegesis, and Proclamation,* Herder & Herder, 1971.

Translator: *Les Epitres de saint Paul aux Philippiens, a Philemon, aux Colossiens, aux Ephesiens,* 3rd edition, revised, Editions du Cerf, 1959.

Contributor to symposia and journals.

WORK IN PROGRESS: Three books, *Commentaire des Epitres de la Captivite, Introduction theologique a la Bible,* and *Evangiles de l'Enfance.*

*   *   *

BENSON, Ruth Crego 1937-

PERSONAL: Born March 15, 1937, in Watkins Glen, N.Y.; daughter of Stanley Eugene (a machinist) and Lora (a home and child-care specialist; maiden name, Ripley) Crego; married Robert Louis Benson (a historian). *Education:* Elmira College, A.B. (summa cum laude), 1959; Yale University, Ph.D., 1969. *Residence:* Portland, Conn.

CAREER: University of Maine at Portland-Gorham, Gorham, director of equal employment opportunity in office of chancellor, beginning 1972. Visiting assistant professor of letters at Wesleyan University, 1970-71. Staff associate and faculty member of U.S. Office of Education Institute at University of Pittsburgh, 1971. *Member:* National Organization for Women, National Women's Party, Women's Equity Action League, Phi Beta Kappa.

WRITINGS: Women in Tolstoy: The Ideal and the Erotic, University of Illinois Press, 1973. Contributor to *Female Studies IV* and *American Association of University Professors Bulletin.*

WORK IN PROGRESS: The Feminism of George Gissing, a monograph.†

BENTHALL, Jonathan 1941-

PERSONAL: Born September 12, 1941, in Calcutta, India; son of Sir Arthur Paul (a company director) and Mary L. (Pringle) Benthall; married Zamira Menuhin, 1975; children: one son, one stepson. *Education:* King's College, Cambridge, B.A., 1962, M.A., 1965. *Home:* 212 Hammersmith Grove, London, England. *Office:* Royal Anthropological Institute, 56 Queen Anne St., London, England.

CAREER: International Business Machines, United Kingdom, systems engineer, 1965-68; Institute of Contemporary Arts, London, England, secretary, 1971-73; Royal Anthropological Institute of Great Britain and Ireland, London, director, 1974—. *Member:* Association of Societies of Art and Design (member of council of management). *Awards, honors:* Chevalier de l'Ordre des Arts et des Lettres (France).

WRITINGS: Science and Technology in Art Today, Praeger, 1972; (editor) *Ecology in Theory and Practice,* Viking, 1972 (published in England as *Ecology: The Shaping Enquiry,* Longmans, Green, 1972); (editor) *The Limits of Human Nature,* Dutton, 1973; (co-editor) *The Body as a Medium of Expression,* Dutton, 1975; *The Body Electric: Patterns of Western Industrial Culture,* Thames & Hudson, 1976. Correspondent on art and technology, *Studio International,* 1969-72; author of annual London letter for *Coloquio-Artes* (Lisbon), 1972—. Editor, *Rain* (Royal Anthropological Institute News), 1974—.

*   *   *

BENTLEY, Gerald Eades 1901-

PERSONAL: Born September 15, 1901, in Brazil, Ind.; son of Layton Coval (a minister) and Josephine (Eades) Bentley; married Esther Greenwood Felt, September 12, 1927 (died, 1961); married Ellen Voigt Stern, August 25, 1965; children: (first marriage) Gerald Eades, Jr. *Education:* DePauw University, B.A., 1923; University of Illinois, M.A., 1926; University of London, Ph.D., 1929. *Home:* 24 Brookstone Dr., Princeton, N.J. 08540.

CAREER: University of Illinois at Urbana-Champaign, instructor in English, 1923-26; New Mexico Military Institute, Roswell, instructor in English, 1926-27; University of Chicago, Chicago, Ill., instructor, 1929-31, assistant professor, 1931-39, associate professor, 1939-43, professor of English, 1943-45; Princeton University, Princeton, N.J., professor, 1945-50, Murray Professor of English, 1950-70, assistant librarian for rare books and special collections, 1971-73. Lecturer at California Institute of Technology, 1942, Shakespeare Institute, 1947, 1953, 1957, 1959, 1962, Cambridge University, 1952, and Harvard University, 1956.

MEMBER: Shakespeare Association of America (president, 1972-74), Modern Humanities Research Association, American Society for Theatre Research, American Philosophical Society, Malone Society (Oxford; president), Bibliographical Society (London), Princeton Club, Century Club. *Awards, honors:* Huntington Library research fellow, 1938-39; Guggenheim fellow, 1944-45; Litt.D., DePauw University, 1948; Fulbright fellow, 1952-53; Litt.D., University of Birmingham, 1959; L.H.D., Indiana University, 1970; Litt.D., Long Island University, 1975.

WRITINGS: (With F. B. Millett) *The Art of the Drama,* Appleton, 1935; (editor with Millett) *The Play's the Thing,* Appleton, 1936; *The Jacobean and Caroline Stage,* seven volumes, Clarendon Press, 1941-68; *Shakespeare and Jonson,* two volumes, University of Chicago Press, 1945, revised edition, 1965; (editor) *Jonson's "The Alchemist,"* Appleton, 1947; *The Swan of Avon and the Bricklayer of Westminster,* Princeton University Press, 1948.

(Editor) *The Development of English Drama,* Appleton, 1950; *The Arte of Angling: 1577,* Princeton University Press, 1956; (editor) William Shakespeare, *Othello,* Penguin, 1958, revised edition, 1970; *Shakespeare: A Biographical Handbook,* Yale University Press, 1961; *Shakespeare and His Theatre,* University of Nebraska Press, 1964; (editor) *The Seventeenth Century Stage,* University of Chicago Press, 1968.

The Profession of Dramatist in Shakespeare's Time, Princeton University Press, 1971. Member of editorial board, *Modern Philology, English Literary History,* American Society for Theatre Research, *Shakespeare Studies,* Malone Society, Renaissance Texts Society, and *Shakespeare Quarterly.*

WORK IN PROGRESS: The Profession of Player in Shakespeare's Time.

* * *

BENTON, William 1900-1973

April 1, 1900—March 18, 1973; American publisher, writer, university vice-president, UNESCO delegate, and director of public service organizations. Obituaries: *New York Times,* March 19, 1973; *Publishers Weekly,* March 26, 1973; *Time,* April 2, 1973. (See index for *CA* sketch)

* * *

BENZ, Frank L(eonard) 1930-

PERSONAL: Born March 14, 1930, in Dunn Center, N.D.; son of Frank L. (a farmer) and Barbara (Unterseher) Benz; married Joyce Schumann, June 20, 1959; children: Steven Frank, Samuel Paul. *Education:* Wartburg College, B.A., 1954; Wartburg Theological Seminary, B.D., 1958; Johns Hopkins University, Ph.D., 1970. *Home:* 1530 Earl Dr., Dubuque, Iowa 52001. *Office:* Division of Bible, Wartburg Theological Seminary, 333 Wartburg Pl., Dubuque, Iowa 52001.

CAREER: Ordained minister of the American Lutheran Church, 1962. Worked as a camp director, carpenter, farmer, and elementary school teacher; Wartburg Theological Seminary, Dubuque, Iowa, assistant professor, 1960-69, associate professor, 1969-74, professor of Old Testament studies, 1974—, head of Division of Bible, 1969-72, acting registrar and director of admissions, 1969-70, dean of students, 1970-75, director of Interm, 1976—, chairman of graduate studies and continuing education committee, 1977—. Theologian-in-residence, Hothorpe Hall (Theddingworth, England), 1975-76. Member of colloquy committee, American Lutheran Church, 1978—. Charter vice-president, Dubuque Area Citizens Council on Community Relations, 1967-68. *Member:* American Schools of Oriental Research, Society of Biblical Literature, Chicago Society of Biblical Research. *Awards, honors:* American Association of Theological Schools fellow, 1968; Hebrew Union College predoctoral fellow, 1968.

WRITINGS: Personal Names in the Phoenician and Punic Inscriptions, Pontifical Biblical Institute, 1972. Contributor of reviews to *Lutheran Quarterly* and *Journal of Biblical Literature;* writer of abstracts for *Old Testament Abstracts.*

WORK IN PROGRESS: Research on the Philistines, Palestinian archaeology, and Biblical prophets.

AVOCATIONAL INTERESTS: Ecology, boy scouts, gardening, and conservation of natural resources.

* * *

BERCOVITCH, Sacvan 1933-

PERSONAL: Born October 4, 1933, in Montreal, Quebec, Canada; son of Alexander and Bertha (Avrutik) Bercovitch; married Gila Malmquist, April 1, 1956; children: Eytan (son). *Education:* Sir George Williams College, B.A., 1961; Claremont Graduate School and University Center (now Claremont Graduate School), M.A., 1962, Ph.D., 1965. *Religion:* Jewish. *Home:* 445 Riverside Dr., New York, N.Y. 10027. *Office:* Department of English, Columbia University, New York, N.Y. 10027.

CAREER: Brandeis University, Waltham, Mass., assistant professor of English, 1966-68; University of California, San Diego, associate professor of English, 1968-70; Columbia University, New York, N.Y., professor of English, 1970—. *Member:* Modern Language Association of America, Institute of Early American History and Culture. *Awards, honors:* Fellowships from Huntington Library, 1968, John Carter Brown Library, 1969, and American Council of Learned Societies, 1972; Guggenheim award, 1970.

WRITINGS: Typology and Early American Literature, University of Massachusetts Press, 1972; *The American Puritan Imagination,* Cambridge University Press, 1973; *The Puritan Origins of the American Self,* Yale University Press, 1975; *The American Jeremiad,* University of Wisconsin Press, 1978. Contributor of numerous essays and articles to journals in history, literature, and interdisciplinary studies.

WORK IN PROGRESS: Revolution and Literature in America.

BIOGRAPHICAL/CRITICAL SOURCES: New York Times Book Review, December 24, 1978.

* * *

BERG, Larry L(ee) 1939-

PERSONAL: Born July 30, 1939, in Fort Dodge, Iowa; son of Carl O. and Zene M. (Anderson) Berg; married Mary Ellen Randall, June 12, 1960; children: Andrea Less, Mary Michelle. *Education:* Attended Iowa State University, 1957-58; University of Iowa, B.A., 1962, M.A., 1963; University of California, Santa Barbara, Ph.D., 1972. *Home:* 5302 Marburn Ave., Los Angeles, Calif. 90043. *Office:* Department of Political Science, University of Southern California, Los Angeles, Calif. 90007.

CAREER: University of California, Santa Barbara, lecturer in American politics, 1967-68, 1969; University of Southern California, Los Angeles, instructor, 1969-72, assistant professor, 1972-74, associate professor of political science, 1974—, director of Institute of Politics and Government. Visiting associate professor at University of California, Davis, 1975-76, and University of California, Santa Barbara, summer, 1976. Executive assistant to Congressman John R. Schmidhauser, 1965-67; coordinator of election campaign for California assemblyman Winfield A. Shoemaker, 1968; delegate and expert witness for platform committee on national policy and American Indian programs, Democratic National Convention, 1968. Member of board of directors, Southern California Center for Education in Public Affairs, Inc., 1978—. Consultant to numerous government offices, educational institutions, and other groups.

MEMBER: American Political Science Association, American Society for Public Administration, American Association of University Professors (University of Southern California chapter; vice-president, 1977—), Western Political Science Association (member of executive council, 1973-75), Southern California Political Science Association (member of governing board, 1971-78; vice-president, 1973; president, 1974-76). *Awards, honors:* National Defense Education Act fellowship, 1963-65; Haynes Foundation, summer faculty research fellowships, 1970, 1972, Town Hall of California Ballot Proposition research grant, 1974, 1976, 1978, research grant, 1977; faculty research and publications grant, 1970, 1973, 1975, 1976, Faculty Innovative Education Fund grant and nomination for Outstanding Teacher Award, both 1975, all from University of Southern California.

WRITINGS: (With John R. Schmidhauser) *The Supreme Court and Congress: Conflict and Interaction, 1945-1968,* Free Press, 1972; (with Eugene Lee) *The Challenge of California,* Little, Brown, 1976; (with Harlan Hahn and Schmidhauser) *Corruption in the American Political System,* General Learning Corp., 1976. Contributor of articles to numerous journals, including *Southern Public Administration Review, Judicature, Western Political Quarterly, Jahrbuch des Oeffertlichen Rechts, Notre Dame Lawyer, Journal of Social Research,* and *Emory University Law Review.* Associate editor, *American Politics Quarterly,* 1972-77; book review consultant, *Choice,* 1973—; member of editorial policy board, *Western Political Quarterly,* 1976—.

* * *

BERGER, Andrew J(ohn) 1915-

PERSONAL: Born August 30, 1915, in Warren, Ohio; son of Anton Andrew (a steelworker) and Mary (Rodenberger) Berger; married Edith Grace Denniston, August 13, 1942 (divorced, 1969); children: John D., Diana M. *Education:* Oberlin College, A.B., 1939; University of Michigan, M.A., 1947, Ph.D., 1950. *Politics:* None. *Religion:* None. *Office:* Department of Zoology, University of Hawaii, Honolulu, Hawaii 96822.

CAREER: University of Michigan, School of Medicine, Ann Arbor, instructor, 1950-54, assistant professor, 1954-57, associate professor of anatomy, 1957-64; Maharaja Sayajirao University of Baroda, Baroda, India, senior Fulbright lecturer, 1964-65; University of Hawaii, Honolulu, professor of zoology, 1965—, chairman of department, 1965-71. Visiting professor at University of California, Los Angeles, summer, 1960; Carnegie visiting professor at University of Hawaii, spring, 1964; member of task force of International Biological Program for Hawaii Terrestrial Biology Project, 1967-68; member of governor's committee to prepare program for preservation of scientific areas in Hawaii, 1969-70, and acting chairman of governor's animal species advisory commission, 1970-71; member of advisory committee on land vertebrates of Board of Agriculture, 1970-72; honorary member of Laboratory of Ornithology at Cornell University, 1968—; honorary associate in ornithology of Bernice P. Bishop Museum, 1965—. Member of editorial committee, East-West Center Press, 1968-70. *Military service:* U.S. Army Air Forces, 1941-46. U.S. Air Force Reserve, 1946-48; became lieutenant colonel.

MEMBER: International Committee for Avian Anatomical Nomenclature, American Association of Anatomists, American Ornithologists Union (fellow), American Society of Zoologists, Association for Tropical Biology, American Association for the Advancement of Science (fellow), Oceanic Institute Alliance, Wilson Ornithological Society

(member of council, 1967-70; vice-presdient, 1971-75; president, 1975-77), Cooper Ornithological Society, Explorers Club (New York), Hawaiian Academy of Science, Conservation Council for Hawaii (member of executive board, 1966-68), Hawaiian Audubon Society (vice-president, 1966-68), Science Research Club (University of Michigan), Senior Research Club (University of Michigan), Sigma Xi, Phi Sigma, Phi Kappa Phi. *Awards, honors:* American Philosophical Society research grant, 1957; McGregor Fund grant, summer, 1958; Guggenheim fellowship, 1963; National Science Foundation grants, 1966-69, 1970-75.

WRITINGS: (With Josselyn Van Tyne) *Fundamentals of Ornithology,* Wiley, 1959, 2nd edition, 1976; (contributor) A. J. Marshall, editor, *Biology and Comparative Physiology of Birds,* Volume I, Academic Press, 1960; *Bird Study,* Wiley, 1961; *Elementary Human Anatomy,* Wiley, 1964; (with J. C. George) *Avian Myology,* Academic Press, 1966; (contributor) Olin Sewall Pettingill, Jr., editor, *Seminars in Ornithology,* Laboratory of Ornithology, Cornell University, 1972; *Hawaiian Birdlife,* University of Hawaii Press, 1972; *The Exotic Birds of Hawaii,* Island Heritage, 1977. Contributor to *Merit Student's Encyclopedia, Atlas of Hawaii, Grzimek's Animal Life Encyclopedia,* and *Endangered Birds: Management Techniques for Threatened Species.* Contributor of about 130 articles to scientific journals. Assistant editor of *Wilson Bulletin,* 1950-51, and *Auk* (of American Ornithological Union), 1953-54; member of editorial board, *Medical Bulletin* (of University of Michigan), 1961-64.

WORK IN PROGRESS: A book.

* * *

BERGER, Joseph 1924-

PERSONAL: Born April 3, 1924, in Brooklyn, N.Y.; son of Harry and Rose (Diner) Berger; married Margaret Smith, July 9, 1966; children: Adam, Rachel, Gideon. *Education:* Brooklyn College (now Brooklyn College of the City University of New York), A.B. (magna cum laude), 1949; Harvard University, M.A., 1952, Ph.D., 1958. *Religion:* Jewish. *Home:* 955 Mears Ct., Stanford, Calif. 94305. *Office:* Department of Sociology, Stanford University, Stanford, Calif. 94305.

CAREER: Dartmouth College, Hanover, N.H., instructor, 1954-56, assistant professor of sociology, 1956-59; Stanford University, Stanford, Calif., assistant professor, 1959-62, associate professor, 1962-68, professor of sociology, 1968—, chairman of department, 1977—, director of Laboratory for Social Research, 1968-70, 1971-74. Licensed counselor. *Military service:* U.S. Army, military intelligence and information control, 1943-46; served in Germany; became first lieutenant; received Bronze Star Medal. *Member:* American Sociological Association, Pacific Sociological Association. *Awards, honors:* National Institute of Mental Health fellowships, 1964, 1970-71.

WRITINGS: (With B. P. Cohen, J. L. Snell, and Morris Zelditch, Jr.) *Types of Formalization in Small Groups Research,* Houghton, 1962; (editor and contributor with Zelditch and Bo Anderson) *Sociological Theories in Progress,* Houghton, Volume I, 1966, Volume II, 1972; (contributor) I. L. Horowitz, editor, *Sociological Self-Images: A Collective Portrait,* Sage Publications, 1969; (editor and contributor with Thomas L. Conner and Hamit Fisek) *Expectation-States Theory: A Theoretical Research Program,* Winthrop, 1974; (with Fisek, Robert Z. Norman, and Zelditch) *Status Characteristics and Social Interaction: An Expectation-*

States Approach, Elsevier, 1977. Contributor of articles to professional journals, including *American Sociological Review, Sociometry, Acta Sociologica, Human Relations,* and *Administrative Science Quarterly.*

* * *

BERKELEY, David S(helley)   1917-

PERSONAL: Born January 13, 1917, in Pittsburgh, Pa.; son of Frank Waldron (a jeweler) and Flora (Shelly) Berkeley; married Carolin Snider, August 20, 1943. *Education:* Juniata College, A.B., 1938; Harvard University, A.M., 1941, Ph.D., 1949. *Politics:* Republican. *Religion:* Protestant Christian. *Home:* 610 Lakeshore Dr., Stillwater, Okla. 74074. *Office:* Department of English, Oklahoma State University, Stillwater, Okla. 74074.

CAREER: Oklahoma State University, Stillwater, instructor, 1948-49, assistant professor, 1949-54, associate professor, 1954-60, professor of English, 1960—, head of graduate studies, 1969-76. Visiting professor at University of Oklahoma, 1965. *Military service:* U.S. Army, 1941-45. *Member:* Modern Language Association of America, Milton Society of America, South-Central Modern Language Association, South Central Renaissance Conference, Oklahoma Council of Teachers of English.

WRITINGS: (Contributor) Harold B. Allen, editor, *Readings in Applied English Linguistics,* Appleton, 1958; *Inwrought with Figures Dim: A Reading of Milton's Lycidas,* Mouton, 1973. Contributor to *Notes and Queries, Explicator, Papers on Milton, American Speech, College English, Bulletin of the Oklahoma Agricultural and Mechanical College: Arts and Sciences Studies, Studies in English Literature, Studies in Philosophy, Shakespeare Quarterly, Modern Philology, University of Tulsa Monographs, Huntington Library Quarterly, National Poetry Association Anthology, Nineteenth Century Fiction, Bulletin of the Oklahoma State University: Arts and Sciences Studies,* and *Bucknell Review.*

WORK IN PROGRESS: Origins of Sentimental Comedy; Blood Will Tell in Shakespeare's Plays.

* * *

BERMAN, Bruce D(avid)   1944-

PERSONAL: Born September 27, 1944, in Boston, Mass.; son of Frank E. (an attorney) and Rose (Rosenberg) Berman. *Education:* Attended Northeastern University, 1965. *Politics:* Independent. *Religion:* Hebrew.

CAREER: Mariners Press, Inc., Boston, Mass., historical researcher and graphic artist, beginning 1967, officer and director of corporate affairs, beginning 1971.

WRITINGS: Published by Mariners Press: *Encyclopedia of American Shipwrecks,* 1972; *The Art of Shipwrecks,* 1978.

WORK IN PROGRESS: Continuing research on shipwrecks, ships, and shipping; cataloging nautical charts dating back to mid-1700's.

AVOCATIONAL INTERESTS: Diving, designing and constructing miniature submarines for salvage, underwater cinematography, and sight inspection of shipwrecks.

BIOGRAPHICAL/CRITICAL SOURCES: Boston Globe, May 24, 1972.

* * *

BERMAN, William C(arl)   1932-

PERSONAL: Born January 9, 1932, in Cleveland, Ohio; son of Sam and Esther (Appell) Berman; married Deborah Smith, August 5, 1962; children: Rachel, Daniel. *Education:* Ohio State University, B.A., 1954, M.A., 1959, Ph.D., 1963. *Office:* Department of History, University of Toronto, Toronto, Ontario, Canada.

CAREER: California State College, California, Pa., historian, 1963-65; University of Louisville, Louisville, Ky., historian, 1965-68; University of Toronto, Toronto, Ontario, historian, 1968—. *Military service:* U.S. Army, 1954-56. *Member:* Organization of American Historians.

WRITINGS: The Politics of Civil Rights in the Truman Administration, Ohio State University Press, 1970.

WORK IN PROGRESS: Research on America since 1945; *Cold War America, at Home and Abroad: 1945-1975.*

* * *

BERNARD, H(arvey) Russell   1940-

PERSONAL: Born June 12, 1940, in New York, N.Y.; son of Herman F. (a retailer) and Lillian (Rosenthal) Bernard; married Carole M. Phillips, January 28, 1962; children: Elyssa, Sharyn. *Education:* Queens College of the City University of New York, B.A., 1961; University of Illinois, M.A., 1963, Ph.D., 1968. *Office:* Department of Anthropology, West Virginia University, Morgantown, W. Va. 26506.

CAREER: Washington State University, Pullman, assistant professor of anthropology, 1966-72; West Virginia University, Morgantown, associate professor, 1972-76, professor of anthropology, 1977—. Research associate at Scripps Institution of Oceanography, 1972. *Member:* American Anthropological Association (fellow), Current Anthropology (associate member), Society for Applied Anthropology (fellow), Human Marine Adaptations Studies Group (founding member), American Association for the Advancement of Science (fellow), Sigma Xi. *Awards, honors:* Fulbright scholarship, Greece, 1969-70.

WRITINGS: (Editor) *Los Otomies,* Laboratory of Anthropology, Washington State University, Volume I, 1969, Volume II, 1972; *Anthropologika Themata* (title means "Introduction to Anthropology"), Kavalis (Athens), 1970; (editor with Michael Kenny) *The Inland Empire,* Laboratory of Anthropology, Washington State University, 1971; (editor with Perth Pelto) *Technology and Social Change,* Macmillan, 1972; (editor with Livie Duran) *Introduction to Chicano Studies,* Macmillan, 1973; (editor) *The Human Way,* Macmillan, 1975; (with Jesus Salinas) *Otami Folktales, Parables, and Jokes,* University of Chicago Press, 1976; (with Salinas) *The Fauna of the Mezquital,* University of New Mexico Press, 1978. Contributor of articles and reviews to professional journals, including *American Anthropologist, Anthropological Quarterly, International Journal of American Linguistics, Ethnologia Europea, Human Organization, Human Communications Research, Social Science Research, Sign Language Studies, Journal of American Folklore,* and *Journal of Social Networks.* Editor, *Human Organization,* 1976-79.

WORK IN PROGRESS: Numerical social network analysis; ethnography of the Otomi Indians of Mexico.

SIDELIGHTS: H. Russell Bernard has worked on Otomi linguistics since 1962 (Otomi is a native language in Mexico spoken by eighty to ninety thousand people).

* * *

BERNARD, Kenneth   1930-

PERSONAL: Born May 7, 1930, in Brooklyn, N.Y.; son of

Otis and Mary (Travaglini) Bernard; married Elaine Reiss (a teacher), September 2, 1952; children: Lucas, Judd, Kate. *Education:* City College (now City College of the City University of New York), B.A., 1953; Columbia University, M.A., 1956, Ph.D., 1962. *Home:* 788 Riverside Dr., New York, N.Y. 10032. *Office:* Department of English, Long Island University, Brooklyn, N.Y. 11201.

CAREER: Long Island University, Brooklyn, N.Y., instructor, 1959-62, assistant professor, 1962-66, associate professor, 1967-70, professor of English, 1971—. Vice-president, New York Theater Strategy, 1974—. Consultant to state arts grants in New York, 1974-75, Massachusetts, 1975, Wisconsin, 1975, and Maryland, 1978. *Military service:* U.S. Army, 1953-55. *Awards, honors:* Office for Advanced Drama Research grant, 1971; Guggenheim fellowship in playwriting, 1972-73; New York Creative Artist Public Service grants, 1973, in playwriting, 1976, in fiction; Rockefeller Foundation grant in playwriting, 1975; National Endowment for the Arts grant in fiction, 1978.

WRITINGS: Night Club and Other Plays, Winter House, 1971; *Two Stories,* Perishable Press, 1973. Contributor of fiction, poetry, and drama to *New American Review, Paris Review, Harper's, Massachusetts Review, Minnesota Review, Tri-Quarterly,* and *Iowa Review.* Fiction editor, *Confrontation,* 1977—.

WORK IN PROGRESS: Plays, including "La Justice" and "Cirque."

*   *   *

BERNER, Robert B(arry) 1940-

PERSONAL: Born September 1, 1940, in Council Bluffs, Iowa; son of Hal and Josephine (Barry) Berner; married Cecilia Marie Riedel, August 8, 1966. *Education:* University of Iowa, B.A., 1968; Bowling Green State University, M.F.A., 1972. *Office:* Department of English, Virginia State College, Petersburg, Va. 23803.

CAREER: Worked as a bartender, postal clerk, and cook; San Francisco Public Library, San Francisco, Calif., publicist, 1969; Virginia State College, Petersburg, Va., instructor in English, 1973—. *Military service:* U.S. Army, 1964-66.

WRITINGS: Geography Lessons and Other Poems, Fulcourt Press, 1973.

WORK IN PROGRESS: Translation of contemporary German poets.††

*   *   *

BERST, Charles A(shton) 1932-

PERSONAL: Born September 30, 1932, in Seattle, Wash.; son of Charles A., Sr. (a government employee) and Esther (Weage) Berst; married Roelina G. Den-Ouden, June 8, 1962; children: Nelina, Caroline. *Education:* University of Washington, Seattle, B.A., 1955, Ph.D., 1965. *Home:* 2800 Roscomare Rd., Los Angeles, Calif. 90024. *Office:* Department of English, University of California, Los Angeles, Calif. 90024.

CAREER: In real estate investment business, Seattle, Wash., 1955-60; University of Alberta, Edmonton, Alberta, assistant professor of English, 1965-67; University of California, Los Angeles, assistant professor, 1967-73, associate professor of English, 1973—. *Member:* Modern Language Association of America, Philological Association of the Pacific Coast.

WRITINGS: Bernard Shaw and the Art of Drama: The Major Plays, University of Illinois Press, 1973. Contributor of articles to *Publications of the Modern Language Association of America, English Literary History, Modern Language Quarterly, Journal of English and Germanic Philology,* and *College Literature.*

WORK IN PROGRESS: Shaw the Devil: The Myth of G.B.S.; The Plays of John Millington Synge.

*   *   *

BESSER, Gretchen R(ous) 1928-

PERSONAL: Born December 1, 1928, in Brooklyn, N.Y.; daughter of Ben (a businessman) and Sidonya (Menkes) Rous; married Albert G. Besser (an attorney), December 28, 1952; children: James, Neal, Brian. *Education:* Wellesley College, B.A., 1949; Sorbonne, University of Paris, graduate study, 1949-50; Middlebury College, M.A., 1950; Columbia University, Ph.D., 1967. *Home and office:* 227 Tillou Rd., South Orange, N.J. 07079.

CAREER: Fairleigh Dickinson University, Teaneck, N.J., instructor in French, 1955-57; Columbia University, New York, N.Y., preceptor in French, 1957-59, 1963-67; Herbert H. Lehman College of the City University of New York, Bronx, N.Y., assistant professor of French, 1967-70; Rutgers University, Newark, N.J., lecturer in French, 1972-73. *Member:* Modern Language Association of America, American Association of Teachers of French, Phi Beta Kappa. *Awards, honors:* Wellesley scholar, 1949; Fulbright scholar in France, 1949-50.

WRITINGS: (Translator) Jean Filloux, *The Crossing of the Copula,* Dodd, 1954; *Balzac's Concept of Genius,* Droz (Geneva), 1969; (translator) Gabriel Cousin, *Journey to the Mountain Beyond,* Avon, 1973; (translator) Georges Michel, *Aggression,* Avon, 1973; *Nathalie Sarraute,* G. K. Hall, in press. Contributor to *Columbia Dictionary of Modern European Literature.* Contributor of articles and reviews to *French Review, Romanic Review, Orbis Litterarum, Annee Balzacienne, Hebrew Studies in Literature, Modern Language Journal, Stanford French Review, Centennial Review, World Literature Today, Nineteenth-Century French Studies,* and *L'Esprit Createur.*

WORK IN PROGRESS: Articles on the People's Republic of China; a book tracing the history of the National Ski Patrol in the United States.

SIDELIGHTS: In her review of *Balzac's Concept of Genius,* Lucille Becker commends Gretchen Besser for her thoroughness, commenting, "While various books have treated limited aspects of Balzac's thought on genius and the creative artist, Professor Besser's lucid and penetrating work is the first to deal with the question of genius as a whole, examining and documenting it in all of its manifestations." This thoroughness is augmented by Besser's methodical approach to her work. "In the course of writing a book about her, I made the acquaintance of the French novelist, Nathalie Sarraute," she explained to *CA.* "Her work habits have strongly influenced my own. She writes every morning from nine to twelve, winter and summer, Sundays and weekdays, without interruption. I try to follow her regimen as nearly as I can, for she has taught me that writing is a ceaseless discipline."

AVOCATIONAL INTERESTS: Tennis, skiing (Besser is a member of the National Ski Patrol).

BIOGRAPHICAL/CRITICAL SOURCES: Books Abroad, winter, 1971.

BEWLEY, Marius 1918-1973

January 23, 1918—January 24, 1973; American educator, editor, critic, anthologist, and author of books on American literature and the English Romantic movement. Obituaries: *New York Times,* January 25, 1973; *Publishers Weekly,* February 5, 1973. (See index for *CA* sketch)

* * *

BHATNAGAR, Joti 1935-

PERSONAL: Born December 4, 1935, in Moradabad, India; son of Raghunandan Prasad (a police officer) and Vidya (Devi) Bhatnagar; married Sheila Srivastava (a teacher), May 28, 1966; children: Rita, Anuj. *Education:* Agra University, B.Sc., 1955, LL.B., 1957; University of London, P.G.C.E., 1962, M.A., 1964, Ph.D., 1969. *Politics:* Liberal. *Home:* 12425 Richer Blvd., Pierrefonds, Quebec, Canada. *Office:* Department of Education, Concordia University, Sir George Williams Campus, Montreal, Quebec, Canada.

CAREER: High school teacher in India, 1955-57, and Great Britain, 1960-66; Enfield College, Middlesex, England, senior lecturer in psychology and acting head of department, 1967-69; Concordia University, Sir George Williams Campus, Montreal, Quebec, assistant professor, 1969-71, associate professor of education and chairman of department, 1971—. *Awards, honors:* Grant from Government of Quebec, 1970, 1971, 1972; Canada Council grant, 1971; grant from Saidye Bronfman Foundation.

WRITINGS: Immigrants at School, Cornmarket Press, 1970; (editor) *Current Perspectives in Social Psychology of Education,* Selected Academic Readings, 1971. Creator of about fifteen education tests, published by Commonwealth Press, 1963-67. Contributor to proceedings; contributor to professional publications, including *Race Today, Psychological Studies, Socialist Worker, Research in Education, Journal of Experimental Education, Vocational Aspects of Education, Canadian Journal of Behavioral Science,* and *Remedial Education.*

WORK IN PROGRESS: A Social Psychology of Education; research on academic achievement of immigrant children in Montreal.

* * *

BIGELOW, Donald N(evius) 1918-

PERSONAL: Born August 19, 1918, in Danbury, Conn.; son of Harry R. and Bessie M. (Nevius) Bigelow; married Louise M. Fournel, September 21, 1957; children: Pierre Nevius. *Education:* Amherst College, B.A., 1939, M.A., 1945; Columbia University, Ph.D., 1950. *Religion:* Episcopalian. *Home:* 3036 New Mexico Ave. N.W., Washington, D.C. 20016. *Office:* U.S. Office of Education, Washington, D.C. 20202.

CAREER: Amherst College, Amherst, Mass., instructor in history, 1943-45; Columbia University, New York, N.Y., instructor, 1947-50, assistant professor of history, 1951-55; Brandeis University, Waltham, Mass., associate professor of history, 1955-60; U.S. Office of Education, Washington, D.C., member of staff, 1961—. Professor of humanities, New York School of Music, 1949-56; moderator of seminar for American Broadcasting Corp. series, 1954-55. Consultant to Ford Foundation and Carnegie Corp. *Member:* American Historical Association.

WRITINGS: William Conant Church and the Army and Navy Journal, Columbia University Press, 1952; (editor

with Hiram Haydn) *Makers of the American Tradition,* four volumes, Bobbs-Merrill, 1953-55; (with Joseph Axelrod) *Resources for Language and Area Studies,* American Council on Education, 1960; *The Non-Western World in Higher Education,* Annals, 1964; (editor) *The Liberal Arts and Teacher Education,* University of Nebraska Press, 1971; (editor) *Schoolworlds,* McCutchan, 1976.

* * *

BIMLER, Richard William 1940-

PERSONAL: Born August 28, 1940, in Hillside, Ill.; son of Arthur M. (a florist) and Mildred (a florist; maiden name Schultz) Bimler; married Hazel J. Reichmann, June 10, 1961; children: Diane, Robert, Michael. *Education:* Valparaiso University, B.A., 1963; Concordia Teachers' College, graduate study, 1965; University of Houston, graduate study, 1967-68; University of Missouri—Kansas City, M.A., 1972. *Religion:* Lutheran Church-Missouri Synod. *Office:* Board of Youth Ministry, Lutheran Church-Missouri Synod, 500 North Broadway, St. Louis, Mo. 63102.

CAREER: St. Andrew Lutheran Church, Houston, Tex., director of youth, 1963-68; Trinity Lutheran Church, Mission, Kan., director of education and youth, 1968-73; Lutheran Church-Missouri Synod, assistant to the president in youth ministry, social ministry, and evangelism of the Minnesota south district in Minneapolis, 1973-77, assistant executive secretary, Board of Youth Ministry in St. Louis, Mo., 1977—. Active in inner-city work, and a former Big Brother. Manager of All-Lutheran Youth Gathering, Houston, Tex., 1973; Global Village manager for All-Lutheran Young Adult Gathering, New Orleans, La., 1976. *Member:* Lutheran Human Relations Association, Religious Education Association, Lutheran Education Association (former president), Department of Pastors and Christian Educators (president, 1968-72), Lutheran Camping Association.

WRITINGS—All published by Concordia: *Youth Ministry Resources,* 1970; *Pray, Praise, and Hooray!,* 1972; *77 Ways of Involving You in the Church,* 1977. Contributor to *Issues, Advance, Interaction, Director of Christian Education Journal.*

WORK IN PROGRESS: Youth ministry research; a sex education series; parish organization handbook; a youth prayer book; retreats for youth.

* * *

BINDER, Frederick Moore 1920-
(Andrew Moore)

PERSONAL: Born November 18, 1920, in Atlantic City, N.J.; son of Paul Reginald and Kathryn (Moore) Binder; married Grace Irene Brandt, May 27, 1943; children: Janet Karen, Roberta Lynn. *Education:* Ursinus College, A.B., 1942; University of Pennsylvania, M.A., 1948, Ph.D., 1955. *Politics:* Republican. *Religion:* Episcopalian. *Home address:* R.D. 4, Taylor Highlands, Huntingdon, Pa. 16652. *Office:* Office of the President, Juniata College, Huntingdon, Pa. 16652.

CAREER: High school teacher in Somerville, N.J., 1946; Temple University, Philadelphia, Pa., assistant registrar, 1946-47, instructor in history, 1946-55; Thiel College, Greenville, Pa., associate professor, 1955-57, professor of history, 1957-59, dean, 1955-59; Hartwick College, Oneonta, N.Y., president, 1959-69, professor of history, 1959-69; New York State Education Department, Albany, associate commissioner for higher education, 1969-70; Whittier College, Whittier, Calif., president, 1970-75; Juniata College, Huntingdon, Pa., president, 1975—. Member of the New York State Regents Examinations Board, 1962-68; Fulbright lecturer in Yugoslavia, 1967-68; trustee, J. C. Blair Hospital, 1975—. *Military service:* U.S. Naval Reserve, 1942-45, 1954—; current rank, lieutenant commander. *Member:* American Historical Association, Organization of American Historians, American Association of University Professors, Empire State Foundation for Independent Liberal Arts Colleges (chairman, 1962-63), Phi Alpha Theta, Alpha Chi Rho (national scholarship officer, 1957-59), California Club, Los Angeles Club, Newcomen Society, Cosmos Club, Rotary. *Awards, honors:* LL.D., Ursinus College, 1960; Litt.D., Wagner College, 1964; L.H.D., Rider College, 1967; Pd.D., Susquehanna University, 1969.

WRITINGS: (Under pseudonym Andrew Moore) *The Serbian Assignment* (novel), Apollo Books, 1972; *Coal Age Empire: Pennsylvania Coal and Its Utilization,* Pennsylvania Historical and Museum Commission, 1974. Contributor to *Journal of Negro History, Pennsylvania Magazine of History and Biography, Pennsylvania History, Military Affairs,* and *National Lutheran.*

*   *   *

BIRCH, Herbert G.   1918-1973

April 21, 1918—February 4, 1973; American professor of pediatrics, researcher, and authority on child development and brain disorders. Obituaries: *New York Times,* February 5, 1973.

*   *   *

BIRKLEY, Marilyn   1916-

PERSONAL: Born May 17, 1916, in Toledo, Ohio; daughter of Martin and Augusta Heyna; married James I. Birkley (an English professor), August 26, 1966. *Education:* College of St. Teresa, B.A. (summa cum laude), 1947; University of Notre Dame, M.A., 1957; University of Michigan, Ph.D., 1964. *Home:* 5 Daytona Beach Pl., Coram, N.Y. 11727. *Office:* Hunter College of the City University of New York, 695 Park Ave., New York, N.Y. 10021.

CAREER: High school English teacher in parochial schools in Michigan, 1947-51; high school mathematics teacher in parochial schools in Toledo, Ohio, 1951-55, and Sandusky, Ohio, 1955-58; Mary Manse College of Toledo, Toledo, instructor in English, 1956-57; San Diego College for Men (now University of San Diego), San Diego, Calif., assistant professor of English, 1964; Hunter College of the City University of New York, New York, N.Y., assistant professor, 1965-70, associate professor of English and education, 1970—. Instructor in English and chairman of department Lourdes Junior College (Sylvania, Ohio), summers, 1955-58; director of reading and writing workshops in state of New York, 1967—. Proposal writer and consultant, Institute for Evaluation of Educational Products, 1970; consultant to Random House, Inc., 1959, Harcourt Brace Jovanovich, Inc., 1971, and Addison-Wesley Publishing Co., Inc., 1977. *Member:* National Council of Teachers of English, International Reading Association, New York State Council of English Teachers, Pi Lambda Theta.

WRITINGS: (With Maurice Eash and others) *Reading and Thinking,* Doubleday, 1966; (with husband, James Birkley) *Pattern Practices to Learn to Write By,* College Skills Center (New York), 1969; (with J. Birkley and Louis Rivers) *Pattern Practices to Learn to Write By,* Level II, College Skills Center, 1972. Contributor to *Catholic School Journal,*

English Record, High Points, Journal of Reading, and *Secondary School Journal.* Editor of divisional publications, *Dateline* and *Viewpoint,* 1976—.

WORK IN PROGRESS: Every Teacher's Primer in Reading; Adult Sight Word List and an accompanying word test, with James Birkley and Harry Miller.

*   *   *

BISHIR, John (William)   1933-

PERSONAL: Surname is pronounced *By*-sher; born September 23, 1933, in Joplin, Mo.; son of Earl William and Virginia (Oldham) Bishir; married Mary Katherine Tims, December 27, 1954 (divorced, 1976); married Catherine Ward, February, 1977; children: (first marriage) Robert, Carol, Patricia, Diane. *Education:* University of Missouri, A.B., 1955; University of Iowa, M.S., 1957; North Carolina State University, Ph.D., 1961. *Religion:* None. *Home:* 305 West Park Dr., Raleigh, N.C. 27605. *Office:* Department of Mathematics, North Carolina State University, Raleigh, N.C. 27607.

CAREER: Florida State University, Tallahassee, assistant professor of statistics, 1962-63; North Carolina State University at Raleigh, instructor, 1957-61, assistant professor, 1961-62, associate professor, 1963-68, professor of mathematics, 1968—. *Member:* Mathematical Association of America, Institute of Mathematical Statistics, Phi Beta Kappa, Sigma Xi.

WRITINGS: (With D. W. Drewes) *Mathematics in the Social and Behavioral Sciences,* Harcourt, 1970. Contributor to *Biometrics, Journal of the Royal Statistical Society, Journal of Mathematical Psychology,* and *Silvae Genetica.*

WORK IN PROGRESS: Research in forest genetics; a book, *Calculus for Business and Economics;* a book on probability.

AVOCATIONAL INTERESTS: Building stringed musical instruments.

*   *   *

BJERKE, Robert Alan   1939-

PERSONAL: Born December 23, 1939, in Eau Claire, Wis.; son of Carl Edward (a tirebuilder) and Beryl (Elkinton) Bjerke. *Education:* University of Wisconsin, B.A., 1961, M.A., 1962, Ph.D., 1966; University of Minnesota, M.A., 1973. *Residence:* Manitowoc, Wis. *Office:* University of Wisconsin Center—Manitowoc County, 705 Viebahn St., Manitowoc, Wis. 54220.

CAREER: St. Olaf College, Northfield, Minn., assistant professor of Norwegian, 1966-71; University of Wisconsin Center—Manitowoc County, Manitowoc, librarian and assistant professor of German, 1973—.

WRITINGS: A Contrastive Study of Old German and Old Norwegian Kinship Terms, Indiana University Publications in Anthropology and Linguistics, 1969; (editor) *Fifteen Modern Norwegian Stories: An Intermediate Norwegian Reader,* St. Olaf College Press, 1971.

*   *   *

BLACK, Robert C(lifford) III   1914-

PERSONAL: Born February 11, 1914, in New York, N.Y.; son of R. Clifford (a jeweler) and Beatrice (Cluett) Black; married Regina Ann Maleham, September 5, 1939; children: Maleham, Clifford, Beatrice (Mrs. Rolland W. Hoverstock), John, Peter, James. *Education:* Williams College, B.A.,

1937; University of Denver, M.A., 1947; Columbia University, Ph.D., 1951. *Politics:* Republican. *Religion:* Episcopal. *Home:* Sky Valley Ranch, Tabernash, Colo. 80478. *Office:* Department of History, Colorado Women's College, Denver, Colo. 80220.

CAREER: Rensselaer Polytechnic Institute, Troy, N.Y., instructor in history, 1945-48; Trinity College, Hartford, Conn., instructor, 1950-53, assistant professor, 1953-58, associate professor of history, 1958-66; Colorado Women's College, Denver, Colo., professor of history, 1966—. *Military service:* U.S. Army, 1942-45; became captain. *Member:* American Historical Association, Canadian Historical Association, Southern Historical Association, State Historical Society of Colorado (director, 1971—), Connecticut Historical Society. *Awards, honors:* Award of merit from American Association for State and Local History, 1970, for *Island in the Rockies*.

WRITINGS: The Railroads of the Confederacy, University of North Carolina Press, 1952; *The Younger John Winthrop,* Columbia University Press, 1966; *Island in the Rockies (History of Grand County, Colorado),* Grand County Pioneer Society, 1969, revised edition, 1978. Contributor of articles to *Journal of Southern History, Vermont History,* and *Civil War History.*

WORK IN PROGRESS: Research on United States and Canadian history, especially materials for biographical studies.

AVOCATIONAL INTERESTS: Mountains, birds, photography, railroads, travel.

BIOGRAPHICAL/CRITICAL SOURCES: New York Times, December 2, 1966; *Times Literary Supplement,* March 9, 1967.

* * *

BLACKMORE, Dorothy S. 1914-

PERSONAL: Born November 19, 1914, in Willows, Calif.; married Edwin L. Blackmore, September 2, 1935 (died April 23, 1978); children: Willis E., Margaret (Mrs. Michael Henwood). *Education:* Chico State College (now California State University, Chico), A.B. (cum laude), 1935; Dominican College of San Rafael, M.S.Ed., 1957; University of California, Berkeley, Ed.D., 1963. *Home:* 620 Coolidge St., Davis, Calif. 95616.

CAREER: Chico State College (now California State University, Chico), demonstration teacher and head of primary department, 1939-41; Dominican College of San Rafael, San Rafael, Calif., professor of education and director of student teaching, 1951-66; University of California, Davis, associate head of teacher education, lecturer, and supervisor, 1966-69; California State Department of Education, Sacramento, Calif., coordinator of teacher recruitment and director of rural internship project, 1969-71, consultant in early childhood education and staff consultant to task force on early childhood education, 1971-72; consultant, Elementary Field Services, 1972-77; California State Facilitator, National Diffusion Network, 1977—. *Member:* International Reading Association, National Education Association, Association for Student Teaching (California president, 1962-64), California Association for Leadership and Curriculum Development, California Teachers Association, California Council on the Education of Teachers (vice-president, 1971-73; president, 1974-76), Phi Delta Kappa, Delta Kappa Gamma, Pi Lambda Theta, Delta Phi Upsilon. *Awards, honors:* Distinguished Achievement Award for Excellence in Teacher Education, American Association of Colleges for Teacher Education, 1966, for the Dominican College of San Rafael elementary program.

WRITINGS: The Teaching Internship, California State Department of Education, 1960; *A Comparison of Selected Personological Attributes of Women Elementary Teachers Perceived during Pre-Service Preparation and First-Year Teaching* (doctoral dissertation), University of California Press, 1963; (co-author) *A Rural Internship Program Model,* California State Department of Education, 1971; *Report of the Task Force on Early Childhood Education,* California State Department of Education, 1971. Contributor to education journals.

* * *

BLACKMORE, John T(homas) 1931-

PERSONAL: Born September 13, 1931, in Washington, D.C.; son of Philip Guillou (retired Brigadier General of U.S. Army) and Emily (Van Patten) Blackmore; married Erica Ellen Felber Steuber, November, 1958 (divorced, 1962); children: Catherin Steuber, Annette Steuber. *Education:* University of New Mexico, B.A., 1953; graduate study at University of California, Berkeley, 1955-57, spring, 1959, Universitat Freiburg, 1957-59, and National University of Taiwan, 1959-60; University of California, Los Angeles, Ph.D., 1970. *Office:* Department of History and Philosophy of Science, Cambridge University, Free School Lane, Cambridge, England.

CAREER: Soochow University, Taipei, Taiwan, English instructor, 1959-60; Bundeswehr Sprachschule, Uetersen, Germany, English teacher, 1960-62; University of California, Santa Cruz, preceptor, 1965-67; California State University, Northridge, assistant professor of history, 1971-72; Harvey Mudd College, Claremont, Calif., assistant professor of history, 1972-77; Cambridge University, Cambridge, England, visiting scholar in the department of history and philosophy of science, 1977—. *Military service:* U.S. Air Force, 1953-55.

WRITINGS: Ernst Mach: His Life, Work, and Influence, University of California Press, 1972. Also author of *A Balanced Philosophy of the Space Age.* Contributor of articles, essays, and reviews to *British Journal for the Philosophy of Science, Isis, Historia Mathematica,* and *Annals of Science.*

WORK IN PROGRESS: Three articles for *British Journal for the Philosophy of Science.*

* * *

BLAFFER-HRDY, Sarah C(ampbell) 1946-
(Sarah C. Blaffer)

PERSONAL: Born July 11, 1946, in Dallas, Tex.; daughter of John H. and Camilla (Davis) Blaffer; married Daniel Bruce Hrdy. *Education:* Radcliffe College, B.A. (summa cum laude), 1969; Harvard University, Ph.D., 1975. *Address:* c/o Peabody Museum, Cambridge, Mass. 02138.

WRITINGS: (Under name Sarah C. Blaffer) *The Black-Man of Zinacantan,* University of Texas Press, 1972; *The Langurs of Abu,* Harvard University Press, 1977. Contributor of articles to *Science, Natural History, American Scientist,* and *Advances in the Study of Behavior.*

WORK IN PROGRESS: A book on the primate origins of womanhood.

AVOCATIONAL INTERESTS: Skiing, art.

BLAIR, Philip M(ark)   1928-

PERSONAL: Born September 7, 1928, in New York, N.Y.; son of Max and Fay G. (Gluck) Blair; married Lois Lee (a teacher), August 25, 1953; children: Laura Anne, Jeffrey Alan. Education: Syracuse University, B.S. (magna cum laude), 1949; Massachusetts Institute of Technology, M.S., 1950; graduate study at Purdue University, 1953-54, and Colorado State University, summer, 1961; Stanford University, Ph.D., 1971. Religion: Jewish. Home: 673 Winggate Dr., Sunnyvale, Calif. 94087. Office: Department of Mechanical Engineering, San Jose State University, San Jose, Calif. 95192.

CAREER: General Dynamics, Convair Division, San Diego, Calif., thermodynamics engineer, 1950-53; Robert College, Istanbul, Turkey, assistant professor of mechanical engineering, 1954-57; San Jose State University, San Jose, Calif., assistant professor, 1957-61, associate professor, 1961-70, professor of mechanical engineering, 1970—. U.S. Agency for International Development, adviser in Industrial Productivity Center, Quito, Ecuador, 1965-67, education adviser, Lima, Peru, 1974-75. Engineer, during summers, for Westinghouse, General Electric, and Boeing Corps. Consultant to Academy for Educational Development and to Oak Ridge Associated Universities. Member: American Society for Engineering Education, American Society of Mechanical Engineers, Tau Beta Pi, Phi Kappa Phi.

WRITINGS: Job Discrimination and Education: An Investment Analysis–A Case Study of Mexican-Americans in Santa Clara County, California, Praeger, 1972; (contributor) Martin Carnoy, editor, Schooling in a Corporate Society: The Political Economy of Education in America, McKay, 1972. Contributor to Americas, Engineering Education, and Comparative Education Review.

SIDELIGHTS: Philip M. Blair told CA: "My writing is technical and not (intentionally) fiction. Since I go through eight or ten drafts on an article or report, I'm awaiting electronic word processors to help the logistics of transforming thought to copy."

*   *   *

BLAKE, David H(aven)   1940-

PERSONAL: Born June 5, 1940, in Long Branch, N.J.; son of Edgar Bond (an educator) and Haven (Johnstone) Blake; married Susan Baird, June 24, 1961; children: David H., Jr., Jennifer, Kimberly. Education: Dartmouth College, A.B., 1961; University of Pittsburgh, M.B.A., 1962; Rutgers University, M.A., 1966, Ph.D., 1968. Home: 221 Guyasuta Rd., Pittsburgh, Pa. 15215. Office: Graduate School of Business, University of Pittsburgh, Pittsburgh, Pa. 15260.

CAREER: Smith, Kline & French Laboratories (drug firm), Philadelphia, Pa., in public affairs, 1962-63; Wayne State University, Detroit, Mich., assistant professor of political science, 1966-69; University of Pittsburgh, Pittsburgh, Pa., associate professor of business administration and political science, 1969-77, professor of business administration, 1977—, associate dean, Graduate School of Business, 1976—. Member: International Studies Association, Academy for International Business.

WRITINGS: (Editor and contributor) The Multinational Corporation, American Academy of Political and Social Science, 1972; (with R. S. Walters) The Politics of Global Economic Relations, Prentice-Hall, 1976; (with others) Social Auditing: Evaluating the Impact of Corporate Programs, Praeger, 1976; (with R. E. Driscoll) The Social and

Economic Impacts of Transnational Corporations: Case Studies of the U.S. Paper Industry in Brazil, Fund for Multinational Management Education, 1977; (co-author) Opinion Leaders and Private Investments: An Attitude Survey in Chile and Venezuela, Fund for Multinational Management Education, 1977; Managing the External Relations of Multinational Corporations, Fund for Multinational Management Education, 1977. Contributor to Columbia Journal of World Business, Foreign Policy, and Journal of International Business Studies.

WORK IN PROGRESS: Managing Corporate Social Policy; The International Flow of Industrial Welfare Ideas.

*   *   *

BLANCHARD, B(irdsall) Everard   1909-

PERSONAL: Born October 19, 1909, in Chicago, Ill.; son of Birdsall Everard (an engineer) and Mary Alice (Vandervest) Blanchard; married Ann Quaglia, October 25, 1949; children: Sharon Reyn, David Everard. Education: Western State Teachers College (now Western Michigan University), B.S., 1931; State University of Iowa, M.S., 1932; University of Chicago, M.A., 1946, Ph.D., 1957. Home and office: 303 Astor Ct., Villa Park, Ill. 60181.

CAREER: Methodist minister, 1936-51. Director of health and physical education in junior high school in Villa Park, Ill., 1932-36; McKendree College, Lebanon, Ill., director of athletics and physical education, 1936-38; State of Illinois, Glen Ellyn, assistant supervisor of adult and vocational education, 1938-41; director of health and physical education in junior high school in Fort Myers, Fla., 1941-42; principal of high school in Cross City, Fla., 1943-46; superintendent of public schools in Minden City, Mich., 1946-47; Elmhurst College, Elmhurst, Ill., professor of education, 1947-48; Erskine College, Due West, S.C., professor of education and director of teacher education, 1948-49; University of Maryland, College Park, dean of graduate and undergraduate studies and of Overseas Division, 1949-51; Plymouth Teachers College (now Plymouth State College), Plymouth, N.H., professor of education and director of student teaching, 1951-55; National College of Education, Evanston, Ill., visiting professor of education, 1961-62; DePaul University, Chicago, Ill., professor of education, 1962-75, professor emeritus, 1975—, director of Educational Field Service, 1962-75, director of Opinion Poll Survey Center, 1963-75, coordinator of graduate programs office, 1966-75; Villa Educational Research Associates, Villa Park, Ill., president. Visiting professor of education, Defiance College; member of executive committee, Association for Field Service in Teacher Education, 1963-69. Superintendent, Military Dependent Schools, 1949-51. Military service: U.S. Air Force, director of Information and Education Section, 1949-51; became lieutenant colonel.

MEMBER: International Association for the Advancement of Educational Research, National Education Association (life member), Phi Delta Kappa, Kappa Delta Pi, Sigma Theta Gamma. Awards, honors: Citation from National Education Association and National School Board Association, 1960, for distinguished research in political science; George Washington Honor Medal and citation from Freedoms Foundation at Valley Forge, 1960; citation from Association for Field Services in Teacher Education, 1968, for outstanding research in higher education; Outstanding Teacher of the Year citation from Notre Dame University, 1968; citation from Princeton University, 1973, for distinguished research in higher education.

WRITINGS: Destination Teaching, Pageant, 1960; *Introductory Statistics for Student of Education,* School of Education, DePaul University, 1963; *A Survey of Illinois Catholic Secondary Schools,* Thomas F. Smith, 1966; *Illinois Index for Selecting Textbooks,* Educational Studies and Development, 1968; *A Profile of Behavioral Characteristics Peculiar to Articulation in American Educational Programs,* University of Dayton Press, 1972; *A New System of Education,* Etc Publications, 1975; *Evaluating Educational Leadership in Higher Education,* World Association for the Advancement of Educational Research, 1979. Author of tests published by Western Psychological Services: "Illinois Index of Scholastic Aptitude," 1967; "Illinois Rating of Teacher Effectiveness," 1968; "Illinois Rating of Character in Physical Education," 1969. Also author of a four-year study of masters degree graduates. Contributor of more than two-hundred-fifty articles to education and health journals, including *Journal of Sports Medicine and Physical Fitness, Improving College and University Teaching,* and *Journal of Experimental Education.*

WORK IN PROGRESS: Working to develop an electronic means of enabling the blind to see by transmitting images directly to the brain for interpretation.

AVOCATIONAL INTERESTS: Aviation (has held private pilot's license), international travel.

* * *

BLANK, Blanche D(avis)

PERSONAL: Born in New York, N.Y.; married Joseph S. Blank, Jr.; children: three daughters. *Education:* Hunter College (now Hunter College of the City University of New York), B.A., 1941; Syracuse University, M.A., 1945; Columbia University, Ph.D., 1951. *Home:* 13 Withington Rd., Scarsdale, N.Y. 10583. *Office:* Division of Social Sciences, Hunter College of the City University of New York, 695 Park Ave., Room 1220, New York, N.Y. 10021.

CAREER: College of the City of New York (now City College of the City University of New York), New York City, lecturer in political science, 1946-49; New School for Social Research, New York City, lecturer in political science, 1951-52; Hunter College of the City University of New York, New York City, instructor, 1956-59, assistant professor, 1960-62, associate professor, 1963-67, professor of political science, 1968—, dean of Division of Social Sciences, 1972—. Research associate at National Tax Foundation, 1945; visiting professor of political science at Sarah Lawrence College, 1969-70; vice-president for academic affairs, Yeshiva University, 1977—. Executive director of Mayor's Task Force on City Personnel (New York City), 1965-66; member of urban affairs task force of American Jewish Congress, 1971—; organized conferences for Urban Research Center (New York City).

MEMBER: American Political Science Association, American Society for Public Administration, American Association of University Professors, Comparative Administration Group, American Civil Liberties Union, Phi Beta Kappa, Pi Sigma Alpha. *Awards, honors:* National Science Foundation research grant, 1966, for a project in comparative administration.

WRITINGS: Codification of Syracuse Licensing Ordinance, [Syracuse, N.Y.], 1945; *The Measurement of National Bureaucracies: A Statistical Approach to Comparative Administration,* Comparative Administration Group (Bloomington, Ind.), 1965; *Report of the Mayor's Task Force on City Personnel,* [New York, N.Y.], 1966; *A*

Handbook for Federal Administrative Internship Programs, Federal Administration Internship Program, 1966; (contributor) Samuel Hendel, editor, *The Politics of Confrontation,* Appleton, 1971; *American Government and Politics: A Critical Introduction,* Aldine-Atherton, 1973; *The Political Clubs of New York City Revisited,* Praeger, 1973. Contributor of more than twenty articles and reviews to popular and professional journals, including *Nation, Public Management, National Civic Review, School and Society, New Republic,* and *Urban Affairs Quarterly.*

* * *

BLATT, Burton 1927-

PERSONAL: Born May 23, 1927, in Bronx, N.Y.; son of Abraham W. (a manufacturer) and Jennie (Starr) Blatt; married Ethel Draizen, December 24, 1951; children: Edward Richard, Steven David, Michael Lawrence. *Education:* New York University, B.S., 1949; Columbia University, M.A., 1950; Pennsylvania State University, Ed.D., 1956. *Religion:* Jewish. *Home:* 106 Cedar Heights Dr., Jamesville, N.Y. 13078. *Office:* School of Education, 150 Huntington Hall, Syracuse University, Syracuse, N.Y. 13210.

CAREER: Teacher of special class for mentally retarded, New York, N.Y., 1949-56; Southern Connecticut State College, New Haven, associate professor, 1956-59, professor of special education and chairman of department, 1959-61; Boston University, Boston, Mass., professor of special education and chairman of department, 1961-69; Syracuse University, Syracuse, N.Y., Centennial Professor, director of Division of Special Education and Rehabilitation, and director of Center on Human Policy, 1969-76, dean of School of Education, 1976—. Assistant commissioner and director, Division of Mental Retardation, Massachusetts Department of Mental Health, 1968-69. Appointed to first Connecticut State Advisory Council on Mental Retardation, 1959; former member of Massachusetts Special Commission on Retarded Children and State of New York Committee for Children. Past member of national advisory committees, R & D Center for Handicapped Children at University of Indiana, United Cerebral Palsy, and National Society for the Prevention of Blindness; consultant to U.S. Office of Education and other federal and state agencies. *Military service:* U.S. Navy, 1945-46.

MEMBER: American Association on Mental Deficiency (vice-president of education, 1971-73; president, 1976-77), Council for Exceptional Children (president of Connecticut chapter, 1960; president of Teacher Education Division, 1969), Phi Delta Kappa. *Awards, honors:* Outstanding Teacher Award, Boston University, 1965; Massachusetts Psychological Association Annual Award, 1967; Massachusetts Association for Retarded Children Annual Award, 1968; Northeast Region Education Award, American Association on Mental Deficiency, 1973; National Humanitarian Award, American Association on Mental Deficiency, 1974; Newell C. Kephart Memorial Award, Purdue University, 1974; New York Schools Teacher of Mentally Handicapped Bicentennial Award, 1976.

WRITINGS: (With Seymour B. Sarason and Kenneth Davidson) *The Preparation of Teachers: An Unstudied Problem in Education,* Wiley, 1962; (with Fred Kaplan) *Christmas in Purgatory: A Photographic Essay on Mental Retardation,* Allyn & Bacon, 1965, second edition, 1966; *The Intellectually Disfranchised: Impoverished Learners and Their Teachers,* Massachusetts Department of Mental Health, 1967; *Exodus from Pandemonium: Human Abuse and a*

Reformation of Public Policy, Allyn & Bacon, 1970; *Souls in Extremis: An Anthology on Victims and Victimizers,* Allyn & Bacon, 1973; *Revolt of the Idiots,* Exceptional Press, 1976; (with Douglas B. Klein and Robert Bogdan) *An Alternative Textbook in Special Education,* Love Publishing, 1977; (with A. Ozolins and J. McNally) *The Family Papers,* Exceptional Press, 1978; *The Professor,* Exceptional Press, 1978.

Contributor: Jerome Hellmuth, editor, *Learning Disorders,* Volume I, Special Child Publications, 1966; Hellmuth, editor, *The Disadvantaged Child,* Volume I, Special Child Publications, 1967; Robert B. Kugel and Wolf Wolfensberger, editors, *Changing Patterns in Residential Services for the Mentally Retarded,* President's Committee on Mental Retardation, 1969; Norman R. Bernstein, editor, *Diminished People: The Problems and Care of the Retarded,* Little, Brown, 1970; Jerome H. Rothstein, editor, *Mental Retardation: Readings and Resources,* Holt, 1971; Don L. Walker and Douglas P. Howard, editors, *Special Education: Instrument of Change in Education for the 70's,* University Press of Virginia, 1972; Robert M. W. Travers, editor, *Handbook of Research on Teaching,* 2nd edition, Rand McNally, 1973.

Author of foreword: Frances Kaplan and Sarason, *The Psycho-Educational Clinic,* Massachusetts Department of Mental Health, 1969; Donald Maietta and Don Sandy, *Baby Learns to Talk,* Stanwix, 1969; and various publications of Division of Special Education and Rehabilitation, Syracuse University.

Project director or co-author of a number of research reports, including *The Educability of Intelligence,* Council for Exceptional Children, 1969. Contributor of more than a hundred articles and reviews to journals. Co-editor of series, "Segregated Settings and the Problem of Change," Division of Special Education and Rehabilitation, Syracuse University, 1972—. Member of editorial staff, *American Journal of Mental Deficiency,* 1957-63; consulting editor, *Mental Retardation,* 1963-72; member of editorial board, *Seminars in Psychiatry,* 1968-70; member of publications committee, *Council for Exceptional Children,* 1969-72; member of editorial advisory board, *Exceptional Parent,* 1971—; book review editor, *Exceptional Children,* 1972-76.

WORK IN PROGRESS: Unmailed Letters and *Ernest, Ruth, and Uncle Waldo.*

* * *

BLAUSTEIN, Elliott H(arold) 1915-

PERSONAL: Born November 16, 1915, in New York, N.Y.; son of Abraham Joseph (a physician) and Sophie (Siegal) Blaustein; married Rose Temkin (a science coordinator), November 23, 1936; children: Carole (Mrs. Michael Barr), Richard. *Education:* Brooklyn College (now Brooklyn College of the City University of New York), B.S., 1936. *Home:* 296 Forest Glenn Ave., Franklin Lakes, N.J. 07417.

CAREER: Teacher of biology and physics in New York, N.Y., public schools, 1959-72; full-time writer, 1972—. *Military service:* U.S. Navy, 1945-46. *Member:* National Science Teachers Association, New York City Physics Teachers Association, New York City Biology Teachers Association, Pi Mu Epsilon.

WRITINGS: Antipollution Lab: Elementary Research Experiments and Science Projects on Air, Water, and Solid Pollution in Your Community, Sentinel Books, 1972; (with

wife, Rose Blaustein, and Peter Greenleaf) *Your Environment and You: Understanding the Pollution Problem,* Oceana, 1974; (with R. Blaustein) *Investigating Ecology,* Arco, 1977; *Experiences in Science,* Globe Book Co., 1977; (with Greenleaf) *Insights in Science,* Globe Book Co., 1977; (with others) *Your Environment and You: Understanding Ecology,* Oceana, 1978. Also author of twenty-six films of "Family Living Series" for Sterling, overhead projectuals for Clearvue, and Science Filmstrips, 1967—.

* * *

BLISS, Carey S(tillman) 1914-

PERSONAL: Born December 13, 1914, in Albany, N.Y.; son of Leslie Edgar (a librarian) and Alice (Burnett) Bliss; married Amelia Baker (a bookseller), September 5, 1942; children: Anthony Stillman. *Education:* Pomona College, A.B., 1936. *Politics:* Liberal Republican. *Religion:* None. *Residence:* San Gabriel, Calif. *Office:* Huntington Library, San Marino, Calif. 91108.

CAREER: Huntington Library, San Marino, Calif., supervisor of reading room, 1940-46, assistant curator of rare books, 1946-62, curator, 1962—. *Member:* Book Club of California, Zamorano Club, Rounce and Coffin Club, Camellia Society of Southern California (member of board of governors, 1968-69, 1973-74), Camellia Society of Temple City. *Awards, honors:* Award of Merit, California Historical Society, 1976.

WRITINGS: (Author of introduction) Charles White, *Letter from San Jose, California, March 18, 1848,* Glen Dawson, 1955; (with wife, Amelia Bliss) *Catalogue of Books and Manuscripts in the Estelle Doheny Collection,* Volume III, privately printed, 1955; (author of introduction) Daniel D. Heustis, *Remarkable Adventures: California, 1845,* Glen Dawson, 1957; (author of introduction and notes) William Hayes Hilton, *Sketches in the Southwest and Mexico: 1858-1877,* Dawson's Book Shop, 1963; *Some Aspects of Seventeenth Century English Printing with Special Reference to Joseph Moxon,* W. A. Clark Memorial Library, University of California, 1965; *Autos across America: A Bibliography of Transcontinental Auto Travel, 1903-1940,* Dawson's Book Shop, 1972; *A Bibliography of Cheney Miniatures,* Dawson's Book Store, 1975; *The Willow Dale Press,* Dawson's Book Store, 1975; (contributor) *The First School Book Printed in California,* Zamorano Club, 1976; (contributor) *A Leaf from the 1583 Dodoens Herbal,* San Francisco Book Club of California, 1977. Compiler, *Catalogues of the Western Books Exhibitions,* Rounce and Coffin Club, 1950, 1956, 1963, 1964, 1965, 1966, 1967. Author of column in *Huntington Library Quarterly,* 1952—. Contributor to *Book Club of California Newsletter, Book Collector,* and *Camellia Review.*

AVOCATIONAL INTERESTS: Raising camellias and collecting early books on camellias.

* * *

BLISS, Edward, Jr. 1912-

PERSONAL: Born July 30, 1912, in Foochow, China; son of Edward (a physician) and May (Bortz) Bliss; married Lois Arnette, August 26, 1940; children: Anne Bliss Mascolino, Lois Bliss Abshire. *Education:* Yale University, B.A., 1935. *Politics:* Democrat. *Religion:* Protestant. *Home:* 14 Marlboro St., Newburyport, Mass. 01950.

CAREER: Bucyrus Telegraph-Forum, Bucyrus, Ohio, reporter, 1935-36; *Columbus Citizen,* Columbus, Ohio, reporter and state editor, 1936-43; Columbia Broadcasting Company, New York, N.Y., writer, 1943-45, editor, 1945-68; American University, Washington, D.C., associate professor, 1968-72, professor of journalism, 1972-77. Consultant to Public Broadcasting Service, 1971-72, Canadian Broadcasting Corp., 1978, and CBS News, 1978—. *Member:* Association for Education in Journalism, Radio-Television News Directors Association, Sigma Delta Chi.

WRITINGS: (Editor) *In Search of Light: The Broadcasts of Edward R. Murrow, 1938-1960,* Knopf, 1967; (with John M. Patterson) *Writing News for Broadcast,* Columbia University Press, 1971. Contributor of articles to *Argosy, Christian Herald, T.V. Guide, Quill, Variety,* and *Television Quarterly.*

WORK IN PROGRESS: A history of broadcast journalism, completion expected in 1981.

BIOGRAPHICAL/CRITICAL SOURCES: Christian Century, June 14, 1967; *Atlantic,* August, 1967; *New York Times Book Review,* September 10, 1967.

* * *

BLISSETT, Marlan 1938-

PERSONAL: Born July 24, 1938, in Paris, Tex.; son of Harold Kenneth and Marie (Ellis) Blissett; married Karen Parker (a lawyer), May 26, 1968 (divorced). *Education:* Texas Technological College (now Texas Tech University), B.A. (honors), 1960; University of California, Berkeley, M.A., 1963; University of Texas at Austin, Ph.D., 1969. *Home:* 804 Edgecliff Ter., Austin, Tex. 78704. *Office:* Lyndon B. Johnson School of Public Affairs, University of Texas, Austin, Tex. 78712.

CAREER: Texas Technological College (now Texas Tech University), Lubbock, instructor in political science, 1962-64; University of Nebraska at Lincoln, assistant professor of political science, 1968-69; Purdue University, Lafayette, Ind., assistant professor of political science, 1969-71; University of Texas at Austin, Lyndon B. Johnson School of Public Affairs, associate professor of public policy, 1971—.

WRITINGS: Politics in Science, Little, Brown, 1972; (editor) *Environmental Impact Assessment,* Engineering Foundation, 1976.

WORK IN PROGRESS: An administrative history of the Johnson administration; an assessment of regional energy policies and solar technology.

* * *

BLOCH, Ariel A(lfred Karl) 1933-

PERSONAL: Born May 14, 1933, in Heidelberg, Germany; married Florence Faerstein, October, 1969. *Education:* Hebrew University of Jerusalem, B.A., 1957; University of Munster, Ph.D., 1962. *Office:* Department of Near Eastern Studies, University of California, Berkeley, Calif. 94270.

CAREER: Assistant, teaching Arabic and ancient Syriac, at University of Munster, Munster, Germany, 1962-64, and University of Erlangen, Erlangen, Germany, 1964-65; University of California, Berkeley, lecturer, 1965-66, assistant professor, 1966-70, associate professor, 1970-74, professor of Semitic languages and linguistics, 1974—. *Member:* American Oriental Society, Linguistic Society of America, Middle East Studies Association, American Association of Teachers of Arabic.

WRITINGS: (With H. Grotzfeld) *Damaszenisch-Arabische Texte mit Uebersetzung, Ammerkungen und Glossar*

(monograph), [Wiesbaden], 1964; *Die Hypotaxe im Damaszenisch-Arabischen mit Vergleichen zur Hypotaxe im Klassisch-Arabischen* (monograph), [Wiesbaden], 1965; *A Chrestomathy of Modern Literary Arabic,* Harrassowitz, 1973. Contributor of articles and reviews to language journals.

WORK IN PROGRESS: Topics in Arabic Syntax and Semantics, completion expected in 1979.

* * *

BLOOD, Marje
(Paige McKenzie)

PERSONAL: Born in Kansas City, Mo.; daughter of Oran C. and Goldie (Fortune) Burkhart; married Raymond Blood (self-employed); children: Iven, Rae Nora Blood Haynie, Pieter, Nikke Blood Strahota.

CAREER: Free-lance writer, 1942—. Administration secretary, County School Districts, Lowell, Ore., 1953-63, and Lane Community College, Eugene, Ore., 1964-68; instructor in adult education classes in creative writing, Willamalane Park District, Springfield, Ore., 1970-72, Maude Kerns Art Center, Eugene, 1971-72, and Linn-Benton Community College, Albany, Ore., 1973; owner and director, Editorial Services Agency, Eugene, beginning 1973. *Member:* National League of American Pen Women (state president, Oregon, 1964-66; Eugene, Ore. branch president 1962-64); Oregon Press Women. *Awards, honors:* National League of American Pen Women, first place awards, 1962, 1964.

WRITINGS: (Under pseudonym Paige McKenzie) *Heavens Help the Working Girl,* Franconia Publishing, 1972; (under pseudonym Paige McKenzie) *Circle of the Suns: Compatability through Astrology,* Vulcan Books, 1975. Also author of television and radio scripts for National Broadcasting Co. Contributor of fiction to *Ingenue* and *St. Anthony;* contributor of articles to *American Astrology* and Popular Library Publications; contributor of poetry to periodicals.

WORK IN PROGRESS: A book, *An Outcry of Silences.*†

* * *

BLOOM, Pauline

PERSONAL: Born in Poltava, Russia; daughter of Max and Meta (Landau) Bloom. *Education:* Attended Brooklyn College (now Brooklyn College of the City University of New York), Hunter College (now Hunter College of the City University of New York), New York University, and Columbia University. *Home and office:* 20 Plaza St., Brooklyn, N.Y. 11238.

CAREER: Brooklyn College of the City University of New York, New York City, instructor in fiction writing, 1949-69; director of Pauline Bloom Workshop Writers (correspondence course), New York City, 1950—. *Member:* Authors Guild (council member), Mystery Writers of America (secretary and member of board of directors, 1960-72), National League of American Pen Women (New York State president; Manhattan Branch president, 1970-74).

WRITINGS: (Contributor) Herbert Brean, editor, *Mystery Writers Handbook,* Harper, 1956; *Toby, Law Stenographer,* Messner, 1959; *Book Notes on Vanity Fair,* Barnes & Noble, 1967; (contributor) Frank A. Dickson and Sandra Smythe, editors, *Handbook of Short Story Writing,* Writer's Digest, 1970; (contributor) *Killers of the Mind* (anthology), edited by Lucy Freeman, Random House, 1974; (contributor) *Mystery Writers' Handbook,* Writer's Digest, 1976.

WORK IN PROGRESS: A suspense novel; a book dealing with writing techniques; a novel.

* * *

BLOOMBERG, Edward (Michael) 1937-

PERSONAL: Born December 23, 1937, in New Rochelle, N.Y.; son of John (an engineer) and Zelda Bloomberg. *Education:* Yale University, A.B., 1959, Ph.D., 1968. *Home:* 59 College Park, Davis, Calif. 95616. *Office:* Department of French and Italian, University of California, Davis, Calif. 95616.

CAREER: Yale University, New Haven, Conn., instructor in French and Italian, 1964-66; University of California, Davis, assistant professor, 1966-73, associate professor of French and Italian, 1974—. *Member:* Modern Language Association of America, Philological Association of the Pacific Coast.

WRITINGS: Student Violence, Public Affairs Press, 1970; *Les Raisons de Pascal,* Debresse, 1973. Contributor to *Wall Street Journal, Romanic Review, Orbis Litterarum, French Review,* and other journals.

WORK IN PROGRESS: Research on Pascal and Rousseau.

* * *

BLOOMFIELD, Arthur Irving 1914-

PERSONAL: Born October 2, 1914, in Montreal, Quebec, Canada; came to United States in 1936, naturalized in 1945; son of Samuel (a businessman) and Hanna (Brown) Bloomfield. *Education:* McGill University, B.A., 1935, M.A., 1936; University of Chicago, Ph.D., 1942. *Religion:* Jewish. *Home:* 201 South 18th St., Philadelphia, Pa. 19103. *Office:* Department of Economics, University of Pennsylvania, Philadelphia, Pa. 19104.

CAREER: Federal Reserve Bank of New York, New York, N.Y., economist, 1941-46, chief of Division of Balance of Payments, 1946-51, senior economist, 1951-57; University of Pennsylvania, Philadelphia, professor of economics and finance, 1958—. Visiting professor at Johns Hopkins University, 1961, Princeton University, 1963, City University of New York, 1965, and University of Melbourne, 1972. Consultant to Bank of Korea, 1949-50, United Nations Civil Assistance Command (Korea), 1952, and U.S. Government missions to Indo-China, 1953, 1954, to Korea, 1956, 1960, and to the Congo, 1966, 1967, 1968. Consultant to Foreign Economic Administration, 1944-45, Ford Foundation (in Malaysia), 1964, Agency for International Development, 1966-68, and U.S. Department of State, 1970-71, 1977.

MEMBER: American Economic Association, Royal Economic Society. *Awards, honors:* Social Science Research Council fellowship, 1939-40; Guggenheim Foundation fellowship, 1956; Rockefeller Foundation award, 1957-58; Ford Foundation faculty research fellowship, 1962-63.

WRITINGS: Capital Imports and the American Balance of Payments: 1934-39, University of Chicago Press, 1950; (with John P. Jensen) *Banking Reform in South Korea* (monograph), Federal Reserve Bank of New York, 1951; *Speculative and Flight Movements of Capital in Postwar International Finance* (monograph), International Finance Section, Princeton University, 1954; *Monetary Policy under the International Gold Standard: 1880-1914* (monograph), Federal Reserve Bank of New York, 1959; *Short-Term Capital Movements under the Pre-1914 Gold Standard* (monograph), Princeton University Press, 1963; *Patterns of Fluc-*

tuation in International Investment before 1914, International Finance Section, Princeton University, 1968. Contributor of articles to professional journals and symposia.

WORK IN PROGRESS: International Monetary Reform, Nineteenth-Century Theories of Trade and Growth.

* * *

BLOUSTEIN, Edward J. 1925-

PERSONAL: Born January 20, 1925, in New York, N.Y.; son of Samuel and Celia (Einwohner) Bloustein; married Ruth Ellen Steinman (a pediatrician), October 6, 1951; children: Elise, Lori. *Education:* New York University, B.A., 1948; Wadham College, Oxford, B.Phil., 1950; Cornell University, Ph.D., 1954, J.D., 1959. *Home:* 1245 River Rd., Piscataway, N.J. 08854. *Office:* Rutgers University, New Brunswick, N.J. 08903.

CAREER: Admitted to Bar of Vermont and Bar of State of New York, 1959; Brooklyn College (now Brooklyn College of the City University of New York), Brooklyn, N.Y., lecturer in philosophy of law and social philosophy, 1950-51; U.S. Department of State, Washington, D.C., political analyst, 1951-52; Cornell University, Ithaca, N.Y., instructor in logic and philosophy, 1954-55; U.S. Department of State, political analyst, 1955-56; law clerk to Chief Judge Stanley H. Fuld of Court of Appeals of the State of New York, 1959-61; New York University, New York, N.Y., assistant professor, 1961, associate professor, 1962-64, professor of law, 1964-65; Bennington College, Bennington, Vt., president, 1965-71; Rutgers University, New Brunswick, N.J., president, 1971—. Member of panel on privacy and behavior research, President's Office of Science and Technology, 1966-67; member of commission on faculty and students, Association of American Colleges, 1968—. *Military service:* U.S. Army, 1943-46; became staff sergeant. *Member:* Phi Beta Kappa. *Awards, honors:* Fulbright fellowship, Oxford University, 1949-50; LL.D., Cedar Crest College, 1970, New York University, 1972.

WRITINGS: (Editor with Willcox, Roemer, and McQuillan, and contributor) *Due Process: Report and Recommendations on Admission to Mental Hospitals under New York Law,* Cornell University Press, 1962; (editor) *Nuclear Energy: Public Policy and the Law,* Oceana, 1964; (with Metzger, Kadish, and Debardeleben) *Dimensions of Academic Freedom,* Illinois University Press, 1969; *The University and the Counterculture,* Rutgers University Press, 1972; *Individual and Group Privacy,* Transaction Books, 1978. Contributor to law, education, and psychology journals, and to *Look.* Editor-in-chief, *Cornell Law Review.*

AVOCATIONAL INTERESTS: Music, tennis, hiking, sailing.

* * *

BLUE, Rose 1931-

PERSONAL: Surname originally Bluestone; born December 3, 1931, in New York, N.Y.; daughter of Irving (a pharmacist) and Frieda (Rosenberg) Bluestone. *Education:* Brooklyn College (now Brooklyn College of the City University of New York), B.A., 1953; Bank Street College of Education, further study, 1966-67. *Politics:* Democrat. *Home:* 1320 51st St., Brooklyn, N.Y. 11219.

CAREER: Teacher in public schools of New York, N.Y., 1955—, teaching in Bedford Stuyvesant Headstart program, 1967—. Lyricist of popular songs. *Member:* Authors Guild, Authors League of America, Mensa, Professional Women's

Caucus, Broadcast Music, Inc.

WRITINGS—Juvenile; all published by F. Watts, except as indicated: *A Quiet Place*, 1969; *Black, Black, Beautiful Black*, 1969; *How Many Blocks Is the World*, 1970; *Bed-Stuy Beat*, 1970; *I Am Here: Yo Estoy Aqui*, 1971; *Grandma Didn't Wave Back*, 1972; *A Month of Sundays*, 1972; *Nikki 108*, 1973; *We Are Chicano*, 1973; *The Preacher's Kid*, 1975; *Seven Years from Home*, Raintree, 1976; *The Yo Yo Kid*, Raintree, 1976; *The Thirteenth Year*, 1977. Also author of high-interest, low-reading-level books for slow readers, including *Camp Thirteen* and *Sabotage Rock*.

Writer of lyrics for published and recorded songs, including "Drama of Love," "Let's Face It," "My Heartstrings Keep Me Tied to You," "Give Me a Break," and "Homecoming Party." Contributing editor, *Teacher*.

WORK IN PROGRESS: A serious and realistic young adult novel dealing with the problems of a Russian immigrant family new to the United States, tentatively entitled *Cold Rain on the Water*.

SIDELIGHTS: Rose Blue found available books about black children inadequate when she was taking a course in children's literature at Bank Street College of Education, so she wrote *A Quiet Place*. "I feel that more sensitive, perceptive books dealing with realities of life and feelings of children are essential to children's literature," she says. "I have attempted to contribute this in my work."

BIOGRAPHICAL/CRITICAL SOURCES: New York Times Book Review, February 4, 1973.

*   *   *

BLUMBERG, Nathan(iel) Bernard 1922-

PERSONAL: Born April 8, 1922, in Denver, Colo.; son of Abraham Moses and Jeannette Blumberg; married Lynne Stout, June 29, 1946 (divorced, 1970); children: Janet Leslie (Mrs. Will Knedlik), Jenifer Lyn, Josephine Laura (Mrs. Larry Loewen). *Education:* University of Colorado, B.A., 1947, M.A., 1948; Oxford University, D.Phil, 1950. *Office:* School of Journalism, University of Montana, Missoula, Mont. 59801.

CAREER: Associated Press, Boulder, Colo., correspondent, 1947; *Denver Post*, Denver, Colo., staff writer, 1948; University of Nebraska at Lincoln, assistant professor, 1950-55, associate professor of journalism, 1955; Michigan State University, East Lansing, associate professor of journalism, 1955-56; University of Montana, Missoula, professor of journalism, 1956—, dean of School of Journalism, 1956-68. Visiting professor at Pennsylvania State University, fall, 1964, Northwestern University, 1966-67, and University of California, Berkeley, fall, 1970. Associate editor and editorial writer, *Lincoln Star*, 1950-53; assistant to editor, *Ashland Gazette*, summers, 1954-55; associate city editor, *Washington Post & Times Herald*, summer, 1956. American Council on Education for Journalism, member of accreditation team, 1958-70, vice-chairman, 1965-67, chairman, 1967-69; U.S. Department of State, American specialist in Thailand, 1961, and Caribbean, 1964; member of National Defense Executive Reserve, Office of Emergency Planning, Executive Office of the President, 1965-68. Member of Nebraska selection committee for Rhodes scholars, 1950-54, Montana selection committee, 1956—, and district selection committee, 1967—. *Military service:* U.S. Army, Artillery, 1943-46; served as editor in Germany and Austria, 1945; received three battle stars and Bronze Star Medal.

MEMBER: National Conference of Editorial Writers, Association of American Rhodes Scholars, Kappa Tau Alpha (national president, 1969-71), Phi Kappa Phi. *Awards, honors:* Rhodes scholar, Oxford University 1948-50.

WRITINGS: One-Party Press? Coverage of the 1952 Presidential Campaign in Thirty-Five Daily Newspapers, University of Nebraska Press, 1954; (editor with Warren J. Brier) *A Century of Montana Journalism*, Mountain Press, 1971; (contributor) Bernard Rosenberg and David Manning White, editors, *Mass Culture Revisited*, Van Nostrand, 1971; (contributor) Peter M. Sandman, David H. Rubin, and Donald B. Sachsman, editors, *Media Casebook: An Introductory Reader in American Mass Communications*, Prentice-Hall, 1972. Author of reports. Contributor to *Masthead, Montana Journalism Review, American Oxonian, Commonweal*, and *Columbia Journalism Review*.

*   *   *

BLUMENFELD, Samuel L(eon) 1926-

PERSONAL: Born May 31, 1926, in New York, N.Y.; son of Louis (a businessman) and Sarah (Sheinfeld) Blumenfeld. *Education:* City College of New York (now City College of the City University of New York), B.A. (cum laude), 1950; Sorbonne, University of Paris, graduate study, 1951-52. *Politics:* "Libertarian Republican." *Religion:* Non-practicing Jew. *Home:* 171 West Seventh St., Boston, Mass. 02127. *Agent:* Oscar Collier, 280 Madison Ave., New York, N.Y. 10016.

CAREER: Rinehart & Co., New York City, assistant editor, 1953-54; World Publishing Co., New York City, associate editor, 1954-55; Viking Press, New York City, first reader, 1955-57; Grosset & Dunlap, Inc., New York City, editor of "Universal Library," 1957-62; Coleridge Press, Inc., New York City, president, 1964-65; *Review of the News*, Belmont, Mass., analysis editor, 1965-67; *Modern Materials Handling*, Cahners Publishing Co., Boston, Mass., associate editor, 1967-69; free-lance writer, 1969—. *Military service:* U.S. Army, 1944-46. *Member:* Reading Reform Foundation (Massachusetts chairman, 1973—), Institute for Humane Studies (fellow).

WRITINGS: How to Start Your Own Private School—And Why You Need One, Arlington House, 1972; *The New Illiterates*, Arlington House, 1973; *How to Tutor*, Arlington House, 1973; (editor) *Property in a Humane Economy*, Open Court, 1974; *The Retreat from Motherhood*, Arlington House, 1975.

WORK IN PROGRESS: A revisionist history and critique of public education, tentatively entitled *Is Public Education Necessary?; Alpha-Phonics: Basic Skills for Reading*, a textbook, for Fundamental Education Press.

SIDELIGHTS: In researching his first book, *How to Start Your Own Private School—And Why You Need One*, Samuel L. Blumenfeld served for a year and a half as a substitute teacher in the high schools and junior high schools of Quincy, Mass., in order to gain firsthand experience of present-day public school practices. His second book, *The New Illiterates*, was inspired by his teaching experiences. In researching it, he uncovered the origin of the sight-vocabulary method. This method was conceived by Rev. Thomas H. Gallaudet, first director of the Hartford Asylum of the Deaf and Dumb. Gallaudet thought he could adapt the method he used in teaching the deaf to read for use by normal children. Gallaudet's first sight-vocabulary primer, *The Mother's Primer*, was the forerunner of Dick and Jane. Blumenfeld believes that this teaching method has been the basic cause of the reading problem in this country.

Although he has spent his entire life dealing with the written word, Blumenfeld told *CA:* "I regret not having started writing full time much earlier, for there is so much a writer must learn about the commercial side of his profession, and he learns this only by being published and finding out what happens to his books *after* they are published. I took lots of courses in English literature in college and developed a reverence for 'literature,' but was never taught a bloody thing about the literary 'business.' I have a feeling that English professors are engaged in a sort of self-serving conspiracy to create a mystique about 'literature' that removes it from its commercial realities and elevates it into a kind of academic religion. Actually, I was sidetracked from becoming a young struggling author by my psychoanalyst, who insisted that I have a steady job so that I could pay for her services (which, for reasons of ego and self-scrutiny, I was convinced I needed). Twenty years later I regard psychoanalysis as the greatest form of self-indulgence ever invented. It's something writers should stay away from."

* * *

BOCHNER, Salomon 1899-

PERSONAL: Born August 20, 1899, in Cracow, Austria-Hungary (now Poland); came to United States in 1933, naturalized in 1938; son of Joseph and Rude (Haber) Bochner; married Naomi Weinberg, November 26, 1937 (died, 1971); children: Deborah Susan (Mrs. Charles Frederick Kennel). *Education:* University of Berlin, Dr.Phil., 1921. *Home:* 4100 Greenbriar, Apt. 239, Houston, Tex. 77006. *Office:* Department of Mathematics, Rice University, Houston, Tex. 77001.

CAREER: International Education Board fellow at Oxford University, Cambridge University, and University of Copenhagen, 1925-27; University of Munich, Munich, Germany, lecturer in mathematics, 1927-32; Princeton University, Princeton, N.J., associate, 1933-34, assistant professor, 1934-39, associate professor, 1939-46, professor of mathematics, 1946-59, Henry Burchard Fine Professor of Mathematics, 1959-68, professor emeritus, 1968—; Rice University, Houston, Tex., Edgar Odell Lovett Professor of Mathematics, 1968—. Visiting professor, University of California, Berkeley, 1953. Consultant on Los Alamos Project, Princeton, 1951, to National Science Foundation and Air Research and Development Command, 1952. *Member:* National Academy of Sciences, American Mathematical Society, American Association for the Advancement of Science.

WRITINGS: Vorlesungen ueber Fouriersche Integrale, Akademische Verlagsgesellschaft, 1932, translation by Morris Tenebaum and Harry Pollard, with new supplement by the author, published as *Lectures on Fourier Integrals,* Princeton University Press, 1959; (with W. T. Martin) *Several Complex Variables,* Princeton University Press, 1948; (with Komaravolu Chandrasekharan) *Fourier Transforms,* Princeton University Press, 1949; (with Kentaro Yano) *Curvature and Betti Numbers,* Princeton University Press, 1953; *Harmonic Analysis and the Theory of Probability,* University of California Press, 1955; *The Role of Mathematics in the Rise of Science,* Princeton University Press, 1966; *Eclosion and Synthesis: Perspectives on the History of Knowledge,* W. A. Benjamin, 1969; *Selected Mathematical Papers of Salomon Bochner,* W. A. Benjamin, 1969; *Problems in Analysis: A Symposium in Honor of Salomon Bochner,* Princeton University Press, 1970; (member of editorial board and contributor) *Dictionary of History of Ideas,* Scribner, 1973; (with others) *History of Analysis,* edited by

R. J. Stanton, Jr. and R. O. Wells, Jr., Rice University, 1978. Consulting editor, *McGraw-Hill Encyclopedia of Science and Technology,* 1960—.

SIDELIGHTS: Two of Bochner's books, *Lectures on Fourier Integrals* and *Curvature and Betti Numbers,* have been published in Russian translation in Moscow, and *The Role of Mathematics in the Rise of Science* has been translated into Japanese.†

* * *

BOCK, Alan W(illiam) 1943-

PERSONAL: Born December 3, 1943, in Trona, Calif.; son of William Zenter (a chemical engineer) and F(rances) Marjorie (Baecht) Bock; married Joyce Griffith, November 7, 1970; children: Justin Guy. *Education:* Attended University of California, Los Angeles, 1961-65. *Politics:* "Libertarian." *Religion:* Episcopal. *Office:* Prospect House, 7777 Leesburg Pike, Tysons Corner, Va.

CAREER: Human Events, Washington, D.C., journalistic intern, 1967; *Village Square,* Los Angeles, Calif., associate editor, 1967-70; California Consumers Council Management Corp. (group marketing), Hollywood, Calif., communications director, 1971-72; Audiotronics Corp. (electronics manufacturing), North Hollywood, Calif., advertising administrator, 1972-73; Prospect House, Inc. (publishing), Tysons Corner, Va., editor, 1973—.

WRITINGS: The Ecology Action Guide, Nash Publishing, 1971. Contributor of articles to *Country Music, Classics West, Environmental Quality, Educational/Industrial TV, Rap,* and *Human Events.*

WORK IN PROGRESS: A book on natural childbirth; research on the energy crisis; a book on a philosophy of ecology incorporating new information on the biological nature of man; collaborating with a former prisoner of war on a book on his experiences.

SIDELIGHTS: Alan Bock told *CA:* "My major interest is exploring the philosophy of individual freedom in a social context. To provide a philosophical framework for a free society. I'm exploring the biological nature of man as well as ethical and moral philosophy. While this kind of work needs to be done, I also think libertarians must prove in action that freedom works—that services now provided by the coercive State can be provided by voluntary exchange. To destroy tyranny will require a worldwide revolution, which will take different forms in different countries—but it must begin in peoples' minds, so there is much to be done."††

* * *

BODIE, Idella F(allaw) 1925-

PERSONAL: Surname is pronounced Body; born December 2, 1925, in Ridge Spring, S.C.; daughter of Robert Grady (a farmer) and Grace Pearl Fallaw; married James E. Bodie (an engineer for DuPont), August 15, 1947; children: Susanne (Mrs. Robert Rhoden), Edwin, John, Beth. *Education:* Attended Mars Hill College, 1942-44; Columbia College, B.A., 1946; University of South Carolina, additional study, 1950-51. *Religion:* Methodist. *Home:* 1113 Evans Rd., Aiken, S.C. 29801. *Office:* Department of English, Aiken High School-Schofield Campus, 220 Sumter St., Aiken, S.C. 29801.

CAREER: Kennedy Junior High School, Aiken, S.C., English teacher and chairman of department, 1960-70; Aiken High School, Schofield Campus, Aiken, S.C., English teacher, 1970—. *Member:* National Education Association,

National Council of English Teachers, Association of Teacher Educators, South Carolina Education Association, Poetry Society of South Carolina, Friends of Library (Aiken County), Delta Kappa Gamma.

WRITINGS—All published by Sandlapper Store: *The Secret of Telfair Inn,* 1971; *The Mystery of the Pirate's Treasure,* 1973; *Ghost in the Capitol,* 1976; *Famous South Carolina Women,* 1978. Contributor of poems to *National Poetry Anthology.*

WORK IN PROGRESS: A teenage book for girls.

SIDELIGHTS: "The most enjoyable part of writing for me is building characters," Idella Bodie remarked to *CA.* "The people in my books are a blending of real people I know. I never make my characters all good or all bad because real people are not that way. No one is all bad. Perhaps a person has a reason for acting the way he does, and the reader has a chance to find out why and attempt to understand him. Also, no one likes a goody-goody so I never make my protagonist this type."

* * *

BOELEN, Bernard J(acques) 1916-

PERSONAL: Born August 22, 1916, in Amsterdam, Holland; came to United States in 1950, naturalized in 1959; son of Louis Joseph (a financial expert) and Jacqueline (Ides) Boelen; married Mary Poels, July 13, 1948; children: Josephine (Mrs. Arlen Gould), Louis, Miriam. *Education:* Berchmans College, Baccalaureate, 1942, Licentiate, 1944; University of Louvain, Doctor of Philosophy (magna cum laude), 1948. *Home:* 102 North Emerson St., Mount Prospect, Ill. 60056. *Office:* Department of Philosophy, DePaul University, 2323 North Seminary Ave., Chicago, Ill. 60614.

CAREER: Institute for Higher Education, Tilburg, Holland, instructor in philosophy, 1947-50; Dutch Institute for Foreign Relations, Breukelen, Holland, assistant professor of philosophy, 1948-50; St. Mary's College, Winona, Minn., assistant professor, 1950-51, associate professor, 1951-53, professor of philosophy, 1953-55, acting head of department, 1953-55; Duquesne University, Pittsburgh, Pa., professor of philosophy, 1955-66; DePaul University, Chicago, Ill., professor of philosophy, 1966—. *Member:* American Catholic Philosophical Association, Metaphysical Society of America, Society for Phenomenology and Existential Philosophy, American Association of University Professors.

WRITINGS: Eudaimonie en het Wezen der Ethiek (title means "Eudaimonia and the Being of Ethics"), Nauwelaerts, 1949; *Existential Thinking,* Duquesne University Press, 1968, reprinted, Herder & Herder, 1971; (contributor) M. Frings, editor, *Heidegger and the Quest for Truth,* Quadrangle, 1968; (contributor) Philip J. Bossert, editor, *Phenomenological Perspectives,* Nijhoff, 1975; *Personal Maturity,* Seabury, 1978.

* * *

BOESEL, David 1938-

PERSONAL: Born February 23, 1938, in Lima, Ohio; son of Paul Otto (an attorney) and Dorothy (Delscamp) Boesel; married Gail Turner; children: Kyle, Justin. *Education:* Wesleyan University, Middletown, Conn., B.A., 1960; Cornell University, M.A., 1963, Ph.D., 1972. *Residence:* Washington, D.C.

CAREER: National Advisory Commission on Civil Disorders, Washington, D.C., research analyst, 1967-68; Johns Hopkins University, Group for Research on Social Policy,

Baltimore, Md., research analyst, 1968-70; Office of Economic Opportunity, Research Division, Washington, D.C., research analyst in political science, beginning 1970.

WRITINGS: (Contributor) *Supplemental Studies for the National Advisory Commission on Civil Disorder,* Praeger, 1968; (editor with Peter Rossi) *Cities under Siege: An Anatomy of the Ghetto Riots,* Basic Books, 1971. Also contributor, Gary Marx, editor, *Racial Conflict,* Little, Brown. Contributor to *Psychiatry* and *Trans-Action.*

WORK IN PROGRESS: A book based on his doctoral dissertation, *The Ghetto Riots: 1964-68;* conducting a survey to learn efficacy of two-year community colleges in promoting upward social mobility for low-income and minority students.†

* * *

BOGART, Leo 1921-

PERSONAL: Born September 23, 1921, son of Jacob (a jurist) and Rachel (Blum) Bogart; married Agnes Cohen, August 8, 1948; children: Michele, Gregory. *Education:* Brooklyn College (now Brooklyn College of the City University of New York), B.A., 1941; University of Chicago, M.A., 1948, Ph.D., 1950. *Home:* 135 Central Park West, New York, N.Y. 10023. *Office:* Newspaper Advertising Bureau, 485 Lexington Ave., New York, N.Y. 10017.

CAREER: Standard Oil Company of New Jersey, New York City, opinion and communications research specialist, 1948-51; McCann-Erickson, Inc., New York City, vice-president of market planning division, 1952-58; Revlon, Inc., New York City, director of market research, 1958-60; Newspaper Advertising Bureau, New York City, vice-president of market planning and research, 1960-66, executive vice-president and general manager, 1966—. Lecturer, Columbia University, 1953-60. *Military service:* U.S. Army, 1942-46. *Member:* American Sociological Association (fellow), World Association for Public Opinion Research (president, 1965-66), International Newspaper Advertising Executives (honorary life member), American Association for Public Opinion Research (president, 1966-67), American Psychological Association (fellow; president, consumer psychological division, 1971-72), Market Research Council (president, 1965-66), Radio-Television Research Council, American Marketing Association. *Awards, honors:* Sidney Goldish Award of International Newspaper Promotion Association, 1966; Media/Scope medals, 1967 and 1969; award from American Association for Public Opinion Research, 1977; Market Research Council first achievement award, 1978.

WRITINGS: Age of Television, Ungar, 1956, revised edition, 1972; *Strategy in Advertising,* Harcourt, 1968; (editor) *Current Controversies in Marketing Research,* Markham, 1969; (editor) *Social Research and the Desegregation of the U.S. Army,* Markham, 1969; *Silent Politics: Polls and the Awareness of Public Opinion,* Wiley, 1972; *Premises for Propaganda: The Cold War Operating Assumptions of the U.S. Information Agency,* Free Press, 1976. Contributor of more than eighty articles to journals in his field. Member of editorial board, *Public Opinion Quarterly,* 1970—.

* * *

BOLGAN, Anne C(atherine) 1923-

PERSONAL: Born August 22, 1923, in Buffalo, N.Y. *Education:* D'Youville College, B.A. (cum laude), 1945; University of Toronto, M.A., 1950, Ph.D., 1960. *Home:* 23

Hampton Crescent, London, Ontario, Canada. *Office:* Department of English, University of Western Ontario, London, Ontario, Canada.

CAREER: D'Youville College, Buffalo, N.Y., instructor in English, 1946-50; St. Mary's College, Notre Dame, Ind., assistant dean of women, 1953-54; University of Toronto, Toronto, Ontario, instructor in English, 1954-59; University of Alaska, Fairbanks, assistant professor, 1959-60, associate professor of English, 1960-64; University of Western Ontario, London, associate professor, 1964-73, professor of English, 1973—. *Awards, honors:* Humanities Research Council of Canada leave fellowship, 1958-59; Canada Council leave fellowship, 1968-69.

WRITINGS: (Editor) T. S. Eliot, *Knowledge and Experience in the Philosophy of F. H. Bradley,* Faber, 1964; *What the Thunder Really Said: A Retrospective Essay on the Making of "The Waste Land,"* McGill-Queens Press, 1973.

WORK IN PROGRESS: Visions and Revisions: The Philosophy of F. H. Bradley and the Mind and Art of T. S. Eliot.

* * *

BOMAR, Cora Paul 1913-

PERSONAL: Born September 8, 1913, in Memphis, Tenn.; daughter of Paul C. (a railroad engineer) and Rosa (Adams) Bomar. *Education:* University of Tennessee, B.S. in Ed., 1939; George Peabody College for Teachers, B.S. in L.S., 1946; University of North Carolina, M.A., 1950. *Politics:* Democrat. *Religion:* Baptist. *Home:* 107 West Avondale Dr., Greensboro, N.C. 27403. *Office:* Department of Education, University of North Carolina, Greensboro, N.C. 27412.

CAREER: Elementary and high school teacher in Tennessee, 1932-34; Procter & Gamble Arsenal, Milan, Tenn., production supervisor, 1942-45; junior high school librarian in Atlanta, Ga., 1945-46; University of Tennessee Martin Branch (now University of Tennessee at Martin), reference librarian, 1946-47; elementary school librarian in Chapel Hill, N.C., 1947-49; instructional supervisor in Orange County, N.C., 1949-51; North Carolina State Board of Education, Raleigh, state school library supervisor, 1951-65, state supervisor of Library and Instructional Materials Services, 1965-66, director of Division of Educational Media, 1966-69; University of North Carolina at Greensboro, assistant professor of library education and instructional media, 1969—. Visiting lecturer, University of North Carolina at Chapel Hill, 1950, 1953, 1954, 1960, 1961, 1964, and 1972; visiting lecturer at library science and educational media institutes at Louisiana State University, Oklahoma State University, Syracuse University, and other universities. Vice-president, North Carolina State Legislative Council, 1966-68. Member of U.S. Office of Education advisory committee on new educational media, 1966-68, and National Catholic Educational Association advisory council on educational technology, 1968-70.

MEMBER: American Library Association (member of council, 1962-67; president of Library Education Division, 1969-70; member of executive board, Library Education Division, 1970—), American Association of School Librarians (member of executive board, 1958-60; president, 1962-63), Association of State School Library Supervisors (president, 1957), Association for Educational Communications and Technology, Association of American Library Schools, American Association of University Women, Southeastern Library Association (president, 1967-68), North Carolina

Library Association (member of executive board, 1958-62, 1964-67), North Carolina Association of School Librarians, North Carolina Association for Social Legislation (vice-president, 1968, 1970; member of executive board, 1970—), Beta Phi Mu (national president, 1965-66), Delta Kappa Gamma (president of Alpha chapter, 1974-76), Pi Gamma Mu.

WRITINGS: (With others) *A Guide to the Development of Educational Media Selection Centers,* American Library Association, 1973. Also author, co-author, or director of six publications for North Carolina Department of Public Instruction, including *Demonstration School Libraries,* three volumes, 1966-68. Contributor to library journals. Editorial consultant, *School Library Journal,* 1968-70; review editor, *School Libraries,* 1969-72.

* * *

BONACHEA, E(nrique) Rolando 1943-

PERSONAL: Born December 18, 1943, in Havana, Cuba; son of Ramon L. (a lawyer) and Ana (Yanes) Bonachea. *Education:* University of New Mexico, B.A., 1968; Georgetown University, M.A., 1970, doctoral candidate. *Office:* Department of Latin American Studies, Georgetown University, Washington, D.C. 20007.

CAREER: Georgetown University, Washington, D.C., fellow of Center for Strategic Studies, 1971-72.

WRITINGS: (Editor with Nelson P. Valdes) *Che: Selected Works of Ernesto Guevara,* M.I.T. Press, 1969; *Cuba in Revolution: A Book of Readings,* Doubleday, 1972; (editor) *Revolutionary Struggle: The Collected Works of Fidel Castro,* Volume I, M.I.T. Press, 1972; *A Briefly Annotated Bibliography of Fidel Castro's Works, 1959-1970,* Center for Latin American Studies, University of Pittsburgh, 1973. Contributor to journals of Latin American affairs. Contributing editor, *Handbook of Latin American Studies,* Hispanic Foundation, Library of Congress, 1972—.

WORK IN PROGRESS: A History of United States-Cuban Relations, 1959-1972; editing with Valdes, Volumes II and III of the collected works of Fidel Castro.†

* * *

BONANSEA, Bernardino M(aria) 1908-

PERSONAL: Born September 27, 1908, in Pinerolo, Turin, Italy; came to United States, 1950; son of Giuseppe and Giuseppina (Savino) Bonansea. *Education:* Attended Studio Liceale, 1924-27, and Studio Teologico, 1927-28; Collegio Internazionale Sant' Antonio, B.A., 1931; Catholic University of America, M.A., 1952, Ph.D., 1954. *Home:* Franciscan Monastery, 1400 Quincy St. N.E., Washington, D.C. 20017. *Office:* School of Philosophy, Catholic University of America, Washington, D.C. 20017.

CAREER: Roman Catholic priest of Order of Friars Minor (Franciscan; O.F.M.); missionary in China, 1931-48; Catholic Middle School, Changsha, Hunan, China, professor of English, religion, and music, 1933-48; Siena College, Loudonville, N.Y., assistant professor of philosophy, 1955-57; Catholic University of America, Washington, D.C., instructor, 1957-58, assistant professor, 1958-60, associate professor, 1960-64, professor of philosophy, 1964—. Superintendent of Catholic schools, Archdiocese of Changsha, 1940-48; superintendent, Catholic Hospital (Changsha), 1945-48; professor of English, Catholic Nursing School (Changsha), 1946-48; professor of Italian, Hunan Province Music School, 1946-47; secretary, Hunan Province Catholic

Relief Committee, 1945-48. Visiting professor of philosophy, St. John's University, Jamaica, N.Y., 1968; ad interim secretary, Apostolic Delegation (Washington, D.C.), 1954, 1960.

MEMBER: American Catholic Philosophical Association (constituent member), Renaissance Society of America, Societas Internationalis Scotistica. *Awards, honors:* Named Lector Generalis by Order of Friars Minor, 1960; Distinguished Service Award, Catholic University of America, 1974.

WRITINGS: Sangue nella Cina Rossa, Gattiglia, 1950; *The Theory of Knowledge of Tommaso Campanella: Exposition and Critique,* Catholic University of America Press, 1954; (contributor) John K. Ryan, editor, *Studies in Philosophy and the History of Philosophy,* Volumes I, II, III, IV, and V, Catholic University of America Press, 1961; (editor and translator) Efrem Bettoni, *Duns Scotus: The Basic Principles of His Philosophy,* Catholic University of America Press, 1961; (contributor) John Clover Monsma, editor, *Science and Religion,* Putnam, 1962; (contributor) Ryan, editor, *Twentieth-Century Thinkers,* Alba House, 1965; (editor with Ryan, and contributor) *John Duns Scotus: 1265-1965,* Catholic University of America Press, 1965; *Tommaso Campanella: Renaissance Pioneer of Modern Thought,* Catholic University of America Press, 1969; (editor and translator) Gabriel M. Allegra, *My Conversations with Teilhard de Chardin on the Primacy of Christ: Peking, 1942-1945,* Franciscan Herald Press, 1971; *God and Atheism: A Philosophical Approach to the Problem of God,* Catholic University of America Press, 1979. Contributor to *Encyclopedia Americana, Encyclopedia of Philosophy,* and *New Catholic Encyclopedia;* contributor to *New Scholasticism, Franciscan Studies, Catholic Biblical Quarterly,* and other philosophical theological publications.

SIDELIGHTS: Bernardino M. Bonansea told *CA:* "In my latest work, *God and Atheism,* the whole problem of God's existence is subjected to a careful analysis, with a view to answering the objections of those philosophers who either deny or question the existence of God or challenge the very possibility of a rational approach to the issue itself. The work contains the most extensive treatment of the classical arguments for God's existence." Bonansea speaks French, Chinese, Latin, German, and Spanish, in addition to his native Italian. He has also studied Greek and Hebrew.

AVOCATIONAL INTERESTS: Classical music.

* * *

BONDURANT, Joan V(alerie) 1918-

PERSONAL: Born December 16, 1918, in Great Bend, Kan.; daughter of Price and Minnie (McGee) Bondurant. *Education:* University of Michigan, A.B. and B.Mus., 1942; University of California, Berkeley, Ph.D., 1952. *Home:* 7433 Woodside Dr., Stockton, Calif. 95207. *Office:* Department of Comparative Politics, University of the Pacific, 3601 Pacific Ave., Stockton, Calif. 95211.

CAREER: University of California, Berkeley, research political scientist, 1953-70, lecturer in political science, 1954-70; University of the Pacific, Stockton, Calif., professor of comparative politics, 1970—. *Member:* International Political Science Association, American Political Science Association, American Society for Legal and Political Philosophy, American Association of Asian Studies. *Awards, honors:* Social Science Research Council fellowship, 1952-53; Institute of International Studies fellowships, 1962 and 1965; American Institute for Indian Studies faculty research fellowship, India, 1965-66.

WRITINGS: Conquest of Violence: The Gandhian Philosophy of Conflict, Princeton University Press, 1958, revised edition, University of California Press, 1971; (editor with Margaret W. Fisher) *Conflict: Violence and Nonviolence,* Aldine-Atherton, 1971; (author of introductory essays) Blanche Cook and others, editors, *Harijan, 1933-1955: A Journal of Non-Resistance,* nineteen volumes, Garland Publishing, 1973. Also author of monographs on Indian politics and government, 1953-70. Contributor to *Encyclopedia Americana.* Contributor to journals, including *Journal of Asian Studies, Journal of Conflict Resolution, Journal of Modern History, American Historical Review,* and *Australian Journal of Politics and History.* Co-editor, *Indian Press Digests,* 1953-70.

WORK IN PROGRESS: Sources of Power and Leadership in India; Aspects of Creative Conflict.

* * *

BONELLIE, Helen-Janet 1937-

PERSONAL: Born March 21, 1937, in Toronto, Ontario, Canada; daughter of William Bonellie (a publishers' representative). *Education:* Studied at New York School of Design and Ontario College of Art. *Residence:* Toronto, Ontario, Canada.

CAREER: Robert Simpson Co., Toronto, Ontario, designer, 1955-60; Shelagh's of Canada, Toronto, designer, 1960-64; residential designer, newspaper columnist, and writer, 1964-71; editor, Southam Business Publications, 1971—. *Member:* Canadian National Press Club, Interior Designers of Ontario. *Awards, honors:* Memorial award for best radio-television script, from Canadian Press Club, 1968, 1969; Canada Council grant, 1970.

WRITINGS: Introduction to Interior Design, A. S. Barnes, 1968; *The Status Merchants,* A. S. Barnes, 1972. Author of the following radio plays for Canadian Broadcasting Corp.: "Freedom of the Cage," 1968, "Sundance," 1969, "No Clocks in Eden," 1970, "Garden of the Sun," 1972. Contributor of monthly features to *Homemakers' Magazine, Canadian Doctor, Furniture and Furnishings,* and *Winnepeg Free Press.* Columnist, *Toronto Globe and Mail* and *Toronto Telegram.* Art reviewer, *Toronto Sun.* Contributor to *Canadian Antique Collector, Canadian Architect, Canada Crafts,* and *Art Magazine.*

WORK IN PROGRESS: A collection of short stories.

AVOCATIONAL INTERESTS: Egyptology, antiques (art nouveau and Bauhaus), contemporary European writers, Canadian art.

* * *

BONEY, F(rancis) N(ash) 1929-

PERSONAL: Born November 10, 1929, in Richmond, Va.; son of David McKinnie (a businessman) and Mary (Francis) Boney; married France Alice Bernard (a teacher), March 28, 1959; children: Bernard David, Claire Nash. *Education:* Hampden-Sydney College in Virginia, B.S., 1952; University of Virginia, M.A., 1960, Ph.D., 1963. *Religion:* Presbyterian. *Home:* 525 Brookwood Dr., Athens, Ga. 30605. *Office:* Department of History, University of Georgia, Athens, Ga. 30602.

CAREER: D. M. Boney & Co., Richmond, Va., salesman and office manager, 1952-54, 1956-57; Murray State College (now University), Murray, Ky., assistant professor of history, 1962-63; University of Georgia, Athens, assistant professor of history, 1963-65; Washington State University,

Pullman, assistant professor, 1965-67, associate professor of history, 1967-68; University of Georgia, associate professor, 1968-72, professor of history, 1972—. *Military service:* U.S. Army, Counter-Intelligence Corps, 1954-56. *Member:* Organization of American Historians, Southern Historical Association, Georgia Historical Society, Phi Beta Kappa. *Awards, honors:* Certificate of commendation from American Association for State and Local History, 1970, for *A Union Soldier in the Land of the Vanquished.*

WRITINGS: John Letcher of Virginia: The Story of Virginia's Civil War Governor, University of Alabama Press, 1967; *A Union Soldier in the Land of the Vanquished: The Diary of Sergeant Mathew Woodruff, June-December, 1865,* University of Alabama Press, 1969; *Slave Life in Georgia: A Narrative of the Life, Sufferings, and Escape of John Brown, a Fugitive Slave, Now in England,* Beehive Press, 1972; (contributor) Kenneth Coleman, editor, *A History of Georgia,* University of Georgia Press, 1977. Contributor to *Encyclopedia Americana.* Contributor of articles and reviews to journals, including *Centennial Review, Civil War Times Illustrated, South Atlantic Quarterly, Civil War History, Intellectual Digest, Phylon, America, Georgia Review,* and *Midwest Quarterly.*

WORK IN PROGRESS: Continued research on the antebellum South; studying Southern stereotypes.

* * *

BONJEAN, Charles M. 1935-

PERSONAL: Born September 7, 1935, in Pekin, Ill.; son of Bruno (a businessman) and Catherine (Dancey) Bonjean. *Education:* Drake University, B.A., 1957; University of North Carolina at Chapel Hill, M.A., 1959, Ph.D., 1963. *Home address:* 16310 Clara Van Tr., Austin, Tex. 78734. *Office:* Hogg Foundation for Mental Health, University of Texas, Austin, Tex. 78712.

CAREER: University of Texas at Austin, assistant professor, 1963-66, associate professor, 1966-70, professor of sociology, 1970-74, Hogg Professor of Sociology and executive associate of Hogg Foundation for Mental Health, 1974—, head of department of sociology, 1972-74. *Member:* American Sociological Association (chairman, section on community, 1976-78; member of publications committee, 1978—), American Political Science Association, Society for the Study of Social Problems, Southwestern Sociological Association (president, 1972—), Southwestern Social Science Association (member of executive council, 1966—), Phi Beta Kappa.

WRITINGS: (With Richard J. Hill and S. Dale McLemore) *Sociological Measurement,* Chandler Publishing, 1967; (editor with Norval D. Glenn) *Blacks in the United States,* Chandler Publishing, 1969; (editor with Louis A. Zurcher) *Planned Social Intervention,* Chandler Publishing, 1970; (editor with Terry N. Clark and Robert L. Lineberry) *Community Politics,* Free Press, 1971; (editor with Dan D. Nimmo) *Politcal Attitudes and Public Opinion,* McKay, 1972; (editor with Louis Schneider) *The Idea of Culture in the Social Sciences,* Cambridge University Press, 1973; (editor with Schneider and Lineberry) *Social Science in America,* University of Texas Press, 1976. Contributor to *American Journal of Sociology, Journalism Quarterly, Sociology and Social Research, Administrative Science Quarterly, Sociology of Education, Pacific Sociological Review, Social Forces, Social Science Quarterly, Journal of Applied Behavioral Science, Sociological Quarterly, Journal of Politics, Western Political Quarterly, American Sociological*

Review, and *Nursing Research.* Editor of *Social Science Quarterly,* 1966.

* * *

BONNETTE, Jeanne 1907-
(Jeanne DeLamarter)

PERSONAL: Born December 29, 1907, in Wausau, Wis.; daughter of Eric (a musician) and Rubee (a musician; maiden name Wilson) DeLamarter; married Arthur Edward Bonnette (in real estate), December 29, 1957; children: (previous marriage) Judith (Mrs. W. W. Barrick IV), Haven (Mrs. H. J. Tobias). *Education:* Attended Hazel Sharp School of Ballet, 1921-27, and University of Chicago, 1925-26; Cosmopolitan School of Music and Dramatic Art, Teacher's Certificate, 1929. *Politics:* Republican. *Home:* 235 Coronado Village, 8901 West Frontage Rd. N.E., Albuquerque, N.M. 87113.

CAREER: Free-lance writer, especially of poetry, 1924—. Teacher of music and ballet; director of summer theater; producer of television series, "The Creative Process," for KNME-TV, Albuquerque, N.M., 1970-71, 1972; composer of orchestral music; poetry contest judge. *Member:* World Poetry Society, National League of American Pen Women (poetry chairman for New Mexico, 1972-73), Poetry Society of America, National Federation of State Poetry Societies (secretary, 1968-74), New Mexico Poetry Society (vice-president, 1973-74; president, 1975—), New Mexico Historical Outdoor Drama Society, Friends of the Little Theatre. *Awards, honors:* Several awards for poetry; Zia Award, New Mexico Press Women, 1973.

WRITINGS—Under name Jeanne DeLamarter: *Colored Sails,* Robert Packard, 1930; *Seven Stars,* R. F. Seymour, 1939; *Chess Game and Other Poems,* R. F. Seymour, 1952.

Under name Jeanne Bonnette: *Oh, the Wide Sky,* Roy F. Thompson, 1968; *In This Place,* South & West, 1971. Also author of *Pueblo Poems,* 1975.

Work represented in anthologies, including *Some Haystacks Don't Even Have Any Needle* and *Poetry of the Desert Southwest.* Also editor of three anthologies. Contributor to *Poet Lore, Christian Science Monitor,* and other publications.

WORK IN PROGRESS: A seventh book.

* * *

BONTEMPS, Arna Wendell 1902-1973

October 13, 1902—June 4, 1973; American educator, anthologist, poet, and author of novels, plays, biographies, and juvenile fiction on Black life and culture. Obituaries: *New York Times,* June 6, 1973; *Time,* June 18, 1973; *Library Journal,* July, 1973; *Publishers Weekly,* July 9, 1973. (See index for *CA* sketch)

* * *

BOOKSPAN, Martin 1926-

PERSONAL: Born July 30, 1926, in Boston, Mass.; son of Simon and Martha (Schwartz) Bookspan; married Janet S. Sobel (an actress and singer), October 24, 1954; children: Rachel Raissa, David Israel, Deborah Joy. *Education:* Harvard University, B.S., 1947. *Home:* 65 Parkview Dr., Bronxville, N.Y. 10708.

CAREER: Boston Symphony Orchestra, Boston, Mass., coordinator of radio, television, and recording, 1954-56; WQXR-Radio, New York City, director of recorded music,

music director, program director, and program consultant, 1956-67; WNAC-Television, Boston, critic-at-large, 1969-70; WPIX-Television, New York City, drama critic, 1970-74. Tape critic, *New York Times*, 1963-65; WABC-Television, music and dance critic, 1965-68. Consultant to Rockefeller Foundation, 1963-67. Radio commentator for New York Philharmonic Orchestra. *Member:* National Association of American Composers and Conductors (vice-president, 1968-75), American Music Center (vice-president, 1970—), National Music Council. *Awards, honors:* Citation from National Association of American Composers and Conductors, 1972.

WRITINGS: 101 Masterpieces of Music and Their Composers, Doubleday, 1968, revised edition, 1973; (co-author) *Zubin: The Zubin Mehta Story*, Harper, 1978. Author of "The Basic Repertoire," a column appearing monthly in *Stereo Review;* columnist, *New York Times*, 1963-65. Contributor to *New Book of Knowledge*, and *New York Times Guide to Recorded Music;* contributor to professional journals, including *High Fidelity* and *Music Journal*, and to *House Beautiful*. Contributing editor of *Stereo Review*, 1958-76.

* * *

BOONE, Louis E(ugene) 1941-

PERSONAL: Born May 5, 1941, in Robertsdale, Ala.; son of Louis W. (a research technician) and Helen (Hadley) Boone; married Pat Jones, May 28, 1964; children: Barry Eugene, Christopher Scott. *Education:* Delta State College, B.S., 1963; University of Southern Mississippi, M.S., 1964; University of Arkansas, Ph.D., 1968. *Home:* 7711 South Jamestown, Tulsa, Okla. 74136. *Office:* Department of Management and Marketing, University of Tulsa, Tulsa, Okla. 74104.

CAREER: Auburn University, Auburn, Ala., instructor in marketing, 1964-65; University of Arkansas, Fayetteville, instructor in economics, 1965-67; University of Southern Mississippi, Hattiesburg, assistant professor, 1967-69, associate professor of marketing, 1969; University of Tulsa, Tulsa, Okla., professor of marketing and chairman of department of management and marketing, 1969—. Advisory editor, PPC Books. *Member:* American Marketing Association, Academy of Management, Southwestern Marketing Association (president), Southern Marketing Association, Ozark Economic Association.

WRITINGS: Identifying the Consumer Innovator, Bureau of Business Research, University of Southern Mississippi, 1969; *Marketing Strategy*, C. E. Merrill, 1971, 2nd edition (with Edwin C. Hackleman), 1975; *Management Perspectives in Marketing*, Dickenson, 1972; (with David L. Kurtz) *The Sales Management Game*, General Learning Press, 1972; *Consumer Behavior: Marketing Applications of the Behavioral Sciences*, Dickenson, 1973, published as *Classics in Consumer Behavior*, PPC Books, 1977; *Contemporary Marketing*, Dryden, 1974, 2nd edition, 1977; (with Kurtz) *Contemporary Business*, Dryden, 1976; (with Kurtz) *Foundations of Marketing*, 1977. Contributor to proceedings; contributor to *Journal of Business, Journal of Retailing, Journal of Purchasing, Southern Journal of Business, Journal of Marketing, Business Horizons*, and *Business Topics*.

* * *

BOORMAN, Howard L(yon) 1920-

PERSONAL: Born September 11, 1920, in Chicago, Ill.; son of William Ryland (a social worker) and Verna (Lyon) Boorman; married Margaret Echlin, April 10, 1948 (divorced, 1971); married Mary Houghton, January 20, 1972; children: (first marriage) Scott A. Boorman. *Education:* Attended Grinnell College, 1937-38; University of Wisconsin, B.A., 1941; Yale University, graduate study, 1946-47. *Politics:* Independent. *Home:* 3603 Hoods Hill Rd., Nashville, Tenn. 37215. *Office:* Department of History, Vanderbilt University, Nashville, Tenn. 37240.

CAREER: U.S. Department of State, Washington, D.C., foreign service officer in China and Hong Kong, 1947-55; Columbia University, New York, N.Y., general editor of biographical dictionary project, 1955-67; Vanderbilt University, Nashville, Tenn., professor of history, 1967—. *Military service:* U.S. Navy, 1943-46; served in Pacific theater; became lieutenant. *Member:* American Historical Association, American Political Science Association, Association for Asian Studies, National Committee on United States-China Relations, Council on Foreign Relations. *Awards, honors:* Rockefeller Public Service Award, 1954-55.

WRITINGS: (Editor) *Biographical Dictionary of Republican China*, Columbia University Press, Volume I, 1967, Volume II, 1968, Volume III, 1970, Volume IV, 1971; (contributor) Albert Feuerwerker, editor, *History in Communist China*, M.I.T. Press, 1968.

WORK IN PROGRESS: A biography of Henry S. Houghton, M.D., former director of Peking Union Medical College.†

* * *

BORDEN, Henry 1901-

PERSONAL: Born September 25, 1901, in Halifax, Nova Scotia, Canada; son of Henry Clifford and Mabel (Ashmere) Barnstead Borden; married Jean Creelman MacRae, June 1, 1929; children: Robert, Ann, Perry, Mary Jean, Henry. *Education:* McGill University, B.A., 1921; Dalhousie University, law student, 1922-24; Exeter College, Oxford, B.A., 1926. *Religion:* Anglican. *Home:* Tannery Hill Farm, R.R. 2, King City, Ontario, Canada. *Office address:* P.O. Box 125, Commerce Court Postal Station, Toronto, Ontario, Canada.

CAREER: Employed by Royal Bank of Canada, 1921-22; called to the Bar of Lincolns Inn, London, England, and Bars of Nova Scotia and Ontario, 1927; King's Counsel, 1938; Bordon, Elliot, Kelley & Palmer, Toronto, Ontario, senior member, 1936-46; Brazilian Light & Power Co., Ltd., Toronto, president, 1946-63, chairman of board, 1963-65. Government of Canada, general counsel, Department of Munitions and Supply, 1939-42, chairman of Wartime Industries Control Board, and Coordinator of Controls, Department of Munitions and Supply, 1942-43. Former director and member of executive committee, G.B.M. Canada Ltd., Bell Canada, IBM Canada Ltd.; former director of Canadian Investment Fund, Ltd., and Canadian Fund, Inc.; director emeritus, Canadian Imperial Bank of Commerce. Chairman, Canada Security Assurance Co.; chairman of Canadian board, Norwich Union Fire Insurance Society Ltd. and Norwich Union Life Insurance Society. Vice-chairman of board of governors, University of Toronto, 1945-64, chairman, 1964-68, honorary chairman, 1968-72; chairman, Royal Commission on Energy, 1957-59.

MEMBER: Phi Kappa Pi, York Club, Toronto Club. *Awards, honors:* Rhodes scholar, 1924; Companion of Order of St. Michael and St. George, 1943; LL.D., St. Francis Xavier University (Antigonish, Nova Scotia), 1960, Dalhousie University, 1968, University of Toronto, 1972; D.C.L., Acadia University, 1960; Grand Officer of National Order of the Southern Cross (Brazil), 1962; Medal of Service of Order of Canada, 1969.

WRITINGS: (With William K. Fraser) *Handbook on Companies,* 3rd edition (Borden was not associated with earlier editions), Carswell, 1931; (editor and author of preface) *Sir Robert Laird Borden: His Memoirs,* two volumes, Macmillan (Toronto), 1939; (editor) Robert Laird Borden, *Letters to Limbo,* University of Toronto Press, 1971.

AVOCATIONAL INTERESTS: Farming, fishing.

*   *   *

BOREHAM, Gordon F. 1928-

PERSONAL: Born May 29, 1928, in Ottawa, Ontario, Canada; son of Henry (a printer) and Ann (O'Meara) Boreham; married Marilyn L. Southwell, June 26, 1954; children: Susan, Mark, Lisa. *Education:* Attended St. Patrick's College, Ottawa, 1948; University of Ottawa, B.Comm., 1952, M.A., 1955; Columbia University, Ph.D., 1962; National Defence College of Canada, diploma, 1974. *Religion:* Roman Catholic. *Home:* 2360 Ryan Dr., Ottawa, Ontario, Canada K2C 1K7. *Office:* Department of Economics, University of Ottawa, Ottawa, Ontario, Canada K1N 6N5.

CAREER: Bell Telephone of Canada, Ottawa, Ontario, management trainee in commercial department, 1952-55; University of Ottawa, Ottawa, lecturer, 1955-57, assistant professor, 1958-62, associate professor, 1962-70, professor of economics, 1970—, member of board of governors, 1965-67. Research officer, Canadian Royal Commission on Taxation, 1963, and Canadian Royal Commission on Health Services, 1964; co-chairman of Social Life Conference, 1966, and world service committee, YMCA-YWCA, 1970-71; consultant, Economic Council of Canada, 1973-75; speaker on television and radio and lecturer in twenty nations including the United States, China, India, Germany, and Great Britain. *Military service:* Canadian Army, Fourth Princess Louise Dragoon Guards, 1949-62; became major.

MEMBER: Canadian Economic Association, Canadian Association of University Teachers, American Economic Association, Association of the Professors of the University of Ottawa (past vice-president and member of board of directors). *Awards, honors:* Canadian Social Science Research Council grant, 1957-58; Canada Council grants, 1958, 1966-67, 1969, 1973-74, 1975; research fellowship from Italian Ministry of Foreign Affairs, 1967; University of Ottawa research grants, 1972, 1975.

WRITINGS: The Basic Preconditions of Economic Development (monograph), National Bank of Egypt, 1967; *Banking Problems: With Special Reference to Developing Countries* (monograph), Institute of Banking Studies, Bank of Greece, 1967; *Economic Aid: A Sino-African Case Study* (monograph), China Publishing, 1968; (with Eli Shapiro, Ezra Solomon, and William White) *Money and Banking: Analysis and Policy in a Canadian Context,* Holt (Canada), 1969, 2nd edition, 1979; (with Richard Leftwich) *An Introduction to Economic Thinking,* with student workbook and study guide, Holt (Canada), 1971; (editor) *Contemporary Economic Thinking: Selected Readings,* Holt (Canada), 1971; *Banking in a World Context* (monograph), Institute of Banking Studies, Bank of Greece, 1973; *Current Banking Policy and Practice in the United Kingdom, West Germany, and Australia* (monograph), Economic Council of Canada, 1976. Contributor to proceedings. Contributor of more than twenty-five articles and reviews to *Canadian Banker, Cana-*

dian Journal of Economics, South African Journal of Economics, Institute of Canadian Banker's Review, Indian Economic Journal, and other publications.

WORK IN PROGRESS: A World Survey of Contemporary Banking Development, completion expected in 1980.

SIDELIGHTS: Gordon F. Boreham told *CA:* "I write primarily to inform my students and to influence policy makers, primarily in the field of money and banking and largely within the 'Third World.' In this latter context, my aim is to help such countries accelerate their rates of growth and thereby improve their living levels. In short, my writing is my way of being 'socially responsible.'"

Some of Boreham's writings have been translated into French and Spanish.

*   *   *

BOREN, James H(arlan) 1925-

PERSONAL: Born December 10, 1925, in Wheatland, Okla.; son of James Basil (a businessman) and Una Lee (Hamilton) Boren; married Irene Cheek, August 16, 1946 (divorced January, 1977); married Alice Irene Peters, October 23, 1977; children: (first marriage) Richard Vincent, James Stanley. *Education:* University of Texas at Austin, B.A. (economics), 1948, Ph.D., 1969; California State College (now University), Long Beach, B.A. (education), 1950; University of Southern California, M.A., 1950. *Politics:* Democrat. *Religion:* Methodist. *Home:* 7801 Winona Ct., Annandale, Va. 22003. *Office:* International Association of Professional Bureaucrats, 1032 National Press Building, Washington, D.C. 20045.

CAREER: High school teacher and evening recreation director in Oxnard, Calif., 1950-52; Texas Department of Agriculture, Austin, chief of Accounting Division, 1952-54; Arlington College (now University of Texas at Arlington), professor of education and head of department, 1954-56; Boren Oil & Gas Corp., president, 1956-57; administrative assistant to U.S. Senator Ralph Yarborough, 1957-61; U.S. Foreign Service, Agency for International Development, Washington, D.C., deputy director of mission to Peru, 1961-63, founder and director of Partners of the Alliance and special assistant to U.S. coordinator of Alliance for Progress, 1963-70; Development Services International, Washington, D.C., president, 1970-76; president, Mumbles Ltd., 1976—. Lecturer, political satirist, and columnist; has appeared on many talk shows on national television. *Military service:* U.S. Naval Reserve, active duty, 1943-46.

MEMBER: National Press Club, International Association of Professional Bureaucrats (founder and president, 1968—), Authors Guild, American Freedom from Hunger Foundation (member of board of directors, 1976—), Phi Delta Kappa. *Awards, honors:* Meritorious honor award, Agency for International Development, 1964; L.H.D., Hawthorne College, 1967; Communication through Humor Award, Toastmasters International, 1977.

WRITINGS: When in Doubt, Mumble: A Bureaucrat's Handbook, Van Nostrand, 1972; *Have Your Way with Bureaucrats,* Chilton, 1974; *The Bureaucratic Zoo,* EPM Publications, 1976. Also author of monthly newsletter, *Mumblepeg: The Voice of the Bureaucrat.* Contributor to *Nation's Business, Transportation and Distribution, TWA Ambassador, Texas Observor,* and *Independent Petroleum.*

WORK IN PROGRESS: A Citizen's Handbook on Bureaucracy, a satire; *Special Advice to Bureaucrats; The Boren Dictum: If You're Going to be a Phoney, Be Sincere about It.*

SIDELIGHTS: Among James H. Boren's guidelines for bureaucrats are "When in charge, ponder. When in trouble, delegate."

BIOGRAPHICAL/CRITICAL SOURCES: Time, November, 1971, November, 1976.

*   *   *

BORING, Phyllis Zatlin 1938-

PERSONAL: Born December 31, 1938, in Green Bay, Wis. *Education:* Rollins College, B.A. (with highest distinction), 1960; University of Florida, M.A., 1962, Ph.D., 1965. *Home:* 5 Timber Rd., East Brunswick, N.J. 08816. *Office:* Department of Spanish, Rutgers University, New Brunswick, N.J. 08903.

CAREER: Rutgers University, New Brunswick, N.J., assistant professor of Romance languages, 1963, associate professor of Spanish, 1963—, and associate dean. Member of conference planning committee, New Jersey State Commission on Women, 1972. *Member:* Modern Language Association of America, American Association of Teachers of Spanish and Portuguese, American Association of University Professors, Women's Equity Action League (former president of New Jersey Division), American Civil Liberties Union, Phi Sigma Iota. *Awards, honors:* Woodrow Wilson fellowship; Fulbright fellowship at University of Grenoble, 1960-61.

WRITINGS: (With Matilde O. Castells) *Lengua y lectura: un repaso y una continuacion,* Harcourt, 1970; (editor) *Francisco Ayala, El rapto,* Harcourt, 1971; *Elena Quiroga,* Twayne, 1977; *Victor Ruiz Iriate,* Twayne, 1979. Contributor to education and language journals, and to newspapers.

WORK IN PROGRESS: Editing, *El lando de seis caballos,* for Almar; *Jaime Salom.*

*   *   *

BOTWINICK, Jack 1923-

PERSONAL: Born January 9, 1923, in Brooklyn, N.Y.; son of Samuel Meyer (a businessman) and Annie (Liebson) Botwinick; married Joan Garfein, September 9, 1956; children: Laura Kay, Karen Ruth, Paula Jean. *Education:* Brooklyn College (now Brooklyn College of the City University of New York), B.A., 1946, M.A., 1950; New York University, Ph.D., 1953. *Office:* Department of Psychology, Box 1125, Washington University, St. Louis, Mo. 63130.

CAREER: Research psychologist, U.S. Public Health Service, 1949-50; New York University, New York, N.Y., instructor in psychology, 1955; National Institute of Mental Health, Bethesda, Md., research psychologist, 1955-63; Duke University, Durham, N.C., 1963-69, began as associate professor, professor of medical psychology, 1963-69; Washington University, St. Louis, Mo., professor of psychology and director of aging and development program, 1969—. *Member:* American Psychological Association (president of division twenty, 1963), Gerontological Society (chairman of Psychological and Social Science Division, 1962).

WRITINGS: Cognitive Processes in Maturity and Old Age, Springer Publishing, 1967; *Aging and Behavior,* Springer Publishing, 1973, 2nd revised edition, 1978; (co-author) *Memory Related Functions and Age,* C. C Thomas, 1974. Contributor of more than eighty articles to journals in his field.

BOUGHTON, James M(urray) 1940-

PERSONAL: Surname is pronounced Boo-tone; born April 8, 1940, in Turkey Run, Ind.; son of Stanley R. (a politician) and Erminee (Bloyd) Boughton. *Education:* Duke University, B.A., 1966, Ph.D., 1969; University of Michigan, M.A., 1967. *Politics:* Peace and Freedom. *Religion:* Rasha Harvan. *Home:* 1607 Nancy St., Bloomington, Ind. 47401. *Agent:* William S. Doyle II, 3419 Burton Ridge Rd., Grand Rapids, Mich. *Office:* Department of Economics, Indiana University, Bloomington, Ind. 47401.

CAREER: Federal Reserve Bank, Atlanta, Ga., economist, 1967; Econometric System Simulation Program, Durham, N.C., economist, 1967-70, acting director, 1969-70; Duke University, Durham, assistant professor of economics, 1969-70; Indiana University at Bloomington, assistant professor, 1970-73, associate professor of economics, 1973—. *Member:* American Economic Association, American Finance Association, Hoosier Forecasters (honorary chairman, 1970-72), Order of Green Friars (treasurer, 1968), Economists for Stromsdorfer (president, 1972), Bloomington Civil Liberties Union.

WRITINGS: Monetary Policy and the Federal Funds Market, Duke University Press, 1972; (with Elmo Wicker) *Principles of Monetary Economics,* Irwin, 1975. Contributor to *Journal of Money, Credit and Banking, Southern Economic Journal, Journal of Bank Research, Public Finance Quarterly, Buddhist Monthly,* and *Applied Economics.*

WORK IN PROGRESS: Mathematical Models of Political and Religions Systems, completion expected in 1980.

*   *   *

BOUMA, Donald H(erbert) 1918-

PERSONAL: Born February 9, 1918, in Grand Rapids, Mich.; married Ailene Batchelor, July 30, 1940 (divorced February, 1968); married Elisabeth Hetherington (a dance instructor and chairman of department of dance), May 18, 1968; children: (first marriage) Gary, Margene (Mrs. Phil Burnett), Jack. *Education:* Calvin College, A.B., 1940; University of Michigan, M.A., 1944; Michigan State University, Ph.D., 1952. *Home:* 78 Lake Doster Dr., Plainwell, Mich. 49080. *Office:* Department of Sociology, Western Michigan University, Kalamazoo, Mich. 49001.

CAREER: Calvin College, Grand Rapids, Mich., associate professor, 1946-52, professor of sociology and head of department, 1952-60; Western Michigan University, Kalamazoo, associate professor, 1960-62, professor of sociology, 1962—. Chairman, Michigan Commission on Fulbright Scholarships, 1956-72. *Military service:* U.S. Navy, 1944-46; became lieutenant junior grade. *Member:* American Sociological Association, North Central Sociological Association, Michigan Sociological Association (president, 1958).

WRITINGS: (With James Hoffman) *Dynamics of School Integration,* Eerdmans, 1968; *Kids and Cops: A Study in Mutual Hostility,* Eerdmans, 1969. Contributor of about forty articles to professional journals. Associate editor, *USA Today,* 1974—.

*   *   *

BOWDEN, Elbert Victor 1924-

PERSONAL: First syllable of surname rhymes with "how"; born November 25, 1924, in Wilmington, N.C.; son of James Owen (a seafood producer and wholesaler) and Dovie Ellen (Phelps) Bowden; married Mary Mariani, May 30, 1948 (divorced, 1950); married Doris Fales (a registered nurse), September 11, 1951; children: (first marriage) Elbert Victor, Jr.; (second marriage) Richard A., Doris Ellen, William Austin, Jack B., Joyce Leigh. *Education:* University of Connecticut, B.A. (with distinction), 1950; Duke University, M.A., 1952, Ph.D., 1957. *Home address:* P.O. Box 186, Fredonia, N.Y. 14063. *Office:* Department of Economics, State University of New York College, Fredonia, N.Y. 14063.

CAREER: Duke University, Durham, N.C., instructor in economics, 1952-54; University of Kentucky, Lexington, research associate at Bureau of Business Research, 1954-55; Duke University, instructor in economics, 1955-56; College of William and Mary in Norfolk (now Old Dominion University), Norfolk, Va., associate professor, 1956-57, professor of economics and chairman of department, 1958-63; Elmira College, Elmira, N.Y., professor of economics, 1963-64; Upper Peninsula Committee for Area Progress, Escanaba, Mich., executive director, 1964-65; Robert R. Nathan Associates (trust territory economic development team), Saipan, Mariana Islands, chief economist and chief of mission, 1965-67; Texas A & M University, College Station, associate professor of economics and research economist, 1967-70; State University of New York College at Fredonia, professor of economics, 1970—. Has conducted symposia, workshops, and seminars; testified at hearings of Interstate Commerce Commission and U.S. Senate committees, and presented material to Federal Communications Commission, Federal Power Commission, and U.S. Trust Territory of the Pacific Islands. *Military service:* U.S. Maritime Service, instructor, 1943. U.S. Merchant Marine, 1943-45; served in Atlantic and European theaters. U.S. Maritime Service, student at officer's training school, 1945. U.S. Merchant Marine, deck officer, 1945-46; served in Pacific theater.

MEMBER: American Association for the Advancement of Science, American Economic Association, American Business Writers Association, American Association of University Professors, Northeast Regional Science Association (vice-president, 1971-72), Rocky Mountain Social Science Association, Southern Economic Association, Southwestern Social Science Association, Western Regional Science Association, New York State Economic Association, Gamma Chi Epsilon, Omicron Delta Epsilon. *Awards, honors:* Ford Foundation fellowship, University of North Carolina at Chapel Hill, 1960; State University of New York College at Fredonia nominee for Chancellor's Award for teaching excellence, 1973.

WRITINGS: (With Thomas W. Carlin) *Economics,* Alexander Hamilton Institue, 1960, revised edition, 1969; *Development Opportunities for Virginia's Eastern Shore* (monograph), Area Redevelopment Administration, U.S. Department of Commerce, 1963; *Multi-County Programming and Implementation for Economic Development* (monograph), Robert R. Nathan Associates, 1964; (principal author) *Economic Development Plan for Micronesia: A Proposed Long-Range Plan for Developing the Trust Territory of the Pacific Islands,* three volumes, Robert R. Nathan Associates, for High Commissioner of Trust Territory, 1966; *Economic Development Plan for Micronesia: Summary Report* (monograph), Robert R. Nathan Associates, 1967; *WIDE: A Mic-American Concept for the Economic Development of the Western Pacific Islands,* Industrial Economics Research Division, Texas A & M University, 1968; (editor) *Urban and Regional Development Planning in Texas,* Division of Planning Coordination, Office of the Governor of Texas, 1969; (with E. A. Copp) *The Houston-Galveston Area: An Overview of Resources, Population,*

Economic Activities, and Projections (monograph), Industrial Economics Research Division, 1969; (with Copp) *Analysis of Land Use Alternatives and Industrial Potential for the Houston Farms Properties* (monograph), Industrial Economics Research Division, 1969; (with Copp) *Future Industry Demand and Land Development Patterns for the Houston Farms Properties* (monograph), Industrial Economics Research Division, 1969.

Location Factors for Nuclear Energy Centers (monograph), Industrial Economics Research Division, Texas A & M University, 1970; *University and Community: Principles, Issues and Case Studies of Faculty-Student Involvement in Urban and Regional Problems* (monograph), Department of Economics, Texas A & M University, 1970; *Nuclear Energy Research and Development in the Pacific Northwest* (monograph), Industrial Economics Research Division, 1970; (editor) *Intergovernmental Relations and Regional Planning in Texas* (monograph), Division of Planning Coordination, Office of the Governor of Texas, 1970; *Fundamentals of Economics: Simple Explanations of Basic Micro and Macro Concepts,* privately printed, 1971; *Economics in Historical Perspective: The Continuing Evolution of Economics Conditions, Problems, Theories, and Systems,* State University of New York College at Fredonia, 1973; *Economics: The Science of Common Sense,* South-Western Publishing, 1974, 2nd edition, 1977.

Contributor to conferences, proceedings, and annals. Contributor of articles and reviews to *Land Economics, Southern Economic Review, Regional Science Journal, Social Science Quarterly, American Economic Review, Journal of Economic Literature, Journal of Developing Areas, Annals of Regional Science,* and *Growth and Change: A Journal of Development.*†

*   *   *

BOWDEN, Gregory Houston   1948-

PERSONAL: Born July 1, 1948, in London, England; son of Frank Bowden (an industrialist and baronet). *Education:* Mansfield College, Oxford, B.A., 1970. *Religion:* Church of England. *Home:* Thame Park, Thame, Oxfordshire, England. *Agent:* Peter Janson-Smith, 31 Newington Green, Islington, London N16 9PU, England.

MEMBER: Royal College of Organists.

WRITINGS: Morgan: First and Last of the Real Sports Cars, Gentry Books, 1972, Dodd, 1973; *British Gastronomy: The Rise of Great Restaurants,* Chatto & Windus, 1975; *The Story of the Raleigh Cycle,* foreword by Alan Sillitoe, W. H. Allen, 1975; (with Reginald Hargreaves Harris) *Two Wheels to the Top,* W. H. Allen, 1976; *More Morgan: A Pictorial History of the Morgan Sports Car,* Gentry Books, 1976, Dodd, 1977.

SIDELIGHTS: Gregory Houston Bowden told *CA:* "My two greatest interests are music and good food. Of the two music is the greater love, and I have changed my prime interest since leaving school from the organ to the harpsichord. My interest in good food probably comes from being brought up in a family which takes an interest in gastronomy and also as a result of travel. I am fluent in French and can get by in German and Italian. My love of cars is strictly limited to Morgans of which I own three."†

*   *   *

BOWEN, Elizabeth (Dorothea Cole)   1899-1973

June 7, 1899—February 22, 1973; Irish-born novelist, short

story writer, scriptwriter, and literary critic. Obituaries: *New York Times,* February 23, 1973; *Washington Post,* February 24, 1973; *Publishers Weekly,* March, 1973; *Newsweek,* March 5, 1973; *Time,* March 5, 1973. (See index for *CA* sketch)

* * *

BOWEN, Haskell L. 1929-

PERSONAL: Born August 13, 1929, in Vinson, Okla.; son of Elmus Carmack (a salesman) and Mary (Lanning) Bowen; married Anita Turpin (a teacher), March 24, 1951 (divorced, 1976); married Donna Raleigh (a secretary), June 18, 1977; children: Cheryl Marie, Stephen Douglas. *Education:* Coalinga College, A.A., 1949; San Jose State College (now University), B.A., 1957, M.A., 1958. *Politics:* Democrat. *Religion:* Baptist. *Home:* 185 Giddings Ct., San Jose, Calif. 95139. *Agent:* VanDeBurg-Linkletter Associates, 1800 Ave. of the Stars, Gateway East, Suite 208, Los Angeles, Calif. 90067.

CAREER: Campbell Union High School District, San Jose, Calif., 1957—, began as teacher and coach, now supervisor of physical education and director of athletics. On leave of absence to do an in-depth study of the drug problem, 1966-67. Member, California Governor's Task Force on Drug Abuse; education delegate, Commission of the Californias to Stem Drug Abuse in Mexico and California. Part-time teacher of courses on drug abuse education, University of California, San Jose, and San Jose State College.

WRITINGS: Drug Abuse Information: Teacher Resource Materials, Santa Clara County Office of Education, 1967; (with Gordon McLean) *High on the Campus,* Tyndale, 1970. Writer of booklets; contributor to journals.

WORK IN PROGRESS: High Risk Living: A Look at Youth Today.

SIDELIGHTS: High on the Campus was filmed as a documentary, 1970.

* * *

BOWER, Julia Wells 1903-

PERSONAL: Born December 27, 1903, in Reading, Pa.; daughter of Andrew Park and Maude (Weightman) Bower. *Education:* Syracuse University, A.B., 1925, A.M., 1926; University of Chicago, Ph.D., 1933. *Religion:* Baptist. *Home and office:* 151 Oneco Ave., New London, Conn. 06320.

CAREER: Vassar College, Poughkeepsie, N.Y., instructor in mathematics, 1926-27; Sweet Briar College, Sweet Briar, Va., instructor in mathematics, 1927-30; Connecticut College, New London, instructor, 1933-38, assistant professor, 1938-42, associate professor, 1942-53, professor of mathematics, 1954-69, professor emerita, 1969—, chairman of department, 1942-72. *Member:* American Mathematical Society, Mathematical Association of America, American Association for the Advancement of Science, Phi Beta Kappa, Sigma Xi, Pi Lambda Theta.

WRITINGS: Introduction to Mathematical Thought, Holden-Day, 1965; *Mathematics: A Creative Art,* Holden-Day, 1973.

* * *

BOWERS, John Waite 1935-

PERSONAL: Born November 28, 1935, in Alton, Iowa; son of George E. (a journalist) and Clara (Wathier) Bowers; children: John Steven, Jeanne Terese, Julie Michelle. *Education:* University of Kansas, Lawrence, B.S., 1958, M.A., 1959; University of Iowa, Iowa City, Ph.D., 1962. *Home:* 302 Fourth Ave., Coralville, Iowa. *Office:* Department of Communication Research, University of Iowa, Iowa City, Iowa 52240.

CAREER: University of Iowa, Iowa City, assistant professor, 1962-65, associate professor, 1965-68, professor of communication research, 1968—, chairman of communication studies, 1975—. *Member:* Speech Communication Association of America (senior associate editor, 1968-71), International Communication Association, American Association of University Professors.

WRITINGS: Designing the Communication Experiment, Random House, 1970; (with Donovan J. Ochs) *The Rhetoric of Agitation and Control,* Addison-Wesley, 1971.

Contributor: Gerald Miller and Thomas Nilsen, editors, *Perspectives on Argumentation,* Scott, Foresman, 1966; Nilsen, editor, *Essays on Rhetorical Criticism,* Random House, 1968; Philip Emmert and William Brooks, editors, *Methods of Research in Communication,* Houghton, 1970; Serge Moscovici, editor, *The Psychosociology of Language,* Markham, 1972; Douglas Ehninger, editor, *Contemporary Rhetoric,* Scott, Foresman, 1972; Gerald Miller and Herbert Simons, editors, *Perspectives on Communication in Social Conflict,* Prentice-Hall, 1974; Walter Fisher, editor, *Rhetoric: A Tradition in Transition,* Michigan State University Press, 1974. Editor, *Communication Monographs,* 1978-80.

* * *

BOWERS, Q(uentin) David 1938-

PERSONAL: Born October 21, 1938, in Honesdale, Pa.; son of Quentin H. (a civil engineer) and Ruth (Garratt) Bowers; married Mary Masters, June 4, 1960 (divorced, 1973); children: Wynnewood, Leland. *Education:* Pennsylvania State University, B.S., 1960. *Office address:* Box 1669, Beverly Hill, Calif. 90210.

CAREER: Bowers and Ruddy Galleries, Inc., Hollywood, Calif., director, 1969—; Mekanisk Musik Museum, Copenhagen, Denmark, director, 1971—; American Auction Association, Hollywood, director, 1971—.

WRITINGS: U.S. Half Cents, 1793-1857, Windsor Research Publications, 1963; *Coins and Collectors,* Windsor Research Publications, 1964; *Put Another Nickel In,* Vestal, 1966; (editor) *A Guide Book of Automatic Musical Instruments,* Vestal, 1967; *Early American Car Advertisements,* Crown, 1971; *Encyclopedia of Automatic Musical Instruments,* Vestal, 1972; *The American Auction Association Presents the Matt Rothert Collection . . . ,* photographs by Robert Budinger, American Auction Association, 1973; *The American Auction Association Presents the Stanislaw Herstal Collection . . . ,* American Auction Association, 1974; *High Profits from Rare Coin Investment,* Bowers and Ruddy Galleries, 1974; *Collecting Rare Coins for Profit,* Harper, 1975; *A Time for a Token: A Catalogue of Tokens and Medals Relating to Automatic Musical Instruments, circa 1850-1930,* Token and Medal Society (Thiensville, Wis.), 1975. Contributor of articles to *Encyclopedia Americana Annual, Coin World Magazine,* and other publications relating to rare coins, music boxes and automatic musical instruments, and other items in the antique field.†

BOWERS, Ronald (Lee) 1941-

PERSONAL: Born June 2, 1941, in Jersey Shore, Pa.; son of Harry Thomas (a steel worker) and Natalie (Runner) Bowers. Education: Lock Haven State College, B.A., 1963. Politics: Democrat. Religion: "Religious Science." Home: 155 East 52nd St., New York, N.Y. 10022.

CAREER: Saks Fifth Ave., New York, N.Y., editor of in-house publication, Saks Fifth Ave-News, 1967—. Member: National Board of Review of Motion Pictures.

WRITINGS: (With James Robert Parish) The M-G-M Stock Company, Arlington House, 1973; The Selznick Players, A. S. Barnes, 1976. Contributor of interviews, film and book reviews, and a periodic column, "Hors D'Oeuvre," to Films In Review, 1965—. Fashion editor, Photoplay magazine.

SIDELIGHTS: Ronald Bowers has a large and extensive collection of motion picture memorabilia, stills, clips, books (approximately 2,000 books), interviews, and letters. Included in this collection are such items as the original program to the movie, "Gone With the Wind," and original Time magazine cover stories on movie personalities, for example, one on Jean Harlow.

In June, 1978, the Ronald Bowers Film and Theatre Collection in the library of Jersey Shore High School was established with over 200 books and other items donated by Bowers.

*   *   *

BOWKER, Francis E. 1917-

PERSONAL: Born August 10, 1917; son of Francis Edwin (a realtor and farmer) and Alice (Chaffee) Bowker; married Carole Moran (a secretary), June 2, 1943; children: Candace Bowker Wheeler, Jonathan R., Alice C. Education: Educated in Massachusetts. Politics: Republican. Religion: Protestant. Home: 26 Denison Ave., Mystic, Conn. 06355. Office: Marine Historical Association, Inc., Mystic, Conn. 06355.

CAREER: Worked on sail boats and steam boats, 1934-44; employed by Patch-Wegner Co., Inc., Rutland, Vt., 1944-47, and 1950-58; owned Bowker Office Equipment Co., Inc., 1947-50; Marine Historical Association, Inc., Mystic, Conn., mate and captain of sail training vessel "Brilliant," 1959—. Wartime service: U.S. Merchant Marine during World War II. Member: Masons (Pawcatuck Lodge).

WRITINGS: Hull-Down, privately printed, 1963; Blue Water Coaster, International Marine Publishing, 1972. Contributor to magazines including Ships and the Sea, Yankee, and Down East.

WORK IN PROGRESS: Research on ships and people involved in coastal trade from Parrsboro, Nova Scotia, from 1900 to 1945.

SIDELIGHTS: Francis Bowker dropped out of school and went to sea on the last of the big American and Canadian commercial schooners. Even as a teenager he had an idea he would someday write about ships and the men with whom he sailed. Despite objections from his parents and advice from captains and old seamen, he continued his career. He says: "At this point in my life I am convinced that my choice was right. I lived through some wonderful experiences, have a fine family, and my position as captain of the schooner 'Brilliant' excites the envy of many who love the sea and ships of sail." He works with young people, taking them to sea as the working crew of a vessel under sail, inspiring either a love

for the sea or a desire to avoid further experience on it at all costs.

*   *   *

BOWLES, Jane (Sydney) 1917-1973

February 22, 1917—May 4, 1973; expatriate American novelist and playwright. Obituaries: New York Times, May 31, 1973; Newsweek, June 11, 1973; Publishers Weekly, June 11, 1973. (See index for CA sketch)

*   *   *

BOWMAN, Albert Hall 1921-

PERSONAL: Born January 16, 1921, in Evanston, Ill.; son of Francis Brainerd and Gertrude (Bowman) Bowman; married Joyce Duschl (a teacher), June 5, 1948; children: Victoria, Elizabeth, Catherine. Education: Trinity College, Hartford, Conn., A.B., 1947; Columbia University, M.A., 1948, Ph.D., 1954. Politics: Democrat. Religion: Episcopalian. Home: 511 James Blvd., Signal Mountain, Tenn. 37377. Office: Department of History, University of Tennessee, Chattanooga, Tenn. 37401.

CAREER: New York University, New York, N.Y., instructor in history, 1948-49; U.S. Government, Washington, D.C., foreign affairs analyst, 1951-57; Tennessee Wesleyan College, Athens, professor of history and chairman of Division of Social Sciences, 1957-62; University of Chattanooga, Chattanooga, Tenn., librarian and professor of history, 1962-69; University of Tennessee at Chattanooga, professor of history, 1969—. Fulbright professor at Catholic University, Louvain, Belgium, 1967-68. Military service: U.S. Army, 1942-45; became first lieutenant; received Bronze Star and Purple Heart. New York National Guard, 1947-50; became captain. Member: American Historical Association (chairman, George Louis Beer Prize committee, 1976-78), Organization of American Historians, Society for Historians of American Foreign Relations, American Association of University Professors (chapter president, 1960-62, 1964-65), Society for French Historical Studies (member of Gilbert Chinard Prize committee, 1978—), United Nations Association (Chattanooga chapter president, 1964-65; member of executive committee, 1964—), National Council of Christians and Jews (member of board of directors, 1965—), American Civil Liberties Union, Southern Historical Association, Chattanooga Historical Association. Awards, honors: Gilbert Chinard Prize, Society for French Historical Studies and Institut Francais de Washington, 1975, for The Struggle for Neutrality.

WRITINGS: (Editor with Omer De Raeymaeker) American Foreign Policy in Europe, Humanities, 1968; The Struggle for Neutrality: Franco-American Diplomacy during the Federalist Era, University of Tennessee Press, 1975. Contributor, Alexander DeConde, editor, Encyclopedia of American Foreign Policy, Scribners, 1978. Contributor of articles to Political Science Quarterly, William and Mary Quarterly, Journal of Canadian History, Reporter, Diplomatic History, American Historical Review, Journal of American History, and Journal of Southern History.

WORK IN PROGRESS: Jefferson and Napoleon: Diplomatic Relations between France and the United States, 1801-1815, for University of Tennessee Press.

*   *   *

BOWMAN, Karl M. 1888-1973

November 4, 1888—March 2, 1973; American psychiatrist,

researcher, professor, and writer on his speciality. Obituaries: *New York Times*, March 4, 1973.

* * *

BOWMAN, Ned A(lan) 1932-

PERSONAL: Born April 6, 1932, in Lyons, Ind.; son of Starlin Ermal (a government employee) and Mary (Jeffers) Bowman; married Gloria Toribia Orduna (a teacher), December 27, 1956; children: Ishmael, Mary, Margaret, Rebekah. *Education:* Attended Indiana University, 1949-52, 1958; University of Iowa, B.A., 1953, M.A., 1956; Universidad Veracruzana, graduate study, 1957; Stanford University, Ph.D., 1963. *Home:* 38 East Ave., Norwalk, Conn. 06851. *Office:* Rosco Laboratories, 36 Bush Ave., Port Chester, N.Y. 10573.

CAREER: University of North Dakota, Grand Forks, instructor in theater, 1956-58; University of Pittsburgh, Pittsburgh, Pa., 1960—, began as assistant professor, currently adjunct professor of theater arts; Rosco Laboratories, Port Chester, N.Y., manager of production and research, 1976—. Fulbright-Hays lecturer in theater, Asociacion Colombiana de Universidades, 1967; director, Arts Information International, 1970-76; president, U.S. Institute for Theatre Technology, 1972-74. *Military service:* U.S. Army, 1953-55; served in Germany; became sergeant. *Member:* American Theatre Association, American Society of Theatre Research, International Organization of Scenographers and Theatre Technicians. *Awards, honors:* Field-Hotaling Fund grant, 1960; Arts of the Theatre Foundation grant, 1963-64; U.S. Office of Education grant, 1966; Pittsburgh Foundation grant, 1966; University of Pittsburgh Center for International Studies grant, 1966, 1968, 1969; U.S. Institute for Theatre Technology, founder's award, 1970, grant, 1977; grants from Government of West Germany, 1971, and International Research and Exchanges Board, 1972.

WRITINGS: (Translator with Harriet Allen) Jacques Polieri, editor, *Scenographie Nouvelle,* [Paris], 1964; (with Maxwell Silverman) *Theatre Architecture,* New York Public Library, 1965; (with William Coleman and Glorianne Engel) *Planning for Theatre,* University of Pittsburgh, 1965; *Indice collective de obras teatrales en seis bibliotecas de Bogota, Colombia,* Center for Latin American Studies, 1965; (with wife, Gloria O. Bowman) *Materials sobre technologia del teatro,* International Dimensions Program, 1966; *Comprehensive Index to the Merriman Collection of Materials on Pittsburgh and New York Theatre,* University of Pittsburgh, 1967; (with others) *Recent Publications on Theatre Architecture,* Scenographic Media, 1972; *Handbook of Technical Practice for the Performing Arts,* Scenographic Media, Volume I, 1972, Volume II, 1975. Contributor to *Educational Theatre Journal, Theatre Survey, Journal of Communications Research, Theatre Design and Technology, Buehnentechnische Rundschav,* and other professional journals in the United States and abroad. Editor, *Recent Publications on Theatre Architecture,* 1960—; editor, *Theatre Design and Technology,* 1965-70; editorial adviser, *Theatre Communication* (Sao Paulo) and *Interscaena.* (Prague).

WORK IN PROGRESS: Studying technical literature for television, theater, and film.

* * *

BOYD, Myron F(enton) 1909-1978

PERSONAL: Born July 19, 1909, in Shelbyville, Ill.; son of Edward P. (a clergyman) and Greta A. (Pierce) Boyd; married Ruth E. Putnam, June 28, 1932; children: Donald Eugene, Darold D., Carolyn R. (Mrs. Dale Martin). *Education:* Seattle Pacific College, A.B., 1932, D.D., 1949; American University, graduate study, 1939; University of Washington, Seattle, graduate study, 1943. *Politics:* Republican. *Home:* 1304 Chestnut, Greenville, Ill. 62246. *Office:* College and Elm Sts., Greenville, Ill. 62246.

CAREER: Ordained minister of Free Methodist Church, 1931; pastor in Tonasket, Wenatchee, and Mt. Vernon, Wash., 1932-41; Seattle Pacific College, Seattle, Wash., pastor, 1941-48; director and speaker on Light and Life Hour, worldwide broadcast, 1945-65; bishop of Free Methodist Church of North America, 1964-76; Greenville College, Greenville, Ill., professor, 1977-78. *Member:* National Holiness Association (president, 1954-58, 1968-72), National Association of Evangelicals (vice-president, 1968-72; president, 1972-74), National Religious Broadcasters (president, 1954-56). *Awards, honors:* LL.D. from Houghton College, 1954; National Religious Broadcasters award, 1955.

WRITINGS—All published by Light and Life Press, except as indicated: *God's Masterpieces,* 1949; *America under God,* 1952; *A More Excellent Way,* 1953; *Personalized Pointers for Heart and Life,* 1956; *To Tell the World,* 1964; (with Merne A. Harris) *Projecting Our Heritage,* Beacon Hill Press, 1969. Contributor of articles to religious periodicals.

WORK IN PROGRESS: A study of the church, its growth, influence, weaknesses, and strengths.†

(Died July 31, 1978)

* * *

BOYD, William 1885-

PERSONAL: Born June 21, 1885, in Portsoy, Scotland; son of Dugald Cameron (a clergyman) and Elizabeth Boyd; married Enid G. Christie. *Education:* Attended Glasgow Academy and Trent College; University of Edinburgh, M.B. and Ch.B., 1908, M.D., 1911, diploma in psychiatry, 1912; F.R.C.S. (Canada), 1949; F.R.C.P., 1955; F.R.C.S. (Scotland), 1966. *Politics:* Conservative. *Religion:* United Church. *Home:* 40 Arjay Crescent, Toronto, Ontario, Canada.

CAREER: Derby Borough Asylum, Derby, England, medical officer, 1909-12; pathologist at Winwick Asylum, Warrington, England, 1912-13, and Royal Wolverhampton Hospital, Wolverhampton, England, 1913-14; University of Manitoba, Winnipeg, professor of pathology, 1915-37; University of Toronto, Toronto, Ontario, professor of pathology and bacteriology, 1937-51, professor emeritus, 1951—; researcher and writer, 1951—. Professor of pathology, University of British Columbia, 1951-54; visiting professor of pathology, University of Alabama, 1955-61. Pathologist at Winnipeg General Hospital, 1919-37, and Toronto General Hospital, 1937-51. *Military service:* British Army, Medical Corps, 1914-15; became captain. *Member:* College of American Pathologists (honorary fellow), American Association of Pathologists and Bacteriologists (president, 1935), International Association of Medical Museums (American and Canadian section; past president), Pathological Society of Great Britain and Ireland (honorary member). *Awards, honors:* LL.D. from University of Saskatchewan, 1937, and Queen's University, 1956; M.D. from University of Oslo, 1945; D.Sc. from University of Manitoba, 1948; Gold-head Cane of American Association of Pathologists and Bacteriologists, 1962; Companion of the Order of Canada, 1968.

WRITINGS: With a Field Ambulance at Ypres, George H. Doran, 1916; *The Physiology and Pathology of the Cerebrospinal Fluid,* Macmillan, 1920; *Surgical Pathology,* Saunders, 1925, 7th edition published as *Pathology for the Surgeon,* 1955, 8th edition published as *Boyd's Pathology for the Surgeon,* edited by William Anderson, 1967; *The Pathology of Internal Diseases,* Lea & Febiger, 1931, 6th edition published as *Pathology for the Physician,* 1958, 8th edition, 1967; *A Textbook of Pathology,* Lea & Febiger, 1932, 8th edition, 1970; *An Introduction to Medical Science,* Lea & Febiger, 1937, 5th edition published as *An Introduction to the Study of Disease,* 1962, 7th edition (with Sheldon Huntington), 1977; *The Spontaneous Regression of Cancer,* C. C Thomas, 1966.

AVOCATIONAL INTERESTS: Mountaineering, golf, gardening.†

*   *   *

BOYER, Robert E(rnst) 1929-

PERSONAL: Born August 3, 1929, in Palmerton, Pa.; son of Merritt Ernst (a civil engineer) and Lizzie Boyer; married Elizabeth Bakos, September 1, 1951; children: Robert M., Janice E., Gary K. *Education:* Colgate University, B.A., 1951; Indiana University, M.A., 1954; University of Michigan, Ph.D., 1959. *Religion:* Protestant. *Home:* 7644 Parkview Cir., Austin, Tex. 78731. *Office:* Department of Geological Sciences, University of Texas, Austin, Tex. 78712.

CAREER: University of Texas at Austin, instructor, 1957-59, assistant professor, 1959-62, associate professor, 1962-67, professor of geology, 1967—, chairman of department, 1971—. *Member:* Geological Society of America (fellow), American Association of Petroleum Geologists, National Science Teachers Association, American Association for the Advancement of Science (fellow), Society of American Photogrammetry, Texas Academy of Science (honorary life fellow), Phi Kappa Phi, Sigma Xi. *Awards, honors:* National Science Foundation fellowship, 1956-57; Autometric Award, first honorable mention, 1972; received honorable mention, Fifth Annual Children's Science Book Award, New York Academy of Sciences, 1976.

WRITINGS: (With Jon L. Higgins) *Activities and Demonstrations for Earth Science,* Parker Publishing, 1970; *Field Guide to Rock Weathering,* Houghton, 1971; (with P. B. Snyder) *Geology,* Hubbard Press, 1972; *Oceanography,* Hubbard Press, 1974; *The Story of Oceanography,* Harvey House, 1975. Also author, *Solo-Learn Units in Earth Science.* Editor, *Texas Journal of Science,* 1962-64, and *Journal of Geological Education,* 1965-68.

WORK IN PROGRESS: Geo-logic System, for Ward's Natural History Establishment, Inc.

*   *   *

BOYLE, John Hunter 1930-

PERSONAL: Born October 6, 1930, in Huron, S.D.; son of John D. and Catherine (Hunter) Boyle; married Barbara Shipley, October 18, 1958; children: Thomas Lawrence, Martha Shipley. *Education:* Georgetown University, B.S., 1953; Harvard University, M.A., 1958; Stanford University, Ph.D., 1968. *Home:* 944 Bryant Ave., Chico, Calif. *Office:* History Department, California State University, Chico, Calif. 95926.

CAREER: California State University, Chico, 1968—, currently professor of history. *Military service:* U.S. Army, Intelligence Corps, 1950-53; became sergeant. *Member:*

Association for Asian Studies, American Historical Association, Pacific Area Intercollegiate Council on Asia Studies. *Awards, honors:* Fulbright grant, 1969-70.

WRITINGS: China and Japan at War, 1937-1945: The Politics of Collaboration, Stanford University Press, 1972.

*   *   *

BOYLE, Stanley E(ugene) 1927-

PERSONAL: Born September 4, 1927, in Sandpoint, Idaho; son of Stanley Cleveland and Bessie (Watkins) Boyle; married Phyllis Patricia Weiler, April 26, 1949 (died February 29, 1972); married Martha Lee York, December 9, 1972; children: (first marriage) Michael Brian, John Patrick. *Education:* Washington State College (now University of Maine at Machias), B.A., 1954, M.A., 1955; University of Wisconsin, Ph.D., 1959. *Politics:* Democrat. *Religion:* Unitarian-Universalist. *Home:* 39 Brown Thrasher, Hilton Head Island, S.C. 29928. *Office:* SERA, Inc., Suite 512, 430 Highway 278, Hilton Head Island, S.C. 29928.

CAREER: St. Louis University, St. Louis, Mo., assistant professor, 1958-59, associate professor, 1959-62; U.S. Department of Justice, Antitrust Division, Washington, D.C., senior economist, 1962; Federal Trade Commission, Washington, D.C., chief of Division of Industry Analysis, 1963-66; Virginia Polytechnic Institute and State University, Blacksburg, professor of economics, 1966-76; Southern Economic Research Associates, Inc., Hilton Head Island, S.C., president, 1977—. Visiting professor, Naval War College, 1961, and University of South Carolina, 1977—. *Military service:* U.S. Army Air Forces, 1945-47. U.S. Air Force, 1947-48. *Member:* American Economic Association, Western Economic Association, Southern Regional Science Association.

WRITINGS: (With J. A. Guthrie) *County Income Payments in Washington,* Washington State College Press, 1954; (with J. P. McKenna) *The Participation of Missouri Firms in Export Trade,* St. Louis University Press, 1961; *Industrial Organization,* Holt, 1972; *Economics of Industry Analysis,* Winthrop Publishing, 1979. Author of monographs for Federal Trade Commission. Contributor to professional journals, including *Federal-Bar Journal, Antitrust Bulletin, Antitrust Law and Economics Review, Journal of Industrial Economics, Journal of Political Economy,* and *American Economic Review.* Member of board of editors, *Southern Economic Journal,* 1967-70; managing editor, *Review of Regional Studies,* 1969-74; managing editor, *Industrial Organization Review.*

WORK IN PROGRESS: Research associated with development of new consulting firm.

*   *   *

BRABB, George J(acob) 1925-

PERSONAL: Born May 9, 1925, in Buhl, Idaho; son of Leslie E. and Nellie (Spainhower) Brabb; married Betty L. Lenz, June 4, 1949; children: Lloyd J., Thea L. *Education:* University of Idaho, B.S., 1950, M.S., 1954; University of Illinois, Ph.D., 1958. *Politics:* Independent. *Office:* Department of Management and Marketing, Illinois State University, Normal, Ill. 61761.

CAREER: University of Washington, Seattle, assistant professor, 1956-60, associate professor of business statistics, 1961-67; University of Montana, Missoula, professor of management, 1967-75; Illinois State University, Normal, professor of management and chairperson of department of management and marketing, 1975—. Research assistant, Employment Security Agency, State of Idaho, 1950-52; Foundation for Economic Education fellow, American Laundry Machinery Industries, Inc., 1965. Specialist in measurements, General Electric Co., summer, 1961; part-time professor of economics and statistics, Pacific Coast Banking School, University of Washington, Seattle, 1959-64; visiting professor of business administration, Harvard University, summer, 1965; research associate and visiting professor of business statistics, Office of Institutional Research, University of Colorado, 1966-67. Director, Computer Institute for Professors of Business Administration, summer, 1969; co-director, Experienced Teacher Fellowship Program, 1968-70. Member, National Science Foundation-Association for Computer Science, 1968, and Conference on Applications of the Computer to the Undergraduate Curriculum, 1970, 1971, 1973. Secretary-treasurer, Montana Computing Associates (a consulting and service firm), 1971-74; president, Five Valleys River Park Association, 1972-74. Has developed training programs for accountants, managers, and educators. *Military service:* U.S. Navy, 1943-46; became aviation radioman third class; received Air Medal.

MEMBER: American Institute for Decision Sciences (member of council; vice-president of Western region, 1972-74; vice-president of organization, 1974-75), American Economic Association, American Statistical Association, Association for Computing Machinery, Institute of Management Sciences, Missoula Athletic Aquatic Club (president, 1973), Sentinel Kiwanis Club. *Awards, honors:* Data educator of the year, Society of Data Educators, 1970.

WRITINGS: (With Philip J. Borque) *Seasonality in Washington State Employment* (monograph), Bureau of Business Research, University of Washington, Seattle, 1960; (with Bourque) *Geographic Differences in Seasonal Instability* (monograph), U.S. Department of Labor and Rhode Island Department of Labor, 1961; (with Kermit O. Hanson) *Managerial Statistics,* 2nd edition (Brabb was not associated with earlier edition), Prentice-Hall, 1961; (contributor) Peter P. Schoderbeck, editor, *Management Systems,* Wiley, 1967, revised edition, 1970; *Introduction to Quantitative Management,* Holt, 1968; *Computers and Information Systems in Business,* Houghton, 1968. Contributor to business journals.

WORK IN PROGRESS: Business Data Processing Principles and Practices, for Houghton.

AVOCATIONAL INTERESTS: Fishing, bowling, writing, backpacking, camping, bridge.

*   *   *

BRACK, O M, Jr.   1938-

PERSONAL: Born November 30, 1938, in Houston, Tex.; son of O M (in sales) and Olivia Mae (Rice) Brack; married Sheila Delfeld, January 21, 1961; married second wife, Vida Katkin, June 16, 1968; married third wife, Gae Holladay, December 31, 1976. *Education:* Baylor University, B.A., 1960, M.A., 1961; University of Texas, Ph.D., 1965. *Office:* Department of English, Arizona State University, Tempe, Ariz. 85281.

CAREER: William Woods College, Fulton, Mo., assistant professor of English, 1964-65; University of Iowa, Iowa City, assistant professor, 1965-68, associate professor of English, 1968-73, director of Center for Textual Studies, 1967-73; Arizona State University, Tempe, Arizona, professor of English, 1973—. Chairman, Eighteenth-Century Short-Title Catalogue Committee, 1970-73; fellow, Hun-

tington Library, 1978. *Member:* Modern Language Association of America, American Society for Eighteenth-Century Studies, Bibliographical Society of America, Printing Historical Society, Bibliographical Society, National Council of Teachers of English, Midwest Modern Langauge Association, Bibliographical Society of the University of Virginia. *Awards, honors:* American Philosophical Society grant, 1967.

WRITINGS: (Editor with Warner Barnes, and author of introduction) *Bibliography and Textual Criticism: English and American Literature, 1700 to the Present,* University of Chicago Press, 1969; (with Robert E. Kelley) *Samuel Johnson's Early Biographers,* University of Iowa Press, 1971; (editor) *Journal Relative to Dr. Johnson's Last Illness,* Windhover Press, 1972; (editor with William Kupersmith and Curt A. Zimansky) Henry Fielding, *Pasquin,* University of Iowa, 1973; (with D. H. Stefanson) *A Catalogue of the Leigh Hunt Manuscripts in the University of Iowa Libraries,* Friends of the University of Iowa Libraries, 1973; (editor with Kelley) *The Early Biographies of Samuel Johnson,* University of Iowa Press, 1974; (editor) *American Humor,* Arete Publications, 1977; (editor with Donald Greene) *The Shorter Prose Writings of Samuel Johnson,* privately printed, 1979. Contributor to encyclopedias and to literary and bibliographical publications. Assistant editor, *Eighteenth Century Bibliography,* 1964-74, and *Books at Iowa,* 1966-73. Member of editorial committee, Yale Edition of the *Works of Samuel Johnson,* 1977—.

WORK IN PROGRESS: A critical edition of the poetry of Michael Wigglesworth; editing Crousaz's *"Commentary on Pope's Essay on Man,"* translated and annotated by Samuel Johnson for the Yale University edition of the works of Johnson; general and textual editor for a ten-volume edition of the works of Tobias Smollett.

*   *   *

BRADLEY, Bert E(dward)   1926-

PERSONAL: Born June 2, 1926, in Birmingham, Ala.; son of Adelbert Edward and Odie (Self) Bradley; married Jeanne Moore, December 4, 1948; children: Susan Ann, Deborah Jeanne. *Education:* Birmingham-Southern College, A.B., 1950; University of Alabama, M.A., 1951; Florida State University, Ph.D., 1955. *Politics:* Republican. *Religion:* Methodist. *Home:* 1104 Ferndale Dr., Auburn, Ala. 36830. *Office:* Department of Speech Communication, Auburn University, Auburn, Ala. 36830.

CAREER: University of Richmond, Richmond, Va., assistant professor, 1955-58, associate professor, 1958-66, professor of speech, 1966-67, head of department, 1958-67; University of North Carolina at Chapel Hill, associate professor, 1967-70, professor of speech, 1970-73, head of department, 1970-73; Auburn University, Auburn, Ala., professor and head of department of speech, 1973—. *Military service:* U.S. Navy, 1944-46. *Member:* International Communication Association, Speech Communication Association of America, American Forensic Association, Southern Speech Communication Association, Alabama Speech Communication and Theatre Association.

WRITINGS: (Contributor with Gifford Blyton) James H. McBath, editor, *Argumentation and Debate,* Holt, 1963; *Speech Performance,* W. C. Brown, 1967; (contributor) Russell R. Windes and Arthur N. Kruger, editors, *Championship Debating,* Volume II, Walch, 1967; (contributor) Waldo W. Braden, editor, *Oratory in the Old South,* Louisiana State University Press, 1970; *Fundamentals of Speech*

Communication: The Credibility of Ideas, W. C. Brown, 1974, 2nd edition, 1978; (contributor) Braden, editor, Oratory in the New South, Louisiana State University Press, in press. Contributor to Southern Speech Journal, Speech Monographs, Speech Teacher, and North Carolina Historical Review. Editor, Speaker, 1959-63, Journal of American Forensics Association, 1965-66, North Carolina Speech Journal, 1969-71, and Southern Speech Communication Journal, 1972-75.

*   *   *

BRAIN, George B(ernard) 1920-

PERSONAL: Born April 25, 1920, in Thorp, Wash.; son of George (a farmer) and Alice Pearl (Ellison) Brain; married Harriet Gardinier, September 28, 1940; children: George Calvin, Marylou. Education: Central Washington State College (now Central Washington University), B.A., 1946, M.A., 1949; Columbia University, Ed.D., 1957; also studied at University of Washington, Seattle, Washington State University, Harvard University, University of Colorado, and Stanford University. Home: 640 Southeast Spring, Pullman, Wash. 99163. Office: Cleveland Hall 163, Washington State University, Pullman, Wash. 99163.

CAREER: High school mathematics and science teacher in Yakima, Wash., 1946-49; Central Washington State College (now Central Washington University), Ellensburg, instructor in mathematics and science, 1949-50; elementary school principal in Ellensburg, Wash., 1950-51; elementary school principal, assistant superintendent, and superintendent of schools in Bellevue, Wash., 1951-59; superintendent of schools in Baltimore, Md., 1960-65; Washington State University, Pullman, dean of College of Education and professor of educational administration, 1965—. Chairman of Fulbright Group Western European Seminar in Comparative Education, 1959, National Committee on Assessing the Progress of Education, 1969—, and Pacific Northwest Regional Manpower Commission, 1970—; member of board of directors of Maryland Academy of Science, 1960-65, National Academy for School Executives, 1969—, Index Publishing Co., 1977—, and Pacific American Institute, 1978—; chairman of board of directors, Northwest Regional Education Laboratory, 1966—; member, National Council on Education for Health Professions, 1969—; member of advisory board, Foreign Study League, 1969—. Visiting professor at Central Washington State College, 1953, Washington State University, 1959, and University of Maryland, 1964; lecturer at Columbia University, University of Connecticut, Harvard University, University of Georgia, University of Delaware, Johns Hopkins University, Morgan State College, University of Oklahoma, Towson State College, Stanford University, and University of Washington, Seattle. Military service: U.S. Naval Reserve, active duty, 1941-42. U.S. Marine Corps Reserve, 1942-46; served in Far East; became major.

MEMBER: American Association of School Administrators (honorary life member; member of executive committee, 1964-66; president, 1965), National Education Association, National Congress of Parents and Teachers, Washington Association of School Administrators (honorary life member; president, 1959), Maryland Association of School Administrators. Awards, honors: Fulbright scholar, 1959; man of the year and distinguished service award for education, National Conference of Christians and Jews, 1963.

WRITINGS: Crisis in Child Mental Health: The Challenge for the 1970's, Harper, 1971; (with Orland F. Furno and George C. Collins) Planning, Programming, Budgeting Systems: A Practical Approach, Atlantic Publishing Co., 1972; (contributor) Thorsten R. Carlson, editor, Administrators and Reading, Harcourt, 1972. Contributor to education journals. Member of editorial advisory board, Scholastic, 1963-69, Education U.S.A., 1964—, Journal of Education, 1966-70, World Book Encyclopedia, 1966—, American Schools and Universities, 1960-64, and Education Digest, 1970—; member of editorial board, World Book Childcraft International, 1966—.

WORK IN PROGRESS: Uses of Encyclopedias in Secondary Schools; School Organization and Administration Theory.

SIDELIGHTS: George B. Brain speaks Chinese and Japanese.

*   *   *

BRAKHAGE, Stan 1933-

PERSONAL: Born January 14, 1933, in Kansas City, Mo.; adopted son of Ludwig (a shoe salesman) and Clara (Dubberstein) Brakhage; married Mary Jane Collom, December 28, 1957; children: Myrrena, Crystal, Neowyn, Bearthm, Rarc. Education: Attended Dartmouth College, two months. Home and office address: P.O. Box 170, Rollinsville, Colo. 80474.

CAREER: Independent motion picture producer having films distributed by Film-Makers Co-Op, Canyon Cinema Co-Op, Audio-Brandon, Pyramid, Grove Press, and London Co-Op, and including among more than seventy films: "Interim," 1952; "Desistfilm," 1954; "Anticipation of the Night," 1958; "Window Water Baby Moving," 1959; "Blue Moses," 1962; "Dog Star Man," 1964; "The Art of Vision," 1965; "Songs," 1967; "Scenes from Under Childhood," 1970; "The Act of Seeing with Ones Own Eyes," 1971; "The Riddle of Lumen," 1972; "Sincerity," 1973-78; "Star Garden," 1974; "The Text of Light," 1974; "Short Films: 1975," 1975; and "The Domain of the Moment," 1977. Lecturer in film history and aesthetics at Art Institute of Chicago, and colleges in the United States and Europe. Member of selection committee, Anthology of Cinema, 1968-69. Awards, honors: Independent Film Award from Film Culture Magazine, 1962; Avon Foundation grant, 1965-69; Rockefeller Foundation fellowship, 1967-69; Brandeis citation, 1973; Colorado Governors Award for Arts and Humanities, 1974; National Endowment for the Arts grants, 1975, 1975, 1977; Guggenheim fellowship, 1978.

WRITINGS: Metaphors on Vision, Film Culture, 1962; A Moving Picture Giving and Taking Book (translation originally published in Sweden as Liten hjalpredafor film makaren, published by Filmcentrum, 1970), Harvey Brown, 1972; The Brakhage Lectures, Good Lion, Volume I, 1970, Volume II, 1972; Seen, Pasteurize Press, 1975; Film Biographies, Turtle Island Press, 1977. Contributor of articles and interviews to journals in the arts, including Film Culture, Art Forum, and Caterpillar.

WORK IN PROGRESS: Two more volumes of The Brakhage Lectures; Scrapbook.

SIDELIGHTS: "Underground" movie-maker Stan Brakhage is known for his original and influential contributions to avant-garde film as well as for his abundant productivity. Brakhage writes in Metaphors on Vision: "Imagine an eye unruled by man-made laws of perspective, an eye unprejudiced by compositional logic, an eye which does not respond to the name of everything but which must know each object encountered in life through an adventure of perception. How many colors are there in a field of grass to the crawling baby unaware of 'green'? How many rainbows can light create for the untutored eye? How aware of variations in heat waves can that eye be? Imagine a world alive with incomprehensible objects and shimmering with an endless variety of movement and innumerable gradations of color. Imagine a world before the 'beginning was the word.'"

BIOGRAPHICAL/CRITICAL SOURCES: Stan Brakhage, *Metaphors on Vision,* Film Culture, 1962; Sheldon Renan, *An Introduction to the American Underground Film,* Dutton, 1967; P. Adams Sitney, editor, *Film Culture Reader,* Praeger, 1970; David Curtis, *Experimental Cinema,* Universe Books, 1971; Sitney, *Visionary Film,* Oxford University Press, 1974; *Modern Photography,* February, 1975; *Film Quarterly,* spring, 1976.

*   *   *

BRANCH, Melville C(ampbell) 1913-

PERSONAL: Born February 16, 1913, in Richmond, Va.; son of Melville C. and Martha (Bowie) Branch; married Hilda S. Rollman, 1951. *Education:* Princeton University, B.A. (with high honors), 1934, M.F.A., 1936, Ecole des Beaux-Arts, Fountainbleau, France, Diplome, 1934; Cranbrook Academy of Art, independent research in planning, 1937-38; Harvard University, Ph.D. (first doctorate granted in field of planning), 1949. *Home:* 1505 Sorrento Dr., Pacific Palisades, Calif. 90272. *Office:* University of Southern California, Los Angeles, Calif. 90007.

CAREER: Norman Bel Geddes & Co. and George Wittbold, Inc., New York, N.Y., head of urban planning section for General Motors Futurama at New York World's Fair, 1938-39; Executive Office of the President, Washington, D.C., research assistant for National Resources Planning Board, 1939-41; Princeton University, Princeton, N.J., director of Bureau of Urban Research, 1941-43; University of Chicago, Chicago, Ill., associate professor of planning, 1947-51; U.S. Government, Los Angeles, Calif., civil servant, 1951-54; Thompson Ramo Wooldridge, Inc., Los Angeles, corporate associate for planning and member of senior staff, 1954-62; University of California, Los Angeles, lecturer in planning, College of Engineering, 1962-66; University of Southern California, Los Angeles, professor of planning, 1966—. Director of "The City" exhibit, Baltimore Museum of Art, 1940-41; planning consultant, Douglas Aircraft Co., 1962-64, Los Angeles City Planning Commission, member, 1961-70, vice-president, 1964-65, president, 1965-66. *Military service:* U.S. Naval Reserve, active duty, 1943-46, as lieutenant.

MEMBER: American Society of Planning Officials (member of board of directors, 1966-69), American Institute of Planners (trustee, California chapter scholarship fund, 1963-69), Institute of Management Sciences (vice-president of College of Planning, Los Angeles, 1961-62), American Association for the Advancement of Science (fellow), Operations Research Society of America, American Society of Photogrammetry. *Awards, honors:* Social Science Research Council demobilization award, 1946-47; Ford Foundation grant, 1969-70; National Endowment for the Arts grants, 1976, 1977; Samuel H. Kress Foundation grant, 1977; Irvine Co. grant, 1978; Robert G. and Maude Morgan Cabell Foundation grant, 1978.

WRITINGS: (Editor) *Federal Aids to Local Planning,* National Resources Planning Board, 1941; *Aerial Photography*

in Urban Planning and Research, Harvard University Press, 1948; (contributor) Harvey Perloff, editor, *Planning and the Urban Community,* Carnegie Press and University of Pittsburgh Press, 1960; *The Corporate Planning Process,* American Management Association, 1962; *Planning: Aspects and Applications,* Wiley, 1966; *Selected References for Corporate Planning,* American Management Association, 1966; *Comprehensive Urban Planning: A Selective Annotated Bibliography with Related Materials,* Sage Publications, 1970; *City Planning and Aerial Information,* Harvard University Press, 1971; (contributor) Ira M. Robinson, editor, *Decision-Making in Urban Planning: An Introduction to New Methodologies,* Sage Publications, 1972; *Air Pollution and City Planning: Case Study of a Los Angeles District Plan, Findings-Recommendations-Explanation,* Environmental Science and Engineering, University of California, 1972; *Urban Air Traffic and City Planning: Case Study of Los Angeles County,* Praeger, 1973; (contributor) *Manual of Remote Sensing,* Volume II, American Society of Photogrammetry, 1975; *Planning Urban Environment,* Dowden, 1975; (editor) *Urban Planning Theory,* Dowden, 1975; *Comparative Urban Design, Rare Engravings, 1830-1840,* Arno, 1978.

Other publications: *Photographic Identification and Analysis of Japanese Antiaircraft Defences,* U.S. Navy Department, 1945; *Toward City Planning of Ocean Environment* (booklet), Department of Engineering, University of California, 1964, also special publication of American Society of Planning Officials, 1964; *Outdoor Noise and the Metropolitan Environment: Case Study of Los Angeles with Special Reference to Aircraft,* Los Angeles Department of City Planning, 1970; *Continuous City Planning,* American Society of Planning Officials, 1973; and other research and technical reports. Contributor to *Planning,* 1965, and to other planning, management, and engineering journals. Advisory editor, *Journal of AIP* (American Institute of Planners), 1958-62, 1975—.

*   *   *

BRANDABUR, Edward 1930-

PERSONAL: Born October 19, 1930, in Cleveland, Ohio; son of John Joseph (a physician) and Genevieve (O'Hara) Brandabur; married Agnes McSharry (an assistant professor of English), June 23, 1956; children: Melanie, Theresa, Jean, Susan, Paula, Keiran, Matthew. *Education:* Xavier University, Cincinnati, Ohio, A.B., 1952, M.A., 1957; University of Cincinnati, Ph.D., 1961. *Politics:* Democrat. *Religion:* Roman Catholic. *Home:* 1206 South Elm Blvd., Champaign, Ill. 61820. *Office:* Department of English, University of Illinois, Urbana, Ill. 61801.

CAREER: University of Illinois at Urbana-Champaign, instructor, 1961-63, assistant professor, 1963-67, associate professor, 1967-71, professor of English, 1971—. Chairman of board of directors, Depot, Inc., 1969-71. *Military service:* U.S. Army, tank gunner, tank commander, and medic, 1953-55; served in Germany. *Member:* International Association for the Study of Anglo-Irish Literature, Modern Language Association of America, American Committee for Irish Studies, American Association of University Professors, James Joyce Foundation, Midwest Modern Language Association. *Awards, honors:* University of Illinois faculty fellowships, 1963, 1965; Guggenheim fellowship, 1972-73.

WRITINGS: A Scrupulous Meanness: A Study of Joyce's Early Work, University of Illinois Press, 1971. Contributor of articles and reviews to professional journals, including

Renascence, New Letters, and *Journal of Aesthetic Education.*

WORK IN PROGRESS: A study of modern literature and the graphic arts in the early twentieth century; a study of James Joyce's *Ulysses;* a book of poems on American ethnic groups; a novel.

AVOCATIONAL INTERESTS: Painting in acrylics and oils.†

*   *   *

BRANFIELD, John (Charles) 1931-

PERSONAL: Born January 19, 1931, in Burrow Bridge, Somerset, England; son of Allan Frederick (a civil servant) and Bessie (Storey) Branfield; married Kathleen Elizabeth Peplow, 1955; children: Susan, Frances, Stephen, Peter. *Education:* Queens' College, Cambridge, M.A., 1956; University of Exeter, M.Ed., 1972. *Home address:* Mingoose Villa, Mingoose, Mount Hawke, near Truro, Cornwall, England. *Agent:* A. P. Watt & Son, 26/28 Bedford Row, London WC1R 4HL, England.

CAREER: Camborne Grammar School, Cornwall, England, English teacher and head of department, 1961-76; teacher, Camborne Comprehensive School, 1976-78.

WRITINGS: A Flag in the Map, Eyre & Spottiswoode, 1960; *Look the Other Way,* Eyre & Spottiswoode, 1963; *In the Country,* Eyre & Spottiswoode, 1966; *The Poison Factory* (juvenile), Harper, 1972 (published in England as *Nancekuke,* Gollancz, 1972); *Why Me?* (juvenile), Harper, 1973 (published in England as *Sugar Mouse,* Gollancz, 1973); *The Scillies Trip,* Gollancz, 1975. Also author of television script, "The Day I Shot My Dad," produced by British Broadcast Corp., 1975.

AVOCATIONAL INTERESTS: Walking, sailing.

*   *   *

BRANSON, David 1909-

PERSONAL: Born July 13, 1909, in King's Lynn, Norfolk, England; son of John Charles Sydney (an inventor and business owner) and May (Boulton) Branson. *Education:* Royal Academy of Music, L.R.A.M. (Performer's Diploma), 1925; studied at Sheffield Art School, 1926-27, and at Royal College of Music, under Harold Samuel and John Ireland, 1927-31. *Home and studio:* Rock House, Exmouth Pl., Hastings, Sussex, England. *Agent:* David Higham Associates Ltd., 5-8 Lower John St., London W.1, England.

CAREER: Pianist, composer, and painter. First appeared in London as pianist at age of eleven at Steinway Hall and obtained L.R.A.M. (performer's diploma) from Royal Academy of Music at 16; besides solo performances as concert pianist has played with chamber music groups, including Cecilia Hansen trio, and as radio artist; composer of orchestral and piano works, works for violin, cello, flute, and guitar, and songs; private teacher of music; adjudicator for music festivals. As artist has exhibited in Royal Academy and Royal Watercolour Society shows, in other London galleries, and provincially; designer of covers for own musical compositions. *Member:* Performing Right Society, British Federation of Music Festivals.

WRITINGS: John Field and Chopin, St. Martin's, 1972. Contributor to music and other journals.

Musical compositions have been published by Bosworth, J. B. Cramer, Elkin/Novello, Oxford University Press, and Melicon. Compositions include "Paraphrases" (orchestral work), 1942, "Pavane and Toccato" (concerto), 1944, "Mediterranean" (for piano and strings), 1956, and "The Mortal Pastime" (for tenor, harp, and strings), 1973. His first songs were set to his own poems, 1929-34, and about fifty other songs set to works of Housman, de la Mare, John Masefield, Hardy, Heine, and others. Major piano solos are "Spanish Jazz," 1939, "The Flung Spray," 1942, "Variations on a Negro Spiritual," 1943, "Two Brazilian Dances," 1967, "Alla Cubana," 1968, "Impromptu," 1973, and "Six Preludes," 1974.

WORK IN PROGRESS: An orchestral work based on the sea, "Piano Sonata: Festival Concertino."

SIDELIGHTS: David Branson is interested in "unusual musical works and research into those of neglected composers (have included many such works in radio and other recitals)." He also has a general interest in the mysterious—herbs, yoga, oriental philosophies, and alchemy. He lived in Spain for the better part of a year, and visited the United States in 1966 to conduct a piano workshop in Raleigh, N.C.

*   *   *

BRAUN, Lev 1913-

PERSONAL: Born November 23, 1913, in Novy Bydzov, Czechoslovakia; son of Emanuel (a businessman) and Louise (Stern) Braun; married Micheline Tison (a professor), April 1, 1949. *Education:* Charles University, Prague, Doctor of Law and Political Science, 1938; Columbia University, M.A., 1961. *Politics:* Liberal Democrat. *Religion:* Jewish. *Home:* 50 Central Park W., New York, N.Y. 10023. *Office:* Department of Social Sciences, Fairleigh Dickinson University, Rutherford, N.J. 07070.

CAREER: British Broadcasting Corp., London, England, program assistant and announcer, 1940-49; Free Europe Committee, New York, N.Y., senior editor and broadcaster, 1950-67; Fairleigh Dickinson University, Rutherford, N.J., 1967—, began as associate professor, currently professor of history. *Member:* Overseas Press Club of America, American Association of University Professors, American Political Science Association, University Centers for Rational Alternatives.

WRITINGS: Witness of Decline: Albert Camus, Moralist of the Absurd, Fairleigh Dickinson University Press, 1973.

WORK IN PROGRESS: The Changing Balance of Power.

*   *   *

BREAN, Herbert 1908(?)-1973

1908(?)—May 7, 1973; American novelist, mystery-story writer, and editor. Obituaries: *New York Times,* May 9, 1973.

*   *   *

BREESE, Gerald (William) 1912-

PERSONAL: Born June 4, 1912, in town of Horseheads, N.Y.; son of Bert M. and Leona (Goodrich) Breese; married Alice Janette Bailey, July 4, 1937 (deceased February, 1972); children: Adele (Mrs. Robert Richards, Jr.), James, Dana Sue, Brinda Sue (Mrs. Gary Coleman). *Education:* Ohio Wesleyan University, A.B., 1935; Yale University, B.D., 1938; University of Southern California, additional study, 1939; University of Chicago, Ph.D., 1947. *Politics:* Independent. *Home:* 47 Deer Path, Princeton, N.J. 08540. *Office:* Department of Sociology, Princeton University, Princeton, N.J. 08540.

CAREER: Pacific University, Forest Grove, Ore., assistant professor of sociology and dean of men, 1938-41; Shrivenham American University, Shrivenham, England, teacher of urban sociology, 1945; University of Chicago, Chicago, Ill., teacher of urban sociology, 1947; Social Science Research Council, Washington, D.C., staff member, 1947-49; Princeton University, Princeton, N.J., assistant professor, 1949-51, associate professor, 1951-59, professor of sociology, 1959-77, professor emeritus, 1977—. Director, Bureau of Urban Research, Princeton, N.J., 1950-66; consultant to Community Planning Associates, Inc., Princeton and Trenton, N.J., 1953-72. Fulbright professor at American University at Cairo, 1954-55; visiting lecturer at University of Natal, 1963; visiting fellow at Institute of Advanced Studies, Australian National University, 1966. Coordinator for Ford Foundation Consulting Team, Delhi, India, 1957-58. *Military service:* U.S. Army, 1942-45. *Member:* American Institute of Planners, American Sociological Association, Population Association of America, American Society of Planning Officials, Eastern Sociological Association. *Awards, honors:* Social Science Research Council grant, 1946-47.

WRITINGS: Daytime Population of Central Business District of Chicago, University of Chicago Press, 1949; *Industrial Site Selection,* Bureau of Urban Research, Princeton University, 1954; *Urbanization in Newly Developing Countries,* Prentice-Hall, 1966; (with others) *Impact of Large Installations on Nearby Areas,* Sage Publications, 1969; (editor and contributor) *The City in Newly Developing Countries: Readings on Urbanism and Urbanization,* Prentice-Hall, 1969; *Urban and Regional Planning in the Delhi-New Delhi Area: Capital for Conquerors and Country,* Tempa Communication Graphics, 1974. Also editor and contributor, *Urban Southeast Asia,* 1973.

WORK IN PROGRESS: Comparative Analysis of the Structure and Growth of Large Metropolitan Areas in Newly Developing Countries; The Southeast Asian City.

* * *

BREGMAN, Jacob I(srael Jack) 1923-

PERSONAL: Born September 17, 1923, in Providence, R.I.; son of Aaron (a junk dealer) and Jennie (Katzoff) Bregman; married Mona Madan (a teacher), June 27, 1948; children: Janet Paula, Marcia Lynn, Barbara Jean. *Education:* Providence College, B.S., 1943; Polytechnic Institute of Brooklyn, M.S., 1948, Ph.D., 1951. *Politics:* Democrat. *Religion:* Judaism. *Home:* 5630 Old Chester Rd., Bethesda, Md. 20014. *Office:* WAPORA, Inc., 6900 Wisconsin Ave. N.W., Washington, D.C. 20015.

CAREER: Nalco Chemical Company, Chicago, Ill., head of physics and chemistry laboratory, 1952-59; Illinois Institute of Technology Research Institute, Chicago, director of chemistry sciences, 1959-67; U.S. Department of Interior, Washington, D.C., deputy assistant secretary, 1967-69; WAPORA, Inc., Washington, D.C., president, 1969—. Chairman of Illinois Air Pollution Control Board, 1963-67. *Military service:* U.S. Army, 1944-46; became technical sergeant. *Member:* American Chemical Society, American Water Resources Association, American Institute of Chemists (fellow), Water Resources Research Council (chairman, 1965-68), New York Academy of Sciences, Explorers Club, Sigma Xi, Phi Lambda Upsilon.

WRITINGS: Corrosion Inhibitors, Macmillan, 1963; (editor with A. J. Dravnieks) *Surface Effects in Detection,* Spartan, 1965; (with Sergei Lenormand) *The Pollution Para-*

dox, Spartan, 1966; (with H. Gehm) *Water Resources and Pollution Control,* Van Nostrand, 1977.

WORK IN PROGRESS: Editor of a series on water pollution, for Academic Press; a book on thermal pollution.

* * *

BRIGHAM, John C(arl) 1942-

PERSONAL: Born December 19, 1942, in Glen Ridge, N.J.; son of John C. (a civil engineer) and Jean (Dipman) Brigham; married Gayle Bradley, September 17, 1962 (divorced, 1975); children: Susan Gayle, Tracy Lynne, David John. *Education:* Duke University, B.A., 1964; University of Colorado, M.A., 1968, Ph.D., 1969. *Office:* Department of Psychology, Florida State University, Tallahassee, Fla. 32306.

CAREER: Florida State University, Tallahassee, assistant professor, 1969-74, associate professor of social psychology, 1974—. *Member:* American Psychological Association, Society for the Psychological Study of Social Issues, Southeastern Psychological Association, Sigma Xi.

WRITINGS: (Editor with T. A. Weissbach) *Racial Attitudes in America,* Harper, 1972; (editor with L. S. Wrightsman) *Contemporary Issues in Social Psychology,* Brooks-Cole, 1973, revised edition, 1977; (with L. J. Severy and B. R. Schlenker) *A Contemporary Introduction to Social Psychology,* McGraw, 1976. Contributor to *Psychological Bulletin, Journal of Experimental Social Psychology, Journal of Personality, Journal of Applied Social Psychology, Representative Research in Social Psychology,* and *Personality and Social Psychology Bulletin.*

WORK IN PROGRESS: Research and writing on attitude change, racial prejudice, stereotypes, and factors affecting accuracy of eyewitness identifications.

* * *

BRIGOLA, Alfredo L(uigi) 1923-

PERSONAL: Born November 23, 1923, in Shanghai, China; naturalized U.S. citizen in 1958; son of Carlo (a diplomat) and Maria (Cereda) Brigola; married Bobbie R. Martin, 1954; children: Gina Maria, Carlo Alfredo. *Education:* University of Chanchun, Chinese language diploma, 1942; University of Mississippi, B.A., 1953, M.A., 1954; studies at University of California, Los Angeles, 1963; University of Madrid, certificado de estudios del doctorado, 1968. *Home:* 229 Grand View Dr., Redlands, Calif. 92373. *Office:* Department of Foreign Languages, University of Redlands, Redlands, Calif. 92373.

CAREER: Nicolis S.A. (an Italian import and export company), Tientsin, China, assistant manager of import department, 1942-44; Bulova Watch Co., Hong Kong, assistant sales manager, 1948-50; Firestone Tire & Rubber Co., Memphis, Tenn., junior accountant, 1953-56; McFadden Cotton Co., Memphis, assistant manager of export department, 1956-57; University of Redlands, Redlands, Calif., 1957-61, began as instructor, became assistant professor of Spanish and French; University of California, Los Angeles, lecturer in Italian and director of Italian Language Laboratory, 1962-64; University of Redlands, professor of Romance languages and coordinator of department of foreign languages, 1965-68; University of Hong Kong, Hong Kong, lecturer in English, 1969-70; University of Redlands, professor of Romance languages and coordinator of department of foreign languages, 1970—. Executive regional manager for Australia, the South Pacific islands, and the Far East, Bar-dahl International Oil Corp., 1969-70; language specialist in Spanish, Italian, and Mandarin Chinese, and official escort interpreter, U.S. Department of State, 1972—. Planned and presented language program series for television station in Los Angeles, Calif., 1962-64. *Member:* Instituto de Cultura Hispanica (honorary life member), Modern Language Association of America. *Awards, honors:* Bronze medal, Cultural Office of Government of Italy, 1963.

WRITINGS: Italian Language Workbook, Holt, 1965; *Practicing Italian,* Holt, 1965, 3rd edition, 1977.†

*   *   *

BRKIC, Jovan 1927-

PERSONAL: Born February 13, 1927, in Belgrade, Yugoslavia; naturalized U.S. citizen; son of Dragisa (a craftsman) and Vida (Markovic) Brkic; married Beverly Thomas (a librarian), 1953; children: Vida, Alexandra. *Education:* University of Goettingen, Cand. Theol., 1950; Pacific School of Religion, B.D., 1952; Columbia University, Ph.D., 1959. *Religion:* Eastern Orthodox. *Home:* 213 Forest Ave., Fargo, N.D. 58102. *Office:* Department of Philosophy, North Dakota State University, Fargo, N.D. 58102.

CAREER: Gustavus Adolphus College, St. Peter, Minn., instructor, 1959-61, assistant professor of philosophy, 1961-63; University of Vermont, Burlington, assistant professor of philosophy, 1963-65; North Dakota State University, Fargo, assistant professor, 1965-66, associate professor, 1966-67, professor of philosophy, 1967—. *Member:* American Philosophical Association, American Society for Political and Legal Philosophy, American Judicature Society, Metaphysical Society of America.

WRITINGS: Moral Concepts in Traditional Serbian Epic Poetry, Mouton, 1961; *Norm and Order: An Investigation into Logic, Semantics and the Theory of Law and Morals,* Humanities, 1970. Contributor of articles to *Sociologia Internationalis, Archiv fuer Rechts-und Sozialphilosophie,,* and other publications.

WORK IN PROGRESS: Research in logic of law.

*   *   *

BROADRIBB, Violet

PERSONAL: Born in Batavia, N.Y.; daughter of James Clark and Elsie (Glidden) Holly; married Samuel Charles Broadribb (deceased); children: Marilyn Broadribb Zweig, Donald Richard. *Education:* Highland Hospital School of Nursing, R.N., 1927; University of Utah, B.S., 1956; Syracuse University, M.S., 1959; University of Washington, Seattle, additional study, 1967-68. *Politics:* Democrat. *Religion:* Society of Friends (Quaker). *Home and office:* 1501 North Miracle Mile, Tucson, Ariz. 85705.

CAREER: Registered nurse; Holy Cross School of Nursing, Salt Lake City, Utah, instructor in pediatric nursing, 1956-58; instructor in pediatric nursing in Wilmington, Del., 1959-60; University of Oregon, Portland, assistant professor of pediatric nursing, 1961-67. Has served as head of nursing in charge of nursing home. *Member:* National League of American Pen Women (Tucson branch), American Nurses Association, American Association on Mental Deficiency, Association for the Care of Children in Hospitals, Common Cause, Pi Lambda Theta.

WRITINGS: Foundations of Pediatric Nursing, Lippincott, 1967, revised edition, 1973; (with Charlotte Corliss) *Maternal–Child Nursing,* Lippincott, 1973; (with Henry Lee) *The Modern Parents' Guide to Baby and Child Care,* Lippincott, 1973.

AVOCATIONAL INTERESTS: Classical music, travel (Australia, Fiji, Great Britain, Switzerland).

*   *   *

BROCK, Alice May 1941-

PERSONAL: Born February 28, 1941, in Brooklyn, N.Y.; daughter of Joseph F. and Mary (Dubro) Pelkey; married Ray Brock, 1962 (divorced, 1969). *Education:* Attended Sarah Lawrence College. *Politics:* "Unaffiliated extreme left." *Residence:* Stockbridge, Mass. 01262.

CAREER: Alice Brock lists her vocations as cook, artist, writer; she left New York City in 1964 to become librarian at the progressive Stockbridge School in Stockbridge, Mass.; established and operated Alice's Restaurant in Stockbridge, 1966-67; appeared as an extra in the film, "Alice's Restaurant"; proprietor and chef of "Take Out Alice," a restaurant and motel near Stockbridge, June, 1972-79.

WRITINGS: (Self-illustrated) *Alice's Restaurant Cookbook,* with recorded introduction by Arlo Guthrie, Random House, 1969; (self-illustrated) *My Life As a Restaurant,* Overlook Press, 1975.

SIDELIGHTS: Alice Brock started "Alice's Restaurant" in 1966 on an investment of $1,500. Serving "gourmet cooking at a roadside joint at roadside prices," as Alice put it, the menu included such diverse items as borscht, tacos, salmon mousse, egg creams, stuffed grape leaves, and carrot juice. Business was good and the restaurant's reputation grew.

Alice and her husband Ray met Arlo Guthrie, son of folksinger Woody Guthrie, when he was a high school student. "We were sort of a young, hip couple," she says, "and we lived in a church that had really great acoustics. There were always kids hanging around the house and Arlo was one of them." Arlo wrote and recorded "Alice's Restaurant," a "talking blues" song that became a hit in 1967. Arthur Penn, a restaurant patron, decided to make the song into a movie. Filming took place at the restaurant with Arlo, Alice, and the entire staff, and United Artists released the movie in 1969.

The basic philosophy of *Alice's Restaurant Cookbook,* which has been described as enjoyable reading even for those who only enter a kitchen to eat, is that the cook should master the cooking and not be intimidated into strictly following recipes and instructions. Alice Brock's carefree, spontaneous method simplifies even foreign cookery: "Tomatoes and oregano make it Italian; wine and tarragon make it French. Sour cream makes it Russian; lemon and cinnamon make it Greek. Soy sauce makes it Chinese; garlic makes it good." "Recipes," writes the author, "aren't as important as the philosophy behind them. Good food is food you eat with your friends, when everybody is having a good time. . . . It's a lovely thing—everyone sitting down together sharing food. Breaking bread or eating together is a traditional symbol of peace, so take a moment, before you dig in, to smile at your friends."

Alice's book *My Life As a Restaurant* has been described as "an autobiography that includes recipes, helpful kitchen hints, and even an acrostic puzzle." It covers the founding and management of "Alice's Restaurant" from Alice's viewpoint and those of her kitchen co-workers.

BIOGRAPHICAL/CRITICAL SOURCES: Life, March 28, 1969; *New York Times,* July 30, 1969, July 8, 1973; *Newsweek,* September 29, 1969; *Time,* October 24, 1969; *McCall's,* February, 1970; *Library Journal,* March 15, 1976; *Detroit Free Press,* November 14, 1978.†

BRODINE, Virginia Warner 1915-
(Virginia Warner)

PERSONAL: Born February 18, 1915, in Seattle, Wash.; daughter of Hayward Dare (an insurance agent) and Grace (McKibben) Warner; married Russell V. Brodine (a symphony musician), October 19, 1941; children: Cynthia (Mrs. Roger Snow), Marc Russell. *Education:* Attended Reed College, 1933-34, 1937-38, and Cornish School of Arts, 1936. *Home:* 26 B. St., Roslyn, Wash. 98941.

CAREER: C. V. Mosby Publishing Co., St. Louis, Mo., copy editor of *Surgery Journal,* 1951-52; public relations director of central states region, International Ladies' Garment Workers's Union, 1954-62; *Environment,* St. Louis, Mo., editor, 1962-69, consulting editor, 1969-74. Editor of environmental workbooks, Scientists' Institute for Public Information, New York, N.Y., 1970. *Member:* Institute for Public Information (vice-chairman of board of directors, 1973-74), Women's International League for Peace and Freedom, St. Louis Committee for Environmental Information (founding member; member of board of directors, 1958-62, 1972—; secretary, 1960-62, 1972-74; president, 1974-76).

WRITINGS—All under name, Virginia Warner: (Editor and author of opening essay with Mark Selden) *Open Secret: The Kissinger-Nixon Doctrine in Asia,* Harper, 1972; *Air Pollution,* Harcourt, 1973; *Radioactive Contamination,* Harcourt, 1975. Author of cantata, "Women Are Dangerous," 1947, with music by Fred Warren; was performed in 1947 and 1948 for the Congress of American Women.

WORK IN PROGRESS: A historical novel dealing with several generations of American women.

AVOCATIONAL INTERESTS: Outdoor living.

* * *

BRODSKY, Iosif Alexandrovich 1940-
(Joseph Brodsky)

PERSONAL: Born May 24, 1940, in Leningrad, Soviet Union; son of Alexander I. and Maria M. (Volpert) Brodsky; children: Andrei (son). *Education:* Attended schools in Leningrad until 1956. *Office:* Department of Slavic Languages and Literatures, University of Michigan, Ann Arbor, Mich. 48104.

CAREER: Russian poet; exiled by the Soviet government, he left his homeland in June, 1972, for refuge in America; poet-in-residence at University of Michigan, Ann Arbor, 1972—. *Member:* Bavarian Academy of Sciences (Munich; corresponding member), American Academy of Arts and Sciences. *Awards, honors:* D.Litt., Yale University, 1978.

WRITINGS—Poetry, except as indicated: *Stikhotvoreniia i poemy* (in Russian), Inter-Language (Washington), 1965; "Xol 'mi," translated by Jean-Jacques Marie and published in France as *Collines et autres poemes,* Editions de Seuil, 1966; *Ausgewahlte Gedichte* (in German), Bechtle Verlag, 1966; (under name Joseph Brodsky) *Elegy to John Donne and Other Poems,* selected, translated, and introduced by Nicholas Bethell, Longmans, Green, 1967; *Velka elegie* (in Czech), Edice Svedectvi (Paris), 1968; *Ostanovka v pustyne* (in Russian), Chekhov (New York), 1970; (under name Joseph Brodsky) *Poems by Joseph Brodsky,* Ardis, 1972; (under name Joseph Brodsky) *Selected Poems, Joseph Brodsky,* translated by George L. Kline, Harper, 1973; (editor under name Joseph Brodsky with Carl Proffer) *Modern Russian Poets on Poetry: Blok, Mandelstam, Pasternak, Mayakousky, Gumilev, Tsvetaeva* (nonfiction), Ardis, 1976; *Konets prekrasnoi epokhi: stikhotvoreniia 1964-1971,* Ardis, 1977; *Chast' rechi: stikhotvoreniia 1972-1976,* Ardis, 1977.

Poems have been published in anthologies in twelve languages, and in *Russian Review, New York Review of Books, Nouvelle Revue Francaise, Unicorn Journal, Observer Review, Kultura, La Fiera Letteraria, New Yorker, New Leader,* and other journals. He also has done translations of poetry from English and Polish into Russian, and from Russian into Hebrew.

WORK IN PROGRESS: Original poems; translations from English into Russian; an English translation of *Chast' rechi* and a collection of essays, both for Farrar, Straus.

SIDELIGHTS: Inside Russia and out, Brodsky is considered to be one of the Soviet Union's finest poets, although his work has never been published in the U.S.S.R. That and other puzzling aspects of Brodsky's exile have been the subject of wide press coverage since he stopped over in Vienna in June, 1972, en route to the United States.

According to *Time,* the poet's expulsion was "the culmination of an inexplicable secret-police vendetta against him that has been going on for over a decade." Brodsky, who is Jewish, said: "They have simply kicked me out of my country, using the Jewish issue as an excuse." The vendetta first came to a head in a Leningrad trial in 1964, when Brodsky was charged with writing "gibberish" instead of doing honest work, and sentenced to five years hard labor. He was released after eighteen months, but his poetry still was banned. Despite the pressures, Brodsky reportedly wrote to Leonid Brezhnev before leaving Moscow asking for "an opportunity to continue to exist in Russian literature and on Russian soil." According to a *Times Literary Supplement* reviewer, "his poetry is religious, intimate, depressed, sometimes confused, sometimes martyr-concious, sometimes elitist in its views, but it does not constitute an attack on Soviet society or ideology unless withdrawal and isolation are deliberately construed as attack: of course they can be, and evidently were."

His confrontations with the Russian authorities have apparently left their mark on his poetry. "Brodsky is someone who has tasted extremely bitter bread," writes Stephen Spender in *New Statesman,* "and his poetry has the air of being ground out between his teeth.... It should not be supposed that he is a liberal, or even a socialist. He deals in unpleasing, hostile truths and is a realist of the least comforting and comfortable kind. Everything nice that you would like him to think, he does not think. But he is utterly truthful, deeply religious, fearless and pure. Loving, as well as hating."

More than one critic holds the view expressed by Arthur C. Jacobs in *The Jewish Quarterly* that Brodsky is "quite apart from what one thinks of as the main current of Russian verse." A critic in *New Leader* writes: "The noisy rant and attitudinizing rhetoric of public issues are superfluous to Brodsky's moral vision and contradictory to his craft. As with all great lyric poets, Brodsky attends to the immediate, the specific, to what he has internally known and felt, to the lucidities of observation heightened and defined by thought.... Poetry of such rare power does not need the sustenance of biography.... At the age of thirty-three, he has the unfaltering intellectual authority that poets rarely achieve before middle age."

Thus, though one might expect Brodsky's poetry to be basically political in nature, this is not the case. "Brodsky's recurrent themes are lyric poets' traditional, indeed timeless concerns—man and nature, love and death, the ineluctability of anguish, the fragility of human achievements and attachments, the preciousness of the privileged moment, the 'unrepeatable.' The tenor of his poetry is not so much apolitical as antipolitical,'' writes Victor Erlich. ''[His] besetting sin was not 'dissent' in the proper sense of the word, but a total, and on the whole quietly undemonstrative, estrangement from the Soviet ethos.''

Though most agree that he is one of the finest living Russian poets, several critics believe that the English translations of his poetry leave a great deal to be desired, thus casting some doubt on his true poetic abilities. Commenting on George L. Kline's translation of *Selected Poems,* Stephen Spender writes: ''These poems are impressive in English, though one is left having to imagine the technical virtuousity of brilliant rhyming [in the originals]. . . . One is never quite allowed to forget that one is reading a second-hand version.'' F. D. Reeve is somewhat more abrupt: ''In *Selected Poems,* the translations and their footnotes seem full of rectitude but lacking poetic rigor. Translating is difficult, I know, and thankless. . . . I think these translations are soupy. . . . How can any of us know who is Joseph Brodsky?'' Though he resists the temptation to place him in the ''academically certified pantheon of Russian poets,'' Reeve agrees that ''Brodsky is an extremely sensitive, alert, skilled, independent, and suggestive poet'' whose Russian poems (as distinguished from their English translations) contain ''a dignity, a grandeur, and a sadness deeply reflective of Russian culture and of our own world.''

Victor Erlich also feels that some of the lines in *Selected Poems* come out ''strained or murky,'' but that Brodsky at his best has ''originality, incisiveness, depth and formal mastery which mark a major poet.'' He concludes an analysis of some of Brodsky's major poems by remarking: ''The richness and versatility of his gifts, the liveliness and vigor of his intelligence, and his increasingly intimate bond with the Anglo-American literary tradition, augur well for his survival in exile, indeed for his further creative growth.''

BIOGRAPHICAL/CRITICAL SOURCES:Times Literary Supplement, July 20, 1967; *Jewish Quarterly,* winter, 1968-69; *Time,* June 19, 1972, August 7, 1972; *Detroit Free Press,* September 17, 1972; *New Leader,* December 10, 1973; *New Statesman,* December 14, 1973; *Partisan Review,* fall, 1974; *Choice,* April, 1974, September, 1977; *Poetry,* October, 1975; (under name Joseph Brodsky) *Contemporary Literary Criticism,* Gale, Volume IV, 1975, Volume VI, 1976.

*   *   *

BROEKER, Galen   1920-

PERSONAL: Born October 1, 1920, in Norfolk, Neb.; son of George Lewis and Blanche (Williams) Broeker; married Harriet Durkee (a chairman, college English department), April 14, 1948. *Education:* University of Wyoming, B.A., 1950; University of Oregon, M.A., 1952; King's College, London, additional study, 1955-56; University of Minnesota, Ph.D., 1957. *Home:* 1808 Chickadee Dr., Knoxville, Tenn. 37919. *Office:* Department of History, University of Tennessee, Knoxville, Tenn. 37916.

CAREER: University of Tennessee, Knoxville, assistant professor, 1957-61, associate professor, 1961-69, professor of history, 1969—. *Military service:* U.S. Army Air Forces, 1943-46. *Member:* Conference on British Studies, American Committee for Irish Studies, American Historical Association, American Association of University Professors. *Awards, honors:* Fulbright scholar at King's College, London, 1955-56; American Council of Learned Societies grant, 1958.

WRITINGS: Rural Disorder and Police Reform in Ireland,

1812-1836, University of Toronto Press, 1970; *London,* Routledge & Kegan Paul, 1970. Contributor of articles and reviews to various journals.

WORK IN PROGRESS: The Liverpool Ministry, 1812-27.

*   *   *

BROGAN, James E(dmund)   1941-

PERSONAL: Born July 26, 1941, in Hastings-on-Hudson, N.Y.; son of James Edmund and Helen (Kazura) Brogan. *Education:* Princeton University, A.B., 1963; Yale University, M.A., 1964, Ph.D., 1967. *Home:* 1048 Union St., San Francisco, Calif. 94133. *Office:* Department of English, San Francisco State University, 1600 Holloway Ave., San Francisco, Calif. 94132.

CAREER: San Francisco State University, San Francisco, Calif., associate professor of English, 1967—.

WRITINGS: (Editor) *The American's Search for Identity: A Reader,* Harcourt, 1972.†

*   *   *

BROMLEY, David G(rover)   1941-

PERSONAL: Born February 25, 1941, in Winchester, Mass.; son of Everett H. (a salesman) and Mary (Krajewski) Bromley; married. *Education:* Colby College, A.B., 1963; Duke University, M.A., 1966, Ph.D., 1971. *Office:* Department of Sociology, University of Virginia, Charlottesville, Va. 22903.

CAREER: National Institute of Mental Health, Bethesda, Md., trainee, 1966-67; Duke University, Durham, N.C., instructor in sociology, 1967-68; University of Virginia, Charlottesville, acting assistant professor, 1968-71, assistant professor of sociology, 1971—. *Member:* American Sociological Association, American Political Science Association, Southern Sociological Society, Virginia Social Science Association.

WRITINGS: (Editor with Charles F. Longino, Jr.) *White Racism and Black Americans,* foreword by Shirley Chisholm, Schenkman, 1972; (contributor) Jack Dennis, editor, *Socialization to Politics: A Reader,* Wiley, 1973. Contributor to *Canadian Journal of Political Science, Canadian Review of Sociology and Anthropology, Land Economics,* and *Newsletter* of University of Virginia.

WORK IN PROGRESS: An essay for *Party Organization: A Comparative Reader,* edited by William Wright; research on sources of non-medical drug use, inter-city comparisons of mass transit use for commutation, socioeconomic characteristics of suburbs and forms of government, latent functions of the draft lottery law, annexation law and municipal expansion, and on factors related to change in boundary coincidence in urban areas in the 1950's.†

*   *   *

BRONSON, William (Knox)   1926-1976

PERSONAL: Born October 30, 1926, in Oakland, Calif.; son of Tingley Knox (a businessman) and Helen (Hempstead) Bronson; married Marilyn Moen, December 16, 1949; children: Knox, Megan, Nathan Moen, Benjamin Hempstead. *Education:* University of California, Berkeley, A.B., 1952; Stanford University, M.A., 1956. *Residence:* Nevada City, Calif. *Office:* Columbus Tower, San Francisco, Calif. 94133.

CAREER: Hanford Sentinel, Hanford, Calif., sports editor, 1953-54; Hiller Aircraft Corp., Palo Alto, Calif., technical editor, 1954-55; Sunset Books, Menlo Park, Calif., assistant editor, 1956-57; Lockheed Space and Missile Division, Sunnyvale, Calif., senior research reports editor, 1957-58; Hiller Aircraft Corp., graphic arts supervisor, 1958-60; free-lance writer, 1961-65; *Cry California,* San Francisco, Calif., founding editor, 1965-72; Sierra Club *Bulletin,* San Francisco, Calif., editor, 1972-73; William Bronson Film Productions, San Francisco, general partner, beginning 1972.

MEMBER: California Historical Society (trustee), Friends of the Bancroft Library (member of council). *Awards, honors:* California Medal from Commonwealth Club of California, 1960, for *The Earth Shook, the Sky Burned;* certificate of meritorious participation from San Francisco Film Festival, 1962, for "The Day San Francisco Burned"; first prize in Commerical Division from Photographic Society of America, 1963, for "These Are the Perils."

WRITINGS: The Earth Shook, the Sky Burned, Doubleday, 1959; *Still Flying and Nailed to the Mast,* Doubleday, 1963; *How to Kill a Golden State,* Doubleday, 1968; (with Richard Reinhardt) *The Last Grand Adventure,* McGraw, 1977. Also author and producer of motion pictures "Disaster 1906," 1961, "The Day San Francisco Burned" (with Barnaby Conrad; based on *The Earth Shook, the Sky Burned*), 1962, and "These Are the Perils," 1963.

WORK IN PROGRESS: Home Is a Freeway, a collection of his environmental writings.

BIOGRAPHICAL/CRITICAL SOURCES: Best Sellers, June 15, 1968; *American Forests,* October, 1968.†

(Died July 13, 1976)

* * *

BROOKS, Gary D(onald) 1942-

PERSONAL: Born September 3, 1942, in Ogden, Utah; son of William Monroe (with North Central Airlines) and Aline (Smith) Brooks; married Bonnie S. Brooks, August 9, 1964 (divorced, 1971); married Donna Riley, January 28, 1972. *Education:* Millikin University, B.M.E., 1964; Indiana University, M.S., 1966, Ed.D., 1967. *Home:* 500 Thunderbird Dr., Apt. 83, El Paso, Tex. 79912. *Office:* Department of Education Administration and Supervision, University of Texas, Box 133, El Paso, Tex. 79968.

CAREER: Millikin University, Decatur, Ill., assistant professor of education and dean of men, 1967-68; University of Texas at El Paso, director of Office of Institutional Studies, 1968-71, assistant to vice-president for academic affairs, 1968-69, vice-president for student affairs, 1971-73, chairman of department of educational administration and supervision, 1973—. *Member:* American Association for Higher Education, American Educational Research Association, American Association of School Administrators, American Personnel and Guidance Association, Association for Institutional Research, National Association of Student Personnel Administrators, Phi Delta Kappa.

WRITINGS: (With wife, Bonnie S. Brooks) *The Literature on Student Unrest,* Educational Technology Publications, 1970; (editor with Richard W. Burns) *Curriculum Design in a Changing Society,* Educational Technology Publications, 1970; (contributor) E. W. Eisner and E. Vallance, editors, *Conflicting Conceptions of Curriculum,* McCutchan, 1974. Also contributor to *Education for Affective Achievement.* Contributor to *Secondary Education Research Journal, Science Teacher, Educational Technology, Sound Education Reports, Phi Delta Kappan, Research in Higher Education, College and University Business, Journal of College Personnel, College and University Journal,* and other journals in his field.

WORK IN PROGRESS: Public School Law.

* * *

BROOKS, Maria (Zagorska) 1933-

PERSONAL: Born January 11, 1933, in Warsaw, Poland; daughter of Karol and Irene Zagorska; married James O. Brooks, August 17, 1958; children: Christopher Charles, James Stanley. *Education:* University of Warsaw, M.A., 1955; University of Michigan, M.A., 1958, Ph.D., 1963; University of Pennsylvania, M.A., 1963. *Office:* Department of Slavic Languages, University of Pennsylvania, Philadelphia, Pa. 19104.

CAREER: University of Warsaw, Warsaw, Poland, instructor in English, 1955-57; University of Pennsylvania, Philadelphia, lecturer in Polish, 1961-63, instructor, 1963-65, assistant professor, 1965-68, associate professor of Polish, Russian, and Slavic linguistics, 1968—. *Member:* Linguistic Society of America, Modern Language Association of America, American Association of Teachers of Slavic and East European Languages, Polish Institute of Arts and Sciences.

WRITINGS: Nasal Vowels in Contemporary Standard Polish: An Acoustic Phonetic Analysis, Mouton, 1969; *Polish Reference Grammar,* Mouton, 1975. Contributor of articles on Slavic and Polish linguistics and folklore to professional journals.

WORK IN PROGRESS: Survey of Slavic Linguistics; Sociolinguistics and Syntactic Analysis of Stylistic Varieties of Contemporary Standard Polish.

* * *

BROOME, Charles L(arue) 1925-

PERSONAL: Born May 26, 1925, in Prentiss, Miss.; son of Claude Andrew (a farmer) and Zudia (McPhail) Broome; married Wanza Joy Walker, July 14, 1951; children: Belinda. *Education:* Louisiana State University, B.S., 1950, M.B.A., 1961; University of Alabama, Ph.D., 1964. *Home:* 102 Kenilworth Rd., Greenville, N.C. 27834. *Office:* School of Business, East Carolina University, P.O. Box 2767, Greenville, N.C. 27834.

CAREER: Industrial engineer for General Gas Corporation, 1950-51; owner of farm equipment business, 1951-54; analyst for Ford Motor Company, 1954-56, and for AMF-Beird, 1956-59; Texas Christian University, Fort Worth, assistant professor of marketing, 1964-66; University of Houston, Houston, Texas, associate professor of marketing, 1966-70; East Carolina University, Greenville, N.C., professor of marketing, 1970—, assistant dean, 1970-71, associate dean, 1971—, director of graduate studies, 1970—. *Military service:* U.S. Army, 1943-46; became staff sergeant. *Member:* American Marketing Association, American Institute of Decision Sciences, Southern Economic Association, Southern Marketing Association, Southwestern Marketing Association, Beta Gamma Sigma.

WRITINGS: (With Ben Enis) *Marketing Decisions: A Bayesian Approach,* Intext, 1971.

* * *

BROSE, Olive J(ohnson) 1919-

PERSONAL: Born December 8, 1919, in New York, N.Y.; daughter of Ole Christian (a marine engineer) and Annie

(Allen) Johnson; married C. Richard Brose (president of F. Schumacher & Co.), April 19, 1941. *Education:* Columbia University, B.S., 1949, M.A., 1951, Ph.D., 1956. *Politics:* Democrat. *Religion:* Episcopalian. *Home:* Hie Hill Farm, Westbrook, Conn. 06498.

CAREER: Brooklyn College (now Brooklyn College of the City University of New York), Brooklyn, N.Y., instructor in history, 1956-59; Columbia University, New York, N.Y., lecturer in history, 1960-62. President, Westbrook Land Conservation Trust, 1968-70. *Member:* American Historical Association, American Society of Church History, Conference on British Studies.

WRITINGS: Church and Parliament: The Reshaping of the Church of England, 1828-1860, Stanford University Press, 1959; *Frederick Denison Maurice: Rebellious Conformist, 1805-1872,* Ohio University Press, 1971. Contributor to *Victorian Studies, Christian Century, Journal of Ecclesiastical History,* and *Worldview.*

*   *   *

BROWDER, Olin L(orraine), Jr. 1913-

PERSONAL: Born December 19, 1913, in Urbana, Ill.; son of Olin Lorraine and Nellie (Taylor) Browder; married Olive Forsythe, September 9, 1939; children: Ann (Mrs. William Sorensen), Catherine (Mrs. Robert Demeritt), John. *Education:* University of Illinois, A.B., 1935, LL.B., 1937; University of Michigan, S.J.D., 1941. *Religion:* Presbyterian. *Home:* 1520 Edinborough, Ann Arbor, Mich. 48104. *Office:* Law School, University of Michigan, Ann Arbor, Mich. 48109.

CAREER: Admitted to the Bar of Illinois, 1939; practiced law in Chicago, Ill., 1938-39; University of Alabama, Tuscaloosa, assistant professor of business law, 1939-41; University of Tennessee, Knoxville, assistant professor of law, 1941-42; member of legal department, Tennessee Valley Authority, 1942-43; Federal Bureau of Investigation, Washington, D.C., special agent, 1943-45; University of Oklahoma, Norman, professor of law, 1946-53; University of Michigan, Ann Arbor, professor of law, 1953—. *Member:* American Bar Association, American Association of University Professors, Phi Beta Kappa, Beta Theta Phi, Phi Alpha Delta, Phi Kappa Phi.

WRITINGS: (Contributor) *American Law of Property,* Little, Brown, 1952; (with L. W. Waggoner and R. V. Wellman) *Family Property Settlements,* Bobbs-Merrill, 1965, 2nd edition, 1973; (with R. A. Cunningham and J. R. Julin) *Basic Property Law,* West Publishing, 1966, 2nd edition, 1973. Also author of *Palmer's Cases on Trusts and Succession,* with Waggoner and Wellman.

*   *   *

BROWER, Daniel R(oberts) 1936-

PERSONAL: Born January 9, 1936, in Evanston, Ill.; son of Daniel R. (an administrator) and Edith (Gibson) Brower; married Francoise Lemenez de Kerdelleau, August 13, 1959; children: Eric, Caroline, Valerie. *Education:* Carleton College, B.A., 1957; Institut d'Etudes Politiques, graduate study, 1955-56; Columbia University, M.A., 1959, Ph.D., 1963. *Home:* 1829 Tacoma Ave., Berkeley, Calif. 94707. *Office:* Department of History, University of California, Davis, Calif. 95616.

CAREER: Bowdoin College, Brunswick, Me., instructor in history, 1962-63; Oberlin College, Oberlin, Ohio, assistant professor of history, 1963-68; University of California,

Davis, associate professor, 1968-76, professor of history, 1976—. *Member:* American Historical Association, American Association for the Advancement of Slavic Studies.

WRITINGS: The New Jacobins: The French Communist Party and the Popular Front, 1934-38, Cornell University Press, 1968; (editor) *The Soviet Experience: Success or Failure?,* Holt, 1971; *Training the Nihilists: Education and Radicalism in Tsarist Russia,* Cornell University Press, 1975; (editor) *The Russian Revolution,* Forum Press, 1978. Contributor to *Slavic Review, Journal of Social History, American Historical Review, History of Education Quarterly,* and *Journal of Economic History.*

WORK IN PROGRESS: A research project on the rise of the Russian urban classes, 1860-1905.

*   *   *

BROWER, Millicent

PERSONAL: Born in Jersey City, N.J. *Education:* Douglass College, Rutgers University, B.L. in Journalism. *Home:* 200 West 20th St., New York, N.Y. 10011.

CAREER: Radio, television, and stage actress (star of "Young Widder Brown," a radio serial). Radio reporter on "Dimension," WCBS-Radio, 1967. Feature writer, reporter, and drama critic, *Village Voice,* 1955, 1963; syndicated feature writer, Women's News Service; drama critic, *Broadside,* 1970. Appointed member of New York Mayor John V. Lindsay's Task Force on Noise Control.

WRITINGS: Ingenue (novel), Ballantine, 1959 (published in England as *Make Me a Star,* Panther, 1960); (contributor) *The Village Voice Reader,* edited by Daniel Wolf and Edwin Fancher, Doubleday, 1962; *I Am Going Nowhere* (poems for children), Putnam, 1972; (contributor) *The Scribner Anthology for Young People,* edited by Anne Diven, Scribner, 1976. Also contributor to report of the Task Force on Noise Control; contributor of fiction, nonfiction, and poetry to national and international magazines.

WORK IN PROGRESS: Poetry and fiction for children; poetry, fiction, and nonfiction for adults.

BIOGRAPHICAL/CRITICAL SOURCES: Newsweek, July 9, 1956; *Village Voice,* March 4, 1959; *Variety,* September 24, 1969; *Elementary English,* November-December, 1973, April, 1975.

*   *   *

BROWN, Bert R(obert) 1936-

PERSONAL: Born June 18, 1936, in New York, N.Y.; son of Alexander (a businessman) and Faye Brown; married Dorothy Slater, December 31, 1960; children: Joslin Anna. *Education:* Colgate University, B.A., 1958; Columbia University, M.A., 1963, Ph.D., 1967.

CAREER: Psychological Corp., New York City, research assistant, 1958-60; New York Medical College, New York City, instructor in psychiatry, 1960-64; New York University, New York City, instructor in psychology and research associate at Institute for Developmental Studies, 1964-67; Cornell University, Ithaca, N.Y., assistant professor of organizational behavior, beginning 1967. Instructor in educational psychology, Yeshiva University, 1963-64; fellow, National Training Laboratories; consultant to Social Science Research Council, National Science Foundation, U.S. Department of the Treasury, and U.S. Department of State. *Member:* American Association for the Advancement of Science, American Psychological Association, Society for the Psychological Study of Social Issues, Eastern Psychological Association.

WRITINGS: (Contributor) M. Deutsch, editor, *The Disadvantaged Child,* Basic Books, 1967; *The Assessment of Self-Concept among Four-Year-Old Negro and White Children: A Comparative Study Using the Brown IDS Self-Concept Reference Test,* Institute for Developmental Studies, New York University, 1967; *The Effects of Need to Maintain Face on Interpersonal Bargaining* (originally appeared in *Journal of Experimental Social Psychology*), New York State School of Industrial and Labor Relations, Cornell University, 1968; (with Jeffrey Rubin) *The Social Psychology of Bargaining and Negotiation,* Academic Press, 1973. Contributor to proceedings and to journals, including *Journal of Experimental Social Psychology, Psychology Today, Sociometry, Journal of Social Issues,* and *Psychiatric Research Reports.*†

* * *

BROWN, Carl F(raser) 1910-

PERSONAL: Born January 25, 1910, in McCall, S.C.; son of John Jackson (a minister) and Myrtie (Grady) Brown; married Ione M. (a teacher), May 23, 1929; children: Carl, Jr., Mac Henry, Roderick. *Education:* University of South Carolina, A.B., 1930, M.A., 1931; George Peabody College for Teachers, Ph.D., 1946. *Religion:* Presbyterian. *Office:* Department of Reading, School of Education, Peabody Hall, University of North Carolina, Chapel Hill, N.C. 27514.

CAREER: Lees Junior College, Jackson, Ky., instructor in English, 1931-33; school teacher and principal in Greenville, S.C., 1933-36; Winthrop College, Rock Hill, S.C., supervisor of laboratory school, 1939-41; Princess Anne College (now University of Maryland Eastern Shore), Princess Anne, Md., director of teacher education, 1946-47; Winthrop College, director of teacher education, 1947-49; University of Florida, Gainesville, director of elementary education, 1948-50; University of North Carolina at Chapel Hill, chairman of reading department, 1950—. Visiting professor, University of South Carolina, 1974. *Military service:* U.S. Naval Reserve, 1943-46; became lieutenant commander. *Member:* International Reading Association (regional chairman, 1952-54), National Education Association, Kappa Delta Pi, Phi Delta Kappa.

WRITINGS: (Editor) *Evaluating the Elementary School,* Southern Association of Colleges and Schools, 1964; (with Mabel O'Donnell) *Harper, Row Basic Spellers,* Books 1-6, Harper, 1965; (with Marion Hodes) *First Experiences with Vowels and Consonants,* Instructo, 1969; (with Hodes) *The Kingdom of Kibalakaboo,* Instructo, 1969; (with O'Donnell) *The Reading Road to Spelling,* Books 1-6, Harper, 1970; (with Hodes) *Second Experiences with Vowell and Consonants,* McGraw, 1972.†

* * *

BROWN, Charles T(homas) 1912-

PERSONAL: Born March 22, 1912, in Braddock, Pa.; son of Charles W. (a salesman) and Mabel (Losey) Brown; married Martha P. Clark (an auditor), September 19, 1936; children: Judith Brown Wright, Charles H. *Education:* Westminster College, B.B.A., 1934; University of Wisconsin, M.A., 1940, Ph.D., 1949. *Politics:* Democrat. *Religion:* Methodist. *Home:* 1828 Hillsdale, Kalamazoo, Mich. 49007. *Office:* Department of Communication Arts and Sciences, Western Michigan University, Kalamazoo, Mich. 49008.

CAREER: Florida Southern College, Lakeland, assistant professor, 1940-42, associate professor, 1942-44, professor of speech, 1946-47; Western Michigan University, Kalamazoo, professor of speech, 1948—. *Military service:* U.S. Naval Reserve, 1944-46; became lieutenant. *Member:* Speech Association of America.

WRITINGS: Introduction to Speech, Houghton, 1955; (with Charles Van Riper) *Speech and Man,* Prentice-Hall, 1966; (with Van Riper) *Communication and Human Relationships,* National Textbook Company, 1973; (with Paul W. Keller) *Monologue to Dialogue,* Prentice-Hall, 1973, 2nd edition, 1978. Contributor to *Quarterly Journal of Speech, Speech Monographs,* and other periodicals. Associate editor of *Journal of Communication,* 1967.

* * *

BROWN, Denise Scott 1931-
(Denise Scott Brown Venturi)

PERSONAL: Born October 3, 1931, in Nkana, Zambia; daughter of Simon (a businessman) and Phyllis (Hepker) Lakofski; married Robert Scott Brown, July 21, 1955 (died, 1959); married Robert Venturi (an architect), July 23, 1967; children: (second marriage) James C. *Education:* Attended University of the Witwatersrand, 1948-51; Architectural Association, London, England, A.A., 1952, and certificate in tropical architecture, 1955; University of Pennsylvania, M.C.P., 1960, M.Arch., 1965. *Politics:* Democrat. *Religion:* Jewish. *Residence:* Philadelphia, Pa. *Office:* Venturi & Rauch, Architects and Planners, 333 South 16th St., Philadelphia, Pa. 19102.

CAREER: University of Pennsylvania, Philadelphia, assistant professor of architecture and planning, 1960-65; Venturi & Rauch (architects and planners), Philadelphia, Pa., architect and planner, 1967—, partner, 1969—. Associate professor of architecture and planning, University of California, Berkeley and Los Angeles, 1965-68; visiting professor of architecture, Yale University, 1968-70. Has worked on various planning projects, and has exhibited planning projects in the Renwich Galley, Smithsonian Institute. *Member:* Architectural Association, Alliance of Women in Architecture, Royal Institute of British Architects, Architects' Registration Council (United Kingdom). *Awards, honors:* Honorary doctorate of Fine Arts, Oberlin College, 1977.

WRITINGS: (With Robert Venturi and Steven Izenour) *Learning from Las Vegas,* M.I.T. Press, 1972, revised, 1977. Contributor of articles and reviews to architecture and planning journals, including *Progressive Architecture, Architectural Forum, Architectural Design, Arts and Architecture, Journal of the American Institute of Planners, Architectural Record, Perspecta, Landscape, Oppositions, Casabella,* and *Werk.*

WORK IN PROGRESS: A planning project for Miami Beach, Fla., and Jim Thorpe, Pa.

BIOGRAPHICAL/CRITICAL SOURCES: Pennsylvania Gazette, December, 1971; *New Republic,* December 2, 1972; *Atlantic Monthly,* May, 1973; Susana Torre, *Women in American Architecture,* Whitney Library of Design, 1977.

* * *

BROWN, Donald Fowler 1909-

PERSONAL: Born May 31, 1909, in Brooklyn, N.Y.; son of Walter Everette (an engineer) and Harriet (Fowler) Brown; married Alice Emmert (a librarian), June 17, 1935; children: Timothy, Sara Lisbeth (Mrs. Frank Clevenger), Abigail,

Prudence (Mrs. Michael Jacobs), Anthony. *Education:* Wheaton College, Wheaton, Ill., A.B., 1932; University of Illinois, M.A., 1933, Ph.D., 1935. *Politics:* Democrat. *Religion:* Presbyterian. *Home:* 108 Wooded Lane, Villanova, Pa. 19085. *Office:* Department of Modern Languages, Villanova University, Villanova, Pa. 19085.

CAREER: McPherson College, McPherson, Kan., professor of French and German, 1935-36; Missouri Valley College, Marshall, Mo., professor of French and German, 1936-38; U.S. Naval Academy, Annapolis, Md., instructor in French and Spanish, 1938-41; Oberlin College, Oberlin, Ohio, instructor in Spanish, 1942-44; MacMurray College for Women (now MacMurray College), Jacksonville, Ill., professor of Spanish, 1944-46; Johns Hopkins University, Baltimore, Md., assistant professor of Spanish, 1946-49; Hope College, Holland, Mich., professor of Spanish, 1949-61; Villanova University, Villanova, Pa., professor of Spanish, 1961—. Visiting professor, University of Delaware, 1970-71. *Member:* Modern Language Association of America, American Association of Teachers of Spanish and Portuguese, Northeast Modern Language Association, Phi Beta Kappa.

WRITINGS: (Translator) Carlos Monge, *Acclimatization in the Andes,* Johns Hopkins Press, 1948; *The Catholic Naturalism of Pardo Bazan,* University of North Carolina Press, 1957, 2nd edition, 1971. Contributor of articles and reviews to *New Catholic Encyclopedia, Romanic Review, Modern Language Notes, Hispanic Review, Hispania, Modern Language Quarterly,* and *Modern Language Journal.*

SIDELIGHTS: Donald Fowler Brown told *CA:* "I have been especially interested in the spread of Emile Zola's literary school of Naturalism to Spain and Latin America. I have traveled and studied abroad extensively, having had eleven summers in Europe and eleven in Mexico. In 1941-42 I was on a year of travel and study in South America, concentrating especially on Brazil and Chile."†

*   *   *

BROWN, Donald Robert   1925-

PERSONAL: Born March 5, 1925, in Albany, N.Y.; son of Julius Edward (a businessman) and Natile (Rosenberg) Brown; married June E. Gole (an information retrieval researcher), August 14, 1945; children: Peter Douglas, Thomas Matthew, Jacob Noah. *Education:* Harvard University, A.B., 1948; University of California, Berkeley, M.A. and Ph.D., 1951. *Home:* 2511 Hawthorn Dr., Ann Arbor, Mich. 48104. *Office:* 109 East Madison, Ann Arbor, Mich. 48104.

CAREER: Worcester Foundation for Experimental Biology and Worcester State Hospital, Worcester, Mass., research psychologist, 1948; Bryn Mawr College, Bryn Mawr, Pa., assistant professor, 1951-57, associate professor of psychology, 1957-64; University of Michigan, Ann Arbor, professor of psychology and senior research scientist at Center for Research on Learning and Teaching, 1964—, fellow of Residential College. Research associate, Mary Conover Mellon Foundation, Vassar College, 1952-55; senior staff engineer, Laboratories for Research and Development, Franklin Institute, 1955-57; fellow, Center for Advanced Study in the Behavioral Sciences, Stanford, Calif., 1960-61; honorary research fellow, University College, University of London, 1970-71. Visiting professor at Swarthmore College, 1955-57, 1960-62, University of California, Berkeley, summer, 1961, University of Pennsylvania, spring, 1964. Member of Dan-

forth Conferences on liberal arts, summers, 1962, 1965, 1966, 1967; member of Three College India Seminar, 1962-63. Institute for Services to Education, Inc., member of board of directors, 1966—. Consultant to Peace Corps, 1964-71. *Military service:* U.S. Army, 1943-46; served in Europe.

MEMBER: American Psychological Association (fellow; member of council, 1967-70), Society for the Study of Social Issues (fellow), American Association for the Advancement of Science, American Association of University Professors (past president of Bryn Mawr chapter), Sigma Xi (past president of Bryn Mawr chapter), Psi Chi.

WRITINGS: (Contributor) R. N. Sanford, editor, *The American College,* Wiley, 1962; (editor) *The Role and Status of Women in the Soviet Union,* Teachers College Press, 1968; (contributor) Lawrence C. Grebstein, editor, *Toward Self Understanding,* Scott, Foresman, 1969; (contributor) E. E. Sampson and H. A. Korn, editors, *Student Activism and Protest,* Jossey-Bass, 1970; (contributor) Jerry Gaff, editor, *The Cluster College,* Jossey-Bass, 1970; (contributor) Clifton D. Bryant, editor, *Social Problems Today,* Lippincott, 1971; (contributor) Paul L. Dressel, editor, *The New Colleges: Toward an Appraisal* (monograph), American College Testing Program and American Association for Higher Education, 1971. Contributor to yearbooks. Also contributor of articles and reviews to professional journals, including *Journal of Social Issues, Contemporary Psychology, American Psychology, Journal of Personality,* and *Educational Record.* Member of editorial board, *Journal of Abnormal and Social Psychology,* 1961-64, and *Journal of Personality and Social Psychology,* 1964-67.

*   *   *

BROWN, F(rancis) Andrew   1915-

PERSONAL: Born August 19, 1915, in Lewiston, N.Y.; son of Frank Berne and Libbie (Deering) Brown; married Mary Killian, October 4, 1941; children: Steven Hamilton, Terence Killian. *Education:* Hamilton College, B.S., 1937; Cornell University, M.A., 1938; University of California, Los Angeles, Ph.D., 1947. *Home:* 1322 West St., Grinnell, Iowa 50112. *Office:* Department of German, Grinnell College, Grinnell, Iowa 50112.

CAREER: University of Michigan, Ann Arbor, 1946-48, began as lecturer, became instructor in German; University of California, Los Angeles, instructor in German, 1948-49; University of Michigan, assistant professor of German, 1949-55; Grinnell College, Grinnell, Iowa, associate professor, 1955-61, professor of German and chairman of department, 1961—. Member of national advisory screening committee for Germanic languages and literatures, Fulbright-Hays awards, 1962-67. National Endowment for the Humanities, consultant, 1974, member of screening panel, 1975. *Military service:* U.S. Navy, 1942-45; served in Pacific and European theaters; became lieutenant. *Member:* Modern Language Association of America, American Association of Teachers of German, Lessing Society. *Awards, honors:* Fulbright-Hays senior award for research in Germany, 1959-60; American Philosophical Society research grant, 1959-60; National Endowment for the Humanities research award in Germany and Austria, 1972-73.

WRITINGS: On Education: John Locke, Christian Wolff, and the "Moral Weeklies", Publications in Modern Philology, University of California, 1952; *Gotthold Ephraim Lessing,* Twayne, 1971. Contributor to yearbooks and to *Encyclopedia of World Biography.* Contributor of about twenty-five articles to academic journals, including *Germanic Re-*

view, Modern Language Quarterly, Journal of English and Germanic Philology, and *Review of Religion.*

WORK IN PROGRESS: Studies in G. E. Lessing's dramatic theory and practice, completion expected in 1980; research on German popular journals as mediators of English literature, 1982.

* * *

BROWN, Francis R(obert) 1914-

PERSONAL: Born December 19, 1914, in Fairbury, Ill.; son of Edwin Henry (a farmer) and Annie (Besgrove) Brown; married Helen Tucker, August 22, 1940; children: Robert Alan, David Lee, Bruce William, Mark Leslie. *Education:* Illinois State University, B.E., 1937; Columbia University, M.A., 1940; University of Illinois, Ed.D., 1954. *Religion:* Disciples of Christ. *Home:* 601 Normal Ave., Normal, Ill. 61761. *Office:* Division of Continuing Education and Public Service, Illinois State University Normal, Ill. 61761.

CAREER: High school mathematics teacher in Decatur, Ill., 1937-42; U.S. Army Air Forces, Chanute Field, Rantoul, Ill., civilian instructor in airplane mechanics and administrator, 1942-43; Millikin University, Decatur, instructor, 1946-47, assistant professor of mathematics, 1947-49; Illinois State University, Normal, instructor, 1949-51, assistant professor, 1951-55, associate professor, 1955-58, professor of mathematics, 1958—, director of Division of University Extension and Field Services, 1958—, director of Division of Continuing Education and Public Service, 1972—. Member of McLean County Regional Planning Board, 1970—, and Illinois Law and Justice Policy Committee, 1970—. Consultant to Scott, Foresman & Co. *Military service:* U.S. Army Air Forces, 1943-46; became staff sergeant.

MEMBER: Mathematical Association of America, National Council of Teachers of Mathematics, National Education Association, Adult Education Association of the U.S.A. (president, 1962-63; director, 1963-66), National University Extension Association, Association of Field Services for Teacher Education (president, 1964-65), Associated Organization for Teacher Education (chairman, 1969-70), American Association of Colleges for Teacher Education (member of executive board, 1968-70), Illinois Council of Teachers of Mathematics (president, 1961-62), Illinois Adult Education Association (president, 1962-63), Phi Delta Kappa, Kappa Phi Kappa, Phi Kappa Phi, Kappa Mu Epsilon, Kappa Delta Pi, Kiwanis (director, 1973-75).

WRITINGS: (With Gussie Phillips and Frances Hewett) *Number and Operation,* Illinois Office of the Superintendent of Public Institutions, 1962; (editor with Vernon C. Pohlmann and Kenneth K. Marcus) *Intergovernmental Cooperation: A Report on Two Conferences,* Adjacent Municipalities Institute, Illinois State University, 1967; (with Charles H. D'Augustine, James W. Heddens, and Charles F. Howard) *New Dimensions in Mathematics,* Grades 1 to 6, Harper, 1970; (with Anthony J. Pettofrezze, Heddens, Donald W. Hight, Howard, and James Rollins) *Mathematics Course 1,* Grade 7, Harper, 1973; *Mathematics Course 2,* Grade 8, Harper, 1973. Contributor to *Illinois Journal of Education, Teacher Education, Mathematics Teacher, Arithmetic Teacher,* and other professional journals. Member of editorial committee, *Illinois Quarterly;* member of committee for reviewing manuscripts, *Mathematics Teacher.*

WORK IN PROGRESS: Updating materials for mathematics teaching.

AVOCATIONAL INTERESTS: Sports (timer and scorer for football and basketball games), travel (Europe, India, China).†

* * *

BROWN, James Wilson 1913-

PERSONAL: Born September 18, 1913, in Hanford, Wash.; son of Harrison (a farmer) and Sophia Estelle (Tuttle) Brown; married Winifred Louise Weersing, December 31, 1940; children: Martha Lee, Pamela Jean, Gregory James. *Education:* Attended University of Washington, Seattle, 1931-32; Central Washington State College (now Central Washington University), B.A., 1937; University of Chicago, M.A., 1939, Ph.D., 1947. *Home:* 1678 Sweetbriar Dr., San Jose, Calif. 95125. *Office:* School of Education, San Jose State University, San Jose, Calif. 95114.

CAREER: Marine radio operator, 1930-31; social science teacher in Wapato and Ellensburg, Wash., 1935-39; Virginia State Department of Education, Richmond, state supervisor of teaching materials, 1941-42, 1946-47; Syracuse University, Syracuse, N.Y., assistant professor of education, 1947-48; University of Washington, Seattle, director of university film center, 1948-53; San Jose State University, San Jose, Calif., associate professor, 1953-54, professor of education, 1954—, dean of graduate studies and research, 1954-72. Information specialist, Marshall Plan, U.S. Department of State, 1951-52; director, Educational Media Institute Evaluation Project, 1965-68. Director, Fruitland Grove, Inc. *Military service:* U.S. Naval Reserve, active duty, 1942-45; became lieutenant commander. *Member:* Association for Educational Communications and Technology (past president), California Media and Library Education Association, California State Employees Association, Phi Delta Kappa, Phi Kappa Phi.

WRITINGS: *Virginia Plan for Audio-Visual Education,* University of Chicago, 1947; (with Richard B. Lewis) *AV Instructional Materials Manual,* Spartan Shops, 1956, 5th edition, McGraw, 1977; (with Lewis and Fred F. Harcleroad) *AV Instruction: Media and Methods,* McGraw, 1959, 5th edition published as *AV Instruction: Technology, Media, and Methods,* 1977; (with James W. Thornton, Jr.) *College Teaching: Perspectives and Guidelines,* McGraw, 1963, 2nd edition, 1971; (with Kenneth D. Norberg) *Administering Educational Media,* McGraw, 1965, 2nd edition (with Norberg and Sara K. Srygley), 1972; (with Thornton) *Going to College in California,* Fearon, 1965; (with Thornton) *New Media and College Teaching,* Association for Educational Communication and Technology, 1968; (editor) *Nonprint Media Information Networking: Status and Potentials,* ERIC Clearinghouse on Information Resources, 1976; *New Media in Public Libraries,* Jeffrey Norton, 1976; (with others) *ERIC: What It Can Do for You, How to Use It,* ERIC Clearinghouse on Information Resources, 1976. Also editor of *Educational Media Yearbook,* published annually by Bowker, 1973—. Contributor to professional journals. Member of editorial advisory board, *Educational Screen.*

AVOCATIONAL INTERESTS: Photography, travel (to Europe, South America, Middle East, Canada, and the Caribbean).

* * *

BROWN, Judith M(argaret) 1944-

PERSONAL: Born July 9, 1944, in India; daughter of Wilfred George (a parson) and Joan Margaret (Adams)

Brown. *Education:* Girton College, Cambridge, M.A. (honors), 1965, Ph.D., 1968. *Residence:* Cheshire, England. *Office:* Department of History, University of Manchester, Manchester M13 9PL, England.

CAREER: Cambridge University, Girton College, Cambridge, England, research fellow, official fellow in history, and director of studies in history, 1968-71; University of Manchester, Manchester, England, lecturer in history, 1971—. *Member:* Royal Historical Society (fellow).

WRITINGS: Gandhi's Rise to Power: Indian Politics, 1918-1922, Cambridge University Press, 1972; (contributor) M. R. D. Foot, editor, *War and Society: Historical Essays in Honour of J. R. Western, 1928-1971,* Elek, 1973; (contributor) W. H. Morris-Jones, editor, *The Making of Politicians: Studies from Africa and Asia,* Athlone, 1976; *Gandhi and Civil Disobedience: The Mahatma in Indian Politics, 1928-1934,* Cambridge University Press, 1977; (contributor) B. N. Pandey, editor, *Leadership in South Asia,* Vikas (New Delhi), 1977; (contributor) D. A. Low, editor, *Congress and the Raj,* [New Delhi], 1978.

WORK IN PROGRESS: Contemporary Hinduism; a textbook on modern India for first and second year university students, to be published by Oxford University Press.

*   *   *

BROWN, Lyle C(larence)   1926-

PERSONAL: Born August 7, 1926, in Hume, N.Y.; son of Forrest John (a farmer) and Laura (Hoagland) Brown; married Sylvia Sills, May 28, 1949; children: Alita, Gloria, Paul. *Education:* Attended Louisiana Technological University, 1944-45; University of Oklahoma, B.A., 1948, M.A., 1952; Instituto Tecnologico de Monterrey, graduate study, 1952; University of Texas at Austin, Ph.D., 1964. *Religion:* Baptist. *Home:* Route 2, Box 97, Waco, Tex. 76710. *Office:* Department of Political Science, Baylor University, Waco, Tex. 76703.

CAREER: University of the Americas, Mexico City, Mexico, instructor in history and political science, 1956-58; Texas College of Arts and Industries (now Texas A&I University), Kingsville, assistant professor of government, 1958-62; Wayland Baptist College, Plainview, Tex., assistant professor of history and political science, 1962-63; Baylor University, Waco, Tex., assistant professor, 1963-65, associate professor, 1965-68, professor of political science, 1968—, director of graduate studies and co-director of Master of International Management Program. *Military service:* U.S. Naval Reserve, 1943-72; became commander. *Member:* American Political Science Association, Latin American Studies Association, Southern Political Science Association, Southwestern Social Science Association, Southwestern Council on Latin American Studies (vice-president, 1972-73; president, 1973-74). *Awards, honors:* Winner of annual Walter Prescott Webb Essay Contest, University of Texas at Arlington, 1978.

WRITINGS: (Contributor) James W. Wilkie and Albert L. Michaels, editors, *Revolution in Mexico: Years of Upheaval, 1910-1940,* Knopf, 1969; (editor with Eugene W. Jones, Joe C. Ericson, and Robert S. Trotter, Jr.) *Practicing Texas Politics,* Houghton, 1971, 3rd edition, 1977; (contributor) John Braeman, Robert H. Bremner, and David Brody, editors, *Twentieth-Century American Foreign Policy,* Ohio State University Press, 1971; (contributor) Richard E. Greenleaf and Michael C. Meyer, editors, *Research in Mexican History: Topics, Methodology, and a Practical Guide to Field Research,* University of Nebraska Press, 1973;

(contributor) Wilkie, Meyer, and Edna Monzon de Wilkie, editors, *Contemporary Mexico,* University of California Press, 1976; *Study Guide: Practicing Texas Politics,* Houghton, 1977; (contributor) George Wolfskill and Douglas W. Richmond, editors, *The Mexican Revolution,* University of Texas Press, 1979. Contributor to *Antologia MCC,* Mexico City College Press, 1956. Contributor to journals, including *Journal of Church and State, Revista de la Universidad de Mexico,* and *Social Studies.*

WORK IN PROGRESS: Editing, with William F. Cooper, *Religion in Latin American Life and Literature,* for Baylor University Press; 2nd edition of *Study Guide: Practicing Texas Politics;* 4th edition of *Practicing Texas Politics,* with Jones, Ericson, and Trotter.

SIDELIGHTS: Lyle C. Brown told *CA:* "My writing is directly related to a variety of courses that I teach. Unhappily, I must confess that writing is not a labor of love. Usually I write because an editor has requested a contribution, or because there is money involved and I am greedy for a royalty check. Writing is the hardest of work, even cruel and unusual punishment that I bring upon myself; but my natural inclination tempts me to read, or to hunt and fish, or to devote more time to my garden and my pecan grove."

AVOCATIONAL INTERESTS: Pecan culture.

*   *   *

BROWN, Marcia   1918-

PERSONAL: Born July 13, 1918, in Rochester, N.Y.; daughter of Clarence Edward (a minister) and Adelaide Elizabeth (Zimber) Brown. *Education:* Studied at Woodstock School of Painting, summers, 1938-39; New York College for Teachers (now State University of New York at Albany), B.A., 1940; also studied at New School for Social Research, Art Students League (New York, N.Y.), and Columbia University. *Address:* P.O. Box 113, West Redding, Conn. 06896.

CAREER: Artist and author of children's books; high school English and drama teacher in Cornwall, N.Y., 1940-43; New York Public Library, New York, N.Y., library assistant for rare book collection, 1943-48; University College of the West Indies, Jamaica, British West Indies, teacher of puppetry, 1953. Woodcuts have been exhibited at Brooklyn Museum, Peridot Gallery, Hacker Gallery, Library of Congress, Carnegie Institute, and Philadelphia Print Club. Work is part of permanent collections at Library of Congress, New York Public Library, and numerous private collections.

MEMBER: International Institute of Arts and Letters (life fellow), Print Council of America, Authors League, Authors Guild, Art Students League (life member), Metropolitan Museum of Art. *Awards, honors:* Caldecott Medal for most distinguished American picture book, Children's Services Division of American Library Association, 1955, for *Cinderella,* and 1962, for *Once a Mouse;* American nominee for Andersen Award for Illustration, 1966, 1975; honor book award of Book World Spring Book Festival, 1969, for *How, Hippo!;* Distinguished Service to Children's Literature Award, University of Southern Mississippi, 1972.

WRITINGS—All self-illustrated children's books; published by Scribner, except as indicated: *The Little Carousel,* 1946; *Stone Soup,* 1947; *Henry-Fisherman,* 1949; *Dick Whittington and His Cat* (an adaptation), 1950; *Skipper John's Cook,* 1951; *The Flying Carpet* (an adaptation), 1956; *Felice,* 1958; *Peter Piper's Alphabet* (an adaptation), 1959; *Tamarindo!,* 1960; *Once a Mouse* (an adaptation), 1961;

Backbone of the King, 1966; *The Neighbors,* 1967; *How, Hippo!,* 1969; *The Bun* (an adaptation), Harcourt, 1972; *All Butterflies: An ABC,* 1974; *The Blue Jackal,* 1977.

Translator and illustrator: Charles Perrault, *Puss in Boots,* 1952; Perrault, *Cinderella,* 1954.

Illustrator: Virginia Watson, *The Trail of Courage,* 1948; Hans Christian Andersen, *The Steadfast Tin Soldier,* translation by M. R. James, 1953; Philip Sherlock, *Anansi,* Crowell, 1954; Peter C. Asbjoernsen and J. E. Moe, *The Three Billy Goats Gruff,* Harcourt, 1957; Andersen, *The Wild Swans,* translation by James, 1963; Theophile Gautier, *Giselle,* translation by Violette Verdy, McGraw, 1970; Andersen, *The Snow Queen,* Scribner, 1972. Also author of filmstrip, ''The Crystal Cavern,'' Lyceum Productions, 1974.

AVOCATIONAL INTERESTS: Music, ballet, reading, travel (Mexico, Virgin Islands, Europe, Near and Middle East, Denmark, Far East, Soviet Union).

BIOGRAPHICAL/CRITICAL SOURCES: Young Wings, February, 1948; *American Artist,* January, 1963; Diana Klemin, *The Art of Art for Children's Books,* Clarkson Potter, 1966; *Young Readers' Review,* November, 1966; *National Observer,* May 27, 1968; Lee Bennett Hopkins, *Books Are by People,* Citation, 1969; *Times Literary Supplement,* April 16, 1970; *Christian Science Monitor,* May 1, 1974.†

*　　*　　*

BROWN, Maurice F(red)   1928-

PERSONAL: Born February 1, 1928, in Geneva, Ill.; son of Maurice F. (a lumberman) and Valeria (a pianist; maiden name, Hill) Brown; married Judith Kredel (a college professor), January, 1957; children: Frederick, Mathilde. *Education:* Lawrence College (now University), B.A., 1949; Harvard University, M.A., 1950, Ph.D., 1958. *Politics:* ''Conservative Thoreauvian Anarchist.'' *Religion:* Christian. *Office:* Department of English, Oakland University, Rochester, Mich. 48063.

CAREER: Lawrence College (now University), Appleton, Wis., instructor in English, 1953-55; Harvard University, Cambridge, Mass., tutor in English, 1955-58; Colby College, Waterville, Me., assistant professor of English, 1958-61; Oakland University, Rochester, Mich., 1961—, began as associate professor, currently professor of English. *Military service:* U.S. Marine Corps, 1951-53, served as combat correspondent; became staff sergeant. *Member:* American Association of University Professors, American Studies Association, Modern Language Association of America, Emerson Society, Michigan Academy, Michigan Historical Society, Phi Beta Kappa.

WRITINGS: Estranging Dawn: The Life and Works of William Vaughn Moody, Southern Illinois University Press, 1973. Contributor to *New England Quarterly, Bulletin of Bibliography, American Literary Realism,* and *Emerson Society Quarterly.*

WORK IN PROGRESS: Research on the American transcendentalists, the theory of biography, American poetry since 1950, and the American 1890's.

*　　*　　*

BROWN, Re Mona   1917-

PERSONAL: Born October 31, 1917, in Menomonie, Wis.; daughter of Herman Robert and Mollie (Brunn) Brown. *Education:* Superior State University, B.E., 1941. *Religion:* Presbyterian. *Home:* 1020 Green Valley Dr., Waukesha, Wis. 53186.

CAREER: Kindergarten teacher in Goodman and Antigo, Wis., 1941-45, in Waukesha, Wis., 1945-65, in San Diego, Calif., 1965-66, and in Waukesha, 1966—. Kindergarten critic teacher at Whitewater State University (now University of Wisconsin—Whitewater), Whitewater, Wis., 1948. *Member:* National Education Association, Tri-Wauk and Waukesha Teachers Association, Delta Kappa Gamma.

WRITINGS—All published by Denison: *Kindergarten Calendar,* 1970; *Kindergarten Bulletin Board Ideas,* 1971; *Third Grade Bulletin Board Ideas,* 1973; *The Three R's in the Kindergarten Calendar,* 1974; *Projects and Ideas for the Kindergarten Calendar,* 1978.

*　　*　　*

BROWN, T(illman) Merritt   1913-

PERSONAL: Born October 22, 1913, in Windsor, Ontario, Canada; son of George W. (a railroad yard conductor) and Alice (Merritt) Brown; married Elizabeth Jean DeWaard, May 30, 1942; children: Garry, Ronald, David. *Education:* University of Western Ontario, B.A., 1934; University of Toronto, M.A., 1947; Australian National University, Ph.D., 1958.

CAREER: Department of trade and Commerce, Ottawa, Ontario, head of econometrics and development research, 1947-59; Royal Military College of Canada, Kingston, Ontario, professor of economics, 1959-62; Queen's University, Kingston, professor of economics, 1962-67; University of Western Ontario, London, professor of economics, beginning 1967. Economist on analysis of growth potential, Royal Commission on Health Services, 1962-64. *Military service:* Royal Canadian Air Force, navigation instructor, 1941-45; became flight lieutenant. *Member:* American Economic Association, Canadian Economics Association, Econometric Society (fellow).

WRITINGS: (Contributor) John W. Kendrick, editor, *Studies in Income and Wealth,* Princeton University Press, 1964; *Canadian Economic Growth,* Queen's Printer, 1965; *Specification and Uses of Econometric Models,* St. Martin's, 1970; (contributor) John F. Chant, editor, *Canadian Perspectives in Economics,* Collier-Macmillan, 1973. Contributor to *International Economic Review* and *Econometrica.* Associate editor, *International Economic Review,* 1960-68.

WORK IN PROGRESS: A textbook on macroeconomic theory and policy; research on the efficacy of various econometric methods using ''Monte Carlo'' techniques.†

*　　*　　*

BRUNDAGE, Burr Cartwright   1912-

PERSONAL: Born December 15, 1912, in Buffalo, N.Y. *Education:* Amherst College, A.B. (with honors), 1936; University of Chicago, Ph.D., 1939. *Home:* 4411 Cortez Way S., St. Petersburg, Fla. *Office:* Department of History, Eckerd College, St. Petersburg, Fla. 33733.

CAREER: MacMurray College, Jacksonville, Ill., instructor in history, 1939-41; Office of Coordinator of Inter-American Affairs, Washington, D.C., area officer, 1941-42; Carleton College, Northfield, Minn., assistant professor, 1942-43; Department of State, Washington, D.C., political desk officer for Chile, 1943-47; Cedar Crest College, Allentown, Pa., professor of history, and head of department, 1947-61; Eckerd College, St. Petersburg, Fla., professor of history, 1961-78, professor emeritus, 1978—. *Awards, honors:* Three research grants for travel to Peru and Mexico from the Board of Higher Education, Presbyterian Church; Six grants for pre-Columbian research from the Research Committee of Florida Presbyterian College; American Philosophical Society research grant for the study in Mexico of Aztec religion.

WRITINGS: *The Juniper Palace* (poems), A. B. Bookman, 1951, revised edition, with introduction by Giles Gunn, Valkyrie Press, 1976; *The Empire of the Inca,* University of Oklahoma Press, 1963; *Lords of Cuzco,* University of Oklahoma Press, 1963; *A Rain of Darts: The Mexican Aztecs,* University of Texas Press, 1972; *No Chance Encounter* (poems), Valkyrie Press, 1974; *Two Earths, Two Heavens,* University of New Mexico Press, 1975; *The Fifth Sun: Aztec Worlds, Aztec Gods,* University of Texas Press, 1979. Contributor to *Christian Scholar, History, Historian, American Historical Review,* and *Journal of Near Eastern Studies.*

WORK IN PROGRESS: A detailed study of the Aztec god Quetzalcoath and his many avatars.

SIDELIGHTS: Burr Cartwright Brundage speaks French and Spanish, and has a reading knowledge of Italian, German, Latin, Egyptian Hieroglyphic (Old, Middle and New Kingdoms), Demotic, Hebrew, Coptic, Quechua and Nahuatl.

* * *

BRUNO, James Edward   1940-
(Eldon Sumner)

PERSONAL: Born December 12, 1940, in Brooklyn, N.Y.; son of John (a lithographer) and Madeline (Nardi) Bruno. *Education:* University of California, Los Angeles, B.A., 1963, M.A., 1965, Ph.D., 1967. *Politics:* Independent. *Religion:* Roman Catholic. *Office:* Department of Education, University of California, Los Angeles, Calif. 90024.

CAREER: Teacher of mathematics and chemistry at schools for girls, 1963-68; University of California, Los Angeles, assistant professor, 1968-73, associate professor of education, 1973—. Operations research engineer, Rome Cable Corp., summer, 1964. Participant, Latin American Study Center, Venezuela, 1973. Consultant to RAND Corp., 1967—, to Institute for Government and Public Affairs, 1969-70, and to Southwest Educational Research Laboratory, 1970. *Member:* Operations Research Society of America, American Educational Research Association.

WRITINGS: (Editor) *Emerging Issues in Education: Policy Implications for the Schools,* Heath, 1972; (with Marvin A. Nottingham) *Collegial Teams: Educational Innovation for the Future,* Lexington Books, 1976; *Educational Policy Analysis: A Quantitative Approach,* Crane, Russak, 1976. Also author of monographs on management techniques in school administration; contributor to symposia, seminars, and transactions. Author of a column on graphology for a Los Angeles newspaper, under pseudonym Eldon Sumner. Contributor to academic journals, including *Education and Urban Society, National Tax Journal, Management Science, Journal of Operations Research,* and *Journal of Socio-Economic Planning Sciences.*

WORK IN PROGRESS: *Quantitative Methodologies for Eduational Planning: Operations Research in the Preparation of Educational Administrators; The Binary Race,* a science fiction novel; studying non-linear relationships affecting school district outputs; research on use of log transformation functions as alternatives to fixed-choice responses in standardized test taking.

AVOCATIONAL INTERESTS: Skiing and swimming (has taught courses), travel (South Seas, South America, Mexico, Europe, Eurasia), scouting.†

* * *

BRUNTON, David W(alter)   1929-

PERSONAL: Born November 9, 1929, in Oak Park, Ill.; son of Walter (an investment broker) and Ethyl (Williams) Brunton; married Marilyn Halbe (a children's librarian), June 25, 1950 (divorced, 1974); children: Jane, Ruth (deceased, 1978), Tom. *Education:* Ripon College, B.A., 1954; University of Illinois, M.S., 1955; University of Santa Clara, additional study, 1967, 1968. *Home address:* P.O. Box 184, Englewood, Colo. 80151. *Office:* Englewood Public Library, Englewood, Colo. 80110.

CAREER: Has worked as surveyor's assistant, stock controller, and receiving foreman in cannery; Retail Credit Co., Evanston, Ill., special investigator, 1954-55; University of Illinois, Newspaper Library, Champaign-Urbana, assistant, 1954-55; *Our Wonderful World* (children's encyclopedia), researcher, 1955-56; Earlham College, Richmond, Ind., catalog librarian, 1956-57, assistant librarian, 1957-60; Elmhurst College, Elmhurst, Ill., head librarian, 1960-61; Nevada State Library, Carson City, director, Cooperative Processing Center, 1961-62, law and documents librarian, 1962-63, director, Technical Processes Division, 1962-63; California Library Association, Berkeley, executive director, 1964-69; University of California, Irvine, staff development officer, 1969-70; Longmont Public Library, Longmont, Colo., assistant city librarian, 1970-73; Douglas County (Colo.) Library, director, 1973-74; Englewood Public Library, Englewood, Colo., assistant to the director, 1974—. Executive director of National Library Week in Nevada, 1962; trustee, National Freedom Fund for Librarians, 1969-71. *Military service:* U.S. Army, 1946-48. U.S. Air Force, 1948-49. U.S. Army Reserve, 1950-61; became first lieutenant. *Member:* American Library Association (secretary of Personnel Administration Section, 1973-74; chairman of Intellectual Freedom Round Table, 1975), American Association for State and Local History, Nevada Library Association, Colorado Library Association, Georgetown Society. *Awards, honors:* Citation from California Library Association, 1969.

WRITINGS: *Index to the Contemporary Scene,* Gale, Volume I, 1973, Volume II, 1975. Contributor of reviews to *American Reference Books Annual;* contributor to *Encyclopedia of Library and Information Science;* contributor of articles to library journals. Member of publications committee, American Society of Association Executives, 1966.

* * *

BRY, Gerhard   1911-

PERSONAL: Surname is pronounced "Bree"; born June 29, 1911, in Berlin, Germany; son of Egon Isaac (a pharmacist) and Olga (Kamnitzer) Bry; married Thea Hackelberg (a psychologist), December 29, 1939; children: Peter, Ava. *Education:* Attended University of Heidelberg and University of Berlin, 1930-32; Columbia University, Ph.D., 1955. *Religion:* Jewish. *Home:* Shady Glen, West Orange, N.J. 07052. *Office:* Department of Economics, Pace University, One Pace Plaza, New York, N.Y. 10038.

CAREER: Consulting economist in private practice, New York City, 1949—. National Bureau of Economic Research, New York City, staff economist, 1940-44, 1952-67; Brooklyn College (now Brooklyn College of the City University of

New York), Brooklyn, N.Y., instructor in economics, 1943-45; Econometric Institute, Inc., New York City, department head, 1945-48; Conmar Products Corp., Newark, N.J., director of market research, 1953-55; Rutgers University, Newark, N.J., lecturer, 1955-58, associate professor of economics, 1958-61; New York University, New York City, professor of economics, 1961-76; Pace University, New York City, adjunct professor of economics, 1976—. Consultant to Economic Policy Council of New Jersey, 1967-70. *Member:* Economic History Association, American Economic Association, American Statistical Association, Regional Science Association.

WRITINGS: The Average Workweek As an Economic Indicator, National Bureau of Economic Research, 1959; *Wages in Germany: 1871-1945,* Princeton University Press, 1960; (with Charlotte Boschan) *Cyclical Analysis of Time Series,* National Bureau of Economic Research, 1971. Author of monographs and articles. Editor of and contributor to *Annual Reports of New Jersey Economic Policy Council,* 1968-70.

WORK IN PROGRESS: Methods of Forecasting; Resistance: Recollections from the Nazi Years, a historical autobiography.

* * *

BRYANT, Shasta M(onroe) 1924-

PERSONAL: Born July 12, 1924, in Mt. Airy, N.C.; married, 1946; children: two boys. *Education:* University of North Carolina, A.B., 1950, M.A., 1956, Ph.D., 1958. *Home:* 2141 Royall Dr., Winston-Salem, N.C. 27106. *Office:* Department of Foreign Languages, Wake Forest University, Winston-Salem, N.C. 27109.

CAREER: University of Miami, Coral Gables, Fla., assistant professor, 1958-64, associate professor of Spanish, 1964-66; Wake Forest University, Winston-Salem, N.C., associate professor, 1966-75, professor of Spanish, 1975—. Resident director, Associated Mid-Florida Colleges "year abroad program in Spain," 1970-71. *Military service:* U.S. Army Air Forces, pilot, 1942-46; served in Pacific theater. U.S. Air Force, assistant professor of air sciences at North Texas State College and University of Miami, 1951-55. U.S. Air Force Reserve, 1955-68; retired as lieutenant colonel.

MEMBER: Modern Language Association of America, American Association of Teachers of Spanish and Portuguese (vice-president of Florida chapter, 1959-61), American Association of University Professors, South Atlantic Modern Language Association, Southeastern Conference on Latin American Studies, Phi Beta Kappa, Phi Delta Kappa, Sigma Delta Pi. *Awards, honors:* Fulbright fellowship, Spain, 1964.

WRITINGS: (Editor with J. Riis Owre) Carlos Loveira y Chirino, *Generales y doctores,* Oxford University Press, 1965; *A Selective Bibliography of Bibliographies of Hispanic American Literature,* Pan American Union, 1966, 2nd revised and enlarged edition, University of Texas at Austin, 1976; (contributor) Balkrishna Gokhale, editor, *Images of India: Asian Studies Two,* Popular Prakashan (Bombay), 1971; *The Spanish Ballad in English,* University Press of Kentucky, 1973. Contributor of articles and reviews to language journals, including *Hispania, Modern Language Journal,* and *South Atlantic Bulletin.* Associate editor of *South Atlantic Bulletin,* 1971-78.

WORK IN PROGRESS: A scholarly edition of Gines Perez de Hita's *Las guerras civiles de Granada.*

SIDELIGHTS: Shasta M. Bryant has worked as a commercial pilot and civilian flight instructor. He has traveled in Europe, the Far East, the Caribbean, Latin America, and the Pacific Islands.

* * *

BUCCELLATI, Giorgio 1937-

PERSONAL: Born February 8, 1937, in Milano, Italy; son of Mario and Maria (Rodolfi) Buccellati; married Marilyn Kelly, April 11, 1966. *Education:* Catholic University, Milan, Italy, Ph.D., 1958; Fordham University, M.A., 1960; University of Chicago, Ph.D., 1965. *Home:* 6760 Dome Dr., Malibu, Calif. 90265. *Office:* Departments of Near Eastern Languages and History, University of California, 405 Hilgard Ave., Los Angeles, Calif. 90024.

CAREER: Loyola University of Chicago, Chicago, Ill., assistant professor of history, 1963-65; University of California, Los Angeles, associate professor of history and near Eastern languages, 1968-74, professor of history and ancient near Eastern languages, 1974—, chairman of graduate archaeology program, 1970-73, director of Institute of Archaeology, 1973—. Director, Joint American Expedition to Terqa, Syria, 1976, 1977, 1978.

WRITINGS: The Amorites of the Ur III Period, Oriental Institute (Naples), 1966; *Cities and Nations of Ancient Syria,* University of Rome, 1967; (editor) *Studi sull'oriente e la Bibbia,* Studio e Vita (Genoa), 1967; (with Robert D. Biggs) *Cuneiform Texts from Nippur,* University of Chicago Press, 1969; (editor) *Approaches to the Study of the Ancient Near East,* Pontifical Biblical Institute (Rome), 1973.

WORK IN PROGRESS: Structural grammar of Babylonian; stylistic analysis of Akkadian literature.

* * *

BUCHER, Magnus 1927-

PERSONAL: Born February 15, 1927, in Grosskemnat, Germany; son of George (a clerk) and Anna (Echteler) Bucher; married Juliane Litzfelder, December 29, 1961; children: Susanne. *Education:* University of Munich, graduate of Sportakademie, 1950; University of Denver, B.A., 1952; University of Colorado, M.A., 1954, Ph.D., 1959. *Home:* Grillparzerstrasse 1, 8201 Kolbermoor, West Germany. *Office:* Physical Education Division, University of Maryland, College Park, Md. 20742.

CAREER: Ski School, Garmisch Partenkirchen, Germany, ski instructor, 1947-50; U.S. Army Dependent School, Dachau, Germany, teacher of German, 1954-55; junior high school teacher of German in Kokomo, Colo., 1955-56; Adams State College, Alamosa, Colo., assistant professor of history, 1958-61; University of Maryland, Germany campus, Munich, professor of history, 1961-73, director of Physical Education Division, 1976—. Director of ski schools in Climax, Colo., 1955-57, and Cuchara Pass, Colo., 1959-61. *Member:* National Education Association, National Political Science Association, American Association of University Professors, Rocky Mountain Social Science Association, Colorado Education Association.

WRITINGS: Anyone Can Yodel: A Musical Theory, Big Mountain Press, 1956; *Englisch Im Schlaf,* Vereinigte Velagswerke, Franke & Co., 1967; *Handbuch des Modernen Skilaufs,* Komar Sportpresse, 1970; *Geschichte des Tennisspiels,* Langer Press, 1977. Contributor to *Ski.*

SIDELIGHTS: Magnus Bucher was a member of the German National Ski Team, 1948-49, and captain of U.S.

National Ski Champions at University of Denver, 1951-52. He has traveled throughout Europe and to Greece and Libya; he speaks French, Italian, German, Greek, and has studied Latin, Dutch, Arabic, Spanish, and Gothic.

*   *   *

BUCHMAN, Herman 1920-

PERSONAL: Born May 20, 1920, in Germany; son of Benjamin and Edith (Brendzel) Buchman; married Dian Dincin (a writer), February 10, 1949; children: Caitlin Dincin. *Home:* 640 West End Ave., New York, N.Y. 10024.

CAREER: Free-lance make-up artist for stage, films, and television; instructor in make-up at State University of New York College at Purchase, Pace University, New York City, and Julliard School of Music, New York City, 1971—. *Military service:* U.S. Army, World War II. *Member:* International Alliance of Theatrical Stage Employees (charter member of make-up artists and hair stylists local; past president and past business agent).

WRITINGS: Stage Make-up, Watson-Guptill, 1971; *Film and T.V. Make-up,* Watson-Guptill, 1972. Also author of two film scripts and three television plays.

WORK IN PROGRESS: Make-up for Shakespearean Roles.

AVOCATIONAL INTERESTS: History (ancient, military, current), archeology, ancient weapons.

*   *   *

BUCK, Pearl S(ydenstricker) 1892-1973

June 26, 1892—March 6, 1973; American educator, publisher, lecturer, philanthropist, translator and author of novels, biographies, plays, essays, and juvenile fiction predominantly about China. Obituaries: *New York Times,* March 7, 1973, March 10, 1973; *Washington Post,* March 7, 1973; *Detroit Free Press,* March 7, 1973; *Publishers Weekly,* March 12, 1973; *Newsweek,* March 19, 1973; *Time,* March 19, 1973; *Current Biography,* April, 1973. (See index for CA sketch)

*   *   *

BUCKLEY, Julian Gerard 1905-

PERSONAL: Born January 21, 1905, in Geneseo, N.Y.; son of Julian Gerard (a lawyer) and Josephine (Gilbert) Buckley; married Christina Boardman, April 26, 1938; children: Christina Buckley Hoff, Sara Gilbert, James Lawrence. *Education:* Harvard University, A.B., 1928; New York University, M.B.A., 1937, Ph.D., 1952. *Politics:* Republican. *Religion:* Episcopalian. *Home:* 34 Goose Hill Rd., Cold Spring Harbor, N.Y. 11724.

CAREER: Fiduciary Trust, New York City, security analyst, 1941-52; New York University, New York City, instructor, 1952-53, assistant professor, 1953-56, associate professor, 1956-63, professor of finance, 1963-73. Deputy comptroller, City of New York, 1970-71. Director of First Investors Fund and First Investors Fund for Growth, 1965-70. *Military service:* National Guard, 1940-45. *Member:* New York Society of Security Analysts, Lawyers Club of New York, Harvard Club of New York, Harvard Club of Boston.

WRITINGS: (With Leo M. Loll) *Over the Counter Securities Markets,* Prentice-Hall, 1961, 3rd edition, 1973; (with D. H. Bellemore) *Problem Manual for Investments,* Boardman, 1962; (with Loll) *Questions and Answers on Securities Markets,* Prentice-Hall, 1968.

BUCZKOWSKI, Leopold 1905-

PERSONAL: Born in 1905, in Nakwasza, Podolia, Ukraine; son of Tomasz and Anna Buczkowski; married, 1945; wife's name, Maria; children: Tadeusz, Agnieszka. *Education:* Studied at Art Academy, Warsaw. *Home:* Konstancin, ul. Piasta 28, Poland. *Agent:* Agencja Atorska, Warsaw, Poland.

CAREER: Writer. *Military service:* Polish Army, 1939-44.

WRITINGS: Czarny potok, Pax, 1954, translation by David Welsh published as *Black Torrent,* M.I.T. Press, 1970; *Wortepy,* Panstwowy Instytut Wydawnictwo, 1957; *Dorycki kruzganek,* Pax, 1957; *Mlody poeta w zamku,* Pax, 1959; *Pierwsza swietnosc,* Panstwowy Instytut Wydawnictwo, 1966; (illustrator) Kornelia Dobkiewiczowa, *Ofka z Kamiennej Gory,* Nasza Ksieg, 1968; *Kapiele w lucca,* Panstwowy Instytut Wydawnictwo, 1975; *Oficer na nieszporach,* Wydawnictwo Literackie, 1976; *Kamien w pieluszkach,* Wydawnictwo Literackie, 1978. Also author of *Uroda na cazsie;* illustrator, Charles Dickens, *David Copperfield.*

*   *   *

BUERKLE, Jack Vincent 1923-

PERSONAL: Born August 9, 1923, in West Frankfort, Ill.; son of Henry Adam and Clemence (Henderson) Buerkle; married Martha Louise Edwards (a junior college professor), June 1, 1946; children: Stephen Vincent, Melanie Lake. *Education:* University of Illinois at Urbana-Champaign, B.A., 1948, M.A., 1949; University of Iowa, Ph.D., 1954. *Religion:* Presbyterian. *Home:* 526 Revere Rd., Merion Station, Pa. 19066. *Office:* Department of Sociology, Temple University, Philadelphia, Pa. 19122.

CAREER: Lake Forest University (now College), Lake Forest, Ill., assistant professor of sociology, 1954-55; Yale University, New Haven, Conn., assistant professor of sociology, 1955-60; Temple University, Philadelphia, Pa., associate professor, 1960-65, professor of sociology, 1965—, head of department, 1962-71. Visiting professor at Der Wirtschaftshochschule, Mannheim, West Germany, 1966-67. *Military service:* U.S. Army, 1943-46. *Member:* American Sociological Association, Institut Internationale de Sociologie, American Psychological Association, Eastern Sociological Society, Sigma Xi, Corinthian Yacht Club (commodore, 1970).

WRITINGS: (With Danny Barker) *Bourbon Street Black,* Oxford University Press, 1973. Contributor of articles to journals in his field.

WORK IN PROGRESS: A biography of Danny and "Blue Lu" Barker, tentatively entitled *The Jazzman and the Blues Singer.*

SIDELIGHTS: Jack Buerkle told *CA,* "My past and present work dealing with New Orleans black jazzmen grows out of a desire to uncover new facts concerning ... the descendants of those who produced America's only unique art form—Jazz."

*   *   *

BUGLIARELLO, George 1927-

PERSONAL: Surname is pronounced Bu-lya-*reh*-lo; born May 20, 1927, in Trieste, Italy; naturalized U.S. citizen; son of Federico (a physician) and Spera (Gefter-Wondrich) Bugliarello; married Virginia U. Harding, January 23, 1960; children: Federico D., Nicolas L. *Education:* University of Padua, Dott.Ing., 1951; University of Minnesota,

M.S.C.E., 1954; Massachusetts Institute of Technology, Sc.D., 1959. *Home:* 5 Terrace Dr., Port Washington, N.Y. 11050. *Office:* Polytechnic Institute of New York, 333 Jay St., Brooklyn, N.Y. 11201.

CAREER: Carnegie-Mellon University, Pittsburgh, Pa., assistant professor, 1959-63, associate professor of civil engineering, 1963-66, professor of biotechnology and civil engineering, 1966-69, chairman of biotechnology program, 1964-69; University of Illinois at Chicago Circle, Chicago, professor of biotechnology and civil engineering and dean of engineering, 1969-73; Polytechnic Institute of New York, Brooklyn, president, 1973—. American specialist in Venezuela, U.S. Department of State, 1968; member of scientific advisory panel, Armed Forces Safety Explosives Board, U.S. Department of Defense, 1968-69; member of hydraulics advisory board, U.S. Waterways Experiment Station (Vicksburg, Miss.), 1968—; American specialist in Zaire and Cameroon, U.S. Department of State, 1977. Executive secretary, First International Hemorheology Conference (Iceland), 1966. Alza Lecturer, Biomedical Engineering Society, 1976. Member of executive committee, ANSER, Washington, D.C.; trustee, Lord Corp., Comtech, Inc., and Teagle Foundation. Member of advisory board, Institute of Computer Science.

MEMBER: American Society of Civil Engineers (chairman, engineer mechanics division, 1972-73), American Society of Engineering Education, Biomedical Engineering Society (member of board of directors, 1969-72), National Academy of Engineering (member of commission on education), American Association for the Advancement of Science (fellow), Society of Rheology, International Society of Hemorheology, National Institutes of Health, Society for Natural Philosophy, International Association for Hydraulic Research, New York Academy of Science. *Awards, honors:* Fulbright scholar at University of Minnesota, 1952-54; Huber Research Prize from American Society of Civil Engineers, 1967; North Atlantic Treaty Organization (NATO) senior postdoctoral fellow at Technical University of Berlin, 1968.

WRITINGS: (Editor) *Bioengineering: An Engineering View,* San Francisco Press, 1967; (editor with V. G. Cardwell, Olive Salembier, and Winifred White) *Women in Engineering,* University of Illinois at Chicago Circle, 1972; (with F. J. Gunther) *Computer Systems and Water Resources,* American Elsevier, 1974; *Towards the Technological University: The Story of Polytechnic Institute of New York,* Newcomen Society, 1975; (with H. A. Simon) *Technology, the Community, and the University,* Pergamon, 1976; (with A. Alexandre, J. Barnes, and C. Wakstein) *The Impact of Noise: A Socio-Technological Introduction,* Pergamon, 1977; (editor) *Invention and Education,* Polytechnic Press, 1977; (editor) *Engineering Colleges, Legislatures, and the Community,* Polytechnic Press, 1978. Contributor of more than a hundred articles to scientific journals. Editor, *Biorheology;* member of board of editors, *American Journal of Cybernetics, World Development, Environmental Letters, Annals of Biomedical Engineering,* and *Journal of Hydraulic Research;* member of advisory board, *Fluid Mechanics-Soviet Research, Journal of Educational Technology Systems, Mechanics Research Communications,* and *Episteme;* member of editorial board, *Philosophy and Technology, Journal of Environmental Systems, Journal of Water Supply and Management,* and *Research in Philosophy and Technology;* editor-in-chief, *Journal of Technology in Society.*

WORK IN PROGRESS: *The Mechanics of Biological Flows; The History and Philosophy of Technology.*

AVOCATIONAL INTERESTS: Philosophy, history, international development.

* * *

BUKALSKI, Peter J(ulian) 1941-

PERSONAL: Born June 5, 1941, in Milwaukee, Wis.; married Anne Gardner. *Education:* University of Wisconsin, B.A., 1963, M.A., 1964; University of California, Los Angeles, M.F.A., 1966; Fordham University, graduate study, 1969; Ohio State University, Ph.D., 1975. *Home:* 1204 West College, Carbondale, Ill. 62901. *Office:* Department of Cinema and Photography, Southern Illinois University, Carbondale, Ill. 62901.

CAREER: Milwaukee Repertory Theatre, Milwaukee, Wis., assistant, 1962-63; Whitefish Bay Community Recreation Department, Whitefish Bay, Wis., director, 1963; Theatre Group, Los Angeles, Calif., assistant director and production assistant, 1964-65; Franklin College, Franklin, Ind., assistant professor of theater arts, 1966-70; Wright State University, Dayton, Ohio, assistant professor of library administration, 1970-72, acting assistant director of university library for instructional services and acting chairman of department of library and communication sciences, 1970-72, director of motion picture studies, 1972-74; Southern Illinois University at Carbondale, chairperson of department of cinema and photography, 1974—. Adviser on graduate financial aids, University of California, Los Angeles, 1964-66. *Member:* University Film Association, Speech Communication Association, Society for Cinema Studies.

WRITINGS: *Film Research: A Critical Bibliography with Annotations and Essay,* G. K. Hall, 1972. Contributor to *Film Heritage, American Libraries, Cue,* and *Theatre Crafts.*

* * *

BULLOCK, Henry 1907(?)-1973

1907(?)—February 8, 1973; American educator, author and authority on Black life in America. Obituaries: *New York Times,* February 10, 1973; *Washington Post,* February 13, 1973.

* * *

BUMSTED, J(ohn) M(ichael) 1938-

PERSONAL: Born December 12, 1938, in White Plains, N.Y.; son of John F. (a clerk) and Mary A. Bumsted; married second wife, Rosalie Stott, August 6, 1973; children: Jonathan, Carla, Hannah. *Education:* Tufts University, B.A. (summa cum laude), 1959; Brown University, Ph.D., 1965. *Politics:* Progressive-Conservative. *Home:* R.R. 1, Ganges, British Columbia, Canada. *Office:* Department of History, Simon Fraser University, Burnaby, British Columbia, Canada V5A 1S6.

CAREER: Tufts University, Medford, Mass., instructor in history, 1963-65; McMaster University, Hamilton, Ontario, assistant professor of history, 1967-69; Simon Fraser University, Burnaby, British Columbia, assistant professor, 1965-67, associate professor, 1967-75, professor of history, 1975—. *Member:* American Historical Association, Organization of American Historians, Canadian Historical Association, Pilgrim Society (fellow).

WRITINGS: (Editor) *Documentary Problems in Canadian*

History, two volumes, Dorsey, 1969; (editor) *The Great Awakening in America*, Blaisdell, 1970; *Henry Alline, 1748-1784*, University of Toronto Press, 1971; (editor) *Canada before Confederation: Essays and Interpretations*, Dorsey, 1972; (with John Van der Wetering) *What Must I Do to Be Saved?: The Great Awakening in Colonial America*, Dryden, 1976.

WORK IN PROGRESS: A three-volume biography of Thomas Douglas, Fifth Earl of Selkirk.

* * *

BUNKER, Edward 1933-

PERSONAL: Born December 31, 1933, in Hollywood, Calif.; son of Edward N. (a set designer) and Sarah (Schwartz) Bunker; married. *Politics:* Socialist. *Religion:* Atheist. *Residence:* New York, N.Y. *Agent:* A. Watkins, Inc., 77 Park Ave., New York, N.Y. 10016.

CAREER: Writer.

WRITINGS: No Beast So Fierce, Norton, 1972; *The Animal Factory*, Viking, 1977. Co-author of screenplay of film, "Straight Time," based on his novel, *No Beast So Fierce*. Contributor to *Harper's, New York Times Sunday Magazine*, and *Los Angeles Times*.

WORK IN PROGRESS: A novel about a child being raised in foster homes, reform schools and mental hospitals ("In other words, a novel showing how 'hard' criminals are created").

SIDELIGHTS: Edward Bunker was sent to reform school at the age of ten, and since has been imprisoned at San Quentin State Prison and other institutions for crimes including robbery, burglary, and selling illegal drugs; at one time he was on the FBI's Ten Most Wanted list. Bunker writes: "It has always been as if I carry chaos with me the way others carry typhoid. My purpose in writing is to transcend my existence by illuminating it. Simultaneously, in the act of writing I discover truth rather than impose a rationality on facts."

* * *

BURCHFIELD, Robert William 1923-

PERSONAL: Born January 27, 1923, in Wanganui, New Zealand; son of Frederick (an electrician) and Mary (Blair) Burchfield; married Ethel May Yates, July 2, 1949 (divorced, 1976); married Elizabeth Austen Knight, November 5, 1976; children: (first marriage) Jennifer Catherine, Jonathan Robert, Elizabeth Jane. *Education:* Attended Wanganui Technical College, 1934-39; Victoria University College, Wellington, New Zealand, M.A., 1948; Magdalen College, Oxford, B.A., 1951, M.A., 1955. *Religion:* Protestant. *Home:* The Barn, 14 Green End, Sutton Courtenay, Oxfordshire, England. *Office:* Oxford English Dictionary, 37a St. Giles, Oxford, England.

CAREER: Oxford University, Oxford, England, junior lecturer in English language and literature at Magdalen College, 1952-53, lecturer in English language and literature at Christ Church, 1953-57, lecturer, 1955-63, fellow and tutor in English language and literature at St. Peter's College, 1963—. *Military service:* Royal New Zealand Artillery, 1941-46; served in Italy; became sergeant. *Member:* Early English Text Society (honorary secretary, 1955-68; member of council, 1968—), Philological Society (London), American Academy of Arts and Sciences (foreign honorary member). *Awards, honors:* Rhodes scholarship, 1949-51; Commander, Order of the British Empire, 1975; D.Litt., University of Liverpool, 1978.

WRITINGS: (With C. T. Onions and G. W. S. Friedrichsen) *The Oxford Dictionary of English Etymology*, Oxford University Press, 1966; (contributor) *Pocket Oxford Dictionary*, Oxford University Press, 1969; (editor) *A Supplement to the Oxford English Dictionary*, Oxford University Press, Volume I, *A-G*, 1972, Volume II, *H-N*, 1976. Chief editor, "Oxford English Dictionaries," Oxford University Press, 1971—. Contributor to *Medium Aevum, Essays and Studies, Notes and Queries*, and other journals. Co-editor, *Notes and Queries*, 1959-62.

WORK IN PROGRESS: Editing *A Supplement to the Oxford English Dictionary*, Volume III, *O-S*.

AVOCATIONAL INTERESTS: Rugby (member of New Zealand Army team in Italy, 1945), travel in the United States, the Far East, and Australia.

BIOGRAPHICAL/CRITICAL SOURCES: Rising Generation (Tokyo), January 1, 1973, February 1, 1973, March 1, 1973.

* * *

BURD, Van Akin 1914-

PERSONAL: Born April 19, 1914, in Miami, Fla.; son of Melvin S. (a contractor) and Elizabeth (Van Akin) Burd; married Julia E. Robinson, June 18, 1943; children: Joyce Ellen (Mrs. Garland Hicks, Jr.). *Education:* University of Chicago, B.A., 1936; Stanford University, M.A., 1941; University of Michigan, Ph.D., 1951. *Home:* 22 Forrest Ave., Cortland, N.Y. 13045. *Office:* Department of English, State University of New York College, Cortland, N.Y. 13045.

CAREER: Teacher in public schools in Michigan, 1936-40; State University of New York College at Cortland, instructor, 1951, assistant professor, 1952-53, associate professor, 1954-58, professor of English, 1959—, Distinguished Professor, 1973—, chairman of department, 1959-60, 1961-63, 1965-68, director of arts and sciences, 1963-64. *Military service:* U.S. Navy, 1942-46. U.S. Naval Reserve, 1942—; present rank, lieutenant commander. *Member:* Modern Language Association of America, Thoreau Society, Victorian Society (London). *Awards, honors:* Grants for research on John Ruskin from American Philosophical Society, 1960, 1965, and from American Council of Learned Societies, 1960-61, 1968.

WRITINGS: (Editor) *The Winnington Letters: John Ruskin's Correspondence with Margaret Alexis Bell and the Children at Winnington Hall*, Harvard University Press, 1969; (editor) *The Ruskin Family Letters: The Correspondence of John James Ruskin, His Wife, and Their Son, John: 1801-1843*, two volumes, Cornell University Press, 1973; (editor) *Ruskin and Rose La Touche: Her Unpublished Diaries of 1863 and 1867*, Oxford University Press, in press. Contributor to literature journals.

WORK IN PROGRESS: A book, *Ruskin's Christmas Story of 1876*.

* * *

BURFORD, Lolah

CAREER: Author.

WRITINGS—All published by Macmillan: Vice Avenged: A Moral Tale, 1971; *The Vision of Stephen: An Elegy*, 1972; *Edward, Edward: A Part of His Story and of History 1795-1816 Set out in Three Parts in This Form of a New-Old Picaresque Romance That Is Also a Study in Grace*, 1973; *Mac Lyon*, 1974; *Alyx*, 1977.

BURFORD, Roger L(ewis) 1930-

PERSONAL: Born January 19, 1930, in Independence, Miss.; son of Roger W. (a farmer) and Christene (Lewis) Burford; married Bettye Jane Marshall, November 25, 1948; children: Roger Marshall, Pamela. *Education:* University of Mississippi, B.B.A., 1956, M.A., 1957; Indiana University, Ph.D., 1961. *Politics:* Democrat. *Religion:* Presbyterian. *Home:* 590 Castlekirk Ave., Baton Rouge, La. 70808. *Office:* College of Business Administration, Louisiana State University, Baton Rouge, La. 70803.

CAREER: Indiana University at Bloomington, lecturer in economics and statistics, 1959-60; Georgia State College (now University), Atlanta, assistant professor, 1962, associate professor of economics, 1962-63; Louisiana State University, Baton Rouge, associate professor of business statistics, 1963-67, professor of quantitative methods, 1967—, director of Division of Research, 1969-74. Fulbright lecturer in economics and statistics, National Taiwan University, 1967-68; executive vice-president, Economic & Industrial Research, Inc., 1968—; chairman, Governor's Council of Economic Advisors, State of Louisiana, 1973—; consultant to numerous organizations. *Military service:* U.S. Air Force, 1951-53.

MEMBER: American Economic Association, American Statistical Association, Econometric Society, American Institute of Decision Sciences, Western Regional Science Association, Southern Economic Association, Beta Gamma Sigma, Pi Kappa Pi. *Awards, honors:* Ford Foundation fellowships, 1957-58, 1958-59, summer, 1962.

WRITINGS: Net Migration for Southern Counties: 1940-50 and 1950-60, Bureau of Business and Economic Research, Georgia State College, 1963; (with P. F. Boyer) *The Impact of NASA Programs on the New Orleans Area Economy,* Division of Research, College of Business Administration, Louisiana State University, 1964; *Louisiana's Human Resources, Part IV: Migration of Working Aged Population* (bulletin), Agricultural Experiment Station, Louisiana State University, 1965; *Probability Projections of Net Migration for Southern Counties and Other Applications of Markov Chains,* Division of Research, College of Business Administration, Louisiana State University, 1966; *A Projections Model for Small Area Economics,* Bureau of Business and Economic Research, Georgia State College, 1966; *Methodology of Regional Economic Research,* Gulf South Research Institute, 1967; *Introduction to Finite Probability,* C. E. Merrill, 1967; *Statistics: A Computer Approach,* C. E. Merrill, 1968; *Basic Statistics for Business and Economics: A Computer Oriented Text,* C. E. Merrill, 1970. Also author of *Net Migration for Louisiana and Its Parishes, 1960-70,* 1972, *Population Projections for Louisiana and Its Parishes, 1970-1985,* 1972, and *An Input-Output Study of Louisiana,* 1973.

Contributor of over seventy-five articles to professional journals, including *Atlanta Economic Review, Economic Journal, Decision Sciences, Southern Economic Journal,* and *Louisiana Economy.* Book review editor, *Annals of Regional Science.*

*   *   *

BURGER, Henry G. 1923-

PERSONAL: Born June 27, 1923, in New York, N.Y.; son of B. W. and Terese Burger. *Education:* Columbia University, B.A. (with honors), 1947, M.A., 1965, Ph.D., 1967. *Politics:* Independent. *Religion:* Protestant. *Home:* 7306 Brittany, Shawnee Mission, Kan. 66203. *Office:* Department of Anthropology, University of Missouri, Kansas City, Mo. 64110.

CAREER: Industrial engineer for Standard Products, Cleveland, Ohio, and other firms, 1947-51; Midwest manufacturers representative, specializing in field testing of new products, 1952-55; social science consultant to research consultancies, based in New York City, 1956-67; Southwestern Cooperative Educational Laboratory, Albuquerque, N.M., anthropologist, 1967-69; University of Missouri—Kansas City, associate professor, 1969-73, professor of anthropology and education, 1973—, founding member of University Doctoral Faculty, 1974—. Lecturer in innovational strategy, City College of the City University of New York, New York City, 1957-65; adjunct professor of educational anthropology, University of New Mexico, 1969. Social science speaker at over sixty-five conferences in America and Europe. Anthropological consultant to U.S. Veterans Administration, Kansas City, 1971-72, and to Prentice-Hall, Inc. and Little, Brown & Co. *Military service:* U.S. Army, Engineers, 1943-46; served in Philippines and Japan; became captain.

MEMBER: International Union of Anthropological and Ethnological Sciences (fellow), International Foundations of Education Society, Association Internationale pour la recherche, Association Internationale pour des methodes, Association Internationale pour structuro-globales, World Academy of Art and Science (fellow), Council on Anthropology and Education (fellow), American Anthropological Association (life fellow), Society of Professional Anthropologists, Society for Medical Anthropology, American Association for the Advancement of Science (fellow), Current Anthropology (fellow), Society for Applied Anthropology (fellow), Royal Anthropological Institute of Great Britain and Ireland (life fellow), Society for General Systems Research (president of New York chapter, 1963-64), American Ethnological Society, American Educational Studies Association, American Association of University Professors, Dictionary Society of North America (charter member), Central States Anthropological Society, Phi Beta Kappa. *Awards, honors:* National Science Foundation faculty research grant, 1970.

WRITINGS: Ethno-Pedagogy, Southwestern Cooperative Educational Laboratory, 1968, 3rd edition, Holt, 1972; *Ethnic Live-In,* Bookstore, University of Missouri—Kansas City, 1969, 2nd edition, 1970; *Ethno-Strategy,* Bookstore, University of Missouri—Kansas City, 1972, 2nd edition, 1976; (contributor) Bernardo Bernardi, editor, *The Concept and Dynamics of Culture,* Mouton, 1977. Compiler of "Ethno-Education," an annotated bibliography of current literature for improving teaching by fitting cultural patterns, published in seven installments of *SWCEL Newsletter,* 1967-69. Contributor to anthropology, education, linguistics, and marketing journals. Advisory editor, *Anthropology and Education Quarterly,* 1975—.

WORK IN PROGRESS: An add-on concept-finder defining words by their processes and forming a handbook of physical and social engineering.

SIDELIGHTS: Henry G. Burger told *CA:* "Culture is the selective accumulation of adaptive techniques. And the trend in science is from descriptivism to codification. Yet social science still wallows in archaic essays. Therefore the ultimately great names will not be the Franz Boases and the Sigmund Freuds. Rather, they will be the Carl Linnaeuses, the Melvil Deweys (perhaps even the Niccolo Machiavellis!) and their technical facilitators like Eugene Garfield.

Hence the person who authors an article, lives a month; who authors a textbook, lives a year; but who creates a new kind of reference book, lives forever. Now, another major trend in science is to work from effect back to cause. When applied to behavior, this fact suggests that we should stop criticism of motivational engineering, and instead codify it. For as organizations grow more complex and global, they will consist increasingly of the computerizers versus the computerized, the transitivizers versus the transitivized. But the human distinctiveness is symboling, and vocabulary is the roll-call of the important and successful procedures of life. Thus it has gradually dawned on me that a key to the perpetually-sought handbook of human nature should be a tree-like codification of all action words. And so I have spent parts of 21 years in rostering and computer-branching all of English's transitive verbs—producing the taxonomy of processes that I am proofreading now.''

* * *

BURNETT, Avis 1937-

PERSONAL: Born May 11, 1937, in Scott City, Kan.; daughter of O. Ray (a minister) and Sylva (Potter) Pomeroy; married Ted L. Burnett, August 1, 1958 (divorced, 1960); children: Christopher. *Education:* Colorado Woman's College (now Temple Buell College), A.A., 1957; Fort Hays Kansas State College, B.A., 1963, M.A., 1965. *Home:* 826 College, Boulder, Colo. 80302. *Office:* 505 College, Boulder, Colo. 80302.

CAREER: Northwest Missouri State College (now University), Maryville, instructor in English, 1965-68; free-lance writer, 1968—.

WRITINGS: Gertrude Stein, Atheneum, 1972.

* * *

BURNETT, Whit(ney Ewing) 1899-1973

August 14, 1899—April 22, 1973; American writer and editor. Obituaries: *Time,* May 7, 1973; *Publishers Weekly,* May 28, 1973. (See index for *CA* sketch)

* * *

BURNHAM, Sophy 1936-

PERSONAL: Born December 12, 1936, in Baltimore, Md.; daughter of George Cochran (an attorney) and Sophy Tayloe (Snyder) Doub; married David Bright Burnham (a journalist), March 12, 1960; children: Sarah Tayloe, Molly Bright. *Education:* Attended University of Florence, 1956-57; Smith College, B.A. (cum laude), 1958. *Religion:* Episcopalian. *Home:* 1405 31st St. N.W., Washington, D.C. 20007.

CAREER: Smithsonian Institution, Washington, D.C., assistant curator for Museum Services, 1962-64; free-lance writer, 1964—; David McKay Co., Inc., New York, N.Y., associate editor, 1972-74. Vice-president, Studio Theatre, Washington, D.C., 1978-79; member of board, Children's Radio Theatre, Washington, D.C., 1978—; member of planning committee for District of Columbia, National Endowment for the Humanities, 1979—. *Member:* Authors Guild, Washington Independent Writers. *Awards, honors:* Best magazine feature award from National Steeplechase and Hunt Association, 1970; Daughter of Mark Twain, Mark Twain Society, 1974.

WRITINGS: The Exhibits Speak, Smithsonian Institution, 1964; *The Art Crowd* (selection of Book-of-the-Month Club and Saturday Review Book Club), McKay, 1973; *Buccaneer*

(young adult), Warne, 1977; *The Landed Gentry,* Putnam, 1978; *The Dogwalker,* Warne, 1979.

Work in anthologized in *Crime in the Cities,* edited by Dan Glaser, Harper, 1970; *Cities in Trouble,* edited by Nathan Glazer, Quadrangle, 1970. Author of ''Music of Shakespeare's England,'' a half-hour television program, for Smithsonian Institution, 1962; ''The Smithsonian's Whale,'' a short film, Smithsonian Institution, 1963; ''The Leaf Thieves,'' a half-hour film, Smithsonian Institution, 1964; documentary film on Civil War Museum in Vicksburg, Miss., for U.S. Department of Interior National Parks Service, 1967; ''Penelope,'' a play, 1976. Contributor of more than fifty articles on current issues to magazines, including *New York Times Magazine, Redbook, Ms, Esquire,* and *New York.* Contributing editor, *Town and Country,* 1975—.

WORK IN PROGRESS: A play and a novel.

SIDELIGHTS: Sophy Burnham told *CA:* ''I first guessed I was a writer at the age of ten, when I failed my fifth-grade English exam. The reason I failed was because the first question was: 'finish this paragraph.' Forty-five minutes and two bluebooks later I was still scribbling away without having finished the paragraph—but I'd discovered what fun it is to write. It took another fifteen years to screw up my courage to try. . . .

''If I don't write a certain amount of time in a given period, I get ugly, like a junkie without a fix. . . . The fact that people pay me to write is a surprise bonus of the craft.

''My goal, as Tacitus put it, is 'to move the hearts and minds of men.' And sometimes tickle their sides. But much of art is craft, fashioned in hours of painstaking thought and work; . . . the immediate aim is to forge words so clear, simple, precise and entertaining that the reader can't keep from turning the page. . . .

''For me the writing itself—the singing of the song—gives as pure pleasure as the later realization . . . that the song has touched another's heart. There's the miracle; it fills me with humility.''

BIOGRAPHICAL/CRITICAL SOURCES: Newsday, March 22, 1973, July 9, 1978; *Washington Post Book World,* March 25, 1973; *New York Times Book Review,* March 25, 1973, July 2, 1978; *New York Times,* March 27, 1973; *Newsweek,* April 9, 1973; *Milwaukee Journal,* May 20, 1973; *Progressive,* September, 1978.

* * *

BURNS, Thomas (Jr.) 1928-

PERSONAL: Born May 6, 1928, in Arena, Wis. *Education:* University of Wisconsin—Madison, B.B.A., 1950; University of Michigan, M.B.A., 1957; University of Minnesota, Ph.D., 1963. *Office:* Department of Accounting, Ohio State University, Columbus, Ohio 43210.

CAREER: Certified public accountant in Wisconsin and Illinois. Lawrence University, Appleton, Wis., assistant professor of accounting, 1952-55; University of Michigan, Ann Arbor, lecturer in accounting, 1955-57; Southern Illinois University at Carbondale, assistant professor of accounting, 1957-58; University of Minnesota, Minneapolis, instructor in accounting, 1958-63; Ohio State University, Columbus, 1963—, began as associate professor, currently professor of accounting, chairperson of department, 1977—, director of doctoral program in accounting, 1965-71, 1974—, moderator, accounting research colloquium, 1967—. Visiting associate professor, Stanford University, 1964; visiting professor of accounting, Harvard University, 1964, University of Chicago, 1965, University of California, Berkeley, 1972-73. *Member:* Beta Alpha Psi (national president, 1978—).

WRITINGS: Accounting Trends I, McGraw, 1967, 12th edition, 1978; (with H. S. Hendrickson) *The Accounting Sampler,* McGraw, 1967, 3rd edition, 1976; *The Use of Accounting Data in Decision Making,* Ohio State University, 1967; *The Behavioral Aspects of Accounting Data for Performance Evaluation,* Ohio State University, 1969, revised edition, 1971; (with J. L. Livingstone) *Income Theory and Rate of Return,* Ohio State University, 1971; (with Hendrickson) *The Accounting Primer: An Introduction to Financial Accounting,* McGraw, 1972; *Behavioral Experiments in Accounting,* Ohio State University, 1972. Book review editor, *Accounting Review.*

* * *

BURNS, Vincent Godfrey 1893-1979
(Bobby Burns)

PERSONAL: Born October 17, 1893, in Brooklyn, N.Y.; son of James Howard (a clerk) and Katherine (Rossberg) Burns; married Edna Rodenberger, June 13, 1921; married second wife, Katherine Howard, August 25, 1945; children: (first marriage) Barbara (Mrs. Richard Zalmstra); (second marriage) Vincent Howard, Victor David. *Education:* Pennsylvania State College (now University), B.S., 1916; Harvard University, A.M., 1917; Union Theological Seminary, B.D., 1922; Columbia University, graduate study, 1922-24. *Politics:* Independent. *Home and office address:* Route 1, Box 480, Annapolis, Md. 21401.

CAREER: Ordained a Congregational minister, 1920; pastor of churches in Brooklyn, N.Y., Pittsfield, Mass., New York, N.Y., and Palisade, N.J., 1920-52; Community Church, Washington, D.C., pastor, 1953-58. Named poet laureate of the State of Maryland, 1962. Leader, Log Cabin Shrine, 1936-40; chairman of board of directors, Fort Lee Public Library; special lecturer at University of Kansas, 1952-53, and University of Wisconsin, 1953-54. Performed on radio programs as Bobby Burns, "poet of the air"; has given recitals and lectures. *Military service:* U.S. Army, Field Artillery, 1918; became lieutenant. *Member:* Composers, Authors and Artists of America (president), Maryland State Poetry Society (past president). *Awards, honors:* George Washington Gold Medal from Freedoms Foundation, 1955.

WRITINGS—Published by New World Books, except as indicated: *The Master's Message for the New Day,* Association Press, 1926; (editor) *The Red Harvest* (anthology), Macmillan, 1930; (with brother, Robert Burns) *I Am a Fugitive from a Chain Gang,* Vanguard, 1932; *Female Convict* (novel), Macauley, 1932; *I'm in Love with Life* (poems), Dutton, 1933; *Heavenly Vision,* 1939; *I Am My Brother's Keeper* (play), Los Angeles Press, 1942; *Out of These Chains,* 1942; *Redwood and Other Poems,* 1952; *America, I Love You* (poems), 1957; *Vagabond's Luck,* 1958; *Flame against the Night* (poems), 1959.

(Editor) *An American Poet Speaks* (essays), 1960; *Poetry for Young Americans,* Frank E. Richards, 1963, Volume I: *The Poet and Nature,* Volume II: *The Poet and His Country,* Volume III: *The Poet and His Ideals; The Man Who Broke a Thousand Chains* (biography), Acropolis, 1963; *Memories and Melodies of Maryland,* 1964; (editor) *The Four Tests of a Loyal American* (essay), Robert Dilley, 1965; *Maryland's Revolutionary Hero,* 1965; *Thirteen Songs,* 1966; *Ballads of the Free State Bard,* 1967; (editor) *Songs of the Free State Bards* (anthology), 1967; *Still Life* (poems), 1969; *World on*

Fire (play), 1969; *Red Fuse on a World Bomb,* 1969; *Heart on Fire* (poems), 1969; *The Sunny Side of Life* (poems), 1970; *Poetry Is Fun,* 1971; *The Story of Old Glory* (anthology), 1972; *New Light on the Lindbergh Kidnapping,* 1973. Also author of *Secrets of Eternal Youth.*

Author of brochures, including *Fosdick and the Fundamentalists* and *Health Is Life.* Contributor to literary magazines. Editor of *Rainbow,* Maryland's poetry magazine, and *Youth Dreams;* associate editor, *Poetry Caravan.*

WORK IN PROGRESS: A collection of his sonnets and a collection of his sermons.

SIDELIGHTS: I Am a Fugitive from a Chain Gang, which is based on Vincent Godfrey Burns' brother's escapes from a Georgia chain gang, was made into a motion picture by Warner Brothers. *Female Convict* has sold one million copies in paperback.

(Died February 3, 1979)

* * *

BURRIS-MEYER, Harold 1902-

PERSONAL: Born April 6, 1902, in Madison, N.J.; son of Henry H. and Minna (McEuen) Meyer; married Anita Mersfelder (an actress), April 12, 1945; children: Anita Gay, Peter Winthrop. *Education:* College of the City of New York (now City College of the City University of New York), B.S., 1923; Columbia University, M.A., 1926, additional graduate study, 1926-32. *Residence:* Boca Raton, Fla. *Office:* Florida Atlantic University, Boca Raton, Fla. 33432.

CAREER: Washington and Jefferson College, Washington, Pa., assistant professor of speech and drama, 1927-29; Stevens Institute of Technology, Hoboken, N.J., 1929-54, began as assistant professor, professor of dramatic arts, 1947-54, director of theater, 1930-54; full-time theater consultant, specializing in sound systems, acoustics, and theater planning, 1954-65; Florida Atlantic University, Boca Raton, professor of drama and director of university theater, 1965-72. Vice-president and director, Muzak Corp., 1943-47; director, Associated Program Service, 1945-47; vice-president and director, Magnetic Programs, Inc., 1948-57; director, Control, Inc., 1951—. Sound consultant for Broadway productions, beginning with "Hamlet" at Broadhurst Theatre, 1931; designer of sound control systems for Metropolitan Opera productions. Member of board of directors, American Council for Arts in Education. *Military service:* U.S. Naval Reserve, 1943-45; became commander; received commendation for development of new and unconventional military devices and techniques.

MEMBER: Organization Internationale des Scenographes et Techniciens de Theatre, Acoustical Society of America (fellow; member of executive committee, 1942-45; current representative to American National Standards Committee for Motion Picture and Television Equipment), American National Theatre and Academy, American Theatre Association, U.S. Institute for Theatre Technology (member of board of directors), Audio Engineering Society (fellow), National Council of Acoustical Consultants (honorary life member), New York Academy of Sciences.

WRITINGS: (With Edward C. Cole) *Scenery for the Theatre: The Organization, Processes, Materials and Techniques Used to Set the Stage,* Little, Brown, 1938, 2nd revised edition, 1971; (with Cole) *Theatres and Auditoriums,* Reinhold, 1949, 2nd edition, 1964; (with Lewis S. Goodfriend) *Acoustics for the Architect,* Reinhold, 1957; (with Vincent Mallory) *Sound in the Theatre,* Radio Magazines, 1959. Contributor to *Theatre Arts* and technical journals.

SIDELIGHTS: Scenery for the Theatre has been published in Japanese.

* * *

BURROWS, David J(ames) 1936-

PERSONAL: Born August 30, 1936, in Paterson, N.J.; son of James and Roslyn (Zimmerman) Burrows; married Sandra Thomson, March 30, 1958; children: Mark, Dara, James, Juliet. *Education:* University of North Carolina, A.B., 1956, A.M., 1957; New York University, Ph.D., 1964. *Home address:* P.O. Box 20, East Millstone, N.J. 08873. *Office:* Department of English, Douglass College, Rutgers University, New Brunswick, N.J. 08903.

CAREER: Hobart College, Geneva, N.Y., instructor in English, 1958-60; Rutgers University, Douglass College, New Brunswick, N.J., instructor, 1960-64, assistant professor, 1964-70, associate professor of English, 1970—. Fulbright-Hays lecturer, University of Lund, 1965-66. *Member:* Modern Language Association of America, American Association of University Professors.

WRITINGS: Private Dealings, Almqvist & Wiksell, 1969; (editor and author of introduction and notes) William Dean Howells, *The Son of Royal Langbrith,* Indiana University Press, 1969; (editor with F. L. Lapides) *Alienation,* Crowell, 1969; (editor with Lapides) *Racism,* Crowell, 1971; (editor with Lapides and Robert Hayden) *Afro-American Literature,* Harcourt, 1971.

* * *

BURTIS, C(harles) Edward 1907-

PERSONAL: Born June 18, 1907, in New York, N.Y.; son of Charles S. (an inventor) and Bertha (Behman) Burtis; married Viola Ida Rizzo (an office manager), June 19, 1943. *Education:* Studied privately with tutors (due to lengthy illness) and at Broughton School of Orthodietetics, New York, N.Y. *Politics:* "No party affiliations or alliances." *Religion:* None. *Agent:* Kenan Bal, BAL Agency, 299 Madison Ave., New York, N.Y. 10017.

CAREER: Sales representative of Nestle Co., 1940-44, and Vitamin Products Co., Milwaukee, Wis., 1945-46; self-employed in real estate, 1946—. *Member:* Nutritional Education Research Foundation, National Health Federation.

WRITINGS: The Real American Tragedy, Lee Foundation for Nutritional Research (Milwaukee), 1960; *The Fountain of Youth,* Fell, 1964; *Nature's Miracle Medicine Chest,* Arco, 1971. Author of two unpublished plays, "The 365 Day Christman" and "The Lallapaloozas."

WORK IN PROGRESS: Four books, *Wait? I'm Not Dead Yet,* with H. Rudolph Alsleben, *The Civilization, The Wonderful World Beyond,* a study of the continuity of life in the dimension beyond physical death, and *Angelo's World,* a novel.††

* * *

BUSHNELL, David S(herman) 1927-

PERSONAL: Born January 7, 1927, in Whittier, Calif.; son of David Sherman (an architect) and Lillian (Dudley) Bushnell; married Shirley Willis, August 7, 1952 (divorced, 1964); married Alice Mencher, August 14, 1965; children: (first marriage) Beckie Lynn, Kimberlie Anne, Karen Jo. *Education:* University of Chicago, Ph.B., 1947, M.A., 1950; University of Washington, Seattle, graduate study, 1951-53. *Politics:* Republican. *Religion:* Unitarian Universalist. *Office:*

American Association of Community and Junior Colleges, 1 Dupont Cir. N.W., Washington, D.C. 20036.

CAREER: University of Michigan, Ann Arbor, assistant study director in Institute of Social Research, 1953-55; International Business Machines Corp., Poughkeepsie, N.Y., Rochester, Minn., and New York, N.Y., administrative assistant, 1955-56, personnel administrator, 1956-60, management communication consultant, 1960-61; Stanford Research Institute, Menlo Park, Calif., social psychologist, 1961-64; U.S. Office of Education, Washington, D.C., consultant, 1964-65, research director for secondary and post-secondary education research, 1965-69; Battelle Memorial Institute, Washington, D.C., fellow in behavioral sciences, 1969-70; American Association of Junior Colleges, Washington, D.C., research director for "Project Focus," 1970-72; Human Resources Research Organization, Alexandria, Va., senior staff scientist, 1972-76; American Association of Community and Junior Colleges, Washington, D.C., project director, 1976—. Visiting lecturer at University of Washington, Seattle, 1955, and at Ohio State University, 1970. Consultant to Battelle Memorial Institute, 1970—, and to American Council on Education and Empire State College, 1972—. *Military service:* U.S. Navy, 1944-45.

MEMBER: American Psychological Association, American Association for the Advancement of Science, American Educational Research Association, American Vocational Association.

WRITINGS: (Contributor) Robert Gordon, editor, *Toward a Manpower Policy,* Wiley, 1967; (editor with Donald Rappaport) *Planned Change in Education: A Systems Approach,* Harcourt, 1971; (contributor) Joseph Axelrod, editor, *New Teaching, New Learning: Current Issues in Higher Education,* Jossey-Bass, 1971; *Organizing for Change: New Priorities for Community Colleges,* McGraw, 1973. Also author of *Alternative Strategies for Implementing Interinstitutional Cooperation,* a report for U.S. Office of Education, 1978. Contributor of over thirty-five articles to education journals.

* * *

BUTLER, David Francis 1928-

PERSONAL: Born February 20, 1928, in New York, N.Y.; son of David (an executive) and Gladys (Donahue) Butler; married Wanda Lee Clarke (a teacher); children: David Eliot, Donald Woodbridge. *Education:* Webb Institute, B.S. in Naval Architecture and B.S. in Marine Engineering, 1949; Yale University, M.S. (M.E.), 1950. *Religion:* Unitarian Universalist. *Home:* 600 Southeast 5 Ct., Pompano Beach, Fla. 33061. *Office:* Central Engineering, Chris Craft Corp., Pompano Beach, Fla. 33060.

CAREER: Todd Shipyard Corp., New York, N.Y., executive trainee and field supervisor, 1950-53; Olin Corporation, Winchester-Western Division, New Haven, Conn., manager of arms research section, 1956-60, senior research associate, 1960-61, manager of advanced design section, 1962-63, manager of Ramset products engineering, 1964, manager of mechanics systems section, 1964-67, staff senior research associate of Winchester Group Research, 1968-71, supervisor of government proposals, 1971-73; Chris Craft Corp., Pompano Beach, Fla., chief mechanical engineer, 1973—. Holder of major patents on firearms mechanisms and explosively operated industrial tools. Director, Sleeping Giant Park Association, 1968-72. *Member:* Society of Naval Architects and Marine Engineers, American Boat and Yacht Council, National Rifle Association (life member).

WRITINGS: The New Archery, A. S. Barnes, 1968, revised edition, 1973; *Winchester '73 and '76,* Winchester Press, 1970; *Simplified Furniture Design and Construction,* A. S. Barnes, 1970; *United States Firearms: The First Century, 1776-1875,* Winchester Press, 1971; *The American Shotgun,* Winchester Press, 1973. Contributor to journals.

*   *   *

BUTLER, James H(armon) 1908-

PERSONAL: Born December 16, 1908, in Cathlamet, Wash.; son of Don Carlos (a building contractor) and Maude (Kimball) Butler; married Etta Willena Barnhart, June 7, 1937. *Education:* Western Washington College of Education (now Western Washington University), A.B., 1937; University of Southern California, A.M., 1939, Ph.D., 1948. *Home:* 5030 West Slauson, Los Angeles, Calif. 90056. *Office:* Department of Drama, University of Southern California, Los Angeles, Calif. 90007.

CAREER: Elementary school and junior high school teacher in Kelso, Wash., 1934-38; high school speech and drama teacher in Tulare, Calif., 1939-40; West Texas State College (now University), Canyon, assistant professor of speech, drama, and acting, 1940-44, head of department of speech, 1943-44; San Jose State College (now University), San Jose, Calif., assistant professor of speech and drama, 1945-46; University of Southern California, Los Angeles, assistant professor, 1946-48, associate professor, 1948-51, professor of drama, 1951—, de Mille Professor of Drama and chairman of department, 1953-71. Has acted in plays in Pasadena and Los Angeles; director of plays with Longview Community Players, 1935-38. Member of advisory committee, American College Theatre Festival, 1969, 1970; member of national advisory board of Aesthetic Education Program, Central Midwestern Regional Educational Laboratory, Inc.; educational adviser, Olesen Filmstrips. *Military service:* U.S. Army, Infantry, 1941-43.

MEMBER: American Theatre Association (president, 1968; member of overseas touring committee, 1957-68), U.S. Institute for Teacher Technology, National Theatre Conference, Theatre Library Association, American Association of University Professors, National Collegiate Players (president, 1958-63), Phi Beta Kappa (president of University of Southern California chapter, 1960-61), Phi Delta Kappa, Phi Kappa Phi, Alpha Psi Omega.

WRITINGS: Theatre and Drama of Greece and Rome, Chandler Publishing, 1972.

Filmstrips; produced by Comma, except as indicated: "The Development of the Physical Theatre," 1951; "Electra," 1955; "The California Missions," 1955; "The Ancient Greek Theatre of Epidauros," 1957; "The Theatre of Dionysis," in two parts, 1957; "The Roman Theatre of Orange," 1957; "The Greek Hellenistic Theatre of Priene," 1957; "Roman Circuses, Amphitheatres, and Naumachiae," a series of two films, 1959; "English Playhouses," six films, 1963; "Italian Renaissance Theatres," three films, 1964; "History of the Physical Theatre," four films, 1965; "The American Theatre to 1850," in two parts, 1965; "Introduction to the Ancient Greek Theatre," in two parts, Olesen, 1972.

Contributor to *Encyclopaedia Britannica.* Contributor of articles and reviews to theatre and speech journals, including *Theatre Survey, Theatre Research, Dramatics, Educational Theatre News, Educational Theatre Journal, Players, Western Speech Journal,* and *Personalist.*

AVOCATIONAL INTERESTS: Collecting theatre books, travel (Western Europe, Greece, Turkey).

*   *   *

BUTLER, Robert N(eil) 1927-

PERSONAL: Born January 21, 1927, in New York, N.Y.; married Diane McLaughlin, September 2, 1950 (divorced, 1973); married Myrna Lewis (a social worker), May 19, 1975; children: (first marriage) Ann Christine, Carole Melissa, Cynthia Lee. *Education:* Columbia University, B.A., 1949, M.D., 1953. *Politics:* Independent. *Home:* 3815 Huntington St. N.W., Washington, D.C. 20015. *Office:* National Institute on Aging, National Institutes of Health, Bethesda, Md. 20014.

CAREER: Private practice in gerontology and psychiatric researcher; National Institute of Mental Health, Bethesda, Md., researcher, 1958-62; Washington School of Psychiatry, Washington, D.C., research psychiatrist and gerontologist, 1962-76, member of executive committee, 1961-76; National Institute on Aging, Bethesda, Md., director, 1976—. Associate clinical professor, Howard University School of Medicine and George Washington University School of Medicine; member of faculty, Washington School of Psychiatry. U.S. Public Health Service, member of staff, 1955—, senior surgeon, 1961, inactive reserve, 1962-76, medical director, 1976—. Member of subcommittee on employment, District of Columbia Inter-departmental Committee on Aging, 1966-67. Member of board of trustees, National Council on Aging, National Caucus on the Black Aged, Legal Research and Services for the Elderly, and District of Columbia Commission on Aging. Founding member, National Ballet, 1962-75. Member of District of Columbia Advisory Committee on Aging, 1969—, chairman, 1969-72; member of Mental Health Technical Advisory Committee to Health Planning Advisory Committee, District of Columbia Department of Public Health, 1970-71. Consultant to U.S. Senate Special Committee on Aging, St. Elizabeth Hospital, Langley Porter Neuropsychiatric Institute, and Center for Law and Social Policy.

MEMBER: American Psychiatric Association (fellow), American Geriatrics Society (founding fellow), Group for the Advancement of Psychiatry, American Medical Association, National Council on Aging (member of board of directors, 1969—), National Council of Senior Citizens, Gerontological Society, Forum for Professionals and Executives (founding member), National Ballet Society (member of board of directors, 1961-75), District of Columbia Medical Society, Washington Psychiatric Society, Cosmos Club. *Awards, honors:* Pulitzer Prize, 1976; certificate of appreciation from American Medical Writers Association, 1976; Community Service Award, District of Columbia Medical Society, 1976.

WRITINGS: (Editor with James E. Birren, Samuel W. Greenhouse, Louis Sokoloff, Marian R. Yarrow, and Seymour Perlin, and contributor) *Human Aging: A Biological and Behavioral Study,* U.S. Government Printing Office, 1963; (contributor) Samuel Granick and Robert Patterson, editors, *Human Aging II: An Eleven Year Followup Biomedical and Behavioral Study,* U.S. Government Printing Office, 1971; *Why Survive? Being Old in America,* Harper, 1975.

With wife, Myrna Lewis: *Aging and Mental Health: Positive Psychosocial Approaches,* Mosby, 1973, 2nd edition, 1977; *Sex after Sixty: A Guide for Men and Women for Their Later Years,* Harper, 1976.

Contributor of more than one hundred articles related to aging to professional journals. Member of editorial board of *Journal of Geriatric Psychiatry*, 1967—, and *Aging and Human Development*, 1970—.

WORK IN PROGRESS: Introductory Handbook on Aging, for Mosby; *Growing Older* and *The Graying of Nations*, for Harper.

SIDELIGHTS: Robert Butler told *CA:* "I am deeply distressed by the human tendency to deny reality self-destructively (beyond healthy illusions and hopefulness). One major subject of denial is aging. I seek to help myself and others to confront the facts of age—and its rich possibilities as well." *Avocational interests:* Travel, politics, reading history and autobiographies, and jogging.

* * *

BUTTS, Porter (Freeman) 1903-

PERSONAL: Born February 23, 1903, in Pana, Ill.; son of Robert Freeman and Cornelia Ann (Paddock) Butts; married Mary Louise Campbell, May 31, 1932; children: Sherrill P. (Mrs. Douglas Randall), Priscilla G. *Education:* University of Wisconsin, B.A., 1924, M.A., 1936. *Home:* 2900 Hunter Hill, Madison, Wis. 53705. *Office:* Wisconsin Union, 800 Langden St., Madison, Wis. 53706.

CAREER: University of Wisconsin—Madison, alumni recorder, 1924-26, director of Wisconsin Union, 1927-68, director of development, Wisconsin Union, 1968—, professor of social education, 1935—. Chairman, Wisconsin Centennial Art Exhibition, 1936; member of board of directors, Metropolitan Madison War Memorial Association, 1945-53; secretary-treasurer, Madison Community Welfare Council, 1950-55. Member of National Housing Advisory Committee, 1956-62; planning consultant for more than one hundred college union buildings and for Milwaukee War Memorial Cultural Center.

MEMBER: Association of College Unions-International (president, 1932; member of executive committee, 1936-70), Madison Art Association (secretary-treasurer, 1928-35), Phi Kappa Phi, Sigma Delta Chi, Rotary Club of Madison. *Awards, honors:* First recipient of Butts-Whiting Award established by Association of College Unions-International, 1967; Porter Butts Creative Arts Award was established in his honor by trustees of Memorial Union Building Association at University of Wisconsin, 1968; the 1970 conference of Association of College Unions-International was designated the Porter Butts Conference; University of Wisconsin Alumni Association Distinguished Service Award, 1975.

WRITINGS: Art in Wisconsin, Madison Art Association, 1936; *State of the College Union around the World*, Association of College Unions-International, 1967; *The College Union Idea* (writings and addresses of Butts), Association of College Unions-International, 1971. Author of *Planning and Operating College Union Buildings* and other booklet-manuals published by Association of College Unions-International; also author of "Ivan Ho!," a musical play, produced in 1925. Contributor to *Handbook of College and University Administration*, McGraw, 1970, *College Student Personnel Readings*, Houghton, 1970, and to *International Encyclopedia of Higher Education*, Jossey-Bass, 1977. Editor of publications, including quarterly bulletin, Association of College Unions-International, 1936-70; member of editorial board, *College and University Business* (magazine), 1949-53.

AVOCATIONAL INTERESTS: Canoeing in Wisconsin and Canada, regional art history, billiards, skiing, snorkeling, fishing.

BIOGRAPHICAL/CRITICAL SOURCES: Bulletin of Association of College Unions-International, March, 1970.

* * *

BUXTON, Edward F(ulton) 1917-

PERSONAL: Born May 8, 1917, in Boston, Mass.; son of Edward W. (a businessman) and Grace (Hurlburt) Buxton; married Susan Abrams (an editor); children: (previous marriage) Gail, Leslie. *Education:* University of Wisconsin, B.A., 1941; graduate study at Northwestern University. *Politics:* Democrat. *Home:* 185 East 85th St., New York, N.Y. 10028. *Agent:* Arthur Pine Associates, Inc., 1780 Broadway, New York, N.Y. 10019. *Office:* 400 East 54th St., New York, N.Y. 10022.

CAREER: Writing and creative supervision positions with major ad agencies, including J. Walter Thompson, 1946-65; Executive Communications, Inc., New York, N.Y., founder and president, 1965—, owner, publisher, and editor of *Ad Day/USA*, 1965—. *Military service:* U.S. Navy, Amphibious Forces, 1941-45; became lieutenant junior grade.

WRITINGS: Promise Them Anything, Stein & Day, 1972; *New Business Tactics*, Executive Communications, 1976; *Creative People at Work*, Executive Communications, 1977. Also author of reports and studies; compiler of management and marketing portfolios.

WORK IN PROGRESS: Research on advertising marketing and management; public speaking; business seminars.

C

CADENHEAD, Ivie E(dward), Jr. 1923-

PERSONAL: Born November 23, 1923, in Montgomery, Ala.; son of Ivie Edward and Annie (Slocomb) Cadenhead; married Margaret Alice Shugart, August 9, 1947; children: Karen, Edward, Kristin, Patricia. *Education:* Attended Vanderbilt University, 1943-44; Alabama Polytechnic Institute (now Auburn University), B.S., 1946, M.S., 1947; University of Missouri, Ph.D., 1950. *Politics:* Democrat. *Religion:* Unitarian Universalist. *Home:* 5125 East 25th Pl., Tulsa, Okla. 74114. *Office:* History Department, University of Tulsa, 600 South College, Tulsa, Okla. 74104.

CAREER: Alabama Polytechnic Institute (now Auburn University), Auburn, part-time instructor in mathematics, 1946; *Baldwin Times,* Bay Minette, Ala., assistant editor, 1947-48; University of Tulsa, Tulsa, Okla., assistant professor, 1950-55, associate professor, 1955-63, professor of history, 1963—. Democratic nominee for Congress from Oklahoma, 1966. Member of Gilcrease Institute Library Commission, 1959-63. *Military service:* U.S. Army Air Forces, communications officer, 1943-46; became second lieutenant. *Member:* Conference on Latin American History, American Association of University Professors, Organization of American Historians, Midcontinent American Studies Association (member of board of directors, 1962-63), Southern Historical Association, Phi Alpha Theta, Omicron Delta Kappa. *Awards, honors:* Organization of American States Essay Prize, 1972.

WRITINGS: Literature and History (monograph), University of Tulsa, 1970; *Jesus Gonzalez Ortega and Mexican National Politics,* Texas Christian University Press, 1972; *Juarez y su Obra,* Colegio de Mexico, 1973; *Benito Juarez,* Twayne, 1973; (editor with Kenneth Colegrove) *Theodore Roosevelt: The Paradox of Progressivism,* Barron, 1974. Contributor of articles and reviews to history and social science journals, and to *Liberal Context, Journal of Church and State, Craftsman,* and newspapers.

WORK IN PROGRESS: Research on the history of Mexico and Guatemala.

*   *   *

CAFFERTY, Bernard 1934-

PERSONAL: Born June 27, 1934, in Blackburn, England; son of Austin and Mary Margaret (Croft) Cafferty. *Education:* University of Birmingham, B.A. (honors), 1954; also studied at Birmingham College of Commerce, 1960-65. *Home:* 4-46 Sheepcote St., Birmingham B16 8AJ, England.

CAREER: Schoolmaster, 1959-70; free-lance writer, 1970—. *Military service:* British Army, 1954-56; became second lieutenant. *Member:* Institute of Linguists (London; fellow).

WRITINGS: (Translator) *Candidates Matches: Chess Player,* 1965 edition, 1966, 1968 edition, 1969, 1971 edition, 1972; (translator) Alexander Kotov, *Think Like a Grandmaster,* Batsford, 1971; (translator) Mikhail M. Botvinnik, *Botvinnik's Best Games: 1947-1970,* Batsford, 1972; *Spassky's Best Games,* Batsford, 1972; *Tal's One Hundred Best Games: 1960-73,* Batsford, 1975; (with Tim Harding) *Play the Evans Gambit,* R. Hale, 1976; (with D. V. Hooper) *Play for Mate,* Bell & Hyman, 1977; *A Complete Defence to 1P-Q4,* Pergamon, 1979. Chess columnist, *Birmingham Evening Mail,* 1966—. Contributor to *Chess* and *British Chess.*

*   *   *

CAINE, Stanley P(aul) 1940-

PERSONAL: Born February 11, 1940, in Huron, S.D.; son of Louis Vernon (a former college president) and Elizabeth (Holland) Caine; married Karen Mickelson, July 11, 1963; children: Rebecca, Kathryn, David. *Education:* Macalester College, B.A., 1962; University of Wisconsin, M.S., 1964, Ph.D., 1967. *Religion:* Presbyterian. *Home and office:* Department of History, Hanover College, Hanover, Ind. 47243.

CAREER: Lindenwood Colleges, St. Charles, Mo., assistant professor of history, 1967-71; DePauw University, Greencastle, Ind., assistant professor of history, 1971-77; Hanover College, Hanover, Ind., professor of history and vice-president for academic affairs, 1977—. *Member:* Organization of American Historians, American Historical Association, National Association for the Advancement of Colored People. *Awards, honors:* D. C. Everest Prize in Wisconsin Economic History given by State Historical Society of Wisconsin for *The Myth of a Progressive Reform,* 1968.

WRITINGS: The Myth of a Progressive Reform, State Historical Society of Wisconsin, 1970; (editor with Roger Wyman) Emanuel Philipp, *Political Reform in Wisconsin,* State Historical Society of Wisconsin, 1973; (contributor) Lewis Gould, editor, *The Progressive Era,* Syracuse University Press, 1974. Contributor to *Business History Review*.

* * *

CALABRESI, Guido 1932-

PERSONAL: Born October 18, 1932, in Milan, Italy; brought to United States in 1939, naturalized in 1948; married Anne Gordon Audubon Tyler, May 20, 1961; children: Bianca Contini, Anne Gordon Audubon, Massimo Franklin Tyler. *Education:* Yale University, B.S. (summa cum laude), 1953, LL.B. (magna cum laude), 1958; Magdalen College, Oxford, B.A. (first class honors), 1955, M.A., 1959. *Office:* Law School, Yale University, New Haven, Conn. 06520.

CAREER: Simpson, Thacher & Bartlett (law firm), New York, N.Y., law clerk, summer, 1957; admitted to Connecticut Bar, 1958; law clerk to Justice Hugo Black of U.S. Supreme Court, 1958-59; Yale University, New Haven, Conn., assistant professor, 1959-61, associate professor, 1961-62, professor, 1962-70, John Thomas Smith Professor of Law, 1970-78, Sterling Professor of Law, 1978—, fellow of Timothy Dwight College, 1960—. Visiting professor at University of Florence, spring, 1969 and winter and spring, 1973, Harvard University, 1969-70, and Kyoto-Doshisha Universities, summer, 1972. Consultant to U.S. Department of Transportation, 1968-70, and State of New York, 1969-70. Member of Connecticut Commission on Medicolegal Investigations, 1969-71, Committee on Legal Issues in Medical Care, 1970-76, Center for Consumer Product Safety, 1973-75, and National Commission on Critical Choices for Americans, 1973-76; selectman, Woodbridge, Conn. Member of board of directors of Crosby Co. and First New Haven National Bank. Trustee of St. Thomas More Chapel (Yale University), Connecticut State College, Catholic University of America, Lehrman Institute, Russell Sage Foundation, and Carolyn Foundation; president of board of trustees, Hopkins Grammar School. Member of advisory board, Joseph and Rose Kennedy Institute for the Study of Bioethics.

MEMBER: National Academy of Sciences (member of council, 1974-76), American Academy of Arts and Sciences (fellow), Associazione Italiana di Diritto Comparato, Elizabethan Club (Yale University; member of board of directors), Yale Club of New York, New Haven Lawn Club, Phi Beta Kappa. *Awards, honors:* Rhodes scholar, 1953; M.A., Yale University, 1962.

WRITINGS: The Costs of Accidents: A Legal and Economic Analysis, Yale University Press, 1970; (with P. Bobbitt) *Tragic Choices,* Norton, 1978.

Contributor: R. L. Landau, editor, *Regulating New Drugs,* University of Chicago Press, 1973; E. S. Phelps, editor, *Altruism, Morality, and Economic Theory,* Russell Sage, 1975; B. Schwartz, editor, *American Law: The Third Century,* Fred B. Rothman, 1976; Simon Rottenberg, editor, *The Economics of Medical Malpractice,* American Enterprise Institute for Public Policy Research, 1978. Also contributor to *Ethics of Medical Care,* edited by L. Tancredi. Contributor to law, labor, and economics journals, and to *Forum* and *Daedalus.* Member of advisory board, *Environmental Law Reporter,* 1970—.

WORK IN PROGRESS: Concerning Cause and the Law of Torts; The Common Law Function in the Age of Statutes.

BIOGRAPHICAL/CRITICAL SOURCES: New York Times Book Review, June 25, 1978.

CALKIN, Homer Leonard 1912-

PERSONAL: Born May 5, 1912, in Clearfield, Iowa; son of Henry Orlando (a farmer) and Ina (Leonard) Calkin; married E. Corrine Reynolds, June 2, 1938 (died, 1969); married Mary K. Ferriss (a secretary), June 12, 1971. *Education:* Attended Simpson College, 1930-32; University of Iowa, B.A., 1935, M.A., 1936, Ph.D., 1939. *Religion:* Methodist. *Home:* 3830 Columbia Pike, Arlington, Va. 22204.

CAREER: U.S. Department of Justice, Washington, D.C., propaganda analyst, 1942-43; National Archives, Washington, D.C., archivist, 1946-50; U.S. Department of State, Washington, D.C., historian, management analyst, and records management officer, 1950-77, consultant, 1977—. *Military service:* U.S. Army, 1943-46; became first lieutenant. *Member:* American Historical Association, Organization of American Historians, Society of American Archivists, Irish Military History Society, Southern Historical Association, Iowa Historical Society, Cosmos Club.

WRITINGS: Casting from the Foundry Mold, Parthenon, 1968; (with Warren H. Reynolds) *German Documents: 1944-1971,* Foreign Relations Committee, U.S. Senate, 1971; (contributor) Gordon P. Baker, editor, *Those Incredible Methodists,* Parthenon, 1972; *Women in the Department of State,* U.S. Government Printing Office, 1978. Contributor to *Palimpsest, School Review, Military Affairs, Civil War History, Social Education, National Historical Magazine, Public Administration Review, Social Science, Irish Historical Studies, Methodist History,* and other journals.

WORK IN PROGRESS: History of Columbia Historical Society; Minorities in the Department of State.

AVOCATIONAL INTERESTS: Travel (Europe, Middle East, Japan, Hong Kong, Canada, Mexico), music, photography, philately, conchology.

* * *

CALLENDER, Charles 1928-

PERSONAL: Born October 30, 1928, in Union Grove, Wis.; son of Vincent (a gunsmith) and Nellie (Bice) Callender; married Marie L. Furey, November 21, 1949. *Education:* University of Chicago, Ph.B., 1948, M.A., 1955, Ph.D., 1958. *Politics:* Democrat. *Home:* 2512 Edgehill Rd., Cleveland Heights, Ohio 44106. *Office:* Department of Anthropology, Case Western Reserve University, Cleveland, Ohio 44106.

CAREER: Current Anthropology, Chicago, Ill., assistant editor, 1959-61; American University at Cairo, Cairo, Egypt, research associate, 1961-63; University of Delaware, Newark, assistant professor of anthropology, 1963-65; Case Western Reserve University, Cleveland, Ohio, associate professor of anthropology, 1965—. Callender did fieldwork among the Fox Indians, 1954-55, and the Sauk and Prairie Potawatomi, 1955; also in Cairo and Alexandria, Egypt, 1961-62, and Egyptian Nubia, 1962-63. *Member:* American Anthropological Association, Middle East Studies Association.

WRITINGS: (Editor with Sol Tax) *Issues in Evolution,* University of Chicago Press, 1960; *Central Algonkian Social Organization,* Milwaukee Public Museum, 1962; (with Fadwa el Guindi) *Life-Crisis Rituals among the Kenuz,* Case Western Reserve University Press, 1971.

WORK IN PROGRESS: Social Organization of the Kenuz.

CALLOW, James T(homas) 1928-

PERSONAL: Born June 17, 1928, in Toledo, Ohio; son of Wayne (an architect) and Mildred (Machen) Callow; married Patricia Henry, June 12, 1954; children: Kathryn (deceased). *Education:* John Carroll University, B.S.S., 1950; University of Toledo, M.A., 1952; Western Reserve University (now Case Western Reserve University), Ph.D., 1964. *Religion:* Roman Catholic. *Home:* 1014 Key West, Clawson, Mich. 48017. *Office:* Department of English, University of Detroit, College Park Station, Detroit, Mich. 48221.

CAREER: University of Detroit, Detroit, Mich., instructor, 1954-60, assistant professor, 1960-66, associate professor, 1966-69, professor of English, 1969—, director of computerized Folklore Archive. *Member:* Modern Language Association of America, American Folklore Society, Archives of American Art, American Studies Association, Michigan Folklore Society (president, 1977—). *Awards, honors:* National Endowment for the Humanities grant, 1973, 1978; Burroughs Corporation grant, 1977.

WRITINGS: Kindred Spirits: Knickerbocker Writers and American Artists, 1807-1855, University of North Carolina Press, 1967; (with Robert J. Reilly) *Guide to American Literature,* two volumes, Barnes & Noble, 1976-77; (contributor) Andrew B. Myers, editor, *A Century of Commentary on the Works of Washington Irving,* Sleepy Hollow Restorations, 1976; (contributor) *Robert Weir: Artist and Teacher of West Point,* Cadet Fine Arts Forum, 1976. Contributor to literature journals, including *American Literature.*

WORK IN PROGRESS: The History and Minutes of the Sketch Club, 1829-1869; A Manual for Computerized Archiving.

* * *

CALTER, Paul (William) 1934-

PERSONAL: Born June 18, 1934, in New York, N.Y.; son of Arthur and Frances Calter; married Margaret Carey, May 13, 1959; children: Amy, Michael. *Education:* Cooper Union, B.S., 1962; Columbia University, M.S., 1966. *Home:* 33 South Pleasant St., Randolph, Vt. 05060. *Office:* Department of Mathematics, Vermont Technical College, Randolph, Vt. 05061.

CAREER: Columbia University, New York, N.Y., senior research assistant, Heat and Mass Flow Analyzer Laboratory, 1952-57, 1959-60; Kollsman Instrument Corp., Elmhurst, N.Y., development engineer, 1960-65; Intertype Co., Brooklyn, N.Y., senior project engineer, 1965-68; Vermont Technical College, Randolph, 1968—, began as associate professor, currently professor of mathematics. Independent consultant in the design of optical and mechanical instruments and apparatus. *Military service:* U.S. Army, 1957-59. *Member:* Volunteers for International Technical Assistance, Optical Society of America, American Society of Mechanical Engineers, Authors Guild, University Club.

WRITINGS: Problem Solving with Computers, McGraw, 1973; *Graphical and Numerical Solution of Differential Equations,* Educational Development Center, 1977; *Magic Squares* (novel), Thomas Nelson, 1977; *Outline of Technical Mathematics,* McGraw, 1978. Contributor to *Review of Scientific Instruments* and *Journal of Engineering Graphics.*

WORK IN PROGRESS: Place of Oaks, a novel; *Technical Mathematics,* a textbook.

AVOCATIONAL INTERESTS: Painting, sculpture, mountaineering.

CAMPBELL, Jane 1934-

PERSONAL: Born June 4, 1934, in Parry Sound, Ontario, Canada; daughter of Charles Scholfield (a physician) and Edith (Ditchburn) Appelbe; married Craig Campbell (a conservation consultant), April 19, 1965. *Education:* Queen's University, B.A. (honors), 1956; Oxford University, B.Litt., 1959; University of Toronto, Ph.D., 1965. *Home:* 188 Lester St., Apt. 7B, Waterloo, Ontario, Canada. *Office:* Department of English, Wilfrid Laurier University, Waterloo, Ontario, Canada.

CAREER: Wilfrid Laurier University, Waterloo, Ontario, lecturer, 1961-65, assistant professor, 1965-68, associate professor of English, 1968—. *Member:* Canadian Association of University Teachers, Association of Canadian University Teachers of English. *Awards, honors:* Canadian Federation of University Women fellowship, 1958; Canada Council predoctoral fellowship, 1959-60, 1960-61; Canada Council postdoctoral fellowship, 1969.

WRITINGS: The "Retrospective Review" (1920-1928) and the Revival of Seventeenth Century Poetry, Waterloo Lutheran University Press, 1972; (editor with James Doyle, and contributor) *The Practical Vision: Essays in English Literature in Honour of Flora Roy,* Wilfrid Laurier University Press, 1978.

AVOCATIONAL INTERESTS: Conservation, ecology, music.

* * *

CAMPBELL, Jeff(erson) H(olland) 1931-

PERSONAL: Born January 19, 1931, in Beaumont, Tex.; son of William Holland (a court reporter) and Eula (Owens) Campbell; married Shelia Ann Trapp (a freelance writer), September 4, 1952; children: Cary Elizabeth, Susan Holland, William Charles. *Education:* Lamar Union Junior College (now Lamar University), A.A., 1950; Southern Methodist University, B.A., 1952, B.D., 1955; Duke University, Ph.D., 1963. *Politics:* Democrat. *Home:* 410 Morningside, Wichita Falls, Tex. 76301. *Office:* Department of English, Midwestern State University, Wichita Falls, Tex. 76308.

CAREER: Ordained Methodist minister, 1956. Southwestern University, Georgetown, Tex., assistant professor, 1962-64, associate professor, 1964-65, professor of English and chairman of department, 1966-74; Midwestern State University, Wichita Falls, Tex., professor of English and chairman of department, 1974—. Chairman, Georgetown Citizens Advisory Committee, 1969-72; member, Georgetown Urban Renewal Commission, 1972-74; member of board of directors, Wichita Falls Symphony Orchestra, 1976—. *Member:* College English Association, American Studies Association, South Central Modern Language Association (chairman, contemporary literature, 1970), American Studies Association of Texas (vice-president, 1970; president, 1971), Conference of College Teachers of English of Texas (president, 1977-78), South Central Association of Departments of English (president, 1977-78), Texas Association of Departments of English (president, 1970, 1971).

WRITINGS: John Howard Griffin, Steck, 1970. Contributor of articles to *Religion in Life, Studies in the Novel, American Literary Realism, Journal of American Studies Association of Texas, CEA Critic, New Mexico Humanities Review,* and *Southwestern American Literature.*

WORK IN PROGRESS: A book-length study of the novels of John Updike entitled *Thorns Spell a Word.*

CAMPBELL, Randolph B(luford) 1940-

PERSONAL: Born November 16, 1940, in Charlottesville, Va.; son of John Landon (a farmer) and Virginia (Lyon) Campbell; married Diana Snow, June 9, 1962; children: James Landon, Jonathan Clay. Education: University of Virginia, B.S., 1961, M.A., 1963, Ph.D., 1966. Politics: Democrat. Home: 924 Imperial Dr., Denton, Tex. 76201. Office: Department of History, North Texas State University, Denton, Tex. 76203.

CAREER: Virginia Polytechnic Institute and State University, Blacksburg, instructor in history, 1963-64; North Texas State University, Denton, assistant professor, 1966-69, associate professor, 1969-73, professor of history, 1977—. Member: Organization of American Historians, Southern Historical Association, Texas State Historical Association. Awards, honors: H. Bailey Carroll Award from Texas State Historical Association, for best article in Southwestern Historical Quarterly, 1969-70; Charles W. Ramsdell Award, 1973, 1974.

WRITINGS: (With Donald Chipman and Robert Calvert) The Dallas Cowboys and the NFL, University of Oklahoma Press, 1970; (with Richard G. Lowe) Wealth and Power in Antebellum Texas, Texas A & M University Press, 1977. Contributor of articles to Virginia Magazine of History and Biography, Americas, Southwestern Historical Quarterly, Journal of Southern History, Journal of American History, Historian, Louisiana Studies, and East Texas Historical Journal.

WORK IN PROGRESS: A book, The Biography of a Nineteenth Century Southern Community: Harrison County, Texas, 1850-1880; a book, Antebellum Texas Agriculture: A Quantitative View.

* * *

CAMPBELL, Rex R. 1931-

PERSONAL: Born January 8, 1931, in Jasper, Mo.; son of Philip Edward (a farmer) and Lucy (Stricker) Campbell; married Mary Higgins, July 12, 1955. Education: University of Missouri, B.S., 1952, M.S., 1959, Ph.D., 1965. Home: 905 Edgewood, Columbia, Mo. 65201. Office: 104 Sociology, University of Missouri, Columbia, Mo. 65201.

CAREER: University of Missouri—Columbia, county extension agent, 1954-59, instructor, 1960-65, assistant professor, 1965-66, associate professor, 1966-72, professor of rural sociology, 1972—, director of Demographic Data Service, 1970-72. Director, Campbell & Associates (consultants). Military service: U.S. Army, 1952-54. Member: Population Association of America, American Sociological Association, Rural Sociological Association, Midwest Sociological Association, Gamma Sigma Delta.

WRITINGS: Highways and Growth Centers in Missouri, University of Missouri Press, 1967, revised edition, 1969; (with Wayne H. Oberle) Beyond the Suburbs: The Changing Rural Life, Lucas Brothers, 1967; Population and Higher Education in Missouri, University of Missouri Press, 1967; (with Peter C. Robertson) Negroes in Missouri, 2nd edition, Missouri Commission on Human Rights, 1967; (with Robert J. Mahoney and Joseph T. Kunce) The Concrete Jungle, Regional Rehabilitation Research Institute, University of Missouri, 1969; (with Jerry L. Wade) Society and Environment: The Coming Collision, Allyn & Bacon, 1972; (with Dan Johnson) History of Black Migration, Duke Press, 1978. Writer of about thirty research bulletins; contributor of twenty articles to sociology journals.

WORK IN PROGRESS: A book in the area of population.

CAMPBELL, Sheldon 1919-

PERSONAL: Born September 8, 1919, in San Diego, Calif.; son of Arthur Ross and Marion (Sheldon) Campbell; married Florence Officer, August 17, 1947; children: Gregory, Kim (daughter). Education: San Diego State College (now University), B.A., 1947; Stanford University, M.A., 1950. Politics: Republican. Home: 6748 Dwane Ave., San Diego, Calif. 92120. Agent: Knox Burger, 39½ Washington Sq. S., New York, N.Y. 10012. Office: Wagenseller & Durst, 6748 Dwane Ave., San Diego, Calif. 92120.

CAREER: Stockbroker. Rohr Corp., San Diego, Calif., director of manager development and training, 1951-60; Lester, Ryons & Co., San Diego, manager of local office, 1960-67; Roberts, Scott & Co., San Diego, senior vice-president, 1967-74; Wagenseller & Durst, San Diego, vice-president, 1974—. Instructor in business administration, University of California. San Diego Planetarium Authority, president, 1968-76, member, 1976—. Military service: U.S. Army, 1941-45; served in European theater; became technical sergeant. Member: American Association for the Advancement of Science, National Wildlife Federation, Fauna Preservation Society, East African Wildlife Society, Zoological Society of San Diego (trustee), San Diego Hall of Science, San Diego Natural History Society.

WRITINGS: (With Philip S. Campbell and John M. Lexcen) History of the 64th Fighter Wing in World War II, U.S. Army, 1945; (with Charles E. Shaw) Snakes of the American West, Knopf, 1973; Lifeboats to Ararat, Time-Life, 1978. Contributor to San Diego (magazine).

WORK IN PROGRESS: Predators of North America, with James Dolan; The Snakes of Planet Earth.

SIDELIGHTS: Sheldon Campbell told CA: "What turned me back to writing as a nearly full-time occupation was the opportunity brought by the income from some successful investments and a deepening interest in animals and conservation sparked by my long-time association with the San Diego Zoo and in particular a milestone conference on 'The Role of Zoos in Conservation,' which I helped organize in 1966. While I anticipate writing about subjects other than wildlife, most of my time and work will be devoted to saving some of the unique forms that live on this earth with us. In this effort, I hope, my writing will help."

* * *

CANFIELD, Cass 1897-

PERSONAL: Born April 26, 1897, in New York, N.Y.; son of Augustus Cass and Josephine (Houghteling) Canfield; married Katharine Emmet, May 24, 1922 (divorced, 1937); married Jane White Fuller, May 27, 1938; children: (first marriage) Cass, Michael Temple. Education: Harvard University, A.B., 1919; additional study at Oxford University, 1919-20. Politics: Democrat. Residence: Mount Kisco, N.Y. Office: Harper & Row, 10 East 53rd St., New York, N.Y. 10022.

CAREER: Harris, Forbes & Co., New York City, salesman, 1921-22; New York Evening Post, New York City, reporter, 1922-23; Harper & Brothers, New York City, manager of London office, 1924-27, president, 1931-45, chairman of the board, 1945-55, chairman of executive committee and editorial board, 1955-62; Harper & Row, New York City, chairman of executive committee and editorial board, 1962-67, senior editor, 1967—, vice-chairman of Harper's Magazine, Inc., 1967—. Member, New York State Council on the Arts, 1960-64. Military service: U.S. Army,

World War I; became second lieutenant. *Member:* National Association of Book Publishers (president, 1932-34), American Association for the United Nations, Planned Parenthood Federation of America (chairman of executive committee of world population emergency campaign, 1962-67), International Planned Parenthood Federation (chairman of governing body, 1963-70, honorary chairman, 1970—), Century Association, Phi Beta Kappa (honorary).

WRITINGS: The Publishing Experience, University of Pennsylvania Press, 1969; *Up and Down and Around: A Publisher Recollects the Time of His Life,* Harper Magazine Press, 1971; *The Incredible Pierpont Morgan,* Harper, 1974; *Sam Adams' Revolution,* Harper, 1976; *The Iron Will of Jefferson Davis,* Harcourt, 1978.

SIDELIGHTS: Cass Canfield has traveled around the world five times.

* * *

CANNING, Ray R(ussell) 1920-

PERSONAL: Born May 7, 1920, in Afton, Wyo.; son of P. J. (a postmaster) and Mary (Gomm) Canning; married Lois Cook (a teacher), September 23, 1941; children: Craig N., Curtis R., Robin Ann (Mrs. Byron Rice), Russel Lyn. *Education:* Utah State University, B.S., 1942; Brigham Young University, M.S., 1948; University of Utah, Ph.D., 1956. *Politics:* Democrat. *Religion:* None. *Home:* 3397 South 2910 E., Salt Lake City, Utah 84109. *Office:* Department of Sociology, University of Utah, Salt Lake City, Utah 84109.

CAREER: Brigham Young University, Provo, Utah, 1946-59, began as assistant professor, became professor of sociology; University of Utah, Salt Lake City, professor of sociology, 1959—, director of summer school, 1959-61, assistant dean of College of Letters and Science, 1961-63, acting dean, 1963-64. President, Social Research Corp. Board member, Utah Association for Mental Health, 1959-62; president, Family Service Society of Salt Lake, 1969; board member, Salt Lake County Detention Center, 1965-71. *Military service:* U.S. Army, 1942-45; received the Silver Star, Bronze Star with one cluster, and Purple Heart with two clusters; became captain. *Member:* American Sociological Association, American Association for the Advancement of Science, Pacific Sociological Society, Utah Historical Society, Utah Academy of Science, Arts and Letters.

WRITINGS: Social Psychiatry: Readings in Mental Health, Leswing Communications, 1972; (with Gary Madsen) *Introduction to Statistics and the Research Process for Sociologists,* Social Research Corp., 1972; *Danny Climbs the Family Tree,* Social Research Corp., 1973; *The Genteel Gentile: Letters of Elizabeth Cumming, 1857-1858,* Tanner Trust Fund, University of Utah Library, 1977. Contributor of seventy articles to journals in his field. Also author of sheet music including, "Hair of Silver, Heart of Gold," "Who Knows," "My Summer Sweetheart Waltze," "December Is Spring," and others.

SIDELIGHTS: Ray R. Canning is chairman of the board of directors of Writers Assistant Institute, a non-profit corporation organized to encourage and assist creative and scientific writing.

* * *

CANTERBERY, E(stes) Ray 1935-

PERSONAL: Born May 26, 1935, in Corning, Ark.; son of Ottis R. and Elizabeth (House) Canterbery; married Ann K.

Pazdera, January 2, 1960 (divorced October, 1975); married Barbara Post Christensen, December 22, 1975; children: (first marriage) Kathryn Lynn, Jennifer Ann. *Education:* Southern Illinois University, B.A., 1958, M.A., 1960; Washington University, St. Louis, Ph.D., 1966. *Office:* Department of Economics, Florida State University, Tallahassee, Fla. 32306.

CAREER: Arizona State University, Tempe, assistant professor of economics, 1964-65; University of Maryland, College Park, assistant professor of economics, 1965-69; Florida State University, Tallahassee, associate professor, 1970-71, professor of economics, 1972—. *Member:* American Economic Association, Canadian Economic Association, Southern Economic Association. *Awards, honors:* Rockefeller Foundation grant, 1971-73; National Science Foundation grant, 1977—.

WRITINGS: Foreign Exchange, Capital Flows, and Monetary Policy, Princeton University Press, 1965; *Economics on a New Frontier,* Wadsworth, 1968; (contributor) John H. Lindauer, editor, *Macroeconomic Readings,* Free Press, 1968; (contributor) D. Mermelstein, editor, *Economics: Mainstream Readings and Radical Critiques,* Random House, 1970; *The Making of Economics,* Wadsworth, 1976; (with Frederick W. Bell) *Aqua-Culture and the Developing Countries: A Feasibliity Study,* Ballinger, 1976; (contributor) M. Sharpe, editor, *The Challenge of Economics,* Random House, 1977. Contributor of articles to *American Economic Journal, Journal of Political Economy, Canadian Economic Journal, National Banking Review, Quarterly Journal of Economics, American Journal of Agricultural Economics, Eastern Economic Journal, Challenge,* and *Western Economic Journal.*

WORK IN PROGRESS: Macroeconomic Theory: A New Macroeconomics with a New Microanalytic Foundation; Economics: Its Decline as a Moral Science.

* * *

CAPIZZI, Michael 1941-

PERSONAL: Born August 31, 1941, in New York, N.Y.; son of Anthony (a welder) and Mildred (Waldman) Capizzi. *Education:* Educated in public schools in Brooklyn, N.Y. *Politics:* "Anarchist-Libertarian." *Religion:* None. *Office:* Easton Memorial Hospital, Easton, Md. 21601.

CAREER: Brooklyn Public Library, Brooklyn, N.Y., clerk-typist, 1958-61; United Nations, New York, N.Y., administrative assistant, 1961-66; Pennsylvania State University Library, State College, library assistant, 1970-71; Easton Memorial Hospital, Easton, Md., part-time junior outpatient registrar, 1971—. Community worker on New York City's Lower East Side.

WRITINGS: The Boy Who Came Up Quietly, World Publishing, 1971; *Getting It All Together,* Delacorte, 1972. Contributor to national magazines. Publisher and editor, *Peace/La Paz* (community newspaper of Lower East Side).

WORK IN PROGRESS: Utopia Sandwich, a novel on visionary political themes; *US: A First Album,* a novel about a rock and roll band, with music; "Son of Bach Strikes Back," a play; short stories.

AVOCATIONAL INTERESTS: Dance, music, drama, reading contemporary fiction and nonfiction, and travel.††

* * *

CAPLAN, Edwin H(arvey)

PERSONAL: Born in Boston, Mass. *Education:* University

of Michigan, B.B.A., 1950, M.B.A., 1952; University of California, Ph.D., 1965. *Office:* School of Business and Administrative Sciences, University of New Mexico, Albuquerque, N.M. 87131.

CAREER: Certified public accountant in Michigan, 1952, and California, 1956; J. B. Colten & Co., Detroit, Mich., staff accountant, 1950-53; J. J. Gotlieb & Co., Detroit, partner, 1953-56; Humboldt State College (now California State University), Arcata, Calif., assistant professor, 1956-58, associate professor of business administration, 1958-61; University of Oregon, Eugene, associate professor of accounting, 1964-67; University of New Mexico, Albuquerque, professor of business and administrative sciences, 1967—. Visiting professor of accounting, University of California, Berkeley, summer, 1968; co-director of American Accounting Association symposium on behavioral science research in accounting, 1970. *Military service:* U.S. Army, Armored Division, 1944-46.

MEMBER: American Accounting Association, American Institute of Certified Public Accountants, American Economic Association, National Association of Accountants, New Mexico Society of Certified Public Accountants (member of board of directors, 1969-70), Beta Alpha Psi, Beta Gamma Sigma.

WRITINGS: Case Study in Public Administration: Sandia Corporation, Joint Task Force II, Division of Public Administration, University of New Mexico, 1970; *Management Accounting and Behavioral Science,* Addison-Wesley, 1971; (co-author) *Human Resource Accounting: Past, Present and Future,* National Association of Accountants, 1974. Contributor to proceedings. Contributor of articles and reviews to professional journals, including *Accounting Review, Abacus,* and *Management Accounting.*

*   *   *

CAPLOVITZ, David   1928-

PERSONAL: Born February 29, 1928, in New Haven, Conn.; son of Samuel Harry and Jennie (Jablonovsky) Caplovitz; married Paulann Hosler (an attorney), June 8, 1968; children: Abigail. *Education:* University of Connecticut, B.A., 1949; Columbia University, Ph.D., 1961. *Politics:* Democrat. *Religion:* Jewish. *Home:* 325 Riverside Dr., New York, N.Y. 10025. *Office:* Hunter College of the City University of New York, 695 Park Ave., New York, N.Y. 10021.

CAREER: University of Chicago, Chicago, Ill., assistant professor of sociology, 1962-64; Columbia University, New York City, associate professor of sociology and research associate in Bureau of Applied Social Research, 1964-69; Hunter College of the City University of New York, New York City, associate professor of sociology, 1970—. Study director, National Opinion Research Center, 1962-64; member of board of directors, National Institute for Consumer Justice; consultant to U.S. Department of Consumer Affairs, 1970-72. *Member:* American Sociological Association, Law and Society Association (trustee).

WRITINGS: The Poor Pay More, Free Press, 1963; (with Norman Bradburn) *Reports on Happiness,* Aldine, 1965; *The Merchants of Harlem,* Sage Publications, Inc., 1973; *Consumers in Trouble: A Study of Debtors in Default,* Free Press, 1974; *The Religious Drop-Outs: Apostasy among College Graduates,* Sage Publications, Inc., 1977; *The Working Addict,* M. E. Sharpe, 1978.

WORK IN PROGRESS: Making Ends Meet: How Families Cope with Inflation and Recession.

CARDEN, Patricia J.   1935-

PERSONAL: Born October 11, 1935, in Burlington, N.C. *Education:* University of North Carolina, A.B., 1958; Columbia University, M.A., 1960, Certificate of Russian Institute, 1960, Ph.D., 1966. *Home:* 1009 Hector St., Ithaca, N.Y. 14850. *Office:* Department of Russian Literature, 192 Goldwin Smith Hall, Cornell University, Ithaca, N.Y. 14850.

CAREER: Cornell University, Ithaca, N.Y., instructor, 1962-65, assistant professor of Russian literature, 1965-71, associate professor, 1971-77, professor of Slavic studies, 1978—. *Member:* Phi Beta Kappa. *Awards, honors:* Clark Award for the Advancement of Teaching, 1969-70.

WRITINGS: The Art of Isaac Babel, Cornell University Press, 1972.

*   *   *

CAREW, Dorothy   1910(?)-1973

1910(?)—June 14, 1973; American journalist, editor, and author of books on the Netherlands and Portugal. Obituaries: *New York Times,* June 16, 1973.

*   *   *

CARFAGNO, Vincent R.   1935-

PERSONAL: Born March 17, 1935, in Norristown, Pa.; son of Vincent and Rose (DiDonato) Carfagno; married Ursula Schmitt (a professor), June 8, 1957; children: Manfred, Roland. *Education:* Self-educated. *Home:* 6 Township Line Rd., Jenkintown, Pa. 19046.

CAREER: Writer. *Military service:* U.S. Army, 1954-56.

WRITINGS—Translator: Wilhelm Reich, *Mass Psychology of Fascism,* Farrar, Straus, 1970; Reich, *Character Analysis,* Farrar, Straus, 1972.

WORK IN PROGRESS: Translating *Function of the Orgasm,* by Wilhelm Reich, for Farrar, Straus; *Creators of Mind,* a volume of essays examining teachings and visions of Melville, Shaw, Jesus, Blake, and Nietzsche.

BIOGRAPHICAL/CRITICAL SOURCES: New Leader, February 8, 1971.

*   *   *

CARLILE, Clark S(tites)   1912-

PERSONAL: Born March 28, 1912, in Jetmore, Kan.; son of George Edward (a realtor) and Ola L. (Stites) Carlile; married Flora B. Smith (manager of a publishing company), September 3, 1941. *Education:* Fort Hays Kansas State College, A.B., 1939; Colorado State College of Education (now University of Northern Colorado), M.A., 1942; University of Iowa, graduate study, 1943, 1946. *Politics:* "Don't vote a straight ticket." *Religion:* Protestant. *Home:* 1430 Sunset Rd., Pocatello, Idaho 83201.

CAREER: Elementary school teacher in Jetmore, Kan., 1932-35; high school teacher in Medicine Lodge, Kan., 1939-41, and Salina, Kan., 1941-43; Beech Aircraft Corp., Wichita, Kan., member of staff in education and personnel departments, 1943-45; Texas College of Arts and Industries (now Texas A & I University), Kingsville, associate professor of speech and acting head of department, 1946-67; Idaho State University, Pocatello, assistant professor, 1947-52, associate professor, 1956-62, professor of speech, 1962-73, professor emeritus, 1973—. Owner, Clark Publishing Co., 1948—. *Member:* Speech Association of America, National Society for the Study of Communication, American Association of University Professors, Pi Kappa Phi, Pi Kappa Delta.

WRITINGS: Thirty-Eight Basic Speech Experiences, Clark Publishing, 1948, 6th edition, 1977; *Project Text for Public Speaking,* Harper, 1953, 3rd edition, 1972; *Brief Project Text for Public Speaking,* Harper, 1957. Contributor of articles and reviews to professional journals.

WORK IN PROGRESS: Fourth edition of *Project Text for Public Speaking.*

AVOCATIONAL INTERESTS: Fishing, skiing, travel in North America, the Pacific, and Europe.

* * *

CARLSON, Lewis H(erbert) 1934-

PERSONAL: Surname changed in infancy; born August 1, 1934, in Muskegon, Mich.; son of Robert and Margaret (Carlson) Lavine; married Semona Conrad (a teacher), December 26, 1960; children: Ann Margaret, Linda Louise. *Education:* University of Michigan, B.A., 1957, M.A.,1962; Michigan State University, Ph.D., 1967. *Politics:* Mostly Democrat. *Home:* 3530 Meadowcroft Dr., Kalamazoo, Mich. 49007. *Office:* Department of History, Western Michigan University, Kalamazoo, Mich. 49001.

CAREER: High school teacher in Muskegon, Mich., 1960-61, Los Angeles, 1962-63; Ferris State College, Big Rapids, Mich., assistant professor of history, 1965-68; Western Michigan University, Kalamazoo, assistant professor, 1968-71, associate professor of history, 1971—. *Military service:* U.S. Army, 1957-59. *Member:* American Studies Association, Association for the Study of Negro Life and History, National Association of Popular Culture, Michigan American Studies Association (president, 1971-72).

WRITINGS: (Contributor) Joseph S. Roucek and Thomas Kiernan, editors, *The Negro Impact on Western Civilization,* Philosophical Library, 1970; (editor with Colburn George) *In Their Place,* introduction by George McGovern, Wiley, 1972.

WORK IN PROGRESS: A History of American Spectator Sports.

AVOCATIONAL INTERESTS: Trout fishing, wine tasting, travel.

* * *

CARLSON, Robert E(ugene) 1922-

PERSONAL: Born January 22, 1922, in Johnstown, Pa.; son of Thomas L. and Mary M. (Nelson) Carlson; married Marjorie J. Sprengel (a personnel supervisor), August 10, 1946; children: Neal, Valerie L. *Education:* University of Pittsburgh, B.A. (with highest honors), 1943, M.A., 1950, Ph.D., 1955. *Home:* 843 Church Ave., West Chester, Pa. 19380. *Office:* Department of History, West Chester State College, West Chester, Pa. 19380.

CAREER: University of Pittsburgh, Pittsburgh, Pa., lecturer, 1947-52, instructor, 1952-55, assistant professor of history, 1955-61; West Chester State College, West Chester, Pa., professor of history, 1961—, chairman of department, 1967-70, 1975—, associate dean for graduate studies, 1970-72. *Military service:* U.S. Navy, 1943-46; became commander. *Member:* American Historical Association, American Association of University Professors, Society for the History of Technology, U.S. Naval Institute, Pennsylvania Historical Association, Chester County Historical Society.

Awards, honors: Grant-in-aid from American Council of Learned Societies, 1961, and from American Philosophical Society, 1961, and 1969.

WRITINGS: The Liverpool and Manchester Railway Project, 1821-1831, Augustus M. Kelley, 1969. Contributor to *Encyclopaedia Britannica.* Contributor of articles and book reviews to *American Historical Review, Journal of Southern History, Technology and Culture, Business History Review, Pennsylvania Magazine of History and Biography, Pennsylvania History,* and *Pennsylvania Heritage.*

WORK IN PROGRESS: Research on American and British transportation subjects, 1820-1835; a bibliography of Chester County and Countians.

* * *

CARLSON, Roy L(incoln) 1930-

PERSONAL: Born June 25, 1930, in Bremerton, Wash.; son of Peter Lincoln (a shipbuilder) and Margaret Mary (Clark) Carlson; married Maureen J. Kelly, June 13, 1953; children: Catherine Carroll, Daniel James, Arne Kelly, Christopher Clark. *Education:* University of Washington, Seattle, B.A., 1952, M.A., 1955; University of Arizona, Ph.D., 1961. *Home:* 888 Seymour Dr., Coquitlam, British Columbia, Canada. *Office:* Department of Archaeology, Simon Fraser University, Burnaby, British Columbia, Canada V5A 1S6.

CAREER: Klamath County Museum, Klamath Falls, Ore., curator and director, 1957-58; University of Colorado, Boulder, assistant professor, 1961-66, curator of Southwestern archaeology, 1962-66, field director of Fourth Nubian Expedition, 1965-66; Simon Fraser University, Burnaby, British Columbia, assistant professor of anthropology, 1966-67, associate professor, 1967-71, professor of archaeology, 1971—, director of archaeological studies, 1969—, currently chairman of department of archaeology. *Military service:* U.S. Army, Medical Service, 1955-56. *Member:* American Association for the Advancement of Science, Society for American Archaeology, Canadian Archaeological Association.

WRITINGS: Basket Maker III Sites near Durango, Colorado, University of Colorado Press, 1963; *Eighteenth Century Navajo Fortresses of the Governador District,* University of Colorado Press, 1965; (editor) *Archaeology in British Columbia: New Discoveries,* University of British Columbia Press, 1970; *White Mountain Redware,* University of Arizona Press, 1970; (editor) *Salvage '71: Reports on Salvage Archaeology Undertaken in British Columbia in 1971,* Department of Archaeology, Simon Fraser University, 1972; (with Daniel R. Birch and Arlene Birch) *Early Indian Cultures of North America,* Fitzhenry & Whiteside, 1974; (editor) *Current Research Reports,* Simon Fraser University, 1976. Contributor to professional journals.

WORK IN PROGRESS: Archaeology and Prehistory of the Pacific Northwest; Prehistory of Northwest Coast Indian Art; Paleolithic Industries of the Sudan.

* * *

CARLTON, Henry F(isk) 1893(?)-1973

1893(?)—April 25, 1973; American playwright and radio scriptwriter. Obituaries: *New York Times,* April 26, 1973.

* * *

CARMICHAEL, Leonard 1898-1973

PERSONAL: Born November 9, 1898, in Philadelphia, Pa.;

son of Thomas Harrison (a doctor) and Emily Henrietta (Leonard) Carmichael; married Pearl Kidston, June 30, 1932; children: Martha (Mrs. S. Parker Oliphant). *Education:* Tufts College (now University), B.S., 1921; Harvard University, Ph.D., 1924; University of Berlin, graduate study, 1924. *Religion:* Episcopalian. *Home:* 4520 Hoban Rd. N.W., Washington, D.C. 20007. *Office:* National Geographic Society, 17th and M Sts. N.W., Washington, D.C. 20036.

CAREER: Tufts College (now University), Medford, Mass., part-time instructor in biology, 1923-24, president of the college and director of laboratory of sensory psychology and physiology, 1938-52; Princeton University, New Brunswick, N.J., instructor, 1924-26, assistant professor of psychology, 1926-27; Brown University, Providence, R.I., associate professor, 1927-28, professor of psychology, 1928-36, director of psychology laboratory, 1927-36, director of laboratory of sensory physiology, 1934-36; University of Rochester, Rochester, N.Y., chairman of department of psychology and dean of Faculty of Arts and Sciences, 1936-38; Smithsonian Institution, Washington, D.C., seventh secretary, 1953-64; National Geographic Society, Washington, D.C., vice-president for research and exploration, 1964-73. Harvard University, lecturer, 1927-31, visiting professor of psychology, 1935; visiting professor, Clark University, 1931-32, Radcliffe College, 1935, and University of Washington, 1940; lecturer, Naval War College; Arthur D. Little Lecturer, Massachusetts Institute of Technology, 1953; Herbert Langfeld Lecturer, Princeton University, 1968. Member of science committee, National Resources Planning Board, 1941-43; member of applied psychology panel, Office of Science Research and Development, 1942-45; Yerkes Laboratories in Primate Biology, member of board of scientific directors, 1942-69, chairman, 1942-60; member of administrators special committee, Veterans Administration, 1945-52; member, Naval Research Advisory Committee, 1947-52; member of committee on human resources, Research and Development Board, 1952-53; member of committee on research, Educational Testing Service, 1952-57; member of board of science directors and trustee, Roscoe B. Jackson Memorial Laboratory, 1952-73; Army Scientific Advisory Panel, member, 1956-62, consultant, 1963-73; National Advisory Committee for Aeronautics, member, 1952-58, vice-chairman, 1956-58; member of scientific advisory board, Tulane Delta Regional Primate Research Center, 1964-73. Chairman of committee on science research personnel, War Manpower Commission, 1941-43; vice-chairman, Harvard Foundation for Advanced Study and Research, 1951-54, 1958-64; chairman of U.S. Delegation, International Conference and signer for United States of Treaty for Protection of Cultural Property in Time of War, The Hague, 1954. Director, National Roster of Scientific and Specialized Personnel, 1940-44; director of human resources, National Security Resources Board, 1948; director, Research Corp.; member board of trustees, Brookings Institution, Tufts University, George Washington University, and Brown University; Science Service, president of the board of trustees, 1955-67, president emeritus, 1972-73. Member of building committee, Washington Cathedral. *Military service:* U.S. Army, 1917.

MEMBER: International Union of Biological Sciences (president, experimental psychology and animal behavior section, 1961-69), International Primatogical Society (president, 1964-68), International Union of Scientific Psychology, Newcomen Society of North America, Ergonomics Research Society of England (honorary member), Societe

Francaise de Psychologie (honorary member), American Academy of Arts and Sciences (fellow), American Association for the Advancement of Science (fellow), American Philosophical Society (president, 1970-73), American Psychological Association (president, 1939-40), American Physiological Society, National Academy of Sciences (chairman, psychology section, 1950-53), National Research Council (chairman, anthropology and psychology division, 1941-44), National Geographic Society (member of board of trustees), Society of Experimental Psychologists, Society for Research in Child Development, Society for Experimental Biology and Medicine, Literary Society, White House Historical Association (director), Phi Beta Kappa, Sigma Xi, Society of the Cincinnati, Sons of the American Revolution, American Legion; St. Botolph Club and Algonquin Club (both Boston); Century Association (New York); National Press Club, Alfalfa Club, Metropolitan Club, Chevy Chase Club, Cosmos Club (all Washington, D.C.).

AWARDS, HONORS—Degrees: Sc.D., Tufts College (now University), 1937, Brown University, 1952, Lowell Technological Institute (now University of Lowell), 1955, George Washington University, 1956, Tulane University, 1958, Trinity College, 1960, Worcester Polytechnic Institute, 1964; LL.D., Boston University, 1938, Colgate University, 1938, Northeastern University, 1941, Rhode Island State College (now University of Rhode Island), 1942, St. Lawrence University, 1943, Boston College, 1951, Harvard University, 1952, Amherst College, 1954, University of Massachusetts—Amherst, 1954, Fairleigh Dickinson University, 1959; Litt.D., Portia College, 1939, Clark University, 1953; L.H.D., University of Maine at Orono, 1952; D.C.L., Dickinson College, 1955; D.Sc., Drexel Institute of Technology (now Drexel University), 1959. Other: Knight Commander, Order of Alfonso the Wise (Spain); Knight Commander Cross with star, Order of Merit of Federal Republic of Germany; Commander, Order of Dannebrog (Denmark); Commendatore dell' Ordine al Meriot della Repubblica Italiana; Presidential Citation of Merit, 1942; Hartley Public Welfare Medal, National Academy of Sciences, 1972.

WRITINGS: (With H. C. Warren) *Elements of Human Psychology,* Houghton, 1930; *An Experimental Study into the Prenatal Guinea-Pig of the Origin and Development of Reflexes and Patterns of Behavior in Relation to the Stimulation of Specific Receptor Areas during the Period of Active Fetal Life,* Clark University, 1934; (contributor) Edwin G. Boring, H. S. Landfeld, and H. P. Weld, editors, *Psychology: A Factual Textbook,* Wiley, 1935; (with others) *National Roster of Scientific and Specialized Personnel,* U.S. Government Printing Office, 1943; (editor and contributor) *Manual of Child Psychology,* Wiley, 1946, 3rd edition, edited by Paul H. Mussen, published as *Carmichael's Manual of Child Psychology,* 1970; (with Walter F. Dearborn) *Reading and Visual Fatigue,* Houghton, 1947, reprinted, Greenwood Press, 1972.

(Editor with Leonard C. Mead) *The Selection of Military Manpower: A Symposium,* National Academy of Sciences, 1951; *Tufts College: Its Science and Technology: A Centennial View (1852-1952),* Newcomen Society in North America, 1952; *Psychology, the Machine, and Society,* Arthur MacGibbon, 1953; *Laziness and the Scholarly Life,* Brown University, 1954; *Joseph Henry 1797-1878, and His Smithsonian Institution,* Newcomen Society in North America, 1956; *The Making of Modern Mind,* Elsevier Press, 1956; (editor) Carl Random Rogers, *Counseling and Psychotherapy: Newer Concepts in Practice,* Houghton,

1957; *Basic Psychology: A Study of the Modern Healthy Mind,* Random House, 1957; *Karl Spencer Lashby, Experimental Psychologist,* [New York], 1959; *Reading and Education Reevaluated,* privately printed, 1959; *The Smithsonian: Magnet on the Mall,* National Geographic Society, 1960; (with J. C. Long) *James Smithson and the Smithsonian Story,* Putnam, 1965; (editor) Marvin David Glock, *The Improvement of College Reading,* 2nd edition, Houghton, 1967. Contributor of articles to psychology journals. Editor, series of books on psychology for Houghton Mifflin Co.; associate editor, *Journal of Genetic Psychology, Genetic Psychology Monographs,* and *British Journal of Educational Psychology.*

WORK IN PROGRESS: The ethology of prenatal and early postnatal mammalian behavior development.

SIDELIGHTS: Leonard Carmichael had a long and distinguished career as a scientist, educator, and official of two large American institutions. He pioneered the research into the role of heredity in development. While chairman of the psychology department at Brown University, Carmichael and Dr. Herbert Jasper developed electroencephalography, the measurement of brain waves. At the age of 39 Carmichael became the president of Tufts College, one of the youngest in the school's history.

While he was the secretary of the Smithsonian Institution, Carmichael oversaw the erection of the Museum of History and Technology and the expansion and renovation of the Museum of Natural History and the National Zoo. As vice-president and head of research and exploration at the National Geographic Society, he sponsored the work of Dr. Louis S. B. Leakey in East Africa, Jacques-Yves Cousteau's explorations in the Mediterranean, and a successful expedition to the summit of Mount Everest. Dr. Leakey said of Carmichael: "He was one of the greatest men I have ever met. His foresight, and his ability to see the human aspect of research and to inspire people, have contributed substantially to our present store of knowledge."

BIOGRAPHICAL/CRITICAL SOURCES: Edwin G. Boring and Gardner Lindzey, editors, *A History of Psychology in Autobiography,* Volume V, Appleton, 1967; *New York Times,* September 17, 1973; *National Geographic,* December, 1973.†

(Died September 16, 1973)

* * *

CARMILLY, Moshe 1908-

PERSONAL: Surname legally changed, 1949; born April 7, 1908, in Budapest, Hungary; U.S. citizen; son of Solomon and Rosalia (Spitzer) Weinberger; married Rhoda Trotzky, 1975. *Education:* Pazmany Peter University, Ph.D., 1934; Jewish Theological Seminary, Budapest, Rabbi, 1935. *Home:* 65 Central Park W., New York, N.Y. 10023. *Office:* Department of Jewish Studies, Yeshiva University, 186th St. & Amsterdam Ave., New York, N.Y. 10033.

CAREER: Chief rabbi of the Jewish community in Cluj-Kolozsvar, Transylvania, Romania, 1934-44; educator in Israel, 1944-57; Yeshiva University, New York, N.Y., instructor, 1957-58, assistant professor, 1958-64, associate professor, 1964-69, professor of Jewish studies, 1969-77, professor emeritus, 1977—. *Member:* American Association of University Professors, World Union of Jewish studies.

WRITINGS: Jubilee Volume Honoring Dr. P. Lowy, [Cluj], 1939; *Antal Mark Memorial Volume,* [Kolozsvar], 1943; *Sepher Ve-Sayyiph* (title means "Book and Sword:

Freedom of Expression and Thought among the Jewish People"), Sura Institute for Research and Publication, Yeshiva University, 1966; *Memorial Volume for the Jews of Cluj-Kolozsvar,* [New York], 1970; *Censorship and Freedom of Expression in Jewish History,* Sepher–Hermon Press, 1977; (compiler) *Hebrew Poets of Hungary,* Eked Publication, 1977. Contributor to *Encyclopedia Judaica,* and several scholarly journals.

WORK IN PROGRESS: Research on Hebrew literature and Jewish history.

* * *

CARMODY, Jay 1900(?)-1973

1900(?)—June 18, 1973; American drama critic. Obituaries: *Washington Post,* June 20, 1973.

* * *

CAROTHERS, J. Edward 1907-

PERSONAL: Born September 12, 1907, in Las Animas, Colo.; son of John Lewis (a merchant) and Sarah (Brown) Carothers; married Leta Hicks, June 1, 1930; children: Bettie Lee (Mrs. Ken C. Thomas), Joan Marsan (Mrs. Thomas Murphine). *Education:* Asbury College, A.B., 1930; Iliff School of Theology, Th.M., 1935, Th.D., 1938. *Politics:* Independent. *Home:* The Drumlin, Salisbury, Vt. 05769.

CAREER: Ordained minister of United Methodist Church, 1932; served in churches in Colorado, Vermont, and New York, 1930-64; United Methodist Church, National Missions, chief executive, 1964—, executive director of an ecumenical task force on the church and technology, 1970—. Member of general board, and secretary of department of church and economic life, National Council of Churches, 1952-64. Participant in six United Methodist General Conferences. Industrial consultant on the family in society.

WRITINGS: Personal Religious Living, Abingdon, 1948; *Keepers of the Poor,* Board of Missions of the Methodist Church, 1966; *Can Machines Replace Man?,* Friendship, 1966; *The Pusher and Puller: A Concept of God,* Abingdon, 1968; *The Churches and Cruelty Systems,* Friendship, 1970; (editor with Margaret Mead, Roger L. Shinn, and Daniel D. McCracken) *To Love or to Perish: Technological Crisis and the Churches,* Friendship, 1972; *Caring for the World,* Friendship, 1978.

WORK IN PROGRESS: The Tireless Guardian, completion expected in 1980; *The Sun in My Eyes,* 1982.

SIDELIGHTS: J. Edward Carothers told *CA* he is "deeply concerned about the relationship of Christian theology to science and technology. This anxiety for mankind's future motivates my research and writing. [I] took early retirement in order to live in Vermont where I will have time to write popular treatments of the two related themes: (1) Human life is precarious, and (2) God is alive and is holding us responsible for what we do that generates consequences."

* * *

CARPENTER, Elizabeth Sutherland 1920-
(Liz Carpenter)

PERSONAL: Born September 1, 1920, in Salado, Tex.; daughter of Thomas Shelton and Mary Elizabeth (Robertson) Sutherland; married Leslie Carpenter (a press correspondent), June 17, 1944; children: Scott, Christy. *Education:* University of Texas, B.J., 1942. *Politics:* Democrat.

Religion: Methodist. *Home:* 116 Skyline Dr., Austin, Tex. 78746. *Office:* 2313 Red River, Austin, Tex. 78705.

CAREER: Reporter for United Press International, Philadelphia, Pa., 1944-45, and Tufty News Bureau, Washington, D.C., 1945-51; Washington correspondent for a number of newspapers in Texas and elsewhere, 1951-61, and operator with her husband of Carpenter News Bureau; executive assistant to Vice-President Lyndon B. Johnson, 1961-63; press secretary and staff director for Lady Bird Johnson at the White House, 1963-69; Hill & Knowlton International, Washington, D.C., vice-president, 1972—. Member of board of advisors, National Parks Service. Member of council, National Women's Political Caucus. *Member:* Women's National Press Club (president, 1956), Washington Press Club, Theta Sigma Phi, Alpha Phi. *Awards, honors:* Headliner Award of Theta Sigma Phi, 1962; received Woman of the Year award in politics and public affairs from *Ladies Home Journal,* 1977.

WRITINGS—Under name Liz Carpenter: *Ruffles and Flourishes: The Warm and Tender Story of a Simple Girl who Found Adventure in the White House,* Doubleday, 1970; (editor) *L.B.J.: Images of a Vibrant Life,* Friends of the L.B.J. Library, 1973. Also author of a training cassette, "Moving Women into the Organization Mainstream for Profit," produced by CREDR Corp., 1974. Contributor to *Vogue, McCall's, Redbook,* and other magazines and newspapers.

SIDELIGHTS: Portions of *Ruffles and Flourishes,* memoires of the author's days at the White House, were prepublished in two issues of *McCall's* and Pocket Books paid a reported $75,000 for paperback rights to the book.

BIOGRAPHICAL/CRITICAL SOURCES: Life, January 30, 1970; *Best Sellers,* February 1, 1970; *New York Times Book Review,* February 8, 1970; *Esquire,* March, 1970; *Booklist,* April 15, 1970, May 1, 1970.†

* * *

CARR, Gwen B. 1924-

PERSONAL: Born February 6, 1924, in Crookston, Minn.; daughter of Joseph E. (a researcher) and Constance (a teacher; maiden name Enje) Briden; married Harold Geiger (deceased); married Ira T. Carr (a member of U.S. State Department), December 11, 1947 (divorced); children: Jeffrey, William, David, John Michael. *Education:* San Diego State College (now University), B.A., 1951; George Washington University, M.A., 1956; University of Southern California, graduate study. *Home:* 4928 Vista Arroyo Rd., La Mesa, Calif. 92041. *Office:* Department of Psychology, San Diego Mesa College, San Diego, Calif. 92111.

CAREER: Teacher in public schools in Hobart, Washington, 1944-45, Orange County, Calif., 1945-46, and Oceanside, Calif., 1949-50; San Diego State College (now University), San Diego, Calif., play therapist in speech clinic, 1955-57; Carlsbad College, Carlsbad, Calif., instructor in adult education program, 1957-58; Arlington High School, Arlington, Va., teacher, 1959-60; San Diego Mesa College, San Diego, member of faculty in department of psychology, 1961-66; American Schools, Vientiane, Laos, teacher guidance, 1966-67; San Diego Mesa College, professor of psychology, 1968—. Member of vocational education advisory committee, San Diego Community Colleges, 1973, and advisory board, Child Development Center, 1971—. *Member:* American Psychological Association, Psi Chi.

WRITINGS: (Editor) *Marriage and Family in a Decade of Change: A Humanistic Reader,* Addison-Wesley, 1972.

CARRITHERS, Gale H(emphill), Jr. 1932-

PERSONAL: Born April 24, 1932, in Chadron, Neb.; son of Gale Hemphill (a civil engineer) and Hope (Rose) Carrithers; married Joan Lambert, September 8, 1956; children: Sandra, Mary Fay. *Education:* College of William and Mary, B.A., 1953; Yale University, M.A., 1957, Ph.D., 1960; State University of New York at Buffalo, M. Arch., 1973. *Politics:* Republican. *Religion:* Episcopalian. *Residence:* Hamburg, N.Y. *Office:* English Department, Clemens, State University of New York, Buffalo, N.Y. 14260.

CAREER: Duke University, Durham, N.C., instructor in English, 1958-62; State University of New York at Buffalo, assistant professor, 1962-66, associate professor, 1966-71, professor of English, 1971—, research associate in architecture and environmental design, 1969-72, director of Graduate Studies in English, 1974-76, chairman of department, 1977—. Member of Hamburg School District Curriculum Council, 1971-73, and Mayor's Committee on Tax Structure, Hamburg, 1972-73. *Military service:* U.S. Army, Artillery, 1953-55; served in Korea. U.S. Army Reserve, 1955-68; completed Command and General Staff School; became captain.

WRITINGS: Donne at Sermons: A Christian Existential World, State University of New York Press, 1972. Contributor to *College English, Genre, Modern Language Quarterly,* and *English Literary History.*

WORK IN PROGRESS: The 2000 Days, a book on educational programming ideas.

* * *

CARROLL, Berenice A(nita) 1932-

PERSONAL: Born December 14, 1932, in New York, N.Y.; daughter of Morris B. (a chemist) and Margaret (a teacher; maiden name Segall) Jacobs; married Robert W. Carroll (a professor of mathematics), September 7, 1957; children: David L., Malcolm S. *Education:* Queens College of the City University of New York, B.A. (magna cum laude), 1953; Brown University, Ph.D., 1960. *Home:* 2010 Silver Court E., Urbana, Ill. 61801. *Office:* Department of Political Science, University of Illinois, Urbana, Ill. 61801.

CAREER: American Historical Association, Washington, D.C., researcher for War Documents Microfilming Project, 1957-59; City College of the City University of New York, New York, N.Y., lecturer in history, fall, 1960; Douglass College of Rutgers University, New Brunswick, N.J., lecturer in history and political science, 1961-62; Newark State College, Newark, N.J., lecturer in history and political science, 1963-64; University of Illinois at Urbana-Champaign, lecturer, 1965-66, assistant professor of history, 1966-69, assistant professor of political science, 1969-71, associate professor, 1971—. Visiting associate professor, University of Texas at Austin, spring, 1975; director of women's studies and visiting associate professor, University of Maryland, 1975-76. Member of international workshop in world order models project, World Law Fund, 1972; member of symposium on the military and society, U.S. Air Force Academy, 1972; invited participant at UNESCO symposium on causes of violence, 1975, and UNESCO-CPRED international conference on political participation of women, 1978. Treasurer, Champaign-Urbana Legal Defense Fund, 1969-72; founding member, A Woman's Place, Urbana, 1971. Lecturer at various universities in the United States.

MEMBER: American Historical Association (member of professional division committee, 1975-77), American Political Science Association, International Studies Association, Consortium on Peace Research, Education and Development (CPRED; member of executive committee, 1971-75, vice-chairwoman, 1972-73), Conference on Peace Research in History (member of council, 1970-78), Women's Caucus for Political Science (member of executive committee, 1969-70), Coordinating Committee on Women in the Historical Profession (chairwoman, 1969-71), University Women's Caucus (chairwoman, 1971-72), Phi Beta Kappa. *Awards, honors:* Fulbright scholar in Frankfurt-am-Main and Goettingen, Germany, 1956-57; Social Science Research Council faculty research grant, 1968-69; National Endowment for the Humanities research grants, 1975-77, 1977-79.

WRITINGS: Design for Total War: Arms and Economics in the Third Reich, Mouton & Co., 1968; (contributor) Charles A. Barker, editor, *Power and Law: An American Dilemma in World Affairs,* Johns Hopkins Press, 1971; (contributor) Thomas E. Hachey, editor, *The Politics of Partition,* Rand McNally, 1972; (editor) *Liberating Women's History: Theoretical and Critical Essays,* University of Illinois Press, 1976; (contributor) *Encyclopedia of U.S. Foreign Policy,* Scribner, in press. Contributor of articles and reviews to *Journal of Peace Research, Massachusetts Review, Annals, Journal of Conflict Resolution, Feminist Studies,* and to other journals. Guest editor of *Journal of Peace Research,* December, 1969. Co-editor, *Peace and Change: A Journal of Peace Research,* 1972-79.

WORK IN PROGRESS: Research on social and political theory by women; research on powers of the "powerless," on non-organizational forms of communication and social action.

* * *

CARROLL, Daniel B(ernard) 1928-1977

PERSONAL: Born August 24, 1928, in Philadelphia, Pa.; son of Francis M. (a sales representative) and Elizabeth E. (Tarbell) Carroll; married Dolores Anne Sims, November 18, 1961; children: Daniel, John Francis, Mary Elizabeth, Monica, Paula, Dolores, Megan. *Education:* St. Charles Seminary, B.A. (philosophy), 1950; Villanova University, B.A. (general arts), 1951; University of Pennsylvania, M.A., 1955, Ph.D., 1968. *Politics:* Democratic. *Religion:* Roman Catholic. *Home:* 10 Williams Rd., Haverford, Pa. 19041. *Office:* Department of History, Villanova University, Villanova, Pa. 19085.

CAREER: Bishop Neumann High School, Philadelphia, Pa., social studies and English teacher, 1952-57; Archmere Academy, Claymont, Del., teacher of English, 1957-63; Villanova University, Villanova, Pa., instructor, 1963-65, assistant professor, 1965-69, associate professor, 1969-73, professor of history, 1973-77. *Member:* American Historical Association, Organization of American Historians, Society for Historians of American Foreign Relations, American Catholic Historical Association. *Awards, honors:* Gilbert D. Chinard prize from Society for French Historical Studies and the Institute Francais de Washington for *Henri Mercier and the American Civil War,* 1968.

WRITINGS: Henri Mercier and the American Civil War, Princeton University Press, 1971; (contributor) *Diplomacy in an Age of Nationalism,* Nijhoff, 1971.

WORK IN PROGRESS: A book on Franco-American relations in the nineteenth-century period, especially 1848-1852, during which both were republics.

AVOCATIONAL INTERESTS: Classical music, art.†

(Died July, 1977)

CARROLL, Stephen J(ohn), Jr. 1930-

PERSONAL: Born August 23, 1930, in Boston, Mass.; son of Stephen John and Helen (Roach) Carroll; married Donna June Freeman, June 24, 1961; children: Christopher, Alisa. *Education:* University of California, Los Angeles, B.S., 1957; University of Minnesota, M.A., 1959, Ph.D., 1964. *Politics:* Democratic. *Religion:* Unitarian Universalist. *Home:* 3901 Foreston Rd., Beltsville, Md. 20705. *Office:* College of Business and Management, University of Maryland, College Park, Md. 20742.

CAREER: University of Minnesota, Minneapolis, instructor in industrial relations, 1958-61; Villanova University, Villanova, Pa., assistant professor of industrial administration, 1961-64; University of Maryland, College Park, professor of business administration, 1964—. Training and research consultant to more than two dozen organizations. *Military service:* U.S. Navy, 1947-53. *Member:* American Psychological Association, Academy of Management, Industrial Relations Research Association.

WRITINGS: (Contributor) Max S. Wortman, Jr. editor, *Creative Personnel Management,* Allyn & Bacon, 1967; (contributor) *Readings in Management,* Volume I, U.S. Army, 1971; (contributor) Henry L. Tosi, Marvin D. Dunnette, and Robert J. House, editors, *Managerial Motivation and Compensation,* Michigan State University, 1972; (editor with Frank T. Paine and John B. Miner) *The Managerial Process: Cases and Readings,* Macmillan, 1973, 2nd edition, 1977; (with Tosi) *Management by Objectives: Research and Applications,* Macmillan, 1973; (with A. Nash) *The Management of Compensation,* Brooks/Cole, 1974; (with Tosi) *Management: Contingencies, Structure, and Process,* St. Clair, 1976; (with Tosi) *Organizational Behavior,* St. Clair, 1977. Contributor of more than fifty articles to scholarly journals.

WORK IN PROGRESS: With C. Schneier, *The Evaluation of Performance,* for Goodyear Publishing; with Tosi, a second edition of *Management: Contingencies, Structure, and Process.*

* * *

CARSON, Mary 1934-

PERSONAL: Born May 19, 1934, in Baldwin, N.Y.; daughter of Joseph G. (a printer and engraver) and Amelia (Reisert) Koelbel; married Daniel J. Carson (an advertising executive), May 22, 1954; children: Paul, John, Joseph, Theresa, Bernadette, Virginia, Celia, Roberta. *Education:* Attended schools in New York. *Politics:* "Mixed." *Religion:* Roman Catholic. *Home and office:* 2692 Grand Ave., Baldwin, N.Y. 11510. *Agent:* Gary Mac Eoin, 17 Dodd St., Nutley, N.J. 07110.

CAREER: Daniel J. Carson Associates (advertising and marketing firm), Baldwin, N.Y., partner, 1959—. *Member:* Greater City Aquarium Society (Queens, N.Y.).

WRITINGS: Ginny: A True Story, Doubleday, 1971; *A Guide for Friends, Neighbors & Relatives of Retarded Children,* Claretian, 1977; (contributor) John Delaney, editor, *Saints for All Seasons,* Doubleday, 1978; *Making Marriage Last for a Lifetime,* Claretian, in press. Author of "One Mother's View," a column syndicated by Daniel J. Carson Associates, 1970—. Assistant editor, *Modern Aquarium,* 1968-70; editor, *Metropolitan Bride.*

WORK IN PROGRESS: Understanding the Handicapped, for elementary school children; *Kaffe Klatsch with Mary,* a modern view of the Virgin Mary; "Little Lessons in Living,'' a series of children's books; *Bobbie,* story of the author's mongoloid daughter.

BIOGRAPHICAL/CRITICAL SOURCES: New York Daily News, September 26, 1971, January 30, 1972; *Monitor,* October 29, 1971; *Long Island Catholic,* January 6, 1972; *Marriage,* July, 1972.

* * *

CARTER, Henry Hare 1905-

PERSONAL: Born June 28, 1905, in Staten Island, N.Y.; son of Lewis Shelburne and Elizabeth (Ensminger) Carter; married Gloria Maria de Gouveia, April 5, 1945 (divorced, 1956); children: Bruce Edward de Gouveia, Christine Elizabeth Carter Daltro. *Education:* University of Pennsylvania, B.S., 1928, A.M., 1931, Ph.D., 1937; also studied at Centro de Estudios Historicos, 1931, Sorbonne, University of Paris, 1933, Istituto Inter-Universitario, 1937, and Universidade de Coimbra, 1939. *Politics:* Republican. *Address:* P.O. Box 76, Notre Dame, Ind. 46556.

CAREER: Lehigh University, Bethlehem, Pa., instructor in Romance languages, 1928-32; Cedar Crest College, Allentown, Pa., professor of modern languages, 1932-37; Northwestern University, Evanston, Ill., instructor, 1937-40, assistant professor of modern languages, 1940-42; U.S. Naval Academy, Annapolis, Md., instructor in Portuguese, 1945-46; U.S. Department of State, Sao Paulo, Brazil, cultural attache, 1946-47; University of Pennsylvania, Philadelphia, assistant professor of Romance languages, 1947-51; De Paul University, Chicago, Ill., associate professor of modern languages, 1951-52; Colorado College, Colorado Springs, professor of foreign languages and chairman of department, 1952-56; University of Notre Dame, Notre Dame, Ind., associate professor, 1956-62, professor of modern languages, 1962-70, professor emeritus, 1970—. Smith-Mundt traveling lecturer in Spain and Portugal, U.S. Department of State, 1955; visiting professor of general linguistics, University of Recife, 1956. *Military service:* U.S. Naval Reserve, active duty, 1942-46; became commander.

MEMBER: American Association of Teachers of Spanish and Portuguese, Brazilian Academy of Philology, Portuguese Language Society (Lisbon), Academy of Sciences of Lisbon. *Awards, honors:* American Philosophical Society grant, 1959, 1970; American Council of Learned Societies grant, 1967; Gulbenkian Foundation fellow, 1970-71.

WRITINGS: Paleographical Edition and Study of the Language of a Portion of Codex Alcobacensis 200, University of Pennsylvania Press, 1938; *Cancioneiro da Ajuda: A Diplomatic Edition,* Modern Language Association of America, 1941; *Contos e anedotas brasileiros* (graded Portuguese reader), Heath, 1942; *The Portuguese Book of Joseph of Arimathea,* University of North Carolina Press, 1967; *Cuentos de Espana Hoy,* Holt, 1974. Contributor of articles and reviews to language journals.

WORK IN PROGRESS: A Paleographical Edition of the Old-Portuguese Vienna Manuscript of the Quest of the Holy Grail.

* * *

CARTER, Lin 1930-

PERSONAL: Born June 9, 1930, in St. Petersburg, Fla.; son of Raymond Linwood and Lucy (Vrooman) Carter; married Noel Vreeland, August 19, 1964. *Education:* Attended Columbia University, 1953-54. *Religion:* "None, but anti-all." *Home:* 100-15 195th St., Hollis, Long Island, N.Y. 11423.

Agent: Henry Morrison, Inc., 58 West 10th St., New York, N.Y. 10011.

CAREER: Copywriter for advertising agencies and book publishers, 1957-69; full-time free-lance writer of science fiction and heroic fantasy, 1969—. Editorial consultant, Ballantine Books, Inc. *Military service:* U.S. Army, Infantry, 1951-53; served in Korea. *Member:* Swordsmen and Sorcerers' Guild of America (SAGA), Sons of the Desert, Sax Rohmer Society, Trap Door Spiders, James Branch Cabell Society, Dark Brotherhood.

WRITINGS: The Wizard of Lemuria, Ace Books, 1965, revised and expanded edition published as *Thongor and the Wizard of Lemuria,* Berkley Publishing, 1969; *Thongor of Lemuria,* Ace Books, 1966; *The Star Magicians* (bound with *The Off-Worlders* by Howard Hunt), Ace Books, 1966; *The Man without a Planet,* Ace Books, 1966; *Flame of Iridar* (bound with *Peril of the Starmen* by Kris Neville), Belmont Books, 1967; (with Robert E. Howard) *King Kull,* Lancer Books, 1967; (with David Grinnell) *Destination: Saturn,* Avalon, 1967; *Thongor against the Gods,* Paperback Library, 1967; (with L. Sprague de Camp and Howard) *Conan,* Lancer Books, 1967; *Tower at the Edge of Time,* Belmont Books, 1968; "The Thief of Thoth," published in *Two Complete Science Fiction Novels,* Belmont Books, 1968; *Thongor in the City of Magicians,* Paperback Library, 1968; (with de Camp) *Conan of the Isles,* Lancer Books, 1968; *Thongor at the End of Time,* Paperback Library, 1968; (with de Camp and Howard) *Conan the Wanderer,* Lancer Books, 1968; *The Giant of World's End,* Belmont Books, 1969; (with de Camp and Howard) *Conan of Cimmeria,* Lancer Books, 1969; *Tolkien: A Look Behind "The Lord of the Rings,"* Ballantine, 1969; *Beyond the Gates of Dream,* Belmont Books, 1969; *Lost World of Time,* Signet Books, 1969; *Tower of the Medusa,* Ace Books, 1969.

Star Rogue, Lancer Books, 1970; *Thongor Fights the Pirates of Tarakus,* Berkley Publishing, 1970; *Outworlder,* Lancer Books, 1971; (with de Camp) *Conan the Buccaneer,* Lancer Books, 1971; *The Quest of Kadji,* Belmont Books, 1971; *Lovecraft: A Look behind the "Cthulhu Mythos,"* Ballantine, 1972; *Under the Green Star,* Daw Books, 1972; *Jandar of Callisto,* Dell, 1972; *Black Legion of Callisto,* Dell, 1972; *Sky Pirates of Callisto,* Dell, 1973; *The Man Who Loved Mars,* Gold Medal Books, 1973; *The Black Star,* Dell, 1973; (with de Camp) *Conan of Aquilonia,* Lancer Books, 1973; *Imaginary Worlds: The Art of Fantasy,* Ballantine, 1973; *When the Green Star Calls,* Daw Books, 1973; *The Valley Where Time Stood Still,* Doubleday, 1974; *Warrior of World's End,* Daw Books, 1974; *By the Light of the Green Star,* Daw Books, 1974; *Time War,* Dell, 1974; *Dreams from R'lyeh,* Arkham, 1975; *As the Green Star Rises,* Daw Books, 1975; *Lankar of Callisto,* Dell, 1975; *Mad Empress of Callisto,* Dell, 1975; *Mind Wizards of Callisto,* Dell, 1975; *Realms of Wizardry,* Doubleday, 1976; *The Immortal of World's End,* Daw Books, 1976; *The Stone Form Mnar: A Fragment from the Necronomicon,* Mirage Press, 1976; *The Barbarian of World's End,* Daw Books, 1977; *The City outside the World,* Berkley, 1977; (with David Wenzel) *Middle Earth: The World of Tolkien Illustrated,* Centaur, 1977; *Ylana of Callisto,* Dell, 1977; *Pirate of World's End,* Daw Books, 1978; *Renegade of Callisto,* Dell, 1978; *Tara on the Twilight,* Zebra Publications, 1978; *The Wizard of Zao,* Daw Books, 1978; (with de Camp) *Conan the Liberator,* Bantam, 1979.

"Zarkon, Lord of the Unknown" series; published by Doubleday: *Invisible Death,* 1975; *The Nemesis of Evil,* 1975; *The Volcano Ogre,* 1976.

Contributor: John Brunner, *The Evil that Men Do* (contains "The Purloined Planet"), Belmont Books, 1969; Harlan Ellison, *Doomsman* (contains "The Thief of Thoth"), Belmont/Tower, 1972.

Editor: *Dragons, Elves, and Heroes*, Ballantine, 1969; *The Young Magicians*, Ballantine, 1969; *At the Edge of the World*, Ballantine, 1970; *The Dream-Quest of Unknown Kadath*, Ballantine, 1970; *Zothique*, Ballantine, 1970; *Golden Cities, Far*, Ballantine, 1970; *The Magic of Atlantis*, Lancer Books, 1970; *The Doom that Came to Sarnath*, Ballantine, 1971; *Hyperborea*, Ballantine, 1971; *New Worlds for Old*, Ballantine, 1971; *The Spawn of Cthulhu*, Ballantine, 1971; *Xiccarph*, Ballantine, 1972; *Discoveries in Fantasy*, Ballantine, 1972; *Beyond the Fields We Know*, Ballantine, 1972; *Great Short Novels of Adult Fantasy 1*, Ballantine, 1972; *Evenor*, Ballantine, 1972; *Great Short Novels of Adult Fantasy 2*, Ballantine, 1973; *Poseidonis*, Ballantine, 1973; *Flashing Swords 1*, Doubleday, 1973; *Flashing Swords 2*, Doubleday, 1973; *Kingdoms of Sorcery*, Doubleday, 1976; *Flashing Swords 3*, Dell, 1976; *Flashing Swords 4*, Dell, 1977; *The Year's Best Fantasy Stories 3*, Daw Books, 1977; *The Year's Best Fantasy Stories 4*, Daw Books, 1978.

WORK IN PROGRESS: Khymyrium, a multi-volume "epic fantasy in the Tolkien tradition."

SIDELIGHTS: Lin Carter's interests range from the Oz books to archaeology and ancient literatures, and include fairy tales, occult philosophy, oriental verse and mythology, and children's books. He collects antiquities (Egyptian, Etruscan, Greek, Roman), ancient coins, swords, paintings, sculpture, and art nouveau. Some of his heroic fantasies have been published in England, Japan, France, Italy, and Germany.

* * *

CARTERETTE, Edward C(alvin) 1921-

PERSONAL: Born July 10, 1921, in Mount Tabor, N.C.; son of John Calvin (an electrical engineer) and Alma (Fowler) Carterette; married Teresa Sosa, January 18, 1941 (divorced, 1951); married Patricia Speidel Blum, January 18, 1955; children: (second marriage) Christopher. *Education:* U.S. Army Command and General Staff College, graduate, 1943; University of Chicago, B.A., 1949; Harvard University, B.A. (cum laude), 1952; Indiana University, Ph.D., 1957. *Home:* 456 Greencraig Rd., Los Angeles, Calif. 90049. *Office:* Department of Psychology, University of California, Los Angeles, Calif. 90024.

CAREER: U.S. Army, 1937-46, leaving service with rank of lieutenant colonel in Adjutant General's Corps; Massachusetts General Hospital, Boston, research student in Brain Wave Laboratory, 1951-52; Massachusetts Institute of Technology, Cambridge, Acoustics Laboratory, research staff member, 1952; University of California, Los Angeles, instructor, 1956-57, assistant professor, 1958-62, associate professor, 1963-67, professor of experimental psychology, 1968—, member, Brain Research Institute, 1974—. Visiting associate professor, University of California, Berkeley, 1966. University of California Press, editorial committee, member, 1968-77, chairman, 1972-77. Chairman of regional selection board, Woodrow Wilson National Fellowship Foundation, 1966-73. American Psychological Association, visiting scientist, 1964, 1966, consultant, 1968; special reviewer, Division of Psychobiology, National Science Foundation, 1961—, National Institute of Mental Health, 1967—, National Research Council-National Academy of Sciences, 1968-73, National Research Council of Canada, 1976. Con-

sultant, Veterans Administration Wadsworth Hospital Center, Los Angeles, 1978—.

MEMBER: Acoustical Society of America (fellow), American Association for the Advancement of Science (fellow), American Psychological Association (fellow), Society of Experimental Psychologists, International Neuropsychology Society, Institute of Electronic and Electrical Engineers, Association for Computing Machinery, Psychonomic Society, Western Psychological Association, Sigma Xi. *Awards, honors:* Social Science Research Council fellow at Stanford University, 1957; National Science Foundation postdoctoral fellow at Royal Institute of Technology, Stockholm, and Cambridge University, 1960-61, and senior postdoctoral fellow at Stanford Institute for Mathematical Studies in the Social Sciences, 1964-65.

WRITINGS: (Editor) *Speech, Language and Communication*, University of California Press, 1966; (with Margaret H. Jones) *Informal Speech: Alphabetic and Phonemic Texts with Statistical Analyses*, University of California Press, 1975.

Contributor: Joan H. Criswell, Herbert Solomon, and Patrick Suppes, editors, *Mathematical Methods in Small Group Processes*, Stanford University Press, 1962; Weiant Wather-Dunn, editor, *Models for the Perception of Speech and Visual Form*, M.I.T. Press, 1967; K. N. Goodman, editor, *The Psycholinguistic Nature of the Reading Process*, Wayne State University Press, 1968; R. Reinier Plomp and G. F. Smoorenburg, editors, *Frequency Analysis and Periodicity Detection in Hearing*, Sijthoff, 1970; E. F. Beckenbach and C. B. Tompkins, editors, *Concepts of Communication: Interpersonal, Intrapersonal and Mathematical*, Wiley, 1971. Also contributor to numerous other books.

Editor with M. P. Friedman, *Handbook of Perception*, eleven volumes, Academic Press, 1973-78. Also editor, with Friedman, "Cognition and Perception" series, Academic Press, 1973—. Contributor of about sixty articles to professional journals. Review editor, *Journal of Auditory Research*, 1959-70; *Perception & Psychophysics*, consulting editor, 1971, member of editorial board, 1972-73, associate editor, 1973—; editorial consultant at various times to *Journal of the Acoustical Society of America, Science, Journal of Experimental Psychology*, and a number of other journals.

* * *

CARVER, Norman F., Jr. 1928-

PERSONAL: Born January 27, 1928, in Kalamazoo, Mich.; son of Norman F. and Louise (Blackaller) Carver; married Joan Willson (a designer), August 15, 1953; children: Norman, III, Cristina. *Education:* Yale University, B.A., 1951, graduate study, 1951-53; Kyoto University, Kyoto, Japan, graduate study, 1953-54. *Home:* 3201 Lorraine Ave., Kalamazoo, Mich. 49008.

CAREER: Self-employed architect in Kalamazoo, Mich., 1955—. Teacher of advanced photography, Kalamazoo Institute of Arts, 1970—. *Military service:* U.S. Army, 1946-48. *Member:* American Institute of Architects.

WRITINGS—Photographic essays: *Form and Space of Japanese Architecture*, Tuttle, 1955; *Silent Cities: Mexico and the Maya*, Wittenborn, 1966; *Italian Hilltowns*, Documan Press, 1978. Contributor of articles to *This Is Japan*. Contributor of photographs to *House Beautiful* and *Architectural Record*.

WORK IN PROGRESS: Photographic books on Spanish

and Portuguese towns, Japanese farm villages, and the villages of North Africa.

* * *

CASEBIER, Virginia (Eleanor) 1918-

PERSONAL: Born August 26, 1918, in Carmi, Ill.; daughter of George Lawrence (a farmer) and Nelle (Matz) Casebier. *Education:* University of Illinois, B.S., 1945, M.S., 1949; Northwestern University, Ph.D., 1957. *Politics:* Democrat. *Religion:* Baptist. *Permanent address:* 1007 South Locust, Champaign, Ill. 61820. *Office:* Department of Management, University of West Florida, Pensacola, Fla. 32504.

CAREER: Southern Illinois University at Carbondale, instructor and supervisor of business education, 1949-53; Northwestern University, Evanston, Ill., assistant professor of secretarial science, 1954-58; Northern Illinois University, DeKalb, associate professor, 1958-65, professor of finance, 1965-68; University of West Florida, Pensacola, professor of management, 1968—. *Member:* American Institute for Decision Sciences. *Awards, honors:* Ford fellow at Indian University, summer, 1962.

WRITINGS: Quantitative Approaches to Management: A Study Guide, Kendall/Hunt, 1972; *Managerial Statistics,* Interstate, 1977.

All with Manning Hanline, published by Intercollegiate Case Clearing House: *The Devil's Own Wine Shoppe,* 1975; *The Leading Chief and Dr. Likert,* 1975; *A Bank Is a Bank–Is a Bank?,* 1976, revised edition, 1978; *Dues Checkoff: When, at What Cost?,* 1976; *District Hub Proposal,* 1977; *Collective Bargaining in the Sunshine,* 1977; *Do's and Don'ts,* 1977; *Deep Division,* 1978. Contributor of articles to *Southern Journal of Business, Business Education World, United Business Education Association Forum, Illinois Vocational Journal,* and *Small Business Administration.*

WORK IN PROGRESS: A study of personnel reactions at Westinghouse Corp.

* * *

CASH, Joseph H(arper) 1927-

PERSONAL: Born January 3, 1927, in Mitchell, S.D.; son of Joseph R. (a judge) and Claudia (Harper) Cash; married Margaret Ann Halla, December 18, 1952; children: Sheridan Lisa, Joseph Mark, Meredith Ann. *Education:* University of South Dakota, B.A., 1949, M.A., 1959; University of Iowa, Ph.D., 1966. *Politics:* Republican. *Home:* 609 Catalina, Vermillion, S.D. 57069. *Office:* Department of History, University of South Dakota, Vermillion, S.D. 57069.

CAREER: High school teacher in South Dakota, 1952-62; Eastern Montana College, Billings, assistant professor, 1965-66, associate professor of history, 1966-68; University of South Dakota, Vermillion, associate professor of history, 1968-72, Duke Research Professor of History, 1972—, dean of College of Arts and Sciences, 1977—. Chairman, South Dakota Board of Historic Preservation, 1971-73. *Military service:* U.S. Marine Corps Reserve, active duty, 1945-46. *Member:* Organization of American Historians, Oral History Association, Western History Association, South Dakota State Historical Society (president, 1976—).

WRITINGS: (Editor with Herbert T. Hoover) *To Be an Indian,* Holt, 1971; *Working the Homestake,* Iowa State University Press, 1973; (with Ramon Harris, Stephen Ward, and Hoover) *The Practice of Oral History,* Microfilming Corp., 1975; (editor) *American Indian Oral History Collec-*tion, Clearwater Publishing, 1977. Also author of books in "Indian Tribal" series, *The Sioux People,* 1971, *The Mandan, Arikara, Hidatsa Peoples,* 1971, *The Ponca People,* 1975, *The Ottawa People,* 1976, and *The Potawatomi People,* 1976.

WORK IN PROGRESS: The Teton Sioux, for Knopf.

* * *

CASPARI, Ernest W(olfgang) 1909-

PERSONAL: Born October 24, 1909, in Berlin, Germany; son of Wilhelm (a physiologist and director of cancer research) and Gertrud (Gerschel) Caspari; married Hermine B. Abraham (a psychologist), August 16, 1938. *Education:* Studied at University of Freiburg, University of Berlin, and University of Frankfurt; University of Goettingen, Ph.D., 1933. *Home:* 80 Penarrow Rd., Rochester, N.Y. 14618. *Office:* Department of Biology, University of Rochester, Rochester, N.Y. 14627.

CAREER: University of Istanbul, Istanbul, Turkey, assistant in microbiology, 1935-38; Lafayette College, Easton, Pa., 1938-44, began as research fellow, became assistant professor of biology; University of Rochester, Rochester, N.Y., assistant professor of zoology and research associate, 1944-46; Wesleyan University, Middletown, Conn., associate professor of biology, 1946-47; Carnegie Institute of Washington, Cold Spring Harbor, N.Y., research associate, 1947-49; Wesleyan University, associate professor of biology, 1949-60; University of Rochester, professor of biology, 1960-75, professor emeritus, 1975—, chairman of department, 1960-65. Visiting professor, Justus Liebig University, Giessen, Germany, 1975-76. Member of board of trustees, Associated Universities, 1961-67.

MEMBER: Genetics Society of America (president, 1966), American Association for the Advancement of Science (vice-president and chairman, zoology section, 1962), American Society of Naturalists (vice-president, 1961), American Society of Zoologists, Behavior Genetics Association, Society for the Study of Evolution, Society for the Study of Development, American Academy of Arts and Sciences, Phi Beta Kappa, Sigma Xi. *Awards, honors:* M.A., Wesleyan University, 1950.

WRITINGS: (Contributor) Mileslav Demerec, editor, *Advances in Genetics,* Volume II, Academic Press, 1947; (contributor) G. J. Simpson and Anne Roe, editors, *Evolution and Behavior,* Yale University Press, 1958; (contributor) Sherwood L. Washburn, editor, *Social Life of Early Man,* Viking, 1961; (editor with A. W. Ravin) *Genetic Organization,* Volume I, Academic Press, 1969; (contributor) E. Tobach, L. R. Aronson, and E. Shaw, editors, *The Biopsychology of Development,* Academic Press, 1971; (contributor) B. Campbell, editor, *Sexual Selection and the Descent of Man, 1871-1971,* Aldine-Atherton, 1972; (editor with L. Ehrman and G. S. Omenn) *Genetics, Environment and Behavior,* Academic Press, 1973; (contributor) R. J. King, editor, *Handbook of Genetics,* Volume III, Plenum, 1975; (contributor) D. K. Belyaev, editor, *Problems of Experimental Biology,* Nauka Publishing House (Moscow), 1977; (contributor) A. Oliverio, editor, *Genetics, Environment and Intelligence,* North-Holland Publishing, 1977. Contributor of more than a hundred articles to professional journals. Editor, *Advances in Genetics,* 1960—, and *Genetics,* 1968-72; member of editorial boards, *Behavior Genetics* and *Behavioral Science.*

WORK IN PROGRESS: Writing chapters for *Development and Evolution of Brain Size: Behavioral Implications,* for

Academic Press, and *Female Hierarchies,* for Aldine-Atherton.

* * *

CASSARA, Ernest 1925-

PERSONAL: Surname is accented on second syllable; born June 5, 1925, in Everett, Mass.; son of Gaetano Thomas (a clothing designer) and Amelia (St. George) Cassara; married Beverly Benner (a professor), February 7, 1949; children: Shirley, Catherine, Nicholas E. *Education:* Tufts University, A.B., 1952, B.D., 1954; Boston University, Ph.D., 1957; Cambridge University, postdoctoral study, 1962-63. *Politics:* Democrat. *Religion:* Unitarian. *Home:* 10421 Courthouse Dr., Fairfax, Va. 22030. *Office:* Department of History, George Mason University, Fairfax, Va. 22030.

CAREER: Radio news broadcaster in Worcester and Brockton, Mass., 1945-50; Tufts University, Medford, Mass., instructor, 1955-56, assistant professor, 1956-62, associate professor of history, 1964-66; Albert Schweitzer College, Churwalden, Switzerland, director, and professor of history, 1963-64; Goddard College, Plainfield, Vt., professor of history, and dean, 1966-70; George Mason University, Fairfax, Va., professor of history, 1970—, chairman of department, 1970-74. Fulbright professor of history, University of Munich, 1975-76. *Member:* American Association of University Professors, American Historical Association, Organization of American Historians, American Studies Association (president of Chesapeake chapter, 1972-74), Southern Historical Association.

WRITINGS: Hosea Ballou: The Challenge to Orthodoxy, Beacon Press, 1961; (contributor) Frank N. Magill, editor, *Masterpieces of Christian Literature,* two volumes, Salem Press, 1963; (contributor) Edward T. James, editor, *Notable American Women,* three volumes, Harvard University Press, 1970; *Universalism in America: A Documentary History,* Beacon Press, 1971; (editor) *The History of the United States of America: A Guide to Information Sources,* Gale, 1977; *The Enlightenment in America,* Twayne, in press. Contributor to *Encyclopaedia Britannica, Collier's Encyclopedia,* and to professional journals, including *History: Reviews of New Books, Journal of American Studies, Vermont History, American Quarterly, Choice,* and *Revue Internationale de Philosophie.* Member of board of editors, *Current,* 1969-73.

* * *

CASTANEDA, James A(gustin) 1933-

PERSONAL: Born April 2, 1933, in Brooklyn, N.Y.; son of Ciro and Edna (Sincock) Castaneda; married Terrill Lynn McCauley, September 14, 1957 (divorced, 1963); married Mary Sibley, December 12, 1964 (divorced, 1976); children: (first marriage) Christopher James. *Education:* Drew University, B.A. (summa cum laude), 1954; Yale University, M.A., 1955, Ph.D., 1958; University of Paris, Certificat, 1957; University of Madrid, additional study, 1957. *Religion:* Methodist. *Home:* 5467 Loch Lomond, Houston, Tex. 77096. *Office:* Department of Spanish, Portuguese, and Classics, Rice University, Houston, Tex. 77001.

CAREER: Hanover College, Hanover, Ind., 1958-61, began as assistant professor, became associate professor of Spanish and French; Rice University, Houston, Tex., assistant professor, 1961-62, associate professor, 1963-67, professor of Spanish, 1967—, chairman of department of Classics, Italian, Portuguese, Russian, and Spanish, 1964-72. Visiting professor, Western New Mexico University, 1970;

Florence Purington Visiting Professor, Mount Holyoke College, 1976-77. Visiting assistant professor, University of Southern California, 1959. University of North Carolina, visiting lecturer, 1962-63, director of University of North Carolina Year-at-Lyon, France, 1967-68, visiting professor, 1968.

MEMBER: American Association of Teachers of Spanish and Portuguese (former vice-president; president of Indiana chapter, 1959-61; member of executive council, 1976-79), Modern Language Association of America, National Federation of Modern Language Teachers Association (president, 1974), American Association of Teachers of French, American Association of University Professors, Society for Values in Higher Education, Renaissance Society of America, Modern Humanities Research Association, American Society for Aesthetics, International Good Neighbor Council, South-Central Modern Language Association (member of executive committee, 1965-67; executive secretary, 1968-75), Instituto de Cultura Hispanica de Houston (president, 1972), Alliance Francaise (member of board of directors, 1972-74) and Interamerican Club (both Houston). *Awards, honors:* Fulbright scholar in Paris, 1956-57; elected Miembro Titular of the Instituto de Cultura Hispanica de Madrid, 1972; alumni achievement award, Drew University, 1973.

WRITINGS: (Editor) *A Critical Edition of Lope de Vega's "Las paces de los reyes, y Judia de Toledo,"* University of North Carolina Press, 1962; (with others) *Lope de Vega Studies, 1937-1962: A Critical Survey and Annotated Bibliography,* University of Toronto Press, 1964; (contributor) John E. Keller, editor, *Hispanic Studies in Honor of Nicholson B. Adams,* University of North Carolina Press, 1966; (with others) *Calderon de la Barca Studies 1951-1969: A Critical Survey and Annotated Bibliography,* University of Toronto Press, 1971; *Agustin Moreto,* Twayne, 1974; *Mira de Amescua,* Twayne, 1977. Contributor, Andrew Debicki and Enrique Pupo-Walker, editors, *Homenaje a Jose Juan Arrom,* University of North Carolina Press. Contributor to *Studia hispanica in honorem R. Lapesa;* contributor of articles and reviews to language journals. Editor-in-chief, *Hanover Forum,* 1960-61; member of publications committee, *Comediantes* (Spanish III section of Modern Language Association of America), 1962—.

WORK IN PROGRESS: A critical edition of Mira de Amescua's *El esclavo del demonio; Spanish Reader,* Book D, for Houghton.

SIDELIGHTS: "Self-indulgence is perhaps the strongest motivation my writing receives," James A. Castaneda wrote *CA.* "Far from aspiring to enlighten readers, I modestly hope that the accumulation and organization of my research on the Spanish Theatre of the Golden Age, and the attempt at expressing my thoughts, opinions, and judgments on this material will progressively discipline and strengthen my scholarship, while enhancing its communicability." Castaneda continued, "My great enthusiasm for scholarship and writing is maintained by frequent and drastic vacations from the academic mode: ever since my first faculty appointment, I have served as a baseball coach for my college or university . . . and recently I have spent summers as a ranch hand in San Felipe, Texas."

BIOGRAPHICAL/CRITICAL SOURCES: Hispania, December, 1963; *Renaissance News,* summer, 1964; *Hispanic Review,* April, 1966.

CATTELL, Psyche 1893-

PERSONAL: Born August 2, 1893, in Garrison, N.Y.; daughter of James McKeen (a psychologist and editor) and Josephine (Owen) Cattell; children: (adopted) Hudson, Jowain Brinkley. Education: Cornell University, M.A., 1925; Harvard University, Ed.M., 1925, Ed.D., 1927; also studied at Sargent School for Physical Education, New York University, Columbia University, Stanford University, Woods Hole Marine Biological Laboratory, Mount Desert Island Biological Laboratory, University of Vienna, and Temple University. Home: 314 North West End Ave., Lancaster, Pa. 17603.

CAREER: Diplomate of American Board of Examiners in Professional Psychology; Stanford University, Stanford, Calif., research assistant in psychology, 1925-26; private practice in psychology, 1939-71. Founder, and director, Cattell School, 1941-74. Research fellow in School of Public Health, Harvard University, 1932-39; instructor in mental testing, Nursery Training School of Boston, 1936-38; psychologist, Lebanon County Mental Health Clinic, 1939-42; chief psychologist, Guidance Clinic of Lancaster, 1939-63, chief psychologist emeritus, 1963—. Collected and assembled Cattell Infant Intelligence Scale kits, 1940—.

MEMBER: American Psychological Association (fellow), Society for Research in Child Development (fellow), American Ortho-Psychiatric Association (fellow), National Education Association, National Educational Research Association, National Association of Nursery Education, American Association for the Advancement of Science (fellow).

WRITINGS: Dentition as a Measure of Maturity, Harvard University Press, 1928; The Measurement of Intelligence of Infants and Young Children, Psychological Corp., 1940; Raising Children with Love and Limits, Nelson-Hall, 1972. Contributor to annals. Contributor of about twenty-five articles to education and psychology journals, including Mothers' Manual, Review of Educational Research, School and Society, Understanding the Child, Human Biology, Journal of Educational Psychology, Journal of Dental Research, and Journal of Genetic Psychology. Writer of column, "Children Under Eight," in Lancaster New Era, 1964-75.

*   *   *

CAVANAGH, Gerald F(rancis) 1931-

PERSONAL: Born September 13, 1931, in Cleveland, Ohio; son of Gerald F., Sr. and Margaret (Gilmore) Cavanagh. Education: Case Institute of Technology (now Case Western Reserve University), B.S., 1953; St. Louis University, M.B.A., 1958, Ph.L. and M.Ed., 1959; Loyola University of Chicago, S.T.L., 1965; studied theology in Dublin and Paris, 1965-66; Michigan State University, D.B.A., 1970. Politics: Liberal. Home: 4001 West McNichols Rd., Detroit, Mich. 48221. Office: Department of Management and Organization Sciences, School of Business Administration, Wayne State University, Detroit, Mich. 48202.

CAREER: Cleveland Pneumatic Tool Co., Cleveland, Ohio, staff assistant to production manager, 1953; Loyola University of Chicago, Chicago, Ill., instructor in mathematics and physics, 1959-61; ordained Roman Catholic priest of Society of Jesus (Jesuit), 1964; Cambridge Center for Social Studies, Cambridge, Mass., research fellow, 1968-70; Wayne State University, Detroit, Mich., assistant professor, 1970-73, associate professor of business administration, 1973—, chairperson of Department of Management, 1976—. Distinguished lecturer on corporate management

and society, Michigan State University, spring, 1972; University of Detroit, member of board of trustees, 1972—, chairman of board, 1973-75. Member of board of trustees, Fordham University, 1976—. Member: Industrial Relations Research Association, Academy of Management, National Affiliation of Concerned Business Students, Society for the History of Technology, Beta Gamma Sigma.

WRITINGS: (With Theodore V. Purcell) Blacks in the Industrial World: Issues for the Manager, Free Press, 1972; Businessmen in Search of Values, Benziger, 1973, 2nd edition published as Businesspersons in Search of Values, 1976; American Business Values in Transition, Prentice-Hall, 1976. Contributor to proceedings. Contributor of articles and reviews to Contact, Benedictine Review, Catholic Digest, Victorian, and Monthly Labor News.

WORK IN PROGRESS: Research on governance and legitimacy of the corporation, and values undergirding business.

*   *   *

CAWLEY, Robert Ralston 1893-1973

July 18, 1893—May 11, 1973; American educator and authority on Milton and English Renaissance literature. Obituaries: New York Times, May 13, 1973. (See index for CA sketch)

*   *   *

CELL, John W(hitson) 1935-

PERSONAL: Born June 25, 1935, in Champaign, Ill.; son of John Wesley (a university professor) and Louise (Keith) Cell; married Gillian Townsend (a university professor), October 19, 1962; children: Thomas, Katherine, John. Education: Duke University, A.B., 1957, Ph.D., 1965. Politics: Democrat. Home: 1011 Highland Woods, Chapel Hill, N.C. 27514. Office: Department of History, Duke University, Durham, N.C. 27708.

CAREER: Duke University, Durham, N.C., instructor, 1962-65, assistant professor, 1965-71, associate professor of history, 1971—. Military service: U.S. Army, 1957-59. Member: American Association of University Professors, American Historical Association. Awards, honors: Social Science Research Council research training fellow, 1970-71; National Endowment for the Humanities summer fellow, 1973; National Endowment for the Humanities research fellow, 1977-78; Rhodes visiting fellow, Saint Antony's College, Oxford University, 1978.

WRITINGS: British Colonial Administration in the Mid-Nineteenth Century, Yale University Press, 1970; (editor and author of introduction) By Kenya Possessed: The Correspondence of J. H. Oldham and Norman Leys, 1918-1926, University of Chicago Press, 1976.

WORK IN PROGRESS: Research on decolonization in the British Empire; a research project on British attitudes toward Africa, 1918-1939.

*   *   *

CHAMBERS, Clarke A(lexander) 1921-

PERSONAL: Born June 3, 1921, in Blue Earth, Minn.; son of Winslow C. (a physician) and Anna E. (Anderson) Chambers; married Florence Wood (an instructor in rhetoric), February 6, 1944; children: Jenny E., Katherine E., Robert W., Sarah C. Education: Carleton College, B.A., 1943; University of California, Berkeley, M.A., 1947, Ph.D.,

1950. *Home:* 2285 Folwell St., St. Paul, Minn. 55108. *Office:* Department of History, University of Minnesota, Minneapolis, Minn. 55455.

CAREER: University of California, Berkeley, lecturer in American history, 1950-51; University of Minnesota, Minneapolis, instructor, 1951-52, assistant professor, 1952-57, associate professor, 1957-64, professor of history, 1964—, chairman of department, 1971-76, director of Social Welfare History Archives Center, 1964—. *Military service:* U.S. Army Air Forces, 1943-45; served in Pacific theatre; became sergeant. *Member:* American Historical Association, Organization of American Historians, Committee on the History of Social Welfare (past president).

WRITINGS: California Farm Organizations, 1929-1941, University of California Press, 1952; *Seedtime of Reform, 1918-1933,* University of Minnesota Press, 1963; (editor) *The New Deal at Home and Abroad,* Free Press, 1964; *Paul U. Kellogg and the Survey,* University of Minnesota Press, 1971; (editor) *A Century of Concern,* National Conference of Social Welfare, 1973.

* * *

CHANELES, Sol 1926-

PERSONAL: Born September 23, 1926, in New York, N.Y.; married Janine Volski, December 22, 1946; children: Claudie Chaneles Grandberg, Katherine. *Education:* Brooklyn College (now Brooklyn College of the City University of New York), B.A., 1948; New York University, M.A., 1950, Ph.D., 1960. *Politics:* None. *Religion:* None. *Home:* 54 West 74th St., New York, N.Y. 10023. *Office:* Department of Criminal Justice, Rutgers University, New Brunswick, N.J. 08903.

CAREER: Dartmouth College, Hanover, N.H., instructor in sociology, 1957; Brooklyn College (now Brooklyn College of the City University of New York), Brooklyn, N.Y., instructor in sociology, 1958; City College of the City University of New York, New York City, assistant professor, 1960-63; City of New York Department of Correction, New York City, director of research, 1962-65; director of project dealing with children sex victims, American Humane Association, 1965-67; director of Urban Studies Division, Simulmatics Corp., 1967-68; president, Urban Resources, Inc., 1968-71; free-lance writer, 1971-76; Rutgers University, New Brunswick, N.J., associate professor, 1976—, chairman of department of criminal justice, 1976—. Member of President's Task Force on Prisoner Rehabilitation; consultant to presidential commission on crime and civil disorders. *Military service:* U.S. Army, 1943-45. *Awards, honors:* Ford Foundation research grants, 1961-62; New Jersey Bar Association media award, 1978.

WRITINGS: Santa Makes a Change, Parents' Magazine Press, 1970; *Losing in Place,* Avon, 1972; *That Pestilent Comestic: Rhetoric,* Grossman, 1972; *The Open Prison,* Dial, 1973; *Children of the Holocaust,* Avon, 1973; *The New Civility,* Grossman, 1973; *Introduction to Security Administration,* McGraw, 1978.

BIOGRAPHICAL/CRITICAL SOURCES: New York Times, November 21, 1972.

* * *

CHANG, Kwang-chih 1931-

PERSONAL: Born April 15, 1931, in Peking, China; came to United States in 1955, naturalized citizen in 1970; son of Wo-chun (a professor) and Hsin-hsiang (Lo) Chang; married

Hwei Li, May 19, 1957; children: Julian Po-keng, Nora Chung-chi. *Education:* National Taiwan University, B.A., 1954; Harvard University, Ph.D., 1960. *Office:* Department of Anthropology, Peabody Museum, Harvard University, Cambridge, Mass. 02138.

CAREER: Harvard University, Cambridge, Mass., lecturer in anthropology, 1960-61; Yale University, New Haven, Conn., instructor, 1961-63, assistant professor, 1963-66, associate professor, 1966-69, professor of anthropology, 1969-77, director of graduate studies, 1966-69, head of department, 1970-73; Harvard University, professor of anthropology, 1977—. *Member:* American Anthropological Association (fellow), Association for Asian Studies.

WRITINGS: The Archaeology of Ancient China, Yale University Press, 1963, revised edition, 1977; *Rethinking Archaeology,* Random House, 1967; (editor) *Settlement Archaeology,* National Press, 1968; *Fengpitou, Tapenkeng, and the Prehistory of Taiwan,* Department of Anthropology, Yale University, 1969; (editor) *Food in Chinese Culture,* Yale University Press, 1977. Contributor to anthropology journals.

* * *

CHAPIN, Dwight Allan 1938-

PERSONAL: Born June 16, 1938, in Lewiston, Idaho; son of Don Merel and Lucille (Walker) Chapin; married Susan Enid Fisk, February 14, 1962 (divorced, 1973); children: Carla Marie, Adam Charles. *Education:* University of Idaho, B.A. (with honors), 1960; Columbia University, M.S. (with honors), 1961. *Politics:* Democrat. *Home:* 350 Glenview, No. 11, San Francisco, Calif. 94131. *Agent:* Michael Hamilburg, 1105 Glendon, Westwood, Calif. 90024. *Office: San Francisco Examiner,* 110 Fifth St., San Francisco, Calif. 94103.

CAREER: Lewiston Morning Tribune, Lewiston, Idaho, reporter and editor, 1956-62; *Vancouver Columbian,* Vancouver, Wash., reporter and editor, 1962-65; *Seattle Post-Intelligencer,* Seattle, Wash., sports writer, 1965-67; *Times,* Los Angeles, Calif., sports writer, 1967-77; *San Francisco Examiner,* San Francisco, Calif., city columnist, 1977—. *Military service:* U.S. Army National Guard, 1961-67. *Member:* Sigma Delta Chi. *Awards, honors:* Several state and national awards for sports writing, including Sigma Delta Chi award, 1968, National Baseball Writers Association award, 1968, National Basketball Writers Association awards, 1969, 1970, Los Angeles *Times* special award for best news story in any department under pressure, 1972, and finalist for California State Sportswriter of the Year, 1973.

WRITINGS: (With Jeff Prugh) *The Wizard of Westwood* (biography of Coach Wooden of University of California, Los Angeles), Houghton, 1973. Work is anthologized in *Best Sports Stories: 1971,* edited by Irving T. Marsh and Edward Ehre, Dutton, 1971. Contributor to football and basketball annuals and other yearbooks. Contributor to *Pro, Sporting News, Today's Health, Calendar, TV Guide, California Magazine, San Francisco Magazine,* and *California Living.*

* * *

CHAPMAN, James (Keith) 1919-
(Hamish Keith)

PERSONAL: Born April 24, 1919, in Gagetown, New Brunswick, Canada; son of Harry Keith (a barber) and Hazel E. (McGowan) Chapman; married Rhoda Ellen Wilson, October 15, 1941. *Education:* University of New

Brunswick, B.A., 1950, M.A., 1952; University of London, Ph.D., 1954. *Home:* 509 Montgomery, Fredericton, New Brunswick, Canada. *Office:* Department of History, University of New Brunswick, Fredericton, New Brunswick, Canada.

CAREER: University of New Brunswick, Fredericton, instructor, 1951-54, assistant professor, 1954-58, associate professor, 1958-64, professor of history, 1964—, chairman of department, 1970-74. *Military service:* Royal Canadian Air Force, navigator and instructor, 1940-46. *Member:* Royal Commonwealth Society, New Brunswick Historical Society, Fredericton Heritage Trust.

WRITINGS: Dr. Edwin Jacob: A Biography, University of New Brunswick Press, 1963; *The Career of Arthur Hamilton Gordon, First Lord Stanmore: 1829-1912,* University of Toronto Press, 1964; *A Political Correspondence of the Gladstone Era: The Letters of Lady Sophia Palmer and Sir Arthur Gordon, 1884-1889,* American Philosophical Society, 1971; (contributor) J. M. Bumstead, editor, *Canadian History before Confederation: Essays and Interpretations,* Dorsey, 1972. Contributor to *Canadian Forum, Canadian Historical Review, Acadiensis,* and *Historical Reflections;* contributor under pseudonym Hamish Keith to *Atlantic Advocate.*

WORK IN PROGRESS: British Liberal Leadership and the Irish Plan of Campaign; Gossip, Ghosts and Goldenrod: Wayside Wanderings of Warren Franklin Hatheway, 1850-1923.

*   *   *

CHAPMAN, Stepan
(Steven Chapman)

HOME: 3035 South East Ankeny St., No. 1, Portland, Ore. 97214.

CAREER: Writer and puppeteer.

WRITINGS: (Under name Steven Chapman) *How Many? How Much?: A Funny Numbers Book,* Follet, 1972. Work is anthologized in *Analog 8,* edited by John W. Campbell, Doubleday, 1971; *Year's Best Horror Stories #2,* edited by Richard Davis, Sphere Books, 1973, and *Orbit,* edited by Damon Knight, Number 12, Putnam, 1973, Number 13, Putnam, 1974, Number 17, Harper, 1975, Number 20, Harper, 1978.

*   *   *

CHAPPLE, Eliot D(ismore)   1909-

PERSONAL: Born April 29, 1909, in Salem, Mass.; married first wife, 1931; married second wife, 1954; children: William D., Della Chapple Bates. *Education:* Harvard University, A.B., 1931, Ph.D., 1933. *Office:* Rockland Research Institute, Orangeburg, N.Y. 10962; and 103 Bedney St., Nyack, N.Y. 10960.

CAREER: Harvard University, Cambridge, Mass., instructor in anthropology, 1935-40, tutor, 1936-40, Arnold research fellow in contemporary civilization, 1940-41, research associate in School of Medicine, 1941-45; partner in Chapple Co., 1945-47; president, E. D. Chapple Co., Inc., 1947-61, chairman of board of directors, 1961—; Rockland State Hospital Research Center, Orangeburg, N.Y., principal research scientist in department of mental health, 1961—. Visiting professor of anthropology, Cornell University, 1965-68. Columbia University, adjunct professor in Graduate School of Business, 1959-60; U.S. Bureau of the Budget, administration consultant, 1942-43. *Member:* Amer-

ican Anthropological Association, Society for Applied Anthropology, American Institute of Biological Sciences, Animal Behavior Society, Ecological Society of America, American Society of Zoologists.

WRITINGS: (With Carlton S. Coon) *Principles of Anthropology,* Holt, 1942, reprinted, Krieger, 1978; (with Leonard R. Sayle) *The Measure of Management,* Macmillan, 1961; *Culture and Biological Man,* Holt, 1970; *Rehabilitation, Dynamic of Change: An Anthropological View,* Center for Research in Education, Cornell University, 1970. Contributor to professional journals.

WORK IN PROGRESS: The Adolescent Sociopath; Dilemma of the Hardcore Unemployed.

*   *   *

CHASE, Judith Wragg   1907-

PERSONAL: Born February 18, 1907, in Augusta, Ga.; daughter of Samuel Alston (a clergyman) and Emma Louise (Sparks) Wragg; married Richard Chase (an army officer), July 18, 1931; children: Richard Conant, Alston Sparks, Pamela (Mrs. Peter M. Hain). *Education:* Attended William Smith College, 1923-24, and Cooper Union Art School, 1924-27; Syracuse University, B.A., 1960. *Address:* Box 446, Sullivan's Island, S.C. 29482; (summer) Box 335, Squirrel Island, Me. 04570. *Office:* Old Slave Mart Museum, 6 Chalmers St., Charleston, S.C. 29401.

CAREER: Started career as artist in 1927 in New York City, where she also acted professionally on stage, 1927-28; Barron Collier, Inc., New York City, advertising illustrator, 1928-30; continued painting and illustrating, doing free-lance advertising art in Panama, 1931-33, and teaching art privately and in schools at various locations, including Fort Benning, Ga., and Charlottesville, Va.; Pine Manor Junior College, Chestnut Hill, Mass., housemother, 1954-55; Lancaster School for Delinquent Girls, Lancaster, Mass., guidance counselor, 1956-57; Manlius Military School, Manlius, N.Y., art director, 1957-60; Old Slave Mart Museum, Charleston, S.C., curator and educational director, 1960—; professional photographer, 1968—. Lecturer on Negro history and art in United States and Canada; representative at First World Festival of Negro Arts, Dakar, Senegal, 1966. Secretary and trustee, Miriam B. Wilson Foundation, Charleston. Vice-president and member of board of directors, Young Womens Christian Association of Greater Charleston, 1967-72.

MEMBER: Association for the Study of Negro Life and History, American Association of Museums, Authors Guild, National Society of Literature and Arts, American Association for State and Local History, Southeastern Conference of Museums, South Carolina Historical Society, Southern Association of Africanists, Charleston Library Society. *Awards, honors:* Awards in art shows, among them exhibitions of Georgia Artists, Southern States Art League, and Virginia Artists; Alpha Phi Alpha Fraternity Community Service Award, 1973.

WRITINGS: Books to Build World Friendship, Oceana, 1964; *Afro-American Art and Craft,* Van Nostrand, 1972; (editor and author of preface and introduction) *Catalogue of the Old Slave Mart Museum and Library,* G.K. Hall, 1978.

*   *   *

CHASE, Mary Ellen   1887-1973

February 24, 1887—July 28, 1973; American author and educator. Obituaries: *Washington Post,* August 1, 1973. (See index for *CA* sketch)

CHEEK, Frances Edith 1923-

PERSONAL: Born December 4, 1923, in Toronto, Ontario, Canada; naturalized U.S. citizen; daughter of George and Emily (Markham) Gowans; married Ernest C. Cheek, March 31, 1948 (deceased); married William Whipple, Jr., 1974; children: (first marriage) Gael Frances. Education: University of Toronto, B.A., 1946; Duke University, M.A., 1953; Columbia University, Ph.D., 1962. Politics: Democrat. Religion: Agnostic. Home: 395 Mercer Rd., Princeton, N.J. 08540. Office: New Jersey Department of Corrections, P.O. Box 7387, Trenton, N.J. 08628.

CAREER: Marlboro State Hospital, Marlboro, N.J., psychiatric attendant, summers, 1946, 1947; New York State Psychiatric Institute, New York, N.Y., assistant in biometrics research, 1954-58; New Jersey Bureau of Research in Neurology and Psychiatry, Princeton, chief of experimental sociology, 1958-77; New Jersey Department of Corrections, Trenton, director of behavior modification training program, 1977—. Visiting lecturer, Princeton University, 1967-69; adjunct associate professor of sociology, Medical School, Temple University, 1967-73. Member: American Association of Behavior Therapists.

WRITINGS: (Editor with Henri Yaker and Humphrey Osmond, and contributor) The Future of Time: Man's Temporal Environment, Doubleday, 1971.

Contributor: Benjamin Pasamanick, editor, Epidemiology of Mental Disorder, American Association for the Advancement of Science, 1959; Leon Salzman and Jules H. Masserman, editors, Modern Concepts of Psychoanalysis, Philosophical Library, 1962; Kurt Salzinger and Suzanne Salzinger, editors, Research in Verbal Behavior and Some Neurophysiological Implications, Academic Press, 1967; H. A. Abramson, editor, The Use of LSD in Psychotherapy and Alcoholism, Bobbs-Merrill, 1967; Bernard Aaronson and Humphrey Osmond, editors, Psychedelics: The Uses and Implications of Hallucinogenic Drugs, Doubleday-Anchor, 1970. Contributor to Current Approaches to Psychoanalysis, Advances in Behavior Therapy, Current Psychiatric Therapies, Group Treatment of Behavior Problems, and to sociology and medical journals.

WORK IN PROGRESS: Research in the development of behavior modification training programs in self-control for inmates, drug addicts, alcoholics, and mental patients, and in stress awareness and coping techniques for correctional staffs.

* * *

CHEN, Jack 1908-

PERSONAL: Original name, Bernard Ivan Felix Acham; born July 2, 1908, in Port-of-Spain, Trinidad; son of Eugene (a lawyer; former foreign minister of China) and Agatha (Ganteaume) Acham (later Chen); married Yuantsung (a writer), 1958; children: three sons. Education: Studied at Law Society School, London, England; attended Vishe Hodestveniye Technicheskiye Masterskiye and Polygraphic Institute, both in Moscow, Soviet Union, 1927-30. Office: Chinese Culture Foundation, 750 Kearny St., San Francisco, Calif. 94108.

CAREER: Journalist and cartoonist in Wuhan, China, Soviet Union, and England, 1927-72. Founder and editor, New China News Agency, London, England, 1947-50; artist and editorial consultant, People's China, Peking, 1950-58, and Peking Review, Peking, 1968-71; free-lance journalist and lecturer in China, 1971-72; consultant on Chinese studies,

New York State Education Department, 1972-73; senior research associate in Chinese studies and writer-in-residence, Cornell University, Ithaca, N.Y., 1973-78; currently affiliated with Chinese Culture Foundation, San Francisco, Calif. Has lectured at major American universities, including Harvard University, Yale University, Princeton University, University of Chicago, University of Michigan, University of California, Berkeley, and Columbia University. Military service: British Army, 1943. Member: Authors Guild, Authors League of America.

WRITINGS: Japan and the Pacific Theatre of War, Lawrence & Wishart, 1942; Soviet Art and Artists, Pilot Press, 1944; Russian Painting: 1700-1917, Society for Cultural Relations (London), 1948; The Chinese Theatre, Dobson, 1948; Folk Arts of New China, Foreign Languages Press (Peking), 1955; New Earth, Foreign Languages Press, 1957, enlarged edition, Southern Illinois University Press, 1972; A Year in Upper Felicity (a book about life on a Chinese commune), Macmillan, 1973; Inside the Cultural Revolution, Macmillan, 1975; The Sinkiang Story, Macmillan, 1977. Contributor to journals and newspapers including Far Eastern Economic Review, Esquire, Foreign Policy, and New York Times.

WORK IN PROGRESS: The Chinese in America, 1820-1980, a pictorial exhibition, book and television project of the Chinese Culture Foundation.

* * *

CHEN, Kuan I. 1926-

PERSONAL: Born June 17, 1926, in Shanghai, China; came to United States in 1948, naturalized in 1961; son of S. P. and Tseng H. (Wei) Chen; married Jui Hsueh (a part-time teacher), October 14, 1960; children: Pauline, Ronald. Education: St. John's University, Shanghai, China, B.S., 1948; Michigan State University, M.S., 1950; Pennsylvania State University, Ph.D., 1954. Religion: Protestant. Home: 4 Williams Ct., McKownville, Albany, N.Y. 12203. Office: Department of Economics, State University of New York, Albany, N.Y. 12222.

CAREER: Pennsylvania State University, University Park, instructor in economics, 1953-54; Kansas State College (now University), Manhattan, assistant instructor in economics, 1954-55; Talladega College, Talladega, Ala., associate professor, 1954-55, professor of economics, 1955-56; Fairleigh Dickinson University, Rutherford, N.J., assistant professor of economics, 1956-61; State University of New York at Albany, associate professor, 1961-64, professor of economics, 1964—. Member: American Economic Association, Association for Evolutionary Economics, Phi Gamma Mu.

WRITINGS: World Population Growth and Living Standards, Bookman Associates, 1960; (editor with J. S. Uppal, and contributor) China and India: A Comparative Development, Free Press, 1971. Author of research monographs on New York local government finances and Pennsylvania farm topics. Contributor of articles to Pennsylvania Farm Economics, Science for the Farmers, New Leader, International Peasant Union Bulletin, Keio Economic Studies, Asian Survey, and Current History.

WORK IN PROGRESS: The Economy of Mainland China.

* * *

CHEN, Samuel Shih-Tsai 1915-

PERSONAL: Born July 18, 1915, in China; son of Shou-

Chen (a teacher) and Hsiu-yin (Liu) Chen; married Winifred Wan (died, 1964); married Welthy Kiang, August 17, 1969; children: (first marriage) Arthur, Lincoln, Victor; (second marriage) David. *Education:* National Central University, B.A., 1935; Harvard University, M.A., 1939, Ph.D., 1941. *Religion:* Christian. *Office:* Department of Political Science, Central Connecticut State College, New Britain, Conn. 06050.

CAREER: National Chengchi University, Nanking, China, professor of political science, 1941-49; China Artware Co., New York, N.Y., president, 1950-65; Central Connecticut State College, New Britain, professor of political science and Chinese art, 1965—. Adviser to Chinese Mission to the United Nations. *Member:* American Political Science Association, American Society of International Law, American Society for Political and Legal Philosophy, Association for Asian Studies, American Association of University Professors. *Awards, honors:* LL.D., South China University, 1968.

WRITINGS: Kuo Chi Fa Hsueh (title means "The Science of International Law"), Chin Hua (Taipei), 1954; *Liang Han Chien Cha Chih Tu Yen Chiu* (title means "A Study of the Control System of the Two Han Dynasties"), Commercial Press (Taipei), 1968; (co-editor) *Yun Wu She Hui Ko Hsueh Ta Tzu Tien* (title means "Yun Wu Encyclopaedia of Social Sciences"), Commercial Press, 1971; *The Theory and Practice of International Organization,* MSS Educational Publishing, 1971, revised edition, Kendall/Hunt, 1979; *Basic Documents of International Organization,* MSS Educational Publishing, 1971, revised edition, Kendall/Hunt, 1979.

WORK IN PROGRESS: Research on problems of Communist China's foreign policy and world peace.

*   *   *

CHENEY, Thomas E. 1901-

PERSONAL: Born November 2, 1901, in Victor, Idaho; son of Thomas E. (a farmer) and Eliza (Hutchings) Cheney; married Fern Allred, June 1, 1927; children: Renee (Mrs. Marvin N. Nelson), Karla Dawn (Mrs. Grant T. Wagner). *Education:* Utah Agricultural College (now Utah State University), B.S., 1930; University of Idaho, M.A., 1936; University of Southern California, graduate study, 1945-52. *Politics:* Independent. *Religion:* Mormon. *Home:* 1720 North Lambert Lane, Provo, Utah 84601. *Office:* Department of English, Brigham Young University, A236 JKB, Provo, Utah 84601.

CAREER: Superintendent of public schools in Idaho, 1930-36; Latter-day Saints Seminary, Blackfoot, Idaho, principal, 1936-44; Brigham Young University, Provo, Utah, professor of literature, 1945-72, professor emeritus, 1972—. *Member:* National Council of Teachers of English, National Folk Festival Association, American Folklore Society, Utah Folklore Society (former president), Utah Academy of Arts and Sciences.

WRITINGS: Mormon Songs of the Rocky Mountains, Texas University Press, 1967; *Love of Faith and Folly,* University of Utah Press, 1971; *The Golden Legacy,* Brigham Young University Press, 1973. Contributor to folklore journals.

*   *   *

CHENG, Ronald Ye-lin 1933-

PERSONAL: Born May 27, 1933, in Shanghai, China; married Teresia Benn, August 25, 1963; children: Anita, Theo-

dore. *Education:* University of London, B.Sc., 1960; University of Hong Kong, M.A., 1963; University of California, Berkeley, Ph.D., 1969. *Religion:* Roman Catholic. *Office:* Fuller Theological Seminary, Pasadena, Calif. 91101.

CAREER: University of Hawaii, Honolulu, assistant professor of sociology, 1969-73; University of Colorado, Boulder, assistant professor of sociology, 1973-77; Fuller Theological Seminary, Pasadena, Calif., post-doctoral fellow, 1978-79. *Member:* International Sociological Association, International Civilization Society, American Sociological Association, Association for Asian Studies, Society for Ch'ing Studies, American Academy of Political and Social Science.

WRITINGS: (Editor) *The Sociology of Revolution: Readings on Political and Popular Unrest,* Regnery, 1973; *The First Revolution in China: A Theory,* Vantage, 1973; *On Some Questions of the Future Development of Chinese Society* (collection of essays in Chinese), Ta Kung Pao Press (Hong Kong), 1978.

WORK IN PROGRESS: Historical-comparative studies of Eastern and Western societies and religions.

*   *   *

CHENG, Ying-wan

PERSONAL: Born in London, England; daughter of Tien-Hsi (a jurist-diplomat) and Siu-chu (Teng) Cheng. *Education:* Attended Ginling College, Nanking, China, 1935-36, and Westfield College, London, 1938-39; Smith College, B.A., 1943; Radcliffe College, M.A., 1945, Ph.D., 1960. *Office:* Department of History, Dowling College, Oakdale, N.Y. 11769.

CAREER: Harvard University, East Asian Research Center, Cambridge, Mass., research assistant, 1955-57; Vassar College, Poughkeepsie, N.Y., instructor in history, 1954-55; Hunter College (now Hunter College of the City University of New York), New York, N.Y., lecturer in history, 1958-60; Dowling College, Oakdale, N.Y., assistant professor, 1960-64, associate professor, 1964-71, professor of history, 1971—. Contributor to British Broadcasting Corp. Chinese program, 1950-53. *Member:* American Historical Association, Association for Asian Studies, Ch'ing Society, Conference on British Studies. *Awards, honors:* Post-doctoral fellowship from American Association of University Women, 1965-66.

WRITINGS: Postal Communication in China and Its Modernization, 1860-1896, Harvard University Press, 1970.

WORK IN PROGRESS: Research on the Chinese post office; Chinese diplomats in nineteenth-century England.

BIOGRAPHICAL/CRITICAL SOURCES: American Historical Review, June, 1971.

*   *   *

CHERNIAVSKY, Michael 1923(?)-1973

1923(?)—July 12, 1973; American educator, scholar, and author of books on Russian history. Obituaries: *New York Times,* July 18, 1973.

*   *   *

CHEW, Ruth 1920-
(Ruth Silver)

PERSONAL: Born April 8, 1920, in Minneapolis, Minn.; daughter of Arthur Percy (a writer) and Pauline (Foucar) Chew; married Aaron B. Z. Silver (a lawyer), April 18, 1948;

children: David, Eve (Mrs. Hugh Hamilton Sprunt, Jr.), George, Anne (Mrs. Mark Gloekler), Helen. *Education:* Attended Corcoran School of Art, 1936-40, and Art Students League of New York, 1973—. *Religion:* None. *Home:* 305 East Fifth St., Brooklyn, N.Y. 11218.

CAREER: Artist for *Washington Post*, Washington, D.C., 1942-43, Grey Advertising Agency, New York, N.Y., 1944-46, and Kresge-Newark Department Store, Newark, N.J., 1946-48. *Awards, honors:* Four Leaf Clover Award for Author of the Year, Lucky Book Club, 1976-77; *Witch in the House* was nominated for Colorado Children's Book Award; *The Witch's Buttons* was nominated for Arizona Young Readers' Award.

WRITINGS—All self-illustrated books for children; published by Scholastic Book Services, except as indicated: *The Wednesday Witch*, 1969; *Baked Beans for Breakfast*, 1970, published as *The Secret Summer*, 1974; *No Such Thing as a Witch*, 1971; *Magic in the Park*, 1972; *What the Witch Left*, 1973; *The Hidden Cave*, 1973, published as *The Magic Cave*, Hastings House, 1978; *The Witch's Buttons*, 1974; *The Secret Tree House*, 1974; *Witch in the House*, 1975; *The Would-Be Witch*, 1976; *The Trouble with Magic*, 1976; *Summer Magic*, 1977; *Witch's Broom*, Dodd, 1977; *The Witch's Garden*, 1978; *Earthstar Magic*, 1979.

Illustrator: Carol Morse, *Three Cheers for Polly*, Doubleday, 1967; E. W. Hildick, *The Questers*, Hawthorn, 1970; Val Abbott, *The Mystery of the Ghost Bell*, Dodd, 1971; Ann McGovern, *Shark Lady*, Scholastic Book Services, 1978.

SIDELIGHTS: "'I write about things I think would be fun to happen,'" Ruth Chew told Michael Tucker of the *New York Times*. Tucker describes some of her themes: "Magic scissors cut objects down to dollhouse size, a mystical robe allows invisibility, enchanted confectionery transforms people into animals and an umbrella grants your heart's desires (if you ask politely). All are common occurrences in the bewitching world of Ruth Chew.... Her method is simplicity. 'Write short words, short sentences, short paragraphs and short books.... One sentence can do the work of three,'" Chew comments. She writes what she thinks children want to read, not what the reviewers like. Tucker comments that she "refuses to proselytize in her books. There are no morals in her stories, no precedents or regulation—just good, clean fun. The tales are an escape for kids ... 'and that's the joy of being a child—being away from adults, being your own boss,'" Chew adds.

AVOCATIONAL INTERESTS: Travel (especially to England and France).

BIOGRAPHICAL/CRITICAL SOURCES: New York Times, May 22, 1977; *Flatbush Life*, May 30, 1977.

*   *   *

CHILCOTT, John H(enry) 1924-

PERSONAL: Born February 21, 1924, in Evanston, Ill.; married Martha Jane Dunkel, August 18, 1950; children: Kurt Apfel, Bret Blaine, Cynthia Jane. *Education:* Harvard University, A.B., 1948; University of Colorado, M.Ed., 1952; University of Oregon, Ph.D., 1956; also studied engineering at Texas Agricultural and Mechanical University (now Texas A & M University), 1943-44. *Office:* Department of Education, University of Arizona, Tucson, Ariz. 85721.

CAREER: Science teacher in Marion, Mass., 1949-51; high school principal in Glenwood, Wash., 1952-54; Menlo

School and College, Menlo Park, Calif., academic assistant to president, 1956-58; University of California, Santa Barbara, assistant professor of education, 1958-63; University of Arizona, Tucson, associate professor, 1963-68, professor of education and anthropology, 1968—. National Science Foundation, director of summer institutes in anthropology, 1961, 1963, 1965, 1968, director of Cooperative College School Science Program in Anthropology, 1970-71; Fulbright lecturer, Universidad Nacional de Trujillo, 1967; director of southwest center, National Study of American Indian Education, 1968-70. *Military service:* U.S. Army, Infantry, 1942-45; served in European theater; received Bronze Star Medal.

MEMBER: American Anthropological Association, American Educational Research Association, American Ethnological Association, American Academy of Political and Social Science, Society for Applied Anthropology (fellow), Council on Anthropology and Education, American Association for the Advancement of Science, American Association of University Professors, Phi Delta Kappa.

WRITINGS: Manual para la Auto-Evaluacion de la Facultad de Letras y Educacion de la Universidad Nacional de Trujillo, Universidad Nacional de Trujillo, 1966; (with Flora Esperanza Acevedo Rebaza, Teresa Rodriguez Sanchez, Nelly Escalante Ludena, Lorenzo E. Matos Deza, and Nunez Alarcon) *Una investigacion para apreciar las tecnicas empleadas en los colegios nacionales y particulares de la ciudad de Trujillo* (monograph), Universidad Nacional de Trujillo, 1966; *Un programa postgraduado para el entrenamiento de los administradores escolares en la facultad de letras y educacion* (monograph), Universidad Nacional de Trujillo, 1966; *El papel de la investigacion en la facultad de letras y educacion*, Universidad Nacional de Trujillo (monograph), Universidad Nacional de Trujillo, 1966; *Una Guia para La Practica Docente en el Colegio*, Universidad Nacional de Trujillo, 1967; (contributor) F. Robert Paulsen, editor, *Contemporary Issues in American Education*, University of Arizona Press, 1967; (editor with Norman C. Greenberg and Herbert B. Wilson and contributor) *Readings in the Socio-cultural Foundations of Education*, Wadsworth, 1968.

(With Arthur D. Dempsey) *Handbook for Pima and Maricopa Indian Teacher Aides*, Bureau of Educational Research and Services, College of Education, University of Arizona, 1970; (with Robert L. Nuss, Roger F. Pfeuffer, and Dempsey) *A Photographic Essay of Pima and Maricopa Indians*, Volume I, Parts A and B, Bureau of Educational Research and Services, College of Education, University of Arizona, 1970; (with Ned Anderson) *Formal Education on the White Mountain Apache Reservation* (monograph), Southwest Center, National Study of American Indian Education, Department of Anthropology, University of Arizona, 1970; *The Navajo Bordertown Dormitory in Flagstaff, Arizona* (monograph), Southwest Center, National Study of American Indian Education, Department of Anthropology, University of Arizona, 1970; (with Ibrahim S. Shalaby) *The Education of a Black Muslim*, Impresora Sahuaro, 1972; (with Angel I. Gomez) *Outline of Mexican American Education*, Impresora Sahuaro, 1973; (with William H. Strand and Ronald E. Mertz) *A High School Feasibility Study for the San Carlos Apache Reservation*, Bureau of School Services, University of Arizona, 1977.

Contributor of about twenty-five articles and reviews to professional journals, including *School Science and Mathematics, Journal of Educational Sociology, Clearing House*, and

American Antiquity. Editor, *Anthropology and Education Quarterly,* 1973-76.

* * *

CHILD, Irvin L(ong) 1915-

PERSONAL: Born March 11, 1915, in Deming, N.M.; son of Arthur H. (a businessman) and Martina A. (Long) Child; married Alice D. Blyth, March 29, 1941; children: Richard Blyth, Pamela Colman. *Education:* University of California, Los Angeles, B.A., 1935; Yale University, Ph.D., 1939. *Home:* 2 Cooper Rd., North Haven, Conn. 06473. *Office:* Department of Psychology, Yale University, New Haven, Conn. 06520.

CAREER: Harvard University, Cambridge, Mass., instructor in psychology, 1939-41; Yale University, New Haven, Conn., assistant professor, 1942-47, associate professor, 1947-54, professor of psychology, 1954—. *Member:* American Psychological Association, Parapsychological Association, Eastern Psychological Association, Phi Beta Kappa, Sigma Xi.

WRITINGS: Italian or American? The Second Generation in Conflict, Yale University Press, 1943, revised edition, with introduction by Francesco Cordasco, Russell, 1970; (editor with Marjorie Van de Water) *Psychology for the Returning Serviceman,* Penguin, 1945; (with John W. M. Whiting) *Child Training and Personality: A Cross-Cultural Study,* Yale University Press, 1953; (with Whiting, W. W. Lambert, and others) *Field Guide for a Study of Socialization,* Wiley, 1966; *Humanistic Psychology and the Research Tradition: Their Several Virtues,* Wiley, 1973; (editor with Edward F. Zigler) *Socialization and Personality Development,* Addison-Wesley, 1973.

* * *

CHILD, Julia 1912-

PERSONAL: Born August 15, 1912, in Pasadena, Calif.; daughter of John (a farm consultant) and Carolyn (Weston) McWilliams; married Paul Child (a U.S. Foreign Service officer, painter, and photographer), September 1, 1945. *Education:* Smith College, B.A., 1934. *Politics:* Democrat. *Office:* WGBH-TV, 125 Western Ave., Boston, Mass. 02134.

CAREER: W. & J. Sloane (department store), New York, N.Y., member of advertising department, 1939-40; U.S. Office of Strategic Services, civilian employee in Washington, D.C., Ceylon, and China, 1941-45; WGBH-TV, Boston, Mass., star of "The French Chef," 1962-72, and "Julia Child and Company," 1978—. *Awards, honors:* George Foster Peabody Award, 1964, and Emmy Award, 1966, both for television work; Ordre de Merite Agricole, 1970.

WRITINGS—All published by Knopf; illustrations and photographs by husband, Paul Child, except as indicated: *Mastering the Art of French Cooking,* Volume I (with Simone Beck and Louisette Bertholle), illustrations by Sidonie Corvin, 1961, Volume II (with Beck), 1970; *The French Chef Cookbook,* 1968; *From Julia Child's Kitchen,* 1975; *Julia Child and Company,* 1978. Author of column, "From Julia Child's Kitchen," for *McCall's.* Contributor to *House and Garden, House Beautiful,* and *Boston Globe.*

WORK IN PROGRESS: More books resulting from television series, "Julia Child and Company."

SIDELIGHTS: Julia Child originally intended to become a "Great Woman Novelist." However, people "'laughed when I sat down at the typewriter,'" she commented in an interview, "'and they were right, too, because nothing ever came of the plan. I wrote for the Smith College *Tattler,* and after I graduated I went home for a while, and then I went to New York and tried to get a job with *The New Yorker,* but they turned me down. The woman-novelist idea was very vague and unformed. I just thought it would develop at some time or other.'" With her life at loose ends, she eventually joined the Office of Strategic Services, where she volunteered for overseas duty in the Far East. She met Paul Child in the O.S.S. office in Ceylon. They married two years later and, by fortunate coincidence, he was transferred to the U.S. Information Service office in Paris. Julia has admitted that she knew little about cooking before or during the early years of her marriage. However, in 1949 she enrolled in a morning course at the Cordon Bleu, a cooking school where she studied under some fine French chefs, and her interest in cooking blossomed. She once remarked, "'Until I got into cooking, I was never *really* interested in anything.'"

Describing the cookbook writing odyssey, Betty Suyker tells how Simone Beck, called Simca by her friends, had joined Louisette Bertholle in trying to write a French cookbook for Americans. They needed an American collaborator. The historic meeting of Beck and Child took place in 1950. "The next decade was a frenzy of activity; . . . [a great deal of it carried on in] an incredible correspondence . . . between Julia and Simca, which is still going on. . . . Although they both test and taste and consult endlessly over what will go into the *Masterings,* there is some division of labor between them. Julia does the writing; Simca accumulates ideas for recipes and rides herd on how the product tastes when Julia has fitted the American ingredients into it."

The original manuscript of the cookbook contained over 800 pages on poultry and sauces alone, and the American publisher who had contracted the book refused to publish it. Child rewrote it in a much condensed, and less academic, manner and Knopf accepted the manuscript. The resulting first volume of *Mastering the Art of French Cooking* was hailed by Craig Claiborne as "a masterpiece. . . . It will probably remain the best in its class for decades to come." A *Time* reviewer remarked: "If Julia Child's TV show is the 'Sesame Street' of the food world, the cookbook she wrote with Simone Beck is its Dr. Spock. Step by rational step, it dispels the fears and dreads involved in cooking more than the simplest meal."

In 1962, Child was invited to appear on a book review program of WGBH, Boston's public television station, to talk about her cookbook. On the show she explained the preparation of an omelette and demonstrated beating egg whites. The response of the programs' viewers was overwhelmingly enthusiastic and Child's famous series, "The French Chef," resulted. As told by Suyker, "Julia's surprise success making an omelette on television . . . led to a 134-show series and her enshrinement as an American folk heroine. If she had not had the least idea of what she was talking about, no doubt many of her fans would still have tuned her in. . . . In fact, she knew exactly what she was talking about, and it showed."

BIOGRAPHICAL/CRITICAL SOURCES: New York Times Book Review, December 3, 1961; *New York Times,* March 5, 1964; *Time,* November 25, 1966, November 26, 1968, December 12, 1970; *National Observer,* July 22, 1968; *Atlantic,* December, 1970; *Antioch Review,* fall/winter, 1970-71; *New Yorker,* December 23, 1974; *People,* December 1, 1975.

CHILDRESS, William 1933-

PERSONAL: Born February 5, 1933, in Hugo, Okla.; son of J. W. (a migrant worker and share-crop farmer) and Lorraine Childress; married Rose Marie Hanemian, June 30, 1962 (divorced April, 1975); married Diana Benson, 1978; children: (first marriage) Christopher Brandon, Jason William, David Daniel. *Education:* Fresno State College (now California State University, Fresno), B.A., 1965; University of Iowa, M.F.A., 1968. *Politics:* "Changeable—basically liberal." *Religion:* Agnostic. *Home:* Route 1, Anderson, Mo. 64831.

CAREER: U.S. Army, 1951-58, demolitions expert and secret courier in Korea, 1952-53, paratrooper, 1955-58; ranch foreman in Clovis, Calif., 1961-65; juvenile counselor in San Francisco, Calif., 1965-66; *Student Magazine*, Cedar Rapids, Iowa, co-founder and editor, 1967-68; Lincoln College, Lincoln, Ill., instructor in English, 1968-69; National Geographic Society, Washington, D.C., editor and writer, 1969-70; free-lance writer and reviewer, 1971—; field editor, *Saga* magazine, 1973-78. *Member:* Poetry Society of America. *Awards, honors:* Joseph Henry Jackson Poetry Award, 1965, 1967; Stephen Vincent Benet Award, 1969, for "The Fires of August"; Devins Award, 1971, for *Lobo; Today's Education* essay award, 1971; Carnegie grant, 1972; Poetry Society of America prize, 1972; Illinois State Arts Commission poetry prize, 1974; State of Illinois literary award, 1976, for poems appearing in *December Magazine; Story* and Martha Foley fiction awards for story, "Uncle Roman."

WRITINGS—Poems: Burning the Years, Smith-Horizon, 1971; *Lobo,* Barlenmir House, 1972. Also author of novella, *Where the Sun Never Shines,* published in *Smith Literary Magazine,* 1978.

Contributor to numerous anthologies, including: *Modern Poets British and American,* Pflaum/Standard, 1966; *Human Voice Anthology* (poetry and fiction), Human Voice Press, 1968; *America Forever New,* edited by S. and J. Brewton, 1968; *Story Anthology,* Scholastic Press, 1969; *Down at the Santa Fe Depot: The Fresno Poets,* Giligia Press, 1970; *Sounds and Silences: Poetry for Now,* edited by Richard Peck, Delacorte, 1970; *Man, in the Poetic Mode,* edited by Joy Zweigler,* McDougal-Littell, 1971; *Some Haystacks Don't Have Any Needles,* edited by Leudecker and Smith, Scott, Foresman, 1971; *Reflections in Literature,* edited by McFarland, Breakstone, and Peckham, Houghton, 1972; *Messages: A Thematic Anthology of Poetry,* edited by X. J. Kennedy, Little, Brown, 1973; *Image: Reflections on Language,* edited by Clark McKowen, Macmillan, 1973; *The Garden and the Wilderness,* edited by Lee and Lee, Harcourt, 1973; *Within You, Without You,* edited by Betsy Ryan, Scholastic Press, 1973; *From the Belly of the Shark,* edited by Walter Lowenfels, Vintage, 1973.

Author of column, "Between Friends," *Friends,* 1979—. Contributor of articles, short stories, and poems to national magazines, including *Westways, Smithsonian, Harper's, Mademoiselle, Saga, Family Circle, New Republic, Nevada, Motorland, Holiday, Saturday Evening Post, Good Housekeeping, Reporter,* and to literary journals.

WORK IN PROGRESS: Another book of poems, for Bookmark Press.

SIDELIGHTS: William Childress told *CA:* "Until American writers get off their egos and form a union or guild, they had better discourage anyone else from playing in the literary fields. These days they are cheap, barren, stingy fields indeed—thanks to publishers who, although rich themselves, lower the rates they pay writers.... American writers have few rights and are being jailed for exercising those few. Meanwhile, the nation's leaders make a mighty fuss over Russian writers. It has become the worst field anyone could enter." Childress also relates that "my hard life as a cottonpicker in my youth lends impetus—and also gives me material for both my literary and humorous short stories and articles."

* * *

CHITTICK, William O(liver) 1937-

PERSONAL: Born April 22, 1937, in Aberdeen, S.D.; son of William Douglas Martin (a college professor) and Bernice (Herther) Chittick; married Marilyn Anne Vickers (a clinical psychologist), August 17, 1968; children: William Vickers, Laura Vickers. *Education:* South Dakota State University, B.S., 1959; Johns Hopkins University, Ph.D., 1964. *Home:* 40 West Lake Dr., Athens, Ga. 30606. *Office:* Department of Political Science, University of Georgia, Athens, Ga. 30602.

CAREER: Florida State University, Tallahassee, assistant professor of political science, 1965-66; University of Georgia, Athens, assistant professor, 1966-70, associate professor of political science, 1970—. *Military service:* U.S. Army Intelligence, 1963-65; became first lieutenant. *Member:* American Political Science Association, International Studies Association, International Peace Research Society, Southern Political Science Association. *Awards, honors:* Woodrow Wilson fellow, 1959-60.

WRITINGS: State Department, Press, and Pressure Groups, Wiley, 1970; *The Analysis of Foreign Policy Outputs,* C. E. Merrill, 1975.

WORK IN PROGRESS: Research on building the competence of individuals and groups within society on world affairs.

* * *

CHORNY, Merron 1922-

PERSONAL: Born August 31, 1922, in Ranfurly, Alberta, Canada; son of Nick and Mary (Malisky) Chorny; married Margaret Johnstone, June 7, 1945; children: John, Jo Anne, Joyce. *Education:* University of Alberta, B.Ed., 1947, M.Ed., 1949, Ed.D., 1965. *Home:* 3831 Brooklyn Cres. N.W., Calgary, Alberta, Canada. *Office:* Department of English Education, University of Calgary, Calgary, Alberta, Canada.

CAREER: Principal of Grimshaw Public School, Grimshaw, Alberta, 1949-58; University of Calgary, Calgary, Alberta, assistant professor, 1960-66, associate professor, 1966-72, professor of English education, 1972—. *Military service:* Royal Canadian Air Force, 1943-45; became flying officer. *Member:* International Steering Committee of English (chairman, 1969-71), Canadian Council of Teachers of English (charter president, 1967; life member), National Council of Teachers of English (director-at-large, 1968-71), Alberta Teachers Association (president of English Council, 1967-68), Alberta Council of Teachers of English (life member), Phi Delta Kappa. *Awards, honors:* Imperial Relations Trust senior fellow at University of London, 1969-70.

WRITINGS: (With M. Kostek and P. Weston) *Just English,* J. M. Dent (Toronto), Volume I, 1966, Volume II, 1967, Volume III, 1968. Editor of *English Teacher,* 1961-67.†

CHOU, Ya-luu 1924-

PERSONAL: Born July 7, 1924, in Chungking, China; son of Yuen-cheng (a businessman) and Nu (Mei-Yin) Chou; married Pauline Ruth Honadel, May 9, 1956; children: Carole, Allan, Barbara. *Education:* National Southwest Associated University, B.A., 1945; University of Cincinnati, M.A., 1948; University of Pennsylvania, Ph.D., 1950. *Politics:* Independent Democrat. *Home:* 61-11 171st St., Fresh Meadows, N.Y. *Office:* Department of Qualitative Analysis and Statistics, St. John's University, Jamaica, N.Y. 11432.

CAREER: Hampton Institute, Hampton, Va., director of Business Division, 1950-54; Rensselaer Polytechnic Institute, Troy, N.Y., assistant professor of economics, 1954-56; Pace College (now University), New York, N.Y., associate professor, 1956-60, professor of economics, 1960-66, research professor, 1966-69; St. John's University, Jamaica, N.Y., professor of economics, 1969—. *Member:* International Platform Association, American Economic Association, American Statistical Association.

WRITINGS: Applied Business Statistics, Holt, 1963; *Statistical Analysis, with Business and Economic Applications,* Holt, 1969, 2nd edition, 1976; *Probability and Statistics for Decision Making,* Holt, 1972; *Applied Business Statistics: A Modern Approach,* Holt, 1979. Contributor to economic, financial, and statistical journals.

WORK IN PROGRESS: Research in economic and business forecasting methods.

*   *   *

CIECHANOWSKI, Jan 1888(?)-1973

1888(?)—April 16, 1973; Polish diplomat and author. Obituaries: *New York Times,* April 18, 1973.

*   *   *

CLANTON, (Orval) Gene 1934-

PERSONAL: Born September 14, 1934, in Pittsburg, Kan.; son of Orval Elmer (a railroad laborer) and Verl Ann (Troxel) Clanton; married Jane Ann Buffington, August 5, 1959; children: Spencer Miles, Kimberley Jean. *Education:* Kansas State College of Pittsburg (now Pittsburg State University), B.S.Ed., 1959, M.S., 1961; University of Kansas, Ph.D., 1967. *Home address:* Route 1, Box 145, Palouse, Wash. 99161. *Office:* Department of History, Washington State University, Pullman, Wash. 99163.

CAREER: Texas A & M University, College Station, 1966-68, began as instructor, became assistant professor of history; Washington State University, Pullman, assistant professor, 1968-71, associate professor, 1971-78, professor of history, 1978—. *Military service:* U.S. Army, 1954-57. *Member:* Organization of American Historians.

WRITINGS: Kansas Populism: Ideas and Men, University Press of Kansas, 1969. Contributor to *Kansas Quarterly, Kansas Historical Quarterly,* and *Agricultural History.*

WORK IN PROGRESS: A book tentatively entitled *Congress, Populism and the 1890's.*

*   *   *

CLARK, Alice S(andell) 1922-

PERSONAL: Born November 24, 1922, in Oneonta, N.Y.; daughter of G(eorge) Harold (a mechanic) and Gertrude (Northrup) Sandell; married Dewey Clark, Jr. (a bank manager), September 13, 1941 (divorced June 3, 1967); children: M. Bruce, Peter D. *Education:* Attended New York College for Teachers (now State University of New York at Albany), 1940-41; State University of New York College at Oneonta, B.A., 1967; State University of New York at Albany, M.L.S., 1968. *Politics:* Republican. *Religion:* Protestant. *Home:* 8608 Chambers Pl. N.E., Albuquerque, N.M. 87111. *Office:* General Library, University of New Mexico, Albuquerque, N.M. 87131.

CAREER: State University of New York at Albany, lecturer in library science, 1968; Ohio State University, Columbus, assistant head of personnel for libraries, 1968-69, undergraduate reference librarian, 1969-70, head of undergraduate libraries, 1970-74; University of New Mexico, Albuquerque, assistant dean for readers' services, 1974—. *Member:* American Library Association, American Association of University Professors, New Mexico Library Association, Greater Albuquerque Library Association, Phi Kappa Phi, Kappa Delta Pi, Beta Phi Mu.

WRITINGS: (With Irene Braden Hoadley) *Quantitative Methods in Librarianship: Standards, Research, Management,* Greenwood Press, 1972; (contributor) Sul A. Lee, editor, *A Challenge for Academic Libraries,* Pierian Press, 1973; (contributor) John Lubans, editor, *Educating the Library User,* Bowker, 1974. Contributor of articles to *RQ, Educational Technology, Journal of Library Automation,* and other periodicals.

WORK IN PROGRESS: Research for M.A. in history, a biography of Wallace Nutting; a series of short computer-assisted instruction courses designed to teach students to use the library; a contribution to *Collection Development in Libraries,* edited by George B. Miller and Robert D. Stueart.

*   *   *

CLARK, (Robert) Brian 1932-

PERSONAL: Born June 3, 1932, in Bournemouth, England; son of Leonard (a blacksmith) and Selina (Smith) Clark. *Education:* Redland College of Education, teaching certificate, 1954; attended Central School of Speech and Drama, 1954-55; University of Nottingham, B.A., 1964. *Religion:* Agnostic. *Home:* Amber Lane Farm, the Slack, Ashover S45 0EB, Derbyshire, England. *Agent:* Judy Daish Associates, Globe Theatre, Shaftsbury Ave., London W.C.1, England.

CAREER: University of Hull, Hull, Yorkshire, England, staff tutor in drama, 1966-70; currently a director of Astramead Ltd. *Military service:* British Army, Signal Corps, 1950-52. *Member:* Writers Guild.

WRITINGS: Group Theatre, Pitman, 1971, Theatre Arts, 1972; (with others) *Lay-By* (play), Calder & Boyars, 1972; "Truth or Dare" (play), first produced at Hull Arts Centre, 1972; *Whose Life Is It Anyway?* (play; first produced in London at Mermaid Theatre, March 6, 1978; produced in Washington, D.C. at Folger Shakespeare Theatre, 1978; also see below), Amber Lane Press, in press.

Television plays; all produced on BBC-TV, except as indicated: "Ten Torrey Canyons," 1972; "Operation Magic Carpet," produced by ITV, 1973; "Achilles Heel," produced by ITV, 1973; "The Greeting" (from a short story by Osbert Sitwell), produced by ITV, 1973; "Parole," produced by Granada, 1975; "Post Mortem," 1976; "The Saturday Party," 1976; "Campion's Review," 1977; "Happy Returns," produced by Granada, 1977; "There's No Place," 1977; "The Country Party," 1977; "Telford's Change" (ten-part serial), 1979. Also author of a television adaptation of his play, "Whose Life Is It Anyway?"; author of about twenty other television plays and two radio plays.

WORK IN PROGRESS: Stage and television plays, including "Can You Hear Me at the Back" and a Broadway production of "Whose Life Is It Anyway?".

BIOGRAPHICAL/CRITICAL SOURCES: Guardian, December 23, 1972; *New York Times,* November 10, 1978.

*   *   *

CLARK, Dora Mae 1893-

PERSONAL: Born June 10, 1893, in Derby, Vt.; daughter of E. Warren (a physician) and Isadore Melissa (Aldrich) Clark. *Education:* Mount Holyoke College, A.B., 1915; Columbia University, A.M., 1916; Yale University, Ph.D., 1924. *Politics:* Independent. *Religion:* Congregationalist. *Home:* 134 Pennsylvania Ave., Chambersburg, Pa. 17201.

CAREER: Wilson College, Chambersburg, Pa., professor of American history and political science, 1925-61, professor emerita, 1961—. *Member:* American Historical Association, American Archaeological Society, Conference on British Studies, Royal Historical Society.

WRITINGS: British Opinion and the American Revolution, Yale University Press, 1930; *Rise of the British Treasury,* Yale University Press, 1960.

WORK IN PROGRESS: American Experience under English Law as Interpreted by the Law Officers of the Crown: 1689-1776.

*   *   *

CLARK, Robert E(ugene) 1912-

PERSONAL: Born May 16, 1912, in Litchfield, Ohio; son of Norris Parker and Jeannette (Watters) Clark; married Lucille E. Lukens, September 14, 1940; children: Thomas E., William R. *Education:* University of Akron, B.A., 1935; University of Chicago, M.A., 1939, Ph.D., 1947. *Politics:* Republican. *Religion:* Methodist. *Home:* 534 Waring Ave., State College, Pa. 16801. *Office:* Department of Sociology, Pennsylvania State University, University Park, Pa. 16802.

CAREER: State Penitentiary, Pontiac, Ill., actuary sociologist, 1938-40; State Penitentiary, Joliet, Ill., actuary sociologist, 1941-43; Pennsylvania State University, University Park, assistant professor, 1947-52, associate professor, 1952-57, professor of sociology, 1957-75, professor emeritus, 1975—. *Military service:* U.S. Naval Reserve, active duty, 1943-46; became commander. *Member:* American Sociological Association.

WRITINGS: (Editor with Clyde Vedder and Samuel Koenig) *Criminology: A Book of Readings,* Dryden, 1953; *Critical Values for 2 x 2 Tables,* Department of Sociology, Pennsylvania State University, 1970; *Reference Group Theory and Delinquency,* Behavioral Publications, 1972. Contributor to *American Journal of Sociology, American Sociological Review,* and *American Statistical Association Journal.*

*   *   *

CLARK, Sue C(assidy) 1935-

PERSONAL: Born May 15, 1935, in Milwaukee, Wis.; daughter of Russell Joseph (an investment counselor) and Catherine (a wholesale bakery board chairman; maiden name, Taft) Clark. *Education:* Attended University of Wisconsin, 1953-56, Columbia University, 1968-70, 1977—, and New School for Social Research, 1972-74. *Home:* 470 West End Ave., Apt. 10E, New York, N.Y. 10024. *Office:* Trans-

Electronic Music Production, Inc., 133 West 87th St., New York, N.Y. 10024.

CAREER: Command-Probe Records, New York City, director of creative services, 1969-70; Trans-Electronic Music Production Inc., New York City, vice-president, 1970—. New York representative of *Rolling Stone* (magazine), 1967-68.

WRITINGS: (Editor with Douglas Kent Hall) *Rock: A World Bold as Love,* Cowles, 1970; *The Superstars: In Their Own Words,* Music Sales, 1972. Contributor of articles and record reviews to *Creem, Rolling Stone, Fusion, Billboard, Rock, Now Sound,* and *Black Stars.*

SIDELIGHTS: Since 1972 Sue Clark has become very involved with photography, contributing photographs to *Black Stars, Basketball Digest,* and *New York.* She lived in Brazil for two years and has traveled to Japan twice and is very interested in the languages and cultures of those two countries.

*   *   *

CLARKE, Lige 1942-

PERSONAL: Born February 22, 1942, in Hindman, Ky.; son of James B. (a merchant) and Corinne (Hicks) Clarke. *Education:* Attended George Washington University, 1964-67. *Residence:* New York, N.Y. *Office:* Gay Newspaper, 116 West 14th St., New York, N.Y. 10011.

CAREER: Gay (newspaper), New York, N.Y., editor, 1968—. *Member:* Mattachine Society of New York (member of board, 1970). *Military service:* U.S. Army, 1963-65. *Awards, honors:* Mattachine Society of New York, Newspaperman of the Year, 1971.

WRITINGS: (With Jack Nichols) *I Have More Fun with You Than Anybody,* St. Martin's, 1972; (with Nichols) *Roommates Can't Always Be Lovers: An Intimate Guide to Male-Male Relationships,* St. Martin's, 1974. Regular columnist, *Screw,* 1968-73.

AVOCATIONAL INTERESTS: Travel, yoga teaching and writing, experiencing different peoples and cultures.

BIOGRAPHICAL/CRITICAL SOURCES: Donn Teal, *The Gay Militants,* Stein & Day, 1971; Angelo D'Arcangelo, *Lovebook: Inside the Sexual Revolution,* Lancer Books, 1971; Derek Miles, *The Dirtiest Dozen,* Midwood Books, 1971; George Weinberg, *Society and the Healthy Homosexual,* St. Martin's 1972; Kay Tobin and Randy Wicker, *The Gay Crusaders,* Paperback Library, 1972; John Francis Hunter, *The Gay Insider, U.S.A.,* Stonehill Publishers, 1972.†

*   *   *

CLARKE, William M(alpas) 1922-

PERSONAL: Born June 5, 1922, in Ashton-under-Lyne, England; son of Ernest and Florence Clarke; married Margaret Braithwaite, June 1, 1946 (divorced, 1973); married Faith Elizabeth Dawson, May 3, 1973; children: (first marriage) Deborah, Pamela. *Education:* Attended University of Manchester, 1941-42, 1946-48, B.A. (honors), 1948. *Home:* 37 Park Vista, Greenwich, London S.E. 10, England. *Office:* Committee on Invisible Exports, 7th Floor, Stock Exchange, London E.C.2, England.

CAREER: Manchester Guardian (now *Guardian*), editorial writer in Manchester and London, England, 1948-55; *Times,* London, assistant city editor, 1955-57; city editor, 1957-62, financial and industrial editor, 1962-66; Committee on Invisible Exports, London, director, 1967-76, director-general and deputy chairman, 1976—. Also a director of U.K. Provident Institution Ltd., London, 1968, Cincinnati Milacron, Birmingham, 1969, Trade Indemnity Co., London, 1971—, Grindlays Bank Ltd., Grindlay Brandts Ltd., Swiss Reinsurance Co. Ltd., Euromoney Publications, Romney Trust Ltd., and City Communications Organization. *Military service:* Royal Air Force, 1941-46; flying instructor, 1942-44, lecturer on law and administration, 1944-46; became flight lieutenant. *Member:* Royal Institute of International Affairs (London; member of council), Reform Club.

WRITINGS: The City's Invisible Earnings: How London's Financial Skill Serves the World and Brings Profit to Britain, Institute of Economic Affairs (London), 1958; *The City in the World Economy,* Institute of Economic Affairs, 1965, revised edition, Penguin, 1967; *Private Enterprise in Developing Countries,* Pergamon, 1966; (editor) *Britain's Invisible Earnings,* British National Export Council, 1967; *Money Markets of the City: What the Future May Bring,* Laurie, Milbank & Co., 1970; (with George Pulay) *The World's Money: How It Works,* Allen & Unwin, 1970, Praeger, 1971. Regular writer on world financial centers. Editor of *Banker,* 1966; editorial consultant to *Banker,* 1966-76, and *Euromoney,* 1977—.

WORK IN PROGRESS: Inside the City, for Allen & Unwin.

AVOCATIONAL INTERESTS: Books, opera.

*   *   *

CLARKSON, Stephen 1937-

PERSONAL: Born October 21, 1937, in London, England; son of George Elliott (a businessman) and Helene (Mannaberg) Clarkson; married Christina McCall (a writer), September 1, 1978; children: (previous marriage) Kyra Antoinette, Blaise Dominique. *Education:* University of Toronto, B.A., 1959; Oxford University, M.A., 1961; University of Paris, Ph.D., 1964. *Religion:* Christian. *Residence:* Toronto, Ontario, Canada. *Office:* Department of Political Economy, University of Toronto, 100 St. George St., Toronto, Ontario, Canada M4W 2Y6.

CAREER: University of Toronto, Toronto, Ontario, assistant professor, 1965-67, associate professor of political science, 1967—. Leader of City of Toronto Municipal Liberal Party, 1969-72; director, Social Planning Council of Metropolitan Toronto, 1970-72; president, University League for Social Reform, 1971-72; director, Maison Francaise de Toronto, 1972. *Military service:* Royal Canadian Naval Reserve, 1955-59; became sub-lieutenant. *Member:* International Political Science Association, Canadian Political Science Association (past secretary-treasurer), Canadian Association of Asian Studies, American Political Science Association, American Association for the Advancement of Slavic Studies. *Awards, honors:* Rhodes scholar, 1958; Woodrow Wilson fellow, 1961.

WRITINGS: (Editor) *An Independent Foreign Policy for Canada?,* McClelland & Stewart, 1968; (editor) *Visions 2020: Fifty Canadians in Search of a Future,* M. G. Hurtig, 1970; *L'Analyse Sovietique des problemes indiens du sous-developpement, 1955-64,* Mouton, 1970; *City Lib: Parties and Reform in Toronto,* A. M. Hakkert, 1972; *The Soviet Theory of Development,* University of Toronto Press, 1978. Contributor of about a hundred articles to academic journals and to newspapers. Member of editorial board, *Canadian Forum.*

WORK IN PROGRESS: A book on participatory democracy in the Liberal Party of Canada.

AVOCATIONAL INTERESTS: Travel through Asia and Europe.

*   *   *

CLASEN, Claus-Peter 1931-

PERSONAL: Born February 8, 1931, in Berlin, Germany; son of Willi (a musician) and Senta (Caspar) Clasen. *Education:* Attended Hamilton College, 1950-51; Free University of Berlin, Staatsexamen, 1957, Dr.Phil., 1962; St. Antony's College, Oxford, graduate study, 1959-62. *Office:* Department of History, University of California, Los Angeles, Calif. 90024.

CAREER: Yale University, New Haven, Conn., assistant professor of history, 1962-66; University of California, Los Angeles, assistant professor, 1966-68, associate professor of history, 1968—. *Member:* Society for Reformation Research.

WRITINGS: Die Wiedertaeufer im Herzogtum Wuerttemberg und in benachbarten Herrschaften. Ausbreitung, Geisteswelt und Soziologie, Kohlhammer, 1965; *Anabaptism, A Social History, 1525-1618: Switzerland, Austria, Moravia, and South and Central Germany,* Cornell University Press, 1972; *Die Augsburger Steuerbuecher um 1600,* Muehlberger, 1976; *The Anabaptists in South and Central Germany, Switzerland and Austria,* Mennonite Historical Society, 1978. Contributor to *Church History* and *Mennonite Quarterly Review.*

WORK IN PROGRESS: Research on Germany's social structure in the Reformation period, with emphasis on Augsburg.

*   *   *

CLASPY, Everett M. 1907(?)-1973

1907(?)—April 16, 1973; American educator, government analyst, and author of books on regional history. Obituaries: *Washington Post,* April 18, 1973.

*   *   *

CLAYTON, Thomas (Swoverland) 1932-

PERSONAL: Born December 15, 1932, in New Ulm, Minn.; son of Robert Schoonmaker (a businessman) and Vida (Swoverland) Clayton; married Ruth Madson, September 24, 1955; children: Pamela Alison, Katherine Anne, John Robert Madson, David Montgomery. *Education:* Attended University of Chicago, 1949-51; University of Minnesota, B.A., 1954; Wadham College, Oxford, D.Phil., 1960. *Politics:* Democrat. *Religion:* Anglo-Catholic. *Office:* Department of English, University of Minnesota, Minneapolis, Minn. 55455.

CAREER: Yale University, New Haven, Conn., instructor in English, 1960-62; University of California, Los Angeles, assistant professor, 1962-67, associate professor of English, 1967-68; University of Minnesota, Minneapolis, associate professor, 1968-70, professor of English, 1970—. *Military service:* U.S. Army, 1955-57. *Member:* International Shakespeare Association, Modern Language Association of America, Renaissance Society of America, Renaissance English Text Society, Shakespeare Association of America, American Association of University Professors, American Association of Rhodes Scholars. *Awards, honors:* Distinguished Teaching Award from College of Liberal Arts, University of Minnesota, 1971; Guggenheim fellowship, 1978.

WRITINGS: The Booke of Thomas Moore: Some Aids to

Scholarly and Critical Shakespearean Studies, Center for Shakespeare Studies, 1969; *The Non-Dramatic Works of John Suckling,* Clarendon Press (of Oxford University), 1971; *Cavalier Poets,* Oxford University Press, 1978. Has written video-tape scripts for a series on Shakespearean plays, for KTCA-Television. Contributor to *Simbolica, Epos, Notes and Queries, Times Literary Supplement, Renaissance Quarterly, English Literary Renaissance, Shakespeare Studies, Pucred, Literature/Film Quarterly, Shakespeare Quarterly,* and other literature journals.

WORK IN PROGRESS: Research on Shakespeare, earlier seventeenth-century poetry, textual criticism, and literary theory.

* * *

CLEARY, Robert E(dward) 1932-

PERSONAL: Born February 27, 1932, in East Orange, N.J.; son of Charles A. and Mary J. (Solomon) Cleary; married Marilyn F. Jacoby (a university instructor), April 21, 1956; children: Barbara, Kevin, Charles. *Education:* Montclair State College, B.A., 1953, M.A. (social studies), 1957; Rutgers University, M.A. (political science), 1959, Ph.D., 1962; American University, LL.D., 1977. *Home:* 7503 Elmore Lane, Bethesda, Md. 10034. *Office:* Department of Government, American University, Washington, D.C. 20016.

CAREER: High school teacher in Irvington, N.J., 1955-58; Rutgers University, New Brunswick, N.J., assistant director of secondary school project, 1959-61; George Peabody College for Teachers, Nashville, Tenn., assistant professor of political science, 1961-64; American Political Science Association, Washington, D.C., congressional fellow, 1964-65, assistant director, 1966-67; American University, Washington, D.C., associate professor, 1965-69, professor of government, 1969—, associate dean, 1967-70, dean for academic development, 1970-72, provost, 1972-76. Executive secretary, Harry S Truman Scholarship Foundation, 1976-78. Consultant to U.S. Office of Education, Fairfax County, Va., Macmillan Co., and Xerox Corp. *Military service:* U.S. Army, 1953-55. *Member:* National Council for the Social Studies, American Political Science Association, American Society for Public Administration, Pi Sigma Alpha, Pi Gamma Mu.

WRITINGS: (Editor with Donald H. Riddle) *The Problems and the Promise of American Democracy,* McGraw, 1964; *Political Education in the American Democracy,* Intext, 1971. Contributor to yearbooks and to *Today's Education, Social Education,* and *Education Forum.*

* * *

CLECAK, Peter (E.) 1938-

PERSONAL: Born July 22, 1938, in Oakland, Calif.; son of Nicholas P. and Jean (Peter) Clecak; married Vivian Bozman, February 26, 1966; children: Aimee Elizabeth, Lisa Nicole. *Education:* University of California, Berkeley, A.B. (cum laude), 1960; Stanford University, Ph.D., 1964. *Home:* 1486 Morningside Cir., Laguna Beach, Calif. 92651. *Office:* Program in Comparative Culture, University of California, Irvine, Calif. 92717.

CAREER: Stanford University, Stanford, Calif., lecturer in English, 1963-64; University of California, Irvine, assistant professor of English and comparative literature, 1966-71, associate professor of English and acting director of Program in Comparative Culture, 1972-74, professor of social

thought and comparative culture, 1975—. Consultant to National Endowment for the Humanities, 1977—. *Military service:* U.S. Army, 1964-66. *Member:* American Historical Association, American Studies Association, Organization of American Historians, Phi Beta Kappa. *Awards, honors:* Woodrow Wilson fellow, 1960-61; Stanford University fellow, 1962-63; University of California Humanities Institute fellow, summer, 1967; *Radical Paradoxes* selected by *Choice* as one of the outstanding academic books for 1974; American Council on Education fellow in higher administration, 1974-75; Phi Beta Kappa fellow, 1974-75, to work on *Crooked Paths.*

WRITINGS: (Contributor) Leo Huberman and Paul M. Sweezy, editors, *Paul Baran: A Collective Portrait,* Monthly Review Press, 1965; (contributor) Louis Manashe and Ronald Radosh, editors, *Teach-Ins: U.S.A.,* Praeger, 1967; (contributor) Ralph Miliband and John Saville, editors, *The Socialist Register: 1969,* Monthly Review Press, 1969; *Radical Paradoxes: Dilemmas of the American Left, 1945-1970,* Harper, 1973; *Crooked Paths: Reflections on Socialism, Conservatism and the Welfare State,* Harper, 1977; (with Howard R. Bowen and others) *Investment in Learning: The Individual and Social Value of Higher Education,* Jossey-Bass, 1977. Contributor of articles and reviews to *Frontier, College Composition and Communication, Studies on the Left, Monthly Review, MR: Seleccions en Castellano, Nation, Per Se, Our Generation Against Nuclear War, Science and Society, MR: Edizone Italiana, Massachusetts Review, American Scholar, Journal of Social Theory and Practice, Modern Occasions, Saturday Review, Antioch Review, Social Policy, Dissent, Chronicle of Higher Education, Change, Book Forum, Social Research,* and *Journal of American History.* Consulting editor, *Book Forum,* 1973; member of editorial board, *Marxist Perspectives,* 1973—.

WORK IN PROGRESS: The Idea of Competition in America, for Oxford University Press.

* * *

CLELAND, Charles C(arr) 1924-

PERSONAL: Born May 15, 1924, in Murphysboro, Ill.; son of Homer W. (a merchant) and Stella (Carr) Cleland; married Betty Lou Woodburn (executive secretary, Texas Board of Psychology), July 18, 1948. *Education:* Southern Illinois University, B.S. in Ed., 1950, M.S. in Ed., 1951; University of Texas, Ph.D., 1957. *Religion:* Presbyterian. *Home:* 3427 Monte Vista, Austin, Tex. 78731. *Office:* Education Bldg. 408-A, University of Texas, Austin, Tex. 78712.

CAREER: Salesman, coal miner, and surveyor's assistant during student days; Brown Schools for Exceptional Children, Austin, Tex., The Oaks, assistant director, 1951-52; Austin State School, Austin, psychologist, 1952-55; Lincoln State School, Lincoln, Ill., chief psychologist, 1956-57; Austin State School, chief of psychology, education, and research, 1957-59; Abilene State School, Abilene, Tex., superintendent, 1959-63; University of Texas at Austin, lecturer, 1963-64, associate professor, 1964-68, professor of special education and educational psychology, 1969—. Lecturer in management, Illinois Wesleyan University, 1956-57; member of cooperative graduate faculty, James Millikin University, 1956-57. Member, Texas Board of Psychological Examiners, 1961; member of task force on residential care, Texas Plan to Combat Mental Retardation. Chairman of board of directors, Brown Schools for Exceptional Children; president of board of directors, Austin Child Guidance Center. *Military service:* U.S. Army, 1943-46; served in Pacific theater.

MEMBER: Interamerican Society of Psychology, American Psychological Association (fellow), International Association for Scientific Study of Mental Deficiency, American Academy on Mental Retardation, American Association on Mental Deficiency (fellow; member of executive board, Southwest region, 1962; representative of national association to White House Conference on Aging, 1971), Southwestern Psychological Association (secretary-treasurer, 1963-65), Texas Psychological Association (president, 1961-62), Phi Kappa Phi, Phi Delta Kappa, Psi Chi. *Awards, honors:* Grants from Illinois Psychiatric Research Board, 1956, Brown Foundation, 1969, 1971, and Hogg Foundation for Mental Health, 1971; Education Award, American Association on Mental Deficiency, 1978.

WRITINGS: (With Jon D. Swartz) *Mental Retardation: Approaches to Institutional Change,* Grune, 1969; (contributor) A. A. Baumeister and E. C. Butterfield, editors, *Mental Retardation,* Aldine-Atherton, 1970; (with Swartz) *Administrative Issues in Institutions for the Mentally Retarded,* Hogg Foundation for Mental Health, 1972; *Mental Retardation: A Developmental Approach,* Prentice-Hall, 1978. Also contributor to *Mental Retardation: Theory and Research,* edited by Richard Eyman and George Tarjan, American Association on Mental Deficiency. Contributor of more than 200 articles and reviews to journals in his field.

WORK IN PROGRESS: Editing with Jon D. Swartz and Albert Shafter, *Readings in Institutional Management;* research and writing on the profoundly retarded.

*   *   *

CLEMMONS, Francois 1945-

PERSONAL: Born April 23, 1945, in Birmingham, Ala.; son of Willie (a laborer) and Inez (Scarbrough) Clemmons. *Education:* Oberlin College, B.M., 1967; Carnegie-Mellon University, M.F.A., 1969. *Office:* Metropolitan Opera Studio, New York, N.Y. 10025.

CAREER: "Misterogers' Neighborhood," Pittsburgh, Pa., actor and singer, 1968—; Metropolitan Opera Studio, New York, N.Y., solo singer, 1969—. *Member:* Phi Mu Alpha.

WRITINGS: (Contributor) Dennis Hartman, editor, *America Sings,* National Poetry Press, 1968; (contributor) R. Baird Chuman, editor, *A Galaxy of Black Writing,* Moore Publishing, 1970; (contributor) Patricia Brown, Don L. Lee, and Francis Ward, editors, *To Gwen with Love,* Johnson Publishing Co., 1971. Contributor of poems to *Black World, Black Creation, Music Journal, Aim,* and *Journal of Black Poetry.*

WORK IN PROGRESS: Three Eyed King, a biography.††

*   *   *

CLEVENGER, Theodore, Jr. 1929-

PERSONAL: Born December 2, 1929, in Kansas City, Mo.; son of Theodore and Alice (Dorcet) Clevenger; married Charlotte Ruth Dorrill (a breeder and exhibitor of Afghan hounds), April 27, 1951; children: Theodore III, Ruth Alice, Frederick William, Elizabeth Anne. *Education:* Attended Phillips University, 1947-49; Baylor University, B.A., 1951, M.A., 1952; Florida State University, Ph.D., 1958. *Home:* 2108 Trainon Ct., Tallahassee, Fla. 32303. *Office:* Department of Communication, Florida State University, 424 Diffenbaugh, Tallahassee, Fla. 32306.

CAREER: Instructor in speech at Henderson State College, Arkadelphia, Ark., 1953-54, Florida State University, Tallahassee, 1955-57, and University of Illinois at Urbana-Champaign, 1957-59; University of Wisconsin—Madison, assistant professor, 1959-62, associate professor of speech, 1962; University of Pittsburgh, Pittsburgh, Pa., associate professor of speech, 1962-65; University of Texas at Austin, professor of speech, 1965-67; Florida State University, professor of speech and chairman of department, 1967-73, acting provost, 1973—. Visiting professor, University of California, Los Angeles, summer, 1964; distinguished visiting professor, University of Nebraska, Omaha, 1970. Recorded lecture series, "Your Speech," for educational television, 1966; speech consultant to political figures in Texas and Florida. Member of board of directors, Asolo Theatre Festival, Sarasota, 1967-69 and State Theatre of Florida, Tallahassee, 1967-69.

MEMBER: American Psychological Association, Speech Communication Association (president, 1972), Speech Association of America (member of administrative council, 1968-70), Society for Psychophysiological Research, American Association for the Advancement of Science, American Association of University Professors, Central States Speech Association, Southern Speech Association, Florida Speech Association.

WRITINGS: Audience Analysis, Bobbs-Merrill, 1966; (with Huber W. Ellingsworth) *Speech and Social Action,* Prentice-Hall, 1967; (with Jack Matthews) *The Speech Communication Process,* Scott, Foresman, 1970.

Contributor: (And editor of texts of debates) Sidney Kraus, principal editor, *Great Debates,* University of Indiana Press, 1962; Ronald Reid, editor, *Introduction to the Field of Speech,* Scott, Foresman, 1966; Paul Ried, editor, *Frontiers in Experimental Speech-Communication Research,* Syracuse University Press, 1966; Keith Brooks, editor, *Communicative Arts and Sciences of Speech,* C. E. Merrill, 1967; Philip Emmert and William D. Brooks, editors, *Research Methods in Speech-Communication,* Houghton, 1971; Herman Stelzner, editor, *Studies in Honor of Karl Wallace,* University of Illinois Press, in press.

General editor, "Undergraduate Speech" series, Scott Foresman, 1966-70. Contributor of more than fifty articles to speech and communication journals including *Educational Theatre Journal, Journal of Marketing Research,* and *Public Opinion Quarterly.* Assistant editor, *Quarterly Journal of Speech,* 1959-62; associate editor, *Speaker,* 1959-64, and *Speech Monographs,* 1962-65; research editor, *Journal of Communication,* 1962-65, editor, 1965-68.†

*   *   *

CLOEREN, Hermann J(osef) 1934-

PERSONAL: Born February 15, 1934, in Aachen, Germany; son of Gerhard (a civil engineer) and Erna (Wolter) Cloeren; married Ingrid Eckmann, June 3, 1966; children: Susanne Vivian, Nicole. *Education:* Attended Innsbruck University, 1954-56, and University College, London, 1956-57; University of Muenster, M.A., 1963, Ph.D., 1967. *Religion:* Roman Catholic. *Home:* 335 Green St., Northborough, Mass. 01532. *Office:* Department of Philosophy, College of the Holy Cross, Worcester, Mass. 01610.

CAREER: Collegium Marianum, Muenster, West Germany, tutor, 1960-62; Aaseehaus-Kolleg, Muenster, tutor, 1963-66; College of the Holy Cross, Worcester, Mass., assistant professor, 1967-72, associate professor of philosophy, 1972—. *Member:* American Philosophical Association, American Association of University Professors.

WRITINGS: (Editor and author of introduction) Philosophie als Sprachkritik im 19. Jahrhundert: Textauswahl I, Frommann-Holzboog, 1971. Contributor of articles and reviews to Kant-Studien, Classical Folia, Historisches Woerterbuch der Philosophie, and Journal of the History of Ideas.

* * *

CLOSE, A. Kathryn 1908(?)-1973

1908(?)—June 9, 1973; American magazine editor and writer, child welfare administrator, and author of books on children and on social and medical problems. Obituaries: Washington Post, June 14, 1973.

* * *

CLOUT, Hugh Donald 1944-

PERSONAL: Born April 29, 1944, in London, England; son of Donald (a policeman) and Florence (Allwood) Clout. Education: University College, London, B.A., 1965, M.Phil., 1968. Office: University College, University of London, Gower St., London WC1E 6BT, England.

CAREER: University of London, University College, London, England, lecturer in geography, 1968—. Visiting assistant professor at University of Georgia, 1972, and University of South Carolina, 1972.

WRITINGS: Geography of Post-War France, Pergamon, 1972; Rural Geography, Pergamon, 1972; The Massif Central, Oxford University Press, 1973; The Franco-Belgian Border Region, Oxford University Press, 1975; Regional Development in Western Europe, Wiley, 1975; Migration in Post-War Europe, Oxford University Press, 1976; Themes in the Historical Geography of France, Academic Press, 1977. Contributor to Geographical Review and Transactions. Editor of Geographical Abstracts Series D: Social Geography, 1968-72.

WORK IN PROGRESS: Two books, Agriculture in France on the Eve of the Railway Age and Social Geography of Britain; research on historical geography of nineteenth-century France.

* * *

CLOWARD, Richard Andrew 1926-

PERSONAL: Born December 25, 1926, in Rochester, N.Y.; son of Donald B. and Esther Marie (Fleming) Cloward; married Ethelmarie McGaffin, March 25, 1951 (divorced, 1978); children: Leslie Anne, Mark, Kevin, Keith. Education: University of Rochester, B.A., 1949; Columbia University, M.S.W., 1950, Ph.D., 1958. Office: School of Social Work, Columbia University, 622 West 113th St., New York, N.Y. 10025.

CAREER: Columbia University, New York, N.Y., assistant professor, 1954-58, associate professor, 1958-62, professor of social work, 1962—. Military service: U.S. Navy, 1944-46. U.S. Army, 1951-54; became lieutenant. Member: American Association of University Professors, American Sociology Association, American Association of Social Workers, New York Civil Liberties Union (member of board of directors, 1958—), Poverty/Rights Action Center (member of board of directors, 1966—). Awards, honors: Dennis Carroll Award from International Society of Criminology, 1965, for Delinquency and Opportunity; C. Wright Mills Award from Society for Study of Social Problems, 1971, for Regulating the Poor.

WRITINGS: Social Perspectives on Behavior, Free Press, 1958; Delinquency and Opportunity, Free Press, 1960; Regulating the Poor, Pantheon, 1971; The Politics of Turmoil, Pantheon, 1974; Poor People's Movements, Pantheon, 1977. Contributor to New Republic, Nation, Saturday Review, Transaction, and other journals in his field.

WORK IN PROGRESS: A study of deviant behavior.

* * *

CLUGSTON, Richard 1938-

PERSONAL: Born August 14, 1938, in Dublin, Ireland; son of George Henry (a master mariner) and Margaret (McGowan) Clugston; married Mary Elizabeth Hazel (a teacher), July 25, 1963. Education: University of Liverpool, B.Eng., 1959; Coventry College of Further Education, P.G.C.E., 1971. Religion: Church of England. Home: "Shane," Towsend Lane, Upper Boddington, near Daventry, Northamptonshire, England. Office: Department of Mathematics, Warriner College, Banbury, Oxford, England.

CAREER: A.E.I., Rugby, England, manager trainee, 1959-62, assistant to chief planner, 1962-64; Marconi Co. Ltd., Chelmsford, Essex, England, assistant to divisional industrial engineer, 1964-66; Fuller Electric Transformers, printing equipment estimating manager, 1966-68; Herbert Ingersoll, Ltd., Daventry, Northamptonshire, England, automatic machine tools and process lines estimating manager, 1968-70; Warriner College, Banbury, Oxford, England, head of mathematics, 1970—. Member: Institution of Electrical Engineers (associate member), Daventry Junior Chamber of Commerce. Awards, honors: Scholarship from the French government, 1961, for study of French manufacturing methods in switch gear factories in Southern France.

WRITINGS: Estimating Manufacturing Costs, Gower Press, 1971. Work included in Top Poets of 1968, Golden Eagle Press, 1968.

WORK IN PROGRESS: What Industry Expects from the English Educational System—and What It in Fact Gets.

* * *

CLUTE, Robert E(ugene) 1924-

PERSONAL: Born July 12, 1924, in Earlville, Iowa; son of Henry H. and Leta (Allen) Clute; married M. Doris Reams (a librarian), December 22, 1946; children: Robert E., Jr., Andrea Reams. Education: Attended Maquoketa Junior College, 1943; University of Alabama, B.A., 1947; George Washington University, M.A., 1948; Duke University, Ph.D., 1958. Politics: Democrat. Religion: Episcopalian. Home: 180 Sunnybrook Dr., Athens, Ga. 30601. Office: Department of Political Science, University of Georgia, Athens, Ga. 30601.

CAREER: U.S. Displaced Persons Commission, Frankfurt, Germany, resettlement officer, 1948-50; U.S. Air Force, Salzburg, Linz, and Vienna, Austria, air specialist, 1950-54; University of Nevada, Reno, assistant professor of political science, 1959-62; University of Georgia, Athens, associate professor, 1962-68, professor of political science, 1968—, director of graduate studies, 1962—. Visiting professor, Tulane University, 1958-59; Fulbright scholar and head of University of Sierra Leone, 1967-68. Military service: U.S. Army, 1943-46. Member: American Society of International Law, American Political Science Association, Southern Political Science Association, Pi Sigma Alpha, Phi Alpha Theta.

WRITINGS: The International Legal Status of Austria,

1938-1955, Nijhoff, 1962; (with R. R. Wilson, J. M. Howell, and D. C. Piper) *The International Law Standard and Commonwealth Developments,* Duke University Press, 1966; (contributor) Carl Beck, editor, *De Lege Pactorum,* Duke University Press, 1970; (contributor) David Deener, editor, *Law and Justice,* Duke University Press, 1970. Contributor to *American Journal of International Law, American Journal of Comparative Law, Georgia Journal of International and Comparative Law, Background of World Politics, Journal of Asian and African Studies,* and *UNESCO Encyclopedia of Social Sciences.*

WORK IN PROGRESS: A book, *Social Change and Political Development.*

*   *   *

CLYDE, Norman Asa 1885-1972

PERSONAL: Born April 8, 1885, in Philadelphia, Pa.; son of Charles (a clergyman) and Isabelle (Purvis) Clyde. *Education:* Geneva College, B.A., 1909; also studied at University of California, University of Wisconsin, and University of Southern California. *Religion:* Protestant. *Address:* Big Pine, Calif. 93513.

CAREER: Taught high school in North Dakota, Utah, Arizona, and California, 1898-1910. Professional mountaineer. Consultant to U.S. Army, Alpine Club, and State of California. *Member:* National Rifle Association, American Alpine Club, Appalachian Club (corresponding member), Sierra Club, California Academy of Sciences. *Awards, honors:* Geneva College, Sc.D., 1939, Distinguished Service award, 1962; Francis Farquhar Mountaineering Award.

WRITINGS: Close Ups of the High Sierra, edited by Walt Wheelock, La Siesta Press, 1961, revised edition, 1966; *Norman Clyde of the Sierra Nevada,* Scrimshaw Press, 1971; *El Picacho Del Diablo: The Conquest of Lower California's Highest Peak, 1932 and 1937,* edited by John W. Robinson, Dawson's Book Shop, 1975. Contributor of more than 300 articles to magazines, including *Field and Stream, Touring Topics, Westward, Sierra Club Bulletin, National Motorist,* and *Sports Afield.*

SIDELIGHTS: Clyde is credited with about one hundred "firsts" in mountain climbing, mostly in the Sierra Nevadas. Numerous mountain features in the Sierra are named after him, including Clyde's Minaret, Clyde's Spires, Clyde's Ledge, Clyde Meadow, and Clyde Peak.†

(Died December 23, 1972)

*   *   *

COATES, Robert M(yron) 1897-1973

April 6, 1897—February 8, 1973; American art critic and writer. Obituaries: *New York Times,* February 10, 1973; *Time,* February 19, 1973. (See index for *CA* sketch)

*   *   *

COCHRAN, John R(obert) 1937-

PERSONAL: Born March 12, 1937, in Mount Vernon, Ohio; son of John Conrad and Mary (Carter) Cochran; married Barbara Rogers (an accountant), July 7, 1961. *Education:* Attended Miami University, Oxford, Ohio, 1955-58; Ohio State University, B.Sc., 1960, M.A., 1962, Ph.D., 1968. *Home:* 853 North Medina Line Rd., Akron, Ohio 44313. *Office:* Department of Counseling and Special Education, University of Akron, Buchtel Ave., Akron, Ohio 44304.

CAREER: Hudson High School, Hudson, Ohio, counselor, 1962-65; University of Akron, Akron, Ohio, associate professor of education, 1969—. *Member:* American Personnel and Guidance Association, Ohio Personnel and Guidance Association (president-elect, 1978-79).

WRITINGS: (Editor with Herman J. Peters) *Guidance: An Introduction and Selected Readings,* C. E. Merrill, 1972.

WORK IN PROGRESS: Research on the evaluation of career education programs.

AVOCATIONAL INTERESTS: Travel.

*   *   *

CODEL, Martin 1903(?)-1973

1903(?)—March 20, 1973; American writer, editor, and publisher of works on broadcasting. Obituaries: *Washington Post,* March 22, 1973.

*   *   *

COE, Rodney Michael 1933-

PERSONAL: Born November 10, 1933, in Marquette, Mich.; son of Roy A. (a variety store manager) and Renee (Reeder) Coe; married Elaine Elwell, September 6, 1954; children: Kevin, Curtis, Andrea, Douglas. *Education:* Iowa State University, B.S., 1955; Southern Illinois University, M.A., 1959; Washington University, St. Louis, Mo., Ph.D., 1962. *Home:* 114 South Elm, St. Louis, Mo. 63119. *Office:* Department of Community Medicine, School of Medicine, St. Louis University, 1320 South Grand Blvd., St. Louis, Mo. 63104.

CAREER: Woodward State Hospital, Woodward, Iowa, supervisor of vocational placements, 1955-56; Illinois State Penitentiary, Menard, classification officer, 1958; Anna State Hospital, Anna, Ill., rehabilitation counselor trainee, 1958-59; Washington University, St. Louis, Mo., lecturer, 1960-62, assistant professor, 1962-67, associate professor of sociology, 1967-70, research assistant at Medical Care Research Center, 1960-62, project director, 1962-63, executive director, 1963-73; St. Louis University, St. Louis, associate professor, 1970-72, professor of community medicine, 1972—. Visiting professor, Latin American Faculty of Social Sciences (Santiago, Chile), 1969-70. Consultant to Chilton Research Services, Inc., 1970—, and Pan American Health Organization, 1974. Member of social problems research review committee, National Institute of Mental Health, 1976—; member of ad hoc research review committee, Administration on Aging, 1976; member of technical consultant panel for health interview survey, National Center for Health Statistics, 1977—; member of committee on incorporation of knowledge of aging into medical education, Institute of Medicine, National Academy of Sciences, 1977—. *Military service:* U.S. Army, Corps of Engineers, 1956-58.

MEMBER: International Gerontological Association, International Sociological Association, American Sociological Association, American Public Health Association, Gerontological Society (secretary, 1972-75; chairman of personnel committee, 1976, 1977), Royal Society of Health, Association of American Medical Colleges, Association for Behavioral Sciences and Medical Education, Association of Teachers of Preventive Medicine, Midwest Sociological Society, Midwest Council for Social Research in Aging (president, 1965-67), Phi Beta Kappa. *Awards, honors:* U.S. Public Health Service grants, 1965-73, 1966-70.

WRITINGS: (With Albert F. Wessen) *Survey of Anes-*

thesia Practice in the United States, Medical Care Research Center, 1966; (with Philip A. O'Hare) *Evaluation of the Effectiveness of Training Sessions Conducted by the Gerontological Society under the Implementation of the Gerontological Curriculum Project,* Medical Care Research Center, 1967; *National Survey of Physicians' Attitudes Toward Preventive Health Care Services for the Aged and Toward Aging,* Medical Care Research Center, 1968; (with John M. Goering, Marvin Cummins, and William Read) *Health Status of Low Income Families in an Urban Area,* Medical Care Research Center, 1969; (editor) *Planned Change in the Hospital: Case Studies of Organizational Innovations,* Praeger, 1970; *Sociology of Medicine,* McGraw, 1970, 2nd edition, 1978; (with Eugene A. Friedmann, Warren A. Peterson, and others) *Medicare Report: Evaluation of the Provision and Utilization of Community Health Resources,* Institute for Community Studies, Inc., 1970; (with Henry P. Brehm) *Preventive Health Care for Adults: A Study of Medical Practice,* College & University Press, 1972; (with Max Pepper) *Development and Demonstration of Baseline Clinical Information on a Target Population of a Neighborhood Comprehensive Health Services Center,* Department of Community Medicine, St. Louis University, 1972; (with Goering) *The Community Laboratory: A Final Report,* Medical Case Research Center, 1973; (with Peterson, Jack Sigler, Mary Stroker, and Julie Egerton) *The Impact of Medicare in Selected Communities,* Institute for Community Studies, Inc., 1973; (with Pepper) *Involvement of Medical Students in a Union Sponsored, Prepaid Health Plan,* Department of Community Medicine, St. Louis University, 1975; (with Pepper) *Community Medicine: Some New Perspectives,* McGraw, 1978.

Contributor: Clyde B. Vedder and Barbara A. Day, editors, *Penology,* C. C Thomas, 1964; Arnold M. Rose and Peterson, editors, *Older People and Their Social World,* F. A. Davis, 1965; *Care of the Geriatric Patient,* 4th edition (Coe was not associated with earlier editions), E. M. Cowdry, editor, Mosby, 1968, 5th edition published as *Cowdry's Care of the Geriatric Patient,* Franz U. Steinberg, editor, 1976; Alfred Kadushin, editor, *Child Welfare Services: A Sourcebook,* Macmillan, 1970; Martin E. Bruetman, editor, *Conference on Delivery of Health Care in Relation to Stroke: 1970,* Chicago Heart Association, 1971; Adina M. Reinhart and Mildred D. Quinn, editors, *Family-Centered Community Nursing,* Mosby, 1973; Albert J. Wertheimer and Mickey C. Smith, editors, *Pharmacy Practice: Social and Behavioral Aspects,* University Park Press, 1974; Robert L. Kane, editor, *The Challenges of Community Medicine,* Springer Publishing, 1974; Sylvia Sherwood, editor, *Long-Term Care: A Handbook for Researchers, Planners and Providers,* Spectrum, 1975; Kane and others, editors, *The Health Gap,* Springer Publishing, 1976; Gary L. Albrecht, editor, *Sociology of Rehabilitation and Physical Disability,* University of Pittsburgh Press, 1976. Contributor to proceedings. Contributor to journals in the behavioral sciences, police sciences, and political science, and to nursing and health care journals and *Inquiry.*

WORK IN PROGRESS: Research on alternatives in long-term care and on changing patterns in provision and utilization of health services for the aged; curriculum development in geriatric medicine; a study of the effects of stress on the process of aging.

AVOCATIONAL INTERESTS: Travel (Europe, Latin America, Russia).

COFFEY, J(oseph) I(rving) 1916-

PERSONAL: Born February 13, 1916, in St. Louis, Mo.; son of Joseph Aloysius and Catherine (Burns) Coffey; married Marjorie Ann Strode, 1939 (divorced, 1963); married Rosemary Klineberg, 1963 (divorced, 1977); married Maryann Bishop, 1978; children: (first marriage) John, Catherine, Judith (Mrs. Samuel Russell); (second marriage) Megan, Susan, James. *Education:* U.S. Military Academy, West Point, N.Y., B.Sc., 1939; Columbia University, additional study, 1943-45; Georgetown University, Ph.D., 1954; graduate of Command and General Staff College and Army War College. *Home:* 4305 Centre Ave., Pittsburgh, Pa. 15213. *Office:* Center for Arms Control and International Security Studies, 160 Mervis Hall, University of Pittsburgh, Pittsburgh, Pa. 15260.

CAREER: U.S. Army, regular officer, 1939-60, retiring as colonel; instructor, later assistant professor of history and government at U.S. Military Academy, West Point, N.Y., 1942-45; had various troop assignments up to division staff officer, and then staff assignments with Army Intelligence, 1950-51, Army Plans, 1953-54, and Office of Assistant Secretary of Defense, 1954-56; assistant director for programs, special studies project, Rockefeller Brothers Fund, 1956-57; executive assistant to Special Assistant to President for Security Operations Coordination, Washington, D.C., 1958-60; staff member, President's Committee on Information Activities Abroad, 1960; Institute for Defense Analyses, Arlington, Va., research analyst, 1960-63; Bendix Systems Division, Ann Arbor, Mich., chief of Office of National Security Studies, 1963-67; University of Pittsburgh, Pittsburgh, Pa., professor of public and international affairs, 1967—, associate dean, Graduate School of Public and International Affairs, 1970-72, director, Center for Arms Control and International Security Studies, 1975—. Lecturer at Georgetown University, 1954-56, 1960-63, Canadian Forces Staff College, U.S. Naval War College, Canadian Defence College, (British) National Defence College, Inter-American Defense College, and various universities. Consultant to Department of Defense, U.S. Arms Control and Disarmament Agency, 1967-73, and Agency for International Development, 1973-74.

MEMBER: International Institute for Strategic Studies, International Studies Association, American Academy of Political and Social Sciences, Council on Foreign Relations, Gold Key Society.

WRITINGS: (With William R. Kintner and others) *Forging a New Sword: A Study of Defense Organization,* Harper, 1958; (with V. P. Rock) *The Presidential Staff,* National Planning Association, 1961; (contributor) Bennett Boskey and Mason Willrich, editors, *Nuclear Proliferation: Prospects for Control,* Dunellen, 1970; *Deterrence in the 1970's* (monograph), Social Science Foundation and Graduate School of International Studies, University of Denver, 1971; *Strategic Power and National Security,* University of Pittsburgh Press, 1971; *Arms Control and European Security: A Guide to East-West Negotiations,* Praeger, for International Institute for Strategic Studies, 1977; (contributor) *Tactical Nuclear Weapons: European Perspectives,* Taylor & Francis, for Stockholm International Peace Research Institute, 1978. Contributor to Stockholm International Peace Research Institute *Yearbook,* 1978. Contributor of articles on strategy, military policy, arms control, and foreign affairs to journals, including *Bulletin of the Atomic Scientists, Foreign Affairs, International Affairs, Annals of the American Academy of Political and Social Scientists, U.S. Naval In-*

stitute Proceedings, Orbis, Revue Militaire Generale, and *Worldview.*

WORK IN PROGRESS: Research on "grey area" weapons and arms control; research in cross-national perceptions of security.

*   *   *

COLBURN, George A(bbott) 1938-

PERSONAL: Born January 11, 1938, in Highland Park, Mich.; son of George Allen (a factory worker) and Nora M. (a registered nurse; maiden name, Humpert) Colburn; married Barbara Ann Brunton, August 19, 1962 (divorced); children: Erin Elizabeth, Kerry Lynne. *Education:* Aquinas College, A.B., 1959; Michigan State University, M.A., 1964, Ph.D., 1971. *Home:* Springbrook Hills, Walloon Lake, Mich. 49796.

CAREER: Grand Rapids Press, Grand Rapids, Mich., sports writer, 1957-59; *Detroit Times,* Detroit, Mich., caption writer, 1960; *Sun* Newspapers, Lafayette, Calif., news and associate editor, 1961-63; Michigan State University, East Lansing, assistant to dean of College of Arts and Letters, 1964-66; *Towne Courier* Newspapers, East Lansing, staff writer and columnist, 1965-70; legislative aide to Speaker of Michigan House of Representatives, Lansing, 1970-73; Illinois State University, Normal, associate professor of information sciences and aide to university president, 1973; *Chicago Tribune,* Hinsdale, Ill., area editor, 1973-74; University of California Extension, San Diego, project director of courses by newspapers, 1974—; *Charlevoix County Press,* Boyne City, Mich., publisher, 1977—. City councilman, East Lansing, 1971-73. *Member:* American Committee for Irish Studies, Irish American Cultural Institute, Common Cause (co-chairman of San Diego County chapter). *Awards, honors:* Pulitzer Prize nomination for community reporting, 1969, for series of articles on selection of president at Michigan State University.

WRITINGS: (Editor with Lewis H. Carlson) *In Their Place: White America Defines Her Minorities, 1850-1950,* Wiley, 1972.

WORK IN PROGRESS: A book with Carlson, *America's Fancy: The Rise of Spectator Sports in the United States,* for Nelson-Hall.

*   *   *

COLEMAN, Richard J(ames) 1941-

PERSONAL: Born November 9, 1941, in Lebanon, Pa.; son of James M. (an engineer) and Alberta (Jordan) Coleman; married Ruth Winslow, December 18, 1965; children: Joy Elizabeth, Sharon Ruth, Laura Carol. *Education:* Johns Hopkins University, B.A., 1963; Princeton Theological Seminary, B.D., 1966, Th.M., 1967. *Home:* 23 Faculty Rd., Durham, N.H. 03824. *Office:* Durham Community Church, Durham, N.H. 03824.

CAREER: Clergyman; pastor of Presbyterian and United Church of Christ churches in Pittsfield, Mass. and Perth Amboy, N.J., 1967-69; Miss Hall's School, Pittsfield, chaplain, 1969-70; Christian Center, Pittsfield, executive director, 1970-78; Durham Community Church, Durham, N.H., teaching minister, 1978—.

WRITINGS: Issues of Theological Warfare: Evangelicals and Liberals, Eerdmans, 1972. Contributor to *Pulpit, Worldview, Theology Today, Journal of American Scientific Affiliation,* and *Journal of Evangelical Theological Society.*

WORK IN PROGRESS: Theology and Science: The End and the Beginning of Their Reigns as Queens.

SIDELIGHTS: Richard J. Coleman told *CA:* "I am excited by the prospects of an emerging new/biblical middle ground between Evangelicals and Liberals in America and the prospect of a deepening dialogue between theology and science. More and more scientists are demonstrating an interest in looking at the large philosophical questions, and hopefully more theologians will be looking at the large scientific questions."

AVOCATIONAL INTERESTS: Traveling, camping, boating, woodworking.

*   *   *

COLETTA, Paolo Enrico 1916-

PERSONAL: Born February 3, 1916, in Plainfield, N.J.; son of Alberto Sisto (a tailor) and Maria (Rappoli) Coletta; married Alicevelyn Warner, January 15, 1940 (died, 1967); married Maria Bellina Boyer, September 5, 1967; children: (first marriage) Dana Maria (Mrs. Lawrence Murphy); (stepchildren) Bernarr Boyer, Paula Maria. *Education:* Junior College of Connecticut, A.A., 1936; University of Missouri, B.S., 1938, M.A., 1939, Ph.D., 1942. *Home:* 1519 Riverdale Dr., Winchester-on-Severn, Annapolis, Md. 21401. *Office:* United States Naval Academy, Annapolis, Md. 21402.

CAREER: University of Missouri—Columbia, instructor in history, 1940-42; Stephens College, Columbia, Mo., instructor in social science, 1942-43; South Dakota State College (now University), Brookings, instructor in history, 1946; University of Louisville, Louisville, Ky., instructor in social science, 1946; U.S. Naval Academy, Annapolis, Md., associate professor, 1958-63, professor of history, 1963—, lecturer in sea power and national policy, 1971—. Visiting professor, University of Maryland Extension, 1959-62; Fulbright lecturer, University of Genoa, 1971; visiting summer professor at University of Nebraska, 1949, 1952, 1953, and at Colorado College, 1963. *Military service:* U.S. Navy, 1943-46. U.S. Naval Reserve, 1951-73; retired as captain.

MEMBER: American Historical Association, U.S. Naval Institute, American Military Institute, Society of Historians for Foreign Relations, Organization of American Historians, Pacific Historical Society, Southern Historical Association, Naval Reserve Association, National Geographic Society, Nebraska State Historical Society, Phi Delta Kappa.

WRITINGS: (Contributor) W. W. Jeffries, editor, *Geography and National Power,* U.S. Naval Institute, 1953, 4th edition, 1968; (with Gerald E. Wheeler) *An Outline of World Naval History,* Annapolis Academy Press, 1956; (contributor) H. Wayne Morgan, editor, *The Gilded Age,* Syracuse University Press, 1963; *William Jennings Bryan,* University of Nebraska Press, Volume I: *Political Evangelist, 1860-1908,* 1964, Volume II: *Progressive Politician and Moral Statesman, 1909-1915,* 1969, Volume III: *Political Puritan, 1915-1925,* 1969; (contributing editor) *Threshold to American Internationalism: The Foreign Policies of William McKinley,* Exposition Press, 1970; (contributor) Arthur M. Schlesinger, Jr., editor, *History of Presidential Elections,* Chelsea House, 1971; (contributor) Schlesinger, editor, *History of U.S. Political Parties,* Chelsea House, 1972; *William Howard Taft,* University Press of Kansas, 1973; (contributor) Alexander DeConde, editor, *Encyclopedia of American Foreign Policies,* Scribner, 1978; *The U.S. Navy and Defense Unification, 1947-1953,* University of Delaware

Press, 1979; (contributing editor) *American Secretaries of the Navy,* Naval Institute Press, 1979. Contributor to encyclopedias; contributor of more than fifty articles and reviews to history journals.

WORK IN PROGRESS: A biography of Bradley A. Fiske, for Regents Press of Kansas; a biography of Bowman Hendry McCallai; a biography of Cyrus Vance.

* * *

COLINVAUX, Paul (Alfred) 1930-

PERSONAL: Born September 22, 1930, in St. Albans, England; son of Flora Kingsman (a banker); married Llewellya W. Hillis (a professor), June 17, 1961; children: Catherine Martha, Roger Paul. *Education:* Jesus College, Cambridge, B.A., 1956, M.A., 1960; Duke University, Ph.D., 1962. *Home:* 319 South Columbia Ave., Columbus, Ohio 43209. *Agent:* C & J Wolfers Ltd., 3 Regents Square, London WC1H 8H2, England. *Office:* College of Biological Sciences, Ohio State University, 484 West 12th Ave., Columbus, Ohio 43210.

CAREER: Canadian Government, research officer attached as pedologist to Soil Survey of New Brunswick, 1956-59; Queen's University of Belfast, Belfast, Northern Ireland, postdoctoral fellow, 1962-63; Yale University, New Haven, Conn., postdoctoral research fellow, 1963-64; Ohio State University, Columbus, assistant professor, 1964-67, associate professor, 1967-71, professor of zoology, 1971—. Distinguished visiting professor, University of Washington, spring, 1972. Field work in Portugal, 1954, Nigeria, 1955, Alaska, 1960, 1963, 1965, 1978, Jamaica, 1962, 1969, Bermuda, 1963, Galapagos, 1966, 1969, 1971, Peru, 1977, and Ecuador, 1978. Chairman of sponsoring institutions of the Institute of Ecology (TIE), 1977—. *Military service:* British Army, Royal Artillery, 1949-51; served in Germany; became lieutenant.

MEMBER: INQUA (International Quaternary Association; member of U.S. National Commission), American Society of Naturalists, American Society of Limnology and Oceanography, Ecological Society of America, American Quaternary Association, American Association for the Advancement of Science, Arctic Institute of North America, American Association of University Professors, Society of Authors, Ohio Academy of Sciences, Phi Beta Kappa, Sigma Xi.

AWARDS, HONORS: North Atlantic Treaty Organization postdoctoral fellowship, 1962-63; outstanding or distinguished teaching awards at Ohio State University from Student Council, College of Biological Sciences, 1970, Ohio State University Alumni Association, 1971, and College of Arts and Sciences, 1972; Guggenheim fellowship in London, 1971-72; Ohioana Book Award in field of science, 1978.

WRITINGS: (Contributor) D. M. Hopkins, editor, *The Bering Land Bridge,* Stanford University Press, 1967; (editor) *The Environment of Crowded Men,* MSS Educational Publishing, 1970; *Introduction to Ecology,* Wiley, 1973; *Why Big Fierce Animals Are Rare and Other Essays,* Princeton University Press, 1978. Author of twenty-part television series, "What Ecology Really Says," broadcast on WOSU, Columbus, 1974, 1976, and 1978; also author of column, "Science in Review," in *Yale Review,* 1972-75. Contributor to *Science, Nature, Ecology,* and other journals.

WORK IN PROGRESS: The Fates of Nations, an ecologist's view of history; an account of arctic researches into the environment of the Bering land bridge, tentatively titled *The Land Bridge Problem;* continued studies in the arctic directed at reconstructing the flora and fauna of the old Bering land bridge; studies in the ice age environment of the American equator in Galapagos, Ecuador, and Brazil.

SIDELIGHTS: Paul Colinvaux writes: "I like classes many hundreds strong [about six hundred are enrolled in his classes] and to these I orate. This form of unfashionable teaching has won me every teaching prize available at my university.... I have been able to enjoy writing because my student days were pleasantly and totally immune from the instruction of English literature departments. This history also gives me the chance to enjoy reading. It is my passionate belief that science is so intrinsically interesting that it only has to be written about beautifully for everybody to understand all about it.

"My sports are rowing and beagling. At Cambridge I acquired a certain facility with hounds, an expertise at running expeditions to remote places, and a third class degree in agriculture. Also some useful education.... In my first Canadian winter I read all of Gibbons' *Decline and Fall* in Joe's diners. I believe this to be a record."

* * *

COLLIAS, Joe G. 1928-

PERSONAL: Born April 25, 1928, in East St. Louis, Mo.; son of George Nick (a cleaner) and Martha L. (Vanbuskirk) Collias; married Majorie M. Piel (a realtor), October 1, 1960. *Education:* Washington University, St. Louis, Mo., M.E., 1956. *Politics:* Independent. *Religion:* Lutheran. *Residence:* Crestwood, Mo. *Office:* Boise Cascade Corp., Hazelwood, Mo. 63042.

CAREER: Bemis Bag Co., St. Louis, Mo., design engineer, 1951-61; Boise Cascade Corp., Hazelwood, Mo., art director, 1961—. *Military service:* U.S. Army, 1946-49; became sergeant.

WRITINGS: Last of Steam, Howell-North Books, 1960; *Search for Steam,* Howell-North Books, 1972.

WORK IN PROGRESS: Three books about local railroads.

AVOCATIONAL INTERESTS: Art (paints in oils), photography.

* * *

COLWELL, C(harles) Carter 1932-

PERSONAL: Born August 19, 1932, in Chicago, Ill.; son of Ernest Cadmen (academic administrator and New Testament scholar) and Annette (Carter) Colwell; married Ann Knox, June 16, 1952; children: Christopher James, Knox Cadmen, Joshua Edwards. *Education:* University of Chicago, B.A., 1949; Cambridge University, B.A., 1952, M.A., 1957; Emory University, Ph.D., 1958. *Religion:* Methodist. *Home:* 818 East Church St., DeLand, Fla. 32720. *Office:* Department of English, Stetson University, DeLand, Fla. 32720.

CAREER: Emory-at-Oxford, Oxford, Ga., instructor in English, 1952, 1955; Stetson University, DeLand, Fla., assistant professor, 1958-64, associate professor, 1964-70, professor of English, 1970—. Consultant, Division of Archives, History, and Records Management, Florida Department of State, 1973-74. Director of Wesley Foundation, 1963-69; corresponding secretary, West Volusia Council on Human Relation, 1969; founding member, Board of Home and

Neighborhood Development. *Military service:* U.S. Army, 1953-55; became sergeant. *Member:* American Association of University Professors (secretary and vice-president, Stetson University chapter), South Atlantic Modern Language Association. *Awards, honors:* Danforth fellow, 1955-58, associate, 1968—.

WRITINGS: A Student's Guide to Literature, Washington Square Press, 1968; *The Tradition of British Literature,* Putnam, 1971; *What's the Usage? A Writer's Guide to English Grammar and Rhetoric,* Reston, 1973; (with James Knox) *The Complete Term Paper,* Reston, 1974. Author of eight cassette lectures on Shakespeare published by Everett/Edwards, 1971-73. Contributor of articles and reviews to *Process Studies, Modern Age, FEA Journal,* and *Daytona Beach News-Journal.*

AVOCATIONAL INTERESTS: Photography, fencing, model railroading, and playing the violin.

*   *   *

CONLEY, Robert J(ackson) 1940-

PERSONAL: Born December 29, 1940, in Cushing, Okla.; son of Robert Parris and Peggy Marie (Jackson) Conley; married Evelyn Snell, March, 1978. *Education:* Midwestern University, B.A., 1966, M.A., 1968. *Home address:* P.O. Box 123, Tahlequah, Okla. *Office:* Native American Studies, Bacone College, Muskogee, Okla. 74401.

CAREER: Northern Illinois University, DeKalb, instructor in English, 1968-71; Southwest Missouri State University, Springfield, instructor in English, 1971-74; Eastern Montana College, Billings, coordinator of Indian culture, 1975-77; assistant programs director, Cherokee Nation of Oklahoma, 1977-78; currently affiliated with Native American Studies program, Bacone College, Muskogee, Okla. *Military service:* U.S. Marine Corps Reserve, Infantry, 1958-64. *Member:* International Platform Association, International Poetry Society, Centro Studi e Scambi Internazzionali, Western Writers of America, National Indian Education Association, Midwest Modern Language Association.

WRITINGS: (Editor with Richard Cherry and Bernard Hirsch) *A Return to Vision,* Houghton, 1971; (editor with Cherry) *Poems for Comparison and Contrast,* Macmillan, 1972; (editor with Cherry and Hirsch) *The Shadow Within,* Houghton, 1973. Contributor to anthologies, including *From the Belly of the Shark,* edited by Walter Lowenfels, *The Face of Poetry,* edited by Laverne H. Clark, *The New Breed,* edited by Edward Oliphant, and *The Remembered Earth,* edited by Geary Hobson. Contributor to *Pembroke, Quetzal, Indian Voice, Blue Cloud Quarterly, Academy,* and *Cardinal Poetry Quarterly.* Co-editor, *Blackbird Circle.*

SIDELIGHTS: Robert J. Conley told *CA:* "My poems and stories are becoming more and more Cherokee in the sense of their developing out of tribal experience and tradition. At the same time, of necessity, they are less personal and, I think, more meaningful."

*   *   *

CONLY, Robert Leslie 1918(?)-1973
   (Robert C. O'Brien)

1918(?)—March 5, 1973; American magazine editor and writer, and author of novels and children's books. Obituaries: *New York Times,* March 8, 1973; *Publishers Weekly,* March 12, 1973; *Library Journal,* March 15, 1973; *Time,* March 19, 1973. (See index for *CA* sketch)

CONNERS, Bernard F. 1926-

PERSONAL: Born September 14, 1926, in Albany, N.Y.; married Catherine Connors, November 30, 1957; children: Christopher, Sarah, Jane. *Education:* St. Lawrence University, B.A., 1951. *Home:* 60 Old Niskayuna Rd., Loudonville, N.Y. 12211. *Agent:* Oscar Collier, 280 Madison Ave., New York, N.Y. 10016.

CAREER: Federal Bureau of Investigation, Washington, D.C., special agent, 1951-60; currently owner of soft drink and real estate businesses in New York and New England. *Military service:* U.S. Army, 1945-47, 1951; became lieutenant.

WRITINGS: Don't Embarrass the Bureau (novel), Bobbs-Merrill, 1972. Contributor to magazines and newspapers.

WORK IN PROGRESS: A second novel.

AVOCATIONAL INTERESTS: Tennis, skiing, football.

*   *   *

CONNERY, Robert H(owe) 1907-

PERSONAL: Born October 1, 1907, in St. Paul, Minn.; son of Robert Henry and Nellie Elizabeth (Collins) Connery. *Education:* University of Minnesota, B.A., 1929, M.A., 1930; Columbia University, Ph.D., 1935. *Home:* Mounted Route 210 (B), Oyster Bay, N.Y. 11771. *Office:* Academy of Political Science, 619 West 114th St., New York, N.Y. 10025.

CAREER: Columbia University, New York, N.Y., instructor in political science, 1933-39; Catholic University of America, Washington, D.C., associate professor of political science, 1939-41; Stanford University, Palo Alto, Calif., associate professor of political science, 1946-48; professor of political science, University of Illinois, 1948-49; Duke University, Durham, N.C., professor of political science, 1949-66; Columbia University, professor of government, 1966-76, president of Academy of Political Science, 1966—. Deputy city administrator, New York City, 1965. Consultant to numerous governmental and research organizations. *Military service:* U.S. Naval Reserve, active duty, 1942-46; became commander. *Member:* American Academy of Political Science (president, 1966—), American Political Science Association. *Awards, honors:* Brookings fellow, 1932.

WRITINGS: Governmental Problems in Wildlife Conservation, Columbia University, 1935, reprinted, AMS Press, 1968; *The Navy and the Industrial Mobilization in World War II,* Princeton University Press, 1950, reprinted, DaCapo Press, 1972; (with R. H. Leach) *The Federal Government and Metropolitan Areas,* Harvard University Press, 1960; (with Robert G. Albion) *Forrestal and the Navy,* Columbia University Press, 1962; (with others) *The Politics of Mental Health,* Columbia University Press, 1968; (with Gerald Benjamin) *Rockefeller of New York: Executive Power in the Statehouse,* Cornell University Press, 1979.

Editor; all published by Academy of Political Science, Columbia University, except as indicated: *Teaching Political Science,* Duke University Press, 1965; *Municipal Income Taxes,* 1968; *The Atlantic Community Reappraised,* 1968; (with Demetrios Caraley) *Governing the City; Challenges and Options for New York,* 1969; *Urban Riots: Violence and Social Change,* Vintage Books, 1969; *The Corporation and the Campus,* 1970; *Unionization of Municipal Employees,* 1971; (with Eldon L. Jones) *Control or Fate in Economic Affairs,* 1971; (with Robert S. Gilmour) *The National Energy Problem,* 1974; (with Gerald Benjamin) *Governing New York State: The Rockefeller Years,* 1974.

WORK IN PROGRESS: Research for a book on operations and problems of state government in New York during the past two decades.

* * *

CONNOR, W(alter) Robert 1934-

PERSONAL: Born August 30, 1934, in Worcester, Mass.; son of J. Walter (a salesman) and Helen (Silverbrand) Connor; married Carolyn Loessel, June 14, 1968; children: Christopher, Stephan. *Education:* Hamilton College, B.A., 1956; Princeton University, Ph.D., 1961. *Home:* 114 Mercer St., Princeton, N.J. 08540. *Office:* Department of Classics, Princeton University, Princeton, N.J. 08540.

CAREER: University of Michigan, Ann Arbor, instructor in classics, 1960-63; Center for Hellenic Studies, Washington, D.C., junior fellow, 1963-64; Princeton University, Princeton, N.J., assistant professor, 1964-70, associate professor, 1970-72, professor of classics, 1972—, chairman of department, 1972-77. Has also taught at Breadloaf School of English and University of Colorado; visiting research fellow, American School of Classical Studies, Athens, Greece, 1977-78. *Member:* American Philological Association, Phi Beta Kappa. *Awards, honors:* Fulbright fellow, University College, Oxford University, 1956-57.

WRITINGS: (Editor) *Greek Orations,* University of Michigan Press, 1966; *Theopompus and Fifth Century Athens,* Harvard University Press, 1968; *The New Politicians of Fifth Century Athens,* Princeton University Press, 1971. Contributor to *Encyclopedia Americana;* contributor of about fifteen articles to classical, foreign language, and archaeology journals.

WORK IN PROGRESS: Thucydides: An Interpretation.

* * *

CONRAD, Robert 1928-

PERSONAL: Born September 6, 1928, in Grand Rapids, Mich.; son of Delbert H. (a salesman) and Mary (Doran) Conrad; married Ursula Rupp, September 18, 1958. *Education:* Attended University of Mexico, 1950; Geneva College, B.S., 1951; Columbia University, M.A., 1964, Ph.D., 1967. *Residence:* Berlin, Germany. *Office:* Latein-Amerika Institut, Freie Universitaet Berlin, Ruedesheimerstrasse 54-56, 1000 Berlin 33, Germany.

CAREER: University of Illinois at Chicago Circle, Chicago, associate professor of history, 1967-78; Free University of Berlin, Berlin, Germany, professor of history, 1978—. *Military service:* U.S. Army, 1946-48. *Member:* Conference on Latin American History, American Historical Association, Latin American Studies Association. *Awards, honors:* American Philosophical Society grant, 1969; National Endowment for the Humanities senior fellowship, 1973-74.

WRITINGS: The Destruction of Brazilian Slavery, 1850-1888, University of California Press, 1972; (translator and author of introduction) Joaquim Nabuco, *Abolitionism: The Brazilian Anti-Slavery Struggle,* University of Illinois Press, 1977; *Brazilian Slavery: An Annotated Research Bibliography,* G. K. Hall, 1977.

Contributor: Helen Delpar, editor, *Encyclopedia of Latin America,* McGraw, 1974; Robert Brent Toplin, editor, *Slavery and Race Relations in Latin America,* Greenwood Press, 1974; Ann M. Pescatello, editor, *The African in Latin America,* Knopf, 1975. Contributor of articles to *Hispanic American Historical Review, International Migration Review, Luso-Brazilian Review,* and *Revista de Historia America.*

WORK IN PROGRESS: A comparative study of U.S. and Brazilian slavery; a documentary history of Brazilian slavery.

* * *

CONYERS, James E(rnest) 1932-

PERSONAL: Born March 6, 1932, in Sumter, S.C.; son of Emmett C. and Crenella (Clinkscales) Conyers; married Jean Farris (deputy director, Office of Economic Opportunity, Vigo County, Ind.), June 4, 1956; children: Judith Yolande, James E., Jr., Jennifer June. *Education:* Morehouse College, A.B., 1954; Atlanta University, M.A., 1956; Washington State University, Ph.D., 1962. *Politics:* "Independent, but vote usually Democratic." *Religion:* "No preference." *Home:* 213 Terre Vista Dr., Terre Haute, Ind. 47803. *Office:* Department of Sociology, Indiana State University, Terre Haute, Ind. 47809.

CAREER: Le Moyne College, Memphis, Tenn., instructor in social science, 1955-56; Indiana State College (now University), Terre Haute, assistant professor of sociology, 1962-64; Atlanta University, Atlanta, Ga., associate professor of sociology, 1964-68; Indiana State University, professor of sociology, 1968—. Field reader for Bureau of Research, U.S. Office of Education, 1966—. Member of board of governors, Community Foundation of Wabash Valley, Inc., 1969—. *Military service:* U.S. Army, 1956-58. *Member:* National Association for the Advancement of Colored People, American Sociological Association (fellow), Society for the Study of Social Problems, Association of Social and Behavioral Scientists (president, 1970-71), Southern Sociological Association, Ohio Valley Sociological Association, Indiana Academy of Social Sciences, Alpha Kappa Delta, Kappa Alpha Psi. *Awards, honors:* Russell Sage Foundation grant, 1971-73.

WRITINGS: (With F. Ivan Nye and Lois Hoffman) *The Employed Mother in America,* Rand McNally, 1962; (contributor) *Psycho-Social Dynamics in Miami,* Center for Advanced Studies, University of Miami, 1969; (author of introduction) W.E.B. DuBois, *The Negro American Family,* M.I.T. Press, 1970; (with Charles V. Willie) *The Family Life of Black People,* C. E. Merrill, 1970; (contributor) Fred R. Crawford, editor, *Violence and Dissent in Urban America,* Southern Newspaper Publishers Association, 1970; (editor with Morris Medley) *Sociology for the Seventies,* Wiley, 1972; (with W. L. Wallace) *Black Elected Officials: A Study of Black Americans Holding Governmental Office,* Russell Sage, 1976. Also contributor to *The Negro College and the Black Community,* edited by Ralph Hines and Richard Robbins. Contributor to sociology and education journals. Member of editorial board, *Phylon,* 1966-68.†

* * *

COOK, Alice Rice 1899-1973

June 24, 1899—April 30, 1973; American educator, management consultant, and author. Obituaries: *New York Times,* May 1, 1973.

* * *

COOKE, Edward F(rancis) 1923-

PERSONAL: Born January 14, 1923, in Boston, Mass.; son of Peter J. (a clerk) and Nora (Regan) Cooke; married Dorothy M. Cleary, July 20, 1947; children: Patricia Cooke

Baughman, Nancy J., Mary E. *Education:* Middlebury College, A.B., 1947; Brown University, M.A., 1949; Northwestern University, Ph.D., 1953. *Politics:* Democratic. *Religion:* Roman Catholic. *Home:* 810 Ninth St., Oakmont, Pa. 15139. *Office:* Allegheny County Courthouse, Pittsburgh, Pa. 15219.

CAREER: University of Pittsburgh, Pittsburgh, Pa., assistant professor, 1955-59, associate professor, 1959-66, professor of political science, 1966—; Allegheny County treasurer, Pittsburgh, Pa., 1968—. Mayor of the Borough of Oakmont, 1966-69. Trustee of LaRoche College, 1969-71. *Military service:* U.S. Navy, 1943-46; received Silver Star Medal. *Member:* American Political Science Association, Municipal Finance Officers Association (state chairman, 1970—), Midwest Political Science Association, Northeast Political Science Association, Civic Club of Allegheny County (member of board of directors, 1969—).

WRITINGS: (With Edward G. Janosik) *Pennsylvania Politics,* Holt, 1957, revised edition, 1965; (contributor) M. E. Jewell, editor, *The Politics of Reapportionment,* Aldine-Atherton, 1962; *Detailed Analysis of the U.S. Constitution,* Littlefield, 1966; (contributor) Cornelius P. Cotter, editor, *Practical Politics in the United States,* Allyn & Bacon, 1969.

WORK IN PROGRESS: A study of political financing in the urban community.

*   *   *

COOMBS, Robert H(olman) 1934-

PERSONAL: Born September 16, 1934, in Salt Lake City, Utah; son of Morgan S. (a physician) and Vivian (Holman) Coombs; married Carol Jean Cook, May 29, 1958; children: Robert S., Kathryn, Lorraine, Holly Ann, David Jeremy. *Education:* University of Utah, B.S., 1958, M.S., 1959; Washington State University, Ph.D., 1964; Wake Forest University, postdoctoral study in medicine, summer, 1966. *Religion:* Church of Jesus Christ of Latter-day Saints (Mormons). *Home:* 1612 Hobart Dr., Camarillo, Calif. 93101. *Office:* 414 UNEX Bldg., University of California, Los Angeles, Calif. 90024; and Box A, Camarillo, Calif. 93010.

CAREER: Iowa State University, Ames, instructor, 1963-64, assistant professor of sociology, 1964-66; Wake Forest University, Bowman Gray School of Medicine, Winston-Salem, N.C., assistant professor, 1966-68, associate professor of sociology at Behavioral Sciences Center, 1968-70; California Department of Mental Hygiene, Sacramento, career research specialist, 1970-73; University of California, Los Angeles, chief of Camarillo-Neuropsychiatric Institute Research Program, 1970-77, associate research sociologist in department of psychiatry, 1970-73, assistant director for research at Neuropsychiatric Institute, 1978—, adjunct professor of biobehavioral sciences. Member of adjunct faculty, University without Walls, Antioch College—West, 1971-74. Delegate to White House Conference on Children, 1970. University of California, Los Angeles, member of executive council, Alcohol Research Center, 1977—, member of executive committee, Biobehavioral Sciences Program, director of Family Learning Center. *Military service:* U.S. Army Reserve, Military Police, 1958-64.

MEMBER: International Scientific Commission on the Family, International Sociological Association, Conference on Social Science and Health, Association for the Behavioral Sciences and Medical Education, American Sociological Association (fellow), National Council on Family Relations (member of executive committee, 1967-68, 1969-71), Association of American Medical Colleges, Pacific Socio-

logical Association, Alpha Kappa Delta (chapter president, 1961), Phi Kappa Phi, Kappa Delta Pi. *Awards, honors:* National Institute of Mental Health grant to study marital and socialization stresses in medical training, 1968-73; National Fund for Medical Education grant to study psychosocial adjustment of medical students, 1969-71; California Council on Criminal Justice grant to conduct Camarillo resocialization program for drug abusers, 1971-74; National Institute on Drug Abuse grant to study techniques for reducing youth problems by strengthening families, 1977-79; California Department of Alcohol and Drug Abuse grant to study family and peer influences on polydrug use.

WRITINGS: Marriage, the Family, and Human Sexuality in Medical Education, Bowman Gray School of Medicine, Wake Forest University, 1966; (editor with H. T. Christensen, D. M. Fulcomer, J. C. Green, R. N. Hey, D. F. Hobbs, R. H. Klemer, E. B. Luckey, M. H. McCaulley, and J. H. Meyerowitz, and contributor) *Human Sexuality in Medical Education and Practice,* C. C Thomas, 1968; (editor with C. E. Vincent, and contributor) *Psychosocial Aspects of Medical Training,* C. C Thomas, 1971; (editor) *Junkies and Straights: The Camarillo Experience,* Lexington Books, 1975; (editor with L. J. Fry and P. G. Lewis) *Socialization in Drug Abuse,* Schenkman, 1976; *Mastering Medicine: Professional Socialization in Medical School,* Free Press, 1978; (with J. St. John) *Making It in Medical School,* Spectrum, in press.

Contributor: K. L. Cannon, editor, *Selected Readings in Marriage and Family Relationships,* Brigham Young University Press, 1966; D. L. Schaeffer, editor, *Sex Differences in Personality: A Book of Readings,* Brooks/Cole, 1971; F. M. Vernon, editor, *Research on Mormonism,* Association for the Study of Religion, 1974; M. L. Medley and A. Cline, editors, *Dating and Marriage: An Interactionist Perspective,* Holbrook, 1974; John Lofland, editor, *Doing Social Life: The Qualitative Study of Human Interaction in Natural Settings,* Wiley, 1976; L. H. Lofland, editor, *Toward a Sociology of Death and Dying,* Sage Publications, Inc., 1976; H. P. Chalfant, D. W. Curry, and C. E. Palmer, editors, *Sociological Stuff,* Kendall/Hunt, 1977.

Contributor to conferences. Contributor to social science journals, including *Journal of Medical Education, Medical Aspects of Human Sexuality, Sociometry, Journal of Educational Research, Sociology and Social Research, Social Problems,* and *Journal of Marriage and the Family.* Member of board of editors, *Family Coordinator: Journal of Education, Counseling, and Services,* 1970—, and *Journal of Drug Issues,* 1977.

WORK IN PROGRESS: Strengthening Families: A Community Approach to Youth Problems; Medical Mates; two articles for journals, "Marital Status and Life Stress," and "The Case of the Harried Medical Student."

*   *   *

COONS, William R(ichard) 1934-

PERSONAL: Born February 8, 1934, in Hudson, N.Y.; son of William Silas and Elsie (Melius) Coons; married Camille A. Nappi, February 6, 1960 (separated); children: Joyce Evelyn, Mary Bernice, Cathy Anne. *Education:* State University of New York at Binghamton, B.A., 1961; Cornell University, M.A., 1964. *Politics:* Independent. *Religion:* Unitarian Universalist. *Home:* 526 Clarendon St., Syracuse, N.Y. 13210. *Agent:* Oscar Collier, 280 Madison Ave., New York, N.Y. 10016.

CAREER: Free-lance writer. Skidmore College, Saratoga

Springs, N.Y., instructor in English, 1964-66; City University of New York, New York, N.Y., instructor in English, 1966. Executive secretary, Joe Hornstein, Inc. *Military service:* U.S. Army, 1954-56.

WRITINGS: Attica Diary, Stein & Day, 1972. Contributor to *Wilson Library Bulletin* and *New York Times Sunday Magazine.*

WORK IN PROGRESS: On Parole, a novel about the vicissitudes of being a parolee; poems.

SIDELIGHTS: William R. Coons has published a song, "Scarlet Tree," which is included in an LP album, "Songs for Very Special People."

*   *   *

COOPER, Bernarr   1912-

PERSONAL: Born October 6, 1912, in Brooklyn, N.Y.; son of Louis (a manufacturer) and Jennie (Linker) Cooper; married Adella Shaw (a teacher), June 7, 1945; children: Stephanie Cooper Vanderpool, Janet Louise. *Education:* Wabash College, A.B., 1932; Northwestern University, graduate study, 1932-34; Stanford University, Ph.D., 1955. *Home:* Van Leuven Dr. S., R.D. 1, Rensselaer, N.Y. 12144. *Office:* State University of New York, State Education Department, Albany, N.Y. 12224.

CAREER: Director and producer in professional radio and little theater, 1934-41; Broadcasting Corp. of Japan, Tokyo, adviser and consultant on broadcasting, 1946-52; United Nations chief of radio and theater materials in Japan and Korea, 1952-54; University of New Mexico, Albuquerque, professor of communication and director of university radio and television, 1956-59; Florida State University, Tallahassee, associate professor of speech and director of educational television workshops, 1959-62; State Education Department, State University of New York, Albany, chief of Bureau of Mass Communications, 1962—. Northeast chairman of national advisory committee for full development of ITFS, Federal Communications Commission; executive secretary, Committee on Educational Uses of Satellites. Educational consultant to United Nations, universities, and state departments of instruction; consultant to Federal Interagency Committee on Education. *Military service:* U.S. Army, 1943-46; served in Military Intelligence and Signal Corps; became lieutenant.

MEMBER: National Association of Educational Broadcasters, Speech Communications Association, National Advisory Council on Foreign Languages for Elementary Schools, American Association of University Professors, Phi Beta Kappa. *Awards, honors:* Certificate of achievement from United Nations Command for work in prisoner of war camps; two grants from U.S. Department of Health, Education, and Welfare for children's television series on interethnic understanding; award to produce a young adult series on consumer education; grant from League of Women Voters for documentary on energy problems in New York State; grant for a television series on Puerto Rican culture and history.

WRITINGS: The Microphone Is Yours: Radio Production-Directing (in Japanese), United Nations Command, 1950; (with Robert L. Hilliard) *Understanding Television,* Hastings House, 1964; *ITFS: What It Is . . . How to Plan,* National Education Association, 1967; *Television Broadcasting,* Hastings House, 1978. Also author or editor of twenty publications per year for New York State Department of Education. Contributor to education and communication journals.

WORK IN PROGRESS: The use of airborne satellites for transmission of instructional, educational, and general informational material; specifically, opportunities for cross-cultural study and the teaching of foreign languages as second languages.

*   *   *

COOPER, Charles M(uhlenberg)   1909-

PERSONAL: Born January 7, 1909, in Lima, Ohio; son of Frederick Eugene (a clergyman) and Rosa (Richards) Cooper; married Alta Peterson, May 29, 1934; children: Charles (deceased), Jeremy, Catherine (Mrs. Donald A. Millard, Jr.). *Education:* Harvard University, A.B. (cum laude), 1930; Lutheran Theological Seminary, Philadelphia, Pa., B.D., 1935; Dropsie College for Hebrew and Cognate Learning (now Dropsie University), Ph.D., 1941. *Home:* 22 Acacia Ave., Berkeley, Calif. 94708. *Office:* Pacific Lutheran Theological Seminary, 2770 Marin Ave., Berkeley, Calif. 94708.

CAREER: Clergyman of Lutheran Church; assistant pastor in Akron, Ohio, 1933-36; Lutheran Theological Seminary, Philadelphia, Pa., instructor, 1936-41, assistant professor, 1941-45, Norton Professor of Old Testament, 1945-53; Lutheran Ministerium of Pennsylvania, Philadelphia, president, 1953-61; Pacific Lutheran Theological Seminary, Berkeley, Calif., professor of Biblical languages, 1961—, president, 1961-73. Member of executive board, Lutheran Church in America. *Member:* American Association of Theological Schools (member of executive committee, 1964-70), Graduate Theological Union (chairman of heads of member schools, 1971-72), Society of Biblical Literature (associate in council, 1948-50), Classical Club of Philadelphia (president, 1951-52), Oriental Club of Philadelphia (president, 1952-53), Berkeley City Commons Club (president, 1971). *Awards, honors:* D.D., Muhlenberg College, 1954.

WRITINGS: (Contributing editor) *Westminster Study Bible,* Westminster, 1948, Revised Standard Version, Collins, 1965; (contributor) *Old Testament Commentary,* Muhlenberg Press, 1948; *The Psalms in Life,* Muhlenberg Press, 1959; (with G. K. Wiencke) *The Old Testament for Us,* Lutheran Church in America, 1965; *Jeremiah,* with Pupil's Book and Teacher's Book, Lutheran Church in America, 1971; *A History of Pacific Lutheran Theological Seminary,* Augsburg, 1979. Contributor to *Uniform Lesson Commentary,* Muhlenberg Press, 1954, 1957, 1965. Also author of monthly column for *Pacific Southwest Lutheran,* 1970-73. Contributor to religion journals. Member of editorial board of *Journal of Biblical Literature,* 1950-53; member of editorial committee of *Theological Education,* 1967-70.

WORK IN PROGRESS: Research in the case method in Biblical exegesis and homiletics.

*   *   *

COOPER, Grace Rogers   1924-

PERSONAL: Born November 22, 1924, in Sharon, Pa.; daughter of Byron A. and Wilda (Boyer) Rogers; married Sanford Lee Cooper (a newspaperman, *Time* editor, and manufacturing distributor), December 15, 1961. *Education:* Attended Maryville College, 1942-44; University of Maryland, B.S., 1946. *Politics:* Independent. *Religion:* Lutheran. *Home and office:* Route 9 W., Great Cacapon, W.Va. 25422.

CAREER: Smithsonian Institution, Washington, D.C., assistant curator, 1948-56, associate curator, 1956-61, curator of textiles, 1961-76; museum consultant, 1976—. Consultant to *Encyclopaedia Britannica. Member:* International Institute for Conservation of Historic and Artistic Works, American Association of Museums.

WRITINGS: The Invention of the Sewing Machine, Smithsonian Institution Press, 1969, revised and expanded edition published as *The Sewing Machine: Its Invention and Development,* 1976; *The Copp Family Textiles,* Smithsonian Institution Press, 1971; *Thirteen-Star Flags: Keys to Identification,* Smithsonian Institution Press, 1973.

WORK IN PROGRESS: Research on conservation of baskets for the small museum.

SIDELIGHTS: Grace Rogers Cooper told *CA:* "Each person's research is but a building block to another. It is a resource best used by as many as possible, which is only feasible through publication."

* * *

COOPER, Jeff 1920-
(John Dean Cooper)

PERSONAL: Born May 10, 1920, in Los Angeles, Calif.; son of John Titus (in finance) and Austeene (George) Cooper; married Janelle Marks, February 6, 1942; children: Christina Cooper Hastings, Paralee Cooper Heath, Lindy Cooper Wisdom. *Education:* Stanford University, B.A., 1941; University of California, Riverside, M.A., 1968. *Politics:* Conservative Republican. *Religion:* Agnostic. *Home:* Gunsite Ranch, Paulden, Ariz. 86334.

CAREER: U.S. Marine Corps, 1941-45; became lieutenant colonel; instructor in combat intelligence and military history, Quantico, Va., 1945-48; served with guerrillas in Southeast Asia, 1950-53; *Guns and Ammo* (magazine), Los Angeles, Calif., departmental editor, 1958-65; Valley College, San Bernadino, Calif., lecturer in history and government, 1960-65; American Pistol Institute, Paulden, Ariz., president and course director, 1971—. *Member:* International Practical Shooting Confederation (founding president), National Geographic Society, American Museum of National History, American Security Council, National Rifle Association, American Wildlife Association, American Ordnance Association. *Awards, honors*—Military: Presidential Citation; Southwest Combat Pistol Champion, 1959, 1960, and 1961.

WRITINGS: Fighting Handguns, Trend, 1957; *Handguns Afield,* Spotlight, 1959; *Complete Book of Modern Handgunning,* Prentice-Hall, 1962; (with Jack O'Connor) *Complete Book of Shooting,* Harper, 1965; *Principles of Personal Defense,* edited by Robert K. Brown and Peter C. Lund, Paladin Press, 1972; *Cooper on Handguns,* Petersen, 1974. Author of monthly column, "Cooper on Handguns", in *Guns and Ammo* magazine, 1965-77. Contributing editor, *Soldier of Fortune, Guns, American Handgunner,* and *Personal Survival.*

WORK IN PROGRESS: The Technique of the Pistol; An Anecdotal History of Marksmanship; The Legend of the Forty-five; a Gunsite anthology.

* * *

COOPER, John Irwin 1905-

PERSONAL: Born March 11, 1905, in St. Thomas, Ontario, Canada; son of John (a locomotive engineer) and Hannah (Irwin) Cooper; married Mary Delight Cook, September 18, 1938; children: Daisy Ann, Mary Carolyn. *Education:* University of Western Ontario, B.A., 1930, M.A., 1933; On-

tario College of Education, secondary school teacher's certificate, 1931; McGill University, Ph.D., 1938. *Religion:* Church of England. *Home:* 66 Bidwell St., Tillsonburg, Ontario, Canada. *Office:* Department of History, McGill University, Montreal, Quebec, Canada.

CAREER: Teacher in secondary schools; McGill University, Montreal, Quebec, began as associate professor of Canadian history, currently associate professor emeritus. Visiting professor, University of Guelph, 1970-71. *Member:* Canadian Historical Association, Societe historique de Montreal, Canadian Church Historical Society. *Awards, honors:* Klieforth Award for a history of North America, 1947.

WRITINGS: Montreal: The Story of Three Hundred Years, Lamarande, 1942; *History of the Montreal Hunt,* The Hunt, 1953; *The Blessed Communion,* Diocesan Archives Committee, 1960; *Montreal: A Brief History,* McGill Queen's Press, 1969. Contributor to *Canadian Historical Review, Canadian Journal of Economics, Current History,* and *Dictionary of Canadian Biography.*

WORK IN PROGRESS: Early History of Ontario, 1610-1713; The Common People of Canada and the United States, with emphasis on the nineteenth and twentieth centuries.

* * *

COOPER, Leslie M(uir) 1930-

PERSONAL: Born May 18, 1930, in Salt Lake City, Utah; son of Leslie C. and Annie (Muir) Cooper; married Arlene Jackson, 1954 (divorced, 1963); children: Michele Christine, Debora Lynn, Lisa Diane. *Education:* Attended University of Utah, 1947-49, 1951-52; Brigham Young University, B.S., 1954, M.S., 1958; University of Illinois, Ph.D., 1962. *Home:* 1265 W. Pinewood Dr., Salt Lake City, Utah 84107. *Office:* Department of Psychology, University of Utah, Salt Lake City, Utah 84112.

CAREER: Brigham Young University, Provo, Utah, special instructor, 1957-58, assistant professor of psychology, 1962-64; Stanford University, Stanford, Calif., assistant professor of psychology, 1964-66; Brigham Young University, associate professor, 1966-70, professor of psychology, 1970-76; University of Utah, Salt Lake City, clinical professor of psychology, 1977—. American Board of Examiners in Psychological Hypnosis, diplomate in experimental hypnosis, 1968. Visiting summer professor at Central Washington State College (now Central Washington University), 1967, and University of Southern California, 1969; visiting professor, University of Southern California, 1972-73; consulting psychometrist, Utah State Training School, American Fork, 1957-58; research consultant to Alpine House Project (halfway house), 1963-64, Utah State Prison, 1970-71, and Canada Council, 1970. Private practice, 1963—. *Military service:* U.S. Air Force, 1954-56; became first lieutenant.

MEMBER: American Psychological Association, Psychonomic Society, American Association for the Advancement of Science, Society for Clinical and Experimental Hypnosis, Utah Academy of Arts and Sciences (fellow), Utah Psychological Association, Phi Kappa Phi, Sigma Xi, Pi Mu Epsilon, Psi Chi. *Awards, honors:* U.S. Public Health Service fellow, 1959-61; National Institute of Mental Health research grants, 1963, 1964; faculty research fellowship, Brigham Young University, 1966, 1971; Karl G. Maeser Research Award, Brigham Young University, 1972.

WRITINGS: (Contributor) Irving Wolf, editor, *Current*

Research in General Psychology, Prentice-Hall, 1967; (with E. R. Hilgard, L. W. Lauer, and A. H. Morgan) *Manual for Stanford Profile Scales of Hypnotic Susceptibility,* Consulting Psychologists Press, 1967; (with P. London) *Development of Hypnotic Susceptibility,* Bobbs-Merrill, 1972; (contributor) Erika Fromm and R. E. Shor, editors, *Hypnosis: Research Developments and Perspectives,* Aldine-Atherton, 1972. Contributor of more than sixty articles and reviews to psychology journals. Editorial consultant to *Choice, International Journal of Clinical and Experimental Hypnosis,* to *Journal of Personality and Social Psychology,* and to *Journal of Abnormal Psychology.*

WORK IN PROGRESS: Revision of chapter on hypnotic amnesia, with Erika Fromm and R. E. Shor, for inclusion in the revised edition of *Hypnosis: Research Developments and Perspectives;* an article for *American Journal of Clinical Hypnosis,* with Perry London.

* * *

CORBIN, Claire 1913-

PERSONAL: Born July 16, 1913, in New York, N.Y.; daughter of Herman and Anna (Kessler) Rothenberg; married Arnold Corbin (a professor of marketing and management), August 22, 1937; children: Lee Harrison, Karen Sue. *Education:* New York University, B.S., 1933, M.S., 1941, Ph.D., 1956. *Home:* 330 Harvard Ave., Rockville Centre, N.Y. 11570. *Office:* College of Business Administration, Fordham University, Bronx, N.Y. 10458; and Corbin Associates, 330 Harvard Ave., Rockville Centre, N.Y. 11570.

CAREER: Haire Publishing Co. (trade publications), New York City, editor and fashion editor, 1933-39; Curtis Publishing Co., Philadelphia, Pa., free-lance writer on home fashions for *Country Gentleman* (magazine), 1935-43; R. H. Macy and L. Bamberger & Co., New York City, executive trainee and merchandising executive, 1939-40; Long Island University, Brooklyn, N.Y., assistant professor of retailing and chairman of department, 1939-44; School of Business and Civic Administration of the City College (now Bernard M. Baruch College of the City University of New York), New York City, lecturer, 1944-49; The Guildery and Guildery Gifts, New York City, partner, 1944-45; Loft Candy Corp., Long Island City, N.Y., 'd rector of sales training, 1945-46; Hunter College (now Hunter College of the City University of New York), New York City, lecturer, 1946-47; Fawcett Publications, New York City, merchandising and promotion editor of *Today's Woman,* 1947-48; Corbin Associates (marketing/management consulting firm), Rockville Centre, N.Y., partner with husband, Arnold Corbin, 1949—; Hofstra College (now University), Hempstead, N.Y., associate professor of marketing, 1949-57; Fordham University, Bronx, N.Y., professor of marketing, 1957—. With her husband, has lectured since 1949 in England, Hong Kong, India, Japan, Taiwan, the Philippines, Australia, and New Zealand.

MEMBER: American Marketing Association (secretary-treasurer, 1970-73), American Academy of Advertising (chairman of national finance committee, 1958-62), National Home Fashions League (vice-president, 1958-59), American Institute of Interior Decorators, American Association of University Women, Adult Education Association, The Fashion Group, Advertising Women of New York, Publicity Club of New York, Eta Mu Pi, Gamma Alpha Chi, Kappa Delta Pi, Pi Lambda Theta.

WRITINGS: (Contributor) *Principles of Retailing,* Pitman, 1955; (contributor) *Principles of Advertising,* Pitman, 1963;

(with husband, Arnold Corbin and George Blagowidow) *Decision Exercises in Marketing,* McGraw, 1964; (with A. Corbin) *New Trends in American Marketing,* British Institute of Management, 1965; (with A. Corbin) *Implementing the Marketing Concept,* British Institute of Management, 1966; (editor-in-chief) *Encyclopedic Dictionary of Marketing and Related Business Terms,* American Marketing Association, in press. Contributor to journals and women's magazines. Member of editorial board of *New York Retailer;* woman's page editor of *Brooklyn Times Union.*

WORK IN PROGRESS: A contribution to *Handbook of Marketing; Financial Analysis for Marketing Decisions;* a revision of *Implementing the Marketing Concept; Marketing Planning and Control.*

* * *

CORBIN, H(ayman) Dan 1912-

PERSONAL: Born October 3, 1912, in Brooklyn, N.Y.; son of David (a merchant) and Frieda (Arnold) Corbin; married Lillian Rossen, May 30, 1937; children: Herbert, Stephen, Susan. *Education:* University of Alabama, B.S., 1933; Columbia University, M.A., 1934; New York University, Ph.D., 1946; University of California, Los Angeles, postdoctoral study, 1962. *Home:* 1322 Sunset Lane, West Lafayette, Ind. *Office:* Department of Physical Education, School of Humanities, Social Science, and Education, Purdue University, Lafayette, Ind. 47907.

CAREER: Recreation Training School, New York City, instructor in physical education and social skills, 1934-37; Department of Parks, New York City, director of playgrounds, 1937-42; high school physical education director and coach, 1942-43; Queens College (now Queens College of the City University of New York), Flushing, N.Y., instructor in health and recreation, 1943-46; Lock Haven State College, Lock Haven, Pa., 1947-66, became professor of health and physical education; Purdue University, Lafayette, Ind., professor of recreation education and chairman of section, 1966-78, professor emeritus, 1978—. Fulbright lecturer, Government College of Physical Education, Lahore, Pakistan, 1958; visiting professor at Utah State University and University of Colorado, 1960, University of Washington, Seattle, 1962, Pennsylvania State University, 1963, and West Virginia University, 1964. Member of President's Council on Physical Fitness, 1959; major specialist, UNESCO-International Council on Health, Physical Education and Recreation study of leisure time activities of youth in the Americas, 1964.

MEMBER: American Association for Health, Physical Education, and Recreation (fellow; past vice-president), National Recreation and Parks Association, American College of Sports Medicine (fellow), American Association of University Professors (president of Lock Haven chapter, 1958), Outdoor Writer's Association of America, Phi Delta Kappa, Sigma Lambda Sigma.

WRITINGS: Recreation Leadership (text), Prentice-Hall, 1953, 3rd edition, with instructor's manual, 1970; *Health and Safety,* with workbook, teacher's manual, and testing manual, Holt, 1959; (with others) *The Growing Years: Adolescence,* American Association for Health, Physical Education and Recreation, 1962; (with others) *Getting Through to Our Future Citizens,* Outdoor Writers Association of America, 1970; (with William J. Tait) *Education for Leisure,* Prentice-Hall, 1973. Contributor of articles and reviews to health education and recreation journals, including *Journal of Leisure Research, Society and Leisure, Recreation Man-*

agement, *Pakistan Review, Self, Journal of Health and Physical Education, Recreation,* and *Youth Leaders Digest.* Associate editor, *Journal of American Association for Health, Physical Education and Recreation,* 1958-61; member of editorial board, *JOHPER (Journal of Health, Physical Education and Recreation),* 1958-61.

AVOCATIONAL INTERESTS: Sailing, photography, travel, and music.

*   *   *

CORNISH, Sam(uel James)   1935-

PERSONAL: Born December 22, 1935, in Baltimore, Md.; married Jean Faxon, September, 1967. *Education:* Attended schools in Baltimore, Md. *Home:* 50 Monastery Rd., Brighton, Mass.

CAREER: Enoch Pratt Free Library, Baltimore, Md., writing specialist, 1965-66, 1968-69; bookseller, 1966-67; C.A.R.E.L., Washington, D.C., editorial consultant, 1967-68; teacher, Highland Park Free School, 1969—; former editor of *Chicory* (magazine), for the Enoch Pratt Library, Baltimore, and of *Mimeo,* a poetry magazine; Education Development Center, Open Education Follow Through Project, Newton, Mass., staff adviser and consultant on children's writing, 1973-78. Consultant to Central Atlantic Regional Educational Laboratories. *Military service:* 1958-60. *Awards, honors:* National Endowment for the Arts grant, 1967.

WRITINGS—Juveniles: Your Hand in Mind, Harcourt, 1970; *Grandmother's Pictures,* Bookstore Press, 1974; *Walking the Streets with Mississippi John Hurt,* Bradbury, 1978. Also author of *Harriet Tubman,* published by Third World Press.

Verse: *In This Corner: Sam Cornish and Verses,* Fleming McCallister Press, 1961; *People under the Window,* Sacco Publishers, 1962; *Generations,* Beanbag Press, 1964, Beacon Press, 1971; *Angles,* Beanbag Press, 1965; *Winters,* Sans Souci Press, 1968; (editor with Lucian Dixon) *Chicory: Young Voices from the Black Ghetto* (poetry and prose collection), Association Press, 1969; (editor with Hugh Fox and contributor) *The Living Underground: An Anthology of Contemporary American Poetry,* Ghost Dance Press, 1969; *Streets,* Third World Press, 1973; *Sometimes,* Pym-Randall Press, 1973; *Sam's World,* Decatur House, 1978. Work is represented in anthologies, including: *Black Fire,* edited by LeRoi Jones and Larry Neal, Morrow, 1968; *Smith Poets,* edited by Harry Smith, Horizon Press, 1969; *New Black Poetry,* edited by Clarence Major, International Publishers, 1969; *American Literary Anthology 3,* edited by George Plimpton and Peter Ardery, Viking, 1970; *Natural Process,* edited by Ted Wilentz and Tom Weatherly, Hill & Wang, 1972; *One Hundred Years of Black Poetry,* Harper, 1972; *A Penguin Anthology of Indian, African, and Afro-American Poetry,* Penguin, 1973; *New Voices in American Poetry,* edited by David Alan Evans, Winthrop, 1973. Contributor of poems and reviews to *Ann Arbor Review, Poetry Review, Journal of Black Poetry, Essence, Boston Review of the Arts,* and Boston newspapers.

SIDELIGHTS: Sam Cornish told *CA* that he has been influenced by Robert Lowell, T. S. Eliot, and LeRoi Jones. He said: "Most of my major themes are of urban life, the Negro predicament here in the cities, and my own family. I try to use a minimum of words to express the intended thought or feeling, with the effect of being starkly frank at times. Main verse form is unrhymed, free."†

CORRIGAN, John D(avitt)   1900-

PERSONAL: Born June 13, 1900, in Indiana, Pa. *Education:* U.S. Naval Academy, B.S., 1920. *Home:* 267 Atlantic Ave., Palm Beach, Fla. 33480.

CAREER: David Grimes, Inc., New York City, 1923-26, began as salesman, became assistant general manager; Servel, Inc., New York City, assistant vice-president of engineering and production and sales, 1926-30; Executives Institute, New York City, president, beginning 1930; Franklin Business Services, Inc., New York City, president, beginning 1966. Member of board of directors of Provident Fund for Income and of Porteous Growth Fund. Management consultant. Has lectured nationally on profit making, leadership, motivation, and salesmanship. *Military service:* U.S. Navy, 1920-23. U.S. Naval Reserve; present rank, commander. *Member:* American Management Association, Sales and Marketing Executives International, Sales Executives Club of New York.

WRITINGS: The Three Golden Keys, Fell, 1950; *How to Build Profit Value in Your Sales Dollars,* Ronald, 1955; (with Millard Bennett) *Successful Communications and Effective Speaking,* Prentice-Hall, 1972; *Guide Lines to Success,* Future Unlimited, 1973; *The Art and Science of Persuasion,* National Sales Dynamics, Inc., 1973.

SIDELIGHTS: John D. Corrigan has made two recordings, "Programmed Sales Meetings" and "Blueprint for Success," released by Success Motivation Institute in 1961.

*   *   *

CORSON, Richard

PERSONAL: Born in Genoa, Ill.; son of Vernon Joseph (a salesman) and Myrna (Long) Corson. *Education:* DePauw University, B.A.; Louisiana State University, M.A. *Home:* 121 Lincoln Pl., Park Slope, Brooklyn, N.Y. 11217.

CAREER: Theatre technical director and instructor at Louisiana State University, Baton Rouge, Women's College of the University of North Carolina, Greensboro, and Vassar College, Poughkeepsie, N.Y.; California State College at Long Beach (now California State University, Long Beach), artist professor-in-residence, 1968-69; Southern Methodist University, Dallas, Tex., adjunct professor of theatre arts, 1971—. Visiting lecturer at University of Minnesota, Dartmouth College, Eastern Washington University, Smith College, and Denison University. Has given almost a thousand one-man performances of his character sketches throughout the United States, Canada and England. *Member:* Phi Beta Kappa. *Awards, honors:* International Thespian Society Founders award for distinguished contributions to theatre and to youth.

WRITINGS: Stage Makeup, Appleton, 1960, 5th edition, 1975; *Monologs for Men,* Baker's Plays, 1960; *Fashions in Hair: The First 5000 Years,* P. Owen, 1964, revised edition, 1971; *Fashions in Eyeglasses,* P. Owen, 1967; *Fashions in Makeup,* P. Owen, 1972. Author of "The Sisters McIntosh," part of a 13-week series produced on NBC-TV, 1950. Contributor to *Dramatics Magazine* and *Quarterly Journal of Speech.* Makeup editor for *Players Magazine.*

WORK IN PROGRESS: Revision of *Stage Makeup,* for Prentice-Hall.

SIDELIGHTS: Fashions in Eyeglasses and *Fashions in Makeup* have been published in Japanese.

COSKEY, Evelyn   1932-

PERSONAL: Born November 16, 1932, in Jersey City, N.J.; daughter of Charles E. and Clara (Peters) Coskey. *Education:* Warren Wilson College, A.A., 1958; Berea College, B.A., 1960; University of Kentucky, M.S. in L.S., 1963; attended Copernicus University, summer, 1976, and Jagellonian University, summer, 1977. *Politics:* Independent. *Religion:* Presbyterian. *Home:* 505 Sanford St., Covington, Ky. 41011. *Office:* Kenton County Public Library, Covington, Ky.

CAREER: Kanawha County Public Library, Charleston, W.Va., librarian, 1964-78; Kenton County Public Library, Covington, Ky., assistant director of adult services, 1978—. *Member:* West Virginia Arts and Crafts Guild.

WRITINGS: Easter Eggs for Everyone, Abingdon, 1973; *Christmas Crafts for Everyone,* Abingdon, 1976. Contributor to *Library Trends.*

WORK IN PROGRESS: Research on the Methodist Church in Poland, and on Polish Easter Eggs; writing a second Christmas craft book.

*   *   *

COSTELLOE, M(artin) Joseph   1914-

PERSONAL: Born November 5, 1914, in Ames, Iowa; son of Martin Francis (a professor) and Mathilda Louise (Weckbach) Costelloe. *Education:* St. Louis University, A.B., 1938, M.A., 1941, Ph.L., 1941; St. Mary's College, St. Mary's, Kan., Th.L., 1947; Johns Hopkins University, Ph.D., 1958. *Home and office:* Curia Generalizia della Compagnia di Gesu, Borgo Santo Spirito 5, 00193 Rome, Italy.

CAREER: Entered Roman Catholic order of the Society of Jesus (Jesuits), 1933, ordained, 1946; high school teacher of Greek in Milwaukee, Wis., 1941-43; St. Stanislaus Seminary, Florissant, Mo., instructor in classical languages, 1952-56; Creighton University, Omaha, Neb., assistant professor, 1957-59, associate professor, 1959-62, professor of classical languages, 1962-73, head of department, 1961-70; Pontifical Biblical Institute, Rome, Italy, librarian, 1973-75; Jesuit Curia, Rome, librarian, 1975—. Visiting professor at Loyola University Center of Humanistic Study, Rome, 1963-64. *Member:* American Philological Association. *Awards, honors:* Fulbright scholar in Rome, Italy, 1950.

WRITINGS: (Translator and editor) Ludwig Hertling and Engelbert Kirschbaum, *The Roman Catacombs and Their Martyrs,* Bruce, 1956, revised edition, Darton, Longman & Todd, 1960; (translator) Guiseppe Ricciotti, *Julian the Apostate,* Bruce, 1960; (translator) Louis Bouyer, *Rite and Man,* University of Notre Dame Press, 1963; (translator) Angelo Paredi, *St. Ambrose and His Times,* University of Notre Dame Press, 1964; (translator) Claudio Morino, *Church and State in the Teaching of St. Ambrose,* Catholic University of America Press, 1969; (translator) Georg Schurhammer, *Francis Xavier,* Jesuit Historical Institute (Rome), Volume I, 1973, Volume II, 1977. Contributor of articles to *America, Classical Journal, Catholic Historical Review, Journal of Higher Education,* and *Classical Bulletin.*

WORK IN PROGRESS: Research on acts of early Christian martyrs, theories of translation, problems in the relationship between classical antiquity and early Christianity.

*   *   *

COTTER, Richard V(ern)   1930-

PERSONAL: Born June 27, 1930, in Long Prairie, Minn.; son of Vernon M. and Edith Cotter; married Carolyn Van Duyn Clark, June 12, 1976. *Education:* Lewis and Clark College, B.S., 1952; University of Oregon, M.S., 1963, Ph.D. (with honors), 1965. *Home address:* P.O. Box 14042, Reno, Nev. 89507. *Office:* College of Business Administration, University of Nevada, Reno, Nev. 89557.

CAREER: Oregon Journal Publishing Co., Inc., Portland, Ore., newsboy and station manager, 1942-43; Oregonian Publishing Co., Inc., Portland, newsboy, branch captain, clerk, night-and-weekend-office manager, 1944-48, district manager, 1948-53; Fairbanks Publishing Co., Inc., Fairbanks, Alaska, business manager, 1953-58; self-employed newspaper distributor and consultant, Portland, 1958-61; Oregon State System of Higher Education, Portland Continuation Center, Portland, instructor in business administration, 1962; University of Oregon, Eugene, instructor in finance, 1963-64; University of Nevada, Reno, assistant professor, 1965-67, associate professor, 1967-71, professor of managerial science, 1971—, associate dean for graduate studies, 1971-78. Visiting professor at University of Oregon, 1967, University of Newcastle, Newcastle, Australia, 1973, and University of Western Australia, 1978. *Military service:* Oregon National Guard, 1953-56. *Member:* American Finance Association, Academy of International Business, Association for Business Simulation and Experiential Learning, Financial Management Association, Western Finance Association, Western Economic Association, Phi Kappa Phi, Beta Gamma Sigma.

WRITINGS: The Business Policy Game, Prentice-Hall, 1973; (co-author) *Commercial Banking,* Prentice-Hall, 1976. Contributor to *AACSB Bulletin, Nevada Business Review, Journal of Financial and Quantitative Analysis,* and *National Banking Review.*

WORK IN PROGRESS: Revised edition, *Commercial Banking.*

AVOCATIONAL INTERESTS: Amateur musician, church choir.

*   *   *

COTTLE, William C(ullen)   1913-

PERSONAL: Born August 12, 1913, in Hart Lot, N.Y.; son of William C. III (a merchant) and Anna (Cullen) Cottle; married Martha Odell (a lawyer), August 16, 1938; children: William C. V, Edward C. *Education:* Syracuse University, B.S., 1932, M.S., 1938, Ed.D., 1949. *Politics:* Independent. *Religion:* Roman Catholic. *Home:* 670 West Harvard St., Englewood, Fla. 33533.

CAREER: Teacher in public school in state of New York, 1932-45; Syracuse University, Psychological Services Center, Syracuse, N.Y., instructor in counseling and senior clinical counselor, 1945-47; University of Kansas, Lawrence, assistant professor, 1947-49, associate professor, 1949-52, professor of education, 1952-61, assistant director of Guidance Bureau, 1948-61, director of Rehabilitation Counselor Training Program, 1955-57; Boston College, Boston, Mass., professor of education and director of Counselor Education and Counseling Psychology Program, 1961-78, professor emeritus, 1978—. New England regional consultant, Bureau of Employment Security, U.S. Department of Labor, 1962—; member of subcommittee on counseling and selection, National Manpower Advisory Committee, 1962-70; diplomate in counseling psychology, American Board of Examiners in Professional Psychology.

MEMBER: American Psychological Association (fellow),

American Personnel and Guidance Association (life member), American Catholic Psychological Association (president, 1960-61), National Vocational Guidance Association (president, 1959-60), Sigma Xi, Phi Delta Kappa. *Awards, honors:* Research award from American Personnel and Guidance Association, 1952.

WRITINGS: The MMPI: A Review, University Press of Kansas, 1953; *Procedures and Preparation for Counseling,* Prentice-Hall, 1960; *The School Interest Inventory and Manual,* Houghton, 1966; *Interest and Personality Inventories,* Houghton, 1968; (with N. M. Downie) *Preparation for Counseling,* Prentice-Hall, 1970; *Beginning Counseling Practicum,* Grune, 1973. Contributor to professional journals.

WORK IN PROGRESS: Editing case studies in counseling, for a textbook; research on developing scoring keys for uncovering potential drug users.

* * *

COUSINS, Albert Newton 1919-

PERSONAL: Born May 7, 1919, in Cleveland, Ohio; son of Harry (a businessman) and Anna (Roth) Cousins; married Rose Manitsas (a teacher and librarian), May 18, 1944; children: Julia, Daniel. *Education:* Ohio State University, A.B., 1942; Harvard University, M.A., 1949, Ph.D., 1951. *Office:* Department of Sociology, Cleveland State University, Cleveland, Ohio 44115.

CAREER: Florida State University, Tallahassee, assistant professor of sociology, 1949-51; Fenn College (now Fenn College of Cleveland State University), Cleveland, Ohio, associate professor of sociology, 1951-65; Ohio State University, Columbus, lecturer in labor education, 1965—; Cleveland State University, Cleveland, professor of sociology, 1965—, chairperson of department, 1977—, director of Anti-Poverty Institute, 1967. Lecturer, Case Western Reserve University, 1952. United Area Citizens Agency, Cleveland, vice-president, 1969-71, president, 1978. *Military service:* U.S. Army, 1942-46; became master sergeant. *Member:* American Sociological Association, American Association of University Professors, North Central Sociological Association. *Awards, honors:* National Science Foundation fellowship, 1966.

WRITINGS: (Contributor) Norman Bell and Ezra Vogel, editors, *A Modern Introduction to the Family,* Free Press, 1960; *A Society's Need . . . A University's Duty,* Cleveland State University, 1967; (editor with Hans Nagpaul) *Urban Man and Society,* Knopf, 1970; (with Nagpaul) *Urban Life,* Wiley, 1979.

WORK IN PROGRESS: Sociological, Political, and Economic Trends.

* * *

COVENEY, James 1920-

PERSONAL: Born April 4, 1920, in London, England; son of James and Mary (Sims) Coveney; married Patricia Yvonne Townsend, September 17, 1955; children: Patrick John, Peter Vivian. *Education:* University of Reading, B.A. (first class honors), 1950; University of Strasbourg, Ph.D., 1953. *Home:* 40 Westfield Close, Bath, Avon, England. *Office:* School of Modern Languages, University of Bath, Bath, Avon, England.

CAREER: University of Strasbourg, Strasbourg, France, lecteur d'Anglais, 1951-53; University of Hull, Hull, England, lecturer in French, 1953-58; Civil Service Commis-

sion, London, England, assistant director of examinations (modern languages), 1958-59; United Nations, New York, N.Y., Secretariat, 1959-61; North Atlantic Treaty Organization, Paris, France, International Secretariat, 1961-64; University of Bath, Bath, England, senior lecturer, 1964—, professor of French, 1969—. Language consultant to McKinsey & Co., Inc., 1969-76. *Military service:* Royal Air Force, 1939-45; became flight lieutenant. *Member:* National Council for Modern Languages (secretary, 1972-74), Association of University Professors of French (joint secretary, 1973—). *Awards, honors:* Chevalier de l'Ordre des Palmes Academiques, 1978.

WRITINGS: La Legende de l'Empereur Constant, Les Belles Lettres, 1955; *International Organization Documents for Translation from French,* Pergamon, 1972; (co-author) *Glossary of French and English Management Terms,* Longman, 1972; (co-author) *Le Francais pour l'ingenieur,* Harrap, 1973; (co-author) *Glossary of German and English Management Terms,* Longman, 1977; (co-author) *Glossary of Spanish and English Management Terms,* Longman, 1978; (co-author) *Guide to French Institutions,* Harrap, 1978. Contributor to British, French, and American journals.

WORK IN PROGRESS: Langues de specialite.

* * *

COWARD, Noel (Peirce) 1899-1973

December 16, 1899—March 26, 1973; English playwright, actor, director, producer, and songwriter. Obituaries: *New York Times,* March 27, 1973; *Washington Post,* March 27, 1973, March 28, 1973; *Time,* April 9, 1973. (See index for CA sketch)

* * *

COWDEN, Dudley J(ohnstone) 1899-

PERSONAL: Born January 10, 1899, in Grinell, Iowa; son of George Watson (a newspaper editor) and Bertha (Johnson) Cowden; married Mercedes Siedler, December 25, 1926. *Education:* Grinell College, A.B., 1919; University of Chicago, A.M., 1921; Columbia University, Ph.D., 1931. *Home:* 304 Country Club Rd., Chapel Hill, N.C. 27514. *Office:* Department of Economics, University of North Carolina, Chapel Hill, N.C. 27514.

CAREER: Lafayette College, Easton, Pa., instructor in economics, 1926-29; St. John's University, Brooklyn, N.Y., instructor in economics, 1931-34; Williams College, Williamstown, Mass., instructor in economics, 1934-35; University of North Carolina at Chapel Hill, associate professor, 1935-41, professor of economic statistics, 1941-71, professor emeritus, 1971—. *Member:* American Economic Association, American Statistical Association (fellow), Southern Economic Association, Phi Beta Kappa, Beta Gamma Sigma. *Awards, honors:* Honorary research associate at University College, London, 1958.

WRITINGS: (With Frederick E. Croxton) *Practical Business Statistics,* Prentice-Hall, 1934, (with Croxton and Ben W. Bolch) 4th edition, 1969; (with Croxton) *Exercises and Problems in Business Statistics,* Prentice-Hall, 1935, 2nd edition, 1940; (with Croxton) *Applied General Statistics,* Prentice-Hall, 1939, (with Croxton and Sidney Klein) 3rd edition, 1967; (with wife, Mercedes S. Cowden) *Practical Problems in Business Statistics,* Prentice-Hall, 1948, 2nd edition, 1960; *Statistical Methods in Quality Control,* Prentice-Hall, 1957. Contributor to *Southern Economic*

Journal, Journal of the American Statistical Association, Industrial Quality Control, Metroeconomica, and other periodicals.

WORK IN PROGRESS: Analysis of economic time series.

* * *

COX, Wally 1924-1973
(Wallace Maynard Cox)

December 6, 1924—February 15, 1973; American stage and screen actor and author of plays, short stories, and children's books. Obituaries: New York Times, February 16, 1973; Time, February 26, 1973.

* * *

COYLE, Leo (Perry) 1925-
(Lee Coyle)

PERSONAL: Born March 27, 1925, in Union City, N.J.; son of Leo Francis and Marie (Perry) Coyle; married Betty Marie Hengesbaugh, June 30, 1951; children: Martha Lee, Susan Jane. Education: St. Peter's College, B.S., 1949; Western Reserve University (now Case Western Reserve University), M.A., 1950, Ph.D., 1959; also attended Rutgers University, 1950-53. Politics: Independent. Home: 3405 Hollister Rd., Cleveland Heights, Ohio 44118. Office: Employee Communications Division, Ohio Bell Telephone Co., Cleveland, Ohio 44114.

CAREER: Jersey Journal, Jersey City, N.J., reporter, 1948-49; Rutgers Preparatory School, New Brunswick, N.J., teacher of English, 1951-53; John Carroll University, Cleveland, Ohio, lecturer, 1953-54, instructor in English, 1954-57, research fellow, 1957; Ohio Bell Telephone Co., Cleveland, Ohio, staff writer in public relations department, 1957-60, editor, 1960-63, supervisor, 1963-65, district manager, 1965-72, division information manager, Visual Communications Center, 1972-77, division manager, Employee Communications, 1977—. Vice-president of finance, Council on International Non-Theatrical Events (CINE), 1977-78. Accredited by Public Relations Society of America and by Industrial Audio Visual Association. Military service: U.S. Army, 1943-46. Member: Industrial Audio Visual Association (president, 1970), Public Relations Society of America.

AWARDS, HONORS: Chris awards from Columbus Film Council, 1971, 1972, and 1973, for films on Ohio; award from Industrial Audio Visual Association, 1971, for outstanding accomplishment and leadership in the audiovisual field; CINE Golden Eagles, 1971, for "Wonderful World of Ohio," 1972, for "Ohio . . . Only the Beginning," 1973, for "Simple Gifts," 1976, for "The Making of Ohio—Industry," and 1978, for "The Making of Ohio—Transportation"; Sunset Magazine Travel Film Festival best film award, 1971, for "The Wonderful World of Ohio"; first and second awards from National Visual Communications Association Day of Visuals, 1971, for "The Wonderful World of Ohio" and "Ohio . . . Only the Beginning"; Emmy Award from Cleveland chapter of National Academy of Television Arts and Sciences, 1972, for best community service program; first prize for videotapes and motion pictures from International Association of Business Communicators, 1972, for "A Special Breed" and "Don't Make It Easy"; Gold Medal from International Film and Art Festival for "Ohio . . . Only the Beginning," 1972; "Ohio . . . Only the Beginning" was named one of the most honored films of 1972 by Business Screen Magazine, March, 1973; Distinguished Achievement Award from Industrial Audio Visual Association, 1977, for "What Killed the Bell System?".

WRITINGS: (Under name Lee Coyle) George Ade, Twayne, 1964; (contributor) Frank Siedel and J. N. Siedel, editors, Pioneers in Science, Houghton, 1968; (contributor) James C. Austin and Donald A. Koch, editors, Popular Literature in America, Bowling Green University Popular Press, 1972.

Author of films, "The Wonderful World of Ohio," "Ohio . . . Only the Beginning," "Simple Gifts" (on folk life in Ohio). Also author of scripts for motion pictures and television, including "A Special Breed," "Don't Make It Easy," "Cleveland," "The Making of Ohio—Industry," and "The Making of Ohio—Transportation."

Contributor to Georgia Review, Ohio Historical Quarterly, Mark Twain Journal, Photomethods, Telephony, Colby Library Quarterly, and Business Screen.

WORK IN PROGRESS: A biographical novel about Mark Twain.

AVOCATIONAL INTERESTS: Music, art, reading, travel, nature.

* * *

CRAIG, David 1932-

PERSONAL: Born July 10, 1932, in Aberdeen, Scotland; son of John (a doctor) and Margaret (Simpson) Craig; married Gillian Stephenson (a doctor), October 7, 1957; children: Marian, Peter, Donald, Neil. Education: University of Aberdeen, B.A. (first class honors), 1954; Cambridge University, Ph.D., 1958. Politics: Communist. Religion: None. Home: Hill House, Main St., Burton, Carnforth, Lancashire, England. Office: University of Lancaster, Bailrigg, Lancaster, England.

CAREER: University of Ceylon, Peradeniya, lecturer in English, 1959-61; Workers' Educational Association, Richmond, Yorkshire, England, organizing tutor, 1961-64; University of Lancaster, Lancaster, England, senior lecturer in literature, 1964—.

WRITINGS: Scottish Literature and the Scottish People: 1680-1830, Chatto & Windus, 1961; (editor) Moderne Prosa und Lyrik der Britischen Inseln, Aufbau-Verlag, 1968; (editor) Alan Sillitoe, Saturday Night and Sunday Morning, Longmans, Green, 1968; (editor) Charles Dickens, Hard Times, Penguin, 1969; (editor with John Manson) Hugh MacDiarmid, Selected Poems, Penguin, 1970; The Real Foundations, Chatto & Windus, 1973; (editor) Marxists on Literature, Penguin, 1975; (editor with Margot Heinemann) Experiments in English Teaching, Edward Arnold, 1976.

Poetry anthologized in Young Commonwealth Poets, edited by P. L. Brent, Heinemann, 1968, and Doves for the Seventies, edited by Peter Robins, Corgi, 1969 and 1972. Also author, with Nigel Gray, of a novel, "The Rebels and the Hostage," published in Firewood, 1976. Contributor to New Statesman, New York Review of Books, Spectator, Times Literary Supplement, Times Higher Education Supplement, New Left Review, Scotsman, New Poetry, Tribune, Mosaic, Marxism Today, and Essays in Criticism. Cofounder and editor, Firewood, 1975-78.

WORK IN PROGRESS: Extreme Situations; Literature and Crisis from the Great War to the Atom Bomb, with Michael Egan; a novel, King Cameron.

* * *

CRANDALL, James E(dward) 1930-

PERSONAL: Born November 5, 1930, in Hutchinson,

Kan.; son of Cecil Clyde (a businessman) and M. Louise (Stevenson) Crandall; married Shirley A. Grittner, June 18, 1959; children: Julie Elizabeth, James Kevin, Jonathan Alexander. *Education:* University of Colorado, B.A., 1955, M.P.S., 1956; University of Oregon, Ph.D., 1963. *Home:* 1426 View, Moscow, Idaho 83843. *Office:* Department of Psychology, University of Idaho, Moscow, Idaho 83843.

CAREER: State University of New York College at Oswego, assistant professor, 1963-64, associate professor of psychology, 1964-67; University of Idaho, Moscow, professor of psychology, 1967—. *Military service:* U.S. Army, 1950-53; became sergeant; received Bronze Star. *Member:* American Psychological Association, North American Society of Adlerian Psychology, Idaho Psychological Association, Phi Beta Kappa.

WRITINGS: (Editor) *Facets of Psychology,* Simon & Schuster, 1970. Contributor of more than two dozen articles to *Journal of Personality, Journal of Verbal Learning and Verbal Behavior, Journal of Experimental Psychology, Journal of General Psychology, Psychological Reports, Journal of Psychology, Journal of Social Psychology, Journal of Clinical Psychology, Journal of Psychology and Theology,* and other professional journals.

WORK IN PROGRESS: Research on the relations of social interest (or concern for others) to other aspects of personality and adjustment.

*   *   *

CRANE, Julia G(orham)   1925-

PERSONAL: Born November 8, 1925, in Mount Kisco, N.Y.; daughter of Joseph Harold (a merchant) and Alma (Reynolds) Crane. *Education:* Columbia University, B.S., 1959, Ph.D., 1966. *Home:* 104 Kings Mountain Ct., Chapel Hill, N.C. 27514. *Office:* Department of Anthropology, University of North Carolina, Chapel Hill, N.C. 27514.

CAREER: Research assistant to anthropologist Margaret Mead, 1956-59; University of North Carolina at Chapel Hill, assistant professor, 1966-72, associate professor, 1972-77, professor of anthropology, 1977—. *Member:* American Anthropological Association, American Ethnological Society, Southern Anthropological Society, Phi Beta Kappa. *Awards, honors:* Prince Bernhard Fund Award, 1971, for *Educated to Emigrate.*

WRITINGS: Educated to Emigrate, Royal Van Gorcum, 1971; (with Michael V. Angrosino, Jr.) *Field Projects in Anthropology: A Student Handbook,* General Learning Corp., 1974.

WORK IN PROGRESS: Editing and writing articles for *Saba Silhouettes* and *Lives Around Lago,* two collections of Caribbean life histories.

*   *   *

CRATON, Michael (John)   1931-

PERSONAL: Surname is pronounced Cray-ton; born August 30, 1931, in London, England; son of George Edgar Morris (a trucker) and Edith (Izzard) Craton. *Education:* University College, London, B.A. (honors), 1955; McMaster University, Ph.D., 1968. *Agent:* Christopher Busby, 44 Great Russell St., London WC1, England. *Office:* Department of History, University of Waterloo, Waterloo, Ontario, Canada.

CAREER: History teacher in Nassau, Bahamas, 1956-62; University of Waterloo, Waterloo, Ontario, 1966—, began

as assistant professor, currently professor of history. *Military service:* British National Service, 1950-51; became sergeant. *Awards, honors:* Canada Council awards, 1967, 1970, 1972.

WRITINGS: History of the Bahamas, Collins, 1962; *A Jamaican Plantation,* W. H. Allen, 1970; *Sinews of Empire,* Doubleday, 1974; *Slavery, Abolition, and Emancipation,* Longman, 1976; *Searching for the Invisible Man,* Harvard University Press, 1978. Editor of *Thames,* 1953-54; subeditor of *Nassau Daily Guardian,* 1960; assistant editor of *Bahamas Handbook,* 1963-65.

WORK IN PROGRESS: Testing the Chains, a study of slave revolts; *A History of the People of the Bahamas;* articles; poetry.

*   *   *

CREAN, John Edward, Jr.   1939-

PERSONAL: Born November 15, 1939, in New York, N.Y.; son of John Edward (a textile executive) and Agnes (Connelly) Crean; married Eileen M. Bickman (a teacher of history), June 16, 1962; children: Elisabeth, John III, Linda. *Education:* College of the Holy Cross, A.B. (cum laude), 1962; Yale University, M.A., 1964, Ph.D., 1966. *Home:* 315 Anapalau St., Honolulu, Hawaii 96825. *Office:* Department of European Languages and Literature, Moore Hall, University of Hawaii, 1890 East-West Rd., Honolulu, Hawaii 96822.

CAREER: Yale University, New Haven, Conn., instructor in German, 1965-66; University of Wisconsin—Madison, assistant professor of German, 1966-71; University of Hawaii, Honolulu, associate professor of German, 1971—, chairman of German section, 1972-74. *Member:* American Association of Teachers of German (president of Hawaii chapter, 1972-74), American Council on the Teaching of Foreign Languages, Hawaii Association of Language Teachers (vice-president, 1975-76).

WRITINGS: (With Peter Mollenhauer) *Briefe aus Deutschland,* Harcourt, 1969; (with Klaus Berghahn) *Kritische Gespraeche,* Holt, 1972. General editor, "Holt Series in German Literature," 1973—. Contributor to journals in Germany, Austria, and America.

WORK IN PROGRESS: With Julian Plante, *The Altenburg Rule of St. Benedict,* for Gerstenberg; *Deutsche Sprache und Kultur,* for Random House; pedagogical and philosophic articles.

*   *   *

CREASEY, John   1908-1973

September 17, 1908—June 9, 1973; English writer of mystery novels. Obituaries: *New York Times,* June 10, 1973; *Publishers Weekly,* June 18, 1973; *Newsweek,* June 25, 1973. (See index for *CA* sketch)

*   *   *

CREIGHTON, (Mary) Helen   1899-

PERSONAL: Born September 5, 1899, in Dartmouth, Nova Scotia, Canada; daughter of Charles Edward and Alice Julia (Terry) Creighton. *Education:* Attended University of Toronto, 1921-22, and Indiana University, 1942. *Religion:* Anglican. *Home and office:* 26 Brookdale Crescent, Apt. 207, Dartmouth, Nova Scotia, Canada B3A 2R5.

CAREER: Folklorist, 1928; collector of folk songs, 1928-47; National Museum of Canada, Ottawa, Ontario, member of staff collecting and recording folklore of Canada's Maritime Provinces, 1947-67. Lecturer. *Wartime service:* Royal Flying Corps, civilian subordinate (chauffeur), 1918. *Member:* Canadian Authors Association (national president, 1962-64), American Folklore Society (fellow), Zonta International Club (charter president, Halifax chapter). *Awards, honors:* LL.D., Mount Allison University, 1957; D.esL., Laval University, 1961; D.C.L., University of King's College, 1967; D.Litt., St. Francis University, 1975, and St. Mary's University, 1976; member of Order of Canada, 1976; Queen's Silver Jubilee Medal, 1978.

WRITINGS: Songs and Ballads from Nova Scotia, Dent, 1932, Dover, 1966; *Folklore of Lunenburg County,* National Museum of Canada, 1950; (with Doreen Senior) *Traditional Songs from Nova Scotia,* Ryerson, 1950; *Bluenose Ghosts,* Ryerson, 1957; *Maritime Folk Songs,* Ryerson, 1962, McGraw, 1972; (with Calum MacLeod) *Gaelic Songs in Nova Scotia,* National Museum of Canada, 1964; *Bluenose Magic,* Ryerson, 1968; *Folk Songs from Southern New Brunswick,* National Museum of Canada, 1971; *A Life in Folklore,* McGraw, 1975. Also author, with Eunice Sircom, of *Eight Ethnic Songs for Young Children,* and *Nine Ethnic Songs for Older Children,* 1977. Contributor to magazines.

WORK IN PROGRESS: A book on Acadian folk songs from recordings made since 1944.

SIDELIGHTS: Helen Creighton has made two recordings for Folkways, "Folk Music from Nova Scotia," 1956, and "Maritime Folk Songs," 1962. She has been the subject of three Canadian film documentaries: "Songs of Nova Scotia," National Film Board, 1957; "Land of the Old Songs," Canadian Broadcasting Corp., 1960; "Lady of the Legends," Canadian Broadcasting Corp., 1966.

*   *   *

CRIM, Mort 1935-

PERSONAL: Born July 31, 1935, in West Frankfort, Ill.; son of William Albert (a clergyman) and Ocie Dell (Martin) Crim; married Naomi Ruth Dale, August 21, 1954; children: Albert Morton, Jr., Carey Dale Martin. *Education:* Alan Hancock College, A.A., 1959; University of Nebraska, B.Ed., 1961; Northwestern University, M.S. (with honors), 1964. *Politics:* Democrat. *Religion:* Presbyterian. *Residence:* Grosse Pointe, Mich. *Office:* WDIV-TV, 622 West Lafayette Blvd., Detroit, Mich. 48231.

CAREER: WNEW-Radio, New York City, news correspondent and commentator, 1964-65; American Broadcasting Corp., New York City, correspondent and commentator covering summit meetings, presidential tours abroad, national elections, and Apollo space flights, 1965-69; WHAS-TV, Louisville, Ky., news commentator, 1969-72; Westinghouse Broadcasting Corp., Philadelphia, Pa., news commentator for KYW-TV, anchor man for "Newswatch" and daytime broadcast of "Eyewitness News," 1972-77; WBBM-TV, Chicago, Ill., news commentator, 1977-78; WDIV-TV, Detroit, Mich., news commentator and anchorman, 1978—. Member of Kentucky State Arthritis Board, 1970-72; consultant on morals and ethics in medicine. *Military service:* U.S. Air Force, 1958-62; became airman first class; received commendation medal with oak leaf cluster.

MEMBER: American Federation of Television and Radio Artists, Radio-Television News Directors Association, Sigma Delta Chi, Kappa Alpha Tau.

WRITINGS—Published by Warner Press: *Like It Is,* 1970, revised edition, 1972; *One Moment, Please!* (selections from Crim's nationally syndicated radio series of the same name), 1972. Author of television news documentary program, and programs for local and national radio broadcasts.

SIDELIGHTS: Discussing his role as a television news journalist, Mort Crim remarked: "I think television is too potent a force for the people who control it to pretend to some kind of neutrality—because it doesn't exist. . . . I think we have a responsibility to make people understand truth in a broader sense." *Avocational interests:* Flying (licensed pilot).

BIOGRAPHICAL/CRITICAL SOURCES: Monthly Detroit, November, 1978.

*   *   *

CRITCHFIELD, Richard 1931-

PERSONAL: Born March 23, 1931, in Minneapolis, Minn.; son of Ralph James (a doctor) and Ann Louise (Williams) Critchfield. *Education:* University of Washington, Seattle, B.A., 1953; Columbia University, M.S., 1957; additional graduate study at University of Innsbruck and University of Vienna, 1958-59, and Northwestern University, 1960. *Politics:* Independent. *Religion:* Protestant. *Home:* 1304 Henry St., Berkeley, Calif. 94709. *Agent:* Sterling Lord Agency, 660 Madison Ave., New York, N.Y. 10021. *Office:* c/o Peggy A. Trimble, *Washington Star,* 225 Virginia Ave. S.E., Washington, D.C. 20061.

CAREER: Journalist since 1955; assistant farm editor of *Cedar Rapids Gazette,* Cedar Rapids, Iowa; Washington correspondent, Salt Lake City (Utah) *Deseret News,* 1957-58; free-lance writer in Asia, 1959, 1962-63; *Washington Star,* Washington, D.C., reporter, 1963—. Lecturer, University of Nagpur, 1960-62. Correspondent covering the China-India conflict, 1962, Vietnam war, 1964-68, Indo-Pakistan war, 1965, the White House, 1968-69, and Washington, D.C. in general, 1957-58, 1968, 1971-72. From 1969 to 1971 and from 1972 to date, Critchfield has been engaged in a project as the first American foreign correspondent to specialize wholly in reporting from villages on the lives of ordinary people in Asia, Africa, and Latin America; in addition to the *Washington Star,* he contributes to *Los Angeles Times, Kansas City Star,* and numerous other periodicals. *Military service:* U.S. Army, Engineers, 1953-55; became sergeant; served in Korea. *Member:* Overseas Press Club, Explorers Club. *Awards, honors:* Overseas Press Club award, 1965, for "The Marines in Vietnam" and "The Battle for Five Mountains," as best daily newspaper or wire service from abroad; Alicia Patterson Fund award, 1970; Ford Foundation grants, 1972-75, and 1976-79; Rockefeller Foundation Humanities Fellowship to study cultural change in rural Asia, Africa, and Latin America, 1978.

WRITINGS: (Editor and illustrator) Kesar Lall, *Lore and Legend of Nepal,* Jagat Lall (Kathmandu), 1961; *The Indian Reporter's Guide,* Vakil, Feffer & Simons, 1962; *The Long Charade: Political Subversion in the Vietnam War,* Harcourt, 1968; *The Golden Bow Be Broken: Peasant Life in Four Cultures,* Indiana University Press, 1974; *Shahhat: An Egyptian,* Syracuse University Press, 1978. Also author of two reports, *Look to Suffering, Look to Joy,* and *The Peasant and the West,* published by American Universities Field Staff, 1978. Critchfield's experimental writings on the lives of ordinary peoples have included series on "The Lonely War," 1964, "The Marines in Vietnam" and "The Battle for Five Mountains," 1965, "People at War," 1966-67, "How We Live" (ten-part series about life styles in Washington, D.C.), 1972, and others. Special correspondent on world rural development, *Economist* (London). Contributor to *New Republic, Reporter, Nation, New Leader, New York Times, Observer* (London), *Human Behavior, International Wildlife, Christian Science Monitor,* and other publications. Contributing editor, *RF Illustrated,* journal of the Rockefeller Foundation.

WORK IN PROGRESS: Villages.

SIDELIGHTS: Richard Critchfield has traveled in fifty countries, and lived in Indonesia, Mauritius, Persia, Morocco, and Austria, among others; his notes, including 450 Vietnam notebooks, are at the Mass Communications Library of the State Historical Society of Wisconsin.

Critchfield told *CA:* "Since 1969, except for one year in Washington (1971-72), doing similar sketches of Americans, [I] have experimented with ways to make the world's poor villagers and slum dwellers more comprehensible to American readers, living for periods of three to eighteen months in a dozen villages in Asia, Africa, and Latin America. The results are reported in newspaper and magazine articles, scholarly reports, and a three-volume study, *Villages,* to be completed in 1980. The subjects are chosen to represent some aspect of cultural change affecting poor people today. They include an Arab Bedouin in southwestern Iran (plan to do one in Saudi Arabia next year), a Sikh Punjabi in northwest India who has prospered from the so-called green revolution in wheat, a Javanese rice-peasant who seasonally migrates to Jakarta to find work, a Moroccan ex-villager who became a gangster, migrated to France, and is now serving a fifteen-year prison sentence, a Mexican migrant to Los Angeles who has returned to his village in Mexico's central highlands, a Brazilian frontiersman and his children and what happens to them during the week-long carnival celebration in the northeastern seaport of Salvador, Mauritian fishermen, Filipinos caught up in a Christian-Muslim land war on Mindanao, a Tibetan refugee in the Himalayas, an African witch doctor among the Nuba tribe in southwestern Sudan, villagers in Bangladesh, Pakistan, Nepal, South Vietnam, Bali and elsewhere. Also a long study of Egyptian peasant life on the upper Nile and a shorter study of such life in the northern Nile delta.

"Most of these villagers have been visited at least twice and several three or four times. The work is often mistaken for anthropology but the methods and results are quite different. Dr. George M. Foster, the Berkeley anthropologist who was one of the pioneers of village studies (in Mexico in the 1940's), helped me to make the distinction in a foreword to *Shahhat.* I have also dealt with the differences in a new booklength study, *Look to Suffering, Look to Joy,* about American anthropology and its study of villages and peasants. . . .

"My major finding so far is that *all* of the villagers studied are substantively better off near the end of the 1970's than they were at the beginning. Change is gradual but farm production is rising, birth rates are perceptively falling and the Apocalyptic vision of the over-populated future is no longer a valid one. This has been possible, however, only at great cost to traditional cultures and it has been a great privilege (and good luck) to see many ancient ways of life (Egypt, India, Indonesia) just as they seem to be vanishing for good. This cultural breakdown, especially in the great cities, does suggest grave dangers for the future. But back in the villages, progress is unquestionable and very heartening."

* * *

CRITES, Stephen D(ecatur) 1931-

PERSONAL: Born July 27, 1931, in Elida, Ohio; son of Beryl A. (a lawyer) and Martha Ruth (Hook) Crites; married Gertrude Elizabeth Bremer (a nurse), September 11, 1955; children: Dorothea Elizabeth, Stephanie Ruth, Lilian Alison, Hannah Louise. *Education:* Ohio Wesleyan University, B.A., 1953; Yale University, B.D., 1956, M.A., 1959, Ph.D., 1961. *Politics:* Democrat. *Home:* 89 Bretton Rd., Middletown, Conn. 06457. *Office:* Department of Religion, Wesleyan University, Middletown, Conn. 06457.

CAREER: Ordained to Methodist ministry, 1956; Grace Methodist Church, Southington, Conn., pastor, 1956-58; Colgate University, Hamilton, N.Y., instructor in philosophy and religion, 1960-61; Wesleyan University, Middletown, Conn., assistant professor, 1961-66, associate professor, 1966-69, professor of religion, 1969—, chairman of department, 1972-75, minister of college church, 1963-67. Visiting assistant professor at University of California, Berkeley, fall, 1965, at San Diego, 1969. *Member:* Society for Values in Higher Education, Friends of Hegel's *Phenomenology,* American Philosophical Association, American Association of University Professors, American Academy of Religion, New Haven Theological Discussion Group. *Awards, honors:* Fulbright fellow and Rockefeller fellow at University of Heidelberg, 1959-60, Lilly postdoctoral fellowship, 1966, American Council of Learned Societies research grant, 1967, at University of Heidelberg; Wesleyan Center for the Humanities faculty fellow, 1969-70; National Endowment for the Humanities senior research fellow, 1975-76.

WRITINGS: (Translator and author of introduction) Soeren Kierkegaard, *Crisis in the Life of an Actress and Other Essays on Drama,* Humanities, 1967; *In the Twilight of Christendom: Hegel vs. Kierkegaard on Faith and History* (monograph), Scholars' Press, 1972; (contributor) Josiah Thompson, editor, *Kierkegaard: A Collection of Critical Essays,* Doubleday-Anchor, 1972; (contributor) James B. Wiggins, editor, *Religion as Story,* Harper, 1975. Editor of monograph series, "Studies in Religion" for American Academy of Religion, 1971-78. Contributor of poems and articles to *Encyclopedia of Philosophy, Review of Metaphysics, Atlantic Monthly, Wesleyan University Alumnus, Journal of the History of Ideas, Journal of Religion, Continuities, Soundings, Christian Century, New Creation,* and *Christian Scholar.* Managing editor, *Christian Scholar,* 1963-65.

WORK IN PROGRESS: Gospel and Dialectic in the Philosophy of Hegel; Towards an Aesthetics of Experiences.

* * *

CROOK, J(oseph) Mordaunt 1937-

PERSONAL: Born February 27, 1937, in London, England; son of Austin Mordaunt (a civil servant) and Irene (Woolfenden) Crook; married Margaret Mulholland, July 4, 1964 (divorced, 1975); married Susan Mayor, July 9, 1975. *Education:* Brasenose College, Oxford, D.Phil., 1961, M.A., 1962. *Home:* 47 Kelly St., London N.W. 1, England. *Office:* Bedford College, University of London, Regent's Park, London N.W. 1, England.

CAREER: Institute of Historical Research, London, England, research fellow, 1961-62; University of London, Bedford College, London, research fellow, 1962-63; University of Leicester, Leicester, England, lecturer in history, 1963-65; University of London, Bedford College, lecturer in history, 1965-75, reader in architectural history, 1975—. Research fellow, Warburg Institute, 1970-71; Slade Professor of Fine Arts, Oxford University, 1979-80. Member of Historic Buildings Council, Department of the Environment, 1974—. *Member:* Society of Architectural Historians (member of executive committee, 1964-75), Victorian Society (member of executive committee, 1970-75), Georgian Group (member of executive committee, 1970-75), Society of Antiquaries. *Awards, honors:* Hitchcock Medal for *History of the King's Works, 1782-1851.*

WRITINGS: (Editor) C. L. Eastlake, *History of the Gothic Revival,* Humanities, 1970, revised edition, 1978; *Victorian Architecture: A Visual Anthology,* Johnson, 1971; *The British Museum,* Praeger, 1972; *The Greek Revival: Neo-Classical Attitudes in British Architecture,* J. Murray, 1972; (editor) R. Kerr, *The Gentleman's House,* Johnson, 1972; (editor) J. T. Emmett, *Six Essays,* Johnson, 1972; (with M. H. Port) *History of the King's Works: 1782-1851,* H.M.S.O., 1973; (with H. M. Colvin, J. Newman, and J. Summerson) *History of the King's Works, 1660-1782,* H.M.S.O., 1975. Contributor to *Architectural Review, Country Life, Connoisseur, R.I.B.A. Journal,* and *Burlington Magazine.* Editor, *Architectural History,* 1967-75.

WORK IN PROGRESS: *William Burges,* for J. Murray; *A Dictionary of Victorian Architects,* with Paul Joyce, for J. Murray.

* * *

CROSSLEY-HOLLAND, Kevin　1941-

PERSONAL: Born February 7, 1941, in England; married; wife's name Ruth; children: Kieran, Dominic (sons). *Education:* Oxford University, B.A. (honors), 1962. *Agent:* Deborah Rogers Ltd., 4-11 Mortimer St., London England.

CAREER: Macmillan & Co., Ltd., London, England, editor, 1962-69, poetry editor, 1969-72; Victor Gollancz Ltd., London, editorial director, 1972-77. Writer and translator. *Awards, honors:* Arts Council of Great Britain, award for the best book for children published between 1966-68, for *The Green Children,* poetry award, 1972, for *The Rain-Giver,* grants, 1976, 1978; Poetry Book Society Choice, 1976, for *The Dream-House.*

WRITINGS—Juvenile: *Havelok the Dane,* Macmillan, 1964, Dutton, 1965; *King Horn* (retelling of thirteenth-century folk poem), Macmillan, 1965, Dutton, 1966; *The Green Children* (based on thirteenth-century tale), Macmillan, 1966, Seabury, 1968; (editor) *Winter's Tales for Children: No. 3,* Macmillan, 1967, St. Martin's, 1968; *The Callow Pit Coffer* (folk tale retold), Macmillan, 1968, Seabury, 1969; (with Jill Paton Walsh) *Wordhoard: Anglo-Saxon Stories,* Farrar, Straus, 1969; *Storm and Other Old English Riddles* (in verse), Farrar, Straus, 1970; *The Pedlar of Swaffham* (based on East Anglian legendry), Seabury, 1971; *The Fire-Brother,* Heinemann, 1973, Seabury, 1975; *The Sea Stranger,* Seabury, 1974; *Green Blades Rising: The Anglo-Saxons,* Deutsch, 1975, Seabury, 1976; *The Earth-Father,* Seabury, 1975; *The Wildman,* Deutsch, 1976.

Poetry: *On Approval,* Outposts Publications, 1961; *My Son,* Turret Books, 1966; *Alderney: The Nunnery,* Turret Books, 1968; *Confessional,* Martin Booth/Sceptre Press, 1969; *A Dream of a Meeting,* Sceptre Press, 1970; *Norfolk Poems,* Academy Editions, 1970; *More Than I Am: Broadsheet,* Steam Press, 1971; *The Rain-Giver,* Deutsch, 1972; *The Wake,* Keepsake Press, 1972; *Petal and Stone,* Sceptre Press, 1975; *The Dream-House,* Deutsch, 1976.

Translations: Bruce Mitchell, editor, *The Battle of Maldon, and Other Old English Poems,* St. Martin's, 1965; *Beowulf,* Farrar, Straus, 1968; *The Exeter Riddle-Book,* Folio, 1978.

Other: (Compiler and author of biographical introduction) William Butler Yeats, *Running to Paradise,* (introductory selection of Yeats' poems), Macmillan (London), 1967, Macmillan (New York), 1968; (editor) *Winter's Tales: 14,* Macmillan, 1968, St. Martin's, 1969; *Pieces of Land: A Journey to Eight Islands* (travel), Gollancz, 1972; (editor) *The Faber Book of Northern Legend,* Faber, 1977. Regular reviewer for *Sunday Times, Times Literary Supplement,* and *Spectator;* contributor to newspapers, poetry journals and other periodicals.

WORK IN PROGRESS: A retelling of the complete cycle of Norse myths, for Deutsch and Pantheon; a new anthology, *The Faber Book of Northwest European Folktales;* a collection of poems for children.

SIDELIGHTS: Kevin Crossley-Holland's work has its basis in "roots, the sense of the past embodied in present, the relationship of person to place." *Avocational interests:* Archaeology.

BIOGRAPHICAL/CRITICAL SOURCES: *Young Reader's Review,* January, 1967, June, 1968, October, 1969; *Books and Bookmen,* December, 1967, August, 1968; *Punch,* October 23, 1968; *Children's Book World,* November 3, 1968; *Listener,* November 14, 1968; *Times Literary Supplement,* January 23, 1969, October 16, 1969; *Saturday Review,* March 15, 1969; *Horn Book,* December, 1969, December, 1971; *Observer Review,* February 26, 1970; *New York Times Book Review,* November 8, 1970.

* * *

CUDAHY, Brian J(ames)　1936-

PERSONAL: Born April 25, 1936, in Brooklyn, N.Y.; son of John J. (a fireman) and Mary (Cahill) Cudahy; married Mary Lou Kassebart, May 28, 1960; children: John, Maureen, Kathleen, James. *Education:* Cathedral College, B.A., 1959; St. Bonaventure University, M.A., 1960, Ph.D., 1963. *Politics:* Registered Democrat. *Religion:* Roman Catholic. *Home:* 9036 Brook Ford Rd., Burke, Va. 22015. *Office:* U.S. Department of Transportation, 2100 2 St. S.W., Washington, D.C.

CAREER: Boston College, Chestnut Hill, Mass., assistant professor, 1963-67, associate professor of philosophy, 1967—; Massachusetts Bay Transportation Authority, Boston, Mass., director of community affairs, 1972-75; Regional Transportation Authority, Chicago, Ill., director of marketing, 1975-77; U.S. Department of Transportation, Urban Mass Transportation Division, Washington, D.C., director of Office of Transit Management, 1977—.

WRITINGS: *Change at Park Street Under: The Story of Boston's Subways,* Greene, 1972; *Rails under the Mighty Hudson: The Story of the Hudson Tubes, the Pennsy Tunnels and Manhattan Transfer,* Greene, 1975; *Under the Sidewalks of New York,* Greene, 1979.

WORK IN PROGRESS: A history of Chicago's loop elevated.

* * *

CULL, John G(uinn, Jr.)　1934-

PERSONAL: Born November 9, 1934, in Venice, Ill.; son of John Guinn and Geneva (Crippen) Cull; married Linda C. Abbott, June 29, 1957; children: David Lawrence, Dana Lorene, Rebecca Lynn. *Education:* Agricultural and Mechanical College of Texas (now Texas A&M University), B.S., 1959, M.Ed., 1960; Texas Technological College (now Texas Tech University), Ph.D., 1967. *Religion:* Presbyterian. *Home:* 5317 Callaghan Rd., San Antonio, Tex. 78228. *Office:* Suite 200, Travis Park, North Bldg., 800 Navarro, San Antonio, Tex. 78205; and Department of Psychology, Our Lady of the Lake University, 411 Southwest 24th St., San Antonio, Tex. 78285.

CAREER: Rehabilitation counselor for agencies in Texas, 1960-62, and Texas Institute for Rehabilitation and Research, Baylor University, Houston, 1962-64; South Plains Adult Mental Health Clinic, Lubbock, Tex., staff psychologist, 1964-65; State Department of Vocational Rehabilitation, Richmond, Va., director of Division of Research and Program Development, 1965-66; Virginia Commonwealth University, Richmond, associate professor, 1966-72, professor of rehabilitation counseling, 1972-77, director of regional counselor training program, 1966-77; clinical psychologist in private practice, 1977—; Our Lady of the Lake University, San Antonio, Tex., professor of clinical counseling psychology, 1977—. Adjunct professor of psychology and education, University of Virginia, 1971-77. Central Shenandoah Planning Commission, member of health and human resources committee, 1969-77, member of criminal justice committee, 1971-77. Consultant to Rehabilitation Services Administration, U.S. Department of Health, Education, and Welfare, 1969—; consultant on rehabilitation programs to Puerto Rico, Virgin Islands, University of Maryland, and to agencies in a dozen states and over forty foreign countries. Consulting editor, Charles C Thomas Publishers, 1970—. President of board of directors, Valley Workshops, Inc.; member of board of directors, Lurnmor School and Dunsmore College. *Military service:* U.S. Naval Reserve, 1951-59, 1964-66.

MEMBER: American Association of Workers for the Blind, American Personnel and Guidance Association, American Psychological Association, American Correctional Association, American Association for the Advancement of Science, Council of Rehabilitation Counselor Educators, International Association of Rehabilitation Facilities, National Association for Retarded Children, National Rehabilitation Association, Virginia Association of Rehabilitation Facilities, Virginia Rehabilitation Association, Virginia Association of Workers for the Blind.

AWARDS, HONORS: Community service awards from Peninsula Association for Retarded Children, 1966, and other Virginia rehabilitation agencies; commissioned a Kentucky Colonel, 1970; numerous awards for leadership in and contributions to the field of rehabilitation from various governments, including Iran, 1975, Portugal, 1975, Turkey, 1976, Iraq, 1976, and Israel, 1977, and from National Rehabilitation Association, 1974, Association of Workers for the Blind, 1975, and Connecticut State Department of Education, 1976; commissioned an admiral in Texas Navy, 1975, and Navy of Nebraska, 1977; made honorary citizen of New Orleans, 1977; named Arkansas Traveler, 1977.

WRITINGS—All with Richard E. Hardy, except as indicated; all published by C. C Thomas, except as indicated: (With Craig R. Colvin) *Contemporary Field Work Practices in Rehabilitation,* 1972; *Problems of Disadvantaged and Deprived Youth,* 1974; *Counseling Strategies with Special Populations,* 1974; *Hemingway: A Psychological Portrait,* Banner Books International, 1977.

Editor with Hardy; all published by C. C Thomas: *Vocational Rehabilitation: Professions and Process,* 1972; *Social and Rehabilitation Services for the Blind,* 1972; *Fundamentals of Criminal Behavior and Correctional Systems,* 1973; *Drug Dependence and Rehabilitation Approaches,* 1973;

Applied Volunteerism in Community Development, 1973; *Introduction to Correctional Rehabilitation,* 1973; *Vocational Evaluation for Rehabilitation Services,* 1973; *Adjustment to Work,* 1973; *The Big Welfare Mess: Public Assistance and Rehabilitation Approaches,* 1973; *The Neglected Older American: Social and Rehabilitation Services,* 1973; *Rehabilitation of the Urban Disadvantaged,* 1973; *Understanding Disability for Social and Rehabilitation Services,* 1973; *Applied Psychology in Law Enforcement and Corrections,* 1973; *Law Enforcement and Correctional Rehabilitation,* 1973; *Climbing Ghetto Walls: Disadvantagement, Delinquency and Rehabilitation,* 1973.

Administrative Techniques of Rehabilitation Facility Operations, 1974; *Alcohol Abuse and Rehabilitation Approaches,* 1974; *Behavior Modification in Rehabilitation Settings: Applied Principles,* 1974; *Counseling and Rehabilitating the Diabetic,* 1974; *Counseling High School Students: Special Problems and Approaches,* 1974; *Deciding on Divorce: Personal and Family Considerations,* 1974; *Organization and Administration of Drug Abuse Treatment Programs,* 1974; *Rehabilitation Techniques in Severe Disability: Case Studies,* 1974; *Types of Drug Abusers and Their Abuses,* 1974; *Career Guidance for Young Women: Considerations in Planning Professional Careers,* 1974; *Counseling and Rehabilitating the Cancer Patient,* 1974; *Creative Divorce through Social and Psychological Approaches,* 1974; *Educational and Psychological Aspects of Deafness,* 1974; *Group Counseling and Therapy Techniques in Special Settings,* 1974; *Mental Retardation and Physical Disability: A Book of Readings,* 1974; *Modification of Behavior of the Mentally Ill: Rehabilitation Approaches,* 1974; *Problems of Adolescents: Social and Psychological Approaches,* 1974; *Psychological and Vocational Rehabilitation of the Youthful Delinquent,* 1974; *Rehabilitation of the Drug Abuser with Delinquent Behavior,* 1974; *Severe Disabilities: Social and Rehabilitation Approaches,* 1974; *Techniques and Approaches in Marital and Family Counseling,* 1974; *Therapeutic Needs of the Family,* 1974; *Modification of Behavior of the Mentally Retarded: Applied Principles,* 1974; *Volunteerism: An Emerging Profession,* 1974.

Problems of Disadvantaged and Deprived Youth, 1975; *Career Guidance for Black Adolescents: A Guide to Selected Professional Occupations,* 1975; *Rehabilitation Facility Approaches in Severe Disabilities,* 1975; *Drug Language and Lore,* 1975; *Fundamentals of Juvenile Criminal Behavior and Drug Abuse,* 1975; *Organization and Administration of Service Programs for the Older American,* 1975; *Services of the Rehabilitation Facility,* 1975; *Problems of Runaway Youth,* 1976; *Considerations in Rehabilitation Facility Development,* 1977; *Physical Medicine and Rehabilitation Approaches in Spinal Cord Injury,* 1977. Contributor to education, rehabilitation, and genetic journals.

WORK IN PROGRESS: Two books, *Opthamological Considerations in the Rehabilitation of the Blind* and *International Rehabilitation,* both with Hardy.

*   *   *

CUMMINS, Walter (Merrill)   1936-

PERSONAL: Born February 6, 1936, in Long Branch, N.J.; married Judith Gruenberg, June 14, 1957; children: Pamela, Jennifer. *Education:* Rutgers University, B.A., 1957; University of Iowa, M.A., and M.F.A., 1962, Ph.D., 1965. *Home:* 23 Franklin Pl., Morristown, N.J. 07960. *Office:* Department of English, Fairleigh Dickinson University, Madison, N.J. 07940.

CAREER: General Electric Co., Schenectady, N.Y., editor, 1957-59; University of Iowa, Iowa City, instructor in English, 1962-65; Fairleigh Dickinson University, Madison, N.J., assistant professor, 1965-69, associate professor of English, 1969—. Chairman of advisory committee on literature, New Jersey State Council on the Arts, 1966-72. *Military service:* U.S. Army Reserve, 1958-64. *Member:* College English Association, American Association of University Professors (president of local chapter, 1966-67).

WRITINGS: Into Temptation (novel), Caravelle Books, 1968; *A Stranger in the Deed* (novel), Caravelle Books, 1968; (editor with Martin Green and Margaret Verhurst) *The Other Sides of Reality,* Boyd & Fraser, 1972; *Witness* (short stories), Samisdat, 1975. Contributor of short stories to *Writer's World, Critic* (of College English Association), *Oasis, Contempora, Wisconsin Review, Kansas Quarterly, Texas Quarterly, Aspect, St. Andrew Review,* and *Bulletin* (of American Association of University Professors).

WORK IN PROGRESS: Short stories.

BIOGRAPHICAL/CRITICAL SOURCES: Newark Evening News, August 14, 1968.

* * *

CUNINGGIM, Merrimon 1911-

PERSONAL: Born May 12, 1911, in Nashville, Tenn.; son of Jessee Lee and Maud Lillian (Merrimon) Cuninggim; married Whitty Daniel, June 10, 1939; children: Jessica Lee (Mrs. John M. Neff), Penelope Ann (Mrs. Ira Horowitz). *Education:* Vanderbilt University, A.B., 1931; Duke University, M.A., 1933; Merton College, Oxford, B.A., 1935, diploma (M.A.), 1937; Yale University, B.D., 1939, Ph.D., 1941. *Office:* Salem College, Winston-Salem, N.C. 27108.

CAREER: Duke University, Durham, N.C., director of religious activities, 1936-38; Emory and Henry College, Emory, Va., professor of religion, 1941-42; Denison University, Granville, Ohio, professor of religion, 1942-44; Pomona College, Claremont, Calif., professor of religion, 1946-51; Southern Methodist University, Dallas, Tex., dean of Perkins School of Theology, 1951-60; Danforth Foundation, St. Louis, Mo., executive director, 1960-66, president, 1966-72; Ford Foundation, advisor on program management, 1973-75; consultant to foundations, colleges, and universities, Cuninggim Associates, 1975-76; Salem Academy and College, Winston-Salem, N.C., president, 1976—. Member of board of directors of Duke University, 1963—, Arts and Education Council of Greater St. Louis, 1964-76, Vanderbilt University, 1968—, St. Louis Symphony, 1968-76, Higher Education Coordinating Council of Metropolitan St. Louis, 1972-76, and Association of Governing Boards of Universities and Colleges, 1975—; president, National Methodist Foundation, 1974-76; chairman of distribution committee of St. Louis Community Foundation, 1974-76; chairman, Research Triangle Institute, 1976—, and Independent College Fund of North Carolina, 1976—; member of board of advisors, Fund for Improvement of Postsecondary Education, 1976—. *Military service:* U.S. Naval Reserve, 1944-46; chaplain. *Member:* Society for Values in Higher Education (member of board of directors), Phi Beta Kappa, Omicron Delta Kappa, Blue Key, Delta Kappa Epsilon. *Awards, honors:* Rhodes scholar, Oxford University, 1933-36; Litt. D. from Central College, Fayette, Mo., 1952, and Pomona College, 1961; LL. D. from Duke University, 1963.

WRITINGS: The College Seeks Religion, Yale University Press, 1947; *Freedom's Holy Light,* Harper, 1955; (contributor) John Paul von Grueningen, editor, *Toward a Christian*

Philosophy of Higher Education, Westminster, 1957; *Christianity and Communism,* Southern Methodist University Press, 1958; (contributor) Arthur L. Harding, editor, *Free Man and His Government,* Southern Methodist University Press, 1958; *The Protestant Stake in Higher Education,* Council of Protestant Colleges, 1961; (contributor) Philip H. Phenix, editor, *Philosophies of Education,* Wiley, 1961; (contributor) Paul Sanders, editor, *Stability and Change through Law,* Vanderbilt University, 1964; (co-author) *Foundation and the Tax Bill,* Foundation Center, 1969; *Private Money and Public Service: The Role of Foundations in American Society,* McGraw, 1972; (co-author) *Church-Related Higher Education,* Judson, 1978.

* * *

CUNNINGHAM, Michael A(lan) 1945-

PERSONAL: Born July 8, 1945, in Las Vegas, Nev.; son of Eldon William (an electrician) and Myrtle (Stowe) Cunningham. *Education:* California Institute of Technology, B.S., 1966; University of Pennsylvania, M.S., 1969, Ph.D., 1973. *Politics:* Democrat. *Religion:* Protestant. *Home:* College Eight, University of California, Santa Cruz, Calif. 95064. *Office:* Information Sciences, University of California, Santa Cruz, Calif. 95064.

CAREER: E. G. & G. (instrumentation), Las Vegas, Nev., scientist, 1966-67; Moore School of Electrical Engineering, Philadelphia, Pa., research fellow, 1967-73; University of California, Santa Cruz, assistant professor of information sciences, 1973—. *Member:* American Association of University Professors.

WRITINGS: Intelligence: Its Organization and Development, Academic Press, 1972; (contributor) Robert Shaw and John Bransford, editors, *Perceiving, Acting, and Knowing,* Lawrence Erlbaum Associates, 1977.

WORK IN PROGRESS: Contributing to *Neo-Piagetian Perspectives in Cognition and Development,* edited by Leeland van den Deale, Juan Pascual-Leone, and Claus Witz, for Academic Press.

AVOCATIONAL INTERESTS: Japanese language.

* * *

CUNNINGHAM, Robert Louis 1926-

PERSONAL: Born March 22, 1926, in Birmingham, Ala.; son of Louis John and Marie Virginia (Schillinger) Cunningham; married Margery Ann Winters, August 20, 1949; children: Christine, Michael, Sheila, Mark, Gregory, Virginia, Roberta, Lisa. *Education:* St. Gregory Seminary, Cincinnati, Ohio, A.B., 1947; Laval University, Ph.D., 1951. *Politics:* Republican. *Home:* 2227 19th Ave., San Francisco, Calif. 94116. *Office:* Department of Philosophy, Rm. 532, University Center, University of San Francisco, San Francisco, Calif. 94117.

CAREER: Xavier University, Cincinnati, Ohio, assistant professor of philosophy, 1951-53; San Francisco College for Women (now Lone Mountain College), San Francisco, Calif., assistant professor, 1953-56, associate professor of philosophy, 1956-58; University of San Francisco, San Francisco, associate professor, 1958-63, professor of philosophy, 1963—. Visiting professor at Rockford College, spring, 1966, and Queens College of the City University of New York, summer 1967; research associate in philosophy, University of California, Berkeley, 1967-68; distinguished visiting professor, U.S. Air Force Academy, 1977-78. *Member:* American Catholic Philosophical Association,

American Philosophical Association, Mont Pelerin Society. *Awards, honors:* Research grants from Relm Foundation, 1965-66, and Institute for Interdisciplinary Research, St. Thomas Aquinas Foundation, 1967-68.

WRITINGS: (Contributor) R. M. McInerny, editor, *New Themes in Christian Philosophy,* University of Notre Dame Press, 1968; (compiler) *Situationism and the New Morality,* Appleton, 1970; (contributor) *Toward Liberty,* Volume II, Institute for Humane Studies, 1971; (contributor and compiler) *Liberty and the Rule of Law,* Texas A & M University Press, 1979. Contributor to *Classics of Catholic Literature,* Harper, 1965, and *New Catholic Encyclopedia,* McGraw, 1967. Contributor to philosophical and other journals.

*   *   *

CUPITT, Don 1934-

PERSONAL: Surname is pronounced *Kew*-pit; born May 22, 1934, in Lancashire, England; son of Robert and Norah (Gregson) Cupitt; married Susan Marianne Day (a teacher), December 28, 1963; children: John Robert Gregson, Caroline Mary, Sarah Anne. *Education:* Trinity Hall, Cambridge, B.A., 1955, M.A., 1958; also attended Westcott House, Cambridge, 1957-59. *Politics:* ''Egalitarian, non-ideological.'' *Religion:* Church of England. *Home:* 62 Humberstone Rd., Cambridge CB4 1JF, England. *Office:* Emmanuel College, Cambridge University, Cambridge CB2 3AP, England.

CAREER: Cambridge University, Cambridge, England, fellow, dean, and director of studies in theology and philosophy, 1966—, university assistant lecturer, 1968-73, lecturer in the philosophy of religion, 1973—.

WRITINGS: Christ and the Hiddenness of God, Westminster, 1971; *Crises of Moral Authority,* Westminster, 1972; (contributor) S. W. Sykes and J. P. Clayton, editors, *Christ, Faith and History,* Cambridge University Press, 1972; *The Leap of Reason,* Westminster, 1976; *The Worlds of Science and Religion,* Seabury, 1976; (contributor) John Hick, editor, *The Myth of God Incarnate,* Westminster, 1977; (with Peter Armstrong) *Who Was Jesus?,* British Broadcasting Corp., 1977; *The Nature of Man,* Seabury, 1979; *Jesus and the Gospel of God,* Lutterworth, 1979. Contributor to theology journals, including *Anglican Theological Review, Theology,* and *Journal of Theological Studies.*

WORK IN PROGRESS: Research on philosophical theology.

*   *   *

CURRAN, Ward S(chenk) 1935-

PERSONAL: Born June 26, 1935, in Springfield, Ill.; son of Nathaniel Buckmaster (an accountant) and Clara (Schenk) Curran; married Kathleen Jannett, November 28, 1963; children: Andrea Jannett, Colleen Thayer. *Education:* Trinity College, Hartford, Conn., B.A., 1957; Columbia University, M.A., 1958, Ph.D., 1961. *Politics:* Independent Republican. *Religion:* Christian. *Home:* 6 Stoner Dr., West Hartford, Conn. 06106. *Office:* Department of Economics, Trinity College, 300 Summit St., Hartford, Conn. 06106.

CAREER: Trinity College, Hartford, Conn., instructor, 1960-62, assistant professor, 1962-67, associate professor, 1967-71, professor of economics, 1971—, George M. Ferris Lecturer in Corporation Finance and Investments, 1962—, director of institutional planning, 1971-73, chairperson of department of economics, 1978-81. Visiting associate professor, Wesleyan University, fall, 1967; Yale University, guest

lecturer, 1969 and 1973, visiting faculty member, 1973-74; guest lecturer, University of Virginia, 1971; lecturer and speaker to management and utility company executives. Member of Greater Hartford Council of Economic Education, 1969—. *Member:* American Economic Association, American Finance Association, Financial Management Association, American Association of University Professors. *Awards, honors:* Foundation for Economic Education fellowship in business, summer, 1964.

WRITINGS: Railroad Equipment Obligations (brochure), Halsey Stuart & Co., 1971; *The Financial Crisis of Private Colleges and Universities,* Connecticut Conference on Independent Colleges, 1970; *Principles of Financial Management,* McGraw, 1970; *An Economic Approach to Regulation of the Corporate Securities Markets,* General Learning Press, 1976. Also author of reports and contributor to annals. Contributor of articles and reviews to professional journals, including *Quarterly Review of Economics and Business, Financial Analysts' Journal, Journal of Finance,* and *Journal of Economic Literature.*

WORK IN PROGRESS: Research on monopoly and public policy.

*   *   *

CURTIS, Lindsay R(aine) 1916-

PERSONAL: Born May 23, 1916, in Salt Lake City, Utah; son of Alexander Robertson (a merchant) and Genevieve (Raine) Curtis; married Marjorie Shepard (a secretary), May 31, 1939; children: Elbert, Mark, Lindsay, Karen (Mrs. Paul Taylor), Colleen (Mrs. Clifford Dunn). *Education:* University of Utah, B.S., 1940; University of Colorado, M.D., 1942. *Religion:* Church of Jesus Christ of Latter-day Saints (Mormon). *Home:* 5479 South 925 E., Ogden, Utah 84403. *Office:* 3905 Harrison Blvd., Ogden, Utah 84401.

CAREER: University of Utah, Salt Lake City, assistant clinical professor of medicine, 1946—. President, Educational Information, Inc., 1960—. Diplomate, American Board of Obstetricians and Gynecologists. Has lectured for newspapers, medical and lay groups. Director, Zion's First National Bank, Ogden; director and educational consultant, American Cancer Society (Utah Division); alternate member, Utah Board of Pardons, 1965, 1967. *Military service:* U.S. Army, chief of Women's Surgical Section, 1944-46; became captain. *Member:* American Medical Association, American College of Obstetricians and Gynecologists, American Board of Obstetricians and Gynecolocists, Utah Medical Association, Utah Obstetrical and Gynecological Society (past president), Ogden Medical Association, Ogden Surgical Society (past president).

WRITINGS: 2½ Minute Talk Treasury, Bookcraft, 1962; *Talks that Teach,* Bookcraft, 1963; *Thoughts for 2½ Minute Talks,* Bookcraft, 1965; *Let's Talk: A Series of Discussions on Challenging Topics in Today's Modern World,* Deseret, 1967; *The Making of a Prophet,* Deseret, 1967; (with Wayne Anderson) *Living, Loving and Marrying,* Deseret, 1968; *Sensible Sex: A Guide for Newlyweds,* Publishers Press, 1968; *Talkable Topics,* Bookcraft, 1969; *About My Daughter, Doctor,* Educational Information Institute, 1970; *Tips for 2½s,* Bookcraft, 1972; *Solving Sex Problems in Marriage: Increasing Sexual Fulfillment,* Hawkes, 1974; *To Strengthen Family Ties,* Bookcraft, 1974; *Feminine and Fit,* Hawkes, 1975; *Talks for a Sunday Morn,* Bookcraft, 1976; (with Yvonne Caroles) *Pregnant and Lovin' It,* H. P. Books, 1977. Also author of *El Cigarillo: Contaminante,* Baptist Spanish Publishing House. Author of several dozen booklets for U.S. Navy, pharmaceutical firms, and TANE (Texas Alcohol Narcotics Education) Press, 1965—; author of "For Women Only," a column syndicated in Canada and the United States. Editor of women's section, *Housecall*, 1972.

WORK IN PROGRESS: So You're Pregnant, So You're Growing Up, So You're Out of Shape, So You're Getting Married, and *So You Have Marital Problems,* all for Searle Educational Systems.†

* * *

CUSKEY, (Raymond) Walter 1934-

PERSONAL: Born September 1, 1934, in Boston, Mass.; son of Walter and Doris Cuskey; married wife, Harriet, June 3, 1961; children: Lauren, Walter, John, Lynn. *Education:* Boston College, B.A., 1961, M.S.W., 1963; Brandeis University, Ph.D., 1968.

CAREER: Center for the Spanish Speaking, Boston, Mass., program planner, 1960-61; First District Court of Middlesex, Malden, Mass., probation officer, 1961-62; Massachusetts Department of Public Health, Boston, social worker, 1962-63; Peace Corps Community Development Training Project, San Juan, Puerto Rico, consultant and supervisor, 1963; National Commission on Health Services, Inc., Bethesda, Md., staff associate, 1963-65; director of psychological research, Worcester State Hospital, 1965-67; North Philadelphia Regional Health Affiliates, Inc., Philadelphia, Pa., social science analyst, 1968; instructor in community medicine at Temple University and Women's Medical College Hospital of Pennsylvania, both in Philadelphia, 1968-69; University of Pennsylvania, Philadelphia, assistant professor of community medicine, 1969-77, instructor in industry, Wharton School of Finance and Commerce, 1969-77. Research associate in narcotic addiction research unit, West Philadelphia Community Mental Health Consortium, 1969. Has conducted sensitivity-group training at Philadelphia General Hospital, 1969-71. Consultant to government committees, national associations, and drug treatment programs. *Military service:* U.S. Air Force, 1953-57.

MEMBER: American Public Health Association, National Association of Social Workers, Academy of Certified Social

Workers. *Awards, honors:* National Institute of Mental Health fellowships, 1961, 1965; Public Health Service fellowship, 1966-68.

WRITINGS: (Contributor) J. C. Ball and C. D. Chambers, editors, *The Epidemiology of Opiate Narcotic Addiction in the United States,* C. C Thomas, 1970; (with A. W. Klein and William Krasner) *Drug-Trip Abroad: American Drug-Refugees in Amsterdam and London,* University of Pennsylvania Press, 1972. Contributor to a variety of professional journals, including *Public Health Reports, Bulletin on Narcotics, Medical Care, Clinical Medicine, Medical Affairs,* and *Public Health Reviews.* Advisory editor, *Public Health Reviews,* beginning 1972, and *Urban and Social Change Review,* 1973—.†

* * *

CUSTER, Chester Eugene 1920-

PERSONAL: Born November 5, 1920, in Scio, Ohio; son of Jesse William and Alma Jane (Moreland) Custer; married Elizabeth Ester Earl (an elementary teacher), August 26, 1946; children: David Eugene, Philip Lynn, Margaret Elizabeth. *Education:* Attended University of Denver, 1940; Muskingum College, B.A., 1945; Garrett Theological Seminary, M.S.T., 1948; Northwestern University, M.A., 1948; attended Vanderbilt Divinity School, 1976. *Home:* 831 Rodney Dr., Nashville, Tenn. 37205. *Office:* Board of Discipleship, P.O. Box 840, Nashville, Tenn. 37202.

CAREER: Ordained minister of United Methodist Church; pastor of Renwick-Hardy church, Iowa, 1948-56; pastor in Hawarden, Iowa, 1956-62, and in Grinnell, Iowa, 1962-68; General Board of Evangelism, Nashville, Tenn., writer of confirmation resources, 1968-72; United Methodist Church, Board of Discipleship, Nashville, Tenn., director of theological consultations and programs of continuing education, 1972-76, executive director of discipleship resources, 1976—.

WRITINGS: Resources for Pastors: Design for Witness, Tidings, 1970; (editor) *The Pilgrim Church,* Tidings, 1971; (editor) *All Things New,* Tidings, 1972; *Called to Care,* Tidings, 1974. Also composer of hymns published by Hymn Society of America.

D

DAANE, Calvin J(ohn) 1925-

PERSONAL: Born July 25, 1925, in Sheboygan, Wis.; son of John (a businessman) and Elizabeth (Teacher) Daane; married Jeanette Kalous (a librarian), 1948; children: Jean, Peter, Elizabeth. Education: University of Wisconsin—Milwaukee, B.S., 1950; Columbia University, M.A., 1950; Indiana University, Ed.D., 1955. Home: 2107 Campo Alegre, Tempe, Ariz. 85281. Office: Department of Counselor Education, Arizona State University, Tempe, Ariz. 85281.

CAREER: Certified by Arizona State Board of Psychological Examiners; Arizona State University, Tempe, assistant professor, 1955-59, associate professor, 1959-67, professor of education, 1967—. Consultant to Studies for Urban Man, Inc., Tempe, 1969—. Military service: U.S. Army, 1943-45; served in Europe. Member: American Psychological Association.

WRITINGS: Introduction to College, Allyn & Bacon, 1958; Group Counseling Models, U.S. Department of Labor, 1968; Vocational Exploration Group: Theory and Research, Studies for Urban Man, 1971; Vocational Exploration Group Kit, Studies for Urban Man, 1971. Contributor to professional journals.

WORK IN PROGRESS: Research on programmed group counseling.

*　*　*

DAGENAIS, James J(oseph) 1928-

PERSONAL: Born June 12, 1928, in Blue Island, Ill.; son of Wilfred Andrew and Anne Dagenais; married Francoise Monnoyer de Galland de Carnieres, 1968. Education: Loyola University, Chicago, Ill., A.B., 1951, M.A., 1957; West Baden College, Ph.L., 1953, S.T.L., 1960; attended University of Paris, 1962-64; Institut Superieur de Philosophie (Louvain), Ph.D., 1966. Home: 230 West High St., Oxford, Ohio 45056. Office: Department of Religion, Miami University, Oxford, Ohio 45056.

CAREER: Roman Catholic priest of Society of Jesus (Jesuits), 1946-66; Loyola University, Chicago, Ill., assistant professor of philosophy, 1966-67; Miami University, Oxford, Ohio, associate professor, 1967-75, professor of religion, 1975—. Member: American Academy of Religion, American Philosophical Association, Association for Humanistic Psychology, Society for Phenomenology and Existential Philosophy, Metaphysical Society of America, American Psychological Association, Association for the Study of Man-Environment Relations, Society for the Scientific Study of Religion, American Academy of Political and Social Science, Husserl Circle.

WRITINGS: Models of Man: A Phenomenological Critique of Some Paradigms in the Human Sciences, Nijhoff, 1972. Contributor of articles and reviews to Human Context and other professional journals. Member of editorial board, Human Context, 1972—.

WORK IN PROGRESS: A book, Perception, Projection, and Project.

*　*　*

DANZIGER, Kurt 1926-

PERSONAL: Born June 6, 1926, in Breslau, Germany; son of Ludwig and Margarete (Krause) Danziger; married Mavis Waters, June, 1951 (divorced, 1970); married Flora de Swardt (a child psychologist), December, 1970; children: (first marriage) Ruth, Eve, Peter. Education: University of Cape Town, M.Sc., 1948; Oxford University, D.Phil., 1952. Office: Department of Psychology, York University, Toronto, Ontario, Canada.

CAREER: University of Melbourne, Melbourne, Australia, lecturer in psychology, 1951-54; Gadjah Mada University, Jogjakarta, Indonesia, professor of psychology, 1958-59; University of Cape Town, Cape Town, South Africa, professor of psychology, 1960-65; York University, Toronto, Ontario, professor of psychology, 1965—. Member: Canadian Psychological Association (fellow).

WRITINGS: Readings in Child Socialization, Pergamon, 1970; Socialization, Penguin, 1971; Interpersonal Communication, Pergamon, 1976.

WORK IN PROGRESS: A book on the history of psychology.

*　*　*

DARLINGTON, Alice (Benning) 1906-1973

1906—March 24, 1973; American civic leader and author. Obituaries: New York Times, March 27, 1973. (See index for CA sketch)

DAUGHDRILL, James H(arold), Jr. 1934-

PERSONAL: Born April 25, 1934, in La Grange, Ga.; son of James Harold and Louisa (Dozier) Daughdrill; married Elizabeth Anne Gay, July 26, 1954; children: James Harold III, Louisa Risha, Elizabeth Gay. *Education:* Davidson College, student, 1952-54, D.D., 1973; Emory University, B.A., 1956; Columbia Theological Seminary, Decatur, Ga., M.Div., 1967. *Office:* Southwestern at Memphis, 2000 North Parkway, Memphis, Tenn. 38112.

CAREER: Kingston Mills, Inc., Cartersville, Ga., president, 1956-64; Presbyterian minister in Little Rock, Ark., 1967-70; General Council of the Presbyterian Church of the United States of America, Atlanta, Ga., secretary of stewardship, 1970-73; Southwestern at Memphis, Memphis, Tenn., president, 1973—. Republican Party chairman in Bartow Country, Ga., 1959. Director, Frank E. Seidman Foundation; trustee of Brooks Memorial Art Gallery and Hutchinson School. *Member:* Association of Presbyterian Colleges (president), College Athletic Conference (president), Southern College and University Union (president), Tennessee Council of Private Colleges (chairman), Economic Club of Memphis, Omicron Delta Kappa.

WRITINGS: Man Talk, Harper, 1972. Contributor to *Presbyterian Survey, Lutheran Digest,* and *Christian Ministry.* Associate editor, *Presbyterian Outlook.*

WORK IN PROGRESS: Writing a book on college administration, under an Exxon research grant.

*   *   *

D'AVANZO, Mario Louis 1931-

PERSONAL: Born November 11, 1931, in New Britain, Conn.; son of Michael and Amelia (Angelo) D'Avanzo; divorced; children: Sylvia, Michael. *Education:* Dartmouth College, A.B., 1953; Trinity College, Hartford, Conn., M.A., 1954; Brown University, Ph.D., 1963. *Residence:* New York, N.Y. *Office:* Department of English, Queens College of the City University of New York, Flushing, N.Y. 11367.

CAREER: Providence College, Providence, R.I., instructor, 1960-63, assistant professor, 1963-65, associate professor of English literature, 1965-67; Queens College of the City University of New York, Flushing, N.Y., associate professor, 1968-75, professor of English literature, 1975—. *Military service:* U.S. Navy, 1954-57; became lieutenant. *Member:* Melville Society.

WRITINGS: Keats's Metaphors for the Poetic Imagination, Duke University Press, 1967. Contributor to literature journals, including *New England Quarterly, Modern Fiction Studies, Emerson Society Quarterly, Explicator, Keats-Shelley Journal, American Literature, Wordsworth Circle,* and *Studies in English Literature.*

WORK IN PROGRESS: Studying Herman Melville and Robert Frost.

*   *   *

DAVIDS, Anthony 1923-

PERSONAL: Born August 28, 1923, in Providence, R.I.; son of William J. and Louise (Nahigan) Davids; married Martha Jean St. Germain, September 17, 1949. *Education:* Brown University, A.B. (magna cum laude), 1949; Harvard University, A.M., 1951, Ph.D., 1954. *Religion:* Baptist. *Home:* 218 Burgess Ave., East Providence, R.I. 02914. *Office:* Department of Psychology, Brown University, Providence, R.I. 02912.

CAREER: Harvard University, Cambridge, Mass., lecturer in clinical psychology, 1935-55, research associate in laboratory of social relations, 1953-55; Brown University, Providence, R.I., assistant professor, 1955-57, associate professor, 1957-63, professor of psychology, 1964—, professor of psychiatry, 1976—; Emma Pendleton Bradley Hospital, East Providence, R.I., director of psychology, 1955—. *Military service:* U.S. Naval Reserve, 1943-46; became lieutenant junior grade; received Air Medal and Presidential citation with Bronze Star. *Member:* American Psychological Association (fellow), American Orthopsychiatric Association (fellow), Society for Personality Assessment (fellow), Society for Research in Child Development, Eastern Psychological Association, New England Psychological Association (member of steering committee), Rhode Island Psychological Association (president, 1960-62), Phi Beta Kappa, Sigma Xi.

WRITINGS: Abnormal Children and Youth: Therapy and Research, Wiley, 1972; *Issues in Abnormal Child Psychology,* Brooks/Cole, 1973; *Child Personality and Psychopathology: Current Topics,* Wiley, Volume I, 1974, Volume II, 1975, Volume III, 1976; *Children in Conflict: A Casebook,* Wiley, 1974; (with Trygg Engen) *Introductory Psychology,* Random House, 1975. Advisory editor of *Contemporary Psychology,* 1968-73, and of *Journal of Consulting and Clinical Psychology,* 1964-78. Contributor of articles to *Journal of Personality, Journal of Consulting and Clinical Psychology, Journal of Abnormal and Social Psychology, American Journal of Orthopsychiatry, Child Development,* and other publications.

*   *   *

DAVIDSON, Jessica 1915-

PERSONAL: Born October 3, 1915, in New York, N.Y.; daughter of Israel and Carrie (Dreyfuss) Davidson. *Education:* University of Wisconsin, A.B., 1936; Columbia University, LL.B. (since converted to J.D.), 1939; Danbury State College (now Western Connecticut State College), M.S., 1963. *Politics:* Independent. *Home:* R.F.D. 1, Route 39, New Fairfield, Conn. 06810.

CAREER: U.S. Department of Labor, opinions attorney in Washington, D.C. and regional offices, 1943-53; Middle School, Newtown, Conn., sixth-grade teacher, 1957-72, eighth-grade teacher of mathematics, 1972-77.

WRITINGS—For children, except as noted: (With William G. Martin) *Mind in a Maze,* Prentice-Hall, 1969, published as *Mind-Boggling Brain Benders,* Prentice-Hall, 1974; *Using the Cuisenaire Rods* (photo-text for teachers), Cuisenaire Co., 1969; *What I Tell You Three Times Is True* (introduction to semantics for young teenagers), McCall Books, 1970; *The Square Root of Tuesday* (introduction to logic for young teenagers), McCall Books, 1971; *Is That Mother in the Bottle?* (introduction to linguistics for young teenagers), F. Watts, 1972; *2, 4, 6, 8, Let's Start to Calculate,* Cuisenaire Co., 1976. Work has been anthologized in "Language of Man" series, McDougal, Littell.

WORK IN PROGRESS: A book of mystery stories to be solved by mathematics, tentatively entitled *X Marks the Spot,* for Cuisenaire Co.; a science fiction book, tentatively entitled *The Planet of the Rejects.*

SIDELIGHTS: Jessica Davidson commented to *CA:* "The public is often aroused about the education of children, and the clamor seesaws between demands for 'open' education and 'relevant' subject matter on the one hand to 'back to basics!' on the other. I have found myself outside this battleground, believing strongly that the most important lesson—logical thinking for humanitarian ends—cannot really be taught in the classroom, though, now and then, it may be learned there. The best education is that which is freely sought, so my hope is to reach, through my books, young people interested in educating themselves.''

AVOCATIONAL INTERESTS: Photography, water sports, gardening, carpentry, reading, making up crossword puzzles for *New York Times.*

* * *

DAVIDSON, Sandra Calder 1935-

PERSONAL: Born April 20, 1935, in Concord, Mass.; daughter of Alexander (a sculptor) and Louisa (James) Calder; married Jean Davidson (a writer), October 28, 1955; children: Shawn, Andrea. *Religion:* Atheist. *Home:* Bordebure, Sache 37, France.

WRITINGS: Sylvestre, ou la grenouille de plomb, Maeght (Paris), 1962, translation by father, Alexander Calder, husband, Jean Davidson, and Judy Hyun published as *Sylvester,* Follett, 1967; (illustrator) Ira Ironmonger, *Alligator Smiling in the Sawgrass,* Young Scott Books, 1965; *Sylvester and the Butterfly Bomb,* Doubleday, 1972.

WORK IN PROGRESS: Turkey and the Eagle; Sylvester and Stephanie; It Is Good and They Are Hungry, a children's cookbook; a story book.

* * *

DAVIES, Norman 1939-

PERSONAL: Born June 8, 1939, in Bolton, England; son of Richard and Elizabeth (Bolton) Davies; married Maria Zielinska (a physician), December 26, 1966; children: Daniel. *Education:* Attended University of Grenoble, 1957-58; Magdalen College, Oxford, B.A. (honors), 1962; University of Sussex, M.A., 1966; Jagiellonian University, D.Phil., 1968. *Home:* 22 Rowland Close, Oxford, England. *Office:* School of Slavonic and East European Studies, University of London, Senate House, Malet St., London W.C.1, England.

CAREER: Oxford University, St. Antony's College, Oxford, England, research fellow, 1969-70; University of London, School of Slavonic and East European Studies, London, England, lecturer in history, 1970—. *Member:* Royal Historical Society (fellow).

WRITINGS: White Eagle, Red Star: The Polish-Soviet War, 1919-1920, St. Martin's, 1972; *Poland Past and Present: A Select Bibliography of Works in English on Polish History,* Oriental Research Partners, 1976; *God's Playground: A History of Poland,* Columbia University Press, 1979. Contributor to *Historical Journal, Journal of Contemporary History, Times, European Studies Review, Slavonic Review, Guardian, Daily Telegraph,* and other journals and newspapers.

SIDELIGHTS: Norman Davies' interest in Poland began when a railroad train bearing him to Russia broke down in Warsaw. The accidental stop-over inspired him to return to Poland, learn the language, marry a Polish woman, and develop a strong attachment to the country.

* * *

DAVIS, Forest K(endall) 1918-

PERSONAL: Born February 1, 1918, in Nashua, N.H.; son of Harold M. (an industrial engineer) and L. Evangeline

(Foster) Davis; married Elizabeth Herriott (a social worker), September 2, 1946; children: Margaret V. A. (Mrs. Arthur E. Gordon), William K. L., Charles M. S., Katharine K. R. *Education:* Harvard University, A.B., 1939, S.T.B., 1948. *Politics:* Independent. *Religion:* Unitarian; Presbyterian. *Home address:* R.R. 1, Box 52, Friendsville, Pa. 18818; and Box 7, Adamant, Vt. 05640. *Office:* Empire State College of the State University of New York, 44 Hawley St., Binghamton, N.Y. 13901.

CAREER: Goddard College, Plainfield, Vt., director of admissions and records, 1950-55, administrative dean, 1957-65, dean of Greatwood Campus, 1965-67, faculty of philosophy and religion, 1950-67; Wilberforce University, Wilberforce, Ohio, federal programs administrator, 1967-72, dean of faculty, 1969-72; Empire State College of the State University of New York, Binghamton, associate dean, 1972-74, professor of philosophy and religion, 1972—. President, Precision Paper, Inc., Adamant, Vt., 1961—. *Military service:* U.S. Army Air Forces, 1943-46. *Member:* American Academy of Religion, American Philosophical Association, Vermont Academy of Arts and Sciences.

WRITINGS: (Editor and author of epilogue) Sylvia Bliss, *Quests: Poems in Prose,* Capital City Press, 1965; *Return from Enlightenment,* Adamant Press, 1971; *Journey among Mountains,* Adamant Press, 1974. Contributor of articles and reviews to *Paper Industry Magazine, Choice,* and to professional journals.

WORK IN PROGRESS: A third volume of essays.

* * *

DAVIS, Garold N(eil) 1932-

PERSONAL: Born October 14, 1932, in Downey, Idaho; son of William H. (a clerk) and M. Josephine (Sterrett) Davis; married Norma Stephens (an instructor at Brigham Young University), December 20, 1954; children: Donnette Jo, William S., Jeffrey Clay, Lorelei Diane, Erik Garold. *Education:* Attended Southern Oregon College, 1955-57; Brigham Young University, B.A., 1958, M.A., 1959; Johns Hopkins University, Ph.D., 1962. *Religion:* Church of Jesus Christ of Latter-day Saints. *Office:* Department of Germanic Languages, Brigham Young University, Provo, Utah 84601.

CAREER: University of Pennsylvania, Philadelphia, instructor in German, 1962-63; Southern Oregon College, Ashland, assistant professor, 1963-65, associate professor of German, 1965-66; University of Colorado, Boulder, assistant professor of German, 1966-68; Brigham Young University, Provo, Utah, associate professor of German and comparative literature, 1968—. *Military service:* U.S. Navy, 1951-55. *Member:* Rocky Mountain Modern Language Association.

WRITINGS: German Thought and Culture in England, 1700-1770, University of North Carolina, 1969.

WORK IN PROGRESS: Austrian Regional Realism: A Biographical Bibliographical Survey, completion expected in 1980.

* * *

DAVIS, J(ohn) Cary 1905-

PERSONAL: Born May 18, 1905, in Pinckneyville, Ill.; son of Don (general telegraph foreman for Illinois Central Railroad) and Louella (Spence) Davis; married Ellen Esslinger, November 25, 1936; children: Don Edward, Karan Elizabeth (Mrs. Stephen Joel Cutler). *Education:* Southern Illinois University, Ed.B., 1929; University of Chicago, A.M., 1930, Ph.D., 1936; Sorbonne, University of Paris, summer diploma in French, 1932. *Politics:* Independent. *Religion:* "Nominally Protestant." *Home:* 38 Mira Las Olas, San Clemente, Calif. 92672.

CAREER: Southern Illinois University at Carbondale, instructor, 1930-37, assistant professor of French, 1937-39, associate professor of French and Spanish, 1939-52, professor of Spanish and Portuguese, 1952-71, acting chairman of department of foreign languages, 1950-51, 1961, chairman, 1964-67. Visiting professor of Romance languages, University of Rochester, summer, 1957. National Defense Education Act Institute at University of South Dakota, professor of Spanish, summer, 1961; National Defense Education Act Institute at South Dakota State College, assistant director, summer, 1961; has also taught at National Defense Education Act Institutes in Guatemala and in San Miguel de Allende, Mexico. *Member:* International Arthurian Society, Modern Language Association of America, American Association of Teachers of Spanish and Portuguese, Hispanic Society of America (corresponding member), South Central Modern Language Association. *Awards, honors:* Mitre Medal of Hispanic Society of America, 1971.

WRITINGS: Caminos de Mexico, Heath, 1962; *Recuerdos de Guatemala,* Southern Illinois University Press, 1970; (with D. Lincoln Canfield) *An Introduction to Romance Linguistics,* Southern Illinois University, 1975. General editor, "Contemporary Latin American Classics" series, Southern Illinois University Press, 1964—. Contributor to *Encyclopaedia Britannica* and *World Book;* contributor of articles and reviews to language journals.

SIDELIGHTS: J. Cary Davis told *CA,* "Aside from my first love, linguistics, I have always been interested in music, photography, stamps and coins, and in amateur carpentry." He has traveled and studied in Mexico, Guatemala, Spain, and Portugal; he speaks Spanish, French, German, Italian, Portuguese, Greek, and Swedish.

*   *   *

DAVIS, Johanna   1937-1974

PERSONAL: Born October 2, 1937, in Los Angeles, Calif.; daughter of Herman J. (a screenwriter) and Sara (Aaronson) Mankiewicz; married Peter Davis (a filmmaker), September 13, 1959; children: Timothy Frank, Nicholas Peter. *Education:* Wellesley College, B.A., 1958. *Politics:* Democrat. *Residence:* New York, N.Y. *Agent:* Lynn Nesbit, International Creative Management, 40 West 57th St., New York, N.Y. 10019.

CAREER: Time, New York, N.Y., secretary, 1959-61, contributing editor, 1961-72.

WRITINGS: Life Signs, Atheneum, 1973. Contributor to *Ladies' Home Journal* and *New York.*†

(Died July 25, 1974)

*   *   *

DAVIS, Melton S(amillow)   1910-

PERSONAL: Born December 27, 1910, in New York, N.Y.; son of Charles Samillow and Jean (Zicklin) Davis; married Ferda Firat, November 27, 1968. *Education:* Attended University of Alabama, 1928-30, University of California, 1936-37, American University, 1944, and Centre Culturel International de Royaumont, 1947-48. *Home:* 11 Via Scipione Gaetano, 00197 Rome, Italy 803732. *Agent:* Julian Bach Literary Agency, Inc., 3 East 48th St., New York, N.Y. 10017.

CAREER: U.S. Department of State, Office of the Foreign Liquidation Commissioner, Paris, France, public relations officer, 1946-47; UNESCO, Paris, editor, 1948-50; Economic Cooperation Administration and Mutual Security Administration, Paris, radio director for Europe, Africa, and the Middle East, 1950-52; *World* (magazine), New York City, Mediterranean editor, 1954-55; Mutual Broadcasting System, New York City, chief of bureau in Italy, 1962—. Political columnist, *New York Post,* 1954-55. Editorial consultant, Lancio Publications, 1971—. *Military service:* U.S. Army, 1943-46. *Member:* Society of Magazine Writers.

WRITINGS: All Rome Trembled, Putnam, 1957; *The Voluptuaries,* Avon, 1966; (translator) Enrico Altavilla, *The Art of Spying,* Prentice-Hall, 1967; *Who Defends Rome?,* Dial, 1972. Contributor to popular magazines, including *Reader's Digest, Parade, Cosmopolitan, Esquire, True, Pageant, Good Housekeeping, Argosy, Skiing,* and *New York Times Magazine.*

BIOGRAPHICAL/CRITICAL SOURCES: Detroit News, April 2, 1972.

*   *   *

DAVIS-WEYER, Caecilia   1929-

PERSONAL: Born August 8, 1929, in Hannover, Germany; daughter of Bernard (an insurance executive) and Anna (Petersmann) Weyer; married Charles Till Davis (a historian), September 8, 1961; children: Bernard, Frank. *Education:* Attended University of Hamburg, and University of Paris; University of Cologne, Ph.D., 1959. *Religion:* Roman Catholic. *Home:* 1628 Amelia, New Orleans, La. 70115. *Office:* Department of Art, Newcomb College, Tulane University, New Orleans, La. 70118.

CAREER: Tulane University, New Orleans, La., lecturer, 1962-66, assistant professor, 1967-70, associate professor of mediaeval art history, 1971—. *Member:* College Art Association. *Awards, honors:* American Council of Learned Societies fellowship, 1972-73.

WRITINGS: Early Mediaeval Art, Prentice-Hall, 1971. Contributor to *Muenchner Jahrbuch, Zeitschrift fuer Kunstgeschichte,* and other journals. Member of editorial board of *Art Bulletin,* 1972—.

WORK IN PROGRESS: A book, *Carolingian Mosaics of Rome.*

*   *   *

DEAN, Howard E(dward)   1916-

PERSONAL: Born June 17, 1916, in Pittsburgh, Pa.; son of Howard Edward (a surgeon) and Loretta (McCullough) Dean; married Helen S. Hodges, September 8, 1941; children: Howard, Jr., Philip. *Education:* University of California, Los Angeles, A.B., 1939; University of Washington, Seattle, graduate study, 1939-40; Columbia University, Ph.D., 1950; Harvard University, post-doctoral study, 1955-56. *Home:* 6325 Joseph St. S.E., Salem, Ore. 97301. *Office:* Department of Political Science, Portland State University, Portland, Ore. 97207.

CAREER: City College (now City College of the City University of New York), New York City, tutor in government, 1941-42; Columbia University, New York City, instructor in political science, 1946-47; University of Oregon, Eugene, assistant professor, 1947-56, associate professor, 1956-61; Portland State University, Portland, Ore., professor of political science, 1961—, head of department, 1961-69, 1978—. Visiting professor at University of Washington, Seattle,

1964. *Military service:* U.S. Army, 1942-45, 1950-52. U.S. Army Reserve, 1945-57; became captain. *Member:* American Political Science Association, American Society for Political and Legal Philosophy, Western Political Science Association, Pacific Northwest Political Science Association (president, 1961-62).

WRITINGS: (With Donald E. Tope, Robert Campbell, Richard A. Littman, John M. Foskett, and Fred Fosmire) *The Social Sciences View School Administration,* Prentice-Hall, 1965; *Judicial Review and Democracy,* Random House, 1966. Contributor to *American Political Science Review, Western Political Quarterly,* and *Oregon Law Review.*

WORK IN PROGRESS: The Behavioral Movement in American Political Science; James Bradley Thayer and the Doctrine of Judicial Review.

* * *

DECARIE, Therese Gouin 1923-

PERSONAL: Born September 30, 1923, in Montreal, Quebec, Canada; daughter of Mercier Leon (a lawyer) and Yvette (Ollivier) Gouin; married Vianney Decarie (a professor of philosophy), December 24, 1948; children: Pascale, Dominique, Jean-Claude, Emmanuel. *Education:* University of Montreal, B.A., 1945, L.Ph., 1947, Ph.D., 1960. *Religion:* Roman Catholic. *Home:* 84 Claude-Champagne Ave., Outremont, Montreal, Quebec, Canada. *Office:* Department of Psychology, University of Montreal, P.O. Box 6128, Montreal, Quebec, Canada.

CAREER: University of Montreal, Montreal, Quebec, instructor, 1949-51, associate professor, 1951-65, professor of psychology, 1965—. Member, National Research Council of Canada, 1970-76. *Member:* Societe canadienne de psychologie, Corporation des psychologues de la Province Quebec, Society for Research in Child Development, Societe de psychoanalyse, Societe Royale. *Awards, honors:* Officer, Order of Canada.

WRITINGS: Le developpement psychologique de l'enfant, Fides, 1953, 5th edition, 1961; *De l'adolescence a la maturite,* Fides, 1955, 3rd edition, 1961; *L'intelligence et l'affectivite chez le jeune enfant,* preface by Jean Piaget, Delachaux et Niestle, 1961, translation published as *Intelligence and Affectivity in Early Childhood,* International Universities Press, 1965; (contributor) B. M. Foss, editor, *Determinants of Infant Behavior,* Volume IV, Methuen, 1968; (editor) *La reaction du jeune enfant a la personne etrangere,* Les Presses de l'Universite de Montreal, 1972, translation published as *The Infant's Reaction to the Stranger,* International Universities Press, 1974. Contributor to professional journals in Canada and the United States.

WORK IN PROGRESS: Research on the problem of observation of emotion in infancy.

* * *

deCHARMS, Richard IV 1927-

PERSONAL: Born December 13, 1927, in Wilkes Barre, Pa.; son of Richard (a civil engineer) and Carita (Pendleton) deCharms; married second wife, Marion Muir, October, 1975; children: (first marriage) Christopher. *Education:* Swarthmore College, B.A., 1952; Wesleyan University, M.A., 1954; University of North Carolina, Ph.D., 1956. *Home:* 445 California, St. Louis, Mo. 63119. *Office address:* Box 1183, Washington University, St. Louis, Mo. 63130.

CAREER: Washington University, St. Louis, Mo., assistant professor, 1957-61, associate professor, 1961-65, professor of psychology, 1965—. *Military service:* U.S. Navy, 1945-50; became lieutenant. *Member:* American Psychological Association, American Association for the Advancement of Science, American Educational Research Association, Sigma Xi. *Awards, honors:* Office of Naval Research grants, 1958-65; Carnegie Corp. grants, 1966-70; Office of Education grant, 1969-70.

WRITINGS: Personal Causation, Academic Press, 1968; (with Dennis J. Shea and others) *Enhancing Motivation: Change in the Classroom,* Halsted, 1976. Contributor to seventeen professional journals including *Journal of Applied Social Psychology* and *Journal of Abnormal Social Psychology.*

WORK IN PROGRESS: Personal Responsibility in the Schools.

* * *

de DIENES, Andre 1913-

PERSONAL: Born December 18, 1913, in Transylvania, Hungary; son of Kalman Dienes (a banker). *Education:* Self-educated. *Home and office:* 1401 Sunset Plaza Dr., Los Angeles, Calif. 90069.

CAREER: Professional photo-artist, 1935—.

WRITINGS—All illustrated with photographs: *The Nude,* Bodley Head, 1956; *Nude Pattern,* Bodley Head, 1958; *Best Nudes,* Bodley Head, 1962; *Natural Nudes,* Amphoto, 1966; *Western Akt,* Fravex, 1967; *Nudes, My Camera, and I,* Focal Press, 1973; *Nude Variations,* Amphoto, 1977.

* * *

de FOSSARD, R(onald) A(lfred) 1929-

PERSONAL: Born July 1, 1929, in London, England; son of Charles Alfred (a hotelier) and Rosanne (McDonough) de Fossard; married Agnes Paterson, July 2, 1956; children: Alexandra Louise, Heather Anne, Yvonne Helen. *Education:* University of Edinburgh, B.Sc. (honors), 1954; University of the Witwatersrand, M.Sc., 1964; University of New England, Ph.D., 1968. *Home:* 43 Chessington Estate, Bundarra Rd., Armidale 2350, New South Wales, Australia. *Office:* University of New England, Armidale 2351, New South Wales, Australia.

CAREER: Ministry of Agriculture and Lands, Jamaica, West Indies, agricultural officer, 1955-58; Citrus and Sub-Tropical Fruit Research Institute, Nelspruit, Transvaal, South Africa, professional officer, 1958-61; Commonwealth Scientific and Industrial Research Organization, Division of Food Preservation, Sydney, Australia, research scientist, 1961-64; University of New England, Armidale, New South Wales, Australia, senior lecturer in botany, 1964—, fellow of St. Albert's College, 1969—. *Military service:* British Army, Royal Rhodesian Regiment, 1947. *Member:* International Plant Tissue Culture Association, International Plant Propagators' Society, Australian Society of Plant Physiologists. *Awards, honors:* Research awards from Nuffield Foundation, 1967-68, Rural Credits Development Fund, 1976-77, Australian Research Grants Committee, 1976-79, Australian Paper Manufacturers Ltd., Australian Forest Holding, Ltd., and other foundations and organizations.

WRITINGS: Brown Stem of Oranges Investigation, Jamaica Ministry of Agriculture, 1958; (editor) *A University Perspective,* Wiley, 1970; *Tissue Culture for Plant Propagators,* University of New England, 1976. Contributor to scientific journals in the United States, Europe, South Africa, and Australia.

WORK IN PROGRESS: Research on plant morphogenesis, tissue and organ culture, vegetative propagation of forest trees, development of haploid plants from pollen, microscopy, and the biology of man-made lakes; conducting a bioassy of the flowering hormone.

AVOCATIONAL INTERESTS: Photography, gardening.

* * *

DEGNAN, James Philip 1933-

PERSONAL: Born September 24, 1933, in Memphis, Tenn.; son of James P. and Clare Degnan. *Education:* Memphis State College (now University), B.A., 1954; University of Notre Dame, M.A., 1956. *Home address:* Box 906, Aptos, Calif. 95003. *Office:* Department of English, University of Santa Clara, Santa Clara, Calif.

CAREER: University of Notre Dame, South Bend, Ind., instructor in English, 1956-57; University of Florida, Gainesville, instructor in English, 1957-61; University of Santa Clara, Santa Clara, Calif., assistant professor, 1962-66, associate professor, 1966-69, professor of English, 1969—; currently director of writer's conference. *Member:* Society of Magazine Writers, Modern Language Association of America. *Awards, honors:* Martha Foley Best American Short Story Anthology honor roll, 1966, for "An Existentialist Experience"; Beinecke award, 1969, for public affairs writing; Fund for Investigative Journalism award, 1971.

WRITINGS: (Compiler with William A. Heffernan) *Language and Literature Reader*, Glencoe Press, 1968; (with Heffernan) *Writing Analyses of Literature*, Holt, 1969. Work is represented in anthologies. Contributor of articles to *Atlantic, Esquire, Nation, Kenyon Review, Hudson Review, Virginia Quarterly Review, Commonweal, Critic, Progressive, Reporter* and *Colorado Quarterly*. Editorial consultant, *Sierra Club Bulletin*.†

* * *

DEKOBRA, Maurice 1885-1973

May 28, 1885—June 2, 1973; French novelist and journalist. Obituaries: *New York Times*, June 3, 1973. (See index for CA sketch)

* * *

DELACATO, Carl H(enry) 1923-

PERSONAL: Born September 10, 1923, in Pottstown, Pa.; son of Ercole and Julia (DiBartolomeo) Delacato; married Janice Fernstrom (a teacher), June 20, 1951; children: Elizabeth F., Carl Henry, Jr., David F. *Education:* West Chester State Teachers College (now West Chester State College), B.S., 1945; University of Pennsylvania, M.S., 1948, Ed.D., 1952. *Politics:* Republican. *Religion:* Unitarian. *Home address:* Thomas and Andorra Rds., Philadelphia, Pa. 19118. *Agent:* Julia Coopersmith, 10 West 15th St., New York, N.Y. 10011. *Office:* Delacato & Delacato, Consultants in Learning, Thomas Rd. at Northwestern Ave., Philadelphia, Pa. 19118; and Center for Neurological Rehabilitation, 32 South Morton Ave., Morton, Pa. 19070.

CAREER: Chestnut Hill Academy, Philadelphia, Pa., assistant headmaster, 1945-65; Institutes for the Achievement of Human Potential, Philadelphia, associate director, 1955-73; University of Plano, Plano, Tex., chairman of department of human development, 1965-73; Center for Neurological Rehabilitation, Morton, Pa., director, 1974—; president, Delacato & Delacato, Consultants in Learning, Philadelphia; director, Carl H. Delacato and Robert J. Doman Autistic Unit. Member of board of trustees, Chestnut Hill Hospital, Philadelphia, 1959-65. *Member:* Authors Guild, Philadelphia Cricket Club.

WRITINGS: The Treatment and Prevention of Reading Problems, C. C Thomas, 1959; *The Diagnosis and Treatment of Speech and Reading Problems*, C. C Thomas, 1963; *The Elementary School of the Future*, C. C Thomas, 1964; *Neurological Organization and Reading*, C. C Thomas, 1966; *A New Start for the Child with Reading Problems: A Manual for Parents*, McKay, 1970, revised edition, 1977; *The Ultimate Stranger, the Autistic Child*, Doubleday, 1974. Editor of "American Series in Education and Learning," 1969-73.

WORK IN PROGRESS: Miracle at Ein Gedi.

SIDELIGHTS: Carl H. Delacato has traveled extensively to study the primitive children of Brazil, the Kalahari Desert and around the equator, as well as Eskimos and the American Indians of Texas and Arizona.

* * *

DE LAGE, Ida 1918-

PERSONAL: Born July 16, 1918, in New York, N.Y.; daughter of Joseph Patrick (a teacher) and Mary Catherine (Sheridan) McCourt; married Maurice Francois De Lage (a papermaker), June 9, 1946; children: Patrick Joseph, Marie Louise. *Education:* Attended New York State Teachers College (now State University of New York College at New Paltz). *Home:* 253 Edison St., Clifton, N.Y. 07013.

CAREER: Writer for children.

WRITINGS—Juvenile; all published by Garrard: *The Farmer and the Witch*, 1966; *Weeny Witch*, 1968; *The Witchy Broom*, 1969; *The Old Witch Goes to the Ball*, 1969.

The Old Witch and the Snores, 1970; *What Does a Witch Need?*, 1971; *Hello, Come In*, 1971; *Beware! Beware! A Witch Won't Share*, 1972; *Pink, Pink*, 1973; *Good Morning Lady*, 1974; *The Old Witch and the Wizard*, 1974; *A Bunny Ride*, 1975; *Bunny School*, 1976; *The Old Witch's Party*, 1976; *ABC Firedogs*, 1977; *ABC Halloween Witch*, 1977; *ABC Pigs Go to Market*, 1977; *ABC Pirate Adventures*, 1977; *The Squirrel's Tree Party*, 1978; *Am I a Bunny?*, 1978; *The Old Witch and the Magic Basket*, 1978; *The Old Witch and the Ghost Parade*, 1978; *ABC Christmas*, 1978; *ABC Santa Claus*, 1978; *ABC Easter Bunny*, 1978.

* * *

DeLAMOTTE, Roy Carroll 1917-
(Gregory Wilson)

PERSONAL: Born December 10, 1917, in Lecompte, La.; son of Octave John (a railroad general manager) and Caroline (Jones) DeLamotte; married Araminta Harper (a college instructor), July 21, 1949; children: Eugenia Caroline, Rebecca Heloise. *Education:* Millsaps College, B.A., 1939; Emory University, B.D., 1948; Yale University, Ph.D., 1953. *Politics:* Liberal Democrat. *Religion:* Methodist. *Home:* 3325 Tanglewood Dr., Augusta, Ga. 30909. *Office:* Department of Philosophy and Religion, Paine College, 1235 15th St., Augusta, Ga. 30901.

CAREER: Ordained minister of Methodist Church, 1951; high school English teacher in Moss Point, Miss., 1946-47;

New England Southern Conference of the Methodist Church, minister, 1951-55; Holston Conference of the Methodist Church, minister, 1955-61; Paine College, Augusta, Ga., associate professor, 1961-69, professor of philosophy and religion, 1970—. *Military service:* U.S. Army, 1944-46. *Member:* American Association of University Professors, Authors League of America. *Awards, honors:* Dollar Book Club Award, 1962, for *The Stained Glass Jungle.*

WRITINGS—All under pseudonym Gregory Wilson: *The Stained Glass Jungle* (novel), Doubleday, 1962; *The Valley of Time* (novel), Doubleday, 1967.

WORK IN PROGRESS: Research on the gospel of Thomas and its relation to the teachings of Jesus; research on gnosticism and its mystical components; research for a historical novel about the Jewish War with Rome, 66-70 A.D.; a novel about early missionaries in Africa and the moral ambiguities of their relation to the colonial powers.

SIDELIGHTS: Roy DeLamotte told *CA:* "Young writers should experiment in all possible forms—short-story, poem, novel, play, articles, whatever—before settling into a specialty. I spent the first fifteen years trying (in vain) to write short-stories before I had the nerve to try a novel, which proved to be my true field. With more courage and curiosity at the outset, I might have had a far more productive career." He adds this hint for beginning novelists: "It helps me to visualize some actual individual as the physical model for each character. For example, I tell myself, 'For this salesman I'll think of Johnny Carson.' Thus every time the character appears, I see him, he always looks the same, and I never have to rack my brains to remember what I said about some smorgasbord of mendacities that never existed."

* * *

DELANEY, Daniel J(oseph) 1938-

PERSONAL: Born March 15, 1938, in Fall River, Mass.; son of Joseph Raymond (a police officer) and Jane (Bourke) Delaney; married Grace C. Dobson (a registered nurse), September 12, 1959; children: Ann Mary, Joseph T., Edmund P., Thomas P., Daniel M., Maureen S. *Education:* Stonehill College, A.B., 1960; Massachusetts State College at Bridgewater, M.Ed., 1962; Arizona State University, Ph.D., 1966. *Politics:* Democrat. *Religion:* Roman Catholic. *Home:* 605 Charlecote Dr., Norfolk, Va. 23462. *Office:* Community Mental Health Center, 325 West 21st St., Norfolk, Va. 23501.

CAREER: High school English teacher in Fall River, Mass., 1960-62; high school director of guidance in North Dartmouth, Mass., 1962-63; Arizona State University, Tempe, counselor, 1963-64, veterans administration vocational counseling and counseling practicum supervisor, 1964-65; University of Illinois at Urbana-Champaign, assistant professor, 1966-68, associate professor, 1968-70, professor of educational psychology, 1970-75; Community Mental Health Center, Norfolk, Va., director of community services program, 1975—. Registered psychologist in private practice in Champaign, Ill., 1971-75. Facility consultant for the juvenile division of Illinois Department of Corrections, 1972—. *Military service:* U.S. Army Reserve, 1956-62. *Member:* American Psychological Association, American Personnel and Guidance Association, American Association for the Advancement of Science, Association for Counseling Education and Supervision, Phi Delta Kappa.

WRITINGS: (Editor) *Readings in Child Development,* Educational Services, 1968; (editor with Thomas J. Long) *Readings in Counseling and Psychotherapy,* Educational

Services, 1968; (with Sheldon Eisenberg) *The Counseling Process,* Rand NcNally, 1972, 2nd edition, 1977. Contributor to education journals.

WORK IN PROGRESS: Contingency Management in Corrections.

* * *

De LUCCA, John 1920-

PERSONAL: Born October 8, 1920, in New York, N.Y.; son of Carlo and Adela (Ianiello) De Lucca; married Margaret L. Williams, June 10, 1956; children: Danielle Sue, David Jonathan. *Education:* College of the City of New York (now City College of the City University of New York), B.B.A., 1941; New School for Social Research, M.A., 1950; Harvard University, graduate study, 1952-53; Ohio State University, Ph.D., 1955. *Home:* 10 Copperfield Dr., Kingston, Ontario, Canada. *Office:* Department of Philosophy, Queen's University, Kingston, Ontario, Canada.

CAREER: Johart International Corp., New York City, president and general manager, 1946-51; Pace College (now University), New York City, instructor in philosophy, 1950-52; Washington State University, Pullman, assistant professor of philosophy, 1956-62; University of Victoria, Victoria, British Columbia, associate professor of philosophy and chairman of the department, 1962-68; Queen's University, Kingston, Ontario, professor of philosophy, 1968—. *Military service:* U.S. Army, 1942-45; served in Pacific theater of operations; became technical sergeant. *Member:* American Philosophical Association (member of executive board, Pacific division, 1965-67), Canadian Philosophical Association, Humanities Association of Canada, Beta Gamma Sigma. *Awards, honors:* Ohio State University fellow, 1954-55.

WRITINGS: (Editor and annotator) *Reason and Experience: Dialogues in Modern Philosophy,* Freeman, Cooper, 1973; *Rene Descartes' Meditations on First Philosophy: With an Appendix Containing Selected Passages from Other Works,* Queen's Bookstore, 1975. Contributor to *Dialogue, Convivium, Philosophical Journal, Classical Journal, Philosophical Quarterly, Philosophy of Science,* and *Queen's Quarterly.*

WORK IN PROGRESS: The Uses of Reason: A Reader in Philosophy; An Introduction to the Philosophy of Science.

* * *

de MESNE, Eugene (Frederick)
(Julian Ocean)

PERSONAL: Surname is pronounced de-Main; born in Hove, Sussexshire, England; son of George William (a military man) and Elizabeth (Montfort) de Mesne. *Education:* Studied at London School of Journalism, Newspaper Institute, New York, N.Y., National School, Surrey, England, and University of Exeter, England.

CAREER: Free-lance writer. Northwoods Press, Meadows of Dan, Va., editor and agent for New England region, 1973-74. *Member:* Clover International Society for Poetry (life member), Artists-Authors International, National Writer's Club. *Awards, honors:* Fiction award from Artists-Authors International, 1968.

WRITINGS—Under pseudonym Julian Ocean: *Lost Moments,* Triple "P", 1970; *From Satan's Pit . . . ,* Hendricks Associates, 1971; *How Do You Tell a Woman?,* Whippoorwill, 1973; (editor) *Sky Blue, Grass Green,* Northwoods, 1973. Editor and columnist, *In-Crowd,* 1972; editor, *Person to People,* 1968-72; former editor, *Writer's Profit.*

WORK IN PROGRESS—Novels: *Fool's Choice; A Stygian Smile; Animal, Animal.*

AVOCATIONAL INTERESTS: Travel, mountain climbing, history, vegetarian tastes and styles of life.†

* * *

DENEVAN, William M(axfield) 1931-

PERSONAL: Born October 16, 1931, in San Diego, Calif.; son of Lester W. and Wilda (Maxfield) Denevan; married Patricia Sue French (a teacher), June 21, 1958; children: William Curtis, Victoria Alden. *Education:* University of California, Berkeley, B.A., 1953, M.A., 1958, Ph.D., 1963. *Home:* 5610 Hempstead Rd., Madison, Wis. 53711. *Office:* Department of Geography, 455 Science Hall, University of Wisconsin, Madison, Wis. 53706.

CAREER: University of Wisconsin—Madison, assistant professor, 1963-68, associate professor, 1968-72, professor of geography, 1972—. *Military service:* U.S. Navy, 1953-55. *Member:* Association of American Geographers, American Geographical Society, American Anthropological Association, Society for American Archaeology, American Association for the Advancement of Science, Latin American Studies Association, Hakluyt Society. *Awards, honors:* Ford Foundation research grant, 1965-66; National Academy of Sciences grant, 1972-73; Guggenheim fellowship, 1977-78.

WRITINGS: The Upland Pine Forests of Nicaragua, University of California Press, 1961; *The Aboriginal Cultural Geography of the Llanos de Mojos of Bolivia,* University of California Press, 1966; *The Biogeography of a Savanna Landscape: The Gran Pajonal of Eastern Peru,* McGill University, 1970; (editor) *The Native Population of the Americas in 1492,* University of Wisconsin Press, 1976. Contributor of more than fifty articles and reviews to journals in his field.

WORK IN PROGRESS: Research on pre-Columbian agricultural methods in the Americas.

* * *

DENFELD, Duane (Henry) 1939-

PERSONAL: Born July 27, 1939, in Portland, Ore.; son of George August (a grocer) and Urba (Anderson) Denfeld. *Education:* Portland State College (now University), B.S., 1963; University of Illinois, Ph.D., 1967.

CAREER: University of Connecticut, Storrs, instructor, 1967-70, assistant professor of criminology, 1970-75; affiliated with University of Maryland, 1975-77; editor, 1977—. Executive director of Outmates, a prisoner support group. *Member:* National Prisoner Reform Association, Groves Conference.

WRITINGS: (Editor) *But Morning Refused to Answer,* Times Change Press, 1972; (editor) *Street-Wise Criminology,* Schenkman, 1973. Also author of *The Indestructible Jeep.* Contributor to professional journals, including *Sexual Behavior* and *Journal of Sexual Research.*

WORK IN PROGRESS: World War II: Thirty Years Later; Casual Sex: Europe and the United States.

SIDELIGHTS: The Indestructible Jeep has been published in Spanish and Portuguese.

* * *

DENNIS, Everette E. 1942-

PERSONAL: Born August 15, 1942, in Seattle, Wash.; son of Everette E. (a painter) and Kathryn M. (Platt) Dennis. *Education:* University of Oregon, B.S., 1964; Syracuse University, M.A., 1966; University of Minnesota, Ph.D., 1974. *Religion:* Protestant. *Office:* School of Journalism and Mass Communication, University of Minnesota, Minneapolis, Minn. 55455.

CAREER: New York Department of Mental Hygiene, Albany, public information associate, 1965-66; Illinois Department of Mental Health, Chicago, director of information, 1966-68; Kansas State University, Manhattan, assistant professor of journalism, 1968-74, acting chairman of department, 1971-72, director of mental health mass communications program, 1969-72; University of Minnesota, Minneapolis, assistant professor, 1974-76, associate professor of journalism and mass communication, 1976—, also member of American Studies faculty. Visiting professor, University of Oregon, 1970-71. *Member:* American Orthopsychiatric Association, Association for Education in Journalism, Sigma Delta Chi, Kappa Tau Alpha (honorary member). *Awards, honors:* Sigma Delta Chi writing award, 1962; recipient of fellowships at Syracuse University, 1964-66, Stanford University, 1969, and Harvard University Law School, 1978-79.

WRITINGS: (Editor) *The Magic Writing Machine: Student Probes of the New Journalism,* University of Oregon, 1971; (with W. L. Rivers) *Other Voices: The New Journalism in America,* Canfield, 1973; (with G. S. Hage) *New Strategies for Public Affairs Reporting,* Prentice-Hall, 1976; *The Media Society: Evidence about Mass Communication in America,* W. C. Brown, 1978; (editor with D. M. Gillmor and D. Grey) *Justice Hugo Black and the First Amendment,* Iowa State University Press, 1978; (editor with Gillmor and I. Ismach) *Enduring Issues in Mass Communications,* West Publishing, 1978. Contributor of articles and reviews to psychiatric journals, journalism periodicals and law reviews.

WORK IN PROGRESS: American Editorial Cartoonists and Their Creations: 1880-1940, biographical studies of cartoonists in the Herschel C. Logan collection; with M. L. DeFleur, *Understanding Mass Communication;* with Christopher Allen, *Puck: The Comic Weekly;* with J. C. Bertrand, *Ideology and the American Press; The Press and the Concept of Representations.*

BIOGRAPHICAL/CRITICAL SOURCES: Progressive, October, 1971; *Journalism Quarterly,* spring, 1972; *Presse Actualite,* April, 1977; *New York Times,* February 15, 1977.

* * *

DENNIS, Henry C(harles) 1918-

PERSONAL: Born July 15, 1918, in Brooklyn, N.Y.; son of Edwin F. and Sonja A. (Walgren) Dennis; married Sarah Bane (an administrative assistant), April 13, 1946. *Education:* University of New Mexico, B.A., 1949, M.A., 1952; also studied at University of Mississippi, University of Tennessee, University of Colorado, University of Hawaii, University of Texas, Hardin-Simmons University, New Mexico Highlands University, New Mexico Eastern University, New Mexico Western University, New Mexico State University, New York University, Pratt Institute, and Chengchi University. *Religion:* Presbyterian. *Address:* Box 990 SR, Corrales, N.M. 87048. *Office:* Sandia High School, 7801 Candelaria N.E., Albuquerque, N.M. 87110.

CAREER: U.S. Veterans Administration, New York, N.Y., counselor, 1945-49; New Mexico Employment Commission, Albuquerque, employees relations representative, 1950-51; Mountain Bell Telephone Co., Albuquerque, commercial development engineer, 1952-56; Travel Service Agency, Albuquerque, manager, 1956-58; Henry Dennis Travel Corp., Albuquerque, president, 1958-63; New Mexico Highway Commission, Santa Fe, highway economist, 1958-62; New Mexico State Planning Office, Santa Fe, resources planner, 1962; Sandia High School, Albuquerque, teacher of American history, sociology, and problems of democracy, 1962—. Senior partner, Henry Dennis & Associates (public relations firm); chairman of board, New Mexico Research Bureau; director, Workshop in Alcoholism and Addiction, 1967; coordinator of Summer Institute for Secondary Schools, National Science Foundation, 1968; director, Workshop in Techniques for Training the Disadvantaged, summer, 1969. Guest lecturer at Adams State College, Air Force Academy, and Kansas Wesleyan University. Legislative aide to U.S. Congressman Manuez Lujan, Jr., summer, 1978. Adviser to People's Republic of China, 1974, and New Mexico governor's committee on legal rights of women; member of board of directors, New Mexico Heart Association, 1952-57; member of board of directors, Albuquerque Area Council on Alcoholism, 1965-67. *Military service:* U.S. Army, Joint Assault Signal Forces, 1940-44; served in Pacific theater.

MEMBER: Royal Economic Society (fellow), National Vocational Guidance Association (professional member), American Academy of Political and Social Science, International Platform Association, American Economic Association, American Society for Public Administration (president, 1971-72). *Awards, honors:* National Science Foundation fellow, 1966; Coe Foundation fellow, 1963; Newspaper Fund award, 1964; National Defense Education fellow, 1967; Freedoms Foundation award, 1970.

WRITINGS: The American Indian: A Chronology and Fact Book, Oceana, 1971; *The American Indian, 1492-1976,* Oceana, 1977. Has written for WBYN-Radio and DeMont Television Network, 1945-47. Contributor to *New Mexico Transporter* and *Telephony.* Editor of *Occasional Papers* of New Mexico Council for the Social Studies and of *Round-Up.*

WORK IN PROGRESS: A History of Labor in New Mexico; The Value of Education to Pueblo Indians; An Alien in a Strange Land.

* * *

DENNIS, Peter (John) 1945-

PERSONAL: Born January 18, 1945, in Adelaide, South Australia; son of Arthur Phillip and Alice (Voitkun) Dennis. *Education:* University of Adelaide, B.A. (honors), 1966; Adelaide Teachers College, Diploma of Teaching, 1966; Duke University, M.A., 1968, Ph.D., 1970. *Office:* Department of History, Royal Military College, Kingston, Ontario, Canada K7L 2W3.

CAREER: Royal Military College of Canada, Kingston, Ontario, lecturer, 1969-70, assistant professor of history, 1970—. Visiting professor at University of Western Ontario, 1973-74. *Member:* International Commission of Military History (Canadian national commissioner), Royal Historical Society (fellow), American Historical Association, Royal Commonwealth Society, Canadian Historical Association.

WRITINGS: Decision by Default: Peacetime Conscription and British Defence, 1919-1939, Duke University Press, 1972; (editor with Adrian Preston) *Soldiers as Statesmen,* Harper, 1976; (editor with Preston) *Swords and Covenants,* Rowman & Littlefield, 1976.

WORK IN PROGRESS: The Territorial Army, 1906-40; co-editing the 1914-25 diaries of Sir H. Rider Haggard; studying British policy in Southeast Asia, 1944-48.

* * *

DENNY, M(aurice) Ray 1918-

PERSONAL: Born November 5, 1918, in Terre Haute, Ind.; son of Maurice R. and Marie C. (Williams) Denny; married Audrey Deeks, August 22, 1942; married second wife, Ruth Wehner, June 12, 1964; children: (first marriage) Michael, Richard, Douglas. *Education:* University of Michigan, B.S., 1942, M.A., 1943; University of Iowa, Ph.D., 1945. *Home:* 4565 Hawthorne Lane, Okemos, Mich. 48864. *Office:* Department of Psychology, Michigan State University, East Lansing, Mich. 48823.

CAREER: University of Oklahoma, Norman, instructor in psychology and counselor, 1945-46; Michigan State University, East Lansing, assistant professor, 1946-53, associate professor, 1953-57, professor of psychology, 1957—. Research consultant, Plymouth State Hospital and Training School, 1967-69. *Member:* American Psychological Association, American Association for the Advancement of Science, Psychonomic Society, Midwestern Psychological Association (president, 1973-74), Michigan Psychological Association (president, 1958, 1959), Sigma Xi, Psi Chi, Phi Sigma.

WRITINGS: (Contributor) Harvey A. Stevens and Rick Heber, editors, *Mental Retardation: A Review of Research,* University of Chicago Press, 1964; (with S. C. Ratner) *Comparative Psychology: Research in Animal Behavior,* Dorsey, 1964, revised edition, 1970; (contributor) F. R. Brush, editor, *Aversive Conditioning and Learning,* Academic Press, 1971; (contributor) Howard Kendler and Janet Spence, editors, *Essays in Neobehaviorism: A Memorial Volume to Kenneth W. Spence,* Appleton, 1971. Contributor to *Psychological Review, Intelligence, Journal of Experimental Analysis of Behavior,* and other publications.

WORK IN PROGRESS: Research on relaxation and relief (avoidance learning), and on experimental extinction.

* * *

DENTON, J(effrey) H(oward) 1939-

PERSONAL: Born May 24, 1939, in Yorkshire, England; son of Wilfred and Edna (Gray) Denton; married Marel Margaret Elizabeth Clifford (a child care officer), February 1, 1964; children: Erika R. E., Andrea C. M. *Education:* University of Hull, B.A. (first class honors), 1960; Cambridge University, Ph.D., 1966. *Home:* 62 Manchester Rd., Greenfield, Oldham, England. *Office:* Department of History, University of Manchester, Manchester, England.

CAREER: University of Manchester, Manchester, England, lecturer in history, 1965—.

WRITINGS: English Royal Free Chapels, 1100-1300: A Constitutional Study, Barnes & Noble, 1970.

WORK IN PROGRESS: Robert Winchesey and the Crown, 1294-1313; an edition of the unprinted letters of Winchesey.

* * *

DENUES, Celia 1915-

PERSONAL: Surname is accented on first syllable, rhymes with ''clues''; born September 14, 1915, in Johnson City, N.Y.; daughter of Frank Sidney (a dairy farmer) and Mae

(Sterling) Dunning; married Charles Denues, June 30, 1940; children: Caroline Mae (Mrs. Robert Bliss). *Education:* Asbury College, B.A., 1939; Stanford University, M.A., 1953. *Home:* 451 Baltusral Dr., Aptos, Calif. 95003.

CAREER: Teacher of English and drama in high schools of Louisville, Ky., 1943-45, Seattle, Wash., 1945-46, and San Jose, Calif., 1947-53; San Jose City College, San Jose, teacher of speech, 1952-58, counselor, beginning 1959. *Member:* California Teachers Association, Delta Kappa Gamma.

WRITINGS: (Contributor) *Behind the Scenes,* Dramatic Publishing, 1952; (with Lawrence H. Mouat) *How to Make a Speech and Like It,* Pacific Books, 1957, revised edition published as *To Make a Speech,* Pacific Books, 1966; *Career Perspective: Your Choice of Work,* Charles A. Jones Publishing, 1972, workbook, 1975.

*   *   *

DEPEW, Arthur M(cKinley) 1896-1976

PERSONAL: Born in 1896, in Jonesboro, Tenn. *Education:* Milligan College, B.A., 1922; Duke University, M.A., 1937; University of North Carolina, further graduate study, 1938-42.

CAREER: Protestant clergyman; Young Men's Christian Association (YMCA), Prague and Bratislava, Czechoslovakia, secretary, 1922; high school teacher and pastor of Christian Church (Disciples of Christ) in Tampa, Fla., 1922-24, West Palm Beach, Fla., 1924-41, and Selma, Ala., 1941-42; United Service Organizations, Jacksonville, Fla., director, 1943; pastor of churches in Jacksonville, 1943-48, Shreveport, La., 1949-53, and Joplin, Mo., 1954-56; missionary building supervisor in Congo, 1956-59; director of men's work and church development in North Carolina, 1959-60; pastor of church in St. Petersburgh, Fla., 1961-62; director of men's work, evangelism, and church development in Georgia, 1963-64; co-minister of Christian church in Tampa, 1964-65; Santa Monica Christian Towers (apartment for senior citizens), Santa Monica, Calif., administrator, 1965-71; interim minister of churches in Los Angeles, Calif., 1971-72.

WRITINGS: Cokesbury Party Book, Abingdon, 1932; *Cokesbury Stunt Book,* Abingdon, 1934; *Cokesbury Game Book,* Abingdon, 1939; *Cokesbury Question Book,* Abingdon, 1973.

SIDELIGHTS: Arthur Depew travelled in Egypt, the Holy Land, Europe, Latin America, the Philippines, Hong Kong, Japan, and Australia.†

(Died January 22, 1976)

*   *   *

de RIVERA, Joseph H(osmer) 1932-

PERSONAL: Born August 1, 1932, in Bremerton, Wash.; son of H. L. (a naval officer) and Ruth (Pritchard) de Rivera; married Margaret Rigdon (an educational researcher), September 7, 1954; children: Alice, Eric, Freda, Lucinda. *Education:* Attended Bowdoin College, 1949-50; Yale University, B.A., 1953; Stanford University, Ph.D., 1961. *Home:* 5 Bishop Ave., Worcester, Mass. 01603. *Office:* Department of Psychology, Clark University, Worcester, Mass. 01610.

CAREER: Dartmouth College, Hanover, N.H., instructor, 1960-62, assistant professor of psychology, 1962-63; New York University, New York, N.Y., assistant professor, 1963-68, associate professor of psychology, 1968-70; Clark

University, Worcester, Mass., associate professor, 1970-77, professor of psychology, 1977—. *Military service:* U.S. Navy Medical Service Corps, 1954-57; became lieutenant. *Member:* American Psychological Association (fellow), American Association of University Professors.

WRITINGS: The Psychological Dimension of Foreign Policy, C. E. Merrill, 1968; *Field Theory as Human Science,* Gardiner, 1976; *A Structural Theory of the Emotions,* International University Press, 1977.

WORK IN PROGRESS: Conceptual Encounter: Mapping Personal Experience.

*   *   *

DESATNICK, Robert L(awrence) 1931-

PERSONAL: Born August 16, 1931, in South Chicago, Ill.; son of John Andrew (a steelworker) and Elizabeth G. Desatnick; married Nancy Birk, September 10, 1955; children: Robert L., Jr., Bruce, Diane. *Education:* Franklin College of Indiana, B.S. (cum laude), 1954; Washington University, St. Louis, Mo., M.B.A., 1956. *Religion:* Baha'i.

CAREER: General Electric Co., New York City, division manager, 1956-66, Chicago, Ill., personnel manager, 1967-68; South Bend Lathe Co., South Bend, Ind., director of personnel, 1966-67; Booz, Allen & Hamilton (management consultants), Inc., Chicago, personnel executive, 1968-69; Indian Head, Inc. (textiles), New York City, director of long range planning and executive management, 1969-71; Otis Elevator Co., International, Inc., Paris, France, director of world-wide human resources, 1971-75; affiliated with Chase Manhattan Bank, New York City, 1975-78. Consultant on employee relations and industrial engineering to numerous other firms. Has taught at New York University, Loyola University, Indiana University, Roosevelt University, Marquette University, and University of Wisconsin. Consultant to U.S. poverty program, 1966. *Military service:* U.S. Army National Guard, Missouri, 1955-56, Michigan, 1957. *Member:* American Management Association, American Society for Personnel Administration, American Society for Training and Development, New York Management Development Forum, Sigma Alpha Eta (past president), Phi Alpha Theta.

WRITINGS: A Concise Guide to Management Development, American Management Association, 1970; *Innovative Human Resource Management,* American Management Association, 1972; (with Margo L. Bennett) *Human Resource Management in the Multinational Company,* edited by Raymond Maddison, Teakfield, 1977, Nichols Publishing, 1978. Contributor to *Personnel Journal.*

WORK IN PROGRESS: International Human Resource Management.†

*   *   *

DESCHNER, (Hans) Guenther 1941-

PERSONAL: Born May 14, 1941, in Fuerth, Germany; married Hilda Buts, 1964; children: Sieghild, Irmhild, Gunhild, Diethild, Guenther, Harald. *Education:* University of Erlangen-Nuernberg, Dr.phil., 1967. *Residence:* Koenigswinter, Germany. *Agent:* Ruth Liepmann, Maienburgweg 23, Zurich, Switzerland. *Office: Die Welt,* Godesberger Allee 99, Bonn, Germany.

CAREER: C. Bertelsmann-Verlag, Guetersloh, Germany, editor, 1965-68; Bertelsmann Sachbuch-Verlag, Guetersloh, senior editor, 1968-69, editor-in-chief, 1969-71; Weidenfeld & Nicolson, London, England, editor for short period, 1971;

Ullstein Verlag, Berlin, Germany, member of editorial branch, 1971-73; *Die Welt,* Bonn, Germany, leading political editor, 1973—.

WRITINGS: (Editor with O. E. Schueddekopf) *Der 2. Weltkrieg,* Bertelsmann, 1967; *Menschen im Ghetto,* Bertelsmann, 1969; *The Warsaw Uprising* (translated from the German by K. Rooney and Charles Whiting), Ballantine, 1972; *Reinhard Heydrich-Statthalter der totalen Macht,* Bechtle, 1977. Writer of radio scripts for Deutsch Welle (radio), Cologne; contributor to magazines.

SIDELIGHTS: Guenther Deschner acquired a fluency in Dutch-Flemish during a year's stay in Belgium; he also speaks English and Spanish.

*   *   *

DESFOSSES, Helen 1945-
(Helen Desfosses Cohn)

PERSONAL: Born April 24, 1945, in Dover, N.H.; daughter of Robert Louis and Agnes (Mater) Desfosses; married Daniel R. Cohn (a physicist), August 19, 1967 (divorced); children: Adam. *Education:* Attended Newton College of the Sacred Heart, 1961-63; Mount Holyoke College, B.A. (with distinction), 1965; Harvard University, M.A., 1967; Boston University, Ph.D., 1971. *Home:* 9A Thurlow Ter., Albany, N.Y. 12203. *Office:* 258 Administration Building, State University of New York, Albany, N.Y. 12222.

CAREER: Boston University, Boston, Mass., instructor, 1970-71, assistant professor of political science, 1971-72, chairperson of Soviet and East European Studies Program, 1970-72; Emmanuel College, Boston, associate professor of political science, 1972-74, acting chairperson of department of government, 1972-73, chairperson, 1973-74; Harvard University, Cambridge, Mass, research associate, 1974-76; University of Michigan—Dearborn, associate professor of social sciences, 1976-78, associate dean, College of Arts, Sciences, and Letters, 1976-78; State University of New York at Albany, dean of undergraduate studies and assistant vice-president for academic affairs, 1978—. Guest lecturer, University of Ghana, 1969. *Member:* American Political Science Association, American Association for the Advancement of Slavic Studies, African Studies Association (chairman of committee on the status of women, 1972-73). *Awards, honors:* Population Council grant, 1974-75; Ford Foundation Grant, 1975-76; National Academy of Science exchange scholar, 1975, for study in Rumania and Czechoslovakia.

WRITINGS: (Under name Helen Desfosses Cohn) *Soviet Policy toward Black Africa: The Focus on National Integration,* Praeger, 1971; (editor with Jacques Levesque, and contributor) *Socialism in the Third World,* Praeger, 1975; (contributor) Warren Weinstein, editor, *Sino-Soviet Aid to Africa,* Praeger, 1975, 2nd edition, 1978; (contributor) Bernard Eissenstat, editor, *The Soviet Union: The Seventies and Beyond,* Heath, 1975; (contributor) Leszek Kosinski, editor, *Demographic Developments in Eastern Europe,* Praeger, 1977. Contributor to *Osteuropa, Problems of Communism,* and other journals.

WORK IN PROGRESS: Editing *Africa and the Communist World* for Hoover Institution.

SIDELIGHTS: Helen Desfosses did research in the Soviet Union, Ghana, and Senegal, 1969, and in Hungary and Yugoslavia, 1971.

DEUTSCH, Karl W(olfgang) 1912-

PERSONAL: Born July 21, 1912, in Prague, Czechoslovakia; came to United States in 1938, naturalized in 1948; son of Martin M. and Maria (Scharf) Deutsch; married Ruth Slonitz, April 2, 1936; children: Mary Elizabeth Deutsch Edsall, Margaret Deutsch Carroll. *Education:* German University, Prague, Czechoslovakia, J.U.C., 1934; Charles University, Prague, J.U.Dr., 1938; Harvard University, M.A., 1941, Ph.D., 1951. *Office:* Department of Government, Harvard University, Cambridge, Mass. 02138.

CAREER: Massachusetts Institute of Technology, Cambridge, instructor, 1942-52, professor of political science, 1952-58; Yale University, New Haven, Conn., professor of government, 1958-67; Harvard University, Cambridge, Mass., professor of government, 1967—, Stanfield Professor of International Peace, 1971—, director of International Institute for Comparative Social Research (West Berlin). Lecturer, U.S. National War College, Inter-American Defense College, and other U.S. staff colleges, 1957—. Fulbright visiting professor, Goethe University, Frankfurt, 1968; visiting lecturer at Instituto de Pesquisas Sociais (Rio de Janeiro), 1968; visiting professor at Princeton University, 1953-54, University of Chicago, 1954, Yale University, 1957-58, University of Heidelberg, 1960, Nuffield College, Oxford, 1962, University of Geneva, 1970, 1971, and 1974, University of Mannheim, 1971, University of Paris, 1973, University of Zurich, 1976, and University of Michigan, 1977. Fellow, Center for Advanced Study in the Behavioral Sciences, 1956-57. American specialist for U.S. Department of State in India, 1962, Germany, 1964, 1967, Czechoslovakia and Poland, 1967, and Brazil, 1975.

MEMBER: International Political Science Association (vice-president, 1970-73; president, 1973—), American Political Science Association (president, 1969-70), National Academy of Sciences, American Academy of Arts and Sciences (fellow), Finnish Academy of Science, Austrian Academy of Science, Peace Science Association (president, 1973—), New England Political Science Association (president, 1965-66). *Awards, honors:* Guggenheim fellowship, 1954-55, 1971; International Exchange Fellow, International House of Tokyo, 1965; honorary doctor of economics and social sciences, University of Geneva, 1973; L.L.D., University of Michigan, 1975, and University of Illinois at Urbana-Champaign, 1976; Ph.D., University of Mannheim, 1977; Svdeten German Prize of Culture, 1977.

WRITINGS: Nationalism and Social Communication, M.I.T. Press and Wiley, 1953, revised edition, 1966; (with Sidney A. Burrell, Robert A. Kann, Maurice Lee, Jr., and others) *Political Community and the Northern Atlantic Area,* Princeton University Press, 1957; (with Lewis J. Edinger) *Germany Rejoins the Powers: Mass Opinion Interest Groups and Elites in Contemporary German Foreign Policy,* Octagon, 1959; *The Nerves of Government,* Free Press, 1963, revised edition, 1966; (with S. Finer, R. Macridis, and V. Aspaturian) *Modern Political Systems: Europe,* Prentice-Hall, 1963, 4th edition, 1978; (with B. M. Russett, Hayward R. Alker, Jr., and H. D. Lasswell) *World Handbook of Political and Social Indicators,* Yale University Press, 1964; (editor with Harry T. Moore) *Lewis Mumford, Human Prospect,* Southern Illinois University Press, 1965; *Arms Control and the Atlantic Alliance,* Wiley, 1967; *Analysis of International Relations,* Prentice-Hall, 1968, 2nd edition, 1978; (editor with Stanley Hoffman) *Relevance of International Law,* Schenkman, 1968; *Nationalism and Its Alternatives* (illustrated), Knopf, 1969; *Politics and Govern-*

ment: How People Decide Their Fate, Houghton, 1970, 2nd edition, 1974; (with R. L. Merritt) *Nationalism and National Development: An Interdisciplinary Bibliography,* M.I.T. Press, 1970; (with Hoffman) *The Relevance of International Law,* Anchor, 1968, 2nd edition, 1971; (with Alker and A. Stoetzel) *Mathematical Approaches to Politics,* American Elsevier, 1973; (co-author) *Mathematical Political Analysis,* Olzog (Munich), 1975; (with Bruno Fritsch and others) *Problems of World Modelling,* Ballinger, 1977; *Tides among Nations,* Free Press, 1978. Member of editorial board, *Behavioral Science,* and *Comparative Studies in Society and History;* member of editorial advisory board, *Social Sciences Citation Index.*

* * *

DEVINE, Janice 1909(?)-1973

1909(?)—February 3, 1973; American editor, publicity manager, and author. Obituaries: *New York Times,* February 9, 1973; *Publishers Weekly,* March 5, 1973.

* * *

DEVLETOGLOU, Nicos E. 1936-

PERSONAL: Born February 15, 1936, in Athens, Greece; son of Eudokimos (a businessman) and Anastasia (Hidiroglou) Devletoglou; married Lana Mandilas, 1971. *Education:* McGill University, B.A. (with first class honors), 1959; University of California, Berkeley, M.A., 1961; University of London, Ph.D., 1964. *Politics:* Conservative. *Religion:* Greek Orthodox.

CAREER: University of Athens, Athens, Greece, professor of economics, 1959-66; University of London, London School of Economics and Political Science, London, England, professor of economics, 1966-73; University of Athens, School of Law, Athens, Greece, professor of economics, 1973-75. Director of family-held companies. *Awards, honors:* Grand Master of the Laws of Ecumenical Patriarchate, Constantinople, 1971.

WRITINGS: Montesquieu and the Wealth of Nations, Center of Economic Research (Athens), 1963; (with James M. Buchanan) *Academia in Anarchy: An Economic Diagnosis,* Basic Books, 1970; *Consumer Behavior: An Experiment in Analytical Economics,* Harper, 1971. Frequent contributor to periodicals, newspapers, and scholarly journals.

WORK IN PROGRESS: Books and articles on behavioral economics, economic theory, and political science.

SIDELIGHTS: Academia in Anarchy has been described as a "wittily written" and "deeply conservative" critique of university structure from an economics point of view. H. J. Noah noted that in the book "the university appears as an economic freak literally asking for and deserving its current fundamental turmoil. . . . The authors argue that attention to a few elementary economic principles is a minimum requirement for the restoration of organizational health to the universities."

AVOCATIONAL INTERESTS: Sports, especially water skiing.

BIOGRAPHICAL/CRITICAL SOURCES: Saturday Review, February 21, 1970; *National Review,* June 30, 1970; *The Times* (London), February 24, 1975.†

* * *

DEWEY, Edward R(ussell) 1895-1978

PERSONAL: Born May 2, 1895, in Elmira, N.Y.; son of Edward Wilkens (an industrial developer) and Hattie (Russell) Dewey; married Elenore Stratton, September 22, 1922 (divorced, 1930); married Catherine Doak, February 13, 1935; children: (first marriage) Barbara Whitnah, Edward Stratton. *Education:* Harvard University, S.B. (cum laude), 1920. *Politics:* Independent. *Religion:* Independent. *Home:* 400 Fourth St., Oakmont, Pa. 15139. *Agent:* Julian Bach, Jr., 3 East 48th St., New York, N.Y. 10017. *Office:* Foundation for the Study of Cycles, 124 South Highland, Pittsburgh, Pa. 15206.

CAREER: Instructor at University of California, Los Angeles, and University of Southern California, Los Angeles, 1927-29; U.S. Bureau of the Census, Washington, D.C., statistical posts, 1929-31; U.S. Department of Commerce, Washington, D.C., assistant to director, Bureau of Foreign and Domestic Commerce, 1931-33; National Industrial Conference Board (now The Conference Board), New York, N.Y., assistant director, Institute of Applied Economics, 1963; independent industrial consultant, 1937-39; Foundation for the Study of Cycles, Pittsburgh, Pa., director, 1940-67, executive vice-president, 1963-67, vice-chairman, 1967-69, 1973-78, president, 1969-73. Adjunct research professor, University of Pittsburgh, 1964-78; adminstrator, International Committee for Research and Study of Factors of the Environment, 1968-78; co-director of Center for Interdisciplinary Cycle Research, 1973-78. *Member:* World Academy of Art and Science (fellow), International Society of Biometerology, American Association for the Advancement of Science, New York Academy of Sciences, Cosmos Club (Washington, D.C.), General Society of Mayflower Descendants. *Awards, honors:* Biometerology Research Foundation award, 1972.

WRITINGS: (With Edwin F Dakin) *Cycles: The Science of Prediction,* Holt, 1947, 2nd edition published as *Cycles: The Science of Prediction, with 1950 Postscript,* 1949; *Cycles: Selected Writings,* Foundation for the Study of Cycles, 1970; (with Og Mandino) *Cycles: The Mysterious Forces that Trigger Events,* Hawthorn, 1971.

Research reports published by Foundation for the Study of Cycles include: *The 17, 7-Year Cycle in War, 600 B.C.-A.D. 1957,* 1964; *The "17-1/3 Year" Cycle in Lake Saki Varves 2295 B.C.-A.D. 1894,* 1964; *The 9, 6-year Cycle,* 1965. Writer of more than 650 other scientific papers and articles. Member of editorial board, *Journal of Interdisciplinary Cycle Research,* 1970-78.

WORK IN PROGRESS: Research relating to rhythmic cycles in many aspects of natural and social science.

BIOGRAPHICAL/CRITICAL SOURCES: New Yorker, "Profile," February 3, 1963.†

(Died February 6, 1978)

* * *

DHOKALIA, (Ramaa) Prasad 1925-

PERSONAL: Born October 17, 1925, in Kota, India; son of Ram Chandra (a government official) and Bhagwatidevi (Sriwastava) Dhokalia; married Shyam Kumari Beohar, May 20, 1948; children: Kumkum, Gunjan, Vivek, Bala, Vikram. *Education:* Allahabad University, B.A., 1946, M.A., 1948, LL.B., 1949; University of Manchester, Ph.D., 1964. *Politics:* Liberal Democrat. *Religion:* Hindu. *Home:* 24 Bharat Housing Society, Nagpur Rd., Jabalpur, Madhya Pradesh, India. *Office:* Banaras Hindu University, Malviyanagar, Varansi 5, India 221005.

CAREER: Allahabad University, Allahabad, India, lecturer, 1949-54, assistant professor of international law and jurisprudence, 1954-64; Banaras Hindu University, Varansi, India, senior reader in law, 1964-72, professor of international law and jurisprudence, 1972—, dean of law school, 1977—. *Member:* International Law Association, Commonwealth Law Association, Commonwealth Legal Education Association, Indian Society of International Law, United Nations Association, Apex.

WRITINGS: Village Panchayats in Uttar Pradesh (monograph), All India Institute of Local Fef Government (Bombay), 1953; *International Law,* Central Book Depot (Allahabad), 1963, revised edition, 1973; *The Codificaiton of Public International Law,* Manchester University Press, 1970, Oceana, 1971. Also author of *Democracy in India: Challenges and Perspectives,* 1975, *Human Rights in India,* 1978, *Law as an Instrument of Development,* 1979, and of *Interaction of Science, Technology, and Law in India,* 1979. Editor-in-chief, *Banaras Law Journal,* 1973—.

WORK IN PROGRESS: Modern Law of Treaties; International Law in the Past and Contemporary Practice of India.

SIDELIGHTS: Prasad Dhokalia told *CA:* "I believe that universal harmony on earth has a cosmic significance and law and its institutions are the human instruments controlled by human agencies for attainment of social harmony and development in human groups—local, regional, national, and transnational—by conscious, rational and deliberate striving. Whilst contrariness or variety in human groups should be accepted as an inherent law of life without degenerating into profanity and destruction, unfortunately, our history is replete with aberrations of sectarianism, bigotry, fanaticism, racism, communalism, and even nationalism which have long possessed this beautiful earth to drench it with human blood and destroy civilizations. I believe in promoting a common law of mankind which can enable us to participate in the grand symphony, to see oneness in the universe and oneness of life, and to find unity between men and men, races and races, high and low, and rich and poor. As a writer on law in general and international law in particular, I have been moved by the goal of inculcating in the readers the attitude and the spirit that can make it possible for the human race to grow together into an harmonious single family as the only alternative to destroying mankind. My book on *The Codification of Public International Law* is the story of an evolving common law of mankind."

AVOCATIONAL INTERESTS: Gardening, photography, painting, travel.

* * *

DICK, William M(ilner) 1933-

PERSONAL: Born December 7, 1933, in Dalkeith, Scotland; son of Robert and Agnes (Milner) Dick; married Madelyn Bergen (a professor), June 12, 1967; children: Alexander John, Eleanor Pauline. *Education:* University of Edinburgh, M.A., 1958; University of Oregon, M.A., 1962; University of Toronto, Ph.D., 1966. *Home:* 38 Chaplin Crescent, Toronto, Ontario, Canada M5P 1A1. *Office:* Scarborough College, University of Toronto, West Hill, Ontario, Canada.

CAREER: Ohio State University, Columbus, instructor, 1964-65; University of Toronto, Toronto, Ontario, instructor, 1965-67, assistant professor, 1967-72, associate professor of American history, 1972—.

WRITINGS: Labor and Socialism in America: The Gompers Era, Kennikat, 1972.

WORK IN PROGRESS: Research on national culture and the working class.

* * *

DICKINSON, Peter 1927-
(Malcolm de Brissac)

PERSONAL: Born December 16, 1927, in Livingstone, Northern Rhodesia (now Zambia); son of Richard Sebastian Willoughby (a colonial civil servant) and Nancy (Lovemore) Dickinson; married Mary Rose Barnard (an artist), April 20, 1953; children: Philippa, Polly, John, James. *Education:* Attended Eton College, five years; King's College, Cambridge, B.A., 1951. *Politics:* "Leftish." *Religion:* "Lapsed Anglican." *Home:* 33 Queensdale Rd., London W11 4SB, England.

CAREER: Writer of mystery novels and juvenile books. Assistant editor of *Punch,* London, England, 1952-69. *Military service:* British Army, 1946-48 ("chaotic period as a conscript"). *Awards, honors:* Crime Writer's Association Award for best mystery of the year, 1968, for *Skin Deep,* and 1969, for *A Pride of Heroes; Emma Tupper's Diary* was an American Library Association Notable Book in 1971.

WRITINGS—Adult mystery novels: *The Glass Sided Ants' Nest,* Harper, 1968 (published in England as *Skin Deep,* Hodder & Stoughton, 1968); *The Old English Peep Show,* Harper, 1969 (published in England as *A Pride of Heroes,* Hodder & Stoughton, 1969); *The Sinful Stones,* Harper, 1970 (published in England as *The Seals,* Hodder & Stoughton, 1970); *Sleep and His Brother,* Harper, 1971; *The Lizard in the Cup,* Harper, 1972; *The Green Gene,* Pantheon, 1973; *The Poison Oracle,* Pantheon, 1974; *The Lively Dead,* Pantheon, 1975; *King and Joker,* Pantheon, 1976; *Walking Dead,* Pantheon, 1977.

Books for young people: *Emma Tupper's Diary* (Junior Literary Guild selection), Little Brown, 1971; *The Dancing Bear,* Gollancz, 1972, Little, Brown, 1973; *Chance, Luck and Destiny,* Little, Brown, 1973; *The Gift,* Little, Brown, 1975; *The Blue Hawk,* Little, Brown, 1976. Also author of "Changes" trilogy, including: *The Weathermonger,* Gollancz, 1968, Little, Brown, 1969, *Heartease* (Junior Literary Guild selection), illustrated by Robert Hales, Little, Brown, 1969, and *The Iron Lion,* Little, Brown, 1972.

Writer of science fiction-thriller series for children, for British Broadcasting Corp. television. Contributor to *Atlantic, Tatler,* and other periodicals.

SIDELIGHTS: Peter Dickinson says that he is "fascinated by anything old, no matter how ugly. Enjoy manual labour, the English language, argument, time, dotty hypotheses. Concerned about social justice and the maiming of the future. Greedy. My books come if I'm lucky, and I don't like talking about them for fear it will spoil my luck."

BIOGRAPHICAL/CRITICAL SOURCES: Children's Book World, November 8, 1970.

* * *

DIHOFF, Gretchen 1942-

PERSONAL: Born January 22, 1942, in Allentown, Pa.; daughter of Clayton T. (a chemical engineer) and Mary (Johnson) Kleppinger; married Ivan Dihoff, March 25, 1961 (divorced); children: Ayo, Tanya. *Education:* Attended Muhlenberg College, 1959-62; University of Pittsburgh, B.A., 1963; University of Wisconsin, additional study, 1970-72, 1973-74. *Politics:* Independent.

CAREER: Taught English and French in Nigeria, 1963-65, and Spain, 1965-66.

WRITINGS: Katsina: Profile of a Nigerian City, Praeger, 1970. Contributor to *African Arts.*

WORK IN PROGRESS: The Nigerians: How They Live and Work, for David & Charles; translations of Fulani tales.

SIDELIGHTS: Gretchen Dihoff is fluent in French and Spanish; has some competence in Fulani, Hausa, and Yoruba.††

* * *

DiLELLO, Richard 1945-

PERSONAL: Born September 28, 1945, in New York, N.Y.; son of Francesco Paulo (a restaurateur) and Jewel (Plaitano) DiLello. *Education:* Educated in New York, N.Y., and Paris, France. *Agent:* Monica McCall, International Creative Management, 40 West 57th St., New York, N.Y. 10019.

CAREER: Professional photographer.

WRITINGS: (Illustrated with photographs by the author) *The Longest Cocktail Party,* Playboy Press, 1972.

WORK IN PROGRESS: Novels and biographies; television and motion picture scripts.

AVOCATIONAL INTERESTS: Travel (Europe, North Africa).†

* * *

DILLARD, J(oey) L(ee) 1924-

PERSONAL: Born June 26, 1924, in Grand Saline, Tex.; son of Marvin L. (a wholesaler of produce) and Thelma (Aly) Dillard; married Jane Reed Montgomery, December 28, 1958 (divorced, 1961); married Margie Ivey (an editor), December 22, 1972; children: (first marriage) Kenneth Joseph. *Education:* Southern Methodist University, B.A. (with highest honors), 1946, M.A., 1951; University of Texas, Ph.D., 1956. *Politics:* Liberal Democrat. *Religion:* "Non-conformist."

CAREER: Southern Methodist University, Dallas, Tex., instructor in English, 1949-51; Texas College of Arts and Industries (now Texas A & I University), Kingsville, associate professor of English, 1955-59; Inter-American University, San German, P.R., Teacher of English to Speakers of Other Languages (TESOL) program, director, 1959-60; U.S. Agency for International Development, Yaounde, Cameroun, descriptive linguist, 1963-64; Lamar State College of Technology (now Lamar University), Beaumont, Tex., associate professor of English, 1965-66; Trinity College, Washington, D.C., lecturer in dialectology, 1966-67; University Officielle de Bujumbura, Bujumbura, Burundi, Fulbright lecturer in TESOL program, 1967-68; Yeshiva University, Ferkauf Graduate School of Humanities and Social Sciences, New York, N.Y., visiting lecturer in linguistics, 1968-71. Visiting professor of sociolinguistics, Georgetown University, 1967; visiting professor of English, State University of New York College at Potsdam, summer, 1968; visiting professor of linguistics, University of Southern California, summer, 1969, and Linguistics Institute, University of North Carolina, summer, 1972. Fulbright lecturer, Universidad Central Del Ecuador, Quito, Ecuador, 1959-60. Director of urban language study for District of Columbia, 1966-67. *Military service:* U.S. Navy, 1943-45. *Member:* American Name Society, International P.E.N., International Linguistic Society, Southeastern Conference on Lin-

guistics, Phi Beta Kappa. *Awards, honors:* American Council of Learned Societies grant, University of North Carolina, summer, 1960.

WRITINGS: (With W. P. Lehmann) *The Alliteration of the Edda,* Department of Germanic Languages, University of Texas, 1954; *Afro-American Vehicle and Other Names,* Institute of Caribbean Studies, 1965; (contributor) E. B. Atwood and A. A. Hill, editors, *Language, Literature, and Culture of the Middle Ages and Later,* University of Texas at Austin, 1969; (contributor) John Szwed and Norman Whitten, editors, *Afro-American Anthropology: Current Perspectives,* Free Press, 1970; (contributor) Dell Hymes, editor, *Pidginization and Creolization of Language,* Cambridge University Press, 1971; *Black English: Its History and Usage in the United States,* Random House, 1972; *All American English,* Random House, 1975; (editor) *Perspectives on Black English,* Mouton, 1975; *American Talk: Where Our Words Came From,* Random House, 1976; *Lexicon of Black English,* Seabury, 1977. Contributor to *Linguistic-Cultural Differences and American Education,* 1969; also contributor to proceedings. Contributor of about thirty articles and reviews to academic journals, including *Language Learning, Caribbean Studies, Names,* and *Nueva Revista.*

WORK IN PROGRESS: Research on maritime contact languages, history of American English, and Afro American language and culture.†

* * *

DIMONT, Madelon 1938-

PERSONAL: Surname is pronounced *Die*-mont; born July 29, 1938, in Vienna, Austria; daughter of Charles Francis Dimont (a journalist) and Penelope (Fletcher) Dimont Mortimer. *Education:* Newnham College, Cambridge, Degree in Law (honors), 1959. *Politics:* Liberal. *Home:* Via San Damaso 51, Rome 00165, Italy. *Agent:* A. D. Peters, 10 Buckingham St., London WC2N 6BU, England.

CAREER: London Daily Mirror, Rome, Italy, staff journalist, 1968-72, chief of Rome bureau beginning 1972. *Member:* Associazione della Stampa Estera in Italia (member of directive council, 1972-73).

WRITINGS: Darling Pericles, Atheneum, 1972.

WORK IN PROGRESS: Queen Zenobia of Palmyra.†

* * *

DINGS, John (Garetson) 1939-

PERSONAL: Born January 13, 1939, in Covina, Calif.; son of McClelland G. (a geologist) and Elizabeth (Griffith) Dings; married Prudence Tully, June 30, 1961; children: Jonathan, Susan, Alison, Abigail. *Education:* Carleton College, B.A., 1961; Cornell University, M.A., 1962, Ph.D., 1968. *Residence:* Buffalo, N.Y. *Office:* Department of English, 306 Clemens Hall, State University of New York at Buffalo, Buffalo, N.Y. 14260.

CAREER: Washington University, St. Louis, Mo., instructor, 1965-67, assistant professor of English, 1967-68; State University of New York at Buffalo, assistant professor, 1968-72, associate professor of English, 1972—. *Military service:* U.S. Army Reserve, 1956-64.

WRITINGS: The Mind in Its Place: Wordsworth, "Michael," and the Poetry of 1800, University of Salzburg, 1973. Contributor to *Paunch* magazine.

WORK IN PROGRESS: Research on literature and society in England, 1780-1860.

DINKMEYER, Don C. 1924-

PERSONAL: Born January 20, 1924, in Evanston, Ill.; son of Don and Lillian Dinkmeyer; married Elvira Jane Succop, June 11, 1949; children: Don, James. *Education:* University of Nebraska, B.S., 1946; Northwestern University, M.A., 1948; Michigan State University, Ph.D., 1958; Alfred Adler Institute, certificate in psychotherapy, 1963. *Office address:* Box 8268, Coral Springs, Fla. 33065.

CAREER: DePaul University, Chicago, Ill., professor of educational psychology and counseling, 1966-73; Communication and Motivation Training Institute, Coral Springs, Fla., president, 1973—. *Member:* American Personnel and Guidance Association, American Psychological Association, American Society of Adlerian Psychology, American Group Psychotherapy Association.

WRITINGS: (With Rudolf Dreikurs) *Encouraging Children to Learn: The Encouragement Process,* Prentice-Hall, 1963; *Child Development: The Emerging Self,* Prentice-Hall, 1965; *Guidance and Counseling in the Elementary School: Readings in Theory and Practice,* Holt, 1968; (with Edson Caldwell) *Developmental Counseling and Guidance: A Comprehensive School Approach,* McGraw, 1970; (with James Muro) *Group Counseling: Theory and Practice,* F. T. Peacock, 1971; (with Gary D. McKay) *Raising a Responsible Child: Practical Steps to Successful Family Relationships,* Simon & Schuster, 1973; (with Jon Carlson) *Consulting: Facilitating Human Potential and Change Processes,* C. E. Merrill, 1973; *Developing Understanding of Self and Others,* American Guidance Service, Part I, 1970, Part II, 1973; (with Carlson) *Consultation,* Wiley, 1975; (with McKay) *Systematic Training for Effective Parenting,* American Guidance Service, 1976; (with Muro) *Counseling in the Elementary and Middle School,* W. C. Brown, 1977; (with son, Don Dinkmeyer, Jr., and W. L. Pew) *Adlerian Counseling and Psychotherapy,* Brooks/ Cole, 1978.

* * *

DION, Gerard 1912-

PERSONAL: Born December 12, 1912, in Ste. Cecile, Quebec, Canada; son of Albert and Georgianna (Leblanc) Dion. *Education:* Laval University, B.A., 1935, L.Th., 1939, M.S., 1943, L.Ph., 1943. *Politics:* Independent. *Religion:* Roman Catholic. *Home:* 909 Mgr. Grandin, Quebec, Quebec, Canada G1V 3X8. *Office:* Department of Industrial Relations, Laval University, Quebec, Quebec, Canada.

CAREER: Laval University, Quebec, Quebec, professor of industrial relations, 1944—, assistant director and director of department, 1947-62. Member of Task Force on Industrial Relations, 1966-68; president, Canadian Textile Labour-Management Committee, 1967—. Member of Economic Council of Canada, 1946—, and Social Sciences and Humanities Research Council of Canada, 1948—. *Member:* Royal Society of Canada (fellow), Canadian Industrial Relations Research Institute (president, 1968), Industrial Relations Research Association, Canadian Sociology and Anthropology Association, Industrial Relations Counselors Association, Association Internationale des relations professionnelles. *Awards, honors:* Officer, Order of Canada; received LL.D. from McGill University, 1945, University of British Columbia, 1946, and University of Toronto, 1948.

WRITINGS: Glossary of Terms Used in Industrial Relations (in English and French), Presses de l'Universite Laval, 1972, 2nd edition, 1975; (editor) *Dictionnaire canadien des*

relations du travail, Presses de l'Universite Laval, 1976. Editor, *Relations Industrielles,* 1946—.

* * *

DISSTON, Harry 1899-
  (H.D.N. Hill)

PERSONAL: Born November 23, 1899, in Red Bank, N.J.; son of Eugene John and Frances Matilda Disston Kauffmann; married Valerie Duval, April 30, 1930 (died, 1951); married Catherine Sitler, August 26, 1960; children: (first marriage) Robin J., Geoffrey W. *Education:* Amherst College, A.B., 1921; U.S. Army Command and General Staff College, graduate, 1943. *Politics:* Republican. *Religion:* Episcopalian. *Home:* Hidden Hill Farm, Keswick, Va. 22947. *Office:* AMVEST Leasing Corp., 1 Boar's Head Pl., Charlottesville, Va. 22903.

CAREER: New York Telephone Co., New York City, supervisory and engineering positions, 1921-32; American Telephone & Telegraph Co., New York City, advisory staff, 1932-40, 1945-60; University of Virginia, Charlottesville, placement administrator of Graduate School of Business Administration, 1965-69, chairman of development committee, 1967-69; AMVEST Leasing Corp., Charlottesville, Va., director, horse and cattle leasing, 1972—. *Military service:* New York National Guard (Army), 1921-60; active service, 1940-45; became brigadier general; received Bronze Star with oak leaf cluster, Legion of Merit, Order of Bolivar (Venezuela), and Medal of Merit with Swords (Free Poland). *Member:* Pilgrims of United States, American Red Cross (Central Virginia Branch, director, 1968—, vice-president, 1971-72), American Horse Shows Association (judge; steward and technical delegate), American Legion, Military Order of Foreign Wars, United States Pony Clubs (governor), St. Georges Society, St. Andrews Society, Phi Beta Kappa, Phi Kappa Psi, Union Club of New York, Church Club of New York, Jack Jenett Bridle Trails Club (president, 1964—), Keswick Hunt Club, Greencroft Club.

WRITINGS: Equestionnaire, A. S. Barnes, 1936, revised edition, 1947; *Riding Rhymes for Young Riders,* Wheelwright, 1951; *Quiz Questions for the U.S. Pony Club,* privately printed, 1960, revised edition, 1976; *Know about Horses,* Devin Adair, 1961; *Horse and Rider,* A. S. Barnes, 1964; *Handbook for the Novice Horseman,* Jarman Press, 1965; *Dressage Writers and Reading,* privately printed, 1970; *Elementary Dressage,* A. S. Barnes, 1970; *Beginning Polo,* A. S. Barnes, 1973; *Better Wear Out Than Rust Out,* A. S. Barnes, 1978. Contributor to *Encyclopaedia Britannica,* and to *Polo, Polo Monthly* (England), *Horse and Horseman, Park Avenue Social Review, Military Digest, Infantry Journal, Cavalry Journal, Chronicle of the Horse, Virginia Horse,* and *Dressage.* Writer of regular column in *Central Virginian* and *Rural Virginia,* both under pseudonym H.D.N. Hill.

WORK IN PROGRESS: Economics of the Horse Industry in Virginia.

* * *

DITZEL, Paul C(alvin) 1926-

PERSONAL: Born November 11, 1926, in Buffalo, N.Y.; son of Shirley Michael and Mildred (Henry) Ditzel; married second wife, Merrilyn Holly, June 2, 1965 (divorced); children: Denise (Mrs. Ron Krivitsky), Debbie (Mrs. Roy Stradley III), Bradley, Stacey. *Education:* Northwestern University, B.S., 1950, M.S., 1951. *Address:* Box 814, Northridge, Calif. 91324. *Agent:* Curtis Brown, Ltd., 575 Madison Ave., New York, N.Y. 10022.

CAREER: Free-lance writer, 1950—. Instructor in journalism, California State University, Northridge. Member, Los Angeles Arson Suppression Task Force. *Military service:* U.S. Marine Corps, 1946-48; became sergeant. *Member:* American Society of Journalists and Authors (chairman, Southern California chapter). *Awards, honors:* Received United Firefighters of Los Angeles award.

WRITINGS: Firefighting: A New Look in the Old Firehouse, Van Nostrand, 1969; *Fire Alarm,* Van Nostrand, 1969; *Emergency Ambulance,* Reilly & Lee, 1972; *Fire Engines, Firefighters: The Men, Equipment and Machines, from Colonial Days to the Present,* Crown, 1976; *How They Built Our National Monuments,* Bobbs-Merrill, 1976; *Railroad Yard,* Messner, 1977. Contributor of more than five hundred articles to magazines. Staff correspondent, *Fire Engineering,* 1950—, and *Motorcycle Dealer News,* 1969—.

WORK IN PROGRESS: Writing on arson, American business, urban transportation, and American history.

* * *

DITZION, Sidney 1908-1975

PERSONAL: Born November 23, 1908, in Philadelphia, Pa.; son of Abraham (a designer) and Lena (Diamond) Ditzion; married Grace Finke (a teacher), January 24, 1931; children: Lynn Shaw, Bruce R. *Education:* College of the City of New York (now City College of the City University of New York), A.B., 1929, M.S., 1938; Columbia University, B.S. in L.S., 1934, Ph.D., 1945. *Home:* 3635 Johnson Ave., New York, N.Y. 10463.

CAREER: City College of the City University of New York, New York, N.Y., assistant to librarian, 1928-39, assistant librarian, 1949-59, assistant professor of history, 1960-64, associate professor, 1965-70, professor, 1971-74. Visiting summer professor of librarianship and history, State University of New York at Albany, 1949, 1951, 1953, 1955. *Member:* American Historical Association, Organization of American Historians, American Studies Association (secretary-treasurer, Metropolitan chapter, 1965-66, chairman, 1966-67).

WRITINGS: Arsenals of a Democratic Culture: A Social History of the American Public Library Movement in New England and the Middle States from 1850 to 1900 (foreword by Merle Curti), American Library Association, 1947, reprinted, 1966; *Marriage, Morals and Sex in America: A History of Ideas,* Bookman Associates, 1953, expanded edition, Octagon, 1969.

Contributor: Emily M. Danton, editor, *Pioneering Leaders in Librarianship,* American Library Association, 1953; Harold Eiberson, compiler, *Sources for the Study of the New York Area: A Bibliographic Essay,* Institute of New York Area Studies, City College, 1958; J. D. Marshall, compiler, *An American Library History Reader,* Shoe String, 1961; Conrad Rawski, editor, *Toward a Theory of Librarianship,* Scarecrow, 1973. Contributor to *Encyclopedia of Sexual Behavior, Guide to Historical Literature,* and *Dictionary of American Biography;* contributor of articles and reviews to library and literary journals.

WORK IN PROGRESS: The First Three Hundred Years, a large-scale social history of America from colonial times to 1920.†

(Died June 28, 1975)

* * *

DOBBINS, Marybelle King 1900-

PERSONAL: Born September 6, 1900, in Muncie, Ind.; daughter of Arthur Daniel and Grace Hamilton (Campbell) King; married William Henry Dobbins (an attorney), June 6, 1925 (died, 1954); children: John Bennett. *Education:* Indiana University, A.B., 1923, M.S., 1960; also studied at Ball State University, 1958, 1959. *Politics:* Republican. *Religion:* Presbyterian. *Home:* 611 Lafayette Ave., Columbus, Ind. 47201. *Agent:* John Bennett Dobbins, 1636 Southwest 19th Ter., Miami, Fla. 33145.

CAREER: High school history teacher in Columbus, Ind., 1923-25; teacher of language arts in junior high schools, 1958-66. *Member:* National Retired Teachers Association, Indiana State Teachers Association, Indiana State Historical Society, Bartholomew County Teachers Association, Bartholomew County Historical Society, Daughters of the American Revolution, Kappa Kappa Gamma Alumnae Club, Psi Iota Xi.

WRITINGS: Our First Fifty Years, privately printed, 1954; *Tim Tuttle and the Tomatoes* (juvenile), photographs by son, John Bennett Dobbins, Denison, 1971; (editor with Robert J. Marshall and Mildred Murray, and contributor) *History of Bartholomew County,* privately printed, 1973.

WORK IN PROGRESS: Tim Tuttle and the Wren House, with son, John Bennett Dobbins; *Gracie Campbell: Dakota Pioneer* (tentative title), for children.

AVOCATIONAL INTERESTS: Travel.††

* * *

DODD, Stuart C(arter) 1900-1975

PERSONAL: Born October 3, 1900, in Jalas, Turkey; son of William Schauffler (a physician and missionary) and Mary L. (Carter) Dodd; married Elizabeth M. Cairns, July 28, 1928; children: Peter C., Bruce C. *Education:* Princeton University, B.S. (magna cum laude), 1922, M.A., 1924, Ph.D., 1926. *Politics:* Independent. *Religion:* "Humanist." *Home:* 1140 38th Ave., Seattle, Wash. 98122. *Office:* Department of Sociology, University of Washington, Seattle, Wash. 98105.

CAREER: State Home for Boys, Jamesburg, N.J., psychologist, 1922-23; American University of Beirut, Beirut, Lebanon, adjunct professor, 1927-30, associate professor, 1930-36, professor of sociology, 1936-47, director of social science research section, 1929-47; University of Washington, Seattle, Walker Ames Lecturer in Sociology, 1946, research professor of sociology, 1947-71, professor emeritus, 1971-75, director of Washington Public Opinion Laboratory, 1947-61. National research fellow, Princeton University, 1923-26, and University of London, 1926-27; researcher, Harvard University, 1934-35; lecturer in sociology, University of New Mexico, 1942. *Military service:* U.S. Army, director of surveys, 1943-44; served in Sicily; became lieutenant colonel.

MEMBER: World Association for Public Opinion Research (secretary-treasurer, 1950-54), International Society for General Semantics, Sociological Research Association, Sociometric Association, American Sociological Association, American Statistical Association, American Association for Public Opinion Research, American Psychological Association, Institute of Mathematical Statistics, Society for General Systems Research, American Humanist Association (vice-president, 1960-61), Operations Research Society of America, Behavioral Research Council (secretary, 1960-66), Pacific Sociological Association (president, 1952-53), Northwest Association for Public Opinion Research (president, 1964-66), Phi Beta Kappa. *Awards, honors:*

Rockefeller Foundation fellowship, Biometrika Laboratory, London, England, 1926-27; decorated with Gold Order of the Cedar for Public Instruction, from Republic of Lebanon, 1947; honorable mention for first sociological prize for scientific research from American Association for the Advancement of Science, 1952; merit awards from American Humanist Association, 1963, and Organization of Arab Students, 1966.

WRITINGS: International Group Mental Tests, Princeton University Press, 1926; *Social Relationships in the Near East*, American University of Beirut, 1931, 2nd revised and enlarged edition, 1940, published as *Social Relations in the Near East*, AMS Press, 1975; (editor) *A Post War Bibliography of the Near Eastern Mandates*, American University of Beirut, 1933; *A Controlled Experiment on Rural Hygiene in Syria*, American University of Beirut, 1934; *Dimensions of Society*, Macmillan, 1942; *A Pioneer Radio Poll in Lebanon, Syria, and Palestine*, Government Press (Jerusalem), 1943; *Surveys of Public Opinion Held in Sicily*, privately printed for Psychological Warfare Branch of Allied Forces Headquarters, 1944; *Systematic Social Science*, American University of Beirut, 1947.

(Contributor) William N. Locke and A. Donald Booth, editors, *Machine Translation of Languages*, Wiley, 1955; (contributor) Baljit Singh, editor, *Frontiers of Social Science*, Macmillan (London), 1955; *Probable Acts of Men*, two volumes, State University of Iowa, 1963; *Systemed Studies in Behavioral Sciences: Sociological Microjournal*, Volume IV, University of Copenhagen, 1970.

Contributor to annals, symposia, research studies, memorial volumes, bulletins, conferences, and transactions. Contributor of about a hundred fifty articles to scientific journals, including *Systematics, Journal of Human Relations, Sociological Microjournal, Religious Humanism, Journal of Broadcasting, Arab Journal*, and *American Behavioral Scientist*.

WORK IN PROGRESS: Systemed Studies on Human Transactions, a collection of articles in four volumes.†

(Died December 26, 1975)

*   *   *

DOERR, Arthur H(arry) 1924-

PERSONAL: Born August 28, 1924, in Johnston City, Ill.; son of Arthur H. (a miner) and Nettie (Felts) Doerr; married Dale Lantrip, August 15, 1947; children: Marc M. *Education:* Attended University of California, Berkeley, 1943-44; Southern Illinois University, B.A. (with high honors), 1947; Indiana University, M.A., 1948; Northwestern University, Ph.D., 1951. *Home:* 66 Blithewood Dr., Pensacola, Fla. 32504. *Office:* Department of Geography, University of West Florida, Pensacola, Fla. 32504.

CAREER: University of Puerto Rico and Puerto Rico Department of Agriculture and Commerce, Rio Piedras, field team chief of Social Science Research Center, and cartographer, 1950; University of Oklahoma, Norman, assistant professor, 1951-55, associate professor, 1955-60, professor of geography, 1960-69, Regent's Professor, 1969-70, chairman of department, 1967-70, dean of graduate college, 1960-65; University of West Florida, Pensacola, professor of geography and vice-president for academic affairs, 1970—. Fulbright professor, University of Philippines, 1958-59; chief of party, University of Pennsylvania, U.S. Agency for International Development Project to Pahlavi University, Iran, 1966-67; visiting scientist, American Geophysical Union,

1971-72. Intelligence expert, U.S. Army, summer, 1956; geologist, Oklahoma Geological Survey, summer, 1959. *Military service:* U.S. Army Air Forces, 1943-46; became second lieutenant. *Member:* Association of American Geographers, National Council for Geographic Education, American Association for the Advancement of Science, Southwest Social Science Association, Oklahoma Academy of Science (fellow), Sigma Xi (former vice-president of University of Oklahoma chapter), Gamma Theta Upsilon, Pi Kappa Sigma, Phi Kappa Phi. *Awards, honors:* American Association of Middle Eastern Affairs summer fellow in Israel, 1965.

WRITINGS: Programa de Classificacion de Terrenos Rurales (maps), Departmento de Agricultura y Comercio, Universidad de Puerto Rico, 1951; (contributor) Kent Ruth, editor, *Oklahoma: A Guide to the Sooner State*, University of Oklahoma Press, 1957; (with Lee Guernsey) *Principles of Geography: Physical and Cultural*, Barron's, 1959, 2nd edition, 1975; *Mexico: Next Door Neighbor* (pamphlet), A. J. Nystrom, 1959; *Coal Mining in Oklahoma and Its Landscape Influence*, Oklahoma Geological Survey, 1961; (with Guernsey) *Principles of Physical Geography*, Barron's, 1964, 2nd edition, 1976; (with Edward L. Myles and Stephen M. Sutherland) *Physical Geography Laboratory Manual*, Laird, 1966; (with Eileen Bloch, Thomas Bloch, Robert Burgess, Lawrence L. Monnett, Jr., Lorraine Murphy, Murray Micol, Ruth Silver, Jeris Strain, and Park Teter) *Benchmark*, U.S. Agency for International Development, 1966; (with Burgess and Teter) *Pahlavi University Arts and Sciences Bulletin*, Pahlavi University, 1966; (with Myles and Sutherland) *A Laboratory Manual for Physical Geography*, University of Oklahoma, 1968; (contributor) George L. Cross, editor, *The World of Ideas*, University of Oklahoma Press, 1968; *An Introduction to Economic Geography*, W. C. Brown, 1959. Also contributor to *Northwestern University Studies in Geography*, Volume VI, 1962. Contributor to *Encyclopaedia Britannica;* contributor of geography articles to scientific journals.

*   *   *

DOLE, Gertrude E(velyn) 1915-

PERSONAL: Born October 10, 1915, in Cavendish, Vt.; daughter of Fletcher Enos and Laura Rogena (Harrington) Dole. *Education:* Middlebury College, A.B., 1937; University of North Carolina, M.A., 1949; University of Michigan, Ph.D., 1957. *Residence:* New York, N.Y. *Office:* Department of Anthropology, State University of New York College, Purchase, N.Y.

CAREER: New School for Social Research, New York City, lecturer in anthropology, summer, 1958; Columbia University, New York City, lecturer in anthropology, 1958-60, 1961-62; New York University, New York City, lecturer, 1961-64, adjunct assistant professor of anthropology, 1964-65; Vassar College, Poughkeepsie, N.Y., assistant professor, 1965-67, associate professor of anthropology, 1970-71; State University of New York College at Purchase, associate professor of anthropology, 1972—. Field work includes archaeological study of caves in Matanzas, Cuba, summer, 1952; study of ethnography of Kuikuru Indians of Mato Grosso, Brazil, 1953-54; survey of ethnographic collections of Tropical Forest Indians in Museo Nacional, Rio de Janeiro, 1954; study of ethnography of Amahuaca Indians of Eastern Peru, 1960-61.

MEMBER: American Anthropological Association (fellow), American Ethnological Society, Society of Women

Geographers, American Association for the Advancement of Science (fellow), Sigma Xi, Phi Sigma.

WRITINGS: (Editor with Robert L. Carneiro, and contributor) *Essays in the Science of Culture,* Crowell, 1960; (contributor) Marc J. Swartz, Victor W. Turner, and Arthur Tuden, editors, *Political Anthropology,* Aldine, 1966; (author of preface) Janice H. Hopper, editor, *Indians of Brazil in the Twentieth Century,* Institute for Cross-Cultural Research, 1967; (contributor) Priscilla Reining, editor, *Kingship Studies in the Morgan Centennial Year,* Anthropological Society of Washington, 1972; (contributor) Raoul Naroll, editor, *Main Currents in Ethnological Theory,* Appleton, 1973; (contributor) Carolyn Matthiasson, editor, *The Marriages of Pacho,* Free Press, 1973.

Films: "The Kuikuru Indians of Central Brazil," Bureau of Audio-Visual Instruction, University of Wisconsin, 1957; "Amahuaca: A Tropical Forest People in Southeastern Peru," Center for Documentary Anthropology, 1972. Contributor to transactions and proceedings. Contributor of articles and reviews to professional journals, including *Natural History, American Anthropologist, Southwestern Journal of Anthropology,* and *Current Anthropology.*

WORK IN PROGRESS: The Kuikuru Indians of Central Brazil.†

* * *

DOLMATCH, Theodore B(ieley) 1924-
(Stephen Josephs)

PERSONAL: Born April 22, 1924, in New York, N.Y.; son of Aaron (a physician) and Diana (Bieley) Stessel; married Blanche Ormont (an artist), December 28, 1948; children: Karen Ann, Stephen Joseph. *Education:* New York University, B.A., 1947, M.A., 1948. *Home:* 298 Law Road, Briarcliff Manor, N.Y. 10510. *Office:* Information Please Publishing, Inc., 57 West 57th St., New York, N.Y. 10019.

CAREER: Queens College (now Queens College of the City University of New York), Flushing, N.Y., instructor in English, 1948-50; Brooklyn College (now Brooklyn College of the City University of New York), Brooklyn, N.Y., administrator of School of General Studies, 1950-55; American Management Association, New York City, publications business manager, 1955-62; Pitman Publishing Corp., New York City, president, 1962-71; Intext Publishers Group, New York City, president, 1971-75; Information Please Publishing, Inc., New York City, president of company and editor of *Information Please Almanac,* 1976—. Chairman of the board of Ballantine Books, 1972. *Military service:* U.S. Army, 1942-46; became master sergeant. *Member:* American National Theatre and Academy (treasurer, 1965-66), Abbott House (president, 1969-72), American Shakespeare Theater (trustee, 1973-74).

WRITINGS: (Editor) *Revolution in Training,* American Management Association, 1955; (under pseudonym Stephen Josephs) *The People Zoo,* Windmill Books, 1972. Contributor of articles to *Library Journal, Dun's Review, Management Review, Personnel, Saturday Review, Modern Language Quarterly,* and *Library Trends.*

* * *

DOMVILLE, Eric 1929-

PERSONAL: Born April 27, 1929, in Liverpool, England; son of Wilfred Lawton (a clerk) and May (Priestman) Domville; married Freda Waites (a Montessori teacher), July 4, 1959; children: Elspeth Jane. *Education:* University of London, B.A., 1961, Ph.D., 1965. *Home:* 379 Cleveland St., Toronto, Ontario, Canada. *Agent:* A. D. Peters & Co., 10 Buckingham St., London WC2N 6BU, England. *Office:* New College, University of Toronto, Toronto, Ontario, Canada.

CAREER: British Civil Service, Liverpool, England, clerical officer, 1945-51; Regional Hospital Board, Liverpool, clerical officer, 1951-56; University of Toronto, Toronto, Ontario, lecturer, 1964-66, assistant professor, 1966-69, associate professor of literature, 1969—. *Member:* Modern Language Association of America, Canadian Association for Irish Studies, Canadian Association of University Teachers.

WRITINGS: A Concordance to the Plays of W. B. Yeats, two volumes, Cornell University Press, 1972; (editor) *Editing British and American Literature, 1880-1920,* Garland, 1976. Contributor and member of editorial board, *Four Decades of Poetry,* and *Fugue.*

WORK IN PROGRESS: Editing, with John Kelly, *Collected Letters of W. B. Yeats,* about nine volumes, for Oxford University Press.

AVOCATIONAL INTERESTS: Music and art from late nineteenth century to the present and their relationships with literature.

* * *

DONNELL, John C(orwin) 1919-

PERSONAL: Born August 18, 1919, in Seattle, Wash.; son of John C., Sr. (a salesman) and Helen (Gollnik) Donnell; married Ruth Carpenter (a librarian), October 31, 1953; children: Richard S., Joyce A. *Education:* University of Washington, Seattle, B.A., 1941; University of California, Berkeley, Vietnamese language and Asian area study under U.S. Army specialized training program, 1944, Ph.D., 1964; Chinese language and Asian area study at Yale University and Cornell University, under auspices of U.S. State Department, 1952-53; Columbia University, M.A., 1959. *Home:* 7022 Boyer St., Philadelphia, Pa. 19119. *Office:* Department of Political Science, Temple University, Philadelphia, Pa. 19122.

CAREER: Office of Supreme Commander of the Allied Powers, Tokyo, Japan, war crimes field investigator, 1946; General Headquarters, Far East Command, Tokyo, research analyst in civil intelligence section, 1946-47; U.S. Department of State and U.S. Information Agency (after 1953), press and publications officer in Saigon, 1950, public affairs officer in Hanoi, 1950-52, press and publications officer in Taipei, 1953-55, special projects officer in Saigon, 1955, field operations officer and cultural affairs officer in Saigon, 1956-57, public affairs officer for Northern Malaya in Penang 1957-58; Dartmouth College, Hanover, N.H., assistant professor of government, 1962-64; RAND Corp., Santa Monica, Calif., member of staff in social sciences, 1964-65; Temple University, Philadelphia, Pa., assistant professor, 1965-66, associate professor, 1966-70, professor of political science, 1970—. Lecturer, Foreign Service Institute of U.S. Department of State, 1966-68; senior visiting lecturer in government, Columbia University, 1969-70. *Military service:* U.S. Army, Counter-Intelligence Corps, 1943-46; served in Philippines and Japan.

MEMBER: American Political Science Association, Association for Asian Studies, American Association of University Professors, Southeast Asia Development Advisory Group, Phi Beta Kappa. *Awards, honors:* Ford Foundation training fellowship, South Vietnam, 1961-62; American Council of Learned Societies-Social Science Research Council research fellowship for study of Vietnamese politics, 1968; Asia Society research grant from Southeast Asia Development Advisory Group, South Vietnam, 1972.

WRITINGS: (Contributor) Wesley R. Fishel, editor, *Problems of Freedom: South Vietnam since Independence,* Free Press, 1961; (contributor) Robert A. Scalapino, editor, *The Communist Revolution in Asia,* Prentice-Hall, 1965, second edition, 1969; (contributor) Fishel, editor, *Vietnam: Anatomy of a Conflict,* F. E. Peacock, 1968; (with Guy J. Pauker and Joseph J. Zasloff) *Viet Cong Motivation and Morale in 1964: Preliminary Report,* RAND Corp., 1969; (editor with Charles A. Joiner) *Electoral Politics in South Vietnam,* Heath, 1974. Contributor to professional conventions and conferences. Contributor to *Pacific Affairs, Asia, Asian Survey, Asian Thought and Society, Journal of Asian Studies,* and *Problems of Communism.*

WORK IN PROGRESS: *Vietnam: The Politics of Manipulation.*

* * *

DORST, Tankred 1925-

PERSONAL: Born December 19, 1925, in Sonneberg, Germany; son of Max (an engineer) and Elisabeth (Lettermann) Dorst. *Education:* Studied at University of Munich, 1952-56. *Home:* Schleissheimerstrasse 182, Munich 40, Germany.

CAREER: Author and playwright. Lecturer in United States, 1970, and other countries. *Member:* Akademie der schoenen Kunste (Academy of Fine Arts; Munich), Deutsche Akademie fur Sprache und Dichtung. *Awards, honors:* Prize of National Theater of Mannheim, 1960; State of Munich Prize, 1964; Gerhart Hauptmann Prize (Berlin), 1964.

WRITINGS: *Geheimnis der Marionette* (title means "Secret of Marionettes"; foreword by Marcel Marceau), H. Rinn, 1957; (editor) *Auf kleiner Buehne* (puppet plays), Juventa-Verlag, 1959; *Die Kurve* (play; first produced, 1960), Kiepenheuer & Witsch, 1960, translation published as *Curve* in *New Theatre of Europe,* Volume III, edited by Robert W. Corrigan, Dell, 1968; *Grosse Schmaehrede an der Stadtmauer* (play; first produced in Luebeck, 1962), Kiepenheuer & Witsch, 1962; *Grosse Schmaehrede an der Stadtmauer,* [and] *Freiheit fuer Clemens,* [and] *Die Kurve* (three plays), Kiepenheuer & Witsch, 1962; (adapter) Ludwig Tiek, *Der Gestiefelte Kater order wie man das Spiel spielt* (play; first produced in Hamburg, 1963), Kiepenheuer & Witsch, 1963; (translator and adapter) Denis Diderot, *Rameaus Neffe* (play; first produced in Nuernberg, 1968), Kiepenheuer & Witsch, 1963; *Yolimba* (libretto of musical farce; music by Wilhelm Killmayer; first produced in Wiesbaden, 1965), Schott Music Corp. (New York), 1965; (editor) *Die Muenchner Raeterrepublik: Zeugnisse und Kommentar* (history), Suhrkamp, 1966; *Die mehreren Zauberer* (stories for children), Kiepenheuer & Witsch, 1966; *Toller* (play; first produced in Stuttgart), Suhrkamp, 1968; *Sand* (television-film play), Kiepenheuer & Witsch, 1971; (adapter) *Kleiner Mann was nun* (play; adapted from novel by Fellada; first produced in Bochun, 1972), Suhrkamp Verlag, 1972; *Eiszeit* (play; first produced in Bochun and Hamburg, 1973), Suhrkamp Verlag, 1973; *Dorothea Merz,* Suhrkamp Verlag, 1976; *Stuecke,* two volumes, Suhrkamp Verlag, 1978.

Unpublished plays: "Die Mohrin," first produced in Frankfurt, 1964; (translator) Moliere, "Der Geizige," first pro-

duced in Stuttgart, 1967; Moliere, "Der Eingebildete Kranke," first produced in Kassell, 1969; "Auf dem Chiwborozo," first produced in Berlin, 1975.

Films: "Rotword" (based on Dorst's play, *Toller*), produced, 1968; "Piggies" (television film), produced, 1969.

WORK IN PROGRESS: More plays, including "Dic Villa" and "Merlin," and films.

* * *

DOTY, Gresdna Ann 1931-

PERSONAL: Given name is pronounced *Gres*-na; born February 22, 1931, in Oelwein, Iowa; daughter of James William and Gresdna (Wood) Doty. *Education:* Attended Monticello College, 1949-51; University of Northern Iowa, B.A., 1953; University of Florida, M.A., 1957; Indiana University, Ph.D., 1967. *Religion:* Roman Catholic. *Office:* Department of Speech, Louisiana State University, Baton Rouge, La. 70803.

CAREER: Southwest Texas State University, San Marcos, instructor, 1957-62, assistant professor of speech, 1964-65; Louisiana State University, Baton Rouge, assistant professor, 1967-72, associate professor of speech, 1972—. *Member:* International Federation for Theatre Research, American Theatre Association, American Society for Theatre Research, Speech Communication Association.

WRITINGS: *The Career of Anne Brunton Merry in the American Theatre,* Louisiana State University Press, 1971. Contributor to *Introduction to Speech Communication,* and to journals, including *Southern Speech Journal, Theatre Survey, Quarterly Journal of Speech, The Speech Teacher.*

WORK IN PROGRESS: Editing John Durang's *The History of the Philadelphia Stage.*††

* * *

DOUBLEDAY, Neal Frank 1905-1976

PERSONAL: Born February 19, 1905, in Lake Mills, Wis.; son of Frank Eugene (a minister) and Minnie (Webb) Doubleday; married Frances M. Honey, August 17, 1932; children: James F., Helen M. (Mrs. Ronald Beyers). *Education:* University of Wisconsin, B.A., 1930, M.A., 1932, Ph.D., 1938. *Politics:* Democrat. *Religion:* Episcopalian. *Home:* 1379 West Macon St., Decatur, Ill. 62522.

CAREER: University of Wisconsin—Madison, instructor in English, 1936-39; Montana State University (now University of Montana), Missoula, instructor in English, 1939-40; University of Connecticut, Storrs, instructor, 1940-45, assistant professor of English, 1945-46; Millikin University, Decatur, Ill., associate professor, 1946-51, professor of English, 1951-70, professor emeritus, 1970-76. *Member:* Modern Language Association of America. *Awards, honors:* D.Litt., Millikin University, 1973.

WRITINGS: (Editor) *Studies in Poetry,* Harper, 1949; (editor) *Studies in Reading and Related Writing,* Heath, 1957; (editor) *Mark Twain's Picture of His America,* Heath, 1960; (editor) *Hawthorne: Tales of His Native Land,* Heath, 1962; *Writer to Reader,* Heath, 1966; *Writing the Research Paper,* Heath, 1969, revised edition, 1971; *Hawthorne's Early Tales: A Critical Study,* Duke University Press, 1972; *Variety of Attempt: British and American Fiction in the Early Nineteenth Century,* University of Nebraska Press, 1976. Contributor to journals in his field.

WORK IN PROGRESS: Research in early English and American nineteenth-century fiction.†

(Died August 29, 1976)

DOW, Blanche H(innan)   1893-1973

February 9, 1893—May 24, 1973; American educator, women's rights leader, and author. Obituaries: *Washington Post*, May 25, 1973.

*   *   *

DOWIE, James Iverne   1911-

PERSONAL: Born November 28, 1911, in Sherrard, Ill.; son of James H. (an electrician) and Emelia (Harris) Dowie; married Elenor M. Danielson (a medical record librarian), June, 1949; children: Ruthie. *Education:* Augustana College, A.B., 1936; University of Chicago, M.A., 1940; University of Minnesota, Ph.D., 1957. *Religion:* Lutheran. *Office:* Department of History, Augustana College, Old Main No. 333, Rock Island, Ill. 61201.

CAREER: Luther Junior College, Wahoo, Neb., associate professor, 1941-57, professor of history, 1957-58, vice-president, 1949-52, 1954-58, acting president, 1953; Augustana College, Rock Island, Ill., associate professor, 1958-65, professor of history, 1965—. *Member:* American Historical Association, Organization of American Historians, American Scandinavian Foundation, Phi Beta Kappa.

WRITINGS: Prairie Grass Dividing, Augustana Book Concern, 1959; (editor with Ernest M. Espelie) *Swedish Immigrant Community in Transition: Essays in Honor of Dr. Conrad Bergendoff*, Augustana Historical Society, 1963; (with Fritiof Ander) *In the Trek of the Immigrants*, Augustana College Library, 1964; (editor with Thomas Tredway) *The Immigration of Ideas*, Augustana Historical Society, 1968.

WORK IN PROGRESS: Research on the impact of nonconformist religious groups upon British politics in the 20th century.†

*   *   *

DOXEY, Roy W(atkins)   1908-

PERSONAL: Born February 27, 1908, in Ogden, Utah; son of Thomas and Bessie (Watkins) Doxey; married Alberta Opheikens, August 6, 1934; children: Douglas Allen (deceased), Clarke Benson, Kimball Roy, Cheryl Diane (Mrs. Ronald Julian). *Education:* Weber College (now Weber State College), A.S., 1934; George Washington University, Washington, D.C., A.B., 1938, M.A., 1940. *Religion:* Church of Jesus Christ of Latter-day Saints (Mormon). *Home:* 123 Second Ave., No. 905, Salt Lake City, Utah 84103. *Office:* 50 East North Temple St., Salt Lake City, Utah 84150.

CAREER: Federal Housing Administration, Washington, D.C., economist, 1935-42; National Housing Agency, Washington, D.C., economist, 1942-44; Brigham Young University, Provo, Utah, assistant professor, 1948-62, associate professor, 1962-65, professor of religion, 1965-74, chairman of department of undergraduate studies in religious instruction, 1963-69, assistant dean, College of Religious Instruction, 1970-71, dean, 1971-74. Church of Jesus Christ of Latter-day Saints, president, Provo Stake, 1963-72, regional representative of the Twelve, 1972—, director of correlation review division, 1978—. Vice-chairman of board of directors, Utah Valley Hospital, 1965-78; chairman of board of directors, Utah Valley Genealogical Branch Library, 1964-72. *Member:* Young Men's Mutual Improvement Association (general board member, 1948-61), Phi Kappa Phi, Omicron Delta Gamma, Pi Gamma Mu.

WRITINGS: The Doctrine and Covenants and the Future, Deseret, 1954, 2nd edition, 1972; *The Latter-day Prophets and the Doctrine and Covenants*, Deseret, Volume I, 1963, Volumes II and III, 1964, Volume IV, 1965, revised edition published as one volume, 1978; *The Doctrine and Covenants Speaks*, Deseret, Volume I, 1964, Volume II, 1970; *Zion in the Last Days*, Olympus, 1965; *Prophecies and Prophetic Promises from the Doctrine and Covenants*, Deseret, 1969; (with Walter D. Bowen) *Doctrine and Covenant Study Guide, with Selected Commentaries*, Brigham Young University Press, Volume I, 1971, Volume II, 1972; *Walk with the Lord*, Deseret, 1973; *The Word of Wisdom Today*, Deseret, 1975. Also author of *Tithing: The Lord's Law*, 1976. Contributor to education and religion journals.

WORK IN PROGRESS: Second volume of *Prophecies and Prophetic Promises from the Doctrine and Covenants; Prayer and the Latter-day Saint*.

*   *   *

DOXIADIS, Constantinos Apostolos   1913-1975

PERSONAL: Born May 14, 1913, in Stenimachos, Greece; son of Apostolos (a pediatrician; former Greek Minister of Refugees, Social Welfare, and Public Health) and Evanthia (Mezeviri) Doxiadis; married Emma Scheepers, April 30, 1940; children: Evanthia (Mrs. Gordon Tripp), Calliope, Euphrosyne (Mrs. Alexis Mardas), Apostolos. *Education:* Technical University of Athens, degree in architecture and engineering, 1935; Berlin-Charlottenburg University, Dr. Ing., 1936. *Religion:* Christian Orthodox. *Home:* 2 Stratiotikou Syndesmou St., Athens, Greece. *Office:* Doxiadis Associates International Co., Ltd., 24 Stratiotikou Syndesmou St., Athens, Greece; and 1058 Thomas Jefferson St., N.W., Washington, D.C. 20007.

CAREER: Chief town planning officer of Greater Athens Area, Athens, Greece, 1937-38; Ministry of Public Works, Athens, head of department of regional and town planning, 1939-45; Ministry of Housing and Reconstruction, Athens, under-secretary and director general, 1945-48; Ministry of Coordination, Athens, under-secretary and coordinator of Greek Recovery Program, 1948-51; Doxiadis Associates International Co., Ltd., (consultants on development and ekistics), Athens, president, 1951-72, chairman, 1973-75, chairman of board of directors and chief executive officer of Washington, D.C. office, 1959-75. Lecturer and acting professor of town planning, Technical University of Athens, 1939-43; visiting lecturer at University of Chicago, University of Dublin, Harvard University, University of Michigan, New York University, Oxford University, Princeton University, Massachusetts Institute of Technology, Yale University, University of Massachusetts, Georgia Institute of Technology, and Swarthmore College. Chairman of board of directors, Athens Technological Organization, founder and president of its Center of Ekistics and teacher of ekistics, beginning 1958. Member of Greek delegation to San Francisco Peace Conference, 1945; Greek representative to France, England, and the United States on problems of postwar reconstruction, 1945; head of Greek delegation to United Nations International Conference on Housing, Planning, and Reconstruction, 1947; head of Greek delegation to Greco Italian War Reparation Conference, 1949-50; Greek representative on housing, building, and planning committee of United Nations Economic and Social Council, 1963, 1964; chairman of session on urban problems, United Nations

Conference on Application of Science and Technology for the benefit of less-developed areas, 1963. Major architectural projects included: National ekistic and housing programs for Iraq, Lebanon and Libya, plans and development programs for Islamabad, Pakistan, Greater Rio de Janeiro, Accra-Tema region, and Ghana, urban renewal and development plans for several U.S. cities; new buildings for several universities, and designer of highways, airports, and housing projects. Consultant to United Nations, International Bank for Reconstruction and Development, Inter-American Development Bank, International Cooperation Administration, Agency for International Development, Ford Foundation, Redevelopment Land Agency of Washington, D.C., and to governments of Brazil, Cyprus, Ethiopia, France, Ghana, Greece, India, Iran, Iraq, Jordan, Lebanon, Libya, Pakistan, Saudi Arabia, South Vietnam, Spain, Sudan, Syria, United States, and Zambia. *Military service:* Greek Army, artillery, 1940-41; received Greek Military Cross. National Resistance Group (Hephaestus), 1941-45; became chief of group. Greek Army, 1944-45; became captain.

MEMBER: International Federation for Housing and Planning, Society for International Development, Industrial Designers of America (honorary member), American Management Association, American Institute of Planners, American Society of Planning Officials, Institute on Man and Science (member of international committee), Royal Incorporation of Architects of Scotland (honorary corresponding member), Town Planning Institute of Great Britain (honorary corresponding member), Deutsche Akademie fuer Staedtebau und Landesplanung (corresponding member). *Awards, honors:* Order of British Empire, 1945, for activities in National Resistance Group and collaboration with Allied Forces; Order of Cedar, Government of Lebanon, 1958, for contribution to development of Lebanon; Royal Order of Phoenix, Government of Greece, 1960, for contribution to development of Greece; Sir Patrick Abercrombie Prize of International Union of Architects, 1963; Cali de Oro Award of Society of Mexican Architects, 1963; award of excellence, Industrial Designers of America, 1965; Aspen Institute of Humanistic Studies Award for the Humanities, 1966; Yugoslav Flag Order with golden wreath, 1966; gold medal, Royal Architectural Institute of Canada, 1976. Honorary degrees include LL.D. from Swarthmore College, 1962, Mills College, 1964, University of Michigan, 1967, Tulane University, 1968, Kalamazoo College, 1968; D.H. from Wayne State University, 1964; L.H.D. from Northern Michigan University, 1965, Case Western Reserve University, 1969; D. Sc. from Detroit Institute of Technology, 1966, University of Pittsburgh, 1967, Marietta College, 1969; D.F.A. from University of Rhode Island, 1966.

WRITINGS: Raumordnung im griechischen Staedtebau Vowinckel, 1937, translation by Jaqueline Tyrwhitt published as *Architectural Space in Ancient Greece,* M.I.T. Press, 1972; *Mia Apli Istoria* (title means "A Simple Story"), Ikaros, 1945; *Oikistiki Analysi* (title means "Ekistic Analysis"), Ministry of Reconstruction (Athens), 1946; *Katastzophes Oikismwn* (title means "Destruction of Towns and Villages in Greece"), Ministry of Reconstruction, 1947; (with others) *Epiviwsis tou Ellinikou Laou–To schedion* (title means "A Plan for the Survival of the Greek People"), two volumes, Ministry of Reconstruction, 1947; *Oikistiki Politiki gia tin Anoikodomisi tis hwras me ena eikosachrono schedio* (title means "Ekistic Policies for the Reconstruction of the Country with a Twenty-Year Pro-

gram"), Ministry of Reconstruction, 1947; (with others) *Dwdecanisos* (title means "Dodecanese"), two volumes, Ministry of Reconstruction, 1947; *Poreia twn Lawn* (title means "March of the People"), Ikaros, 1948.

Our Capital and Its Future, Doxiadis Associates, 1960; *Architecture in Transition,* Oxford University Press, 1963; (with T. B. Douglass) *The New World of Urban Man,* United Church Press, 1965; *Urban Renewal and the Future of the American City,* Public Administration Service (Chicago), 1966; *Between Dystopia and Utopia,* Trinity College Press (Hartford), 1966; *Emergence and Growth of an Urban Region: The Developing Urban Detroit Area,* Detroit Edison Co., Volume I, 1966, Volume II, 1967, Volume III, 1970; *Ecumenopolis: The Settlement of the Future,* Athens Center of Ekistics, 1967; *Ekistics: An Introduction to the Science of Human Settlements,* Oxford University Press, 1968.

Campus Planning in an Urban Area: A Master Plan for Rensselaer Polytechnic Institute, Praeger, 1971; *The Two-Headed Eagle: From the Past to the Future of Human Settlements,* Lycabettus Press, 1972; *The Great Urban Crimes We Permit by Law,* Lycabettus Press, 1973; *Anthropolis: City for Human Development,* Norton, 1974; *Building Entopia,* Norton, 1975; *Action for Human Settlements,* Norton, 1976; *Ecology and Ekistics,* edited by Gerald Dix, Westview Press, 1977. Also author of reports on problems of development and ekistics in thirty-six countries.

SIDELIGHTS: After World War I, Constantinos Apostolos Doxiadis developed and matured the concept he named "ekistics." Ekistics (derived from the Greek word meaning home) is the science of human settlement, denoting the interrelationship of man with his environment. Man's total surroundings are studied, encompassing various areas of expertise including sociology, engineering, urban planning, geography, psychology, and architecture, in addition to the future needs of man in his relationship to his environment.

Time magazine reported: "Doxiadis was something of an oracle, the inventor and tireless promoter of ekistics. His practice and precepts combined to make him the world's best-known planner. . . . [Doxiadis] felt that the world was rushing toward increasingly disorderly urbanization and sprawl. Conceding that the trend was inexorable, he insisted that growth could be guided and made rational—but only if all elements of city building were treated together. He therefore urged architects, planners and engineers to get into ekistical harness with geographers, meteorologists, sociologists, and economists. By the year 2100, . . . such a collaboration could create 'Ecumenopolis,' an orderly, beautiful city of perhaps 25 billion people that would virtually cover the continents.''

Doxiadis' feeling for humanity expressed itself in his dedication and the pride he took in the various projects he was involved in. The individual was always of primary concern. Doxiadis believed "people were always the same irrespective of whether they lived in the ranchitos of Caracas or the mountains of Latin America, the peasants of the African jungle, the nomads of the deserts of the Middle East, the refugees of Karachi, the commuters of New York and the nomadic dwellers of the outskirts of the big metropolitan areas. In some way they were always the same men and women and children, they were always humans. To all those, who suffer and live under inhuman conditions and make me suffer with them, I owe my greatest gratitude."

AVOCATIONAL INTERESTS: Swimming, sailing, mountain climbing.

BIOGRAPHICAL/CRITICAL SOURCES: New Yorker, May 11, 1963; *Christian Century,* September 25, 1968; *New Republic,* January 11, 1969; *New York Times,* June 30, 1975; *Washington Post,* June 30, 1975; *Time,* July 14, 1975.†

(Died June 28, 1975)

*   *   *

DOZIER, Craig Lanier 1920-

PERSONAL: Born June 14, 1920, in Spartanburg, S.C.; son of Edward Jordan and Lucy (Ladshaw) Dozier; married Virginia Neely, June 11, 1956; children: Joyn Craig, David Ladshaw. *Education:* Attended University of South Carolina, 1940-42; University of Wisconsin, B.A., 1947; Johns Hopkins University, graduate study at School of Advanced International Studies, 1947-48, Ph.D., 1954; University of Maryland, M.A., 1951. *Home:* 1614 North College Park Dr., Greensboro, N.C. 27403. *Office:* Department of Geography, University of North Carolina, Greensboro, N.C. 27412.

CAREER: American Express Co., employed in travel and banking departments, Rome, Italy, 1948-49; University of Maryland, College Park, instructor in geography, 1951-52; Centro Cultural Brasil-Estados Unidos, Santos, Brazil, teacher of English, 1952; Johns Hopkins University, Baltimore, Md., part-time instructor at McCoy College, 1953-54; Memphis State College (now University), Memphis, Tenn., instructor in geography, 1954; University of South Carolina, Columbia, assistant professor of geography, 1954-56; Rollins College, Winter Park, Fla., assistant professor of geography, 1957-59; Louisiana Polytechnic Institute (now Louisiana Tech University), Ruston, associate professor of geography, 1959-60; University of North Carolina at Greensboro, associate professor, 1960-69, professor of geography, 1969—, chairman of department, 1960—. *Military service:* U.S. Army Air Forces, 1942-45; served in European theater.

MEMBER: Association of American Geographers, Latin American Studies Association, Conference of Latin American Geographers, Southeastern Conference of Latin American Studies, Wilderness Society. *Awards, honors:* National Research Council-National Academy of Sciences area grant for foreign research in Central America, 1956-57; Social Science Research Council grant for work in South America and Mexico, 1965-66.

WRITINGS: Indigenous Tropical Agriculture in Central America: Land Use, Systems and Problems, National Research Council, 1958; *Land Development and Colonization in Latin America: Case Studies of Peru, Bolivia, and Mexico,* Praeger, 1969. Contributor to proceedings. Contributor to *Geographical Review* and other journals.

WORK IN PROGRESS: Research on Central American and Caribbean coastal areas and historical geography.

*   *   *

DRAKE, (Bryant) Stillman 1910-

PERSONAL: Born December 24, 1910, in Berkeley, Calif.; son of Bryant Stillman (a chemist) and Flora (Frickstad) Drake; married Eda Salzmann, November 14, 1937 (divorced, 1950); married Lucille Daneri, February 23, 1951 (divorced, 1961); married Florence Selvin, April 1, 1967; children: (first marriage) Mark, Daniel Lee. *Education:* University of California, Berkeley, A.B., 1932. *Home:* 219 Glen Rd., Toronto, Ontario, Canada.

CAREER: Heller, Bruce & Co., San Francisco, Calif.,

bond analyst, 1946-56; Government Development Bank, San Juan, Puerto Pico, assistant vice-president, 1956-58; Blyth & Co., Inc., San Francisco, Calif., financial consultant, 1958-67; University of Toronto, Toronto, Ontario, professor of history of science, 1967-78, acting director, Centre for Renaissance Studies, 1972-73. *Member:* International Academy of History of Science, History of Science Society, Renaissance Society of America. *Awards, honors:* LL.D., University of California, Berkeley, 1968; Guggenheim Foundation fellow, 1971-72, and 1976-77.

WRITINGS: (Translator and author of introduction and notes) Galileo Galilei, *Dialogue Concerning the Two Chief World Systems,* foreword by Albert Einstein, University of California Press, 1953, 3rd edition, 1967; (editor, translator, and author of introduction and notes) *Discoveries and Opinions of Galileo,* Doubleday, 1957; (translator with C. D. O'Malley, and author of introduction and notes) Galilei, *Controversy on the Comets of 1618,* University of Pennsylvania Press, 1960; (with I. E. Drabkin, translator, and author of introduction and notes) *Galileo on Motion and on Mechanics* (Drake translated *Le Meccaniche* [Mechanics] for this edition, and Drabkin translated *De Motu* [Motion]), University of Wisconsin Press, 1960; (author of introduction and notes; translation by Thomas Salusbury) Galilei, *Discourse on Bodies in Water,* University of Illinois Press, 1960; (translator and author of notes) Ludovico Geymonat, *Galileo Galilei,* McGraw, 1965; (with Drabkin, translator and author of introduction and notes) *Mechanics in Sixteenth-Century Italy,* University of Wisconsin Press, 1969; (author of new introduction) A. B. Johnson, *The Meaning of Words,* reprint of 1854 edition, Greenwood Press, 1969; *Galileo Studies, Personality, Tradition and Revolution,* University of Michigan Press, 1970; (translator and author of introduction and notes) Galilei, *Two New Sciences,* University of Wisconsin Press, 1974; *Galileo Against the Philosophers,* Zeitliad Ver Brugge, 1976; *Galileo At Work: His Scientific Biography,* University of Chicago Press, 1978.

Contributor: H. M. Evans, editor, *Men and Moments in the History of Science,* University of Washington Press, 1959; *Atti del Simposio su Galileo Galilei nella storia e nella filosofia della scienza,* [Florence], 1967; Ernan McMullin, editor, *Galileo, Man of Science,* Basic Books, 1967; Charles S. Singleton, editor, *Art, Science and History in the Renaissance,* Johns Hopkins Press, 1967; Charles L. Todd and R. L. Blackwood, editors, *Language and Value,* Greenwood Press, 1969; Bert S. Hall and Delno C. West, editors, *On Pre-Modern Technology and Science,* University of California Center for Medieval and Renaissance Studies, 1976.

Writer of series of more than twenty "Galileo Gleanings," published in *Isis, Osiris, Physis,* and other journals, 1955-72. Contributor to *Dictionary of Scientific Biography,* Scribner, 1970.

WORK IN PROGRESS: Chronological arrangement and analysis of Galileo's working papers on motion.

*   *   *

DRAKE, W(inbourne) Magruder 1914-

PERSONAL: Born October 28, 1914, in Natchez, Miss.; son of H. Winbourne M. (a banker) and Mildred (Myers) Drake; married Lelia Newland (a college teacher), December 29, 1958. *Education:* Washington and Lee University, B.A., 1936, M.A., 1937; University of North Carolina at Chapel Hill, Ph.D., 1954. *Politics:* Democrat. *Religion:* Presbyterian. *Home:* 409 Marguerite Blvd., Lafayette, La.

70503. *Office:* Department of History, University of Southwestern Louisiana, Lafayette, La. 70504.

CAREER: Fidelity & Deposit Company of Maryland, special representative in Baltimore, Md., Atlanta, Ga., and Louisville, Ky., 1937-40; Washington and Lee University, Lexington, Va., assistant registrar, 1940-42, registrar, 1946-49; University of Mississippi, Oxford, instructor in history, 1952-53; Davidson College, Davidson, N.C., assistant professor of history, 1954-55; University of Southwestern Louisiana, Lafayette, assistant professor, 1955-57, associate professor, 1957-63, professor of history, 1963—. *Military service:* U.S. Navy Reserve, active duty, 1942-46; became lieutenant commander; inactive duty, 1946-63; became commander. *Member:* Organization of American Historians, American Association of University Professors, Southern Historical Association, Mississippi Historical Society, Louisiana Historical Association, Phi Beta Kappa. *Awards, honors:* University fellow at University of North Carolina, 1951-52.

WRITINGS: (Editor with Robert R. Jones) *The Great South,* Louisiana State University Press, 1972. Contributor to *Journal of Southern History, Journal of Mississippi History, Louisiana History, North Carolina Historical Review,* and *Vicksburg Post.*

WORK IN PROGRESS: Editing a collection of Civil War letters and a diary, and a collection of letters from Edward King to George W. Cable.

*   *   *

DREITZEL, Hans Peter   1935-

PERSONAL: Born January 3, 1935, in Berlin, Germany; son of Carl (a teacher) and Anna (Runge) Dreitzel; married Doris Hexel, August 4, 1961. *Education:* Attended Institut de Sciences Politiques, 1958, and Free University of Berlin, 1958-59; University of Goettingen, Ph.D., 1961. *Home:* 69 Goethestrasse, Berlin 12, Germany. *Office:* Free University of Berlin, 21 Gargstrasse, Berlin 33, Germany.

CAREER: New School for Social Research, New York, N.Y., assistant professor of sociology, 1968-69; Free University of Berlin, Berlin, Germany, professor of sociology, 1969—. *Member:* German Association of Sociology, National Council of Family Relations.

WRITINGS: Elitebegriff und Sozial struktur, Enke, 1962; *Sozialer Wandel,* Luihterhand, 1966, 2nd edition, 1972; *Die gesellschaft luben Leiden und das Leiden an der Gesellschaft,* Enke, 1968, 2nd edition, 1972; (compiler) *Family, Marriage, and the Struggle of the Sexes,* Macmillan, 1972; (editor) *Recent Sociology,* Macmillan, Volume I: *Social Basis of Politics,* 1969, Volume II: *Patterns of Communicative Behavior,* 1970, Volume III: *Social Organization of Health,* 1971, Volume IV: *Sexual Revolution and Family Crisis,* 1972, Volume V: *Childhood and Socialism,* 1973; *Einsamkeit als soziologischs Problem,* Arche, 1970. Contributor to European sociology journals.

WORK IN PROGRESS: Research on communal families and on Marxism and symbolic interaction.†

*   *   *

DRUMMOND, Dorothy W(eitz)   1928-

PERSONAL: Born December 19, 1928, in San Diego, Calif.; daughter of Frederick W. (a chemist) and Dora (Weidenhofer) Weitz; married Robert R. Drummond (a professor of geography), September 5, 1953; children: Kathleen, Gael, Martha. *Education:* Valparaiso University, B.A., 1949;

Northwestern University, M.A., 1951. *Religion:* Lutheran. *Home address:* Route 15, Box 354, West Terre Haute, Ind. *Office:* Department of Geography, St. Mary-of-the-Woods College, St. Mary-of-the-Woods, Ind. 47876.

CAREER: Geographical Review, American Geographical Society, New York, N.Y., editorial assistant, 1951-53; Indiana State College (now University), Terre Haute, Laboratory School instructor, 1963-64; St. Mary-of-the-Woods College, St. Mary-of-the-Woods, Ind., instructor in geography, 1969—. *Member:* American Geographical Society, Association of American Geographers, National Council for Geographic Education. *Awards, honors:* Fulbright scholar to Burma, 1957-58.

WRITINGS: (With Clyde Kohn) *The World Today: Its Patterns and Cultures,* McGraw, 1963, 3rd revised edition, 1971; *World Patterns Transparencies Kit,* McGraw, 1967. Contributor to *Britannica Junior Encyclopaedia, Compton's Encyclopedia,* and *Focus.*

*   *   *

DRUMMOND, Richard H(enry)   1916-

PERSONAL: Born December 14, 1916, in San Francisco, Calif.; son of John Albert (a building contractor) and Clara (Jacobson) Drummond; married Pearl Estella Oppegaard, June 5, 1943; children: Donald Craig, Angela Claire, Lowell Henry. *Education:* University of California, Los Angeles, B.A. (with highest honors), 1938, M.A., 1939; University of Wisconsin, Ph.D., 1941; Gettysburg Theological Seminary, B.D., 1944. *Politics:* Democrat. *Home:* 135 Croydon Crest, Dubuque, Iowa 52001. *Office:* Department of Ecumenical Mission and History of Religions, University of Dubuque Theological Seminary, Dubuque, Iowa 52001.

CAREER: Ordained minister of United Presbyterian Church, 1947; United Presbyterian Church, U.S.A., Commission on Ecumenical Mission and Relations, Kamakura, Japan, fraternal worker, 1949-62; University of Dubuque Theological Seminary, Dubuque, Iowa, professor of ecumenical mission and history of religions, 1962—. Visiting professor at Tokyo Union Theological Seminary, 1968-69, 1976-78, Luther Theological Seminary, 1970-71, Divine Word Seminary, 1971-73, and International Christian University, 1978. *Military service:* U.S. Army, 1945-46; became sergeant. *Member:* North American Academy of Ecumenists, American Academy of Religion, Midwest Fellowship of Professors of Mission (president, 1970-71), Phi Beta Kappa. *Awards, honors:* Sealantic Fund faculty fellowship from American Association of Theological Schools, 1968-69.

WRITINGS: A History of Christianity in Japan, Eerdmans, 1971; *Gautama the Buddha: An Essay in Religious Understanding,* Eerdmans, 1974; *Unto the Churches,* A.R.E. Press, 1978. Contributor to *Journal of Ecumenical Studies* and other periodicals.

WORK IN PROGRESS: Research on Japanese Buddhism, the fathers of the early church, especially the Alexandrian theologians, and the history of Christian spirituality.

SIDELIGHTS: Richard H. Drummond told *CA:* "I have continued to teach both in the United States and Japan, [where] I generally lecture in Japanese.... I do not hesitate to say that a major motive in my writing is to deepen the religious faith and understanding of my contemporaries."

Gautama the Buddha has appeared in a Dutch edition. *Unto the Churches* has been translated into Japanese.

BIOGRAPHICAL/CRITICAL SOURCES: International Review of Mission, July, 1975.

DuBRIN, Andrew J(ohn) 1935-

PERSONAL: Born March 3, 1935, in New York, N.Y.; son of Albert E. (a salesman) and Louise (Walsh) DuBrin; married; children: Drew, Douglas. Education: Hunter College (now Hunter College of the City University of New York), A.B., 1956; Purdue University, M.S., 1957; Michigan State University, Ph.D., 1960. Politics: "No party affiliation." Religion: "No preference." Home: 170 Glen Ellyn Way, Rochester, N.Y. 14618. Office: Rochester Institute of Technology, Rochester, N.Y. 14623.

CAREER: Certified psychologist in state of New York; International Business Machines Corp. (IBM), Kingston, N.Y., personnel research psychologist in Data Services Division, 1962-63; Clark, Cooper, Field & Wohl, New York City, psychological consultant, 1963-64; Rohrer, Hibler & Replogle, New York City, psychological consultant, 1964-70, partner in charge of Rochester, N.Y. office, 1967-70; Rochester Institute of Technology, Rochester, N.Y., associate professor, 1970-72, professor of behavioral science, 1972—. Military service: U.S. Army, chief clinical psychology officer, 1960-62; became captain. Member: American Psychological Association, Phi Beta Kappa.

WRITINGS: The Practice of Managerial Psychology: Concepts and Methods for Manager and Organization Development, with instructor's manual, Pergamon, 1971; Women in Transition, C. C Thomas, 1972; The Practice of Managerial Psychology, Pergamon, 1971; Women in Transition, C. C Thomas, 1972; The Singles Game, Major Books, 1973; Survival in the Sexist Jungle, Major Books, 1974; Fundamentals of Organizational Behavior, Pergamon, 1974, 2nd edition, 1978; Managerial Deviance, Van Nostrand, 1976; The New Husbands, Nelson-Hall, 1976; Casebook of Organizational Behavior, Pergamon, 1977; Survival in the Office, Van Nostrand, 1977; Human Relations, Reston, 1978; Winning at Office Politics, Van Nostrand, 1978; Effective Business Psychology, Reston, 1979; The Practice of Supervision, Business Publications, in press. Contributor to professional journals, including Personnel Journal, Sales Management, Search, American Psychologist, Insurance Law Journal, and Public Relations Quarterly.

SIDELIGHTS: Andrew DuBrin told CA: "[I'm] still groping for that big bestseller. I feel pangs of success when I am able to turn down an offer to do a book."

*   *   *

DUCKWORTH, Alistair M(cKay) 1936-

PERSONAL: Born August 4, 1936, in Balmullo, Fife, Scotland; son of Herbert George and Ann (McKay) Duckworth; married Donna Hardy (a microbiologist), June 13, 1964; children: Alexandra, Edward Angus. Education: University of Edinburgh, M.A. (first class honors), 1958; John Hopkins University, M.A., 1964, Ph.D., 1967. Home: 1720 Northwest 26th Way, Gainesville, Fla. 32601. Office: Department of English, University of Florida, Gainesville, Fla. 32611.

CAREER: University of Virginia, Charlottesville, assistant professor of English, 1967-73; University of Florida, Gainesville, associate professor of English, 1973—. Lecturer, Clark Memorial Library, 1977. Military service: Royal Navy, 1959-62; became lieutenant. Member: Modern Language Association of America, South Atlantic Modern Language Association, Phi Beta Kappa, Naval and Military Club. Awards, honors: University of Florida Presidential Scholar, 1976.

WRITINGS: The Improvement of the Estate: A Study of Jane Austen's Novels, Johns Hopkins Press, 1971. Contributor to Jane Austen Today, Georgia University Press, 1975, and Jane Austen: Bicentennial Essays, Cambridge University Press, 1975. Also contributor to Nineteenth-Century Fiction, Modern Philology, English Language Notes, Papers in Language and Literature, Sewanee Review, and New Republic.

WORK IN PROGRESS: Research in novel theory.

*   *   *

DUDLEY, Guilford A(llerton) 1921-1972

PERSONAL: Born May 1, 1921, in New York, N.Y.; son of Guilford Swathel (a surgeon) and Marie (Irwin) Dudley; married Anne Sullivan, September 15, 1945; children: Guilford Alexander. Education: Harvard University, A.B., 1943; University of California at Los Angeles, M.A., 1952, Ph.D., 1956. Home: 1811 North 69th St., Scottsdale, Ariz. 85257. Office: Department of History, Arizona State University, Tempe, Ariz. 85281.

CAREER: Export-import executive in Philippines, China, and Japan, 1946-54; Arizona State University, Tempe, instructor, 1956-57, assistant professor, 1957-60, associate professor, 1960-66, professor of history, 1966-72. Founder and director of Center for Asian studies, 1965-72. Military service: U.S. Navy, 1943-46; became lieutenant junior grade; received four Bronze Stars. Member: American Historical Association, Association for Asian Studies, Pacific Coast Conference on British Studies (former secretary-treasurer, and member of executive council). Awards, honors: American Association for Middle East Studies fellowship, 1962.

WRITINGS: (With Edward R. Tannenbaum and others) A History of the World, edited by Tannenbaum, Wiley, 1973; A History of Eastern Civilizations, Wiley, 1973.††

(Died August 2, 1972)

*   *   *

DUNCAN, Delbert J(ames) 1895-

PERSONAL: Born June 8, 1895, in American Fork, Utah; son of William Ethan (an electrician) and Mary (Harrington) Duncan; married Elizabeth Peairs, March 18, 1929; children: James Bruce. Education: University of Utah, B.S., 1918; Harvard University, M.B.A., 1921; Northwestern University, Ph.D., 1935. Politics: Republican. Religion: Presbyterian. Home: 614 Sage Ct., Pacific Grove, Calif. 93950.

CAREER: University of Colorado, Boulder, assistant professor, 1924-27, associate professor of marketing, 1927-30; Northwestern University, Evanston, Ill., associate professor, 1930-32, professor of marketing, 1932-46; Cornell University, Ithaca, N.Y., professor of marketing and distribution, 1946-51; University of California, Berkeley, professor of marketing, 1951-53; University of Colorado, dean of School of Business, 1953-56; University of California, Berkeley, professor of marketing, 1956-62, professor emeritus, 1962—. Worked for National Recovery Administration, 1934, and Office of Price Administration and War Production Board, 1940-42. Former member of board of directors of National State Bank (Boulder), Wheatley-Jacobsen, Inc., and Klein Institute for Aptitude Evaluation. Military service: U.S. Aviation Service, Aircraft and Production, 1918-19; became second lieutenant.

MEMBER: American Marketing Association (past vice-president; member of board of directors, 1947-49), American Economic Association, Newcomen Society in North America. *Awards, honors:* Named to Hall of Fame in distribution by Boston Conference on Distribution, 1953; University of California, Berkeley citation, 1970, for distinguished achievement and notable service to the University.

WRITINGS: (With Charles F. Phillips) *Retailing: Principles and Methods,* Irwin, 1947, 8th edition published as *Modern Retailing Management: Basic Concepts and Practices,* 1972, 9th edition (with Stanley C. Hollander), 1977; (with Phillips) *Marketing Principles and Methods,* Irwin, 1948, 6th edition, 1968; *Basic Determinates of Behavior in Industrial Purchasing,* Institute of Business and Economic Research, University of California, 1968; *Retailing: Modern Concepts and Practices* (programmed learning aid), Irwin, 1970. Contributor to business and marketing journals.

* * *

DUNCAN, W. Raymond 1936-

PERSONAL: Born March 14, 1936, in Ancon, Panama Canal Zone; son of Walter F. (an electrician) and Francis (Davis) Duncan; married Ute M. Clemetsen, September 13, 1961; children: Erik, Christopher. *Education:* University of California, Riverside, A.B., 1959; Fletcher School of Law and Diplomacy, M.A., 1962, M.A.L.D., 1963, Ph.D., 1964. *Religion:* Protestant. *Home:* 328 Campbell Rd., Brockport, N.Y. 14420. *Office:* Department of Political Science, State University of New York College at Brockport, Brockport, N.Y. 14420.

CAREER: State University of New York College at Brockport, associate professor, 1968-72, professor of political science, 1972—. *Military service:* U.S. Army, 1959-61. *Member:* American Political Science Association, American Association of University Professors.

WRITINGS: (Editor with James Nelson Goodsell) *The Quest for Change in Latin America,* Oxford University Press, 1970; *Soviet Policy in Developing Countries,* Blaisdell, 1970; *Latin American Politics: A Developmental Approach,* Praeger, 1976.

WORK IN PROGRESS: Nationality, Citizenship and Politics in Latin America; research on ethnicity and national identity in the "third world," on the politics of economic growth in the "third world," and on Soviet policy in developing countries.

BIOGRAPHICAL/CRITICAL SOURCES: Washington Post, January 7, 1971.

* * *

DUNNAHOO, Terry

PERSONAL: Born in Fall River, Mass.; daughter of Joseph Alfred (a mill worker) and Emma (Dolbec) Janson; married Thomas William Dunnahoo (a cinematographer), September 18, 1954; children: Kim, Sean, Kelly. *Education:* Attended parochial schools in Massachusetts. *Politics:* "I vote for the man—or the woman." *Religion:* Roman Catholic. *Home:* 4061 Tropico Way, Los Angeles, Calif. 90065. *Agent:* Evelyn Singer Agency, P.O. Box 163, Briarcliff Manor, N.Y. 10510.

CAREER: Writer. Has worked in a civilian capacity for U.S. Navy on Guam and as a teacher of creative writing in the gifted program, Los Angeles Public Schools. Lecturer to private groups, writer's conferences, and seminars, colleges, and schools. Consultant to California Arts Commission. *Member:* International P.E.N. (president, Los Angeles

Center, 1975-77), Authors Guild of America, Society of Children's Book Writers, Southern California Council on Literature for Children and Young People. *Awards, honors:* Southern California Council on Literature for Children and Young People's nonfiction award, for *Before the Supreme Court.*

WRITINGS: Emily Dunning, Regnery, 1970; *Nellie Bly,* Regnery, 1970; *Annie Sullivan,* Regnery, 1970; *Before the Supreme Court: The Story of Belva Ann Lockwood,* Houghton, 1974; *Who Cares about Espie Sanchez?,* Dutton, 1976; *This Is Espie Sanchez,* Dutton, 1976; *Who Needs Espie Sanchez?,* Dutton, 1977. Contributor of reviews to *West Coast Review of Books.*

WORK IN PROGRESS: A book about Ellen Richards.

SIDELIGHTS: Terry Dunnahoo told *CA:* "When I speak to groups of hopeful writers, I tell them I'm the exception to the writer's unwritten rules. As a child, I wasn't an avid reader. I worked my way through high school and business school, which left little time to read. I never had a strong desire to write. No particular incident influenced me. No teacher encouraged me. Writing was something I suddenly decided to do. And, for awhile, I couldn't imagine doing anything else. However, now I've branched out in different areas related to writing. I speak at writers' conferences throughout the United States, I teach creative writing, I review books, I do manuscript analysis, and I've become active in writer's organizations. Each gives me a feeling of helping others. But none gives me more satisfaction than meeting my audience during lecture tours, especially the young people who take Espie Sanchez, one of my fictional characters, so seriously that they believe she's a real person."

* * *

DUNNE, Mary Collins 1914-
(Regina Moore)

PERSONAL: Born January 15, 1914, in County Down, Ireland; daughter of George William (a calker) and Brigid (Byrne) Collins; married Stephen John Dunne (a teamster), January 11, 1937; children: Nancy (Mrs. Thomas Roberts), Mary Anne (Mrs. Jon Ploof), Bernadette, Christine. *Education:* Studied creative writing at University of San Francisco, University of California, San Francisco City College, and California State University, San Francisco (now San Francisco State University). *Politics:* Democrat. *Religion:* Roman Catholic. *Home:* 266 Jules Ave., San Francisco, Calif. 94112.

CAREER: Writer. *Member:* California Writers' Club.

WRITINGS: Alaskan Summer (juvenile), Abelard, 1968; *Reach Out, Ricardo* (juvenile), Abelard, 1970; *Gregory Gray and the Brave Beast* (juvenile), Childrens Press, 1972; *Nurse of the Midnight Sun,* Bouregy, 1973; *Standby Nurse,* Bouregy, 1974; *Cruise of the Coral Queen,* Bouregy, 1975; *Nurse of the Vineyards,* Bouregy, 1975; *The Secret of Captives' Cave* (juvenile), Putnam, 1976; *Nurse of Crystalline Valley,* Bouregy, 1977. Contributor of articles and short stories (some under pseudonym Regina Moore) to *Adventure, Camping Guide, Catholic Boy, Catholic Miss, Christian Home, Classmate, Co-Ed, Ave Maria, Datebook, Extension, Family Digest, Ingenue, Marriage, Story Friends, Straight, Teen, Together, Upward Venture, Young Miss, Young World,* and *San Francisco Record.*

WORK IN PROGRESS: Children's stories and adult suspense fiction.

AVOCATIONAL INTERESTS: Gardening, swimming, spectator baseball, travel.

* * *

DUPREE, Louis 1925-

PERSONAL: Born August 23, 1925, in Greenville, N.C.; son of Chauncey Leary (a postal clerk) and Luna (Tripp) Dupree; married Ann Bradford Kirschner, September 15, 1949 (divorced, 1965); married Nancy Marie Shakuntula Hatch (a writer), February 20, 1966; children: (first marriage) Julie, Louis F. R., Sara G. *Education:* Harvard University, A.B. (cum laude), 1949, A.M., 1953, Ph.D., 1955. *Politics:* Liberal. *Religion:* Muslim. *Home:* Willow Grove Rd., Stony Point, N.Y. 10980. *Office:* American Universities Field Staff, P.O. Box 150, Hanover, N.H. 03755.

CAREER: Member of American Museum of Natural History expeditions in West Pakistan and Afghanistan, 1949, 1950-51, and University of Pennsylvania Museum expedition in Iran, 1951; Harvard University, Cambridge, Mass., assistant to dean of scholarships, 1953; Air University, Maxwell Air Force Base, Ala., area study contractor, 1953-54, assistant professor, 1954-57, associate professor of Middle Eastern studies, 1957; Pennsylvania State University, University Park, associate professor of anthropology, 1957-66, adjunct professor, 1966—; American Universities Field Staff, Hanover, N.H., associate with joint teaching-research appointments at eleven universities, 1959—. Research associate, American Museum of Natural History, 1959-71. Visiting professor, Kabul University, 1962, 1964-66; lecturer at intervals for U.S. Department of State, Foreign Service Institute, 1967—; visiting lecturer; University of Chicago, spring, 1968. Foreign affairs consultant, American University, 1958, 1960-61, 1967; consultant, U.S. Operations Mission-Pakistan, 1963, 1966; Peace Corps, director of area studies in Afghanistan, 1966, consultant on Afghanistan, 1970. Member of Near and Middle East Committee, Social Science Research Council, 1958-59; member, Eisenhower Exchange Fellowship Committee for Afghanistan, 1971. Consultant to U.S. Agency for International Development, 1976, United Nations Development Programme, 1976, and United Nations Educational, Scientific, and Cultural Organization (UNESCO), 1977. *Military service:* U.S. Merchant Marine Reserve, 1943-44. U.S. Army, Paratroopers, 1944-47; served in Philippines, Okinawa, Japan; became first lieutenant.

MEMBER: American Anthropological Association (fellow), American Association for the Advancement of Science (fellow), Society for Applied Anthropology (fellow), American Oriental Society (fellow), American Ethnological Society, Archaeological Institute of America, Middle East Institute, Royal Central Asian Society, Societe Prehistorique Francaise, Asia Society (member of Afghanistan council), British Institute of Persian Studies, Society for Afghan Studies, Gamma Alpha, Explorers Club (New York; fellow), Harvard Travellers Club.

AWARDS, HONORS: Meritorious Service Commendation from U.S. Air Force, 1956, for field work on survival test in the Libyan Sahara; grants for field work in Afghanistan from Wenner-Gren Foundation, 1959-60, 1965, Social Science Research Council, 1964, American Philosophical Society, 1964-65, 1966, Rockefeller Fund, 1965, American Museum of Natural History, 1968, National Science Foundation, 1969-70, and Heinze Foundation, 1970-71; National Endowment for the Humanities fellow and American Council of Learned Societies fellow at King's College (Cambridge),

1972-73; grants from John D. Rockefeller III Fund, L.S.B. Leakey Foundation, and Archaeological Institute of America for research trip to People's Republic of China, 1978.

WRITINGS: The Jungle Survival Field Test, Air University, 1956; *The Desert Survival Field Test,* Air University, 1956; *The Warm Water Survival Field Test,* Air University, 1958; *Shamshir Ghar: Historic Cave Site in Kandahar Province, Afghanistan* (based on doctoral thesis), Volume XLVI, Anthropological Papers of American Museum of Natural History, 1958; (editor) *Anthropology in the Armed Forces,* Social Science Research Center, Pennsylvania State University, 1959; *Deh Morasi Ghundai: A Chalcolithic Site in South-Central Afghanistan,* Volume L, Anthropological Papers of American Museum of Natural History, 1963; (with wife, Ann Dupree and A. A. Motamedi) *A Guide to the Kabul Museum,* National Museum of Afghanistan, 1964, 2nd edition, 1968; (author of notes) G. F. Debets, *Physical Anthropology of Afghanistan,* Volumes I-II, edited by Henry Field and translated by Eugene V. Prostov, Peabody Museum of Archaeology and Ethnology, Harvard University, 1970; *Afghanistan,* Princeton University Press, 1973; (with others) *Prehistoric Research in Afghanistan: 1959-1966,* Volume LXII, Transactions of American Philosophical Society, 1972; (editor) George Scott Robertson, *Kaffirs of the Hindu Kush,* Oxford University Press, 1974; (editor with L. Albert) *Afghanistan in the 1970's,* Praeger, 1974; (with wife, Nancy Hatch Dupree) *The National Museum of Afghanistan: A Pictorial Guide,* Kabul, 1974.

Contributor: L. P. Vidyarthi, editor, *Anthropology and Tribal Welfare in India,* Bihar University, 1959; Vidyarthi, editor, *Aspects of Religion in Indian Society,* [Meerut], 1961; K. H. Silvert, editor, *Expectant Peoples: Nationalism and Development,* Random House, 1963; Robert B. Textor, editor, *Cultural Frontiers of the Peace Corps,* M.I.T. Press, 1965; Donald N. Wilber, editor, *The Nations of Asia,* Hart Publishing, 1966; *The Developing World: AUFS Readings,* Volume I, American Universities Field Staff, 1966; Silvert, editor, *Churches and States: The Religious Institution and Modernization,* American Universities Field Staff, 1967; *City and Nation in the Developing World: AUFS Readings,* Volume II, American Universities Field Staff, 1968; (author of foreword) Hasan Kakar, *Afghanistan: A Study in International Political Developments, 1880-1896,* Punjab Educational Press, 1971; Harrison Brown and Alan Sweezy, editors, *Population: Perspective, 1971,* Freeman, Cooper, 1972.

Author of book-length reports for U.S. Air Force, including *Cultural Study of Afghanistan,* 1953, *. . . of Iran,* 1954, *. . . of West Pakistan and Kashmir, 1954, . . . of North India, Nepal, Bhutan and Sikkim,* 1957. Contributor of about seventy articles to *American Universities Field Staff Reports: South Asia Series,* 1959—. Project officer for U.S. Government "Ethnic Card Study: A Description of the Peoples of the World," 1954-57.

Contributor to *Collier's Encyclopedia, Cowles Comprehensive Encyclopedia, Cowles Encyclopedia of Nations, Americana Annual,* and other annuals. Contributor of more than 150 articles and thirty reviews to *Time, American Antiquity, Nation, Illustrated London News, Arts Asiatiques, U.S. Lady, Afghanistan, Muslim World, Economist, Middle East Journal,* and other periodicals and newspapers. Occasional columnist, *Kabul Times,* 1962—; corresponding member, International News Rights and Royalties (London), 1963—.

DUTTON, John M(ason) 1926-

PERSONAL: Born October 17, 1926, in Sanford, Me.; son of Mason Henry and Irene (Watson) Dutton; married Shirley Reed, September 8, 1956; children: Jane, William, Watson, David. Education: University of New Hampshire, B.S., 1952; Harvard University, M.B.A., 1957. Politics: Independent. Religion: Protestant. Home: 29 Washington Square W., New York, N.Y. 10011. Office: Graduate School of Business Administration, 100 Trinity Pl., New York University, New York, N.Y. 10006.

CAREER: Metcalf & Eddy, Boston, Mass., engineer, 1954-55; Northeastern University, Boston, instructor in industrial management, 1959-60; Purdue University, Lafayette, Ind., assistant professor, 1960-64, associate professor of business administration, 1964-68; Southern Methodist University, Dallas, Tex., professor of business administration and director of research, 1968-71; New York University, New York, N.Y., professor of business administration, 1971—. Lucas Visiting Professor, University of Birmingham, 1963-64. Military service: U.S. Navy, 1945-47, 1952-54; became lieutenant junior grade. Member: American Association for the Advancement of Science, Institute of Management Sciences, Operations Research Society of America, Society for Applied Anthropology. Awards, honors: McKinsey award for management research, 1968.

WRITINGS: (Contributor) A. R. Towl, editor, Intercollegiate Bibliography of Cases in Business Administration, Harvard Business School, 1965; (contributor) M. P. Hottenstein and R. W. Millman, editors, Research Toward the Development of Management Thought, Academy of Management, 1967; (contributor) Millman and Hottenstein, editors, Promising Research Directions, Academy of Management, 1968; (with W. H. Starbuck) Computer Simulation of Human Behavior, Wiley, 1971; (with J. S. Aronofsky and M. T. Tayyabkhan) Managerial Planning with Linear Programming in Process Industries, Wiley, 1978. Contributor to business journals. Editor, International Journal of Production Research.

WORK IN PROGRESS: A book discussing strategy in major integrated international oil firms; studies of technological change in business firms; studies of organizing processes in large task organizations.

AVOCATIONAL INTERESTS: Reading, music, theatre, collecting industrial crafts, sport fishing, wilderness trips.

*   *   *

DYCK, Martin 1927-

PERSONAL: Born January 16, 1927, in Gruenfeld, Ukraine, Russia; Canadian citizen; son of Martin (a teacher and professional linguist) and Helene (a teacher; maiden name, Peters) Dyck; married Marie Wiens, June 12, 1949; children: Vernon, Victor, Martin and Ingrid (twins). Education: University of Manitoba, B.A. (double honors in German literature and mathematics), 1953, M.A., 1954; University of Cincinnati, Ph.D., 1956. Religion: Mennonite and Congregationalist. Home: 18 Red Coat Lane, Lexington, Mass. 02173. Office: Room 14N-236, Massachusetts Institute of Technology, Cambridge, Mass. 02139.

CAREER: Massachusetts Institute of Technology, Cambridge, assistant professor, 1956-58; University of Michigan, Ann Arbor, assistant professor, 1958-60, associate professor, 1960-64, professor of German, 1964-65; Massachusetts Institute of Technology, professor of German, humanities, and literature, 1965—. Member: International Society for

Germanic Languages and Literature, Modern Language Association of America, American Association of University Professors, American Society for Eighteenth Century Studies, Kafka Society of America, Modern Humanities Research Association, History of Science Society, Freies Deutsches Hochstift, Northeast Modern Language Association. Awards, honors: Guggenheim fellow, 1961-62; American Council of Learned Societies fellow, 1961-62; American Philosophical Society award, 1969.

WRITINGS: Novalis and Mathematics, University of North Carolina Press, 1960, 2nd edition, AMS Press, 1969; Die Gedichte Schillers, Francke, 1967; (contributor) Siegfried Mews, editor, Studies in Nineteenth & Twentieth Century German Literature, University of North Carolina Press, 1970; (contributor) Husbanding the Golden Grain, University of Michigan Press, 1973. Contributor to festschriften and to Germanic Review, PMLA, MIT Literary Magazine, Journal of English and Germanic Philology, German Quarterly, Monatschefte, Comparative Literature, Goethe-Jahrbuch, Lessing Yearbook, Germano-Slavica, and others. Member of editorial board, Historia Mathematica, 1972-76.

WORK IN PROGRESS: Research in theory of comedy, Schiller's language and imagination, Goethe and mathematics, Novalis, metaphoric and syntactic analysis of poetry.

*   *   *

DYER, William G(ibb) 1925-

PERSONAL: Born October 4, 1925, in Portland, Ore.; married Bonnie Hansen, January 2, 1952; children: five. Education: Attended University of Oregon, 1943, and Washington State University, 1944; Brigham Young University, B.A., 1950, M.A., 1951; University of Wisconsin, Ph.D., 1955. Home: 3077 Mojave Lane, Provo, Utah 84601. Office: A265 JKBA, Brigham Young University, Provo, Utah 84601.

CAREER: Iowa State University, Ames, instructor in sociology, 1953-55; Brigham Young University, Provo, Utah, assistant professor, 1955-59, associate professor, 1959-63, professor of sociology, 1963—, and chairman of department. Visiting professor at University of California, Utah State University, and University of Utah. National Training Laboratories, training consultant, 1959-60, program director of National Training Laboratory for Applied Behavioral Science, 1966-70, member of board of directors, 1967-70, fellow of National Training Laboratories Institute. Senior associate, Leadership Resources, Inc. Organization development consultant to Danish Technological Institute, 1969, and Danish Agricultural Development Organization, 1969-70. Military service: U.S. Army Air Forces, 1943; became second lieutenant.

MEMBER: International Association of Applied Social Sciences, American Sociological Association, American Association for Humanistic Psychology, American Association of University Professors, Pacific Sociological Association, Alpha Kappa Delta.

WRITINGS: (Editor) Training Designs for Human Relations Laboratories: 1959-60, National Training Laboratories, 1960; (contributor) Arthur B. Shostak and William Gomberg, editors, Blue Collar World, Prentice-Hall, 1964; (with Evan T. Peterson) Family Centered Nursing Care: A Social Science Perspective, College of Nursing, University of Utah, 1966; An Outline of Basic Principles of Sociology Using a Social System Frame of Reference, Brigham Young University Press, 1967; (contributor) Robert F. Winch and Louis Goodman, editors, Selected Studies in Marriage and *the Family,* Holt, 1968; (contributor) Robert V. Guthrie, editor, *Psychology in the World Today,* Addison-Wesley, 1969; (contributor) J. K. Haddon and M. L. Borgatta, editors, *Marriage and Family,* F. E. Peacock, 1969; (contributor) J. N. Edwards, editor, *The Family and Change,* Knopf, 1969; (contributor) Fleming Balveg, editor, *Organization Development,* L.O.K. Publication (Denmark), 1970; (editor) *Modern Theory and Method in Group Training,* Van Nostrand, 1972; *The Sensitive Manipulator: The Change Agent Who Builds with Others,* Brigham Young University Press, 1972, revised edition published as *Insight to Impact: Strategies for Interpersonal and Organizational Change,* 1976; *Creating Closer Families: Principles of Positive Family Interaction,* Brigham Young University Press, 1975; *Team Building: Issues and Alternatives,* Addison-Wesley, 1977. Contributor to about thirty articles and reviews to sociology and education journals.†

*   *   *

DYLAN, Bob 1941-
(Robert Zimmerman)

PERSONAL: Name legally changed August 9, 1962; born May 24, 1941, in Duluth, Minn.; son of Abraham (an appliance dealer) and Beatty (Stone) Zimmerman; married Sara Lowndes, November 22, 1965 (divorced, 1977); children: four, one stepchild. *Education:* Attended University of Minnesota, 1960. *Address:* 264, Cooper Station, New York, N.Y. 10003.

CAREER: Songwriter, composer of more than three hundred songs, including "Blowin' in the Wind," "Don't Think Twice, It's All Right," "The Times They Are A-Changin'," "It Ain't Me Babe," "Mr. Tambourine Man," "Like a Rolling Stone," "Desolation Row," "Just Like a Woman," "Lay Lady Lay," "If Not for You," "Forever Young," "Idiot Wind," and "Senor"; singer and performer (plays guitar, piano, autoharp, and harmonica); recording artist (has sold more than ten million records); poet. Performer on tours and concerts, and on television, including appearances in major concert halls of the United States, England, Europe, Australia, Japan, and at Woodstock, the Newport Jazz Festival, and the Monterey Folk Festival; has appeared in films "Don't Look Back," 1965, "Eat the Document," 1966, "Pat Garrett and Billy the Kid," 1972, "Concert for Bangladesh," 1972, "Rolling Thunder," 1977, and "Renaldo and Clara," 1978. *Awards, honors:* Tom Paine Award, Emergency Civil Liberties Committee, 1963; Mus. D., Princeton University, 1970; has received numerous music awards.

WRITINGS: Tarantula (prose), Macmillan, 1971; *Poem to Joanie,* Aloes Press (London), 1972; *Words* (poem), J. Cape, 1973; *Writings and Drawings,* Knopf, 1973; "Renaldo and Clara" (filmscript), Circuit Films, 1978.

Recordings: "Bob Dylan" (contains two songs written by Dylan), Columbia, 1962; "Freewheelin' Bob Dylan," Columbia, 1963, songbook published by Witmark, 1964; "The Times They Are A-Changin'," Columbia, 1964, songbook published by Witmark, 1964; "Another Side of Bob Dylan," Columbia, 1964, songbook published by Warner Brothers, 1964; "Bringing It All Back Home," Columbia, 1965, songbook published by Warner Brothers/Seven Arts, 1965; "Highway 61 Revisited," Columbia, 1965, songbook published by Witmark, 1965; "Blonde on Blonde," Columbia, 1966, songbook published by Peer-Southern, 1966; "Bob Dylan's Greatest Hits," Columbia, 1967, songbook published by Warner Brothers, 1967; "John Wesley Harding,"

Columbia, 1968, songbook published by Big Three, 1968; "Nashville Skyline," Columbia, 1969, songbook published by Peer-Southern, 1969; "Self Portrait," Columbia, 1970, songbook published by Warner Brothers, 1970; "New Morning," Columbia, 1970, songbook published by Big Three, 1971; "Bob Dylan's Greatest Hits, Volume II," Columbia, 1971; "Pat Garrett and Billy the Kid" (soundtrack), Columbia, 1973; "Planet Waves," Asylum, 1974, songbook published by Alfred Music, 1974; "Before the Flood," Asylum, 1974, songbook published by Warner Brothers, 1974; "Blood on the Tracks," Columbia, 1974, songbook published by Warner Brothers, 1975; "The Basement Tapes," Columbia, 1975, songbook published by Cherry Lane, 1975; "Desire," Columbia, 1975, songbook published by Warner Brothers, 1976; "Hard Rain," Columbia, 1976; "Street-Legal," Columbia, 1978.

Other songbooks: "The Bob Dylan Songbook," Witmark, 1963; "Bob Dylan Himself," Duchess, 1965; "Bob Dylan: A Collection," Witmark, 1966; "Don't Look Back," Witmark, 1967; "Bob Dylan the Original," Warner Brothers, 1968; "Songs for Voice and Guitar," two volumes, Witmark, 1968; "Bob Dylan's Songs for Harmonica," Witmark, 1968; "Approximately Complete Works," De Bezige Bij-Thomas Rap (Amsterdam), 1970; "Bob Dylan: A Retrospective," Warner Brothers, 1973; "Bob Dylan Leatherette Edition," Warner Brothers, 1974; "The Songs of Bob Dylan, 1966-1975," Knopf, 1976.

SIDELIGHTS: Bob Dylan is "the elusive, reclusive poet-songwriter whose songs of protest and love sparked, sensitized and inspired an entire generation," writes *Newsweek*'s Maureen Orth. Though an immensely popular performer, with at least twelve gold albums (selling over 500,000 units each), and two platinum albums (selling over one million units each), Dylan is much more than just popular. "The story of Dylan's art and poetry in the 1960s," writes Gregg M. Campbell in the *Journal of Popular Culture,* "is the story of a personal quest and dialogue in which Dylan led an entire generation of American and Western European youth ... toward a renewed vision of authenticity and human dignity."

The first influence on the development of Bob Dylan's music, in his early teens, were the country music of Hank Williams and black music, including the gospel rock of singer Little Richard. He taught himself piano, guitar and harmonica by listening to their music. Dylan did not discover folksinger Woody Guthrie, generally thought of as his chief influence, until his brief tenure at the University of Minnesota. But once he found Guthrie, Dylan immersed himself in the folk tradition; it was as a folksinger that he attained his first prominence. Dylan's first album, released when he was only nineteen, was a collection of folk songs, only two of which were written by him. It was a limited success and was followed within a year by an album consisting entirely of his own songs of protest and apocalyptic vision. His audience grew steadily. In 1963 the popular trio Peter, Paul and Mary released a version of his "Blowin' in the Wind" which was to become the fastest-selling single in the history of Warner Brothers Records. It was the first of 1500 recordings of his songs that would be made by other performers. By the time his third album was released in 1964, Dylan's role as a leader of the protest movement was established. This role came about because, as Jonathan Cott writes, "like few other persons of the mid-Sixties, . . . Dylan was right in time with the times." As folksinger Joan Baez explained, "Bobby Dylan says what a lot of people my age feel but cannot say." Dylan sang of alienation, rage, anxiety, desperation, and vision at the very moments when young people felt these things in themselves. Dylan's biographer Anthony Scaduto summarizes: "For millions of the young, Dylan has been a poet of the streets, crying out in pain against society's indifference and stupidity; his voice, his words, his visions gave substance to their radicalization."

Uncomfortable with the leadership role, Dylan attempted to dodge it by releasing a fourth album containing nothing but folk stories and love songs. In the meantime, thinking deeply, reading widely, questioning assumptions, Dylan began to see "the Movement" as futile. Scaduto quotes Dylan: "What Joan Baez is doing, and all those people demonstrating, they're not gonna save the world. It's not true they can change men's hearts. . . . Nobody's gonna learn by somebody else showing them or teaching them. People have to learn by themselves." Dylan broke away from folk music and the protest movement which had brought him renown. In his concerts and his next album, symbolically titled "Bringing It All Back Home," he recalled his musical roots and for the first time combined folk with the driving beat and electric sound of rock music. Purists booed and Dylan lost some fans but gained many more than he lost. He widened his audience and in "Highway 61 Revisited" produced what many critics see as his best work, truly integrating folk and rock music and adding as lyrics some of the finest poetry of the decade—mystical, apocalyptic, dense with images and allusions.

Dylan's young fans claimed him ferociously and catapulted him to superstardom. "His words," wrote Ralph Gleason, "not those of Pulitzer Prize winners, are quoted by students, written by them on walls and made into slogans and pasted on notebooks to demonstrate the fervor of their belief." Dave Van Ronk, performer and friend of Dylan, said, "Bobby wanted to be a superstar. When he discovered the reality of being a superstar he freaked out." As Scaduto puts it, Dylan feared "that he would be swallowed by it all, destroyed by fame." He felt his fans demanding that he offer himself as a martyr to their needs, their causes. The album that he released at this time, "'Blonde on Blonde,' marks the apex of Dylan's career as a rock 'n' roll star," writes Alan Rinzler. "At this point in his life he really was as big as Elvis Presley. Moreover, the content of Dylan's songs convinces many idolatrous fans that he *knows,* that he has the cosmic *answer,* that he can tell them the truth about their lives—an assumption which he himself both encourages and disdains. . . . The responsibility is too great, the pressure becomes immense." Then, in July of 1966, Bob Dylan was involved in a motorcycle accident that almost killed him. During his recuperation, and afterward, in the isolation he sought for himself and his family, Dylan has said that he thought about who he was and where he was going. He returned to the Judaic heritage he had once denied and studied and practiced rock music. All this would be evident when he returned to public view.

Dylan's contribution in the early part of his career has been summed up by Gregg Campbell: "By challenging the dominant style of power, arrogance and hubris in the 1950s and 1960s, Bob Dylan and the flower children called America back to that which was most worthy and essential in its tradition and left an artistic statement and an ethical legacy worthy of Melville, Twain or Faulkner. We can ask no more of any individual nor of any generation." The *New Yorker* noted that Dylan "always manages to free himself from the expectations of his audience. When they were expecting folk songs about the struggles of the thirties, he gave them folk songs about the struggles of the sixties. When they were expecting a revolutionary anthem with all the answers, he gave them a revolutionary anthem that was all questions. 'The answer is blowin' in the wind'—was there ever a better summing up of the intuitive, improvisatory, unreflective approach of what we used to call 'the Movement'? When people expected acoustic, he gave them electric. When they expected funk, he gave them mysticism. When they expected psychedelia, he gave them simple country love tunes. When they finally learned not to expect anything in particular except genius, he gave them mediocrity. . . ." Novelist John Clellan Holmes has been quoted as saying that Dylan "has the authentic mark of the bard on him, and I think it's safe to say that no one, years hence, will be able to understand just what it was to live in this time without attending to what this astonishingly gifted young man has already achieved."

"During the seclusion which followed the crash," writes Joe Urschel of the *Detroit Free Press:* "myths spread and [Dylan's] legend grew even faster. The myths fueled record sales and two of his albums went gold. Also during that time, rock music technology grew more and more sophisticated. The Beatles released 'Sgt. Pepper's Lonely Hearts Club Band,' a triumph of production and electronic manipulation. Upon recovery, Dylan ignored the popular trend and released a controversial, slow-paced acoustical, 'John Wesley Harding.' And once again he succeeded." But, as Urschel continues, Dylan's next album, "Nashville Skyline," seemed jarringly out of step: "Pure country, it came at the height of the nation's disillusionment with the war in Vietnam and seemed to say all the wrong things. It appealed to the conservative South, where Dylan's protest songs had once spurred civil rights marchers through streets lined with white bigotry. It seemed to turn its back on the country's angry young people and the tempestuous times," reflecting instead the happiness of Dylan's personal life. While large numbers of his fans followed him in his incursions into country music, there were desertions, and cries of his having sold out to commercial interests. "New Morning," continuing the happy spirit of "Nashville Skyline," was a smash hit, making up for the poor reception of "Self Portrait." But it was 1974 before Dylan had another success. His book, *Tarantula,* written in 1965-66 but not published until 1971, was a disappointment. "*Tarantula* didn't work," writes Scaduto. "It grew less lucid as he went along, more stream of consciousness that both defied meaning and lacked the emotion of poetry. Much of it was absurdist word-play."

Dylan's private life, which he has revealed onstage and protected offstage, was unveiled again in his work of this period. "Planet Waves" is a collection of what Dylan labelled "torch songs," passionate ballads with a hint of loss; by the time "Blood on the Tracks" was released the theme was lost love. Some critics have related these themes to Dylans' 1977 divorce. The theme of loss was continued in three cuts on "Desire" and practically the whole of "Street Legal."

Rinzler confesses his favoritism for "Desire," "an album by a mature artist at the height of his powers. . . . Everything about this album is polished to a new level of perfection." Alan Platt of *New Times* believes that "Street Legal" which "promises to be his most commercially successful ever," will also be one of Dylan's most controversial. Platt describes the album as "a series of the most aggressive and ill-tempered *love* songs that even the unsentimental Dylan ever seemed capable of putting out. They are also brilliant, which is more to the point." Recalling Dylan's talent for timeliness, Platt adds: "The times are ripe for the bitter and witty realism of a Dylan. . . . [This album] conveys the fierce honesty that is seldom presented for popular consumption, and *never* in rock music. The complexities of loss and despair are not pretty, nor is Dylan a sweet-natured boy. . . . Once again, Dylan is right there with his rough-edged verite style of production, in the perfect position to give his estranged admirers another shot of much-needed reality.''

Dylan's fascination with film led him to write and produce ''Renaldo and Clara,'' and because of his growing reputation, the film was widely reviewed. But other than Jonathan Cott of *Rolling Stone,* who thought the film ''audacious and remarkable,'' most critics could find little to praise. Janet Maslin of the *New York Times* says: ''Mr. Dylan, who has a way of insinuating that any viewer-who doesn't grasp the full richness of his work must be intellectually deficient or guilty of some failure of nerve, has seen fit to produce a film that no one is likely to find altogether comprehensible. Yet . . . 'Renaldo and Clara' holds the attention at least as effectively as it tries the patience.'' Several reviewers, including *Time's,* see the marvelous concert footage as the only reason ''his new movie is not a complete waste of time.'' Another group of film critics agree with Jack Kroll, who describes the movie as ''this ego trip disguised as deep-dish Art.'' Karen Durbin of the *Village Voice* writes: '''Renaldo and Clara' is not, as it first seems, an artsy-fartsy muddle about Truth, God, and Identity. It's a monster movie starring Dylan's ego.''

In spite of the intensity of the attack on ''Renaldo and Clara,'' many critics think highly of Dylan's poetry. While some agree with poet Louis Simpson, who says ''I don't think Bob Dylan is a poet at all; he is an entertainer,'' those who admire his verse include poets Allen Ginsberg, Lawrence Ferlinghetti, Kenneth Rexroth, and a host of literary critics. Dylan's poetry has been compared to that of Ginsberg, Whitman, Villon, Blake, Baudelaire, and Rimbaud, and the apparent influence of these writers and others has been traced in his lyrics. Richard Goldstein writes in *New York,* ''Allen Ginsberg once called Dylan 'the Walt Whitman of the jukebox,' but actually he was the Allen Ginsberg of the jukebox, adapting the scathing chant of poems like 'Howl,' and appropriating the syntax of beat poetry.'' Ginsberg also credited Dylan with having ''altered the course of poetics in America. . . . Dylan has almost single-handedly brought language back to its original poetic form which is minstrelsy.''

Critic after critic praises Dylan's use of symbolism, his rich complexity, his mysticism, his unpredictability, and, despite the harshness of his vision, his surprisingly hopeful existentialism. Irwin Silber, who is no fan of Dylan's, nevertheless has written: ''Let there be no mistake about it. Bob Dylan is a terrifyingly gifted artist.'' Writing in *Sing Out!,* Paul Nelson admires ''Dylan's unyielding and poetic point of view [which] represents a total commitment to the subjective over the objective, the microcosm over the macrocosm. . . . The tradition that Dylan represents is that of all great artists; that of projecting, with the highest possible degree of honesty and craftsmanship, a unique and personal vision of the world we live in, knowing full well that unless the personal is achieved, the universal cannot follow.'' In his article in *Saturday Review,* Steven Goldberg notes the mystical experience which dominates Dylan's work, and his concern with salvation. Goldberg concludes, ''This is why Dylan merits our most serious attention. For he stands at the vortex: when the philosophical, psychological and scientific lines of thought are followed to the point where each becomes a cul-de-sac, as logic without faith eventually must, Dylan is there to sing his songs.''

Bob Dylan's works have been published in French, Swedish, German, Finnish, Italian, Hebrew, Dutch, Norwegian, and Spanish.

BIOGRAPHICAL/CRITICAL SOURCES—Books: Sy Ribakove and Barbara Ribakove, *Folk Rock: The Bob Dylan Story,* Dell, 1966; Daniel Kramer, *Bob Dylan,* Citadel, 1967; Stephen Pickering, editor, *Dylan: A Commemoration,* Nowels Publications, 1971; Toby Thompson, *Positively Main Street: An Unorthodox View of Bob Dylan,* Coward, 1971; Craig McGregor, editor, *Bob Dylan: A Retrospective,* Morrow, 1972; Anthony Scaduto, *Bob Dylan,* W. H. Allen, 1972; Michael Gray, *Song and Dance Man,* Dutton, 1972; Craig Karpel, *The Tarantula in Me,* KLONH Books, 1973; Kathleen Beal, *Bob Dylan,* Creative Education Press, 1974; editors of *Rolling Stone* magazine, *Knocking on Dylan's Door,* Pocket Books, 1974; William Yenne, editor, *One Foot on the Highway: Bob Dylan on Tour,* KLONH Books, 1974; Stephen Pickering, *Bob Dylan Approximately: A Midrash,* McKay, 1975; Francois Ducray, *Dylan,* A. Michel (Paris), 1975; *Contemporary Literary Criticism,* Gale, Volume III, 1975, Volume IV, 1975, Volume VI, 1976; Sam Shepard, *Rolling Thunder Logbook,* Viking, 1977; Larry Sloman, *Rolling with the Thunder,* Bantam, 1978; Michael Gross and Robert Alexander, *Bob Dylan: An Illustrated History,* Grosset & Dunlap, 1978; Alan Rinzler, *Bob Dylan: The Illustrated Record,* Harmony, 1978.

Periodicals: *Look,* March 8, 1966; *New Yorker,* March 19, 1966, February 11, 1974, February 18, 1974, April 7, 1975, February 13, 1978; *National Review,* June 28, 1966, February 9, 1971, April 16, 1976; *Saturday Evening Post,* July 30, 1966, November 2, 1968, June, 1974; *New York Times,* December 23, 1967, January 11, 1968, April 13, 1969, January 26, 1978; *Time,* January 12, 1968, April 11, 1969, September 12, 1969, November 14, 1969, June 22, 1970, May 24, 1971, January 21, 1974, February 20, 1978; *Newsweek,* February 26, 1968, April 14, 1969, April 12, 1971, January 14, 1974, February 10, 1975, November 17, 1975, January 30, 1978; *Saturday Review,* May 11, 1968, October 26, 1968, April 26, 1969, May 30, 1970; *New Republic,* May 20, 1972, April 20, 1974, April 5, 1975, February 14, 1976; *New York,* January 28, 1974; *Village Voice,* February 7, 1974, January 20, 1978; *Rolling Stone,* February 14, 1974, March 14, 1974, March 13, 1975, January 26, 1978, March 9, 1978, March 23, 1978, May 18, 1978, June 29, 1978, August 24, 1978, November 16, 1978; *South Atlantic Quarterly,* spring, 1974; *Journal of Popular Culture,* summer, 1974, spring, 1975; *New Times,* February 6, 1978, February 20, 1978, May 15, 1978, August 7, 1978; *Atlantic,* April, 1978; *People,* July 17, 1978; *Detroit Free Press,* October 13, 1978.†

*   *   *

DYMALLY, Mervyn M(alcolm) 1926-

PERSONAL: Born May 12, 1926, in Trinidad, British West Indies; son of Hamid A. and Andried S. (Richardson) Dymally; married Alice M. Gueno, 1968; children: Mark, Lynn. *Education:* California State College (now University), Los Angeles, B.A., 1954; California State College (now University), Sacramento, M.A., 1969; United States International University, Ph.D., 1978. *Home:* 2366 West 23rd St., Los Angeles, Calif. 90018. *Office:* State Capitol, Room 1028, Sacramento, Calif. 95814.

CAREER: California State Assembly, Sacramento, assemblyman, 1962-66, chairman of committee on industrial relations, 1965-66; California State Senate (representing Los Angeles and Watts), Sacramento, senator, 1967-74, chairman of committees on social welfare, 1968-69, military and veterans affairs, 1969-70, and elections and reapportionments, 1971-74, chairman of subcommittees on medical education and health needs, 1972-74, and child development and child care program, 1972-74, chairman of majority caucus, 1970-74; lieutenant governor of the state of California, 1975—. Elementary and secondary school teacher in Los Angeles, Calif., 1954-60; lecturer in government at Claremont Colleges, University of California, Davis and Irvine, and Whittier College. Visiting fellow, Metropolitan Applied Research Center (New York, N.Y.). Member of board of advisors, Joint Center for Political Studies; founder and chairman of board of directors, Urban Affairs Institute; founder and member of board of directors, Job Education and Training Center. Member of California advisory committee, U.S. Civil Rights Commission. Member of board of directors, South Central Area Welfare Planning Council.

U.S. Department of State, goodwill ambassador to East and Central Africa, 1964, and Guyana and the Caribbean, 1965.

MEMBER: American Political Science Association, American Academy of Political and Social Science, American Association of University Professors, National Conference of Black Elected Officials (founder), California Conference of Black Elected Officials (chairman), Phi Delta Phi. *Awards, honors:* LL. D., University of West Los Angeles, 1970; J.D. from Lincoln University, 1975, and California College of Law, 1976.

WRITINGS: The Black Politician: His Struggle for Power, Doxbury, 1971. Contributor to *Urban West.* Founder and editor-in-chief, *Black Politician.*

SIDELIGHTS: Mervyn M. Dymally visited Israel as a guest of the government, 1967; in 1970, he was a guest of the Ditchley Foundation in England.

E

EAMES, Edwin 1930-

PERSONAL: Born March 7, 1930, in New York, N.Y.; son of Morris and Anna (Korn) Eisenberg; married Phyllis Edelstein (a teacher), September 9, 1951; children: Mona, David, Lori. *Education:* College of the City of New York (now City College of the City University of New York), B.S.S., 1951; Lucknow University, graduate study, 1953-54; Cornell University, Ph.D., 1965. *Politics:* Democrat. *Religion:* Jewish. *Home:* 700 Elkins Ave., Philadelphia, Pa. 19117. *Office:* Department of Anthropology, Bernard M. Baruch College of the City University of New York, 17 Lexington Ave., New York, N.Y. 10010.

CAREER: Temple University, Philadelphia, Pa., instructor, 1956-62, assistant professor, 1962-66, associate professor of anthropology, 1966-70; Bernard M. Baruch College of the City University of New York, New York, N.Y., associate professor, 1970-75, professor of anthropology, 1975—. *Member:* American Anthropological Association (fellow), American Association for the Advancement of Science, Philadelphia Anthropological Society (member of council), Phi Beta Kappa, Sigma Xi, Cornell Club of Philadelphia.

WRITINGS: (With Judith Goode) *Urban Poverty in a Cross Cultural Context,* Free Press, 1973; *Anthropology of the City,* Prentice-Hall, 1977. Contributor to anthropology and sociology journals. Consulting editor, *International Journal of Contemporary Sociology,* 1971—.

WORK IN PROGRESS: A cultural anthropological text, for Worth Publishers; research on psychic practitioners in New York.

* * *

EASTIN, Roy B(randon) 1917-

PERSONAL: Born July 1, 1917, in Henderson, Ky.; son of Roy Brandon; married Charlotte Mae Draeger (died, 1971); married Doris M. Bergstrom, August 26, 1972; children: (first marriage) Virginia Ann (Mrs. Morris Levin). *Education:* George Washington University, A.B., 1943, A.M., 1945; American University, Ph.D., 1953. *Religion:* Protestant. *Home:* 4010 25th Pl., Arlington, Va. 22207. *Office:* Department of Business Administration, George Washington University, Washington, D.C. 20006.

CAREER: U.S. Government Printing Office, Washington, D.C., assistant to director of personnel, 1943-45, assistant to

superintendent of documents, 1945-49, superintendent of documents, 1949-53, executive officer, 1953-60; George Washington University, Washington, D.C., professor of business administration, 1960—. Director, Dimension, Inc., 1961—. Licensed psychologist in District of Columbia, 1973—. Consultant, Printing Industries of America, 1960—.

MEMBER: American Psychological Association, American Society for Personnel Administration, Society for Personnel Administration, George Washington Personnel Society. *Awards, honors:* Citation from Rockefeller public service awards committee, 1952; distinguished service gold medal from U.S. Government Printing Office, 1959.

WRITINGS: Government Publications and Their Use, Brookings Institution, 1961, revised edition, 1969; *Management Patterns in Growing Business Forms Companies,* International Business Forms Industries, 1966; *The Difference Makes the Management,* Printing Industries of America, 1967. Contributor to *Forum on the Public Library Inquiry, Hospital Administration Quarterly,* and *Impressions.†*

* * *

EATON, Tom 1940-

PERSONAL: Born March 2, 1940, in Wichita, Kan.; son of Newton A. (an engineer) and Betty (Cooper) Eaton; married Shara Pinkley, June 24, 1967. *Education:* University of Kansas, B.F.A., 1962. *Home and office:* 911 West 100th St., Kansas City, Mo. 64114.

CAREER: Hallmark Cards, Inc., Kansas City, Mo., artist and writer in contemporary cards department, 1962-66; Scholastic Magazines, Inc., New York, N.Y., art editor and cartoonist, 1966-68; free-lance artist, writer, and cartoonist, 1968—. *Military service:* U.S. Army, Medical Field Service School, 1963-65.

WRITINGS—All self-illustrated; published by Scholastic Book Services, except as indicated: *Chicken-Fried Fudge and Other Cartoon Delights,* 1971; *Flap* (novel), Delacorte, 1972; *Otis G. Firefly's Phantasmagoric Almanac,* 1975; *Tom Eaton's Book of Marvels,* 1977; *The Organized Week,* 1977. Also author of *Captain Ecology, Pollution Fighter, Popnut,* and *Holiday Greeting Cards.*

Illustrator; all juveniles: Richard L. Penney, *The Penguins Are Coming,* Harper, 1969; William J. Cromie, *Steven and the Green Turtle,* Harper, 1970; W. Harmon Wilson and Roman F. Wormke, *Life on Paradise Island,* Scott, Foresman, 1970; Z. S. da Dilva, *Nuestro Mundo,* Macmillan, 1970; Richard R. Ricciuti, *An Animal for Alan,* Harper, 1971; Robyn Supraner, *A Sea Parade,* Nutmeg, 1971; Supraner, *Surprises!,* Nutmeg, 1971; *The Big Time Book,* Mulberry, 1971. Illustrator, M. Gerrard and J. McInnes, *Hickory Hollow ABC,* published by Thomas Nelson, and Richard T. Scott, *Pen the Red Hen,* published by Reader's Digest Press; also illustrator of filmstrip, "Folklore and Fables."

All published by Garrard: Donna Pape, *Leo the Lion Looks for Books,* 1972; Pape, *Count on Leo Lion,* 1973; Pape, *The Sleep-Leaping Kangaroo,* 1973; John McInnes, *Have You Ever Seen a Monster?,* 1974; McInnes, *Leo Lion Paints It Red,* 1974; Emily Hearn, *TV Kangaroo,* 1975; Howard Goldsmith, *What Makes a Grumble Smile?,* 1977; Nancy L. Robison, *Where Did My Little Fox Go?,* 1977; Pape, *Where Is My Little Joey?,* 1978.

All published by Scholastic Book Services: *Laugh Your Head Off,* 1969; LaVinia Dobler, *It's Your World: Don't Pollute It!,* 1972; Bud Delaney and Lolo Delaney, *The Daily Laugh,* 1973; Jim Razzi, *Mad Mad Puzzle Parade,* 1975; Mosesson, *The Perfect Put-Down,* 1975; B. Delaney and L. Delaney, *The Laugh Journal,* 1975; Donna Pape and Jeanette Grote, *Pack of Puzzles,* 1976; Leonore Klein, *Mazes & Mysteries,* 1976; Pape, *Puzzle Panic,* 1977; B. Delaney and L. Delaney, *The Beastly Gazette,* 1977. Also illustrator, Gerald Mosler, *Puzzle Fun,* L. Eisenberg and K. Hall, *Chicken Jokes and Puzzles,* Dick Hyman, *Crazy Laws,* Peggy Hudson, *Words to the Wise,* Irwin Silber, *Folksong Festival,* and J. Robinson, B. Van't Hul, and S. Dunning, *Language I* and *Language II.*

Workbooks; published by Scholastic Book Services, except as indicated: Lawrence Charry, *Across and Down,* 1967; Charry and Herber, *Word Puzzles and Mysteries,* 1967; Veryl Goldsweig, *Countdown,* 1969; Goldsweig, *Sprint,* 1970; *Panorama,* Houghton, 1971, revised edition, 1974. Illustrator of *Scope Visuals 1, 2, 3, 4, 5, 9, 10, 11, 14, 17, 19,* and *22;* also illustrator, Goldsweig, *Trackdown,* B. J. Hurwood, *Chillers and Thrillers,* and Miriam Lee, *Jobs in Your Future.*

Contributor of cartoons to *Playboy, Look, Saturday Evening Post,* and *Teen.*

WORK IN PROGRESS: Two adult novels.

SIDELIGHTS: Tom Eaton writes: "My purpose is to write books and draw cartoons which entertain. With the rewards for these labors I hope to maintain the good will of the local tradespeople and the banker who holds the mortgage on my house. This policy was defined several years ago when I tried telling the grocer that I was a big-time author, but he still insisted on cash. Several of my books have had foreign language editions; unfortunately they were issued as part of the Obscure, Iowa University Press's ill-fated Dead-Languages Program, and failed to sell. Or even to be given away. My main literary influences have been Ernest Bushmiller [creator of the "Nancy" comic strip] and the unsung genius who wrote the Ben-Gay ads of the late 1940's starring Peter Pain. The image of that green devil, bewhiskered jaw atwitch with malice, leaping upon some poor wretch's shoulder to jab him with the pitchfork of neuralgia has always seemed to me fraught with symbolism of the entire human condition. That and crabgrass. My working habits are simple—I begin each job when it cannot possibly be put off any longer, and try to get it over with as quickly as possible. This frees my inhibitions, adds to my spontaneity, and interferes less with my daytime television watching. My

greatest spiritual goal is to someday write one positive, believable statement about Amtrak."

AVOCATIONAL INTERESTS: Science fiction, science, travel (Europe and Scandinavia).

* * *

EBER, Dorothy (Margaret) Harley   1930-

PERSONAL: Born March 18, 1930, in Bromeley, England; daughter of George E. (a broker) and Dorothy Vera (Williams) Harley; married George Francis Eber (an architect), July 6, 1958. *Education:* University of Toronto, B.A. *Religion:* Anglican. *Home:* 1455 Sherbrooke St. W., Montreal, Quebec, Canada.

CAREER: Newspaper reporter in Toronto, Ontario, Montreal, Quebec, and London, England, 1950-57; free-lance magazine writer, 1960—. Guest curator, McCord Museum, McGill University. *Member:* Media Club of Canada (chairperson of Montreal branch, 1968-69), Canadian Guild of Crafts (member of Eskimo committee). *Awards, honors:* National Women's Press Club Memorial Award, from Media Club of Canada, 1969, for "Teen Cult in the New North," a magazine article; Canada Council grants, 1970, 1971, 1972, 1973, 1975, and 1976.

WRITINGS: The Computer Centre Party: Canada Meets Black Power, Tundra, 1969; *Pitseolak: Pictures Out of My Life,* Oxford University Press in arrangement with Design Collaborative Books, 1971, Washington University Press, 1972; (with Peter Pitseolak) *People from Our Side,* Hurtig Publishers, 1975, Indiana University Press, 1977; (editor) Peter Pitseolak, *Peter Pitseolak's Escape from Death* (juvenile), McClelland & Stewart, 1977, Delacourt, 1978. Also author of filmscript based on *Pitseolak: Pictures Out of My Life,* produced by National Film Board of Canada, 1973. Contributor to magazines in England and Canada, including *M Magazine* (of Montreal Museum of Fine Arts), *Saturday Night, Maclean's Magazine,* and *Chatelaine.*

WORK IN PROGRESS: A book made up chiefly from interviews with people who worked with Alexander Graham Bell; a book on Cape Dorset prints and print makers.

SIDELIGHTS: Dorothy Eber has made more than ten trips to Baffin Island to interview the artists of Cape Dorset. She is currently a guest curator at McGill University's McCord Museum where an exhibition entitled "Peter Pitseolak: Historian of South Baffin Island" is in progress and will be ready to tour internationally in September, 1979. Her principal interest as a writer is in documentary reportage. Most of her material on south Baffin Eskimos is written from tape recorded interviews. Her greatest influences have been anthropologist Oscar Lewis and Henry Brandon of the *New York Times.*

* * *

EDKINS, Diana M(aria)   1947-

PERSONAL: Born September 13, 1947, in New York, N.Y.; daughter of Walter (a physician) and Lola (Fine) Edkins. *Education:* New York University, B.A., 1969; State University of New York at Buffalo, M.A., 1971. *Office:* Department of Photographic History, Pratt Institute, Brooklyn, N.Y. 11205.

CAREER: Pratt Institute, Brooklyn, N.Y., teacher of photographic history, 1972—.

WRITINGS: Explorers, Time-Life, 1973; *Landscape and Discovery* (catalogue to accompany exhibit of author's photographs), Hofstra University, 1973; (with Beaumont Newhall) *William H. Jackson,* Morgan & Morgan, 1974. Consultant to Time/Life Book Series, 1972.

WORK IN PROGRESS: Work on nineteenth-century American landscape photographers; an exhibition on European and American landscape photographers.†

*   *   *

EDMONSON, Harold A(rthur) 1937-

PERSONAL: Born November 30, 1937, in Chicago, Ill.; son of George Robert and Letty (Worth) Edmonson. *Education:* Wright Junior College, A.A., 1958; University of Illinois at Urbana-Champaign, B.S., 1960. *Relgion:* Lutheran. *Home:* 1040 East Knapp, Milwaukee, Wis. 53202. *Office:* Kalmbach Publishing Co., 1027 North Seventh St., Milwaukee, Wis. 53233.

CAREER: Zonolite Company, Chicago, Ill., member of public relations staff, 1961-64; Rauland Corp., Melrose Park, Ill., editor of company newspaper, 1967-68; Kalmbach Publishing Company, Milwaukee, Wis., associate editor of *Trains Magazine,* 1968-71, books editor, 1971—. *Military service:* U.S. Army Reserve, 1960-66. *Member:* National Railway Historical Society, Railroad Club of Chicago (director, 1965—), Milwaukee Press Club.

WRITINGS: Main Line Mexico, privately printed, 1964; *World Steam in Action,* Ian Allan, 1970; (contributor) *Flying Scotsman,* 2nd edition, Ian Allan, 1970; (contributor) *Trains around the World,* Octopus Books, 1972; (editor) *Journey to Amtrak,* Kalmbach, 1972; (with Victor Hand) *The Love of Trains,* Octopus Books, 1974; *The Railroad Station Planbook,* Kalmbach, 1977; (editor) *Famous Spaceships of Fact and Fantasy,* Kalmbach, 1978.

SIDELIGHTS: Harold A. Edmonson has traveled on the railroads on six continents and in twenty-seven countries. *Avocational interests:* Aviation, photography.

*   *   *

EDWARDS, David C(harles) 1937-

PERSONAL: Born November 24, 1937, in Wisconsin Rapids, Wis.; son of Orrin E. (a shop foreman) and Evelyn (Anderson) Edwards; married Jeanne C. Seidens, August 22, 1959; children: Jennifer, Anna. *Education:* University of Wisconsin, B.S., 1959; University of Iowa, M.A., 1961, Ph.D., 1962. *Home:* R.R. 3, Ames, Iowa 50010. *Office:* Department of Psychology, Iowa State University, Ames, Iowa 50011.

CAREER: Iowa State University, Ames, assistant professor, 1963-67, associate professor, 1967-72, professor of psychology, 1972—. *Military service:* U.S. Naval Reserve, 1955-63. *Member:* Psychonomic Society, American Psychological Association, Sigma Xi.

WRITINGS: General Psychology, with workbook, Macmillan, 1968, 2nd edition, 1972.

WORK IN PROGRESS: Research in psychophysiology of attention and in peripheral vision as it affects visual looking behavior.

*   *   *

EDWARDS, Paul M(adison) 1933-

PERSONAL: Born February 26, 1933, in Independence, Mo.; son of Frank H. (a minister) and Alice (Smith) Edwards; married Carolyn Smith, February 7, 1953; children: Paula Jean, Greggory Madison. *Education:* Washburn Uni-

versity of Topeka, B.A., 1959; University of South Dakota, M.A., 1960; University of St. Andrews, Ph.D., 1972. *Home:* 329 South Silver, Lamoni, Iowa 50140. *Office:* Department of History and Philosophy, Graceland College, Lamoni, Iowa 50140.

CAREER: Graceland College, Lamoni, Iowa, assistant professor, 1960-67, associate professor, 1967-71, professor of history and philosophy, 1971—, vice-president for academic affairs, 1978—. Chief of the Museum Division of the Wyoming Department of History and Archives, 1965-66; chairman of the board of Venture Foundation, Inc., 1970—. *Military service:* U.S. Army, 1953-55; became staff sergeant. *Member:* American Philosophical Association, American Historical Association, Missouri Valley Historical Association.

WRITINGS: Inquiry in Faith, Herald House, 1967; *Essays in Restoration History,* Coronado Press, 1970; *The Hilltop Where . . . ,* Herald Press, 1972.

*   *   *

EICHELBERGER, Clayton L. 1925-

PERSONAL: Born May 3, 1925, in Strang, Neb.; son of Joel V. (a carpenter) and Katie (Lauber) Eichelberger; married Nancy Houston, June 2, 1956; children: Julie, Joel, Jon. *Education:* University of Colorado, B.A., 1949, M.A., 1950; University of Texas, Ph.D., 1956. *Residence:* Arlington, Tex. *Office:* Department of English, University of Texas at Arlington, Arlington, Tex. 76010.

CAREER: University of Texas at Arlington, associate professor, 1956-60, professor of American literature, 1960—. *Military service:* U.S. Army, 1950-52; became sergeant major. *Member:* American Studies Association, Modern Language Association of America (chairman of American Literature Group, 1972), South Central Modern Language Association, Texas College Teachers of English.

WRITINGS: (Compiler) *A Guide To Critical Reviews of United States Fiction, 1870-1910,* Scarecrow, Volume I, 1971, Volume II, 1974; *Published Comment on William Dean Howells through 1920: A Research Bibliography,* G. K. Hall, 1976; *Harper's Lost Reviews: The Literary Notes by Lawrence Hutton, John Kendrick Bangs, and Others,* KTO Press, 1976. Contributor of critical and bibliographic studies of authors to *Georgia Review, Journal of Popular Culture, American Quarterly, Papers of the Bibliographic Society,* and *American Literary Realism.* Editor, *American Literary Realism,* 1967-77.

WORK IN PROGRESS: Studies, critical and bibliographic, of American fiction; further compilations of critical reviews of American fiction, 1870-1910.

*   *   *

EISDORFER, Carl 1930-

PERSONAL: Born June 20, 1930, in Bronx, N.Y.; son of Sam and Fani Eisdorfer; married Susan Elizabeth Gadsby; children: Erica, Marc, Jason. *Education:* New York University, B.A., 1951, M.A., 1953, Ph.D., 1959; Duke University, M.D., 1964, psychiatry training, 1965-67. *Residence:* Seattle, Wash. *Office:* Department of Psychiatry, University of Washington, Seattle, Wash. 98195.

CAREER: City of New York, N.Y., social investigator, 1952-53, school psychologist, 1953-54; Duke University, Durham, N.C., 1956-72, began as research assistant, became professor of medical psychology, head of Division of Medical Psychology, 1970-72, director of behavioral sciences program, School of Medicine, 1968-72, director of Center for the Study of Aging and Human Development, 1970-72; University of Washington, Seattle, professor of psychiatry and chairperson of department of psychiatry and behavioral sciences, School of Medicine, and adjunct professor, department of psychology, 1972—, acting director of Institute on Aging, 1977—. Diplomate in psychiatry, American Board of Psychiatry and Neurology, 1974. Visiting professor, University of Southern California, summers, 1968, 1974, and 1977; visiting professor, University of California, Berkeley, and University of California Medical Center, San Francisco, 1969-70. Halifax County Health Department, coordinator of Community Mental Health Service, 1959-69, program director of Community Mental Health Center, 1969-71. National Institute of Health, co-chairperson of Conference on Learning in the Adult Years, 1967, chairperson of Conference on Longitudinal Studies of Adult Life and Aging, 1967, member of Program Projects Review Committee, Division of Research Grants, 1967-69, member of Research and Training Review Committee, 1969-77. U.S. Department of Health, Education, and Welfare, member of Committee on Older Americans, 1971-73, member of President's Biomedical Research Panel, 1975. Member of board of directors, Carver Research Foundation of Tuskegee Institute, 1971-76; member of panel on death with dignity, National Academy of Sciences, 1971—. Federal Council on Aging, member, 1974-76, chairperson of Research and Manpower Subcommittee, 1974-76, consultant, 1976-77, member of Committee on Aging and Medical Education, 1977. Secretary of Section of Geriatric Psychiatry, World Congress of Psychiatry, 1977; member of Task Force on Aging, American Public Health Association, 1978. Member of professional advisory committee, Brookdale Institute of Gerontology and Adult Human Development, Jerusalem, Israel, 1974; member of advisory committee, Institute for Advanced Studies in the Biomedical Sciences, 1976; member of national advisory council, Davis Institute for the Care and Study of Aging, 1976-78; member of advisory board, National Action Forum for Older Women, 1978. White House Conference on Aging, special consultant, 1961, consultant to Technical Committee on Research and Demonstration, 1971-73; special consultant to World Wide Physician Program, Peace Corps, 1965-70; consultant to Veterans Administration Health Care Resources Committee, 1975-77, Psychiatry Education Branch, National Institute of Mental Health, 1975-77, and to National Advisory Council on Aging, National Institute on Aging, 1976-77. Consultant in behavioral sciences, Collier's Encyclopedia Reference Service, 1956-61. *Military service:* U.S. Army, clinical psychologist, 1954-56.

MEMBER: American Psychological Association (fellow; president of Division 20, 1969-70; chairman of Task Force on Aging, 1970-72), Gerontological Society (fellow; chairman of Division on Psychology and Social Sciences, 1970-71; president, 1971-72), American Geriatrics Society (fellow), American Psychiatric Association (fellow), American College of Psychiatrists (fellow), American Psychopathological Association, American Psychosomatic Society, Society for Psychophysiological Research, American Association for the Advancement of Science (fellow), Society for Research in Child Development, Washington State Psychological Association (fellow), Sigma Xi. *Awards, honors:* National Institute of Mental Health fellow, 1962-64; Robert W. Kleemeier Award of Gerontological Society, 1969, for outstanding research in aging; Edward B. Allen Award of American Geriatrics Society, 1974; Kesten Award and So-

cial Science award of Ethel Percy Andrus Gerontology Center, University of Southern California, 1976.

WRITINGS: (Editor with Stuart E. Golann and contributor) *Handbook of Community Mental Health,* Appleton, 1972; (editor with Lissy F. Jarvik and June Blum and contributor) *Intellectual Functioning in Adults,* Springer Publishing, 1973; (editor with M. P. Lawton) *The Psychology of Aging and Adult Development,* American Psychological Association, 1973; (editor with Edward Fann) *Psychopharmacology and Aging,* Plenum, 1973.

Contributor: Clark Tibbitts and W. T. Donahue, editors, *Social and Psychological Aspects of Aging,* Columbia University Press, 1962; Rosamonde R. Boyd, editor, *Older Americans: Social Participants,* Converse College, 1968; George Talland, editor, *Human Behavior and Aging: Recent Advances in Research and Theory,* Academic Press, 1968; E. W. Busse and Eric Pfeiffer, editors, *Behavior and Adaptation in Later Life,* Little, Brown, 1969; Adeline M. Hoffman, editor, *The Daily Needs and Interests of Older People,* C. C Thomas, 1970; Ira Iscoe and Charles Spielberger, editors, *Community Psychology: Perspectives in Training and Research,* Appleton, 1970; Erdman Palmore, editor, *Normal Aging,* Duke University Press, 1970; Frances Carp, editor, *Retirement,* Behavioral Science Publications, 1972.

Contributor to other symposia; contributor of more than forty articles to mental health, community health, gerontology, psychiatry, and other journals. Member of editorial board, *Annual Review of Gerontology and Geriatrics, Western Journal of Medicine, Gerontological Abstracts, Aging and Human Development, Community Psychology,* and *Law and Contemporary Problems,* 1968-72; contributing editor, *Postgraduate Medicine,* 1969-74, and *Contemporary Psychology,* 1970-75; consulting editor, *Contemporary Psychology,* 1970-75.

WORK IN PROGRESS: Program or project director of studies on various aspects of aging for National Institutes of Health, National Institute of Child Health and Human Development, and American Orthopsychiatric Association.

*   *   *

EISELE, Albert A(lois) 1936-

PERSONAL: Surname is pronounced "Eyes-*lee*"; born June 28, 1936, in Faribault County, Minn.; son of Albert A. (a farmer and writer) and Susan (Frawley) Eisele; married Moira Conway, September 29, 1962; children: Catherine, Ann. *Education:* St. John's University, Collegeville, Minn., B.A., 1958; University of Minnesota, additional study, 1962-64. *Politics:* Democrat. *Religion:* Roman Catholic. *Home:* 1309 Seaton Cir., Falls Church, Va. 22046. *Office:* Ridder Newspapers, 1325 E St. N.W., Washington, D.C. 20004.

CAREER: Ridder Newspapers, Washington correspondent, 1965—. *Military service:* U.S. Army, 1960; became second lieutenant. *Member:* National Press Club, National Capital Democratic Club, Federal City Club. *Awards, honors:* American Political Science Association Award for distinguished reporting of public affairs, 1971.

WRITINGS: Almost to the Presidency: A Biography of Two American Politicians, Piper, 1972. Contributor of articles to *New Republic, Washingtonian,* and *TWA Ambassador.*††

*   *   *

EITZEN, Ruth (Carper) 1924-

PERSONAL: Born July 20, 1924, in Lititz, Pa.; daughter of

Reuben R. and Eva (Weber) Carper; married Allan Eitzen (an artist), June 12, 1954; children: Hilda, Dirk, Ann, Laura, John. *Education:* Goshen College, B.A., 1946; also attended Eastern Mennonite School, Basel Gewerbeschule, and Pennsylvania Academy of Art; studied art privately. *Religion:* Mennonite. *Home address:* Route 1, Box 60, Barto, Pa. 19504.

CAREER: Mennonite Publishing House, Scottdale, Pa., writer and illustrator, 1945-49; Mennonite Central Committee, Akron, Pa., volunteer in editorial and educational capacity in Europe, 1950-54; free-lance artist and writer, 1954—.

WRITINGS: Ti Jacques: A Story of Haiti, Crowell, 1972. Contributor of poems, articles, and short stories to journals.

WORK IN PROGRESS: Writing poems; research in American history for children's books.††

* * *

EL-AREF, Aref (?)-1973

(?)—July 30, 1973; Arab politician and historian. Obituaries: *Washington Post,* August 2, 1973.

* * *

ELDREDGE, H(anford) Wentworth 1909-

PERSONAL: Born October 16, 1909, in New York, N.Y.; son of Hanford Wentworth and Elizabeth (Taylor) Eldredge; married Diana Younger, April 21, 1947; children: James Wentworth, Alan Wentworth. *Education:* Dartmouth College, A.B., 1931; University of Vienna, graduate study at Austro-American Institute, 1933; Yale University, Ph.D., 1935. *Home:* Tarn House, Norwich, Vt. 05055. *Office:* Department of Sociology, Dartmouth College, Hanover, N.H. 03755.

CAREER: Dartmouth College, Hanover, N.H., instructor, 1935-39, assistant professor, 1939-41, 1946-49, professor of sociology, 1949-74, professor emeritus, 1974—, chairman of department of sociology and anthropology, 1953-57, chairman of department of sociology, 1965-68, chairman of international relations program, 1959-62, chairman of city planning and urban studies program, 1959-65. Harvard University, visiting lecturer, 1963, visiting professor, 1974-75; member of faculty, Salzburg Seminar in American Studies, 1965; visiting professor, University of California, Berkeley, 1967; lecturer at Institut des Hautes Etudes de Defense Nationale, Paris, 1960, Fuehrungsakademie der Bundeswehr, Hamburg, 1960, U.S. Air Force Academy, 1961, Ecole de Guerre, Brussels, 1962, and at a number of universities in United States and England; ten-time guest lecturer (eighteen lectures) at NATO Defense College, Paris, 1955-64. Held government posts with Department of Justice and Department of State, 1942; member of president's Citizens Committee for International Development, 1961. Founding trustee of Atlantic Foundation and Outward Bound, Inc. Consultant on White House staff, 1956. *Military service:* U.S. Army, 1942-45; became major; received Bronze Star and five battle stars.

MEMBER: American Sociological Association, American Society of Planning Officials, American Institute of Planners, Society for International Development, Beta Theta Pi, The Brook (New York), Wianno Club (Osterville, Mass.), American Club (London). *Awards, honors:* Visiting scholar as guest of West German Republic, 1964.

WRITINGS: (With Francis E. Merrill) *Culture and Society,* Prentice-Hall, 1952; *The Second American Revolu-*

tion: *The Near Collapse of Traditional Democracy,* Morrow, 1964, revised edition, Washington Square Press, 1966; (editor and author of preface and notes) *Taming Megalopolis: An Introduction to Urban Planning and Urbanism,* two volumes, Praeger, 1967; (contributor) Albert Somit, editor, *Political Futurism,* Holt, 1972; *World Capitals: Toward Managed Urbanism,* Doubleday, 1975. Author of a series of articles on developments in Latin America for *New York Herald Tribune,* 1950. Contributor of articles and reviews to journals, including *Revue de Defense Nationale, Survival,* and *NATO Letter.*

WORK IN PROGRESS: Societal Space: The Behavioral Basis of Urban Planning, with Frank Smallwood.

SIDELIGHTS: H. Wentworth Eldredge told *CA* that he is "reasonably fluent in German and French, barely adequate in Spanish, some slight knowledge of Italian, Portuguese, Dutch, Norwegian, Swedish, and Danish." He has spent seven and one-half years abroad, mainly in Western and Central Europe, with some time spent in Latin America, North Africa, the Middle East, and the Orient.

* * *

ELISOFON, Eliot 1911-1973

April 17, 1911—April 7, 1973; American photographer, painter, art collector, film director, and author of books on primitive art and other topics. Obituaries: *New York Times,* April 8, 1973; *Washington Post,* April 9, 1973.

* * *

ELKIN, Frederick 1918-

PERSONAL: Born August 5, 1918, in Atlantic City, N.J.; son of Charles and Ethel (Markowitz) Elkin; married Madge Brown, June 30, 1955; children: Mark, Lisa, Delia. *Education:* University of Chicago, B.A., 1940, M.A., 1946, Ph.D., 1951. *Home:* 165 Cortleigh Blvd., Toronto, Ontario, Canada M5N 1P6. *Office:* Department of Sociology, York University, 4700 Keele St., Downsview, Ontario, Canada.

CAREER: Motion Picture Association of America, Hollywood, Calif., member of research staff, 1947-50; University of Southern California, Los Angeles, lecturer in cinema department, 1948-51; University of Missouri—Columbia, visiting assistant professor of sociology, 1951-52; McGill University, Montreal, Quebec, assistant professor, 1952-61, associate professor of sociology, 1961-62; University of Montreal, Montreal, associate professor of sociology, 1962-64; York University, Downsview, Ontario, professor of sociology, 1964—, chairman of department, 1964-69, director of Office of Research Administration, 1972-76. Coding supervisor, National Opinion Research Center, summer, 1952; research project director, Defence Research Board, Ottawa, summer, 1955; visiting professor, Sir George Williams University, summer, 1971. Dellcrest Children's Centre, Toronto, research consultant, 1966-69, member of professional advisory committee, 1969—; member of board of directors, Social Planning Council of Metropolitan Toronto, 1967-69. *Military service:* U.S. Army, Signal Intelligence, 1942-45; served in England, France, and Germany. *Member:* American Sociological Association, Canadian Sociology and Anthropology Association (president, 1973-74), Association of Voluntary Action Scholars, Phi Beta Kappa. *Awards, honors:* Canada Council leave fellow, 1969-70, 1976-77.

WRITINGS: Child and Society, Random House, 1960, 2nd edition (with Gerald Handel), 1972, 3rd edition (with Handel), 1978; *The Family in Canada,* Vanier Institute of the

Family, 1964; *Rebels and Colleagues: Advertising and Social Change in French Canada,* McGill-Queens University Press, 1973.

Contributor: Bernard Rosenberg and David M. White, editors, *Mass Culture: The Popular Arts in America,* Free Press, 1957; Joseph S. Roucek, editor, *Contemporary Sociology,* Philosophical Library, 1958; Roucek, editor, *The Unusual Child,* Philosophical Library, 1962; George Zollschan and Walter Hirsch, editors, *Explorations in Social Change,* Houghton, 1964; W. E. Mann, *Canada: A Sociological Profile,* Copp, 1968; A. Isaiah Litvak and Bruce Mallen, editors, *Marketing: Canada,* 2nd edition, McGraw, 1968; Mann, editor, *Social and Cultural Change in Canada,* Volume I, Copp, 1970; Jacques Boucher and Andre Morel, editors, *Le Droit dans le vie familiale,* University of Montreal Press, 1970; R. J. Ossenberg, editor, *Canadian Society: Pluralism, Change and Conflict,* Prentice-Hall, 1971; K. Ishwaran, editor, *The Canadian Family,* Holt, 1971, revised edition, 1976; B. D. Singer, editor, *Communications in Canadian Society,* Copp, 1972, revised edition, 1975; M. D. Beckman and R. H. Evans, editors, *Marketing: A Canadian Perspective,* Prentice-Hall, 1972.

Contributor to *Marriage, Family and Society: Canadian Perspectives,* edited by S. P. Wakil, 1975, and to other books. Writer of research reports for Vanier Institute of the Family, Defence Research Board, and Ontario Human Rights Commission. Contributor to *A Dictionary of the Social Sciences* and to sociology, anthropology, and psychology journals. Member of editorial board, *Canadian Review of Sociology and Anthropology,* 1963-65, and *Sociological Focus,* 1972—; associate editor, *International Journal of Comparative Sociology,* 1967—.

SIDELIGHTS: Child and Society has been translated into both Spanish and Portuguese.

*   *   *

ELLIOTT, Bruce (Walter Gardner Lively Stacy) 1915(?)-1973

(Walter Lively, Bruce Stacy, Walter Stacy)

1915(?)—March 21, 1973; American magazine publisher and editor, novelist, mystery and science fiction writer, and author of books and scripts on magic. Obituaries: *New York Times,* March 25, 1973.

*   *   *

ELLIOTT, Sarah M(cCarn)   1930-

PERSONAL: Born March 6, 1930, in Chicago, Ill.; daughter of David Glessner (a manufacturer) and Ruth (an assistant dean of students at University of Chicago; maiden name, O'Brien); married Paul M. Elliott (a freelance writer and editor), June 16, 1961 (divorced December 21, 1978). *Education:* Attended Stephens College, 1948-49, and National College of Education, 1949-50; Northwestern University, B.S. in Ed., 1952. *Politics:* "Independent-liberal." *Religion:* "Independent." *Home and office:* 333 East 34th St., New York, N.Y. 10016.

CAREER: Elementary teacher in the states of Washington, New York, and Illinois, 1952-54, 1958; commercial artist in garment industry, New York City, 1954-55; text and trade book editor in Chicago, Ill., and New York City, 1957-63, working for Scott, Foresman, Prentice-Hall, Macmillan, Harcourt, Brace & World, and other publishers; Community Gallery, New York City, curator and coordinator of art shows, 1969-72. Artist, with work in group shows in New

York, 1968, 1970, and book illustrator; teacher of course on children's classics at New School for Social Research. Conductor of radio series on children's classics; has appeared on other radio and television programs, including "Today" and "Johnny Carson" shows. *Member:* American Begonia Society, Linnaean Society of New York. *Awards, honors: Our Dirty Land* was named an outstanding science book for children by National Science Teachers Association-Children's Book Council Joint Committee, 1976.

WRITINGS—All published by Messner; all self-illustrated: *Our Dirty Air* (juvenile; Library of Congress selection for *Books 1971*) 1971; *Our Dirty Water* (juvenile), 1973; *Our Dirty Land,* 1976.

Contributor: *Freedom's Sound,* Holt, 1968; *Sprint Reading Skills,* Scholastic Book Services, 1978; *Back to Basics,* Reader's Digest Educational Books, 1979.

AVOCATIONAL INTERESTS: Gardening on city roof ("despite pollution"), bird watching, jazz.

*   *   *

ELLWOOD, Robert S(cott), Jr.   1933-

PERSONAL: Born July 17, 1933, in Normal, Ill.; son of Robert Scott (a teacher) and Knola (Shanks) Ellwood; married Gracia Fay Bouwman (a writer), August 28, 1965. *Education:* University of Colorado, B.A. (magna cum laude), 1954; Berkeley Divinity School, New Haven, Conn., M.Div. (cum laude), 1957; University of Chicago, M.A., 1965, Ph.D., 1967. *Residence:* Pasadena, Calif. *Office:* School of Religion, University of Southern California, Los Angeles, Calif. 90007.

CAREER: Minister in Episcopal church in Central City, Neb., 1957-60; University of Southern California, Los Angeles, assistant professor, 1967-71, associate professor, 1971-75, professor of religion, 1975—, Bishop James W. Bashford Professor of Oriental Studies, 1977—, director of East Asian Studies Center, 1977—. Lecturer at churches, colleges, and universities. *Military service:* U.S. Navy, chaplain, 1961-62; became lieutenant. *Awards, honors:* Rockefeller Foundation fellowship in religion, 1964-65; Fulbright-Hays fellowship, Japan, 1966-67.

WRITINGS: Religious and Spiritual Groups in Modern America, Prentice-Hall, 1973; *One Way: The Jesus Movement and Its Meaning,* Prentice-Hall, 1973; *The Feast of Kingship: Accession Ceremonies in Ancient Japan,* Sophia University Press (Tokyo), 1973; *The Eagle and the Rising Sun: Americans and the New Religions of Japan,* Westminster, 1974; *Many Peoples, Many Faiths,* Prentice-Hall, 1976; *Words of the World's Religions: An Anthology,* Prentice-Hall, 1977; *Introducing Religion: From Inside and Outside,* Prentice-Hall, 1978; *Readings in Religion: From Inside and Outside,* Prentice-Hall, 1978; *Alternative Altars,* University of Chicago Press, in press; *Mysticism and Religion,* Prentice-Hall, in press. Contributor to *Encyclopaedia Britannica.* Contributor of about twenty articles to academic journals, including *History of Religions, Sewanee Review, Asian Folklore Studies, Journal of Church and State,* and *Anglican Theological Review.*

WORK IN PROGRESS: Three books, *Japanese Civilization: Past and Present,* for Duxbury Press, *Tenrikyo: A Pilgrimage Faith,* for Cornell University Press, and *Christianity, A Cultural Perspective,* for Prentice-Hall.

*   *   *

EMBODEN, William A., Jr.   1935-

PERSONAL: Born February 24, 1935; son of William A. (a

priest) and Mildred (an artist; maiden name, Hagquist) Emboden. *Education:* Purdue University, B.S., 1957; Indiana University, M.A., 1960; University of California, Los Angeles, Ph.D., 1965. *Politics:* "Monarchist." *Office:* Department of Biology, California State University, Northridge, Calif. 91324.

CAREER: California State University, Northridge, assistant professor, 1965-70, associate professor, 1970-74, professor of biology, 1974—. Senior curator of botany, Los Angeles Natural History Museum, Los Angeles, Calif., 1967-70. *Member:* Sigma Xi.

WRITINGS: Narcotic Plants, Macmillan, 1972; (contributor) Peter T. Furst, editor, *Flesh of the Gods: The Ritual Use of Hallucinogens,* Praeger, 1972; *Bizarre Plants,* Macmillan, 1974; *Narcotic Plants of the World,* Macmillan, 1979. Editor and contributor, *Terra.*

WORK IN PROGRESS: Three books, *Plants of Shakespeare, Botany of Leonardo da Vinci,* and *The Artist as a Scientist.*

SIDELIGHTS: William A. Emboden told *CA:* "I travel and live graciously in a French Normandy chateau situated in the Santa Monica Mountains. During the summer I retire to Paris and Venice where I write."

*   *   *

EMERSON, William K(eith)   1925-

PERSONAL: Born May 1, 1925, in San Diego, Calif.; son of Horace Paine and Vera (Vaught) Emerson. *Education:* San Diego State College (now University), A.B., 1948; University of Southern California, M.S., 1950; University of California, Berkeley, Ph.D., 1956. *Home:* 10 East End Ave., New York, N.Y. 10021. *Office:* American Museum of Natural History, Central Park W. at 79th St., New York, N.Y. 10024.

CAREER: Malacologist; University of California, Museum of Paleontology, Berkeley, paleontologist, 1950-55; American Museum of Natural History, New York, N.Y., assistant curator, 1955-61, associate curator, 1961-66, curator of living vertebrates, 1966—, chairman of department, 1960-74. Research associate of San Diego Natural History Museum, 1962—; member of Belvedere expedition to Gulf of California, 1962; leader of Puritan-American Museum of Natural History expedition to western Mexico.

MEMBER: American Association for the Advancement of Science (fellow), American Malacological Union (president, 1961-62), Society of Systematic Zoology (member of council, 1960-63), Paleontological Society, Western Society of Malacologists (president, 1969-70).

WRITINGS: (With M. K. Jacobson) *Shells of the New York City Area,* Argonaut Books, 1961, revised edition published as *Shells from Cape Cod to Cape May with Special Reference to the New York Area,* Dover, 1971; (with Jacobson) *Wonders of the World of Shells: Sea, Land, and Fresh-water,* Dodd, 1971; *Shells,* photographic illustrations by Andreas Feininger, Viking, 1972; (with Arnold Ross) *Wonders of Barnacles,* Dodd, 1976; (with Jacobson) *The American Museum of Natural History Guide to Shells: Land, Freshwater, and Marine, from Nova Scotia to Florida,* Knopf, 1976; (with Jacobson) *Wonders of Starfish,* Dodd, 1977. Contributor to encyclopedias; contributor of articles and reviews to scientific journals.

WORK IN PROGRESS: Two books on mollusks and other invertebrates.

ENGEL, (Aaron) Lehman   1910-

PERSONAL: Born September 14, 1910, in Jackson, Miss.; son of Ellis (a salesman) and Juliette (Lehman) Engel. *Education:* Attended Cincinnati Conservatory of Music, 1926-27, Cincinnati College of Music, 1927-29; graduate of Juilliard School, 1934; studied privately with Roger Sessions, 1935. *Politics:* None. *Religion:* None. *Home and office:* 350 East 54th St., New York, N.Y. 10022.

CAREER: Composer of concert works for various solo instruments, orchestra, and voice, and conductor of works for theater, television, films, and radio; conductor of more than sixty recordings for RCA-Victor, Columbia, Decca, Brunswick, and Atlantic. Musical director, Dallas State Fair Musicals, Dallas, Tex., 1949-52; conductor at Lewisohn Stadium, New York City, 1951, and for New Friends of Music at Town Hall, New York City, 1952; guest conductor for St. Louis Municipal Opera, 1968—, and Turkish State Opera, 1968. Lecturer, Salzburg Seminar in American Studies, 1968; lecturer to numerous universities and organizations throughout the United States. President, Arrow Music Press, Inc.; director of music department, American Musical and Dramatic Theater Academy, 1962—. Director of Workshops for Composers and Lyricists for Broadcast Music, Inc.; director of musical theater development for Columbia Pictures-Screen Gems. Member of board of directors of Henry Street Settlement's Music School, Everyman Associates, Inc., and Foundation of the Theatre and Music Collection, Museum of the City of New York; member of advisory board, New York High School of Performing Arts. Consultant on bicentennial recordings, Rockefeller Foundation, 1973-74. *Military service:* U.S. Navy, 1942-46; became lieutenant.

MEMBER: Authors Guild, Concert Artists Guild, Players Club, Sigma Alpha Mu. *Awards, honors:* D.Mus., Boguslawski College of Music (Chicago), 1944; Society for the Publication of American Music award, 1946; Antoinette Perry Awards (Tonys) for musical direction of "The Consul," 1950, and for "Wonderful Town" and Gilbert and Sullivan repertory, both 1953; Bellamann Award, 1964; scroll of honor, 1968, from Consular Law Society; award of merit, 1968, from Cultural Division of Republic of Austria; D.Mus., Cincinnati Conservatory College of Music, 1971; D.H.L., Millsaps College, 1971; citation for outstanding contribution to musical theater, 1971, from Hartford Conservatory.

WRITINGS: Renaissance to Baroque, seven volumes, Flammer, 1931; *Music for the Classical Tragedy,* Flammer, 1953; *Planning and Producing the Musical Show,* Crown, 1957, revised edition, 1966; *The American Musical Theatre: A Consideration,* Macmillan, 1968, revised edition, 1975; *Words with Music,* Macmillan, 1972; *Getting Started in the Theater,* Macmillan, 1973; *This Bright Day* (autobiography), Macmillan, 1973; *Their Words Are Music,* Crown, 1975; *The Critics,* Macmillan, 1976; *The Making of a Musical,* Macmillan, 1977. Works also include an anthology, *Folk Songs,* published by Flammer; contributor to *World Book Encyclopedia,* 1973.

Compositions include "The Shoe Bird," a ballet; "Pierrot of the Minute"; "The Trojan Women"; "The Chaplet"; "The Soldier"; and "The Creation." Composer of incidental music for the theater, including "Anne of the Thousand Days," "The Time of Your Life," "A Streetcar Named Desire," and numerous Shakespearean plays; composer of music for films, radio, and television, including Shakespearean plays produced by Hallmark Hall of Fame.

Contributor to magazines including *Theatre Arts, Woman's Home Companion, Musical America, Musical Leader, Modern Musical,* and *Dance Observer,* and to newspapers.

AVOCATIONAL INTERESTS: Attending the theater, gourmet restaurants, world travel.

* * *

ENGELMANN, Hugo O(tto)   1917-

PERSONAL: Born September 11, 1917, in Vienna, Austria; came to United States in 1939, naturalized in 1944; son of Otto Hugo (a certified public accountant) and Karolina (Skrceny) Engelmann; married Ruth Marie Gould (a free-lance writer), October 4, 1941; children: John Hugh. *Education:* University of Vienna, J.U.C., 1938; University of Wisconsin, Ph.D., 1953. *Politics:* "Independent, leaning to Democrats." *Religion:* "Nonbeliever." *Home:* 421 Hillcrest Dr., DeKalb, Ill. 60115. *Office:* Department of Sociology, Northern Illinois University, DeKalb, Ill. 60115.

CAREER: Michigan State University, East Lansing, instructor in social science, 1945-48; University of Wisconsin—Milwaukee, instructor, 1948-56, assistant professor, 1956-58, associate professor, 1958-60, professor of sociology, 1960-69, chairman of department, 1964-67; Northern Illinois University, DeKalb, professor of sociology, 1969—. Founder and editor, Clearinghouse for Sociological Literature.

MEMBER: International Society for the Comparative Study of Civilizations, American Sociological Association, American Anthropological Association (fellow), American Association for the Advancement of Science (fellow), Society for General Systems Research, American Political Science Association, American Academy of Political and Social Science, National Council on Family Relations, American Association of University Professors, Midwest Sociological Society (former Wisconsin director), North Central Sociological Association, Central States Anthropological Society, Illinois Sociological Association, Wisconsin Sociological Association (former president), New York Academy of Sciences, Michigan Academy of Sciences, Arts and Letters, Wisconsin Academy of Sciences, Arts, and Letters, Alpha Kappa Delta.

WRITINGS: The Evaluation Modality Test, with manual and key, Psychometric Affiliates, 1956; *A Systemic Dynamic Approach to Social Theory,* privately printed, 1957; *Essays in Social Theory and Social Organization,* W. C. Brown, 1966; (contributor) Keshav Dev Sharma, editor, *Basic Issues in Social Sciences,* Academic Journals of India, 1968; *Sociology: A Guided Text,* W. C. Brown, 1969; (contributor) G. C. Hallen and Rajeshwar Prasad, editors, *Sorokin and Sociology,* Satish Book Enterprise, 1970.

Also contributor, Mau Singh Das, editor, *Contemporary Sociology in the United States.* Contributor of more than forty articles and reviews to professional journals, including *Anthropological Quarterly, Sociological Quarterly, Journal of Human Relations, Heuristic,* and *International Review of History and Political Science.* Associate editor, *International Journal of Contemporary Sociology;* editorial adviser, *International Review of Sociology;* member of editorial board, *Indian Journal of Sociology;* former associate editor, *Sociological Quarterly;* member of editorial board, *International Review of History and Political Science;* former editor, *Wisconsin Sociologist.*

WORK IN PROGRESS: The Emergence of Sociology: A Sociohistoric Essay.

BIOGRAPHICAL/CRITICAL SOURCES: Sociological Quarterly, summer, 1970.

* * *

ENGLISH, Edward (H.)   19(?)-1973

19(?)—June 8, 1973; American vagabond poet, jewelry maker, and civil rights worker. Obituaries: *New York Times,* June 13, 1973.

* * *

ENTERLINE, James Robert   1932-

PERSONAL: Born June 29, 1932, in Salunga, Pa.; son of Robert Andes and Mary (Greenly) Enterline; married Esther Goldstein (a psychologist), March 28, 1965. *Education:* Lebanon Valley College, B.S., 1954; New York University, graduate study. *Home:* 144 West 95th St., New York, N.Y. 10025.

CAREER: Researcher. Western Electric Corp., New York City, planning engineer, 1958-59; Systems Research Group, Mineola, N.Y., chief systems engineer, 1959-63; Fox Computer Services, Inc., New York City, vice-president, 1963-65. *Military service:* U.S. Navy Reserve, 1948-52. *Member:* Association for Computing Machinery, Institute of Electronic and Electrical Engineers, Society for History of Discoveries, Explorers Club.

WRITINGS: Viking America: The Norse Crossings and Their Legacy, Doubleday, 1972. Contributor to *Imago Mundi, American Scandinavian Review, Scientific American, International Journal of Nautical Archaeology, Explorers Journal,* and *Computerworld.*

WORK IN PROGRESS: A sequel to *Viking America,* with emphasis on maps.

SIDELIGHTS: When Yale University announced the discovery of a Vinland map in 1965, James Enterline sold a successful computer business interest and devoted himself to research in the matter of Columbus vs. Leif Ericson. His research has included field work in Iceland and Greenland.

BIOGRAPHICAL/CRITICAL SOURCES: American Heritage, August, 1972; *Reader's Digest,* March, 1973.

* * *

ENZ, Jacob J(ohn)   1919-

PERSONAL: Born January 6, 1919, in Newton, Kan.; son of Henry (an auto trimmer) and Lydia (Toews) Enz; married Joan Veston (a choirmaster), May 25, 1944; children: David Veston, John Ewert. *Education:* Bethel College, North Newton, Kan., A.B., 1941; New York Theological Seminary, S.T.B., 1941; University of Chicago, graduate study, 1946-47; Johns Hopkins University, Ph.D., 1960. *Home:* Route 4, 58335, CR 105 S., Elkhart, Ind. 46514. *Office:* Mennonite Biblical Seminary, 3003 Benham Ave., Elkhart, Ind. 46514.

CAREER: Worked as an auto trimmer in Newton, Kan., 1932-41; pastor of First Mennonite Church, Nappanee, Ind., 1944-48; Goshen College, Goshen, Ind., instructor in German, 1947-48; Bethel College, North Newton, Kan., assistant professor of Bible and Christian Education, 1948-50; Mennonite Biblical Seminary, Elkhart, Ind., associate professor, 1954-57, professor of Old Testament and Hebrew, 1958—, acting dean, 1961-62. *Member:* American Oriental Society, American Schools of Oriental Research, Society for Biblical Literature, Chicago Society for Biblical Research. *Awards, honors:* Fulbright travel grant, 1964; faculty fellowship from the American Association of Theological Schools, 1971.

WRITINGS: The Christian and Warfare: The Roots of Pacifism in the Old Testament, Herald Press, 1972. Acting editor of *Mennonite,* 1948-50.

WORK IN PROGRESS: "Light" and "Darkness" in the Dead Sea Scrolls and the Bible.

SIDELIGHTS: Jacob Enz took part in archaeological digs at Ashdod, 1963, and Massada, 1964. He writes, "My concern is to show that the Scriptures are not a dusty literary museum but a battle manual under Christ in conflict with the sum of all evil—institutionalized hatred."

* * *

EPSTEIN, Dena J. 1916-

PERSONAL: Born November 30, 1916, in Milwaukee, Wis.; daughter of William Sampson and Hilda (Satt) Polacheck; married Morton Batlan Epstein (a clinical chemist), October 24, 1942; children: William Eliot, Suzanne Louise. *Education:* University of Chicago, B.A., 1937; University of Illinois, B.S. in L.S., 1939, M.A., 1943. *Office:* University of Chicago Library, Chicago, Ill. 60637.

CAREER: University of Illinois Library, Urbana, cataloger, 1939-43; Newark Public Library, Newark, N.J., senior music librarian, 1943-45; Library of Congress, Washington, D.C., music cataloger in Copyright Cataloging Division, 1946-48; University of Chicago, Chicago, Ill., assistant music librarian, 1964—. Lecturer, University of Tennessee Library, 1978. *Member:* American Library Association, Music Library Association (member of board of directors, 1970-73; president, 1977-79), American Musicological Society, International Folk Music Council, International Association of Music Libraries, American Association of University Women. *Awards, honors:* Grants from American Council of Learned Societies, 1970, Illinois Arts Council, 1970, and National Endowment for the Humanities, 1971, all for research on black folk music; Chicago Folklore Prize, 1978, for *Sinful Tunes and Spirituals.*

WRITINGS: Music Publishing in Chicago before 1871: The Firm of Root & Cady, 1858-1871, Information Coordinators, 1969; (author of preface) *Complete Catalogue of Sheet Music and Musical Works Published by the Board of Music Trade of the U.S.A., 1870,* reprint edition, Da Capo, 1973; *Sinful Tunes and Spirituals: Black Folk Music to the Civil War,* University of Illinois Press, 1977. Contributor to *Dictionary of American Biography, Notable American Women, 1607-1950, New Grove Dictionary of Music and Musicians,* and music and library journals.

SIDELIGHTS: Dena J. Epstein told *CA:* "The lack of an historic record for Black American music before the Civil War seemed unbelievable to me. In the enormous literature of slavery, it seemed inconceivable that no mention of music could be found. As a librarian, I realized that most of the existing works relied on a handful of sources known to discuss music. A wide-ranging search of every potential source of information seemed an appropriate project for someone trained in library techniques. About 1953, while I was raising my children, I decided to see what could be found. I had no idea where the search might lead, and was prepared to end in failure. I certainly did not expect to be able to document conclusively the transplantation of African music in the New World, its persistence for as long as 150 years in some areas, and its acculturation into what is now known as Afro-American music. But that's what happened."

ERICSON, Joe Ellis 1925-

PERSONAL: Born June 9, 1925, in Throckmorton County, Tex.; son of Lester Y. and Lena A. (Ellis) Ericson; married Carolyn Reeves, July 16, 1955; children: Linda Dianne (Mrs. Michael Devereaux), Joseph R., John Ellis. *Education:* Texas Technological College (now Texas Tech University), B.S. in Ed., 1946, M.A., 1948, Ph.D., 1957. *Politics:* Democrat. *Religion:* Methodist. *Home:* 1614 Redbud St., Nacogdoches, Tex. 75961. *Office address:* Department of Political Science, Stephen F. Austin State University, Box 3045, Nacogdoches, Tex. 75962.

CAREER: West Texas State College (now University), Canyon, instructor in political science, 1951-53; Arlington State College (now University of Texas at Arlington), instructor in social sciences, 1955-57; Stephen F. Austin State University, Nacogdoches, Tex., assistant professor, 1957-62, associate professor, 1962-67, professor of political science and chairman of department, 1967—. Election judge of Nacogdoches County, Tex., 1967-72; county chairman, Democratic Party, 1972-74. *Member:* American Political Science Association, American Studies Association (Texas branch president, 1971-72), Southern Political Science Association, Southwestern Social Science Association, Texas Association of College Teachers.

WRITINGS: (With Eugene Jones, Lyle Brown, and Robert Trotter) *Practicing Texas Politics,* Houghton, 1971, revised edition, 1977; *Banks and Bankers in Early Texas,* Polyanthos, 1976. Contributor of articles and reviews to *West Texas Historical Association Yearbook, Southwestern Historical Quarterly, Southwestern Social Science Quarterly, East Texas Historical Journal, Alpha Chi Recorder, Rocky Mountain Social Science Journal,* and *American Quarterly.*

WORK IN PROGRESS: Biographical Directory of Judges of the Republic of Texas; constitutional and legal history of Texas.

* * *

ETCHESON, Warren W(ade) 1920-

PERSONAL: Born May 15, 1920, in Bainbridge, Ind.; son of Raymond W. (a merchant) and Rosetta (Evans) Etcheson; married Marianne Newgent, May 30, 1947; children: Denise Elene, Crayton Wade. *Education:* Indiana University, B.S., 1942; University of Iowa, M.A., 1951, Ph.D., 1954. *Home:* 6625 Northeast 132nd St., Kirkland, Wash. 98033. *Office:* School of Business Administration, University of Washington, Seattle, Wash. 98195.

CAREER: University of Iowa, Iowa City, instructor in business administration, 1952-54; University of Washington, Seattle, assistant professor, 1954-56, associate professor, 1956-60, professor of business administration, 1960—, director of bureau of business research, 1957-63, assistant dean, 1961-63, associate dean, 1974—. Fulbright lecturer to Istanbul, Turkey, 1963-64. Trustee of Delta Chi Educational Foundation, 1954-62. *Military service:* U.S. Army, 1942-46; became first lieutenant. *Member:* American Marketing Association, American Economic Association, Order of Artus, Delta Chi (national secretary, 1954-56), Phi Eta Sigma.

WRITINGS: Pazarlama, Turkish Ministry of Education, 1964; *Consumerism,* Canfield Press, 1972. Writer of monographs and journal articles on economic development and marketing practices.

* * *

EUBANK, Nancy 1934-

PERSONAL: Born March 4, 1934, in Beloit, Kan.; daughter

of Neal H. (a carpenter) and Eva (Teasley) Jamison; married Dillard M. Eubank, Jr. (a psychologist), February 27, 1960; children: Laurie Ellen. *Education:* University of Kansas, A.B., 1955; University of Minnesota, graduate study, 1956-58. *Home:* 4100 Queen Ave. S., Minneapolis, Minn. 55410. *Office:* Minnesota Historical Society, Bldg. 25, Fort Snelling, St. Paul, Minn. 55111.

CAREER: Western Mineral Products Co., Minneapolis, Minn., public relations writer, 1960-61; KUOM (University of Minnesota radio station), Minneapolis, program supervisor, 1965-68; Minnesota Historical Society, St. Paul, Minn., historic sites interpretation supervisor, 1969—. *Member:* American Association for State and Local History, Women Historians of the Midwest, Phi Beta Kappa, Pi Sigma Alpha.

WRITINGS: A Living Past: Fifteen Historic Places in Minnesota, Minnesota Historical Society, 1973; *The Russians in America,* Lerner, 1973; (with Gordon Lothson) *A Journey through Time,* Minnesota Historical Society, 1974; *The Lindberghs: Three Generations,* Minnesota Historical Society, 1975. Author of a film script, "Building Yesterday," 1976. Also author of booklets, brochures, museum exhibit texts, and radio scripts on Minnesota history. Contributor to *Minnesota History* and other magazines.

WORK IN PROGRESS: Research for Minnesota Historical Society on exhibits, publications, and films on historic sites, Chippewa and Dakota Indian history, and early Indian prehistory.

AVOCATIONAL INTERESTS: Radio, television, and film production.

*   *   *

EUNSON, (John) Dale   1904-

PERSONAL: Surname is pronounced Un-son; born August 15, 1904, in Neillsville, Wis.; son of Robert Strong (a farmer and local politician) and Isla (Heath) Eunson; married Katherine Albert (a writer), September 18, 1931 (died, 1970); married Berenice Tolins Dratler, June, 1971; children: (first marriage) Joan (Mrs. Kirby Weatherly). *Education:* Attended University of Southern California, 1922-23. *Politics:* Democratic. *Religion:* Atheist. *Home and office:* 509 Lado Dr., Santa Clara, Calif. 93111. *Agent:* Harold Ober Associates, Inc., 40 East 49th St., New York, N.Y. 10017.

CAREER: Worked as publicity writer for Metro-Goldwyn-Mayer and as secretary to novelist Rupert Hughes; Hearst Magazines, New York, N.Y., *Cosmopolitan,* secretary to the editor, 1930-33, associate editor, 1933-35, fiction editor, 1943-48; free-lance writer at other periods. *Member:* Writers Guild of America, West.

WRITINGS: Homestead (fiction), Farrar & Rinehart, 1934; (ghost-writer) Peter Freuchen, *Arctic Adventure,* Farrar & Rinehart, 1936; *The Day They Gave Babies Away* (juvenile), Farrar, Straus, 1946, reprinted, 1970; *Up on the Rim* (juvenile), Farrar, Straus, 1970.

Plays: (With Hagar Wilde) "Guest in the House," first produced on Broadway at Plymouth Theatre, 1942; "Public Relations," 1944; (with wife, Katherine Albert Eunson) "Loco," first produced on Broadway at Biltmore Theatre, 1946.

Screenplays; all with Katherine Albert Eunson: "On the Loose," RKO, 1951; "The Star," Twentieth Century-Fox, 1953; "Sabre Jet," United Artists, 1953; "All Mine to Give" (based on Dale Eunson's book *The Day They Gave Babies Away),* Universal, 1957; "Eighteen and Anxious,"

Republic, 1957; "Young Mother," Republic, 1958; (and with Ruth Brooks Flippen) "Gidget Goes to Rome," Columbia, 1963. Also author of screen story for "All Women Have Secrets," Paramount, 1939.

Author of several dozen television plays, in collaboration with Katherine Albert Eunson. Also author of scripts for television series, including "The Waltons" and "Love Story." Contributor of about fifty short stories to *Cosmopolitan, Ladies' Home Journal, Redbook, Collier's, Woman's Home Companion, McCall's,* and other national magazines.

WORK IN PROGRESS: A play, "Southern Comfort"; short stories ("have returned to the short story medium after an absence of a good many years"); a novel tentatively entitled *The Boy Who Spoke to Nuns.*

SIDELIGHTS: Dale Eunson's play "Guest in the House" was filmed under the same title in 1944 with Anne Baxter and Ralph Bellamy. The play "Loco" is the basis for the film "How to Marry a Millionaire."

*   *   *

EVANS, David S(tanley)   1916-

PERSONAL: Born January 28, 1916, in Cardiff, Wales; son of Arthur Cyril (a clerk) and Kate (Priest) Evans; married Betty Hall Hart, March 8, 1948; children: Jonathan Gareth Weston, Barnaby Huw Weston. *Education:* King's College, Cambridge, B.A., 1937, M.A. and Ph.D., 1941, Sc.D., 1971. *Home:* 6001 Mountainclimb Dr., Austin, Tex. 78731. *Office:* Department of Astronomy, University of Texas, Austin, Tex. 78712.

CAREER: Oxford University, University Observatory, Oxford, England, research assistant, 1938-46; Radcliffe Observatory, Pretoria, South Africa, second assistant, 1946-51; Royal Observatory, Cape Province, South Africa, chief assistant, 1951-68; University of Texas at Austin, professor of astronomy, 1968—. Former trustee, South African Museum (Cape Town).

MEMBER: International Astronomical Union (former commission president), Royal Astronomical Society (London; fellow), Institute of Physics (London; fellow), American Astronomical Society, Astronomical Society of Southern Africa (honorary member; former president and member of council), Royal Society of South Africa (fellow; former member of council). *Awards, honors:* National Science Foundation senior visiting scientist, 1965-66; McIntyre Award from Astronomical Society of Southern Africa, 1972.

WRITINGS: Frontiers of Astronomy, Sigma Books, 1946; *Teach Yourself Astronomy,* English Universities Press, 1952, 3rd edition, 1970; *Observation in Modern Astronomy,* American Elsevier, 1968; (editor with wife, Betty H. Evans, T. J. Deeming, and S. Goldfarb) *Herschel at the Cape,* University of Texas Press, 1969; (editor and author of introduction) Guenther Buttmann, *The Shadow of the Telescope,* Scribner, 1970; (editor with Derek Wills and Beverly H. Wills) *External Galaxies and Quasi-Stellar Objects,* Reidel, 1972. Former editor, *Discovery* and *Observatory.*

WORK IN PROGRESS: Research in astronomy.

*   *   *

EVANS, Donald (Dwight)   1927-

PERSONAL: Born September 21, 1927, in Thunder Bay, Ontario, Canada; son of Ira Dwight (a businessman) and Jessie (Milliken) Evans; married Sybil Ruth Blenkinsop,

June 28, 1952; children: Stephen, Gregory, Luke, Nicholas. *Education:* University of Toronto, B.A., 1950; Oxford University, B.Phil., 1953, D.Phil., 1962; McGill University, B.D., 1955. *Home:* 35 Walmer Rd., Toronto, Ontario, Canada. *Office:* Department of Philosophy, University of Toronto, Toronto, Ontario, Canada.

CAREER: Ordained minister of United Church of Canada, 1955; minister in Grand Forks, British Columbia, 1955-58; McGill University, Montreal, Quebec, assistant professor of philosophy of religion, 1960-64; University of Toronto, Toronto, Ontario, associate professor, 1964-68, professor of philosophy, 1968—. *Awards, honors:* Canada Council fellowship, 1960-62, 1969-70, 1975-77.

WRITINGS: The Logic of Self Involvement: A Philosophical Study of Everyday Language with Special Reference to the Christian Use of Language about God as Creator, SCM, 1963, 2nd edition, Herder & Herder, 1969; *Communist Faith and Christian Faith,* Ryerson, 1964; (editor and contributor) *Peace, Power, and Protest,* Ryerson, 1967; *Faith, Authenticity, and Morality,* University of Toronto Press, 1979.

WORK IN PROGRESS: Religion and Morality; research on varieties of religious experiences and their relation to psychotherapeutic experiences.

*   *   *

EVANS, Harold Matthew   1928-

PERSONAL: Born June 28, 1928, in Manchester, England; son of Frederick (a rail driver) and Mary (Haselum) Evans; married Enid Parker (a teacher), August 15, 1953; children: Ruth, Katherine, Michael. *Education:* University of Durham, B.A. (honors), 1952, M.A., 1962; also studied at University of Chicago and Stanford University. *Religion:* Church of England. *Residence:* London, England. *Agent:* A. D. Peters, 10 Buckingham St., London WC2N 6BU, England. *Office: Sunday Times,* Thomson House, London W.C. 1, England.

CAREER: Ashton-u-Lyne Reporter, Ashton-u-Lyne, England, reporter, 1943-46, 1949; *Manchester Evening News,* Manchester, England, assistant editor, 1952-56, 1958-61; *Northern Echo,* Darlington, England, editor, 1961-66; *Sunday Times,* London, England, chief assistant to editor, 1966, editor, 1967—. Editor-in-chief, North of England Newspaper Co., 1963-66; member of National Council for the Training of Journalists; consultant to International Press Institute Abroad, 1960—. *Military service:* Royal Air Force, 1943-64. *Member:* Ski Club of Great Britain, Garrick Club, Royal Automobile Club. *Awards, honors:* Hannen Swaffer International Publishing Corporation awards, campaigning journalist of the year, 1967, and journalist of the year, 1972.

WRITINGS: The Active Newsroom, International Press Institute, 1962; *Editing and Design,* Holt, Volume I: *Newsman's English,* 1971, Volume II: *Text Editing,* 1973, Volume III: *News Headlines,* 1973, Volume IV: *Pictures on a Page,* 1978, Volume V: *Newspaper Design,* 1973; *Handling Newspaper Text,* Holt, 1974; (co-author) *We Learned to Ski,* Collins, 1974. Author of television scripts. Contributor to *Punch, Guardian, Times,* and other publications.

WORK IN PROGRESS: Deadline Suez, for Deutsch.

AVOCATIONAL INTERESTS: Table tennis, skiing, music, writing.

BIOGRAPHICAL/CRITICAL SOURCES: Leonard Russell, Phillip Knightly, Harold Hobson, *Pearl of Days,* Hamish Hamilton, 1972.†

EVANS, (William Edis) Webster   1908-

PERSONAL: Born August 26, 1908, in London, England; son of William (a clergyman, Church of England) and Helen (Jones) Evans; married Jean Hilda Marshall, November 30, 1956. *Education:* Attended Merchant Taylors' School, London. *Politics:* Conservative. *Religion:* Church of England. *Home:* 16 Chatterton Ct., Kew Rd., Richmond, Surrey TW9 2AR, England. *Agent:* Donald Copeman Ltd., 52 Bloomsbury St., London WC1B 3QT, England.

CAREER: John O' London's Weekly, London, England, member of editorial staff, 1928-39, deputy editor, 1952, editor, 1953-54; Country Life Books, London, general editor, 1954-69; David & Charles Ltd. (publishers), London, consultant, 1971—. *Military service:* Royal Air Force, 1940-47; served in Middle East, Italy, and Germany; became wing commander; mentioned in dispatches. *Member:* Sherlock Holmes Society of London (former member of council), Royal Mid-Surrey Golf Club, Nineteenth Club (London).

WRITINGS: (Editor with Tom Scott) *In Praise of Golf* (anthology), Muller, 1950; (editor with Scott) *The Golfers' Year* (annual), Nicholas Kaye, 1950, 1951; *Rubs of the Green: Golf's Triumphs and Tragedies,* Pelham Books, 1969, Transatlantic, 1970; (compiler) *Encyclopedia of Golf,* St. Martin's, 1971, 2nd edition, 1973.

WORK IN PROGRESS: A new edition of *Encyclopedia of Golf.*

SIDELIGHTS: "Have always been connected with books and golf, sometimes separately, sometimes together," Webster Evans writes. He is an acknowledged authority on the history and rules of golf, which he has played since the age of six. He lives in Richmond to be within walking distance of the Royal Mid-Surrey Golf Club.†

*   *   *

EVERGOOD, Philip   1901-1973
(Howard Francis Dixon)

October 26, 1901—March 11, 1973; American artist. Obituaries: *New York Times,* March 13, 1973; *Current Biography,* April, 1973.

*   *   *

EWING, Elizabeth   1904-

PERSONAL: Born February 26, 1904, in Glasgow, Scotland; daughter of James Cameron (a librarian) and Grace Young (King) Ewing; married John Milligan, August, 1930 (divorced); children: David Quoys. *Education:* Glasgow University, M.A. (first class honors), 1927. *Politics:* Conservative. *Home:* 25 Westfield Way, Ruislip, Middlesex, England.

CAREER: Worked as a reporter, feature writer, and columnist on various national and provincial newspapers, including Kemsley Newspapers, *Glasgow Herald, Daily Sketch, News of the World, Scotsman,* and *Sunday Graphic,* 1928-50, and for E. M. Wright and Current Affairs (public relations firms), London, England, 1936-47; operated own public relations firm in London, 1947-71.

WRITINGS: Fashion in Underwear, Theatre Arts, 1972; *History of Twentieth Century Fashion,* Scribner, 1974; *Women in Uniform through the Centuries,* Batsford, 1975; *History of Children's Costume,* Scribner, 1977; *Dress and Undress: A History of Women's Underwear,* Scribner, 1978. Contributor to magazines, including *Scottish Field, Women's Journal, Chamber's Journal, Everybody's,* and

London Mercury. Editor of house magazines, brochures, and pamphlets.

WORK IN PROGRESS: Fashion in Furs.

SIDELIGHTS: Elizabeth Ewing writes *CA:* "My academic and writing instincts [are] both satisfied by writing on fashion history, which I see as always closely linked with social history and conditions of life. I find the research laborious and exacting but rewarding and try to tackle subjects or aspects of subjects not already dealt with by other fashion writers."

* * *

EYESTONE, Robert 1942-

PERSONAL: Born September 11, 1942, in Fort Bragg, N.C.; son of John D. (a professional engineer) and Pauline (Gross) Eyestone; married Susan Anne Wodicka, September 11, 1965; children: David, Elisabeth. *Education:* Massachusetts Institute of Technology, S.B., 1964; Stanford University, M.A., 1965, Ph.D., 1967. *Home:* 5055 Dupont Ave. S., Minneapolis, Minn. 55419. *Office:* Department of Political Science, University of Minnesota, 1414 Social Science, Minneapolis, Minn. 55455.

CAREER: University of Minnesota, Minneapolis, assistant professor, 1967-73, associate professor of political science, 1973—. *Member:* American Political Science Association, Policy Studies Organization, Midcontinent Regional Science Association, Midwest Political Science Association.

WRITINGS: The Thread of Public Policy, Bobbs-Merrill, 1971; *Political Economy,* Markham, 1972; *From Social Issues to Public Policy,* Wiley, 1979.

WORK IN PROGRESS: Coordination of state environmental policy; evaluation of planning decisions.

* * *

EYKMAN, Christoph 1937-

PERSONAL: Born December 6, 1937, in Frankfurt, Germany; son of Alfred (an opera conductor) and Irmgard (von Muller) Eykman; married Elke Schmidt, May 9, 1970; children: Alexander, Mathias. *Education:* University of Bonn, Ph.D., 1964. *Religion:* Lutheran. *Home:* 10 Alfred Rd., Framingham, Mass. 01701. *Office:* Department of German, Boston College, Chestnut Hill, Mass. 02167.

CAREER: Antioch College, Yellow Springs, Ohio, assistant professor, 1964-68; Boston College, Chestnut Hill, Mass., assistant professor, 1968-72, associate professor of German, 1972—, chairperson of department, 1976—. *Member:* International Association of Philosophy and Literature, Modern Language Association of America.

WRITINGS: Die Funktion des Haesslichen, Bouvier, 1965, second edition, 1969; *Geschichtspessimismus in der It. Lit. des 20. Iahrh,* Francke, 1970; *Denk-und Stilformen des deutschen Expressionismus,* Francke, 1973; *Phaenomenologie der Interpretation,* Francke, 1977.

WORK IN PROGRESS: Die Schwierigkeit des Schreibens.

F

FACOS, James F(rancis) 1924-

PERSONAL: Surname is pronounced *Fay*-kus; born July 28, 1924, in Lawrence, Mass.; son of Chris and Theresa (McAdam) Facos; married Cleo Chigos, December 1, 1956; children: Theresa-Katina, Elizabeth Joy, Anthony John. *Education:* Bates College, A.B., 1949; Florida State University, M.A., 1958. *Home:* 333 Elm St., Montpelier, Vt. 05602. *Office:* Department of English, Vermont College Division, Norwich University, Montpelier, Vt. 05602.

CAREER: Norwich University, Vermont College Division, Montpelier, Vt., instructor, 1959-72, assistant professor, 1972-73, associate professor of English, 1973—. *Military service:* U.S. Army Air Forces, 1943-45; became staff sergeant; served in European theater; received Air Medal with three oak leaf clusters and Distinguished Flying Cross. U.S. Air Force Reserve, 1948—; present rank, second lieutenant. *Member:* National Council of Teachers of English, Academy of American Poets, American Association of University Professors, New England Poetry Club. *Awards, honors:* Bates writing prize, 1949; Alden Award from Dramatists' Alliance, 1956, for "Felicia," a one-act play; Walter Peach Award from Poetry Society of Vermont, 1962, for "Agates and Whistles"; Corinne Davis Award from Poetry Society of Vermont, 1970, for "Room 304."

WRITINGS: The Piper O' the May (one-act verse play), Pioneer Drama Co., 1962; *The Legacy* (one-act play), Eldridge Publishing, 1967; *Morning's Come Singing* (collection of poems), Dorrance, 1967; *A Day of Genesis* (folk play), Eldridge Publishing, 1969; *The Silver Lady* (novel), Atheneum, 1972; *Silver Wood* (one-act play), Eldridge Publishing, 1977; *One Daring Fling* (three-act play), Dramatic Publishing, 1978. Also author of "Felicia," a one-act play.

SIDELIGHTS: The James Facos Collection (manuscripts, notes, and papers) is now part of the twentieth-century archives of the Mulgar Memorial Library, Boston University.

* * *

FAGAN, Brian Murray 1936-

PERSONAL: Born August 1, 1936, in Birmingham, England; naturalized U.S. citizen; son of Brian Walter and Margaret (Moir) Fagan; married Judith Ann Fontana (a registered nurse), December 6, 1969. *Education:* Pembroke College, Cambridge, B.A. (honors), 1959, M.A., 1962, Ph.D., 1963. *Home:* 665 Las Alturas, Santa Barbara, Calif.

93103. *Office:* Department of Anthropology, University of California, Santa Barbara, Calif. 93106.

CAREER: Livingstone Museum, Livingstone, Northern Rhodesia (now Zambia), keeper of prehistory, 1959-65; British Institute of History and Archaeology in East Africa, Nairobi, Kenya, director of Bantu studies project, 1965-66; University of Illinois at Urbana-Champaign, visiting associate professor of anthropology, 1966-67; University of California, Santa Barbara, associate professor, 1967-68, professor of anthropology, 1969—, director of Center for the Study of Developing Nations, 1969-70, associate dean of research and graduate affairs, 1970-72, associate dean of College of Letters and Science, 1972-73, dean of instructional development, 1973-76. Lecturer, University of Capetown, 1960; Munro Lecturer, University of Edinburgh, 1967; Richard M. Nixon Visiting Scholar and Lecturer, Whittier College, 1976; lecturer of African history at campuses throughout United States. Zambia Monuments Commission, member, 1960-65, secretary, 1960-62; director of Kalomo/Choma Iron Age project, 1960-63, of Lochinvar research project, 1963-64, and of Bantu studies project in Kenya, Uganda, and Tanzania; conducted archaeological research in Zambia and Northern Nigeria, 1969-70. Has presented papers to numerous conferences in the United States, Africa, England, and Europe. Consultant on innovative instruction, New Mexico State University, 1973; consultant to administrator and head of mission, Evaluation of International Audio-Visual Resource Service, United Nations Fund for Popular Activities, 1976. *Military service:* Royal Navy, 1954-56.

MEMBER: Royal Geographical Society (fellow), Royal Anthropological Institute (fellow), African Studies Association (United States; fellow; chairman of archaeology committee, 1968-69), American Anthropological Association (fellow), Society for American Archaeology, South African Archaeological Society, Prehistoric Society, Current Anthropology (associate), New York Academy of Sciences (fellow), Santa Barbara Yacht Club, Cruising Association (London). *Awards, honors:* Grants from Wenner Gren Foundation, 1967, 1968, and National Science Foundation, 1968-70, 1970-71; Guggenheim fellow, 1972-73; Commonwealth Club Gold Medal for Nonfiction, 1975, for *The Rape of the Nile;* Hanson Cup from Cruising Association, 1975, for a cruise to Scandanavia.

WRITINGS: Southern Africa during the Iron Age, Praeger,

1966, revised edition published as *Southern Africa,* Thames & Hudson, 1971; (editor) *A Short History of Zambia,* Oxford University Press, 1966, revised edition, 1968; *Iron Age Cultures in Zambia,* Humanities, Volume I: *Kalomo and Kangila,* 1967, Volume II (with S.G.H. Daniels and D. W. Phillipson): *Dambwa, Ingombe Ilede and the Tonga,* 1969.

(Editor) *Introductory Readings in Archaeology,* Little, Brown, 1970; (author of introduction and editorial note) Randall MacIver, *Medieval Rhodesia,* Cass & Co., 1971; (editor) L.S.B. Leakey, *The Stone Age Cultures of Kenya Colony,* Cass & Co., 1971; *In the Beginning: An Introduction to Archaeology,* Little, Brown, 1972, 3rd edition, 1978; *People of the Earth,* Little, Brown, 1974, 2nd edition, 1977; (editor) *Corridors in Time,* Little, Brown, 1974; *The Rape of the Nile,* Scribner, 1975; (with Roland Oliver) *Africa in the Iron Age,* Cambridge University Press, 1975; (editor) *Avenues to Antiquity,* W. H. Freeman, 1976; *Elusive Treasure,* Scribner, 1977; (editor) *Civilization,* W. H. Freeman, 1978; *Archaeology: A Brief Introduction,* Little, Brown, 1978; *Quest for the Past,* Addison-Wesley, 1978; (with Graham Pomeroy) *A Cruising Guide to Santa Barbara Channel,* Capra, 1978.

Contributor: W. W. Bishop and J. D. Clark, editors, *Background to Evolution in Africa,* University of Chicago Press, 1967; Roland Oliver, editor, *The Middle Age of African History,* Oxford University Press, 1968; Leonard M. Thompson, editor, *African Societies in Southern Africa,* Praeger, 1969; Roland Oliver and J. D. Fage, editors, *Papers in African Prehistory,* Cambridge University Press, 1970; J. R. Gray and David Birmingham, editors, *Pre-Colonial African Trade,* Oxford University Press, 1970; P. L. Shinnie, editor, *The African Iron Age,* Oxford University Press, 1971. Contributor of over one hundred articles and reviews to professional journals and newspapers.

WORK IN PROGRESS: A history of Mesopotamian archaeology.

SIDELIGHTS: Brian Fagan told *CA:* "I became interested in popular writing about archaeology while working in Zambia, where national history had to be created from excavations rather than written records. There I was involved in radio and TV as well as in guidebooks and newspaper writing and scientific articles and monographs. Since coming to the U.S. in 1966, I have been involved in the teaching of large introductory archaeology courses and in much popular lecturing, occupations which led me into textbook writing and then into trade books.

"My trade career began with a chance letter from Scribners about an article I wrote for *Archaeology* on tomb robbers, a letter that led to *The Rape of the Nile* and a whole new vista of writing opportunity. I have continued to write about archaeology for the general public ever since, for the subject is becoming increasingly specialized as it grows. There is a real danger that undisturbed archaeological sites will vanish in North America in the next generation unless the public realizes the immorality of collecting artifacts from Indian sites for personal gain. Such sites are, after all, the archives of American Indian history. I told some of the story of the destruction of American Indian history in my *Elusive Treasure.*

"A lifetime interest has been cruising under sail. We have spent the last three summers sailing in Europe on our 41-foot cutter, *Catticus Rex,* and won the Cruising Association's Hanson Trophy for a cruise to Finland in 1975. I have just completed *Cruising Guide to the Santa Barbara Channel,* with Graham Pomeroy, and plan to do more writing about sailing in the future.

"I speak French, and [am] deeply involved in the use of media for undergraduate teaching, have an abhorrence for bureaucrats developed when I served as an academic dean, and love cats. Two of them dominate our lives, indeed did everything they could to prevent this paragraph being written by sitting on my pen."

BIOGRAPHICAL/CRITICAL SOURCES: New Statesman, July 28, 1967.

*   *   *

FAIRFIELD, Richard   1937-

PERSONAL: Born November 18, 1937, in Gardiner, Me.; son of George W. and Daisy (House) Fairfield; divorced, 1969; children: April. *Education:* Studied at Emerson College, 1959-61, and University of Maine, 1962-64; Tufts University, B.A., 1967; Starr King School, M.Div., 1969. *Politics:* Democrat ("at present"). *Home and office:* School of Living-West, 442½ Landfair Ave., Los Angeles, Calif. 90024.

CAREER: R. I. Fairfield Insurance Agency, Wiscasset, Me., owner, 1961-65; Alternatives Foundation, San Francisco, Calif., owner, 1966-72; School of Living-West, Los Angeles, Calif., director, 1973—. *Military service:* U.S. Army, Chinese Mandarin specialist in Security Agency, 1956-59. *Member:* Mutual Insurance Agents Association, Junior Chamber of Commerce, Grange.

WRITINGS: In Search of Utopia, Alternatives Foundation, 1971; *Communes, U.S.A.: A Personal Tour,* Penguin, 1972; *Communes: Europe,* Alternatives Foundation, 1972; *Communes: Japan,* Alternatives Foundation, 1972; (editor) *Utopia: U.S.A.,* Alternatives Foundation, 1972. Editor, *Modern Utopian,* 1966-72, *Visions,* 1971, *Alternatives Newsmagazine,* 1971-72, and *Alternatives Journal,* 1971—.

WORK IN PROGRESS: The Green Revolution: Perspectives on Living, a periodical about the major problems of living.††

*   *   *

FALL, Frieda Kay   1913-

PERSONAL: Born July 1, 1913, in Lebanon, Ind.; daughter of Cecil George and Willa Kay (Irwin) Fall; married Joseph Michael Farraday, March 12, 1952 (divorced, 1952); children: Jonathan Fall Farraday. *Education:* Texas State College for Women (now Texas Woman's University), B.A., 1935, M.A., 1941; private study in painting and lithography, 1932, 1940-42. *Politics:* Republican. *Home:* 6051 Embury St., Pacific Palisades, Calif. 90272. *Agent:* Raymond Marlowe, 9917 Robbins Dr., Beverly Hills, Calif. 90212.

CAREER: Art teacher in Texas, 1935-44; Frieda Kay Fall Gallery, Dallas, Tex., operator, 1944-51; Los Angeles County Museum of History, Science and Art, Los Angeles, Calif., registrar of collections, 1951-62; Los Angeles County Museum of Art, Los Angeles, teacher of children's painting classes, 1961, registrar of collections, 1962-67, executive assistant in museum operations, 1967-68, assistant to deputy director for fine arts, 1968-78. Instructor in painting and drawing, Dallas Museum of Fine Arts, summers, 1938-44. Artwork has been exhibited in New York, Texas, Washington, Pennsylvania, and Tennessee.

MEMBER: International Institue of Arts and Letters (fellow), American Association of Museums, National Association of Women Painters, College Art Association, Society of Architectural Historians, International Council of Museums, Western Museums League (secretary-treasurer,

1957-59), Western Association of Art Museums, Art Historians of Southern California. *Awards, honors:* Painting awards from Texas State Fair and Dallas Museum of Fine Arts, 1926-32; Edith Penman Prize from National Association of Women Artists, 1938.

WRITINGS: Art Objects: Their Care and Preservation—A Reference for Museums and Collectors, Museum Publications, 1967, new edition published as *Art Objects: Their Care and Preservation—A Handbook for Museums and Collectors,* Laurence McGilvery, 1973. Contributor to museum journals.

SIDELIGHTS: Frieda Kay Fall is descended from Sir Henry Cole, founder of Victoria and Albert Museum (London, England), and from Thomas Cole, the American painter.

*   *   *

FALLON, Carlos 1909-

PERSONAL: Born January 21, 1909, in Bogota, Colombia; son of Diego Jose and Blanca (Convers) Fallon; married Maureen Byrne, June 16, 1934; children: Daniel, Patricia (Mrs. Patrick Conner). *Education:* Colombian Government Military Academy, certificate, 1936.

CAREER: Destroyer captain, Colombian Navy, 1931-41, served as chief of staff and commander of Upper Amazon Squadron, retiring as captain; Vitro Silver Spring Laboratories, Silver Spring, Md., systems engineer, 1956-57; Nems-Clarke Co., Silver Spring, chief mechanical engineer, 1957-59; Tele-Dynamics, Inc., Philadelphia, Pa., manager of manufacturing, 1959-61; Radio Corp. of America (RCA), Camden, N.J., manager of value analysis and purchasing research, 1961-72; OMR, Inc., Silver Spring, planning consultant, beginning 1972. Has lectured at Northwestern University, 1943, Royal Canadian Air Force Staff College, 1946, 1947, Oklahoma Agricultural and Mechanical College (now Oklahoma State University), 1948, University of North Dakota, 1948, University of Minnesota, 1948, National Defense College of Canada, 1948, 1949, DePauw University, 1951, University of Idaho, 1953, Assumption College (Canada), 1958, Purdue University, 1964, 1965, 1969, Rutgers University, 1970, and Pennsylvania State University, 1971. *Military service:* U.S. Army Air Forces, 1943-46; became captain.

MEMBER: Mathematical Association of America, Society of American Mechanical Engineers, Society of American Naval Engineers, Canadian Mathematical Congress, Royal Astronomical Society of Canada.

WRITINGS: A Variety of Fallon, Little, Brown, 1950; *Varde Och Beslut* (monograph; title means "Value and Decision"), Byggforlaget, 1969; *Value Analysis to Improve Productivity,* Wiley, 1971, revised edition published in German as *Produktivitaetssteigerung durch Wertanalyse: Einsatz von Meschen–Mitteln–Maschinen,* Herder & Herder, 1973; (contributor) H. B. Maynard, editor, *Industrial Engineering Handbook,* McGraw, 1971. Contributor to *American Mathematical Monthly, Naval Engineers Journal, IEEE Transactions* of Institute of Electrical and Electronics Engineers, and *RCA Engineer.*

WORK IN PROGRESS: A Practical Decision Method (tentative title), simplified mathematical approaches to choice and decisions; research on motives and accomplishments of South American privateers operating against Spanish shipping off the coast of Louisiana and Texas in the early nineteenth century.††

FALLON, Frederic (Michael) 1944-1970

PERSONAL: Born July 28, 1944, in Boston, Mass.; son of Frederic C. (a U.S. Naval officer) and Helen (Walker) Fallon. *Education:* Attended University of San Francisco, 1963, and Chabot College, 1964; California State College (now California State University), Hayward, B.A., 1967, M.A., 1968; doctoral candidate, University of California, Davis, at time of death. *Politics:* Democrat. *Religion:* Roman Catholic. *Home:* 5331 Radele Court, Fremont, Calif. 94536.

CAREER: Teacher of English at University of California, Davis, 1969. An artist, Fallon sold his paintings to help finance his college education.

WRITINGS: The White Queen (historical novel), Doubleday, 1972. Editor of *Manibus,* 1964, and *Amaranth,* 1966-67.

WORK IN PROGRESS: A novel, concerning the draft and Robert F. Kennedy, left uncompleted at time of death.

SIDELIGHTS: In honor of the author, the Frederic Fallon Scholarship Fund has been established at Chabot College, Hayward, Calif.†

(Died June 7, 1970)

*   *   *

FARAH, Caesar Elie 1929-

PERSONAL: Born March 13, 1929, in Portland, Ore.; son of Selim Kahlil (a businessman) and Lawrice (Nasrallah) Farah; married Lorraine Teresa Jerro (an artist), 1954 (divorced, 1975); married Marsha Bernadette McDonald, 1977; children: (first marriage) Ronald, Christopher, Ramsey, Laurence, Raymond, Alexandra. *Education:* Attended International College of Beirut, 1941-46; Stanford University, B.A., 1952; Princeton University, M.A., 1955, Ph.D., 1957. *Politics:* Republican. *Religion:* Eastern Orthodox. *Home:* 3847 York Ave. S., Minneapolis, Minn. 55410. *Office:* Department of Near and Middle Eastern Studies, University of Minnesota, Minneapolis, Minn. 55455.

CAREER: U.S. Information Service, Delhi, India, and Karachi, Pakistan, public affairs assistant and educational exchange attache, 1957-59; Portland State University, Portland, Ore., assistant professor of history and Semitic Languages, 1959-63; Los Angeles State College of Applied Arts and Sciences (now California State University, Los Angeles), assistant professor, 1963-64; Indiana University at Bloomington, associate professor of Asian studies and Near Eastern languages, 1964-69; University of Minnesota, Minneapolis, professor of Arabic and Islamic studies, 1969—. Visiting lecturer at University of Baghdad and Lebanese University, 1966-67, and Universidad Autonoma de Madrid, 1977. *Member:* American Oriental Society, American Association of Teachers of Arabic (member of executive board, 1965), Royal Asiatic Society of Great Britain, Middle East Studies Association, American Historical Association. *Awards, honors:* Ford Foundation grant, 1966; American Research Center grant to Egypt, 1966-67; Fulbright-Hays grant to Turkey, 1967-68; American Philosophical Society grant, 1970-71.

WRITINGS: (Translator from the Arabic) *The Eternal Message of Muhammad,* Devin-Adair, 1964; *Islam: Beliefs and Observances,* Barron, 1968; *The Addendum in Medieval Arabic Historiography,* American Oriental Society, 1968.

WORK IN PROGRESS: A Bibliographical Guide to Islamic Philosophy and Mysticism; editing and writing introduction to *Al-Mustafad min Dhayl Ta'rih Bagdad* by Ibu al-Najjar (in Arabic), for Hyderabad; *The Lebanon in the Eastern Question; The Syro-Lebanese Humanists of the Arab Revivalist Movement.*

* * *

FAUSTI, Remo P(hilip) 1917-

PERSONAL: Born April 11, 1917, in Walla Walla, Wash.; son of Joseph and Marie (Zaro) Fausti; married Bonnie R. Hungate, 1941; children: James V., Jannis M. (Mrs. Keith Peterson), Deborah A. (Mrs. Robert Haft). *Education:* State College of Washington (now Washington State University), B.A., 1939, M.A., 1947; University of Northern Colorado, Ed.D., 1956. *Religion:* Roman Catholic. *Home:* 930 Fisk St. N.W., Pullman, Wash. 99163. *Office:* Department of Speech, Washington State University, Pullman, Wash. 99163.

CAREER: Worked as a speech and English teacher in Washington high schools, 1940-43; Washington State University, Pullman, instructor, 1946-51, assistant professor, 1951-56, associate professor, 1956-61, professor of speech, 1961—, head of department, 1964-68. Guest instructor at University of Northern Colorado, 1963, and Western Washington State College (now University), 1969; visiting professor at Pennsylvania State University, 1972. *Military service:* U.S. Navy, 1943-46. *Member:* Speech Communications Association of America, American Association of University Professors, American Institute of Parlimentarians, Western Speech Communication Association, Washington Speech Communications Association.

WRITINGS: (With Arthur B. Miller) *Elements of Deliberative Debating,* Wadsworth, 1969; *Introductory Readings in Oral Communication,* Cummings, 1972; (with Edward L. McGlone) *Understanding Oral Communication,* Cummings, 1972. Contributor to professional journals in communications.

WORK IN PROGRESS: A book, *A History of Debate at Washington State University.*

* * *

FEDER, Lillian

PERSONAL: Born in New York, N.Y.; daughter of Solomon and Celia (Kirschner) Feder. *Education:* Brooklyn College (now Brooklyn College of the City University of New York), B.A., 1945; Columbia University, M.A., 1947; University of Minnesota, Ph.D., 1951. *Office:* Program in English, Graduate Center, City University of New York, 33 West 42nd St., New York, N.Y. 10036.

CAREER: Queens College and the Graduate Center of the City University of New York, assistant professor, 1960-64, associate professor, 1964-67, professor of English and comparative literature, 1967—. *Member:* Modern Language Association of America, Classical Association of the Atlantic States, P.E.N. *Awards, honors:* American Association of University Women fellowship, 1962-63; National Endowment for the Humanities fellowship, 1974-75.

WRITINGS: Crowell's Handbook of Classical Literature, Crowell, 1964, reissued as *Apollo Handbook of Classical Literature,* Apollo, 1970; *Ancient Myth in Modern Poetry,* Princeton University Press, 1971. Contributor to academic and literary journals.

WORK IN PROGRESS: Madness in Literature.

FEILER, Seymour 1919-

PERSONAL: Surname rhymes with "Tyler"; born April 11, 1919, in New York, N.Y.; son of Max and Sarah (Loeb) Feiler. *Education:* College of the City of New York (now City College of the City University of New York), B.A., 1948; University of Grenoble, graduate study, 1948-50; Columbia University, M.A., 1951; Northwestern University, Ph.D., 1957. *Home:* 1127 West Brooks St., Norman, Okla. 73069. *Office:* Department of French, University of Oklahoma, Norman, Okla. 73069.

CAREER: Teacher of French and English at Oxford Academy, Pleasantville, N.J., 1951-53; University of Oklahoma, Norman, instructor, 1955-57, assistant professor, 1957-62, associate professor, 1962-67, professor of French, 1967—, David Ross Boyd Professor of French, 1975. *Military service:* U.S. Army, 1942-46; became captain. *Member:* Modern Language Association of America, American Association of Teachers of French, American Council on the Teaching of Foreign Languages, South Central Modern Language Association, Oklahoma Foreign Language Teachers Association, Oklahoma Education Association. *Awards, honors:* Smith-Mundt grant to the French West Indies, 1957-58.

WRITINGS: (Translator and editor) *Jean-Bernard Bessu's Travels in the Interior of North America, 1751-1762,* University of Oklahoma Press, 1962; (translator) Gaston Wiet, *Cairo: City of Art and Commerce,* University of Oklahoma Press, 1964; (translator) *On the Western Tour with Washington Irving: The Journal and Letters of Count de Pourtales,* University of Oklahoma Press, 1968; (translator) Wiet, *Baghdad: Metropolis of the Abbasid Caliphate,* University of Oklahoma Press, 1971.

AVOCATIONAL INTERESTS: Travel.

* * *

FEIST, Aubrey (Noel Lydston) 1903-

PERSONAL: Surname rhymes with "beast"; born December 26, 1903, in Norwich, Norfolk, England; son of Lydston Frith (an accountant) and Ethel Beatrice (Huitson) Feist; married Kathleen Mary Binks (collaborator with and assistant to her husband), June 22, 1940. *Education:* Attended school in London, England. *Politics:* Conservative. *Religion:* Church of England. *Home and office:* Little Garth, Singleton, near Chichester, Sussex, England. *Agent:* Harvey Unna Ltd., 14 Beaumont Mews, Marylebone High St., London W1N 4HE, England.

CAREER: Employed in insurance business, 1922-35; fulltime writer, except for the war years, 1935—, doing the bulk of his writing for British Broadcasting Corp. Radio. *Military service:* British Army, Intelligence Corps, 1942-46; became sergeant. *Member:* Society of Authors.

WRITINGS—Adult: Key Men (novel), Melrose, 1937, abridged edition, Mellifont Press, 1945; *The Eyes of St. Emlyn* (novel), John Long, 1938, abridged edition, Mellifont Press, 1944; *The Lion of St. Mark* (historical nonfiction), Bobbs-Merrill, 1971; *Italian Lakes,* Batsford, 1975.

Books for boys: *High Barbary,* Heinemann, 1950; *Spread Eagle,* Heinemann, 1952; *The Dagger and the Rose,* Heinemann, 1961; *The Field of Waterloo, June 18, 1915,* Lutterworth, 1969.

One-act stage plays: *The Black Cabinet,* Samuel French, 1947; *Among Those Present,* Evans Plays, 1950; *Drums of Deliverance,* Evans Plays, 1953; *The Devil's Four-Poster* (comedy), Evans Plays, 1953; *Crime at the Cedars,* Kenyar Deane, 1972.

Television screenplays: "The Devil's Dungeon," Columbia Screen Gems, 1958; "Arms and the Woman" (adaptation of original story by Geoffrey Orme), Columbia Screen Gems, 1958.

Television and radio programs include nineteen historical serials, historical plays, history units, and talks, broadcast in England, South Africa, New Zealand, and Southern Rhodesia; many of the programs originated on BBC's "Children's Hour" and "Story-Time." Collaborator with his wife, Kay Feist, on the books and lyrics of two-part dog opera, "The Dog Next Door," with music by Alan Paul, first broadcast on "Children's Hour," and later presented in a shortened adult version and new two-part version. Contributor of short stories to periodicals in England, other Commonwealth countries, and the United States; some of the stories have been published in anthologies.

WORK IN PROGRESS: A possible serial for British Broadcasting Corp.; *The Story of the Minstrels,* with wife, for young people.

AVOCATIONAL INTERESTS: Military history, uniforms, and armour.†

* * *

FELDMAN, M(aurice) P(hilip) 1933-

PERSONAL: Born August 2, 1933, in Leeds, England; son of Nathaniel and Betty (Cohen) Feldman; married Stella Moscoe, July 12, 1959; children: Ariella, Naomi. *Education:* University of Manchester, B.A. (honors), 1959; University of London, diploma in clinical psychology (with distinction), 1960, Ph.D., 1962. *Politics:* "Centre." *Religion:* Jewish. *Home:* 5 Wake Green Rd., Birmingham 15, England. *Office:* Department of Clinical Psychology, University of Birmingham, P.O. Box 36, Birmingham B15 2TJ, England.

CAREER: Research worker, London Institute of Psychiatry, 1960-62; clinical psychologist, Crumpsall Hospital, 1962-66; University of Birmingham, Birmingham, England, lecturer, 1966-68, senior lecturer, 1968-72, reader in clinical psychology, 1972—. Visiting professor at University of Hawaii, 1972—. *Military service:* British Army, 1951-52. *Member:* British Psychological Society.

WRITINGS: Psychology in the Industrial Environment, Butterworth & Co., 1971; (with M. J. MacCulloch) *Homosexual Behaviour: Therapy and Assessment,* Pergamon, 1971; *Theoretical and Experimental Bases of Behavior Therapies,* Wiley, 1976; *Animal Behavior,* Wiley, 1977. Contributor to *American Journal of Psychiatry, Behaviour Research and Therapy, Psychological Bulletin,* and *Acta Psychiatrica Scandinavica.*

WORK IN PROGRESS: Human Sexual Behaviour, with MacCulloch; *The Social Psychology of Psychological Problems,* with J. F. Orford; research on alcoholism and crime.

AVOCATIONAL INTERESTS: Theatre, rugby football, literature, single malt whiskey.

* * *

FELDMAN, Sandor S. 1891(?)-1973

1891(?)—March 23, 1973; Hungarian-born psychiatrist, educator, and author of books on the significance of gestures and mannerisms, and other topics. Obituaries: *New York Times,* March 24, 1973.

* * *

FELDMAN, Saul D(aniel) 1943-

PERSONAL: Born September 28, 1943, in Philadelphia, Pa.; son of Benjamin and Beatrice Feldman. *Education:* Temple University, B.A., 1965; Western Reserve University (now Case Western Reserve University), M.A., 1967; University of Washington, Seattle, Ph.D., 1972. *Home:* 16000 Terrace Rd., Apt. 2204, East Cleveland, Ohio 44112.

CAREER: University of Washington, Seattle, instructor in sociology, 1967-69; University of California, Berkeley, research sociologist at Survey Research Center, 1969-71, instructor in sociology, 1970-75; Case Western Reserve University, Cleveland, Ohio, 1975-77, began as assistant professor, became associate professor of sociology; director, Cleveland Area Survey, 1977—. Manager, Cleveland Opera Theater. *Member:* American Sociological Association, Popular Culture Association.

WRITINGS: (With Gerald Thielbar) *Life Styles: Diversity in American Society,* Little, Brown, 1972, 2nd edition, 1975; (editor with Thielbar, and contributor) *Issues in Social Inequality,* Little, Brown, 1972; *Escape from the Doll's House: Women in Graduate and Professional Education,* McGraw, 1973; *Deciphering Deviance,* Little, Brown, 1978. Contributor to professional journals, including *Social Forces* and *American Journal of Sociology.*

* * *

FELDT, Allan Gunnar 1932-

PERSONAL: Born April 20, 1932, in Tonawanda, N.Y.; son of Gunnar Axel (a factory foreman) and Alma (Ahnberg) Feldt; married Barbara McVittie, January 30, 1954; children: David, Linda, Laurie. *Education:* University of Michigan, B.S., 1954, A.M., 1958, Ph.D., 1963. *Politics:* Democrat. *Religion:* None. *Home:* 3105 Sunnywood Dr., Ann Arbor, Mich. 48103. *Office:* 2204 College of Architecture and Urban Planning, University of Michigan, Ann Arbor, Mich. 48109.

CAREER: Cornell University, Ithaca, N.Y., assistant professor, 1962-66, associate professor of sociology and city and regional planning, 1966-71; University of Michigan, Ann Arbor, associate professor, 1971-73, professor of urban and regional planning, 1973—, chairperson of Program in Urban and Regional Planning, 1973-74. Alderman, Ithaca Common Council, 1967-71. *Military service:* U.S. Army, 1954-56. *Member:* International and North American Simulation and Gaming Association, American Society of Planning Officials.

WRITINGS: CLUG: Community Land Use Game, Free Press, 1972; *WALRUS I and II: Water and Land Resource Utilization Simulation,* University of Michigan Sea Grant Program, 1972; *GEPS: Generelles Entwicklungs Plan Spiel,* DATUM (Bonn), 1972; *Planspiel: Simulation aus Hilfsmittel fur die Stadtebauliche Planung und die Planerausbildung,* Der Bandminister fur Raumordnung, Bauwesen, und Stadtebau, 1977.

Contributor: Becker and Goudappel, editors, *Developments in Simulation and Gaming,* Boom Meppel (Netherlands), 1972; Patterson, editor, *Recent Developments in Urban Gaming,* Simulation Council, Inc., 1976; Coppard and Goodman, editors, *Urban Gaming/Simulation,* University of Michigan Press, 1977; Greenblatt and Dulce, editors, *Gaming-Simulation,* Wiley, 1978. Contributor to *American Sociological Review, Journal of American Statistical Association, Journal of American Institute of Planners,* and *Demography.*

WORK IN PROGRESS: A textbook or novel on decentralist theory and practice.

SIDELIGHTS: Allan Feldt told *CA:* "Up to this time, my writing has been incidental to my research and teaching activities—primarily in the area of urban theory and simulation/gaming. I have recently become involved in decentralist theory and philosophy, however, and have become convinced that a novel is the most suitable form to develop these ideas—allowing a suitable interplay of both philosophy and imagery to get the central idea across. Novel writing appears to be vastly more difficult than academic writing, however, and I anticipate many years before I can develop a satisfactory manuscript."

* * *

FELLOWS, Donald Keith 1920-

PERSONAL: Born March 31, 1920, in Los Angeles, Calif.; son of John Lee (a salesman) and Ruth (Parker) Fellows; married Virginia Lady Neil (an elementary school teacher); children: Scott Emery, Leslie Ellen, Karen Lee. *Education:* University of California, Los Angeles, B.A., 1942; San Fernando Valley State College (now California State University, Northridge), M.A., 1968. *Politics:* Republican. *Religion:* Unitarian Universalist. *Home:* 15002 Kittridge St., Van Nuys, Calif. 91405. *Office:* Department of Earth Science, Los Angeles Mission College, 1101 San Fernando Rd., San Fernando, Calif. 91340.

CAREER: John L. Fellows & Son (retail floor coverings), Burbank, Calif., owner-manager, salesman, 1946-72; substitute and evening class instructor in physical geography, physical geology, and anthropology, Los Angeles City College and Los Angeles Pierce College, both Los Angeles, Calif., 1968-75; part-time lecturer in physical and cultural geography at California State University, Northridge, 1968-75; lecturer in geography and anthropology, Los Angeles Mission College, San Fernando, Calif., 1975—. *Military service:* U.S. Naval Reserve, active duty, 1943-46; served in Okinawa; became lieutenant; received Bronze Star Medal. *Member:* Association of American Geographers, National Council for Geographic Education, Association of Pacific Coast Geographers, California Council for Geographic Education, Los Angeles Geographic Society, Magnolia Park Optimist Club (president, 1964-65).

WRITINGS: A Mosaic of America's Ethnic Minorities, Wiley, 1972; *The Environment of Mankind: An Introduction to Physical Geography,* Wiley, 1975. Contributor to *California Geographer.*

WORK IN PROGRESS: Second edition of *The Environment of Mankind.*

* * *

FELSTEIN, Ivor 1933-
(Frank Steen)

PERSONAL: Born May 14, 1933, in Glasgow, Scotland; son of Myer and Boonie (Greenberg) Felstein; married Juliet Miller; children: one son, one daughter. *Education:* University of Glasgow, M.B., 1956, Ch.B., 1956. *Residence:* Manchester, England. *Office:* Department of Geriatric Medicine, Bolton Group Hospitals, Farnworth, Lancashire, England.

CAREER: Kingston Group Hospitals, Surrey, England, medical registrar, 1960-63; Bolton District General Hospital, Farnworth, Lancashire, England, physician in geriatrics, 1963—; free-lance medical journalist, 1964—. *Member:* British Geriatrics Society, Society of Authors (London).

WRITINGS: Later Life: Geriatrics Today and Tomorrow,

Penguin, 1969; *Sex and the Longer Life,* Penguin, 1970; *Snakes and Ladders: Medical and Social Aspects of Modern Management,* Constable, 1971; *A Change of Face and Figure,* Constable, 1971; *Living to Be a Hundred: A Study of Old Age,* David & Charles, 1973; *Sex in Later Life,* Penguin, 1973; (with Joyce Mitson and Mavis Barnard) *The Medical Shorthand Typist,* Pitman, 1974; *Sexual Pollution: The Fall and Rise of Veneral Diseases,* David & Charles, 1974; *Looking at Retirement,* British Medical Association, 1977. Author of columns appearing in *Bolton Evening News, Hospital World,* and *On Call.* Contributor of short stories, under pseudonym Frank Steen, to *Hospital World, Glasgow University Magazine, Scottish Thistle,* and *Nursing Mirror.* Contributor to *Marshall-Cavendish Encyclopedias;* contributor to medical journals and to newspapers. Consulting editor, *British Journal of Sexual Medicine,* 1973—.

AVOCATIONAL INTERESTS: Writing short stories, cinema.†

* * *

FENWICK, Charles G(hequiere) 1880-1973

May 26, 1880—April 24, 1973; American political scientist, expert on international law, and author. Obituaries: *New York Times,* April 26, 1973; *Washington Post,* April 26, 1973.

* * *

FERNANDEZ-MARINA, R(amon) 1909-

PERSONAL: Born September 16, 1909, in San Juan, Puerto Rico; son of Ramon (an engineer) and Sofia (Marina) Fernandez-Abarca; married Luz M. Petrovich (a social worker), August 31, 1941; children: Ramon. *Education:* Attended St. John's College, Annapolis, Md., 1926-27; University of Madrid, M.S., 1931, M.D., 1933; Washington Psychoanalytic Institute, diploma, 1948. *Home:* B4-16 R. de Arellano, Guaynabo, P.R. 00917. *Office:* 404 Professional Bldg., Santurce, P.R. 00909.

CAREER: Medical practice specializing in internal medicine, Bayamon, P.R., 1933-45, specializing in psychiatry and psychoanalysis, Santurce, P.R., 1947; Munic Hospital, Ponce, P.R., intern, 1933-34; private practice, San Juan, P.R., 1937-39; Bayamon District Hospital, Bayamon, chief of medical services, 1937-43; affiliated with St. Elizabeth's Hospital, Washington, D.C., 1945, and Chestnut Lodge, Rockville, Md., 1945-47; medical director, Puerto Rico Insular Psychiatric Hospital, 1947-52; Hato Tejas Hospital, Bayamon, psychiatrist, 1952-70; psychiatrist and director of drug dependence program, Puerto Rico Psychiatric Hospital, 1970—. Civilian medical director, Roosevelt Roads Naval Base, 1941-43; University of Puerto Rico, lecturer, 1948-50, assistant professor of psychiatry, 1952-57, lecturer in Law School, 1963-65. Consultant to Commonwealth of Puerto Rico, 1969—. Member of national board of advisors, Hampshire College. President, Mountain Camp Resort, 1956—.

MEMBER: American Medical Association, Puerto Rico Medical Association, American Psychiatric Association, American Psychoanalytic Association, American Academy of Psychoanalysis (fellow), American Association for the Advancement of Science, American College of Psychoanalysts, Argentine Adolescent Psychiatric Association (honorary member), Academy of Arts and Sciences of Puerto Rico, Puerto Rico Public Health Association (president, 1965), New York Academy of Science. *Awards, honors:* Literary Society of Puerto Rico, first prize for poetry, 1958;

Puerto Rico Atheneum, second prize for short story, 1963; named psychiatrist of the year by the Puerto Rico Medical Association, 1971.

WRITINGS: (With Ursula V. Eckardt) *The Horizons of the Mind,* Philosophical Library, 1965; (with Eckardt) *The Sober Generation,* University of Puerto Rico, 1968. Also author of *Poemas en Tres Claves.* Contributor of poems, short stories, and scientific articles to journals.

WORK IN PROGRESS: A book, *The Fourth Horizon.*†

* * *

FERRES, John H(oward) 1932-

PERSONAL: Born October 17, 1932, in Perth, Australia; son of Ernest F. (a grocer) and Gladys (Howard) Ferres; married Mary B. Elliott (a secretary), April 12, 1958 (divorced June, 1976); children: Joselyn, Christine, John. *Education:* University of West Australia, B.A. (honors), 1954; Louisiana State University, M.A., 1956, Ph.D., 1959. *Religion:* Roman Catholic. *Home:* 4383 Stoneycroft Dr., Okemos, Mich. 48864. *Office:* Department of American Thought and Language, Michigan State University, East Lansing, Mich. 48823.

CAREER: Carlow College, Pittsburgh, Pa., assistant professor of English, 1960-64; Michigan State University, East Lansing, assistant professor, 1964-67, associate professor, 1967-72, professor of American thought and language, 1972—. *Member:* Modern Language Association of America, American Studies Association (vice-president, 1973-75; president of Michigan chapter, 1975-78), Association for Canadian Studies in the United States. *Awards, honors:* Fulbright scholarship, 1955-58.

WRITINGS: (Editor) Sherwood Anderson, *Winesburg, Ohio,* Viking, 1965; (editor) *Twentieth Century Interpretations of Arthur Miller's "The Crucible",* Prentice-Hall, 1972; (editor and compiler) *Modern Commonwealth Literature,* Ungar, 1977; *Arthur Miller: A Reference Guide,* G. K. Hall, 1978.

* * *

FETTER, Elizabeth Head 1904-1973

September 4, 1904—January 21, 1973; American author and civic leader. Obituaries: *New York Times,* January 22, 1973. (See index for *CA* sketch)

* * *

FIELER, Frank B(ernard) 1933-

PERSONAL: Born January 8, 1933, in Dayton, Ky.; son of Frank Bernard (a trucker) and Laura (Styer) Fieler; married Jean Fair, August 29, 1956; children: Laura, Therese, Karl. *Education:* Morehead State College (now University), B.S., 1955; University of Florida, M.A., 1958, Ph.D., 1960. *Home:* 34 Morris Ave., Athens, Ohio 45701. *Office:* Department of English, Ohio University, Athens, Ohio 45701.

CAREER: Ohio University, Athens, instructor, 1960-62, assistant professor, 1962-66, associate professor, 1966-71, professor of English, 1971—, head of department, 1971—, director of remedial English, 1962-64, director of graduate program, 1966-69. *Member:* Modern Language Association of America, Renaissance Society of America, Bibliographical Society, Printing Historical Society, Private Libraries Association, Phi Beta Kappa.

WRITINGS: Tamburlaine, Part I, And Its Audience, University of Florida Press, 1962; (editor with Henry Green)

Geoffrey Whitney, *Choice of Emblems,* Benjamin Blom, 1967; (editor) Barnabe Googe, *Eglogs, Epytaphes, and Sonettes (1563),* Scholars' Facsimiles & Reprints, 1968; *The David McCandless McKell Collection,* G. K. Hall, 1973. Contributor to *Studies in English Literature, Renaissance Papers, Studies in Short Fiction, Journal of English and Germanic Philology,* and *Western Humanities Review.*

WORK IN PROGRESS: Research on bibliographical and textual problems concerning Tennyson's "Idylls of the King."†

* * *

FINCH, Henry LeRoy 1918-

PERSONAL: Born August 8, 1918, in Monmouth Beach, N.J.; son of Henry LeRoy (an investment banker) and Mary (Baker) Finch; married Margaret Rockwell, June 12, 1948; children: Mary Dabney, Annie Ridley Crane, Henry LeRoy III. *Education:* Yale University, B.A., 1940; Columbia University, M.A., 1949, Ph.D., 1951. *Politics:* Independent. *Religion:* Episcopal. *Home:* 106 Liberty Ave., New Rochelle, N.Y. 10805. *Office:* Department of Philosophy, Hunter College of the City University of New York, New York, N.Y. 10021.

CAREER: Sarah Lawrence College, Bronxville, N.Y., professor of philosophy, 1953-73; Hunter College of the City University of New York, New York, N.Y., professor of philosophy, 1973—. *Member:* American Philosophical Society.

WRITINGS: (Editor with Lucie B. Gutkind) Eric Gutkind, *The Body of God,* Horizon Press, 1969; (editor) A. B. Goldenweiser, *Talks with Tolstoi,* Horizon Press, 1969; (editor) Charles Woodbury, *Talks with Emerson,* Horizon Press, 1969; *Wittgenstein: The Early Philosophy,* Humanities, 1971; *Wittgenstein: The Later Philosophy,* Humanities, 1976.

* * *

FINCHER, Cameron Lane 1926-

PERSONAL: Born November 4, 1926, in Douglas County, Ga.; son of Andrew Jackson and Ada (Swafford) Fincher; married Mary Frances Cutts, June 15, 1957; children: Marcel, Matthew, Mandy, Melissa. *Education:* Atlanta Division, University of Georgia (now Georgia State University), B.C.S., 1950; University of Minnesota, M.A., 1951; Ohio State University, Ph.D., 1956. *Politics:* Democrat. *Religion:* Protestant. *Home:* 230 Pine Forest Dr., Athens, Ga. 30606. *Office:* Institute of Higher Education, University of Georgia, Athens, Ga. 30602.

CAREER: Georgia State College (now University), Atlanta, instructor, 1951-54, assistant professor, 1956-58, associate professor, 1958-61, professor of psychology, 1961-65, director of testing and counseling, 1956-65; University of Georgia, Athens, associate director, 1965-69, director of Institute of Higher Education, 1969—. Visiting summer professor at North Carolina State College of Agriculture and Engineering (now North Carolina State University at Raleigh), 1959, at Emory University, 1960, 1961. *Military service:* U.S. Navy, 1944-46; received three combat ribbons. *Member:* American Psychological Association, American Educational Research Association, Association for Institutional Research, Society for College and University Planning (member of board of directors, 1971—), American Association for Higher Education, National Council on Measurement in Education, Alpha Kappa Psi, Phi Delta Kappa.

WRITINGS: Nursing and Paramedical Personnel in Georgia, Georgia State College, 1962; *A Preface to Psychology,* Harper, 1964, 2nd edition, 1972; (editor) *Institutional Research and Academic Outcomes,* Association for Institutional Research, 1968; (editor) *Challenge and Response of Institutional Research,* Association for Institutional Research, 1970. Also author of a monograph, *Atlanta Studies Its Bond Issue: A Survey of Public Opinion.* Author of a monthly column, "University Spotlight," in *Athens Banner-Herald,* 1970—. Contributor of articles to journals in his field.

WORK IN PROGRESS: A book on planning, decision-making, and policy-formulation in higher education; policy and evaluation research; two books on Southern history, culture, and regionalism, "long in progress but still unfinished."

SIDELIGHTS: Cameron Fincher writes that he has "tried short stories without satisfaction" and has "survived an infatuation with the Civil War but scars sometimes show."

*   *   *

FINER, Samuel Edward   1915-

PERSONAL: Born September 22, 1915, in London, England; son of Max and Fanny Finer; married Margaret Ann McFadyean, 1949 (divorced, 1975); married Catherine J. Jones, 1977; children: (first marriage) two sons, one daughter. *Education:* Trinity College, Oxford, B.A. (first class honors), 1937, M.A., 1946. *Home:* 48 Lonsdale Rd., Oxford, England. *Office:* All Soul's College University Offices, Wellington Sq., Oxford OX1 2JD, England.

CAREER: Oxford University, Balliol College, Oxford, England, lecturer in politics, 1946-49, junior research fellow, 1949-50; University of Keele, Keele, England, professor of political institutions, 1950-66, deputy vice-chancellor, 1962-64; University of Manchester, Manchester, England, professor of government, 1966-74; Oxford University, All Soul's College, Gladstone Professor of Government and Public Administration, 1974—. Visiting professor and faculty member, Institute of Social Studies, The Hague, 1957—; visiting professor at Cornell University, 1962, Hebrew University of Jerusalem, 1969, Simon Fraser University, 1976, and European University Institute, 1977. *Military service:* British Army, Royal Signals, 1940-46; became captain. *Member:* Royal Historical Society (fellow), International Political Science Association (vice-president, 1969; member of executive board, 1969-74), Political Studies Association (chairman, 1965-69).

WRITINGS: A Primer of Public Administration, Muller, 1950; *The Life and Times of Sir Edwin Chadwick,* Methuen, 1952, reprinted, Barnes & Noble, 1970; (with Sir John P. R. Maud) *Local Government in England and Wales,* 2nd edition (Finer was not associated with earlier edition), Oxford University Press, 1953; *Anonymous Empire: A Study of the Lobby in Great Britain,* Pall Mall, 1958, 2nd revised and enlarged edition, Humanities, 1966; *Private Industry and Political Power* (expansion of Ramsey Muir memorial lecture for 1958), Pall Mall, 1958; (with H. B. Berrington and D. J. Bartholomew) *Backbench Opinion in the House of Commons, 1955-59,* Pergamon, 1961; *The Man on Horseback: The Role of the Military in Politics,* Praeger, 1962; (with others) *Modern Political Systems: Europe,* edited by Roy C. Macridis and R. E. Ward, Prentice-Hall, 1963, 4th edition, 1978; *Comparative Government,* Penguin, 1970, Basic Books, 1971; (contributor) Gillian Sutherland, editor, *Studies in the Growth of 19th Century Government,*

Rowman & Littlefield, 1972; (contributor) Geraint Parry, editor, *Participation,* Manchester University Press, 1972; (contributor) C. Tilly, editor, *The Formation of National States in Western Europe,* Princeton University Press, 1975.

Editor: (And author of historical notes) Emmanuel J. Sieyes, *What Is the Third Estate?,* translation from the French by M. Blondel, Pall Mall, 1963, Praeger, 1964; (and author of introduction) Vilfredo Pareto, *Sociological Writings,* translation from the Italian by Derick Mirfin, Praeger, 1966; *Adversary Politics and Electoral Reform,* Wigram, 1975. Also editor of *Five Constitutions.*

Contributor of articles and reviews to periodicals and newspapers.

WORK IN PROGRESS: Change and Persistency in the British Party System; studies on the role of the military in politics.

AVOCATIONAL INTERESTS: Painting, writing poetry (for his own pleasure, not publication), and translating French poetry.

*   *   *

FINK, William B(ertrand)   1916-

PERSONAL: Born May 11, 1916, in Yonkers, N.Y.; son of Perley C. (a realtor) and Agnes (Heuchele) Fink; married Esther Cheney (director of Head Start), April 16, 1941; children: William B., Jr., Marilyn C. *Education:* Wesleyan University, B.A., 1937; Columbia University, M.A., 1939, Ph.D., 1950. *Politics:* Democrat. *Religion:* Presbyterian. *Home:* Main St., Laurens, N.Y. 13796. *Office:* Department of History, State University of New York College, Oneonta, N.Y. 13820.

CAREER: High school social studies teacher in New York, 1937-38, in Maryland, 1939-42; New York College for Teachers (now State University of New York at Albany), Albany, instructor in Campus School, 1946-49; Columbia University, New York, N.Y., instructor in history, 1949-51; State University of New York College at Oneonta, professor of history, 1953—, head of social science department, 1960-70, head of social science education department, 1970—. Fulbright lecturer in Philippines, 1961-62; visiting lecturer, Trent Polytechnic, Nottingham, England, winter, 1978; fellow of Hughes Hall, Cambridge University, spring, 1978. *Military service:* U.S. Naval Reserve, 1942-46; became lieutenant. *Member:* American Historical Association, Organization of American Historians, National Council for the Social Studies, New York State Historical Association, New York State Council for the Social Studies, Phi Beta Kappa.

WRITINGS: (With David Ellis and James Frost) *New York: The Empire State,* Prentice-Hall, 1961; (with Frost, Ellis, and Ralph Brown) *A History of the United States,* Follett, 1968; *Getting to Know the Hudson,* Coward, 1970; *Getting to Know New York State,* Coward, 1971.

WORK IN PROGRESS: A collection of documents of New York history, 1975.

*   *   *

FIRESTONE, Harvey S(amuel), Jr.   1898-1973

April 20, 1898—June 1, 1973; American industrialist. Obituaries: *New York Times,* June 1, 1973; *Washington Post,* June 2, 1973.

FIRESTONE, O(tto) J(ohn) 1913-

PERSONAL: Born January 17, 1913, in Austria; son of Bruce M. (a lawyer) and Regina (Seaman) Firestone; children: Brenda Ruth, Catherine Paula, Bruce Murray, John Mitchell Peter. *Education:* University of Vienna, Dr. juris et rerum politicarum, 1936; London School of Economics and Political Science, graduate study, 1938-40; McGill University, M.A., 1942. *Home:* 375 Minto Pl., Ottawa, Ontario, Canada K1M 0B1. *Office:* University of Ottawa, 500 Cumberland St., Ottawa, Ontario, Canada K1N 6N5.

CAREER: Department of Pensions and Health (later Privy Council), Ottawa, Ontario, research assistant on Advisory Committee on Reconstruction, and Advisory Committee on Economic Policy, 1942-44; Department of Reconstruction (later Department of Reconstruction and Supply), Ottawa, Ontario, assistant to director general of economic research and director of economic research, 1944-48; Department of Trade and Commerce, Ottawa, Ontario, director of economic research, 1948-50; economic adviser to minister of trade and commerce, 1950-60; University of Ottawa, Ottawa, Ontario, professor of economics, 1960—, vice-dean of faculty of social science, 1964-70. Visiting professor, Cambridge University, 1972, Australian National University, 1975, and University of Nevada, 1978. Member of Royal Commission on Health Services, 1962-65; sessional lecturer, Banff School of Advanced Management, 1965, 1967. Economic adviser to Central Mortgage and Housing Corp., 1946-60, and to Special Committee of Senate on Poverty, 1969-70.

MEMBER: International Association for Research in Income and Wealth, Canadian Economics Association, Canadian Historical Association, Canadian Political Science Association, Institute of Public Administration of Canada, Canadian Tax Foundation, Royal Economic Society, Conference on Research in Income and Wealth, American Economic Association, American Academy of Political and Social Science, Association of Evolutionary Economics, Economic History Society (Great Britain). *Awards, honors:* Coronation Medal, from Queen Elizabeth II, 1953; Doctor of Economics, Hanyang University, Korea, 1975.

WRITINGS: Residential Real Estate in Canada, University of Toronto Press, 1951; (contributor) *Short-Term Economic Forecasting,* Princeton University Press, for National Bureau of Economic Research, 1955; *Canada's Economic Development: 1867-1953,* Bowes, 1958.

(Contributor) *Trends in the American Economy in the Nineteenth Century,* Princeton University Press, for National Bureau of Economic Research, 1960; *Problems of Economic Growth,* University of Ottawa Press, 1965; *Broadcast Advertising in Canada: Past and Future Growth,* University of Ottawa Press, 1966; *Economic Implications of Advertising,* Methuen, 1967; (contributor) J.M.S. Careless and R. C. Brown, editors, *The Canadians,* Macmillan (of Canada), 1967; *Industry and Education: A Century of Canadian Development,* University of Ottawa Press, 1969; (contributor) Victor Fuchs, editor, *Production and Productivity in the Service Industries,* Columbia University Press, for National Bureau of Economic Research, 1969.

The Public Persuader, Methuen, 1970; *Economic Implications of Patents,* University of Ottawa Press, 1971; (editor and contributor) *Economic Growth Reassessed,* University of Ottawa Press, 1972; (contributor) Bert G. Hickman, editor, *Econometrics Models of Cyclical Behaviour,* Columbia University Press, for National Bureau of Economic Research, 1972; (editor and contributor) *Regional Economic*

Development, University of Ottawa Press, 1974; *Canada's Anti-Inflation Program and Kenneth Galbraith,* University of Ottawa Press, 1977; (contributor) Tullio Bagiotti and Giampiero Franco, editors, *Pioneering Economics,* CEDAM (Italy), 1978.

Also author of about a dozen government reports. Contributor to proceedings, conferences, and symposia. Contributor of more than twenty-five articles and reviews to professional journals, including *Canadian Journal of Agricultural Economics, Canadian Patent Reporter, Canadian Tax Journal,* and *Review of Income and Wealth.*

* * *

FISCHEL, Walter J(oseph) 1902-1973

November 12, 1902—July 14, 1973; German-born American professor of Semitic languages and literature, historian, Orientalist, and author. Obituaries: *New York Times,* July 16, 1973. (See index for *CA* sketch)

* * *

FISCHER, Donald E(dward) 1935-

PERSONAL: Born November 8, 1935, in St. Louis, Mo.; son of Charles and Marie Fischer; married Mary Sharpe (an accountant), August 14, 1966. *Education:* Washington University, St. Louis, Mo., B.S., 1957, D.B.A., 1964; University of Detroit, M.B.A., 1960. *Home:* Codfish Falls Rd., Storrs, Conn. 06268. *Office:* Department of Finance, University of Connecticut, Box U-41, Storrs, Conn. 06268.

CAREER: Haskins & Sells, St. Louis, Mo., accountant, 1957-58; Chrysler Corp., Detroit, Mich., financial analyst, 1958-60; Arizona State University, Phoenix, assistant professor of finance, 1964-66; University of Connecticut, Storrs, assistant professor, 1966-68, associate professor, 1968-75, professor of finance, 1975—. *Military service:* U.S. Army Reserve, 1957-62; became captain. *Member:* American Economic Association, American Finance Association, Financial Management Association, Financial Analysts Federation, Eastern Finance Association, Hartford Society of Financial Analysts, Beta Gamma Sigma.

WRITINGS: Contemporary Financial Management, Scott, Foresman, 1969; (with Ronald J. Jorden) *Security Analysis and Portfolio Management,* Prentice-Hall, 1975, 2nd edition, 1979. Contributor to *Journal of Finance, Journal of Financial Education, Public Utilities Fortnightly, Atlanta Economic Review,* and *Encyclopedia Americana.*

AVOCATIONAL INTERESTS: Culinary arts, classical music, travel.

* * *

FISHBEIN, Meyer H(arry) 1916-

PERSONAL: Born May 6, 1916, in New York, N.Y.; son of Jacob and Celia (Brownstein) Fishbein; married Evelyn Centner (a teacher), March 30, 1947; children: Daniel, Diane. *Education:* American University, M.A., 1954, graduate study, 1954-62. *Religion:* Jewish. *Home:* 5005 Elsmere Ave., Bethesda, Md. 20014. *Office:* Military Archives Division, National Archives, Washington, D.C. 20408.

CAREER: National Archives, Washington, D.C., archivist, 1940-57, chief of Business Economics Branch, 1957-61, senior records appraisal specialist, 1962-67, deputy director of Records Appraisal Division, 1967-68, director, 1968-74, director, Military Archives Division, 1974—. Director, Conference on National Archives and Statistical Research,

1968. Adjunct professor, American University, 1977—. *Military service:* U.S. Army, 1943-46. *Member:* Society of American Archivists (fellow), Social Science History Association, Organization of American Historians, International Council on Archives, Cosmos Club.

WRITINGS: Early Business Statistical Operations of the Federal Government, National Archives, 1958; *The Censuses of Manufactures: 1810-1890,* National Archives, 1963; *The National Archives and Statistical Research,* Ohio University Press, 1973. Contributor to *American Archivist, Social Forces, Illinois Libraries, Labor History,* and other professional journals. Member of editorial advisory board, *Business History Review,* 1963-69.

WORK IN PROGRESS: Handbook for Archivists on Automatic Data Processing, completion expected in 1979.

* * *

FISHER, Gene H. 1922-

PERSONAL: Born August 20, 1922, in Indianapolis, Ind.; son of Ora and Grace A. (Martin) Fisher; married Susan M. Hoskinson (a social worker), October, 1965; children: Bruce, Gail, Scot. *Education:* University of Southern California, B.S. in B.A., 1947, M.B.A., 1947; Ohio State University, Ph.D., 1951. *Home:* 16915 Dulce Ynez Lane, Pacific Palisades, Calif. 90272. *Office:* RAND Corp., 1700 Main St., Santa Monica, Calif. 90406.

CAREER: Statistician, Indiana Bell Telephone Co., 1947-48; University of Southern Califonia, Los Angeles, instructor in monetary theory, money, and banking, 1948; Ohio State University, Columbus, instructor in statistics, 1950-51; RAND Corp., Santa Monica, Calif., economist and member of research staff, 1951-62, member of senior research staff, 1962—, associate head of resource analysis department, 1969-72, head of management sciences department, 1972—. Conductor of seminars at University of California, Los Angeles, and University of California, Irvine, 1970-71. *Military service:* U.S. Army, Infantry, 1943-46; served in European theater, 1944-45; became captain; received Bronze Star and Purple Heart with oak-leaf cluster. *Member:* American Economic Association, Econometric Society, Beta Gamma Sigma, Phi Kappa Phi.

WRITINGS: Cost Considerations in Systems Analysis, American Elsevier, 1971. Author or co-authors of various classified and unclassified research reports published by RAND Corp.

Contributor: J. A. Stockfisch, editor, *Planning and Forecasting in the Defense Industries,* Wadsworth, 1962; E. S. Quade, editor, *Analysis for Military Decisions,* Rand McNally, 1964; Davis Novick, editor, *Program Budgeting: Program Analysis and the Federal Budget,* Harvard University Press, 1965; F. J. Lyden and E. G. Miller, editors, *Planning, Programming, Budgeting: A Systems Approach to Management,* Markham, 1967; Quade and W. I. Boucher, *Systems Analysis and Policy Planning,* American Elsevier, 1967; Robert T. Golembiewski, editor, *Public Budgeting and Finance,* F. E. Peacock, 1968; David I. Cleland and William R. King, *Systems, Organizations, Analysis, Management,* McGraw, 1969; Julius Margolis, editor, *The Economics of Public Output,* National Bureau of Economic Research, 1970. Contributor to economic and business journals.

WORK IN PROGRESS: Studies on policy analysis concepts and methods.

AVOCATIONAL INTERESTS: Working on problems in

minority communities, skeet and trap shooting, tennis, bowling.

* * *

FISHER, John C(harles) 1927-

PERSONAL: Born November 27, 1927, in Mendon, N.Y.; son of John C. (a safety engineer) and Helen (Laramie) Fisher; married Joanne Marie Byrnes, August 18, 1956; children: Gerard David, Elizabeth Ann. *Education:* Champlain College (State University of New York), B.A., 1953; University of Michigan, M.A., 1954, Ed.D., 1962. *Politics:* Democrat. *Religion:* Roman Catholic. *Home address:* Perry Hill, Oswego, N.Y. 13126. *Office:* Department of English, State University of New York College, Oswego, N.Y.

CAREER: State University of New York College at Oswego, instructor, 1957-58, assistant professor, 1958-61, associate professor, 1961-62, professor of English, 1963—, chairman of department, 1972-74, chairman of Oswego Faculty Assembly, 1977-78. Fulbright lecturer at University of Rome, 1963-64. Visiting professor at University of Michigan, 1958-61, University of Hawaii, 1970, and Inter American University, 1970. In charge of instruction for State University of New York-Ford Foundation Indonesia Project, 1962-63. *Military service:* U.S. Navy, 1945-47, 1951-52. *Member:* Modern Language Association of America, College English Association, National Council of Teachers of English, Keats-Shelley Association, New York State English Council (fellow; executive secretary, 1968-70; president, 1973—), Rotary Club.

WRITINGS: Linguistics in Remedial English, Mouton, 1966; *Workbook in Transformational Grammar,* Books 3 and 4, Ginn, 1970; *Transparencies in Transformational Grammar,* Ginn, 1970. Contributor to *College English* and other journals.

* * *

FISHER, Ralph Talcott, Jr. 1920-

PERSONAL: Born April 5, 1920, in Washington, D.C.; son of Ralph Talcott (a banker) and Margaret (Merriam) Fisher; married Ruth Meads (a social worker), December 20, 1942; children: Ralph T. III, Margaret M., Albert M. *Education:* University of Montpellier, certificate, 1938; University of California, Berkeley, B.A., 1942, M.A., 1948; Columbia University, certificate of Russian Institute, 1950, Ph.D., 1955. *Politics:* Independent. *Religion:* Congregationalist. *Home:* 2115 Burlison Dr., Urbana, Ill. 61801. *Office:* Department of History, University of Illinois, Urbana, Ill. 61801.

CAREER: Yale University, New Haven, Conn., instructor, 1952-55, assistant professor of history, 1955-58; University of Illinois at Urbana-Champaign, associate professor, 1958-60, professor of history, 1960—, director of Russian and East European Center, 1960—. *Military service:* U.S. Army, 1942-46; became major. *Member:* American Historical Association, American Association for Advancement of Slavic Studies (secretary, 1960-69), Phi Beta Kappa, Alpha Delta Phi. *Awards, honors:* Social Science Research Council grant, 1951-52; Rockefeller Foundation grant, 1956-58; Fulbright-Hays grant, 1964-65; American Council of Learned Societies grant, 1965.

WRITINGS: Pattern for Soviet Youth: A Study of the Congresses of the Komsomol, 1918-1954, Columbia University Press, 1959; (editor with George Vernadsky) Sergei Pushkarev, compiler, *Dictionary of Russian Historical Terms,*

Yale University Press, 1970; (editor with Vernadsky and others) *Source Book for Russian History to 1917*, Yale University Press, 1972. Member of editorial board of *Russian Review*, 1958—, and *Slavic Review*, 1969—.

* * *

FISHMAN, Joshua A(aron) 1926-

PERSONAL: Born July 18, 1926, in Philadelphia, Pa.; son of Aaron Samuel (a dental technician) and Sonia (Horwitz) Fishman; married Gertrude Jeanne Schweid, December 23, 1951; children: M. Manuel, David Eliot, Avrom. *Education:* University of Pennsylvania, B.S. and M.S., 1948; Columbia University, Ph.D., 1953. *Religion:* Jewish. *Home:* 3340 Bainbridge Ave., Bronx, N.Y. 10467. *Office:* Ferkauf Graduate School of Humanities and Social Sciences, Yeshiva University, 55 Fifth Ave., New York, N.Y. 10003.

CAREER: Teacher at elementary and secondary levels in Jewish schools, 1945-50; Jewish Education Committee of New York, Inc., New York City, research assistant, 1951-52, senior research associate and educational psychologist, 1952-54; College Entrance Examination Board, New York City, research assistant, 1955-56, assistant director of research, 1956-57, director of research 1957-68; City College (now City College of the City University of New York), New York City, lecturer, 1955-57, visiting professor of psychology at Uptown Branch, 1957-58; University of Pennsylvania, Philadelphia, associate professor of human relations and psychology and director of research at A. M. Greenfield Center for Human Relations, 1958-60; Yeshiva University, New York City, professor of psychology and sociology and dean of Ferkauf Graduate School of Education, 1960-66, distinguished research professor of social sciences, Ferkauf Graduate School of Humanities and Social Sciences, 1966—, vice-president for academic affairs, 1973—. Fellow, Center for Advanced Study in the Behavioral Sciences, 1963-64; senior specialist, Institute of Advanced Projects, East-West Center, University of Hawaii, 1968-69; fellow, Institute for Advanced Study, Princeton University, 1975-76. Member of UNESCO planning committee, International Seminar on Bilingualism, 1966-67; chairman of research planning committee, Yivo Center for Advanced Jewish Studies, 1967—. Member of advisory planning committee, Center for Applied Linguistics, 1966-68; member of advisory committee, International Research Center on Bilingualism, 1967—.

MEMBER: American Psychological Association (fellow), American Sociological Association (fellow), American Association for the Advancement of Science (fellow), American Anthropological Association (fellow), Linguistic Society of America, American Association of University Professors, New York State Psychological Association (president of Applied Social Division, 1962-63), Sigma Xi, Pi Gamma Mu. *Awards, honors:* Social Science Research Council postdoctoral fellowship, 1954-55, and travel grants, 1961, 1966; National Science Foundation conference travel grants, 1960, 1963, 1966; American Sociological Association conference travel grant, 1966; Ped.D., Yeshiva University, 1968.

WRITINGS: (With Lucy Davidowicz and others) *For Max Weinreich on His Seventieth Birthday*, Mouton, 1965; *Yiddish in America*, Research Center in Anthropology, Folklore and Linguistics, Indiana University, 1965; (with others) *Language Loyalty in the United States*, Mouton, 1966; *Hungarian Language Maintenance in the United States*, Research Center in Anthropology, Folklore and Linguistics,

Indiana University, 1966; (editor) *Readings in the Sociology of Language*, Mouton, 1968; (editor with Charles A. Ferguson and Jyotirindra Das Gupta, and contributor) *Language Problems of Developing Nations*, Wiley, 1968.

Sociolinguistics: A Brief Introduction, Newbury House Publications, 1970; (with Robert L. Cooper, Roxana Ma, and others) *Bilingualism in the Barrio*, Research Center in Anthropology, Folklore and Linguistics, Indiana University, 1971; (editor) *Advances in the Sociology of Language*, Mouton, Volume I, 1971, Volume II, 1972; *Language and Sociocultural Change: Essays by Joshua A. Fishman*, Stanford University Press, 1972; *The Sociology of Language*, Newbury House Publications, 1972; (editor) *Studies in Modern Jewish Social History*, Ktav, 1972; *Language and Nationalism*, Newbury House Publications, 1973; *Advances in Language Planning*, Mouton, 1973; *Bilingual Education: An International Sociological Perspective*, Newbury House Publications, 1976; (with Cooper) *The Spread of English*, Newbury House Publications, 1977; (editor) *The Creation and Revision of Writing Systems*, Mouton, 1977; (editor) *Societal Multilingualism*, Mouton, 1978; (with others) *Language Planning Processes*, Mouton, 1978.

Contributor: Nevitt Stanford, editor, *The American College*, Wiley, 1961; Warren A. Findley, editor, *The Impact and Improvement of School Testing*, University of Chicago Press, 1963; Albert Valdman, editor, *Trends in Language Teaching*, McGraw, 1966; Milton L. Baron, editor, *Minorities in a Changing World*, Knopf, 1967; Paul Lazarsfeld, William H. Sewell, and Harold L. Wilensky, editors, *The Uses of Sociology*, Basic Books, 1967; Albert H. Marckwardt, editor, *Language and Language Learning*, National Council of Teachers of English, 1968; *Language Development*, Ford Foundation, 1968; L. G. Kelly, editor, *The Description and Measurement of Bilingualism*, University of Toronto Press, 1969; W. H. Whiteley, editor, *Language Use and Social Change*, Oxford University Press, 1970; C. Cazden and others, editors, *Functions of Language in the Classroom*, Teachers College Press, 1970; J. Gumperz and D. Hymes, editors, *Directions in Sociolinguistics*, Holt, 1973; H. Giles, editor, *Language and Ethnicity in Intergroup Relations*, Academic Press, 1977.

Also author of research reports for College Entrance Examination Board and U.S. Office of Education. Contributor of more than one hundred articles to psychology, education, anthropology, linguistic, and other journals. Associate editor, *Sociology of Education*, 1962-65; editor, *Journal of Social Issues*, 1965-69; member of editorial boards, *Journal of Psycholinguistic Research*, 1967—, *Yivo-Bleter, Yivo Annual*, and *Yidishe Shprakh*, 1970—, *Interamerican Review*, 1971—, and *Review of Nationalism*, 1974—.

WORK IN PROGRESS: *The Sociology of Language in Education*, with R. L. Cooper; *Never Say Die!: The Sociology of Yiddish; The Rebirth of Ethnicity; Language and Life; The View of Ethnicity in Euro-Mediterranean Social Theory*, with V. Nahirny.

SIDELIGHTS: Joshua Fishman told *CA:* "My life and my work have been a joyful struggle to integrate Jewishness and Americanness, science and religion, Yiddish, English, Hebrew, the U.S.A. and Israel, Objectivity and emotion, theory and practice, sociology and linguistics, in order to grow [and] resist (arbitrary) boundaries."

BIOGRAPHICAL/CRITICAL SOURCES: Joshua Fishman, *Language and Sociocultural Change*, Stanford University Press, 1972.

FISZMAN, Joseph R. 1921-

PERSONAL: Born October 5, 1921, in Poland; son of Jacob H. (a writer) and Gala (Zajac) Fiszman; married Rachele Noto (a research assistant), September 7, 1951; children: Gale Theresa, Sula Rachele. *Education:* Emory University, M.A., 1956; Michigan State University, Ph.D., 1964; Charles University, Prague, postdoctoral study, 1965-66. *Home:* 2700 Central Blvd., Eugene, Ore. 97403. *Office:* Department of Political Science, University of Oregon, Eugene, Ore. 97403.

CAREER: Michigan State University, East Lansing, instructor, 1958-59; University of Oregon, Eugene, assistant professor, 1964-66, associate professor, 1968-71, professor of political science, 1971—, teaching director, Institute of Comparative Study, Communist Systems and Ideology, 1964-65, acting director of research, Institute for Comparative Experimental Behavioral Systems, 1969-71. Visiting associate professor, Wayne State University, 1967-68. Consultant to U.S. Department of Labor, 1956-60, International Association of Machinists, 1961-68, and Lane County Human Resources, Office of Economic Opportunity, 1969-71. *Member:* American Political Science Association, American Association for the Advancement of Slavic Studies, American Association of University Professors, Industrial Relations Research Association, Association for Asian Studies, Western Political Science Association (member of board of editors, 1966-69, 1972—), Far Western Slavic Conference. *Awards, honors:* Research fellowships from University of Ohio, 1959-62, Eagleton Foundation, 1962, and U.S. Office of Education, 1966-67; grants from Inter-University Committee on Travel, 1964, 1965, American Council of Learned Societies, 1970, International Exchange and Research Board, 1973, and London School of Economics and Political Science, 1973.

WRITINGS: (Editor) *The American Political Arena,* Little, Brown, 1962, (with Gene Peschman) 3rd edition, 1972; *Between Rome and Moscow Is Warsaw: Education and Socialization in People's Poland,* University of Oregon, 1969, revised edition published as *Revolution and Tradition in People's Poland: Education and Socialization,* Princeton University Press, 1972; *Education and Sociopolitical, Cultural, and Economic Change,* Institute of Sociology and Philosophy, University of Ljubljana, 1970; (contributor) Peter Toma, editor, *The Changing Face of Communism in Eastern Europe,* University of Arizona Press, 1970. Columnist for *New Leader,* 1952-55. Contributor to journals in his field. Member of board of editors, *Western Political Quarterly,* 1966-69.

WORK IN PROGRESS: Research on the problem of socialization and sociocultural adaptation; research on attitudes toward sex morality as a reflection of political attitudes and beliefs.†

*   *   *

FITZ-GERALD, Carolyn 1932-

PERSONAL: Born March 1, 1932, in Cuero, Tex.; daughter of Stillwell M. (president of Melton Book Co.) and Alice (Wood) Melton; married James Fitz-Gerald (an attorney), March 14, 1953; children: Lyn, Jeanne, James IV, Mary Mab. *Education:* Attended Southern Methodist University, 1949-51; University of Texas, Main University (now University of Texas at Austin), B.J. and B.S. in Ed., 1953. *Religion:* Presbyterian. *Home:* 1603 Seaboard, Midland, Tex. 79701.

CAREER: Former teacher; Melton Book Co., Dallas, Tex.,

director, 1967—, secretary of board of directors, 1969—; Leslie Press, Dallas, Tex., education editor, beginning 1970. Partner, Writers' Ink, Midland, Tex. *Member:* Theta Sigma Phi.

WRITINGS: (Editor) *Five Minutes with God,* Broadman, 1969; (with Dolores Gunter) *Creative Storytelling,* Leslie Press, 1971.†

*   *   *

FitzGERALD, Frances 1940-

PERSONAL: Born October 21, 1940, in New York, N.Y.; daughter of Desmond FitzGerald (a deputy director of the CIA) and Mary Endicott (an urbanist; maiden name Peabody) FitzGerald Tree. *Education:* Radcliffe College, B.A. (magna cum laude), 1962. *Agent:* Robert Lescher, 155 East 71st St., New York, N.Y. 10021.

CAREER: Free-lance journalist. *Awards, honors:* Overseas Press Club award, 1967, for best interpretation of foreign affairs; American Academy of Arts and Letters and National Institute for Arts and Letters award, and National Book Award, both 1973, for *Fire in the Lake;* Pulitzer Prize for contemporary affairs writing, 1973; Bancroft Prize, 1973.

WRITINGS: Fire in the Lake: The Vietnamese and Americans in Vietnam (excerpts first published in *New Yorker,* 1972), Little, Brown, 1972, revised edition, 1973. Contributor to *Atlantic, Herald Tribune, New York Review of Books, New York Times Magazine, Village Voice, New Yorker,* and others.

WORK IN PROGRESS: An American Drama: U.S. History for Children in the Twentieth Century.

SIDELIGHTS: Frances FitzGerald went to Vietnam in 1966, equipped with excellent French, and stayed as a free-lance writer for almost a year. Subsequent research, including informal study with Paul Mus (a Vietnam authority), together with personal observations, resulted in *Fire in the Lake,* a "major work," "essential reading for all Americans" according to many critics. Despite some complaints of "little new information," of inaccuracies, of lack of scholarship, and of faulty judgment in selection of authorities, most reviewers find this work rich in historical perspective and cultural insight, "among the best books [on Vietnam] yet available."

FitzGerald has a family background of involvement in public affairs. Her mother is a former U.S. ambassador to the United Nations; her father, an expert on Southeast Asia, served in Burma under Gen. Joseph Stillwell.

*   *   *

FLOOD, Charles Bracelen 1929-

PERSONAL: Born November 14, 1929, in New York, N.Y.; son of John L. and Ellen (Bracelen) Flood; married Kathryn Burnham, April 5, 1975; children: James Caperton Thornton. *Education:* Harvard University, B.A., 1951. *Politics:* Republican. *Religion:* Roman Catholic. *Address:* Box 8, Richmond, Ky. 40475. *Agent:* Sterling Lord Agency, 660 Madison Ave., New York, N.Y. 10021.

CAREER: Writer. Sophia University, Tokyo, Japan, instructor in creative writing and world literature, 1963-65. Has worked as free-lance reporter. *Military service:* U.S. Army, 1952-53. *Member:* Authors League (member of governing body), Authors Guild (member of governing body), National Book Committee (member of governing body), International P.E.N. (president of American Center, 1969-

71), Century Association (New York City), Arlington Association (Richmond, Ky.). *Awards, honors:* Houghton Mifflin Literary Award, 1953, for *Love Is a Bridge;* Senior Fulbright award for study in Taiwan, 1963; American Revolution Round Table award, 1976, for *Rise, and Fight Again.*

WRITINGS: Love Is a Bridge, Houghton, 1953; *A Distant Drum,* Houghton, 1957; *Tell Me, Stranger,* Houghton, 1959; *Monmouth,* Houghton, 1961; *More Lives Than One,* Houghton, 1967; *The War of the Innocents,* McGraw, 1970; *Trouble at the Top,* McGraw, 1972; *Rise, and Fight Again,* Dodd, 1976. Contributor of articles and short stories to *New Yorker, Atlantic Monthly,* and *Esquire.*

WORK IN PROGRESS: A book on the postwar years of Robert E. Lee.

SIDELIGHTS: "In Charles B. Flood the fighting troops in Vietnam have found their Ernie Pyle," John Reed wrote in his review of *The War of the Innocents* in *Saturday Review.* Flood spent 1967 in Vietnam gathering information for his documentary. He "avoided Saigon and the mandarins, Oriental and Occidental, who [ran] the war. Instead, his time was spent out in the 'boonies' . . . in the company of middle-grade officers and lesser ranks." The result, Thomas Lask writes, is "an unending panagyric to the courage and selflessness of the American G.I. and the officers that lead them." Lask concedes that the "hero worship in the book" is not entirely unfounded but objects to the "larger than life" status that Flood gives to "virtually everyone . . . [he] encounters in the fighting area. . . ." He is also troubled by the fact that "almost nowhere in the book do Americans show any regard for the Vietnamese as a people or express any firm committment to a just cause." Lask concludes that "in spite of its mettlesome heroics, the book leaves the reader with as much a sense of disquiet as of pride."

BIOGRAPHICAL/CRITICAL SOURCES: New York Times Book Review, March 19, 1967; *New Yorker,* March 25, 1967; *Saturday Review,* April 1, 1967; *New York Times,* October 23, 1970; *New York Times Book Review,* November 8, 1970; *Saturday Review,* November 28, 1970; *National Observer,* November 30, 1970; *New York Times Book Review,* May 7, 1972; *National Review,* June 9, 1972.

* * *

FLORESCU, Radu R. 1925-

PERSONAL: Born October 23, 1925, in Bucharest, Romania; naturalized U.S. citizen; son of Radu A. (a diplomat) and Vera (de Soepkez) Florescu; married Nicole Elizabeth Michel (self-employed in fashions), December 31, 1950; children: Nicholas, John, Radu, Alexandra. *Education:* Christ Church, Oxford, B.A., 1947, M.A., 1950, B.Litt., 1951; further study at University of Texas at Austin, 1951-52; Indiana University at Bloomington, Ph.D., 1959. *Home:* 38 Jerusalem Rd., Cohasset, Mass. 02025. *Agent:* David Higham Associates Ltd., 5-8 Lower St. John St., Golden Square, London W1R 3PE, England. *Office:* Department of History, Boston College, Chestnut Hill, Mass. 02167.

CAREER: Boston College, Chestnut Hill, Mass., instructor, 1953-57, assistant professor, 1957-63, associate professor of East European history, 1963—. Senior fellow, St. Anthony College, Oxford University, 1962. Consultant, U.S. Department of State, 1953-54. Has lectured widely on Romania and Eastern Europe at universities. *Member:* American Historical Association, American Association for the Advancement of Slavic Studies, American Catholic History Association, Mediaeval Academy of America, International Institute for South East European Studies, Romanian

Academic Society, Oxford Society (secretary of New England branch). *Awards, honors:* Ford Foundation fellowship to United States, 1951-52; Mid-European research scholar, 1952-53; American Philosophical Society grants, 1961-62, 1968, 1970; Fulbright faculty fellowship, 1967.

WRITINGS: The Struggle against Russia in the Roumanian Principalities, Romanian Academic Society (Munich), 1962; *Capidava,* Meridiane (Bucharest, Romania), 1965; *Le Monastere de Gorvona,* Meridiane, 1965; (with C. Cioranesco, G. Filitl, and others) *Aspects des relations Russo-Roumaines retrospectives et orientations,* Minard (Paris), 1967; *Ghid archeologic al Debrogei,* Meridiane, 1968; *Arta Dacilor,* Meridiane, 1968; (with Raymond T. McNally) *In Search of Dracula,* New York Graphic Society, 1972; (with Cristian Moisescu) *Adamclisi,* Meridiane, 1973; (with Alan Barbour and Matei Cazacu) *In Search of Frankenstein,* New York Graphic Society, 1975; (with McNally) *Dracula: A Biography of Vlad the Impaler 1431-1476,* Hawthorn, 1976. Also co-editor of *Contemporary Eastern Europe.*

Contributor: Miloslav Recheigl, Jr., editor, *Czechoslovakia Past and Present,* Mouton & Co., 1970, Humanities, 1971; Paul L. Horecky, editor, *Southeastern Europe: A Guide to Basic Publications,* University of Chicago Press, 1970. Contributor of articles and reviews to history and science journals.

WORK IN PROGRESS: Bram Stoker, with Raymond T. McNally.

SIDELIGHTS: Florescu and McNally teamed up in 1967 to track down leads in Romania on the original Dracula, a fifteenth-century counterpart of the fictional vampire that Irish novelist, Bram Stoker, portrayed in his best selling *Dracula.* The Florescu-McNally book, *In Search of Dracula,* resulted in a documentary film on their research in Romania's Dracula country and a series of escorted tours to the scene.

AVOCATIONAL INTERESTS: The revival of American railroads, medical history.

BIOGRAPHICAL/CRITICAL SOURCES: Time, January 15, 1973; *London Times,* January 6, 1978.†

* * *

FLORY, Charles D(avid) 1902-

PERSONAL: Born September 28, 1902, in Nokesville, Va.; son of Samuel H. (a minister) and Lydia Frances (Kerlin) Flory; married Mary Grossnickle, 1925; children: Elaine (Mrs. Leslie J. Fisher), Frances Ann. *Education:* Manchester College, North Manchester, Ind., A.B., 1924; University of Chicago, M.A., 1928, Ph.D., 1933. *Home:* 621 Douglas Rd., Salisbury, Md. 21801.

CAREER: High school teacher in Indiana, 1924-27; Park College, Parkville, Mo., instructor in education, 1928-30; University of Chicago, Chicago, Ill., General Education Board fellow in child development, 1934-35; Lawrence College (now University), Appleton, Wis., 1935-43, began as assistant professor, professor of education and psychology, 1940-43; Stevenson, Jordan & Harrison, New York City, consultant, 1943-45; Rohrer, Hibler & Replogle (consultants), New York City, general partner, 1945-70. Visiting summer professor at University of Wisconsin, North Texas State University, and other colleges. Member of board of governors, White Plains Hospital, 1966—; president of School District No. 6 School Board, Greenborough, Scarsdale, N.Y., 1959.

MEMBER: American Association for the Advancement of Science, American Psychological Association, Academy of Religion and Mental Health, Eastern Psychological Association, New York State Psychological Association, New York Academy of Sciences. Awards, honors: LL.B., Manchester College, 1968.

WRITINGS: The Physical Growth of Mentally Deficient Boys (doctoral thesis at University of Chicago, 1933), Society for Research in Child Development and National Research Council, 1936, reprinted, Kraus Reprint Co., 1966; Osseous Development in the Hand as an Index of Skeletal Development, Society for Research in Child Development and National Research Council, 1936, reprinted, Kraus Reprint Co., 1966; (with Franklin N. Freeman) Growth in Intellectual Ability as Measured by Repeated Tests, National Research Council, 1937; (editor) Managers for Tomorrow, New American Library, 1965; (editor) Managing through Insight, New American Library, 1968; (with R. Alec Mackenzie) The Credibility Gap in Management, Van Nostrand, 1971. Contributor to psychology, education, and business journals.

*   *   *

FLYNN, Gerard (Cox) 1924-

PERSONAL: Born August 14, 1924, in New York, N.Y.; son of John Francis (a New York State court clerk) and Katharine (Cox) Flynn; married Geraldine Monahan, January 20, 1945; children: Matthew, Peter, Geraldine, Mary (Mrs. Steven Fleming), Paul, Andrew, Alexander, Grace, Julia, Amy, Gerard. Education: Fordham University, A.B., 1947; Columbia University, M.A., 1950; New York University, Ph.D., 1958. Home: Route 1, Random Lake, Wis. 53075. Office: Department of Spanish and Portuguese, University of Wisconsin, Milwaukee, Wis. 53201.

CAREER: St. John's University, Brooklyn, N.Y., assistant professor of history, 1949-55; Rutgers University, New Brunswick, N.J., assistant professor of Spanish, 1956-63; University of Wisconsin—Milwaukee, associate professor, 1963-68, professor of Spanish, 1969—. Military service: U.S. Marine Corps Reserve, 1942-45; became captain.

WRITINGS: (Editor) El arbol de la ciencia, Appleton, 1970; Sor Juana Ines de la Cruz, Twayne, 1971; Tamayo y Baus, Twayne, 1972; Spanish for Urban Workers, Pruett, 1972; Manuel Breton de los Herreros, Twayne, 1973. Also author of unpublished novels, The Mysteries of Mr. Garibaldi Patch and How He Hated Children, Captain Nelly McKelly and the Basque Jewel Mystery, The Bronx, 1930, The Associate Professor, and The St. Patrick's Day Parade. Contributor of articles to Hispania, HR, and other journals.

WORK IN PROGRESS: A book on Spanish novelist, Luis Coloma, for Twayne.

*   *   *

FORBES, Thomas Rogers 1911-

PERSONAL: Born January 5, 1911, in New York, N.Y.; son of James B. (a businessman) and Stella (Rogers) Forbes; married Helen Frances Allen, June 19, 1934; children: Thomas R., Jr., William M. Education: University of Rochester, B.A., 1933, Ph.D., 1937. Residence: Hamden, Conn. Office: Department of Surgery, School of Medicine, Yale University, New Haven, Conn. 06510.

CAREER: Johns Hopkins University, Baltimore, Md., assistant, 1937-38, instructor in anatomy, 1938-45; Yale University, New Haven, Conn., instructor, 1945-46, assistant

professor, 1946-51, associate professor, 1951-62, professor of anatomy, 1962—, E. K. Hunt Professor of Anatomy, 1977—, assistant dean of School of Medicine, 1948-60, associate dean, 1960-69, fellow of Branford College, 1951—. Technical aide, National Research Council and Office of Scientific Research and Development, 1942-45. Gideon de Laune Lecturer, Worshipful Society of Apothecaries, 1975. Producer of films on the history of medicine.

MEMBER: International Society for the History of Medicine, American Association of Anatomists, American Association for the History of Medicine, Society for Experimental Biology and Medicine, Endocrine Society, American Association for the Advancement of Science, Royal Society of Medicine, Society for Social History of Medicine (London), Faculty of the History and Philosophy of Pharmacy and Medicine of the Worshipful Society of Apothecaries (London), Connecticut Academy of Arts and Sciences, Sigma Xi, Phi Beta Kappa, Psi Upsilon. Awards, honors: Guggenheim fellowship, 1942; M.A., Yale University, 1962; George Rosen Award in History of Medicine, 1978.

WRITINGS: The Midwife and the Witch, Yale University Press, 1966; Chronicle from Aldgate: Life and Death in Shakespeare's London, Yale University Press, 1971; Crowner's Quest, American Philosophical Society, 1978. Contributor to scientific and medical history journals. Journal of the History of Medicine and Allied Science, member of board of editors, 1956-68, acting editor, 1960-62, editor, 1962-63.

WORK IN PROGRESS: Research on endocrinology and on history of medicine.

*   *   *

FORCE, Roland W(ynfield) 1924-

PERSONAL: Born December 31, 1924, in Omaha, Neb.; son of Richard Erwin and Edna Fern (Collins) Force; married Maryanne Tefft, September 16, 1949. Education: Stanford University, A.B., 1950, M.A. (education), 1951, M.A. (anthropology), 1952, Ph.D., 1958. Home: 37 Rockleigh Rd., Rockleigh, N.J. 07647. Office: Museum of the American Indian, Broadway at 155th St., New York, N.Y. 10032.

CAREER: Bernice P. Bishop Museum, Honolulu, Hawaii, associate in ethnology, 1954-56; Chicago Natural History Museum, Chicago, Ill, curator of oceanic archaeology and ethnology, 1956-61; Bernice P. Bishop Museum, Honolulu, director, 1962-76; Museum of the American Indian, New York, N.Y., director, 1977—. Military service: U.S. Army, 1943-46; became sergeant. Member: International Council of Museums, American Association for the Advancement of Science (fellow), American Anthropological Association (fellow), American Association of Museums, National Trust for Historic Preservation, Pacific Science Association, Sigma Xi.

WRITINGS: Leadership and Cultural Change (monograph), Field Museum of Natural History, 1960; (editor) Induced Political Change in the Pacific, Bishop Museum Press, 1965; (with wife, Maryanne Force) Art and Artifacts of the Eighteenth Century, Bishop Museum Press, 1968; (with M. Force) The Fuller Collection of Pacific Artifacts, Bishop Museum Press, 1971; (with M. Force) Just One House, Bishop Museum Press, 1972. Contributor to Science.

*   *   *

FORD, Brian J(ohn) 1939-

PERSONAL: Born May 13, 1939, in Corsham, Wiltshire,

England; son of William John (a designer, company director, chartered engineer, and lecturer) and Cicely Beryl Pryn (Biddick) Ford; married Janice May Smith (a high school governor); children: Anthony John Kevin Stuart Pryn, Sarah Rose Pryn, Tamsin Emily May; (foster children) Leigh Roy Mills, Timothy James Harvard. *Education:* Educated at schools in London and Peterborough, England, and Cardiff, Wales; studied at University of Wales, 1959-61. *Home:* Mill Park House, 57 Westville Rd., Cardiff CF2 5DF, Wales.

CAREER: Wrote weekly column, "Science and You," for South Wales Echo at the age of nineteen; Medical Research Council, London, England, junior research assistant, 1958-59; British Broadcasting Corp., regional science specialist for BBC radio, 1961-67, regional scientific contributor for BBC-TV, 1962-68, advisor to "The Burke Special" TV program, 1972-73, chairman of "Where Are You Taking Us?" TV program, 1974-75; Independent Television System, Bristol, England and Cardiff, Wales, science telecaster, 1964-67; *New Scientist,* London, book critic, 1970-72. Guest producer of science programs, BBC Wales, 1965. Lecturer in science and technology, College of Art and Design, Newport, England, 1965-66; visiting lecturer, Foreign and Commonwealth Office, British Council Division, 1978. Scientific consultant, BBC Science Unit, 1962—; consultant to Medical Development Trust, London, 1962-63; consulting editor, Northwood Publishing, 1967-68. *Member:* Royal Microscopical Society (fellow), Royal Society of Health (associate member), British Interplanetary Society (associate fellow), Quekett Microscopical Club, BBC Club, Society for Basic Irreproducible Research (honorary member), Savage Club (London), Architecture Club of London. *Awards, honors:* Italia Prize nomination for TV program "Heart Attack," 1974.

WRITINGS: (Editor) *Science Diary,* Letts, 1967, 13th edition, 1979; *German Secret Weapons: Blueprint for Mars,* Ballantine, 1969; *Microbiology and Food,* Northwood, 1970; *Allied Secret Weapons: The War of Science,* Ballantine, 1971; *Nonscience and the Pseudotransmogrificationalific Egocentrified Reorientational Proclivities Inherently Intracorporated in Expertistical Cerebrointellectualised Redeploymentation with Special Reference to Quasi-Notional Fashionistic Normativity, the Indoctrinationalistic Methodological Modalities and Scalar Socio-economic Promulgationary Improvementalisationalism Predelineated Positotaxically Toward Individualistified Mass-acceptance Gratificationalistic Securipermanentalisationary Professionism, or, How to Rule the World* (scientific satire), Wolfe Publishing, 1971; *The Earth Watchers,* Frewin, 1973; *The Revealing Lens: Mankind and the Microscope,* Harrap, 1973; *The Optical Microscope Manual: Past and Present Uses and Techniques,* Crane Russak, 1973; (with others) *The Cardiff Book,* Stewart Williams, 1973; *Microbe Power: Tomorrow's Revolution,* Stein & Day, 1976.

Also author of *The New Dark Age, The Wartime Rocket Race, Chemical Warfare, Doctors at War,* and *Eyes in the Sky,* for Purnell; scientific editor, *History of the Second World War,* 1966-69. Contributor to *Know Britain.* Author of a number of published research programs. Research papers have been published in *Museums Journal, Journal of the Royal Microscopical Society, New Scientist,* and other scientific journals; guest contributor to *MIT Journal, Times* (London), *Nature, Listener, Observer, Private Eye, Guardian, Oz,* and other publications.

WORK IN PROGRESS: Patterns of Sex and *The Carriers;* "research into the development of science and technology, in particular studying criteria of selection, (both societal and psychological) and the concept of quantifying 'areas of ignorance' as an adjunct to orthodox education. Campaigns for wider study of micro-organisms and for legislation governing their safe handling in laboratories. Several books 'in the pipeline' examine relationships between society's pressures and the future of scientific progress."

SIDELIGHTS: Brian J. Ford told *CA* that he "retired from the media and scientific scene in 1968 (at age 28) to remain free of pressures, considering it of prime importance to evolve a lifestyle that combines freedom with personal integrity." Ford holds that "the best years for retirement are in the thirties." His travels have taken him through Europe, and to the United States, India, Southeast Asia, Africa, Australia, New Zealand, and the Pacific Islands.

Ford's microscopical research has been referred to in *New Knowledge* and *International Yearbook of Science and Technology,* among other works. Some of his writings have been translated into Russian, Italian, Chinese, French, German, and other languages. His book *Nonscience . . . or How to Rule the World* was the subject of the BBC TV program, "Down With the Experts." His TV program "Cancer" holds the record for the highest audience reaction index in British broadcasting. He has been guest host on such TV programs as "It's Your Line" and "Kaleidoscope."

Ford, a descendant of the inventor Sir James Watt, has lectured world-wide on such topics as "the democratisation of science." He believes that "clear communication of science [should] become a professional specialty" and that "the fundamental re-thinking of textbooks and educational material" is long overdue.

AVOCATIONAL INTERESTS: Photography (some of his scientific photographs received a gold commendation at an international exhibition of the Royal Photographic Society), playing jazz piano on radio and TV (had weekly solo spot at the Cardiff Jazz Club, 1960-66), "spending time at the beach, in or on the ocean, celebrating the phenomenon of living."

BIOGRAPHICAL/CRITICAL SOURCES: Mensa Journal, Number 115, 1968; *Medical News,* October 18, 1968; *Times* (London), September 17, 1971, March 17, 1973, April 7, 1973; *Sunday Times,* October 24, 1971, March 25, 1973; *Irish Press,* October 30, 1971; *Nature,* December 3, 1971, February 8, 1974, August 16, 1974; *Punch,* May 9, 1973, July 28, 1976; *Times Literary Supplement* (London), December 10, 1976; *Mercury* (Hobart, Australia), February 7, 1978, February 10, 1978.

* * *

FORD, Donald H(erbert) 1926-

PERSONAL: Born August 15, 1926, in Sioux City, Iowa; son of Herbert Owen and Ester (Sanow) Ford; married Carol Clark, May 30, 1948; children: Russell, Martin, Douglas, Cameron. *Education:* Kansas State College of Agriculture and Applied Science (now Kansas State University), B.S., 1948, M.S., 1950; Pennsylvania State University, Ph.D., 1956. *Office:* 203 Myra Dock Bldg., Pennsylvania State University, University Park, Pa. 16802.

CAREER: Certified psychologist in Pennsylvania; Kansas State College of Agriculture and Applied Science (now Kansas State University), Manhattan, counselor, 1948-52, assistant dean of students, 1950-51; Pennsylvania State University, University Park, instructor, 1955-56, assistant professor, 1956-64, associate professor, 1964-72, professor of human development, 1972—, assistant director of Division of Counseling, 1956-63, director, 1963-65, director of Placement Service, 1963-64, assistant to president for federal affairs, 1965-66, dean of College of Human Development, 1967-77. Member of board of directors, Community Services of Pennsylvania. *Military service:* U.S. Army Air Forces, 1944-45.

MEMBER: American Psychological Association, American Association for the Advancement of Science, American Personnel and Guidance Association, Eastern Psychological Association, Pennsylvania Psychological Association, Phi Delta Kappa, Psi Chi, Phi Kappa Phi, Pi Mu Epsilon.

WRITINGS: (With H. B. Urban) *Systems of Psychotherapy: A Comparative Study,* Wiley, 1963; (contributor) A. M. Freedman and H. I. Kaplan, editors, *Comprehensive Textbook of Psychiatry,* Williams & Wilkins, 1967; (contributor) M. H. Goldberg and J. R. Swinton, editors, *Blindness Research: The Expanding Frontiers,* Pennsylvania State University Press, 1969; (contributor) S. H. Osipow and W. B. Walsh, editors, *Behavior Change in Counseling: Readings,* Appleton, 1970; (contributor) Garfield and Bergin, editors, *Handbook of Psychotherapy and Behavior Change,* Wiley, 1970. Author of monographs and contributor to proceedings. Contributor to *Journal of Individual Psychology, Educational Record, Psychology Today,* and *Annual Review of Psychology.*

* * *

FORD, Josephine Massyngbaerde (J. Massingberd Ford)

PERSONAL: Born in Nottingham, England; daughter of Hector Patrick (an engineer) and Winifred (Husband) Ford. *Education:* Middlesex Hospital, S.R.N., 1956; University of Nottingham, B.A. (honors), 1957, Ph.D., 1965; King's College, London, B.D., 1963. *Politics:* Conservative. *Religion:* Roman Catholic. *Home:* 18701 Kintz Rd., South Bend, Ind. 46637. *Office:* Department of Theology, University of Notre Dame, Notre Dame, Ind. 46556.

CAREER: Registered nurse. University of Durham, Durham, England, lecturer in Latin, 1959-61; Makerere University College, Makerere, Uganda, lecturer in Biblical studies, 1963-65; University of Notre Dame, Notre Dame, Ind., assistant professor, 1965-68, associate professor of theology, 1968—. *Member:* American Academy of Religion, Catholic Biblical Society, Association of Women Aspiring to the Presbyteral Office, Society for New Testament Studies, Society of Biblical Literature, Chicago Society for Biblical Research, Side Saddle Association.

WRITINGS—Under name J. Massingberd Ford: *A Trilogy on Wisdom and Celibacy,* University of Notre Dame Press, 1966; *Wellsprings of Scripture: A Rabbinic and Thematic Introduction,* Sheed, 1967; *The Spirit and the Human Person: A Meditation,* Pflaum, 1969; (with Ralph A. Kiefer) *We Are Easter People: A Commentary for the Time of Resurrection,* Herder & Herder, 1970; *The Pentecostal Experience,* Paulist-Newman, 1970; *Baptism in the Spirit,* Claretian, 1971; (author of introduction and commentary, and translator) *Revelation,* Doubleday, 1975; *The Hospital Prayer Book,* Paulist Press, 1975; *Which Way for Catholic Pentecostals?,* Harper, 1976. Contributor to *New Catholic Encyclopedia;* contributor of about forty articles to theology journals.

WORK IN PROGRESS: Luke, a Book of Consolation for the Disappointed Zealots; Social Consciousness in the Judeo-Christian Tradition.

FOREMAN, Carl 1914-

PERSONAL: Born July 23, 1914, in Chicago, Ill.; son of Isadore and Fanny (Rozin) Foreman; married second wife, Evelyn Smith, August 7, 1965; children: Carla, Jonathan, Amanda. *Education:* Attended University of Illinois, Northwestern University, and John Marshall Law School. *Address:* 1370 Avenue of the Americas, New York, N.Y. 10019.

CAREER: Film writer, director, and producer. Has also worked as a waiter, salesman, ballet dancer, sideshow barker, and elephant handler. Managing director, Open Road Films (London), 1952-75. *Military service:* U.S. Army, 1941-45.

MEMBER: Royal Society of Arts (fellow), Film Production Association (member of executive council, 1967-75), British Film Institute (member of board of governors, 1965-71), National Film School (governor, 1971-75), Writer's Guild of Great Britain (president, 1968-75), Saville Club, Garrick Club, Royal Automobile Club. *Awards, honors:* Decorated Commander of Royal Order of Phoenix, Greece, 1962; Distinguished Service Award from Writer's Guild of Great Britain, 1968; Laurel Award for achievement in screenwriting, from Writer's Guild of America, 1969; decorated Commander of Order of British Empire, 1970; Show Business Writer Award from Variety Club of Great Britain, award for best British screenplay from Writer's Guild of Great Britain, and Academy Award nomination, all 1972, for "Young Winston." Academy Award nominations from Academy of Motion Picture Arts and Sciences, 1949, for "Champion," 1950, for "The Men," 1952, for "High Noon," 1961, for "The Guns of Navarone," and 1973, for "Young Winston."

WRITINGS: A Cast of Lions, Collins, 1966; *Young Winston,* John M. Fontana, 1972.

Screenplays: "Champion," 1948; "Home of the Brave," 1948; "The Men," 1949; "Cyrano de Bergerac," 1950; "High Noon," 1951 (published in *Three Major Screenplays,* Globe Books, 1972); "The Bridge over the River Kwai," 1956; "The Key," 1957; "The Mouse That Roared," 1960; "The Guns of Navarone," 1961; "The Victors," 1964; "Born Free," 1965; "Mackenna's Gold," 1969; "Young Winston," 1972.

Contributor to *Journal of Screen Producers Guild, Film Comment, Films and Filming, Saturday Review,* and *New York Times Magazine.*

WORK IN PROGRESS: Screenplays, "Tai-Pan," "The Day the World Ended," and "The Yellow Jersey"; a novel, *Bannister's Bridge,* for Dutton; an autobiography for Simon & Schuster.

SIDELIGHTS: Although he has been called "one of the most famous and honored film writers and producers in the world," Carl Foreman was one of many who found it difficult to work in the fifties because he was on the Hollywood blacklist. His approach to the accusations of the House Un-American Activities Committee led to two landmark cases. By taking what would later be called the "diminished Fifth" amendment, he neither went to jail nor named names. When the committee tried to arrange the revocation of his passport to keep him from writing for foreign film-makers, the courts agreed that the State Department had no legal grounds for the action. This gave Foreman a chance to resume his work abroad. Several of the films he wrote were never attributed to him because of his past political associations. Although many were recognized, some remain unknown even today. Foreman was executive producer of "The Mouse That

Roared'' and ''Born Free,'' 1965, ''Otley'' and ''The Virgin Soldiers,'' 1969, ''Living Free,'' 1971, and ''Young Winston,'' 1972.

BIOGRAPHICAL/CRITICAL SOURCES: Commonweal, May 10, 1957; *Reporter,* May 15, 1958; *Sight and Sound,* summer, 1958; *Saturday Review,* December 28, 1963; *Washington Post,* April 9, 1971; *Publishers Weekly,* April 25, 1977.

*　*　*

FORGUS, Ronald (Henry)　1928-

PERSONAL: Born May 18, 1928, in Cape Town, South Africa; son of William A. (a retail owner) and Marie (Kleinhaus) Forgus; married Silvia Parvei, May 5, 1951 (divorced, 1965); married Valerie Lamont, August 8, 1965; children: (first marriage) Michael, Sandra; (second marriage) Tristan, Kilian. *Education:* McGill University, B.Sc., 1950, M.Sc., 1951; Cornell University, Ph.D., 1953. *Politics:* Independent. *Religion:* Episcopalian. *Home:* 659 Green Briar, Lake Forest, Ill. 60045. *Office:* Department of Psychology, Lake Forest College, Lake Forest, Ill. 60045.

CAREER: University of Pennsylvania, Philadelphia, assistant professor of psychology, 1953-58; private practice in clinical psychology, Lake Forest, Ill., 1961—; Lake Forest College, Lake Forest, associate professor, 1958-62, professor of psychology, 1963—, head of department, 1958—. Visiting professor at Harvard University, 1965-66; adjunct professor, Chicago Medical School, 1978—. Consultant to Hume, Mansfield & Silber, organization psychologists, 1973—. *Military service:* Royal Canadian Air Force, 1948-52. *Member:* American Psychological Association, American Association of University Professors, Canadian Psychological Association, American Board of Professional Psychologists, Illinois Psychological Association, Sigma Xi.

WRITINGS: Perception: The Basic Process in Cognitive Development, McGraw, 1966, 2nd edition, 1976; (contributor) Leon Eisenberg, C. J. Kagan, and Nathan Talbot, editors, *Application of Behavioral Science to Pediatric Practice,* Saunders, 1972; (with B. Shulman) *Personality: A Cognitive View,* Prentice-Hall, 1979.

*　*　*

FORKOSCH, Morris D(avid)　1908-

PERSONAL: Born February 26, 1908, in New York, N.Y.; married Selma V. Milner, November 26, 1934 (deceased). *Education:* St. John's University, Jamaica, N.Y., LL.B., 1930, LL.M., 1932; New York University, B.A., 1936, M.A., 1938, J.S.D., 1948; New School for Social Research, Ph.D., 1952, M.S.Sc., 1956. *Office:* School of Law, Woodland University, Van Nuys, Calif. 91401.

CAREER: Admitted to Bar of New York State, 1931, U.S. Supreme Court, 1939, Supreme Court of the Philippines, 1946, and Bar of Minnesota, 1976; private practice of law, 1931-44, 1947-49; Brooklyn Law School, Brooklyn, N.Y., professor of Law, 1949-71, chairman of department, 1952-72; University of San Diego, School of Law, San Diego, Calif., professor of law, 1972-73; University of Gonzaga, School of Law, Spokane, Wash., professor of law, 1973-74; San Fernando Valley School of Law, Sepulveda, Calif., professor of law, 1974-75; University of Melbourne, School of Law, Melbourne, Victoria, Australia, professor of law, 1975; National Taiwan University, Taipei, Fulbright-Hays fellow, 1975-76; Hamline University, School of Law, St. Paul, Minn., professor of law, 1976-77; Pace University, School of

Law, White Plains, N.Y., professor of law, 1977-78; Woodland University, School of Law, Van Nuys, Calif., professor of law, 1978—. Lecturer at Latin-American Institute, 1946-50, Walter Hervey, Jr. College, 1946-52, International Ladies Garment Workers Union Training Institute, 1954-55; New School for Social Research, 1968, 1969, Tokoyo Law School, 1970, Free University of Berlin, 1971, and at other universities and law conferences in the United States and abroad. Member of panel of arbitrators, Federal Mediation and Conciliation Service, 1949—, and American Arbitration Association, 1949—; special trial examiner, New York State Labor Relations board, 1953-54; arbitrator, Civil Court of City of New York, 1954—; member of National Public Employment Disputes Settlement Panel, 1969—; mediator, Federal Housing and Development Administration, 1971—. Member of board of advisers, Court Practice Institute, 1976—.

MEMBER: International Association of Lawyers, International Political Science Association, American Society for Legal History (president, 1958-61; member of board of directors, 1961—), American Political Science Association, American Economic Association, American Philosophical Association, Fulbright Alumni Association, American Society for Political and Legal Philosophy, British Society for the Philosophy of Science, Labor Relations Research Association, Societe Jean Bodin pour l'Histoire Comparative des Institutions, Societe d'Histoire du Droit, Academy of Political Science, American Academy of Political and Social Science, American Association of University Professors, Association of the Bar of the City of New York.

WRITINGS: A Treatise on Labor Law, Bobbs-Merrill, 1953, 2nd edition, 1965; (editor) *The Political Philosophy of Arnold Brecht,* Exposition, 1954; *A Treatise on Administrative Law,* Bobbs-Merrill, 1956; *Antitrust and the Consumer,* Dennis (Buffalo), 1956; (reviser) Francis X. Carmody, *New York Practice,* 7th edition (Forkosch was associated only with earlier supplements), Boardman, 1956, 8th edition (revised with Abraham Wilson) published as *Carmody-Forkosch New York Practice,* 1963, annual supplements, 1964-69; *Constitutional Law,* Foundation Press, 1963, 2nd edition 1969; (general editor and contributor) *Essays in Legal History in Honor of Felix Frankfurter,* Bobbs-Merrill, 1966.

Contributor to three-volume study, *Freedom of Information in the United States,* University of Torino, and to other symposia and festschrifts published abroad. Also contributor to *Dictionary of the History of Ideas, Dictionary of American History, Encyclopaedia Judaica, Universal World Reference Encyclopaedia,* and to *Nation.* About fifty articles have been published in *New York Law Journal,* and more than one hundred articles and forty reviews in other professional journals.

WORK IN PROGRESS: Continuing research in idea of equality, in legal history, First Amendment rights, and political theory.

SIDELIGHTS: Morris Forkosch told *CA:* ''The pain and joy of giving birth is unique to the female. The nearest approach for the male is creating something original, be it with hands or mind. When a written bit of me finds expression in print it is like a child which then grows and flowers and itself may be the spur for another's creation. But, I confess, there is so much of Churchill's blood, sweat, and tears involved in all this that at times one wonders if it's worth it all—and when someone remarks on it, or when it is cited or quoted, everything falls into place and the answer is yes. If there is anything more exciting to do in this world then I'd like to hear about it, and I confess that I scuba dive, ski, fly, and do things which are physically exciting and even dangerous. But put all these beside your own creation, and there's nothing more exciting, a consummation devoutly recommended to Everyman.''

* * *

FORSTER, Merlin H(enry) 1928-

PERSONAL: Born February 24, 1928, in Delta, Utah; son of Henry (a police officer) and Ila (Rawlinson) Forster; married Vilda Naegle, April 25, 1952; children: Celia, David, Angela, Daniel, Elena. *Education:* Brigham Young University, B.A., 1956; University of Illinois, M.A., 1957, Ph.D., 1960. *Religion:* Latter-day Saint (Mormon). *Office:* Department of Spanish and Portuguese, University of Texas, Austin, Tex. 78712.

CAREER: University of Texas, Main University (now University of Texas at Austin), instructor, 1960-61, assistant professor of Romance languages, 1961-62; University of Illinois at Urbana-Champaign, assistant professor, 1962-65, associate professor, 1965-69, professor of Spanish and Portuguese, 1969-78, director of Center for Latin American Studies, 1972-78, associate of Center for Advanced Study, 1976; University of Texas at Austin, professor of Spanish and Portuguese, 1979—, chairman of department, 1979—. Director, National Endowment for the Humanities summer seminar on experimental literary forms in twentieth century Latin America, 1978. *Military service:* U.S. Army, 1951-54; active reserve, 1954—; current rank, colonel. *Member:* American Association of Teachers of Spanish and Portuguese, Latin American Studies Association. *Awards, honors:* Research grant from Social Science Research Council for work in Mexico, 1965-66; Fulbright-Hays research fellowship for work in Argentina, Chile, Brazil, and Peru, 1971.

WRITINGS: Los Contemporaneos: 1920-1932, Ediciones de Andrea, 1964; *An Index to Mexican Literary Periodicals,* Scarecrow, 1966; *La muerte en la poesia mexicana,* Editorial Diogenes, 1970; *Letras de Mexico (1937-47): Indice anotado,* Universidad Iberoamericana, 1972; (editor, contributor, and author of introduction) *Tradition and Renewal: Essays on Twentieth Century Latin American Literature and Culture,* University of Illinois Press, 1975; *Fire and Ice: The Poetry of Xavier Villaurrutia,* Department of Romance Languages, University of North Carolina at Chapel Hill, 1976; *Historia de la poesia hispanoamericana,* American Hispanist, 1978. Contributor to *Encyclopedia Americana.* Contributor of articles and reviews to *Hispania, Revista Iberoamericana, Luso-Brazilian Review, Symposium,* and other journals in Mexico and the United States. Member of editorial board, *Latin American Theatre Review,* 1969—.

WORK IN PROGRESS: A history of Latin American avant-garde literature, 1920-45.

* * *

FORSTER, Robert 1926-

PERSONAL: Born June 7, 1926, in New York, N.Y.; son of Theodore (a paint distributor) and Elise Caroline (Strobel) Forster; married Elborg Hamacher (a translator and editor), July 8, 1955; children: Marc Richard, Thomas Theodore. *Education:* Swarthmore College, B.A., 1949; Harvard University, M.A., 1950; Johns Hopkins University, Ph.D., 1956; University of Toulouse, graduate study, 1953-55. *Home:* 208 Oakdale Rd., Baltimore, Md. 21210. *Office:* Department of History, Johns Hopkins University, Baltimore, Md. 21218.

CAREER: University of Nebraska, Lincoln, assistant professor, 1958-61, associate professor of history, 1961-62; Dartmouth College, Hanover, N.H., associate professor of history, 1962-65; Johns Hopkins University, Baltimore, Md., professor of history, 1966—. Fellow, Institute of Advanced Study, Princeton University, 1975-76. U.S. delegate to International Congress of Historical Sciences, 1975-80. *Military service:* U.S. Army, Infantry, 1944-46; served in Italy. *Member:* American Historical Association, Society for French Historical Studies (president, 1973-74), Economic History Association, Phi Beta Kappa. *Awards, honors:* Social Science Research Council grant, 1962, 1964; John Simon Guggenheim grant, 1969-70.

WRITINGS: The Nobility of Toulouse in the 18th Century, Johns Hopkins Press, 1960; (editor with wife, Elborg Forster) *European Society in the 18th Century,* Harper, 1969; (editor with Jack P. Greene) *Preconditions of Revolution in Early Modern Europe,* Johns Hopkins Press, 1970; *The House of Saulx-Tavanes: Versailles and Burgundy, 1700-1830,* Johns Hopkins Press, 1971; *Seeds of Change: Peasants, Nobles, and Rural Revolution in France,* Macmillan, 1975. Editor, with Orest Ranum, of *Selections from the Annales,* annual publication of Johns Hopkins Press, 1975—. Contributor of articles to *American Historical Review, Past and Present, Economic History Review, Annales* (Paris). Member of editorial board, *Annales historiques de la Revolution francaise,* 1976—.

WORK IN PROGRESS: Research on French notables in the eighteenth and nineteenth centuries.

SIDELIGHTS: Robert Forster has done research in France, including Toulouse, 1953-55, 1957-58, Bordeaux, 1958, Rennes, 1960, La Rochelle, 1962, Dijon, 1964, and Paris, 1969-70.

* * *

FORSYTH, David J(ames) C(ameron) 1940-

PERSONAL: Born June 4, 1940, in Elgin, Scotland; son of J.S.M. (a bank manager) and M. J. (Smith) Forsyth; married Gillian A. Dunmore, September 8, 1969; children: James, John, Ben, Robert. *Education:* University of Aberdeen, M.A. (first class honors), 1962. *Office:* Department of Economics, University of Strathclyde, George St., Glasgow G1 1XW, Scotland.

CAREER: University of Strathclyde, Glasgow, Scotland, assistant lecturer, 1963-64; University of Aberdeen, Aberdeen, Scotland, lecturer in political economy, 1964-65; University of Strathclyde, lecturer, 1966-70, senior research fellow, 1970-74, senior lecturer in economics, 1974—.

WRITINGS: (With D. M. Kelly) *Studies in the British Coal Industry,* Pergamon, 1969; *United States Investment in Scotland,* Praeger, 1972; *The Choice of Manufacturing Technology in Sugar Production in Developing Countries,* H.M.S.O., 1979. Contributor to professional journals.

* * *

FORSYTHE, Sidney A. 1920-

PERSONAL: Born July 7, 1920, in Lexington, Ky.; son of Frederick Alexander (a businessman) and Carolyn (Baker) Forsythe; married Amelia Spielberger, June 5, 1941 (divorced, 1964); married Mary Victoria De Luca (an elementary school teacher), September 7, 1969; children: (first marriage) Bruce D., Marilyn D. (Mrs. James Todesco), Norman L. *Education:* University of Kentucky, A.B. (cum laude), 1942; Southern Baptist Theological Seminary, B.D.,

1946; University of Louisville, M.A., 1949; Harvard University, Ph.D., 1963. *Politics:* Democrat. *Religion:* Roman Catholic. *Home:* 154 East Main St., Norton, Mass. 02766. *Office:* Knapton Hall, Wheaton College, Norton, Mass. 02766.

CAREER: Joseph E. Seagram Co., Louisville, Ky., production operator, 1942-46; Alabama State College at Montevallo (now University of Montevallo), instructor, 1946-49, assistant professor of sociology, 1949-54; Queens College, Charlotte, N.C., associate professor of sociology, 1954-57; Wheaton College, Norton, Mass., assistant professor, 1957-64, associate professor, 1964-69, professor of sociology, 1969—. Visiting professor at Bridgewater State College, Stonehill College, Rhode Island College, and University of Rhode Island Division of University Extension. *Member:* American Association of University Professors, American Sociological Association, Phi Beta Kappa. *Awards, honors:* Ford Foundation grant for research, 1971-72.

WRITINGS: An American Missionary Community in China, 1895-1905 (monograph), Harvard University Press, 1971. Contributor to *Public Opinion Quarterly.*

WORK IN PROGRESS: A book tentatively entitled *The Response of British Protestant Missionaries to Chinese Nationalism, 1911-1951.*

AVOCATIONAL INTERESTS: Forsythe participates in "a good many" amateur choral and operatic societies.

* * *

FORTE, Allen 1926-

PERSONAL: Born December 23, 1926, in Portland, Ore.; son of M. Palmer and Marion (Eastman) Forte; married Sharland Waitzfelder, February 4, 1950. *Education:* Columbia University, B.S., 1950, M.A., 1952. *Home:* 10 Mulberry Hill, Hamden, Conn. 06517. *Office:* Department of Music, Yale University, Stoeckel Hall, New Haven, Conn.

CAREER: Columbia University, Teachers College, New York, N.Y., instructor in music, 1954-59; Mannes College of Music, New York, N.Y., teacher of music theory, 1957-59; Yale University, New Haven, Conn., instructor, 1959, assistant professor, 1960-64, associate professor of music theory, 1964-1967; Massachusetts Institute of Technology, Cambridge, professor of music, 1967-68; Yale University, professor of music, 1968—, director of graduate studies in music, 1970-77. Instructor in music at Manhattan School of Music, 1957-58. *Military service:* U.S. Navy Reserve, 1944-46 (active service). *Member:* American Musicological Society, College Music Society, Society for Music Theory (president, 1977-79). *Awards, honors:* American Council of Learned Societies fellowship, 1965-66.

WRITINGS: Contemporary Tone-Structures, Teachers College Press, 1955; *The Compositional Matrix,* Music Teachers National Association, 1961; *Tonal Harmony in Concept and Practice,* Holt, 1962, 3rd edition, 1979; *SNOBOL 3 Primer: An Introduction to the Computer Programming Language,* M.I.T. Press, 1967; *The Structure of Atonal Music,* Yale University Press, 1973; *The Harmonic Organization of "The Rite of Spring,"* Yale University Press, 1978. Editor of *Journal of Music Theory,* 1960-67.

* * *

FOSTER, Carno A(ugustus) 1916-

PERSONAL: Born October 16, 1916, in Barbados; naturalized U.S. citizen in 1920; son of Fitz Hurbert (a schooner captain) and Elizabeth (Rock) Foster; married Phyllis Barnes (a supervisory clerk), September 17, 1950; children: Marie, Philip, Stephen. *Education:* Utilities Engineering Institute, Chicago, diploma, 1960. *Religion:* "Esoteric Science and Transcendental Philosophy." *Home:* 235 Sterling St., Brooklyn, N.Y. 11225.

CAREER: Mechanic in machine industry, Barbados, 1939-46; manager of grocery store, Brooklyn, N.Y., 1948-54; New York City Transit Authority, New York, N.Y., road car inspector, 1956—; Carno Realty Corp., Brooklyn, real estate operator, 1965-70. Trustee and member of executive council of Barbados Workers' Union, 1943-47; member of Barbados Labor Board, 1944-47; president of Adelphi Civic Association, 1964-67; organizer of block associations in Brooklyn, 1964-67; officer of block associations in Brooklyn, 1964-67; officer of U-Care Co-ordinating Council, Brooklyn, 1964-67, and Lafayette Gardens Co-ordinating Council, Brooklyn, 1965-67.

WRITINGS: Justice in Man, Philosophical Library, 1972. Contributor of articles to *New York Daily News.*

WORK IN PROGRESS: Research on the component parts of the human soul, and Einstein's Theory of Relativity.††

* * *

FOWLER, George P(almer) 1909-

PERSONAL: Born August 1, 1909, in Marietta, Ohio; son of George Edward (a salesman) and Mary E. (Palmer) Fowler; married Lorene McClure, April 16, 1931; children: Mrs. Theron D. Oxley, Janet Fowler Ross. *Education:* Butler University, B.S.L., 1933; Vanderbilt University, B.D., 1943; Yale University, Ph.D., 1954. *Home:* 2616 Rogers Ave., Ft. Worth, Tex. 76109.

CAREER: Ordained clergyman of Disciples of Christ, 1929; minister in Indiana, Kentucky, and Tennessee, 1933-43; Texas Christian University, Ft. Worth, assistant professor, 1947-54, associate professor, 1954-57, professor of religion, 1957-77. *Member:* Theta Phi.

WRITINGS: Fundamentals of Grammar of the Greek New Testament, with workbook, Stafford-Lowden, 1967, revised edition, 1971; *Our Religious Heritage: A Guide to the Study of the Bible,* Kendall/Hunt, 1969, revised edition, 1972.

* * *

FOX, Allan M(ark) 1948-

PERSONAL: Born January 6, 1948, in Philadelphia, Pa.; son of Jack and Ruth (Gelman) Fox; married Harriette Brownstein, June 14, 1970. *Education:* Temple University, B.A., 1969, J.D., 1972; Yale University, LL.M., 1975. *Home:* 821 Duke St., Alexandria, Va. 22314. *Office:* Office of Senator Jacob K. Javits, 321 Russell Bldg., U.S. Senate, Washington, D.C. 20510.

CAREER: Admitted to the Bar of Pennsylvania, 1972; Temple University, Drug Education Activities Center, Philadelphia, Pa., assistant director, 1968-69, director, 1969-72; District Attorney's Office, Philadelphia, Pa., assistant district attorney, 1972; assistant attorney general in Harrisburg, Pa., 1972-74; U.S. Senate, Washington, D.C., Committee on Labor and Public Welfare, Subcommittee on Health, counsel, 1975-77, administrative assistant and chief legislative assistant to Senator Jacob Javits, 1977—. General counsel, Governor's Council on Drug and Alcohol Abuse, Harrisburg, 1972-74; commissioner of Commission on Human Medical Research in Pennsylvania, Harrisburg, 1973-74; counsel, Commission on the Status of Women, Investigative Hearings on Women and Health Care, 1974; special counsel to commissioner, Departments of Health and Public Welfare, Commonwealth of Pennsylvania, Philadelphia, 1974. *Member:* American Bar Association, Federal Bar Association, National Health Lawyers Association, American Public Health Association, Institute of Society, Ethics, and the Life Sciences, American Association for the Advancement of Science, Philadelphia Bar Association.

WRITINGS: (Editor with Richard E. Harman) *Drug Awareness,* Avon, 1970.

* * *

FOX, Douglas A(llan) 1927-

PERSONAL: Born March 20, 1927, in Mullumbimby, New South Wales, Australia; son of Cecil Edwin Madison and Lilly (Tucker) Fox; married Margaret Porter, September 12, 1958; children: Elizabeth Rachel, Michael Glenn. *Education:* University of Sydney, B.A., 1956; University of Chicago, M.A., 1958; Pacific School of Religion, S.T.M., 1958, Th.D., 1963. *Home:* 1320 North Tejon St., Colorado Springs, Colo. 80903. *Office:* Department of Religion, Colorado College, Colorado Springs, Colo. 80903.

CAREER: Protestant clergyman, 1956-63; minister in New South Wales, Australia, 1956-61, and San Francisco, Calif., 1962-63; Colorado College, Colorado Springs, assistant professor, 1963-68, associate professor, 1968-74, professor of religion, 1974—. *Member:* American Association of University Professors.

WRITINGS: Buddhism, Christianity, and the Future of Man, Westminster, 1972; *The Vagrant Lotus: An Introduction to Buddhist Philosophy,* Westminster, 1973; *Mystery and Meaning,* Westminster, 1976. Contributor to *Journal of Bible and Religion, Encounter, Philosophy East and West, Religion in Life, Contemporary Religions in Japan,* and other journals.

WORK IN PROGRESS: Oriental Philosophy: The Relation of Ideas in Christian and Oriental Philosophy; An Introduction of Mahayana and Theravada Buddhist Philosophy.

* * *

FOX, Richard G(abriel) 1939-

PERSONAL: Born March 3, 1939, in New York, N.Y.; son of Joseph and Elizabeth (Cetron) Fox; married Judith Huff, 1974. *Education:* Columbia University, A.B. (cum laude), 1960; University of Michigan, M.A., 1961, Ph.D., 1965. *Home:* 1601 Kent St., Durham, N.C. *Office:* Department of Anthropology, Duke University, Durham, N.C. 27710.

CAREER: Brandeis University, Waltham, Mass., assistant professor of anthropology, 1965-68; Duke University, Durham, N.C., associate professor, 1968-73, professor of anthropology, 1973—. Member of Institute for Advanced Study, 1971-72.

WRITINGS: From Zamindar to Ballot Box, Cornell University Press, 1969; (editor) *Urban India: Society, Space, and Image,* Duke University Press, 1971; *Kin, Clan, Raja, and Rule in Northern India,* University of California Press, 1971; (editor) *Realm and Region in Traditional India* (monograph), South Asia Program, Duke University, 1977; *Cities in Their Cultural Setting: An Introduction to Urban Anthropology,* Prentice-Hall, 1977. Editor, *American Ethnologist,* 1976-79.

WORK IN PROGRESS: Research on urban anthropology, ethnicity in complex societies, and anthropology of anthropology.

FOX, Siv Cedering 1939-

PERSONAL: Given name rhymes with "Steve"; born February 5, 1939, in Oeverkalix, Sweden; came to United States, 1953, naturalized, 1958; daughter of Hilding (a businessman) and Elvy (Wikstroem) Cedering; married David Lawrence Fox; children: Lisa, Lora, David. *Politics:* Democrat. *Home:* Polly Park Rd., Rye, N.Y. 10580.

CAREER: Poet. Has given poetry readings in Japan, Australia, and France, and at universities throughout the United States. Visiting lecturer, University of Massachusetts, 1973; visiting writer, Columbia University, 1976. Her photographs were exhibited in New York at Modernage Galleries, summer, 1973. Coordinator of poets and writers bicentennial programs, 1975-76. Contributing editor for Pushcart Prize, 1978; member of American-Scandanavian Foundation publication committee, 1978. Consultant to board, Coordinating Council of Literary Magazines, 1972-75. *Member:* Poetry Society of America. *Awards, honors:* Poetry prize from Annapolis Fine Arts Festival, 1968; John Masefield Narrative Poetry Award from Poetry Society of America, 1969; William Marion Reedy Award from Poetry Society of America, 1970, for "Ceremonial"; photography prize, from *Saturday Review,* 1970; Borestone Mountain Poetry Award, 1973; Creative Artists Public Service fellowship, 1973, for *Mother Is;* Pushcart Prize, 1977, for *The Juggler;* Emily Dickinson Award, 1977.

WRITINGS: Letters from the Island, Fiddlehead, 1973; *Der Blommande traedet* (title means "The Flowering Tree"), Forum (Stockholm), 1973; *Cup of Cold Water* (poems and photographs), New Rivers Press, 1973; *Letters from Helge* (prose poems), calligraphy by George Gintole, New Rivers Press, 1974; (editor and translator) *Friberg and Palm/Two Swedish Poets,* New Rivers Press, 1974, bilingual hardcover edition published as *Two Swedish Poets: Gosta Friberg and Goran Palm,* 1978; *Mother Is* (poems), Stein & Day, 1975; *How to Eat a Fortune Cookie* (poems), illustrated by Sally Soper Bowers, New Rivers Press, 1976; *Joys of Fantasy* (nonfiction), illustrated with photographs by Ed Rothkowitz, Stein & Day, 1977, hardcover edition, Playboy Press, 1978; *The Juggler,* with etchings by Bill Braer, Sagarin Press, 1977; *Color Poems,* Calliopea Press, 1978; *The Blue Horse* (poems for children), Seabury, 1978; (editor and translator) *Twenty-Seven Swedish Poems,* Calliopea Press, 1978.

Poetry included in anthologies, including *New Voices in American Poetry,* Winthrop, 1973, *Rising Tides: 20th Century American Women,* Pocket Books, 1973, *Best Poems of 1973,* Capstan, 1976, and *Short Stories by Contemporary American Women.* Contributor of poetry, prose, and translations to numerous newspapers and literary magazines, including *Prairie Schooner, Partisan Review, Massachusetts Review, Chicago Tribune, New York Times, Paris Review, Kayak,* and to periodicals in Sweden and Japan; contributor of children's poetry to *Cricket.*

WORK IN PROGRESS: Playing in the Pig House, a novel; *Letters to Zakarias,* poems; *The Two-Headed Reindeer Calf,* short prose.

* * *

FOX, Sonny 1925-

PERSONAL: Born June 17, 1925, in Brooklyn, N.Y.; son of Julius A. and Gertrude (Goldberg) Fox; children: Christopher, Meredith, Dana, Tracy. *Education:* New York University, B.A., 1947. *Residence:* Los Angeles, Calif.

CAREER: Television and stage performer; producer, currently with Alan Landsburg Productions, Beverly Hills, Calif. Vice-president, Forum Communications, 1969—; consultant on telecommunications for the Asia Society, 1972—. *Military service:* U.S. Army, 1943-45; became sergeant; received Purple Heart. *Member:* International Academy of Television Arts and Sciences (member of board of directors, 1972—), National Academy of Television Arts and Sciences (chairman of board of directors, 1970-72). *Awards, honors:* Received nominations for Emmy Awards from National Academy of Television Arts and Sciences, 1961, 1962, 1963, 1964, and 1965, for performing and programming.

WRITINGS: (With Bob Grey) *Jokes and How to Tell Them,* Putnam, 1965; (with Grey) *Funnier Than the First One,* Putnam, 1972; *Jokes and Tips for the Joke Teller,* Putnam, 1976. Contributor to *T.V. Quarterly.*

* * *

FRAMO, James L(awrence) 1922-

PERSONAL: Born June 25, 1922, in Philadelphia, Pa.; son of James (a singing waiter) and Madeline (Regina) Framo; married Mary B. D'Adamo (a social worker), September 14, 1946; children: Joan E., Patricia M. *Education:* Pennsylvania State University, B.A., 1947, M.S., 1948; University of California, graduate study, 1948-49; University of Texas, Ph.D., 1953. *Politics:* Democrat. *Religion:* Roman Catholic. *Home:* 400 Hidden River Rd., Narberth, Pa. 19072. *Office:* Department of Psychology, Temple University, Philadelphia, Pa. 19122.

CAREER: Worcester State Hospital, Worcester, Mass., intern in clinical psychology, 1951-52; staff psychologist at U.S. Veterans Administration Hospital, Perry Point, Md., 1952-54, and U.S. Naval Hospital, Philadelphia, Pa., 1954-56; Eastern Pennsylvania Psychiatric Institute, Philadelphia, research scientist and family therapist, 1956-69; Thomas Jefferson University, department of psychiatry and human behavior, Philadelphia, instructor, 1960-63, assistant professor, 1963-71, associate professor of clinical psychology, 1971—; Jefferson Community Mental Health Clinic, Philadelphia, chief of Family Therapy Unit, 1969-73; Temple University, Philadelphia, adjunct associate professor, 1972-73, professor of psychology, 1973—. *Military service:* U.S. Army, 1943-45; served in Italian campaign. *Member:* American Psychological Association (fellow), American Orthopsychiatric Association, National Council on Family Relations, American Family Therapy Association (founding member), American Association of Marriage and Family Counselors.

WRITINGS: (Editor with Ivan Boszormenyi-Nagy) *Intensive Family Therapy,* Harper, 1965; (editor) *Family Interaction: A Dialogue between Family Researchers and Family Therapists,* Springer Publishing, 1972. Contributor to professional journals and other magazines. Member of advisory board of editors, *Family Process.*

WORK IN PROGRESS: A book tentatively entitled, *Families Are Where You Live;* researching ways to evaluate progress in family and marital therapy; *A Dynamic Approach to Family and Marital Therapy.*

* * *

FRANCIS, Wayne L(ouis) 1935-

PERSONAL: Born October 27, 1935, in Chicago, Ill.; son of Louis and Alice (Cross) Francis; married Barbara Wat-

kins, January 30, 1960; children: Wendy, Scott. *Education:* Wabash College, A.B., 1957; Indiana University, Ph.D., 1961. *Office:* Department of Political Science, University of Missouri, Columbia, Mo. 65201.

CAREER: Indiana University at Bloomington, instructor in political science, 1961-62; Syracuse University, Syracuse, N.Y., assistant professor of political science, 1962-67; University of Washington, Seattle, associate professor of political science, 1967-73; University of Missouri—Columbia, professor of political science, 1973—, chairman of department, 1976—. *Member:* American Political Science Association, Western Political Science Association, Midwest Political Science Association.

WRITINGS: Legislature Issues in the Fifty States, Rand McNally, 1967; *Formal Models of American Politics,* Harper, 1972; (with David C. Leege) *Political Research: Design, Measurement and Analysis,* Basic Books, 1974; *American Politics: Analysis of Choice,* Goodyear Publishing, 1976. Contributor to *American Political Science Review, Journal of Politics, Western Political Quarterly,* and *Simulation and Games.*

* * *

FRANKEL, Zygmunt 1929-

PERSONAL: Born June 10, 1929, in Wieliczka, Poland; son of Leon (a lawyer) and Giza (an ethnographer) Frankel; married Alona Goldman (a graphic artist), 1958; children: two sons. *Education:* Attended Lublin University, Poland, 1946, Battersea Polytechnic, London, England, and Cardiff Technical College, 1947-52. *Religion:* Jewish. *Home and office:* 4 Nathan St., Ramat-Gan, Israel. *Agent:* Philip G. Spitzer, 111-25, 76th Ave., Forest Hills, N.Y. 11375.

CAREER: Self-employed machine designer, specializing in automation research and development. *Military service:* Israel Army, 1954-58. *Awards, honors:* ADAM International Review (London) novel award, 1968, for *The Octopus.*

WRITINGS: Short War, Short Lives (novel), Abelard, 1971. Also author of *The Octopus.* Contributor to *ADAM International Review, London Magazine, London Magazine Stories,* and *Transatlantic Review.*

WORK IN PROGRESS: Siberian Diary, an autobiography to age 16; a novel, *The Motivation of a Pearl Oyster;* short stories and poems.

SIDELIGHTS: Zygmunt Frankel's family was deported from Poland to Siberia when he was ten. After World War II he lived five years in England, one year in Belgium, and then settled in Israel; he spent two years (1968-70) in New York City. *Avocational interests:* Zoology, skin-diving, gliding, painting, film-making, photography.

* * *

FRANKFURT, Harry Gordon 1929-

PERSONAL: Born May 29, 1929, in Langhorne, Pa.; son of Nathan (a bookkeeper) and Bertha (Gordon) Frankfurt; married Marilyn Rothman (a social worker), December 18, 1960; children: Katherine, Jennifer. *Education:* Johns Hopkins University, B.A., 1949, M.A., 1953, Ph.D., 1954; Cornell University, graduate study, 1949-51. *Home:* 545 Ellsworth Ave., New Haven, Conn. 06511. *Office:* Department of Philosophy, Yale University, New Haven, Conn. 06520.

CAREER: Ohio State University, Columbus, instructor, 1956-59, assistant professor of philosophy, 1959-62; Harpur College (now State University of New York at Binghamton), associate professor of philosophy, 1962-63; Rockefeller University, New York, N.Y., research associate, 1963-64, professor of philosophy, 1964-76; Yale University, New Haven, Conn., professor of philosophy, 1976—, chairman of department, 1978—. *Military service:* U.S. Army, 1954-56. *Member:* American Philosophical Association, Phi Beta Kappa. *Awards, honors:* Visiting fellow at All Souls College, Oxford University, 1971-72.

WRITINGS: Demons, Dreamers, and Madman, Bobbs-Merrill, 1970. Contributor to *Philosophical Review, Journal of Philosophy,* and *American Philosophical Quarterly.*

WORK IN PROGRESS: Research in seventeenth-century philosophy; metaphysics and philosophy of mind.

*　　*　　*

FRANZEN, Gosta Knut   1906-

PERSONAL: Born June 14, 1906, in Soderkoping, Sweden; son of Frans and Amalia (Svensson) Franzen; married Karin Franson (a university lecturer), August 5, 1939; children: Lars, Lena. *Education:* Uppsala University, Fil.Kand., 1927, M.A., 1929, Ph.D., 1937; attended University of Heidelberg, 1926; University of Marburg, postdoctoral study, 1937. *Home:* Sunnerstavaegen 19B, 75251 Uppsala, Sweden.

CAREER: Uppsala University, Uppsala, Sweden, assistant professor of Scandanavian languages, 1937-41; Swedish Consulate General, Information Bureau, San Francisco, Calif., information director, 1943-44; University of California, Berkeley, instructor in Swedish, 1943-44; University of Chicago, Chicago, Ill., associate professor, 1944-56, professor of Scandinavian languages, 1956-74. *Member:* Royal Gustavus Adolphus Academy, Royal Academy of Humanities (Uppsala), Royal Society of Science (Uppsala), Iceland Society (Uppsala), Society for Advancement of Scandinavian Study, Swedish Pioneer Society, American-Scandinavian Foundation. *Awards, honors:* Knight of Order of Vasa, Sweden, 1950; Knight of Order of North Star, Sweden, 1966; Knight of Order of St. Olaf, Norway, 1971.

WRITINGS: Vikbolandets by och gardnamn, Nomina Germanica, 1937; *Amerikansk kateder och svensk,* KF's Bokforlag, 1947; *Runo ortnamn,* Kungl Gustav Adolfs Akademien, 1959; *Laxdoelabygdens ortnamn,* Kungl Gustav Adolfs Akademien, 1964; *Prose and Poetry of Modern Sweden,* University of Nebraska Press, 1969; *Gustavia on Saint Barthelemy,* Acta Academiae Regiae Scientiarum Upsaliensis, 1974. Contributor of approximately one hundred articles to scholarly journals.

WORK IN PROGRESS: Two books, *The Place Names of Sweden* and *Province of Ostergotland.*

*　　*　　*

FRASE, Larry E.   1945-

PERSONAL: Born May 30, 1945, in Wadsworth, Ohio; son of Dale E. (a contractor) and Maxine (Musser) Frase. *Education:* University of Arizona, B.A., 1967; Arizona State University, M.A., 1969, Ed.D., 1971; post-doctoral study, Western Illinois University. *Home:* 1201 East Via Entrada, Tucson, Ariz. *Office:* Flowing Wells Schools, Prince Rd., Tucson, Ariz. 85705.

CAREER: Elementary school teacher in Mesa, Ariz., 1967-73; employed with Uniondale Public Schools, Uniondale, N.Y., 1973-75; Flowing Wells Schools, Tucson, Ariz., assistant superintendent, 1975—. Instructor in education at Arizona State University, 1967-73; University of Arizona,

instructor in education, 1971-72, currently instructor in administration and supervision. National and international consultant.

WRITINGS: (With G. E. Talbert) *Individualized Instruction: A Book of Reading,* C. E. Merrill, 1972. Contributor to Arizona-Mesa Differentiated Staffing Consortium. Contributor to *Audio-Visual Instruction, Arizona Teacher, National Elementary School Principal, Forum on Open Education, Lutheran Education,* and *Educational Technology.*

WORK IN PROGRESS: Enhancing Quality in Instruction: Apply the Locus of Control.

*　　*　　*

FREED, Arthur   1894-1973

September 9, 1894—April 12, 1973; American songwriter and motion picture producer. Obituaries: *New York Times,* April 13, 1973; *Washington Post,* April 14, 1973; *Time,* April 23, 1973.

*　　*　　*

FREEDMAN, Arthur M(erton)   1916-

PERSONAL: Born March 16, 1916, in Toledo, Ohio; son of Louis S. and Sylvia H. (Weisz) Freedman; married Fay Diamond (an artist), September 6, 1946; children: Daryl Michal, Deborah T. *Education:* University of Toledo, A.B., 1938; University of Cincinnati, A.M., 1939; University of Pennsylvania, Ph.D., 1959. *Religion:* Judiasm. *Residence:* Springfield, Pa. *Office:* Wharton School, University of Pennsylvania, Philadelphia, Pa. 19104.

CAREER: Brown University, Providence, R.I., instructor in economics, 1946-48; Bates College, Lewiston, Me., assistant professor of economics, 1948-55; University of Pennsylvania, Philadelphia, lecturer, 1955-59, assistant professor, 1959-63, associate professor of finance, 1963—, associate chairman of department, 1977—. *Military service:* U.S. Army, 1942-46; became captain. *Member:* American Economic Association, American Finance Association, Royal Economic Society.

WRITINGS: (With Charles R. Whittlesey and Edward S. Herman) *Money and Banking: Analysis and Policy,* Macmillan, 1963, revised edition, 1968. Contributor to the *Special Study of the Securities Markets,* Securities Exchange Commission, 1962.

WORK IN PROGRESS: Research in monetary theory; research in mechanisms and effects of monetary and fiscal policies.

*　　*　　*

FREEDMAN, Daniel X.   1921-

PERSONAL: Born August 17, 1921, in Lafayette, Ind.; son of Harry and Sophia (Feinstein) Freedman; married Mary C. Neidigh, March 20, 1945. *Education:* Harvard University, B.A. (cum laude), 1947; Yale University, M.D., 1951; Western New England Institute for Psychoanalysis, graduate, 1966. *Home:* 4950 South Chicago Beach Dr., Chicago, Ill. 60615. *Office:* Department of Psychiatry, University of Chicago, 950 East 59th St., Chicago, Ill. 60637.

CAREER: Intern in pediatrics, 1951-52; Yale University, School of Medicine, New Haven, Conn., resident, 1952-55, chief resident in psychiatry, 1955-56, instructor of psychiatry, 1955-58; National Institute of Mental Health, Bethesda, Md., training in Laboratory of Clinical Sciences, 1957-58; Yale University, School of Medicine, assistant professor,

1958-61, associate professor, 1961-64, professor of psychiatry, 1964-66; University of Chicago, Chicago, Ill., professor of psychiatry and chairman of department, 1966—, Louis Block Professor of Biological Sciences, 1969—. Attending psychiatrist, Yale-New Haven Community Hospital, 1958-66. National Academy of Sciences-National Research Council, chairman of panel on psychiatric drugs, Drug Efficacy Study, 1966-68, member of committee on problems of drug dependence, 1971-72; chairman of clinical psychopharmacology research review committee, National Institute of Mental Health, 1967-69; vice-president, National Coordinating Council on Drug Education, 1971; member of scientific and professional board, International Council on Alcohol and Alcoholism, 1971—. Member of board of directors, Social Science Research Council, 1967-73, Foundation's Fund for Research in Psychiatry, 1969-72, Drug Abuse Council, Inc., 1972—, and Drug Abuse Council of Illinois, 1972—. Medicine in the Public Interest, Inc., member of board of directors, 1973—, vice president, 1977—. Member of advisory board, Institute for Sex Research, Indiana University, 1966-68. Consultant to juvenile courts, 1955-57, Fairfield State Hospital, 1958-66, and to U.S. Department of Army, 1965-67. *Military service:* U.S. Army, 1942-46.

MEMBER: American Psychiatric Association (fellow; chairman of Commission on Drug Abuse, 1971—; vice-president, 1975-77), American Medical Society on Alcoholism, American Association of Chairmen of Departments of Psychiatry (president, 1972), American Medical Association, American Psychopathological Association, American Psychosomatic Society (councilor, 1970-73), American Society for Pharmacology and Experimental Therapeutics, Collegium Internationale Neuro-Psychopharmacologium, American Association for the Advancement of Science, Association of American Medical Colleges (member of executive council, 1977-79), Group for the Advancement of Psychiatry, International Brain Research Organization, Psychiatric Research Society, Society of Biological Psychiatry, Society for Neuroscience, Western New England Psychoanalytic Society, Western New England Institute for Psychoanalysis, Illinois Psychiatric Society (president, 1971), Chicago Psychoanalytic Society, Yale Medical Society (president, 1962-63), Sigma Xi, Alpha Omega Alpha. *Awards, honors:* Received distinguished achievement award from *Modern Medicine*, 1973; William C. Menninger award from American College of Physicians, 1975.

WRITINGS: (With F. C. Redlich) *The Theory and Practice of Psychiatry,* Basic Books, 1966; (author of foreword and contributor) C. P. Rosenbaum, editor, *The Meaning of Madness,* Science House, 1970; (editor with David Offer, and contributor) *Modern Psychiatry and Clinical Research: Essays in Honor of Roy R. Grinker, Sr.,* Basic Books, 1971; (editor and contributor) *Biology of the Major Psychoses: A Comparative Analysis,* Raven Press, 1975; (editor with Jarl E. Dyrud, and contributor) *American Handbook of Psychiatry,* Volume V: *Treatment,* 2nd edition, Basic Books, 1975.

Contributor: G. J. Sarwer-Foner, editor, *The Dynamics of Psychiatric Drug Therapy,* C. C Thomas, 1960; G. H. Glaser, editor, *EEG and Behavior,* Basic Books, 1963; Philip Solomon, editor, *Psychiatric Drugs,* Grune, 1965; D. Efron, editor, *Ethnopharmacologic Search for Psychoactive Drugs,* U.S. Government Printing Office, 1967; Zubin and Shagrass, editors, *Neurobiological Aspects of Psychopathology,* Grune, 1969; J. R. Wittenborn and others, editors, *Drugs and Youth,* C. C Thomas, 1969; R. J. Mandell and

M. P. Mandell, editors, *Psychochemical Research in Man,* Academic Press, 1969.

What Everyone Needs to Know about Drugs, U.S. News & World Report, 1970; editorial staff of Communications Research Machines, *Psychology Today: An Introduction,* Communications Research Machines, 1970; W. W. Stewart, editor, *Drug Abuse in Industry,* Halos & Associates, 1970; J. R. Gamage and E. L. Zerkin, editors, *Hallucinogenic Drug Research: Impact on Science and Society,* Stash Press, 1970; C. C. Brown and C. Savage, editors, *The Drug Abuse Controversy,* National Education Consultants, 1971; Sherman C. Feinstein and others, editors, *Adolescent Psychiatry,* Volume I, Basic Books, 1971; Joseph Mendels, editor, *Biological Psychiatry,* Wiley, 1972; Francis Braceland and others, editors, *Drug Abuse: Medical and Criminal Aspects,* MSS Information Corp., 1972; S. Btesh, editor, *Drug Abuse: Nonmedical Use of Dependence-producing Drugs,* Plenum, 1972; Mendels, editor, *Textbook of Biological Psychiatry,* Wiley, 1973; R. H. Williams, editor, *To Live and to Die: When, How and Why?,* Springer-Verlag, 1973; J. Barchas and E. Usdin, editors, *Serotonin and Behavior,* Academic Press, 1973; S. Fisher and A. M. Freedman, editors, *Opiate Addiction: Origins and Treatment,* V. H. Winston, 1973; E. Costa, G. Gessa, and M. Sandler, editors, *Advances in Biochemical Psychopharmacology,* Volume X: *Serotonin—New Vistas,* Raven Press, 1974; *American Handbook of Psychiatry,* Basic Books, Volume IV, edited by M. F. Reiser, 1975, Volume VI, edited by D. A. Hamburg, 1975; J. R. Tinklenberg, editor, *Marijuana and Health Hazards: Methodological Issues in Current Research,* Basic Books, 1975; P. H. Hughes, editor, *Behind the Wall of Respect: Community Experiments in Heroin Addiction Control,* University of Chicago Press, 1977; H. Akiskal and W. Webb, editors, *Psychiatric Diagnosis: Exploration of Biological Predictors,* Spectrum, 1977; Usdin, Hamburg, and Barchas, editors, *Neuroregulators and Psychiatric Disorders,* Oxford University Press, 1977; J. O. Cole, A. Schatzberg, and G. Frazier, editors, *Depression: Biology, Psychodynamics and Treatment,* Plenum, 1978; J. P. Brady and H.K.H. Brodie, editors, *Controversy in Psychiatry,* Saunders, 1978; van Praag, Rafaelsen, Lader, and Sachar, editors, *Handbook of Biological Psychiatry,* Volume II, Dekker, 1978.

Contributor to *McGraw-Hill Encyclopedia of Science and Technology,* to proceedings of international conferences on drug dependence, and to yearbooks. Contributor of more than one hundred articles and reviews to scientific journals, *Federal Probation, Midway,* and *Nature.* Editor-in-chief, *Archives of General Psychiatry,* 1970—; member of editorial board, *Journal of Experimental Research in Personality,* 1965-69, *Biochemical Pharmacology,* 1966—, University of Chicago Press, 1967—, *Journal of Nervous and Mental Disease,* 1967—, *Communications in Behavioral Biology,* 1967—, *Life Sciences,* 1968-70, *Year Book of Psychiatry and Applied Mental Health,* 1969—, *Journal of Autism and Childhood Schizophrenia,* 1970—, *Journal of Youth and Adolescence,* 1971—, and *Psychosomatic Medicine,* 1972—; member of international editorial board for drug dependence, *Excerpta Medica.*

SIDELIGHTS: As a medical student at Yale, Daniel X. Freedman studied the central mode of action of antihistamines, which won him the Keese Prize for student research in 1951. In the early 1960's he discovered the long postulated (but never demonstrated) link of LSD to the metabolism and disposition of serotonin in the brain. In drug abuse work, he emphasizes the need for bridges between basic, clinical, and community programs.

* * *

FREEDMAN, M(orris) David   1938-

PERSONAL: Born May 23, 1938, in Toronto, Ontario, Canada; son of Nathan and Freda (Glicksman) Freedman; married Roberta Ephron, August 12, 1962; children: Sandra, Craig. Education: University of Toronto, B.A.Sc. (honors), 1960; University of Illinois, M.S.E.E., 1962, Ph.D.E.E., 1965. Residence: Southfield, Mich. Office: Bendix Corp., Southfield, Mich. 48076.

CAREER: University of Illinois at Urbana-Champaign, research associate at Biological Computer Laboratory, 1965-66; Bendix Corp., Research Laboratories, Southfield, Mich., senior engineer, 1966-69, staff engineer, 1969-72, senior staff engineer, 1972-74, principal engineer, 1974-75, senior principal engineer, 1975—. Lecturer, Wayne State University, 1967; University of Michigan, Dearborn Campus, adjunct lecturer, 1972-73, adjunct assistant professor, 1973-78, adjunct associate professor, 1978—. Member: Institute of Electrical and Electronic Engineers (member of Computer Society), Association for Computing Machinery, Society of Manufacturing Engineers, Engineering Society of Detroit, Sigma Xi, Eta Kappa Nu, Tau Beta Pi, Phi Kappa Phi, Pi Mu Epsilon.

WRITINGS: (Contributor) H. M. Von Foerster and J. W. Beauchamp, editors, Music by Computers, Wiley, 1969; Principles of Digital Computer Operation, Wiley, 1972. Author of technical reports. Contributor to proceedings and to professional journals, including Journal of the Audio Engineering Society, Journal of the Acoustical Society of America, and Bendix Technical Journal. Associate editor, Computer Architecture News.

WORK IN PROGRESS: Research on computer-aided design and interactive graphics systems; a book on designing systems containing small computers.

SIDELIGHTS: M. David Freedman holds patents on proximity-focused image storage tube, shadow edge position detector, optical image data processing system, character recognition systems, coordinate determining device, and lumber inspection system.

* * *

FREEMAN, Eugene   1906-

PERSONAL: Born February 16, 1906, in New York, N.Y.; son of Alexander Samuel (a designer and worker in ornamental iron) and Rose (Farkas) Freeman; married Ann Sternberg (an editor), November 30, 1930; children: James Montague, Thomas Parry. Education: University of California, Los Angeles, A.B., 1926; University of Chicago, fellow, 1928-31, Ph.D., 1937; Northern Illinois College of Optometry, O.D., 1934. Home and office address: P.O. Box 1908 (15401 Blackberry Hill Rd.), Los Gatos, Calif. 95030.

CAREER: Northern Illinois College of Optometry, Chicago, assistant professor, 1933-36, associate professor, 1936-39, professor of physiologic optics and professional ethics, 1939-43; Illinois Institute of Technology, Chicago, assistant professor of philosophy, 1947-53; Chicago College of Optometry, Chicago, professor of ethics and vice-president, 1949-56; free-lance writer and editor, 1956-59; Open Court Publishing Co., La Salle, Ill., editor-in-chief, 1959-65, editor of Scholarly Books Division, and editor of Monist, 1959—; San Jose State University, San Jose, Calif., associate pro-

fessor, 1965-67, professor of philosophy, 1967-73, professor emeritus, 1973—, chairman of department, 1966-69; Open Court Publishing Co., Los Gatos, Calif., director of philosophy division, 1973—.

MEMBER: American Philosophical Association, Charles S. Peirce Society, Metaphysical Society of America. Awards, honors: D.O.S., Chicago College of Optometry, 1949; other awards for contributions to optometric education include Distinguished Service Foundation Award, Omega Epsilon Phi Award, and Gold Medal of Beta Sigma Kappa, all 1949.

WRITINGS: The Categories of Charles Peirce, Open Court, 1934; (editor with David Appel) The Great Ideas of Plato, Lantern Press, 1952, reissued as The Wisdom and Ideas of Plato, Fawcett, 1956; (editor with William L. Reese and contributor) Process and Divinity: The Hartshorne Festschrift, Open Court, 1967; (editor with Joseph Owens) The Wisdom and Ideas of St. Thomas Aquinas, Fawcett, 1968; (editor with Wilfrid Sellars) Basic Issues in the Philosophy of Time, Open Court, 1971; (editor with Maurice Mandelbaum) Spinoza: Essays in Interpretation, Open Court, 1975; The Abdication of Philosophy; Philosophy and the Public Good: Essays in Honor of Paul Schlipp, Open Court, 1976. Co-author with I. M. Borish of Manual of Accreditation, American Optometric Association, 1942. Contributor to Yale Review, Monist, and optometry journals.

Series editor and co-editor, "Monist Library of Philosophy," Open Court, three volumes published; member of editorial advisory board, "Library of Living Philosophers," Open Court. Member of editorial advisory board of the journals, Folia Humanistica (Barcelona), Studi Internazionali di Filosofia (Turin), and Rassegna Internazionale di Logica (Bologna).

WORK IN PROGRESS: An essay on Blanshard's philosophy of education for a forthcoming volume on Blanshard in "Library of Living Philosophers."

* * *

FREEMAN, Ruth B(enson)   1906-

PERSONAL: Born December 5, 1906, in Methuen, Mass.; daughter of Wilbur Milton (a trucker) and Elsie (Lawson) Freeman; married Anselm Fisher, September 20, 1927; children: Nancy Ruth (Mrs. Bernard Smith). Education: Mount Sinai Hospital School of Nursing, graduate, 1927; Columbia University, B.S., 1934; New York University, M.A., 1939, Ed.D., 1951. Politics: Democrat. Religion: Protestant. Home and office: 616 Massachusetts Ave. N.E., Washington, D.C. 20002.

CAREER: Visiting Nurse Service of New York, staff nurse, 1928-37; New York University, New York, N.Y., instructor in nursing, 1937-41; University of Minnesota, Minneapolis, professor of public health, 1941-46; American National Red Cross, Washington, D.C., director of nursing, 1946-50; Johns Hopkins University, Baltimore, Md., associate professor, 1950-62, professor of public health, 1962-71, professor emeritus, 1971—. Member: National League for Nursing (president, 1955-59), National Health Council (president, 1959-60), American Public Health Association (fellow; member of executive board, 1951-56), American Nurses' Association, Minnesota Nurses' Association (president, 1944-46). Awards, honors: Pearl McIver Award for distinguished work in public health nursing, 1958; Bronfman Prize from American Public Health Association, 1972, for excellence in public health.

WRITINGS: *Techniques of Supervision in Public Health Nursing,* Saunders, 1945, revised edition, 1949; *Public Health Nursing Practice,* Saunders, 1950, 3rd revised edition, 1963; (with E. M. Holmes) *Administration in Public Health Services,* Saunders, 1960; *Community Health Nursing Practice,* Saunders, 1970.

SIDELIGHTS: Ruth Freeman's book, *Community Health Nursing Practice,* has been translated into Spanish, French, and Hebrew. Freeman told *CA,* "The greatest stimulus for writing and source of validation in professional writing are students and young practitioners."

* * *

FRERE, Emile (George) 1917-1974

PERSONAL: Surname rhymes with "air"; born October 3, 1917, in Point Marion, Pa.; son of Emile Georges (a glass worker) and Regina (Cabaret) Frere; married Hazel Wilma Woods, 1940 (deceased); children: Emile Eugene, Raymond Guy. *Education:* West Virginia University, B.S.Ed., 1940, M.A., 1949; additional graduate study at Sorbonne, University of Paris, and University of Bordeaux; University of Pittsburgh, Ph.D. (with honors), 1961. *Home:* 508 Beechurst Ave., Morgantown, W.Va. 26505. *Office:* Department of Foreign Languages, 440 A.H., West Virginia University, Morgantown, W.Va. 26506.

CAREER: Coal miner in West Virginia, 1940-41; employee at railroad terminal in Washington, D.C., 1941-47, began as clerk, became supervisor; professional photographer, 1944-56; West Virginia University, Morgantown, instructor, 1949-61, associate professor, 1961-71, professor of French, 1971-74. Fulbright exchange teacher in Bordeaux, France, 1957-58; member, Foreign Language Council of West Virginia. *Member:* Modern Language Association of America, American Association of Teachers of French, American Association of University Professors, West Virginia State Philological Society, Kappa Delta Pi, Izaak Walton League of America. *Awards, honors:* Andrew Mellow fellow at University of Pittsburgh, 1960-61; West Virginia University Foundation grant for research in France, summer, 1965; West Virginia University Foundation, Inc., research for publication grant, 1966.

WRITINGS: *The Moralism of Jean Anouilh,* Greenwich Book, 1967; (with Robert Laborde) *Quelques Journees francaises,* with laboratory recordings, Blaisdell, 1969. Contributor to journals. Associate editor of *West Virginia Language Bulletin,* 1954-57.

WORK IN PROGRESS: *The Aphorisms in the Works of Anouilh; Phonetics for Prospective Teachers of French.*

AVOCATIONAL INTERESTS: Fishing, music, auto mechanics, electronics, manual arts.†

(Died July 1, 1974)

* * *

FRIEDMAN, Alice R. 1900-

PERSONAL: Born March 17, 1900, in Vienna, Austria; naturalized citizen; daughter of Carl E. and Paul (Steiner) Friedman. *Education:* University of Vienna, Ph.D., 1925. Studied under Alfred Adler in Vienna. *Politics:* Democrat. *Religion:* Jewish.

CAREER: School for Problem Children, Vienna, Austria, director and psychotherapist, 1924-38; clinical psychologist, Veterans' Administration, 1947-51; chief psychologist, mental hygiene clinic, Lebanon Hospital (New York), 1952-

57; group psychotherapist, Valley State Hospital, 1959-67; clinical psychologist, State Diagnostic Center (New Jersey), 1967-69; psychotherapist, Queens County Neuropsychiatric Institute, 1969—. Psychotherapist, Vienna public schools child guidance clinic, 1928-36, Vienna University extension, 1929-35; private practice, 1957-60, 1964-67; member of teaching staff, New School of Social Research, 1969-73. *Member:* American Psychological Association, Society for Personality Assessment, American Group Psychotherapy Association, New York Society of Clinical Psychologists.

WRITINGS: *The Birth of Psychotherapy,* Norton, 1972. Contributor to psychological journals.†

* * *

FRIEDMANN, Arnold 1925-

PERSONAL: Born May 12, 1925, in Nuremberg, Germany; son of Max (a lawyer) and Else (Bacharach) Friedmann; married Susanne Kirsch (a teacher), 1949; children: Daniel Peter, Ronald David. *Education:* Pratt Institute, B.F.A., 1953, M.S., 1960; Union Graduate School, Ph.D., 1976. *Religion:* Jewish. *Home:* 42 North Maple St., Hadley, Mass. 01035. *Office:* Department of Design, University of Massachusetts, Amherst, Mass. 01002.

CAREER: Interior designer, Kew Gardens, N.Y., 1955-72; Pratt Institute, Brooklyn, N.Y., assistant professor, 1957-60, associate professor, 1961-65, professor of design, 1966-72, head of department, 1970-72; University of Massachusetts—Amherst, professor of design, 1972—, head of department, 1972-73. *Military service:* British Army, 1943-46. *Member:* American Society of Interior Designers, Interior Design Educators Council (president, 1965-67), American Association of University Professors, International Federation of Interior Architects (honorary corresponding member).

WRITINGS: *A Critical Study of Interior Design Education,* Interior Design Educators Council, 1968; (with John Pile and Forrest Wilson) *Interior Design: An Introduction to Architectural Interiors,* American Elsevier, 1970, revised edition, 1976; *Commonsense Design,* Scribner, 1976; (with Craig Zimring and Ervin Zube) *Environmental Design Evaluation,* Plenum, 1978. Contributor to *Encyclopaedia Britannica* and to journals in his field.

* * *

FRONDIZI, Risieri 1910-

PERSONAL: Born November 20, 1910, in Posadas, Argentina; son of Julio and Isabel (Ercoli) Frondizi; married Josefina Barbat, December 30, 1938; children: Josefina Isabel, Carlos Alberto. *Education:* Instituto Profesorado, Buenos Aires, M.A. (philosophy), 1935; University of Michigan, M.A. (philosophy), 1943; National University of Mexico, Ph.D., 1950. *Home:* 1309 West Walnut St., Carbondale, Ill. 62901. *Office:* Department of Philosophy, Southern Illinois University, Carbondale, Ill. 62901.

CAREER: Professor of philosophy at University of Tucuman, Tucuman, Argentina, 1938-46, University of Venezuela, Caracas, 1947-48, University of Pennsylvania, Philadelphia, 1948-49, Yale University, New Haven, Conn., 1949-50, University of Puerto Rico, Rio Piedras, 1951-54, and Columbia University, 1955; University of Buenos Aires, Buenos Aires, Argentina, professor of philosophy, 1956-66, dean of Faculty of Philosophy and Letters, 1957, president of university, 1957-62; University of California, Los Angeles, visiting professor of philosophy, 1966-68; University of Texas at Austin, visiting professor of philosophy, 1968-69; Southern Illinois University at Carbondale, professor of philosophy, 1970—. Member of Institute for Advanced Study, Princeton, 1964. President, Union of Latin American Universities, Mexico City, 1958-62; member of administrative board, International Association of Universities, Paris, 1960-70. *Member:* International Phenomenological Society, International Institute of Philosophy (Paris; permanent member), Inter-American Philosophical Society (former president), Council on Higher Education of the American Republics (CHEAR; former co-chairman), American Society of Value Inquiry.

WRITINGS: El punto de partida del filosofar, Losada, 1945, 2nd edition, 1957; *Substancia y funcion en el problem del yo,* Losada, 1952, translation published as *The Nature of the Self: A Functional Interpretation,* Yale University Press, 1953, reissued in Spanish as *El yo como estructura dinamica,* Editorial Paidos, 1970, and under original English title, Southern Illinois University Press, 1971; *Que son los valores? Introduccion a la axiologia,* Fondo de Cultura Economica (Mexico), 1958, 5th revised edition, 1972, translation by Solomon Lipp published as *What Is Value? An Introduction to Axiology,* Open Court, 1963, 2nd edition, 1971; *La universidad en un mundo de tensiones,* Editorial Paidos, 1971; *Introduccion a los problemas fundamentales del hombre,* Fondo de Cultura Economica, 1977.

Editor: George Berkeley, *Tratado sobre los principios del conocimiento humano,* Losada, 1939, 3rd edition, 1968; (and translator) Rene Descartes, *Discurso del metodo,* University of Puerto Rico, 1954; *Descartes,* Centro Editor de America Latina, 1967; (with Jorge Gracia) *El hombre y los valores en la filosofia latinoamericana del siglo XX,* Fondo de Cultura Economica, 1975.

Work included in several anthologies in English and Spanish. Contributor of more than 50 articles on philosophy and education to American and European journals. Consulting editor, *Monist* and *Philosophy and Phenomenological Research.*

WORK IN PROGRESS: A book on man as a creative animal.

SIDELIGHTS: Risieri Frondizi has traveled extensively and lectured in Europe, Latin-America, Japan, India, Middle East, Australia, and New Zealand. His brother, Arturo Frondizi, was president of Argentina, 1958-62.

*   *   *

FROST, Leslie Miscampbell 1895-1973

September 20, 1895—May 4, 1973; Canadian statesman and historian, former premier of Ontario. Obituaries: *Washington Post,* May 5, 1973.

*   *   *

FROST, William 1917-

PERSONAL: Born June 8, 1917, in New York, N.Y.; son of John William (a lawyer) and Christina (Gurlitz) Frost; married Marjorie Pangburn (a painter), August 4, 1942; children: Marjorie Augusta Frost McCracken, Christina Emily, Clifford William. *Education:* Bowdoin College, B.A. (summa cum laude), 1938; Columbia University, M.A., 1942; Yale University, Ph.D., 1946. *Home:* 2820 Verde Vista Dr., Santa Barbara, Calif. 93103. *Office:* 1720 South Hall, University of California, Santa Barbara, Calif. 93106.

CAREER: Instructor in English at Carnegie Institute of Technology (now Carnegie-Mellon University), Pittsburgh,

Pa., 1942-44, and Yale University, New Haven, Conn., 1946-47; Wesleyan University, Middletown, Conn., assistant professor of English, 1947-51; University of California, Santa Barbara, assistant professor, 1951-55, associate professor, 1955-61, professor of English, 1961—, chairperson of department, 1974-79. Visiting associate professor, Yale University, 1958-59. *Member:* Modern Language Association of America, Mediaeval Academy of America, Philological Association of the Pacific Coast, California State Employees Association, Phi Beta Kappa. *Awards, honors:* Guggenheim fellow, 1959; American Council of Learned Societies research grant, 1966-67, 1978-79; National Endowment for the Humanities grant, 1972-73.

WRITINGS: Fulke Greville's "Caelica": An Evaluation (monograph), privately printed, 1942; (editor or co-editor of cited volumes; Maynard Mack, principal editor) *English Masterpieces: An Anthology of Imaginative Literature from Chaucer to T. S. Eliot,* Prentice-Hall, 1950, 2nd edition (does not include Volume VIII), 1961, Volume I: *The Age of Chaucer,* Volume VI: *Romantic and Victorian Poetry,* Volume VII: *Modern Poetry,* Volume VIII: *Selected Prose;* (editor and author of introduction and commentaries) *Selected Works of John Dryden,* Rinehart, 1953, 2nd edition, Holt, 1971; *Dryden and the Art of Translation* (monograph), Yale University Press, 1955, reprinted, Shoe String, 1969; (with others) *Bibliography of Studies in Victorian Literature for the Ten Years 1945-54,* edited by Austin Wright, University of Illinois Press, 1956; (associate editor; Mack, editor) *The Iliad of Homer,* translation by Alexander Pope, two volumes, Yale University Press, 1967; (associate editor; Mack, editor) *The Odyssey of Homer,* translation by Alexander Pope, two volumes, Yale University Press, 1967. Also editor with A. B. Chambers, John Dryden, *Juvenal and Persius and Other Poems,* Volume IV, University of California Press; author of *Dryden and Future Shock,* 1976.

Contributor: Richard J. Schoeck and Jerome Taylor, editors, *Chaucer Criticism: The Canterbury Tales,* University of Notre Dame Press, 1960; Maynard Mack, editor, *Essential Articles for the Study of Alexander Pope,* Archon, 1964; Clifford Leech, editor, *Shakespeare: The Tragedies* (critical essays), University of Chicago Press, 1965; Horst Meller and Hans-Joachim Zimmerman, editors, *Lebende Antike,* Erich Schmidt Verlag, 1967; G. S. Rousseau, editor, *Twentieth Century Interpretations of "The Rape of the Lock,"* Prentice-Hall, 1969; Bruce King, editor, *Dryden's Mind and Art,* Oliver & Boyd, 1969, Barnes & Noble, 1970; Roger Lonsdale, editor, *Dryden to Jonson,* Sphere Books, 1971; Earl Miner, editor, *John Dryden,* G. Bell, 1972. Contributor of articles and reviews to professional journals, including an omnibus review of all new books published in 1972 on the 1660-1800 period for *Studies in English Literature,* summer, 1973.

WORK IN PROGRESS: Editing Volumes V and VI (Dryden's Virgil) in the California edition of Dryden; co-editing Volume VII (*The Fables*), with Earl Miner; a book on Chaucer and Richardson as innovators.

SIDELIGHTS: "I distrust holders of picturesque or flamboyant views, and try to avoid such views myself," William Frost writes. He spent 1966-67 doing research in England (Oxford area), and has made three other trips to England and two to France in the past decade or so.

AVOCATIONAL INTERESTS: Music, poker, chess, cinema, bicycling.

FRUHAN, William E(dward), Jr. 1943-

PERSONAL: Born March 5, 1943, in Lakewood, Ohio; son of William E. (a sales manager) and Elizabeth (McPhilliamy) Fruhan; married Virginia J. Warren, September 2, 1967; children: Matthew W. and William E. III (twins). *Education:* Yale University, B.S., 1965; Harvard University, M.B.A., 1967, D.B.A., 1970. *Home:* 39 Dolphin Rd., Newton, Mass. 02159. *Office:* Harvard Business School, Boston, Mass. 02163.

CAREER: Harvard University, Business School, Boston, Mass., assistant professor, 1970-74, associate professor of finance, 1974—. Director of Epsilon Data Management, Inc., Burlington, Mass., Pittsburgh & Lake Erie Railroad Co., Pittsburgh, Pa., and Detroit, Toledo & Ironton Railroad Co., Dearborn, Mich. *Member:* Financial Management Association.

WRITINGS: The Fight for Competitive Advantage, Division of Research, Harvard Business School, 1972; (editor with J. K. Butters and T. R. Piper) *Case Problems in Finance,* Irwin, 1975. Contributor to *Harvard Business Review.*

WORK IN PROGRESS: Financial Strategy, for Irwin.

* * *

FUKUYAMA, Yoshio 1921-

PERSONAL: Born April 29, 1921, in Los Angeles, Calif.; son of Keikichi (a businessman) and Shizu (Yokota) Fukuyama; married Toshiko Kawata (an artist), December 29, 1950; children: Yoshihiro Francis. *Education:* Doane College A.B., 1943; University of Chicago, B.D., 1950, Ph.D., 1960. *Home:* 107 Redwood Lane, State College, Pa. 16801. *Office:* 1001 Liberal Arts Tower, Pennsylvania State University, University Park, Pa. 16802.

CAREER: Ordained minister in Congregational Christian Church (now United Church of Christ), 1950. Teacher at American School, Talas-Kayseri, Turkey, 1945-48; United Church of Christ, New York, N.Y., director of research, 1955-67; Pennsylvania State University, University Park, associate professor, 1967-71, professor of religious studies, 1971—, chairman of department, 1975—, graduate officer, 1971-74. *Member:* American Sociological Association, Society for the Scientific Study of Religion, Religious Research Association (president, 1961-63), Religious Education Association.

WRITINGS: (Contributor) J. Robert Nelson, editor, *Christian Unity in North America: A Symposium,* Bethany Press, 1958; (contributor) Roger L. Shinn, editor, *Essays on the American Character,* Harper, 1964; (contributor) Donald M. Valdes and Dwight G. Dean, editors, *Sociology in Use: Selected Readings for the Introductory Course,* Macmillan, 1965; (contributor) Arthur Shostok, editor, *Sociology in Action: Case Studies in Social Problems and Directed Social Change,* Dorsey Press, 1966; (with Thomas C. Campbell) *The Fragmented Layman: An Empirical Study of Lay Attitudes,* Pilgrim Press, 1970; *The Ministry in Transition: A Case Study of Theological Education,* Pennsylvania State University Press, 1972; (contributor) Joseph Faulkner, editor, *Religion's Influence in Contemporary Society: Readings in the Sociology of Religion,* C. E. Merrill, 1972. Contributor of articles on sociology of religion to professional journals. Contributing editor of *Review of Religious Research.*

FULLER, William A(lbert) 1924-

PERSONAL: Born May 10, 1924, in Moosomin, Saskatchewan, Canada; son of Albert Thomas and Marguerite (Williams) Fuller; married C. Marie Turtle (a teacher), May 31, 1947; children: Karen (Mrs. Richard E. Braun), James, Kathleen, Gordon. *Education:* University of Saskatchewan, B.A., 1946, M.A., 1947; University of Wisconsin, Ph.D., 1957. *Religion:* None. *Home:* 6552 112th St., Edmonton, Alberta, Canada T6H 4R2. *Office:* Department of Zoology, University of Alberta, Edmonton, Alberta, Canada T6G 2E9.

CAREER: Research biologist, Canadian Wildlife Service, 1947-59; University of Alberta, Edmonton, assistant professor, 1959-63, associate professor, 1963-67, professor of zoology, 1967—. *Member:* American Association for the Advancement of Science (fellow), American Society of Mammalogists, Canadian Society of Environmental Biologists, Arctic Institute of North America (fellow), Wildlife Society, Societas pro Fauna et Flora Fennica (foreign member), Sigma Xi.

WRITINGS: The Life of the Far North, McGraw, 1972.

* * *

FUNDABURK, Emma Lila 1922-

PERSONAL: Born December 14, 1922, in Luverne, Ala.; daughter of Albert Donlin and Lila (Douglass) Fundaburk. *Education:* Attended Alabama College (now University of Montevallo), 1940-42, and University of Mexico City, summer, 1942; George Washington University, A.B., 1944; Northwestern University, M.A., 1946; Ohio State University, Ph.D., 1963. *Home:* 225 Baldwin St., Bowling Green, Ohio 43402; and Luverne, Ala. 36049. *Office:* Department of Economics, Bowling Green State University, Bowling Green, Ohio 43403.

CAREER: U.S. State Department, Washington, D.C., economic analyst, 1944-45; Alabama Department of Industrial Relations, Montgomery, economic researcher and writer, 1946-48; University of Alabama Center, Montgomery, instructor in economics, 1947-48; Alabama Department of Planning and Economic Development, Montgomery, economic researcher and writer, 1948-49; Huntingdon College, Montgomery, instructor in economics, 1950; U.S. Office of Price Stabilization, Montgomery, district economist, 1951-52; accountant with Maxwell Air Force Base, Montgomery, 1952-53, and with Jefferson Standard Life Insurance, 1954; free-lance writer, 1955-57; Ohio State University, Columbus, instructor in economics, 1958-63; University of Hawaii, Honolulu, assistant economist at Economic Research Center and assistant professor of economics, 1963-66; Bowling Green State University, Bowling Green, Ohio, assistant professor, 1966-68, associate professor, 1968-76, professor of economics, 1977—.

MEMBER: American Economic Association, Eastern Economics Association, Midwest Economics Association, Ohio Academy of Science, Ohio Association of Economics and Political Science, Omicron Delta Epsilon. *Awards, honors:* First prize from National Tax Equality Association, 1946, for essay on taxation; book awards from Southeastern U.S. Library Association and Alabama Library Association, both in 1959, for *Sun Circles and Human Hands;* Alabama Pen Women award, 1959; Economics in Action Institute scholar, 1969; National Science Foundation scholar, 1970.

WRITINGS: Unemployment Compensation: History and Meaning, Alabama Department of Industrial Relations,

1947; (editor with Mary D. Foreman) *Sun Circles and Human Hands: Southeastern Indians, Arts and Industries,* privately printed, 1957; *Southeastern Indians: Life Portraits,* Scarecrow, 1959; *Parade of Alabama,* privately printed, 1960; *The Economic Complex of Kauai,* Economic Research Center, University of Hawaii, 1964; *Diversified Manufacturing in Kauai,* Economic Research Center, University of Hawaii, 1964; *The Garment Manufacturing Industry of Hawaii,* four volumes, Economic Research Center, University of Hawaii, 1965; *Garment Manufacturing on the Outer Islands,* Economic Research Center, University of Hawaii, 1966; *Reference Materials and Periodicals in Economics,* Scarecrow, Volume I, 1971, Volume IV, 1972; *Bibliography of the History of Economic Thought,* Volume I, Scarecrow, 1973; (with Thomas Davenport) *Art at Educational Institutions in the United States,* Scarecrow, 1974; (with Davenport) *Art in Public Places in the United States,* Bowling Green University Press, 1975; *Art in the Environment in the United States,* privately printed, 1976. Also author of *Guide to Location of Art in the United States.*

WORK IN PROGRESS: Four more volumes of *Reference Materials and Periodicals in Economics* and five additional volumes of *Bibliography of the History of Economic Thought,* for Scarecrow.

SIDELIGHTS: Emma Fundaburk has traveled and studied in Mexico, Europe, and the Soviet Union. She attended the Second International Conference of Economic Historians at Aix-en-Provence, France, 1962.

G

GALBREATH, Robert (Carroll) 1938-

PERSONAL: Surname is pronounced *Gal*-breth; born October 24, 1938, in Cincinnati, Ohio; son of Frank Hubert (a civil engineer) and Betty (Carroll) Galbreath; married Naomi Paster, June 5, 1964; children: Nicholas Paul. *Education:* University of Michigan, A.B. (with high honors), 1960, Ph.D., 1970; Harvard University, A.M., 1961. *Home:* 4217 North Woodburn St., Shorewood, Wis. 53211. *Office:* Honors Program, University of Wisconsin, Milwaukee, Wis. 53201.

CAREER: Bowling Green State University, Bowling Green, Ohio, 1965-70, began as instructor, became assistant professor of history, instructor in experimental studies, 1970-72; University of Wisconsin—Milwaukee, post-doctoral fellow at Center for Twentieth Century Studies, 1972-74, lecturer in history and English, 1973-74, coordinator of honors program, College of Letters and Sciences, 1974—. *Member:* Modern Language Association, American Academy of Religion, American Society for Psychical Research, Science Fiction Research Association (secretary, 1979-80), Phi Beta Kappa, Phi Eta Sigma. *Awards, honors:* Woodrow Wilson fellowship, 1960-61.

WRITINGS: (Editor and contributor) *The Occult: Studies and Evaluations*, Bowling Green University Popular Press, 1972. Contributor of articles and reviews to journals in his field of interest, including *Journal of Popular Culture, Journal of American Folklore, History of Religions, Political Theory, Book Forum, Science Fiction Studies, Journal of the American Society for Psychical Research, Bulletin of Bibliography, Journal of American History,* and *Extrapolation.* Contributor of papers to scholarly meetings. *Abstracts of Folklore Studies,* associate editor, 1966-75, bibliographical notes editor, 1966-68; advisory editor, *Journal of Popular Culture,* 1970-77, and *Book Forum,* 1974-77; associate editor, *Explorations: A Newsletter of Research into the Occult.*

WORK IN PROGRESS: Research on Hermann Hesse, Rudolf Steiner, science fiction, modern gnosticism, modern occultism and their cultural impact.

* * *

GALEWITZ, Herb 1928-

PERSONAL: Born July 9, 1928, in Brooklyn, N.Y.; son of Philip and Beckie (Bernstein) Galewitz; married Miriam Nodelman, July 1, 1962; children: Eve, Philip. *Education:* College of the City of New York (now City College of the City University of New York), B.B.A., 1956. *Home:* 143 North Parkway, Plainview, N.Y. 11803. *Office:* 299 Madison Ave., New York, N.Y. 10017.

CAREER: Pocket Books, Inc., New York City, sales administration, 1953-59; Golden Records, New York City, business manager, 1959-65; MGM Records, New York City, artists and repertoire producer, 1965-68; independent record producer and licensing agent, New York City, 1968—. *Military service:* U.S. Army, 1951-53. *Awards, honors:* Nominated for a National Academy of Recording Arts and Sciences "Grammy," 1969, for best record of a musical show in 1968, "You're A Good Man Charlie Brown."

WRITINGS: (Editor) *The Celebrated Cases of Dick Tracy,* Chelsea House, 1971; (editor) *Toonerville Trolley,* Scribner, 1972; (editor) *Great Comics of the New York News and Chicago Tribune,* Crown, 1972; (editor) *Bringing up Father,* Scribner, 1973; (editor) *The Gumps,* Scribner, 1974; (editor) *Dick Tracy: The Early Thirties,* Chelsea House, 1978.

WORK IN PROGRESS: A life of Rose O'Neill.

* * *

GARDNER, Eldon J(ohn) 1909-

PERSONAL: Born June 5, 1909, in Logan, Utah; son of John William and Cynthia (Hill) Gardner; married Helen Richards, August 21, 1939; children: Patricia (Mrs. Jerome L. Mahrt), Donald Eldon, Betty Ann (Mrs. George T. Morrison), Cynthia (Mrs. Stephen R. Pulley), Alice, Mary Jane (Mrs. Joseph M. Neville). *Education:* Utah State University, B.S., 1934, M.S., 1935; University of California, Berkeley, Ph.D., 1939, additional study, 1957-58; postdoctoral study at University of London, 1971. *Religion:* Church of Jesus Christ of Latter-day Saints (Mormon). *Home:* 369 North 500 East Street, Logan, Utah 84321. *Office:* Department of Natural Resources, 137 Biology, Utah State University, Logan, Utah 84321.

CAREER: Salinas Junior College, Salinas, Calif., instructor in biology and dean of lower division, 1939-46; University of Utah, Salt Lake City, assistant professor, 1946-47, associate professor of biology, 1947-49; Utah State University, Logan, professor of zoology, 1949-74, professor emeritus, 1974—, dean of College of Science, 1962-67, dean of School of Graduate Studies, 1967-74. Research professor of medical biophysics and computing, University of Utah, 1977—. Geneticist, Bureau of Plant Industry (Salinas, Calif.), 1943-46; U.S. Department of Health, Education and Welfare, member of scientific review and evaluation committees, 1967-71, chairman, 1969-71; member of Logan Board of Education, 1962-63.

MEMBER: American Society of Human Genetics (director, 1953-57; secretary, 1957-60; vice-president, 1961), Genetics Society of America, American Society of Naturalists, American Institute of Biological Sciences, American Association for the Advancement of Science, Western Society of Naturalists, Utah Academy of Sciences, Arts and Letters (president, 1969), Sigma Xi (chapter president, 1953-54), Phi Kappa Phi (chapter president, 1950-52). *Awards, honors:* Distinguished service award from Utah Academy of Sciences, Arts and Letters, 1957; Utah Science Teachers Award, 1967; Willard Gardner Science Award, 1975.

WRITINGS: Principles of Genetics, Wiley, 1960, 5th edition, 1975; *History of Biology,* Burgess, 1960, 3rd edition, 1972; *Genetics Laboratory Exercises,* Burgess, 1956, 5th edition, 1970; (with T. R. Mertens) *Genetics Laboratory Investigations,* Burgess, 1970, 6th edition, 1975; *Genetics of Cancer and Other Abnormal Growths* (monograph), Utah State Agricultural College, 1954; *Evolution and the Bible* (monograph), Utah State University, 1960; *Mechanics of Organic Evolution* (monograph), Utah State University, 1962. Chairman, *Rocky Mountain Science Council Newsletter,* 1970-72.

WORK IN PROGRESS: Genetic and cytological investigations of abnormal growths and cancer in Drosophila melanogaster and man since 1946; research project supported by the National Cancer Institute; 6th edition of *Principles of Genetics;* 4th edition of *History of Biology;* 7th edition of *Genetics Laboratory Investigations.*

* * *

GARLICK, Peter C(yril) 1923-

PERSONAL: Born March 7, 1923, in New Paltz, N.Y.; son of Cyril Givens (a civil servant) and Lilian C. (Keeton) Garlick; married Irma Fortune Moonie, August 10, 1960; children: Peter Nicholas, Sarah Helen. *Education:* University of Sheffield, B.A. (honors), 1949, Dipl.Educ., 1950, M.A., 1951; University of London, Ph.D., 1962. *Home:* 37 Center St., New Paltz, N.Y. 12561. *Office:* Department of African Studies, State University of New York, New Paltz, N.Y. 12561.

CAREER: University of Science and Technology, Kumasi, Ghana, lecturer in economics, 1952-57; University of Ghana, Accra, research fellow, 1957-62; University of New England, New South Wales, Australia, lecturer in economics, 1962-63; Howard University, Washington, D.C., assistant professor of economics, 1964-67; State University of New York at New Paltz, associate professor, 1967-70, professor of economics in department of African studies, 1970—. *Military service:* Royal Navy, 1942-46. *Member:* American Economics Association, African Studies Association, African Studies Association of the United Kingdom, Society for International Development, Royal Commonwealth Society, State University of New York African Studies Faculty Association (vice-chairman, 1968-70).

WRITINGS: African Traders in Kumasi, University of Ghana, 1959; *African Traders and Economic Development in Ghana,* Clarendon Press, 1971. Contributor to journals in his field.

WORK IN PROGRESS: Research in current economic affairs in Africa and recent African economic history.

* * *

GARVEY, Edward B. 1914-

PERSONAL: Born November 13, 1914, in Farmington, Minn.; son of Edward (a real estate dealer) and Mary M. (Bohan) Garvey; married Mary I. Quick, 1938; children: Dennis P., Daniel M., Kathleen M. (Mrs. Hector A. Menendez), Sharon H., Kevin Q. *Education:* Attended Mankato State College, 1932-34, and Marquette University, 1942-43. *Politics:* Democrat. *Religion:* Roman Catholic. *Home:* 1015 Parker St., Falls Church, Va. 22046. *Office:* Appalachian Outfitters, Oakton, Va. 22124.

CAREER: U.S. Department of Agriculture, Soil Conservation Service, various posts in Winona, Minn., Milwaukee, Wis., and Washington, D.C., 1935-58; National Science Foundation, Washington, D.C., finance officer, 1958-69. Assistant general manager, Appalachian Outfitters, Oakton, Va., 1971—. Outdoor recreation exhibits specialist, U.S. Information Agency, representative at International Trade Fair in Zagreb, Yugoslavia, 1972, and at exhibits in Skopje, Yugoslavia, Moscow and Irkutsk, USSR, all in 1973, representative at exhibit in Budapest, Hungary, 1974. *Member:* Federal Government Accountants Association, Appalachian Trail Conference (secretary, 1964-67; member of board of managers, 1964-72, 1977—; chairman of shelters committee, 1970—), Potomac Appalachian Trail Club (supervisor of trails, 1959-65; president, 1972-74).

WRITINGS: Appalachian Hiker: Adventure of a Lifetime, Appalachian Books, 1971 revised edition, 1978; *Hiking Trails in Mid-Atlantic States,* Great Lakes Living Press, 1976. Contributor to U.S. Department of Agriculture *Yearbook,* 1967 and 1974, and of articles relating to the Appalachian Trail to magazines.

WORK IN PROGRESS: Yugoslavian Wanderers.

SIDELIGHTS: Edward B. Garvey hiked the 2,000-mile Appalachian Trail from Georgia to Maine in 1970, starting on April 4 and completing the trip on October 7. In July and August of 1978, Garvey hiked through the Alps of Yugoslavia, Austria, and Italy.

* * *

GARZILLI, Enrico 1937-

PERSONAL: Born August 12, 1937, in Providence, R.I.; son of Frank (a baker) and Fannie (Parrillo) Garzilli. *Education:* Our Lady of Providence Seminary, B.A., 1959; Gregorian University, S.T.B., 1961, S.T.L., 1963; University of Rhode Island, M.A., 1967; Brown University, Ph.D., 1970. *Home:* 33 Vermont St., Cranston, R.I. 02920.

CAREER: Member of Roman Catholic secular priesthood, ordained, 1962; assistant pastor in Smithfield, R.I., 1963-64; Our Lady of Providence Seminary, Warwick, R.I., head of literature department, 1967-74; North American College, Vatican City, academic dean, 1974-78; professor at Gregorian University, Rome, Italy and Angelicon University, Rome, 1974-78. Special lecturer, Providence, R.I., 1979. *Member:* Modern Language Association of America, American Association of University Professors.

WRITINGS: Circles without Center, Harvard University Press, 1972; *Ashen Victors,* Blue Guitar, 1978.

WORK IN PROGRESS: A musical play, "Canticle"; a book on contemporary understanding of time in literature and philosophy.

SIDELIGHTS: Enrico Garzilli has given concerts in piano and organ in the United States and Rome, has composed musical settings for liturgy, and produced and directed plays. He knows Latin, Greek, Italian, French, and German. His poem, "Caro Santo Padre Sorridente," was read over national television during Pope John Paul I's funeral. It has since been translated into nine languages.

*   *   *

GASPARINI, Graziano 1926-

PERSONAL: Born July 31, 1926, in Venice, Italy; son of Luciano (owner of an estate and a businessman) and Anita Viola Gasparini; married Luise Margolies (an anthropologist), August 7, 1970; children: four. Education: University of Venice, B.A., 1948; University of Heidelberg, M.A., 1959; University of Venezuela, B.A., 1965. Residence: Caracas, Venezuela. Office: Apartado 3305, Caracas, Venezuela.

CAREER: Architect in Caracas, Venezuela, 1950—. Has designed restoration and conservation monuments in Caracas and other parts of Latin America. Professor of architecture and art history, University of Venezuela, 1955—, president of Consejo de Desarrollo Cientifio y Humanistio and director of Centro de Investigaciones Historicas y Esteticas of the University of Venezuela. Director of Patrimonio Historico, Artistico y Ambiental de la Nacion, 1974—. President of Venezuela Conseil International des Monuments et des Sites, 1968—. Consultant to UNESCO and Organization of American States.

MEMBER: Colegio de Arquitectos, Colegio de Ingenieros, Academy of Historians (Venezuela), Society of Architectural Historians, Association of Venezuela Writers. Awards, honors: Francisco de Miranda award, 1972, for outstanding architectural contributions in Venezuela; Jose Maria Vargas award, 1971, for outstanding teaching; diploma from Instituto Nacional de Culturas, Peru, for outstanding activity regarding preservation of national patrimony; several prizes for paintings.

WRITINGS: Templos coloniales de Venezuela, Ediciones "A" (Caracas), 1959, 3rd edition, Ediciones Armitano, 1976; La arquitectura colonial de Coro, Ediciones "A", 1961; Templos coloniales del estado Barinas, Ediciones "A", 1961; La casa colonial venozolana, Universidad Central de Venezuela, 1962; (with Mariano Picon Salas) Promesa de Venezuela, Ediciones de la Presidencia de la Republica (Caracas), 1964; La arquitectura colonial en Venezuela, Ediciones Armitano (Caracas), 1965; Venezuela: Monumentos Historicos y Arqueologicos, Edicion del Instituto de Geografia y Historia (Mexico), 1966; (with Jeannette Abouhamad) Amuay 64: su gente, su vivienda, Centro de Investigaciones Historicas y Esteticas, Universidad Central de Venezuela, 1966; (photographic illustrator) Guillermo Meneses, Muros de Venezuela, Ediciones Armitano, 1967; Restauracion de templos coloniales en Venezuela, Edicion del Ministerio de Justicia, Direccion de Cultos (Caracas), 1969; (with Juan Pedro Posano) Caracas a traves de su arquitectura, Edicion de la Fundacion Fina Gomez (Caracas), 1969; Caracas colonial, Centro Editor de America Latina (Buenos Aires), 1969; (with Isaac Chocron) Color Natural, Ediciones del Grupo Montana (Caracas), 1969; (with Frank Elgar) Poleo, Ediciones Armitano, 1970; (photographic illustrator) Alfredo Armas Alfonso, Que de recuerdos en Venezuela, Ediciones Armitano, 1970, English edition published as Memories of Venezuela, 1973; Los Retablos del Periodo Colonial en Venezuela, Ediciones Armitano, 1972; America:

Baroco y Arquitectura, Ediciones Armitano, 1972; (photographic illustrator) Pablo Neruda, Alturas de Macchu Picchu, Editorial Losada, 1972; (with Carlos Duarte) El Arte Colonial en Venezuela, Editoriale Arte, 1974; (with wife, Luise Margolies) Arquitectura Inka, Universidad Central de Venezuela, 1977; Caracas: La Ciudad Colonial y Guzmancista, Ediciones Armitano, 1978; Muros de Mexico (photographic essay), Celanese de Mexico, 1978. Contributor to scholarly journals, magazines, and newspapers. Editor, Boletin (of Centro de Investigaciones Historicas y Esteticas).

WORK IN PROGRESS: Norms of Conservation and Restoration; The Urban History of the Port City of La Guaira, Venezuela.

AVOCATIONAL INTERESTS: Photography, painting, travel (Latin America, Europe, United States, and Russia).

*   *   *

GAY-CROSIER, Raymond 1937-

PERSONAL: Born August 30, 1937, in Basel, Switzerland; son of Gaston and Alice (Huez) Gay-Crosier; married Ruth Spiess, July 13, 1963; children: Pascale Michele. Education: Studied at University of Basel, 1958-60, and Sorbonne, University of Paris, 1960-61; University of Berne, Ph.D., 1965. Home: 7717 Southwest 42nd Ave., Gainesville, Fla. 32601. Office: Department of Romance Languages, University of Florida, Gainesville, Fla. 32601.

CAREER: Lycee Louis-le-Grand, Paris, France, assistant in German literature, 1960-61; Lycee de Berthoud, Berne, Switzerland, professor of French and philosophy, 1962-66; Trent University, Peterborough, Ontario, assistant professor of French, 1966-67; University of Florida, Gainesville, associate professor, 1967-73, professor of French, 1973—. Military service: Swiss Air Force, 1961-62; became first lieutenant. Member: Modern Language Association of America, American Association of University Professors (president of chapter), Association des Amis d'Andre Gide, Malraux Society, South Atlantic Modern Language Association of America (member of executive committee, 1978-81). Awards, honors: Research grants from University of Basel, 1958, Trent University, 1966, and University of Florida, 1968, 1970, 1971.

WRITINGS: Les envers d'un echec: Etude sur le theatre d'Albert Camus, Minard, 1967; Religious Elements in the Secular Lyrics of the Troubadors, University of North Carolina Press, 1971; (editor) Albert Camus: 1970, University of Sherbrooke Press, 1971. Also author of "Albert Camus" series, Wissensehafte, 1975—. Contributor of about fifty articles and reviews to professional journals.

WORK IN PROGRESS: Towards a Heuristics of Irony, a consolidation and theoretical articulation of several former projects; an essay on Merleau-Ponty as a literary critic.

SIDELIGHTS: Raymond Gay-Crosier told CA: "As a critic I see myself not as the opponent or detractor of the creative author but as a professional reader pointing out empathetically the strengths and weaknesses of a textual message and its fabrication. Good critical and good creative writing are two sides of the same coin. Ultimately, my task as a critic is to demonstrate to the uninitiated reader the multiplicity of reading levels and depths, the fact that active reading amounts to writing, the correlation between literature and literacy."

*   *   *

GEIST, Robert John 1912-

PERSONAL: Born February 6, 1912, in Buffalo, N.Y.; son

of J. C. Otto (a tinsmith) and Katharine (Nill) Geist; married Margaret A. Story, June 5, 1937; children: Gretel G. Rutledge, Kathe B. *Education:* Cornell University, B.S., 1932; University of Missouri, M.A., 1934; University of Illinois, Ph.D., 1940. *Politics:* Democrat. *Home:* 947 Marigold, East Lansing, Mich. 48823.

CAREER: University of Missouri—Columbia, instructor in English, 1935-37; University of Illinois at Urbana-Champaign, instructor in English, 1937-42, 1945-47; Michigan State University, East Lansing, assistant professor, 1947-56, associate professor, 1956-61, professor of English, 1961-75, professor emeritus, 1975—. Visiting professor, University of the Ryukyus, 1957-60, 1964-66. *Military service:* U.S. Army Air Forces, 1942-45; became captain. *Member:* Modern Language Association of America, American Association of University Professors.

WRITINGS: (With Richard Summers) *Current English Composition,* Rinehart, 1951; (with Thomas A. Bledsoe) *Current Prose: A College Reader,* Rinehart, 1953; (with Hiroshi Yabiku and Yoshimitsu Narita) *English Pronunciation for Speakers of Japanese,* University of the Ryukyus, 1959, revised edition, 1965; (with Yabiku and Narita) *English Sentences for Speakers of Japanese,* University of the Ryukyus, 1959, revised edition, 1960; (with Seiki Kinjo and Okifumi Komesu) *English Reader for Okinawan Students,* Tuttle, 1961; *An Introduction to Language,* Macmillan, 1970; *An Introduction to Modern Grammar,* Macmillan, 1970; *A Short History of English,* Macmillan, 1970; *An Introduction to Transformation Grammar,* Macmillan, 1971. Co-author, "Macmillan Language Series," Volumes III, IV, V, and VI, 1967, 5th edition, 1973. Contributor to language journals.

*   *   *

GELDARD, Frank A(rthur) 1904-

PERSONAL: Surname is accented on both syllables; born May 20, 1904, in Worcester, Mass.; son of Arthur (manager of produce business) and Margaret Hardy (Gordon) Geldard; married Jeannette Manchester, June 20, 1928; children: Deborah Rea (Mrs. Wallace Emmett Tobin III). *Education:* Clark University, A.B., 1925, A.M., 1926, Ph.D., 1928. *Politics:* Democrat. *Home:* 551 Lake Dr., Princeton, N.J. 08540. *Office:* Department of Psychology, Princeton University, Princeton, N.J.

CAREER: University of Virginia, Charlottesville, associate professor, 1928-37, professor of psychology, 1937-62, director of Psychological Laboratory, 1928-60, chairman of department, 1946-50, dean of Graduate School of Arts and Sciences, 1960-62; Princeton University, Princeton, N.J., Stuart Professor of Psychology, 1962-72, professor emeritus and senior research psychologist, 1972—. Research chief, Human Resources Division, U.S. Air Force, 1949-50; chairman of human resources committee, Office of Secretary of Defense, 1950-56; chairman of military psychology committee and member of committee on international relations in psychology, National Research Council, 1953-59; member of committee on biological and medical sciences, National Science Foundation, 1953-59; scientific liaison officer, Office of Naval Research (London, England), 1956-57; chairman, North Atlantic Treaty Organization (NATO) advisory group on human factors, 1959-65; member of scientific advisory board, Delta Regional Primate Laboratory, 1964-71; member of board of directors, Psychological Corp., 1963-75; member of International Brain Research Organization (of UNESCO). Consultant to National Military Estab-

lishment. *Military service:* U.S. Army Air Forces, Office of Air Surgeon, commanding officer of psychological mission to Philippines and Japan, 1942-45; became colonel; received Legion of Merit. U.S. Air Force Reserve, 1946-57.

MEMBER: American Psychological Association (fellow; past president of divisions of experimental psychology and military psychology; member of board of directors), Psychonomic Society (president, 1965-66), Society of Experimental Psychologists, American Association for the Advancement of Science (fellow; past vice-president), Royal Society of Medicine (England; fellow), Phi Beta Kappa, Sigma Xi. *Awards, honors:* Sc.D., Washington and Lee University, 1969; Sc.D., Clark University, 1978.

WRITINGS: (Contributor) E. G. Boring, H. S. Langfeld, and H. P. Weld, editors, *Foundations of Psychology,* Wiley, 1948; (contributor) Leonard Carmichael and L. C. Mead, editors, *The Selection of Military Manpower,* National Academy of Sciences and National Research Council, 1951; *The Human Senses,* Wiley, 1953, 2nd edition, 1972; (contributor) W. A. Rosenblith, editor, *Sensory Communication,* Wiley, 1961; *Fundamentals of Psychology,* foreword by Boring, Wiley, 1962; (editor) *Defence Psychology,* Pergamon, 1962; *Communication Processes,* Pergamon, 1963; (contributor) D. R. Kenshalo, editor, *The Skin Senses,* C. C Thomas, 1968; (contributor) W. D. Neff, editor, *Contributions to Sensory Physiology,* Volume IV, Academic Press, 1970; (editor) *Cutaneous Communication Systems and Devices,* Psychonomic Society, 1974; *Sensory Saltation: Metastability in the Perceptual World,* Halsted, 1975; (contributor) T. A. Sebeok, editor, *How Animals Communicate,* Indiana University Press, 1978.

Author of technical reports. Contributor to proceedings and to *Encyclopedia of Science and Technology.* Contributor to professional journals and popular magazines, including *Saturday Review, American Journal of Psychology, Psychology Today, American Psychologist, Science,* and *Occupational Psychology.* Associate editor, *Journal of Perception and Psychophysics,* 1965-70; former consulting editor, *Contemporary Psychology, Journal of Psychology, Journal of Comparative and Physiological Psychology, Journal of Experimental Psychology,* and *Journal of Genetic Psychology.*

*   *   *

GELINAS, Paul J. 1911-

PERSONAL: Born July 17, 1911, in Woonsocket, R.I.; son of Edmond J. (an engineer) and Anna (Desaultnier) Gelinas; married Eva Jane MacFarlane, June, 1933; children: Robert P. *Education:* Acadia University, B.A., 1933; Columbia University, M.A., 1949; College of the City of New York (now City College of the City University of New York), M.Sc., 1950; New York University, Ed.D., 1954. *Politics:* Independent. *Religion:* Baptist. *Home:* 31 West Meadow Rd., Setauket, Long Island, N.Y. 11733.

CAREER: Reporter and feature writer, 1940-41; Setauket, N.Y. public schools, superintendent, 1942-60; adjunct professor of psychology at Adelphi University, State University's Long Island Center (now State University of New York at Stony Brook), Hofstra University, and Long Island University, 1942-60; psychologist in private practice, 1961—; writer, 1961—. *Military service:* National Guard, 1934-36. *Member:* National Education Association, New York State Psychological Association, Suffolk County Psychological Association. *Awards, honors:* The Paul J. Gelinas High School in Setauket, N.Y., was named in his honor.

*WRITINGS—*Mainly for young people: *The How and Why*

Wonder Book of Coins and Currency, Wonder Books, 1965; *So You Want to be a Teacher,* Harper, 1965; *Geography of the World for Young Readers,* Grosset, 1965; *History of the World for Young Readers,* Grosset, 1965; *Frightened Women,* Tower, 1967; *Teenagers and Their Hangups,* Richards Rosen, 1975; *Coping with Anger,* Richards Rosen, 1978.

With son, Robert P. Gelinas; all published by Richards Rosen: *Your Future in School Psychology,* 1968; *The Teenager and Psychology,* 1971; *How Teenagers Can Get Good Jobs,* 1971; *The Teenager in a Troubled World,* 1972; *Teenagers Look at Sex in Nature,* 1973.

WORK IN PROGRESS: The Teenager and Social Action; The Madness in All of Us; Getting a Job Is Easy When You Know How.

SIDELIGHTS: Paul J. Gelinas wrote *CA:* "Most of my writings have sprung from my desire to simplify and to make clear what is often hidden in scientific jargon. As a clinical psychologist, I have been fascinated with the popularization of the psychology, personality, and the motives of young people. Somehow, that seems more important to me than to engage in esoteric research largely for the benefit of other scientists."

* * *

GEORGE, Emery E(dward) 1933-

PERSONAL: Born May 8, 1933, in Budapest, Hungary; son of Larry H. (a tool designer) and Julianna (Deutsch) George; married Mary G. Weidenbeck (a librarian), 1969. *Education:* University of Michigan, B.A., 1955, M.A., 1959, Ph.D., 1964. *Office:* Department of German, 3142 Modern Languages Building, University of Michigan, Ann Arbor, Mich. 48104.

CAREER: University of Illinois at Urbana-Champaign, instructor, 1964-65, assistant professor of German, 1965-66; University of Michigan, Ann Arbor, assistant professor, 1966-69, associate professor of German, 1969-75, professor of German, 1975—. *Military service:* U.S. Army, 1955-58. *Member:* Modern Language Association of America, Poetry Society of America, International Poetry Society, International P.E.N., Authors' Guild of America, American Society for Aesthetics, Hoelderlin-Gesellschaft (Germany), University of Michigan Research Club, Spoon River Society. *Awards, honors:* Avery and Jule Hopwood Major Award for Poetry, 1960.

WRITINGS: (Editor) *Friedrich Hoelderlin: An Early Modern,* University of Michigan Press, 1972; (editor with L. T. Frank) *Husbanding the Golden Grain: Studies in Honor of Henry W. Nordmeyer,* Department of German, University of Michigan, 1973; *Hoelderlin's "Ars Poetica,"* Mouton, 1973; *Mountainwild* (poetry), Kylix Press, 1974; *Black Jesus* (poetry), Kylix Press, 1974; (translator) Miklos Radnoti, *Subway Stops: Fifty Poems,* Ardis, 1977; *A Gift of Nerve: Poems 1966-1977,* Kylix Press, 1978. Work is anthologized in *Lyrics of Love: A Treasury of Romantic Poetry,* Young Publication, 1972, *The Ardis Anthology of New American Poetry,* Ardis, 1977, *Shaping: New Poems in Traditional Prosodies,* Dryad, 1978. Contributor of translations to Willis Barnstone, editor, *Modern European Poetry,* Bantam, 1966; Anna Akhmatova, *Sochineniia tom vtoroi* (means "Works: Volume II"), Inter-Language Literary Associates, 1968; Aleksis Rubulis, editor, *Baltic Literature,* University of Notre Dame Press, 1970; *Hoelderlin's Ars Poetica,* Mouton, 1973. Contributor of poems, articles, and reviews to literature journals, including *Beloit Poetry Journal, Laurel*

Review, Literary Review, Saturday Review, Slavic Review, Language and Style, and *Modern Language Review.* Associate editor, *Russian Literature Triquarterly,* 1972—; founding editor, *Michigan Germanic Studies,* 1975-76; co-editor, *Frankfurter Hoelderlin-Ausgabe,* 1978—.

WORK IN PROGRESS: A book on Goethe's poetic language; three volumes of poems; translations of Hungarian poems; editing an anthology of contemporary American poetry and translations, with wife, Mary W. George.

SIDELIGHTS: Emery George writes *CA:* "By background I am both a European and an American; by training and inclination, both a scholar and a writer. In my academic profession—German language, literature, and culture taught at the university level—great emphasis is placed upon the missionary nature of our activity. In scholarship I aim at finding and training the exceptional student; in my writing, on the other hand, I hope to reach people everywhere. Despite widespread feeling among the best of us that, as one distinguished poet recently put it, everyone writes poetry and yet no one buys or reads it, I remain impressed by the number of people in all walks of life who do in fact read, and read perceptively."

BIOGRAPHICAL/CRITICAL SOURCES: Choice, December, 1972, March, 1978; *Cross Currents,* spring, 1973; *Monatshefte,* summer, 1975.

* * *

GERLACH, Luther P(aul) 1930-

PERSONAL: Born October 25, 1930, in Reading, Pa.; married Ursula M. M. Soelter, April 3, 1958; children: Douglas, Suzanne, Andrew. *Education:* University of Minnesota, B.A. (with honors), 1952; University of London, certificates in African and Islamic law, 1958, Ph.D., 1961. *Home:* 1879 Cloud Dr., Blaine, Minn. *Office:* Department of Anthropology, University of Minnesota, Minneapolis, Minn. 55455.

CAREER: University of Minnesota, Minneapolis, visiting lecturer in anthropology, 1961; Lafayette College, Easton, Pa., assistant professor of anthropology and sociology, 1961-63; University of Minnesota, assistant professor, 1963-65, associate professor, 1965-71, professor of anthropology, 1971—, director of human ecology program, 1964-67, member of Urban Affairs Center, 1968. Lecturer and consultant, National Endowment for the Arts, 1970-71; visiting associate in anthropology and environmental studies, 1971-72; senior consultant at Aspen Institute for Humanistic Studies, 1972-73; member of various task forces and committees of Upper Midwest Council, 1973—; member of State Department Energy Resources lecture team, 1974; consultant to Solar Energy Research Institute, 1978—; peer reviewer for Sandia Laboratory, 1978—. Photographer and producer of films, television series, and multi-media kits, including "People, Power, Change: A Study of Movements of Revolutionary Change," 1968, "Afro-American Insights," 1968, "People Eco-Action," 1970, "Zanj Africa," 1970, "Systems, Symbols and Change," 1971, "Winds of Change," 1971, "Jamaica: Why Don't You Stop and Say Hello?," 1973, "Systemic Thinking," 1974, "Trucker's Shutdown: Social Response to Resource Shortage," 1975, "Independence, Interdependence?," 1976, "Can Independence Survive Interdependence?," 1976, "They Say: A Report on Farmers' Attitudes," 1977, "Grassroots Energy," 1978. Also photographer and producer of a ten-program series on movements of revolutionary change, 1969, two films made in collaboration with *Encyclopaedia Britannica,* 1973, and a ten-program series paralleling and illustrating his book, *Lifeway Leap*, 1974. Lecturer for church and community organizations. Member of community information task force, Minneapolis Urban Coalition, 1968-69. *Military service:* U.S. Army Reserve, 1950-70, active duty, 1952-54; served in Japan and Korea; became major.

MEMBER: American Anthropological Association, Society for Applied Anthropology, American Association for the Advancement of Science, Visual Anthropology Society. *Awards, honors:* Fulbright fellowship for field research in Kenya, Tanganyika and Uganda, 1958-60; Office of International Programs grant, 1964; National Defense Education Act grant, 1965-68; Ferndale Foundation grant, 1966-68; Northwest Area Foundation grant, 1967—; Water Resources grant, 1969-72, 1976-79; Rockefeller Foundation grant, 1969-70.

WRITINGS: (Contributor) David Brokensha, editor, *Ecology and Economic Development in Tropical Africa*, Institute of International Studies, University of California, 1965; (contributor) L. Riddick Lynch, editor, *The Cross-Cultural Approach to Health Behavior*, Fairleigh Dickinson University Press, 1970; (contributor) Norman E. Whitten, Jr. and John F. Szwed, editors, *Afro-American Anthropology: Contemporary Perspectives*, Free Press, 1970; (with Virginia Hine) *People, Power, Change: Movements of Social Transformation*, Bobbs-Merrill, 1970; (contributor) Stanley M. Davis, editor, *Comparative Management*, Prentice-Hall, 1971; *Lifeway Leap: The Dynamics of Change in America*, University of Minnesota Press, 1973; (contributor) Irving Zaretsky and Mark Leone, editors, *Religious Movements in Contemporary America*, Princeton University Press, 1974; (contributor) Kenneth D. Wilson, editor, *Prospects for Growth: Changing Expectations for the Future*, Praeger, 1977; (contributor) Magorah Maruyama, editor, *Cultures of the Future*, Mouton, 1978. Also contributor to *Handbook of Organizational Design*, edited by William Starbuck and Paul C. Nystrom. Contributor to proceedings and bulletins. Contributor to *Encyclopaedia Britannica;* contributor to professional publications, including *Bio-Science, McCormick Quarterly, Anthropological Quarterly, Natural History, Spirit,* and *American Behavioral Scientist.*

WORK IN PROGRESS: Research on how movements of social protest affect and are affected by established institutions and cultural values; writing articles and a book.

*   *   *

GEROLD, Karl   1906-1973

August 29, 1906—February 28, 1973; German journalist, editor, and publisher. Obituaries: *New York Times,* March 1, 1973.

*   *   *

GERSON, Walter (Max)   1935-

PERSONAL: Born April 1, 1935, in Great Falls, Mont.; son of Max Charles (a farmer) and Ella (Clawiter) Gerson; married Stephanie Brown (an opera singer), September 1, 1962; children: Mark, Greer. *Education:* University of Montana, B.A., 1957, M.A., 1958; University of Washington, Seattle, Ph.D., 1963. *Residence:* Salem, Ore. *Office:* Department of Sociology, Willamette University, Salem, Ore. 97301.

CAREER: Washington State Census Board, Seattle, field representative, 1959-61; *Sociological Inquiry,* Seattle, Washington, circulation manager, 1960-62; Stanford University, Stanford, Calif., instructor in sociology, 1962-63; Uni-

versity of Minnesota, Minneapolis, assistant professor of sociology, 1963-67; University of Toronto, Toronto, Ontario, associate professor of sociology, 1967-73; Willamette University, Salem, Ore., professor of sociology and chairman of department, 1973—. Planned and broadcast a series of sociology courses on educational WTCA-Television, 1965-66, and a similar series on KUCM-Radio, 1967. Research consultant to U.S. Department of Agriculture, 1966, and Task Force on Mass Media and Violence, 1968-69. *Member:* American Sociological Association. *Awards, honors:* Research grant from University of Toronto, 1968-70, for studying a proposed theory of popular culture.

WRITINGS: (Contributor) Otto N. Larsen, editor, *Violence and the Mass Media,* Harper, 1968; (editor and contributor) *Social Problems in a Changing World: A Comparative Reader,* Crowell, 1969; (contributor) Mark Abrahamson, editor, *Readings on Sociological Concepts, Methods and Data,* Van Nostrand, 1970. Contributor to social science journals.

WORK IN PROGRESS: Mass Entertainment and Popular Culture; Neglected Social History; Mobile Occupations; Nostalgia, Collecting and Flea Markets: The Regeneration of America.

AVOCATIONAL INTERESTS: Railroad enthusiast, collecting materials on forms of popular culture (including comic books, brochures, magazines, newspapers, newspaper comic strips), baseball, and the American West.

*   *   *

GESCHWENDER, James A(rthur)   1933-

PERSONAL: Born November 30, 1933, in Niagara Falls, N.Y.; son of Elmer E. (a laborer) and Susie (Coty) Geschwender; married Barbara Ann Norbut, June 24, 1961; children: Laura. *Education:* State University of New York College for Teachers at Buffalo (now State University of New York College at Buffalo), B.S. (magna cum laude), 1955; Michigan State University, M.A., 1959, Ph.D., 1962. *Home:* 1517 Drexel Dr., Binghamton, N.Y. 13903. *Office:* Department of Sociology, State University of New York, Binghamton, N.Y. 13901.

CAREER: State University of New York College for Teachers at Buffalo (now State University of New York College at Buffalo), acting assistant professor of social studies, 1957-58; Florida State University, Tallahassee, assistant professor of sociology, 1962-64; Wayne State University, Detroit, Mich., assistant professor of sociology, 1964-68; University of Western Ontario, London, visiting associate professor of sociology, 1968-70; State University of New York at Binghamton, associate professor, 1970-71, professor of sociology, 1971—, chairman of department, 1971-75. *Member:* American Sociological Association, Society for the Study of Social Problems, Eastern Sociological Society.

WRITINGS: (Contributor) Herbert Hyman and Eleanor Singer, editors, *Readings in Reference Group Theory and Research,* Free Press, 1968; (with Benjamin D. Singer and Richard W. Osborn) *Black Rioters,* Heath, 1970; (editor and contributor) *The Black Revolt: Readings on the Civil Rights Movement, Ghetto Uprisings, and Separatism,* Prentice-Hall, 1971; *Race, Class and Worker Insurgency: The League of Revolutionary Black Workers* (monograph), Cambridge University Press, 1977; *Racial Stratification in America,* W. C. Brown, 1978. Contributor to symposia. Contributor to sociology journals, including *Sociological Inquiry, Social Forces,* and *Phylon.*

WORK IN PROGRESS: Research on evolution of tactics in Black revolt; student activism in Canada.

SIDELIGHTS: James Geschwender told *CA* that he is "one of a growing number of scholars who rejects the notion that good scholarship requires value neutrality and emotional detachment." Geschwender attempts to relate his research "to significant social concerns and is willing to combine scholarly research and social activism in the same endeavor."

*   *   *

GETHING, Thomas W(ilson)   1939-

PERSONAL: Born March 30, 1939, in Jackson, Mich.; son of Garrett C. and Laura E. (Wilson) Gething; married Judith R. Dean (a college teacher), August 25, 1962; children: Katherine L., Elizabeth D. *Education:* University of Michigan, B.A., 1961, M.A., 1963, Ph.D., 1966; postdoctoral study at Indiana University, 1964, and Yale University, 1964-65. *Home:* 514 Kekupua St., Honolulu, Hawaii 96825. *Office:* Department of Indo-Pacific Languages, University of Hawaii, Honolulu, Hawaii 96822.

CAREER: University of Michigan, Ann Arbor, assistant professor of Southeast Asian liguistics and languages, 1966-67; Ohio University, Athens, associate professor of linguistics, 1970-71; University of Hawaii, Honolulu, associate professor, 1967-77, professor of Southeast Asian linguistics and languages, 1977—. *Member:* Linguistic Society of America, Siam Society, American Oriental Society, Association for Asian Studies. *Awards, honors:* American Council of Learned Societies grant, 1964; Ford Foundation grant, 1965-66.

WRITINGS: Aspects of Meaning in Thai Nominals, Mouton, 1973; *Basic Thai Reader,* Korean Studies, University of Hawaii at Manoa, 1977. Contributor of articles and reviews to *Journal of Asian Studies, Journal of the American Oriental Society,* and *Modern Language Journal.*

WORK IN PROGRESS: Research on Thai linguistics.

SIDELIGHTS: Thomas Gething lived and travelled in Southeast Asia in 1965, 1972, and 1976.

*   *   *

GIACUMAKIS, George, Jr.   1937-

PERSONAL: Born July 6, 1937, in New Castle, Pa.; son of George and Stavroula (Pappas) Giacumakis; married Joan Elizabeth Gillies (a registered nurse), September 3, 1960; children: Stephen, Deborah, Mark, Andrew. *Education:* Shelton College, B.A., 1959; Brandeis University, M.A., 1961, Ph.D., 1963. *Politics:* Republican. *Religion:* Protestant. *Home and office:* Institute of Holy Land Studies, Mt. Zion, P.O. Box 1276, Jerusalem, Israel.

CAREER: California State University, Fullerton, assistant professor, 1963-68, associate professor, 1968-73, professor of history, 1973-79, head of department, 1972-75; Institute of Holy Land Studies, Jerusalem, Israel, president-elect, 1977-79, president, 1979—. Member of editorial board, Lockman Foundation. *Member:* American Scientific Affiliation, American Schools of Oriental Research, American Oriental Society, Middle East Studies Association, Near East Archaeology Society, Evangelical Theological Society, Phi Alpha Theta.

WRITINGS: The Akkadian of Alalah, Mouton, 1969.

GIANNONI, Carlo Borromeo   1939-

PERSONAL: Born July 26, 1939, in Chicago, Ill.; son of Natale (a restaurateur) and Lidwina (Curielli) Giannoni; married Janet Delia, August 3, 1963; children: Carla Marie, Deborah Carol. *Education:* University of Chicago, B.A., 1961; University of California, Berkeley, graduate study, 1961-62; University of Pittsburgh, M.A., 1963, Ph.D., 1966. *Home:* 2107 Addison Rd., Houston, Tex. 77025. *Office:* Department of Philosophy, Rice University, Houston, Tex. 77001.

CAREER: University of Texas at El Paso, assistant professor of philosophy, 1964-67; Rice University, Houston, Tex., associate professor of philosophy, 1967—. Visiting professor at Florida Agricultural and Mechanical University, 1968-69. *Member:* Philosophy of Science Association, American Association of University Professors, American Philosophical Association, Western Division.

WRITINGS: Conventionalism in Logic, Mouton, 1971.

WORK IN PROGRESS: Research on conventionalism in physics and the philosophy of special relativity.

AVOCATIONAL INTERESTS: Amateur radio (W5RYT).

*   *   *

GIBBS, John G(amble)   1930-

PERSONAL: Born August 25, 1930, in Asheville, N.C.; son of Robert S. (an electrical engineer) and Isabella (Gamble) Gibbs; married third wife, Karen Louise Johnson, December 31, 1972. *Education:* Davidson College, A.B., 1952; Union Theological Seminary, Richmond, Va., B.D. (now M.Div.), 1955, Th.M., 1958; University of Basel, additional study, 1955-56; Princeton Theological Seminary, Th.D. (now Ph.D.), 1966. *Home:* 442 Cedar Lane, Moorhead, Minn. 56560. *Office:* Department of Humanities, Moorhead State College, Moorhead, Minn. 56560.

CAREER: Clergyman of Presbyterian Church; pastor in South Carolina, West Virginia, and New Jersey, 1956-64; Princeton Theological Seminary, Princeton, N.J., research assistant, 1962-63; Macalester College, St. Paul, Minn., interim instructor in religion, 1964-65; Blake School, Hopkins, Minn., teacher of Latin, 1965-67; Moorhead State College, Moorhead, Minn., assistant professor, 1967-72, associate professor, 1972-78, professor of humanities, 1978—. Member of part-time graduate faculty, Ecumenical Institute, Concordia College, Moorhead, Minn., 1971—. Fellow of Institute for Ecumenical and Cultural Research, St. John's Abbey, Collegeville, Minn., 1973-74. *Member:* Studiorum Novi Testamenti Societas, Society of Biblical Literature, Red River Valley Theological Consortium.

WRITINGS: Creation and Redemption: A Study in Pauline Theology, E. J. Brill, 1971. Contributor of book reviews and articles to *Interpretation, Scottish Journal of Theology, Journal of the American Academy of Religion, Catholic Biblical Quarterly, Journal of Biblical Literature, Minneapolis Tribune, Christian Century, Presbyterian Survey, Novum Testamentum, Dialog, Enquiry,* and other periodicals. Also contributor to *International Standard Bible Encyclopaedia.*

WORK IN PROGRESS: Research in biblical and theological studies; proposed college-level anthology, *Perspectives on Ultimate Reality;* research of the religious history of the northern plains, history of the relation between concepts of creation and redemption; study of cosmic Christology, interdisciplinary humanities; grant supported study of myth and symbol.

GIBLIN, Charles Homer 1928-

PERSONAL: Born January 22, 1928, in Chicago, Ill.; son of Homer Michael and Jessie E. (Wruck) Giblin. *Education:* Loyola University, Chicago, A.B., 1950, M.A., 1952; West Baden College, S.T.L., 1959; Pontifical Biblical Institute, Rome, S.S.D., 1967. *Home:* Fordham University, Faber Hall, Bronx, N.Y. 10458. *Office:* Department of Theology, Fordham University, Collins Hall, Bronx, N.Y. 10458.

CAREER: Entered Roman Catholic Society of Jesus (Jesuits), 1945, ordained, 1958; Bellarmine School of Theology, Chicago, Ill., assistant professor of New Testament, 1963-66; Fordham University, New York, N.Y., assistant professor, 1967-69, associate professor of New Testament, 1969—. Visiting professor at Xavier University, Cincinnati, Ohio, 1967, 1968, University of San Francisco, 1972, and Ecole Biblique et archeologique Francaise, Jerusalem, 1974. *Member:* Catholic Biblical Association of America, Society of Biblical Literature, Society of New Testament Studies (Studiorum Novi Testamenti Societas).

WRITINGS: The Threat to Faith: An Exegetical and Theological Re-examination of 2 Thessalonians 2, Pontifical Biblical Institute, 1967; *In Hope of God's Glory: Pauline Theological Perspectives,* Herder & Herder, 1970; (contributor) W. C. Bier, editor, *Conscience: Its Freedom and Limitations,* Fordham University Press, 1971.

WORK IN PROGRESS: Research in theology of Matthew, Luke, and John.

* * *

GIBSON, Arrell Morgan 1921-

PERSONAL: Born December 1, 1921, in Pleasanton, Kans.; son Arrell Morgan (a miner) and Lorene (Davis) Gibson; married Dorothy Deitz, December 24, 1942 (divorced, April, 1971); children: Patricia Ann Butler, Michael Morgan, Kathleen Camille. *Education:* Joplin Junior College (now Missouri Southern State College), A.B.A., 1946; University of Oklahoma, B.A., 1947, M.A., 1948, Ph.D., 1954. *Politics:* Democratic. *Religion:* Protestant. *Home:* 909 Birch Dr., Norman, Okla. 73069. *Office:* Faculty Exchange, University of Oklahoma, Norman, Okla. 73069.

CAREER: Phillips University, Enid, Okla, assistant professor, 1949-51, associate professor, 1951-54, professor of history and government, 1954-57; University of Oklahoma, Norman, assistant professor, 1957-60, associate professor, 1960-64, professor of history, 1964-72, George Lynn Cross Research Professor, 1972—, chairman of department, 1964, 1970—, curator of Phillip's Collection and head of the university library's Division of Manuscripts, 1957-70, curator of history at Stovall Museum, 1959—. Visiting professor at Arizona State University, 1973-74, and University of New Mexico, summer, 1975; Montgomery Lecturer at University of Nebraska, 1978. Member of advisory board, Museum of the Great Plains, 1962—. *Military service:* U.S. Navy, 1942-46. *Member:* American Historical Association, Organization of American Historians, Southern Historical Association, Western Historical Association, Southwestern Social Science Association, Oklahoma Historical Society (member of board of directors, 1960—), Phi Alpha Theta, Phi Beta Kappa. *Awards, honors:* University of Oklahoma faculty research grants, 1957-71; Rockefeller Foundation University of Oklahoma Press award, 1961; American Philosophical Society research grants, 1963, 1969; Duke Foundation research grant, 1968, 1969; Oklahoma Writer of the Year, 1971, from University of Oklahoma School of Journalism; Distinguished Alumnus, 1972, Missouri Southern State College; Pulitzer Prize nominee, 1972, for *The Chickasaws;* American Association for State and Local History Award of Merit for *Wilderness Bonanza.*

WRITINGS: The Kickapoos: Lords of the Middle Border, University of Oklahoma Press, 1963; *Life and Death of Colonel Albert Jennings Fountain,* University of Oklahoma Press, 1965; *Oklahoma: A History of Five Centuries,* Harlow Publishing, 1965; *Fort Smith: Little Gibraltar on the Arkansas,* University of Oklahoma Press, 1969; *The Chickasaws,* University of Oklahoma Press, 1971; *Wilderness Bonanza,* University of Oklahoma Press, 1972; *Edward Everett Dale: Frontier Historian,* University of Oklahoma Press, 1975; *The West in the Life of the Nation,* Heath, 1976; *The Oklahoma Story,* University of Oklahoma Press, 1978. Contributor of articles on Western and Indian history to scholarly journals. Member of editorial advisory board, *Arizona and the West;* regional editor, *Journal of the West.*

WORK IN PROGRESS: Pacific Basin Frontier; The American Indian: Pre-History to the Present, for Heath.

* * *

GIBSON, James W(illiam) 1932-

PERSONAL: Born July 15, 1932, in Marysville, Ohio; son of James W. (a foreman) and Avalyn (Laird) Gibson; married Joanne McNamee, July 16, 1960; children: James, Jr., Matthew, Stephen, Timothy. *Education:* Otterbein College, B.A., 1954; Ohio State University, M.A., 1960, Ph.D., 1962. *Religion:* Roman Catholic. *Home:* Route 4, Columbia Mo. 65201. *Office:* Department of Speech and Dramatic Art, University of Missouri, Columbia, Mo. 65201.

CAREER: Butler University, Indianapolis, Ind., assistant professor of speech, 1962-66; University of Nebraska at Omaha, assistant professor of education, 1966-67; University of Missouri—Columbia, associate professor, 1967-70, professor of speech and dramatic art, 1970—. *Military service:* U.S. Army, 1954-56. *Member:* International Communication Association, American Psychological Association, Speech Communication Association, Central States Speech Association. *Awards, honors:* Outstanding Young Teacher Award from Central States Speech Association, 1967.

WRITINGS: (With George Lewis, Russell Everett, and Kathryn Schoen) *Teaching Speech,* C. E. Merrill, 1969; (editor) *A Reader in Speech Communication,* McGraw, 1971; *Speech Organization: A Programmed Approach,* Rinehart Press, 1971; (with Michael Hanna) *Audience Analysis,* Prentice-Hall, 1976; (with Clifton Cornwell) *Creative Speech,* Macmillan, 1979. Editor of *Central States Speech Association Journal,* 1970-73.

* * *

GIBSON, Janice T(horne) 1934-

PERSONAL: Born February 26, 1934, in Hartford, Conn.; daughter of Peter A. (a building constructor) and Marjorie (Greenberg) Thorne; married Robert H. Gibson, February 13, 1957 (divorced, 1970); married Eugene D. Vinogradoff, September 13, 1973; children: Robin Lynne, Mark Gregory. *Education:* University of Connecticut, A.B. (with honors), 1955; Brown University, M.S., 1957; University of Virginia, Ed.D., 1962. *Home:* 1825 Wightman St., Pittsburgh, Pa. 15217. *Office:* School of Education, University of Pittsburgh, Pittsburgh, Pa. 15260.

CAREER: University of Virginia, School of Medicine, Charlottesville, research psychologist, 1958-60, extern in psychology, 1960-61, Extension Division, instructor in psychology, 1959-63; University of Pittsburgh, Pittsburgh, Pa., assistant professor, 1962-68, associate professor of psychology, 1968-72, associate professor of education, 1968-72, professor of educational psychology, 1972—. Professor of psychology and education, Aegean School, Naxos, Greece, summers, 1977—. Fulbright professor in Greece, Yugoslavia, Bulgaria, Cyprus, and Israel, 1971-72. Program director and professor, Summer Program in Russia, National Endowment for the Arts, 1976. Research exchange scholar to Russia, National Academy of Sciences, 1976-77. Consultant, Allyn & Bacon, 1963, and Prentice-Hall, 1964.

MEMBER: International Education Research Association, American Psychological Association, Society for Research in Child Development, Regional Council for International Studies, Eastern Psychological Association, Pennsylvania Psychological Association, Pittsburgh Psychological Association, Kappa Delta Pi, Pi Lambda Theta. *Awards, honors:* Grant from Kennan Institute of Advanced Russian studies.

WRITINGS: (Contributor) Irving Berg and Bernard Bass, editors, *Conformity and Deviation,* Harper, 1961; (with Arthur J. Bachrach and Douglas K. Candland) *Arithmetic Tutor: A Programmed Textbook in Arithmetic,* Division of Educational Research, University of Virginia, 1961; *Effects of Programmed and Traditional Review on Learning,* U.S. Office of Education and U.S. Department of Health, Education and Welfare, 1965; *Educational Psychology: A Programmed Text,* with instructor's manual, Appleton, 1968, revised edition, 1972.

Educational Psychology: Revised Study Guide, New Century Educational Division, Meredith Corp., 1970; (editor) *Managing Learning in Urban Schools,* Appleton, 1972; (editor) *Teaching Parents Teaching,* Appleton, 1972; *Psicologia Educativa,* Trillas Publishing Co., 1974; *Psychology for the Classroom,* Prentice-Hall, 1976; *Growing Up: A Study of Children,* Addison-Wesley, 1978; (with Phyllis Blumberg) *Growing Up: Readings on the Study of Children,* Addison-Wesley, 1978. Editor, "Managing Learning in Urban Schools" series, Appleton, 1969—. Contributor of articles to education journals, including *Virginia Journal of Education, Contemporary Educational Psychology,* and *Journal of Educational Research.* Member of editorial board, *Contemporary Educational Psychology,* 1975—.

WORK IN PROGRESS: With husband, Eugene D. Vinogradoff, *Growing Up in Moscow;* revising *Psychology for the Classroom.*

SIDELIGHTS: Janice T. Gibson told *CA:* "I am a psychologist, and my writing to date has dealt with psychological issues. I find it much more exciting, however, to write books for the public to read than for students of psychology. My latest work, *Growing Up in Moscow,* is my first venture into the 'real world' of general readers. It has been a challenge to write in ways that people want to read when they don't have to. I'm sure that this has helped me in my role as professor. At the minimum, it has made me humble."

* * *

GIBSON, Richard (Thomas) 1931-

PERSONAL: Born May 13, 1931, in Los Angeles, Calif.; son of Clarence Louis and Alice (Thomas) Gibson; married Sarah Joy Kaye, March 24, 1956; children: Dominique, Frederick, Monique. *Education:* Attended Kenyon College, 1950-51, University of Rome, 1951-52, Sorbonne, University of Paris, 1955-56, Columbia University, 1961-62. *Home:* 32 Hartswood Rd., London W12 9NA, England. *Office:* Tricontinental Development Consultants, Rue St. Georges, Bte. 4, Brussels 1050, Belgium.

CAREER: Philadelphia Afro-American, Philadelphia, Pa., reporter, 1949-50; *Christian Science Monitor,* Mediterranean Bureau, Rome, Italy, reporter, 1951-52; *Agence France-Presse,* Paris, France, sub-editor, 1955-58; Columbia Broadcasting System, New York, N.Y., newswriter, 1960-61; *Revolution Africaine,* Algiers, Algeria, Lausanne, Switzerland, and Paris, France, editor, 1962-64; Negro Press International, London, England, correspondent, 1966-70; Tuesday Publications, Inc., London, England, international correspondent, 1970-76; overseas representative, International Art Associates, Ltd., 1976—. Director, Tricontinental Development Consultants, Brussels, Belgium. *Military service:* U.S. Army, 1952-54. *Member:* Association of American Correspondents in London, Association de la Presse Internationale of Brussels, Foreign Press Association, American Friends of China in Europe (secretary-treasurer, 1972—), Institute of Race Relations (London).

WRITINGS: A Mirror for Magistrates (novel), Anthony Blond, 1958; *African Liberation Movements,* Oxford University Press, 1972.

WORK IN PROGRESS: Research on the liberation struggles in Africa (especially Southern Africa), and the growing economic relationship between Europe, China, and Africa.

* * *

GIFFIN, Frederick Charles 1938-

PERSONAL: Born September 10, 1938, in Pittsburgh, Pa.; son of Frederick Sylvester (a business executive) and Sarah (Beam) Giffin; married Martha Knapp, October 30, 1959; children: Frederick Scott, Shawn Russell. *Education:* Denison University, B.A. (summa cum laude), 1960; Emory University, M.A., 1961, Ph.D., 1965. *Residence:* Tempe, Ariz. *Office:* Department of History, Arizona State University, Tempe, Ariz. 85281.

CAREER: Southern Methodist University, Dallas, Tex., assistant professor of history, 1964-67; Arizona State University, Tempe, associate professor, 1967-74, professor of history, 1974—, assistant dean of Graduate College, 1970-72, chairman of advisory board, Russian and East European Publications, 1977—. *Military service:* U.S. Marine Corps Reserve, 1958-64. *Member:* American Association for the Advancement of Slavic Studies, Phi Beta Kappa, Omicron Delta Kappa. *Awards, honors:* National Endowment for the Humanities fellow, 1970.

WRITINGS: (Editor with Ronald D. Smith) *Against the Grain: An Anthology of Dissent, Past and Present,* Mentor, 1971; *Woman as Revolutionary,* Mentor, 1973; *Six Who Protested: Radical Opposition to the First World War,* Kennikat, 1977. Contributor to *Slavic Review, Historian, European Studies Review,* and other professional journals.

WORK IN PROGRESS: The Death of Walter Krivitsky; The Kravchenko Affair; American Reactions to the Beilis Case.

* * *

GILBERT, Charles 1913-

PERSONAL: Born June 6, 1913, in London, England; son of Aaron and Ann (Swedlow) Gilbert; married Diane Freedenthal, January 1, 1960. *Education:* New York University, B.S., 1949, Ph.D., 1953; Pennsylvania State University, M.A., 1950. *Politics:* Independent. *Home:* 19 Barry Dr., Glen Cove, N.Y. 11542. *Office:* Hofstra University, Hempstead, N.Y. 11550.

CAREER: Wagner College, Staten Island, N.Y., instructor

in economics and finance, 1950-53; New York University, New York, N.Y., assistant professor of economics, 1953-58; University of Hartford, West Hartford, Conn., associate professor of economics and finance and chairman of department, 1958-60; Hofstra University, Hempstead, N.Y., professor of banking and finance, 1960—. *Member:* American Finance Association, Economic History Association (member of board of trustees), Business History Association.

WRITINGS: The Meaning of Profits, Institute of Economic Affairs, 1958; *American Financing of World War I,* Greenwood Press, 1970; (with Herman E. Krooss) *American Business History,* Prentice-Hall, 1972. Contributor to *Solicitor, Commercial and Financial Chronicle,* and other professional publications. Associate editor of *Journal of Economic History,* 1955-60.

*   *   *

GILBERT, Sandra M(ortola)   1936-

PERSONAL: Born December 27, 1936, in New York, N.Y.; daughter of Alexis Joseph (a civil engineer) and Angela (Caruso) Mortola; married Elliot Lewis Gilbert (a professor of English), December 1, 1957; children: Roger, Katherine, Susanna. *Education:* Cornell University, B.A., 1957; New York University, M.A., 1961; Columbia University, Ph.D., 1968. *Home:* 53 Menlo Pl., Berkeley, Calif. 94707. *Office:* Department of English, University of California, Davis, Calif. 95616.

CAREER: Queens College of the City University of New York, Flushing, lecturer in English, 1963-64, 1965-66; Sacramento State College (now California State University, Sacramento), lecturer in English, 1967-68; California State College (now California State University, Hayward), assistant professor of English, 1968-71; St. Mary's College, Moraga, Calif., lecturer in English, 1972; Indiana University at Bloomington, associate professor of English, 1973-75; University of California, Davis, associate professor of English, 1975—. *Member:* Modern Language Association of America.

WRITINGS: Shakespeare's "Twelfth Night," Thor Publishing, 1964; *Two Novels by E. M. Forster,* Thor Publishing, 1965; *D. H. Lawrence's "Sons and Lovers,"* Thor Publishing, 1965; *The Poetry of W. B. Yeats,* Thor Publishing, 1965; *Two Novels by Virginia Woolf,* Thor Publishing, 1966; *Acts of Attention: The Poems of D. H. Lawrence,* Cornell University Press, 1973; *In the Fourth World: Poems,* University of Alabama Press, 1978; (co-author) *The Madwoman in the Attic,* Yale University Press, 1979; (author and editor with Susan Gubar) *Shakespeare's Sisters: Feminist Essays on Women Poets,* Indiana University Press, 1979. Represented in anthologies, including *Best Little Magazine Fiction,* 1971, *Bicentennial Poetry Anthology,* 1976, *Contemporary Women Poets,* 1978, and *The Poetry Anthology,* 1978. Contributor of fiction and poetry to *Mademoiselle, Poetry, Epoch, Nation, New Yorker,* and other magazines.

WORK IN PROGRESS: Emily's Bread, a collection of poems; *The Madwoman in the Attic,* Volume II, with Gubar.

SIDELIGHTS: Sandra M. Gilbert told *CA:* "Although I write in three different genres—poetry, fiction, and criticism—and I'm often asked how I reconcile work in such 'contradictory' modes, I feel that I am always doing essentially the same thing. In some sense, I see myself as an interpreter of wonders, a reader of signs and portents, an analyst of texts and pretexts and contexts. Thus, whether I write a

poem, a critical essay, or a short story, I am always trying to see 'through' reality to the darker world (or the brighter one) behind appearances. . . ."

*   *   *

GILDZEN, Alex   1943-

PERSONAL: Born April 25, 1943, in Monterey, Calif.; son of Al (a machine operator) and Helen (Kovach) Gildzen. *Education:* Kent State University, B.A., 1965, M.A., 1966. *Home:* 1520 South Blvd., Kent, Ohio 44240. *Office:* University Libraries, Kent State University, Kent, Ohio 44242.

CAREER: Kent State University, Kent, Ohio, lecturer in English, 1966-70, assistant professor, 1970-77, associate professor of library administration, 1977—, assistant curator of special collections at university library, 1970-77. Member of board of trustees, Kent Acting & Touring Co. *Member:* Society of Cinephiles.

WRITINGS—Poems: *Into the Sea,* Abraxas Press, 1969; *December '70: Ohio,* Toucan Press, 1971; (editor) *Six Poems: Seven Prints,* University Libraries, Kent State University, 1971; *The Origin of Oregano,* Tarragon Graphics, 1971; *Twenty Sonnets Bound in Gold,* Killaly Press, 1972; (editor) *A Festschrift for Djuna Barnes on Her Eightieth Birthday,* University Libraries, Kent State University, 1972; *Funny Ducks,* Ghost Dance Press, 1973; *The Year Book,* North Atlantic Books, 1974; *Swimming,* Ground Zero, 1976; *New Notes: Poems 1971-76,* Shelly's Press, 1978; *Postcard Poems,* Viscerally Press, 1978. Contributor to *American Reference Books Annual.* Editor, *Toucan,* 1967-73; co-editor of *Serif: Quarterly of the Kent State University Libraries.*

WORK IN PROGRESS: Cat Scratches, a portfolio of poems and prints, with Linda Lyke; *Vanilla Angel,* a book of autobiographical poems.

*   *   *

GILL, Richard   1922-

PERSONAL: Born May 5, 1922, in New York, N.Y.; son of Sidney Lionel and Anne (Clarke) Gill. *Education:* New York University, B.A. (cum laude), 1947; Columbia University, M.A., 1948, Ph.D. (with distinction), 1966. *Residence:* New York, N.Y. *Office:* Department of English, Pace University, Pace Plaza, New York, N.Y. 10038.

CAREER: State University of New York College for Teachers (now State University of New York College at Buffalo), instructor in English, 1950-51; Clarkson College of Technology, Potsdam, N.Y., instructor in liberal studies, 1951-52; Pace University, New York City, professor of English, 1954—. *Military service:* U.S. Army, 1943-45; served in European theater; received Purple Heart. *Member:* Modern Language Association of America, Phi Beta Kappa.

WRITINGS: Happy Rural Seat: The English Country House and the Literary Imagination, Yale University Press, 1972; (editor with Ernest Sherman) *The Fabric of Existentialism: An Anthology of Philosophy and Literature,* Appleton, 1973. Contributor to *Twentieth Century Literature, Saturday Review,* and *Literature/Film Quarterly.*

WORK IN PROGRESS: A comparative study of the nineteenth-century novel.

SIDELIGHTS: Richard Gill has traveled and studied in England and Ireland.

GILLEN, Mollie 1908-

PERSONAL: Born November 1, 1908, in Sydney, Australia; daughter of Robert Edmund (a physician) and Bertha (Youdale) Woolnough; children: Ian Richard, Barbara Clare. *Education:* University of Sydney, B.A., 1930. *Address:* c/o Royal Bank of Canada, 2 Cockspur St., London SW1Y 5BQ, England.

CAREER: Copywriter in Sydney, Australia, 1937; secretary and office manager in England and Scotland, 1938-40; Ministry of Food, London, England, office manager, 1940-41; Department of Public Works, Ottawa, Ontario, information officer, 1957-60; Department of Northern Affairs, Ottawa, editor of *North,* 1960-62; Maclean-Hunter Ltd., Toronto, Ontario, associate editor of *Chatelaine,* 1963-74. Has lectured on fiction writing at Carleton University's Extension Department, and at Metro Toronto Adult Education Department. *Awards, honors:* Medal from University of Western Ontario for "The Masseys," an article appearing in *Chatelaine,* 1965; Canada Council grant, 1967, for *The Prince and His Lady,* and 1972, for *Royal Duke.*

WRITINGS: Star of Death (mystery fiction), Geoffrey Bles, 1960; *The Masseys: Founding Family,* Ryerson, 1965; *The Prince and His Lady,* Sidgwick & Jackson, 1970, St. Martin's, 1971; *Assassination of the Prime Minister,* Sidgwick & Jackson, 1972, St. Martin's, 1973; *The Wheel of Things: A Biography of L. M. Montgomery, Author of Anne of Green Gables,* Fitzhenry & Whiteside, 1975, abridged text edition published as *L. M. Montgomery,* 1978; *Royal Duke,* Sidgwick & Jackson, 1976. Contributor of stories to *Saturday Evening Post, Ladies' Home Journal, Farm Journal,* and British, Australian, and European magazines; contributor of articles to *Ottawa Citizen, History Today,* and other journals.

WORK IN PROGRESS: Historical research.

AVOCATIONAL INTERESTS: Travel, including a trip to the Arctic Circle.

* * *

GILLIN, John P(hilip) 1907-1973

PERSONAL: Born August 1, 1907, in Waterloo, Iowa; son of John Lewis (a sociologist) and Etta (Shaffner) Gillin; married Helen Norgord, March 29, 1934; children: John Christian. *Education:* University of Wisconsin, B.A., 1927, M.A., 1930; Harvard University, A.M., 1931, Ph.D., 1934. *Religion:* Unitarian Universalist. *Home:* 1115 Sourwood Dr., Chapel Hill, N.C. 27514.

CAREER: Harvard University, Peabody Museum, Cambridge, Mass., member of staff, 1934-35; University of Utah, Salt Lake City, assistant professor of anthropology and curator, 1935-36; Ohio State University, Columbus, assistant professor of anthropology and curator, 1936-41; Duke University, Durham, N.C., associate professor of anthropology, 1941-46; University of North Carolina at Chapel Hill, professor of anthropology, 1946-59; University of Pittsburgh, Pittsburgh, Pa., dean of social sciences, 1959-63, research professor of anthropology, 1963-72; National Institute for Mental Health, research professor of anthropology, 1962-72. Anthropological field work in Algeria and Europe, 1930, New Mexico, 1931, British Guiana, 1932-33, Ecuador and Peru, 1934-35, Utah, 1936-37, Wisconsin, 1938-39, Guatemala, 1942, 1946, 1948, Peru, 1944-45, Cuba, 1948, and various parts of Latin America and Europe, 1958-73. Import-export officer for Board of Economic Welfare, U.S. Embassy (Lima, Peru), 1942-44; representative in Peru,

Smithsonian Institution, 1944-45. Fellow, Center for the Advanced Study of the Behavioral Sciences, 1954-55.

MEMBER: American Anthropological Association (member of executive board, 1944-45; president, 1965-66), Society for Applied Anthropology (president, 1959-60), American Association for the Advancement of Science (fellow), Sigma Xi, Phi Beta Kappa, Phi Kappa Phi, Alpha Kappa Delta.

WRITINGS: The Barama River Caribs of British Guiana, Peabody Museum, Harvard University, 1936, reprinted, Kraus Reprint, 1967; *The Quichua-Speaking Indians of the Province of Imbabura, Ecuador and Their Anthropometric Relations with the Andean Area,* Bureau of American Ethnology, 1941; *Archaeological Investigations in Central Utah,* Peabody Museum, Harvard University, 1941, reprinted, Kraus Reprint, 1967; (with father, J. L. Gillin) *An Introduction to Sociology,* Macmillan, 1942, revised edition published as *Cultural Sociology,* Macmillan, 1948; *Moche: A Peruvian Coastal Community,* Institute of Applied Anthropology, Smithsonian Institution, 1947, reprinted, Greenwood Press, 1973; *The Ways of Men,* Appleton, 1948; *The Culture of Security in San Carlos,* Tulane University, 1951; (editor and contributor) *For a Science of Social Man,* Macmillan, 1954; *Archaeological Investigations in Nine Mile Canyon, Utah: A Republication,* University of Utah, 1955; (editor) *Human Ways: Selected Essays in Anthropology,* University of Pittsburgh Press, 1969; *Both Human and Humane,* University of Pennsylvania, 1960.

WORK IN PROGRESS: Tales from the Guiana Woods and Elsewhere, a book of memoirs.†

(Died August 4, 1973)

* * *

GILLIS, Everett A(lden) 1914-

PERSONAL: Born March 4, 1914, in Cameron, Mo.; son of Earle Adrien (a postal clerk) and Pearle (Owens) Gillis; married Lizzie Mae Allen, August 14, 1943 (died May 25, 1978). *Education:* Texas Christian University, B.A., 1936, M.A., 1939; University of Texas, Ph.D., 1948; University of California, Los Angeles, additional study, 1955-56. *Politics:* Democrat. *Religion:* Baptist. *Home:* 3209 26th St., Lubbock, Tex. 79410. *Office:* Department of English, Texas Tech University, Lubbock, Tex. 79409.

CAREER: University of Texas at Austin, instructor in English, 1940-42; Texas College of Arts and Industries (now Texas A&I University), Kingsville, assistant professor of English, 1947-49; Texas Tech University, Lubbock, associate professor, 1949-55, professor of English, 1956—, chairman of department, 1964-69. *Military service:* U.S. Army, Field Artillery, 1942-46.

MEMBER: Modern Language Association of America, National Council of Teachers of English, National Writers Club, American Folklore Society, International Poetry Society (fellow), Poetry Society (London), South Central Modern Language Association, Southwestern American Literature Association (president, 1970), Texas Association of College Teachers, Poetry Society of Texas (life member; vice-president, 1951; councillor, 1952—), Texas Folklore Society (vice-president, 1960; president, 1961), Texas Institute of Letters.

AWARDS, HONORS: Silver Spur Award from Texas Border Poets, 1948, for "Portrait of a Professor"; Ford Foundation fellowship, 1955-56.

All from the Poetry Society of Texas: Alamo Prize, 1945, for

"Growth of the Violin"; Texas Prize, 1946, for "Parson John," and 1951, for "Ballad of Captain Bill McDonald"; Critics Award Prize, 1947, for "Speech Beyond Speech," and 1948, for "The Hunter: An Autumn Metaphor"; Portrait Poem Prize, 1952, for "The Water Finder"; Old South Prize, 1953, for "Estevanico the Black Seas Cibola," 1958, for "Seascape: Santa Monica Palisades," and 1973, for "The Door"; All State Prize, 1955, for "Memories."

WRITINGS: Hello the House! (poems), Kaleidograph, 1944; *Who Can Retreat?* (poems), Wagon and Star, 1944; *Sunrise in Texas* (poems), Fotolith, 1949; *Angles of the Wind* (poems), Kaleidograph, 1954; *Sing Your America: Discussion Leader's Guide,* Adult Education Department, Texas Tech University, 1954; (with Joseph Doggett and Rosa Bludworth) *A College Forum* (textbook), Odyssey, 1963; *Ballads for Texas Heroes* (songs; music by John Q. Anderson), privately printed, 1963; *Oliver La Farge,* Steck, 1967; *"The Waste Land" As Grail Romance: Eliot's Use of the Medieval Grail Legends,* Texas Tech University Press, 1974; (author of introduction) Oliver La Farge, *The Enemy Gods,* University of New Mexico Press, 1976. Composer of choral work, "West Texas Suite," commissioned by Lubbock Public Schools. Contributor to literature journals, including *South Atlantic Quarterly, Prairie Schooner, Western Folklore, Southwestern American Literature,* and *Descant.*

WORK IN PROGRESS: The Cowboy and His Songs, with Jack Wages; *John A. Lomax's Cowboy Songs and Other Frontier Ballads: A Critical Listing,* with Wages and Lawrence Clayton, completion expected in 1980; *West Texas Proverbs and Superstitions,* with Kenneth W. Davis, 1980; *Far Beyond Distance,* a collection of poems; *Heart Singly Vowed,* a collection of memorial sonnets.

BIOGRAPHICAL/CRITICAL SOURCES: Lola Beth Green and Dahlia Terrell, editors, *Gold Land: A Bibliography,* Texas Tech University Press, 1970.

*   *   *

GILLMOR, Donald M(iles) 1926-

PERSONAL: Born April 27, 1926, in Fort Frances, Ontario, Canada; son of Ralph H. (a mechanic and merchant) and Margaret (McLeod) Gillmor; married Sophie Anastasia Kryzanowski, August 31, 1949; children: Vivian Ellen (Mrs. Derek R. Cathcart), Peter Ralph. *Education:* University of Manitoba, B.A., 1949; University of Minnesota, M.A., 1950, Ph.D., 1961. *Home:* 2016 North Wheeler St., St. Paul, Minn. 55113. *Office:* 34 Murphy Hall, University of Minnesota, Minneapolis, Minn. 55455.

CAREER: Winnipeg Free Press, Winnipeg, Manitoba, reporter, 1950-53; University of North Dakota, Grand Forks, assistant professor, 1952-56, associate professor, 1956-63, professor of journalism, 1963-65, director of University Honors Program, 1961-65; University of Minnesota, Minneapolis, professor of journalism, 1965—, director of graduate studies, 1965-72. *Military service:* Royal Canadian Air Force, 1943-45. *Member:* American Association of University Professors (president of Twin Cities chapter, 1970-71), Association for Education in Journalism (chairman of law division, 1974-75), Fair Trial-Free Press Council of Minnesota (vice-president, 1970-72). *Awards, honors:* University of North Dakota distinguished teacher award, 1958; runner-up, Sigma Delta Chi Award for distinguished research in journalism, 1967; Frank Luther Mott/Kappa Tau Alpha Award for research in journalism, 1970; Minnesota Press Club distinguished teaching award, 1975 and 1978.

WRITINGS: Free Press and Fair Trial, Public Affairs Press, 1966; *Mass Communication Law: Cases and Comment,* West Publishing, 1969, 3rd edition, 1979; (contributor) Frederick Wirt and Willis Hawley, editors, *New Dimensions of Freedom in America,* Chandler Publishing, 1969; *Judicial Restraints on the Press,* Freedom of Information Foundation, 1974; (contributor) Steven Chaffee, editor, *Political Communication Issues and Strategies for Research,* Sage Publications, Inc., 1976; (contributor) L. S. Harms and Jim Richstad, editors, *Evolving Perspectives on the Right to Communicate,* East-West Center, 1977; (with Everette Dennis and Arnold Ismach) *Enduring Issues in Mass Communication,* West Publishing, 1978; (with David Grey and Dennis) *Hugo L. Black and the First Amendment,* Iowa State University Press, 1978; (contributor) Bruce Westley and Guido Stempel III, editors, *Research Methods in Mass Communication,* Prentice-Hall, 1979.

WORK IN PROGRESS: Research on law and economics of mass communication.

*   *   *

GINANDES, Shepard 1928-

PERSONAL: Born June 7, 1928, in New York, N.Y.; son of Elias A. (an optometrist) and Esther (Welinsky) Ginandes; married Lois Condon (a dancer and choreographer), December 27, 1949 (died, 1975); married Sheila Hamilton (a yoga teacher and women's counselor), 1976; children: (first marriage) David, Clifford, Nicholas, Paul. *Education:* Harvard University, B.A., 1948, M.D., 1951. *Religion:* Yogi. *Home address:* P.O. Box 93, Kingshill, St. Croix, U.S. Virgin Islands 00850.

CAREER: Licensed to practice medicine in Massachusetts and Hawaii; Boston University, Boston, Mass., assistant professor of adolescent psychiatry, 1968-72; The School We Have, Concord, Mass., director, beginning 1968. *Military service:* U.S. Army, 1953-55; became first lieutenant. *Member:* American Psychiatric Association.

WRITINGS: The School We Have, Seymour Lawrence, 1973; *Coming Home: How Parents and Grown Children Can Confront Each Other More Openly, Communicate More Freely, and Become Friends,* Delacorte, 1976. Editor, "Living and Loving" (KHET-TV series), 1966.

*   *   *

GITTINGER, J(ames) Price

PERSONAL: Born in Berkeley, Calif.; married Mattiebelle Stimson (an art historian), 1954. *Education:* University of California, Davis, B.S., 1949; Iowa State University, Ph.D., 1955. *Office:* International Bank for Reconstruction and Development, 1818 H St. N.W., Washington, D.C. 20433.

CAREER: U.S. International Cooperation Administration, Washington, D.C., agricultural economist, 1955-60; Harvard Advisory Group, Plan Organization of Iran, Tehran, agricultural economist, 1961-62; National Planning Association, Agricultural Development Council, Washington, D.C., associate, 1962-65; National Planning Association, Center for Development Planning, Washington, D.C., associate director, 1965-66; International Bank for Reconstruction and Development, Economic Development Institute, Washington, D.C., agricultural economist, 1966—. *Member:* American Economic Association, American Agricultural Economics Association, Society for International Development.

WRITINGS: Planning for Agricultural Development: The Iranian Experience, National Planning Association, 1965; *The Literature of Agricultural Planning,* National Planning Association, 1966; *North American Agriculture in a New World,* National Planning Association, 1970; *Economic Analysis of Agricultural Projects,* Johns Hopkins Press, 1972; (editor) *Compounding and Discounting Tables for Project Evaluation,* Johns Hopkins Press, 1973.

WORK IN PROGRESS: A revised edition of *Economic Analysis of Agricultural Projects.*

* * *

GLADE, William P(atton), Jr. 1929-

PERSONAL: Born July 29, 1929, in Wichita Falls, Tex.; son of William Patton and Billie (Hatcher) Glade; married Marlene Joseph, July 10, 1954; children: Anita, Genie, Patton, John. *Education:* University of Texas, B.B.A., 1950, M.A., 1951, Ph.D., 1955. *Residence:* Austin, Tex. *Office:* Institute of Latin American Studies, Sid Richardson Hall-Unit I, University of Texas, Austin, Tex. 78712.

CAREER: University of Maryland, College Park, instructor, 1957-58, assistant professor of economics, 1958-60; University of Wisconsin—Madison, assistant professor, 1960-63, associate professor, 1963-66, professor of business and economics, 1966-71; University of Texas at Austin, professor of economics, 1970—, Institute of Latin American Studies, associate director, 1970-71, director, 1971—. *Member:* Latin American Studies Association (member of executive council, 1974-76; vice-president, 1978; president, 1979), American Economic Association, Association for Evolutionary Economics, Council for International Exchange of Scholars, Midwest Association for Latin American Studies (vice-president, 1961-62; president, 1962-63), Southwest Council of Latin American Studies, Cosmos Club.

WRITINGS: (With C. W. Anderson) *Two Studies of the Political Economy of Mexico,* University of Wisconsin Press, 1963; *The Latin American Economies: A Study of Their Institutional Evolution,* Van Nostrand, 1969; (with Jon Udell, James Littlefield, and William Strang) *Marketing in a Developing Economy: The Case of Peru,* Heath Lexington Books, 1970. Contributor to *Journal of Economic Issues, Journal of Inter-American Studies, Inter-American Economic Affairs, Economic Development and Cultural Change, Explorations in Entrepreneurial History,* and *Revista de Integracion.*

* * *

GLADISH, David F(rancis) 1928-

PERSONAL: Born March 18, 1928, in Chicago, Ill.; son of David Francis and Eleanor (Lindrooth) Gladish; married Shirley Glebe (a teacher), May 17, 1951; children: Frances, Frea, Andrew. *Education:* Attended University of Illinois, Chicago campus (now University of Illinois at Chicago Circle), 1946-47, and College of the Academy of the New Church, Bryn Athyn, Pa., 1947-48; Lake Forest College, B.A., 1950; University of Illinois, M.A., 1954, Ph.D., 1961. *Residence:* St. James, Mich. 49782.

CAREER: Franklin College of Indiana, Franklin, assistant professor, 1961-63, associate professor, 1964-67, professor of English, 1968-72. WFCI-Franklin, producer of "The Pais-Lis Prince," a ten-part comedy drama, 1971. *Military service:* U.S. Army, 1950-52. *Member:* Modern Language Association of America, Renaissance Society of America,

Phi Sigma Iota, Alpha (Franklin College). *Awards, honors:* Second prize in Indiana Sesquicentennial state poetry contest, 1967.

WRITINGS: (Editor) William Davenant, *Gondibert,* Oxford University Press, 1971; *All in Favor Say Island!,* Whiskey Point Press, 1975; *About Thirty Animals,* Whiskey Point Press, 1977. Poems represented in anthologies, including *I Love You All Day, It Is That Simple: Modern Poems of Love and Marriage,* edited by Philip Dacey and Gerald M. Knoll, Abbey Press, 1970, and *Since Feeling Is First,* edited by Mecklenburger and Simmons, Scott, Foresman, 1971. Contributor of poems to *Accent* and *Epos,* and of travel feature articles to *Franklin Star, Grand Rapids Press,* and *Charlevoix County Press.*

WORK IN PROGRESS: A free-verse translation of *Beowulf* into modern English; *What a Song Can Do,* a book of fables in verse form; designing a series of film scripts on literary techniques and their correspondence to techniques of other art forms; *How to Get Out On a Limb: The Practical Techniques of Tree Surgery; A Hole in the Wind,* the sights, sounds, and personality of a small town, in verse; *The Kit Came Crated,* fifty poems; *You Can Get There from Here: The Old Testament and Other Great Books,* about a new way to read the Old Testament.

* * *

GLASRUD, Bruce (Alden) 1940-

PERSONAL: Born September 20, 1940, in Plainview, Minn.; son of Leslie E. (a businessman) and Margaret (Rud) Glasrud; married Pearlene Vestal, October 17, 1964. *Education:* Luther College, B.A., 1962; Eastern New Mexico University, M.A., 1963; Texas Tech University, Ph.D., 1969. *Politics:* Liberal. *Religion:* Lutheran. *Home:* 21258 Birch St., Hayward, Calif. 94541. *Office:* Department of History, California State University, Hayward, Calif. 94542.

CAREER: Texas Lutheran College, Seguin, instructor in history, 1964-65; California State University, Hayward, assistant professor, 1968-73, associate professor, 1973-78, professor of history, 1978—, chairman of department, 1977—. *Member:* Organization of American Historians, American Studies Association, Southern Historical Association, Western History Association, Texas State Historical Association, United Professors of California.

WRITINGS—Editor: (with Alan M. Smith) *Promises to Keep: Portrayal of Nonwhites in the United States,* Rand McNally, 1972; (with James A. Halseth) *The Northwest Mosaic: Minority Conflicts in Pacific Northwest History,* Pruett, 1977; (with Smith) *Race Relations in British North America, 1607-1763,* Nelson-Hall, in press. Contributor to *Journal of the West, Mid-America, Southwestern Historical Quarterly, Pacific Historical Review, Canadian Review of Studies in Nationalism, American Studies, East Texas Historical Journal, North American Mentor, Red River Valley Historical Review,* and numerous other periodicals and journals.

WORK IN PROGRESS: Blacks in White Texas.

* * *

GLASSNER, Martin Ira 1932-

PERSONAL: Born July 7, 1932, in Plainfield, N.J.; married Renee Gewirtzman (a high school teacher); children: Karne Aline, Aleta Bonny, Cindy Miriam. *Education:* Syracuse University, B.A., 1953; California State College (now University), Fullerton, M.A., 1964; Claremont Graduate School, Ph.D., 1968; also studied at Columbia University, University of Wisconsin, George Williams College, and University of the Americas; postdoctoral study at Baldwin-Wallace College, summer, 1970, and Yale University, 1970-71. *Home:* 742 Paradise Ave., Hamden, Conn. 06514. *Office:* Department of Geography, Southern Connecticut State College, New Haven, Conn. 06515.

CAREER: Lincoln-Chicago Boys' Club, Chicago, Ill., program director, 1957; Glassner's Department Store, Cliffside Park, N.J., manager, 1957-58; U.S. Department of State, exchange program officer in Washington, D.C., 1958-60, vice-consul in Kingston, Jamaica, 1960-62, vice-consul in Antofagasta, Chile, 1962-63; Chapman College, Orange, Calif., lecturer in political science, 1964-65; California State Polytechnic College (now University), Pomona, instructor, 1965-66, assistant professor of social sciences, 1966-67; University of Puget Sound, Tacoma, Wash., assistant professor of political science, 1967-68; Southern Connecticut State College, New Haven, assistant professor, 1968-77, associate professor of geography, 1977—, acting chairman of department, spring, 1970. Visiting senior lecturer in geography, University of Haifa, 1971-72; lecturer in political science, University of New Haven; visiting scholar, Yale Law School, 1974-75. Advisor to Government of Nepal, United Nations Development Program, 1976. Presented weekly radio programs in Washington, D.C., Jamaica, and Chile, on traditional music of the United States and the world. *Military service:* U.S. Army, 1955-56.

MEMBER: International Law Association, Association of American Geographers, American Geographical Society, American Society of International Law, Society for International Development, New England-St. Lawrence Valley Geographical Society, New England Council of Latin American Studies. *Awards, honors:* Fellowship from U.S. Office of Education, including study in Morocco, Tunisia, and Egypt, 1970-71; Southern Connecticut State College faculty scholar award, 1975.

WRITINGS: Access to the Sea for Developing Landlocked States, Nijhoff, 1970. Contributor to *Americas, Economic Geography, Caribbean Studies, Nepal Review, Geographical Review, Focus,* and other professional journals. Founding editor, *Inquiry/Update,* 1973-75.

WORK IN PROGRESS: A book on political geography; a book, *Systematic Political Geography,* for Wiley; a bibliography on land-locked states, for Sijthoff; a book on Bolivia's access to the sea.

SIDELIGHTS: Martin Glassner is an extensive traveller. He has visited "forty-eight states of the U.S., all ten provinces of Canada and much of Mexico, in addition to numerous countries including Puerto Rico, Cuba, Ecuador, Yugoslavia, Greece, Italy, Switzerland, Monaco, Portugal, Luxembourg, India and Iceland." *Avocational interests:* Folk and square dancing, traditional music and folklore, mountaineering and canoeing; collecting stamps, maps, and flags.

*   *   *

GLEIMAN, Lubomir 1923-

PERSONAL: Surname rhymes with "layman"; born May 21, 1923, in Trnava, Slovakia; son of Jan Frndak (a lawyer) and Anna (Urbanek) Gleiman; married Nancy Waeber, May 10, 1941; children: Mary Melanie, Cyril Edward, Jan Kenneth. *Education:* University of Bratislava, M.U.C., 1945; University of Innsbruck, Rev. Pol. Cand., 1948; Thomas

More Institute, B.A., 1952; University of Montreal, M.A., 1954, Ph.D. (summa cum laude), 1957. *Politics:* Democrat. *Religion:* Roman Catholic. *Home:* 80 Brook St., Franklin, Mass. 02038. *Office:* Department of Philosophy, Salve Regina, the Newport College, Newport, R.I. 02840.

CAREER: Clarke Steamship Co., Montreal, Quebec, accountant, 1949-54; Thomas More Institute, Montreal, lecturer in philosophy, 1954-57; University of Montreal, Montreal, instructor in medieval political doctrines, 1956-57; Newton College of the Sacred Heart, Newton, Mass., assistant professor, 1957-58, associate professor, 1958-61, professor of political science, 1961-75; Boston College, Chestnut Hill, Mass., Newton senior fellow, 1975-78; Salve Regina, the Newport College, Newport, R.I., professor of philosophy, 1978—. *Member:* Mediaeval Academy of America, American Political Science Association, Institute of Medieval Studies (University of Montreal), Phi Alpha Theta.

WRITINGS: Origin of Treuga Dei, Vrin, 1962. Also author of *Medieval Roots of the Contemporary Totalitarian Syndrome.* Contributor to *Thought, Proceedings of American Catholic Philosophical Association, Slovak Studies, Revue Thomiste,* and *Esprit.*

WORK IN PROGRESS: Essays in Political Anthropology.

SIDELIGHTS: Lubomir Gleiman is competent in Slovak, French, German, Latin, Russian, Polish, and Hungarian.

*   *   *

GLENDON, Mary Ann 1938-

PERSONAL: Born October 7, 1938, in Pittsfield, Mass.; daughter of Martin Francis (a journalist) and Sarah (Pomeroy) Glendon; married Edward R. Lev (a lawyer), August 29, 1970; children: Elizabeth Ann, Katherine Glendon, Sarah Pomeroy. *Education:* Attended Mount Holyoke College, 1955-56; University of Chicago, B.A., 1959, J.D., 1961, M.Comp.L., 1963; Universite Libre de Bruxelles, graduate study, 1962-63. *Religion:* Roman Catholic. *Residence:* Chestnut Hill, Mass. *Office:* Law School, Boston College, Newton, Mass. 02167.

CAREER: European Economic Communities, Brussels, Belgium, legal intern, 1962-63; Mayer, Brown & Platt (law firm), Chicago, Ill., attorney, 1963-68; Boston College, Law School, Newton, Mass., assistant professor, 1968-71, associate professor, 1971-73, professor of law, 1973—. Visiting professor, Law School, Harvard University, 1974-75.

WRITINGS: (With Max Rheinstein) *The Law of Decedents' Estates,* Foundation Press, 1971; *State, Law and Family,* North-Holland, 1977. Member of editorial board, *American Journal of Comparative Law,* 1969—; contributing editor, *International Encyclopedia of Comparative Law,* 1970—.

WORK IN PROGRESS: Treatise on comparative conflict of laws.

*   *   *

GNAROWSKI, Michael 1934-

PERSONAL: Born September 27, 1934, in Shanghai, China; son of Daniel (an industrialist) and Nina (Dudko) Gnarowski; married Diana Paquet, October 21, 1961; children: Franceska, Sybille, Daniel. *Education:* McGill University, B.A., 1956; Indiana University, additional study, 1959; University of Montreal, M.A., 1960; University of Ottawa, Ph.D., 1967. *Home:* 15 Ossington Ave., Ottawa, Ontario,

Canada. *Office:* Department of English, Carleton University, Ottawa, Ontario, Canada.

CAREER: University of Sherbrooke, Sherbrooke, Quebec, lecturer in English, 1961-62; Lakehead University, Port Arthur (now Thunder Bay), Ontario, assistant professor of English, 1962-65; Sir George Williams University, Montreal, Quebec, associate professor of English, 1966-72; Carleton University, Ottawa, Ontario, professor of English, 1972—. Visiting professor at University of Ottawa, 1969-72; exchange visiting professor, University of Leningrad, 1977. Research officer of Royal Commission on Bilingualism and Biculturalism, 1964-66. *Military service:* Canadian Intelligence Corps, 1960-65; became lieutenant. *Member:* Association of Canadian University Teachers, Virginia Bibliographical Society. *Awards, honors:* C. D. Howe fellowship, 1965-66.

WRITINGS: Postscript to St. James Street (poems), Delta Canada, 1965; (editor with Louis Dedek) *The Making of Modern Poetry in Canada,* Ryerson Press, 1967; (editor) *The Rising Village of Oliver Goldsmith,* Delta Canada, 1968; *The Gentlemen Are Also Lexicographers* (poems), Delta Canada, 1968; (editor) *Three Early Poems from Lower Canada,* Lande Foundation, 1969; (editor) *Archibald Lampman,* Ryerson Press, 1970; (editor) *Selected Poems and Songs of Joseph Quesnel,* Lande Foundation, 1970; *Contact Press: 1952-1967,* Delta Canada, 1971; (editor) *Selected Stories of Raymond Knister,* Ottawa University Press, 1972; (compiler) *Concise Bibliography of English Canadian Literature,* McClelland & Stewart, 1973, revised edition, 1978; (editor) *Leonard Cohen: The Artist and His Critics,* McGraw, 1976; (editor) *New Provinces: Poems of Several Authors,* University of Toronto Press, 1976. General editor of McGraw-Hill Ryerson "Critical Views on Canadian Writers" series; general editor of the Carleton Library series for McClelland & Stewart, Ltd.; editor of *Yes: A Magazine of Poetry and Prose,* 1956-69; co-editor of *Le Chien D'Or/The Golden Dog Magazine,* 1972-74, and *Canadian Poetry: Studies, Documents and Reviews,* 1977—.

WORK IN PROGRESS: Editing *Selected Poems of Archibald Lampman.*

*   *   *

GOBAR, Ash 1930-

PERSONAL: Born April 7, 1930, in Georgia, U.S.S.R.; naturalized U.S. citizen; son of Imir (an historian) and Salia (Mirian) Gobar; married Anne Boeke (curator of Headley Museum), June 15, 1957; children: Penelope, Peter, Karina. *Education:* College of Wooster, A.B., 1952; University of Chicago, M.A., 1954; University of Geneva, M.Sc., 1959; University of Wisconsin, Ph.D., 1959. *Politics:* Republican. *Religion:* Christian Church. *Home:* 989 Holly Springs Rd., Lexington, Ky. 40504. *Office:* Department of Philosophy, Transylvania University, Lexington, Ky. 40508.

CAREER: Columbia University, New York, N.Y., guest scholar, 1960-61; Concord College, Athens, W.Va., instructor, 1961-62, assistant professor, 1962-65, associate professor of philosophy, 1965-67; Transylvania University, Lexington, Ky., professor of philosophy, 1968—. *Member:* World Congress of Philosophy, American Philosophical Association, National Wildlife Federation. *Awards, honors:* American Philosophical Society grant, 1968.

WRITINGS: Philosophic Foundations of Psychology, Nijhoff, 1968. Contributor to *Proceedings* of American Philosophical Society, *World Congress of Philosophy, Philosophical Forum, Philosophy Today, Studies in Soviet Thought,* and *Philosophical Studies.*

WORK IN PROGRESS: Modern Philosophy: An Exposition of the Methods and Concepts of Philosophy As an Integral Science; An Essay on Truth; Philosophy and Mountain Climbing.

SIDELIGHTS: Ash Gobar wrote *CA:* "I am a philosophical author. I write about a set of fundamental questions: questions concerning truth, reality, value, the meaning of life, among others. What distinguishes contemporary philosophers from each other, and most of them from some, is their approach to the fundamental questions. I (and some philosophers) handle these questions logically and dialectically. This means that I deal with concepts almost exclusively. I call this approach logical realism. And this accounts for the exactness of style in my philosophic writings."

Gobar continues: "My aim, however, remains constant throughout: to proceed from the immediate order to the ultimate order—from sight to insight—to view the world integrally. In my world all worlds hang together: the subjective and the objective, fact and value, art and science are philosophically interrelated. This integral ideology is my answer to the fragmented ideologies which plague the contemporary scene: reductionism and absurdism, to name but two extreme cases."

*   *   *

GODSHALK, William Leigh 1937-

PERSONAL: Born July 12, 1937, in Pen Argyl, Pa.; son of Melvin LeRoy (a slater) and Doris (Curl) Godshalk; married Eleanor Wilkie, July 2, 1960 (divorced, 1967); married Anne McFarlane (a teacher), July 28, 1967 (divorced, 1973); married Lauri Brown, 1974 (divorced, 1975); married Vicki Lehman, 1976 (divorced, 1977); children: (first marriage) Heather; (third marriage) Elihu. *Education:* Attended University of St. Andrews, 1957-58; Ursinus College, B.A., 1959; Harvard University, M.A., 1960, Ph.D., 1964. *Politics:* Democrat. *Religion:* Protestant. *Home:* 231 Atkinson St., Cincinnati, Ohio 45219. *Office:* Department of English, University of Cincinnati, Cincinnati, Ohio 45221.

CAREER: Tufts University, Medford, Mass., instructor in English literature, 1960-61; Harvard University, Widener Memorial Room, Cambridge, Mass., Renaissance consultant, 1963-64; College of William and Mary, Williamsburg, Va., assistant professor of English literature, 1964-67; University of Cincinnati, Cincinnati, Ohio, associate professor, 1967-72, professor of English literature, 1972—. *Member:* Modern Language Association of America, Modern Humanities Research Association, Renaissance Society of America. *Awards, honors:* Fellow of Cooperative Program in the Humanities, University of North Carolina at Chapel Hill, 1965-66; Folger Library fellow, 1970.

WRITINGS: (Editor and author of introduction and bibliography) James Branch Cabell, *Beyond Life,* Johnson Reprint, 1970; (editor) Ellen Glasgow, *Voice of the People,* College & University Press, 1973; *Patterning in Shakespearean Drama,* Mouton, 1973; *The Marlovian World Picture,* Mouton, 1974; *In Quest of Cabell,* Revisionist Press, 1975. Contributor to *Journal of Modern Literature, Studies in Philology, Renaissance Quarterly, Shakespeare Studies,* and other professional journals. Editor, *Kalki: Studies in James Branch Cabell.*

WORK IN PROGRESS: Sir Philip Sidney: A Reference Guide, with A. J. Colianne; editing Garland Publishing's Shakespeare bibliographies series.

GOERDT, Arthur L(inus) 1912-

PERSONAL: Born January 13, 1912, in Dyersville, Iowa; son of Joseph (a farmer) and Wilhelmina (Koopmann) Goerdt. *Education:* University of Dayton, B.S.Ed., 1935; Our Lady of the Lake College, B.S.L.S., 1942; St. Louis University, M.Ed., 1950. *Home and office:* St. Mary's University, San Antonio, Tex. 78284.

CAREER: Roman Catholic brother of The Society of Mary (S.M.); high school English teacher and librarian in Illinois, Missouri, Texas, Michigan, and Wisconsin, 1935-57; St. Mary's University, San Antonio, Tex., instructor, 1957-63, assistant professor, 1963-70, associate professor of English, 1971—, chairman of department, 1971-73. *Member:* National Council of Teachers of English, Catholic Library Association (life member; president, 1959-61), South Central Modern Language Association, Texas Conference of College Teachers of English, Texas Council of Teachers of English, San Antonio English Teachers Club (president, 1969-70). *Awards, honors:* Grants from Kaltenborn Foundation, 1968, 1969, 1970, to study student university newspapers abroad.

WRITINGS: Campus Unrest, St. Mary's University, 1970. Contributor of about twenty articles to professional journals.

WORK IN PROGRESS: A book of interviews with Canadian university student editors; compiling results of research on Canadian student newspapers.

* * *

GOH, Cheng-Teik 1943-

PERSONAL: Born October 16, 1943, in Butterworth, Malaysia; son of Soon-Tit (a lorry-driver) and Kim-Khuan (Ooi) Goh; married Yoon-Lin Ng (a teacher), August, 1969; children: Eng-Gi, Eng-Leh, Miao-Ling. *Education:* Harvard University, A.B. (honors), 1965; Leiden University, Doctorandus, 1967, Ph.D., 1974. *Office:* Ministry of Transport, Kuala Lumpur, Malaysia.

CAREER: University of Malaya, Kuala Lumpur, lecturer in history, 1967-74; Government of Malaysia, Kuala Lumpur, parliamentary secretary to prime minister, 1974-76, deputy minister of works and utilities, 1976-78, deputy minister of transport, 1978—; member of parliament, 1974—.

WRITINGS: The May Thirteenth Incident and Democracy in Malaysia, Oxford University Press, 1971; *Integration in a Plural Society: The Chinese in Malaysia,* Straits Echo Press, 1978.

* * *

GOLD, Seymour M(urray) 1933-

PERSONAL: Born October 20, 1933, in Detroit, Mich.; son of Max and Betty (Smith) Gold; married Susan Williams, September 2, 1962; children: Daniel, David, Robert. *Education:* Michigan State University, B.S., 1957, M.S., 1958; Wayne State University, M.U.P., 1962; University of Michigan, Ph.D., 1969. *Home:* 1001 Cornell Dr., Davis, Calif. 95616. *Office:* College of Agricultural and Environmental Sciences, Division of Environmental Planning and Management, University of California, Davis, Calif. 95616.

CAREER: Parks Department, Detroit, Mich., landscape assistant, 1951-53; City Plan Commission, Detroit, junior city planner, 1959-60, intermediate city planner, 1960-63; Vilican-Leman & Associates, Southfield, Mich., senior planner, 1963-64; Illinois Department of Conservation, Springfield, state recreation planner, 1964-66; City Planning

Department, Ann Arbor, Mich., principal planner, 1966-69; University of California, Davis, associate professor of environmental planning, 1969—. Visiting lecturer at University of Illinois, 1965-66, Southern Illinois University, winter, 1966. University of California, Berkeley, visiting lecturer, 1972, visiting scholar, 1976-77. Research associate, School of Natural Resources, University of Michigan, 1967-68. *Military service:* U.S. Army Signal Corps., active duty, 1959-60; reserve, 1960-66; became captain.

MEMBER: American Institute of Planners, American Society of Planning Officials, American Association for the Advancement of Sciences, American Association of University Professors, World Future Society, National Recreation and Park Association, Society of Park and Recreation Educators, American Association for the Advancement of Science, Sierra Club, California Park and Recreation Society, California Planning and Conservation League, Alpha Phi Omega. *Awards, honors:* National Wildlife Federation Conservation fellowship, 1967; Beatrix Farrand Research fellowship, 1976-77.

WRITINGS: Urban Recreation Planning, Lea & Febiger, 1973; (contributor) William B. Stapp, editor, *Environment and the Citizen,* Holt, 1973; (contributor) Robert McNally, editor, *Biology: An Uncommon Introduction,* Harper, 1974; *Recreation Planning and Design,* McGraw, 1978. Contributor of material on urban and recreation planning to University of California Extension publications and co-author of various city planning reports. Contributor of many articles to journals in his field. Reviewer, *Journal of Human Ecology,* 1970-71, *Journal of Leisure Research,* 1971-72, *AIP Newsletter,* 1971-72, and *International Journal of Environmental Studies,* 1972-73. Editor, "Man-Environment Information Guide" series.

WORK IN PROGRESS: User Response to Landscape Quality in Urban Parks; Mystique of Environmental Planning; Open Space Preservation in Urbanizing Areas.

* * *

GOLDBERG, Alvin Arnold 1931-

PERSONAL: Born August 18, 1931, in Detroit, Mich.; son of Irving and Eva (Burnstein) Goldberg; married Judith Hiller (lecturer in a community college), June 9, 1955; children: Jonathan, Benjamin, Elissa, Adam. *Education:* Wayne University (now Wayne State University), B.A., 1953; University of Hawaii, M.A., 1955; Northwestern University, Ph.D., 1959. *Politics:* Democrat. *Religion:* Jewish. *Home:* 661 Lafayette, Denver, Colo. 80218. *Office:* Department of Speech Communication, University of Denver, Denver, Colo. 80208.

CAREER: University of Hawaii—Hilo Branch, instructor in speech, 1955; Northern Illinois University, DeKalb, assistant professor of speech, 1958-61; University of Denver, Denver, Colo., associate professor, 1961-66, professor of speech, 1966-69, director of graduate studies, 1961-69; Northwestern University, Evanston, Ill., professor of public address and director of group communication, 1970-71; University of Denver, professor of speech communication and chairman of department, 1971—. Has presented papers at conventions and conferences around the United States. Member of Denver Crime Commission. *Member:* International Communication Association, Speech Communication Association of America, American Association of University Professors, Western Speech Association.

WRITINGS: (Editor with Johnnye Akin, Gail Myers, and Joseph Stewart) *Language Behavior: A Book of Readings,*

Mouton, 1970; (contributor) Ken Johnson, editor, *Research Designs in General Semantics,* Gordon & Breach, 1972; (with Carl Larson) *Group Communication,* Prentice-Hall, 1975. Also author, with Alton Barbour, of *Interpersonal Communication: Teaching Strategies and Resources.* Contributor to speech, education, and social science journals, including *Speaker, Speech Teacher, Speech Monographs, Interaction, Journal of Communication,* and *Journal of Applied Behavioral Science.*

*   *   *

GOLDBERG, Miriam Levin 1914-

PERSONAL: Born July 18, 1914, in Baku, Russia; daughter of Jacob Leon (an educator) and Rebecca (Altman) Levin; married Carl Goldberg, June 30, 1936 (died June 8, 1972); children: Daniel David. *Education:* Columbia University, B.A., 1946, M.A., 1947, Ph.D., 1955. *Religion:* None. *Home:* 3820 Sedgwick Ave., Bronx, N.Y. 10463. *Office:* Department of Psychology, Teachers College, Columbia University, 525 West 120th St., New York, N.Y. 10027.

CAREER: Grove School (residential school for emotionally disturbed children), Madison, Conn., teacher, administrative assistant, and camp head counselor, 1937-45; nursery school teacher in Bronx, N.Y., 1945-49; Columbia University, Teachers College, New York, N.Y., research associate in evaluation and citizenship education, 1950-54, research associate at Horace Mann Lincoln Insitute's talented youth project, 1954-58, professor of psychology education, 1957—. Director of beginning reading project, Center for Urban Education, 1966-71. *Member:* American Psychological Association, American Educational Research Association, American Association of University Professors, Society for Research in Child Development, Association for the Gifted, Metropolitan Association for the Study of the Gifted (president, 1964), Sigma Xi, Kappa Delta Pi.

WRITINGS: (With A. Harry Passow, and others) *Planning for Talented Youth,* Bureau of Publications, Teachers College, Columbia University, 1955; *Research on the Talented,* Teachers College Press, 1965; *The Effects of Ability Grouping,* Teachers College Press, 1966; *A Comparison of Mathematics Programs for Able Junior High School Students,* two volumes, Teachers College, Columbia University, 1966; (with Passow and Jane B. Raph) *Bright Underachievers,* Teachers College Press, 1966; (editor with Passow and Abraham J. Tannenbaum) *The Education of the Disadvantaged: A Book of Readings,* Holt, 1967; (editor with Martha Werle) *Psychological Foundations of Education: Readings,* MSS Information, 1974. Also author of *Effects of Various Approaches to Beginning Reading for Disadvantaged Children,* Center for Urban Education. Contributor to *Childhood Education, Exceptional Children, Educational Leadership,* and *School Psychologist.*

*   *   *

GOLDENBERG, Herbert 1926-

PERSONAL: Born July 19, 1926, in New York, N.Y.; son of Philip (an insurance agent) and Eva (Cooper) Goldenberg; married Bernice Gesner, June 27, 1948 (divorced, 1962); married Irene Feinstein (a psychologist), February 17, 1963; children: (first marriage) Philip Scott; (second marriage) Erica Joan, Karen Louise. *Education:* City University of New York, B.S., 1949; University of California, Los Angeles, M.A., 1952, Ph.D., 1953. *Home:* 869 Malcolm Ave., Los Angeles, Calif. 90024. *Office:* Department of Psychology, California State University, Los Angeles, Calif. 90032.

CAREER: California State University, Los Angeles, instructor, 1953-54, assistant professor, 1954-60, associate professor, 1960-65, professor of psychology, 1965—; clinical psychologist in private practice, Los Angeles, Calif., 1953—. *Military service:* U.S. Navy, 1944-46. *Member:* American Psychological Association, Western Psychological Association, California State Psychological Association, California Teachers Association, United Professors of California, Los Angeles County Psychological Association (president, 1965-66), Los Angeles Society of Clinical Psychologists (president, 1963-65).

WRITINGS: Contemporary Clinical Psychology, Brooks/Cole, 1973; *Abnormal Psychology: A Social/Community Approach,* Brooks/Cole, 1977; *Family Therapy: An Overview,* Brooks/Cole, in press.

AVOCATIONAL INTERESTS: Collecting African art, Oriental rugs, American Indian and pre-Columbian pieces.

*   *   *

GOLDMAN, Marcus Selden 1894-

PERSONAL: Born May 12, 1894, in Middletown, Ohio; son of Charles Trine (a realtor) and Minnie (Sheafor) Goldman; married Olive Mortimer Remington, September 12, 1925; children: Agnes Redfearn (Mrs. John Francis Burke), Marcia Elizabeth (Mrs. Malcolm Douglas Widenor), Charles Remington, Olive Mary Louise (Mrs. John Alfred Malcolm). *Education:* Miami University, Oxford, Ohio, A.B., 1916; University of Illinois, A.M., 1917, Ph.D., 1931; Sorbonne, University of Paris, graduate study, 1919-21; Harvard University, A.M., 1926. *Politics:* Independent. *Religion:* Episcopalian. *Home:* 203 West Michigan Ave., Urbana, Ill. 61801. *Office:* Department of English, University of Illinois, Urbana, Ill. 61801.

CAREER: New York Herald, dramatic and fine arts critic on European edition in Paris, France, 1921-23; Hoosac School, Hoosic, N.Y., classical master, 1923-24; University of Illinois at Urbana-Champaign, instructor, 1929-31, associate in English, 1931-36, assistant professor, 1936-46, associate professor, 1946-58, professor of English, 1958-62, professor emeritus, 1962—. Visiting professor, Stephens College, 1936-37; Taft Foundation lecturer, University of Cincinnati, 1941. *Military service:* U.S. Army, American Expeditionary Forces in France, 1917-19; became sergeant first class; received three battle stars. U.S. Army Air Forces, 1942-46; became colonel; received Legion of Merit. U.S. Army Reserve, 1946-53; commander of 5961st Army Reserve School, Champaign, 1951-53.

MEMBER: Modern Language Association of America (life member), Mediaeval Academy of America (life member), Modern Humanities Research Association (life member), American Military Institute (life member), Reserve Officers Association, Retired Officers Association, American Church Union, English-Speaking Union, Izaak Walton League of America, Phi Beta Kappa, Sigma Delta Chi, Delta Upsilon, Champaign Country Club. *Awards, honors:* American Field Service fellowship at University of Paris, 1919-21; Distinguished Service Citation of Champaign County chapter, Izaak Walton League; Distinguished Service Award, Champaign-Urbana Jaycees, 1973 (received jointly with wife); honorary doctorate, Miami University, 1974.

WRITINGS: Sir Philip Sidney and the Arcadia, University of Illinois, 1934; (with Bernard L. Jefferson and S. E. Glenn) *A Progressive Study of English Composition,* Odyssey, 1941; (translator with wife, Olive Remington Goldman)

Henri Gheon and Henri Brochet, *St. Anne and the Gouty Rector and Other Plays,* Longmans, Green, 1950; *Poems of the Past,* Stinehour Press, 1970; *In Praise of Little Fishes,* David R. Godine, 1977. Essays, reviews, articles, and poems have been published in journals and included in anthologies, festschriften, and other collections. Literary editor, *Paris-Review* (fortnightly English-language magazine), 1921-23.

WORK IN PROGRESS: Continuing research on Sir Philip Sidney, Sir John Harington, and Izaak Walton; a book on fish and fishing in the Middle West.

AVOCATIONAL INTERESTS: Fishing, conservation, national defense.

*   *   *

GOLDSMITH, Arnold L(ouis)   1928-

PERSONAL: Born February 7, 1928, in Boston, Mass.; son of Max (a salesman) and Dora (Lavine) Goldsmith; married Gladys Wasserman (a music teacher), June 22, 1950; children: Janet, Marsha, Steven. *Education:* Boston University, B.A., 1948; University of Wisconsin, M.A., 1949, Ph.D., 1953. *Home:* 27369 Everett, Southfield, Mich. 48076. *Office:* Department of English, Wayne State University, Detroit, Mich. 48202.

CAREER: Wayne State University, Detroit, Mich., instructor, 1953-57, assistant professor, 1957-63, associate professor, 1963-70, professor of English, 1970—. Visiting professor, University of Tulsa, 1967. *Member:* American Association of University Professors, Phi Beta Kappa.

WRITINGS: (Contributor) A. Dayle Wallace and Woodburn O. Ross, editors, *Studies in Honor of John Wilcox,* Wayne State University Press, 1958; (editor with Milton Bruce Byrd) *Publication Guide for Literary and Linguistic Scholars,* Wayne State University Press, 1958; (contributor) Robert Murray Davis, editor, *Steinbeck: A Collection of Critical Essays,* Prentice-Hall, 1972; *Modern American Literary Criticism: 1905-1965,* G. K. Hall, 1979. Contributor to literature and education journals, including *Modern Drama* and *Renascence.*

*   *   *

GOLDSTEIN, Irwin L.   1937-

PERSONAL: Born October 4, 1937, in New York, N.Y.; son of Ben (a retail-store owner) and Molly (Stone) Goldstein; married Arlene E. Isaccson, December, 1960; children: Harold, Beth. *Education:* Attended Queens College of the City of New York (now Queens College of the City University of New York), 1955-57; College of the City of New York (now City College of the City University of New York), B.B.A., 1959; University of Maryland, M.A., 1962, Ph.D., 1964. *Home:* 8806 Gramercy Lane, Laurel, Md. 20810. *Office:* Department of Psychology, University of Maryland, College Park, Md. 20742.

CAREER: Executive Appraisal, Queens, N.Y., research assistant, 1957-58; Human Sciences Research, Arlington, Va., research assistant, summer, 1961; Ohio State University, Columbus, assistant professor of psychology and research associate of Human Performance Center, 1963-66; University of Maryland, College Park, professor of psychology, 1966—, assistant chairman of department, 1968—, director of graduate studies in psychology, 1969—. *Member:* American Psychological Association (fellow), American Association for the Advancement of Science, Psychonomic Society, Sigma Xi, Psi Chi. *Awards, honors:* National Insti-

tutes of Health research grant, 1967-69; U.S. Air Force Office of Scientific Research grant, 1967-71; National Aeronautics and Space Administration summer fellow, 1967.

WRITINGS: (With W. C. Howell) *Engineering Psychology: Current Perspectives in Research,* Appleton, 1971; *Training: Program Development and Evaluation,* Brooks/Cole, 1974. Writer of research reports; contributor of about thirty articles to psychology journals. Editor, engineering psychology section of *Journal Supplement Abstract Service;* associate editor, *Human Factors Journal;* member of editorial board, *Journal of Organizational Behavior and Human Performance.*

*   *   *

GOLDSTEIN, Martin E(ugene)   1939-

PERSONAL: Born November 26, 1939, in Philadelphia, Pa.; son of Morris and Nettie Goldstein; married Janet Mendell (an English teacher), June 12, 1966. *Education:* Cornell University, B.A., 1961; University of Pennsylvania, M.A., 1964, Ph.D., 1968. *Home:* 31 Price's Lane, Rose Valley, Pa. 19065. *Office:* Department of Political Science, Widener College, Chester, Pa. 19013.

CAREER: Widener College, Chester, Pa., assistant professor, 1968-73, associate professor of political science, 1973—, director of paralegal studies, 1973—. *Military service:* U.S. Air Force Reserve, 1962-67. *Member:* International Studies Association (member of Philadelphia chapter executive committee, 1972-74; president, 1977-78), American Political Science Association.

WRITINGS: American Policy in Laos, Fairleigh Dickinson University Press, 1973. Contributor of articles to professional journals including *Political Science* and *Intellect.*

WORK IN PROGRESS: An anthology of readings in American foreign policy.

*   *   *

GOLDWATER, Barry (Morris)   1909-

PERSONAL: Born January 1, 1909, in Phoenix, Ariz.; son of Baron (a department store merchant) and Josephine (Williams) Goldwater; married Margaret Johnson, September 22, 1934; children: Joanne (Mrs. Eugene Butler), Barry Morris, Jr., Michael Prescott, Margaret (Mrs. Richard Holt). *Education:* Attended University of Arizona, 1928. *Religion:* Episcopalian. *Home address:* P.O. Box 1601, Scottsdale, Ariz. 85252. *Office:* U.S. Senate, Washington, D.C. 20510.

CAREER: Goldwater's Inc. (department store), Phoenix, Ariz., salesman, manager-president, 1929-37, president, 1937-53, chairman of board of directors, 1953-60. City councilman in Phoenix, Ariz., 1949-52; U.S. Congress, Washington, D.C., Republican senator from Arizona (member of Armed Services Committee, Labor and Public Welfare Committee, and Aeronautical and Space Sciences Committee), 1953-64, 1968—. Republican candidate for U.S. presidency, 1964. Member of advisory committee on Indian affairs, U.S. Department of the Interior, 1948-50. Member of board of directors, Heard Museum, Museum of Northern Arizona, and St. Joseph's Hospital. *Military service:* U.S. Army Air Forces, pilot and instructor in fighter gunnery, 1941-45; served in Asia and Pacific theaters; received Air Medal. U.S. Air Force Reserve, 1945-67, retiring as major general.

MEMBER: American Institute of Foreign Trade (director), American Association of Indian Affairs (director), Royal Photographic Society (England), American Legion, Veterans of Foreign Wars, Municipal League (vice-president), Eta Mu Pi, Sigma Chi, Masons (Shriner), Elks. *Awards, honors:* Award, U.S. Jaycees, 1937; Man of the Year, Phoenix, Ariz., 1949.

WRITINGS: Arizona Portraits, two volumes, privately printed, 1940; *An Odyssey of the Green and Colorado Rivers,* privately printed, 1941, published as *Delightful Journey, Down the Green and Colorado Rivers,* Arizona Historical Foundation, 1970; *Speeches of Henry Ashurst,* privately printed, 1954; *The Conscience of a Conservative,* Victor, 1960, 14th edition, Manor Books, 1974; *The Face of Arizona,* F. P. Middleton, 1964; *People and Places,* Random House, 1967; (contributor) *The Goldwater Kachina Doll Collection,* Arizona Historical Foundation, 1969; *The Conscience of a Majority,* Prentice-Hall, 1970; *Barry Goldwater and the Southwest,* Troy's Publications, 1976; *The Coming Breakpoint,* Macmillan, 1976. Also author of several published speeches. Contributor to *Human Events, National Review, Saturday Review, Reader's Digest, Saturday Evening Post,* and *McCalls.*

WORK IN PROGRESS: His memoirs, for Harcourt.

SIDELIGHTS: Barry Goldwater is the primary spokesman for political conservatives in the United States today. As a U.S. senator for 20 years, the Republican presidential candidate in 1964, a lecturer on college campuses, and an author of several books, Barry Goldwater has consistently expounded the conservative political position. He has warned of the dangers of government bureaucracy, big labor unions, and communism. He has supported the national defense, limited government, and the business community. Although many people might disagree with his politics (he consistently scores zero in the Americans for Democratic Action ratings), Emmet John Hughes has described him as "a thoroughly decent and conscientious citizen, a man of generous instincts, personal charm, and authentic patriotism."

Born to a wealthy department store owner, Barry Goldwater enjoyed an affluent upbringing. He graduated from the Staunton Military Academy in 1928 and, when his father died in 1929, began working in the family department store. In 1934, he married Borg-Warner heiress Margaret Johnson, and in 1937 he became president of the family business, Goldwater's Inc. During the Second World War, he served as a pilot in the U.S. Army Air Forces.

It wasn't until 1949 that Goldwater entered politics. He ran for the Phoenix City Council on a nonpartisan, reformist ticket and won in a landslide. During his first year in office, he helped reorganize the Phoenix Police Department. In 1952, he ran for the U.S. senate against Democratic incumbent Ernest W. McFarland. It was a hard-fought race in which Goldwater charged McFarland with being a "socialist." McFarland called in such Democratic notables as Vice-President Alben W. Barkley and House Speaker Sam Rayburn to deliver speeches on his behalf. Goldwater won the election by a slim seven thousand votes. He later admitted that Republican Dwight Eisenhower's presidential win that same year helped to insure his own victory. Six years later, when running for re-election against McFarland, Goldwater won by 35,000 votes.

Goldwater emerged as a leading figure in the Republican Party in 1960, when his book *The Conscience of a Conservative* was published and greeted enthusiastically by the nation's conservatives. At the 1960 Republican Party National Convention, his newly-won prominence was made evident by a move by some delegates to nominate him for president. Goldwater discouraged the move, supporting Richard Nix-

on's nomination instead and giving a number of speeches on Nixon's behalf during the campaign.

In 1964, Goldwater sought and won the Republican presidential nomination. His foremost concern, as he later explained it, was to keep the Republican Party under the control of its conservative wing. Winning the presidency, he said, "was never life or death for me." Running against the incumbent Democrat Lyndon Johnson, Goldwater faced an experienced political opponent. Democratic President John F. Kennedy's recent assassination was still fresh in the public's memory. Some observers questioned whether any Republican candidate could win the election.

Declaring himself to be "a choice, not an echo," Goldwater campaigned in a spontaneous, straight-talking, and highly controversial style. "He was continuously giving answers off the top of his head to the most serious questions," Roy Reed commented later in the *New York Times*. "His spontaneity had a dual effect. To his friends, he was candid and refreshing; to his enemies, he was insane and dangerous." Emmet John Hughes complained, "It is as though a child were speaking on the problems of the times, with a child's directness and lack of complexity." Conservative Russell Kirk disagreed, "His words carry conviction, because men perceive that they come from a sound head." James J. Kilpatrick later observed that "Goldwater's candor was forever at war with discretion, honesty struggled with tact, and tact often lost; the impulse to pop off proved hard to resist." Goldwater jokingly proposed "sawing off" the liberal eastern seaboard of the United States and "setting it adrift in the ocean." He supported "courageous nuclear brinkmanship," sending the Marines to Cuba, breaking off diplomatic relations with the Soviet Union, and abolishing the graduated income tax. He expressed the opinion that the nation's poor were poor because they had either low intelligence or low ambition.

Goldwater drew the support of right-wing organizations like the John Birch Society with his opinions on the Civil Rights Act, the United Nations, and the minimum wage laws (opposed to all three), the Vietnam war ("bomb the living hell out of them"), and the Cold war ("victory over communism"). This support, together with his campaign statement that "extremism in the defense of liberty is no vice" (a phrase he adapted from Cicero), alarmed more moderate observers, but Goldwater refused to back down. He stated on several occasions that the Birch Society was composed of fine, intelligent people who were often model citizens in their community. Some observers noted with concern the Society's tendency to label people, including every American president since Franklin Roosevelt, as "communist." "I refused to write them [the John Birch Society] out of the human race," Goldwater later said. Goldwater's refusal to denounce his extremist supporters appeared to many observers as a tacit approval of them. "To be sure," James J. Kilpatrick wrote in the *National Review*, "he was warmly loved by millions of old-line, conservative Republicans, but he lost the support of party moderates."

Called "The Great Divider" of the Republican Party, his campaign met with such resistance within his own ranks that it became a largely personal effort. Moderate and liberal political figures of both parties were alarmed by him. Governor Nelson Rockefeller found Goldwater's views "dangerous, irresponsible, and frightening." Union leader George Meany saw "a parallel between Senator Barry Goldwater and Adolph Hitler." The Reverend Doctor Martin Luther King Jr. warned of "dangerous signs of Hitlerism in the Goldwater campaign."

This image of extremism followed Goldwater throughout the campaign. James Reston, writing in the *New York Times,* examined this image and wrote: "Mr. Goldwater may attract all the ultras and antis—the forces that are anti-Negro, anti-labor, anti-foreigner, anti-intellectual—but he also attracts something else that is precisely the opposite of these vicious and negative forces. Mr. Goldwater touches the deep feeling of regret in American life: regret over the loss of religious faith; regret over the loss of simplicity and fidelity; regret over the loss of the frontier spirit of pugnacious individuality; regret, in short, over the loss of America's innocent and idealistic youth." Despite the heated controversy his campaign had elicited, Goldwater chose to end the race by repeating the first speech of his campaign; it was his way of showing that his beliefs had remained the same.

When the election results were tabulated, his opponent, President Lyndon Johnson, had won by a landslide. Goldwater had carried only six states; he carried his home state of Arizona by less than 5,000 votes. Republican congressional candidates who aligned themselves with the Goldwater platform, including such popular figures as Robert Taft and Howard Baker, were also defeated. "The size of the vote that Johnson got was a bit of a surprise," Goldwater would later say, "but it didn't bug me; it didn't stay with me. When you've lost an election by that much, it isn't a case of whether you made the wrong speech or wore the wrong necktie. It just was the wrong time." Soon after the election, Goldwater was approached by a stranger who asked if he were the famous senator. "No," replied Goldwater, his good spirits still intact, "and I didn't vote for the son of a bitch."

Goldwater returned to his senate seat in 1968 where he has continued his frank observations on the issues of the day, much to the delight of his conservative supporters. During the Watergate scandals of the Nixon administration, Goldwater was an outspoken critic of Mr. Nixon, repeatedly suggesting that he "tell the truth." He has spoken out on the dangers of computer data-gathering by the government, worried that the practice endangers personal privacy. In 1976, he criticized the special privileges and benefits afforded congressmen and scolded them for cutting back on similar benefits available to military personnel. His latest book, *The Coming Breakpoint,* explores the problems of government bureaucracy and predicts a time in the near future when the citizenry will refuse to support it any longer. In 1979, he emerged as the leader of the conservative opposition to the American recognition of the People's Republic of China. He filed a lawsuit against the Carter administration to halt official recognition and prevent the renouncing of the American-Taiwan mutual defense treaty.

A man of many interests, Barry Goldwater is a photographer, an expert on the Indian tribes of Arizona, a builder of model airplanes and automobiles, a ham radio enthusiast, and the only jet pilot in congress. He has made a number of camping expeditions on the Colorado River. During one of these expeditions in 1954, he discovered a natural stone bridge in Grand Canyon National Park. His book, *An Odyssey of the Green and Colorado Rivers,* tells of one of his expeditions and is illustrated with his own photographs. The book *People and Places* contains many of his photographs as well. His collection of Kachina dolls (Hopi Indian spirit representations) was donated to the Heard Museum and is described in the book *The Goldwater Kachina Doll Collection.*

In recent years, Goldwater's image among more liberal observers has undergone a change. Many of those who were opposed to him in 1964 have become his friends. Roy Reed, writing in the *New York Times Magazine,* has noted that Goldwater is "an elder and now respectable statesman." Some of his views have changed (he now supports detente, for instance), as have those of his former opponents so that the once seemingly vast distance between them has narrowed. Although still a leading conservative, he has become quite popular with people across the entire political spectrum. He spends much of his time giving speeches across the country. Perhaps, as he observed in a recent *New York Times* interview, "when you lay a real liberal alongside a real conservative, there's not enough difference to put in your hat."

BIOGRAPHICAL/CRITICAL SOURCES: Stephen C. Shadegg, *Barry Goldwater: Freedom Is His Flight Plan,* Fleet Press, 1962; *Human Events,* April 27, 1963; *New York Times,* July 9, 1963; *U.S. News & World Report,* July 15, 1963, September 2, 1963, September 7, 1964, April 25, 1966, September 2, 1966, April 28, 1969, February 16, 1976; *Newsweek,* October 21, 1963, August 3, 1964; Jack Bell, *Mr. Conservative: Barry Goldwater,* Macfadden, 1964; Edwin McDowell, *Barry Goldwater: Portrait of an Arizonan,* Regnery, 1964; Frank R. Donovan, *The Americanism of Barry Goldwater,* Macfadden, 1964; Arthur Frommer, *Goldwater from A to Z,* Frommer-Pasmantier, 1964; *McCalls,* January, 1964; *Look,* April 21, 1964; *Life,* September 18, 1964; *Vital Speeches,* October 1, 1964, February 15, 1969, May 15, 1978; *New York Times Magazine,* November 1, 1964, April 7, 1974; Bernard Cosman, *Five States for Goldwater: Continuity and Change in Southern Voting Patterns, 1920-1964,* University of Alabama Press, 1965; John H. Kessel, *Goldwater Coalition: Republican Strategies in 1964,* Bobbs-Merrill, 1968; *National Review,* January 16, 1968, December 19, 1975, April 30, 1976; *Time,* May 17, 1968, January 1, 1979; *Saturday Review,* October 17, 1970; *Cincinnati Enquirer,* July 21, 1974; *Washington Post Book World,* May 2, 1976.

*   *   *

GOLDWATER, Robert   1907-1973

November 23, 1907—March 26, 1973; American art critic, scholar, and teacher. Obituaries: *New York Times,* March 27, 1973.

*   *   *

GOLLEDGE, Reginald G(eorge)   1937-

PERSONAL: Born December 6, 1937, in Dungog, New South Wales, Australia; son of Lancelot George (a railway employee) and Rose (Gilbert) Golledge; married Margaret Ruth Mason (assistant director of special education in Ohio), January 21, 1961 (divorced, 1975); married Allison Louise Cahill (assistant professor of art history at University of Houston); children: (first marriage) Stephanie Kim, Linda Rae. *Education:* University of New England, Armidale, Australia, B.A. (honors), 1960, M.A. (honors), 1961; University of Iowa, Ph.D., 1966. *Home:* 267 Forest Dr., Goleta, Calif. 93017. *Office:* Department of Geography, Ellison Hall, University of California, Santa Barbara, Calif. 93106.

CAREER: University of Canterbury, Christchurch, New Zealand, lecturer in geography, 1961-63; University of British Columbia, Vancouver, assistant professor of geography, 1965-66; Ohio State University, Columbus, assistant professor, 1966-67, associate professor, 1967-71, professor of geography, 1971-77; University of California, Santa Barbara, professor of geography, 1977—. Visiting professor at

University of California, Berkeley, 1967, University of California, Los Angeles, 1969, University of Sydney, 1970, University of Texas at Austin, 1972, 1973, 1974, and University of Auckland, 1976.

MEMBER: Association of American Geographers, Regional Science Association, Environmental Design and Research Association, Institute of Australian Geographers, Psychometric Society, U.S. Classification Society. *Awards, honors:* Grants from Ohio State University's Transportation Research Center, 1967-68; National Science Foundation grants, 1969-70, 1973, 1974, 1975-76, and 1978-79.

WRITINGS: (With B. W. Johnson, L. J. King, and Alan Williman) *Traffic in a New Zealand City,* Whitcomb & Tombs, 1965; (editor with K. R. Cox) *Behavioral Models in Geography,* Northwestern University Press, 1969; (with J. N. Rayner) *Special Analysis of Settlement Patterns,* Department of Geography, Ohio State University, 1971; (with Gerard Rushton) *Multidimensional Scaling: Review and Geographic Applications,* Commission on College Geography, 1972; (with Douglas Aenedea) *Introduction to Scientific Reasoning in Geography,* Wiley, 1975; (with Rushton) *Spatial Choice and Spatial Behaviour,* Ohio State University Press, 1976; (with Gary T. Moore) *Environmental Knowing,* Dowden, 1976; (with Leslie J. King) *Cities, Space and Behavior,* Prentice-Hall, 1978.

Contributor: R. F. Warner, editor, *New England Essays,* University of New England (Armidale, Australia), 1963; Conrad Blythe, editor, *Manufacturing in New Zealand,* Pegasus, 1965; G. H. Drury and M. Logan Heinemann, editor, *A Geography of Australia,* Educational Books (Sydney), 1968; J. F. Schwar and others, editors, *A Study of Highway Research Needs and Resources,* Transportation Research Center, Ohio State University, 1968; *Cognitive Configurations of a City,* Ohio State University Research Foundation, 1975; *Essays in Honor of G. J. Butland,* University of New England Press, 1976; I. Altman and J. Wohlwill, *Human Behavior and Environment,* Plenum, 1977; R. Taaffe and J. Dolland, *Geographical Horizons,* Kendall/Hunt, 1978; N. Thrift, T. Carlstein and D. Parkes, *Timing Space and Spacing Time,* Aldine, 1978; S. Gale and G. Olsson, *Philosophy and Theory of Decision Making,* Reidel, 1978. Contributor to proceedings; over fifty articles have been published in *Geographical Analysis, Economic Geography, Journal of Regional Science, Australian Geographer,* and other geography journals in the United States, Australia, and New Zealand. *Geographical Analysis,* associated editor, 1971-73, editor, 1974-78; consulting editor, *Environment and Behavior,* 1971—, and *Professional Geographer,* 1972—.

WORK IN PROGRESS: *Behavioral Basis of Geography,* with K. R. Cox, for Wiley; *Proximity and Preference,* with J. N. Rayner; *Behavioral Models in Geography: Retrospect and Prospect.*

*   *   *

GOMEZ-GIL, Alfredo 1936-

PERSONAL: Born November 1, 1936, in Alicante, Spain; son of Alfredo (a government employee) and Natividad (Gil-Escoto) Gomez-Torre. *Education:* School of Hermanos Maristas, B.A., 1953; University of Granada, additional study, 1956-58; University of Madrid, license, 1965. *Politics:* "Liberty inherent to justice; peace inherent to liberty." *Home:* 1265 Asylum Ave., Hartford, Conn. 06105. *Office:* Hartford College for Women, Hartford, Conn. 06105.

CAREER: Yale University, New Haven, Conn., lecturer in

Spanish language and literature, 1965-66; Hartford College for Women, Hartford, Conn., assistant professor, 1968-72, associate professor, 1972—. Visiting professor, Middlebury College, summer, 1969. *Military service:* Spanish Army, Infantry, summers, 1962-63; became sergeant. *Member:* Modern Language Association of America, American Association of Teachers of Spanish and Portuguese. *Awards, honors:* Golden plaque of City of Murcia.

WRITINGS: *Escalas imprecisas* (poems), [Barcelona], 1960; *Pesada arena* (poems), Timon, 1962; *Brumas y cartones* (poems), Timon, 1963; *El exconde Sucanor,* Arcel, 1964; *Chispas y confetis,* Orozco, 1966; *Por la distancia* (poems), Agora, 1968; *Norte, Este, Oeste y Sur* (poems), Oliveros, 1968; *Cerebros espanoles en USA,* Plaza & Janes, 1971; *Introduccion a la esperanza* (poems), El Toro de Granito, 1971; *Veinti cuatro Poemas de Nieve,* Cuadernos del Sur, 1971; *Desde al arca del Profeta* (poems), Caja de Ahorros de la Diputacion Provincial, 1971; *Entre fetiches y Amuletos,* Caffarena, Malaga, 1974; *Paisajes y formas de Schlotter a traves de ur poeta,* Ediciones de Arte, 1975; *La Vuelta de los Cerebros,* Plaza & Janes, 1976; *La frente en el Suelo,* Alicante, 1976; *The Vibrations of Silence,* Ediciones Cultura Hispanica, 1978.

WORK IN PROGRESS: Anthology of Spanish Poetry; *Dissection of the American Woman; Sobre la Marcha,* a book of poems.

BIOGRAPHICAL/CRITICAL SOURCES: Gustavo Gili, editor, *Historia de la Literatura Espanola,* Valbuena Prat, 1968; Francisco Carenas, editor, *Antologia Poetas Espanoles en USA,* Editorial Adonais, 1972; Camilo Jose Cela, editor, *Papeles de San Armadans,* Number 206, Mallorca, 1973.

*   *   *

GONZALEZ, Alfonso 1927-

PERSONAL: Born March 21, 1927, in New York, N.Y.; son of Frank and Angustias (Perez) Gonzalez; married Avelina Gomez (a nurse anesthetist), June 24, 1956; children: Robert, Linda, Lisa. *Education:* Clark University, A.B., 1949; Northwestern University, M.A., 1950; University of Texas, Main University (now University of Texas at Austin), Ph.D., 1962. *Home:* 3927 Vardell Rd. N.W., Calgary, Alberta, Canada T3A 0C3. *Office:* Department of Geography, University of Calgary, Calgary, Alberta, Canada T2N 1N4.

CAREER: Army Map Service, Washington, D.C., military intelligence research specialist, 1954-55; San Diego State College (now University), San Diego, Calif., 1957-60, began as instructor, became assistant professor of geography; Northeast Louisiana State College (now Northeast Louisiana University), Monroe, assistant professor of geography, 1960-62; Southern Illinois University, Alton, assistant professor of geography, 1962-63; University of South Florida, Tampa, 1963-67, began as assistant professor, became associate professor of geography, chairman of department, 1965-67; University of Calgary, Calgary, Alberta, 1967—, began as associate professor, currently professor of geography. Visiting professor, Kent State University, summer, 1962, University of Texas, summer, 1966. Member of Florida Governor's Committee on resource-use education, 1964-67. *Military service:* U.S. Army, 1945-46, 1950-51; became sergeant.

MEMBER: Association of American Geographers, National Council for Geographic Education, Latin American Studies Association, Conference of Latin American Geographers, Canadian Association of Latin American Studies, Canadian Association of University Professors, Population Reference Bureau, Southeast Conference on Latin American Studies, Southwest Council for Latin American Studies, Rocky Mountain Council for Latin American Studies, Midwest Association for Latin American Studies, Pacific Coast Council for Latin American Studies. *Awards, honors:* National Science Foundation grants, 1966-67; Fulbright-Hays senior fellowship in Colombia, 1971.

WRITINGS: (Assistant to Donald D. Brand, with Pablo Guzman-Rivas) *Coastal Study of Southwest Mexico,* University of Texas Press, Part I, 1957, Part II, 1958; (contributor) *La Geografia y los Problemas de Poblacion,* Volume I, Sociedad Mexicana de Geografia y Estadistica, 1966; (contributor) Paul Kramer and Robert E. McNicoll, editors, *Latin American Panorama: An Anthology,* Putnam, 1968; (contributor) George Demko, Harold M. Rose, and George A. Schnell, editors, *Population Geography: A Reader,* McGraw, 1970; (contributor) *Discussion Papers,* University of Calgary, 1970; (contributor) Robert N. Thomas, editor, *Population Dynamics of Latin America: A Review and Bibliography,* Conference of Latin American Geographers, 1973. Author of classified reports for Army Map Service, 1954-55. Contributor to Richard P. Momsen, Jr., editor, *Change in Latin America: An Interdisciplinary Approach,* and *Grolier Encyclopedia Universal.* Contributor to *Journal of Inter-American Studies, World Affairs Digest, Caribbean Studies, Florida Geographer, Journal of Geography,* and other professional journals.

WORK IN PROGRESS: Agriculture and Population: Comparison of World Regions; Latin America: Population and Settlement.

* * *

GOODMAN, Grant K(ohn) 1924-

PERSONAL: Born October 18, 1924, in Cleveland, Ohio; son of Lewis Meyer (a manufacturer) and Elaine (Kohn) Goodman. *Education:* Princeton University, B.A., 1948; University of Michigan, M.A., 1949, Ph.D., 1955. *Religion:* Jewish. *Home:* 934 Pamela Lane, Lawrence, Kan. 66044. *Office:* Department of History, University of Kansas, Lawrence, Kan. 66045.

CAREER: University of Washington, Seattle, acting assistant professor of history, 1955-56; University of Delaware, Newark, instructor in history, 1956-58; State University of New York at Fredonia, assistant professor of history, 1958-62; University of Kansas, Lawrence, associate professor, 1962-65, professor of history, 1965—. Visiting Fulbright lecturer in history at University of Philippines, 1959-60; visiting professor at Sophia University, Tokyo, summers, 1967 and 1969, 1970-71, and University College, Dublin, 1975; fellow, Netherlands Institute for Advanced Study in the Humanities and Social Sciences, Wassenaar, 1976-77. *Military service:* U.S. Army, 1943-46; became first lieutenant. *Member:* American Historical Association, Association for Asian Studies, Asia Society, Japan Society, Midwest Conference on Asian Affairs. *Awards, honors:* Fulbright scholar, University of Leyden, 1952-53; Fulbright-Hays faculty research grant, 1964-65; American Council of Learned Societies and Leverhulme Foundation travel grants, 1969, 1973; Japan Pen Club award, 1972, Japan Foundation grant, 1973; Sumitomo-Rockefeller grant, 1976-78.

WRITINGS: The Dutch Impact on Japan, 1640-1853, E. J. Brill, 1967; *Four Aspects of Philippine-Japanese Relations, 1930-1940,* Yale University, Southeast Asia Studies, 1967;

(editor) *Imperial Japan and Asia: A Reassessment,* East Asian Institute, Columbia University, 1967; *Davao: A Case Study in Japanese-Philippine Relations,* University of Kansas, East Asian Series, 1967; (editor) *The American Occupation of Japan: A Retrospective View,* University of Kansas, East Asian Series, 1968.

WORK IN PROGRESS: Japan and the Indian National Movement, 1905-1941; Japan: The Dutch Experience; From Bataan to Tokyo: Diary of a Filipino Student in Wartime Japan.

* * *

GOODWIN, Leonard 1929-

PERSONAL: Born October 11, 1929, in Brooklyn, N.Y.; son of Cecil M. (a civil engineer) and Ida (Cohen) Goodwin; married Mary T. Doyle (a public health nutritionist), June 4, 1960; children: Jonathan, Micah, Rachel. *Education:* University of Michigan, B.S. (engineering mathematics), 1950, B.S. (engineering physics), 1951, B.A., 1953; University of Chicago, M.A., 1954; graduate study at Brandeis University, 1954-55, and Columbia University, 1955-57. *Home:* 818 Hillsboro Dr., Silver Spring, Md. 20902; and 123 Newton Ave. N., Worcester, Mass. 01609. *Office:* Department of Social Science and Policy Studies, Worcester Polytechnic Institute, Worcester, Mass. 01609.

CAREER: Industrial Scientific Co., New York, N.Y., physicist, 1951-52; Clifford Manufacturing Co., Waltham, Mass., research engineer, 1954-55; Earlham College, Richmond, Ind., assistant professor of psychology and community dynamics, 1957-60; National Academy of Sciences, Washington, D.C., research associate and head of administrative operations for Committee on International Exchange of Persons, 1960-66; Brookings Institution, Washington, D.C., research associate, 1966-74; Worcester Polytechnic Institute, Worcester, Mass., professor and chairman of department of social science and policy studies, 1974—. *Member:* American Sociological Association, American Parents Committee (member of board of directors, 1974—).

WRITINGS: American Professors in Asia: A Study of the Selection and Adaptation of American Professors under the Fulbright Program (monograph), Bureau of Educational and Cultural Affairs, U.S. Department of State, 1964; *Do the Poor Want to Work?: A Social Psychological Study of Work Orientation,* Brookings Institution, 1972; *Can Social Science Help Resolve National Problems?: Welfare, a Case in Point,* Free Press, 1975; *The Work Incentive Program and Related Experiences: A Review of Research with Policy Implications* (monograph), U.S. Department of Labor, 1977. Contributor to *American Psychologist* and *Social Problems.* Associate editor, *Journal of Applied Behavioral Science,* 1974—.

WORK IN PROGRESS: A book tentatively entitled *The Social Psychological Impact of Welfare and Unemployment Insurance.*

* * *

GORDON, Giles (Alexander Esme) 1940-
(Boswell)

PERSONAL: Born May 23, 1940, in Edinburgh, Scotland; son of Alexander Esme and Betsy Balmont (McCurry) Gordon; married Margaret Anna Eastoe (a book illustrator), March 21, 1964; children: Callum Giles, Gareth Alexander, Harriet Miranda. *Education:* Attended Edinburgh Academy, 1952-58. *Politics:* Labour. *Residence:* London, England. *Agent:* Ilsa Yardley, Elaine Greene Ltd., 31 Newington Green, London N16 9PU, England. *Office:* Anthony Sheil Associates Ltd., 2 Morwell St., London WC1B 3AR, England.

CAREER: Oliver & Boyd Ltd. (book publishers), Edinburgh, Scotland, trainee, 1959-63; Secker & Warburg Ltd. (book publishers), London, England, advertising manager, 1963-64; Hutchinson & Co. (book publishers), London, editor, 1964-66; Penguin Books Ltd., Harmondsworth, Middlesex, England, editor, 1966-67; Victor Gollancz Ltd. (book publishers), London, editorial director, 1967-72; Anthony Sheil Associates Ltd. (literary agents), London, partner, 1972—. Lecturer in creative writing, Tufts University-in-London, 1972-77. *Member:* Arts Council of Great Britain (member of literature panel, 1966-70), Society of Young Publishers (past chairman), Society of Authors (member of committee of management, 1973-76), Writers' Guild of Great Britain, Garrick Club.

WRITINGS—Poetry: *Two and Two Make One,* Akros, 1966; *Two Elegies,* Turret Books, 1968; *Twelve Poems for Callum,* Akros, 1970; *Eight Poems for Gareth,* Sceptre Press, 1970; *Between Appointments,* Sceptre Press, 1971; *One Man, Two Women,* Sheep Press, 1974; *The Egyptian Room, Metropolitan Museum of Art,* Sceptre Press, 1974; *The Oban Poems,* Sceptre Press, 1977.

Short story collections: *Pictures from an Exhibition,* Dial Press, 1970; *Farewell, Fond Dreams,* Hutchinson, 1975; *The Illusionist,* Harvester Press, 1978.

Novels: *The Umbrella Man,* Allison & Busby, 1971; *About a Marriage,* Stein & Day, 1972; *Girl with Red Hair,* Hutchinson, 1973; *100 Scenes from Married Life,* Hutchinson, 1976; *Enemies,* Harvester Press, 1977.

Juvenile: *Walter and the Balloon,* Heinemann, 1975.

Editor: (With Alex Hamilton, and contributor) *Factions,* M. Joseph, 1974; *Beyond the Words,* Hutchinson, 1975; (with Dulan Barber) *Members of the Jury,* Wildwood House, 1975; *Prevailing Spirits: A Book of Scottish Ghost Stories,* Hamish Hamilton, 1976; *A Book of Contemporary Nightmares,* M. Joseph, 1977; (with Fred Urquhart) *Modern Scottish Short Stories,* Hamish Hamilton, 1978.

Contributor to *Transatlantic Review, Punch, New Review, New Statesman, Spectator, Guardian,* and to *The Scotsman,* under pseudonym Boswell. Co-editor, *New Saltire* (Scottish literary magazine), 1960-62.

BIOGRAPHICAL/CRITICAL SOURCES: *Listener,* April 9, 1970; *Times Literary Supplement,* April 23, 1970; *Observer Review,* June 21, 1970; Giles Gordon, editor, *Beyond the Words,* Hutchinson, 1975.

*   *   *

GORDON, Leland J(ames) 1897-

PERSONAL: Born September 28, 1897, in Janesville, Minn.; married Doris Gilbert, June 23, 1923; children: Leland J., Janet W. (Mrs. Gordon M. Forbes). *Education:* University of Pennsylvania, B.S., 1922, M.A., 1924, Ph.D., 1928. *Politics:* Democrat. *Religion:* Baptist. *Home:* 830 North Shore Dr., St. Petersburg, Fla. 33701. *Office:* Library, Denison University, Granville, Ohio 43023.

CAREER: Chippewa Milling Co., Montevideo, Minn., assistant sales manager, 1919-20; University of Pennsylvania, Wharton School of Finance and Commerce, Philadelphia, instructor, 1922-29, assistant professor of economics, 1930-31, assistant director of admissions, 1927-29; Haverford Col-

lege, Haverford, Pa., lecturer in economics, 1927-29; Denison University, Granville, Ohio, professor, 1931-59, John E. Harris Professor of Economics and Research, 1959-63, professor emeritus, 1963—, chairman of department of economics, 1931-57, special assistant to president, 1966-70, director of Weights and Measures Research Center, 1955-74. Lecturer, Kanzanjian Foundation, 1957; Fulbright lecturer, Hiroshima University, 1963-64; guest lecturer in Japan, 1969; visiting professor at Willamette University, Louisiana State University, Northwestern University, University of Maryland (Overseas Program in Europe), University of Colorado, University of Wisconsin, and Pennsylvania State University. Research specialist in Office of Consumer Advisor, Advisory Commission to the Council of National Defense, 1940-41; member of board of directors, Consumers Union, 1942-49; arbitrator, Fifth Regional War Labor Board, 1944-45; member of consumers advisory committee, Council of Economic Advisers, 1948-52. Member of Commission on Church and Economic Life, National Council of Churches, 1950-69.

MEMBER: American Council on Consumer Interests (charter member; president, 1958-59), American Association of University Professors, Midwest Economic Association (president, 1957-58), Ohio Association of Economists and Political Scientists (president, 1959-60), Phi Beta Kappa, Pi Gamma Mu, Tau Kappa Alpha, Omicron Delta Kappa. *Awards, honors:* Penfield fellow in international relations, 1929-30; Fulbright lecturer; American Council on Consumer Interests, distinguished fellow, 1973.

WRITINGS: *American Relations with Turkey, 1830-1930: An Economic Interpretation,* University of Pennsylvania Press, 1932; *Economics for Consumers,* American Book Co., 1939, (with Stewart M. Lee) 7th edition, Van Nostrand, 1977; *Consumers in Wartime,* Harper, 1943; *Elementary Economics,* American Book Co., 1950; (with Reinhold Niebuhr) *Your Christian Conscience and American Abundance,* Department of Church and Economic Life, 1955; *The Function of the Consumer in a Free Choice Economy,* Calvin K. Kazanjian Economics Foundation, 1958; *Weights and Measures and the Consumer,* Consumers Union, 1966, 2nd edition, 1970. Contributor of about two hundred articles, pamphlets, and reviews to professional periodicals. Member of board of editors, *Social Science,* 1939-75.

SIDELIGHTS: Leland Gordon writes: "My purpose in writing my first consumer book, was enlightenment about consumer economics. The first one was published in 1939, when it was a pioneering adventure in a new field."

*   *   *

GORDON, Michael 1940-

PERSONAL: Born November 14, 1940, in Brooklyn, N.Y.; son of Julius and Ann Gordon; married Roberta Ruth Rosenberg (a special education teacher), June 7, 1964; children: Jennifer Lyn, Andra Leigh. *Education:* City College of the City University of New York, B.A., 1962; University of Connecticut, M.A., 1964, Ph.D., 1967. *Home:* 57 Bundy Lane, Storrs, Conn. 06268. *Office:* Department of Sociology, University of Connecticut, Storrs, Conn. 06268.

CAREER: Temple University, Philadelphia, Pa., instructor, 1966-67, assistant professor of sociology, 1967-69; University of Connecticut, Storrs, assistant professor, 1969-71, associate professor, 1971-77, professor of sociology, 1977—. *Member:* American Sociological Association, National Council for Family Relations, Eastern Sociological Society. *Awards, honors:* Fulbright lectureship to Ireland, 1973;

Younger Humanist fellowship from National Endowment for the Humanities, 1974-75.

WRITINGS: Juvenile Delinquency in the American Novel, 1905-1965: A Study in the Sociology of Literature, Bowling Green University Press, 1971; (editor) The Nuclear Family in Crisis: The Search for an Alternative, Harper, 1972; (editor with Robert R. Bell) The Social Dimension of Human Sexual Behavior, Little, Brown, 1972; (editor with Bell, and contributor) The Social Dimension of Human Sexuality, Little, Brown, 1972; (editor) The American Family in Social Historical Perspective, St. Martin's, 1973, 2nd edition, 1978; The American Family: Past, Present, and Future, Random House, 1978. Contributor to Journal of Marriage and the Family, Medical Aspects of Human Sexuality, Journal of Sex Research, Social Forces, Social Problems, Journal of Popular Culture, Family Coordinator, Pacific Sociological Review, Sociology and Social Research, Journal of Comparative Family Studies, and International Journal of Sociology of the Family. Editor of special issue, Journal of Marriage and the Family, August, 1973; member of editorial board, Journal of Marriage and the Family and Sociological Symposium.

WORK IN PROGRESS: Research on change in American courtship customs.

*   *   *

GORDON, Percival Hector   1884-1975

PERSONAL: Born January 27, 1884, in Qu'Appelle, Northwest Territories (now Saskatchewan), Canada; son of Leslie and Clara E. (Hector) Gordon; married Harriet Sarah Kennedy, October 7, 1908 (died September 27, 1959); children: Helen Jessie (Mrs. Francis Gordon Venables). Education: University of Toronto, B.A., 1905, M.A., 1906, B.C.L., 1909. Politics: Conservative. Religion: Anglican. Home: 2424 College Ave., Regina, Saskatchewan, Canada S4P 1C8.

CAREER: Admitted to the Bar of Saskatchewan, 1908, Bar of Ontario, 1934; private law practice in Regina, Saskatchewan, 1908-33, Toronto, Ontario, 1933-35, Regina, 1961-75. Examiner of law students, 1910-22; created King's Counsel, 1928 (later Queen's Counsel); judge of Saskatchewan Court of Appeals, Regina, 1935-61. President, Regina Daily Star, Regina, Saskatchewan, 1924-35. Chancellor of Anglican Diocese of Qu'Appelle, 1921-42; head of Canadian Red Cross Society, 1940-44. Volunteer lecturer at University of Saskatchewan, College of Law, 1962-71. Director of Toronto General Trust Corp.; honorary counsel to Federation of Indian Tribes of Saskatchewan. Member: Canadian Law Society, Saskatchewan Law Society, Assiniboia Club. Awards, honors: Commander of Order of the British Empire, 1943; Officer of the Order of Canada, 1972; LL.D., Manitoba University, 1943; holder of Polish, Greek, and British decorations.

WRITINGS: Fifty Years in the Canadian Red Cross, Ryerson Press, 1970. Contributor to magazines, newspapers, and law journals.

WORK IN PROGRESS: Working on all Indian treaties in their application to the federal government.†

(Died April 6, 1975)

*   *   *

GORMAN, John Andrew   1938-

PERSONAL: Born August 28, 1938, in Hoboken, N.J.; son of Thomas and Edith (Ward) Gorman. Education: Manhattan College, B.A., 1960; University of Freiburg, additional study, 1962-63; Johns Hopkins University, M.A., 1961, Ph.D., 1967. Politics: Radical. Religion: Unitarian Universalist. Home: 6004 Southwest 62nd Ave., South Miami, Fla. 33143.

CAREER: Fisher School of Languages, New York, N.Y., part-time instructor in English, 1961-62; Lamar State College of Technology (now Lamar University), Beaumont, Tex., assistant professor of German, 1965-66; University of Miami, Coral Gables, Fla., assistant professor of German, 1967-74; free-lance writer, 1974—. Language director, Netherlands National Student Organization, summer, 1964; language director, Council on Student Travel, summer, 1965. Member: American Civil Liberties Union. Awards, honors: Danforth fellowship, 1960-67; Woodrow Wilson fellowship, 1960-61; fifth prize in Writer's Digest poetry contest, 1971.

WRITINGS: (Translator) Lorenz Winter, Heinrich Mann and His Public, University of Miami Press, 1969; The Reception of Federico Garcia Lorca in Germany, Goeppinger Arbeiten fuer Germanistik, 1973. Contributor to American Motorcycle News, National Zeitung, Aufbau, National Fisherman, Mensa Bulletin, Go Boating, ABC International, Soundings, and numerous other periodicals.

WORK IN PROGRESS: Studying contemporary intellectual, social, and political developments with an eye to a nonjudgemental anticipation and understanding of the future; a study of "white terror" and its effects on our society.

SIDELIGHTS: John A. Gorman writes: "The greatest encouragement to take up writing seriously was the reading of so much bad prose already in print and so well rewarded. My pain could only be assuaged by taking up the pen myself." Avocational interests: Travel, the outdoors, diving, sailing, boating.

*   *   *

GOSNELL, Harold F(oote)   1896-

PERSONAL: Surname is pronounced Goz-nel; born December 24, 1896, in Lockport, N.Y.; son of James (a Methodist minister) and Sylvia (Foote) Gosnell; married Florence Lucy Fake (a teacher), June 30, 1928; children: David Foote, John Scammon. Education: University of Rochester, A.B., 1918; University of Chicago, Ph.D., 1922. Politics: Independent. Religion: Protestant. Home: 5408 Wilson Lane, Bethesda, Md. 20014.

CAREER: University of Chicago, Chicago, Ill., instructor, 1922-26, assistant professor, 1926-32, associate professor of political science, 1932-42; U.S. Government, Washington, D.C., analyst, Office of Price Administration, 1941-42, administrative analyst, Bureau of the Budget, 1942-46, member of staff, Division of Historical Policy, Department of State, 1946-50; American University, Washington, D.C., adjunct professor of government, 1947-60; Special Operations Research Office, Washington, D.C., senior research scientist, 1950-60, chairman of Exploit-USRR project, 1960-61; Howard University, Washington, D.C., professor of government, 1961-70. Visiting professor, University of Washington, Seattle, 1955. Research consultant to National Resources Committee, 1937, 1938, and Bureau of the Budget, 1940. Military service: U.S. Army, 1918-19; became sergeant. Member: Phi Beta Kappa. Awards, honors: Social Science Research Council fellowship to study European election procedures, 1925-26; Spelman Fund fellowship to study British Royal Commission of Inquiry, 1933; first winner of John Anisfield Award for best book in field of race relations, 1935, for Negro Politicians.

WRITINGS: *Boss Platt and His New York Machine: A Study of the Political Leadership of Thomas C. Platt, Theodore Roosevelt, and Others,* University of Chicago Press, 1924, reprinted, Russell, 1969; (with C. E. Merriam) *Non-Voting: Causes and Methods of Control,* University of Chicago Press, 1924; *Getting Out the Vote: An Experiment in the Stimulation of Voting,* University of Chicago Press, 1927; *Why Europe Votes,* University of Chicago Press, 1930; *Negro Politicians: The Rise of Negro Politics in Chicago,* University of Chicago Press, 1935, 2nd edition, 1968; *Machine Politics: Chicago Model,* University of Chicago Press, 1937, 2nd edition, 1969; *Grass Roots Politics,* American Council on Public Affairs, 1942, reprinted, Russell, 1970; *Democracy: The Threshold of Freedom,* Ronald, 1948; (with Merriam) *The American Party System,* 4th edition (Gosnell was not associated with earlier editions), Macmillan, 1949; *Champion Campaigner: Franklin D. Roosevelt,* Macmillan, 1952; (with Smolka) *American Parties and Elections,* C. E. Merrill, 1976.

Contributor: T. V. Smith and L. D. White, editors, *An Experiment in Social Science Research,* University of Chicago Press, 1929; Roy V. Peel and Joseph S. Roucek, editors, *Introduction to Politics,* Crowell, 1941; Douglas Waples, editor, *Print, Radio and Film in a Democracy,* University of Chicago Press, 1942; L. D. White, editor, *The Future of Government in the United States,* University of Chicago Press, 1942; *The United States at War: Development and Administration of the War Program by the Federal Government,* U.S. Government Printing Office, 1946; E. Franklin Frazier, editor, *Integration of the Negro in American Life,* Howard University, 1952. Contributor to *Encyclopedia of the Social Sciences, Encyclopaedia Britannica,* and *Collier's Encyclopedia.* Contributor of about sixty articles to journals and proceedings.

WORK IN PROGRESS: A biography of President Harry S Truman, tentatively entitled *Truman's Crises;* an article on Black mayors; an autobiography, *Professor Meets Teacher.*

*   *   *

GOULD, Lewis L(udlow) 1939-

PERSONAL: Born September 21, 1939, in New York, N.Y.; son of John L. (a journalist) and Carmen (Lewis) Gould; married Karen D. Keel (an art historian and author), October 24, 1970. *Education:* Brown University, A.B., 1961; Yale University, M.A., 1962, Ph.D., 1966. *Home:* 2602 La Ronde, Austin, Tex. 78731. *Office:* Department of History, University of Texas, Austin, Tex. 78712.

CAREER: Yale University, New Haven, Conn., assistant professor of history, 1966-67; University of Texas at Austin, assistant professor, 1967-71, associate professor, 1971-76, professor of history, 1976—. *Member:* Organization of American Historians, American Historical Association, Phi Beta Kappa. *Awards, honors:* Carr P. Collins Prize, Texas Institute of Letters, 1973, for *Progressives and Prohibitionists;* National Endowment for the Humanities fellowship, 1974-75.

WRITINGS: *Wyoming: A Political History, 1868-1896,* Yale University Press, 1968; (editor with James C. Curtis) *The Black Experience in America: Selected Essays,* University of Texas Press, 1970; *Progressives and Prohibitionists: Texas Democrats in the Wilson Era,* University of Texas Press, 1973; (editor and contributor) *The Progressive Era,* Syracuse University Press, 1974; (with Richard Greffe) *Photojournalist: The Career of Jimmy Hare,* University of Texas Press, 1977; *Reform and Regulation: American Politics, 1900-1916,* Wiley, 1978.

WORK IN PROGRESS: *The Presidency of William McKinley,* completion expected in 1979.

*   *   *

GOULED, Vivian G(loria) 1911-
(Marcia Peters)

PERSONAL: Surname is pronounced *Goo*-lay; born June 12, 1911, in Los Angeles, Calif.; daughter of Peter (an industrialist) and Mary (Kaufman) Gouled. *Education:* Newark Normal School, teacher certification for kindergarten and primary grades, 1932. *Home:* 65 Hawthorne Pl., Montclair, N.J. 07042.

CAREER: Kindergarten-elementary school teacher. *Member:* Authors Guild, National League of American Pen Women, Society of Children's Book Writers. *Awards, honors:* More than twenty-five poetry awards, including prizes from Ocean Park Writer's Conference, 1956, and Suffield Writer's Conference, 1959.

WRITINGS—For children: *1 2 3 I Can Count,* Rand McNally, 1972. Work is represented in forty-six anthologies, including: *Young America at the Piano,* Book II, edited by Raymond Burrows and E. M. Ahearn, Birchard, 1946; *For a Child: Great Poems Old and New,* edited by Wilma McFarland, Westminster, 1947; *A Child's First Playbook,* edited by Caroline Horowitz, Hart Publishing, 1953; *Poems Children Enjoy,* edited by Elizabeth F. Noon, F. A. Owen, 1953; *Away We Go: One Hundred Poems for the Very Young,* compiled by C. S. McEwen, Crowell, 1956; *Treasure Trails Parade,* edited by Marjorie Barrows, Spencer Press, 1958; *V Is for Verses,* edited by Odille Ousley, Ginn, 1964; *Happy Rhythms and Rhymes: Favorite Songs and Poems from "My Weekly Reader,"* edited by Patricia M. Cavanaugh, American Education Publications, 1971; *Humpty Dumpty's Holiday Stories,* Parents' Magazine Press, 1973; and in music readers, manuals, readers, and primers. Author of verses for more than sixty greeting card companies. Contributor of more than twenty-five hundred poems to children's magazines and educational journals, occasionally under pseudonym, Marcia Peters, including *My Weekly Reader, Instructor, Humpty Dumpty, Grade Teacher, Early Years,* and *Wee Wisdom,* and to more than fifty church school publications.

WORK IN PROGRESS: *Good Bye, Kangaroo* (tentative title), a collection of poems about animals for young children; *Doodles,* for Rand McNally.

AVOCATIONAL INTERESTS: Playing piano, word games, word puzzles, writing songs for young children, cactus and other indoor plants, art, music, nature, travel.

*   *   *

GOULET, Denis A. 1931-

PERSONAL: Born May 27, 1931, in Fall River, Mass.; son of Fernand J. and Lumena (Bouchard) Goulet; married Ana Maria Reynaldo Alves, November 21, 1964; children: Andrea, Sinane (daughters). *Education:* Attended Providence College, Providence, R.I., 1948-50; St. Paul's College, Washington, D.C., B.A., 1954, M.A., 1956; Institut de Recherche et de Formation en Vue du Developpement (Paris), M.A. (social planning), 1960; University of Sao Paulo, Ph.D., 1963. *Residence:* Washington, D.C. *Office:* Overseas Development Council, 1717 Massachusetts Ave. N.W., Washington, D.C. 20036.

CAREER: Worked on census of immigrants in Toronto, Ontario, 1957, and later that year as laborer in proletarian areas of St. Remy, France; lived in slums and worked as factory hand in Madrid, Spain, 1957-58; shared life of two nomadic tribes in northern Sahara, Algeria, 1958; Institut de Recherche et de Formation en Vue du Developpement (IFRED), Paris, France, foreign student adviser, 1959-60, member of development mission to Lebanon, 1960, visiting professor, 1962-63; U.S. Agency for International Development, adviser in Brazil on development, 1964, and on higher education and manpower, 1965; University of Saskatchewan, Regina Campus, visiting professor of social sciences, 1965-66; Indiana University at Bloomington, visiting associate professor, 1966-67, associate professor of government, 1967-68; Center for the Study of Development and Social Change, Cambridge, Mass., research fellow, 1968-69; Center for the Study of Democratic Institutions, Santa Barbara, Calif., visiting fellow, 1969; University of California at San Diego, La Jolla, visiting professor of sociology, 1969-70; Center for the Study of Development and Social Change, fellow, 1970-74; Overseas Development Council, Washington, D.C., visiting fellow, 1974-76, senior fellow, 1976—. Visiting fellow, Organization of American States, Washington, D.C., 1974-76.

MEMBER: Society for International Development. *Awards, honors:* Chevalier, Ordre du Cedre (Lebanon), 1960; grants for research in Brazil from governments of United States and Brazil, 1961-62, and Organization of American States, 1963.

WRITINGS: (With L. J. Lebret and others) *Besoins et possibilites de developpement du Liban,* three volumes, Lebanon Ministry of Planning, 1960-61; *Etica del desarrollo,* Editora Estela/IEPAL (Barcelona/Montevideo), 1965; (contributor) Samuel Shapiro, editor, *Cultural Factors in Interamerican Relations,* University of Notre Dame Press, 1968; (with Michael Hudson) *The Myth of Aid,* Center for the Study of Development and Social Change, 1970; *The Cruel Choice: A New Concept in the Theory of Development,* Atheneum, 1971; (contributor) E. Philip Morgan, editor, *The Administration of Change in Africa,* Dunellen, 1973; *A New Moral Order: Studies in Development Ethics and Liberation Theology,* Orbis, 1974; *The Uncertain Promise: Value Conflicts in Technology Transfer,* Idoc Books, 1977; *Looking at Guinea-Bissau: A New Nation's Development Strategy,* Overseas Development Council, 1978.

Contributor of over sixty articles to *Contact* (Paris), *World Justice, Christian Century, Developpement et Civilisations, Comparative Studies in Society and History, Harvard Educational Review, International Development Review,* and other journals.

WORK IN PROGRESS: A book-length study of the role of indigenous values in development.

SIDELIGHTS: In his work on the ethics of development, Denis Goulet has done field research by living the life of poverty in Algeria, Lebanon, Brazil, Spain, and other countries. His theoretical work concentrates on values conflict, multidisciplinary research, and new pedagogies, as these relate to development. He is competent in Spanish, Portuguese, and French.

BIOGRAPHICAL/CRITICAL SOURCES: *Vista* (publication of U.S. Association for the United Nations), November-December, 1971.

*   *   *

GOW, Donald John   1920-1973

PERSONAL: Born July 13, 1920, in Calgary, Alberta,

Canada; son of Walter Donald and Georgia (Boyd) Gow; married Nellie Cockburn, March 4, 1945; children: Andrew Duncan. *Education:* University of Manitoba, B.A., 1940; studied at Imperial Defence College, England, 1957; Queen's University, Kingston, Ontario, Ph.D., 1967. *Religion:* Anglican. *Home:* 99 Collingwood St., Kingston, Ontario, Canada. *Office:* School of Public Administration, Queen's University, Kingston, Ontario, Canada.

CAREER: Public Service Commission, Ottawa, Ontario, personnel selection officer, 1945-52; Canada Government, Treasury Board Staff, Ottawa, Ontario, budget analyst, 1953-56, Public Service Division chief, 1960-65; North Atlantic Treaty Organization (NATO) Secretariat, Paris, France, program control officer of infrastructure, 1957-59; Queen's University, Kingston, Ontario, executive assistant to the principal, 1967-70, director of School of Public Administration, 1970-73. Consultant to Prime Minister's Task Force on Labor Relations, 1967-68, Economic Council of Canada, 1970-71, and Secretary of State for Canada, 1971. *Military service:* Canadian Army, 1941-45; became captain. *Member:* Canadian Political Science Association, Canadian Institute of Public Administration, Canadian Tax Foundation. *Awards, honors:* Canada Council fellow, 1966; research fellow of Institute of Public Administration of Canada, 1966-67.

WRITINGS: The Progress of Budgetary Reform in the Government of Canada, Economic Council of Canada, 1973. Contributor to *Public Personnel Review* and *Public Administration Review.*

WORK IN PROGRESS: A study of employee earnings in the public sector in Canada; research grant to study policy-making at federal, provincial, and metropolitan levels of government; *Public Administration in Canada,* for University of Toronto Press.†

(Died June, 1973)

*   *   *

GOYER, Robert S(tanton)   1923-

PERSONAL: Born October 7, 1923, in Kokomo, Ind.; son of Clarence V. and Genevieve (Sober) Goyer; married Patricia Ann Stutz, 1950; children: Karen (Mrs. James Brodzinski), Susan, Linda, Amy. *Education:* DePauw University, B.A., 1948; Miami University, Oxford, Ohio, M.A., 1950; Ohio State University, Ph.D., 1955. *Home:* 19 Mulligan Rd., Athens, Ohio 45701. *Office:* College of Communication, Ohio University, Athens, Ohio 45701.

CAREER: Miami University, Oxford, Ohio, instructor in speech, 1948-51; Ohio State University, Columbus, instructor, 1955-56, assistant professor of speech, 1956-58, research associate in psychology at Research Foundation, 1956-63; Purdue University, Lafayette, Ind., assistant professor, 1958-61, associate professor, 1961-64, professor of communication, 1964-66, associate director, Communication Research Center, 1959-66; Ohio University, Athens, professor of interpersonal communication, 1966—, director of Center for Communication Studies, 1966-74, associate dean of Graduate College, 1978—. Visiting professor, University of Kansas, 1965. *Military service:* U.S. Army, 1943-46, 1951-52; became first lieutenant; received Bronze Star and Combat Infantryman's Badge. U.S. Army Reserve, 1946-55.

MEMBER: International Communication Association (president, 1969-70), American Association for the Advancement of Science, American Psychological Association, Speech Communication Association, Sigma Delta Chi. *Awards, honors:* National Aeronautics and Space Administration-American Society for Engineering Education faculty fellow at Marshall Space Flight Center, 1970.

WRITINGS: (With W. C. Redding and J. T. Rickey) *Interviewing Principles and Techniques,* revised edition, W. C. Brown, 1968; (with Michael Z. Sincoff) *Interviewing Methods,* Kendall/Hunt, 1977. Co-author of research reports on training devices for Office of Naval Research. Contributor to journals and to collected readings in his field. Editor, *Central States Speech Journal,* 1961-64.

WORK IN PROGRESS: Theories of Communication; Theories of Persuasion.

* * *

GRACEY, Harry L(ewis) 1933-

PERSONAL: Born April 18, 1933, in Upper Darby, Pa.; son of Harry F. (a foreign service officer) and Elizabeth (Hood) Gracey. *Education:* Antioch College, A.B., 1956; graduate study at University of Kentucky, 1956-58, and University of Michigan, 1958-60; New School for Social Research, M.A., 1964, Ph.D., 1967. *Politics:* Democrat. *Religion:* Society of Friends (Quaker). *Residence:* Schenectady, N.Y. *Office:* Department of Sociology, Union College, Schenectady, N.Y. 12308.

CAREER: Bank Street College of Education, New York City, research assistant and member of faculty, 1960-64; Brooklyn College of the City University of New York, New York City, instructor in sociology, 1964-67; Political and Economics Planning Ltd., London, England, research associate, 1967-70; City College of the City University of New York, New York City, assistant professor of sociology, 1970-71; Union College, Schenectady, N.Y., associate professor of sociology, 1971—, chairman of department, 1971—. Consultant, Social Science Research Council of Great Britain, 1969—. *Member:* American Sociological Association, British Sociological Association.

WRITINGS: (Editor with Dennis Wrong) *Readings in Introductory Sociology,* Macmillan, 1968, second edition, 1972; *Curriculum or Craftsmanship: The Elementary Teacher in the Bureaucratic System,* University of Chicago Press, 1972; (with Peter Hall, Roy Drewett, and Ray Thomas) *The Containment of Urban England,* Allen & Unwin, Volume I, 1972, Volume II, 1973.

WORK IN PROGRESS: Research on alternative schools, counterculture communes, and multi-national corporations.†

* * *

GRAF, Le Roy Philip 1915-

PERSONAL: Born March 17, 1915, in Fremont, Ohio; son of John Charles (a lunch-room proprietor) and Rose (Hammel) Graf; married Ruth Adena Peal (a preparatory school teacher), June 12, 1942; children: Christina, Melissa, Jeremy Peal. *Education:* Oberlin College, A.B., 1936; Harvard University, M.A., 1937, Ph.D., 1942. *Religion:* Unitarian. *Home:* 5717 Westover Dr., Knoxville, Tenn. 37919. *Office:* Department of History, University of Tennessee, Knoxville, Tenn. 37916.

CAREER: Harvard University and Radcliffe College, both Cambridge, Mass., instructor in history, 1942-43; Tufts College (now University), Medford, Mass., instructor in history, 1943-44; Ohio State University, Columbus, instructor in history, 1944-45; University of Tennessee, Knoxville,

associate professor, 1945-50, professor of history, 1950—, distinguished service professor, 1972—, head of department, 1965—. Visiting professor at Tufts College, summer, 1947, University of Houston, summer, 1956, and Vanderbilt University, summer, 1960. Member of Tennessee State Historic Sites Advisory Committee; member of advisory board, Region IV National Archives and Records Service. *Member:* American Historical Association, Organization of American Historians, American Association of University Professors (member of council, 1964-66), National Conference of Christians and Jews, Knoxville Round Table, Southern Historical Association (member of council, 1956-58), Phi Beta Kappa (senator, united chapters, 1977—), Phi Kappa Phi.

WRITINGS: (Editor with Ralph W. Haskins) *The Papers of Andrew Johnson,* University of Tennessee Press, Volume I, 1967, Volume II, 1970, Volume III, 1972, Volume IV, 1975. Contributor of about ten articles to professional journals. *Publications of East Tennessee Historical Society,* associate editor, 1945-74, senior editor, 1974—.

WORK IN PROGRESS: Additional volumes of *The Papers of Andrew Johnson,* a series of about a dozen volumes.

* * *

GRAFF, George 1886-1973

August 5, 1886—January 24, 1973; American songwriter. Obituaries: *New York Times,* January 26, 1973; *Washington Post,* January 27, 1973; *Newsweek,* February 5, 1973.

* * *

GRAHAM, Gene S(wann) 1924-

PERSONAL: Born August 26, 1924, in Murray, Ky.; son of Carmon McWade (a teacher) and Opal (Swann) Graham; married Martha Fentress, October 20, 1945; children: Susan Marie (Mrs. James Erwin Fox), Betty Jane (Mrs. Michael White), Philip Gene. *Education:* Murray State University, B.S., 1948; Harvard University, graduate study, 1962-63. *Politics:* "Independent, leaning Democrat." *Religion:* Christian Church (Disciples of Christ). *Home and office:* 806 Meartop Dr., Nashville, Tenn. 37205.

CAREER: Nashville Tennessean, Nashville, Tenn., reporter, cartoonist, columnist, editorial writer, and public affairs editor, 1948-64; University of Illinois at Urbana-Champaign, visiting lecturer, 1964-65, associate professor, 1965-71, professor of journalism, 1972—. Director of summer training, *Boston Globe,* 1966-67, 1968-69. *Military service:* U.S. Navy, aviator, 1943-45; became ensign. *Member:* Association of American Editorial Cartoonists, Associated Press Managing Editors Association, Sigma Delta Chi. *Awards, honors:* Pulitzer Prize, 1962, for national affairs reporting.

WRITINGS: One-Man, One-Vote, Atlantic-Little Brown, 1972. Contributor of chapters to numerous books. Contributor to *New South, Quill, Nieman Reports, Harper's, Living History of the World,* and *Accent USA.*

* * *

GRANT, John E(rnest) 1925-

PERSONAL: Born August 28, 1925, in Newburyport, Mass.; son of Albert M. (a town official) and Christine (Currier) Grant; married Mary Lynn Johnson, March 6, 1974; children: (previous marriage) Michael E., Kenneth M. *Education:* Attended Hamilton College, 1947-49; Harvard University, A.B., 1951, A.M., 1954, Ph.D., 1960. *Home:* 15 Seventh Ave. S., Iowa City, Iowa 52240. *Office:* Department of English, University of Iowa, Iowa City, Iowa 52242.

CAREER: University of Connecticut, Storrs, instructor, 1956-60, assistant professor, 1960-64, associate professor of English, 1964-65; University of Iowa, Iowa City, professor of English, 1965—. Visiting professor at University of Alberta, 1968 and 1973, and Emory University, 1976. Military service: U.S. Army, 1943-46. Member: American Association of University Professors, Modern Language Association of America, Midwest Modern Language Association. Awards, honors: American Council of Learned Societies fellowship, England, 1968-69; American Philosophical Society fellowship, 1971; National Endowment for the Humanities fellowship, 1977.

WRITINGS: (Editor) Discussions of William Blake, Heath, 1961; (contributor) Northrop Frye, editor, Blake: A Collection of Critical Essays, Prentice-Hall, 1966; (contributor) Murray Krieger, editor, Northrop Frye in Modern Criticism: English Institute Essays, 1965, Columbia University Press, 1966; (contributor) Alvin Rosenfeld, editor, William Blake: Essays for S. Foster Damon, Brown University Press, 1969; (contributor) Willi Erzgraber, editor, Interpretationen, Fischer Bucherei, 1970; (editor with David V. Erdman) Blake's Visionary Forms Dramatic, Princeton University Press, 1970; (contributor) Robert N. Essick, editor, Blake: The Artist, Hennessey & Ingalls, 1973; (contributor) Stuart Curran and Joseph A. Wittreich, Jr., editors, Blake's Sublime Allegory, University of Wisconsin Press, 1973; (contributor) John Karl Franson, editor, Milton Reconsidered, Universitat Salzburg, 1976; (editor with wife, Mary Lynn Johnson) Blake's Poems and Designs, Norton, 1978. Contributor to Yale Review, Modern Philology, Philological Quarterly, Bulletin of the New York Public Library, Modern Language Quarterly, Nation, Keats-Shelly Journal, Journal of Aesthetics and Art Criticism, Southern Review, Blake Newsletter, Blake Studies, PMLA, James Joyce Quarterly, Studies in Romanticism, English Language Notes, Texas Studies in Literature and Language, and Essays in Criticism.

WORK IN PROGRESS: With E. J. Rose, M. J. Tolley, and D. V. Erdman, William Blake's Designs for Young's Night Thoughts: A Complete Edition, five volumes, for Clarendon Press.

* * *

GRAUPE, Daniel 1934-

PERSONAL: Born July 31, 1934, in Jerusalem, Palestine (now Israel); son of Moshe Heinz (a professor of philosophy) and Nehama Hella (Neumann) Graupe; married Dalia Smilansky (a teacher), July 9, 1968; children: Menahem Henny, Pelleg Pinhas, Oren. Education: Technion, Israel Institute of Technology, B.S.M.E., 1958, B.S.E.E., 1959, Dipl. Ing., 1960; University of Liverpool, Ph.D., 1963. Religion: Jewish. Home: 1006 Marion Ave., Highland Park, Ill. 60035. Office: Department of Electrical Engineering, Illinois Institute of Technology, Chicago, Ill. 60616.

CAREER: Israeli Government Industries, Tel Aviv, automatic control engineer, 1959-60; University of Liverpool, Liverpool, England, lecturer in engineering, 1963-67; Israel Institute of Technology, Haifa, senior lecturer in engineering, 1967-70; Colorado State University, Fort Collins, associate professor, 1970-74, professor of electrical engineering, 1974-78; Illinois Institute of Technology, Chicago, professor of electrical engineering, 1978—. Visiting professor, University of Notre Dame, 1976-77; visiting Russell Springer Pro-

fessor, University of California, Berkeley, 1977. Military service: Israeli Air Force, 1952-56, 1973; became sergeant. Member: Institute of Electrical and Electronics Engineers, Institute of Electrical Engineers (United Kingdom), Institute of Mathematics and Applications (associate fellow), American Association of University Professors, New York Academy of Science, Sigma Xi.

WRITINGS: Identification of Systems, Van Nostrand, 1972, 2nd edition, Robert E. Krieger, 1976; Time Series Analysis and Adaptive Filtering, Robert E. Krieger, 1979. Contributor of articles and reviews to Man and Cybernetics, Cybernetica, International Journal of Control, International Journal of Systems Science, Journal of British Nuclear Energy Society, IEEE Transactions on Automatic Control, IEEE Transactions of Systems, Automatica (journal of International Federation of Automatic Control), Technometrics, and Bulletin of Prosthetics Control.

WORK IN PROGRESS: Research in identification and prediction theory, filtering theory, optimal and adaptive control and bio-engineering.

* * *

GRAVEL, Mike 1930-

PERSONAL: Surname is pronounced Gra-vell; born May 13, 1930, in Springfield, Mass.; son of Alphonse and Maria (Bourassa) Gravel; married Rita Jeannette Martin, April 25, 1959; children: Martin Anthony, Lynne Denise. Education: Attended Assumption College, Worcester, Mass., 1949-50, and American International College, 1950-51; Columbia University, B.S., 1956. Religion: Unitarian Universalist. Residence: Oxon Hill, Md. Agent: David Obst, 527 Madison Ave., No. 1614, New York, N.Y. 10022. Office: 3121 Dirksen Senate Office Building, Washington, D.C. 20510.

CAREER: Realtor, 1958; Alaska Legislature, Juneau, Democratic party representative from Anchorage, 1962-68, speaker of House of Representatives, 1965-68; U.S. Senate, Washington, D.C., senator from Alaska, 1969—. Military service: U.S. Army, Counter Intelligence Corps, 1951-54; became second lieutenant. Awards, honors: D.H. L., Assumption College and University of Alaska.

WRITINGS: Jobs and More Jobs, Mt. McKinley, 1968; (editor) The Pentagon Papers: Gravel Edition, Beacon Press, 1971; Citizen Power, Holt, 1972.

* * *

GRAVES, Barbara Farris 1938-

PERSONAL: Born January 18, 1938, in Bartlesville, Okla.; daughter of Elmer (an assistant postmaster) and Laura (Larimore) Farris; married Mark T. Graves, Jr. (a computer graphics engineer), August 17, 1957; children: Mark Steven, Lauren Kay. Education: University of Oklahoma, B.A., 1963, Ph.D., 1975; University of Tulsa, M.A., 1969. Politics: "Democrat, nominally." Religion: Disciples of Christ. Home: 21227 Southwest Yachats Ct., Tualatin, Ore. 97062.

CAREER: University of Oklahoma Press, Norman, Okla., bookkeeper, 1956-59; University of Oklahoma, College of Liberal Studies, Norman, instructional materials coordinator, 1975-77, program development specialist, 1977-78. Member: Wallace Stevens Society, Phi Beta Kappa. Awards, honors: Modern Language Association of America—Association of Departments of English Certificate of Excellence in Teaching, 1972-73.

WRITINGS: (With Donald J. McBain) Lyric Voices: Approaches to the Poetry of Contemporary Song, Wiley, 1972;

(contributor) *Interpreting Literature*, Holt, 1973. Contributor to *Orbit*.

WORK IN PROGRESS: A book on French influences on Wallace Stevens' later poetry; research in Surrealist poetry, Wallace Stevens, Ashbery and Koch.

AVOCATIONAL INTERESTS: Skiing, camping, learning guitar.

* * *

GRAVES, Susan B(ernard) 1933-
(Marley Bernard)

PERSONAL: Born May 21, 1933, in Philadelphia, Pa.; daughter of E. (a manufacturer's agent) and Opal (Marley) Bernard; married Philip F. Graves (an attorney), 1955; children: Alison. *Education:* Attended University of Edinburgh, 1953-54; University of Pennsylvania, A.B. (with distinction), 1955; Columbia University, M.A., 1963. *Agent:* Anita Diamant, Writer's Workshop, Inc., 51 East 42nd St., New York, N.Y. 10017.

CAREER: Has worked as newspaper reporter, public relations writer, editor, researcher, and rewriter. Former community relations adviser, Tuckahoe Urban Renewal Agency, Tuckahoe, N.J. *Member:* Phi Beta Kappa.

WRITINGS: Tower, Institute for the Crippled and Disabled, 1967; *Evins of Tennessee: Twenty-five Years in Congress,* Popular Library, 1971; (with Wilbur Cross) *The New Age of Medical Discovery,* Hawthorn, 1972. Author of "Under Twenty," a column syndicated by Columbia Features, 1970. Contributor of articles to national magazines, sometimes under name Marley Bernard, including *Good Housekeeping, Vista, Cosmopolitan, True, Cavalier, Saturday Review, Family Health, Writer's Digest, Girl Talk,* and *Penthouse.* Contributing editor, *My Baby,* 1970-71, *Private Practice,* and *Congratulations.*

WORK IN PROGRESS: Magazine articles.†

* * *

GRAY, Edwyn 1927-

PERSONAL: Born July 17, 1927, in London, England; son of Alfred Edward (an engineer) and Edith (Beadle) Gray; married Gilberte Milo, February 25, 1950 (divorced, June 21, 1972); married Susan Bowers, July 1, 1972; children: Mark Anthony (stepson). *Education:* Attended Royal Grammar School, High Wycombe, England, 1940-46. *Home:* 11 Hillcroft Rd., Penn, High Wycombe, Buckinghamshire HP10 8EA, England. *Agent:* Curtis Brown Ltd., 1 Craven Hill, London W2 3EP, England.

CAREER: Former professional musician: British Civil Service, England, Her Majesty's Inspector of Taxes, 1946—. *Member:* Society of Authors, Authors Guild, Authors League of America.

WRITINGS—Non-fiction: The Underwater War: 1914-1918, Scribner, 1971 (published in England as *A Damned Un-English Weapon,* Seeley Service, 1971); *The Killing Time* (Military Book Club selection), Scribner, 1972; *The Devil's Device* (Miltary Book Club selection), Seeley Service, 1975.

Fiction: *No Survivors,* Seeley Service, 1974, Pinnacle Books, 1975; *Action Atlantic,* Seeley Service, 1975, Pinnacle Books, 1976; *The Tokyo Torpedo,* Seeley Service, 1976, Pinnacle Books, 1977; *Last Command,* Seeley Service, 1977, Pinnacle Books, 1978; *Fighting Submarine,* Seeley Service, 1978; *Devil Flotilla,* Seeley Service, in press;

Diving Stations, Seeley Service, in press. Contributor of several hundred short stories and features to magazines in the United Kingdom, United States, and Australia, 1952-68, and of articles on naval history to professional journals.

WORK IN PROGRESS: Another "submarine" novel, as yet untitled; a four-book series on the German E-boat flotillas of World War II.

AVOCATIONAL INTERESTS: Showing and breeding of dachshunds, collecting antiques, photography; formerly a rifle and pistol marksman and rally driver.

* * *

GRAY, Peter 1908-

PERSONAL: Born June 4, 1908, in London, England; came to United States in 1937, naturalized in 1944; son of Oscar Crommelin (a writer) and Dorothy (Selby) Gray; married Freda Dolman, July 29, 1933; children: Peter John (deceased). *Education:* University of London, B.Sc., 1929, Ph.D., 1931; Imperial College of Science, London, A.R.C.S., 1929, D.I.C., 1933. *Home:* 5131 Ellsworth Ave., Pittsburgh, Pittsburgh, Pa. 15232. *Office:* 117 Clapp Hall, University of Pittsburgh, Pittsburgh, Pa. 15260.

CAREER: Royal College of Science, London, England, assistant, 1927-29; Norwich Castle Museum, Norwich, England, zoologist, 1929-31; University of Edinburgh, Edinburgh, Scotland, lecturer in embryology, 1931-37; University of Rochester, Rochester, N.Y., Rockefeller traveling fellow, 1937-38; University of Pittsburgh, Pittsburgh, Pa., associate professor, 1939-43, professor of biology, 1943-64, Andrey Avinoff Professor of Biology, 1964-78, professor emeritus, 1978—, acting head of department, 1945, head of department of biology, 1947-64. Director of research projects for U.S. Office of Scientific Research Development, 1941-45, U.S. Army Air Forces, 1941-45, and U.S. Maritime Commission, 1944.

MEMBER: American Society of Zoologists, American Association of Anatomists, American Association for the Advancement of Science (fellow), American Microscopical Society (president, 1963-64), Society for Industrial Microbiology (director, 1962-65), Society of Amateur Microscopists, Royal Microscopical Society, American Association of University Professors, National Education Association, Sigma Xi, Phi Beta Kappa, Phi Sigma, Alpha Epsilon Delta.

WRITINGS: French Grammar for Science Students, Pitman, 1931; *Basic Microtechniques* (illustrated), Blakiston, 1952, 3rd edition published as *Handbook of Basic Microtechnique,* McGraw, 1964; *Microtomist's Formulary and Guide* (illustrated), Blakiston, 1954, reprinted, Kriegar, 1975; *The Mistress Cook* (illustrated), Oxford University Press, 1956; (with wife, Freda Gray) *Bibliography of Works in Microtechnique in Latin Alphabet Languages* (illustrated), W. C. Brown, 1956; (editor) *Encyclopedia of Biological Sciences,* Reinhold, 1961, 2nd edition, Van Nostrand, 1969; (with Clarence Goodnight and Marie Goodnight) *General Zoology* (illustrated), Reinhold, 1964; *Dictionary of Biological Sciences,* Reinhold, 1967; *The Use of the Microscope,* McGraw, 1967; *Student Dictionary of Biology,* Van Nostrand, 1973; (editor) *Encyclopedia of Microscopy and Microtechnique,* Van Nostrand, 1973; *Directory of Bioscience Departments and Faculties in the United States and Canada,* Dowden, 1975. Contributor to scientific journals.

AVOCATIONAL INTERESTS: Hunting, fishing, gardening, lapidary work.

GRAYSON, A(lbert) K(irk)   1935-

PERSONAL: Born April 1, 1935, in Windsor, Ontario, Canada; son of Albert Kirk and Helen (Smith) Grayson; married Eunice Marie Service, August 3, 1956; children: Vera Lorraine, Sally Frances. *Education:* University of Toronto, B.A., 1955, M.A., 1958; University of Vienna, graduate study, 1959-60; Johns Hopkins University, Ph.D., 1962. *Home:* 118 Heddington Ave., Toronto, Ontario, Canada M5N 2K8. *Office:* Department of Near Eastern Studies, University of Toronto, Toronto, Ontario, Canada M5S 1A1.

CAREER: University of Chicago, Chicago, Ill., research assistant for Assyrian dictionary project, 1962-63; Temple University, Philadelphia, Pa., assistant professor of history, 1963-64; University of Toronto, Toronto, Ontario, assistant professor, 1964-67, associate professor, 1967-72, professor of Near Eastern studies, 1972—. University of Pennsylvania, visiting lecturer in Assyriology, 1963-64; member, British School of Archaelogy in Iraq. *Member:* American Oriental Society, Toronto Oriental Club, Rencontre Assyriologique Internationale. *Awards, honors:* Canada Council research awards, 1959-61, 1968-78.

WRITINGS: (Contributor) J. B. Pritchard, editor, *Ancient Near Eastern Texts Relating to the Old Testament,* Princeton University Press, 3rd edition (Grayson was not associated with earlier editions), 1969; *Assyrian Royal Inscriptions,* Harrassowitz, Volume I, 1972, Volume II, 1976; (with D. B. Redford) *Papyrus and Tablet,* Prentice-Hall, 1973; *Assyrian and Babylonian Chronicles,* Augustin, 1975; *Babylonian Historical-Literary Texts,* University of Toronto Press, 1975. Contributor to *Chicago Assyrian Dictionary;* contributor of articles and reviews to professional journals.

WORK IN PROGRESS: A *Textbook of Ancient History,* with A. Spalinger, L. Casson, and L. Warren; preparing a catalogue of the Babylonian collection in the British Museum; writing the history of the Assyrian Empire for the revised *Cambridge Ancient History,* Volume III.

SIDELIGHTS: A. K. Grayson told *CA:* "Assyrian and Babylonian history and literature is my passion, a passion which I wish to share with all my readers, for this culture has played a highly significant role in the formation of modern civilization. My greatest joy is to read a newly discovered text, one that has not been read by anyone for thousands of years."

*   *   *

GRAYSON, Charles   1905-1973

1905—May 4, 1973; American novelist and screenwriter. Obituaries: *New York Times,* May 9, 1973.

*   *   *

GRAYSON, Henry (Wesley)   1910-

PERSONAL: Born May 24, 1910, in Moose Jaw, Saskatchewan, Canada; son of Albert Kirk (a rancher) and Wilhelmina (Simpson) Grayson; married Helen Mary Galloway, April 30, 1942; children: David Kirk, Geraldine Helen. *Education:* University of Saskatchewan B.A. (honors), 1937; University of Toronto, M.A., 1947, Ph.D., 1950. *Politics:* Independent. *Religion:* Protestant. *Home address:* P.O. Box 715, R.R. 2, Harper's Ferry, W.Va. 25425. *Office:* Department of Economics, University of Hawaii, 2404 Maile Way, Honolulu, Hawaii 96822.

CAREER: University of Maryland, College Park, associate

professor of economics, 1951-62; University of Hawaii, Honolulu, 1962—, began as professor of economics, currently professor emeritus. *Military service:* Royal Canadian Air Force, flying officer, 1942-45.

WRITINGS: Economic Planning under Free Enterprise, Public Affairs Press, 1954; *The Crisis of the Middle Class,* Rinehart, 1955; (with Philipp H. Loman) *Principles of Economics,* American Book Co., 1958; *Price Theory in a Changing Economy,* Macmillan, 1965; *The Theory of Relativity Revisited,* Dorrance, 1978.

WORK IN PROGRESS: The Theory of a Discrete, Finite and Nonsimultaneous Universe; research on relativistic physics and on modifications in Riemann geometry.

*   *   *

GREEN, Abel   1900-1973

June 3, 1900—May 10, 1973; American magazine editor and author. Obituaries: *Newsweek,* May 21, 1973; *Time,* May 21, 1973.

*   *   *

GREEN, David M(arvin)   1932-

PERSONAL: Born June 7, 1932, in Jackson, Mich.; son of George E. and Carrie (Crawford) Green; married Clara Lofstrom (died July 11, 1978); children: Allan, Phillip, Katherine, George. *Education:* University of Chicago, B.A., 1952; University of Michigan, B.A., 1954, M.A., 1955, Ph.D., 1958. *Home:* 9 Lakeview Ter., Winchester, Mass. 01890. *Office:* Department of Psychology and Social Relations, Harvard University, Cambridge, Mass. 02138.

CAREER: Massachusetts Institute of Technology, Cambridge, assistant professor of psychology, 1958-63; University of Pennsylvania, Philadelphia, associate professor of psychology, 1963-66, vice-chairman of department, 1964-66; University of California at San Diego, La Jolla, professor of psychology, 1966-73; Harvard University, Cambridge, professor of psychophysics, 1973—, chairman of department of psychology and social relations, 1978—. *Member:* American Psychological Association (fellow), Society of Experimental Psychologists, Psychonomic Society, Psychometric Society, Acoustical Society of America (fellow), American Association for the Advancement of Science (fellow), American Association of University Professors, National Academy of Sciences, Phi Beta Kappa. *Awards, honors:* Sigma Xi Biennial Award, from Acoustical Society of America, 1966, for contributions to the area of psychological acoustics; Guggenheim fellowship, 1973-74; Overseas fellow, St. John's College, Cambridge University.

WRITINGS: (With J. A. Swets) *Signal Detection Theory and Psychophysics,* Wiley, 1966; *An Introduction to Hearing,* Halsted, 1976.

*   *   *

GREEN, Mark J(oseph)   1945-

PERSONAL: Born March 15, 1945, in Brooklyn, N.Y.; son of Irving Arthur (a lawyer) and Ann (Suna) Green; married Denisse Frand, August 13, 1977. *Education:* Cornell University, B.A., 1967; Harvard University, J.D., 1970. *Religion:* Jewish. *Home:* 5359 Nevada Ave. N.W., Washington, D.C. 20009.

CAREER: Center for Study of Responsive Law, Washington, D.C., legal consultant, 1970-71; Corporate Accountability Research Group, Washington, D.C., lawyer and director, 1971-76; Public Citizen's Congress Watch, Washington, D.C., director, 1977—.

WRITINGS: (Editor with Bruce Wasserstein) *With Justice for Some*, Beacon Press, 1971; (with Beverly Moore and Wasserstein) *The Closed Enterprise System: Ralph Nader's Study Group Report on Antitrust Enforcement*, Grossman, 1972; (with James Fallows and David Zwick) *Who Runs Congress?*, Grossman, 1972; (editor with Ralph Nader) *Corporate Power in America: Ralph Nader's Conference on Corporate Accountability*, Grossman, 1973; (editor) *Monopoly-Makers: Ralph Nader's Study Group Report on Regulation and Competition*, Grossman, 1973; *The Other Government: The Unseen Power of Washington Lawyers*, Viking, 1975; (with Nader) *Verdicts on Lawyers*, Crowell, 1976; (with Nader) *Taming the Giant Corporation*, Norton, 1976. Contributor to *New Republic, Nation, Village Voice, New York, Washington Post, New York Times*, and other periodicals.

SIDELIGHTS: After publishing his own "public interest law" book, *With Justice for Some*, Mark Green wrote several Nader group reports. In a review of one of these, *The Closed Enterprise System*, a *New Republic* critic writes: "By now nearly everyone knows what to expect from Ralph Nader and his study groups: shocking revelations of industry's abuse of the consumer and his environment, governmental indifference, and bold and imaginative proposals for remedies." In that tradition, continues the reviewer, this report "is massive, convincing, and merciless." *The New York Review of Books*, reviewing *Monopoly-Makers*, praises Green for "sensibly" recommending that "agencies that serve no function other than managing cartels of their corporate clientele should . . . simply be abolished." In a review of Green's *The Other Government*, the *New Yorker* critic says: "Green is highly critical of the ethical standards of the successful Washington firms. . . . [He] is knowing, temperate, and readable—qualities that make his argument persuasive." But F. M. Oppenheimer, who reviewed the same book for *National Review*, describes it as "inaccurate and illiterate . . . permeated with the odor of juvenile sanctimoniousness." John Kenneth Galbraith, whose review appeared in the *New York Times Book Review*, says, "Green is careful in his language, keeps his indignation under control, has researched his subject with care and skill and is altogether persuasive."

BIOGRAPHICAL/CRITICAL SOURCES: Saturday Review, August 7, 1971, April, 1973; *Atlantic*, May, 1972; *New Republic*, July 15, 1972; *Campaign*, September 1, 1972; *Nation*, September 25, 1972; *New York Times Book Review*, March 4, 1973, May 18, 1975; *New York Review of Books*, June 28, 1973; *National Review*, August 15, 1975, December 10, 1976; *New Yorker*, August 18, 1975; *Christian Science Monitor*, May 20, 1976, November 3, 1976; *America*, October 2, 1976, December 4, 1976.

* * *

GREEN, Milton D(ouglas) 1903-

PERSONAL: Born May 16, 1903, in Central City, Colo.; son of William S. and Josephine (Anderson) Green; married Geraldine Knight, December 21, 1928; children: Ann Green Collins, Daniel Edward. *Education:* University of Michigan, A.B., 1926, J.D., 1928; Columbia University, LL.M., 1938, J.S.D., 1944. *Home:* 1728 La Tierra Ct., Lake San Marcos, Calif. 92069.

CAREER: Admitted to Bar of State of Colorado, 1929, State of Washington, 1947, and State of Missouri, 1954; private law practice with Denver, Colo., law firms Hodges, Wilson & Rogers, 1929, McComb & Strong, 1929-30, and McComb & Green, 1930-37; University of Colorado, Boulder, instructor, 1937-38, associate professor, 1940-41, professor of law, 1941-45, acting dean of Law School, 1943-45; University of Utah, Salt Lake City, associate professor of law, 1938-40; University of Washington, Seattle, professor of law, 1945-53; Washington University, St. Louis, Mo., professor of law and dean of Law School, 1953-59; New York University, New York, N.Y., professor of law, 1959-67, acting director, 1959-60, associate director of Institute of Judicial Administration, 1960-63; University of California, Hastings College of Law, San Francisco, professor of law, beginning 1967. Visiting summer professor of law, University of Michigan, 1941, Stanford University, 1948, and University of Southern California, 1953, 1958. Compliance commissioner of War Production Board and Civilian Production Administration, 1943-47; public panel member of War Labor Board, 1943-45; hearing commissioner of National Production Authority,1951-53. Chairman of Clayton, Mo., charter commission, 1956-57. *Member:* American Bar Association, San Francisco Bar Association, St. Louis Bar Association, Washington Bar Association, Phi Beta Kappa, Coif, Phi Delta Phi.

WRITINGS: (Contributor) Harry W. Jones, editor, *The Courts, The Public, and the Law Explosion*, Prentice-Hall, 1965; *Basic Civil Procedure*, Foundation Press, 1972, 2nd edition, 1979. Contributor of articles to legal periodicals and journals.

* * *

GREEN, Norma B(erger) 1925-

PERSONAL: Born September 15, 1925, in Providence, R.I.; daughter of C. Albert (an orthodontist) and Florence (Bomstein) Berger; married Norman S. Green, May 21, 1950 (divorced, 1969); children: John, William. *Education:* Rhode Island School of Design, B.F.A., 1945; also studied at Positano Art Workshop (Italy), Grande Chaumiere (Paris), and New School for Social Research. *Politics:* Democrat. *Home:* 443 Sea Rocket Ct., Kiawah Island, John's Island, S.C. 29455.

CAREER: Artist; paints in water color and designs textiles; had a solo show in New York, N.Y., 1970.

WRITINGS: (Self-illustrated) *Bears, Bees, Birch Trees* (juvenile), Doubleday, 1973; *The Hole in the Dike* (juvenile), illustrations by Eric Carle, Crowell, 1975; (adaptor) *Wings and Wishes*, Harper, 1977.

WORK IN PROGRESS: Research on Greek and Irish songs, verse, and superstitions, for a children's book; obscure riddles from around the world.

SIDELIGHTS: Norma B. Green told *CA* that she writes early in the day, "every day," and hopes that her books can deliver some message to her readers. *Avocational interests:* Travel, photography, nature.

* * *

GREEN, Rose Basile 1914-

PERSONAL: Born December 19, 1914, in New Rochelle, N.Y.; daughter of Salvatore (a businessman) and Caroline (Galgano) Basile; married Raymond S. Green (a broadcasting executive), June 20, 1942; children: Carol-Rae (Mrs. Alfred R. Hoffmann), Raymond Ferguson St. John. *Education:* College of New Rochelle, B.A. (cum laude), 1935; Columbia University, M.A., 1941; University of Pennsylvania, Ph.D., 1962. *Politics:* Independent. *Religion:* Roman Catholic. *Home:* Manor Rd., Route 2824, Philadelphia, Pa. 19128.

CAREER: U.S. Works Progress Administration, wrote history of Litchfield County, Conn. for Federal Writers' Project, 1935-36; high school teacher of English, Italian, and drama in Torrington, Conn., 1936-42; University of Tampa, Tampa, Fla., registrar and associate professor of English, 1942-43; free-lance writer of radio scripts for National Broadcasting Co., 1943-53; Temple University, Philadelphia, Pa., instructor in English, 1953-57; Cabrini College, Radnor, Pa., associate professor, 1957-62, professor of English and chairman of department, 1962-70; free-lance writer, 1970—. Member of board of directors of Balch Institute of Ethnic Studies, American Institute of Italian Studies, National Italian American Foundation, Free Library of Philadelphia, and Opera Company of Philadelphia.

MEMBER: Academy of American Poets, American Poetry Society, International Society of Poets, American Academy of Political and Social Science, American Studies Association, National Council of Teachers of English, Modern Language Association of America, American Italian Historical Association, American Association of University Women, Pennsylvania Poetry Society, Women for Greater Philadelphia (member of board of directors), Philadelphia Council of Teachers of English, Kappa Gamma Pi, Philadelphia Art Alliance (member of literary board), America-Italy Society of Philadelphia, Cosmopolitan Club of Philadelphia.

AWARDS, HONORS: Humanities Award, Nationalities Service Center (Philadelphia), 1975, for *The Italian-American Novel;* Woman of the Year Award, Sons of Italy of America, 1975, for *The Italian-American Novel* and *Primo Vino;* City of Philadelphia citation, 1975; Agnes C. Brothers Pathway of Life Award, National Federation of State Poetry Societies, 1976; National Literary Award, Daughters of the American Revolution, 1976, for *76 for Philadelphia;* National Award ("Amita"), Association of Italian American Women, 1976, 1978; National Award from National Italian American Foundation, 1978, and appointment as Distinguished Daughter of Pennsylvania from state of Pennsylvania, 1978, both for *Woman, the Second Coming.*

WRITINGS: To Reason Why (poems), A. S. Barnes, 1971; *The Italian-American Novel: A Survey,* Fairleigh Dickinson University Press, 1972; *Primo Vino* (poems), A. S. Barnes, 1972; *76 for Philadelphia* (poems), A. S. Barnes, 1975; *Woman, the Second Coming,* A. S. Barnes, 1977. Author of pamphlet, "The Cabrinian Philosophy of Education," of scripts on American life for "Voice of America," and of two plays. Contributor to literary journals. Editor, *Azimuth,* 1962-69.

WORK IN PROGRESS: A book of poems, *The Pennsylvania People;* researching and writing an anthology of American literature to include all major ethnic groups; a biography of St. Frances Cabrini; "Eyes for an Eye," a play.

SIDELIGHTS: Rose Basile Green told *CA:* "Poetry is the most aesthetic articulation of the aspirations of an age, the positioned call of the golden horn brassed to the sound of both hunters and hounds in pursuit of a running dream. The call, however, should not deafen the ear with too much brass."

*   *   *

GREENBERG, Bernard L(ouis) 1917-

PERSONAL: Born May 31, 1917, in New York, N.Y.; son

of Louis and Esther (Solomon) Greenberg; married Sally Henry (a psychologist), May 22, 1947; children: Elisabeth, Mary, Tom. *Education:* Oberlin College, B.A., 1941; George Washington University, M.A., 1949; Johns Hopkins University, graduate study, 1949-51, 1952-54; Queens' College, Cambridge, graduate study, 1951-52. *Home:* 7004 Wake Forest Dr., College Park, Md. 20740. *Office:* Office of Admissions, Gallaudet College, Washington, D.C. 20002.

CAREER: George Washington University, Washington, D.C., instructor in English, 1948-49; Johns Hopkins University, Baltimore, Md., instructor in English, 1949-54; Gallaudet College, Washington, D.C., assistant professor, 1954-57, associate professor, 1957-64, professor of English, 1964—, director of admissions and records, 1968—. *Military service:* U.S. Army Air Forces, 1942-46; received commendation ribbon and ten battle stars; U.S. Air Force Reserve, 1946—; present rank, lieutenant colonel.

WRITINGS: A Short Guide to Better English, Gallaudet College, 1960; (with Sara Withers) *Better English Usage,* Bobbs-Merrill, 1965. Contributor of articles on the college potential of the hearing handicapped to *American Annals of the Deaf* and *College and University.*

WORK IN PROGRESS: Editing, with Melvin New and Richard Davies, an annotated edition of Lawrence Sterne's *Tristram Shandy,* for University of Florida Press; *France: As You Like It,* with wife, Sally Greenberg.

*   *   *

GREENBERGER, Allen J(ay) 1937-

PERSONAL: Born March 18, 1937, in Chicago, Ill.; son of Harold Herbert and Alice (Ross) Greenberger. *Education:* University of Michigan, B.A., 1958, M.A., 1960, Ph.D., 1966. *Home:* 660 Wedgewood, Upland, Calif. 91786. *Office:* Department of History, Pitzer College, Claremont, Calif. 91711.

CAREER: Smith College, Northampton, Mass., instructor in history, 1965-66; Pitzer College, Claremont, Calif., assistant professor, 1966-70, associate professor, 1970-75, professor of history, 1975—. *Member:* American Historical Association, Association for Asian Studies, Conference of British Studies, Phi Beta Kappa.

WRITINGS: The British Image of India: A Study in the Literature of Imperialism, Oxford University Press, 1969.

WORK IN PROGRESS: Research on the social history of the British in India.

*   *   *

GREENFIELD, Norman S(amuel) 1923-

PERSONAL: Born June 2, 1923, in New York, N.Y.; son of Max (a printer) and Dorothy (Hertz) Greenfield; married Marjorie Hanson (a psychologist); children: Ellen, Jennifer, Susan. *Education:* New York University, B.A., 1948; University of California, Berkeley, M.A., 1952, Ph.D., 1953. *Office:* Department of Psychiatry, University Hospitals, Madison, Wis. 53706.

CAREER: University of Wisconsin—Madison, assistant professor, 1954-59, associate professor, 1959-63, professor of psychiatry, 1963—, associate director of Wisconsin Psychiatric Institute, 1962—. *Military service:* U.S. Army Air Forces, 1943-46. *Member:* American Psychological Association, American Psychosomatic Society, Society for Psychophysiological Research, American Association for the Advancement of Science, American Association of University Professors.

WRITINGS: (Editor with Robert Roessler) *Physiological Correlates of Psychological Disorder,* University of Wisconsin Press, 1962; (editor with W. C. Lewis) *Psychoanalysis and Current Biological Thought,* University of Wisconsin Press, 1965; (editor with L. M. Roberts and M. H. Miller) *Comprehensive Mental Health,* University of Wisconsin Press, 1968; (editor with G. M. Abroms) *The New Hospital Psychiatry,* Academic Press, 1971; (editor with R. H. Sternbach) *Handbook of Psychophysiology,* Holt, 1972.

* * *

GREENLICK, Merwyn R(onald) 1935-

PERSONAL: Born March 12, 1935, in Detroit, Mich.; son of Emanuel and Fay (Ettinger) Greenlick; married Harriet Cohen, August 19, 1956; children: Phyllis, Michael, Vicki. *Education:* Wayne State University, B.S., 1957, M.S., 1961; University of Michigan, Ph.D., 1967. *Politics:* Liberal. *Home:* 712 Northwest Spring, Portland, Ore. 97229. *Office:* Health Services Research Center, Kaiser Foundation Hospitals, 4707 Southeast Hawthorne, Portland, Ore. 97215.

CAREER: Wayne State University, Detroit, Mich., instructor in pharmacy administration, 1958-62; Kaiser Foundation Hospitals, Portland, Ore., director of Health Services Research Center, 1964—. Portland State University, Portland, lecturer, 1965-68, adjunct professor of sociology, 1969—; associate clinical professor of preventive medicine and public health, University of Oregon, Medical School, 1971—. Member of board of directors, Washington County Community Action Organization, 1966-70; member of committee to evaluate national center for health statistics, U.S. Department of Health, Education, and Welfare; member of Oregon Health Manpower Council.

MEMBER: American Public Health Association (fellow; member of board of governors, 1970—), American Association for the Advancement of Science, American Sociological Association, American Statistical Association, Institute of Medicine of National Academy of Sciences, Group Health Association of America, Delta Omega, Omicron Delta Kappa, Rho Chi.

WRITINGS: (Editor) *Conceptual Issues in the Analysis of Medical Care Utilization Behavior,* U.S. Government Printing Office, 1970; (contributor) Anne R. Somers, editor, *The Kaiser Permanent Medical Care Program,* Commonwealth Fund, 1971; (with A. V. Hurtado and E. W. Saward) *Integration of Home Health and Extended Care Facility Services into a Comprehensive, Prepaid Group Practice Plan* (monograph), Hospital Research and Educational Trust, 1972. Contributor of about thirty articles to *Medical Care* and other journals.

* * *

GREGORY, Peter 1924-

PERSONAL: Born September 29, 1924, in New York, N.Y.; son of Praxiteles and Despina (Iatrides) Gregory; married Doris Diaz, September 28, 1955; children: Beate B., Thomas P. *Education:* Ohio Wesleyan University, B.A., 1948; Harvard University, M.A., 1950, Ph.D., 1957. *Home:* 102 Juniper Hill Pl. N.E., Route 13, Albuquerque, N.M. 87122. *Office:* Department of Economics, University of New Mexico, Albuquerque, N.M. 87131.

CAREER: University of Puerto Rico, Rio Piedras, assistant director of Manpower Resources Project, 1953-57; University of Minnesota, Minneapolis, assistant professor, 1958-

65, associate professor of economics, 1965-71; University of New Mexico, Albuquerque, professor of economics, 1971—. Visiting professor at Yale University, 1957-58, and Cornell University-University of Chile Program, 1962-64. Visiting economist at International Labour Office, Geneva, Switzerland, 1966-67; consultant to World Bank, Organization of American States, and International Labour Office. *Member:* American Economic Association, Industrial Relations Research Association, Latin American Studies Association.

WRITINGS: (With L. G. Reynolds) *Wages, Productivity and Industrialization in Puerto Rico,* Irwin, 1965; *Sueldos Y Salarios en la Industria Manufacturera,* Universidad de Chile, 1966; *Industrial Wages in Chile,* Cornell University Press, 1967; *Industrialization and Wages in Japan,* International Labour Office, 1973.

WORK IN PROGRESS: Research in labor markets in developing countries and public policy in labor matters.

* * *

GREGORY, Robert G(ranville) 1924-

PERSONAL: Born May 16, 1924, in Denver, Colo.; son of Robert L. (a civil engineer) and Mina Clare (Williams) Gregory; married Patricia D. Rio, September 4, 1955; children: Theresa M., Robert J. *Education:* University of California, Los Angeles, B.A., 1948, M.A., 1950, Ph.D., 1956; University of London, graduate study, 1953-54. *Home:* 3479 Watervale Rd., Manlius, N.Y. 13104. *Office:* Department of History, Syracuse University, Syracuse, N.Y. 13210.

CAREER: March Air Force Base, Riverside, Calif., civilian historian, 1956; Wake Forest University, Winston-Salem, N.C., assistant professor, 1957-62, associate professor of history, 1962-66; Syracuse University, Syracuse, N.Y., associate professor, 1966-72, professor of history, 1972—. *Military service:* U.S. Army, 1943. *Member:* African Studies Association, Association of African Studies Programs (chairman, 1974-77; member of executive committee, 1977—).

WRITINGS: *Sidney Webb of East Africa,* University of California Press, 1962; (with Robert Maxon and Leon Spencer) *A Guide to the Kenya National Archives,* Program of Eastern African Studies, Syracuse University, 1968; *India and East Africa,* Clarendon Press, 1971. Contributor to *South Atlantic Quarterly, AICC Economic Review, Journal of Indian History, Africana Library Journal,* and *Vivekananda Kendra Patrika.*

WORK IN PROGRESS: An economic and social history of the Asians in East Africa; history of the Indian Overseas Association, 1919-1947.

* * *

GREINKE, (Lawrence) Eric 1948-

PERSONAL: Born July 15, 1948, in Grand Rapids, Mich.; son of Harold Howard (a die-maker) and Alice May (Hill) Greinke; married Pamela May Wilbur (a graphic artist), March 28, 1969. *Education:* Attended Grand Rapids Junior College, 1968-70; Grand Valley State College, B.A., 1972. *Home:* 3103 Peckheath Dr. S.W., Wyoming, Mich. 49509.

CAREER: Poet and novelist; owner of Pilot Press Books. Maple Grove Medical Facility, Grand Rapids, Mich., orderly, 1968-70; Grand Valley Nursing Home, Grand Rapids, orderly, 1970; B. Dalton Bookseller, Grand Rapids, assistant manager, 1976—. Creative writing teacher, City High School, Grand Rapids, 1974-75. Worked with Artists in the

Schools, Michigan Council for the Arts, 1976. *Military service:* U.S. Coast Guard, 1966-68. *Member:* Committee of Small Magazine Editors and Publishers. *Awards, honors:* National Poetry Festival fellow, 1972; nominated for Pulitzer Prize for letters, 1972, for *The Last Ballet.*

WRITINGS: Earth Songs, privately printed, 1970; *Canary Wine,* Metamorphosis, 1970; *Milk Run and Other Poems,* Metamorphosis, 1971; *Sand and Other Poems,* Metamorphosis, 1971; *The Cymbal Crashes,* Pilot Press, 1971; *Caged Angels,* Pilot Press, 1972; (editor and contributor) *Ten Michigan Poets,* Pilot Press, 1972; *The Last Ballet,* Pilot Press, 1972; (with Ben Tibbs and Ronnie Lane) *Grape Wishes,* Pilot Press, 1973; *Iron Rose,* Pilot Press, 1973; (with wife, Pam Greinke) *For You,* Pilot Press, 1974; *Black Milk: Ghazal Sequences,* Free Press, 1974; (translator and author of preface) *The Drunken Boat and Other Poems from the French of Arthur Rimbaud,* Free Books, 1975, 2nd edition, 1976; (editor) Tibbs, *Bombs: Selected Poems,* Pilot Press, 1975; *The Broken Lock: Selected Poems, 1960-1975,* Pilot Press, 1975.

Work is anthologized in: *Being '71,* edited by Cor Barendrecht, Being Press, 1971; *Best of Four,* edited by Walter Lockwood, Dyer-Ives, 1971; *Best College Poetry of 1971,* edited by Dennis Hartman, National Poetry Press, 1971; *Michigan Hot Apples,* edited by Gay Rubin, Hot Apples Press, 1972; *Midwest Poetry 1972,* edited by Ray Burrows, Burrow Books, 1973; *Contemporary American Poets,* edited by Maurice Custodio, Peace & Pieces, 1973; *Mantras,* edited by Alan Britt, Floating Hair Press, 1974; *For Neruda/For Chile,* edited by Walt Lowenfels, Beacon Press, 1975. Book reviewer, *Grand Rapids Press,* 1972—. Contributor to over forty literary journals and newspapers, including *Bitterroot, Brown Penny Review, Cape Rock Journal, Cloven Hoof, Display, Essence, For the Time Being, Lanthorn, Magazine Six, Metamorphosis, Midnight, Happiness Holding Tank, Once Again, Pegasus, Root, Stone Drum, Voices, Free-Lance, Detroit Free Press, Grand Rapids Journal,* and *The Whole COSMEP Catalog.* Former poetry editor of *Amaranthus* (magazine).

WORK IN PROGRESS: Whole Self/Whole World, a psychological monograph; *Essays and New Atlantis,* sociological essays; an autobiographical novel.

SIDELIGHTS: Eric Greinke told *CA:* "I have been writing for survival and growth since the age of seven. I hope that my books track the elusive atoms of love, resulting in a fusion between myself and others. I try to identify and communicate humanistic/existential realities and contribute same to human union. I write only when inspired, though I've learned that all inspiration does not require recording, and thus quantity of output has decreased while quality increases.... A writer should never imitate other writers, nor should writing be done 'for practice,' uninspired and misconnected to the real self and its true tides.

"My influences have been those writers who have dealt with self-exploration and aesthetic revolution, both of which are always needed: Poe, Whitman, Thoreau, Emerson, Rimbaud, Baudelaire, Artaud, Eliot, Pound, Dylan Thomas, Frank O'Hara, and Henry Miller." Greinke cites other influences as being Germanic mythology, expressionist art, surrealism, rock and roll and such philosophers and psychologists as Kant, Thoreau, Jung, Perls, and Laing.

Greinke believes that "much contemporary writing never goes beyond the therapeutic into the universal. The power of words is yet narrowly understood. I believe the best novelists today are Jerzy Kosinski and John Gardner. My favorite

poet is the brilliant verbal revolutionary Ben Tibbs, now seventy-three years old and still mainly unrecognized. The only contemporary poet whom we *know* to be 'great' is Allen Ginsberg. Robert Bly is runner-up."

*   *   *

GRENDLER, Paul F(rederick) 1936-

PERSONAL: Born May 24, 1936, in Armstrong, Iowa; son of August P. and Josephine (Girres) Grendler; married Marcella McCann, June 16, 1962; children: Peter, Jean. *Education:* Oberlin College, B.A., 1959; University of Wisconsin, M.A., 1961, Ph.D., 1964. *Home:* 115 Sheldrake Blvd., Toronto, Ontario, Canada M4P 2B1. *Office:* Department of History, University of Toronto, Toronto, Ontario, Canada M55 1A1.

CAREER: University of Pittsburgh, Pittsburgh, Pa., instructor in history, 1963-64; University of Toronto, Toronto, Ontario, assistant professor, 1964-69, associate professor, 1969-73, professor of history, 1973—. *Member:* Renaissance Society of America, American Historical Association, American Catholic Historical Association. *Awards, honors:* Fulbright fellowship for study in Italy, 1962-63; Institute for Research in Humanities fellowship, 1967-68; Harvard University Center for Italian Renaissance Studies, I Tatti fellow, 1970-72; Canada Council fellowship, 1971; American Council of Learned Societies fellowship, 1971-72; Cornell University Society for the Humanities senior fellow, 1973-74; Guggenheim fellowship, 1978-79; Marraro Prize from American Catholic Historical Association, 1978, for *The Roman Inquisition and the Venetian Press, 1540-1605.*

WRITINGS: Critics of the Italian World 1530-1560: Anton Francesco Doni, Nicolo Franco, and Ortensio Lando, University of Wisconsin Press, 1969; *The Roman Inquisition and the Venetian Press, 1540-1605,* Princeton University Press, 1977. Member of editorial board, *Collected Works of Erasmus,* for University of Toronto Press.

WORK IN PROGRESS: A monograph, *Primary and Secondary Education in Renaissance Italy, 1500-1650,* completion expected in 1981.

*   *   *

GRENNAN, Margaret R(ose)

PERSONAL: Born in New York, N.Y.; daughter of Benjamin (an inventor) and Helen (an educator; maiden name, Donovan) Grennan; married Charles V. Lehmann, December 28, 1954. *Education:* Hunter College (now Hunter College of the City University of New York), B.A., 1934; Columbia University, M.A., 1935, Ph.D., 1943. *Religion:* Roman Catholic. *Residence:* New York, N.Y.

CAREER: Hunter College of the City University of New York, New York, N.Y., assistant professor, 1943-52, associate professor, 1952-62, professor of English, 1962-67; Herbert H. Lehman College of the City University of New York, Bronx, N.Y., professor of English, 1967-72, professor emerita, 1973—. *Member:* Phi Beta Kappa.

WRITINGS: The Heart of Newman's Apologia, Longmans, 1934, reprinted, Russell, 1970; *William Morris, Medievalist and Revolutionary,* Kings Crown Press, 1945, reprinted, Russell, 1970; (editor) *Shakespeare's Julius Caesar,* Loyola University Press, 1942; (editor of Victorian Section) *English Voices: An Anthology,* Sadlier, 1946. Contributor of reviews and articles to *Catholic World, America, Modern Language Notes, English Literary History,* and other periodicals.

WORK IN PROGRESS: Research in the Celtic background of Anglo-Irish literature; a novel, *The Days that Were Shortened;* a play, *The Hostage.*†

* * *

GRIBBLE, Charles E(dward) 1936-

PERSONAL: Born November 10, 1936, in Lansing, Mich.; son of Charles Percy and Elizabeth Keturah (McGee) Gribble. *Education:* University of Michigan, B.A., 1957; Harvard University, A.M., 1958, Ph.D., 1967; Moscow State University, graduate study, 1960-61. *Office:* Slavic Department, Ohio State University, Columbus, Ohio 43210.

CAREER: Brandeis University, Waltham, Mass., 1961-68, began as instructor, became assistant professor of Russian; Indiana University at Bloomington, assistant professor of Slavic languages, 1968-75; Ohio State University, Columbus, associate professor of Slavic languages, 1975—. President and editor, Slavica Publishers, Inc., Columbus, Ohio, 1967—. *Member:* Linguistic Society of America, American Association for Advancement of Slavic Studies, Association of Teachers of Slavic and East European Languages, Phi Beta Kappa. *Awards, honors:* Woodrow Wilson fellowship, 1957-58; American Council of Learned Societies fellowship, 1972; International Research and Exchanges Board award to Union of Soviet Socialist Republics, 1972.

WRITINGS: (Editor) *Readings in the History of the Russian Language,* Schoenhof's Foreign Books, 1964, revised and enlarged edition published as *Medieval Slavic Texts,* Slavica, Volume I: *Old and Middle Russian Texts,* 1973; (editor) *Studies Presented to Professor Roman Jakobson by His Students,* Slavica, 1968; *Russian Root List,* Slavica, 1973; *A Short Dictionary of Eighteenth-Century Russian,* Slavica, 1976. Editor-in-chief, *Folia Slavica* (journal), 1977—.

WORK IN PROGRESS: Computer-aided description of Old Russian language; studies of medieval Slavic manuscripts and Bulgarian grammar.

* * *

GRIEDER, Walter 1924-

PERSONAL: Born November 21, 1924, in Basel, Switzerland; divorced; children: Lorenz-Alain. *Education:* Studied at a normal school in France and at art schools in Basel and Paris. *Politics:* None. *Religion:* "My own." *Home:* Baeumleingasse 16, 4051 Basel, Switzerland.

CAREER: Painter, graphic artist, and writer, designer, and illustrator of books. *Member:* Swiss Graphic Designers. *Awards, honors:* Prizes for posters and for books.

WRITINGS: Die Geburtstagsreise, Herder Verlag, 1961; *Pierrot and His Friends in the Circus* (originally published in German), Delacorte, 1967; *Das Grosse Fest,* translation published as *The Great Feast,* Parents' Magazine Press, 1968; *Die Verzauberte Trommel,* Sauerlaender, 1968, translation by Doris Orgel published as *The Enchanted Drum,* Parents' Magazine Press, 1969; *Nimm Mich Mit, Frau Vogeluase,* Otto Maier Verlag, 1972; *Die Gute Tat dev Dicken Kinder,* Auuelle Betz Verlag, 1972; *The Wonderchild,* Broschek Verlag, 1972; *Das Geschuk des Oparis,* Atlantis Verlag, 1972. Contributor of short stories and articles on art to periodicals.

WORK IN PROGRESS: Designing "very modern books" for Diogenes, Atlantis, Otto Maier, Broschek, and other publishers.

SIDELIGHTS: Walter Grieder has traveled in most countries of Europe, in Africa, and in India, where he designed a booklet, *Grieder Meets the Maharajah,* for Air India. *Avocational interests:* Grieder told *CA* he is "open for everything worth[y] of interest."

* * *

GRIESSMAN, Benjamin Eugene 1934-

PERSONAL: Born August 12, 1934, in Spartanburg, S.C.; son of Benjamin F. (a machinist) and Irene (Hill) Griessman; children: Katrina Margene, Sharon Joanna, Gloria Gay. *Education:* Tennessee Temple College, B.A., 1956; Baylor University, M.A., 1958; Louisiana State University, Ph.D., 1966. *Politics:* Democrat. *Office:* Department of Sociology, Auburn University, Auburn, Ala. 36830.

CAREER: College of William and Mary, Williamsburg, Va., lecturer in sociology, summer, 1965; North Carolina State University, Raleigh, assistant professor, 1966-68, associate professor of sociology and anthropology, 1968-70, associate professor of forestry, 1968-70, project director at Center for Occupational Education, 1967-70; Auburn University, Auburn, Ala., professor of sociology and head of department, 1970—.

MEMBER: American Sociological Association, American Anthropological Association.

WRITINGS: (With Alvin L. Bertrand) *Factors Related to the Communication of Forest Fire Prevention Messages in Selected Rural Communities,* Agricultural Experiment Station, Louisiana State University, 1967; *The Concerted Services Approach to Developmental Change in Rural Areas: An Interim Evaluation,* Center for Occupational Education, North Carolina State University, 1968; (with Kenneth Densley) *Vocational Education in Rural Areas,* Educational Resources Information Center Clearinghouse, New Mexico State University and Ohio State University, 1969; *Planned Change in Low-Income Rural Areas: An Evaluation of Concerted Services in Training and Education* (monograph), Center for Occupational Education, North Carolina State University, 1969; *Minorities,* Dryden, 1975; (with W. David Lewis) *The Southern Mystique,* University of Alabama Press, 1976. Contributor to *Journal of Range Management, American Forests, Journal of Human Relations, Journal of Cooperative Extension, Rural Sociology, Adult Leadership, Educational Technology, Sociological Focus, Washington Post,* and others. Series editor, *The American Anthropologist.*

WORK IN PROGRESS: Up Close: Profiles of Important People of Our Time.

* * *

GRINDAL, Bruce T. 1940-

PERSONAL: Born June 21, 1940, in Geneva, Ill.; son of Baard and Marie (Roggaman) Grindal; married Mary Ann Gleason, June 12, 1965; married second wife, Lourdes Ruiz Ortegon, June 14, 1975; children: (first marriage) Matthew Bruce; (second marriage) Lourdes Angela. *Education:* Northwestern University, B.A., 1963; Indiana University, Ph.D., 1969. *Home:* 2221 Amelia Cir., Tallahassee, Fla. 32304. *Office:* Department of Anthropology, Florida State University, Tallahassee, Fla. 32306.

CAREER: Middlebury College, Middlebury, Vt., assistant professor of anthropology, 1969-72; Florida State University, Tallahassee, 1972—, began as assistant professor, currently associate professor of anthropology. *Member:*

American Anthropological Association, African Studies Association. *Awards, honors:* Foreign Area Fellowship Program grant, 1966-68, to do research in Ghana.

WRITINGS: Growing Up in Two Worlds: Education and Transition among the Sisala of Northern Ghana, Holt, 1971; (contributor) George Spindler, editor, *Education and Cultural Process,* Holt, 1974; (contributor) *Humanistic Anthropology: Essays in Honor of David Bidney,* University Press of America, 1978. Contributor to anthropology journals. Editor of *Anthropology and Humanism Quarterly.*

WORK IN PROGRESS: Further writing on the Sisala; research on rural Black folk culture.

* * *

GROFF, Patrick J(ohn) 1924-

PERSONAL: Born January 30, 1924, in Crescent City, Calif.; widowed, 1963; children: Christopher. *Education:* University of Oregon, B.S., 1948, M.S., 1950; University of California, Ed.D., 1955. *Home:* 5152 College Gardens Ct., San Diego, Calif. 92115. *Office:* Department of Elementary Education, San Diego State University, San Diego, Calif. 92182.

CAREER: Elementary school teacher in Coos Bay, Ore., 1950-53; San Diego State University, San Diego, Calif., assistant professor, 1955-60, associate professor, 1960-64, professor of education, 1964—. Visiting professor at Stanford University, 1963, University of North Dakota, 1967, and Webster College, 1968. Member of elementary section, National Council of Teachers of English Institutes. *Military service:* U.S. Navy, 1943-45. *Member:* National Council of Teachers of English, International Reading Association, Phi Delta Kappa, Beta Theta Pi.

WRITINGS: (With Fred and Corinne Guggenheim and others) *New Frontiers in Education,* Grune, 1966; (with Paul Anderson) *Resource Materials for Teachers of Spelling,* Burgess, 1968; (with William Anderson) *A New Look at Children's Literature,* Wadsworth, 1972; *Phonics: Why and How,* General Learning Corp., 1977. Contributor of more than one hundred and fifty articles to *Reading Teacher, Horn Book, School Librarian,* and professional journals.

WORK IN PROGRESS: A book on processes involved in stimulating children to write; a book on the effectiveness of phonics teaching.

* * *

GROGAN, Emmett 1942-1978
(Fastlife; Kenny Wisdom)

PERSONAL: Born November 28, 1942, in Brooklyn, N.Y.; son of Eugene Leo (a margin clerk) and Margaret Grogan; married Louise Latraverse (an actress and theater owner), June 24, 1972. *Education:* Studied film making at Center of Experimental Cinema (Rome, Italy). *Politics:* "Independent radical democratic American." *Religion:* "Non-sectarian self-introspection." *Address:* c/o Grossman, Suite 404, 75 East 55th St., New York, N.Y. 10022.

CAREER: Wrote, directed, and acted in plays for San Francisco Mime Troupe Co., San Francisco, Calif., during the 1960's; founded and organized "Digger Movement," in San Francisco, Calif., 1966-69. *Military service:* U.S. Army, 1965-66. *Awards, honors:* First prize for best actor in his own film, "Let Them Look Me Up and Take Their Own Sweet Time," Salerno Film Festival Ridotto, 1964.

WRITINGS: (Editor) *The Digger Papers* (anthology), privately printed, 1968; *Ringolevio: Or, a Life Played for Keeps,* Little, Brown, 1972; *Final Score,* Holt, 1976. Contributor of articles, occasionally under pseudonyms, to underground magazines and newspapers, including *Cream, Los Angeles Free Press,* and *International Times of London.*

WORK IN PROGRESS: One Percent Free: Or, Alive on the Other Side, a novel; a film adaptation of *Ringolevio.*

SIDELIGHTS: Emmett Grogan was a professional burglar and jewel thief and a dealer in stolen objects of art; he resided in a number of penal institutions.

BIOGRAPHICAL/CRITICAL SOURCES: Ramparts, March, 1967.†

(Died April 6, 1978)

* * *

GROSS, Hanns 1928-

PERSONAL: Born June 20, 1928, in Stockerau, Austria; son of Arthur (a bank official) and Gabriele (Schneider) Gross. *Education:* University of London, B.A., 1950; University of Chicago, A.M., 1963, Ph.D., 1966. *Home:* 6415 North Sheridan Rd., Chicago, Ill. 60626. *Office:* Department of History, Loyola University, 6525 North Sheridan Rd., Chicago, Ill. 60626.

CAREER: Emmanuel Grammar School, Swansea, Wales, teacher of classics and history, 1948-61; Consolidated Book Publishers, Chicago, Ill., social science editor, 1962; Roosevelt University, Chicago, lecturer in history, 1965-66; Southern Illinois University at Carbondale, assistant professor of history, 1966-67; Loyola University, Chicago, assistant professor, 1967-73, associate professor, 1973-78, professor of history, 1978—. *Member:* American Historical Association, American Society of Legal History, Conference Group of Central European Historians, Conference on Faith and History, Istituto di Studi Romani, Society for Italian Historical Studies.

WRITINGS: (Editor) *An Illustrated Outline History of Mankind,* Consolidated Book Publishers, 1963; *Empire and Sovereignty: A History of the Public Law Literature of the Holy Roman Empire, 1599-1804,* University of Chicago Press, 1973.

WORK IN PROGRESS: Research in the social and intellectual history of the city of Rome in the seventeenth and eighteenth centuries.

BIOGRAPHICAL/CRITICAL SOURCES: American Historical Review, April, 1978.

* * *

GROSS, Milton 1912(?)-1973

1912(?)—May 9, 1973; American sports journalist. Obituaries: *New York Times,* May 10, 1973; *Time,* May 21, 1973.

* * *

GROSS, Theodore L(awrence) 1930-

PERSONAL: Born December 4, 1930, in New York, N.Y.; son of David (a teacher) and Anna Gross; married Selma Bell (a teacher), August 27, 1955; children: Donna, Jonathan. *Education:* University of Maine, B.A., 1952; Columbia University, M.A., 1957, Ph.D., 1960. *Home:* 113 Old Mill Rd., Great Neck, N.Y. 11023. *Office:* Department of English, City College of the City University of New York, 131st St. at Convent Ave., New York, N.Y. 10031.

CAREER: City College of the City University of New York, New York, N.Y., instructor, 1958-61, assistant professor, 1961-64, associate professor, 1964-68, professor of English, 1968—, chairman of department, 1970-72, dean of humanities, 1972—. Visiting professor at University of Nancy, 1963-64, 1968-69, and Kyoto American Studies summer seminar, 1978. *Member:* Modern Language Association of America, National Council of Teachers of English (director of commission on literature), Association of Departments of English (member of executive committee).

WRITINGS: Albion W. Tourgee, Twayne, 1963; *Thomas Nelson Page,* Twayne, 1967; (editor with Norman Kelvin) *An Introduction to Fiction,* Random House, 1967; (editor with James A. Emanuel) *Dark Symphony: Negro Literature in America,* Free Press, 1968; (editor) *Representative Men: Cult Heroes of Our Time,* Free Press, 1970; *Annotated Bibliographies: Hawthorne, Melville,* Free Press, 1971; *The Heroic Ideals in American Literature,* Free Press, 1971; (editor) *A Nation of Nations: Ethnic Literature in America,* Free Press, 1971; (editor) *The Literature of American Jews,* Free Press, 1973; (general editor) *America in Literature,* two volumes, with teachers manual, Wiley, 1978.

Contributor: Seymour L. Gross and John Edward Hardy, editors, *Images of the Negro in American Literature,* University of Chicago Press, 1966; Clayton L. Eichelberger, editor, *American Literary Realism: 1870-1910,* University of Texas Press, 1967; Louis D. Rubin, editor, *Bibliographical Checklist of Southern Literature,* Louisiana State University Press, 1968; C.W.E. Bigsby, editor, *The American Negro Writer,* Everett Edwards, 1969. General editor, "Studies in Language and Literature," Harper, 1975-77. Contributor of articles and reviews to professional journals, including *Phylon, Critique, College English,* and *South Atlantic Quarterly.*

WORK IN PROGRESS: The Humanities in Urban Education, for Doubleday.

SIDELIGHTS: Reviewer Michael Thelwell writes: "In *Dark Symphony* Professors Gross and Emanuel have supplied us with the most comprehensive anthology of black writing—fiction, poetry, and the essay—since Sterling Brown and his associates published *The Negro Caravan* in 1941. . . . Intended as an introduction to the finest achievements in Negro literature, the book succeeds splendidly." But, Thelwell continues, "the editors were guided in their selections by traditionally formal critical assumptions. . . . This emphasis . . . is unfortunate . . . because it violates, fragments and excludes so much of indigenous black expression." Addressing this question in an article in *Antioch Review,* Gross writes, "By maintaining the highest criteria in judging Negro writing, one honors the Negro's culture."

BIOGRAPHICAL/CRITICAL SOURCES: New York Times, November 26, 1968, July 22, 1971; *Christian Science Monitor,* December 12, 1968; *Ramparts,* October, 1969; *Books Abroad,* winter, 1970; *New Republic,* December 29, 1973; *Prairie Schooner,* fall, 1974.

* * *

GROTH, Alexander J(acob) 1932-

PERSONAL: Surname legally changed, 1953; born March 7, 1932, in Warsaw, Poland; became U.S. citizen, 1953; son of Jacob (an accountant) and Maria (Hazenfus) Goldwasser; married Marilyn Wineburg, December 15, 1961; children: Stevin James, Warren Adrian. *Education:* College of the City of New York (now City College of the City University of New York), B.A. (magna cum laude), 1954; Columbia

University, M.A., 1955, Ph.D., 1960. *Politics:* Independent. *Religion:* Jewish. *Home:* 603 Georgetown Pl., Davis, Calif. 95616. *Office:* Department of Political Science, University of California, Davis, Calif. 95616.

CAREER: City College of the City University of New York, New York, N.Y., instructor in political science, 1960-61; Harpur College (now State University of New York at Binghamton), assistant professor of political science, 1961-62; University of California, Davis, assistant professor, 1962-67, associate professor, 1967-71, professor of political science, 1971—. *Member:* American Political Science Association, Western Political Science Association, Far Western Slavic Conference. *Awards, honors:* Grant from American Council of Learned Societies and Social Science Research Council, 1965-66.

WRITINGS: Revolution and Elite Access, Institute of Governmental Affairs, University of California, 1966; *Eastern Europe after Czechoslovakia,* Foreign Policy Association, 1969; *Comparative Politics: A Distributive Approach,* Macmillan, 1971; *Major Ideologies: An Interpretative Survey of Democracy, Socialism, and Nationalism,* Wiley, 1971; *People's Poland: Government and Politics,* Chandler Publishing, 1972; (co-author) *Contemporary Politics: Europe,* Winthrop Publishing, 1976. Contributor to political science journals.

WORK IN PROGRESS: Research on public policy aspects of comparative politics.

* * *

GROTJAHN, Martin 1904-

PERSONAL: Born July 8, 1904, in Berlin, Germany; came to United States in 1936, naturalized in 1942; son of Alfred (a physician) and Charlotte (Hartz) Grotjahn; married Etelka Grosz (a physician), August 18, 1927; children: Michael. *Education:* University of Berlin, M.D. (summa cum laude), 1929. *Politics:* Liberal. *Religion:* None. *Office:* 416 North Bedford Dr., No. 303, Beverly Hills, Calif. 90210.

CAREER: Kaiser Frederick Hospital (of University of Berlin), Berlin, Germany, intern, 1929-30, head physician in neuropsychiatry, 1930-36; Menninger Clinic, Topeka, Kan., staff physician, 1936-38; Institute of Psychoanalysis, Chicago, Ill., staff physician and instructor in psychiatry, 1938-42; Southern California Institute for Psychoanalysis, Beverly Hills, director and training psychoanalyst, 1946—. Former member of Berlin Psychoanalytic Institute; University of Southern California, instructor, 1950-56, assistant professor, 1956-57, associate professor of psychiatry, 1957-69, clinical professor emeritus, 1969—. Diplomate of American Board of Neurology and Psychiatry. *Military service:* U.S. Army, 1942-46; became major. *Member:* American Psychiatric Association (life fellow), American Psychoanalytic Association (life member), American Medical Association (life member).

WRITINGS: Beyond Laughter, McGraw, 1957; *Psychoanalysis and the Family Neurosis,* Norton, 1960; (editor with Franz Alexander and Samuel Eisenstein) *Psychoanalytic Pioneers,* Basic Books, 1966; *The Voice of the Symbol,* Mara Publishers, 1972; *The Art and Technique of Analytic Group Therapy,* Jason Aronson, 1977; *Carl Jung: Life and Work of the Psychiatrist,* [Mainz, Germany], 1977.

WORK IN PROGRESS: Clinical Observations from Group Psychotherapy in Mental Institutions; Memoirs of a Psychoanalyst.

BIOGRAPHICAL/CRITICAL SOURCES: Werner Mendel, editor, *A Celebration of Laughter,* Mara Publishers, 1972.

*   *   *

GUARINO, M(artin) Vincent 1939-

PERSONAL: Born April 1, 1939, in Chicago, Ill.; son of Martin C. (a printing salesman) and Margaret (Shearin) Guarino; married Karen Marie Shedd, December 28, 1964 (divorced February 5, 1977); children: Kristy Lee, Martha Marie. *Education:* Attended University of Texas, Main University (now University of Texas at Austin), 1961-65. *Office:* 1334 South Kirkwood, Houston, Tex. 77077.

CAREER: Subscription Television, Inc., Santa Monica, Calif., assistant to vice-president of marketing, 1964; *'Teen* (magazine), Los Angeles, Calif., senior editor, 1965-68; Pennzoil Co., Houston, Tex., public relations manager, 1970-77; self-employed communications consultant, 1977—. *Military service:* U.S. Navy, 1957-61. *Member:* Information Film Producers of America, Association of Petroleum Writers, Houston Press Club. *Awards, honors:* Gold Quill of International Association of Business Communicators, 1970, 1973; Gold Cindy from Information Film Producers of America, 1972.

WRITINGS—Adaptations of screenplays: James Collier, *The Restless Ones,* Word, Inc., 1973; Collier, *For Petes Sake,* Word, Inc., 1973.

Author of filmscripts: "The Drafting Technician," A.I.E. Studios, 1970; "The Long Haul North," A.I.E. Studios, 1970; "Sea Robin" (rewrite), Motion Picture Service, 1971; "Something to Build On," A.I.E. Studios, 1971; "New Barrels on the Bayou," A.I.E. Studios, 1972; "P.O.G.O.," Pennzoil Company, 1972; "A Story of People," Pennzoil Company, 1973; "A Pennzoil Day," Pennzoil Company, 1975. Financial writer for Pennzoil and subsidiary firms. Author of column in *'Teen.* Contributor to *Writer's Digest* and *Expecting.*

*   *   *

GUEMPLE, Lee 1930-

PERSONAL: Surname rhymes with "simple"; born July 10, 1930, in Kansas City, Mo.; son of John Ernest and Jacqueline (Lawson) Guemple; married Josephine Miller, May 23, 1952; children: Matthew, Elizabeth. *Education:* University of Chicago, B.A., 1959, M.A., 1961, Ph.D., 1966. *Home:* 49 Heathcote Ave., London, Ontario, Canada. *Office:* Department of Anthropology, University of Western Ontario, London, Ontario, Canada N6A 3K7.

CAREER: Singer of popular music in Kansas City, Mo., 1948-52; interior decorator in Kansas City, 1948-56; Chicago City College, Wright Branch (now Wright College), Chicago, Ill., instructor in social science, 1960-64; Florida State University, Tallahassee, assistant professor of anthropology, 1964-66; Southern Illinois University at Carbondale, assistant professor of anthropology, 1966-70; University of Western Ontario, London, associate professor of anthropology, 1970—, chairman of department, 1972-77. Visiting professor at Arctic Research and Training Center, University of Saskatchewan, 1969, Institute of Social and Economic Research, Memorial University of Newfoundland, 1969-70. Research fellow, University of Aberdeen, 1977-78. *Military service:* U.S. Army, 1952-54. *Member:* Royal Anthropological Institute (fellow), American Anthropological Society (fellow), Central States Anthropological Society (member of executive board, 1972-75). *Awards, honors:* Research

awards, National Museum of Canada, 1962, 1967; National Science Foundation grant, 1969-70.

WRITINGS: Inuit Spouse Exchange, Department of Anthropology, University of Chicago Press, 1961; (editor) *Alliance in Eskimo Society,* American Ethnological Society, 1972; *Eskimo Adoption,* National Museum of Man (Canada), 1978.

WORK IN PROGRESS: Research on alliance theory from an institutional point of view; analysis of cultural symbolism.

*   *   *

GUERS-VILLATE, Yvonne 1924-

PERSONAL: Born June 22, 1924, in Senas, France; daughter of Rene (a physician) and Jeanne (Rech) Guers; married Jose T. Villate (an engineer), May 18, 1963. *Education:* University Aix-Marseille, Licence-es-Lettres, 1944; University of Paris, Concours du C.A., 1948; Bryn Mawr College, M.A., 1951, Ph.D., 1960. *Home:* 1133 North Greenway Dr., Coral Gables, Fla. 33134. *Office:* Department of Modern Languages, Florida International University, Miami, Fla. 33199.

CAREER: Bryn Mawr College, Bryn Mawr, Pa., directress of French House, 1950-51; Baldwin School, Bryn Mawr, teacher of French, 1951-53; Mount Holyoke College, South Hadley, Mass., instructor in French, 1953-55; Chapin School, New York, N.Y., head of French department, 1955-59; Syracuse University, Syracuse, N.Y., assistant professor of French, 1959-65; University of Wisconsin—Milwaukee, associate professor, 1965-69, professor of French, 1969-73; Florida International University, Miami, professor of French, 1974—. *Member:* Modern Language Association of America, American Association of Teachers of French, South Atlantic Modern Language Association, Amis de Cerisy.

WRITINGS: (Editor) Georges Bernanos, *Dialogues des Carmelites,* Macmillan, 1965; *C. F. Ramuz: L'Authenticite, ethique et esthetique de l'oeuvre,* Buchet-Chastel, 1966. Contributor to *French Review, Symposium, Revue des Lettres Modernes, Etudes bernanosiennes, Revue de l'universite Laval, P.L.L., Renascence, USF Language Quarterly,* and *Les Letters Romanes.*

WORK IN PROGRESS: A book on Marguerite Duras.

*   *   *

GUGGENHEIMER, Richard 1906-1977

PERSONAL: Born April 2, 1906, in New York, N.Y.; son of Samuel H. (a lawyer and writer) and Caroline (Koenig) Guggenheimer; married Katharine Pease Beardsley, July 2, 1940 (divorced, 1950); married Marjorie-May Sidenberg, July 14, 1950. *Education:* Attended Sorbonne, University of Paris, 1926-27; Johns Hopkins University, B.A., 1927. *Home:* 784 Park Ave., New York, N.Y.

CAREER: Briarcliff College, Briarcliff Manor, N.Y., lecturer in philosophy of arts and chairman of art department, 1942-72, professor emeritus, 1972-77. *Member:* American Society for Aesthetics.

WRITINGS: Sight and Insight: A Prediction of New Perceptions in Art, Harper, 1945, 3rd edition, Kennikat, 1968; *Creative Vision for Artist and Audience,* Harper, 1960, revised edition published as *Creative Vision for Art and Life,* 1960; *New Dimensions of Destiny: A Further Measure of Man's Reach,* CSA Press, 1971. Contributor to *Art Education, Johns Hopkins Magazine,* and other journals.

WORK IN PROGRESS: A sequel to *New Dimensions of Destiny: A Further Measure of Man's Reach.*

SIDELIGHTS: Richard Guggenheimer displayed his paintings in museums and galleries throughout the United States, and held one-man exhibits in the Van Diemen-Lilienfeld, Macbeth, Passedoit, and Georges Seligmann Galleries, as well as in Paris.

BIOGRAPHICAL/CRITICAL SOURCES: New York Times, March 13, 1977; *AB Bookman's Weekly,* May 9, 1977.†

(Died March 11, 1977)

* * *

GUGLIOTTA, Bobette 1918-

PERSONAL: Surname is pronounced Gu-*lyot*-ta; born November 8, 1918, in Chicago, Ill.; daughter of Irving M. (a music composer) and Aline (Waite) Bibo; married Guy Frank Gugliotta (a military officer and marine engineer), June 2, 1940; children: Guy Bibo. *Education:* Studied creative writing at Stanford University, University of Southern California, and University of California, Los Angeles. *Home:* 25351 Moody Rd., Los Altos Hills, Calif. 94022. *Agent:* Amy Berkower, Writer's House, Inc., 132 West 31st St., New York, N.Y. 10001.

CAREER: Foothill International League, Los Altos Hills, Calif., founder and first chairman, 1962-65; Young Women's Christian Association (YWCA), Honolulu, Hawaii, master of ceremonies on beach club radio program, 1965-66; Recording for the Blind, Palo Alto, Calif., reader and auxiliary member, 1969—. Founded University of Hawaii foreign student program, 1965-66.

WRITINGS: Nolle Smith: Cowboy, Engineer, Statesman, Dodd, 1971; *Katzimo, Mysterious Mesa,* Dodd, 1974. Contributor to *Good Housekeeping, Virginia Quarterly Review, Woman,* and other periodicals and newspapers.

WORK IN PROGRESS: Ring of the Serpent, a young adult adventure story set in Ecuador in 1857; an adult novel set in Brazil.

SIDELIGHTS: Bobette Gugliotta wrote her first story (about Mickey Mouse) at age eleven, for Walt Disney. She recently returned home from a three-year stay in Quito, Ecuador, where she renewed her interest in South America and "all that pertains to it."

BIOGRAPHICAL/CRITICAL SOURCES: Los Altos Town Crier, December 29, 1971; *Palo Alto Times,* January 11, 1972.

* * *

GUHIN, Michael A(lan) 1940-

PERSONAL: Born August 30, 1940, in Pomona, Calif.; son of Alan Edward and Marion (Naisbitt) Guhin. *Education:* University of Southern California, B.A., 1962, M.A., 1964; London School of Economics and Political Science, Ph.D., 1967. *Office:* National Security Council, Old Executive Office Building, Washington, D.C. 20506.

CAREER: National Security Council, Washington, D.C., staff member, 1969—. *Member:* Phi Beta Kappa, Phi Kappa Phi.

WRITINGS: John Foster Dulles: A Statesman and His Times, Columbia University Press, 1972; *Nuclear Paradox: Security Risks of the Peaceful Atom,* American Enterprise Publications, 1976. Contributor to *International Affairs* and *Orbis.*†

GUICE, John D(avid) W(ynne) 1931-

PERSONAL: Surname rhymes with "rice"; born March 24, 1931, in Biloxi, Miss.; son of William Lee and Lee Dicks (Guice) Guice; married Carol Thomas, February 15, 1958; children: Soni Jo, John D. W., Jr. *Education:* Yale University, B.A., 1952; Texas Western College (now University of Texas at El Paso), M.A., 1953; University of Colorado, Ph.D., 1969. *Religion:* Methodist. *Home:* 3010 Mesa Dr., Hattiesburg, Miss. 39401. *Office:* Department of History, University of Southern Mississippi, Hattiesburg, Miss. 39401.

CAREER: White House (department store), El Paso, Tex., administrative assistant, 1952-53, merchandise manager, 1956-61; Harrison Business Equipment, El Paso, sales manager, 1961-66; University of Southern Mississippi, Hattiesburg, assistant professor, 1969-71, associate professor, 1971-78, professor of history, 1978—, director of American studies program, 1977—. University of Colorado, instructor in history, summer, 1968, visiting assistant professor, summer, 1970. *Military service:* U.S. Army, cryptographic specialist, 1954-56; served in France.

MEMBER: American Historical Association, Organization of American Historians, Western History Association, Colorado State Historical Society, Mississippi Historical Society, Rotary Club. *Awards, honors:* American Philosophical Society grants, 1970, 1972, and 1978; LeRoy Hafen Award for best article in volume of *Colorado.*

WRITINGS: The Rocky Mountain Bench: The Territorial Supreme Courts of Colorado, Montana, and Wyoming, 1861-1890, Yale University Press, 1972; (contributor) John Porter Bloom, editor, *The American Territorial System,* Ohio University Press, 1973; (contributor) Richard A. McLemore, editor, *A History of Mississippi* (two volumes), University and College Press of Mississippi, 1973. Contributor to *Southern Quarterly, Western Historical Quarterly, Colorado,* and *American Journal of Legal History.*

WORK IN PROGRESS: A history of Mississippi territory; editing a reprint of the *Confession of James Copeland* (noted outlaw hanged at Augusta, Miss. in 1857).

SIDELIGHTS: "Though my first serious scholarship related to the Rocky Mountains," John D. W. Guice told *CA,* "my interests have turned to the Southern frontier for mainly two reasons. First, my teaching position placed me near the research materials; secondly, my roots are in this frontier where my ancestors settled near Natchez prior to 1773.

"On returning to Mississippi after an absence of over two decades and following my formal training in history, I was astounded at the degree to which the topics of slavery and the Civil War dominate historiography. The region's frontier heritage so lingers in the shadows of sectionalism that historians of the trans-Mississippi West virtually ignore the cis-Mississippi antecedents of so many of the institutions which they describe.... So in a sense, those of us who probe into the Southern frontier work in land that has been passed over quickly—fertile soil for research during the rising interest in comparative frontiers."

* * *

GURR, Ted Robert 1936-

PERSONAL: Born February 21, 1936, in Spokane, Wash.; son of Robert Lucas and Anne (Cook) Gurr; married Erika Brigitte Klie (a research assistant), February 20, 1960; children: Lisa Anne, Andrea Mariel. *Education:* Reed College,

B.A., 1957; Princeton University, additional study, 1958-59; New York University, Ph.D., 1965. *Politics:* Independent. *Home:* 2417 Central Park Ave., Evanston, Ill. 60201. *Office:* Department of Political Science, Northwestern University, Evanston, Ill. 60201.

CAREER: American Behavioral Scientist, Princeton, N.J., assistant to the editor, 1958-60, assistant editor, 1960-61, associate editor, 1963-64; Princeton University, Center of International Studies, Princeton, research associate, 1965-67, faculty associate, 1967-69, assistant professor of political science, 1967-69; Northwestern University, Evanston, Ill., associate professor, 1969-72, professor of political science, 1972-74, Payson S. Wild Professor of Political Science, 1974—, chairman of department 1977—. Visiting assistant professor of political science, New York University, 1966-67; visiting fellow, Cambridge University Institute of Criminology, 1976. Co-director of task force on history of violence, National Commission on the Causes and Prevention of Violence, 1968-69.

MEMBER: American Political Science Association, International Studies Association, International Society for the Study of Aggression (fellow), Social Science History Association, International Peace Science Society, Phi Beta Kappa. *Awards, honors:* Woodrow Wilson fellowship, 1957; Ford Foundation fellowship, England, 1970; Woodrow Wilson Foundation Prize from American Political Science Association, 1971, for *Why Men Rebel;* Guggenheim fellowship, 1972-73; German Marshall Fund senior fellowship, 1976.

WRITINGS: (With Alfred de Grazia) *American Welfare,* New York University Press, 1961; *New Error-Compensated Measures for Comparing Nations: Some Correlates of Civil Violence* (monograph), Center for International Studies, Princeton University, 1966; (with Charles Ruttenberg) *The Conditions of Civil Violence: First Test of a Causal Model* (monograph), Center for International Studies, Princeton University, 1967; (with Ruttenberg) *Cross-National Studies of Civil Violence,* Center for Research in Social Systems, American University, 1968; (editor with Hugh Davis Graham) *Violence in America: Historical and Comparative Perspectives,* National Commission on the Causes and Prevention of Violence, 1969, reissued as *History of Violence in America,* Praeger, 1969, revised edition, in press.

Why Men Rebel, Princeton University Press, 1970; (editor with Francisco J. Moreno) *Basic Courses in Comparative Politics: An Anthology of Syllabi,* Sage Publications for the International Studies Association, 1970; (with Muriel McClelland) *Political Performance: A Twelve-Nation Study,* Sage Publications, 1971; *Politimetrics: An Introduction to Quantitative Macropolitics,* Prentice-Hall, 1972; (editor with Ivo K. Feierabend and Rosalind Feierabend) *Anger, Violence, and Politics,* Prentice-Hall, 1972; (with Harry Eckstein) *Patterns of Authority: A Structural Basis for Political Inquiry,* Wiley-Interscience, 1975; *Rogues, Rebels, and Reformers: A Political History of Urban Crime and Conflict,* Sage Publications, 1976; (with Peter N. Grabosky and Richard C. Hula) *The Politics of Crime and Conflict: A Comparative History of Four Cities,* Sage Publications, 1977; *Comparative Studies of Political Conflict and Change,* Inter-University Consortium for Political and Social Research, 1978.

Contributor: Feliks Gross, editor, *World Politics and Tension Areas,* New York University Press, 1966; Wolfgang Friedman and John Norton Moore, editors, *Law and Civil*

War in the Modern World, Johns Hopkins Press, 1975; Lewis A. Coser and Otto N. Larsen, editors, *The Uses of Controversy in Sociology,* Free Press, 1976; Michael Stohl, editor, *The Politics of Terror: A Reader in Theory and Practice,* Dekker, 1978. Co-editor, "Sage Professional Papers in Comparative Politics," Sage Publications, 1969—. Associate editor, *World Politics,* 1967-68, member of editorial board, 1970—; member of editorial board, *Comparative Political Studies,* 1969—.

WORK IN PROGRESS: Editing and contributing to *Handbook of Political Conflict,* completion expected in 1979; a book for Sage Publications, tentatively entitled *World Patterns of Civil Conflict; Conflict and Society: A Formal Theory;* research on the origins and development of the state.

AVOCATIONAL INTERESTS: Antiquities, travel, photography, camping.

BIOGRAPHICAL/CRITICAL SOURCES: New York Times, July 30, 1969; *New York Times Book Review,* April 12, 1970; *Virginia Quarterly Review,* summer, 1970; *American Journal of Sociology,* January, 1971; *American Political Science Review,* March, 1971; *Saturday Review,* May 22, 1971; *Social Research,* spring, 1971; *Journal of Politics,* August, 1973, November, 1977, February, 1978; *Contemporary Sociology,* September, 1977; *Annals of American Academy of Political and Social Science,* November, 1977; *Social Science Quarterly,* December, 1977.

*   *   *

GURWITSCH, Aron 1901-1973

January 17, 1901—June 25, 1973; Russian-born American professor of philosophy and author. Obituaries: *New York Times,* June 27, 1973. (See index for *CA* sketch)

*   *   *

GUTERMAN, Simeon L(eonard) 1907-

PERSONAL: Born December 25, 1907, in New York, N.Y.; son of Henry (a rabbi) and Lena (Hurwitz) Guterman; married Bette Adler (an arts and crafts instructor), September 1, 1972. *Education:* Harvard University, A.B. (with honors), 1930, A.M., 1932, Ph.D., 1944. *Religion:* Jewish. *Home:* 511 West 232nd St., Riverdale, New York, N.Y. 10463. *Office:* New York Law School, 57 Worth St., New York, N.Y. 10013.

CAREER: Head of high school history department in Scranton, Pa., 1935-45; Ohio Northern University, Ada, professor of history, 1945-46; Pennsylvania State College, Stroudsburg, professor of social studies, 1946-53; Yeshiva University, New York, N.Y., professor of history, 1953-73, professor emeritus, 1973—, dean of Yeshiva College, 1953-59, professor of history at Ferkauf Graduate School of Humanities and Social Sciences, 1959-73, chairman of department of social sciences, 1959-65. Visiting professor, University of Idaho, 1953; adjunct professor, New York Law School, 1974—. *Member:* American Historical Association, Mediaeval Academy of America, American Society for Legal History, American Association of University Professors.

WRITINGS: Religious Toleration and Persecution in Ancient Rome, Aiglon Press, 1951, reprinted, Greenwood Press, 1971; (contributor) N. Lamm and W. S. Wurzburger, editors, *A Treasury of Tradition,* Hebrew Publishing Co., 1967; *From Personal to Territorial Law: Aspects of the History and Structure of the Western Legal-Constitutional Tra-*

dition, Scarecrow, 1972. Contributor of a dozen articles to historical journals.

WORK IN PROGRESS: Two books, *Historical Background of Modern Democracy* and *The Western Legal Tradition.*

* * *

GUTHKE, Karl S(iegfried) 1933-

PERSONAL: Born February 17, 1933, in Lingen, Germany; son of Karl H. (a government official) and Helene (Beekman) Guthke; married Dagmar von Nostitz, April 24, 1965; children: Carl Ricklef. *Education:* Studied at University of Heidelberg, 1952, 1953-54; University of Texas at Austin, M.A., 1953; University of Goettingen, Ph.D., 1956. *Home:* Hillside Rd., Lincoln, Mass. 01773. *Office:* Department of German, Harvard University, Cambridge, Mass. 02138.

CAREER: University of California, Berkeley, instructor, 1956-58, assistant professor, 1958-59, associate professor, 1959-62, professor of German literature, 1962-65; University of Toronto, Toronto, Ontario, professor of German literature, 1965-68; Harvard University, Cambridge, Mass., professor of German literature, 1968-78, Kuno Francke Professor of German Art and Culture, 1978—. Visiting professor at University of Colorado, 1963, and University of Massachusetts, 1967. *Member:* Modern Language Association of America, International Association of Germanists, American Lessing Society (vice-president, 1969-71; president, 1971-72), Schiller Society, Freies Deutsches Hochstift, Academy for Library Studies. *Awards, honors:* American Philosophical Society grant, 1961-62; Guggenheim fellowship, 1965; American Council of Learned Societies fellowship, 1973; Walter Channing Cabot prize, 1977.

WRITINGS: *Englische Vorromantik und deutscher Sturm und Drang: M. G. Lewis' Stellung in der Geschichte der deutsch-englischen Literaturbeziehungen,* Vandenhoeck & Ruprecht, 1958; (with Hans M. Wolff) *Das Leid im Werke Gerhart Hauptmanns: Fuenf Studien,* University of California Press, 1958; *Geschichte und Poetik der deutschen Tragikomoedie,* Vandenhoeck & Ruprecht, 1961; *Gerhart Hauptmann: Weltbild im Werk,* Vandenhoeck & Ruprecht, 1961; *Haller und die Literatur,* Vandenhoeck & Ruprecht, 1962; *Der Stand der Lessing-Forschung: Ein Bericht ueber die Literatur 1932-1962,* Metzler, 1965; *Modern Tragicomedy: An Investigation into the Nature of the Genre,* Random House, 1966; *Wege zur Literatur: Studien zur deutschen Dichtungs-und Geistesgeschichte,* A. Francke, 1967; (with Heinrich Schneider) *Gotthold Ephraim Lessing,* Metzler, 1967, 3rd edition, 1979; *Die Mythologie der entgoetterten Welt: Ein literarisches Thema von der Aufklaerung bis zur Gegenwart,* Vandenhoeck & Ruprecht, 1971; *Das deutsche buergerliche Trauerspiel,* Metzler, 1972, 2nd edition, 1976; *G. E. Lessing,* Metzler, 1973; *Literarisches Leben im achtzehnten Jahrhundert in Deutschland und in der Schweiz,* A. Francke, 1975.

Editor: Friedrich Schiller, *Turandot, Prinzessin von China, ein tragikomisches Maerchen nach Gozzi,* Reclam, 1959; Johann Heinrich Fuessli, *Remarks on the Writings and Conduct of J. J. Rousseau,* Augustan Reprint Society, 1960; *Dichtung und Deutung: Gedaechtnisschrift fuer Hans M. Wolff,* A. Francke, 1961; (reviser and author of introduction) Hans M. Wolff, *Die Weltanschauung der deutschen Aufklaerung in geschichtlicher Entwicklung,* 2nd edition, A. Francke, 1963; Jakob M. R. Lenz, *Der Hofmeister* Reclam, 1963; Gotthold E. Lessing, *D. Faust und die Matrone von*

Ephesus, Reclam, 1968; Gerhart Hauptmann, *Fasching: Der Apostel,* Reclam, 1969; *Hallers Literaturkritik,* Niemeyer, 1970; Gotthold E. Lessing, *Werke,* Carl Hanser, Volume I, 1971, Volume III, 1973; F. M. Klinger, *Die Zwillinge,* Reclam, 1972; Johann Heinrich Fuessli, *Saemtliche Gedichte,* Orell Fuessli, 1973.

Contributor: M. Bircher and A. Haas, editors, *Barocklyrik,* A. Francke, 1973; S. Bauschinger, H. Denkler, and W. Haas, editors, *Amerika in der deutschen Literatur,* Reclam, 1975; B. von Wiese, editor, *Deutsche Dichter des 18. Jahrhunderts,* Erich Schmidt, 1977; *Deutsches Literatur-Lexikon,* A. Francke, 1978; H. Michel, editor, *Albrecht von Haller,* Birkhauser (Basel), 1978; W. Hinck, editor, *Handbuch des deutschen Dramas,* Bagel, 1979; W. Hinderer, editor, *Schillers Dramen,* Reclam, 1979. Contributor to journals in United States, Germany, and Italy.

WORK IN PROGRESS: *Science Fiction and the Image of Man.*

AVOCATIONAL INTERESTS: Skiing, old maps, nineteenth-century graphics, pre-Columbian archaeology.

* * *

GUTHRIE, James W. 1936-

PERSONAL: Born August 28, 1936, in Chicago, Ill.; son of James W. and Florence (Harvey) Guthrie; children: Sarah, James, Shannon. *Education:* Stanford University, B.A., 1958, M.A., 1960, Ph.D., 1968; Harvard University, postdoctoral study, 1969-70. *Home:* 52 Orhvale St., Berkeley, Calif. *Office:* 3533 Tolman Hall, School of Education, University of California, Berkeley, Calif. 94720.

CAREER: High school science teacher in Arcata, Calif., 1960-61; high school history and social studies teacher in Palo Alto, Calif., 1961-63; U.S. Department of Health, Education, and Welfare, Washington, D.C., intern in education, 1966-67; University of California, Berkeley, assistant professor, 1968-70, associate professor, 1971-77, professor of education, 1977—, director of urban education program, 1968-71. Deputy director, New York State Education Commission, 1970-72. *Member:* American Educational Research Association, American Association of School Administrators, Phi Delta Kappa. *Awards, honors:* Alfred North Whitehead postdoctoral fellow at Harvard University, 1969-70.

WRITINGS: (Contributor) Irwin T. Johnson and David N. Evans, editors, *An Evaluation of NDEA Title III in California,* California State Department of Education, 1966; (contributor) *Toward Improved Urban Education,* Charles A. Jones Publishing, 1970; (contributor) George B. Kleindorfer, Henry M. Levin, and Robert T. Stout, editors, *Do Teachers Make a Difference?,* U.S. Government Printing Office, 1970; (contributor) Kleindorfer, Levin, and Stout, editors, *A Time for Priorities: Financing the Schools for the 70's,* National Education Association, 1970; (editor with Edward Wynne) *New Models for American Education,* Prentice-Hall, 1971; (with Kleindorfer, Levin, and Stout) *Schools and Inequality,* M.I.T. Press, 1971; (with Walter I. Galms and Lawrence C. Pierce) *School Finance,* Prentice-Hall, 1978. Contributor of about twenty articles to *Saturday Review* and to education journals.

WORK IN PROGRESS: Two books, *Educational Administration* and *Local Government: The Vanishing Vision;* a Ford Foundation sponsored study of school resource allocation.

GUTIERREZ-VEGA, Zenaida 1924-

PERSONAL: Born June 23, 1924, in Union de Reyes, Cuba; daughter of Maximino (a businessman) and Maria (a grammar school director; maiden name Vega) Gutierrez. *Education:* Institute of Secondary Education, Matanzas, Cuba, B.A., 1945; University of Havana, Ph.D., 1950, post-doctoral study, 1950-55; postdoctoral study at National College of Doctors in Philosophy (Havana), 1950-53, International University of Manendez Pelayo, 1957, University of Rome, 1956-57, and Institute of Hispanic Culture (Madrid), 1962, 1966; University of Madrid, Ph.D. (summa cum laude), 1966. *Home:* 220 East 63rd St., Apt. 4L, New York, N.Y. 10021. *Office:* Department of Spanish, Hunter College of the City University of New York, New York, N.Y. 10021.

CAREER: High school Spanish teacher in Cardenas, Cuba, 1948-49; American Dominican Academy, Havana, Cuba, professor of Spanish, 1951-52; Instituto del Vedado, Havana, professor of Spanish and Spanish-American literature, 1952-59; University of Las Villas, Santa Clara, Cuba, professor of Spanish-American literature, Italian language and literature, and art history, 1959-62; American Air Base, Torrejon, Madrid, Spain, professor of Spanish, 1966; Institute of European Studies, Madrid, substitute professor of Spanish-American literature, 1967; University of Missouri, St. Louis, assistant professor of Spanish-American literature, 1967-68; University of Puerto Rico, Rio Piedras, associate professor of Spanish-American literature, summer, 1969; State University of New York College at Oswego, associate professor of Spanish and Spanish-American literature, 1968-71; Hunter College of the City University of New York, New York, N.Y., adjunct associate professor of Spanish and Spanish-American literature, 1971—. Visiting professor of Spanish, Fairleigh Dickinson University, 1971-72.

MEMBER: Modern Language Association of America, American Association of Teachers of Spanish and Portuguese, American Association of University Professors, American Association of University Women, Circulo Italo-Cubano de Cultura (founder), Touring Club Italiano (founder). *Awards, honors:* Fellowship from Cuban Ministry of Education, 1956-57; fellowship from Institute of Hispanic Culture, 1958-59, 1962-66, 1967; Panorama espanol contemporaneo prize, Institute of Hispanic Culture, 1963; Tesis doctorales hispanoamericanas prize, Institute of Hispanic Culture, 1966; grant from University of Missouri at St. Louis, 1967.

WRITINGS: Jose Maria Chacon y Calvo: Hispanista cubano, Ediciones Cultura Hispanica, 1969. Contributor of articles and reviews to Spanish language journals.

WORK IN PROGRESS: Alfonso Reyes: Cartas.

BIOGRAPHICAL/CRITICAL SOURCES: Arriba, April 27, 1969; *La Vanguardia,* April 28, 1969; *Mundo Hispanico,* January, 1970.†

H

HAAS, Irvin 1916-

PERSONAL: Born May 4, 1916, in Brooklyn, N.Y.; son of Jacob (a railroad employee) and Emma (Littenberg) Haas; married Irene Basarowitz, August 31, 1938; children: Karin (Mrs. Stuart Clode), Peter. *Education:* Attended New York University. *Politics:* None. *Home:* 65 Diana's Trail, Roslyn, N.Y. 11576.

CAREER: Editor with Book Collector's Packet, 1938-41, and Limited Editions Club and Heritage Club, 1945-46; associate director, Seven Arts Book Society, 1947-51; Marboro Book Club, New York City, director, 1951-55, 1965-68; owner and director of Antiques Book Society, 1955-60, and Arts and Crafts Book Club, 1955-60; A. S. Barnes & Co., Inc., New York City, director of sales, 1961-65; Commentary Library, New York City, director of book club, 1968-71. Consultant to other book clubs. *Military service:* U.S. Navy, 1942-45. *Member:* Book Club Round Table.

WRITINGS: Bibliography of Modern American Presses, Black Cat Press, 1935; *Bruce Rogers: A Bibliography,* Peter Pauper, 1936; *Bibliography of Material Relating to Private Presses,* Black Cat Press, 1937; *Treasury of Great Prints,* Yoseloff, 1960; *America's Historic Houses and Restorations,* Hawthorn, 1966; *America's Historic Inns and Taverns,* Arco, 1972; *America's Historic Villages and Restorations,* Arco, 1974; *America's Historic Ships, Replicas, and Restorations,* Arco, 1975; *Historic Homes of the American Presidents,* McKay, 1976. Also author of *Citadels, Ramparts, and Stockades: America's Historic Forts,* for Everest. Prints editor, *Art News.*

WORK IN PROGRESS: America's Historic Battlefields, for Everest.

AVOCATIONAL INTERESTS: Travel.

* * *

HAAS, J(ohn) Eugene 1926-

PERSONAL: Born October 25, 1926, in Lancaster, Pa.; son of Emanuel Casper and Rhoda (Wolgemuth) Haas; married Mary Helen Kraybill (a professor of home economics education), August 14, 1948; children: Cynthia Louise, Margene Kay. *Education:* Upland College, A.B., 1950; University of California, Los Angeles, M.A., 1953; University of Minnesota, Ph.D., 1957. *Home:* 1712 Ponderosa Place, Loveland, Colo. 80537.

CAREER: Ohio State University, Columbus, assistant professor, 1957-61, associate professor, 1961-66, professor of sociology and anthropology, 1966-67; University of Colorado, Boulder, professor of sociology, beginning 1968. Summer lecturer, Columbia University, 1961. President of Human Ecology Research Services, Inc.; member of disaster relief committee, National Citizens Commission for International Cooperation, 1965; member of task group on human dimensions of atmosphere, National Center for Atmospheric Research, 1966-67; member of committee on Alaska earthquake, National Academy of Science, 1968-71; member of science and engineering advisory committee to National Oceanic and Atmospheric Administration, 1970-72; chairman of Loveland Environmental Quality Commission, 1971-72. Consultant to Columbus Hospital Federation, 1962-64, Ohio State Nurses Association, 1964-67, and Executive Office of the President, Office of Emergency Preparedness, 1971—. *Member:* American Sociological Association, American Meteorological Society, American Association for the Advancement of Science, Midwest Sociological Society.

WRITINGS: (With Thomas E. Drabek) *Complex Organizations: A Sociological Perspective,* Macmillan, 1973; (with Drabek) *Understanding Complex Organizations,* W. C. Brown, 1974; (with Gilbert F. White) *Assessment of Research on Natural Hazards,* M.I.T. Press, 1975; (editor with others) *Reconstruction Following Disaster,* M.I.T. Press, 1977. Author of several monographs. Contributor to *Contemporary Sociology, Trans-Action, American Sociological Review, Indian Sociological Bulletin, Administrative Science Quarterly, Social Forces, Nursing Research,* and *Midwest Sociologist.*†

* * *

HABERSTROH, Chadwick John 1927-

PERSONAL: Born July 19, 1927, in Livingston, Mont.; son of John Casimir (a photographer) and Grace (Smith) Haberstroh (a teacher); married Phyllis Weese (a social worker), January 24, 1959; children: John Christopher, Sarah Catherine. *Education:* University of Minnesota, B.A., 1948, Ph.D., 1958; Columbia University, M.A., 1950. *Home:* 2029 East Newton Ave., Milwaukee, Wis. 53211. *Office:* Department of Business Administration, University of Wisconsin, Milwaukee, Wis. 53201.

CAREER: Teacher in public schools in Montana, 1948-49;

U.S. Department of Labor, Wage and Hour and Public Contracts Division, Washington, D.C., labor economist and administrator, 1950-52; University of Minnesota, Minneapolis, instructor in economics, 1953-54; Carnegie Institute of Technology (now Carnegie-Mellon University), Pittsburgh, Pa., senior research fellow in industrial administration, 1954-57; Massachusetts Institute of Technology, Cambridge, assistant professor of industrial management, 1957-62; University of Denver, Denver, Colo., professor of management, 1962-65, chairman of department, 1962-64; Case Institute of Technology (now Case Western Reserve University), Cleveland, Ohio, associate professor of economics, 1965-67; University of Wisconsin—Milwaukee, professor of business administration and political science, 1967—. Fulbright lecturer in Cuenca, Ecuador, 1959; expert on office mechanization in Argentina for Bureau Technical Assistance Operations, United Nations, 1961; chairman, College on Organization, Institute of Management Sciences, 1964-65, 1968-71. *Military service:* U.S. Naval Reserve, active duty, 1945-46.

MEMBER: American Association for the Advancement of Science, Society for General Systems Research, American Association of University Professors (president-elect of University of Wisconsin—Milwaukee chapter, 1973-74), North American Research Group on Management. *Awards, honors:* Fulbright research scholarship, Barcelona, Spain, 1965-66.

WRITINGS: (With A. H. Rubenstein) *Some Theories of Organization,* Irwin-Dorsey, 1960, revised edition, 1966; (contributor) Martin K. Starr, editor, *Executive Readings in Management Science,* Macmillan, 1964; (contributor) Donald E. Porter and Phillip Applewhite, editors, *Studies in Organizational Behavior and Management,* International Textbook Co., 1964; (contributor) Charles P. Bonini, Robert K. Jaedicke, and Harvey M. Wagner, editors, *Management Controls: New Directions in Basic Research,* McGraw, 1964; (contributor) *Problems of Tax Administration in Latin America,* Johns Hopkins Press, 1965; (contributor) James G. March, editor, *Handbook of Organizations,* Rand McNally, 1965; (with W. C. Frederick) *Management Education in Spain,* Ford Foundation and Sociedad de Estudios y Publicaciones, 1969; (contributor) Russell Ackoff, and others, *Systems and Management Science,* Random House, 1973; (contributor) Ackoff, editor, *Systems and Management Annual,* Petrocelli, 1974; (contributor) Martin Greenberger and others, editors, *Networks for Research and Education: Sharing of Computer and Information Sources Nationwide,* M.I.T. Press, 1974. Contributor to business administration journals. Member of editorial board, *Administrative Science Quarterly,* 1973-76.

*   *   *

HACKNEY, Sheldon 1933-

PERSONAL: Born December 5, 1933, in Birmingham, Ala.; son of Cecil Fain (a businessman) and Elizabeth (Morris) Hackney; married Lucy Durr, June 15, 1957; children: Virginia Foster, Sheldon Fain, Elizabeth Morris. *Education:* Vanderbilt University, B.A., 1955; Yale University, M.A., 1963, Ph.D., 1966. *Office:* Office of the President, Tulane University, New Orleans, La. 70118.

CAREER: Princeton University, Princeton, N.J., instructor, 1965-66, assistant professor, 1966-69, associate professor, 1969-72, professor of American history, 1972-75, provost, 1972-75; Tulane University, New Orleans, La., president, 1975—. *Military service:* U.S. Navy, 1956-61;

became lieutenant. *Member:* American Historical Association, Organization of American Historians, Agricultural History Society, Southern Historical Association. *Awards, honors:* Albert J. Beveridge Award of the American Historical Association, 1970, and Charles Sydnor Award of the Southern Historical Association, 1970, both for *Populism to Progressivism in Alabama.*

WRITINGS: Populism to Progressivism in Alabama, Princeton University Press, 1969; (editor) *Populism: The Critical Issues,* Little, Brown, 1971; (compiler with Barton Bernstein and James M. Banner) *Understanding the American Experience,* Harcourt, 1973. Contributor to *American Historical Review, Journal of Southern History,* and *American Scholar.*

WORK IN PROGRESS: The Civil Rights Movement in the South: 1954-68; Social Change in the Nineteenth-Century South.

BIOGRAPHICAL/CRITICAL SOURCES: Virginia Quarterly Review, summer, 1970; *Detroit Free Press,* December 30, 1970.

*   *   *

HADLEY, Leila 1926-

PERSONAL: Born September 22, 1926, in New York; daughter of Frank Vincent (a sportsman) and Beatrice (Eliott) Burton; married Arthur T. Hadley, March, 1944 (divorced August, 1947); married Yvor H. Smitter, January, 1953 (divorced August, 1969); married William C. Musham, May 29, 1976; children: (first marriage) Arthur T. III; (second marriage) Victoria, Matthew, Caroline. *Education:* Attended University of Witwatersrand. *Religion:* Presbyterian. *Home and office:* 1170 Fifth Ave., New York, N.Y. 10029. *Agent:* International Creative Management, 40 West 57th St., New York, N.Y. 10019.

CAREER: Diplomat (magazine), New York City, associate editor, 1965-67; *Saturday Evening Post,* New York City, cartoon editor, 1967, associate women's editor, 1968; *Palm Beach Life,* Palm Beach, Fla., book reviewer and feature writer, 1970-73. *Member:* Society of American Travel Writers, Society of Women Geographers.

WRITINGS: Give Me the World, Simon & Schuster, 1958; *How to Travel with Children in Europe,* Walker, 1963; (with John Barclay) *Manners for Young People,* Random House, 1966; *Fielding's Guide to Traveling with Children in Europe,* Morrow, 1972, revised edition, 1974; *Traveling with Children in the U.S.A.,* Morrow, 1976. Contributor to *Town and Country, Holiday, Woman's Day, Travel and Camera, Venture, McCall's, Diplomat,* and *Saturday Evening Post.*

WORK IN PROGRESS: A novel; articles.

*   *   *

HAGAN, Kenneth J(ames) 1936-

PERSONAL: Born February 20, 1936, in Oakland, Calif.; son of James A. and Mary (Connolly) Hagan; married Vera Low, February 8, 1964; children: Douglas, Meiling, Kevin. *Education:* University of California, Berkeley, A.B., 1958, M.A., 1964; Claremont Graduate School, Ph.D., 1970. *Politics:* Democrat. *Home:* 1209 Poplar Ave., Annapolis, Md. 21401. *Office:* Department of History, U.S. Naval Academy, Annapolis, Md. 21402.

CAREER: University of California, Irvine, associate in history, 1965-66; Claremont Men's College, Claremont, Calif., instructor in history, 1968-69; Kansas State University,

Manhattan, assistant professor of history, 1969-73; U.S. Naval Academy, Annapolis, Md., assistant professor, 1973-77, associate professor of history, 1977—. *Military service:* U.S. Naval Reserve, 1958-63; became lieutenant. *Member:* Naval Historical Foundation, Society for Historians of American Foreign Relations, Organization of American Historians, American Historical Association, U.S. Naval Institute, Phi Alpha Theta. *Awards, honors:* Research associateships from Smithsonian Institution, summers, 1967, 1968; post-doctoral fellowships from National Endowment for the Humanities, summer, 1974, and Smithsonian Institution, spring, 1975.

WRITINGS: American Gunboat Diplomacy and the Old Navy: 1877-1889, Greenwood Press, 1973; (co-author) *American Foreign Policy: A History,* Heath, 1977; (editor) *In Peace and War: Interpretations of American Naval History, 1775-1978,* Greenwood Press, 1978. Contributor to *Encyclopedia of American Diplomacy,* Scribner, 1978.

WORK IN PROGRESS: Co-editing, *Over the Ramparts: Interpretations of American Military History from Yorktown to the Present,* for Greenwood Press.

* * *

HAGGERSON, Nelson L. 1927-

PERSONAL: Born June 11, 1927, in Silver City, N.M.; son of Nelson Lionel (a construction worker) and Gladys (Jackson) Haggerson; married Bessie Kate Baldwin (a public health nurse), June 1, 1949; children: Patrick, Frederick, Terese, Lionel, Rebecca, Mary. *Education:* Vanderbilt University, B.A. (cum laude), 1949; Western New Mexico University, M.A., 1952; Claremont Graduate School, Ph.D., 1960. *Politics:* Democrat. *Religion:* Roman Catholic. *Home:* 132 West Balboa Dr., Tempe, Ariz. 85282. *Office:* Arizona State University, Tempe, Ariz. 85281.

CAREER: Latin and mathematics teacher in Hurley, N.M., 1949-52; New Mexico Military Institute, Roswell, teacher of Latin and mathematics, 1952-53; principal of high school in Bayard, N.M., 1953-60; Western New Mexico University, Silver City, assistant professor of education, 1960-61; Webster College, Webster Groves, Mo., associate professor of education, 1963-64; Arizona State University, Tempe, professor of secondary education, 1963—, chairman of department, 1967-74. Has taught at hospitals, nursing schools, and for Bureau of Indian Affairs. *Military service:* U.S. Navy, 1945-46. *Member:* National Education Association, Association for Supervision and Curriculum Development, National Council for the Social Studies, Arizona Education Association, Phi Delta Kappa. *Awards, honors:* Arizona Teacher of the Year, 1973.

WRITINGS: (With L. H. Griffith and D. D. Weber) *Secondary Education Today,* McKay, 1967; *To Dance with Joy* (poems), Exposition, 1971. Also author of a video tape production, ''Aesthetics Are Basic,'' Arizona Department of Education; contributor to poetry anthologies. Contributor to education journals.

* * *

HAGGERTY, James J(oseph) 1920-

PERSONAL: Born February 1, 1920, in Orange, N.J.; son of Anna (Morahan) Haggerty; married Marian Smith (an office manager), November 20, 1962. *Education:* Attended schools in Orange, N.J. *Politics:* Independent. *Religion:* Agnostic. *Home and office:* 502 H St. S.W., Washington, D.C. 20024.

CAREER: Orange Daily Courier, Orange, N.J., 1938-41, began as advertising copy boy, became general assignment and sports reporter; American Aviation Publications, Washington, D.C., military editor of *American Aviation Daily* and *American Aviation Magazine,* 1948-53; *Collier's,* New York City, aviation editor, 1953-56 (magazine ceased publication, 1956); *Look,* New York City, contributing editor on aviation and defense, 1957-58; free-lance writer in Washington, D.C., 1958—, covering all forms of aviation, space and missilery, and general science. Consulting editor, Aerospace Industries Association of America, 1957-66, 1975—, and Spartan Books, 1964-66. *Military service:* U.S. Army Air Forces and U.S. Air Force, 1942-48; flew fifty-two combat missions as navigator with 15th Air Force; assigned to Pentagon, 1946-48, with final post as chief of press section, Office of the Secretary of the Air Force; became captain; received Distinguished Flying Cross and Air Medal with four oak-leaf clusters.

MEMBER: Aviation/Space Writers Association (president, 1950-51), National Press Club, National Aviation Club, Touchdown Club of Washington, Bethesda Country Club, Washington Redskins Alumni Association. *Awards, honors:* Winner of Trans World Airlines annual writing competition, 1950 and 1952, and Interavia international writing competition, 1959; James T. Strebig Memorial Trophy of Aviation Writers Association, 1957; U.S. Air Force Award of Appreciation, 1966; Aviation and Space Writers Association best book award, 1966, and magazine writing award, 1976.

WRITINGS: First of the Spacemen (biography of Iven Kincheloe), Duell, Sloan & Pearce, 1960; *Project Mercury,* Scholastic Book Services, 1961; *Spacecraft,* Scholastic Book Services, 1961; (with H. Guyford Stever) *Flight,* Time, Inc., 1965, 8th edition, in press; *Man's Conquest of Space,* Scholastic Book Services, 1966; (with W. R. Smith) *The United States Air Force: A Pictorial History in Art,* Books, Inc., 1966; (with William Henry Sebrell) *Food and Nutrition,* Time, Inc., 1967; *Apollo,* North American Rockwell Corp., 1968; *Apollo: Lunar Landing,* Rand McNally, 1969; *Aviation's Mr. Sam,* Aero, 1974; *Hail to the Redskins,* Seven Seas Press, 1974.

Contributor to *Encyclopaedia Britannica, Grolier's Encyclopedia, Collier's Encyclopedia, National Encyclopedia,* and *Illustrated Encyclopedia of Aviation and Space,* and to general magazines, aviation publications, and industry house organs; also has written film scripts, for radio panel shows, and compiled industrial brochures. Also author and editor of *Spinoff* (annual space report by the National Aeronautics and Space Administration), 1977-79. Editorial consultant and writer for Aerospace Industries Association of America, 1957-66; editor, *Aerospace Year Book* and *Aircraft, Missiles and Spacecraft Year Book,* 1957-70; contributing editor of *Armed Forces Journal,* 1961-69, and *National Aeronautics Magazine,* 1972-74; Washington correspondent, *Flight International,* 1974-75.

WORK IN PROGRESS: Continuing research projects in aviation and space.

AVOCATIONAL INTERESTS: Travel (''particularly via cruise ship''), sports (''committee work and writing'').

* * *

HAGOPIAN, John V. 1923-

PERSONAL: Born March 11, 1923, in Ambridge, Pa.; son of Ardash Arthur (a laborer) and Vera (Avetisoff) Hagopian; married Alexandra Makar, 1947 (divorced, 1948); married Jo Heimann, 1950 (divorced, 1955); married Sue Baxter, 1955 (divorced, 1970); children: (third marriage) Amy, Geoffrey. *Education:* Wayne University (now Wayne State University), A.B., 1945, M.A., 1950; Western Reserve University (now Case Western Reserve University), Ph.D., 1955. *Politics:* Independent. *Religion:* Atheist. *Home:* 35 Davis St., Binghamton, N.Y. 13905. *Office:* Department of English, State University of New York, Binghamton, N.Y. 13901.

CAREER: Wayne University (now Wayne State University), Detroit, Mich., instructor in English, 1946-49; Indiana University at Bloomington, lecturer in English, 1953-55; University of Michigan, Ann Arbor, instructor, 1955-59, assistant professor of English, 1959-60; University of the Saar, Saarbruecken, Germany, professor of American studies and chairman of department, 1960-63; State University of New York at Binghamton, professor of English and comparative literature, 1963—. Fulbright professor at University of Kiel, 1957-58, and University of Regensburg, 1976-77; U.S. Information Service lecturer, 1960-63; visiting professor, Jackson State College, 1967; visiting lecturer, Medical School, University of Mississippi, 1967-69; visiting summer professor at Falkenstein Seminar in American Studies, 1961-63, 1968, Sir George Williams University, 1970, and Institute of Modern Letters, University of Tulsa, 1976. Co-director, State University of New York Semester in London, 1976. Violinist with Binghamton Symphony, 1963-67. *Military service:* U.S. Army, Signal Corps, 1943-46; served in the Pacific; received five battle stars.

MEMBER: International Federation of Modern Language and Literature, International Association of University Professors of English, Modern Language Association of America, College English Association, National Council of Teachers of English.

WRITINGS: (With Martin Dolch and others) *Insight I: Analyses of American Literature,* Hirschgraben-Verlag, 1962, 4th edition, 1971; (with Dolch and others) *Insight II: Analyses of Modern British Literature,* Hirschgraben-Verlag, 1964, 3rd edition, 1969; *J. F. Powers,* Twayne, 1968; *Insight III: Modern British and American Poetry,* Hirschgraben-Verlag, 1969; *Insight IV: Analysis of British and American Drama,* Hirschgraben-Verlag, 1975. Contributor of articles, poems, and short stories to *Southern Review* and other journals. Member of board of editors of *Studies in Short Fiction,* 1965—.

WORK IN PROGRESS: Two books, *Psychology and Technique of the I-Narrative* and *Meaning and Structure of Metaphor.*

SIDELIGHTS: John V. Hagopian made the following "self-observations—not necessarily in order of importance. Professors of literature should not be museum keepers, preservers of the dead past. Encounter with students is more important than research and publication—but both are necessary. I am a Camusian existentialist. I am homo ludens. I love my children. I love women. I abandoned all political activity when I discovered the corrupt personal motives of all leaders, left and right. The symphony orchestra is civilization's highest achievement—any community that doesn't have a good one isn't really civilized!"

AVOCATIONAL INTERESTS: Music, theater, tennis, golf, games, and puzzles.

*   *   *

HAILEY, Oliver 1932-

PERSONAL: Born July 7, 1932, in Pampa, Tex.; son of Oliver D. (a butcher) and Hallie May (Thomas) Hailey; married Elizabeth Ann Forsythe, June 25, 1960; children: Elizabeth Kendall, Melinda Brooke. *Education:* University of Texas, Main University (now University of Texas at Austin), B.F.A., 1954; Yale University, M.F.A., 1962. *Politics:* Democrat. *Religion:* Protestant. *Home:* 11747 Canton Pl., Studio City, Calif. 91604. *Agent:* Shirley Bernstein, Paramuse Artists Associates, 1414 Ave. of the Americas, New York, N.Y. 10019.

CAREER: Dallas Morning News, Dallas, Tex., feature writer, 1957-59; playwright, 1960—. *Military service:* U.S. Air Force, Strategic Air Command, 1954-57; became first lieutenant. *Member:* Writers Guild. *Awards, honors:* Phyllis S. Anderson fellowship in playwriting, 1961-62; Drama Desk-Vernon Rice Award, 1963, for "Hey You, Light Man!"; Certificate of Merit, Los Angeles Drama Critics Circle, 1973, for "Father's Day."

WRITINGS—Plays: *First One Asleep, Whistle* (produced on Broadway at Belasco Theatre, February 26, 1966), S. Fischer Verlag, 1967; *Who's Happy Now?* (three-act; first produced in Los Angeles, Calif. at Mark Taper Forum, November 3, 1967; produced Off-Broadway at Village South Theatre, November 17, 1969; produced on "Theatre in America" series, PBS-TV, May 14, 1975), Random House, 1969; *Hey You, Light Man* (two-act; first produced in Lawrence, Kan. at University of Kansas, May 9, 1961; produced Off-Broadway at Mayfair Theatre, February 26, 1963), Dramatists Play Service, 1970; *"Picture," "Animal," "Crisscross": Three Short Plays* ("Picture" and "Animal" produced together Off-Off-Broadway at Caffe Cino, May, 1965; "Crisscross" produced in Los Angeles, Calif. at Evergreen Theatre, March 6, 1970), Dramatists Play Service, 1970; *Father's Day* (two-act; first produced in Los Angeles, Calif., 1970; produced on Broadway at Golden Theatre, March 16, 1971), Dramatists Play Service, 1971; *Continental Divide* (three-act; produced in Washington, D.C. at Washington Theatre Club, May 6, 1970), Dramatists Play Service, 1973; *For the Use of the Hall* (two-act; first produced in Providence, R.I. at Trinity Square Theatre, January 2, 1974; produced Off-Off-Broadway at Playwrights Horizon, November 13, 1977; produced on "Hollywood Television Theatre" series, PBS-TV, June 2, 1975), Dramatists Play Service, 1976; *Red Rover, Red Rover* (two-act; produced in Minneapolis, Minn. at Cricket Theatre, November 25, 1977), Dramatists Play Service, 1979.

Unpublished plays: "Child's Play: A Comedy for Orphans," produced in New Haven, Conn. at Yale University, October, 1962; "Home by Hollywood," produced in New London, Conn. at Mitchell College, May 15, 1964; "Orphan," produced in Los Angeles, Calif. at Evergreen Stage, June 17, 1970; "And Where She Stops Nobody Knows," produced in Los Angeles, Calif. at Mark Taper Forum, April 1, 1976; "Tryptich," produced in Los Angeles, Calif. at Mark Taper Forum Lab, February 6, 1978; "I Can't Find It Anywhere," produced in Louisville, Ky. at Actors Theatre, February, 1979. Also author of two-act play "I Won't Dance."

Plays represented in anthologies, including: *Three Plays from the Yale School of Drama,* edited by John Gassner, Dutton, 1964; *Collision Course,* edited by Edward Parone, Random House, 1968; *Showcase One Plays from the Eugene O'Neill Foundation,* edited by John Lahr, Grove, 1969; *New Theatre for Now,* edited by Parone, Delta, 1971.

Author of episode for "Bracken's World," NBC-TV and of nine episodes for "McMillan and Wife," NBC-TV. Story editor, "McMillan and Wife," 1972-74.

SIDELIGHTS: Four of Oliver Hailey's full-length plays have been published in Germany.

* * *

HAILSTONES, Thomas J(ohn) 1919-

PERSONAL: Born April 12, 1919, in Hamilton, Scotland; brought to United States, 1921, naturalized, 1926; son of James and Mary (Sweeney) Hailstones; married Catherine Paffhausen, January 25, 1944; children: Barbara (Mrs. Norman Breckel), William, Patrick. *Education:* University of Detroit, B.A., 1947; Wayne University (now Wayne State University), M.A., 1948; St. Louis University, Ph.D., 1951. *Religion:* Roman Catholic. *Home:* 379 Circlewood Lane, Cincinnati, Ohio 45215. *Office:* Office of the Dean, College of Business Administration, Xavier University, Cincinnati, Ohio 45207.

CAREER: Ford Motor Co., Detroit, Mich., auto assembler, 1939-42, 1945-47; University of Detroit, Detroit, instructor in business administration, 1947-48; St. Louis University, St. Louis, Mo., instructor in economics, 1948-52; University of Notre Dame, Notre Dame, Ind., assistant professor of economics, 1951-52; Xavier University, Cincinnati, Ohio, assistant professor, 1952-55, associate professor, 1955-59, professor of economics, 1959—, chairman of department of economics and business, 1952-56, director, Business Administration Division, 1956-61, dean, College of Business Administration, 1961—. Instructor for U.S. Army Air Forces and Royal Air Force during World War II; adjunct professor, General Electric Co. Management Development Institute. Conducted "Economic Trends," a weekly program, for WLW-Radio, 1958-63; WLW-Television, panel member on "World Front," 1958—. Chairman, Full Employment Commission (Cincinnati), 1954-60; chairman of advisory committee, Ohio State Employment Service, 1961—; member of advisory committee, Cincinnati Manpower Development and Training Program, 1962-65; member of economic education committee, National Invest-in-America Council, 1963-67; member of board of trustees, Community Action Commission (Cincinnati), 1965-67. Member of board of directors, Clopay Corp., and A. C. Wahl & Associates.

MEMBER: American Economic Association, National Association of Business Economists, Association of Social Economics (president, 1975), Midwest Economics Association.

WRITINGS: Basic Economics, Southwestern Publishing, 1960, 5th edition, 1975; (with James Harvey Dodd) *Economics: Principles and Applications,* Southwestern Publishing, 4th edition (Hailstones was not associated with 1st or 2nd editions; was consulting editor for 3rd edition, 1957), 1961, 5th edition, 1965; *Readings in Economics,* Southwestern Publishing, 1963, 3rd edition (with Frank V. Mastrianna), 1974; (with Bernard L. Martin and George A. Wing) *Contemporary Economic Problems and Issues,* Southwestern Publishing, 1966, 2nd edition (with Martin and Mastrianna), 1970, 3rd edition, 1973; (with Michael J. Brennan) *Economics: An Analysis of Principles and Policies,* Southwestern Publishing, 1970, 2nd edition, 1975. Author of "Economic Thoughts," weekly newspaper column, 1955-65.

WORK IN PROGRESS: Managerial Economics.

* * *

HAINES, Charles 1928-

PERSONAL: Born March 22, 1928, in New York, N.Y.; son of Charles Everett (a surgeon) and Irene (Hamilton) Haines; married Claudia Persi (a university professor), February 21, 1969; children: Charles Henry Persi. *Education:* Trinity College, Dublin, B.A., 1949, M.A., 1954. *Office:* Department of English, Carleton University, Ottawa, Ontario, Canada.

CAREER: Institute of Physical Medicine and Rehabilitation, New York, N.Y., director of recreational therapy, 1952-54; Bocconi University, Milan, Italy, assistant professor, 1955-59, associate professor of English, 1959-64; Carleton University, Ottawa, Ontario, professor of English, 1965—; CBC-Radio, Ottawa, drama, opera, and dance critic, 1970—. Acting head of English department, University of Leece, Leece, Italy, 1961-62. *Member:* Modern Language Association of America, Association of Canadian University Teachers of English, American Association of University Professors, National Association of Railroad Passengers, Association of Canadian Radio and Television Artists, Bootmakers of Toronto.

WRITINGS: William Shakespeare, F. Watts, 1968; *Charles Dickens,* F. Watts, 1970; *Florence,* F. Watts, 1972; *Edgar Allan Poe,* F. Watts, 1974. Author of introductions to new translations into Italian of works by Twain, Poe, Swift, DeFoe, Dickens, and Shakespeare, for Club del Libro, Milan, Italy. Associate editor, *Between Friends/Entre Amis* (Canada's Bicentennial gift to United States), National Film Board of Canada, 1976. Book reviewer, Ottawa *Citizen.*

WORK IN PROGRESS: A study of Shakespeare's "Comedy of Errors."

AVOCATIONAL INTERESTS: Acting, classical music, travel, and baseball.

* * *

HALE, Julian A(nthony) S(tuart) 1940-
(Anthony Stuart)

PERSONAL: Born November 27, 1940, in Llandrindod Wells, Wales; son of James P. R. (a farmer) and Gillian (Mason) Hale; married Mary Kathleen Benet (a writer), June 28, 1971; children: Laura. *Education:* Attended Winchester College, 1959; Christ Church, Oxford, M.A., 1963. *Home:* 9 Warwick Ave., London W.9, England. *Agent:* Clyde Taylor, 34 Perry St., New York, N.Y. 10014.

CAREER: G. C. Harrap & Co. (publishers), London, England, member of staff, 1963-65; Food and Agriculture Organization/Economic Commission for Europe (FAO/ECE), Palais des Nations, Geneva, Switzerland, member of staff, 1965-67; British Broadcasting Corp., London, member of staff of external services, 1968-73; editor, *European Gazette,* 1973—.

WRITINGS: Ceausescu's Romania, Harrap, 1971; *The Land and People of Romania,* Lippincott, 1972; *Radio Power: Propaganda and International Broadcasting,* Temple University Press, 1975; (under pseudonym Anthony Stuart) *Snap Judgement* (novel), Macdonald & Jane's 1977; (under pseudonym Anthony Stuart) *Vicious Circles* (novel), Macdonald & Jane's, 1978, published as *That Man Gull and Vicious Circles,* Arbor House, 1979.

WORK IN PROGRESS: Two more novels in the "Vladimir Gull" series, under pseudonym Anthony Stuart; other fiction.

* * *

HALEY, Neale

PERSONAL: Born in Buffalo, N.Y.; daughter of Frederick

H. (a research chemist) and Jacqueline (Longaker) Kranz; married Russell I. Haley (a market researcher), May 29, 1948; children: Douglas Frank, Kim Suzanne. *Education:* Barnard College, A.B., 1962. *Politics:* Independent. *Religion:* Christian Scientist. *Residence:* Durham, N.H.

CAREER: Riding director, director, and now consultant at Camp Longacres, East Aurora, N.Y., summers, 1943-68.

WRITINGS: How to Teach Group Riding, A. S. Barnes, 1970; *Judge Your Own Horsemanship,* A. S. Barnes, 1971; *The Schooner Era: A Lost Epic in History,* A. S. Barnes, 1972; *How to Have Fun With a Horse,* A. S. Barnes, 1972; *Understanding Your Horse: Equine Character and Psychology,* A. S. Barnes, 1973; *Grooming Your Horse,* A. S. Barnes, 1974; *Teach Yourself to Ride,* A. S. Barnes, 1974; *Training Your Horse to Show,* A. S. Barnes, 1976; *Birds for Pets and Pleasure: How to Keep Them Alive,* Viking, in press. Contributor to *Christian Science Journal, Christian Science Sentinel, American Cage Bird,* and other periodicals.

WORK IN PROGRESS: Four children's books: *Dark Stranger,* a horse mystery; *The Bull Dancer,* fiction on the Minoan civilization; *Saucy Melody,* a camp horse story; *The Day of the Eclipse,* a fantasy.

SIDELIGHTS: Neale Haley told *CA:* "One's life changes, a bit like a kaleidoscope, retaining the underlying values, but throwing color and form into new fields. An eighteen-foot aviary with artificial lights and plants behind a glass wall in my living room highlights an interest that rivals [my interest in] horses. Here twenty species of finches mingle and breed. But I've turned now to my real love, children's fiction."

* * *

HALL, Gwendolyn Midlo 1929-

PERSONAL: Born June 27, 1929, in New Orleans, La.; daughter of Herman L. (an attorney) and Ethel (Samuelson) Midlo; married Michel H. Yuspeh, June 27, 1949 (divorced, 1955); married Harry Haywood Hall (a writer), April 10, 1956; children: (first marriage) Leonid A.; (second marriage) Haywood, Rebecca. *Education:* Attended Tulane University, 1947-49; University of the Americas, B.A., 1962, M.A., 1963; University of Michigan, Ph.D., 1970. *Office:* Department of History, Livingston College, Rutgers University, New Brunswick, N.J.

CAREER: Elizabeth State College (now Elizabeth City State University), Elizabeth City, N.C., instructor in history, 1965; University of Michigan, Ann Arbor, lecturer in Afro-American studies, 1969; Michigan Historical Collections, Ann Arbor, research associate, 1970—; Rutgers University, New Brunswick, N.J., assistant professor, 1971-73, associate professor of history, 1973—. *Awards, honors:* University of Michigan Gwendolyn Midlo Hall Collection established by Michigan Historical Collections, 1970; Outstanding Service Award, The People's Association (Inmate's Association of Leesburg State Prison, Leesburg, N.J.), 1973.

WRITINGS: Social Control in Slave Plantation Societies: A Comparison of St. Domingue and Cuba, Johns Hopkins Press, 1971; (contributor) Jack Greene and David Cohen, editors, *Neither Slave Nor Free,* Johns Hopkins Press, 1972. Also contributor to *Annals* of the New York Academy of Science, 1977. Contributor to *Black World* and *Freedomways.*

WORK IN PROGRESS: A chapter for *Africans in the Diaspora,* for Harvard University Press; *The Armed Self-Defense Movement against the Ku Klux Klan during the Decade 1956-66; The Gang of Four: Distortion of a Great Revolution.*

SIDELIGHTS: Gwendolyn Hall lived in France between 1949-53, and in Mexico between 1959-63. In November, 1975, she visited the Peoples' Republic of China for three weeks. She made a second trip there during June and July, 1978 as a guest of Vice-Premier Keng Piao. Hall is competent in French and Spanish and can read Portuguese. She has a strong interest in social theory, historical methods, social movements, and race relations.

* * *

HALL, Joseph (Sargent) 1906-

PERSONAL: Born August 23, 1906, in Butte, Mont.; son of Horace Mark (a physician and surgeon) and Nellie (Kirkendall) Hall. *Education:* Stanford University, B.A., 1928; Columbia University, M.A., 1936, Ph.D., 1941; studied at Ecole des Hautes Etudes, University of Paris, 1933-34. *Home and office:* 1455 Lemoyne St., Los Angeles, Calif. 90026.

CAREER: Latin teacher in high school in Anaheim, Calif., 1930-33; historian student technician, National Park Service, 1937; Brooklyn College (now Brooklyn College of the City University of New York), Brooklyn, N.Y., tutor in English, 1939, 1940-41; historical collaborator, National Park Service, 1939-40; University of Montana, Missoula, assistant professor of English, 1946-48; Pasadena City College, Pasadena, Calif., instructor, 1948-63, associate professor, 1963-70, professor of English, 1970-72; researcher and writer, 1972—. Hartford Seminary Foundation Lecturer in Linguistics, Kennedy School of Missions, 1940-42; private secretary and literary adviser, 1941-42. *Military service:* U.S. Army Air Forces, 1942-45; became technical sergeant. U.S. Air Force Reserve, 1945-51. *Member:* American Dialect Society, American Folklore Society, Sierra Club, Tennessee Folklore Society, Kentucky Folklore Society, California Folklore Society, Southern California Folklore Society (president, 1959-60).

WRITINGS: The Phonetics of Great Smoky Mountain Speech, Kings Crown Press, 1942; *Smoky Mountain Folks and Their Lore,* Great Smoky Mountains Natural History Association, 1960; *Sayings from Old Smoky,* Cataloochee Press, 1972; *Yarns and Tales from the Great Smokies,* Cataloochee Press, 1978. Contributor to *American Speech, Journal of American Folklore, Regional Review* (National Park Service), *American Poet, Tennessee Folklore Society Bulletin,* and *Southwestern Historical Quarterly.*

WORK IN PROGRESS: Mountain Medicine; Mountain Tales: Eerie and Humorous; Smoky Mountain Songs and Ballads.

AVOCATIONAL INTERESTS: Travel, music (piano), mountain climbing, hiking, skiing.

BIOGRAPHICAL/CRITICAL SOURCES: Pasadena Independent, Star-News, September 1, 1957.

* * *

HALLE, Katherine Murphy
(Kay Halle)

PERSONAL: Born in Cleveland, Ohio; daughter of Horatio Samuel (a merchant) and Blanche (Murphy) Halle. *Education:* Attended Mary C. Wheeler School, Providence, R.I., Smith College, and Cleveland Institute of Music. *Politics:* Democrat. *Home and office:* 3001 Dent Pl. N.W., Washington, D.C. 20007. *Agent:* Carl Brandt, Brandt & Brandt, 101 Park Ave., New York, N.Y. 10017.

CAREER: Columnist in London for *Cleveland News,* writing "A Chair on the Boulevard," for one year; became feature writer in New York, N.Y. for *Cleveland Press;* returned to Cleveland, Ohio, joined staff of WGAR-Radio, interviewing prominent personalities on own program, "Know Your City," 1938-42; travelled 18,000 miles in Latin America in 1940, collecting material for radio programs and newspaper articles; executive in office of Strategic Services, Washington, D.C., 1942-45; *Cleveland Plain Dealer,* Cleveland, feature writer, 1948—. Music commentator with the Cleveland Sumphony Orchestra for Columbia Broadcasting System Inc., Cleveland, 1938-40. Appointed by President John F. Kennedy to Advisory Committee of National Cultural Center of Washington (now Kennedy Center for the Performing Arts), 1962; chairman of garden committee of Blair House (the President's guest house in Washington, D.C.); member of Bi-Centennial Committees of Washington, D.C. and Cleveland; member of board of directors of International Student House, Washington Performing Arts, Karamu House (Cleveland), and Woman's National Democratic Club; chairman of historic preservation, Citizens Association of Georgetown. *Awards, honors:* Order of the British Empire, 1967.

WRITINGS—Under name Kay Halle: *Irrepressible Churchill: A Treasury of Winston Churchill's Wit,* World Publishing, 1967; (contributor) Morris Ernst, editor, *The Teacher,* Prentice-Hall, 1967; *Winston Churchill: On America and Britain,* Walker & Co., 1970; *The Grand Original Portraits of Randolph Churchill by His Friends,* Houghton, 1971. Contributor to *Christian Science Monitor, Reader's Digest, New York Times Magazine, Look, Coronet, Washington Post,* and *Washington Evening Star.*

WORK IN PROGRESS: Churchill Clairvoyant.

*   *   *

HALLIDAY, Richard   1905-1973

April 3, 1905—March 3, 1973; American film and theatrical producer, film and drama critic, and novelist. Obituaries: *New York Times,* March 4, 1973.

*   *   *

HALLION, Richard P(aul, Jr.)   1948-

PERSONAL: Born May 17, 1948, in Washington, D.C.; son of Richard Paul (a federal government employee) and Marie (Flynn) Hallion. *Education:* University of Maryland, B.A. (with high honors), 1970, Ph.D., 1975. *Home:* 1003 Montrose Ave., Laurel, Md. 20810.

CAREER: Smithsonian Institution, National Air and Space Museum, Washington, D.C., currently curator of department of science and technology. *Member:* Society for the History of Technology, Air Force Historical Foundation, American Aviation Historical Society, U.S. Naval Institute, American Institute of Aeronautics and Astronautics, American Astronautical Society, Aviation/Space Writers Association, Phi Alpha Theta, Pi Sigma Alpha, Phi Kappa Phi. *Awards, honors:* Guggenheim fellowhip, Smithsonian National Air and Space Museum, 1972-73; American Institute of Aeronautics and Astronautics history manuscript award, 1975; Aviation/Space Writers Association regional award, 1978, for *Legacy of Flight.*

WRITINGS: Supersonic Flight: Breaking the Sound Barrier and Beyond, Macmillan (with Smithsonian National Air

and Space Museum), 1972; *Legacy of Flight: The Guggenheim Contribution to American Aviation,* University of Washington Press, 1977; *The Wright Brothers: Heirs of Prometheus,* Smithsonian Institution Press, 1978. Author of column "Out of the Past" in *Astronautics and Aeronautics.* Contributor to various publications, including *Air Enthusiast, Aeroplane Monthly, Aviation Quarterly, Flight International, Cockpit, Flying, Technology and Culture,* and *Aerospace Historian.*

WORK IN PROGRESS: Studying American aeronautical research and development since World War II; research on the history of American flight research and on aeronautical development during and since World War I.

SIDELIGHTS: Richard Hallion told *CA:* "As an aviation historian, I am always pleasantly surprised by the great amount of subjects within the field that have not received their measure of attention. As a result, I have the enjoyable and enviable opportunity of selecting those subjects that I am especially intrigued by for detailed research. Eventually, I believe that we will have the broad sweep of aviation history mapped out, much as the contours of, say, American history are now. And when that time comes, the historian's task may become more tedious—but no less important—than it is now."

*   *   *

HALLPIKE, C. R.   1938-

PERSONAL: Born April 19, 1938, in London, England; son of A. S. and E. D. Hallpike. *Education:* Studied at Clifton College, Bristol; Queen's College, Oxford, B.A., 1962, Diploma in Social Anthropology, 1963, B.Litt., 1964, D.Phil., 1968. *Office:* Department of Anthropology, Dalhousie University, Halifax, Nova Scotia, Canada.

CAREER: Dalhousie University, Halifax, Nova Scotia, postdoctoral fellow, 1968-69, research associate in anthropology, 1972—. Conducted field research in Ethiopia, 1965-67, and in Papua, 1970-72.

WRITINGS: (Contributor) T. O. Beidelman, editor, *The Translation of Culture,* Tavistock Publications, 1971; *The Konso of Ethiopia: A Study of the Values of a Cushitic People* (monograph), Clarendon Press, 1972; *Bloodshed and Vengeance in the Papuan Mountains* (monograph), Clarendon Press, 1977. Contributor to *Africa, Journal of Ethiopian Studies,* and *Man.*

WORK IN PROGRESS: Research on theories of age-grading systems in primitive societies; evaluation of functionalist and ecological theories of primitive society; analysis of primitive thought; the nature of social evolution.†

*   *   *

HALPER, Thomas   1942-

PERSONAL: Born December 1, 1942, in Brooklyn, N.Y.; son of Albert (an author) and Pauline (a textile designer; maiden name, Freedman) Halper. *Education:* St. Lawrence University, A.B., 1963; Vanderbilt University, M.A., 1967, Ph.D., 1970. *Politics:* Democrat. *Religion:* Jewish. *Home:* 245 East 19th St., New York, N.Y. 10003. *Office:* Department of Political Science, Bernard M. Baruch College of the City University of New York, 17 Lexington Ave., New York, N.Y. 10010.

CAREER: Worked as an iron lather, postal worker, and bank clerk; Tulane University, New Orleans, La., instructor in political science, 1967-68; Coe College, Cedar Rapids, Iowa, instructor, 1968-70, assistant professor of political science, 1970-74; Bernard M. Baruch College of the City University of New York, New York, N.Y., assistant professor, 1974-76, associate professor of political science, 1977—. *Member:* American Political Science Association, Pi Sigma Alpha, Phi Sigma Tau.

WRITINGS: Foreign Policy Crises: Appearance and Reality in Decision Making, C. E. Merrill, 1971. Contributor to *Aging and the Elderly,* edited by Spicker and Woodward. Contributor of articles to numerous journals, including *Milbank Memorial Fund Quarterly, Political Studies, New York Law Forum, South Atlantic Quarterly, New York Affairs, Journal of Health Politics, Policy and Law, Texas Quarterly, New York Law School Law Review, Connecticut Medicine, Drake Law Review, Indiana Law Journal,* and *Polity.*

*   *   *

HALPRIN, Lawrence 1916-

PERSONAL: Born July 1, 1916, in New York, N.Y.; son of Samuel W. and Rose (Luria) Halprin; married Ann Schuman (a choreographer), September 19, 1940; children: Daria (Mrs. Dennis Hopper), Rana. *Education:* Cornell University, B.A. (plant sciences), 1939; University of Wisconsin, M.S., 1941; Harvard University, B.S. (landscape architecture), 1942. *Politics:* Democrat. *Religion:* Jewish. *Office:* Roundhouse, 1500 Sansome, San Francisco, Calif.

CAREER: Registered landscape architect in California, Colorado, Connecticut, Massachusetts, New York, Ohio, Oregon, Pennsylvania, Texas, and Washington; Thomas D. Curch & Associates, San Francisco, Calif., senior associate, 1946-49; Lawrence Halprin & Associates, San Francisco and New York, N.Y., principal, 1949-76; Roundhouse, San Francisco, partner, 1976—. Lecturer in landscape architecture, University of California, Berkeley, 1953, 1962-65; visiting lecturer at University of British Columbia, 1954, University of North Carolina at Durham, 1955, and University of Pennsylvania, 1958. Director, Halprin Summer Workshop, 1966, 1968. Appointed to White House Conference on Natural Beauty, 1965, National Council on the Arts, 1966-72, and Advisory Committee on Historical Preservation, 1967-70. Work has been exhibited at San Francisco Museum of Art, 1962 and 1975, and Columbia University, 1972. *Military service:* U.S. Naval Reserve, active duty, 1943-46; became lieutenant junior grade.

MEMBER: World Society for Ekistics (Athens), American Society of Landscape Architects (fellow), American Institute of Interior Designers (honorary fellow), American Academy of Arts and Sciences, Sierra Club, San Francisco Planning and Urban Renewal Association (member of board of directors, 1964-65), San Francisco Dancers Workshop (member of board of directors, 1950—), San Francisco Actors Workshop (member of board of directors, 1965-66). *Awards, honors:* Gold medal for distinguished achievement in an allied profession, American Institute of Architects, 1964.

WRITINGS: Freeways, Reinhold, 1966; *The Freeway in the City,* U.S. Government Printing Office, 1968; *New York, New York,* Housing and Development Administration, City of New York, 1968; *The RSVP Cycles: Creative Processes in the Human Environment,* Braziller, 1970; *Caracas: Environmental Problems and Programs,* Lawrence Halprin & Associates, 1970; *Cities,* M.I.T. Press, 1972; *Lawrence Halprin Notebooks: 1959-71,* M.I.T. Press, 1972; *Take Part,* Lawrence Halprin & Associates, 1972; *Willamette Valley: Choices for the Future,* Willamette Valley

Environmental Protection and Development Planning Council, 1972; (with others) *Taking Part: A Workshop Approach for Collective Creativity,* M.I.T. Press, 1975.

*   *   *

HAMELMAN, Paul W(illiam) 1930-1976

PERSONAL: Born October 8, 1930, in Hempstead, N.Y.; son of George Joseph (an aero-engineer) and Frances (Cotter) Hamelman; married Marilyn Brown, November 14, 1953; children: Bethann, David Christopher, Mark Thomas, Mary Alice. *Education:* Davis and Elkins College, A.B., 1953; University of Pittsburgh, M.B.A., 1958, Ph.D., 1962. *Politics:* Independent Democrat. *Religion:* Roman Catholic. *Home:* 207 Eakin St., Blacksburg, Va. 24060. *Office:* Department of Business Administration, Virginia Polytechnic Institute and State University, Blacksburg, Va. 24061.

CAREER: West Virginia University, Morgantown, assistant professor, 1960-64, associate professor of management, 1964-69, assistant provost, 1966-67, director of business and government science programs, 1967-68; Virginia Polytechnic Institute and State University, Blacksburg, associate professor, 1969-73, professor of business administration, 1973-76. Lecturer at Ohio State University, University of Toledo, Bethany College, Davis and Elkins College, and Bowling Green State University. Consultant to U.S. Department of Health, Education, and Welfare, 1970-71, UNESCO, 1972, and other public and business organizations. *Military service:* U.S. Navy, 1953-56; became lieutenant commander.

MEMBER: American Economic Association, American Institute for Decision Sciences, Institute of Management Sciences, Operations Research Society of America, American Association for the Advancement of Science (fellow), Washington Operations Research Council, Beta Gamma Sigma, Phi Alpha Theta. *Awards, honors:* U.S. Steel Foundation fellowship, 1958-60; West Virginia Foundation grant, 1966; Ford Foundation travel grant, 1972.

WRITINGS: (Contributor) Gerald Rudolph, editor, *The Academic Community Looks at Library Management,* Virginia Polytechnic Institute and State University, 1972; (contributor) Kenneth W. Harris and James L. Crimer, editors, *Public Program Evaluation: Analysis of Performance versus Original Plan and Promise,* Association for Public Program Analysis, 1972; (editor) *Managing the University: A Systems Approach,* Praeger, 1972; (contributor) Steuart H. Britt and Harper W. Boyd, editors, *Marketing Management and Administrative Action,* McGraw, 1973; (contributor) Stanley J. Shapiro, editor, *Marketing Management: Readings in Operational Effectiveness,* Harper, 1973. Author of monographs. Contributor to business administration journals, including *Sloan Management Review, International Journal of Educational Sciences, Journal of Marketing Research, TIMS Interfaces, Journal of Business Policy, Journal of Finance, Journal of Advertising Research,* and *Government Executive.*

WORK IN PROGRESS: Research on diffusion of scientific thought and methodology across disciplinary fields, on implementation of management science in government and industry, and on educational planning.

AVOCATIONAL INTERESTS: Sailing, skiing, exploring, reading novels, history (political, economic, and military, especially contemporary), biographies of contemporary statesmen.†

(Died September, 1976)

HAMILTON, Charles Granville 1905-

PERSONAL: Born July 18, 1905, in Homestead, Pa.; son of Augustus William (a minister) and Mary C. (Frey) Hamilton; married Mary Elizabeth Case (a mathematics teacher), May 23, 1939. *Education:* Berea College, A.B., 1925; Columbia University, B.D., 1928, M.D., 1971; University of Mississippi, M.A., 1947; Vanderbilt University, Ph.D., 1958; additional study at twenty-two other institutions. *Politics:* Democratic. *Home:* Meridian, Monroe and Maple, Aberdeen, Miss. 39730.

CAREER: Clergyman of Episcopal Church; rector in Aberdeen, Miss. and in other Mississippi churches, 1928-72. Radio minister and director of "Quiet Hour," 1941—. Representative in Mississippi State Legislature, 1940-44; official at Democratic national conventions, 1940-72. President, Mississippi Council for Christian Social Action; director, Family Protection League; member, White House Traffic Safety Commission. *Military service:* U.S. Army, Infantry, World War II; became lieutenant. *Member:* Sons of Confederate Veterans, Order of Stars and Bars, Mark Twain Society, Phi Kappa Phi.

WRITINGS: Our Brother Augustus, Examiner, 1936; *Within Whose Memories Abide,* Okolona, 1937; *South,* Okolona, 1937; *Christian Education,* American, 1937; *These Precious Years,* American, 1938; *Ten Commandments,* Okolona, 1938; *Gospel in Ecclesiastes,* American, 1938; *There Came One Running,* Okolona, 1939; *No Frontiers,* Forward, 1940; *Mississippi I Love You,* Harrison Co., 1942; *These United States,* Southern Publishing, 1942; *Hymns We Love,* Okolona, 1944; *Revolution,* Okolona, 1945; *Prophet in Wartime,* Okolona, 1948; *Negro Education in Mississippi,* Okolona, 1951; *Lincoln and the Know Nothings,* Public Affairs Press, 1953; *48 in '48,* Christopher, 1954; *What Time Is It?,* Forward, 1958; *You Can't Steal First Base,* Philosophical Library, 1972; *Mississippi, I Love You Still,* Fulton, 1974; *The Flag Was Flame,* Fulton, 1975; *Justice Standeth Afar Off,* Booneville, 1977; *Any Resemblance,* Fulton, 1978; *Progressive Mississippi,* Booneville, 1978; *Liberty and Justice under God,* Fulton, 1978.

Editor: *Brave Voyage,* Examiner, 1936; *Lyric Monroe,* American, 1937; *Basic Relationships of Science,* American, 1939; *Is the Young Man Safe?,* Okolona, 1941; *Preaching Is Flame,* Branch, 1960; *Singing Spirit,* Superior, 1963; *Moments of Meditation,* Superior, 1964; *Thunder in the Wilderness,* Augsburg, 1964; *Music of Eternity,* Superior, 1965; *Grass on the Mountains,* Superior, 1966; *Land Beyond,* Superior, 1967; *God of the Years,* Superior, 1968; *Look Again,* Superior, 1969; *Christianity in 53 Words,* Superior, 1970; *Life's Benediction,* Superior, 1971; *The North Wind Comes,* Superior, 1972; *A Single Star,* Superior, 1975; *Our Yesterdays,* Fulton, 1978.

Contributor: *Poems of Justice,* Willett, 1929; *Moments with Modern Poets,* Tumasel, 1938; *Verse Harvest,* Tumasel, 1939; *Rendezvous of the Poets,* Tumasel, 1939; *North America Book of Verse,* Harrison, 1939; *Music Unheard,* Harrison, 1939; *Jesus the High Priest,* Archdiocese of Chicago, 1940; *Community Development,* Furman, 1941; *We the People,* Paebar, 1949; *Basic American Documents,* Littlefield, 1951; *American Government,* Stackpole, 1951; *Centennial Sermons,* Berea College Press, 1954; *Mother,* Cavalier, 1957. Contributor to 59 additional volumes, including histories and anthologies, and to periodicals. Editor of *Journal of Mississippi History,* 1943-53, *Churchman,* 1958—, *Crossroads, Anglican Outlook,* and *Christian Outlook.*

WORK IN PROGRESS: Three books, *Mirror of the 1920's, Mental Health Legislation in Mississippi,* and *I Know the Lord Has Laid His Hands on Me.*

* * *

HAMMER, Jefferson J(oseph) 1933-

PERSONAL: Born March 30, 1933, in New York, N.Y.; son of Jefferson Joseph (an electrician) and Mary Agnes (Coghlan) Hammer. *Education:* Manhattan College, B.A., 1955; St. Joseph's Seminary, graduate study 1955-60; Iona College, M.S.Ed., 1970. *Home:* 153 West 11th St., New York, N.Y. 10011. *Office:* St. Vincent's Hospital and Medical Center, New York, N.Y. 10011.

CAREER: Ordained Roman Catholic priest, 1960; St. Margaret Mary's Church, Bronx, N.Y., associate pastor, 1960-65; Bronx Municipal Hospital Center, Bronx, resident chaplain, 1965-71; Montefiore Hospital and Medical Center, Bronx, resident chaplain, 1971-73; St. Vincent's Hospital and Medical Center, New York, N.Y., director of department of pastoral care, 1973—. *Member:* Historical Arms Society of New York. *Awards, honors:* Cardinal Cooke Award for Chaplain of the Year, 1975.

WRITINGS: Frederic Augustus James's Civil War Diary: Sumter to Andersonville, Fairleigh Dickinson University Press, 1973.

SIDELIGHTS: Jefferson Hammer collects items from the Civil War, particularly those related to identified individuals.

* * *

HAMSHERE, Cyril (Eric) 1912-

PERSONAL: Born August 14, 1912, in Kenya, East Africa; son of John Edward (a clergyman) and Maud (Barnett) Hamshere; married Helen Gyles (a teacher), December 28, 1937. *Education:* Trinity College, Cambridge, B.A. (honors), 1934, M.A., 1946; Oxford University, additional study, 1934, 1949. *Home:* Tinkers Lodge, Brockenhurst Rd., South Ascot SL5 9HB, Berkshire, England.

CAREER: Munro College, Jamaica, master, 1934-40; Her Majesty's Overseas Civil Service, Queen's College, Georgetown, British Guiana, master, 1940-46, headmaster of Arusha School, Arusha, Tanganyika, 1946-63; Papplewick School, Ascot, Berkshire, England, master of history and English, 1965—. *Military service:* British Army, intelligence officer, 1943-46; served in British Guiana, the Caribbean, the United States, Italy, Egypt, Ceylon, and Singapore.

WRITINGS: The British in the Caribbean, Harvard University Press, 1972; *Venezuela,* Plata Publishing, 1977. Contributor to *History Today.*

WORK IN PROGRESS: Two historical novels, *The Revenge of John Hawkins* and *The Buccaneer; The Sea Is Round,* a play about Drake's circumnaviagation of the world.

AVOCATIONAL INTERESTS: Travel (India, Malaya, South Africa, Rhodesia, Spain, France, Italy, and Greece).

* * *

HAND, Wayland D(ebs) 1907-

PERSONAL: Born March 19, 1907, in Auckland, New Zealand; U.S. citizen; son of Hyrum and Margaret (Wride) Hand; married Viola White, June 8, 1932 (divorced, 1957); married Celeste Gordon Gilford (a teacher), December 19,

1957; children: (first marriage) Jacqueline Hand Berner, Winifred (Mrs. Daniel E. Marsh); (second marriage) Sydney Gilford. *Education:* University of Utah, A.B., 1933, M.A., 1934; University of Chicago, Ph.D., 1936. *Politics:* Democrat. *Religion:* Church of Jesus Christ of Latter-day Saints (Mormon). *Home:* 716 Courtland St., Venice, Calif. 90291. *Office:* Center for Comparative Folklore and Mythology, University of California, Los Angeles, Calif. 90024.

CAREER: University of Minnesota, Minneapolis, instructor in German, 1936-37; University of California, Los Angeles, instructor, 1937-42, assistant professor, 1942-46, associate professor, 1946-52, professor of German and folklore, 1952-74, chairman of department of Germanic languages, 1947-50, director of Center for Comparative Folklore and Mythology, 1960—. Trustee, American Folklife Center, 1976—. *Member:* International Society for Folk Narrative Research, American Folklore Society (president, 1957-58), Mediaeval Academy of America, American Name Society, American Dialect Society, Deutsche Gesellschaft fuer Volkskunde, Folklore Society (London). *Awards, honors:* Guggenheim fellow, 1952-53, 1960-61; first American to receive Pitre International Folklore Prize, 1965; knighted, First Class of the Order of the Lion of Finland, 1972.

WRITINGS: (Editor) *Humaniora: Essays in Literature, Folklore and Bibliography Honoring Archer Taylor on His Seventieth Birthday,* J. J. Augustin, 1960; (editor) *Popular Beliefs and Superstitions from North Carolina* (Volumes VI and VII of the Frank C. Brown Collection of North Carolina Folklore), Duke University Press, 1961, 1964; (editor) *American Folk Legend: A Symposium,* University of California Press, 1971; (editor) *American Folk Medicine,* University of California Press, 1976. Contributor of about a hundred articles to philological and folklore journals. Editor, *Journal of American Folklore,* 1947-51, and *Western Folklore,* 1954-66.

WORK IN PROGRESS: *Dictionary of American Popular Beliefs and Superstitions,* a multi-volume work begun in 1944; *Index of American Folk Legends.*

BIOGRAPHICAL/CRITICAL SOURCES: D. K. Wilgus, editor, *Folklore International: Essays in Traditional Literature, Belief and Custom in Honor of Wayland Debs Hand,* Folklore Associates, 1967.

* * *

HANLEY, Evelyn A(lice) 1916-

PERSONAL: Born December 14, 1916, in Atlanta, Ga.; daughter of James Bourke (a lawyer) and Alice (Wanamaker) Hanley. *Education:* Brooklyn College of the City University of New York, A.B., 1935; New York University, A.M., 1937, Ph.D., 1944. *Politics:* Republican. *Religion:* Protestant. *Home:* 82-64 170th St., Jamaica, N.Y. 11432. *Office:* Department of English, Hunter College of the City University of New York, 695 Park Ave., New York, N.Y. 10021.

CAREER: Brooklyn College of the City University of New York, Brooklyn, N.Y., instructor in English, 1944-46; Adelphi College (now University), Garden City, N.Y., instructor in English, 1946-49; New Jersey State Teachers College (now The William Paterson College of New Jersey), Wayne, assistant professor of English, 1950-51; Hunter College of the City University of New York, New York, N.Y., lecturer, 1963-65, instructor, 1965-67, assistant professor, 1968-73, associate professor of English, 1973—. *Member:* American Association of University Professors, Modern

Language Association of America, English Graduate Association of New York University, Dickens Fellowship of New York and Philadelphia. *Awards, honors:* Parker Lloyd-Smith Prize in Poetry and Charles Dickens Commemorative Medal, for work on Dickens in his Centennial Year (1970), 1971.

WRITINGS: Poetic Profiles (poems), Arcade Press, 1962; *Antiphony* (poems), Arcade Press, 1963; *Stoicism in Major English Poets of the Nineteenth Century,* Haskell House, 1964; *Nature in Theme and Symbol: Wordsworth to Eliot,* Heathcote, 1972; *The Subjective Vision: Six Victorian Women Poets,* Hippocrene, 1978. Contributor of articles, book reviews, and poems to journals, magazines and newspapers.†

* * *

HANLEY, William 1931-

PERSONAL: Born October 22, 1931, in Lorain, Ohio; son of William Gerald (a housepainter) and Anne (Rodgers) Hanley; married Shelley Post, 1956 (divorced, 1961); married Patricia Stanley, February 19, 1962 (divorced, 1978); children: (second marriage) Katherine, Nell. *Education:* Attended Cornell University, 1950-51, and American Academy of Dramatic Arts, 1954-55. *Home:* 179 Ivy Hill Rd., Ridgefield, Conn. 06877. *Agent:* Georges Borchardt, Inc., 136 East 57th St., New York, N.Y. 10020.

CAREER: Worked as a bank clerk, mail clerk, factory worker, and book salesman, among other jobs; playwright and novelist. *Military service:* U.S. Army, Infantry, 1952-54; became second lieutenant. *Member:* Dramatists Guild, Writers Guild, International P.E.N. *Awards, honors:* Vernon Rice Award, 1963, for "Whisper Into My Good Ear" and "Mrs. Dally Has a Lover"; *Variety* New York Drama Critics' Poll Award for most promising playwright, 1964-65, and Outer Circle Award, 1965, both for "Slow Dance on the Killing Ground."

WRITINGS—Novels: Blue Dreams; or, the End of Romance and the Continued Pursuit of Happiness, Delacorte, 1971; *Mixed Feelings,* Doubleday, 1972; *Leaving Mount Venus,* Ballantine, 1977.

Plays: *Mrs. Dally Has a Lover and Other Plays* (contains "Mrs. Dally Has a Lover" [first produced with "Whisper into My Good Ear" Off-Broadway at Cherry Lane Theatre, October 1, 1962; produced with "Today Is Independence Day" as "Mrs. Dally" on Broadway at Golden Theatre, September 22, 1965], "Whisper into My Good Ear" [first produced with "Mrs. Dally Has a Lover" Off-Broadway at Cherry Lane Theatre, October 1, 1962; produced off the West End at Hampstead Theatre Club, April 3, 1966], and "Today Is Independence Day" [first produced with "Mrs. Dally Has a Lover" as "Mrs. Dally" on Broadway at Golden Theatre, September 22, 1965]), Dial, 1963; *Slow Dance on the Killing Ground* (produced on Broadway at Plymouth Theatre, November 30, 1964), Random House, 1965; *Flesh and Blood* (produced on NBC-TV, January 26, 1968), Random House, 1968. Also author of "Conversations in the Dark," produced in Philadelphia, Pa. at Walnut Street Theatre, December 23, 1963. Author of screenplay, "The Gypsy Moths," produced by Metro-Goldwyn-Mayer, 1969, and of a radio play, "A Country without Rain," 1970.

Plays represented in anthologies, including: *The Best Plays of 1964-1965,* edited by Otis L. Guernsey, Jr., Dodd, 1965; *Collision Course,* edited by Edward Parone, Random House, 1968; *Best American Plays, Sixth Series,* edited by John Gassner and Clive Barnes, Crown, 1971.

SIDELIGHTS: In an interview with Joanne Stang, William Hanley comments: "'The theme of responsibility seems to come and go through everything I've done. I think it will continue to do so, although I hope each play is drastically different from another. When I say responsibility I don't mean just responsibility to other people, but responsibility for one's own acts. I don't think there is anyone who isn't aware of the darkness I'm talking about in "Slow Dance." Most people have a tendency to turn away from it, and that is a negative act when the only constructive thing to do is to face it, and to see that there is the possibility of something better. If, in the final moments of the play, the audience has faced the darkness, and if, at least, the thought is planted that there might be something better, that's all that it's about.'"

BIOGRAPHICAL/CRITICAL SOURCES: New York Times, December 13, 1964; *Washington Post,* June 14, 1969; *Publishers Weekly,* September 18, 1972, February 28, 1977.

* * *

HANSON, Earl Parker 1899-1978

PERSONAL: Born March 16, 1899, in Berlin, Germany; son of American citizens, Albert Parker (an engineer) and Lida (Siboni) Hanson; married Dorothy Lane, February 4, 1933 (divorced, 1938); married Charlotte Leeper (a social worker), October 1, 1938; children: (first marriage) John Parker; (second marriage) David Parker, Nancy Leeper (deceased). *Education:* University of Wisconsin, B.S. in M.E., 1922; additional study at Columbia University, 1930-31, and University of Chicago, 1933. *Politics:* Democrat. *Home address:* P.O. Box 12143 Loiza Station, Santurce, Puerto Rico 00914. *Agent:* Robert P. Mills Ltd., 156 East 52nd St., New York, N.Y. 10022.

CAREER: Lived abroad until the age of twelve; junior engineer on power plant construction, Milwaukee, Wis., 1920-21; engineer in copper mines, Chuquicamata, Chile, 1922-25; Simmons Boardman Publishing Co., New York City, editor and production manager in book department, 1925-27; McGraw-Hill Catalogue and Directory Co., New York City, production manager, 1927-29; lectured and wrote and served as executive secretary of Explorers Club, New York City, between 1929-31; made one-man expedition to Orinoco-Amazon basins and Andes of South America for Carnegie Institution, Washington, D.C., 1931-33; National Resources Committee, Washington, D.C., Mississippi Valley Committee, research technician, 1934-35; Puerto Rico Reconstruction Administration, San Juan, planning consultant, 1935-36; lectured and wrote, 1937-41; worked on publication projects of U.S. Coordinator of Inter-American Affairs, 1941-42, and G-2 Section, U.S. Army, 1942-43; consultant on tropical equipment and survival to Quartermaster General, U.S. Army Air Forces, 1942-44; headed Foreign Economic Administration mission to Liberia, 1944-46; wrote and lectured, 1946-49; professor of geography and chairman of department at University of Delaware, Newark, 1949-55; consultant to Department of State, Commonwealth of Puerto Rico, San Juan, 1955-69. Made trips to Iceland in 1920, 1927, to Canadian Subarctic for *World's Work* (magazine), 1929, to South America to study navigation possibilities in Amazon basin with U.S. Army Engineers expedition, 1943, and to Monagas, Venezuela, for Creole Petroleum Co., 1954-55. Lecturer on these and other countries at U.S. universities, as well as public lecturer from coast to coast.

MEMBER: American Geographical Society (fellow), Asso-

ciation of American Geographers, Explorers Club. *Awards, honors:* Knight Official, Liberian Humane Order of African Redemption, 1946; Knight, Icelandic Order of the Falcon, 1953.

WRITINGS: Journey to Manaos, Reynal & Hitchcock, 1938; (editor) *Highroad to Adventure* (anthology of adventure tales), McBride, 1941; *Chile: Land of Progress,* Reynal & Hitchcock, 1941; *Stefansson: Prophet of the North,* Harper, 1941; *The Amazon: A New Frontier?,* Foreign Policy Association, 1944; *New Worlds Emerging,* Duell, Sloan & Pearce, 1950; *Transformation: The Story of Modern Puerto Rico,* Simon & Schuster, 1955; *Puerto Rico,* Doubleday and American Geographical Society, 1956; *Chile,* Doubleday and American Geographical Society, 1958; *Bolivia,* Doubleday and American Geographical Society, 1959; *Puerto Rico: Land of Wonders,* Knopf, 1960; *Puerto Rico: Ally for Progress,* Van Nostrand, 1962; *South from the Spanish Main,* Delacorte, 1967.

Other publications: (Editor and reviser) *Yankee Caballero,* McBride, 1940; (editor-in-chief) "New World Guides to the Latin American Republics," three volumes, Duell, Sloan & Pearce, 1944, 3rd edition, 1950; (staff director) *Index to the Map of Hispanic America,* American Geographical Society and U.S. Government Printing Office, 1945.

Contributor to *Book of Knowledge Annual, Britannica Junior, Encyclopedia Americana, Encyclopaedia Britannica,* and *World Book Encyclopedia Annual.* Contributor of articles to magazines, including *American Scholar, National Geographic, Harper's, Reader's Digest, Nation, Saint Nicholas, Science, American Mercury, Discovery,* and *Americas;* also has written about two hundred reviews of books on geographical subjects for *Saturday Review, New York Times,* and other newspapers. Weekly columnist for *Island Times,* San Juan, 1955-64.

WORK IN PROGRESS: His autobiography.

SIDELIGHTS: Earl Parker Hanson not only wrote and lectured about Puerto Rico, but was also a consultant for special projects of the Commonwealth's Planning Board and Department of Tourism. *Transformation: The Story of Modern Puerto Rico,* was translated into Spanish and condensed versions were published in Arabic, Burmese, and Hindi, 1956, and the book has been used throughout the world by the U.S. Information Agency.†

(Died July 19, 1978)

* * *

HANSON, F(ridolf) Allan 1939-

PERSONAL: Born May 17, 1939, in Dixon, Ill.; son of Fridolf Ansford and Evelyn (Swanson) Hanson; married Louise Pekrol, June 16, 1962; children: Katherine, George, Brian. *Education:* Princeton University, A.B., 1961; University of Chicago, M.A., 1963, Ph.D., 1966. *Office:* Department of Anthropology, University of Kansas, Lawrence, Kan. 66045.

CAREER: University of Kansas, Lawrence, assistant professor, 1966-70, associate professor, 1970-76, professor of anthropology, 1976—. Field work in Tahiti, 1960, 1961, 1963-64; research in Oxford, 1970, and New Zealand, 1976-77. *Member:* American Anthropological Association (fellow), Association for Social Anthropology in Oceania, Current Anthropology (associate member), Polynesian Society, Societe des Etudes Oceaniennes (life member), Societe des Oceanistes, Central States Anthropological Society. *Awards, honors:* National Institute of Mental Health grant for research in Paris, 1967; Andrew P. Mellon postdoctoral fellow at University of Pittsburgh, 1972-73; American Council of Learned Societies fellow, 1976-77.

WRITINGS: Rapan Lifeways: Society and History on a Polynesian Island, Little, Brown, 1970; (contributor) Alan Howard, editor, *Polynesia: Readings on a Culture Area,* Chandler Publishing, 1971; *Meaning in Culture,* Routledge & Kegan Paul, 1975. Contributor to *Journal of the Anthropological Society of Oxford, American Anthropologist, Ethnology, Current Anthropology,* and other periodicals.

WORK IN PROGRESS: Research in semiotics and the anthropology of art; preparing a book on the art and world view of the New Zealand Maori.

* * *

HANUSHEK, Eric Alan 1943-

PERSONAL: Born May 22, 1943, in Lakewood, Ohio; married Nancy L. Keleher, June 11, 1965; children: Eric A., Jr., Megan E. *Education:* U.S. Air Force Academy, B.S. (with distinction), 1965; Massachusetts Institute of Technology, Ph.D., 1968. *Home:* 7930 Harwood Pl., Springfield, Va. 22152.

CAREER: U.S. Air Force, 1965-73, final rank, captain, instructor at Air Force Academy, 1968-69, assistant professor, 1969-71, associate professor of economics, 1971-73; Cost of Living Council, Executive Office of the President, Washington, D.C., senior economist, 1973-74. Research associate, Harvard University, John F. Kennedy School of Government, 1970-71; senior staff economist, President's Council of Economic Advisers, 1971-72; consultant to RAND Corp. and Urban Institute. *Member:* American Economic Association, Econometric Society, American Statistical Association.

WRITINGS: (Contributor) *Do Teachers Make a Difference?,* U.S. Government Printing Office, 1970; *Education and Race: An Analysis of the Educational Production Process,* Heath, 1972; (contributor) Frederick Mosteller and Daniel P. Moynihan, editors, *On Equality of Educational Opportunity,* Random House, 1972; (editor with John Jackson) *Introduction to Estimation Theory,* Academic Press, 1977. Author of reports for RAND Corp. and Harvard University Program on Regional and Urban Economics. Contributor to *Rocky Mountain Social Science Journal* and *American Economic Review.*

WORK IN PROGRESS: Research on regional differences in the structure of earnings on graduate education training in the U.S. Air Force, on the dynamics of industrial location, on efficient estimators for regressing regression coefficients; studying a method of combining data samples to avoid misspecification.†

* * *

HARDING, Barbara 1926-

PERSONAL: Born August 23, 1926, in Hickory, N.C.; daughter of Glenn Wallick (a mechanical engineer) and Nancy (Halsey) Harding. *Education:* Attended Averett College, 1945-48; further courses at University of Virginia Extension, 1954-55, University of Chicago, 1955-57, and Central Piedmont Community College, 1970-71. *Politics:* Liberal. *Religion:* "Baptist turned Episcopalian."

CAREER: Crabtree Press, Charlotte, N.C., vice-president, beginning 1965. Narrator on tape and cassettes for Protestant Radio and Television Center and for S & P Productions, both Atlanta, Ga.; fashion commentator on radio; lecturer

and conductor of radio programs on rose culture; teacher of hand monogramming at Free University, Charlotte.

WRITINGS: It Wonders Me . . . a fantasy almost, Crabtree Press, 1965; (with Legette Blythe and others) *Charlotte Today and Mecklenburg County, North Carolina,* Crabtree Press, 1967; *The Boy, the Man, and the Bishop,* Barnhardt Brothers, 1970; (editor) Ira David Wood, *A Lover's Guide to the Outer Banks,* Crabtree Press, 1971. Narrator on cassette and record of Kays Gary's book, *When All Else Is Gone . . . love remains,* Crabtree Press, 1972.

WORK IN PROGRESS: The Edge of the World, Poetic prose with art by Scott Howson; *Once upon Another Time,* a collection of essays.

AVOCATIONAL INTERESTS: Designing gardens, sewing.††

* * *

HARDING, D(ennis) W(illiam) 1940-

PERSONAL: Born April 11, 1940, in Poole, Dorsetshire, England; son of Charles Royston (a company representative) and Marjorie Doris (Best) Harding. *Education:* Keble College, Oxford, B.A., 1963, M.A., 1967; Institute of Archaeology, Oxford, D.Phil., 1969. *Home:* 14 Drummond Pl., Edinburgh, Scotland. *Office:* Department of Archaeology, University of Edinburgh, Edinburgh, Scotland.

CAREER: Oxford University, Ashmolean Museum, Oxford, England, assistant keeper, 1965-66; University of Durham, Durham, England, lecturer in Celtic archaeology, 1966-76; University of Edinburgh, Edinburgh, Scotland, Abercromby Professor of Archaeology, 1977—. *Member:* Prehistoric Society.

WRITINGS: The Iron Age in the Upper Thames Basin, Clarendon Press, 1972; *The Iron Age in Lowland Britain,* Routledge & Kegan Paul, 1974; (with A. J. Challis) *Later Prehistory from the Trent to the Tyne,* two volumes, British Archaeological Reports, 1975; (editor and contributor) *Hillforts: Later Prehistoric Earthworks in Britain and Ireland,* Academic Press, 1976; (editor and contributor) *Archaeology in the North: Report of the Northern Archaeological Survey,* University of Durham, 1976; *Prehistoric Europe,* Elsevier, 1978. Contributor to national and local archaeological publications.

WORK IN PROGRESS: Research and fieldwork on the British Iron Age; air survey of northern England and lowland Scotland.

* * *

HARE, Nathan 1934-

PERSONAL: Born April 9, 1934, in Slick, Okla.; son of Seddie Henry (a farmer) and Tishia (Davis) Hare; married Julie Reed (a public relations specialist), December 27, 1956. *Education:* Langston University, A.B., 1954; University of Chicago, M.A., 1957, Ph.D. (sociology), 1962; California School of Professional Psychology, Ph.D., 1975; also studied at Northwestern University, 1959. *Religion:* None. *Home:* 1895 Jackson St., San Francisco, Calif. 94109. *Office:* 1360 Turk St., San Francisco, Calif. 94115.

CAREER: Briefly, a professional boxer; Virginia State College, Petersburg, instructor in sociology, 1957-58; National Opinion Research Center, Chicago, Ill., interviewer, 1959-61; University of Chicago, Chicago, research assistant at Population Research Center, 1960-61; Howard University, Washington, D.C., instructor, 1961-63, assistant professor of sociology, 1964-67; San Francisco State College (now University), director of Black Studies Curriculum, 1968, chairman of department of black studies, 1968-69, director, Center for Educational Innovation, summer, 1968; *Black Scholar*, Sausalito, Calif., founding publisher, 1969-75; Child Development Services, Oakland, Calif., clinical psychologist, 1975-76; psychologist in private practice, 1977—. Part-time visiting professor, Lone Mountain College, 1972-73; chairman of task force on demographic and communal characteristics, Teachers College, Columbia University, 1966-67. Chairman of workshop on education, National Conference on Black Power, 1968; president, Black World Foundation, 1970; member of board of advisors, San Francisco Black Exposition, 1972; member of board of directors of North American Committee, Second World Black and African Festival of Arts and Culture, 1974—; affiliated with C.H.A.N.C.E., 1976. *Military service:* U.S. Army Reserve, 1958-64, active duty, 1958.

MEMBER: American Sociological Association, Association of Behavioral and Social Sciences, American Psychological Association, Association of Orthopsychiatry, American Association of University Professors, Eastern Sociological Association, New York Academy of Sciences, Sigma Gamma Rho. *Awards, honors:* Danforth fellow, 1954-57; "Black Is Beautiful" citation from United Black Artists, 1968; Distinguished Alumni Award, Langston University.

WRITINGS: (Author of introduction) W.E.B. DuBois, *The Souls of Black Folk*, Signet, 1969; *The Black Anglo-Saxons*, Collier, 1970; (author of introduction) Lenneal Henderson, editor, *Black Political Life in the United States*, Chandler Publishing, 1972; (editor) *Contemporary Black Thought*, Bobbs-Merrill, 1973; (editor) *Pan-Africanism*, Bobbs-Merrill, 1974. Contributor of about sixty articles to sociology and black studies journals and to national periodicals, including *Newsweek, Ramparts, Saturday Review,* and *U.S. News and World Report.* Contributing editor, *Journal of Black Studies, Ebony, Black Scholar, Journal of Black Education,* and *Black Law Journal.*

*   *   *

HARKNESS, Gladys Estelle Suiter   1908(?)-1973

1908(?)—June 16, 1973; American author and editor. Obituaries: *New York Times*, June 17, 1973; *Washington Post*, June 18, 1973.

*   *   *

HARPER, James E(dwin)   1927-

PERSONAL: Born July 12, 1927, in Evanston, Ill.; son of Donald and Evelyn (Johnson) Harper. *Education:* University of Chicago, Ph.D., 1962. *Politics:* Democrat. *Religion:* None.

CAREER: Wayne State University, Detroit, Mich., assistant professor of history, 1959-61; Sacramento State College (now California State University, Sacramento), assistant professor of history, 1961-64; Roosevelt University, Chicago, Ill., associate professor of history, 1964-71. *Military service:* U.S. Army, Engineers, 1945-47. *Member:* American Historical Association, Mediaeval Academy of America. *Awards, honors:* Fulbright scholarship to University of Aix-Marseilles, 1953-54.

WRITINGS: (With William Davisson) *European Economic History,* Volume I: *The Ancient World*, Appleton, 1972. Contributor to *Church History, Agricultural History, American Journal of Philology, Discourse,* and other journals.

WORK IN PROGRESS: Volume II of *European Economic History.*††

*   *   *

HARRINGTON, Jeremy   1932-

PERSONAL: Born October 7, 1932, in Lafayette, Ind.; son of Will (a farmer) and Ellen (Caine) Harrington. *Education:* Duns Scotus College, B.A., 1955; Xavier University, Cincinnati, Ohio, M.A., 1965; Northwestern University, M.S.J., 1966. *Home:* 5000 Colerain Ave., Cincinnati, Ohio 45223. *Office:* St. Anthony Messenger, 1615 Republic, Cincinnati, Ohio 45210.

CAREER: Entered Roman Catholic Order of Friars Minor, 1950, ordained priest, 1959; Roger Bacon High School, Cincinnati, Ohio, teacher, 1960-64; *St. Anthony Messenger*, Cincinnati, associate editor, 1964-66, editor, 1966—, publisher, 1975—. *Member:* Catholic Press Association (president, 1975-77). *Awards, honors:* St. Francis de Sales Award for outstanding contribution to Catholic journalism, 1972.

WRITINGS: (Editor) *Conscience in Today's World*, St. Anthony Messenger Press, 1970; (editor) *Jesus Christ: Superstar or Savior?*, St. Anthony Messenger Press, 1972; *Your Wedding: Planning Your Own Ceremony*, St. Anthony Messenger Press, 1974.

*   *   *

HARRISON, Hank   1940-

PERSONAL: Born June 17, 1940, in Monterey Calif.; son of G. H. Harrison (a professor of physical education) and E. V. (a fashion designer; maiden name Cooke) Protine; married; children: Courtney Michelle. *Education:* College of San Mateo, A.A., 1962; San Francisco State College (now University), B.A., 1965; University of Netherlands, M.A., 1968; Antioch College, M.A., 1978. *Politics:* "Radical/Jeffersonian Democrat." *Religion:* Buddhist. *Address:* 1400 Westcott Rd., Colusa, Calif.

CAREER: Social psychologist and free-lance technical writer; De Anza College, Cupertino, Calif., instructor, 1975-76; Antioch College/West, San Francisco, Calif., instructor, 1978-79. Chief administrator, Institute for Contemporary Studies, 1965-68; director of technical publications, Honeywell Corp., Minneapolis, Minn., 1969; writer in residence, Montalvo Association for the Arts, 1975. Adviser and consultant to Grateful Dead Corp. and Ice Nine Publishing, 1966—, Clark County (Nevada) Public Library, 1977, Lockheed Missile and Space Co., 1978, Coherat Laser Corp., 1978, TRW-Vidar, 1978, and Imsai Computer Corp., 1978-79. *Military service:* U.S. Navy, Medical Corps, 1957-59. *Member:* International P.E.N., American Society of Composers, Authors and Publishers, National Freelance Photographers Association, National Association of Science Writers, Society for Technical Communications, Research into Lost Knowledge Organization (London), Project Greenpeace (charter member). *Awards, honors:* Caldecott-Newberry notable book award, 1978-79, for *A Hole in the Wind.*

WRITINGS: Head: The Drug User in America, Putnam, 1968; *The Dead Book: A Social History of the Grateful Dead* (computer-designed illuminated manuscript), Simon & Schuster, 1973; *A Hole in the Wind, Hang Gliding and the Quest for Flight*, Bobbs-Merrill, 1978; *The Holy Grail*, Rudolph Steiner, 1979; *The Dream Place*, Childrens Book Press, 1979; *The Resurrection of the Dead Book*, Warner Communications, 1979. Contributor to *Vancouver Maga-*

zine, Berkeley Barb, and *New Times.* Editor, *Las Vegas Sun* "Sunday Scene Magazine," 1977.

WORK IN PROGRESS: Inside Gifted Children; Ritual Murders; Wonder Cures; The Mystic Missions of California.

SIDELIGHTS: "Any good writer must master all literary forms," Hank Harrison told *CA.* "Gifted generalists are rare but essential to the advancement of human learning." He is currently living on a houseboat in Sausalito.

* * *

HARRISON, Stanley R. 1927-

PERSONAL: Born October 5, 1927, in New York, N.Y.; son of Samuel (a "chicken man") and Janet Charlotte (Weinstein) Harrison; married Patricia Ann Middleton (a potter), October 10, 1959 (divorced, 1975); children: Samantha Jeannette, Stanley Dionysius, Tabitha Ellen, Noah Anthony. *Education:* Brooklyn College (now Brooklyn College of the City University of New York), B.A., 1949, M.A., 1957; Michigan State University, Ph.D., 1964. *Religion:* "Jewish Atheist." *Home:* 21 East Main St., Mansfield, Pa. 16933. *Office:* Department of English, Mansfield State College, Mansfield, Pa. 16933.

CAREER: Michigan State University, East Lansing, instructor in English, 1959-61; University of Rhode Island, Kingston, instructor in English, 1961-64; Tulane University, New Orleans, La., assistant professor of English, 1964-67; Virginia Polytechnic Institute and State University, Blacksburg, associate professor of English, 1967-69; Transylvania College, Lexington, Ky., writer-in-residence, 1969-70; Mansfield State College, Mansfield, Pa., professor of English, 1970—. *Member:* Modern Language Association of America, North East Modern Language Association. *Awards, honors:* "Machiavelli and the Mandrake" named best play by Theatre Americana, 1973-74; appointed to a Commonwealth of Pennsylvania Teaching Chair, 1976.

WRITINGS: Edgar Fawcett, Twayne, 1972.

Plays: "Machiavelli and the Mandrake," first produced by Tulane University Theatre, April, 1967; "The World at January," first produced by Virginia Polytechnic Institute and University Theatre, May, 1969; "The Last Blue Whale," first produced in Elmira, N.Y. at Samuel Clemens Center, 1978. Contributor of stories and poetry to *Western Review, Jewish Frontier, Cimarron Review, Southwestern Review, Midstream, Psychological Perspectives, Encore,* and *Western Poetry;* contributor of articles to literature journals, including *Tulane Studies in English, Walt Whitman Review, Studies in Short Fiction, Markham Review,* and *Mark Twain Journal.* Editor-in-chief, *Falcon,* 1972—.

WORK IN PROGRESS: That Leaves Clubs and Spades, a novel.

* * *

HARRITY, Richard 1907-1973

May 22, 1907—January 19, 1973; American playwright, author, and editor. Obituaries: *New York Times,* January 21, 1973.

* * *

HARROLD, William E(ugene) 1936-

PERSONAL: Born June 24, 1936, in North Carolina; son of William Benton (a businessman) and Helen (Mason) Harrold. *Education:* Wake Forest University, B.A., 1959; Uni-

versity of North Carolina, M.A., 1961, Ph.D., 1967. *Home:* 1982 North Prospect Ave., 2A, Milwaukee, Wis. 53202. *Office:* Department of English, University of Wisconsin, Milwaukee, Wis. 53211.

CAREER: University of Wisconsin—Milwaukee, instructor, 1965-66, assistant professor, 1967-71, associate professor, 1972-78, professor of English, 1978—, coordinator of graduate study in English.

WRITINGS: Beyond the Dream (poems), Brandon Press, 1972; *The Variance and the Unity: The Complementary Poems of Robert Browning,* Ohio University Press, 1973. Contributor to anthologies, including *Heartland II: Poets of the Midwest,* edited by Lucien Stryk and *For Neruda, for Chile,* edited by Walter Lowenfels. Contributor of more than four hundred poems to over one hundred forty-six journals; contributor of articles, essays and reviews to *Small Press Review, Northeast Rising Sun, Margins, Manassas Review, St. Andrew's Review,* and other periodicals.

WORK IN PROGRESS: A book of poems, for Stone Marrow Press.

* * *

HARSTON, Ruth 1944-

PERSONAL: Born December 16, 1944, in Richmond, Calif.; daughter of Richard George and Anna (Woodbury) Harston. *Education:* Utah State University, B.F.A., 1968, M.F.A., 1969; Western States Chiropractic College, 1976—. *Home:* 69 East First N., Logan, Utah 84321.

CAREER: Logan Cold Storage, Logan, Utah, clerk, 1954-65; Utah State University, Photography Laboratory, Logan, clerk and laboratory assistant, 1965-68; Ruth's Studio, Logan, photographer, 1970-75; portrait painter, 1975-76. *Member:* Intermountain Professional Photographers Association. *Awards, honors:* First prize from League of Utah Writers, 1970, for "Fairyfoot," a radio play; first prize from Intermountain Professional Photographers Association for wedding photograph, 1971.

WRITINGS: (With Kalee Larsen and Elyse Larsen) *Bradford and the Burglar* (juvenile), Young Scott Books, 1972.

* * *

HART, Marie 1932-

PERSONAL: Born November 25, 1932, in Watsonville, Calif.; daughter of Thomas Ellsworth (a farmer) and Marjorie Irene (Downer) Hart. *Education:* Seattle Pacific College, B.S., 1954; University of Southern California, Los Angeles, M.S., 1963, Ph.D., 1967. *Home:* 859 Bille Rd., Paradise, Calif. 95969. *Office:* Department of Health and Movement Studies, P.O. Box 9971, Mills College, Oakland, Calif. 94613.

CAREER: Worked as physical education teacher in high schools in California, 1954-57; Selwyn College, Auckland, New Zealand, instructor in physical education, 1957-58; San Bernardino Valley College, San Bernardino, Calif., instructor in physical education, 1958-60, assistant dean of women, 1958-60; University of Southern California, Los Angeles, visiting assistant professor of physical education, 1960-67; California State Polytechnic College (now University), Pomona, assistant professor of physical education, 1967-68; California State University at Hayward, associate professor of physical education, 1968-74, associate professor of kinesiology, 1971-74; Mills College, Oakland, Calif., associate professor of physical education and chairman of department of health and movement studies, 1974—.

WRITINGS: (Editor and contributor) *Sport in the Socio-Cultural Process,* W. C. Brown, 1972, 2nd edition, 1976; (contributor) *Issues in Physical Education,* National Press, 1973; *Sex Discrimination in Physical Education and Athletics Programs in California Higher Education,* Institute for Change in Higher Education, 1974; (contributor) G. H. McGlynn, editor, *Issues in Physical Education,* National Press, 1974; *Sex Discrimination in Physical Education and Athletic Programs in California Higher Education,* Institute for Change in Higher Education, 1974; (contributor) R. Rivenes, editor, *Foundations of Physical Education,* Houghton, 1978. Contributor of articles to *Psychology Today* and *Foil.*

WORK IN PROGRESS: Health and Life Style of Early California Women (most of the women interviewed for this project are over 80 years old and live in rural areas or on family ranches).

* * *

HARTFORD, Margaret E(lizabeth) 1917-

PERSONAL: Born December 12, 1917, in Cleveland, Ohio; daughter of William A. (a businessman) and Inez (Logan) Hartford. *Education:* Ohio University, A.B., 1940; University of Pittsburgh, M.Sc. S.A., 1944; University of Chicago, Ph.D., 1962. *Politics:* "Depends on platform and candidate." *Religion:* Episcopalian. *Home:* 5386 Village Green, Los Angeles, Calif. 90016. *Office:* Leonard Davis School of Gerontology, Andrus Gerontology Center, University of Southern California, Los Angeles, Calif. 90007.

CAREER: American Services Institute, Pittsburgh, Pa., program consultant, 1944-48, executive director, 1948-50; Case Western Reserve University, Cleveland, Ohio, assistant professor, 1950-58, associate professor, 1958-62, professor of social work, 1962-75; University of Southern California, Los Angeles, professor of gerontology and social work, 1977—, research associate in educational gerontology, 1977—, director of Leonard Davis School of Gerontology, 1975-77. Member of board of directors, Welfare Federation of Cleveland, 1969-71. Visiting professor of social work and gerontology, University of Southern California, 1973-75; visiting professor of gerontology at McGill University and San Jose State University, 1978. *Member:* National Association of Social Workers (Cleveland area chapter chairman, 1969-72), American Association of University Professors, Council on Social Work Education, National Conference of Social Work, Gerontological Society, Association for Gerontology in Higher Education, Western Gerontological Society.

WRITINGS: (With Grace L. Coyle) *Social Process in the Community and Group,* Council on Social Work Education, 1958; *Groups in Social Work,* Columbia University Press, 1972; (contributor) Robert W. Roberts and Helen Northen, editors, *Theories for Social Work with Groups,* Columbia University Press, 1976; (contributor) Francine Sobey, editor, *Changing Roles in Social Work Practice,* Temple University Press, 1977; (contributor) James E. Birren, editor, *Handbook of Mental Health and Aging,* Prentice-Hall, 1978. Contributor to *Encyclopedia of Social Work.* Contributor to *Proceedings of National Conference of Social Work, Social Welfare Forum, Social Work, Journal of Education for Social Work, Camping Magazine, Journal of Educational Gerontology, Journal of Sociology, Social Welfare, Gerontology and Higher Education,* and *Journal of Social Work with Groups.* Member of editorial board, *Journal of Educational Gerontology, Journal of Sociology and Social Work,* and *Journal of Social Work with Groups.*

WORK IN PROGRESS: Working with Groups in Social Work; Social Work with Older Adults; Working with Older Adults in the Human Sciences; Making the Best of the Years after Retirement; Curriculum Development in Gerontology.

SIDELIGHTS: Margaret E. Hartford told *CA:* "As a young child I wrote stories and poems [and was] encouraged by teachers in writing essays and papers, and later [by] journalism courses, and extracurricular opportunities in school papers and library magazines. After graduate education in social work [I] was encouraged by my various jobs to prepare written material of professional quality. [I] am hoping that in my retirement I will be able to return to poetry, fiction, and essays. [I] spent most of my professional career writing journal articles, reports, chapters, and books.

"My writing style is to collect as much information as is available on a topic, that is, careful research of all the elements to be covered, as well as a review of similar or comparable writing to be sure the topic has not been covered. Then, I sketch out some of the major notions I wish to cover, much as a painter roughs out a potential picture. Later I outline, based on the rough sketch, and fill in the details. This process is very informal. It takes several days or weeks of thinking and planning, but the first draft comes very quickly in a day or more depending on the length."

AVOCATIONAL INTERESTS: Nature, ecology, birds, flowers, handicrafts, camping, travel, running.

* * *

HARTMAN, George E(dward) 1926-

PERSONAL: Born October 20, 1926, in Newton, Kan.; son of Albert J. and Ellen (Pawlick) Hartman. *Education:* University of Kansas, B.S., 1950; Indiana University, M.B.A., 1951; University of Illinois, Ph.D., 1958; University of Cincinnati, J.D., 1964. *Politics:* Democrat. *Religion:* Presbyterian. *Home:* 310 Bryant, Cincinnati, Ohio 45220. *Office:* College of Business Administration, University of Cincinnati, Cincinnati, Ohio 45221.

CAREER: Agricultural and Mechanical College of Texas (now Texas A & M University), College Station, instructor in marketing, 1951-52; University of North Dakota, Grand Forks, assistant professor of marketing, 1952-55; University of Cincinnati, Cincinnati, Ohio, assistant professor, 1958-61, associate professor, 1961-64, professor of marketing, 1964—. Member of board of directors, Reeves Advertising Agency. Member of U.S. Secretary of Commerce's Regional Export Expansion Council, 1969-73. *Military service:* U.S. Army, 1945-46; served in Asiatic-Pacific theater; became sergeant. *Member:* American Marketing Association, American Bar Association, American Council for Consumer Interests, Ohio Bar Association, Southwestern Ohio Consumers Association (member of board of directors, 1977—), Phi Delta Phi, Beta Gamma Sigma.

WRITINGS: (Editor) *Export Trade Handbook,* Department of Commerce, University of Cincinnati, 1968; *Handbook of Modern Marketing: Contract Section,* McGraw, 1971; (editor) *Mutual Trading Opportunity: U.S.-U.S.S.R.,* Department of Commerce, University of Cincinnati, 1972; (contributor) Henry Baker, editor, *Environment 1984,* Grid Publishing, 1975. Contributor of articles to marketing journals.

WORK IN PROGRESS: An article on advertising and the First Amendment.

HARTMAN, Robert K(intz) 1940-

PERSONAL: Born May 12, 1940, in Greensburg, Pa.; son of Joseph Wilmer (a sales manager) and Helen (Kintz) Hartman; married Nancy Carol Farmer (a college instructor), June 15, 1964 (divorced May, 1973). *Education:* Pennsylvania State University, B.S., 1964; University of Connecticut, M.A., 1968, Ph.D., 1970. *Home:* 38 Meadow Lane, Bridgewater, Mass. 02324. *Office:* Bridgewater-Raynham Regional School District, Mt. Prospect St., Bridgewater, Mass. 02324.

CAREER: Darien Board of Education, Darien, Conn., psychologist, 1970-72, coordinator of special education, 1972-73; Indiana State University, Terre Haute, associate professor of special education, 1973-74; Regional Education Assessment and Diagnostic Service, Inc., Lakeville, Mass., executive director, 1974-77; Bridgewater-Raynham Regional School District, Bridgewater, Mass., director of special education, 1977—. Lecturer in psychology, University of Bridgeport, 1970-73. Consultant in research and evaluation to Mediax, Inc., Westport, Conn., 1972—, and International Education Association, Westport, Conn., 1972—. *Member:* American Psychological Association, National Association of School Psychologists, New England Psychological Association, Connecticut Association for Supervisors of Special Education (vice-president, 1972-73, president, 1973-74), Massachusetts Psychological Association, Orton Society.

WRITINGS: (Editor with Nancy C. Hartman) *New Issues in Educational Psychology,* Simon & Schuster, 1971; (editor with Nancy Hartman) *Psychology in the Classroom,* MSS Educational Publishing, 1971; (editor with Nancy Hartman) *Perspectives in Reading,* MSS Educational Publishing, 1971. Contributor to *Exceptional Children, Journal of School Psychology, Journal of Special Education, Reading Teacher, Journal of Reading Behavior, Journal for Special Educators of the Mentally Retarded,* and *Digest of the Mentally Retarded.*

WORK IN PROGRESS: Research in learning disabilities and special education.

* * *

HARTMANN, Edward George 1912-

PERSONAL: Born May 3, 1912, in Wilkes-Barre, Pa.; son of Louis (a public health officer) and Catherine (Jones-Davis) Hartmann. *Education:* Bucknell University, A.B., 1937, M.A., 1938; Columbia University, Ph.D., 1947, B.S.L.S., 1948. *Home:* 69 Hancock St., Boston, Mass. 02114. *Office:* Department of History, Suffolk University, Beacon Hill, Boston, Mass. 02114.

CAREER: Wilkes College, Wilkes-Barre, Pa., assistant professor of history, 1946-47; College of the City of New York (now City College of the City University of New York), New York, N.Y., fellow in library and lecturer in history, 1947-48; Suffolk University, Boston, Mass., assistant professor, 1948-52, associate professor, 1952-56, professor of history, 1956—, director of libraries, 1948-56. *Military service:* U.S. Army, combat historian, 1944-46. U.S. Air Force Reserve, 1950-72; retired as major. *Member:* American Historical Association, Society of American Historians, Immigration History Society, National Gymanfa Ganu Association, Honourable Society of the Cymmrodorion, St. David's Society of the State of New York, Welsh Society of Philadelphia, United Oxford and Cambridge University Club, Columbia University Club, Boston Athenaeum (proprietor), Society of King's Chapel, Ninetieth Division Association, Phi Beta Kappa, Phi Alpha Theta, Order of Lafayette.

Awards, honors: Gold medallion of Welsh Society of Philadelphia, 1966; Hopkins Medal of St. David's Society of the State of New York, 1970.

WRITINGS: (Editor) *Tough 'Ombres: The Story of the 90th Infantry Division,* Stars and Stripes, 1944; (editor) *A Short History of the 357th Infantry Regiment,* Nickl Press, 1945; *The Movement to Americanize the Immigrant,* Columbia University Press, 1948; (editor) *Centennial History of the Welsh Baptist Association of Pennsylvania,* Payne Printers, 1955; *History of American Immigration,* Rand, McNally, 1967; *Americans from Wales,* Christopher, 1967; *History of the Welsh Congregational Church of the City of New York: 1801-1951,* John Penry Press, 1969; *American Immigration,* Lerner, 1978. Contributor to *Columbia Encyclopedia, Americana Annual,* and to historical and scholarly journals.

* * *

HARTMANN, Susan M(arie) 1940-

PERSONAL: Born May 3, 1940, in St. Louis, Mo.; daughter of Herbert R. (a banker) and Marie (Trog) Meckfessel; married Charles J. Hartmann, Jr., August 26, 1961 (divorced, 1971). *Education:* Washington University, St. Louis, Mo., A.B., 1961; University of Missouri, M.A., 1963, Ph.D., 1966. *Residence:* St. Louis, Mo. *Office:* 8001 Natural Bridge, University of Missouri, St. Louis, Mo. 63121.

CAREER: University of Missouri, St. Louis, assistant professor, 1966-71, associate professor of history, 1972—. Visiting associate professor of history, Boston University, 1971-72. *Member:* American Historical Association, Organization of American Historians, American Studies Association, American Association of University Professors. *Awards, honors:* University of Missouri Curators Award, 1971, and David D. Lloyd Prize from Truman Library Institute, 1972, both for *Truman and the 80th Congress;* American Association of University Women Young Scholar Recognition Award, 1973.

WRITINGS: The Marshall Plan, C. E. Merrill, 1968; *Truman and the 80th Congress,* University of Missouri Press, 1971; *The Paradox of Women's Progress: 1820-1920,* Forum Press, 1973. Contributor to *Journal of American History, American Historical Review, Women's Studies, Encyclopedia of Southern History,* and *Annals of the American Academy of Political and Social Science.* Member of advisory board of *Women Studies Abstracts.*

WORK IN PROGRESS: The Impact of World War II on Sex Roles; Women's Organizations and Feminism.

* * *

HARTNACK, Justus 1912-

PERSONAL: Born May 29, 1912, in Copenhagen, Denmark; son of Valdemar (a military officer) and Nonny Ludvigne (Gruener) Hartnack; married Inge Benedicte Endorph Petersen, March 12, 1937; children: Joergen, Birgitte (Mrs. Ulrik Federspiel). *Education:* University of Copenhagen, M.A., 1946, Ph.D., 1950. *Office:* Department of Philosophy, State University of New York College, Brockport, N.Y. 14420.

CAREER: Colgate University, Hamilton, N.Y., visiting lecturer, 1946-50, assistant professor, 1950-54; Aarhus University, Aarhus, Denmark, professor of philosophy, 1954-72, head of department, 1954-68; State University of New York College at Brockport, professor of philosophy, 1968-

70, university professor, 1970-78. Visiting professor at Vassar College, 1958-59, and New York University, 1966-67. *Military service:* Danish Army, 1931-48, retiring as captain. *Awards, honors:* Gentleman in waiting for His Majesty the King of Denmark, 1938; Knight of Dannebroge, first degree, 1972.

WRITINGS: The Problems of Perception in British Empiricism, Munksgaard, 1950; *Philosophical Problems,* Humanities, 1962; *Wittgenstein and the Modern Philosophy,* Doubleday, 1965; *Kant's Theory of Knowledge,* Harcourt, 1967; *Language and Philosophy,* Mouton, 1973; *History of Philosophy,* Humanities, 1973.

* * *

HARVEY, Donald J(oseph) 1922-

PERSONAL: Born October 4, 1922, in New York, N.Y.; son of William Harold (a business executive) and Helen (Chiampou) Harvey; married Jacqueline Rozendaal (an artist/painter), June 11, 1955; children: Nanette C. *Education:* Princeton University, B.A. (cum laude), 1943; Columbia University, M.A., 1948, Ph.D., 1953; Sorbonne, University of Paris, graduate study, 1950-51. *Politics:* Democrat. *Religion:* Protestant. *Home:* 279 Park Ave., Manhasset, N.Y. 11030. *Office:* Department of History, Hunter College of the City University of New York, 695 Park Ave., New York, N.Y. 10021.

CAREER: Hunter College of the City University of New York, New York, N.Y., instructor, 1951-61, associate professor, 1961-67, professor of history, 1967—, chairman of department, 1968-71. Consultant to Rockefeller Foundation, 1974-77, and National Endowment for the Humanities, 1977-78. *Military service:* U.S. Army, Artillery, 1943-46; served in European Theater; became captain; received five battle stars. *Member:* American Historical Association, Society for French Historical Studies (treasurer, 1957), Phi Alpha Theta.

WRITINGS: (With Edward Mead Earle and others) *Modern France,* Princeton University Press, 1951; *France since the Revolution,* Free Press, 1968. Contributor to *New Republic* and to history journals.

WORK IN PROGRESS: French intellectuals and the problem of twentieth-century war.

* * *

HARVEY, Edward Burns 1939-

PERSONAL: Born October 2, 1939, in Victoria, British Columbia, Canada; son of Richard Burns (a lawyer) and Helen (Nield) Harvey; married Lorna Marsden (a university professor), June 12, 1961. *Education:* University of British Columbia, B.A. (honors), 1964; Princeton University, A.M., 1966, Ph.D., 1967. *Residence:* Toronto, Ontario, Canada. *Office:* Ontario Institute for Studies in Education, 252 Bloor St. W., Toronto, Ontario, Canada.

CAREER: University of Toronto and Ontario Institute for Studies in Education, Toronto, Ontario, associate professor of education, 1967—, professor of sociology, 1974—, chairman of department of sociology in education, 1972-76. *Member:* Canadian Sociology and Anthropology Association (member of executive committee), Canadian Educational Research Association, Social Science Federation of Canada (chairman of statistics committee), National Youth Advisory Group, Princeton Club of New York. *Awards, honors:* Woodrow Wilson fellow at Princeton University, 1965—; Canada Council awards, 1967.

WRITINGS: (Editor) *Perspectives on Modernization: Essays in Memory of Ian Weinberg,* University of Toronto Press, 1972; *Education and Employment of Arts and Science Graduates: The Last Decade in Ontario,* Commission on Post-Secondary Education in Ontario, 1972; (with J. Lennards) *Key Issues in Higher Education,* Ontario Institute for Studies in Education, 1973; *Educational Systems and the Labour Market,* Longman, 1973; *Industrial Society: Structures, Roles and Relations,* Dorsey, 1975; (with K.S.R. Murthy) *Supply of and Demand for New Graduates,* Technical Service Council, 1975; (with L. R. Marsden) *The Fragile Federation,* McGraw, 1979. Contributor to sociology and education journals.

* * *

HARVEY, William Burnett 1922-

PERSONAL: Born September 4, 1922, in Greenville, S.C.; son of Charles Hugh (a railroad employee) and Emma (Ballenger) Harvey; married Mary Louise Geleide, March 28, 1945; children: Anne Constance (Mrs. William Colton Taylor), David Kent. *Education:* Wake Forest University, A.B., 1943; University of Michigan, J.D., 1948; University of Heidelberg, graduate study, 1955-56. *Politics:* Democrat. *Religion:* Episcopalian. *Office:* School of Law, Boston University, 755 Commonwealth Ave., Boston, Mass. 02215.

CAREER: Hogan & Hertson (legal firm), Washington, D.C., lawyer, 1949-51; University of Michigan, Ann Arbor, assistant professor, 1951-54, associate professor, 1954-57, professor of law, 1957-66; Indiana University at Bloomington, professor of law, 1966-73, dean of Law Faculty, 1966-71; Boston University, Boston, Mass., professor of law and professor of political science, 1973—. Professor of law and dean of faculty, University of Ghana, Legon, 1962-64. *Military service:* U.S. Navy, 1943-46. *Member:* American Bar Association, American Association of University Professors, African Law Association.

WRITINGS: (With Dawson) *Contracts and Contract Remedies,* Foundation Press, 1959, 3rd edition, 1977; *Law and Social Change in Ghana,* Princeton University Press, 1966; *Introduction to the Legal Systems of East Africa,* East African Literature Bureau, 1975. Contributor to law journals.

WORK IN PROGRESS: The University in Court.

* * *

HASEL, Gerhard F(ranz) 1935-

PERSONAL: Born July 27, 1935, in Vienna, Austria; naturalized U.S. citizen in 1964; son of Franz Joseph (a clergyman) and Helene (Schroeter) Hasel; married Hilde Schafer (a teacher), June 11, 1961; children: Michael, Marlene, Melissa. *Education:* Marienhoehe Seminary, Germany, L.T., 1958; Atlantic Union College, B.A., 1959, Andrews University, M.A., 1961, B.D., 1962; Vanderbilt University, Ph.D., 1970. *Home address:* Red Bud Trail, Route 2, Box 496D, Berrien Springs, Mich. 49103. *Office:* Department of Old Testament, Andrews University, Berrien Springs, Mich. 49104.

CAREER: Clergyman of Seventh-day Adventist Church; Southern Missionary College, Collegedale, Tenn., assistant professor of religion, 1963-66; Andrews University, Berrien Springs, Mich., 1967—, began as associate professor, currently professor of Old Testament and Biblical theology and assistant dean of theological seminary. *Member:* International Society for the Study of the Old Testament, Society of

Biblical Literature, American Academy of Religion, American Schools of Oriental Research, Chicago Society of Biblical Research, Alpha Gamma Mu. *Awards, honors:* Danforth teacher award, 1967-69.

WRITINGS: The Remnant: The History and Theology of the Remnant Idea from Genesis to Isaiah, Andrews University Press, 1972, 2nd edition 1974; *Old Testament Theology: Basic Issues in the Current Debate,* Eerdmans, 1972, 3rd edition, 1979; *Jonah: Messenger of the Eleventh Hour,* Pacific Press Publishing Association, 1977; *New Testament Theology: Basic Issues in the Current Debate,* Eerdmans, 1978. Contributor to *Theological Dictionary of the Old Testament,* Eerdmans, 1977, and *New International Standard Bible Encyclopedia,* Eerdmans, 1978. Contributor to *Andrews University Seminary Studies, Zeitschrift Alttest Wissenschaft, Journal of Biblical Literature, Bible Translator, Biblical Theology Bulletin, Mennonite Quarterly Review, Evangelical Quarterly, Bibliotheca Orientalis, Zeichen der Zeit,* and *Journal of American Academy of Religion.* Associate editor of *Andrews University Seminary Studies.*

WORK IN PROGRESS: A Theology of the Old Testament; Studies in the Book of Daniel; Understanding the Bible; Commentary on Amos and Hosea; research on ancient Near Eastern and Israelite prophecy; studies in apocalypticism.

* * *

HASKELL, Martin R(oy)   1912-

PERSONAL: Born October 21, 1912, in New York, N.Y.; son of Aaron Munro and Rose (Robbins) Haskell; married Rochelle Joseph (a speech therapist), April 4, 1946. *Education:* College of the City of New York (now City College of the City University of New York), B.A., 1931; Brooklyn Law School, LL.B., 1940; New York University, M.A., 1954, Ph.D., 1957. *Politics:* Democrat. *Religion:* Unitarian Universalist. *Home:* 19 38th Pl., Long Beach, Calif. 90803. *Office:* Department of Sociology, California State University, Long Beach, Calif. 90801.

CAREER: Admitted to New York Bar, 1940; in private practice of law in New York City, 1940-42, 1946-48; Moreno Institute, New York City, training director, 1954-63; California State University, Long Beach, assistant professor, 1963-66, associate professor, 1966-70, professor of sociology, 1970—. Lecturer in sociology, New York University, 1956-59; City University of New York, lecturer, 1958-60, assistant professor of sociology, 1960-63; executive director, California Institute of Socioanalysis, 1965—. Placement director, Berkshire Farm for Boys, 1957-60. *Military service:* U.S. Army Reserve, active duty, 1942-46, 1948-53, 1961-62; became lieutenant colonel.

MEMBER: American Sociological Association (fellow), American Psychological Association, American Society of Group Psychotherapy and Psychodrama (fellow), American Society of Criminology. *Awards, honors:* August Aichhorn Award for contributions in the field of juvenile delinquency, American Society of Social Psychiatry, 1959; De Roy Award for research on juvenile delinquency, Society for the Study of Social Problems, 1960; research grant from U.S. Office of Vocational Rehabilitation, 1960-61.

WRITINGS: (With Burnham Carter) *How to Use Educational Recordings Effectively* (a manual for blind students and guidance counselors), U.S. Department of Health, Education, and Welfare, 1962; *The Psychodramatic Method,* California Institute of Socioanalysis, 1967; *An Introduction to Socioanalysis,* California Institute of Socioan-

alysis, 1967, 2nd edition, 1972; (with Lewis Yablonsky) *Crime and Delinquency,* Rand McNally, 1970, 2nd edition, 1975; (with Yablonsky) *Juvenile Delinquency,* Rand McNally, 1974, 2nd edition, 1978; *Criminology: Crime and Criminality,* Rand McNally, 1974, 2nd edition, 1978; *Socioanalysis: Self-Direction Via Sociometry and Psychodrama,* Role Training Associates, 1975. Contributor to *Group Psychotherapy, Social Problems,* and *Journal of Criminal Law, Criminology and Police Science.* Contributing editor of *Group Psychotherapy* and *Psychodrama.*

* * *

HASSLER, Donald M. (II)   1937-

PERSONAL: Born January 3, 1937, in Akron, Ohio; son of Donald M. (a businessman) and Fran (Parsons) Hassler; married Diana Cain, October 8, 1960 (died September 19, 1976); married Sue Smith, September 13, 1977; children: (first marriage) Donald M. III, David. *Education:* Williams College, B.A., 1959; Columbia University, M.A., 1960, Ph.D., 1967. *Religion:* Presbyterian. *Home:* 1226 Woodhill, Kent, Ohio 44240. *Office:* Department of English, Kent State University, Kent, Ohio 44240.

CAREER: University of Montreal, Montreal, Quebec, instructor in English, 1961-65; Kent State University, Kent, Ohio, assistant professor, 1967-71, associate professor, 1971-77, professor of English, 1977—, director of experimental college, 1973—. *Member:* Modern Language Association of America, American Society for Eighteenth-Century Studies, Keats-Shelley Association, American Association of University Professors, Science Fiction Research Association, Ohio Poets Association, Phi Beta Kappa. *Awards, honors:* Woodrow Wilson fellow, 1959.

WRITINGS: The Comedian as the Letter D: Erasmus Darwin's Comic Materialism, Nijhoff, 1973; *On Weighing a Pound of Flesh* (poetry), Defiance College Publications, 1973; *Erasmus Darwin,* Twayne, 1974; (contributor) Theodore Besterman, editor, *Studies on Voltaire and the Eighteenth Century,* Voltaire Foundation, 1976; (contributor) Joseph Olander and Martin Greenberg, editors, *Issac Asimov,* Taplinger, 1977. Represented in annual anthologies of Ohio Poets Association, 1969—; contributor to *Hiram Poetry Review, Canadian Poetry, Fiddlehead, Descant, Canadian Forum,* and other periodicals.

WORK IN PROGRESS: A collection of poems; a collection of essays on the relation of modern science fiction to the eighteenth century.

* * *

HASTINGS, Margaret   1910-

PERSONAL: Born May 23, 1910, in Springfield, Mass.; daughter of William Walter (a teacher and clergyman) and Elizabeth (Fairbank) Hastings. *Education:* Mount Holyoke College, B.A., 1931, M.A., 1932; Bryn Mawr College, Ph.D., 1939; University of London, graduate study, 1933-34. *Politics:* Democrat. *Home:* 9 Silverwood Ter., South Hadley, Mass. 01075.

CAREER: History teacher at private schools in Waterbury, Conn. and Boston, Mass., 1935-44; U.S. Department of the Army, Security Agency, Arlington, Va., research analyst, 1944-45; Rutgers University, Douglass College, New Brunswick, N.J., lecturer, 1946, instructor, 1946-49; assistant professor, 1949-52, associate professor, 1952-60, professor of history, 1960-75. Educational Testing Service, examiner, 1940-61, reader, 1950-61. *Member:* American Historical

Association, Mediaeval Academy of America, American Association of University Professors, Royal Historical Society (fellow), Selden Society (London), Conference on British Studies, Phi Beta Kappa. *Awards, honors:* Fulbright fellowship, 1950-51; Guggenheim fellowship, 1959-60; American Council of Learned Societies fellowship, 1964-65; Helen Maud Cam fellowship, Girton College, Cambridge, 1972-73.

WRITINGS: The Court of Common Pleas in Fifteenth Century England, Cornell University Press, 1947; (contributor) Elizabeth C. Furber, editor, *Changing Views on British History,* Harvard University Press, 1966; *Medieval European Society,* Random House, 1971. Contributor to *Speculum, Guildhall Miscellany, American Historical Review,* and *Journal of Economic History.*

WORK IN PROGRESS: Research on Sir Thomas More as Chancellor of the Duchy of Lancaster and as a lawyer; research on the legal profession in the Middle Ages.

SIDELIGHTS: Margaret Hastings has lived or traveled in France, Italy, England, and Greece. *Avocational interests:* Mountain walking.†

* * *

HASWELL, Chetwynd John Drake 1919-
(Jock Haswell, George Foster)

PERSONAL: Born July 18, 1919, in Penn, Buckinghamshire, England; son of Chetwynd Henry (a brigadier, Royal Engineers) and Dorothy (Berry) Haswell; married Charlotte Annette Petter, October 25, 1947; children: Richard, Frances, Charles. *Education:* Attended Winchester College, 1933-37, and Royal Military College, Sandhurst, 1938-39. *Politics:* "Deep distrust of all politicians." *Religion:* Church of England. *Home and office:* Grey House, Lyminge, Folkestone, Kent, England.

CAREER: Professional soldier commissioned into The Queen's Royal Regiment, oldest English line regiment, as second lieutenant, 1939; retired with rank of major when regiment was amalgamated in 1959; went into industry as technical writer "and hated every minute of it"; started his own technical writing and publicity firm, Southern Sales Promotion Ltd., 1964, and still is nominal managing director; reemployed by British Ministry of Defence as retired officer-author for Service Intelligence (formerly Military Intelligence) at School of Service Intelligence, 1966—.

WRITINGS—Under name Jock Haswell, except as indicated: (Under pseudonym George Foster) *Indian File,* M. Joseph, 1960; (under pseudonym George Foster) *Soldier on Loan,* M. Joseph, 1961; *The Queen's Royal Regiment,* Cooper, 1967; *The First Respectable Spy: The Life and Times of Colquhoun Grant, Wellington's Head of Intelligence,* Hamish Hamilton, 1969; *James II: Soldier and Sailor,* St. Martin's, 1972; *British Military Intelligence,* Weidenfeld & Nicolson, 1973; *Citizen Armies,* P. Davies, 1973; *The British Army: A Concise History,* Thames & Hudson, 1975; *The Battle for Empire: A Century of Anglo-French Conflict,* Cassell, 1976; *The Ardent Queen: Margaret of Anjou and the Lancastrian Heritage,* P. Davies, 1976; *Spies and Spymasters: A Concise History of Intelligence,* Thames & Hudson, 1977; *Intelligence, Deception and the D-Day Landings,* Batsford, 1979. Contributor to *Argosy* and business, technical, military, and intelligence journals.

WORK IN PROGRESS: A biography of Dr. Wilhelm Stieber, Bismarck's "King of Sleuthhounds," for Albrecht Knaus Verlag.

SIDELIGHTS: As a soldier Chetwynd John Haswell traveled extensively in Africa, the Far East, and Europe, "much of my travelling being on my feet, since I was an infantryman.... History has always fascinated me," he says, "from the point of view of trying to find out what *really* happened. Contemporary accounts always vary so much: for example, what really happened on the village green at Lexington? Who fired first? No one really knows. Perhaps my main motivation is real enjoyment of a good story that is true."

* * *

HATCH, Eric S(towe) 1902(?)-1973

1902(?)—June 4, 1973; American novelist, television and short story writer. Obituaries: *Washington Post,* July 6, 1973; *Publishers Weekly,* July 16, 1973.

* * *

HATCH, James V(ernon) 1928-

PERSONAL: Born October 25, 1928, in Oelwein, Iowa; son of MacKenzie (a boilermaker) and Eunice (Smith) Hatch; married Evelyn Marcussen, 1949 (marriage dissolved, 1963); married Camille Billops (an artist), 1964; children: (first marriage) Susan, Dion. *Education:* State University of Northern Iowa, B.A., 1949; State University of Iowa, M.A., 1955, Ph.D., 1958. *Politics:* Independent. *Office:* Department of English, City College of the City University of New York, New York, N.Y. 10031.

CAREER: High school English and drama teacher, 1949-58; University of California, Los Angeles, assistant professor of theatre arts, 1958-62; High Cinema Institute, Cairo, Egypt, Fulbright lecturer, 1962-65; City College of the City University of New York, New York, N.Y., assistant professor, 1965-72, associate professor, beginning 1973, currently professor of English. Visiting professor, New York University, 1973. Co-founder, director, Hatch/Billops Collection (New York City), 1968—; resident playwright, Idylwild Arts Foundation, 1960, Huntington Hartford Foundation, 1962; U.S. Department of State, theatre specialist in India, Pakistan, and Ceylon, 1968; lecturer in creative writing, Chautauqua Institute, 1969, 1970; consultant to Institute of Dramatic Arts, University of California at Santa Barbara, 1967, New York City Board of Education, 1969, Institute in Dramatic Arts, North Carolina State University, 1970, and Afro-American Institute, Columbia University, 1970. *Awards, honors:* Thomas Wood Stevens Award from Stanford University, and Festival of Arts Award, Birmingham, Ala., both 1957, for "Easter Song"; George Washington Honor Medal Award from Freedoms Foundation, 1958, for "This Is Worth Remembering"; Obie Award of *Village Voice* for best Off-Broadway musical in New York, 1961-62, for *Fly Blackbird;* Unity Award of Better Race Relations Bureau of Hollywood, 1962; first prize at Atlanta Film Festival, and Golden Eagle Cine award, both 1972, for "Denmark 43."

WRITINGS: (With Ibrahim Ibn Ismail) *Poems for Niggers and Crackers,* Schindler Press, 1965; *The Black Image on the American Stage: A Bibliography,* Drama Book Specialist, 1970; (contributor) William Reardon and Thomas Pawley, editors, *The Black Teacher and the Dramatic Arts,* Negro Universities Press, 1970; *Liar, Liar* (a children's musical play; first produced November, 1962, at ANTA Children's Theatre, Los Angeles), General Music Corp., 1972; (editor with Victoria Sullivan) *By and About Women,* Random House, 1973; *Black Theatre USA: 1847-1972,* Free

Press, 1974; (with Omanii Abdullah) *Black Playwrights, 1823-1977*, Bowker, 1977.

Unpublished plays, except as indicated: "Dagzil," first produced at University of Iowa, July, 1956; "Easter Song," first produced at University of Iowa, August, 1956; "Tallest Baby," first produced at University of California, Los Angeles, December 1958; *Fly Blackbird* (published in *The Black Teacher and the Dramatic Arts;* see above), first produced at Theatre Vanguard, Los Angeles, September, 1960; produced Off-Broadway at Mayfair Theatre, February 5, 1962; (co-author) "Conspiracy," first produced at Washington Square Methodist Church, New York, N.Y., April, 1970; (co-author) "If It Do Not Die, It Do Not Die," first produced Off-Off-Broadway at Last Chance Theatre, April, 1970; (co-author) "Safe at Last," first produced Off-Off-Broadway at East Village Theatre, March, 1973; (co-author) "The Divided Bed," first produced at Actors Equity Showcase, New York, N.Y., March, 1977.

Films: "This Is Worth Remembering," 1957; "Autumn," 1957; "The Sole Survivor," 1960; "Modern Arabic Women," 1964; "Three Days of Suez," 1964; "Paper Pulp from Sugar Cane," 1965; "Denmark 43," 1972; "Oelwein Centennial," 1973. Also writer of educational films for the State University of Iowa, 1956-58.

Contributor to *Drama Review, Nation, Village Voice, College English, Changing Education, Black Scholar, Ararat, Black Perspective in Music,* and *Black Art.*

WORK IN PROGRESS: Collecting oral histories from black artists, for City University of New York.

* * *

HAUCK, Paul A(nthony) 1924-

PERSONAL: Born September 15, 1924, in Germany; naturalized U.S. citizen in 1949; son of John and Elizabeth (Koenig) Hauck; married Marceleen T. Steenburgen, 1953; children: Kathryn (Mrs. Henry Holladay), Melanie, Stephanie. *Education:* Drew University, B.A., 1948; University of Utah, M.A., 1951, Ph.D., 1953. *Home:* 2365 18th St., Apt. D, Moline, Ill. 61264. *Office:* Suite 302, Safety Building, Rock Island, Ill. 61201.

CAREER: Psychologist in Butte, Mont., 1953-55; State Hospital, East Moline, Ill., chief psychologist, 1955-60; Western Mental Health Center, Marshall, Minn., director, 1960-67; Peoria Mental Health Center, Peoria, Ill., chief psychologist, 1967-68; clinical psychologist in Rock Island, Ill., 1968—. Diplomate, American Board of Professional Psychology, 1961. *Member:* American Psychological Association (founder; president, 1959-60).

WRITINGS—All published by Westminster, except as noted: *The Rational Management of Children*, Libra, 1967, 2nd edition, 1972; *Reason in Pastoral Counseling*, 1972; *Overcoming Depression*, 1973; *Overcoming Frustration and Anger*, 1974; *Overcoming Worry and Fear*, 1975; (with Edmund S. Kean) *Marriage and the Memo Method*, 1975; *How to Do What You Want to Do: The Art of Self Discipline*, 1976; *Marriage Is a Loving Business*, 1977; *How to Stand Up for Yourself*, 1979. Contributor of weekly column to *Human Scene*.

WORK IN PROGRESS: Brief Therapy with RET.

* * *

HAUSRATH, Alfred Hartmann 1901-

PERSONAL: Born May 1, 1901, in New York, N.Y.; son

of Alfred Hartmann (a musician) and Anna (Bleyer) Hausrath; married Mary Catherine Glassford, March 23, 1923; children: Alfred Hartmann III, Dean Harvey, Donald Craig. *Education:* Iowa State College of Agriculture and Mechanic Arts (now Iowa State University of Science and Technology), B.S., 1922, M.S., 1929; graduate study at University of Iowa, 1933-35, and Columbia University. *Home:* 120 Hilltop Rd., Silver Spring, Md. 20910.

CAREER: Iowa State College of Agriculture and Mechanic Arts (now Iowa State University of Science and Technology), Ames, 1928-42, began as instructor, became assistant professor of education; U.S. Government, Washington, D.C., management specialist, Office for Emergency Management, 1942-45, administrative posts, Office of Naval Research, 1945-49; Educational Testing Service, Princeton, N.J., director of Co-operative Test Division, 1949-51; Johns Hopkins University, Operations Research Office, Bethesda, Md., division chief and research director, 1951-61; Research Analysis Corp., McLean, Va., chief of Conflict Analysis Division, 1961-66; independent researcher and writer, 1966—. Adviser, consultant, or staff member at various times to President's Advisory Committee on Education, U.S. Armed Forces Institute, U.S. Department of State, Vietnam Advisory Group, Saigon, and other government bodies.

MEMBER: American Association for the Advancement of Science (fellow), Operations Research Society of America (charter member), American Personnel and Guidance Association, National Vocational Guidance Association. *Awards, honors:* United Nations Command Service Medal (Korea), 1953.

WRITINGS: (With John H. Harms) *Consumer Science: A Fusion Course in Physical Science Applied to Consumer Problems*, with teacher's manual, Macmillan, 1939; (with Harms) *Let's Investigate: An Experimental Approach to Consumer Science*, Macmillan, 1942; *Venture Simulation in War, Business, and Politics*, McGraw, 1971. Author or co-author of classified and unclassified research reports for U.S. military establishment; contributor to science texts.

WORK IN PROGRESS: Research on visualized history of civilization, both ancient and American.

SIDELIGHTS: Alfred Hausrath has done research on a variety of problems in the Far East, Southeast Asia, Middle East, and Europe.

* * *

HAVEL, J(ean) E(ugene Martial) 1928-

PERSONAL: Born June 16, 1928, in Le Havre, France; Canadian citizen; son of Marc Louis Gustave and Suzanne Celine Marie (Dore) Havel; married Anne Marie Luhr, August 22, 1955 (died January 22, 1977); children: Guillaume, Frederik, Mathilde, Ingrid Lucie. *Education:* University of Paris, LL.B., 1950, Diplome de l'Institut des Etudes Politiques, 1952, study at Institut des Etudes Scandinaves, 1952-53, Doctorat es lettres, 1956; University of Oslo, graduate study, 1953-54. *Office:* Department of Political Science, Laurentian University, Sudbury, Ontario, Canada.

CAREER: University of Stockholm, Stockholm, Sweden, extension teacher, 1956-59; University of Montreal, Montreal, Quebec, assistant professor of political science, 1959-62; Laurentian University, Sudbury, Ontario, assistant professor, 1962-64, associate professor, 1964-69, professor of political science, 1969—. Guest lecturer at University of

New Brunswick, 1968, University of London, University of Helsinki, University of Padova, University of Rouen, and University of Caen, 1969. *Member:* Canadian Political Science Association, Social Science Research Council of Canada (member of executive council, 1968-69). *Awards, honors:* Council of Europe research scholar, 1957-58; Canada Centennial Medal, 1967; Canada Council leave fellowship, 1968-69, 1975-76.

WRITINGS: Cours de journalisme: La redaction, Ecole Universelle, 1956; *La fabrication du journal,* Ecole Universelle, 1957; *Habitat et Logement,* Presses Universitaires de France, 1957; *La condition de la femme,* Armand Colin, 1961; *Politics in Sudbury: A Survey of Mass Communications, Political Behaviour, and Political Parties in Sudbury,* Laurentian University Press, 1966; *Les Etats scandinaves et l'intergration europeenne,* Editions de l' Universite Laurentienne, 1970; *La Finlande et la Suede,* Editions Naaman, in press. Writer of booklets on political science topics; contributor of more than forty articles and reviews to journals.

* * *

HAVENS, Murray Clark 1932-

PERSONAL: Born August 21, 1932, in Council Grove, Kan.; son of Ralph Murray (an economist) and Catherine (Clark) Havens; married Agnes Scharpf, July 5, 1958 (died, 1969); married Elizabeth Maret (a sociologist), December 20, 1969 (divorced, 1975); children: (first marriage) Colin Scott, Theresa Agnes. *Education:* University of Alabama, B.A., 1953; Johns Hopkins University, M.A., 1954, Ph.D., 1958. *Politics:* Democrat. *Home:* 7408 Topeka, Lubbock, Tex. 79424. *Office:* Department of Political Science, Texas Tech University, Lubbock, Tex. 79409.

CAREER: Brookings Institution, Washington, D.C., postdoctoral fellow, 1958-59; Duke University, Durham, N.C., assistant professor of political science, 1959-61; University of Texas at Austin, professor of government, 1961-73, director of graduate program in political science; Texas Tech University, Lubbock, professor of political science and chairperson of department, 1973—. Fulbright lecturer, University of Sydney, 1966. Consultant to National Commission on Violence. *Military service:* U.S. Army, 1954-56; became first lieutenant. *Member:* American Political Science Association, American Association of University Professors, American Civil Liberties Union, Southern Political Science Association (secretary, 1964-65), Midwest Political Science Association, Southwestern Political Science Association.

WRITINGS: City Versus Farm?, University of Alabama, 1957; *The Challenges to Democracy,* University of Texas Press, 1965; (with Carl Leiden and Karl M. Schmitt) *The Politics of Assassination,* Prentice-Hall, 1970, published as *Assassination and Terrorism: Their Modern Dimensions,* Sterling Swift, 1975; (contributor) Benjamin J. Taylor and Thurman J. White, editors, *Issues and Ideas in America,* University of Oklahoma Press, 1976. Book review editor of *Journal of Politics.*

WORK IN PROGRESS: A study of the nature of conflict.

SIDELIGHTS: Murray Havens is a private pilot.

* * *

HAVENS, Thomas R. H. 1939-

PERSONAL: Born November 21, 1939, in Chambersburg, Pa.; son of Paul Swain (a college president) and Lorraine (Hamilton) Havens. *Education:* Princeton University,

A.B., 1961; University of California, Berkeley, M.A., 1962, Ph.D., 1965. *Office:* Department of History, Connecticut College, New London, Conn. 06320.

CAREER: University of Toronto, Toronto, Ontario, assistant professor of history, 1965-66; Connecticut College, New London, assistant professor, 1966-70, associate professor, 1970-75, professor of history, 1975—, chairman of department, 1974-76, director of Asian studies program, 1970-72. Associate, John K. Fairbank Center for East Asian Research, Harvard University, 1973—. *Member:* American Historical Association, Association for Asian Studies, American Association of University Professors. *Awards, honors:* Ford Foundation foreign area fellow at Chuo University, 1964-65; National Endowment for the Humanities fellow in Tokyo, Japan, 1968-69; Fulbright senior research scholar, 1972-73, and Guggenheim fellow, 1976-77, at Institute of Social Sciences, Waseda University.

WRITINGS: Nishi Amane and Modern Japanese Thought, Princeton University Press, 1970; *Farm and Nation in Modern Japan: Agrarian Nationalism, 1870-1940,* Princeton University Press, 1974; *Valley of Darkness: The Japanese People and World War Two,* Norton, 1978; (contributor) Edward R. Beauchamp, editor, *Learning to Be Japanese: Selected Readings on Japanese Society and Education,* Linnet Books, 1978. Contributor to journals of Asian studies and *American Historical Review.*

WORK IN PROGRESS: A study of the arts and postwar Japanese cultural history.

* * *

HAWKINS, Gordon 1919-

PERSONAL: Born July 25, 1919, in London, England; son of Joseph (a teacher) and Elsie (Goddard) Hawkins; married Stephanie Jarvis, May 14, 1940; children: Glynis (Mrs. Stuart Morrison), Caroline, Sarah. *Education:* University of Wales, B.A. (first class honors), 1950; Balliol College, Oxford, graduate study, 1950-54. *Politics:* Radical. *Religion:* Agnostic. *Home:* 16 Carey St., Manly, Sydney 2095, New South Wales, Australia. *Office:* Faculty of Law, University of Sydney, 173-5 Phillip St., Sydney 2000, New South Wales, Australia.

CAREER: Police commandant and magistrate in Kohima Assam, India, 1945-46; English Prison Service, Maidstone, England and Wakefield, England, prison governor and member of staff college, 1954-61; University of Sydney, Sydney, New South Wales, senior lecturer, 1961-70, associate professor of criminology, 1971—. Adviser to Australian Federal Government, 1973—, and Australian Law Reform Commission, 1975—. *Military service:* British Army, Assam Rifles, 1939-45; served in North Africa, Italy and Burma; became captain. *Member:* Australian Academy of Forensic Science, Australia and New Zealand Society of Criminology, Society of Public Teachers of Law, American Society of Criminology.

WRITINGS: (With Norval Morris) *The Honest Politician's Guide to Crime Control,* University of Chicago Press, 1970; (with Morris) *Crime and Modern Society: America's Dilemma,* University of Tokyo Press, 1971; (with Franklin E. Zimring) *Deterrence: The Legal Threat in Crime Control,* University of Chicago Press, 1973; *The Prison: Policy and Practice,* University of Chicago Press, 1976; (with Morris) *Letter to the President on Crime Control,* University of Chicago Press, 1977; *Beyond Reasonable Doubt,* A.B.C. Publications, 1978. Author of column appearing in *Australian* (newspaper).

WORK IN PROGRESS: The Crisis in Corrections, with Michael Sherman, completion expected in 1979.

* * *

HAYNES, Robert Vaughn 1929-

PERSONAL: Born November 28, 1929, in Nashville, Tenn.; son of Robert Raymond (a professor) and Gladys (Vaughn) Haynes; married Martha Farr, December 25, 1952; children: Catherine Anne, Carolyn Alice, Charles Allen. *Education:* Millsaps College, B.A., 1952; George Peabody College for Teachers, M.A., 1953; William M. Rice Institute (now Rice University), Ph.D., 1959. *Politics:* Democrat. *Religion:* Presbyterian. *Home:* 2010 Banks St., Houston, Tex. 77098. *Office:* Department of History, University of Houston, Houston, Tex. 77004.

CAREER: University of Houston, Houston, Tex., instructor, 1956-59, assistant professor, 1959-62, associate professor, 1962-67, professor of history, 1967—, acting director of Afro-American studies, 1969-71, director of Institute of Cultural Understanding, summer, 1971, interim director of libraries, 1976-78, director of libraries, 1978—. Visiting professor, University of Alabama, 1970. Member of the board of directors of Bicentennial Commission of Texas Colleges and Universities, and Ecumenical Houston Campus Ministries. Member, advisory planning committee, Texas Conference on Library and Information Services; treasurer, Houston Committee on the Humanities. *Military service:* U.S. Air Force, 1950-51.

MEMBER: American Library Association, American Historical Association, Organization of American Historians, American Studies Association, Association for the Study of Negro Life and History, Institute for Early American History and Culture, Southwestern Library Association, Southern Historical Association, Texas Historical Association, Texas Library Association, Mississippi Historical Society, Pi Gamma Mu, Phi Kappa Phi, Phi Alpha Theta. *Awards, honors:* Danforth associate, 1969—.

WRITINGS: Blacks in White America before 1865, McKay, 1972; (contributor) Richard Aubrey McLemore, editor, *History of Mississippi,* University & College Press of Mississippi, 1973; *A Night of Violence: The Houston Mutiny and Riot of 1917,* Louisiana State University Press, 1976; *The Natchez District and the American Revolution,* University Press of Mississippi, 1976; (contributor) Richard V. Weekes, editor, *Muslim Peoples: A World Ethnographic Survey,* Greenwood Press, 1978. Contributor to *Journal of Mississippi History, Alabama Review, Louisiana History, Southwestern Historical Quarterly,* and *Journal of the American Studies Association of Texas.*

WORK IN PROGRESS: Houston, Texas and the Progressive Movement.

* * *

HAYTER, Earl W(iley) 1901-

PERSONAL: Born February 25, 1901, in Ridgeway, Ohio; son of Amner Z. (an implement dealer) and Luella E. (Garner) Hayter; married Beulah Overman, June 3, 1927; children: Donna, Mary (Mrs. Edward Harmon). *Education:* Attended Grand Island College, 1922-26; University of Nebraska, A.B., 1927; University of North Dakota, M.A., 1932; Northwestern University, Ph.D., 1934. *Politics:* Democrat. *Home:* 560 Normal Rd., DeKalb, Ill. 60115.

CAREER: Teacher in public schools, 1927-30; McKendree College, Lebanon, Ill., associate professor of history, 1934-

36; Northern Illinois University, DeKalb, professor of American history, 1936-69, university historian, 1969-73, head of history department, 1963-64, director of European seminars to Oxford University, 1959, 1962. Consultant to *Encyclopaedia Britannica* for "Libraries of American Civilization," edited by Mortimer J. Adler. *Member:* Organization of American Historians, Agriculture History Society (member of executive committee, 1960), American Civil Liberties Union, Sigma Xi, Pi Kappa Delta, Alpha Chi Sigma, Phi Alpha Theta. *Awards, honors:* Social Science Research Council grants, 1940, 1946; American Philosophical Society grant, 1962; Earl W. Hayter history fellowship, Northern Illinois University, 1969.

WRITINGS: The Troubled Farmer, Northern Illinois University Press, 1968; *Education in Transition: The History of Northern Illinois University,* Northern Illinois University Press, 1974. Contributor of articles to history and agriculture journals.

* * *

HEAD, Robert V. 1929-

PERSONAL: Born March 27, 1929, in Yankton, S.D.; son of Clarence M. and Ellen (Magirl) Head; divorced; children: Brenda Eileen. *Education:* George Washington University, B.A. (with distinction), 1952.

CAREER: General Electric Co., Palo Alto, Calif., manager of deposit accounting systems, computer department, 1957-59; International Business Machines (IBM), Sabre Project, senior systems engineer, 1959-62, staff member, Systems Research Institute, New York, N.Y., 1962-63; Security Pacific National Bank, Los Angeles, Calif., vice-president and manager of Systems Planning Division, 1963-65; Computer Sciences Corp., Los Angeles, manager of management information technology, 1965-67; Software Resources Corp., Los Angeles, founder and president, 1967-68; independent information systems consultant, writer, and lecturer, 1968—. Chairman of technical advisory panel, National Highway Accident and Injury Analysis Center, U.S. Department of Transportation, 1967-69. National lecturer for Association for Computing Machinery, 1966-67, 1970-71; lecturer at universities and for associations and industry throughout the country. *Military service:* U.S. Army, 1946-48.

MEMBER: Association for Computing Machinery, Society for Management Information Systems (founder; first president, 1968-70), Institute of Management Sciences, Phi Beta Kappa, Pi Gamma Mu, Phi Eta Sigma, Mensa.

WRITINGS: Real-Time Systems, Holt, 1964; *A Guide to Packaged Systems,* Wiley, 1971; *Manager's Guide to Management Information Systems,* Prentice-Hall, 1972.

Contributor: Melvin Klerer and G. A. Korn, *Digital Computer User's Handbook,* McGraw, 1967; *Handbook of Data Processing Management,* Brandon/Systems Press, 1968; *Real-Time Systems Design,* Information and Systems Institute, 1968; *Effective Program Development,* Data Processing Digest, 1969; *Managing Your Information,* Business Press, 1970; *Planning Community Information Utilities,* AFIPS Press, 1972. Contributor of more than forty articles to bank, automation, and computer journals. Contributor of reviews to *Computing Reviews* and *Data Processing Digest.* Contributing editor, *Datamation,* 1965-71; associate editor and columnist, *Journal of Systems Management,* 1966-70.††

HEADY, Eleanor B(utler) 1917-

PERSONAL: Born March 13, 1917, in Bliss, Idaho; daughter of Arthur Harrison and Effie (Carrico) Butler; married Harold F. Heady (a professor of ecology), June 12, 1940; children: Carol Marie (Mrs. Don De Maria), Kent Arthur. *Education:* University of Idaho, B.A., 1939. *Politics:* Liberal Republican. *Religion:* Congregationalist. *Home and office:* 1864 Capistrano Ave., Berkeley, Calif. 94707. *Agent:* Marilyn Marlow, Curtis Brown Ltd., 575 Madison Ave., New York, N.Y. 10022.

CAREER: Has worked as a high school English teacher, radio announcer, and script writer. Member of board of directors, Concerned Berkeley Citizens. *Member:* League of American Penwomen, Authors Guild, California Writer's Club (president, 1972-73), Berkeley City Club.

WRITINGS—Juvenile: Jambo, Sungura, Norton, 1965; *When the Stones Were Soft: East African Fireside Tales,* Funk, 1968; *Coat of the Earth,* Norton, 1968; *Brave Johnny O'Hare,* Parents' Magazine Press, 1969; *Tales of the Nimipoo,* World Publishing, 1970; (with husband, Harold F. Heady) *High Meadow,* Grosset, 1970; *Safiri the Singer,* Follett, 1972; *The Soil That Feeds Us,* Parents' Magazine Press, 1972; (with H. F. Heady) *Sage Smoke,* Follett, 1973; *Make Your Own Dolls,* Lothrop, 1974; *Plants on the Go,* Parents' Magazine Press, 1975; *Trees Are Forever,* Parents' Magazine Press, 1978. Contributor to *Cricket, Ranger Rick's Nature Magazine,* and *Highlights for Children.*

WORK IN PROGRESS: With Harold F. Heady, *Range and Wildlife Management in the Tropics,* for Longman.

BIOGRAPHICAL/CRITICAL SOURCES: New York Times Book Review, May 5, 1965; *Saturday Review,* September 21, 1968, November 14, 1970; *Christian Science Monitor,* October 17, 1970.

*   *   *

HEALY, Timothy S. 1923-

PERSONAL: Born April 25, 1923, in New York, N.Y.; son of Reginald S. (a radio artist) and Margaret (Vaeth) Healy. *Education:* Woodstock College, A.B., 1946, Ph.L., 1947, M.A., 1948; University of Louvain, S.T.L., 1954; Fordham University, M.A., 1958; Oxford University, D.Phil., 1966. *Politics:* Democrat. *Office:* Office of Academic Affairs, City University of New York, 535 East 80th St., New York, N.Y. 10021.

CAREER: Roman Catholic priest of Society of Jesus (Jesuit); Fordham Preparatory School, New York City, instructor in English and Latin, 1947-50; Fordham University, New York City, instructor, 1956-58, assistant professor, 1958-65, associate professor, 1965-68, professor of English, 1968-69, director of alumni relations, 1957-62, executive vice-president, 1965-69; City University of New York, New York City, professor of English and vice-chancellor of academic affairs, 1969—. Chairman of board of directors, New York College Bound Corp., 1966-69; trustee, Marymount College, 1970—; member, New York State Commission on Graduate Education. Member of advisory council, New York State Department of Education, 1970—; member of academic advisory council, New York City Police Department; consultant, President's Commission on Campus Unrest, 1970. *Military service:* U.S. Army Reserve, chaplain; became captain. *Member:* Modern Language Association of America, College English Association, American Association of University Professors, American Oxonians, Lotus Club. *Awards, honors:* Kent-Danforth fellow at Oxford

University, 1963-66; American Philosophical Society grant, 1969; American Council of Learned Societies grant, 1970.

WRITINGS: (Editor with Helen Gardner) *John Donne: Selected Prose,* Clarendon Press, 1967; (editor) *John Donne: Ignatius His Conclave,* Clarendon Press, 1969. Contributor to *Saturday Review, New Republic,* and other periodicals.

WORK IN PROGRESS: Editing Book Six of Hooker's *Laws of Ecclesiastical Polity;* editing John Donne's *Devotions,* for Clarendon Press.

BIOGRAPHICAL/CRITICAL SOURCES: Times Literary Supplement, August 17, 1967.†

*   *   *

HEATH, Peter (Lauchlan) 1922-

PERSONAL: Born May 9, 1922, in Milan, Italy; son of Philip George (an underwriter) and Olga (Sinclair) Heath. *Education:* Magdalen College, Oxford, B.A. (honors), 1946. *Home:* 808 Winston Ter., Charlottesville, Va. 22903. *Office:* Department of Philosophy, University of Virginia, Charlottesville, Va. 22901.

CAREER: University of Edinburgh, Edinburgh, Scotland, lecturer in moral philosophy, 1946-58; University of St. Andrews, St. Andrews, Scotland, senior lecturer in logic, 1958-62; University of Virginia, Charlottesville, professor of philosophy, 1962—. Visiting professor, University of Michigan, 1966, 1969. *Military service:* British Army, 1942-45; became captain. *Member:* Lewis Carroll Society of North America (president, 1978), Aristotelian Society, Mind Association, Southern Society for Philosophy, Reform Club (London).

WRITINGS: (Translator) Max Scheler, *The Nature of Sympathy,* Routledge & Kegan Paul, 1954; (translator) Gustav A. Wetter, *Dialectical Materialism,* Routledge & Kegan Paul, 1958; (translator) Martin von Senden, *Space and Sight,* Methuen, 1962; (editor) Augustus De Morgan, *On the Syllogism,* Routledge & Kegan Paul, 1966; (translator) Wetter, *Soviet Ideology Today,* Heinemann, 1966; *The English Parish Clergy on the Eve of the Reformation,* Routledge & Kegan Paul, 1969; (translator with John Lachs) J. G. Fichte, *Science of Knowledge,* Appleton, 1970; (translator) Werner Heisenberg, *Across the Frontiers,* Harper, 1974; (translator) Hans Kelsen, *Essays in Moral and Legal Philosophy,* D. Reidel, 1974; (editor) Lewis Carroll, *The Philosopher's Alice,* St. Martin's, 1974; (translator) Werner Marx, *Hegel's Phenomenology of Spirit,* Harper, 1976; (translator) F.W.J. Schelling, *System of Transcendental Idealism,* University of Virginia Press, 1978. Contributor to encyclopedias and to philosophy journals.

WORK IN PROGRESS: Translating Moritz Schlick's *Philosophical Papers.*

AVOCATIONAL INTERESTS: Music, golf.

*   *   *

HEATON, Herbert 1890-1973

June 6, 1890—January 24, 1973; English-born American professor and historian. Obituaries: *New York Times,* January 26, 1973; *Washington Post,* January 26, 1973; *Publishers Weekly,* February 19, 1973. (See index for *CA* sketch)

*   *   *

HECK, Harold J(oseph) 1906-

PERSONAL: Born January 7, 1906, in Brusly, La.; son of

Henry J. B. and Hortense (Dupont) Heck; married Lydia Suzanne Holt, September 16, 1935; children: Peter M., Henry d'A., Thomas F. *Education:* Louisiana State University, B.A., 1926, M.A., 1931; University of Pennsylvania, M.B.A., 1933; New York University, D.C.S., 1939. *Politics:* Republican. *Religion:* Roman Catholic. *Residence:* Bozman, Md.

CAREER: Employed with Louisiana National Bank, Baton Rouge, La., 1926-32, and Bank of New York, New York, N.Y., 1933-36; University of Notre Dame, Notre Dame, Ind., instructor in finance, 1937-38; St. Joseph's College, Philadelphia, Pa., lecturer in economics and finance, 1938-41; Georgetown University, Washington, D.C., lecturer, 1941-45; Loyola University, New Orleans, La., professor of economics, 1946-47; Tulane University, New Orleans, La., professor of business administration, 1947-57; U.S. Embassy, Paris, France, commercial attache, 1957-62; U.S. Department of Commerce, Washington, D.C., director of International Trade Analysis Division, 1962-64; Georgetown University, School of Foreign Services, professor of international trade, and chairman of department, 1964-71, director of Master of Science in Foreign Service Program, 1970-71; consultant in private practice, 1965—. Fulbright visiting professor of economics at Waseda University, 1952-53, Helsinki School of Economics, 1971, and University of the Americas, 1973. Assistant secretary, Robert Morris Associates, Philadelphia, 1938-41. *Military service:* U.S. Army, 1941-46; became colonel. *Member:* Association for Education in International Business, American Planning Association, American Economic Association, Cosmos Club (Washington, D.C.).

WRITINGS: Foreign Commerce, McGraw, 1953; *Most-Favored-Nation Principle,* Chamber of Commerce of the U.S.A., 1966; *International Business Environment,* American Management Association, 1969; *International Trade,* American Management Association, 1972. Contributor to *World Book Encyclopedia.*†

*   *   *

HEGARTY, Reginald Beaton   1906-1973

August 5, 1906—January 18, 1973; American whaling historian. Obituaries: *New York Times,* January 20, 1973. (See index for *CA* sketch)

*   *   *

HEINE, Ralph W(illiam)   1914-

PERSONAL: Born December 31, 1914, in Elgin, Ill.; son of Louis William (a musician) and Agnes S. (Green) Heine; married Patricke Ann Johns (a sociologist and writer), August 31, 1942; children: Mark W., Karen A., Peter H., Paul R. *Education:* Attended Elgin Junior College, 1933-35; Northwestern University, B.S., 1938, M.S., 1939, graduate study, 1940-42; New York University, graduate study, 1939-40; University of Chicago, Ph.D., 1950; Washington School of Psychiatry, Certificate, 1952. *Home:* 403 Lenawee Dr., Ann Arbor, Mich. 48104.

CAREER: Clinical psychologist for U.S. Central Intelligence Agency, 1946-47, for Veterans Administration in Washington, D.C., 1947-48, in Chicago, Ill., 1948-53, West Side Hospital, Chicago, chief clinical psychologist, 1953-56; Northwestern University, Evanston, Ill., lecturer in psychology, 1955-56; University of Chicago, Chicago, Ill., associate professor of psychology and chief clinical psychologist in department of psychiatry, 1956-65; University of Michigan, Ann Arbor, professor of psychology in departments of

psychiatry and psychology, 1965-78, director, Institute for Human Adjustment, 1974-78. Certified psychologist in State of Illinois, 1964. Consultant to Peace Corps, 1961-65, 1969-70, to municipal courts of Chicago, 1962-65, to National Institute of Mental Health, 1965—. Diplomate in clinical psychology, American Board of Examiners in Professional Psychology, 1953. *Military service:* U.S. Army, 1942-46; became first lieutenant. *Member:* American Psychological Association (fellow), Midwest Psychological Association, Sigma Xi. *Awards, honors:* National Institute of Mental Health senior fellow and honorary research fellow of Manchester University, 1964-65.

WRITINGS: (Co-author) *Assessment of Men,* Rinehart, 1948; (editor and contributor) *The Student Physician as Psychotherapist,* University of Chicago Press, 1962; (editor with Joseph Wepman) *Concepts of Personality,* Aldine, 1963; *Psychotherapy,* Prentice-Hall, 1971.

Author of foreword: Robert Carson, *Interaction Concepts of Personality,* Aldine, 1969; Donald W. Fiske, *Measuring the Concepts of Personality,* Aldine-Atherton, 1971; Patricke J. Heine, *Personality in Social Theory,* Aldine-Atherton, 1971; Salvatore Maddi and Paul T. Costa, *Humanism in Personology,* Aldine-Atherton, 1972. General editor of Aldine-Atherton's "Perspectives on Personality" series. Contributor of more than seventy articles and reviews to encyclopedias and journals. Consulting editor of *Contemporary Psychology,* 1963-69, and *Journal of Abnormal Psychology,* 1964—.

*   *   *

HEINEN, Hubert (Plummer)   1937-

PERSONAL: Born March 5, 1937, in Houston, Tex.; son of Erwin (a certified public accountant and partner in an accounting firm) and Emily (Plummer) Heinen; married Ursula Jakobiak, October 27, 1959; children: Dirk Detlef, Erika, Doris. *Education:* University of Texas, B.A., 1958, Ph.D., 1964; also studied at University of Freiburg, 1958-59. *Politics:* Democrat. *Religion:* Lutheran. *Home:* 4505 Spanish Oak Trail, Austin, Tex. 78731. *Office:* Department of German, University of Texas, Austin, Tex. 78712.

CAREER: University of Pennsylvania, Philadelphia, instructor in German, 1963-64; University of Pittsburgh, Pittsburgh, Pa., assistant professor, 1964-68, associate professor of German, 1968-69; University of Texas at Austin, associate professor of German, 1969—. *Member:* Modern Language Association of America, American Association of Teachers of German, American Association of University Professors, South Central Modern Language Association.

WRITINGS: Die rhythmisch-metrische Gestaltung des Knittelverse bei Hans Folz (title means "The Rhythmic Form of Hans Folz's Rhymed Couplets"), Elwert, 1966; (with Lore Barbara Foltin) *Paths to German Poetry,* Dodd, 1969; (with J. Alan Pfeffer and others) *Grunddeutsch: A Basic German Grammar,* Prentice-Hall, 1973. Contributor to *Kinder Literatur Lexikon, Modern Language Notes, Speculum, Texas Studies in Language and Literature,* and other language journals.

AVOCATIONAL INTERESTS: Scouting, reading detective novels, organic gardening.

*   *   *

HELD, Richard   1922-

PERSONAL: Born October 10, 1922, in New York, N.Y.; son of Lawrence W. and Tessie (Klein) Held; married Doris

Bernays (an elementary counselor and coordinator of pupil personnel service), June 29, 1951. *Education:* Columbia University, B.A., 1943, B.S., 1944; Swarthmore College, M.A., 1948; Harvard University, Ph.D., 1952. *Home:* 102 Appleton St., Cambridge, Mass. 02138. *Office:* Department of Psychology, Massachusetts Institute of Technology, 79 Amherst St., Cambridge, Mass. 02139.

CAREER: Harvard University, Cambridge, Mass., National Institutes of Health post-doctoral fellow, 1952-53; Brandeis University, Waltham, Mass., instructor, 1953-55, assistant professor, 1955-58, associate professor, 1958-61, professor of psychology, 1961-62, chairman of department, 1961-62; National Science Foundation, Washington, D.C., senior research fellow, 1962-63; Massachusetts Institute of Technology, Cambridge, visiting professor, 1962-63, professor of psychology, 1963—, chairman of department, 1978—. Member, Institute for Advanced Study, Princeton University, 1955-56; National Institutes of Health, member of experimental psychology study section, 1964—, chairman, 1966-68; member of committee on vision, National Research Council. *Military service:* U.S. Navy, 1944-46; became lieutenant junior grade.

MEMBER: International Brain Research Organization, American Psychological Association (fellow), American Academy of Arts and Sciences (fellow), American Association for the Advancement of Science (fellow), American Academy of Optometry (fellow), National Academy of Sciences, Psychonomic Society, Society for Neurosciences, Society of Experimental Psychologists, Eastern Psychological Association (director), Sigma Xi.

WRITINGS: Perception: Mechanism and Models, W. H. Freeman, 1972; (author of introduction) *Recent Progress in Perception: Readings from Scientific American,* W. H. Freeman, 1976. Contributor to psychology and vision journals in the United States and abroad . Co-editor of *Psychologische Forschung;* consulting editor of *Perception.*

* * *

HELFRITZ, Hans 1902-

PERSONAL: Born July 25, 1902, in Hilbersdorf, Germany; son of Kurt and Marie Helfritz. *Education:* Studied music and music history at Hochschule fuer Musik, Berlin; also studied at the University of Berlin and the University of Vienna. *Religion:* Evangelical. *Residence:* San Jose, Isla Ibiza, Baleares, Spain.

CAREER: Writer, composer, explorer, and lecturer on his travels; lived in Chile, and has made his headquarters in the Balearic Islands since 1961.

WRITINGS: Unter der Sonne des Orients, Die Buchgemeinde (Berlin), 1931; *Chicago der wueste,* Hobbing, 1932, translation published in *Land without Shade* (see below); *Land ohne schatten,* P. List, 1934, revised edition published as *Arabien: Die Letzten wunder der wueste,* 1934, translation of original edition published in *Land without Shade* (see below); *Land without Shade* (contains translations of *Chicago der wueste* and *Land ohne schatten),* translation by Kenneth Kirkness, Hurst & Blackett, 1935, McBride, 1936; *Geheimnis um Schobua,* Deutsche Verlagsgesellschaft (Berlin), 1935, revised edition published in *Entdeckungsreisen in Suedarabien* (see below); *Vergessnes Suedarabien: Wadis, Hochhaeuser und Beduinen,* Bibliographisches Institut (Leipzig), 1936; *Im urwald von Malaya,* Deutsche Verlagsgesellschaft, 1936; *Ewigkeit und wandel im Fernen Osten,* Deutsche Verlagsgesellschaft, 1936; *Mexiko frueher und heute,* Deutsche Verlagsgesellschaft, 1939.

Im quellgebiet des Amazonas, Safari Verlag, 1942; *Zum weissen Kontinent,* Editorial El Buen Libro (Buenos Aires), 1948.

Im Lande der weisson Cordillere, Safari Verlag, 1952; *Im Lande der Koenigin von Saba,* Brockhaus, 1952; *De Osterinsel,* Fretz & Wasmuth, 1953; *Mexiko und Mittelamerika,* Safari Verlag, 1954, abridged edition published as *Mexiko: Eine Reise durch alte Kulturen und moderne Zivilisation,* Safari Verlag, 1960; *Zwischen Atlantik und Pacifik: Streifzuege durch Zentralamerika,* Beuchergilde Gutenberg, 1956; *Glueckliches Arabien: Abenteurliche Reise zwischen dem Teufel und dem Roten Meer,* Fretz & Wasmuth, 1956, translation by M. Heron published as *The Yemen: A Secret Journey,* Allen & Unwin, 1958, revised German edition published in *Entdeckungsreisen in Suedarabien* (see below); *Durchs Reich der Sonnengoetter* (youth book), Benziger Verlag (Zurich), 1957; *Schwarze Ritter zwischen Niger und Tschad,* Safari Verlag, 1958; *Belearen: Mallorca, Menorca, Ibiza, Formentera,* Fretz & Wasmuth, 1959.

Kanarische Inseln, Fretz & Wasmuth, 1961, translation published as *Canary Islands,* Fretz & Wasmuth, 1963; *Chile,* Fretz & Wasmuth, 1961; *Zentralamerika: Die Laenderbruecke im karibischen Raum,* Safari Verlag, 1963; *Amerika: Land der Inka, Maya und Azteken,* Ueberreuter, 1965; *Die Goetterburgen Mexikos: Ein Reisefuehrer zur Kunst Alt-Mexikos,* DuMont Schauberg, 1968; *Mexiko: Land der drei Kulturen,* Safari Verlag, 1968, translation published as *Mexican Cities of the Gods: An Archaeological Guide,* Praeger, 1970.

Ethiopie: Musique de tous les temps (with recording of Ethiopian music), Harmonia Mundi, 1970; *Aethiopien, Kunst im Verborgenen,* Verlag Dumont Schauberg, 1972; *Suedamerika: praekolumbische Hochkulturen,* Verlag Dumont Schauberg, 1973; *Indonesien: Java, Sumatra, Bali und Sulawesi,* Verlag Dumont Schauberg, 1977; *Guatemala, Honduras, Belize: die versunkene Welt der Maya,* Verlag Dumont Schauberg, 1977; *Entdeckungsreisen in Suedarabien* (contains revised editions of *Geheimnis um Schobua* and *Glueckliches Arabien),* Verlag Dumont Schauberg, 1977. Composer of numerous works for instrument and orchestra.

* * *

HELLER, Peter 1920-

PERSONAL: Born January 11, 1920, in Vienna, Austria; naturalized U.S. citizen; son of John (a businessman) and Margarete (Steiner) Heller; married Katrina Ely Burlingham, 1944 (divorced, 1951); married Christiane Menzel, August 20, 1951; children: (first marriage) Anne; (second marriage) Joan Heller Humphreys, Vivian, Stephen, Eve. *Education:* McGill University, Licentiate of Music and B.A., 1944; Columbia University, M.A., 1945, Ph.D., 1951. *Home:* 280 Brompton Rd., Williamsville, N.Y. 14221. *Office:* Department of Modern Languages, Clemens Hall, State University of New York, Buffalo, N.Y. 14260.

CAREER: Columbia University, New York, N.Y., instructor in German, 1948-51; Harvard University, Cambridge, Mass., instructor in German, 1951-54; University of Massachusetts—Amherst, associate professor, 1954-59, professor of German, 1959-61, Commonwealth Professor, 1961-68; State University of New York at Buffalo, professor of German and comparative literature, 1968—, head of German department, 1968-71. *Member:* Modern Language Association of America. *Awards, honors:* Fulbright research grants for study in Germany, 1954-56.

WRITINGS: (With F. C. Ellert) *German One,* Heath,

1962; (contributor) *Masterpieces of Western Literature*, W. C. Brown, 1966; *Dialectics and Nihilism: Essays on Lessing, Nietzsche, Mann, and Kafka*, University of Massachusetts Press, 1966; (with Edith Ehrlich) *German Fiction and Prose*, Macmillan, 1967; (with Ehrlich and J. Schaefer) *German Essays and Expository Prose*, Macmillan, 1969; (contributor) *Franz Kafka: His Place in World Literature*, Texas Tech University Press, 1971; (contributor) *Benn-Wirkung Wider Willen*, Athenaeum (Frankfort), 1971; *Von den Ersten und Letzten Dingen*, De Gruyter (Berlin), 1972; *Prosa in Versen* (poetry), Blaeschke, 1974; *Menschentiere* (poetry), Lyrik und Prosa, 1975; *Probleme der Zivilisation*, Bourier, 1978; *Emigrantenlitaneien* (poetry), Blaeschke, 1978. Contributor to *Encyclopaedia Britannica*. Contributor of articles and reviews to *German Life and Letters, Lyrica Germanica, Germanic Review, Massachusetts Review, Modern Language Forum, Malahat Review*, and other publications.

WORK IN PROGRESS: A book, *Studies on Nietzsche;* a volume of essays on German literature; an autobiographical volume; a volume of short stories.

*　　*　　*

HELLER, Robert   1899(?)-1973

1899(?)—January 22, 1973; American management engineer, efficiency expert, and authority on reorganization of Congress. Obituaries: *New York Times*, January 24, 1973.

*　　*　　*

HELLMAN, C(larisse) Doris   1910-1973

August 28, 1910—March 28, 1973; American historian and educator. Obituaries: *New York Times,* March 29, 1973.

*　　*　　*

HELMER, John   1946-

PERSONAL: Born March 6, 1946, in Melbourne, Australia; married Margaret Santi (an actress); children: Jason. *Education:* University of Melbourne, B.A. (first class honors), 1967; Harvard University, A.M., 1970, Ph.D., 1972.

CAREER: Harvard University, Cambridge, Mass., research associate at Institute of Politics, beginning 1973. *Member:* American Sociological Association, Harvard Club of New York City.

WRITINGS: (Editor with Neil A. Eddington) *Urbanman: The Psychology of Urban Survival*, Free Press, 1973; *Bringing the War Home: The American Soldier in Vietnam and After*, Free Press, 1973; *The Deadly Simple Mechanics of Society*, Seabury, 1974; (with Thomas Vietorisz) *Drug Use, the Labor Market, and Class Conflict*, Drug Abuse Council, 1974; *Drugs and Minority Oppression*, Seabury, 1975. Contributor to professional journals. Former associate editor of *Esquire;* editorial consultant to *Fortune.*†

*　　*　　*

HENDERSON, Charles P(ackard), Jr.   1941-

PERSONAL: Born May 10, 1941, in Youngstown, Ohio; son of Charles P. (a judge) and Margaret (Arms) Henderson; married Jane Pataky (a hospital chaplain), May 28, 1966; children: Andrew, Kirsten. *Education:* Princeton University, A.B. (cum laude), 1963; Union Theological Seminary, New York, M.Div., 1966. *Home:* 136 East 64th St., New York, N.Y. 10021. *Office:* Central Presbyterian Church, 593 Park Ave., New York, N.Y. 10021.

CAREER: Ordained minister of Presbyterian Church, 1966; First Presbyterian Church, Hoboken, N.J., minister, 1966-69; Princeton University, Princeton, N.J., assistant dean of the chapel, 1969-73; Noroton Presbyterian Church, Darien, Conn., associate minister, 1973-76; Central Presbyterian Church, New York, N.Y., senior minister, 1977—. Specialist and consultant to National Student Volunteers Program, ACTION, Washington, D.C., 1971—. Visiting lecturer at Princeton University, 1971, 1972. Member of board of directors, Union Theological Seminary, 1972—. *Member:* National Association of College and University Chaplains.

WRITINGS: Student Volunteers/A Manual for Communities, U.S. Government, 1971; *The Nixon Theology*, Harper, 1972. Contributor to *Nation, New York Times, New York Law Forum, Commonweal, Princeton Seminary Bulletin, New World Outlook,* and *Christian Century.*

*　　*　　*

HENDERSON, Dwight F.   1937-

PERSONAL: Born August 14, 1937, in Austin, Tex.; son of Ottis Franklin (an engineer) and Leona (Bradford) Henderson; married Connie Chorlton (an artist), December 24, 1966; children: Patricia Ross. *Education:* University of Texas, B.A., 1959, M.A., 1961, Ph.D., 1966. *Politics:* Democrat. *Religion:* Unitarian Universalist. *Home:* 1730 Kensington Blvd., Fort Wayne, Ind. 46805. *Office:* Division of Arts and Letters, Indiana University, 2101 Coliseum Blvd. E., Fort Wayne, Ind. 46805.

CAREER: Indiana University at Fort Wayne, associate professor of history and dean of Division of Arts and Letters, 1966—. *Military service:* U.S. Army, 1962-64; became captain. *Member:* Organization of American Historians, Southern Historical Association.

WRITINGS: (Editor) *Private Journals of Georgiana Gholson Walker, 1862-1865, with Selections from the Post War Years, 1865-1876*, Confederate Publishing, 1963; *Courts for a New Nation*, Public Affairs Press, 1971. Contributor to history journals.

WORK IN PROGRESS: Jeffersonian Courts.

*　　*　　*

HENDERSON, Nancy   1943-

PERSONAL: Born September 19, 1943, in Clinton, Iowa; daughter of Lyle Louis (head of advertising for a woodwork firm) and Bernadine (Peterson) Sodeman; married Bill Henderson (a writer under pseudonym Luke Walton, and editor), December 23, 1967. *Education:* Bryn Mawr College, B.A. (summa cum laude), 1969; graduate study at Princeton University. *Residence:* Yonkers, N.Y. *Agent:* Philip G. Spitzer, 111-25 76th Ave., Forest Hills, N.Y. 11375. *Office:* College Division, W. W. Norton & Co., 55 Fifth Ave., New York, N.Y. 10003.

CAREER: Editorial assistant in College Division, W. W. Norton & Co. (publishers), New York, N.Y. *Awards, honors:* Award from New Jersey Teachers of English for *Out of the Curtained World.*

WRITINGS: Out of the Curtained World: The Story of an American Nun Who Left the Convent, Doubleday, 1972.

WORK IN PROGRESS: Short fiction; a study of central themes of Christianity; research on frequently-used expressions in American English.†

HENDIN, David (Bruce) 1945-

PERSONAL: Born December 16, 1945, in St. Louis, Mo.; son of Aaron (a physician) and Lillian (Karsh) Hendin; married Sandra Levine, May 16, 1968; children: Sarah Tsvia, Benjamin Judah. *Education:* University of Missouri, B.S., 1967, M.A., 1970. *Religion:* Jewish. *Home address:* P.O. Box 630, West Haverstraw, N.Y. 10993. *Agent:* Russell & Volkening, Inc., 551 Fifth Ave., New York, N.Y. 10017. *Office:* United Feature Syndicate and Newspaper Enterprise Association, 200 Park Ave., New York, N.Y. 10017.

CAREER: Mollie Goodman High School, Ashkelon, Israel, biology teacher, 1967-68; United Feature Syndicate and Newspaper Enterprise Association, New York, N.Y., 1970—, currently vice-president and executive editor. Clinical instructor, University of Missouri graduate journalism program, 1971—; part-time lecturer, Columbia University School of Journalism, 1975-76. Consultant in the humanities at Institute of Neuroscience, St. Barnabas Hospital. Advisor, Thanatology Foundation; editorial consultant, American Friends of the Israel Museum. *Member:* Holy Land Conservation Fund (member of board of directors), Council for the Advancement of Science Writing (member of board of directors), Kappa Tau Alpha. *Awards, honors:* Claude Bernard Science Journalism Award from the National Society for Medical Research, 1972; American Association of Blood Banks award of merit, 1972; American Academy of Family Physicians certificate of commendation, 1973; American Medical Association medical journalism award, 1973; Blakeslee Award, American Heart Association, 1973; American Medical Writers Association Book of the Year Award, 1977, for *The Life Givers*.

WRITINGS: Everything You Need to Know about Abortion, Pinnacle, 1971; (editor) *Acupuncture: What Can It Do for You?*, Award Books, 1972; (with Aileen Claire) *Doctor's Save Your Heart Diet*, Award Books, 1972; *Save Your Child's Life*, Enterprise Publications, 1972; *Death as a Fact of Life*, Norton, 1973; *The Life Givers*, Morrow, 1975; (with Herb Kreindler) *Guide to Ancient Jewish Coins*, Attic, 1975; *The World Almanac Whole Health Guide*, New American Library, 1977; *Collecting Coins*, New American Library, 1978; (with Joan Marks) *The Genetic Connection: How to Protect Your Family against Genetic Disease*, Morrow, 1978. Author of syndicated column, "The Medical Consumer," 1973-77; author of column "Coins of Ancient Israel," *Shekel* (journal of the American Israel Numismatic Association), 1976—. Contributor to *The World Almanac*. Contributor of articles to *Saturday Review, Family Circle, Reader's Digest, Science Digest, Medical Opinion, Quill*, and other periodicals. Member of editorial board, American Israel Numismatic Association.

WORK IN PROGRESS: A book on coins of Biblical times and a novel set in the ancient Near East.

SIDELIGHTS: David Hendin lectures at schools and colleges. He has appeared on radio and television programs including "The Today Show" and "NBC Monitor." His book *Save Your Child's Life* has been translated into Spanish.

BIOGRAPHICAL/CRITICAL SOURCES: Best Sellers, February 1, 1973; *New York Times Book Review*, February 25, 1973; *Nation*, April 23, 1973; *Publishers Weekly*, October 8, 1973.

* * *

HENDRICKS, J(ames) Edwin 1935-

PERSONAL: Born October 19, 1935, in Pickens County, S.C.; son of Jim Ed and Cassie (Looper) Hendricks; married Sue James (a counselor), June 28, 1958; children: James, Christopher, Lee. *Education:* Furman University, B.A., 1957; University of Virginia, M.A., 1959, Ph.D., 1961. *Politics:* Democrat. *Religion:* Baptist. *Residence:* Winston-Salem, N.C. *Office:* Department of History, Wake Forest University, Winston-Salem, N.C. 27109.

CAREER: Wake Forest University, Winston-Salem, N.C., assistant professor, 1961-66, associate professor, 1966-75, professor of history, 1975—, director of Historic Preservation Program. Consultant on historic restoration; director of Historic Bethabara, Inc., and of Historic Winston, Inc.; chairman, Winston-Salem Historic Districts Commission. *Military service:* U.S. Army Reserve, 1957-65. *Awards, honors:* R. J. Reynolds research leave, 1971-72.

WRITINGS: (With C. C. Pearson) *Liquor and Anti-Liquor in Virginia, 1619-1919*, Duke University Press, 1967; (contributor of bibliographic supplement) D. H. Gilpatrick, *Jeffersonian Democracy in North Carolina*, revised edition, Octagon, 1967; (contributor) B. G. Gokhale, editor, *Images of India*, Popular Prakashan, 1971; (contributor) John B. Boles, editor, *America: The Middle Period*, University Press of Virginia, 1973; *The Franklin House*, Surry County Historical Society, 1974; (editor) *Some Trees from the Forest*, Wake Forest University, 1975; (editor and contributor) *Forsyth: The History of a County on the March*, University of North Carolina Press, 1976; (contributor) E. M. Teagarden, editor, *Essays on the History of Myths and Legends*, University of South Dakota Press, 1977. Contributor of articles and reviews to *Journal of Southern History, Winston-Salem Journal, North Carolina Historical Review, Research Studies, Pennsylvania Magazine of History and Biography*, and other periodicals.

WORK IN PROGRESS: A biography of Charles Thomson, 1729-1824, secretary of the Continental Congress.

SIDELIGHTS: J. Edwin Hendricks told *CA:* "I firmly believe that academic historians fail unless they 'people the past.' This can best be done with a fine blending of research in primary sources, secondary writings, and a careful examination of the . . . artifacts relating to the subject. Only then can the historian accomplish his task."

* * *

HENNEDY, Hugh L(ouis) 1929-

PERSONAL: Born September 17, 1929, in Boston, Mass.; son of John F. (a salesman) and Geraldine (Barcelo) Hennedy; married Doris Antonellis (a registered nurse), August 15, 1953; children: Hugh, Elizabeth, Constance, John. *Education:* University of Notre Dame, B.A., 1951; Columbia University, M.A., 1956; Boston University, Ph.D., 1966. *Address:* Biddeford Pool, Me. 04006. *Office:* Department of English, St. Francis College, 605 Pool Rd., Biddeford, Me. 04005.

CAREER: St. Francis College, Biddeford, Me., instructor, 1955-60, associate professor, 1960-66, professor of English, 1966—, chairman of Division of Humanities, 1961-63, and 1968-69. *Military service:* U.S. Army, 1952-54. *Member:* Modern Language Association of America, Mediaeval Academy of America, Shakespeare Association of America, American Association of University Professors, American Civil Liberties Union.

WRITINGS: Unity in Barsetshire, Mouton, 1971. Contributor to *Chaucer Review, Commonweal, Studies in the Novel*, and *Eire-Ireland*.

WORK IN PROGRESS: Research on *King Lear,* Chaucer's "Man of Law's Tale," and Joyce's *Portrait of the Artist as a Young Man.*†

* * *

HENSLEY, Charles S(tanley) 1919-

PERSONAL: Born March 8, 1919, in East St. Louis, Ill.; son of Frank Lee and Muriel Joy (Blackburn) Hensley. *Education:* Washington University, St. Louis, Mo., A.B., 1942, A.M., 1943; Columbia University, graduate study, 1945-47; University of Missouri, Ph.D., 1958. *Politics:* Democrat. *Religion:* Episcopalian. *Home:* 10650 South Hoyne, Chicago, Ill. 60643. *Office:* Department of English, E-357, Chicago State University, Chicago, Ill. 60628.

CAREER: University of Minnesota, Minneapolis, instructor in English, 1947-50; Harris Teachers College, St. Louis, Mo., assistant professor of English, 1950-60; Southern Illinois University, Alton Center, Carbondale, associate professor of English, 1960-63; Humboldt State Teachers College (now Humboldt State University), Arcata, Calif., assistant professor of English, 1963-65; Stanislaus State College (now California State College, Stanislaus), Turlock, Calif., assistant professor of English, 1965-68; Chicago State University, Chicago, Ill., associate professor, 1968-71, professor of English, 1971—. Lecturer at Washington University, St. Louis, Mo., 1948-51. *Member:* Modern Language Association of America, Renaissance Society of America, English Speaking Union, National Council of Teachers of English, College English Association, Eta Sigma Phi, Lambda Iota Tau.

WRITINGS: The Later Career of George Wither, Mouton, 1969; (with Rosemary Freeman) *Introduction, Wither: A Collection of Emblemce,* University of South Carolina Press, 1973. Contributor to *LIT, Ariel,* and *Seventeenth Century News.*

WORK IN PROGRESS: Student's Guide: How To Read and Enjoy Shakespeare; studying Flemish literary engravings of the seventeenth century.

AVOCATIONAL INTERESTS: Violin, piano, opera, chamber music.†

* * *

HENSLIN, James Marvin 1937-

PERSONAL: Born February 5, 1937, in Roseau, Minn.; son of Marvin (a business entrepreneur) and Lucille (Kruger) Henslin; married Linda Kuntz, December 20, 1972; children: (previous marriage) Stephanie Helen, James Marvin, Jr., Greta Anne; (second marriage) Paul Michael. *Education:* Concordia Senior College, Ft. Wayne, Ind., B.A., 1959; Concordia Seminary, St. Louis, Mo., B.D., 1962; Washington University, St. Louis, Mo., M.A., 1966, Ph.D., 1967. *Religion:* "A charismatic Christian." *Home:* 2403 College, Alton, Ill. 62002. *Office:* Department of Sociology, Southern Illinois University, Edwardsville, Ill. 62025.

CAREER: Pastor of Lutheran churches in Oregon, 1962-64; University of Missouri—St. Louis, instructor, 1964-66, assistant professor of sociology, 1966-67; Southern Illinois University at Edwardsville, assistant professor, 1968-72, associate professor, 1972-75, professor of sociology, 1975—. A founder and director of Suicide Prevention Services in Madison and St. Clair counties, Ill. *Member:* American Sociological Association, American Society of Criminology, Society for the Scientific Study of Social Problems. *Awards, honors:* National Institute of Mental Health postdoctoral fellowship to study family response to suicide, 1967-68.

WRITINGS: (Editor) *Studies in the Sociology of Sex,* Appleton, 1971, 2nd edition, 1979; *Down to Earth Sociology,* Free Press, 1972, 2nd edition, 1976; (editor with Larry T. Reynolds) *Social Problems in American Society,* Holbrook, 1973, 2nd edition, 1976; (editor with Reynolds) *American Society,* McKay, 1973; (editor with James R. Hayes) *Introducing Anthropology,* Holbrook, 1975; *Introducing Sociology,* with student guide, Free Press, 1975; (editor) *Introducing Sociology: Selected Readings,* Free Press, 1975; (editor) *Deviant Life-Styles,* Transaction Books, 1977.

WORK IN PROGRESS: Research on drug dealers, gerontological sexual adaptation, and menarche.

SIDELIGHTS: Some of James Marvin Henslin's writings have been translated into German and Spanish.

* * *

HENTHORN, William E(llsworth) 1928-

PERSONAL: Born July 10, 1928, in Cincinnati, Ohio; son of William J. (a merchant) and Anna (Linden) Henthorn; married Taesoon Lee (in real estate), October 28, 1960; children: William Lee, Alexander Lee. *Education:* University of California, Berkeley, B.A., 1957; University of Leiden, A.B., and M.A., 1962, Ph.D., 1963.

CAREER: Resided in Korea, 1957-61, where he studied, taught, and operated a translation service; Princeton University, Princeton, N.J., assistant professor of Oriental languages, 1966-69; University of Hawaii, Honolulu, senior fellow of Institute of Advanced Projects at East-West Center, 1969-70, associate researcher at Social Science Research Institute, beginning 1970. *Military service:* U.S. Merchant Marine, 1943-48; U.S. Air Force, 1948-56.

WRITINGS: Korea: The Mongol Invasions, E. J. Brill, 1963; *A History of Korea,* Free Press, 1971. Contributor to encyclopedias; contributor of about twenty articles on Korea to scholarly journals.

* * *

HERBERGER, Charles F. 1920-

PERSONAL: Born February 29, 1920, in Ilion, N.Y.; son of Charles Frederick (an executive) and Florence L. (Hunt) Herberger; married Melvina Crosby, August 10, 1946; children: Melvina (Mrs. John S. Brock). *Education:* Dartmouth College, A.B., 1942; University of Cincinnati, M.A., 1948; Boston University, Ph.D., 1960. *Home:* R.F.D. 1, Alfred, Me. 04002. *Office:* Department of English, Nasson College, Springvale, Me. 04083.

CAREER: University of Cincinnati, Cincinnati, Ohio, instructor in English, 1948-50; Framingham State College, Framingham, Mass., instructor in English, 1952; Colby Junior College, New London, N.H., instructor in English, 1953; Wayne State University, Detroit, Mich., instructor in English, 1954-58; Nasson College, Springvale, Me., professor of English, 1958—, director of College Study Abroad Program in Vienna, Austria, 1971, 1974, and 1976. Visiting professor, Deree College, 1977. Has done research in prehistory in Crete, Greece, Italy, and Great Britain. *Military service:* U.S. Navy, 1942-46; later commander in U.S. Naval Reserve. *Member:* American Association of University Professors, Gamma Delta Chi.

WRITINGS: The Thread of Ariadne: The Labyrinth of the Calendar of Minos, Philosophical Library, 1972; *The Riddle of the Sphinx: Calendric Symbolism in Myth and Icon,* Vantage, 1978. Also author of plays: The Back of Your Neck," produced at Little Theatre, Sanford, Me., 1965, and "Shadrach, Meshach, and Abendego," produced at Nasson College Theatre, 1966. Contributor to *Deree College Review.*

WORK IN PROGRESS: "Paradise Glossed," a play.

* * *

HERFINDAHL, Orris C(lemens) 1918-1972

PERSONAL: Born June 15, 1918, in Parshall, N.D.; son of Henry (a retailer) and Cecil (Swanson) Herfindahl; married Anna Marie Rogers, August 25, 1940; children: Anne (Mrs. William Sare), Henry, Cynthia, Erika. *Education:* University of Minnesota, B.B.A., 1939; Columbia University, Ph.D., 1950. *Religion:* Protestant. *Home:* 902 Madison Lane, Falls Church, Va. 22046. *Office:* Resources for the Future, Inc., 1755 Massachusetts Ave. N.W., Washington, D.C. 20036.

CAREER: University of Illinois (now University of Illinois at Urbana-Champaign), assistant professor of economics, 1948-51; U.S. Bureau of Mines, Washington, D.C., economist, 1951-53; Committee for Economic Development, Washington, D.C., economist, 1953-56; Resources for the Future, Inc., Washington, D.C., economist, 1956-72. *Military service:* U.S. Navy, 1943-46. *Member:* American Economic Association, Econometric Society, Royal Economic Society.

WRITINGS: Copper Costs and Prices: 1870-1957, Johns Hopkins Press, 1959; *Three Studies in Mineral Economics,* Resources for the Future, 1961; (with Allen Kneese) *Quality of the Environment,* Resources for the Future, 1965; *Natural Resource Information for Economic Development,* Johns Hopkins Press, 1969; (with Kneese) *Introduction to the Economic Theory of Natural Resources Use: With Illustrative Applications,* C. E. Merrill, 1973; David B. Brooks, editor, *Resource Economics: Selected Works of Orris C. Herfindahl,* Johns Hopkins Press, 1974. Contributor to professional journals.

WORK IN PROGRESS: Studies in Mineral Economics.

SIDELIGHTS: Orris C. Herfindahl traveled and worked in Latin America, and was traveling in Nepal when he died.†

(Died December 16, 1972)

* * *

HERLIHY, David 1930-

PERSONAL: Born May 8, 1930, in San Francisco, Calif.; son of Maurice Peter (a workingman) and Irene (O'Connor) Herlihy; married Patricia McGahey (a professor), 1952; children: Maurice, Christopher, David, Felix, Gregory, Irene. *Education:* University of San Francisco, B.A., 1952; Catholic University of America, M.A., 1953; Yale University, Ph.D., 1956. *Home:* Mather House, Harvard University, Cambridge, Mass. 02138. *Office:* Department of History, Harvard University, Cambridge, Mass. 02138.

CAREER: Bryn Mawr College, Bryn Mawr, Pa., assistant professor, 1955-62, associate professor of history, 1962-64; University of Wisconsin—Madison, professor of history, 1964-72, William F. Allen Professor of History, 1970-72; Harvard University, Cambridge, Mass., professor of history, 1972—. Lecturer at Swarthmore College, 1958, 1963, and Princeton University, 1964; associate director of studies, Ecole Pratique des Hautes Etudes, Paris, France, 1969-70.

MEMBER: American Historical Association, Mediaeval Academy of America (fellow), American Catholic Historical Association (president, 1970-71), Economic History Association, Italian Historical Society of America, Agricultural History Society, American Numismatic Society, Midwest Medieval Conference (president, 1970-71). *Awards, honors:* Fulbright fellow in Italy, 1954-55; Guggenheim fellow, 1961-62; American Council of Learned Societies fellowship, 1966-67; fellow of Center for Advanced Research in the Behavioral Sciences, 1971-72.

WRITINGS: Pisa in the Early Renaissance: A Study of Urban Growth, Yale University Press, 1958; (contributor) *Finances et comptabilite urbaines du XIIIe au XVIe siecle,* Pro Civitate, 1964; (contributor) Kenneth M. Setton and Henry R. Winkler, editors, *Great Problems in European Civilization,* Prentice-Hall, 1966; *Medieval and Renaissance Pistoia: The Social History of an Italian Town,* Yale University Press, 1967; (contributor) Nicolai Rubinstein, editor, *Florentine Studies: Politics and Society in Renaissance Florence,* Faber, 1968; *Medieval Culture and Society,* Harper, 1968; (editor with Robert S. Lopez and Vsevolod Slessarev) *Economy, Society, and Government in Medieval Italy,* Kent State University Press, 1969; *The History of Feudalism,* Harper, 1970; *Women in Medieval Society* (Smith lecture), University of St. Thomas, 1971; (contributor) Jacob Price and Val Lorwin, editors, *The Dimensions of the Past,* Yale University Press, 1972; (contributor) Frank Johnson, editor, *Alienation: Concept, Term, and Meaning,* Academic Press, 1973; (with Mortimer Chambers, Theodore K. Rabb, Raymond Grew, and Isser Woloch) *The Western Experience,* two volumes, Knopf, 1974. Contributor of more than thirty articles to history journals. Current or former member of editorial boards of *Catholic Historical Review, Historical Methods Newsletter, Journal of Economic History, Journal of Interdisciplinary History,* and *Speculum.*

WORK IN PROGRESS: Second edition of *The Western Experience;* translating *Les Toscans et leurs familles* into English with Christiane Klapisch.

* * *

HERMAN, Charlotte 1937-

PERSONAL: Born June 10, 1937, in Chicago, Ill.; daughter of Harry (a mattress manufacturer) and Leah (Kossof) Baran; married Melvin Herman (an attorney), January 27, 1957; children: Sharon, Michael, Deborah, Karen. *Education:* Attended University of Illinois, 1955-57; Roosevelt University, B.A., 1960. *Residence:* Lincolnwood, Ill.

CAREER: Teacher in the public schools of Chicago, Ill., 1960-63. Member of Children's Reading Round Table and Off-Campus Writers' Workshop. *Member:* Authors Guild, Society of Midland Authors. *Awards, honors:* Society of Midland Authors Children's Book Award for *Our Snowman Had Olive Eyes.*

WRITINGS—Juvenile: *String Bean,* J. Philip O'Hara, 1972; *The Three of Us,* J. Philip O'Hara, 1973; *The Difference of Ari Stein,* Harper, 1976; *You've Come a Long Way Sybil MacIntosh,* Lamplight, 1977; *Our Snowman Had Olive Eyes,* Dutton, 1977.

WORK IN PROGRESS: Picture books, including *On the Way to the Movies,* for Dutton, completion expected in 1980.

SIDELIGHTS: Charlotte Herman told *CA:* "A skinny childhood prompted the writing of my first book, *String Bean,* and I have been writing ever since. It seems that as my children get older, I write for an older audience, though I still love to do picture books."

HERMAN, Marguerite Shalett   1914-1977

PERSONAL: Born October 12, 1914, in Minneapolis, Minn.; daughter of Benjamin (a surgeon) and Sarah (an insurance agent; maiden name, Yager) Shalett; married Lewis Herman (a writer, director, and producer), March 17, 1940 (died April 6, 1966); children: Stephanie (Mrs. David M. Verharst), Judith, Helmar. *Education:* Attended University of Minnesota, 1932-33, 1934-35, and University of Pennsylvania, 1933-34. *Home address:* P.O. Box 433, Tujunga, Calif. 91042. *Office address:* Rescue Breathing Film Associates, P.O. Box 433, Tujunga, Calif. 91042.

CAREER: Professional play reader in Minneapolis and St. Paul, Minn., 1930-38; radio actress (appearing on such programs as "Ma Perkins," "Arnold Grimm's Daughter," "Bachelor's Children," "Guiding Light," and "This Is Your Life"), 1938-43; Rescue Breathing Film Associates, Tujunga, Calif., owner, 1962-77. *Member:* American Federation of Television and Radio Artists, Mensa. *Awards, honors:* "Rescue Breathing" received awards from Educational Film Library Association, Columbus Film Festival, and National Safety Council, all in 1958; "Poletop Rescue Breathing with Closed Chest Heart Massage" received awards from Columbus Film Festival and Vancouver International Film Festival in 1962; American Institute of Graphic Arts chose *The Cornucopia* as one of the fifty best books published in the United States for 1973.

WRITINGS: (With husband, Lewis Herman) *Manual of Foreign Dialects for Radio, Stage, and Screen,* Ziff-Davis, 1943, new edition, Theatre Arts, 1973; (with Lewis Herman) *Talk American: A Practical Guide for Eliminating a German Accent,* Ziff-Davis, 1944; (with Lewis Herman) *Manual of American Dialects for Radio, Stage, Screen, and Television,* Ziff-Davis, 1947, new edition, Theatre Arts, 1959; (with daughter, Judith Herman) *The Cornucopia: A Kitchen Entertainment and Cookbook, 1390-1899,* Harper, 1973. Writer of scripts for "Tapestry of Life," a radio serial, 1939; writer, director, and producer, with Lewis Herman, of films: "Rescue Breathing," 1958, and "Poletop Rescue Breathing with Closed Chest Heart Massage," 1962. Contributor to *Mensa Journal.*†

(Died January 3, 1977)

*   *   *

HERMAND, Jost   1930-

PERSONAL: Born April 11, 1930, in Kassel, Germany; son of Heinz and Annelies (Hucke) Hermand; married Elisabeth Jagenburg, 1956. *Education:* University of Marburg, D.Phil., 1955. *Home:* 845 Terry Pl., Madison, Wis. 53711. *Office:* Department of German, University of Wisconsin, Madison, Wis. 53706.

CAREER: Free-lance writer, 1955-58; University of Wisconsin—Madison, assistant professor, 1958-61, associate professor, 1961-63, professor of German, 1963-67, Vilas Research Professor of German, 1967—. Visiting professor at Harvard University, Free University of West Berlin, University of Bremen, and University of Texas. *Awards, honors:* American Council of Learned Societies fellowship, 1963.

WRITINGS: (With Richard Hamann) *Deutsche Kunst und Kultur,* five volumes, Akademie, 1959-75; *Von Mainz nach Weimar,* Metzler, 1969; *Pop International,* Athenaeum (Frankfurt), 1971; *Unbequeme Literatur,* Stiehm, 1971; *Der Schein des schoenen Lebens,* Athenaeum, 1972; *Streitobjekt Heine,* Fischer Atheneum, 1975; *Der fruehe Heine,* Wink-

ler, 1976; *Stile, Ismen, Etiketten,* Athenaeum (Frankfurt), 1978. Co-editor, *Basis, Monatschefte,* and *Brecht-Yearbook.*

WORK IN PROGRESS: Research on the culture of the Weimar republic.

*   *   *

HERNADI, Paul   1936-

PERSONAL: Born November 9, 1936, in Budapest, Hungary; son of Lajos (a concert pianist) and Zsuzsanna (Fueredi) Hernadi; married Virginia Tucker (a music teacher), August 18, 1964; children: Charles, Christopher. *Education:* Attended University of Budapest, 1955-56; University of Vienna, Ph.D., 1963; Yale University, Ph.D., 1967. *Home:* 1422 East College St., Iowa City, Iowa 52240. *Office:* Department of Comparative Literature, University of Iowa, Iowa City, Iowa 52242.

CAREER: Drama critic and book reviewer for newspapers in Vienna, Austria, 1963; Colorado College, Colorado Springs, Colo., assistant professor of German, 1967-69; University of Rochester, Rochester, N.Y., associate professor of German and of comparative literature, 1969-75; University of Iowa, Iowa City, professor of English and comparative literature, 1975—. *Member:* Modern Language Association of America, American Comparative Literature Association, Midwest Modern Language Association.

WRITINGS: Beyond Genre: New Directions in Literary Classification, Cornell University Press, 1972; (editor) *What Is Literature?,* Indiana University Press, 1978. Contributor to journals in the United States and Europe.

WORK IN PROGRESS: Work on literary theory, on modern drama, and on Goethe's *Faust.*

*   *   *

HERPEL, George L(loyd)   1921-

PERSONAL: Born August 31, 1921, in St. Louis, Mo.; son of George M. and Irene (Lloyd) Herpel; married June L. Stamm, November 22, 1946; children: John, Mark. *Education:* Vanderbilt University, B.A., 1942; St. Louis University, M.B.A., 1954, Ph.D., 1958. *Religion:* Protestant. *Home:* 9 Single Lane, Wallingford, Pa. 19086. *Office:* School of Business, Temple University, Philadelphia, Pa. 19122.

CAREER: C. V. Mosby Publishing Co., St. Louis, Mo., general sales manager and director of public relations, 1948-54; International Shoe Co. (now Interco), St. Louis, director of management development and planning, 1954-62; Temple University, Philadelphia, Pa., professor of marketing, 1962—, chairman of department, 1962-67; Syracuse University, Graduate School of Sales Management and Marketing, Syracuse, N.Y., dean of faculty, 1964—. Visiting professor at Washington University, St. Louis, 1949, and St. Louis University, 1958-62. Former member of the board and corporate secretary of Chemtech Corp., St. Louis, 1960-62; member of Philadelphia Regional Export Expansion Council, U.S. Department of Commerce, 1966; president of Hedgerow Theatre Corp. (a non-profit theatre and drama school), 1971—; director of W. A. Krueger Co., Scottsdale, Ariz., 1971—. Former vocational counselor for American Red Cross; training chairman for United Fund of St. Louis; advisor for World Congress of Marketing, New York, 1965. *Military service:* U.S. Naval Reserve, 1942-46; became lieutenant. *Member:* American Marketing Association (president of St. Louis chapter, 1959-60; member of national board of directors, 1961-65; national vice-president, 1963-65), Sales and Marketing Executives (St. Louis chapter, member of board of directors, 1951-62; president, 1955-56; member of national board of directors, 1955-64), American Management Association, American Society of Training Directors, American Society of International Executives (corporate secretary to board of directors, 1976—), Society for Advancement of Management, Institute of Management Science, St. Louis Convention Bureau (member of board of directors), Philadelphia Sales and Marketing Executives (member of board of directors and of executive committee), Pi Sigma Epsilon (member of national board of directors, 1962-68).

WRITINGS: Specialty Advertising in Marketing, Dow Jones-Irwin, 1972; (contributor) Vic Buell, editor, *Handbook of Modern Marketing,* McGraw, 1970. Contributor of articles to numerous journals.

WORK IN PROGRESS: Three books, *International Business Cases, Service Businesses,* and *Entrepreneurship: Shakespeare in Modern Business.*

* * *

HERRING, George C., Jr. 1936-

PERSONAL: Born May 23, 1936, in Blacksburg, Va.; son of George C. (a university administrator) and Gordon (Saunders) Herring; married Nancy Walton, March 15, 1958; children: John Walton, Lisa Susanne. *Education:* Roanoke College, B.A., 1957; University of Virginia, M.A., 1962, Ph.D., 1965. *Home:* 432 Bristol Rd., Lexington, Ky. 40502. *Office:* Department of History, University of Kentucky, Lexington, Ky. 40506.

CAREER: Ohio University, Athens, assistant professor of history, 1965-69; University of Kentucky, Lexington, associate professor of history, 1969—, chairman of department, 1973-76. *Military service:* U.S. Navy, 1958-60. *Member:* American Historical Association, Society for the History of American Foreign Relations, Organization of American Historians.

WRITINGS: Aid to Russia, 1941-1946, Columbia University Press, 1973; *The Diaries of Edward R. Stettinius,* New Viewpoints, 1975.

WORK IN PROGRESS: America's Longest War: The United States and Vietnam, 1950-1975, for Wiley.

* * *

HERRMANN, Robert O(mer) 1932-

PERSONAL: Born February 7, 1932, in Washington, D.C.; son of Omer Wesley and Beth (Mickle) Herrmann; married Carol Anne McGuire, October 14, 1967; children: John Martin, Nell Elizabeth. *Education:* University of Wisconsin—Madison, B.S., 1955; Michigan State University, M.S., 1961, Ph.D., 1964. *Home:* 568 Ridge Ave., State College, Pa. 16801. *Office:* Department of Agricultural Economics and Rural Sociology, Pennsylvania State University, Weaver Bldg., University Park, Pa. 16802.

CAREER: University of California, Davis, assistant professor, 1962-65; Pennsylvania State University, University Park, assistant professor, 1965-68, associate professor, 1968-74, professor of agricultural economics, 1974—. *Military service:* U.S. Navy, 1955-58; became lieutenant junior grade. *Member:* American Council on Consumer Interests (president, 1968-69), American Agricultural Economics Association, American Economics Association, American Marketing Association.

WRITINGS: (Editor) *The Consumer Behavior of Children and Teenagers: An Annotated Bibliography,* American Marketing Association, 1969; (with Herbert Jelley) *The American Consumer: Issues and Decisions,* Gregg, 1973, 2nd edition, 1978. Editor, *Journal of Consumer Affairs,* 1977—.

WORK IN PROGRESS: Consumerism and the American Public, completion expected in 1979.

* * *

HERSEY, George Leonard 1927-

PERSONAL: Born August 30, 1927, in Cambridge, Mass.; son of Milton Leonard (an economist) and Katharine (Page) Hersey; married Jane Maddox Lancefield, September 2, 1953; children: Donald, James. *Education:* Harvard University, A.B., 1951; Yale University, M.F.A., 1954, M.A., 1960, Ph.D., 1964. *Politics:* Democrat. *Home:* 167 Linden St., New Haven, Conn. 06511. *Office:* Department of the History of Art, Yale University, New Haven, Conn. 06520.

CAREER: Bucknell University, Lewisburg, Pa., instructor, 1954-55, assistant professor of art, 1956-59; Yale University, New Haven, Conn., assistant professor, 1965-68, associate professor, 1968-74, professor of history of art, 1974—. Director of restoration research, Lockwood-Mathews Mansion Museum, Norwalk, Conn., 1970—; member, Governor's Commission on the Restoration of the Connecticut State Capitol, 1977—. *Military service:* U.S. Army, 1946-47. *Member:* Society of Architectural Historians (member of board of directors, 1970-73), Victorian Society (United States), Victorian Society (Great Britain). *Awards, honors:* Fulbright scholar in Italy, 1962; American Philosophical Society award, 1962; Schepp Foundation fellow of the Harvard Center for Renaissance Studies, Florence, 1971.

WRITINGS: Alfonso II and the Artistic Renewal of Naples, 1485-95, Yale University Press, 1969; *High Victorian Gothic: A Study in Associationism,* Johns Hopkins Press, 1972; *The Aragonese Arch at Naples, 1443-1477,* Yale University Press, 1973; *Pythagorean Palaces: Architecture and Magic in the Italian Renaissance,* Cornell University Press, 1976. Co-editor of *Architectura: Internationale Zeitschrift fur Architektur-Geschichte,* 1971—; editor, Yale Publications on the History of Art, 1971—.

WORK IN PROGRESS: Pygmalion: Episodes in the Development of a Myth; A Dream of Fair Women: The Dialogue on Love in Early Pre-Raphaelite Painting; co-editor with Jill Meredith, *Rossetti Revisited: Essays on the Double Work of Art.*

* * *

HERSHENSON, David Bert 1933-

PERSONAL: Born August 30, 1933, in Boston, Mass.; son of Bert Barnet (a physician) and Judith (Cohen) Hershenson; married Marian Vogel (a city planner), August 18, 1957; children: Joseph Bert, Evan Stuart. *Education:* Harvard University, A.B. (magna cum laude), 1955; Boston University, A.M., 1960, Ph.D., 1964. *Politics:* Independent. *Religion:* Jewish. *Home:* 125 Cedar St., Newton Centre, Mass. 02159. *Office:* Sargent College of Allied Health Professions, Boston University, Boston, Mass. 02215.

CAREER: State University of New York at Buffalo, counseling psychologist, 1963-65; Illinois Institute of Technology, Chicago, assistant professor, 1965-67, associate professor, 1967-70, professor of psychology, 1970-77, chairman of department, 1973-77; Boston University, Sargent College of

Allied Health Professions, Boston, Mass., professor of rehabilitation counseling and dean, 1977—. Member of board of directors, Goodwill Industries of Massachusetts, 1977—. *Member:* American Psychological Association, American Personnel and Guidance Association, National Rehabilitation Association.

WRITINGS: (Editor with R. M. Roth and Thomas Hilliard) *The Psychology of Vocational Development,* Allyn & Bacon, 1970; (contributor) E. Herr, editor, *Vocational Guidance and Human Development,* Houghton, 1974. Contributor to psychology and counseling journals. Member of editorial board of *Journal of Vocational Behavior,* 1970—, and *Journal of Counseling Psychology,* 1976—; associate editor of *Rehabilitation Counseling Bulletin,* 1966-72.

WORK IN PROGRESS: Research on vocational rehabilitation.

AVOCATIONAL INTERESTS: Travel.

*   *   *

HERSHENSON, Maurice (Eugene) 1933-

PERSONAL: Born May 27, 1933, in Brooklyn, N.Y.; son of Harry and Fannie (Zerden) Hershenson; married Amy Gross (a teacher), September 4, 1955; children: Gregg, Eric. *Education:* Brooklyn College (now Brooklyn College of the City University of New York), B.A., 1955, M.A., 1960; Yale University, Ph.D., 1964. *Politics:* Democrat. *Home and office:* 21 Wedgwood Rd., Wellesley, Mass. 02181.

CAREER: University of Wisconsin—Madison, assistant professor, 1963-66, associate professor of psychology, 1966-68; Brandeis University, Waltham, Mass., associate professor of psychology, 1968—, chairman of department, 1973-75. Instructor at Brooklyn College of the City University of New York, summers, 1960, 1961. *Military service:* U.S. Army, 1955-57. *Member:* American Association for the Advancement of Science, American Psychological Association, Psychonomic Society, Eastern Psychological Association, New York Academy of Sciences, Sigma Xi. *Awards, honors:* Research grants from the National Institute of Mental Health, 1965-67, 1967-70, 1970-72.

WRITINGS: (Contributor) H. Moltz, *The Ontogenesis of Vertebrate Behavior,* Academic Press, 1971; (with Ralph N. Haber) *The Psychology of Visual Perception,* Holt, 1973, 2nd edition, 1979. Contributor to professional journals.

WORK IN PROGRESS: Research in perception and perceptual development, specifically in the ability to recognize symbols and the changing ability to function in visual space.

*   *   *

HERSHER, Leonard 1925-

PERSONAL: Born March 30, 1925, in Lancaster, Pa.; son of Morris J. (a grocer) and Mollie (Edelson) Hersher; married Hilda Turoff (a librarian), September 5, 1948; children: Michael E., Jay K., Lisa A. *Education:* New York University, B.A., 1949; University of Chicago, Ph.D., 1955. *Politics:* Liberal. *Home:* 520 Greenwood Pl., Syracuse, N.Y. 13210. *Office:* Department of Pediatrics, State University of New York Upstate Medical Center, Syracuse, N.Y. 13210.

CAREER: State University of New York Upstate Medical Center, Syracuse, instructor, 1954-59, assistant professor, 1959-61, associate professor of pediatrics, 1961—. *Military service:* U.S. Army, 1943-46; became sergeant; received Purple Heart. *Member:* Central New York Psychological Association (president, 1964).

WRITINGS: (Editor) *Four Psychotherapies,* Appleton, 1970. Contributor of articles to *Science, Developmental Psychology,* and other journals. Associate editor of *Child Development,* 1970-71.

WORK IN PROGRESS: Research on minimal cerebral dysfunction in children and immunological incompetence.

*   *   *

HERTLING, G(unter) H. 1930-

PERSONAL: Born June 14, 1930; son of G. C. and Clara (Glaeffcke) Hertling; married Darlene M. Little (a registered physical therapist), 1953; children: Sonja E., Dieter R. *Education:* University of California, Berkeley, B.A., 1954, M.A., 1957, Ph.D., 1963. *Office:* Department of German, University of Washington, Seattle, Wash. 98195.

CAREER: University of Washington, Seattle, assistant professor, 1964-67, associate professor, 1967-74, professor of German, 1974—. *Member:* Modern Language Association of America, American Association of Teachers of German, Philological Association of the Pacific Coast.

WRITINGS: Wandlung der Werte im dichterischen Werke der Ricarda Huch, Bouvier, 1966; *Conrad Ferdinand Meyers Epik: Traumbesseelung, Traumbesinnung and Traumbesitz,* Francke, 1973. Also author of articles on C. F. Meyer, Adalbert Stifter, Thomas Mann, and Heinrich von Kleist.

WORK IN PROGRESS: Research on German literature and thought in the eighteenth and nineteenth centuries.

*   *   *

HERZ, John H(ermann) 1908-

PERSONAL: Born September 23, 1908, in Dusseldorf, Germany; son of Carl (a judge) and Elizabeth (Aschaffenburg) Herz; married Anne Klein (a library clerk), June 22, 1941; children: Stephen. *Education:* University of Cologne, Ph.D., 1931; Graduate Institute of International Studies (Geneva), diplome, 1938; also studied at University of Freiburg, University of Heidelberg, and University of Berlin. *Home:* 193 Nelson Rd., Scarsdale, N.Y. 10583. *Office:* Department of Government, City College of the City University of New York, New York, N.Y.

CAREER: Institute for Advanced Study, Princeton, N.J., member, 1939-41; Howard University, Washington, D.C., instructor in government, 1941-43; U.S. Office of Strategic Services, Washington, D.C., political analyst, 1943-45; U.S. State Department, Washington, D.C., political analyst, 1945-48; Howard University, professor of political science, 1948-52; City College of the City University of New York, New York, N.Y., associate professor, 1952-60, professor of government, 1960-77, professor emeritus, 1977—. Visiting professor, Columbia University, 1952, 1957; member of graduate faculty, New School for Social Research, 1953, 1958. Consultant to RAND Corp. *Member:* American Political Science Association, American Society of International Law, Conference Group on German Politics, Commission to Study the Organization of Peace, Amnesty International. *Awards, honors:* Social Science Research Council award, 1948-49; Woodrow Wilson award, 1951, for *Political Realism and Political Idealism;* Rockefeller Foundation fellow, 1954-55, 1963-64; Fulbright fellow, 1960.

WRITINGS: Political Realism and Political Idealism, University of Chicago Press, 1951; (with G. M. Carter) *Major Foreign Powers,* Harcourt, 1952, 6th edition, 1972; *International Politics in the Atomic Age,* Columbia University Press, 1959, revised edition, 1961; (with Carter) *Government and Politics in the Twentieth Century,* Praeger, 1961, 3rd edition, 1973; *The Government of Germany,* Harcourt, 1967, 2nd edition, 1972; (with Carter and Louise Holborn) *German Constitutional Documents,* Praeger, 1970; *The Nation-State and the Crisis of World Politics,* McKay, 1976. Contributor of articles to scholarly journals. Co-editor, *Comparative Politics.*

SIDELIGHTS: Reflecting on a career which spans nearly a half-century of research and writings in the field of political science and international relations, John Herz told *CA:* "Under the impact of the great global problems that have come to beset mankind (world population explosion, exhaustion of resources, destruction of the environment, and, above all, the threat of nuclear annihilation), I have centered my research and writing over the last two decades around the relation between politics and these problems and the question of what changes in attitude-patterns and political action are required to solve the global problems in ways under which mankind can survive."

* * *

HEWES, Leslie   1906-

PERSONAL: Born February 25, 1906, in Guthrie, Okla.; son of Willis and Pearl (Gifford) Hewes; married Elma Graham Beary, June 14, 1933; children: Carolyn Louise (Mrs. Daniel John Toft), Robert Willis. *Education:* University of Oklahoma, B.A., 1928; University of California at Berkeley, Ph.D., 1940. *Politics:* Democrat. *Religion:* Presbyterian. *Home:* 3022 South 27th St., Lincoln, Neb. 68502. *Office:* Department of Geography, University of Nebraska, Lincoln, Neb. 68508.

CAREER: University of Oklahoma, Norman, instructor, 1932-39, assistant professor, 1939-43, associate professor of geography, 1943-45, tennis coach, 1936-42; University of Nebraska, Lincoln, professor of geography, 1945-74, professor emeritus, 1974—, head of department, 1946-68. Fulbright professor at University of Vienna, 1958-59. Lectured at European universities, 1959; visiting lecturer in geography at Flinders University, Australia, 1978. *Member:* International Geographical Union, Association of American Geographers (council member, 1949-50, 1954-56, 1968-72), American Geographical Society, National Council of Geographical Education, Phi Beta Kappa (president of Nebraska chapter, 1959-60), Sigma Xi (president of Nebraska chapter, 1952-53). *Awards, honors:* Association of American Geographers, grant-in-aid, 1956, certificate for meritorious contribution, 1965.

WRITINGS: (Contributor) *Festschrift, Leopold G. Schiedl Zum 60. Geburtstag,* Volume II, Ferdinand Berg & Son (Vienna), 1967; *The Suitcase Farming Frontier of the Central Great Plains; A Study in Historical Geography,* University of Nebraska Press, 1973; (contributor) Brian W. Blouet and Merlin P. Lawson, editors, *Images of the Plains: The Role of Human Nature in Settlement,* University of Nebraska Press, 1975; *Occupying the Cherokee Country of Oklahoma,* University of Nebraska Studies, 1978; (contributor) Frederick C. Luebke, editor, *Cultural Heritage of the Plains,* University of Nebraska Press, in press. Contributor to *Geographical Review, Economic Geography, Annals of the Association of American Geographers, Die Erde,* and *Geographische Rundschau.*

WORK IN PROGRESS: Historical Geography of the Plains and Prairies.

HEYWOOD, Christopher   1928-

PERSONAL: Born July 2, 1928, in Stellenbosch, South Africa; became British citizen in 1957; son of Arthur Lister (a farmer) and Katherine (Duminy) Heywood; married Annemarie Johanna, December 21, 1951 (divorced, 1972); children: Katherine Tamara, Giles Carl. *Education:* Stellenbosch University, B.A., 1948; Oxford University, B.A., 1952, B.Litt., 1957, M.A., 1957. *Politics:* "Left." *Residence:* Sheffield, England. *Office:* Department of English Literature, University of Sheffield, Sheffield 10, England.

CAREER: University of Ife, Ife, Nigeria, professor of English, 1966-68; University of Sheffield, Sheffield, England, lecturer, 1956, senior lecturer in English, 1970—. *Awards, honors:* Rhodes scholar at Oxford University, 1949-52.

WRITINGS: (Editor and author of introduction) *Perspectives on African Literature,* Heinemann, 1971; (editor) *Aspects of South African Literature,* Holmes & Meier, 1976. Contributor to *Revue de litterature comparee, Comparative Literature, Nineteenth Century Fiction,* and other journals.

WORK IN PROGRESS: Research on the English novel in the later nineteenth century.

AVOCATIONAL INTERESTS: Music, painting, travel.†

* * *

HICKEL, Walter J(oseph)   1919-

PERSONAL: Born August 18, 1919, in Claflin, Kans.; son of Robert A. (a farmer) and Emma (Zecha) Hickel; married Janice Cannon, September 22, 1941 (died August, 1943); married Ermalee Strutz, November 22, 1945; children: (first marriage) Theodore; (second marriage) Robert, Walter, Jr., Jack, Joseph, Karl. *Education:* Attended public schools in Claflin, Kans. *Politics:* Republican. *Religion:* Catholic. *Home:* 1905 Loussac Dr., Anchorage, Alaska 99503. *Office:* 510 L Street, Suite 607, Anchorage, Alaska 99503.

CAREER: Left Kansas, where his father was a tenant farmer at age of twenty, after buying an insurance agency and selling it the next year; made his way to Alaska, where he washed dishes, tended bar, and was a civilian inspector for the U.S. Air Force during World War II; went into construction and real estate business, becoming owner of Hickel Construction Co., Anchorage, Alaska, 1946, builder-owner of Traveler's Inn, 1953, Hotel Captain Cook, Northern Lights Shopping Center, University Shopping Center, (all Anchorage), and Traveler's Inn, Fairbanks, 1955; sole owner of Hickel Investment Co., Anchorage; governor of Alaska, 1966-68; appointed Secretary of the Interior by President Richard Nixon, served 1969-70; lecturer. Republican National Committeeman for Alaska, 1954-64; member of economic development committee, Alaska State Chamber of Commerce; trustee, Alaska Methodist University and National Recreation and Park Association; member of Board of Regents, Gonzaga University; member of board, Western Airlines and Salk Institute; member of World Advisory Council for Buckminister Fuller's Design Science Institute; world observer at United Nations Conference on Human Environment (Stockholm); chairman of National Conference on Geothermal Energy of National Science Foundation, 1972.

MEMBER: American Association for the Advancement of Science (member of committee of scientific freedom and responsibility), Alaska Chamber of Commerce, Boys Club of Alaska, Pioneers of Alaska, Alaska Native Brotherhood, Equestrian Order of the Holy Sepulchre, Knights of Malta, Knights of Columbus, Rotary Club, B.P.O. Elks Lodge,

Washington Athletic Club (member of board of governors, 1961, 1962), Capitol Hill Club (Washington, D.C.). *Awards, honors:* Named "Alaskan of the Year," 1969; De Smet Medal, Gonzaga University, 1969; "Man of the Year," by National Ripon Society; Horatio Alger Award, 1972. Honorary degrees: D.Eng., Stevens Institute of Technology, 1970; LL.D. from St. Mary of the Plains College, 1970, Adelphi University, 1971, University of Maryland, 1971, Saint Martin's College, 1971, and University of Alaska, 1976; D.Pub. Administration, Willamette University, 1971; D.Laws from University of San Diego, 1972, Rensselaer Polytechnic Institute, 1973; D.Eng. from Michigan Technological University, 1973.

WRITINGS: Who Owns America?, Prentice-Hall, 1971. Contributor to *Reader's Digest.*

SIDELIGHTS: In his tenure as Secretary of the Interior, Walter Hickel was known for his environmental protectionism. As Alan Seaburg writes: "The challenge was to find the correct balance between industry and conservation and then to act. Hickel favored a 'wise use without abuse' of the environment." He promised to "prosecute those who pollute" and did so. Hickel was asked to resign on Thanksgiving, 1970. "Being fired was not a disaster," he told M. C. Langan. "It has opened doors to opportunities...." One opportunity was, apparently, to write about his experiences, in *Who Owns America?* Variously described as a "Cabinet memoir," a "buoyant" account of Hickel's efforts for a better environment, the book recounts his struggles with, among others, oil companies, the whaling industry, certain Congressmen, and "the White House clique." It is not, critics agree, an expose of Washington's "dirty laundry." To Ernest Gruening "it is a prospectus of practical idealism which ... could go far to alleviate our nation's most pressing and worsening dilemmas. It ... will have far-reaching political repercussions." At the other extreme, James Ridgeway complained that "Hickel ... offers no substantive description or analysis of the fundamental 'conservation' issues facing the country," although Hickel has been outspoken on these very issues in interviews and lectures. He contends that ugliness in our cities is one of the causes of unhappiness, drug addiction, and crime. He told Langan: "With strong government leadership we can clean up our air and water in less than ten or fifteen years, and anyone who denies it is either uninformed or lying.... We must not allow shortsighted industrialists to exploit our nation's resources for selfish purposes.... Our problem is not lack of space, and it is not lack of resources. The problem has been a lack of concern.... We pay for death-dealing and destructive wars. We can afford to pay the price to live."

BIOGRAPHICAL/CRITICAL SOURCES: Christian Century, December 1, 1971; *American Forests,* December, 1972.

*   *   *

HICKEY, Joseph J(ames) 1907-

PERSONAL: Born April 16, 1907, in New York, N.Y.; son of James B. (a truck driver) and Sarah (Mooney) Hickey; married Margaret Brooks (an editor), June 20, 1942; children: Susan (Mrs. James Nehls). *Education:* New York University, B.S., 1930, graduate student, 1940-41; University of Wisconsin, M.S., 1943; University of Chicago, further graduate study, 1943-44; University of Michigan, Ph.D., 1949. *Residence:* Madison, Wis. *Office:* Russell Laboratories, University of Wisconsin, Madison, Wis. 53706.

CAREER: New York University, New York City, assistant track coach, 1930-33; Consolidated Edison Co., New York City, power salesman, 1933-41; Wisconsin State Soil Conservation Committee, Madison, research assistant, 1941-43; University of Michigan, Ann Arbor, assistant curator, Museum of Zoology, 1944-46; University of Wisconsin—Madison, assistant professor, 1948-49, associate professor, 1949-58, professor of wildlife ecology, 1958-77. Visiting professor of zoology, University of Minnesota Biological Station, 1952, 1959, 1962; visiting scientist, Vogelschutzwarte fuer Hessen, Rheinland-Pfalz und Saarland, 1964. Member of technical advisory council, Wisconsin State Pesticide Review Board, 1969-73; member of ad hoc advisory committees to Smithsonian Institution, National Academy of Sciences, and Environmental Protection Agency; member of Bodega Bay Institute for Pollution Ecology.

MEMBER: American Ornithologists' Union (member of council, 1945-48, 1963-66; vice-president, 1970-72; president, 1972-73), Nature Conservancy (treasurer, 1950-56; member of board of governors, 1963-70), Wilson Ornithological Society, Cooper Ornithological Society, Ecological Society of America, American Association for the Advancement of Science, American Institute of Biological Sciences, National Audubon Society, Rachel Carson Trust for the Living Environment, Cornell Laboratory of Ornithology, Linnaean Society of New York (vice-president, 1935-37; president, 1937-39), Wisconsin Society for Ornithology (president, 1954-55). *Awards, honors:* Guggenheim fellow, 1946-47; Leopold Medal of Wildlife Society, 1972; W. E. Clyde Todd Award of Audubon Society of Western Pennsylvania, 1972; Arthur A. Allen Medal of Cornell University, 1976.

WRITINGS: A Guide to Bird Watching, Oxford University Press, 1943; *Survival Studies of Banded Birds,* U.S. Department of Interior, 1952; (editor) *Peregrine Falcon Populations: Their Biology and Decline,* University of Wisconsin Press, 1969. Editor, *Proceedings* of Linnaean Society of New York, 1940-41, and *Journal of Wildlife Management,* 1956-59; associate editor, *Proceedings* of XIIIth International Ornithological Congress, 1963.

WORK IN PROGRESS: Research on effects of chemical pollutants on bird populations and of coal mining on songbirds.

SIDELIGHTS: Joseph Hickey's *A Guide to Bird Watching,* although a slim book by some standards (250 pages), has gone through many printings and still is considered one of the classics in its field.

*   *   *

HIESBERGER, Jean Marie 1941-

PERSONAL: Born September 18, 1941, in Kansas City, Mo.; daughter of Anton A. and Elizabeth (Nitsche) Hiesberger; married Robert Heyer (an editor), August 19, 1972. *Education:* St. Mary College, Xavier, Kans., B.S., 1963; St. John's University, Collegeville, Minn., M.A., 1969. *Home:* 589 Ridgeland Terrace, Englewood, N.J. 07631. *Office:* Paulist/Newman Press, 1865 Broadway, New York, N.Y. 10023.

CAREER: Paulist/Newman Press, New York, N.Y., general editor of *Come to the Father,* religious education program for the United States, 1971—. Lecturer.

WRITINGS—All published by Paulist/Newman: *Discovery Education,* 1971; (with husband, Robert Heyer and Bernadette Kenny) *Let Us Pray,* Volumes I-IV, 1971-72, Volumes V-VI, 1973; (with Martha Bowes, Heyer, and Kenny) *"Come to the Father" Slide Film Kit-Grade 6,* 1972; (with Bowes, Heyer, and Kenny) *"Come to the Father" Slide Film Kit-Grade 7,* 1972; (editor with Kevin Lynch), *"Come to the Father" Teacher Formation Kit,* 1972; (editor) *"Come to the Father" Teacher Training Cassettes,* 1972; *You Have Given Us Today,* 1973; (editor) *Change My Heart,* 1976; (editor) *Arise, Jerusalem!,* 1978. Contributor of articles to *Religious Education, New Catholic World,* and *Catholic News.* Member of editorial board of *New Catholic World,* 1972—.

* * *

HIESTAND, Dale L(eroy) 1925-

PERSONAL: Surname is pronounced Hee-st'nd; born January 16, 1925, in Salem, Ill.; son of Arthur C. (a salesman) and Rosa E. (Hampsten) Hiestand; married Wanda C. Kowalewich (a professor of nursing), August 4, 1945; children: Gregory K., Susan L. *Education:* Washington University, St. Louis, Mo., B.S.B.A., 1948, M.A., 1949; Columbia University, Ph.D., 1963. *Politics:* Democrat. *Religion:* None. *Home:* 341 Hudson Ter., Piermont, N.Y. 10968. *Office:* 512 Uris, Columbia University, New York, N.Y. 10027.

CAREER: Instructor in money and banking at American Institute of Banking, St. Louis, Mo., 1948-49, and Washington University, St. Louis, 1949; Columbia University, New York, N.Y., Medical Payments Project, lecturer in statistics, 1950-51, research assistant, 1951-53, National Manpower Council, research assistant and then associate, 1953-61, Conservation of Human Resources, research associate, 1961-67, senior research associate, 1967—, Graduate School of Business, assistant professor, 1964-67, associate professor, 1967-71, professor of business, 1971—. Consultant and researcher for U.S. Department of Labor, National Aeronautics and Space Administration, U.S. Department of Health, Education, and Welfare, other national agencies, the state of New Jersey, and the city of New York. *Military service:* U.S. Army, 1943-46. *Member:* American Economic Association, Industrial Relations Research Association.

WRITINGS: Economic Growth and Employment Opportunities of Minorities, Columbia University Press, 1964; (with Eli Ginzberg and others) *The Pluralistic Economy,* McGraw, 1965; (with Ginzberg) *Mobility in the Negro Community: Guidelines for Research on Social and Economic Progress,* U.S. Commission on Civil Rights, 1968; *White Collar Employment Opportunities for Minorities in New York City,* U.S. Equal Employment Opportunity Commission, 1968; (with Ginzberg and others) *Manpower Strategy for the Metropolis,* Columbia University Press, 1968; *Discrimination in Employment: An Appraisal of the Research,* Institute of Labor and Industrial Relations, University of Michigan, 1970; *Changing Careers After 35: New Horizons through Professional and Graduate Study,* Columbia University Press, 1971; (with Ginzberg and others) *Urban Health Services: The Case of New York,* Columbia University Press, 1971; (with Ginzberg and others) *New York Is Very Much Alive: A Manpower View,* McGraw, 1973; *High Level Manpower and Technological Change in the Steel Industry: Implications for Corporate Manpower Planning,* Praeger, 1974; (editor with Miriam Ostow) *Health Manpower Information for Policy Guidance,* Ballinger, 1976; (with Dean W. Morse) *Comparative Metropolitan Employment Complexes: New York, Chicago, Los Angeles, Houston, Atlanta,* Allanheld, Osmun, in press.

Contributor: John P. Davis, editor, *The American Negro Reference Book,* Prentice Hall, 1966; Arthur M. Ross, editor, *Employment, Race and Poverty,* Harcourt, 1967; Jerry M. Rosenberg, editor, *New Conceptions of Vocational and Technical Education,* Teachers College Press, 1967; Orley Ashenfelter and Albert Rees, editors, *Discrimination in Labor Markets,* Princeton University Press, 1973; *Community Hospitals and the Challenge of Primary Care,* Center for Community Health Systems, Columbia University, 1975. Contributor to symposia, including three National Manpower Council publications issued by Columbia University Press.

* * *

HILL, W(illiam) Speed 1935-

PERSONAL: Born January 19, 1935, in Louisville, Ky.; son of Eugene Dubose (an executive) and Lila (Robinson) Hill; married Emita Brady (a university teacher and administrator), July 23, 1960; children: Julie, Christopher, Madeleine. *Education:* Princeton University, A.B., 1957; Harvard University, A.M., 1959, Ph.D., 1964. *Politics:* Independent Democrat. *Religion:* Protestant. *Home:* 47 Wildcliff Rd., New Rochelle, N.Y. 10805. *Office:* Department of English, Herbert H. Lehman College of the City University of New York, Bronx, N.Y. 10468.

CAREER: Case Western Reserve University, Cleveland, Ohio, assistant professor of English, 1964-69; New York University, New York, N.Y., assistant professor of English, 1969-73; Herbert H. Lehman College of the City University of New York, Bronx, N.Y., associate professor, 1973-77, professor of English, 1978—. *Member:* Modern Language Association of America, Renaissance English Text Society, Renaissance Society of America, Columbia University Seminar in the Renaissance, Bibliographical Society, Phi Beta Kappa. *Awards, honors:* Woodrow Wilson fellowship, 1957; American Philosophical Society grant, 1969; Folger Library fellowship, 1969; Newberry Library fellowship, 1969; American Council of Learned Societies research grant, 1970, and senior fellowship in humanities, 1974; Folger Library-British Academy exchange fellowship, 1973.

WRITINGS: Richard Hooker: A Descriptive Bibliography of the Early Editions, 1593-1724, Press of Case Western Reserve University, 1970; *Studies in Richard Hooker: Essays Preliminary to an Edition of the Works,* Press of Case Western Reserve University, 1973; (editor) *Richard Hooker, Of the Laws of Ecclesiastical Polity,* Harvard University Press, 1977. Also general editor of a critical edition of the works of Richard Hooker, six volumes, for Folger Library and Harvard University Press.

WORK IN PROGRESS: Continuing supervision of an old-spelling critical edition of works of Richard Hooker, for Folger Library and Harvard University Press.

* * *

HILLBRUNER, Anthony 1914-

PERSONAL: Born February 10, 1914, in Chicago, Ill.; son of Walter and Hedwig (Senk) Hillbruner; married Laura Ziino (a teacher of adult education classes), 1942; children: Anthony J., Tina Laurie. *Education:* Northwestern University, B.S., 1949, M.A., 1950, Ph.D., 1953. *Politics:* Liberal. *Religion:* Roman Catholic. *Home:* 407 North Mission Dr., San Gabriel, Calif. 91775. *Office:* Department of Speech, California State University, Los Angeles, Calif. 90032.

CAREER: Instructor in speech at University of Denver, Denver, Colo., 1950-51, University of Oregon, Eugene, 1951-52, and Stanford University, Stanford, Calif., 1952-54; California State University, Los Angeles, assistant professor, 1954-57, associate professor, 1957-63, professor of rhetoric and American studies, 1963—, coordinator of American studies program, 1954-68. Visiting scholar at Cambridge University, 1972. Member: American Studies Association, Speech Communication Association of America, Western Speech Communication Association. Awards, honors: Foundation grant, 1965, and Creative Research award, 1968, both from California State University.

WRITINGS: Critical Dimensions: The Art of Public Address Criticism, Random House, 1966; (contributor) David H. Grover, editor, Landmarks in Western Oratory, University of Wyoming Press, 1968; (contributor) John L. Erickson and Robert F. Forston, editors, Public Speaking as Dialogue, Hunter Publishing, 1972. Contributor of more than thirty articles and essays to professional journals and little literary magazines.

WORK IN PROGRESS: Research on British rhetoric and on rhetorical criticism.

AVOCATIONAL INTERESTS: Painting and working at other crafts; art, literature, music, theater in all its forms.

*   *   *

HILLMAN, Howard 1934-

PERSONAL: Born December 8, 1934, in Hollywood, Calif. Education: California State University, B.A., 1959; Harvard University, M.B.A., 1961. Office: The Hillman Company, 220 East 63rd St., New York, N.Y. 10021.

CAREER: National Academy of Sports, New York City, president, 1961-65; Test Publishers of America, New York City, president, 1965; The Hillman Co., New York City, president, 1965—. Lecturer. Awards, honors: The Art of Winning Foundation Grants was named "Outstanding Reference Book of the Year" by American Library Association, 1975.

WRITINGS: Insider's Guide to New York, McKay, 1967; (editor) The Complete New Yorker, McKay, 1972; Hillman's Restaurant Map, Macmillan, 1973; (with Karin Abarbanel) The Art of Winning Foundation Grants, Vanguard, 1975; The Art of Winning Government Grants, Vanguard, 1977; The Diner's Guide to Wines, Hawthorn, 1978; The Penguin Book of World Cuisines, Penguin, in press; The Food Bible, Avon, in press; The Art of Winning Corporate Grants, Vanguard, in press.

"At-a-Glance" series, published by McKay: New York at-a-Glance, 1971; Chicago . . . , 1971; San Francisco . . . , 1971; Hawaii . . . , 1972; Miami . . . , 1972; Washington, D.C. . . . , 1972; Boston . . . , 1972. Contributor to New York Times, Business Week, Institutional Investor, Wall Street Journal, International Review of Food and Wine, and other periodicals.

SIDELIGHTS: CA learned from Howard Hillman that his editorial research "on world cuisines has been supplemented by traveling one million miles around the world to over one hundred countries as well as by actively cooking in those countries."

*   *   *

HINSHAW, Randall (Weston) 1915-

PERSONAL: Born May 9, 1915, in La Grange, Ill.; son of Virgil Goodman (a lawyer and reformer) and Evelyn (Piltz) Hinshaw; married Pearl Stevens, June 19, 1949; children: Frederic Randall, Robert Louis, Elisabeth Mary. Education: Occidental College, A.B., 1937; Princeton University, Ph.D., 1944. Home: 755 West Eighth St., Claremont, Calif. 91711. Office: Department of Economics, Claremont Graduate School, Claremont, Calif. 91711.

CAREER: Federal Reserve Board, Division of International Finance, Washington, D.C., economist, 1943-46, 1947-52; Amherst College, Amherst, Mass., assistant professor of economics, 1946-47; U.S. Mission to North Atlantic Treaty Organization and European Regional Organizations, Paris, France, special adviser on international financial policy, 1952-57; Claremont Graduate School, Claremont, Calif., professor of economics, 1960—, chairman of department, 1967-69, 1977—. Visiting professor, Yale University, 1957-58, Oberlin College, 1958-59, Bologna Center, Johns Hopkins University, 1965-67, spring, 1971, University of California, Los Angeles, spring, 1968. Chairman of planning committee, Bologna-Claremont series of biennial international monetary conferences, 1967—. Member: American Economic Association, Council on Foreign Relations, Econometric Society, Phi Beta Kappa.

WRITINGS: The European Community and American Trade, Praeger, 1964; (editor) Monetary Reform and the Price of Gold, Johns Hopkins Press, 1967; (editor) The Economics of International Adjustments, Johns Hopkins Press, 1971; (editor) Inflation as a Global Problem, Johns Hopkins Press, 1972; (editor) Key Issues in International Monetary Reform, Dekker, 1975; (editor) Stagflation: An International Problem, Dekker, 1977. Contributor to professional journals.

WORK IN PROGRESS: Research on international monetary field.

SIDELIGHTS: Randall Hinshaw told CA: "Astronomy is a fairly serious avocation; I developed a strong interest in my teens, when I seriously considered being an astronomer. I have built 4 telescopes, and spend a good deal of time observing with my latest 8-inch reflector."

*   *   *

HIPPLE, Walter J(ohn), Jr. 1921-

PERSONAL: Born March 14, 1921, in Chicago, Ill.; son of Walter John (a teacher) and Emilie (Scheu) Hipple; married Anne Ruth Poier, November 27, 1962; children: Heidi Kristina, Ethan John. Education: University of Chicago, B.A., 1947, M.A., 1948. Ph.D., 1954; postdoctoral study at Courtauld Institute, London, 1956-57, and Cambridge University, 1961-62. Home address: R.D. 1, Box 380, Fairville Rd., Chadd's Ford, Pa. 19317. Office: Department of Philosophy, West Chester State College, West Chester, Pa. 19380.

CAREER: Roosevelt University, Chicago, Ill., lecturer in English, 1948; University of Chicago, Chicago, Ill., instructor in humanities, 1948-50; University of Arkansas, Fayetteville, instructor in English, 1951-52; University of Florida, Gainesville, assistant professor of humanities, 1952-56; Cornell College, Mt. Vernon, Iowa, associate professor of English and philosophy, 1957-61; University of the Pacific, Stockton, Calif., professor of humanities and English, 1962; Indiana State University, Terre Haute, Professor of philosophy, 1963-72, chairman of department of humanities, 1964-72; Shimer College, Mount Carroll, Ill., dean of college, 1972-76; West Chester State College, West Chester, Pa., academic vice-president, 1976-77, professor of philosophy and associate to president, 1977—. Visiting professor of English, Idaho State University, 1963, and University of Southern California, summer, 1963. Chairman, State Committee on Humanities in Secondary Schools (Indiana), 1965-69. *Military service:* U.S. Army, Signal Corps, 1943-45; became sergeant. *Member:* Modern Language Association of America, American Society for Aesthetics, American Philosophical Association, American Association for Higher Education, Society for College and University Planning, National Association for Humanities Education. *Awards, honors:* Guggenheim fellow at Cambridge University, 1961-62; Litt. D., Shimer College, 1976.

WRITINGS: The Beautiful, the Sublime, and the Picturesque in Eighteenth-Century British Aesthetic Theory, Southern Illinois University Press, 1957; (author of introduction) Alexander Gerard, *An Essay on Taste (1759): Together with Observations Concerning the Imitative Nature of Poetry,* Scholars' Facsimiles and Reprints, 1963; (contributor) Howard Anderson and John Shea, editors, *Studies in Criticism and Aesthetics: 1660-1800,* University of Minnesota Press, 1967; (contributor) Sheila Schwartz, editor, *Teaching the Humanities: Selected Readings,* Macmillan, 1970. Contributor of articles and reviews to professional journals, including *Journal of Aesthetics and Art Criticism, Music Educators Journal, Art Bulletin, University of Toronto Quarterly,* and *Philosophical Quarterly.*

WORK IN PROGRESS: Research on nineteenth-century aesthetic theory, particularly in England.

AVOCATIONAL INTERESTS: Camping, back-packing, ecology, travel (visiting galleries and churches).

* * *

HIRSCH, Herbert 1941-

PERSONAL: Born April 29, 1941, in New York, N.Y.; son of Emeric (a jeweler) and Lillias (Solomon) Hirsch; children: Candace Gail, April Diana. *Education:* Concord College, B.A., 1963; Villanova University, M.A., 1965; University of Kentucky, Ph.D., 1968. *Politics:* Radical. *Religion:* None. *Home:* 11918 Nene Dr., Austin, Tex. 78750. *Office:* Department of Government, University of Texas, Austin, Tex. 78712.

CAREER: University of Texas at Austin, assistant professor, 1968-73, associate professor of political psychology, 1973—. Secretary, Committee for Rural Democracy. *Member:* American Political Science Association, Southern Political Science Association, Western Political Science Association, Mid-Western Political Science Association.

WRITINGS: Poverty and Politicization, Free Press, 1971; (editor with M. Donald Hancock) *Comparative Legislative Systems,* Free Press, 1971; (editor with David Perry) *Violence as Politics,* Harper, 1973; (with Armando Gutierrez) *Learning to Be Militant: Ethnic Identity and the Development of Political Militance in a Chicano Community,* R & E Research Associates, 1977. Contributor of articles to *American Political Science Review, Social Science Quarterly,* and *Western Political Quarterly.*

WORK IN PROGRESS: The Right of the People: The American People and Their Politics, for Allyn & Bacon.

* * *

HIRSCH, Monroe J(erome) 1917-

PERSONAL: Born March 6, 1917, in New York, N.Y.; son of Stanley (a publisher) and Anna (Mandell) Hirsch; married Winifred Maud Wilson (a teacher), May 4, 1940; children:

Geoffrey Alan. *Education:* Attended College of the City of New York (now City College of the City University of New York), 1934-37; University of California, Berkeley, A.B., 1940, certificate in optometry, 1940; Stanford University, Ph.D., 1947. *Home and office address:* P.O. Box 8, Ojai, Calif. 93023.

CAREER: Ohio State University, Columbus, assistant professor of optometry, 1947-48; Stanford University, Stanford, Calif., assistant professor of physiology, 1948-49; Los Angeles College of Optometry, Los Angeles, Calif., professor of optometry, 1949-53; private practice in optometry in Ojai, Calif., 1953—; University of California, Berkeley, professor of optometry and physiological optics, 1967—, director of clinics, 1967-73, dean, 1973-78. *Member:* American Academy of Optometry (fellow; president, 1966-68), American Association of University Professors, American Association for the Advancement of Science (fellow), American Optometric Association, California Optometric Association, Sigma Xi, Lions Club (president, 1963). *Awards, honors:* Silver medal for distinguished service, Optometry Foundation, 1960.

WRITINGS: (Editor with Ralph E. Wick) *Vision of the Aging Patient,* Chilton, 1960; (editor with Wick) *Vision of Children,* Chilton, 1963; (editor) *Refractive State of the Eye,* Burgess, 1967; (with Wick) *The Optometric Profession,* Chilton, 1970. Contributor of about two hundred papers to optometry journals. *American Journal of Optometry and Archives of American Academy of Optometry,* associate editor, 1953-68, editor, 1968-78.

WORK IN PROGRESS: Research on the eye and visual science.

* * *

HIRSHBERG, Al(bert S.) 1909-1973

May 10, 1909—April 11, 1973; American sportswriter and author. Obituaries: *New York Times,* April 13, 1973. (See index for *CA* sketch)

* * *

HITIRIS, Theodore 1938-

PERSONAL: Born January 12, 1938, in Corfu, Greece; son of Gerassimos and Ioanna (Christou) Hitiris; married Marja Aavynen, 1972; children: one son, one daughter. *Education:* Higher School of Economics, Athens, Greece, B.A., 1961; University of York, D.Phil., 1969. *Office:* Department of Economics, University of York, York YO15DD, England.

CAREER: Ministry of Economic Co-ordination, Athens, Greece, economist, 1963-64; Center of Planning and Economic Research, Athens, economist, 1964-65; University of York, York, England, fellow and lecturer, 1967-78, senior lecturer in economics, 1978—. *Military service:* Greek Army, 1961-62. *Member:* Association of University Teachers, Association of University Teachers of Economics, University Association of Contemporary European Studies.

WRITINGS: Trade Effects of Economic Association with the Common Market: The Case of Greece, Praeger, 1972; (with H. P. Burrow) *Macroeconomics: A Mathematical Introduction,* Wiley, 1974. Contributor of articles to *Economic Journal.*

* * *

HOBERMAN, Mary Ann 1930-

PERSONAL: Born August 12, 1930, in Stamford, Conn.;

daughter of Milton and Dorothy (Miller) Freedman; married Norman Hoberman (an architect and illustrator), February 4, 1951; children: Diane, James, Charles, Margaret. *Education:* Smith College, B.A., 1951. *Home:* 98 Huntington Ridge Rd., Greenwich, Conn. 06830. *Agent:* Russell & Volkening, Inc., 551 Fifth Ave., New York, N.Y. 10017.

WRITINGS—Illustrated by husband, Norman Hoberman, except as noted: *All My Shoes Come in Two's* (poems), Little, Brown, 1957; *How Do I Go?,* Little, Brown, 1958; *Hello and Good-by* (poems), Little, Brown, 1959; *What Jim Knew,* Little, Brown, 1963; *Not Enough Beds for the Babies* (poems), illustrated by Helen Spyer, Little, Brown, 1965; *A Little Book of Little Beasts,* illustrated by Peter Parnall, Simon & Schuster, 1973; *The Looking Book,* illustrated by Jerry Joyner, Knopf, 1973; *The Raucous Auk,* illustrated by Joseph Low, Viking, 1973; *Nuts to You and Nuts to Me,* illustrated by Ronni Solbert, Knopf, 1974; *I Like Old Clothes,* illustrated by Jacqueline Chwast, Knopf, 1976; *Bugs,* illustrated by Victoria Chess, Viking, 1976; *A House Is a House for Me,* illustrated by Betty Fraser, Viking, 1978.

WORK IN PROGRESS: A picture book, for Viking.

* * *

HOBHOUSE, Hermione 1934-

PERSONAL: Born February 2, 1934, in Somerset, England; daughter of Arthur Lawrence and Konradin Huth (Jackson) Hobhouse; married; children: two. *Education:* Lady Margaret Hall, Oxford, B.A., 1954. *Home:* Westcombe Stables, Evercreech, Sheptom Mallet, Somerset, England.

CAREER: Architectural historian. Researcher and scriptwriter with Associated-Rediffusion Television, 1956-58, and Granada Television, 1958-63; free-lance journalist, reviewer, and lecturer; part-time tutor at Architectural Association School, London, England. *Member:* Victorian Society (secretary, 1977—). *Awards, honors:* Alice Davis Hitchcock Medallion of Society of Architectural Historians of Great Britain, 1972, for *Thomas Cubitt: Master Builder.*

WRITINGS: The Ward of Cheap in the City of London: A Short History, Ward of Cheap Club, 1963; *Thomas Cubitt: Master Builder,* Universe, 1971; *Lost London,* Macmillan (London), 1971, Houghton, 1972; *History of Regent Street,* Queen Anne Press, 1976. Contributor to *Architectural Design* and *Country Life.*

SIDELIGHTS: Thomas Lask writes of *Lost London:* "Miss Hobhouse . . . is not an intransigent antiquarian. She knows that streets have to be widened, that fire hazards and unsafe structures have to be removed, that large-scale planning must be undertaken. But too often these moves are haphazard, senseless, shortsighted, or motivated by greed. Her passionate scorn and contempt for what she calls 'official vandalism' should blanch the cheek of every bureaucrat."

BIOGRAPHICAL/CRITICAL SOURCES: New York Times, June 16, 1972.

* * *

HODGE, James L(ee) 1935-

PERSONAL: Born September 18, 1935, in Harrisburg, Pa.; son of Earl Henry and Catherine (Ferber) Hodge; married Janice Dunn, June 21, 1958; children: Geoffrey Lee, Stephen Charles. *Education:* Tufts University, A.B. (magna cum laude), 1957; Pennsylvania State University, A.M., 1960, Ph.D., 1961. *Politics:* Republican. *Home:* 37 Meadowbrook Rd., Brunswick, Me. 04011. *Office:* Department of German, Bowdoin College, Brunswick, Me. 04011.

CAREER: Bowdoin College, Brunswick, Me., instructor, 1961-63, assistant professor, 1963-68, associate professor, 1968-74, professor of German, 1974—, George Taylor Files Professor of Modern Languages, 1977—, chairman of department, 1968—. *Member:* Modern Language Association of America, American Association of Teachers of German, American Association of University Professors. *Awards, honors:* National Defense Education Act grant for research in Vienna, Austria, 1966-67.

WRITINGS: (Editor with Sheema Buehne and Lucille Pinto) *Helen Adolf Festschrift,* Ungar, 1968; *The Portable German Tutor,* Prentice-Hall, 1970. Contributor of articles and reviews to language journals.

WORK IN PROGRESS: Research on linguistic motifs in plays of G. E. Lessing; motifs in European mythology.

* * *

HODGES, Richard E(dwin) 1928-

PERSONAL: Born November 21, 1928, in Los Angeles, Calif.; son of Charles Edward (a forester) and Helen (Barnes) Hodges; married Lois M. Sorenson, September 1, 1962; children: Susan Margaret, Charles Richard. *Education:* Oregon State University, B.Ed., 1953, B.S. in Ed., 1954, M.S., 1958; Stanford University, Ed.D., 1964. *Home:* 1030 Claremont Ct., Tacoma, Wash. 98466. *Office:* School of Education, University of Puget Sound, Tacoma, Wash. 98416.

CAREER: Los Angeles Examiner, Los Angeles, Calif., editorial work, 1948-51; worked as a teacher and principal in Salem, Oregon public schools, 1953-60; University of Chicago, Chicago, Ill., assistant professor, 1964-68, associate professor of education, 1968-74; University of Puget Sound, Tacoma, Wash., professor in and director of School of Education, 1974—. *Military service:* U.S. Army, 1946-48. *Member:* International Reading Association (chairman of psycholinguistics and reading committee), National Conference on Research in English (president, 1972-73), National Council of Teachers of English (member of board of directors), American Educational Research Association.

WRITINGS: (With Paul R. Hanna and Jean S. Hanna) *Spelling: Structure and Strategies,* Houghton, 1971; (with E. Hugh Rudorf) *Language and Learning to Read,* Houghton, 1972. Contributor to *Elementary School Journal, Elementary English, Phi Delta Kappan,* and *Journal of Teachers Education.* Editor, *Elementary School Journal,* 1971-74.

WORK IN PROGRESS: Language Development and Implications for Instruction; theories of writing systems.

* * *

HODGES, Zane Clark 1932-

PERSONAL: Born June 15, 1932, in Washington, D.C.; son of Z. C. (a U.S. civil servant) and Virginia (Henderson) Hodges. *Education:* Wheaton College, Wheaton, Ill., B.A., 1954; Dallas Theological Seminary, Th.M., 1958. *Home:* 5735 Gaston Ave., No. 116, Dallas, Tex. 75214. *Office:* Dallas Theological Seminary, Dallas, Tex. 75204.

CAREER: Dallas Theological Seminary, Dallas, Tex., 1959—, began as assistant professor, currently professor of New Testament literature and exegesis.

WRITINGS: The Hungry Inherit, Moody, 1972. Contributor of articles to *Bibliotheca Sacra* and *Journal of the Evangelical Society.*

WORK IN PROGRESS: The Greek New Testament According to the Majority Text, for Thomas Nelson.

SIDELIGHTS: Zane Hodges toured the Bible lands, including Greece, Israel, and Rome, in 1971.

* * *

HODIN, J(osef) P(aul) 1905-

PERSONAL: Born August 17, 1905, in Prague, Czechoslovakia; son of Edouard David (a photographer) and Rosa (Klug) Hodin; married Doris Pamela Simms, May 22, 1945; children: Michael Vivian, Annabelle. *Education:* Charles University, Prague, Dr. Juris, 1924; studied at Art Academy of Dresden, 1931, Art Academy of Berlin, 1932-33, and Courtauld Institute of Art, London, 1946. *Home and office:* 12 Eton Ave., London NW3 3EH, England.

CAREER: Writer and art critic. Press attache, Government of Norway (London), 1944-45; director of studies and librarian, Institute of Contemporary Arts (London), 1949-54; director of international relations, *Studio International Journal of Modern Art* (London). *Member:* Royal Society of London (fellow), International Association of Art Critics (president of British section), American Society of Aesthetics and Art Criticism, British Society of Aesthetics and Art Criticism (member of executive committee). *Awards, honors:* D.S.M. first class (Czech military award), 1947; first international prize for art criticism, Biennale (Venice), 1954; Cavaliere Uffiziale (Italy), 1956; Saint Olav Medal (Norway), 1958; commander of Order of Merit (Italy), 1966; grand cross of Order of Merit (Austria), 1968; Ph.D., Uppsala University, 1969; Order of Merit first class (Germany), 1969; Silver Cross of Merit (Vienna), 1972; honorary professor of art history, Vienna University, 1975.

WRITINGS: Sven Erixson, A. B. Svensk Litteratur, 1940; *Ernst Josephson: Grundlinjer for en nyinstallning till hans konst, hans sjukdom, hans personlighet*, Broderna Lagerstrom, 1942; *Konst och kritik: till den levande konstkritikens problem* (title means "Art and Criticism"), Broderna Lagerstrom, 1944; *Jan Amos Comenius och vartid* (title means "Jan Amos Comenius and Our Time"), Albert Bonniers Forlag, 1944; *Tommaso G. Masaryk, il filosofo della democrazia*, [Rome], 1945; *Edvard Munch: Nordens genius*, Ljus, 1948; *Isaac Gruenewald*, Ljus, 1949.

Moore, De Lange, 1956, Universe Books, 1959; *The Dilemma of Being Modern: Essays on Art and Literature*, Routledge & Kegan Paul, 1956, Noonday Press, 1959; *Ben Nicholson: The Meaning of His Art*, A. Tiranti, 1957.

Barbara Hepworth, Editions du Griffon, 1961, D. McKay, 1962; *Chadwick*, Universe Books, 1961; (author of introduction) *Emilio Greco: Sculptures and Drawings* (exhibition catalog), The Contemporaries, Inc., 1961; *Alan Reynolds*, Redfern Artists Series, 1962; *Bekenntnis zu Kokoschka*, F. Kupferberg, 1963; *Edvard Munch: der Genius des Nordens*, F. Kupferberg, 1963; *Oskar Kokoschka: The Artist and His Time: A Biographical Study*, New York Graphic Society, 1966; *Walter Kern*, Wittenborn, 1966; *Ruszkowski: Life and Work*, Cory, Adams & Mackay, 1966; (author of introduction and biographical note) Bernard Leach, *A Potter's Work*, Evelyn, Adams & Mackay, 1967; *Oskar Kokoschka: sein Leben, seine Zeit*, F. Kupferberg, 1968; *Kafka und Goethe: zur Problematik unseres Zeitalters*, Odysseus, 1968; *Die Bruehlsche Terrasse: Ein Kuenstlerroman*, H. Christians, 1969; (author of introduction) Giacomo Manzu, *Raccolta amici di Manzu* (catalogue), Ardea Roma, 1969.

Oskar Kokoschka: Eine Psychographie, Europa-Verlag, 1971; *Emilio Greco: Sculpture and Drawings* (monograph and biography), New York Graphic Society, 1971; *Manessier*, Praeger, 1972; *Edvard Munch*, Praeger, 1972; *Modern Art and the Modern Mind*, Press of Case Western Reserve University, 1972; *Bernard Stern: Paintings and Drawings*, Three Eagles, 1972; *Kokoschka and Hellas*, Euro Art, 1973; *Hilde Goldschmidt: Leben und Werk*, Hans Christians Verlag, 1973; *Ludwig Meidner: seine Kunst, seine Persoenlichkeit, seine Zeit*, Justus von Liebig Verlag, 1973; *Paul Berger-Bergner: Leben und Werk*, Hans Christians Verlag, 1974; *John Milne, Sculptor*, Latimer, 1977; *Else Meidner, Leben und Werk*, Justus von Liebig Verlag, 1978. Contributor to international journals. Co-editor, *Prisme des Artes* (Paris), 1956-59; co-editor, *Quadrum* (Brussels), 1956-66; member of editorial council, British Society of Aesthetics.

WORK IN PROGRESS: A Prague Youth (autobiographical novel); books on Elisabeth Frink and Franz Luby.

AVOCATIONAL INTERESTS: Reading and international travel.

BIOGRAPHICAL/CRITICAL SOURCES: Walter Kern, editor, *J. P. Hodin: European Critic*, Cory, Adams & Mackay, 1965.

* * *

HOELZEL, Alfred 1934-

PERSONAL: Born February 21, 1934, in Vienna, Austria; son of Simon (a bookkeeper) and Fanny (Stern) Hoelzel; married Helga Y. Wolf, April 7, 1957; children: Esther, Rachel, Daniel. *Education:* University of Massachusetts, B.A., 1955; Northwestern University, M.A., 1956; Boston University, Ph.D., 1964. *Home:* 30 Stetson St., Brookline, Mass. 02146. *Office:* Department of German, University of Massachusetts, Boston, Mass. 02116.

CAREER: Boston Public Latin School, Boston, Mass., teacher of modern languages, 1957-64; Brookline Public Schools, Brookline, Mass., director of foreign languages, 1964-65; University of Massachusetts—Boston, assistant professor, 1965-68, associate professor, 1968-75, professor of German, 1975—. *Military service:* U.S. Army, 1957-58. *Member:* American Association of Teachers of German, Modern Language Association of America.

WRITINGS: (With Jack Moeller, Robert Simmons, and Elfi Tangert) *German One*, Houghton, 1970; (with Moeller, Lynn Dhority, and Tangert) *German Two*, Houghton, 1970, revised edition, 1976. Contributor to *German Quarterly, Monatshefte, Lessing Yearbook*, and *Midstream*.

WORK IN PROGRESS: Translating a book of comedies from the German of Walter Hasenclever; writing articles on *Faust* and on Holocaust literature.

* * *

HOENIGER, F(rederick) David 1921-

PERSONAL: Surname is pronounced *Hen*-ni-ger; born April 25, 1921, in Germany; married Judith Whitaker (a microbiologist), September 13, 1954; children: Brian, Cathleen. *Education:* University of Toronto, B.A. (honors), 1946, M.A. (honors), 1948; University of London, Ph.D., 1954. *Home:* 133 Roxborough Dr., Toronto, Ontario, Canada M4W 1X5. *Office:* English Section, Victoria College, University of Toronto, Toronto, Ontario, Canada M5S 1K7.

CAREER: University of Saskatchewan, Saskatoon, member of faculty, 1946-47; University of Toronto, Victoria College, Toronto, Ontario, instructor, 1948-51, 1953-55, assistant professor, 1955-61, associate professor, 1961-63, professor of English, 1963—, director, Centre for Reformation and Renaissance Studies. *Member:* Renaissance Society of America, Canadian Society for Renaissance Studies (president, 1976-78), Toronto Field Naturalists Club (president, 1961-62). *Awards, honors:* Guggenheim fellowship, 1964-65.

WRITINGS: (Editor) William Shakespeare, *Pericles,* Harvard University Press, 1963; (editor with T. P. Harrison) *Edward Topsell: The Fowles of Heaven,* University of Texas Press, 1972. General editor, "The Revels Plays," Methuen, 1971-75, Manchester University Press, 1976—.

*   *   *

HOFFMAN, Bernard G(ilbert)   1925-

PERSONAL: Born December 14, 1925, in Butte, Mont.; son of Rudolph O. (a professor) and Henrietta (Mahy) Hoffman; married Lillian Miller, September 27, 1957 (died, 1970). *Education:* University of Montana, B.A., 1946; University of California, Ph.D., 1955. *Home:* 2522 Drexel St., Vienna, Va. 22180.

CAREER: U.S. Department of Justice, Lands Division, Indian Claims Section, Washington, D.C., research analyst in anthropology, 1955-56; American University, Foreign Area Study Division, Special Operations Research Organization, Washington, D.C., research associate, 1957-58; National Science Foundation, Washington, D.C., research analyst for Foreign Science Information Program of Office of Scientific Information Service, 1958-64, and assistant director of Course Content Improvement Program of Studies and Curriculum Improvement Section of Division of Pre-College Education in Science, 1964-65; University of Maryland at College Park, associate professor of anthropology, 1965-77; self-employed, 1977—. *Member:* American Anthropological Association, American Association for the Advancement of Science, American Archaeological Society, New York Academy of Sciences.

WRITINGS: Cabot to Cartier: Sources for a Historical Ethnography of Northeastern North America, 1497-1550, University of Toronto Press, 1961, second edition, 1968; *The Structure of Traditional Moroccan Rural Society,* Mouton, 1967.

WORK IN PROGRESS: Micmac Indians of Nova Scotia and New Brunswick; Ethnohistory of Eastern North American Indians.

*   *   *

HOFFMEISTER, Adolf   1903-1973

1903—July 25, 1973; Czech graphic artist, educator, diplomat, author, and translator. Obituaries: *New York Times,* July 26, 1973; *Washington Post,* July 26, 1973.

*   *   *

HOFLING, Charles K(reimer)   1920-

PERSONAL: Born April 22, 1920, in Cincinnati, Ohio; son of Charles Andrew, Jr. (a physician) and Edith (Kreimer) Hofling; married Madelyn Gibson Laymon, December 25, 1945; children: Deborah Gail Hofling Witonski, Charles Andrew III, Karen Clark, Mark Laymon. *Education:* Attended Ohio University, 1937-39; University of Cincinnati, B.A. (with high honors), 1942, M.D., 1946; University of Pennsylvania, medical studies, 1942-43. *Politics:* Independent. *Religion:* Episcopalian. *Home:* 501 North Mosley Rd., St. Louis, Mo. 63141. *Office:* 1221 South Grand Blvd., St. Louis, Mo. 63104.

CAREER: Cincinnati General Hospital, Cincinnati, Ohio,

intern, 1946-47, assistant resident, 1947-48, chief resident, 1949-50; psychiatric resident at Winter Veterans Administration Hospital and Menninger Clinic, Topeka, Kan., and fellow of Menninger Clinic, 1948-49; University of Cincinnati, College of Medicine, Cincinnati, instructor, 1950-52, 1954-56, assistant professor, 1956-64, associate professor of psychiatry, 1964-68, visiting associate professor, 1968-71, visiting professor of psychiatry, 1971—; St. Louis University, School of Medicine, St. Louis, Mo., professor of psychiatry, 1968—. Cincinnati General Hospital, member of attending staff, 1954-68, director of psychiatric consultation service, 1966-68; member of attending staff, St. Louis University Group Hospitals, 1968—. Diplomate and examiner, American Board of Psychiatry and Neurology. Trustee, Pastoral Counseling Institute (St. Louis), 1972—. *Military service:* U.S. Army, 1942-46; became second lieutenant. U.S. Air Force, Medical Corps, 1952-54; became captain.

MEMBER: American College of Psychiatrists (fellow), American College of Psychoanalysts (fellow), American Medical Association, American Psychiatric Association (fellow), American Psychosomatic Society, Association for Applied Psychoanalysis, Association of American Medical Colleges, Association of Directors of Psychiatric Residency Training, Pan-American Medical Association (diplomate), American Association for the Advancement of Science, Society for Health and Human Values, Society of Humanistic Psychology, Society for the Scientific Study of Religion, Institute for Theological Encounter with Science and Technology, American Association of University Professors, New York Academy of Sciences, Missouri Historical Society, Phi Beta Kappa, Sigma Xi, Alpha Omega Alpha, Cosmos Club (Washington, D.C.), University Club (Cincinnati).

WRITINGS: (With Madeleine Leininger) *Basic Psychiatric Concepts in Nursing,* Lippincott, 1960, 4th edition, 1979; (with others) *Textbook of Psychiatry for Medical Practice,* Lippincott, 1963, 3rd edition, 1975; (editor with Paul Ornstein and contributor) *Memos to Maury: Essays in Applied Psychoanalysis,* Grune, 1968; (editor with Gene Usdin) *Aging: The Process and the People,* Bruner/Mazell, 1978.

Contributor: Milton Kramer, editor, *Dream Psychology and the New Biology of Dreaming,* C. C Thomas, 1969; M. D. Faber, editor, *Psychoanalytic Approaches to Shakespeare,* Science House, 1969; Leonard Bickman and Thomas Henchy, editors, *Beyond the Laboratory: Field Research in Social Psychology,* McGraw, 1972; James Robinson, editor, *The Mayor of Casterbridge: Critical Essays,* Norton, 1976; Usdin, editor, *Depression: Clinical, Biological and Psychological Perspectives,* Bruner/Mazell, 1977; Sidney Smith, editor, *The Human Mind Revisited,* Basic Books, 1978. Co-author of section on drug therapy in *Progress in Neurology and Psychiatry,* Grune, annually, 1966-72.

Recorded lectures include "Psychological Aspects of Creative Writing" and "Hemingway's *The Old Man and the Sea,"* McGraw Sound Seminars, 1969. Contributor of articles, reviews, and editorials to medical journals and to *Shakespeare Studies* and *American Imago.*

Member of editorial board, *Journal of Hospital and Community Psychiatry,* 1966-72, and *Bulletin of the Menninger Clinic,* 1970—; American College of Psychiatrists, member of publications committee, 1969—, co-editor, 1978—.

WORK IN PROGRESS: A psychological study of the Hamilton-Burr duel; a clinical study of psychiatric patients who show a favorable response to the deaths of significant figures; a psychohistorical study of General Custer.

SIDELIGHTS: Charles Hofling told *CA* that he has been influenced "among psychiatrists, by Karl Menninger and among historians, by Winston Churchill." His works have appeared in French, Spanish and Japanese editions. *Avocational interests:* Riding, playing piano, tennis, bridge, chess, coin collecting.

*   *   *

HOFSTEDE, Geert H(endrik) 1928-

PERSONAL: Legal given name Gerard; born October 2, 1928, in Haarlem, the Netherlands; son of Gerrit and Evertine G. (Veenhoven) Hofstede; married Maaike A. Van den Hoek, June 4, 1955; children: Gert-Jan, Rokus, Bart P., P. Gideon. *Education:* Delft Institute of Technology, M.Sc., 1953; Groningen University, Ph.D. (cum laude), 1967. *Office:* European Institute for Advanced Studies in Management, 20 Place Stephanie, Box 15/16, 1050 Brussels, Belgium.

CAREER: Berenschot Consultants and Stork Machine Works, Hengelo, Netherlands, management consultant, 1955-59; Jovanda Hosiery Co., Hengelo, plant manager, 1959-60; Menko Textile Co., Enschede, Netherlands, production manager of weaving, 1961-63, director of staff services, 1963-65; IBM European Education Center, Blaricum, Netherlands, manager of personnel research, 1965-71; IMEDE Management Development Institute, Lausanne, Switzerland, visiting lecturer, 1971-73; European Institute for Advanced Studies in Management, Brussels, Belgium, professor of organizational behavior, 1973—. Visiting professor of organizational behavior, INSEAD, Fontainebleau, France, 1973—; visiting scientist, IIASA (Laxenburg Castle, Austria), 1979. *Military service:* Netherlands Army, 1953-55; became first lieutenant. *Awards, honors:* Annual Efficiency Award of Dutch Management Association, 1968, for *The Game of Budget Control.*

WRITINGS: The Game of Budget Control, Van Gorcum, 1967, 2nd edition, 1969; *Baas en Budget,* Samsom, 1968, 2nd edition, 1973; (editor with M. S. Kassem) *European Contributions to Organization Theory,* Van Gorcum, 1976; (editor) *Futures for Work,* Nijhoff, 1979.

Contributor: E.C.H. Marx and A.W.M. Teulings, editors, *Samenspel van Managers en Specialisten,* Spectrum, 1969; *Handboek voor Managers,* Kluwer, 1971; P.J.D. Drenth, P.J. Willems, and C. J. de Wolff, editors, *Arbeids-en Organisatie-psychologie,* Kluwer, 1973; H. C. de Bettignies, editor, *Maitriser le changement dans l'entreprise?,* Editions d'Organisation, 1975; C. B. Tilanus, editor, *Quantitative Methods in Budgeting,* Nijhoff, 1976; Y. H. Poortinga, editor, *Basic Problems in Cross-Cultural Psychology,* Swets & Zeitlinger, 1977; M. Ghertman and J. Leontiades, editors, *European Research in International Business,* North-Holland Publishing, 1978; B. Wilpert and A. R. Negandhi, editors, *Work Organizatiol. Research: European and American Perspectives,* Kent State University Press, 1978; C. L. Cooper and E. Mumford, editors, *The Quality of Working Life in Eastern and Western Europe,* Associated Business Press, 1979; C. J. Lammers and D. J. Hickson, editors, *Organizations Alike and Unlike: Towards a Comparative Sociology of Organizations,* Routledge & Kegan Paul, 1979; L. H. Eckensberger, W. J. Lonner, and Poortinga, editors, *Cross-Cultural Contributions to Psychology,* Swets & Zeitlinger, 1979; E. Grochla, editor, *Handwoerterbuch der Organisation,* 2nd edition (Hofstede was not associated with earlier edition), Poeschel, 1979. Contributor of numerous articles to professional, social science, and man-

agement journals in ten countries, including the Netherlands, United States, and Germany.

WORK IN PROGRESS: Dimensions of National Culture: Value Systems in Organizations in Forty Countries.

SIDELIGHTS: Geert H. Hofstede told *CA:* "*Dimensions of National Culture* is my *chef d'oeuvre.* I have said pathetically that it has been written with blood; I sacrificed two careers in order to be able to do the research for it. However, being able to follow one's own intellectual interests outweighs many a career." *Avocational interests:* European and Middle-Eastern archaeology.

*   *   *

HOGAN, Robert F(rancis) 1927-

PERSONAL: Born August 20, 1927, in Oakland, Calif.; son of John P. and Anne (Murphy) Hogan; married Patricia Stitt, September 2, 1950; children: Anne, John, Mary, Elizabeth. *Education:* University of California, Santa Barbara, B.A., 1950; University of California, Berkeley, M.A., 1958; University of Illinois at Urbana-Champaign, Ph.D., 1972. *Home:* 1105 West Park St., Champaign, Ill. 61820. *Office:* National Council of Teachers of English, 1111 Kenyon Rd., Urbana, Ill. 61801.

CAREER: High school English teacher in Pleasant Hill, Calif., 1953-57; University of California, Demonstration Secondary School, Oakland, English teacher, 1954-60, supervisor of teaching of English, School of Education, 1957-60; Diablo Valley College, Pleasant Hill, Calif., instructor in English, 1957-60; College Entrance Examination Board, New York, N.Y., assistant director of commission on English, 1960-62; National Council of Teachers of English, Urbana, Ill., assistant executive secretary, 1962-65, associate executive secretary, 1965-68, executive secretary, 1968—. *Military service:* U.S. Naval Reserve, active duty, 1945-46. *Member:* National Council of Teachers of English.

WRITINGS: (Editor) Arthur Koestler, *Darkness at Noon,* Macmillan, 1963; (with James R. Squire and Robert S. Whitman) *The National Interest and the Continuing Education of Teachers of English,* National Council of Teachers of English, 1964; (contributor) Glenys Unruh, editor, *New Curriculum Developments,* Association for Supervision and Curriculum Development, 1965; (editor) *The English Language in the School Program,* National Council of Teachers of English, 1966; (with John Frank) *Obscenity, the Law, and the English Teacher,* National Council of Teachers of English, 1966; (contributor) Robert R. Leeper, editor, *Supervision: Emerging Profession,* Association for Supervision and Curriculum Development, 1969; (contributor) John Maxwell and Anthony Tovatt, editors, *On Writing Behavioral Objectives for English,* National Council of Teachers of English, 1970. Contributor to English and education journals.

*   *   *

HOKE, John (Lindsay) 1925-

PERSONAL: Born June 26, 1925, in Pittsburgh, Pa.; son of John (an editor) and Helen Hoke (a writer and editor; surname now Watts); married Sylvia Hyde, June 25, 1950; children: Franklin, Bonnie, Edward, Larry. *Education:* Antioch College, B.A., 1950. *Home:* 5421 Waneta Rd., Washington, D.C. 20016. *Office:* Division of Urban and Environmental Activities, National Capital Parks, National Park Service, U.S. Department of Interior, Washington, D.C. 20242.

CAREER: American Automobile Association, Washington, D.C., technician in motion picture production and photographic laboratory, 1950-57; International Cooperation Administration, communications media officer in Paramaribo, Surinam (Netherlands Guiana), 1957-61; self-employed as writer and inventor, 1961-62; Agency for International Development, Communications Resources Division, Washington, D.C., development officer, 1962-63; Atlantic Research Corp., Alexandria, Va., engineer, 1963-66; U.S. Department of Interior, Washington, D.C., Bureau of Outdoor Recreation, writer-editor in Division of Nationwide Planning, 1966-67, program liaison specialist in Division of Environmental Conservation, 1967-70, National Park Service, program liaison specialist in Division of Urban Park Programs, 1970-72, urban parks program specialist for National Capital Region, 1972—. Designer of Hoke Electric Vehicle, a solar powered boat, and small power sources for remote field operation of electrical equipment, including one for archaeological field use by National Geographic Society; helped develop field incubator to transport eggs of whooping cranes and other endangered species. Photographer and producer of documentary films. *Awards, honors:* Meritorious Service Award of U.S. Department of Interior for conversion of Bolivar Pond into wetlands ecosystem.

WRITINGS—Juvenile books, except as indicated: *The First Book of Snakes,* F. Watts, 1952; *The First Book of Photography,* F. Watts, 1957, revised edition, 1965; *Music Boxes: Their Lure and Lore* (adult), Hawthorn, 1957; *The First Book of the Jungle,* F. Watts, 1963; *The First Book of the Guianas,* F. Watts, 1964; *The First Book of Solar Energy,* F. Watts, 1968, revised edition published as *Solar Energy,* 1978; *Turtles and Their Care,* F. Watts, 1970; *Ecology: The Environment, Its Mechanisms, and Man,* F. Watts, 1971, revised edition, 1977; *Terrariums,* F. Watts, 1972; *Aquariums,* F. Watts, 1975; *Discovering the World of the Three-Toed Sloth,* F. Watts, 1976. Author and illustrator of book-length article on the three-toed sloth for *National Geographic;* contributor to government publications and popular and technical periodicals, including *Popular Science, Ranger Rick, Popular Mechanics, Aquarium,* and *National Geographic School Bulletin.*

SIDELIGHTS: John Hoke's interest in electric power sources antedates the current surge of concern about environment. While in Surinam he designed and fabricated a collapsible light-weight watercraft that could operate on a noiseless electric drive in vegetation-choked waterways. After his return to the United States, he incorporated this concept into the Solar Boat, a craft powered by sunlight. After that he began working on a simple low-cost electric vehicle for urban use, one that could be built "from items already on the shelf" to operate without fouling the air. He took several months leave in 1966 to develop the version he finally settled on, logged 1,600 miles in test drives around Washington, and assisted in the Senate hearings on electric vehicles. Television viewers saw his car and other selected electric prototypes on the "Today" show, March 14, 1967.

In 1968 Hoke suggested putting logs, plants, turtles and fish into one of Washington's many reflecting pools. The conversion of the stagnant Simon Bolivar pool to a living ecosystem has saved the government thousands of dollars a year in maintenance costs because it cleans itself naturally. In addition it has become so popular with the public that several other pools have received the same treatment.

For lack of a better term, Hoke is described by his employer as an "urban parks program specialist." He is perhaps more completely described by UPI reporter Mike Feinsilber as "the village visionary, the class inventor, the technology zealot, the tinkerer who can't accept the way things are."

His current project is convincing officials at the Interior building to put a park on its 70,000 square foot roof. Hoke told a *Washington Post* reporter that the building could easily support the weight and that, like the reflecting pools, this project could save the department money. "[The] earth would act as insulation," he said, and "protect the roof from . . . the wind and weather that make roof maintenance the largest expense of most government buildings." He added, "The roofs of Washington are a vast undiscovered country. . . . Here we have an opportunity to put back—eight, ten, fifteen stories up in the air—the natural environment we destroyed and stripped bare on the ground." And, as he told Feinsilber, "the irony is, the denser the city, the more of this peculiar land there is."

Hoke is the inventor of a solar-powered air-conditioned pith helmet. He also has designed miniature environments for classroom use, devised a simplified system of classification for tropical vegetation, and designed or modified photographic devices. A licensed diver, he served as watch director on the Tektite II program in the Virgin Islands.

BIOGRAPHICAL/CRITICAL SOURCES: New Republic, August 13, 1966; *Life,* October 21, 1966; *Washington Post,* September 22, 1977; *Detroit Free Press,* October 5, 1978.

*   *   *

HOLDEN, David (Shipley)   1924-1977
(David Shipley)

PERSONAL: Born November 20, 1924, in Sunderland, England; son of Thomas Shipley (a journalist) and Ethel (Stocks) Holden; married Ruth Lynam (a journalist and public relations adviser), August 24, 1962. *Education:* Emmanuel College, Cambridge, B.A. (honors), 1946, M.A., 1950; Northwestern University, M.A., 1951. *Politics:* "Independent of any party, liberal inclination." *Residence:* London, England. *Agent:* Julian Bach, 3 East 48th St., New York, N.Y. 10017. *Office: Sunday Times,* 200 Gray's Inn Rd., London W.C.1, England.

CAREER: Teacher of geography in Scottish secondary schools in Duns, 1947-49, and Leith, 1949-50; *The Times,* London, England, Washington correspondent, 1955-56, Middle East correspondent, 1956-60, special foreign correspondent, 1960-61; *The Guardian,* Manchester and London, England, special foreign correspondent, 1961-65; *The Sunday Times,* London, chief foreign correspondent, 1965-77. *Member:* Royal Institute of International Affairs, Royal Society of Arts, National Union of Journalists.

WRITINGS: (Contributor) Mortimer Smith, editor, *The Public Schools in Crisis,* Regnery, 1956; *Farewell to Arabia,* Walker & Co., 1966; *Greece without Columns,* Lippincott, 1972. Author of television documentaries and radio scripts for British Broadcasting Corp.

WORK IN PROGRESS: A book on Africa.

SIDELIGHTS: David Holden told *CA:* "I drifted into journalism out of family habits and lack of other commitments and have taken to writing books occasionally as a way of retaining some sanity. I like bird-watching, gardening, and traveling, especially among the ruins of antiquity. I wish I spoke Arabic, Chinese, Russian, and Italian, but I don't."

Shortly after arriving in Egypt in late 1977, Holden was found shot to death in the desert near the Cairo Airport. Though his killers have never been positively identified, Egyptian police believe he was murdered for political reasons by members of an intelligence organization. A special press award has been created in his memory.

BIOGRAPHICAL/CRITICAL SOURCES: New York Times, December 12, 1977; London *Times,* December 12, 1977, December 18, 1977, December 19, 1977.†

(Died December, 1977)

* * *

HOLDER, Glenn 1906-

PERSONAL: Born October 9, 1906, in Lynnville, Ind.; son of Charles W. (a farmer) and Clara (Seltzer) Holder; married Helen Scales (an elementary school teacher), December 22, 1934; children: William G., John C. *Education:* DePauw University, A.B., 1927; Indiana University, A.M., 1935, Ed.D., 1964. *Home and office:* 101 Northwest Seventh St., Richmond, Ind. 47374.

CAREER: Richmond, Ind. public schools, English teacher, 1931-56, director of secondary education, 1957-66; Ball State University, Muncie, Ind., assistant professor of English, 1966-73. *Member:* National Council of Teachers of English, Midwest English Conference (executive secretary, 1967-73).

WRITINGS: (With Jerome Carlin and Henry Christ) *English on the Job,* Globe Book, Volume I, 1943, 4th edition, 1970, Volume II, 1961, 3rd edition, 1970; (editor with son, William G. Holder) *Saturn: The Moon Rocket,* Messner, 1969, 2nd edition, 1970; *Talking Totem Poles,* Dodd, 1973. Also editor of language films. Contributor to professional journals.

WORK IN PROGRESS: A book on the retrieval, restoration, and protection of authentic totem poles, for Dodd.

* * *

HOLLAND, Lynwood M. 1905-

PERSONAL: Born March 31, 1905, in Bronwood, Ga.; son of John C. (a businessman) and Mary Ann (Martin) Holland; married Wilma Martin, August 18, 1945. *Education:* Emory University, A.B., 1932, A.M., 1933; University of Illinois, Ph.D., 1945. *Politics:* Democrat. *Religion:* Methodist. *Address:* P.O. Box 185, Bronwood, Ga. 31726.

CAREER: Assistant professor of political science, University of Georgia, 1937-40; University of Arizona, Tucson, assistant professor of political science, 1945-46; Emory University, Atlanta, Ga., assistant professor, 1946-47, associate professor, 1947-50, professor of political science, 1950-67, chairman of department, 1950-65; Texas Tech University, Lubbock, professor of political science and chairman of department, 1967-71. *Military service:* U.S. Army Air Forces, 1942-45; became sergeant. *Member:* American Political Science Association, Southern Political Science Association, Western Political Science Association, Phi Beta Kappa, Omicron Delta Kappa, Pi Sigma Alpha.

WRITINGS: The Direct Primary in Georgia, University of Illinois Press, 1947; *The Administrative Agencies of Georgia,* Neff, 1949; *State and Local Government in the United States,* Prentice-Hall, 1951; *Georgia Government,* Steck-Vaughn, 1959; *P.M.B. Young: The Warwick of the South,* University of Georgia, 1962; *The End of the Log,* Levy Press, 1967.

WORK IN PROGRESS: A political novel; research on intergovernmental relations.

* * *

HOLLIS, James R(ussell) 1940-

PERSONAL: Born May 17, 1940, in Springfield, Ill.; son of Harold E. (an industrial manager) and Gladys L. (Lindgren) Hollis; married Bonnie J. Smith (a journalist), May 27, 1962; children: Taryn L., Timothy J. *Education:* Manchester College, A.B., 1962; Drew University, Ph.D., 1967. *Home:* 2497 Venezia Ave., Vineland, N.J. 08360. *Office:* Department of Literature, Stockton State College, Pomona, N.J. 08240.

CAREER: Manchester College, North Manchester, Ind., assistant professor, 1967-69, associate professor of English, 1969-73; Stockton State College, Pomona, N.J., associate professor of humanities, 1973—, on leave to Jung Institute (Zurich, Switzerland), 1977-80. Member of board of directors, Wabash County Arts Council. Team leader for National Humanities Series Program, "Language: The Human Connection." *Member:* Modern Language Association of America, Midwest Modern Language Association. *Awards, honors:* Rockefeller fellow, 1962-63.

WRITINGS: (Contributor) Barbara MacKenzie, editor, *The Process of Fiction,* Harcourt, 1968; *Harold Pinter: The Poetics of Silence,* Southern Illinois University Press, 1970; *Modern Life Styles,* with instructor's manual, Scott, Foresman, 1971; (editor and author of introduction) *Watermarks* (poems), Church of Brethren Press, 1971. Contributor to language journals.

WORK IN PROGRESS: A book, as yet untitled, combining the fields of literature, philosophy, and depth psychology in an examination of the theme of tracing the lost gods in modern culture.

* * *

HOLME, Thea 1903-

PERSONAL: Born December 27, 1903, in London, England; daughter of Philip Mainwaring (an architect) and Florence Anna (Wynne) Johnston; married Leicester Stanford Holme, April 17, 1926; children: Timothy Philip. *Education:* Attended Slade School of Art, University College, London, and Central School for Speech Training and Dramatic Art. *Home:* 13 Coleshill Village, Highworth, SN6 7PR, Wiltshire, England.

CAREER: Actress; radio and television script writer; author. Toured with Ben Greet Players, in England and on one trip to the United States, as a leading Shakespearean actress, 1924-29; played numerous roles in London, England, 1931-39; became member of original British Broadcasting Corp. (BBC) repertory company, 1939; leading actress with Stratford-on-Avon Festival Company, 1940, and Arts Council Tours, 1942-44; actress in BBC-TV "classics." *Member:* Royal Society of Literature (fellow).

WRITINGS: The Carlyles at Home, Oxford University Press, 1965; *Chelsed,* Taplinger, 1972; *Prinny's Daughter: Biography of Princess Charlotte of Wales,* Hamish Hamilton, 1976; *This Most Imprudent Lady,* Hamish Hamilton, in press.

Drama: "Roman Holiday," produced at Oxford, 1937, produced in London under title "Love at Short Sight," 1938; "Northanger Abbey" and "Mansfield Park," adapted from Jane Austen novels, produced at Theatre Royal, Windsor, 1955-56; two episodes of "Dear and Honoured Lady," BBC television, 1976. Also author of adaptations, serials and feature programs for radio, including biographies of Jane Austen, and a series called "Married to a Genius," on the wives of great men.

* * *

HOLMES, Charles S(hiveley) 1916-1976

PERSONAL: Born January 13, 1916, in Oberlin, Ohio; son

of Harry N. and Mary (Shiveley) Holmes; married Marian T. Crain, August 6, 1937. *Education:* Oberlin College, A.B., 1938; Princeton University, Ph.D., 1941. *Politics:* Democrat. *Religion:* Episcopalian. *Home:* 1010 Berkeley Ave., Claremont, Calif. 91711. *Office:* Pomona College, Claremont, Calif. 91711.

CAREER: Pomona College, Claremont, Calif., instructor, 1941-43, assistant professor, 1946-47, associate professor, 1947-58, professor of English, 1958-76. Fulbright professor, University of Graz, 1955-56, University of Vienna, 1962-63. *Military service:* U.S. Naval Reserve, active duty, 1943-46; became lieutenant. *Member:* Modern Language Association of America, Authors Guild, Philological Association of the Pacific Coast. *Awards, honors:* American Council of Learned Societies research grant, 1966-67.

WRITINGS: (Editor with Edwin Fussell and Ray Frazer) *The Major Critics,* Knopf, 1957; *The Clocks of Columbus: The Literary Career of James Thurber,* Atheneum, 1972; (editor) *Thurber: A Collection of Critical Essays,* Prentice-Hall, 1974. Contributor to *Yale Review, South Atlantic Quarterly,* and other journals.

WORK IN PROGRESS: Research on contemporary humorists.

SIDELIGHTS: Charles Holmes's *The Clocks of Columbus: The Literary Career of James Thurber* "concentrates chiefly on Thurber's role as a literary stylist," according to reviewer William Hogan. "Holmes is a dedicated Thurber scholar who has done his homework exhaustively and with affection for his subject. The fact that, in a retelling of many familiar tales . . . his prose generates less magic than Thurber's did is not the biographer's fault. Thurber wrote like some unicorn in a garden, and Holmes is merely a mortal scholar, a solid writer rather than an exciting one. . . . *The Clocks of Columbus* might send a multitude of readers back to the [Thurber] originals . . . and that in itself is a favor to us all."

AVOCATIONAL INTERESTS: Theater, travel, golf, swimming.

BIOGRAPHICAL/CRITICAL SOURCES: Saturday Review, October 21, 1972; *Time,* November 20, 1972; *New York Times,* January 17, 1976; *Washington Post,* January 17, 1976.†

(Died January 15, 1976)

* * *

HOLMES, Douglas 1933-

PERSONAL: Born December 7, 1933, in Bridgeport, Conn.; son of Myron (an architect) and Margaret (Moore) Holmes; married Monica Bychowski (a psychologist), June 9, 1959; children: Deborah, Gregory, Pamela. *Education:* Attended Rensselaer Polytechnic Institute, 1954; Tufts University, B.A., 1958; New York University, Ph.D., 1962. *Home:* 80 Steephill Rd., Weston, Conn. 06680; and 45 East 89th St., New York, N.Y. 10028. *Office:* 1560 Broadway, New York, N.Y. 10036.

CAREER: National Council on Alcoholism, New York City, research coordinator, 1961-63; New York City Department of Health, senior research scientist, 1963; Associated Young Men-Young Women Hebrew Associations of Greater New York, New York City, associate director of research, 1963-65; director of research, 1965-69; Center for Community Research, New York City, director, 1969-74; Community Research Applications, Inc., New York City, president, 1972—. Adjunct assistant professor, New York

University, School of Industrial Engineering and Operations Research, 1964-66. Lecturer, Bernard M. Baruch School of Business and Public Administration of the City College (now Bernard M. Baruch College of the City University of New York), 1964-66. Member of faculty, New School for Social Research (New York City), 1977—. Consultant to various private, governmental, social, medical, educational, and corporate organizations, including National Jewish Welfare Board, Harlem Hospital, Odyssey House, Ford Foundation, and U.S. Department of Health, Education, and Welfare. Certified psychologist, New York State and Connecticut. *Military service:* U.S. Army, 1954-56. *Member:* American Orthopsychiatric Association (fellow), American Psychological Association, Gerontological Society.

WRITINGS: (With wife, Monica Bychowski Holmes, and Lisa Appignanesi), *The Language of Trust: A Dialogue of the Generations,* Science House, 1971; (with wife, M. Holmes, and Judith Field) *The Therapeutic Classroom,* Jason Aronson, 1974; (with wife, M. Holmes) *The Service Handbook for Older Americans,* Science House, 1979. Publications include research reports and monographs for National Institute of Mental Health, U.S. Public Health Service, and other agencies. Contributor to professional journals.

* * *

HOLMES, Jack D(avid) L(azarus) 1930-

PERSONAL: Surname originally Lazarus; born July 4, 1930, in Monmouth County, N.J.; son of John Daniel (a realtor) and Waltrude (Hendrickson) Lazarus; married Anne Elizabeth Anthony, 1952 (divorced, 1965); married Martha Austin Reid, 1966 (divorced, 1967); married Gayle Carlson Pannell, 1967 (divorced, 1970); married Stephanie Pasneker (an elementary teacher), April 10, 1971; children: (first marriage) David H. Jack Forrest, Ann M., (third marriage) Daniel J. *Education:* Florida State University, B.A. (cum laude), 1952, graduate study, 1953-54; University of Florida, M.A., 1953; National University of Mexico, graduate study, 1954; University of Texas, Ph.D., 1959; University of Alabama in Birmingham, postdoctoral study, 1963-64. *Home:* 520 South 22nd Ave., Birmingham, Ala. 35205. *Office:* University of Alabama, University Station, Birmingham, Ala. 35294.

CAREER: Memphis State University, Memphis, Tenn., instructor in history, 1956-58; *Memphis Press-Scimitar,* Memphis, staff writer, 1957-58; McNeese State University, Lake Charles, La., assistant professor of history, 1959-61; lecturer in history, University of Maryland Overseas Division, Constantina, Spain, and researcher for U.S. Parks Service, Seville, Spain, 1962; University of Alabama in Birmingham, associate professor, 1963-68, professor of history and political science, 1968—. Consultant to U.S. Parks Service, 1962, Historic Pensacola Preservation Board, Pensacola, Fla., 1968-70, and Mississippi Department of Archives and History, 1978. *Military service:* U.S. Army, 1951.

MEMBER: American Association for State and Local History, Southern Historical Association, Alabama Academy of Sciences, Florida, Louisiana, and Mississippi state historical societies, Tennessee Squire, Phi Beta Kappa, Phi Kappa Phi, Phi Alpha Theta, Sigma Delta Pi, Pi Kappa Phi.

AWARDS, HONORS: American Philosophical Society and Fulbright grants for research in Spain, 1961-62; McClung Award of East Tennessee Historical Society for best articles of 1962, 1964; Louisiana Library Association Award for best book published in Louisiana in 1965, for *Gayoso,* and Alabama Writers' Conclave Award in biography for same book, 1966; Association for the Study of State and Local History grant, 1966; American Philosophical Society grant, 1966; Louisiana Historical Association Award for best article in *Louisiana History*, 1970.

WRITINGS: The Planned Suburban Shopping Center: An Annotated Bibliography, Bureau of Business Research, University of Texas, 1957, revised edition published as *Selected and Annotated Bibliography of the Planned Suburban Shopping Center*, 1960; (editor) *Documentos ineditos para la historia de la Luisiana, 1792-1810*, Ediciones Turanzas (Madrid), 1963; *Gayoso: The Life of a Spanish Governor in the Mississippi Valley, 1789-1799*, Louisiana State University Press, for Louisiana Historical Association, 1965; (editor) *Jose de Evia y sus reconocimientos del Golfo de Mexico, 1783-1796*, Ediciones Turanzas, 1968; (editor) Francis Baily, *Travels on the Western Waters*, Volume III: *Journal of a Tour in Unsettled Parts of North America in 1796 and 1797*, abridged edition, Southern Illinois University Press, 1969; (with Raymond J. Martinez) *New Orleans: Facts and Legends*, Hope Publications (New Orleans), 1970, revised edition, 1972; *New Orleans Drinks and How To Mix Them*, Hope Publications, 1973; *A History of the University of Alabama Hospitals*, University Hospital Auxiliary, 1974; *The 1779 "Marcha de Galvez:" Louisiana's Giant Step Forward in the American Revolution*, Baton Rouge Bicentennial Corp., 1974.

Editor and publisher: "Louisiana Collection Series of Books and Documents on Louisiana History," Volume I: *Honor and Fidelity: The Louisiana Infantry Regiment and the Louisiana Militia Companies, 1766-1821*, 1965, Volume II: *A Guide to Spanish Louisiana, 1762-1806*, 1970, Volume III: *Louisiana in 1776: A Memoria of Francisco Bouligny*, 1977.

Contributor: John F. McDermott, editor, *The French in the Mississippi Valley*, University of Illinois Press, 1965; Raymond J. Martinez, *The Story of Spanish Moss: What It Is and How It Grows*, Hope Publications, 1968; McDermott, editor, *Frenchmen and French Ways in the Mississippi Valley*, University of Illinois Press, 1969; (author of introduction) Luis de Onis, *Memoria sobre las negociaciones entre Espana y los Estados Unidos de America*, Ediciones Turanzas, 1969; Ernest W. Dibble and Earle W. Newton, editors, *In Search of Gulf Coast Colonial History*, Historic Pensacola Preservation Board, 1970; Dibble and Newton, editors, *Spain and Her Rivals on the Gulf Coast*, Historic Pensacola Preservation Board, 1971; James R. McGovern, editor, *Colonial Pensacola*, Pensacola-Escambia County Development Commission, 1972; *History of Mississippi*, two volumes, University Press of Mississippi, 1973; McDermott, editor, *The Spanish in the Mississippi Valley, 1762-1804*, University of Illinois Press, 1974; Charles M. Hudson, editor, *Four Centuries of Southern Indians*, University of Georgia Press, 1975; *Handbook of Texas*, supplement, Texas State Historical Association, 1976; *Encyclopedia of Southern History*, Louisiana State University Press, 1978. Contributor of more than one hundred articles, mainly historical, to journals.

WORK IN PROGRESS: Biographies of Philip Nolan, early frontiersman, Alexander O'Reilly, governor of Louisiana, 1769-1770, and Bernardo de Galvez, captain-general and governor of Louisiana, 1777-1782; editing correspondence between Stephen Minor and Manuel Gayoso de Lemos, 1792-1799, and the works of Joseph, Baron de Pontalba; also writing on the status of the black man in Spanish Louisiana and West Florida, on Alabama settlers, 1780-1813, and on Pensacola settlers, 1781-1821.

SIDELIGHTS: Jack D. L. Holmes draws his book materials from a collection of 50,000 pages of eighteenth-century documents, mostly microfilmed in archives of Spanish history.

*   *   *

HOLMES, Robert L(awrence)   1935-

PERSONAL: Born December 28, 1935, in Watertown, N.Y.; son of Augustus S. and Rhoda (Lawrence) Holmes; married Charlotte Kellogg, September 6, 1958 (separated, 1978); children: Suzanne Rebecca, Timothy Robert. *Education:* Harvard University, A.B., 1957; University of Michigan, M.A., 1959, Ph.D., 1961. *Home:* 12 Buckingham St., Rochester, N.Y. 14607. *Office:* Department of Philosophy, University of Rochester, Rochester, N.Y. 14627.

CAREER: University of Texas, Main University (now University of Texas at Austin), instructor in philosophy, 1961-62; University of Rochester, Rochester, N.Y., assistant professor, 1962-67, associate professor, 1967-71, professor of philosophy, 1971—. Visiting associate professor at University of Michigan, 1967, 1969. Fellow, Center for Advanced Studies, University of Illinois, 1970-71, and National Humanities Institute, Yale University, 1976-77. *Member:* American Philosophical Association, American Association of University Professors. *Awards, honors:* First Prize from Council for Philosophical Studies, 1970, for "Violence and Nonviolence."

WRITINGS: (With Lewis W. Beck) *Philosophic Inquiry*, 2nd edition (Holmes was not associated with 1st edition), Prentice-Hall, 1968. Contributor to *Journal of Philosophy, Mind, Review of Metaphysics, Inquiry, Monist, Journal of Value Inquiry, Ethics*, and *Bulletin of Atomic Scientists*.

WORK IN PROGRESS: A book on the philosophy of war.

*   *   *

HOLT, Robert R(utherford)   1917-

PERSONAL: Original surname, Watson; name legally changed; born December 27, 1917, in Jacksonville, Fla.; son of Walter John Watson (a business executive) and Grace (Hilditch) Watson Holt; married Louisa Pinkham, February, 1944 (divorced, 1952); married Crusa Adelman, December 27, 1957 (died, 1959); married Joan Esterowitz, August 2, 1963; children: (first marriage) Dorothy O. (Mrs. William F. Prickett), Catherine F.; (third marriage) Daniel W., Michael D. *Education:* Princeton University, B.A. (with highest honors), 1939; Harvard University, M.A., 1941, Ph.D., 1944; attended Washington School of Psychiatry and Topeka Institute for Psychoanalysis, 1944-53. *Politics:* Democrat. *Religion:* None. *Home:* 20 East Eighth St., New York, N.Y. 10003. *Office:* Research Center for Mental Health, New York University, 6 Washington Pl., New York, N.Y. 10003.

CAREER: U.S. Department of Agriculture, Washington, D.C., study director, Division of Program Surveys, 1944-46; Winter Veterans Administration Hospital, Topeka, Kan., clinical psychologist, 1946-49; Menninger Foundation, Topeka, instructor, 1946-49, associate psychologist, 1947-49, senior psychologist, 1949-53, director of psychological staff, 1951-53; New York University, New York, N.Y., associate professor, 1953-59, professor of psychology, 1959—, director of Research Center for Mental Health, 1953-63, co-director, 1963-69, senior staff member, 1969—. Instructor, American University, 1944; clinical assistant professor, University of Kansas, 1946-50; lecturer, Topeka Institute for Psychoanalysis, 1949-53; fellow, Center for Advanced Study in the Behavioral Sciences, 1960-61; visiting professor of clinical psychology, Harvard University, 1967-68. Member of fellowship committee, Foundations Fund for Research in Psychiatry, 1956-61; member of board of directors, Scientists on Survival, 1961-63; member, National Institute of Mental Health Extramural Research Advisory Committee, 1968-69; member of board of trustees, Psychological Service Center of New York Society of Clinical Psychologists; member of scientific advisory board, Environmental Defense Fund, 1971—.

MEMBER: American Psychological Association (fellow; president of Division of Clinical Psychology, 1961-62), American Association for the Advancement of Science (fellow), Society for the Psychological Study of Social Issues, Phi Beta Kappa, Sigma Xi. *Awards, honors:* Research career award, National Institute of Mental Health, 1962—; Great Man Award of Society for Projective Techniques and Personality Assessment, 1969; Distinguished Contribution Awards from New York Society of Clinical Psychologists, 1973, and American Psychological Association Division of Clinical Psychology.

WRITINGS: (With Bruno Klopfer, Mary D. Ainsworth, and W. G. Klopfer) *Developments in the Rorschach Technique,* World Book Co., Volume I: *Technique and Theory,* 1954; (with Lester Luborsky) *Personality Patterns of Psychiatrists,* two volumes, Basic Books, 1958; (editor) *Motives and Thought: Psychoanalytic Essays in Memory of David Rapaport,* International Universities Press, 1967; (editor) David Rapaport, M. M. Gill, and Roy Schafer, *Diagnostic Psychological Testing,* revised edition (Holt was not associated with earlier edition), International Universities Press, 1968; (with I. L. Janis, G. F. Mahl, and Jerome Kagan) *Personality: Dynamics, Development, and Assessment,* Harcourt, 1969, Part IV by Holt reprinted as *Assessing Personality,* Harcourt, 1971; (editor and contributor) *New Horizon for Psychotherapy: Autonomy as a Profession,* International Universities Press, 1971; (with H. B. Barr, R. J. Langs, G. S. Klein, and Leo Goldberger) *LSD: Personality and Experience,* Wiley, 1972; (editor with Emanuel Peterfreund, and contributor) *Psychoanalysis and Contemporary Science,* Volume I, Macmillan, 1972; *Methods in Clinical Psychology,* two volumes, Plenum Press, 1978.

Contributor: T. Newcomb and E. Hartley, editors, *Readings in Social Psychology,* Holt, 1947; G. W. Lasker and F. P. Thieme, *Yearbook of Physical Anthropology,* Viking, 1949; H. H. Anderson and G. L. Anderson, editors, *An Introduction to Projective Techniques,* Prentice-Hall, 1951; G. Devereux, *Reality and Dream,* International Universities Press, 1951; E. Shneidman and others, editors, *Thematic Test Analysis,* Grune, 1951; R. Kotinsky and H. L. Witmer, editors, *Community Programs for Mental Health,* Harvard University Press, 1955; S. J. Beck and H. B. Molish, editors, *Reflexes to Intelligence,* Basic, 1959; M. A. Rickers-Ovsiankina, editor, *Rorschach Psychology,* Wiley, 1960; J. G. Peatman and E. L. Hartley, editors, *Festschrift for Gardner Murphy,* Harper, 1960; P. Solomon and others, editors, *Sensory Deprivation,* Harvard University Press, 1961; J. Kagan and G. Lesser, editors, *Contemporary Issues in Thematic Apperceptive Methods,* C. C Thomas, 1961; B. E. Flaherty, editor, *Psychophysiological Aspects of Space Flight,* Columbia University Press, 1961; S. Messick and J. Ross, editors, *Measurement in Personality and Cognition,* Wiley, 1962; R. A. Baker, editor, *Psychology in the Wry,* Van Nostrand, 1963; R. W. White, editor, *The Study of Lives,* Atherton, 1963; F. H. Sanford and E. J. Capaldi,

editors, *Advancing Psychological Science,* Wadsworth, Volume I: *Philosophies, Methods, and Approaches,* 1964; P. Worchel and D. Byrne, editors, *Personality Change,* Wiley, 1964; E. Southwell and M. Merbaum, editors, *Personality: Readings in Theory and Research,* Wadsworth, 1964; M. Zax and G. Stricker, editors, *The Study of Abnormal Behavior: Selected Readings,* Macmillan, 1964, 2nd edition, 1969; B. Wolman, editor, *Handbook of Clinical Psychology,* McGraw, 1965; N. S. Greenfield and W. C. Lewis, editors, *Psychoanalysis and Current Biological Thought,* University of Wisconsin Press, 1965; I. N. Mensh, editor, *Clinical Psychology: Science and Profession,* Macmillan, 1966; E. I. Megargee, editor, *Research in Clincal Assessment,* Harper, 1966; Byrne and M. L. Hamilton, editors, *Personality Research: A Book of Readings,* Prentice-Hall, 1966; E. L. Hoch and others, editors, *Professional Preparation of Clinical Psychologists,* American Psychological Association, 1966; J. H. Masserman, editor, *Science and Psychoanalysis,* Grune, Volume XI: *Concepts of Ego,* 1967; T. Millon, editor, *Theories of Psychopathology,* Saunders, 1967; Wolman, editor, *Historical Roots of Contemporary Psychology,* Harper, 1968; E. P. Torrance and W. F. White, editors, *Issues and Advances in Educational Psychology: A Book of Readings,* F. E. Peacock, 1969; B. L. Kintz and J. L. Bruning, editors, *Research in Psychology: Readings for the Introductory Course,* Scott, Foresman, 1970; B. Klopfer and others, editors, *Developments in the Rorschach Technique,* Harcourt, Volume III: *Aspects of Personality Structure,* 1970; P. W. Sheehan, editor, *The Function and Nature of Imagery,* Academic, 1972.

Contributor to *International Encyclopedia of the Social Sciences* and to scientific journals. Editor, *TAT Newsletter,* 1946-52; member of editorial board, *Journal of Psychological Researches* (Madras, India), 1956—, *Journal of Nervous and Mental Disease,* 1957—, *Psychological Issues,* 1958—, *Handbook of Clinical Psychology,* 1963-65, and *Psychoanalysis and Contemporary Science,* 1969—; member of editorial advisory board, *Journal of Projective Techniques,* 1949-50, and *Journal of Social Issues,* 1949-51; consulting editor, *Journal of Abnormal and Social Psychology,* 1955-60; member of board of consultants, *American Imago,* 1963—.

WORK IN PROGRESS: A book on Freud, the sources of his ideas and their development; a book on the measurement of primary process thinking; research in measuring and enhancing ego development.

*   *   *

HOLTON, (William) Milne 1931-

PERSONAL: Born November 4, 1931, in Charlotte, N.C.; son of William (a salesman) and Mary (Milne) Holton; married Sylvia Wallace (a professor), July 3, 1964. *Education:* Dartmouth College, A.B. (cum laude), 1954; Harvard University, LL.B., 1957; Alliance Francais, graduate study, 1958; Yale University, M.A., 1959, Ph.D., 1965. *Religion:* None. *Office:* Department of English, University of Maryland, College Park, Md. 20742.

CAREER: Admitted to the Bar of the U.S. Supreme Court and the Bar of the State of Tennessee; Roberts & Weil, Chattanooga, Tenn., attorney, 1957; National Education Association, Washington, D.C., counsel to Federal Relations Division, 1959; University of Maryland, College Park, instructor in English, 1961-65; Uppsala University, Uppsala, Sweden, Fulbright lecturer in English, 1965-66; University of Maryland, assistant professor, 1966-72, associate professor, 1972-78, professor of English, 1978—. Fulbright professor of English, University of Skopje, 1970.

MEMBER: Modern Language Association of America, American Literary Translators Association, American Civil Liberties Union, South Atlantic Modern Language Association, Phi Beta Kappa.

WRITINGS: (With David J. Burrows, Lewis M. Dabney, and Grosvenor S. Powell) *Private Dealings: Eight Modern Writers,* Almqvist & Wiksell, 1970; *The Cylinder of Vision: The Fiction and Journalism of Stephen Crane,* Louisiana State University Press, 1972.

Editor and translator: *The Big Horse and Other Stories of Modern Macedonia,* University of Missouri Press, 1974; (with Graham W. Reid) *Reading the Ashes: An Anthology of the Poetry of Modern Macedonia,* University of Pittsburgh Press, 1977; (with Paul Vangelisti) *The New Polish Poetry,* University of Pittsburgh Press, 1978. Contributor to *Criticism, Studia Neophilologica, Modern Language Journal, Contempora, Proof,* and *Chattanooga Times.*

WORK IN PROGRESS: A critical study of the imitations of Robert Lowell; collecting, translating into English, and editing anthologies of nineteenth and twentieth-century Czech and Serbian poetry; further study of writings of Stephen Crane and Skipwith Cannell.

* * *

HONEYCUTT, Roy L(ee), Jr. 1926-

PERSONAL: Born October 30, 1926, in Grenada, Miss.; son of Roy Lee and Gladys (Carpenter) Honeycutt; married June Williams, August 31, 1948; children: Roy Lee III, Mary Ann. *Education:* Mississippi College, B.A., 1950; Southern Baptist Theological Seminary, B.D., 1952, Th.D., 1958; University of Edinburgh, M.Th., 1971. *Home:* 1823 Bainbridge Row Dr., Louisville, Ky. 40207. *Office:* Office of the Provost, Southern Baptist Theological Seminary, 2825 Lexington Rd., Louisville, Ky. 40206.

CAREER: Clergyman of Southern Baptist Church; Midwestern Baptist Theological Seminary, Kansas City, Mo., associate professor, 1959-63, professor of Hebrew and Old Testament, 1963-75; Southern Baptist Theological Seminary, Louisville, Ky., professor of Old Testament interpretation, 1975, dean of school of theology, 1975—; provost, 1976—, academic dean, 1971-75. *Military service:* U.S. Army, 1944-46. *Member:* Society of Biblical Literature, American Academy of Religion, American Schools of Oriental Research, Association of Baptist Professors of Religion, Society for Old Testament Study.

WRITINGS: Amos and His Message, Broadman, 1963; *Crisis and Response,* Abingdon, 1965; *These Ten Words,* Broadman, 1966; *Amos: A Study Guide,* Seminary Extension Department, 1966; (contributor) Olin T. Binkley, editor, *How to Study the Bible,* Convention Press, 1969; (contributor) Clifford Ingle, editor, *Children and Conversion,* Broadman, 1970; (contributor) J. F. Ward and W. E. Green, editors, *Is the Bible a Human Book?,* Broadman, 1970; *Hosea and His Message,* Broadman, 1975. Contributor to *Southwestern Journal of Theology, Review and Expositor, Foundations,* and *Broadman Bible Commentary.* Consulting editor of *Broadman Bible Commentary,* 1969-72.

* * *

HOOPS, Richard A(llen) 1933-

PERSONAL: Born March 3, 1933, in Fort Wayne, Ind.; son of Marion Elmer and Henrietta (Barnett) Hoops; married

Helen W. Johnson, August 17, 1957; children: Keriann, Mark, Drake, Kent. *Education:* Oberlin College, B.A., 1954; University of Illinois, M.S., 1956, Ph.D., 1961. *Office:* Department of Speech Pathology and Audiology, Ball State University, Muncie, Ind. 47306.

CAREER: University of Wisconsin Hospitals, Madison, director of audiology program in ENT department, 1963-64; Ball State University, Muncie, Ind., director of speech and hearing clinic, 1965-76, chairperson of department of speech pathology and audiology, 1976—. *Member:* American Speech and Hearing Association, Indiana Speech and Hearing Association (president, 1968-70).

WRITINGS: Speech Science, C. C Thomas, 1960, 2nd edition, 1969; (contributor) J. Griffith, editor, *Communication for the Deaf and Hard of Hearing,* C. C Thomas, 1970; (editor) *Neurolinguistic Approaches to Stuttering,* Mouton, 1973.

WORK IN PROGRESS: Co-editing the multi-volume "Neurolinguistic" series.

* * *

HOOVER, F(rancis) Louis 1913-

PERSONAL: Born March 12, 1913, in Sherman, Tex.; son of Guy Frank (a grain dealer) and Marie Louise Elizabeth (Louis) Hoover; married Lucille Eddleman, September 1, 1935; children: Jon Julien. *Education:* North Texas State Teacher's College (now North Texas State University), B.S., 1933; Columbia University, M.A., 1935; New York University, Ed.D., 1942; also studied at Art Students League and New School for Social Research. *Home and office:* 1002 South Crockett St., Sherman, Tex. 75090.

CAREER: La Salle Art Gallery, New York, N.Y., co-director, 1934-36; North Texas State Teacher's College (now North Texas State University), Denton, instructor in art, 1936-40; Eastern Illinois University, Charleston, assistant professor of art, 1941-44; Illinois State University, Normal, professor of art and head of department, 1944-68, director of museums, 1970-73, director of International Collection of Child Art, Research Center, Ewing Museum of Nations. Practicing gemologist, 1975—. Art director, Carden School, 1934-36; free-lance package designer, 1934-36; director, Fairway Gallery of Art, 1962-68. Sponsor of diennial exhibitions of American child art, 1955, 1957, 1959, 1961; member of board of directors, Art Education Foundation, 1956-66; art has been represented in exhibitions in New York, Illinois, and Texas, 1935—. *Member:* Appraisers Association of America, American Society of Appraisers, National Art Education Association (member of executive council, 1959-61), National Education Association, American Association of University Professors, Western Arts Association (president, 1949), Illinois Art Education Association (president, 1951), Delta Phi Delta, Phi Delta Kappa. *Awards, honors:* Award for editorial excellence from Industrial Marketing Association, 1954.

WRITINGS: Guide for Teaching Art Activities in the Classroom, Publisher's Development Corp., 1956; *Art Activities for the Very Young,* Davis Publications, 1962; (editor) *Young Printmakers,* Art Resource Publications, 1964; (editor) *Young Sculptors,* Davis Publications, 1967; (editor) *Young Printmakers II,* Davis Publications, 1969; *African Art,* Illinois State University, 1973. Also created "Art and Activities in the Classroom," a filmstrip, 1955. Editor, *Arts and Activities,* 1952-67; editor and publisher, Art Resource Services, 1963-65.

WORK IN PROGRESS: Research on art of the San Blas Islands; Pre-Columbian Jades of Central America; Gems of the World.

AVOCATIONAL INTERESTS: International travel, studying tribal cultures in various parts of the world, and seeking sources of unusual precious gemstones.

*   *   *

HOOVER, Marjorie L(awson) 1910-

PERSONAL: Born February 1, 1910, in New York, N.Y.; daughter of James T. (an engineer) and Anne (O'Neill) Lawson; married Andrew G. Hoover (a professor), July 16, 1942; children: John, James. Education: Smith College, B.A., 1930; University of Bonn, Ph.D., 1934; Yale University, M.A., 1962. Home: 179 Morgan St., Oberlin, Ohio 44074; and 704 Washington St., No. 2A, New York, N.Y. 10014.

CAREER: St. Xavier College, Chicago, Ill., instructor in German, 1935-36; Swarthmore College, Swarthmore, Pa., instructor in German, 1936-38; Oberlin College, Oberlin, Ohio, instructor, 1938-39, assistant professor, 1939-43, lecturer, 1950-53, 1955-59, associate professor, 1959-72, professor of German and Russian, 1972-76; Wells College, Aurora, N.Y., Campbell Professor, 1977. Member: Modern Language Association of America, American Association for the Advancement of Slavic Studies, American Association of Teachers of Slavic and East European Languages. Awards, honors: National Book Award nomination in arts and letters, 1975, for V. E. Meyerhold: The Autonomous Theater.

WRITINGS: Spannung in der Erzahlung, Mnemosyne 19, 1934; (editor) Das Tagebuch der Anne Frank, Norton, 1959; (editor) Franz Kafka, Die Verwandlung, Norton, 1961; (editor) Tankred Dorst, Two Plays, Holt, 1973; V. E. Meyerhold: The Autonomous Theater, University of Massachusetts Press, 1974; (translator with George Genereux, Jr. and Jacob Volkov) Nikolai Erdman, The Mandate [and] The Suicide, Ardis, 1975.

WORK IN PROGRESS: Alexander Ostrovsky.

*   *   *

HOPPIN, Richard H(allowell) 1913-

PERSONAL: Born February 22, 1913, in Northfield, Minn.; son of Claude Edward (a banker and insurance agent) and Elinor (Hallowell) Hoppin; married Jean Rice, December 23, 1938. Education: Studied at Ecole normale de Musique, 1933-35; Carleton College, A.B., 1936; Harvard University, A.M., 1938, Ph.D., 1952. Home: 331 Brevoort Rd., Columbus, Ohio 43214. Office: School of Music, Ohio State University, Columbus, Ohio 43210.

CAREER: Mount Union College, Alliance, Ohio, assistant professor of music, 1938-42; University of Texas, Main University (now University of Texas at Austin), assistant professor, 1949-56, associate professor, 1956-61; Ohio State University, Columbus, professor of music history, 1961—. Military service: U.S. Marine Corps Reserve, active duty, 1943-45; became captain; receieved Purple Heart. Member: American Musicological Society (member of council, 1964-66; member of executive board, 1965), Renaissance Society of America, International Musicological Society. Awards, honors: Fulbright grant to Belgium, 1954-55; Guggenheim fellow, 1959-60; D.H.L., Carleton College, 1977.

WRITINGS: (Contributor) Randall Thompson, editor, Essays on Music in Honor of Archibald Thompson Davison,

Harvard University, Department of Music, 1957; The Cypriot-French Repertory of the Manuscript Torino, Biblioteca Nazionale J. II. 9, American Institue of Musicology (Rome, Italy), Volume I: Polyphonic Mass Movements, 1960, Volume II: Motets, 1961, Volume III: Ballades, 1963, Volume IV: Virelais and Rondeaux, 1963; (contributor) Jan LaRue, editor, Aspects of Medieval and Renaissance Music: A Birthday Offering to Gustave Reese, Norton, 1966; (contributor) John Glowacki, editor, Paul A. Pisk: Essays in His Honor, College of Fine Arts, University of Texas, 1966; Cypriot Plainchant of the Manuscript Torino, Biblioteca Nazionale J. II. 9, American Institue of Musicology, 1968; Medieval Music, Norton, 1978; Anthology of Medieval Music, Norton, 1978. Contributor of articles and reviews to music journals. Member of editorial board, Journal of American Musicological Society, 1972-77.

*   *   *

HORKHEIMER, Max 1895-1973

February 14, 1895—July 7, 1973; German-born American sociologist and philosopher. Obituaries: New York Times, July 9, 1973.

*   *   *

HOROWITZ, I(srael) A. 1907-1973
(Al Horowitz)

November 15, 1907—January 18, 1973; American chess writer and champion. Obituaries: New York Times, January 19, 1973; Washington Post, January 20, 1973; Time, January 29, 1973.

*   *   *

HOROWITZ, Ira 1934-

PERSONAL: Born February 12, 1934, in New York, N.Y.; son of Robert and Mary (Tell) Horowitz; married Ann R. Holway (an associate professor of economics), June 6, 1958. Education: Johns Hopkins University, B.A. (with honors), 1955; Massachusetts Institute of Technology, Ph.D., 1959. Politics: None. Religion: None. Office: Department of Management, University of Florida, 103 Matherly, Gainesville, Fla., 32601.

CAREER: University of Kansas City (now University of Missouri—Kansas City), Kansas City, Mo., lecturer in economics, 1960; Indiana University at Bloomington, assistant professor, 1960-63, associate professor, 1963-66, professor of economics, 1966-72; University of Florida, Gainesville, professor of economics and chairman of department of management, 1972—. Visiting professor, Catholic University of Louvain, 1968-69, and Michigan State University, 1978-79. Senior economist, U.S. Department of Justice, 1974-75. Member: American Economic Association, Econometric Society, American Statistical Association, Research Society of America, American Association of University Professors, Phi Beta Kappa, Beta Gamma Sigma. Awards, honors: Woodrow Wilson fellow, 1955-56; Ford Foundation faculty research fellowship, 1965-66; Beta Gamma Sigma Distinguished Scholar, 1977-78.

WRITINGS: (With James A. Alcott) Small Business and Government Research and Development, U.S. Small Business Administration, 1962; An Introduction to Quantitative Analysis, McGraw, 1965, revised edition, 1972; (contributor) J. Fred Weston and Sam Petzman, editors, Public Policy toward Mergers, Goodyear Publishing, 1969; Decision Making and the Theory of the Firm, Holt, 1970; Quan-

titative Economic Policy and Planning, Norton, 1978. Contributor of more than fifty articles and reviews to economics journals in the United States and abroad.

* * *

HOROWITZ, Irving Louis 1929-

PERSONAL: Born September 25, 1929, in New York, N.Y.; son of Louis and Esther (Tepper) Horowitz; married Ruth Lenore Narolansky, 1950 (divorced, 1964); children: Carl Frederick, David Dennis. *Education:* College of the City of New York (now City College of the City University of New York), B.S.S., 1951; Columbia University, M.A., 1952; University of Buenos Aires, Ph.D., 1957; Brandeis University, postdoctoral fellow, 1958-59. *Home:* Blawenburg-Rocky Hill Rd., Route 206 and Highway 518, Princeton, N.J. 08540. *Office:* Department of Sociology, Rutgers University, New Brunswick, N.J. 08903.

CAREER: University of Buenos Aires, Buenos Aires, Argentina, assistant professor of social theory, 1955-58; Bard College, Annandale-on-Hudson, N.Y., assistant professor of sociology, 1959-60; Hobart and William Smith Colleges, Geneva, N.Y., assistant professor of sociology and chairman of department, 1960-63; Washington University, St. Louis, Mo., associate professor, 1963-65, professor of sociology, 1965-69; Rutgers University, New Brunswick, N.J., professor of sociology, Graduate Faculty, and chairman of department of sociology at Livingston College, 1969—. Visiting professor at Central University of Venezuela, Caracas, 1957, University of Buenos Aires, 1959, 1961, 1963, State University of New York at Buffalo, 1960, Syracuse University, 1961, University of Rochester, 1962, University of California, Davis, 1966, University of Wisconsin, 1967, Stanford University, 1968-69, University of Calgary, 1970, American University, 1972, Queen's University, 1973, Princeton University, 1976, Boston College, 1976, and University of Mexico, 1978; visiting lecturer at London School of Economics and Political Science, University of London, 1962; Fulbright-Hays lecturer in India, 1977. Senior staff member, Latin American Research Center, 1964-67, 1967-70. Consultant to International Education Division, Ford Foundation, 1959-60; member of advisory board, Institute for Scientific Information, Inc., 1969—. Consulting editor, Oxford University Press, 1964-69, and Aldine-Atherton, 1969-72.

MEMBER: American Sociological Association (fellow), American Philosophical Association, International Studies Association, International Association for the Philosophy of Law and Social Thought, Society for the Study of Social Problems, Society for International Development, American Association for the Advancement of Science, American Association of University Professors, Authors Guild, Midwest Sociological Society, New York State Sociological Society (president, 1961-62). *Awards, honors:* Special citation, Carnegie Endowment for International Peace, 1957, for *Idea of War and Peace in Contemporary Philosophy.*

WRITINGS: Idea of War and Peace in Contemporary Philosophy, Paine-Whitman, 1957, 2nd edition, Humanities, 1973; *Philosophy, Science and the Sociology of Knowledge,* C. C Thomas, 1960; *Radicalism and the Revolt against Reason: The Social Theories of Georges Sorel,* Humanities, 1961, revised edition, Southern Illinois University Press, 1968; *The War Game: Studies of the New Civilian Militarists,* Ballantine, 1963; *Historia y elementos de la sociologia del conocimiento,* University of Buenos Aires Press, 1963; *Revolution in Brazil: Politics and Society in a Developing Nation,* Dutton, 1964; *Three Worlds of Development: The Theory and Practice of International Stratification,* Oxford University Press, 1966, revised edition, 1972; *Professing Sociology: The Life Cycle of a Social Science,* Aldine, 1968; *The Struggle Is the Message: The Organization and Ideology of the Anti-War Movement,* Glendessary, 1970; (with William H. Friedland) *The Knowledge Factory: Student Activism and American Crisis,* Aldine, 1970; *Foundations of Political Sociology,* Harper, 1972.

Editor: *Conference on Conflict, Consensus and Cooperation,* Hobart College, 1962; *The New Sociology: Essays in Social Science and Social Values in Honor of C. Wright Mills,* Oxford University Press, 1964; (and author of introduction) C. Wright Mills, *Sociology and Pragmatism: Higher Learning in America,* Paine-Whitman, 1964; *The Anarchists,* Dell, 1964; *The Rise and Fall of Project Camelot,* M.I.T. Press, 1967; (and author of introduction) C. Wright Mills, *Power, Politics and People,* Oxford University Press, 1968; (with John Gerasi and Josue de Castro) *Latin American Radicalism: A Documentary Report on Left and Nationalist Movements,* Random House, 1969; *Sociological Self-Images: A Collective Portrait,* Pergamon, 1969; *Cuban Communism,* Aldine, 1970, 3rd edition, Transaction Books, 1977; *Masses in Latin America,* Oxford University Press, 1970; (with others) *Sociological Realities: A Guide to the Study of Sociology,* Harper, 1971, 2nd edition published as *Sociological Realities II: A Guide to the Study of Society,* 1975; *The Troubled Conscience,* Center for the Study of Democratic Institutions, 1971; *The Use and Abuse of Social Science,* Dutton, 1971, 2nd edition, 1975; *Israeli Ecstasies/Jewish Agonies,* Oxford University Press, 1974; (with James Everett Katz) *Social Science and Public Policy in the United States,* Praeger, 1975; *Genocide: State Power and Mass Murder,* Transaction Books, 1976; *Ideology and Utopia in the United States, 1956-1976,* Oxford University Press, 1977; *Equity, Income, and Policy: Comparative Studies in Three Worlds of Development,* Praeger, 1977; *Science, Sin and Scholarship: The Politics of Reverend Moon and the Unification Church,* M.I.T. Press, 1978; (with Seymour Martin Lipset) *Dialogues on American Politics,* Oxford University Press, 1978.

Member of editorial staff, *Sociological Abstracts,* 1962-63; senior editor, *Trans-Action/Society,* 1963-68, editor-in-chief, 1968—; editor, *Studies in Comparative International Development,* 1964—; member of editorial board, *International Studies Quarterly,* 1966-70, *Indian Journal of Sociology,* 1971-75, *Journal of Jazz Studies,* 1973—, *Social Indicators,* 1973—, *Social Praxis,* 1973—, *Policy Studies Review Annual,* 1976—, *Civil Liberties Review,* 1976-79, and *Third World Review,* 1976—; associate editor, *Journal of Conflict Resolution,* 1966-72, *Contemporary Jewry,* 1976—, *Journal of Political and Military Sociology,* 1973—; advisory editor, *Indian Sociological Bulletin,* 1963-69, *Social Theory and Practice,* 1970—, *Indian Review,* 1977—, and *Symbolic Interaction,* 1977—.

WORK IN PROGRESS: C. Wright Mills: A Sociological Biography, for Macmillan and Free Press.

SIDELIGHTS: The German poet Walter Hollerer writes of Irving Louis Horowitz, ''He is a kind of poet, with a poet's sense of rhyme, metaphor, gesture, and at times a poet's amiable capacity for presenting his wishes as accomplished facts.''

BIOGRAPHICAL/CRITICAL SOURCES: Times Literary Supplement, August 3, 1967, June 24, 1977; *Motive,* February, 1968; *Nation,* March 3, 1969; *New Leader,* April

28, 1969; *Saturday Review*, June 7, 1969; *Time*, January 5, 1970; *Choice*, January, 1973, September, 1974, June, 1977; *Comparative Literature Studies*, December, 1973; *Social Forces*, March, 1974; *Christian Century*, March 20, 1974; *Progressive*, April, 1974; *America*, May 4, 1974, April 16, 1977; *American Political Science Review*, June, 1974; *American Journal of Sociology*, September, 1974, September, 1975; *Contemporary Sociology*, May, 1976; *Journal of Politics*, November, 1976; *Sociology: Reviews of New Books*, March, 1977, May, 1977; *Virginia Quarterly Review*, spring, 1977; *Annals of American Academy of Political and Social Science*, July, 1977; *Political Science Quarterly*, summer, 1977.

*   *   *

HOROWITZ, Michael M.   1933-

PERSONAL: Born November 2, 1933, in New York, N.Y.; married Sylvia Gordon Huntley, 1955; children: Andrew, Stephanie, Daniel. *Education:* Oberlin College, B.A. (with honors), 1955; Columbia University, M.A., 1956, Ph.D., 1959. *Home:* 22 Crestmont Rd., Binghamton, N.Y. 13905. *Office:* Department of Anthropology, State University of New York, Binghamton, N.Y. 13901.

CAREER: Kent State University, Kent, Ohio, assistant professor of anthropology, 1959-61; State University of New York at Binghamton, assistant professor, 1961-63, associate professor, 1963-69, professor of anthropology, 1969—, chairman of department of anthropology, 1962-66, 1970-72. Fulbright professor, University of Bergen, 1966-67; visiting lecturer, University of Michigan, summer, 1964; field researcher in Martinique, summer, 1956, 1962, and 1957-58; New York State Department of Education educational team representative to Africa and Middle East, 1965; director, Republic of Niger project under National Science Foundation funding, 1967-72; president, Institute for Development Anthropology. Director, Cerebral Palsy and Handicapped Children's Association of Southern New York.

MEMBER: American Anthropological Association (fellow), Society for Applied Anthropology (fellow), Society for Medical Anthropology, Current Anthropology (associate), Centre Nigerien des Recherches en Sciences Humaines, Columbia University Seminar on Ecological Systems and Cultural Evolution (fellow), Phi Beta Kappa, Sigma Xi. *Awards, honors:* Woodrow Wilson fellow, 1955-56; American Anthropological Association fellow in ethnobotany, 1956, 1957; Social Science Research Council grants, 1957-58, 1962; National Science Foundation grant, 1967-72; Carnegie Corporation grant, 1968-69.

WRITINGS: Morne-Paysan: Peasant Village in Martinique, Holt, 1967; (contributor) A. J. Field, editor, *Urbanization and Work in Modernizing Societies*, Glengary Press, 1967; *Peoples and Culture of the Caribbean*, Doubleday, 1971; (contributor) N. Dyson-Hudson, editor, *Perspectives on Nomadism*, Brill, 1972; *Manga of Niger*, three volumes, Human Relations Area File Press, 1972; (co-author) *Anthropology of Rural Development in the Sahel*, Institute for Development Anthropology, 1977. Contributor of more than thirty articles and reviews to professional journals in the United States and Europe.

WORK IN PROGRESS: Editing with J. E. Leavitt, *Readings in Educational Anthropology*.

*   *   *

HORST, Irvin B(uckwalter)   1915-

PERSONAL: Born May 31, 1915, in Lancaster, Pa.; son of Elmer K. (a farmer) and Katie (Buckwalter) Horst; married Ava Rohrer, June 17, 1944; children: Marlise, Rachel, Daniel, Joanna. *Education:* Eastern Mennonite College, Th.B., 1941; Goshen College, B.A., 1949; University of Pennsylvania, M.A., 1950; University of Amsterdam, Ph.D., 1966. *Religion:* Protestant. *Home:* Johan Wagenaarlaan 5, Heemstede, Netherlands. *Office:* University of Amsterdam, Herengracht 514-516, 1017 Amsterdam, Netherlands.

CAREER: Eastern Mennonite College, Harrisonburg, Va. member of faculty, 1955-66; University of Amsterdam, Amsterdam, Netherlands, professor of theology, 1968—. Secretary, Teylers Godgeleerd Genootschap. *Wartime service:* Mennonite Central Committee, civilian public service, 1941-46, foreign relief service in France and Holland, 1946-48. *Member:* American Society of Church History, Renaissance Society of America, Bibliographical Society (London), Pennsylvania German Society.

WRITINGS: A Ministry of Goodwill, Mennonite Central Committee, 1950; *A Bibliography of Menno Simons*, De Graaf, 1962; (editor) *Een Geestelijk Liedt-Boecxken* (Mennonite songbook), F. Knuf, 1971; (editor) *Ausbund* (Mennonite songbook), F. Knuf, 1971; *The Radical Brethren*, De Graaf, 1972; (editor) *De Geest in het Geding*, H. D. Tjeenk Willink, 1978. Editor of *Doopsgezinde Bijdragen;* consulting editor, *Mennonite Quarterly Review*.

WORK IN PROGRESS: Cross Currents in Anglo-Dutch History and Thought of the Tudor Period; Menno Simons: Two Early Writings and an Autobiographical Sketch.

AVOCATIONAL INTERESTS: Walking, swimming, collecting books.

*   *   *

HORVATH, Janos   1921-

PERSONAL: Born November 7, 1921, in Cece, Hungary. *Education:* Columbia University, Ph.D., 1967. *Religion:* Unitarian. *Home:* 3495 Hancock Ridge, Martinsville, Ind. 46151. *Office:* Department of Economics, Butler University, Indianapolis, Ind. 46208.

CAREER: Member of Hungarian Parliament, 1945-47; economist and director of American-Hungarian Relief, and United Nations Relief and Rehabilitation Administration (UNRRA), 1945-47; President of Nostra National Warehouse Corp. Ltd., Hungary, 1945-47; Whitman College, Walla Walla, Wash., associate professor of economics, 1961-68; Butler University, Indianapolis, Ind., distinguished professor of economics, 1968—. Chief economist, Hungarian Farmers' Association, 1956; acting president, National Reconstruction Council of Hungary, 1956. Visiting professor, University of the Philippines, 1958-59, Columbia University, 1961-62. *Member:* International Studies Association, American Economic Association, American Association for the Advancement of Science, Academy of Political Science, Association for the Study of the Grants Economy. *Awards, honors:* Hungarian Academy of Science fellow, 1947; Ford Foundation fellow, 1962; Danforth Faculty fellow, 1963-65.

WRITINGS: Chinese Technology Transfer to the Third World: A Grants Economy Analysis, Praeger, 1976; (editor with Kenneth Boulding) ''Grants Economics Series,'' twelve volumes, Praeger, 1978-1981. Contributor to *American Economist, Journal of Economic Literature, Southern Economic Journal, Political Science Quarterly, Antitrust Bulletin, American Journal of Agricultural Economics,* and other publications.

WORK IN PROGRESS: Research in explicit and implicit international grants and tributes, the inflation-unemployment dilemma, environmental problems, measurement of industrial concentration, and criteria for classifying economic systems.

SIDELIGHTS: Janos Horvath was a youth leader of national resistance against Nazi German occupation, 1942-44, and a political leader against the Sovietization of Hungary, 1945-47, and as a result of this work was a political prisoner in 1944-45 and 1947-50.

*   *   *

HOSFORD, Jessie 1892-

PERSONAL: Born August 19, 1892, in Nebraska; married Lisle Hosford (a professor), April 18, 1917 (deceased); children: Harriett (deceased), Henry, Philip. *Education:* Attended Iliff School of Theology, 1927-28; New Mexico Highlands University, B.A., 1933, M.A., 1934. *Religion:* Protestant. *Home:* 1405 Oregon Ave., Alamogordo, N.M.

CAREER: Formerly active in community affairs in Las Vegas, N.M., serving as secretary of the Las Vegas Hospital Board for eight years, as member of the Las Vegas School Board for six years, and as Girl Scouts commissioner. *Member:* National League of American Pen Women (former president of Las Vegas and Alamogordo branches). *Awards, honors:* New Mexico Federation of Women's Clubs award, 1962; Western Heritage Junior Book Award, 1970, for *An Awful Name to Live Up To.*

WRITINGS—Juvenile: Listen to the Rain, Exposition, 1953; *An Awful Name to Live Up To,* Meredith, 1969; *You Bet Your Boots I Can,* Thomas Nelson, 1972.

WORK IN PROGRESS: A collection of poems.†

*   *   *

HOUSTON, Neal B. 1928-

PERSONAL: Born August 7, 1928, in Dallas, Tex.; son of Neal B., Sr. and Pauline (Carr) Houston; married Ellen Joan Norton, November 10, 1956; children: Alan Kyle, Sharon Lee. *Education:* University of Texas, B.S.Ed., 1949, M.Ed., 1953, M.A., 1960; Texas Technological College (now Texas Tech University), Ph.D., 1965. *Politics:* Democrat. *Religion:* Episcopalian. *Home:* 2933 Dogwood St., Nacogdoches, Tex. 75961. *Office:* Ferguson 306 A and B, Stephen F. Austin State University, Nacogdoches, Tex. 75961.

CAREER: Amarillo College, Amarillo, Tex., professor of English, 1958-63, 1964-65; Angelo State College (now University), San Angelo, Tex., associate professor of English, 1965-66; Stephen F. Austin State University, Nacogdoches, Tex., professor of English, 1966—. Visiting professor, Texas Technological College (now Texas Tech University), summer, 1966, and University of Hawaii, 1970-71. Board president, Episcopal Day School, Nacogdoches. *Military service:* U.S. Army, 1951-53; served in Japan. *Member:* Modern Language Association of America, Conference of College Teachers of English, South Central Modern Language Association.

WRITINGS: Ross Santee, Steck, 1968; (with J. J. Quinn) *Phonetikon,* Scott, Foresman, 1970. Contributor to *Bibliography of Southwestern American Literature.* Contributor of more than fifty poems, articles, reviews, teaching aids, and monographs to *Dalhousie Review, Research Studies, Review of Educational Research, Victorian Newsletter, Ranger,* and other journals and publications. Editor, *Re: Arts and Letters.*

WORK IN PROGRESS: Writing on Nathaniel Hawthorne.

*   *   *

HOWARD, Daniel F(rancis) 1928-

PERSONAL: Born March 30, 1928, in Waterbury, Conn.; son of Daniel F. (a broker) and Etta E. (Hughes) Howard; married Maureen Kearns (a novelist), August 28, 1954 (divorced, 1968); married Barbara Whitlock (a social worker), February 1, 1968; children: (first marriage) Loretta; (second marriage), Peter, Matthew. *Education:* Yale University, B.A., 1949, M.A., 1951, Ph.D., 1956. *Home:* 856 Hoes Lane, Piscataway, N.J. 08854. *Office:* Department of English, Rutgers University, New Brunswick, N.J. 08903.

CAREER: Carnegie Institute of Technology (now Carnegie Mellon University), Pittsburgh, Pa., instructor in English, 1953-54; Williams College, Williamstown, Mass., instructor in English, 1954-58; Kenyon College, Gambier, Ohio, assistant professor of English, 1958-60; Rutgers University, New Brunswick, N.J., associate professor, 1960-66, professor of English, 1966—, chairman of department, 1966—. *Awards, honors:* Fulbright scholarship in Italy, 1956-57; American Council of Learned Societies grants-in-aid, 1959; American Philosophical Society award, 1963-64.

WRITINGS: (Editor) *Samuel Butler's Correspondence with His Sister May,* University of California Press, 1962; (editor) Samuel Butler, *Ernest Pontifex: Or The Way of All Flesh,* Houghton, 1964; *Writing about Reading,* Little, Brown, 1966; *The Modern Tradition: An Anthology of Short Stories,* Little, Brown, 1968, 4th edition, 1979; *Lessons in Critical Reading and Writing: William Shakespeare's "Hamlet,"* Harcourt, 1970; (editor with Hans-Peter Brever) Butler, *Erewohn: Or, Over the Range,* University of Delaware Press, 1979.

WORK IN PROGRESS: A Critical Study of Victorian Fiction.

*   *   *

HOWARD, James H(enri) 1925-

PERSONAL: Born September 10, 1925, in Redfield, S.D.; son of Lewis J. (a county clerk) and Iva (Parsons) Howard; married Elfriede Heinze, August 13, 1948; children: Lance N., Eva M. *Education:* University of Nebraska, B.A., 1949, M.A., 1950; University of Michigan, Ph.D., 1957. *Politics:* Democrat. *Religion:* Unitarian Universalist. *Home:* Route 2, Stillwater, Okla. 74074. *Office:* Department of Sociology, Oklahoma State University, Stillwater, Okla. 74074.

CAREER: North Dakota State Historical Museum, Bismarck, archaeologist and preparator, 1950-53; Kansas City Museum, Kansas City, Mo., lecturer in anthropology, 1955-57; University of North Dakota, Grand Forks, assistant professor, 1957-61, associate professor of anthropology, 1961-63; University of South Dakota, Vermillion, professor of anthropology, 1963-68, director of Institute of Indian Studies, 1963-66; Oklahoma State University, Stillwater, associate professor of sociology and anthropology, 1968—. Chief archaeologist, Fortress of Louisbourg Archaeological Project, Louisbourg, Nova Scotia, 1962; state archaeologist, South Dakota, 1963-66. Consultant and expert witness for law firms representing Turtle Mountain band of Plains-Ojibwa tribe before U.S. Indian Claims Commission, 1953-63, and Ponca tribe, 1960. *Military service:* U.S. Army, 1943-46; received Bronze Star.

MEMBER: American Anthropological Association (fellow), Society for American Archaeology, American Association for the Advancement of Science (fellow), American Society for Ethnohistory, Central States Anthropological Society, Phi Beta Kappa, Sigma Xi. *Awards, honors:* Research grants from National Park Service and North Dakota State Historical Society, 1958, American Philosophical Society, 1959, Wenner-Gren Foundation, 1961, 1965—, and National Park Service, 1964—.

WRITINGS: (Contributor) Gertrude E. Dole and Robert L. Carneiro, editors, *Essays in the Science of Culture in Honor of Leslie A. White*, Crowell, 1960; *Dakota Winter Counts as a Source of Plains History*, Bureau of American Ethnology, 1960; *The Plains Ojibwa, Hunters and Warriors of the Northern Prairies*, South Dakota Museum, 1965; *The Ponca Tribe*, Bureau of American Ethnology, 1965; *The Dakota or Sioux Tribe: A Study in Human Ecology*, South Dakota Museum, 1966; (translator and editor) *The Warrior Who Killed Custer: The Personal Narrative of Chief Joseph White Bull*, University of Nebraska Press, 1968; *The Southeastern Ceremonial Complex and Its Interpretation*, Missouri Archaeological Society, 1968.

Publications include reports of archaeological investigations at Renner, Tony Glas, Huff, Toronto Reservoir, and other sites. Contributor of more than 120 articles and reviews to *Ethnohistory, American Antiquity, Journal of American Folklore, American Indian Hobbyist*, and other journals and museum bulletins. Editor, *Museum News* (South Dakota Museum), 1963-68, and *Newsletter* of Oklahoma Anthropological Society, 1969-71.

WORK IN PROGRESS: A monograph on Shawnee ceremonialism and its cultural background.

SIDELIGHTS: James Howard says that he is "dedicated to presenting American Indian culture from the viewpoint of an 'insider,' that is, a member of the culture being described."

*   *   *

HOWARD, John (Arnold) 1916-

PERSONAL: Born June 21, 1916, in Georgetown, Ill.; son of Fred (a highway commissioner) and Edith (Saylor) Howard; married Lynn Horstman, June 16, 1950; children: Jeffrey, Peter. *Education:* University of Illinois at Urbana-Champaign, B.S., 1939, M.A., 1941; Harvard University, M.S., 1948, Ph.D., 1952. *Religion:* Methodist. *Home:* 22 Kingston Rd., Scarsdale, N.Y. 10583. *Office:* Department of Marketing, Columbia University, New York, N.Y. 10027.

CAREER: University of Illinois at Urbana-Champaign, assistant professor of marketing, 1948-58; University of Chicago, Chicago, Ill., associate professor of marketing, 1950-58; University of Pittsburgh, Pittsburgh, Pa., professor of marketing, 1958-63; Columbia University, New York, N.Y., professor of marketing, 1963—, George E. Warren Professor of Business, 1976. *Military service:* U.S. Army, 1942-46; became lieutenant colonel. *Awards, honors:* P. D. Converse Award, 1976, for work in marketing theory.

WRITINGS: Marketing: Executive and Buyer Behavior, Columbia University Press, 1963; *Marketing Theory*, Allyn & Bacon, 1965; (with J. N. Sheth) *The Theory of Buyer Behavior*, Wiley, 1969; *Marketing Management*, 3rd edition, Irwin, 1973; (with J. O. Farley and L. W. Ring) *Consumer Behavior: Theory and Practice*, Allyn & Bacon, 1973; *Consumer Behavior: Application of Theory*, McGraw, 1977.

WORK IN PROGRESS: Research in theory of human choice with applications to choice of brands by consumers as well as choice of corporate strategies by executives.

HOWARD, Robert 1926-

PERSONAL: Born March 22, 1926, in Chewelah, Wash.; son of Thomas P. (a bridge builder) and Loretta (Buckley) Howard. *Education:* Attended Gonzaga University, 1946-48; University of Washington, Seattle, 1948-51; San Francisco State College (now University), B.A., 1959, M.S., 1961. *Office:* 516 Sutter St., San Francisco, Calif. 94102.

CAREER: University of San Francisco, San Francisco, Calif., counselor, 1961-69, lecturer in psychology, 1964—; private practice in psychotherapy, San Francisco, 1961—. *Military service:* U.S. Naval Reserve, 1944-46. *Member:* American Personnel and Guidance Association, American Psychological Association, National Rehabilitation Association, California Marriage and Family Counselors Association.

WRITINGS: Human Psychology: Experiments in Awareness, Westinghouse Learning Press, 1972; *Roles and Relationships: Exploring Attitudes and Values*, Westinghouse Learning Press, 1973.

WORK IN PROGRESS: Two books, *Intimate Psychology: The Work and Play of Love* and *Insight*.

*   *   *

HOWES, Royce (Bucknam) 1901-1973

January 3, 1901—March 18, 1973. American newspaper editor, author, and teacher. Obituaries: *New York Times*, March 19, 1973, March 20, 1973; *Washington Post*, March 21, 1973. (See index for *CA* sketch)

*   *   *

HSUEH, Chun-tu 1922-

PERSONAL: Born December 12, 1922, in Canton, China; came to United States, 1949, naturalized citizen, 1961; married Cordelia Te-hua Huang (daughter of Huang Hsing, co-founder of Republic of China), December 13, 1952. *Education:* China School of Journalism, Hong Kong, Certificate, 1939; Chaoyang University, LL.B., 1946; Raffles College (since incorporated into University of Singapore), further study, 1946-49; Columbia University, M.A., 1953, Ph.D., 1958. *Office:* Department of Government and Politics, University of Maryland, College Park, Md. 20742.

CAREER: Stanford University, Stanford, Calif., research associate in political science, 1959-62; University of Hong Kong, Hong Kong, lecturer in history, 1962-64; visiting associate professor at State University of New York College at Plattsburgh and faculty scholar at Columbia University, New York, N.Y., 1964-65; University of Maryland, College Park, associate professor, 1965-68, professor of government and politics, 1968—. Columbia University, associate in University Seminar on Modern China, 1966—, professor of government, summer, 1969; visiting scholar, St. Antony's College, Oxford University, 1969; visiting professor and acting head of Division of Chinese and East Asian Politics, Free University of Berlin, 1970; research associate, Fairbank Center for East Asian Research, Harvard University, 1978. Chairman, Washington and Southeast Regional Seminar on China, 1974—; member, National Bicentennial Ethnic-Racial Council, and Maryland Bicentennial Commission advisory committee, 1975-76. Lecturer at numerous universities and institutions in United States and abroad.

MEMBER: American Political Science Association, Association for Asian Studies, International Studies Association, Asian Political Scientists Group in the USA (chairman of executive committee, 1975—). *Awards, honors:* Dimensions *of China's Foreign Relations* was selected by *Asia Mail* for honorable mention on its list of best books on Asian affairs, 1977.

WRITINGS: The Chinese Communist Movement: An Annotated Bibliography, Hoover Institution, Volume I, 1960, Volume II, 1962; *Huang Hsing and the Chinese Revolution,* Stanford University Press, 1961; *Shih-nien tsa-lu* (title means "Selected Writings of a Decade"; collection of his own articles), Universal Book Co. (Hong Kong), 1964; (editor and contributor) *Revolutionary Leaders of Modern China,* Oxford University Press, 1971, abridged edition published as *Les dirigeants de la Chine revolutionnaire,* Calmann-Levy, 1973; *Asian Political Scientists in North America: Professional and Ethnic Problems,* University of Maryland Law School, 1977; *Dimensions of China's Foreign Relations,* Praeger/Holt, 1977.

Contributor: *Contemporary China,* Volume VI, Hong Kong University Press, 1968; *Twenty Years of Communist China,* Centre d'Etude du Sud Est Asiatique et de L'Exreme-Orient (Brussels), 1969; *From Oracle Bones to Oral Records: Sources on Chinese History,* Australian National University Press, 1973. Contributor to *Encyclopaedia Britannica, Biographical Dictionary of Republican China,* and journals in several countries. Member of editorial board, *Ethnicity, New Political Science,* and *Chinese Studies in History;* member of board of directors, *Asia Mail,* 1978—.

WORK IN PROGRESS: Research on foreign policy politics in China; Chinese in the United States and abroad.

SIDELIGHTS: Chun-tu Hsueh told *CA,* "In 1971, I visited China, hence becoming the first professor from America specializing in Chinese politics to visit China in twenty years."

* * *

HU, Sze-Tsen 1914-

PERSONAL: Born October 9, 1914; son of Shao Tang and Su Mei (Tang) Hu; married Shia Zong Wang, March 14, 1948 (died January 30, 1962); children: Herman, Charlotte. *Education:* National Central University, Nanking, China, B.Sc., 1938; University of Manchester, Ph.D., 1947. *Home:* 1076 Tellem Dr., Pacific Palisades, Calif. 90272. *Office:* Department of Mathematics, University of California, Los Angeles, Calif. 90024.

CAREER: Tulane University, New Orleans, La., associate professor of mathematics, 1952-55; University of Georgia, Athens, professor of mathematics, 1955-56; Wayne State University, Detroit, Mich., professor of mathematics, 1956-60; University of California, Los Angeles, professor of mathematics, 1960—. Consultant to Lockheed Missiles and Space Company, Palo Alto, Calif., 1959-64. *Member:* American Mathematical Society, Mathematical Association of America, London Mathematical Society, Sigma Xi. *Awards, honors:* D.Sc., University of Manchester, 1959; Academia Sinica, Republic of China, academician, 1966.

WRITINGS: Homotopy Theory, Academic Press, 1959; *Elements of General Topology,* Holden-Day, 1964; *Theory of Retracts,* Wayne State University Press, 1965; *Elements of Modern Algebra,* Holden-Day, 1965; *Threshold Logic,* University of California Press, 1965; *Introduction to General Topology,* Holden-Day, 1966; *Homology Theory,* Holden-Day, 1966; *Introduction to Contemporary Mathematics,* Holden-Day, 1966; *Elements of Real Analysis,* Holden-Day, 1967; *Cohomology Theory,* Markham, 1968; *Introduction to Homological Algebra,* Holden-Day, 1968;

Mathematical Theory of Switching Circuits and Automata, University of California Press, 1968; *Differentiable Manifolds,* Holt, 1969; *Elementary Functions and Coordinate Geometry,* Markham, 1969; *Calculus,* Markham, 1970; *Linear Algebra with Differential Equations,* Markham, 1971.

* * *

HUFSCHMIDT, Maynard Michael 1912-

PERSONAL: Original surname, Hufschmid; name legally changed in 1939; born September 28, 1912, in Catawba, Wis.; son of John J. (a lumberman) and Emma (Von Arx) Hufschmid; married Elizabeth Leake (a librarian), July 5, 1941; children: Emily, Mark. *Education:* University of Illinois, B.S., 1939; Harvard University, M.P.A., 1955, D.P.A., 1964. *Office:* Department of City and Regional Planning, University of North Carolina, Chapel Hill, N.C. 27514.

CAREER: Illinois State Planning Commission, Chicago, planning technician, 1939-41; U.S. National Resources Planning Board, Washington, D.C., engineer in public works programs, 1941-43; U.S. Bureau of the Budget, Washington, D.C., budget examiner in public investment program, 1943-49; U.S. Department of the Interior, Office of the Secretary, Washington, D.C., member of program and technical review staffs in natural resource program, 1949-55; Harvard University, Cambridge, Mass., research associate in public administration and director of research for Harvard water program, 1955-65; University of North Carolina at Chapel Hill, professor of planning and environmental sciences and engineering, and research professor of Institute for Research in Social Science, 1965—, member of board of directors and technical committee of Water Resources Research Institute. Member of Triangle Universities' Consortium on Air Pollution; member of Environmental Studies Council. Consultant to business and government agencies.

MEMBER: American Society for Public Administration, Regional Science Association (vice-president), Elisha Mitchell Scientific Society, Cosmos Club, Sigma Xi, Tau Beta Pi. *Awards, honors:* Clemens Herschel Award from Boston Society of Civil Engineers, 1959; National Science Foundation senior postdoctoral research fellowship, 1970-71; Kenan Research Professor, 1970-71.

WRITINGS: (Contributor) *America's Needs and Resources,* Twentieth Century Fund, 1947; (with Robert W. Hartley, Eleanor Wolkind, and Sidney Jaffe) *America's Capital Requirements,* Twentieth Century Fund, 1950; (contributor) Franklin L. Pollack, editor, *Resources Development: Frontiers for Research,* University of Colorado Press, 1960; (with Arthur Maass, Robert Dorfman, Harold A. Thomas, Jr., Stephen A. Marglin, and Gordon M. Fair) *Design of Water-Resource Systems,* Harvard University Press, 1962; (contributor) Austin C. Hoggatt and Frederick E. Balderston, editors, *Symposium on Simulation Models: Methodology and Applications to the Behavioral Sciences,* Southwestern Publishing, 1963; (contributor) Robert Kates and Ian Burton, editors, *Readings in Resource Management and Conservation,* University of Chicago Press, 1965; (contributor) *Water Resources and Economic Development in the South,* Agricultural Policy Institute, North Carolina State University, 1965; (with Myron B. Fiering) *Simulation Techniques for Design of Water-Resource Systems,* Harvard University Press, 1966; (editor) *Regional Planning: Challenge and Prospects,* Praeger, 1969; (contributor) Julius Margolis, editor, *The Analysis of Public Output,* Columbia

University Press, 1970; (contributor) Edwin S. Mills, editor, *Economic Analysis of Environmental Problems,* Columbia University Press, 1975. Contributor to professional journals.

WORK IN PROGRESS: Research on state water resource planning and on methodology and policy analysis for water resources and environmental quality.

*   *   *

HUGHES, Catharine R(achel)   1935-

PERSONAL: Born September 4, 1935, in Newark, N.J.; daughter of John (a glassblower) and Eleanor (a nurse; maiden name Woodworth) Hughes. *Education:* Attended schools in Lancaster, Pa. *Religion:* Roman Catholic. *Home:* 79 West 12th St., Apt. 6B, New York, N.Y. 10011.

CAREER: L. B. Herr & Son (distributors of school supplies and equipment), Lancaster, Pa., assistant to president, 1952-57; Sheed & Ward, New York City, director of advertising and publicity, 1957-63; Frederick A. Praeger, New York City, merchandising coordinator, 1963-67; *America,* New York City, drama critic, 1967—; Off and Off-Off Broadway reviewer for *Show Business,* 1968-70; American theatre critic for *Plays and Players,* London, England, 1969-75; arts columnist for *Holiday,* 1976-77; currently fiction reviewer and specialist in Soviet and East European affairs for *Publishers Weekly;* free-lance editor in New York City. Has been assistant director for Off-Broadway plays, theatre consultant for New York State Council on the Arts, editorial consultant to book publishers, and film columnist for *Critic. Member:* New Drama Forum Association (chairman of awards committee), Drama Desk, American Theatre Critics Association.

WRITINGS: "Madame Lafayette" (historical drama), first produced at the Blackfriar's Theatre, New York, N.Y., March 3, 1960; *Plays, Politics and Polemics,* DBS Publications, 1972; *American Playwrights: 1945-75,* Pitman Publishing (London), 1976.

Editor; all published by Sheed: *Darkness and Light: Selections from St. John of the Cross,* 1972; *The Prison of Love: Selections from St. Teresa of Avila,* 1972; *The Clouded Hills: Selections from William Blake,* 1973; *Dreams and Regrets: Selections from the Russian Mystics,* 1973; *The Weeping Sky* (Jewish mystics), 1973; *Leaves in the Dust* (American Indian mystics), 1973.

Editor and photographer; all published by Seabury, 1974: *The Secret Shrine: Islamic Mystical Reflections; The Smokeless Fire: Hindu Mystical Reflections; The Solitary Journey: Buddhist Mystical Reflections; Shadow and Substance: Taoist Mystical Reflections.*

Photographer: Sister Mary Roger Thibodeaux, *A Black Nun Looks at Black Power,* Sheed, 1972; F. J. Sheed, *The Lord's Prayer,* Seabury, 1975; Sheed, *Our Hearts Are Restless,* Seabury, 1976; Sheed, *Death into Life,* Arena Lettres, 1978; Helen Thomas, *Personal Prayers,* Arena Lettres, 1978.

Other: (Adapter) Francis Peter LeBuffe, *My Changeless Friend,* Arena Lettres, 1974. Editor, *New York Theatre Annual,* Gale, 1978—. Contributor to *Nation, Playbill, Ebony, Progressive, After Dark, Commonweal, Christian Century, Congress Bi-Weekly, Critic, Saturday Review, Antioch Review, Arts in Society, New York Times,* and other periodicals.

WORK IN PROGRESS: Tennessee Williams: A Critical Study, completion expected in 1979.

AVOCATIONAL INTERESTS: Travel to Russia, eastern

and western Europe, Britain and Ireland, Canada, and the Caribbean.

*   *   *

HUGHES, Charles C(ampbell)   1929-

PERSONAL: Born January 26, 1929, in Salmon, Idaho; son of Charles Frederick (a mechanic) and Grace Jean (Campbell) Hughes; married Jane Ellen Murphy, February 6, 1951 (divorced, 1962); married Patricia D. Winters, August 7, 1964 (divorced, 1969); married Leslie Ann Medert, March 7, 1970; children: (third marriage) John Charles Campbell, Calisse Marie. *Education:* Harvard University, A.B. (magna cum laude), 1951; Cornell University, M.A., 1953, Ph.D., 1957. *Home:* 7453 Enchanted Hills Dr., Salt Lake City, Utah 84121. *Office:* Department of Family and Community Medicine, University of Utah Medical Center, Salt Lake City, Utah 84132.

CAREER: Cornell University, Ithaca, N.Y., instructor, 1957, acting assistant professor of anthropology, 1959-62; Center for Advanced Study in the Behavioral Sciences, Stanford, Calif., fellow, 1961-62; Michigan State University, East Lansing, associate professor, 1962-64, professor of anthropology, 1964-73, professor in department of psychiatry, 1970-73, director of African Studies Center, 1962-70; University of Utah, Salt Lake City, professor of anthropology, 1973—, professor in department of family and community medicine, 1973—, chairman of department, 1973-78. Has done field work in Nova Scotia, 1952-53, St. Lawrence Island, Alaska, 1954-55, and Nigeria, 1961. Member of behavioral sciences test committee of National Board of Medical Examiners, 1973-77; member of advisory board, East-West Academy of the Healing Arts, 1976—. *Military service:* U.S. Army Reserve, 1951-57.

MEMBER: American Anthropological Association (fellow), American Association for the Advancement of Science (fellow), American Sociological Association (fellow), African Studies Association (fellow), Society for Applied Anthropology (president, 1969-70), Arctic Institute of North America, Association for the Behavioral Sciences and Medical Education (president, 1978-79), International Society for General Semantics, Society for Medical Anthropology, American Ethnological Society, Phi Beta Kappa, Sigma Xi, Phi Kappa Phi. *Awards, honors:* National Institute of Mental Health fellowship, 1961-62; Michigan State University Distinguished Faculty Award, 1967.

WRITINGS: An Eskimo Village in the Modern World, Cornell University Press, 1960; (with Marc-Adelard Tremblay, Robert N. Rapoport, and Alexander H. Leighton) *People of Cove and Woodlot: Communities from the Viewpoint of Social Psychiatry,* Basic Books, 1960; (with Leighton, T. Adeoye Lambo, Dorothea C. Leighton, Jane M. Murphy, and David B. Macklin) *Psychiatric Disorders among the Yoruba,* Cornell University Press, 1963; (editor) *Make Men of Them: Introductory Readings for Cultural Anthropology,* Rand McNally, 1972, revised edition published as *Custom-Made: Introductory Readings for Cultural Anthropology,* 1976; *Eskimo Boyhood: An Autobiography in Psychosocial Perspective,* University Press of Kentucky, 1974.

Contributor: Alexander H. Leighton, editor, *My Name Is Legion,* Basic Books, 1959; T. Adeoye Lambo, editor, *Proceedings of the First Pan-African Psychiatric Conference, 1961,* Government Printer of Nigeria, 1962; Iago Galdston, editor, *Man's Image in Medicine and Anthropology,* International Universities Press, 1963; S. F. Eisenstadt, editor,

Contemporary Social Problems, Free Press, 1964; Jane M. Murphy and Leighton, editors, *Approaches to Cross-Cultural Psychiatry*, Cornell University Press, 1966; Marc J. Swartz, Victor H. Turner, and Arthur Tuden, editors, *Political Anthropology*, Aldine, 1966; *Comparative Theories of Social Change*, Foundation for Research on Human Behavior (Ann Arbor), 1966; Swartz, editor, *Local-Level Politics*, Aldine, 1968; Joseph Finney, editor, *Culture Change, Mental Health, and Poverty*, University Press of Kentucky, 1969; Otto von Mering and Leonard Kasdan, editors, *Relations between Anthropology and Medicine*, University of Pittsburgh Press, 1970; Hans Peter Dreitzel, editor, *The Social Organization of Health*, Macmillan, 1971; Eleanor Leacock and Nancy O. Lurie, editors, *The American Indian in Historical Perspective*, Random House, 1971; M. Taghi Farvar and John P. Milton, editors, *The Careless Technology: Ecology and International Development*, Natural History Press, 1972. Contributor of more than thirty articles and reviews to encyclopedias, anthropology journals, and community medicine journals. Associate editor, *Journal of Psychological Anthropology*, 1978—.

WORK IN PROGRESS: Contributing to *Handbook of North American Indians;* a textbook on behavioral science and medical education.

* * *

HUGHES, John A(nthony) 1941-

PERSONAL: Born March 20, 1941, in Sheffield, England; son of John Eric (a fireman) and Agnes (Jones) Hughes. *Education:* University of Birmingham, B.Soc.Sci. (first class honors), 1963. *Politics:* "Liberal-Anarchist . . . vote Labour." *Religion:* None. *Home:* 19 Fern Bank, Lancaster, England. *Office:* Department of Sociology, University of Lancaster, Bailrigg, Lancaster, England.

CAREER: University of Birmingham, Birmingham, England, temporary lecturer in political sociology, 1964-65; University of Exeter, Exeter, England, lecturer in sociology, 1965-70; University of Lancaster, Lancaster, England, lecturer in sociology, 1970—. *Member:* British Sociological Association.

WRITINGS: (With R. E. Dowse) *Political Sociology*, Wiley, 1972; *Sociological Analysis: Methods of Discovery*, Thomas Nelson, 1976. Contributor to *Sociology* and *British Journal of Sociology*.

WORK IN PROGRESS: *The Philosophy of Social Research*, for Longman.

AVOCATIONAL INTERESTS: Science fiction.

* * *

HUGHES, Leo 1908-

PERSONAL: Born November 20, 1908, in Carlyle, Ill.; son of Peter William (a farmer) and Florence (Ogle) Hughes; married Mildred Robert, August 25, 1936; children: Barbara Jane (Mrs. Jerrold S. Buttrey), Robert Lee. *Education:* University of Illinois, B.A., 1933, M.A., 1934, Ph.D., 1938. *Politics:* Democrat. *Religion:* Roman Catholic. *Home:* 902 West 31st St., Austin, Tex. 78705. *Office:* 201 Calhoun Hall, University of Texas, Austin, Tex. 78712.

CAREER: University of Texas at Austin, instructor, 1938-42, assistant professor, 1942-46, associate professor, 1946-56, professor of English, 1956—, associate dean of Graduate School, 1959-65. Visiting professor of English at New York University, summers, 1949, 1958, Rice University, 1962-63, and Northern Illinois University, summer, 1970. *Member:*

Modern Language Association of America, Scholia, South Central Modern Language Association, Phi Beta Kappa. *Awards, honors:* Decorated Knight Commander of St. Gregory; Folger fellowships, Washington, D.C., 1953, 1966; Guggenheim fellowship, London, England, 1956-57; scholar's library award from Modern Language Association of America and Texas Writers' Roundup award, both in 1971, for *The Drama's Patrons*.

WRITINGS: English Farce in the Restoration, privately printed, 1938; (with A. H. Scouten) *Ten English Farces*, University of Texas Press, 1948; *A Century of English Farce*, Princeton University Press, 1956; (contributor) Carroll Camden, editor, *Restoration and Eighteenth-Century Literature: Essays in Honor of Alan Dugald McKillop*, University of Chicago Press, 1963; (contributor) John Glowacki, editor, *Paul A. Pisk: Essays in His Honor*, College of Fine Arts, University of Texas, 1966; (editor) William Wycherley, *The Plain Dealer*, University of Nebraska Press, 1967; *The Drama's Patrons*, University of Texas Press, 1971. Contributor of about twenty-five articles and reviews to literature journals, including *Philological Quarterly, Modern Language Notes, Theatre Notebook, Notes and Queries, Thought, Review of English Studies*, and *Modern Language Review*.

WORK IN PROGRESS: Editing a promptbook of Fletcher-Buckingham-Garrick *Chances;* nine promptbooks of seventeenth- and eighteenth-century plays formerly part of repertory and library of Drury Lane; a book on English comedy in the Restoration period and in the eighteenth century.

* * *

HULICKA, Karel 1913-

PERSONAL: Born January 3, 1913, in Prague, Czechoslovakia; married Irene Mackintosh (a professor of psychology), May 27, 1957; children: Charles. *Education:* Academy of Commerce, Prague, Czechoslovakia, Diploma, 1934; University of Prague, Diploma, 1939, Ing., 1946; University of California, Berkeley, Ph.D., 1952. *Home:* 98 University Ave., Buffalo, N.Y. 14214. *Office:* Diefendorf Hall, State University of New York, Buffalo, N.Y. 13214.

CAREER: Technical College, Prague, Czechoslovakia, professor of commerce, 1939-47; University of California, Berkeley, instructor in political science, 1952-53; University of Minnesota, Minneapolis, visiting lecturer in political science, 1955-56; University of Oklahoma, Norman, assistant professor of government, 1956-59; State University of New York at Buffalo, assistant professor, 1959-61, associate professor of history and government, 1961-64, professor of history, 1964—. Visiting professor, Institut d'Etudes Americaines, 1968. *Member:* American Political Science Association.

WRITINGS: (Co-author) *European Politics and Government*, Ronald, 1962; (with wife, Irene M. Hulicka) *Soviet Institutions, the Individual, and Society*, Christopher, 1967. Contributor of about thirty-five articles to political science journals in the United States and Europe. Contributing editor of Philosophical Library's *Dictionary of Political Science*, 1964, and *Handbook of Historical Concepts*, 1967.

AVOCATIONAL INTERESTS: Playing violin.

* * *

HULLEY, Clarence C(harles) 1905-

PERSONAL: Born June 29, 1905, in Staffa, Ontario,

Canada; son of Charles Immanuel (a farmer) and Jessie Ellen (Frank-Pitt) Hulley; married Julia Menefee (a registered hospital dietitian), 1955. *Education:* University of British Columbia, B.A., 1934, M.A., 1938; University of Washington, Seattle, Ph.D., 1943; University of Wisconsin, post-doctoral study. *Home and office address:* 313 Oak Ridge Ave., Fayetteville, N.C. 28305.

CAREER: High school teacher of history in Canada, 1934-40; University of Wisconsin—Madison, teaching fellow, 1942-43; Oregon State College (now University), Corvallis, instructor in history, 1944-45; University of Oregon, Portland, instructor in history, 1945; University of Alaska, Fairbanks, professor of history and political science and head of department, 1945-55; Augustana College, Sioux Falls, S.D., associate professor of European history, 1955-59; Southern State College, Magnolia, Ark., chairman of division of social sciences, 1959-60; Western Carolina College (now University), Cullowhee, N.C., associate professor of history, 1960-62; Carthage College, Kenosha, Wis., associate professor of history, 1962-63; Northland College, Ashland, Wis., associate professor of history, 1963-65; Methodist College, Fayetteville, N.C., professor of history and chairman of department, 1966-73. Visiting professor at University of Miami, 1950. *Member:* American Historical Association, American Association of University Professors. *Awards, honors:* American Philosophical Society research grant, 1948-49.

WRITINGS: Alaska, 1741-1953, Binfords, 1953, 2nd edition published as *Alaska: Past and Present,* 1959, 3rd revised and enlarged edition, 1970.

WORK IN PROGRESS: Mary of Guise, Queen Regent of Scotland.

*   *   *

HUMPHRY, Derek   1930-

PERSONAL: Born April 29, 1930, in Bath, Somerset, England. *Education:* Attended secondary school in England. *Politics:* Socialist. *Religion:* None. *Residence:* London, England, and Los Angeles, Calif. *Agent:* Elaine Greene, 31 Newington Green, London N.16, England. *Office: Sunday Times,* 200 Grays Inn Rd., London W.C.1, England; and *Los Angeles Times,* Times-Mirror Sq., Los Angeles, Calif. 90053.

CAREER: Reporter in England for *Yorkshire Post,* 1945-46, *Bristol Evening World,* 1946-51, *Manchester Evening News,* 1951-55, and *Daily Mail,* 1955-61; deputy editor of *Luton News,* 1961-63, and editor of *Havering Recorder,* 1963-67; *Sunday Times,* London, England, race relations, immigration, and civil liberties reporter, 1967-78, special correspondent in U.S., 1978—; *Los Angeles Times,* Los Angeles, Calif., feature writer, 1978—. *Awards, honors:* Co-winner of Martin Luther King Memorial Prize, 1973, for *Because They're Black.*

WRITINGS: (With Gus John) *Because They're Black,* Penguin, 1971; *Police Power and Black People,* Panther, 1972; (with Michael Ward) *Passports and Politics,* Penguin, 1973; (with David Tindall) *False Messiah: The Story of Michael X,* Hart-Davis, McGibbon, 1977; (with Ann Wickett) *Jean's Way,* Quartet Books, 1978; *Policing the Police,* Calder, 1979.

WORK IN PROGRESS: A survey of movements and legislation for voluntary euthanasia and the right to die throughout the world.

SIDELIGHTS: Jean's Way, an appeal for the right to die with dignity, has been published in nine countries.

HUNSBERGER, Warren S(eabury)   1911-

PERSONAL: Born August 28, 1911, in Philadelphia, Pa.; son of Byron Keyser (an educator) and Elizabeth N. (an educator; maiden name, Hume) Hunsberger; married Ruth Pedersen, April 17, 1942; children: Peter Hume, David Hume, Ellen Hume. *Education:* Yale University, A.B., 1933, Ph.D., 1937; National War College, graduate, 1951. *Home:* 3606 35th St. N.W., Washington, D.C. 20016. *Office:* School of International Service, American University, Washington, D.C. 20016.

CAREER: Princeton University, Princeton, N.J., instructor in economics, 1937-40; University of New Hampshire, Durham, assistant professor of economics, 1940-46 (on leave, 1941-46); Office of Export Control, Washington, D.C., economist, 1941; U.S. Department of State, Washington, D.C., chief, Northeast Asia Research Branch, 1946-48, chief, Division of Research for Far East, 1949-50, economist, President's Materials Policy Commission, 1951-52; U.S. International Cooperation Administration and predecessor agencies, program officer in Brazil, 1952-53, and Mexico, 1953; University of Rochester, Rochester, N.Y., Haloid Professor of International Economics, 1954-59; U.S. International Cooperation Administration, Washington, D.C., Far East regional economist, 1959-61; Johns Hopkins University, School of Advanced International Studies, Washington, D.C., professor of economic programming, Institute for International Development, 1961-63; Ford Foundation, adviser to economic planning unit, Prime Minister's Department, Kuala Lumpur, Malaysia, 1963-66; American University, Washington, D.C., adjunct professor, 1960-63, professor of economics, 1966-76, professor emeritus, 1976—, director, Center for Asian Studies, 1971-76. Economist and deputy team leader, United Nations Development Program/World Bank Korean Energy Study, 1978-79. Lecturer at Rutgers University, 1939-40, and Salzburg Seminar in American Studies, 1958, lecturer on international trade and economic development in Japan, Korea, Taiwan, Hong Kong, Thailand, and Indonesia, 1969; lecturer to government and private groups in Washington, D.C. *Military service:* U.S. Naval Reserve, active duty, 1941-46; retired as captain.

MEMBER: American Economic Association, Association for Asian Studies, Asia Society, Japan Society, Indonesian-American Friendship Society, Council on Foreign Relations, National Economists Club, American Foreign Service Association, Japan-American Society (Washington, D.C.; trustee), Pi Gamma Mu. *Awards, honors:* Council on Foreign Relations research fellow, 1958-59; Fulbright lecturer to Japan, 1973; Japan Foundation research fellow in Japan, 1974.

WRITINGS: (Contributor) Vera Micheles Dean, editor, *The Nature of the Non-Western World,* Mentor Press, 1957; (editor) *New Era in the Non-Western World,* Cornell University Press, 1957; *Japan in United States Foreign Economic Policy,* U.S. Government Printing Office, 1961; *Japan and the United States in World Trade,* Harper, 1964; (contributor) *United States-Japanese Political Relations,* Center for Strategic Studies, Georgetown University, 1968; *Japan: New Industrial Giant,* American-Asian Educational Exchange, 1972; (contributor) Jerome B. Cohen, editor, *Pacific Partnership: United States-Japan Trade,* Japan Society, 1972. Consultant on material for programmed text, *An Introduction to Communist China,* Defense Intelligence School, 1969. Contributor to *Worldmark Encyclopedia of the Nations* and to journals.

WORK IN PROGRESS: Research on foreign trade and economic relations of Asian countries.

* * *

HUNT, Kari (Eleanor B.) 1920-

PERSONAL: Born January 29, 1920, in Orange, N.J.; daughter of Jesse Herbert (an executive) and Nell (Stockett) Babcock; married Douglas M. Hunt, July 3, 1940; children: Karen (Mrs. Leon Schnitzspahn). *Education:* Attended Mount Holyoke College, 1937-39; also studied at University of Buffalo (now State University of New York at Buffalo) and Cornell University; studied mask-making with Doane Powell, 1950-51. *Home address:* R.D. 1, Box 386, Glen Gardner, N.J. 08826.

CAREER: Maskmaker for "Masquerade Party," a national network television show, produced from 1951 to 1959, carried by Columbia Broadcasting System, then by American Broadcasting Co., and later by National Broadcasting Co.; lecturer on masks and pantomime performer in masks, 1958—. *Member:* American Institute of Archaeology, Zonta Club of Morristown.

WRITINGS: (With Bernice Wells Carlson) *Masks and Mask Makers,* Abingdon, 1961; (with husband, Douglas Hunt) *Pantomime: The Silent Theater,* Atheneum, 1964; (with D. Hunt) *The Art of Magic,* Atheneum, 1967.

WORK IN PROGRESS: A book on the theater of Punch and Judy in its present forms.

AVOCATIONAL INTERESTS: Travel in Europe, particularly in Denmark, England, and France.

* * *

HUNTER, Howard Eugene 1929-

PERSONAL: Born June 20, 1929, in Lima, Ohio; son of Jesse C. and Zelva (Swan) Hunter; married Doris Leenhouts (a professor), July 5, 1957; children: Amy, Bruce. *Education:* Ohio Northern University, B.S., 1950; Ohio State University, M.A., 1952; Boston University, S.T.B., 1954, Ph.D., 1957. *Home:* 3 Madison Ave. W., Winchester, Mass. 01890. *Office:* Department of Religion, Miner Hall, Tufts University, Medford, Mass. 02155.

CAREER: Clergyman of Methodist Church; minister in Fairhaven and Acushnet, Mass., 1953-58; Tufts University, Medford, Mass., instructor, 1957-58, assistant professor of philosophy of religion and theology, 1958-61; Boston University, School of Theology, Boston, Mass., assistant professor of theology and director of admissions, 1961-66; Tufts University, associate professor of literature of religion, 1966-68, professor of religion and chairman of department, 1969—, director of College Within, 1974-77. Research fellow, Doshisha University Center for Study of Japanese Religions, Kyoto, 1970. Juror, American Film Festival, 1967-70; past president, Winchester Fair Housing. *Member:* American Academy of Religion, Society for the Arts, Religion, and Contemporary Culture (director and president), American Philosophical Association (fellow), American Association of University Professors.

WRITINGS: (Contributor) Frank Magill, editor, *Masterpieces of Christian Literature,* Salem Press, 1963; (editor) *Humanities, Religion, and the Arts Tomorrow,* Holt, 1972. Contributor of about thirty-five articles and reviews to religious journals. Member of editorial board, 1958-67, and managing editor, 1967-68, of *Crane Review.*

WORK IN PROGRESS: Religion and the Arts.†

HUNTER, Louise H(arris)

PERSONAL: Daughter of William H. and Janet (Foran) Harris; married Charles H. Hunter (deceased); children: Elsie Elaine, Evelyn Luella. *Education:* University of Hawaii, B.A. and M.A. *Religion:* Roman Catholic. *Home:* 1332 Makaha Valley Towers, Waianae, Hawaii 96792.

CAREER: High school teacher of history in Honolulu, Hawaii, 1968-73.

WRITINGS: Buddhism in Hawaii: Its Impact on a Yankee Community, University of Hawaii Press, 1971. Also author with husband, Charles H. Hunter, of *Statehood for Hawaii.*

* * *

HUNTER, Robert E(dwards) 1940-

PERSONAL: Born May 1, 1940, in Cambridge, Mass.; son of Robert, Jr. (a businessman) and Inez (Evans) Hunter. *Education:* Wesleyan University, Middletown, Conn., B.A. (with honors), 1962; London School of Economics and Political Science, London, Ph.D., 1969. *Politics:* Democrat. *Religion:* Protestant. *Home:* 613 Maryland Ave. N.E., Washington, D.C. 20002. *Office:* National Security Council, 368 Old Executive Office Bldg., Washington, D.C. 20510.

CAREER: U.S. Department of the Navy, Polaris Project, Washington, D.C. and London, England, administrative management intern, summers, 1961-63; assistant to Douglass Cater (special assistant to President Lyndon B. Johnson), Washington, D.C., 1964-65; London School of Economics and Political Science, University of London, London, England, lecturer in international relations, 1967-69; writer for 1968 presidential candidate Hubert H. Humphrey, 1968, 1969-70; Johns Hopkins University, School of Advanced International Studies, Washington, D.C., professorial lecturer in international studies, 1972-73; foreign policy advisor to Senator Edward Kennedy, 1973-77; National Security Council, Washington, D.C., director of West European Affairs, 1977—. Research associate, International Institute for Strategic Studies (London), 1967, 1968-69; fellow, Overseas Development Council, 1970-72, senior fellow, 1972-73. Associate executive director of platform committee, Democratic National Convention, 1972. *Member:* Council on Foreign Relations, International Institute for Strategic Studies, American Political Science Association, Arms Control Association, Chicago Council on Foreign Relations, Phi Beta Kappa. *Awards, honors:* Fulbright scholarship, London, England, 1962-63.

WRITINGS: (With Michael Howard) *Israel and the Arab World: The Crisis of 1967* (monograph), Institute for Strategic Studies, 1967; *The Soviet Dilemma in the Middle East* (monograph), Institute for Strategic Studies, 1969; *Security in Europe,* Elek, 1969, 2nd edition, Indiana University Press, 1972; (editor and contributor) *The United States and the Developing World: Agenda for Action,* Overseas Development Council, 1973; (editor with John E. Reilly) *Development Today: A New Look at U.S. Relations with the Poor Countries,* Praeger, 1972; (contributor) Henry Owen, editor, *The Next Phase in Foreign Policy,* Brookings Institution, 1973; (contributor) Peter Mansfield, editor, *The Middle East: A Political and Economic Survey,* Oxford University Press, 4th edition (Hunter was not associated with earlier editions), 1973. Contributor to professional journals, including *International Conciliation, Nation, World Review, Foreign Policy, New Republic, Listener,* and to Washington, Baltimore and New York newspapers.

HURLOCK, Elizabeth B. 1898-

PERSONAL: Born July 4, 1898, in Harrisburg, Pa.; daughter of William S. T. (a doctor) and Catharine M. (Bergner) Hurlock; married Irland McKnight Beckman (a banker), December 21, 1931; children: Daryl Elizabeth (deceased), Gail McKnight. *Education:* Bryn Mawr College, A.B., 1919, M.A., 1922; Columbia University, Ph.D., 1924. *Politics:* Democrat. *Religion:* Episcopalian. *Home:* Lenox Forest Apts., 3200 Lenox Rd. N.E., Atlanta, Ga. 30324.

CAREER: Springside School, Chestnut Hill, Pa., head of department of mathematics, 1919-21; Columbia University, New York, N.Y., instructor, 1924-26, associate in psychology, 1926-46, departmental representative for undergraduates, 1926-46; assistant to advisor of women students, 1926-46; University of Pennsylvania, Philadelphia, associate in psychology, 1949, associate in developmental psychology in School of Education, 1949-67; writer, 1946—; lecturer and consultant, 1968—. *Member:* American Psychological Association (fellow), American Association of University Professors, Gerontological Society, National Association for Better Radio and Television, American Association of University Women, Eastern Psychological Association (fellow), St. Andrew's Society of Atlanta, Atlanta Writers' Club, Bryn Mawr Club of Atlanta, Sigma Xi, Bryn Mawr Club of New York, Bryn Mawr Club of Philadelphia, Philadelphia Cricket Club.

WRITINGS: The Psychology of Dress: An Analysis of Fashion and Its Motive, Ronald, 1929, reprinted, Benjamin Blom, 1971; *Modern Ways with Babies,* Lippincott, 1937; *Child Development,* McGraw, 1942, 6th edition, 1978; *Modern Ways with Children,* McGraw, 1943; *Child Growth and Development,* McGraw, 1948, 5th edition, 1978; *Adolescent Development,* McGraw, 1949, 4th edition, 1973; *A Guide and Record of Your Baby's Early Years,* C. R. Gibson, 1952; *Developmental Psychology,* McGraw, 1953, 4th edition, 1974; *Guideposts to Growing Up,* Standard Education, 1954; *Personality Development,* McGraw, 1973. Writer of eleven educational sound films and five film strips on child and adolescent development for McGraw. Author of syndicated newspaper column, "As We Live," 1947-58. Contributor to encyclopedias, books for parents, journals, and magazines. Child training editor of *Today's Health,* 1947-59; member of editorial staff of *Journal of Adolescence,* 1966—.

AVOCATIONAL INTERESTS: Travel, swimming, national and community affairs.

*   *   *

HURSCH, Carolyn J(udge)

PERSONAL: Born in Cranston, R.I.; daughter of Albert and Madeleine (Noque) Judge; married Jack L. Hursch, Jr. (a mathematician), April 1, 1962. *Education:* Indiana University, A.B., 1952; University of California, Los Angeles, graduate study, 1957-58; University of Colorado, M.A., 1961, Ph.D., 1965. *Religion:* Protestant.

CAREER: During early career employed in various occupations, including that of guitar teacher, manager of a secretarial school, and assistant to a private detective; Castleton Teachers College (now Castleton State College), Castleton, Vt., assistant professor of psychology, 1965-66; University of Vermont, Burlington, assistant professor of statistics of psychology, 1965-67; University of Florida, Gainesville, assistant professor of psychology, 1967-73; Veterans Administration Hospital, Gainesville, Fla., research psychologist, 1970-73; Denver General Hospital, Denver, Colo., research psychologist, beginning 1973. *Member:* American

Psychological Association, Association for the Psychophysiological Study of Sleep, Florida Psychological Association, Florida State Museum Association.

WRITINGS: (Contributor) Ernest Hartmann, editor, *Sleep and Dreaming,* Little, Brown, 1970; (with Robert L. Williams and Ismet Karacan), *Electroencephalography (EEG) of Human Sleep: Clinical Applications,* Wiley, 1974; *The Trouble with Rape: A Psychologist's Report on the Legal, Medical, Social and Psychological Problems,* Nelson-Hall, 1977. Contributor of about thirty articles to medical psychological journals; contributor of poetry to *Denver Post, Home Life, Town and Country,* and *Mayflower Log.*

WORK IN PROGRESS: Dark Rainbow, a biographical novel on the life of Rembrandt.

SIDELIGHTS: Carolyn J. Hursch told *CA:* "I sold my first story at age 8, and have been writing ever since between other things, mostly scientific articles, which I write with my head, but in those rare free hours, I write poetry and fiction with my heart." *Avocational interests:* Painting, skiing, mountain climbing, collecting rocks and coins, planting flowers, travel (she has traveled throughout the country and lived in a dozen states and in Holland).†

*   *   *

HUSTON, James Alvin 1918-

PERSONAL: Born March 24, 1918, in Fairmount, Ind.; son of Alva Merrill and Nettie (Caskey) Huston; married Florence Webb, December 29, 1946; children: Nita Diane, James Webb. *Education:* Indiana University, A.B. (with honors), 1939, A.M., 1940; New York University, Ph.D., 1947; also studied at St. John's College, Oxford, 1945, and University of Fribourg, summer, 1951. *Religion:* Christian (Disciples of Christ). *Home:* 300 Langhorne Lane, Lynchburg, Va. 24501. *Office:* Lynchburg College, Lynchburg, Va. 24504.

CAREER: Purdue University, Lafayette, Ind., instructor, 1946-48, assistant professor, 1948-53, associate professor, 1953-60, professor of history, 1960-72; Lynchburg College, Lynchburg, Va., dean, 1972—. Department of the Army, Office of Chief of Military History, historian, 1951-53; Naval War College, E. J. King Professor of Maritime History, 1959-60; National War College, professor of international affairs and director of European studies, 1966-67, 1971-72. *Military service:* U.S. Army, infantry, 1942-46, 1951-53; became major; received Bronze Star Medal with oak leaf cluster. U.S. Army Reserve, 1939-72; became colonel. *Member:* Southern Historical Association, Acacia, Phi Beta Kappa, Phi Delta Kappa.

WRITINGS: Combat History of 134th Infantry, Army & Navy Publishing, 1948; *Biography of a Battalion,* Courier Press, 1950; (contributor) Paul S. Jacobsen and others, editors, *An Introduction to American Government,* Stackpole, 1954; *Across the Face of France,* Purdue University, 1963; *Sinews of War,* Office of Chief of Military History, 1966; (contributor) Eisenhower Foundation, editor, *D-Day: The Normandy Invasion in Retrospect,* University Press of Kansas, 1971; *Out of the Blue,* Purdue University, 1972; (contributor) *Dictionary of American History,* Scribner, 1976. Contributor of articles to history and military journals.

WORK IN PROGRESS: Research on strategy and logistics of North Atlantic Treaty Organization (NATO).

*   *   *

HUTTON, Geoffrey 1928-

PERSONAL: Born May 2, 1928, in Croydon, England; married; children: three. *Education:* University College, London, B.Sc., 1951. *Home:* 17 Combe Park, Bath BA1 3NP, England. *Office:* School of Management, University of Bath, Claverton Down, Bath, England.

CAREER: Tavistock Clinic, London, England, assistant clinical psychologist, 1951-53; Tavistock Institute of Human Relations, London, project officer, 1954-59, associate consultant in Centre for Career Development and Institutional Change, 1958—; University of Edinburgh, Edinburgh, Scotland, director of Social Environment Research Unit, 1959-64; University of Bath, Claverton Down, Bath, England, reader in behavioral sciences, 1965—. *Member:* British Psychological Society (associate member), British Sociological Association, European Institute for Transnational Studies in Group and Organizational Development (general associate member), International Association of Applied Social Scientists (international charter member).

WRITINGS: (With Cyril Sofer) *New Ways in Management Training,* Tavistock Publications, 1958; *Thinking about Organization,* University of Bath Press, 1969, 2nd edition, Tavistock Publications, 1972. Contributor to *Human Relations* and *Journal for the Theory of Social Behaviour.*

WORK IN PROGRESS: Thinking about Systems, Ideas and Action.

*   *   *

HYMAN, Lawrence W.   1919-

PERSONAL: Born January 5, 1919, in New York, N.Y.; son of Joseph (a storekeeper) and Rose (Golub) Hyman; married Virginia Riley (a teacher), May 21, 1949; children: Laura Jean. *Education:* College of the City of New York (now City College of the City University of New York), B.S.S., 1940; Columbia University, M.A., 1947, Ph.D., 1951. *Politics:* Democrat. *Religion:* "Humanist." *Home:* 687 Wyndemere Ave., Ridgewood, N.J. 07450. *Office:* Department of English, Brooklyn College of the City University of New York, Brooklyn, N.Y. 11210.

CAREER: Brooklyn College of the City University of New York, Brooklyn, N.Y., instructor, 1953-60, assistant professor, 1961-68, associate professor, 1969-70, professor of English, 1971—. Democratic county committeeman (Ridgewood, N.J.). *Military service:* U.S. Army Air Forces, 1942-46. *Member:* Modern Language Association of America, National Council of Teachers of English, American Society for Aesthetics.

WRITINGS: Andrew Marvell, Tawyne, 1964; *The Quarrel Within: Art and Morality in Milton's Poetry,* Kennikat, 1972.

WORK IN PROGRESS: A series of articles on the conflict between literature and morality.

*   *   *

HYMAN, Robin P(hilip)   1931-

PERSONAL: Born September 9, 1931, in London, England; son of Leonard and Helen Hyman; married Inge Neufeld; children: James, Peter, Philippa. *Education:* University of Birmingham, B.A. (honors), 1955. *Home:* 101 Hampstead Way, London NW11 7LR, England. *Office:* Bell & Hyman Ltd., Denmark House, 37/39 Queen Elizabeth St., London SE1 2QB, England.

CAREER: Evans Brothers Ltd. (publishers), London, England, 1955-77, managing director, 1972-77; Bell & Hyman Ltd. (publishers), London, chairman and managing director, 1977—. *Member:* Publishers Association (member of council, 1975—).

WRITINGS: (Compiler) *A Dictionary of Famous Quotations,* Bell & Hyman, 1962, published as *The Quotation Dictionary,* Macmillan, 1967; (with John Trevaskis) *The Boys' and Girls' First Dictionary,* Evans Brothers, 1967, published as *The Young Readers Press First Dictionary,* Young Readers Press, 1972.

Juveniles, written with wife Inge Hyman; all originally published by Evans Brothers: *Barnabas Ball at the Circus,* 1967; *Runaway James and the Night Owl,* 1968; *Run, Run, Chase the Sun,* 1969; (compiler) *Three Bags Full,* 1972; *Happy with Hubert,* 1973; *The Hippo Who Wanted to Fly,* 1973; *Caspar and the Lion Cub,* 1974; *The Magical Fish,* 1974; *Caspar and the Rainbow Bird,* 1975; *The Greatest Explorers in the World,* 1978. Member of editorial board, *World Year Book of Education,* 1969-73.

AVOCATIONAL INTERESTS: Theater, travel, reading.

*   *   *

HYSLOP, Lois Boe   1908-

PERSONAL: Born April 3, 1908, in Baltic, S.D.; daughter of Nils (a minister) and Sissel (Finseth) Boe; married Francis E. Hyslop (a professor), September 11, 1948. *Education:* Augustana College, B.A., 1930; University of Wisconsin, M.A., 1931, Ph.D., 1935. *Politics:* Republican. *Religion:* Lutheran. *Home:* 326 Hillcrest Ave., State College, Pa. 16801. *Office:* Department of French, Pennsylvania State University, University Park, Pa. 16802.

CAREER: Susquehanna University, Selinsgrove, Pa., professor of French, 1935-44; Skidmore College, Saratoga Springs, N.Y., associate professor of French and Spanish, 1944-48, head of department of Romance languages, 1947-48; Pennsylvania State University, University Park, associate professor, 1948-55, professor of French and Spanish, 1958—, acting head of department of French, 1963-65, fellow of Institute for the Arts and Humanistic Studies of Pennsylvania State University. *Member:* Modern Language Association of America, American Association of Teachers of French, Phi Sigma Iota, Pi Kappa Delta.

WRITINGS: (Translator with husband, Francis Hyslop) *Baudelaire on Poe,* Bald Eagle Press, 1952; (translator, editor, and author of commentary with Francis Hyslop), *Baudelaire: A Self-Portrait,* Oxford University Press, 1957, reprinted, Greenwood Press, 1978; (with Francis Hyslop) *Baudelaire as a Literary Critic,* Pennsylvania State University Press, 1964; (editor and contributor) *Baudelaire as a Love Poet and Other Essays,* Pennsylvania State University Press, 1969; *Henry Becque,* Twayne, 1972. Contributor to *French Review, Bulletin Baudelairien, Kentucky Quarterly,* and other literature journals.

WORK IN PROGRESS: Another book of essays about Baudelaire.

BIOGRAPHICAL/CRITICAL SOURCES: Books Abroad, spring, 1970.

I

ICKS, Robert J(oseph) 1900-

PERSONAL: Born September 11, 1900, in Kaukauna, Wis.; son of August William (a labor union officer) and Elizabeth (Feister) Icks; married Gertrude Genevieve Duel, August 1, 1923. *Education:* Ripon College, Ph.B., 1922; graduate study at University of Wisconsin. *Politics:* Republican. *Religion:* Congregationalist. *Home:* 438 May St., Elmhurst, Ill. 60126.

CAREER: Salesman for Standard Oil Co. of Indiana, 1922-23; high school teacher in Wisconsin, 1924-29; Hardware Mutual Casualty Co. (now Sentry Insurance Co.), Stevens Point, Wis., department manager, 1929-40; Auto Owners Insurance Co., Lansing, Mich., vice-president, 1946-48; S. Alexander Bell & Co. (now Peat, Marwick, Mitchell & Co.; an accounting firm), Chicago, Ill., department manager, 1948-68. Executive secretary of insurance advisory committee to the Illinois State Director of Insurance, 1966. *Military service:* U.S. Army Reserve, 1927-60; active duty, 1941-46; received Legion of Merit and Army Commendation Medal; retired as colonel. *Member:* American Ordnance Association, U.S. Armor Association, Association of the U.S. Army.

WRITINGS: (With R. E. Jones and G. H. Rarey) *The Fighting Tanks since 1916,* Military Service Publishing Co., 1933; (with O. H. Hacker, Otto Merker, and G. P. Von Zezschwitz) *Heigls Taschenbuch der Tanks,* J. F. Lehmanns Verlag, 1935; *Tanks and Armored Vehicles,* Duell, Sloan & Pearce, 1945; *Profiles in Armour,* Profile Publications, 1969; *Famous Tank Battles,* Doubleday, 1972; (with Duncan Crow) *Encyclopedia of Tanks,* Barrie & Jenkins, 1975; (with Crow) *Encyclopedia of Armored Cars,* Barrie & Jenkins, 1976. Contributor to *Ordnance, Infantry Journal, Armor, Royal Tank Corps Journal, Truppendienst, Feldgrau, Armed Forces Journal,* and *Embassy.*

WORK IN PROGRESS: A book on the development of U.S. military policy.

* * *

IGLITZIN, Lynne 1931-

PERSONAL: Born November 7, 1931, in New York, N.Y.; daughter of Harvey J. (a professor) and Blix (Ruskay) Bresler; married Alan Iglitzin (a musician), June 21, 1953; children: Karen, Lara, Eric. *Education:* Barnard College, B.A., 1953; University of Minnesota, M.A., 1957; Bryn Mawr College, Ph.D., 1966. *Politics:* Democrat. *Home:* 5241 17th St. N.E., Seattle, Wash. 98105. *Office:* Department of Undergraduate Studies, University of Washington, Seattle, Wash. 98105.

CAREER: Beaver College, Glenside, Pa., assistant professor of political science, 1966-67; University of Washington, Seattle, lecturer in American politics, 1968—, associate director of undergraduate studies, 1972—, director of cooperative education and fieldwork studies. *Member:* American Political Science Association, American Civil Liberties Union (member of board of directors of State of Washington unit and head of Women's Rights Committee).

WRITINGS: Violent Conflict in American Society, Chandler Publishing, 1972; (editor with Ruth Ross) *Women in the World: A Comparative Study,* American Bibliographic Center-Clio Press, 1976. Contributor to *Midwest Quarterly, Politics and Society, Journal of Social Issues, American Behavioral Scientist,* and *Teaching Political Science.*

* * *

ILLIANO, Antonio 1934-

PERSONAL: Born April 21, 1934, in Italy; son of Fausto and Luigina (Scotto) Illiano; married Elfriede R. Worsthorn, June 11, 1962; children: Vincent. *Education:* University of Naples, Laurea de Dottore in Lettere, 1958; University of California, Berkeley, Ph.D., 1966. *Home:* 400 Ridgecrest Dr., Chapel Hill, N.C. 27514. *Office:* Department of Romance Languages and Literatures, University of North Carolina, Chapel Hill, N.C. 27514.

CAREER: University of California, Santa Barbara, instructor, 1963-66; University of Texas at Austin, assistant professor of Italian language and literature, 1966-68; University of Oregon, Eugene, assistant professor of Italian language and literature, 1968-69; University of North Carolina at Chapel Hill, assistant professor, 1969-71, associate professor of Romance languages and literatures, 1971—. *Member:* Modern Language Association of America, Dante Society of America. *Awards, honors:* Postdoctoral fellowship from University of Texas Academic Excellence Program, 1966; Pogue leave, University of North Carolina, 1978.

WRITINGS: (Editor and translator with Howard E. Smither) Alfred Einstein, *The Italian Madrigal,* Volume III, Princeton University Press, 1971; (editor and translator with Daniel P. Testa) Luigi Pirandello, *Pirandello: On Humor,* University of North Carolina Press, 1974; (translator with P. Cherchi) Theodore Silverstein, *Poeti e filosofi medievali,* Adriatica Editrice, 1975; *Introduzione alla critica pirandelliana,* Fiorini, 1976. Contributor to *Dictionary of Italian Literature* and *Columbia Dictionary of Modern European Literature.* Contributor to *Italica, PMLA, New York Public Library Bulletin, Forum Italicum, Comparative Literature, Studi Piemontesi, Mark Twain Journal, Modern Drama, Perspectives on Contemporary Literature,* and other journals.

*   *   *

INGBAR, Mary Lee   1926-

PERSONAL: Born May 18, 1926, in New York, N.Y.; daughter of Edward C. (a professor of English literature) and Ruth (Prince) Mack; married Sidney H. Ingbar (William B. Castle Professor of Medicine at Harvard University Medical School), May 28, 1950; children: David, Eric, Jonathan. *Education:* Radcliffe College, S.B. (cum laude), 1946, A.M., 1948, Ph.D., 1953; Harvard University, M.P.H. (cum laude), 1956. *Home:* 305 Dudley St., Brookline, Mass. 02146. *Office:* School of Medicine, University of Massachusetts, 55 Lake Ave. N., Worcester, Mass. 01605.

CAREER: U.S. Government, Washington, D.C., price economist with Department of Labor, 1951-52, and business economist with Department of the Interior, 1952-53; Harvard University, part-time lecturer on medical economics at School of Public Health, Boston, Mass., 1957-61, research associate, Graduate School of Public Administration, Cambridge, Mass., 1961-66; Cambridge Department of Health, Hospital, and Welfare, Cambridge, part-time director of program development, 1968-69, 1970-72; Commonwealth of Massachusetts, Executive Office for Administration and Finance, Boston, consultant in health economics, 1969-70, director of research, Office of Comprehensive Health Planning, 1970-71; University of California, San Francisco, associate professor of health economics, 1972-75, associate program director, Robert Wood Johnson Clinical Scholar Program, 1974-75; U.S. Department of Health, Education, and Welfare, Public Health Service, Boston, regional consultant for health economics and public health advisor, 1975-76; Harvard University Medical School, Boston, principal research associate in preventive and social medicine, 1976—; Beth Israel Hospital, Boston, research associate, 1976—; University of Massachusetts, Worcester, School of Medicine, director of institutional studies and part-time consultant, 1976—, department of family and community medicine, professor of family and community medicine, 1977—. Visiting professor of health economics, Dartmouth College, 1976. Project director of research studies of hospital costs in Massachusetts for U.S. Public Health Service, 1961-66, and of cost-benefit analyses and ambulatory care for National Center for Health Services Research and Development, 1970-72. Overseer, Peter Bent Bingham Hospital, 1976. Friends of Boston City Hospital, recording secretary, 1963-66, chairman of nominating committee, 1966-67, president, 1968-69. Member of Organization of Health Services Panel, National Advisory Commission on Health Manpower, 1966-67; member of Task Force on Alcoholism of the Attorney General of the Commonwealth of Massachusetts, 1969; member of experimental health services delivery systems review committee, U.S. Public Health Service, 1971-72; member, Committee on Humanizing Health Care, Medical Sociology Section of the American Sociology Association, 1974. Director, Center for Chamber Music, 1976—. Consul-

tant or advisor to Town of Brookline and Florence Heller Graduate School for Advanced Studies in Social Welfare, Brandeis University, 1960-61, Brookline-Brigham Nursing Home, 1962-63, U.S. Department of Health, Education, and Welfare, 1966-67, 1972-74, Massachusetts Committee on Children and Youth, 1968, Office of Comprehensive Health Planning, Commonwealth of Massachusetts, 1972, Casa de Amigos Neighborhood Health Center, Texas Medical Center, 1973, California Hospital Association, 1973—, California Hospital Commission, 1973, On Lok Senior Health Services, 1973-74, Los Angeles County Department of Health Services and School of Public Health, University of California, Los Angeles, 1974, and Alpha Center for Health Planning, 1977—.

MEMBER: American Association for the Advancement of Science, American Economic Association, American Hospital Association, American Public Health Association (fellow; co-chairman, medical care-maternal and child health sections liaison committee, 1959-61; member, governing council, 1974-76; chairman, ambulatory care committee, medical care section, 1975-77; chairman, social policy committee, 1977-78; chairman-elect, medical care section, 1977-78; chairman, medical care section, 1978-79), Association for the Behavioral Sciences and Medical Education, Association of Teachers of Preventive Medicine, Association of University Programs in Health Administration, Operations Research Society of America, Society for Advanced Medical Systems, Royal Society of Health (London), Massachusetts Public Health Association (secretary, medical care section, 1960-61; chairman-elect, medical care section, 1964-65; chairman, medical care section, 1965-66; recording secretary, 1966-68), Delta Omega, Phi Beta Kappa, Omicron Chi Epsilon (honorary faculty member).

WRITINGS: (Contributor) *Inter-Industry Analysis,* Bureau of Mines, Department of the Interior, 1953; *MEROPS: Medical Economics Regression Option Programming System,* Graduate School of Public Administration, Harvard University, 1966; (with Lester D. Taylor) *Hospital Costs in Massachusetts: An Econometric Study,* Harvard University Press, 1968; (contributor) Matthew A. Budd, Barney Reiffen, Melvin A. Rodman, and Herbert Sherman, *A Program for an Ambulatory Care Service,* Lincoln Laboratory, Massachusetts Institute of Technology, 1969; *Report on the Rate Setting Commission of the Commonwealth of Massachusetts: Its Problems and Prospects* (monograph), Office of Comprehensive Health Planning, Commonwealth of Massachusetts, 1970; (with Joan M. Gorga) *Mortality of Residents of Massachusetts by Substate Region, Cause of Death and Socio-Demographic Characteristics of the Deceased, 1966, 1967, and 1968* (monograph), Office of Comprehensive Health Planning, Commonwealth of Massachusetts, 1971; (with Kathleen T. Young) *Medical Care of the Ambulatory Patient in Massachusetts: Outpatient Services of Short-Term Hospitals by Substate Region and Area in Relation to Populations, Inpatient Bed Capacities, Medical Manpower, 1965-69* (monograph), Office of Comprehensive Health Planning, Commonwealth of Massachusetts, 1971; (with Jean M. Glancy and Young) *Preliminary Listing of Sources of Information Pertinent to Planning Health Services in Massachusetts* (monograph), Office of Comprehensive Health Planning, Commonwealth of Massachusetts, 1971; *Contributions of Improved Data Systems to Better Ambulatory Care for Disadvantaged Urban Residents* (monograph), Department of Health, Hospital, and Welfare of the City of Cambridge, Massachusetts, 1972; *Hospital Costs and Efficiency: A Report to the California Hospital*

Commission on its Prospects and Problems (monograph), School of Medicine, University of California, San Francisco, 1973; (contributor) Robert L. Kane, editor, *The Behavioral Sciences and Preventive Medicine: Opportunities and Dilemmas*, U.S. Government Printing Office, 1977; (contributor) Michael Zubkoff, Ira E. Raskin, and Ruth S. Hanft, editors, *Hospital Cost Containment: Selected Notes for Future Policy*, Milbank Memorial Fund, 1978; (contributor) George K. Chacko, editor, *Health Handbook, 1976: An International Reference on Care and Cure*, North-Holland Publishing, 1978. Work has been anthologized in *Medical Care in Transition: Reprints from the American Journal of Public Health 1958-62*, Volume II, U.S. Government Printing Office, 1964. Contributor to proceedings. Contributor of articles and reviews to *American Journal of Public Health, Journal of the American Medical Women's Association, Journal of Economic Literature, New England Journal of Medicine*, and *Arthritis and Rheumatism*.

* * *

INGERSOLL, David E(dward) 1939-

PERSONAL: Born November 12, 1939, in Chicago, Ill.; son of Joseph S. and Edna (Young) Ingersoll; married Elizabeth Nybakken, June 16, 1962 (divorced July, 1977). *Education:* Carleton College, B.A., 1961; Claremont Graduate School and University Center (now Claremont Graduate School), Ph.D., 1964. *Home address:* R.F.D. 2, Newark, Del. 19711. *Office:* Department of Political Science, University of Delaware, Newark, Del. 19711.

CAREER: University of Delaware, Newark, assistant professor, 1964-70, associate professor of political science, 1970—, chairperson of department, 1975—. *Member:* American Political Science Association, American Association of University Professors, Southern Political Science Association, Pi Sigma Alpha.

WRITINGS: Communism, Fascism, Democracy: The Origins and Development of Three Ideologies, C. E. Merrill, 1971.

WORK IN PROGRESS: Research on futurology; a book on twentieth-century democratic theory.

* * *

INGLIS, Stuart J(ohn) 1923-

PERSONAL: Born December 16, 1923, in Van Nuys, Calif.; son of John Percy (an educator) and Ruth (Penfield) Inglis; married Elizabeth Eskildsen, December 21, 1958; children: Jeffrey, Adrienne, Jennifer. *Education:* Attended Pomona College, 1942-43, and Occidental College, 1943-44; University of California, Berkeley, B.A., 1947, M.A., 1956. *Politics:* Democrat. *Religion:* Presbyterian. *Home:* 573 Tyler Ave., Livermore, Calif. 94550. *Office:* Department of Physics, Chabot College, Livermore, Calif. 94550.

CAREER: Contra Costa College, San Pablo, Calif., instructor in physics and astronomy, 1956-63; Sonoma State College (now California State College, Sonoma), Rohnert Park, instructor in physics, 1963-64, associate professor of physical science and astronomy, 1964-65; Chabot College, Hayward, Calif., instructor in physics and astronomy, 1965-70, Livermore, Calif. campus, instructor in physics, astronomy, and geology, 1975—; Rogue Community College, Grants Pass, Ore., instructor in physical science, 1971-72. Lecturer in astronomy, Morrison Planetarium, 1956-60. Member of International Geophysical Year solar eclipse expedition to South Pacific, 1958. Visiting associate professor of chemistry, Rensselaer Polytechnic Institute, 1967-68. *Military service:* U.S. Marine Corps, 1943-45; became second lieutenant. *Member:* Astronomical Society of the Pacific, Sigma Xi. *Awards, honors:* National Science Foundation science faculty fellow, 1961-62.

WRITINGS: Planets, Stars, and Galaxies, Wiley, 1961, 4th edition, 1976; (editor and contributor) *An Approach to Physical Science*, Wiley, 1969; *Physics: An Ebb and Flow of Ideas*, Wiley, 1970.

WORK IN PROGRESS: Geology, a textbook for nonscience majors.

AVOCATIONAL INTERESTS: Improving forests on his land, farming, and landscaping.

* * *

INGRAM, William 1930-

PERSONAL: Born November 23, 1930, in Chicago, Ill. *Education:* Grinnell College, B.A., 1953; Columbia University, M.A., 1956; University of Pennsylvania, Ph.D., 1966. *Office:* Department of English, University of Michigan, Ann Arbor, Mich. 48109.

CAREER: University of Michigan, Ann Arbor, assistant professor, 1967-70, associate professor, 1970-78, professor of English, 1978—. *Military service:* U.S. Army, 1953-55.

WRITINGS: (Editor with Peter Bauland) *The Tradition of the Theatre*, Allyn & Bacon, 1970; (with Kathleen Swaim) *A Concordance to John Milton's English Poetry*, Clarendon Press, 1972; *A London Life in the Brazen Age*, Harvard University Press, 1978.

* * *

INNIS, Donald Quayle 1924-

PERSONAL: Born April 21, 1924, in Toronto, Ontario, Canada; came to United States in 1963; son of Harold Adams (a professor) and Mary (Quayle) Innis; married Janet Marion Graham, June 17, 1949 (divorced, 1966); married Winifred Huggins, April 5, 1969; children: (first marriage) Mary Graham, John Williams; (second marriage) Katherine Anne. *Education:* University of Toronto, B.A. (honors), 1947; University of California, Berkeley, Ph.D., 1959. *Home:* 78 Center St., Geneseo, N.Y. 14454. *Office:* Department of Geography, State University of New York College, Geneseo, N.Y. 14454.

CAREER: University of Chicago, Chicago, Ill., instructor in geography, 1948-50; University of Western Ontario, London, instructor in geography, 1952-53; Queen's University, Kingston, Ontario, instructor, 1953-56, assistant professor of geography, 1956-63; State University of New York College at Geneseo, associate professor, 1963-65, professor of geography, 1965—, chairman of department, 1965—, president of faculty senate, 1973-74. Chairman, African Students Foundation (Kingston), 1962-63. *Member:* American Geographical Society, Association of American Geographers, Association of Asian Studies, Canadian Association of Geographers, Friends of the Earth, Sierra Club, Smithsonian Institution, United University Professionals (president, Geneseo chapter, 1974-75). *Awards, honors:* Canada Council grant for field work in Jamaica, 1960; research grant from State University of New York for field work in India, 1966.

WRITINGS: Canada: A Geographic Study, McGraw (Toronto), 1966; (contributor) John Warkentin, editor, *Canada: A Geographical Interpretation*, Methuen, 1968; *New York*

State: Independent Study Course, State University of New York at Albany, 1970. Contributor to *Grolier Encyclopedia* and *These United States Atlas.* Contributor to *Spotlight, Queen's Quarterly, Canadian Geographical Journal, Les Cahiers de Geographie de Quebec, Focus, Canadian Journal of Economics and Political Science, Geographical Review,* and *Organic Gardening.*

WORK IN PROGRESS: Intercropping: The Scientific Basis of Peasant Agriculture, a monograph studying small farm agriculture methods in the tropics; research on radio and television station distributions.

SIDELIGHTS: Donald Innis speaks French, Spanish, German, Russian, and Marathi. He has traveled in the West Indies, Europe, Near East, and South Asia. As a writer, Innis feels that one of his major tasks is to preserve the wealth of unrecorded knowledge possessed by non-literate small farmers in the tropics about the best ways to grow more food.

* * *

IRWIN, George 1910-1971

PERSONAL: Born December 21, 1910, in Timaru, New Zealand; son of George and Mary (Lambert) Irwin; married Judy Judd, June 11, 1937. *Education:* University of Canterbury, New Zealand, M.A., 1934. *Religion:* Church of England. *Home:* Turanga Rd., Henderson R.D. 1, Auckland 8, New Zealand.

CAREER: Teacher in Fiji, 1936-40; principal of Teachers Training College, Western Samoa, and assistant director of education in Western Samoa, 1940-55; researcher and writer, 1955-71. *Military service:* Royal New Zealand Air Force, 1940-45; became lieutenant.

WRITINGS: Samoa: A Teacher's Tale, Cassell, Ltd., 1965, A. S. Barnes, 1966; *Samuel Johnson: A Personality in Conflict,* Oxford University Press, 1971. Contributor of articles to *Johnsonian News Letter* and *Literature and Psychology.*††

(Died February 21, 1971)

* * *

ISAKOVSKY, Mikhail Vasilyevich 1900-1973

January 20, 1900—July 22(?), 1973; Russian poet, lyric writer, and newspaperman. Obituaries: *Washington Post,* July 23, 1973; *New York Times,* July 23, 1973.

* * *

ISHAK, Fayek (Matta) 1922-

PERSONAL: Born October 29, 1922, in Sharkieh, Egypt; married Aida Hanna (a teacher of French), August 3, 1958; children: Hany (son), Hoda (daughter). *Education:* Cairo University, B.A., 1945; Cairo College of Education, diploma in education and psychology, 1947; Cairo Institute of Higher Studies, diploma in English linguistics and translation, 1951; University of Exeter, diploma in graduate studies in English, 1954; University of Liverpool, Ph.D., 1962. *Home:* 135 Woodside St., Thunder Bay, Ontario, Canada. *Office:* Department of English, Lakehead University, Thunder Bay, Ontario, Canada P7B 5E1.

CAREER: High school English teacher in Egypt, 1947-52; Higher Teachers College, Cairo, Egypt, lecturer in English literature, 1954-63; Ain Shams University, Higher Teachers College, Cairo, assistant professor of English, 1963-66; Notre Dame University, Nelson, British Columbia, assis-

tant professor of English, 1966-67; Lakehead University, Thunder Bay, Ontario, assistant professor, 1967-69, associate professor, 1969-77, professor of English, 1977—, chairman of department, 1977—. *Member:* International Society for Neoplatonic Studies, Association of Canadian University Teachers of English, American Oriental Society, Renaissance Society of America, Medieval Academy of America. *Awards, honors:* Scholarship from Cairo Ministry of Education at University of Exeter, 1952-54; grants from Chancellor's Fund of Lakehead University, for research in England and the United States, 1968, 1969, 1970, 1971, 1972; plaques for distinguished scholarly achievement, International Biographical Association, 1975, 1976.

WRITINGS: (With H. M. Hanna) *Comprehension Practice and Precis Writing,* Darel-Fikr, 1957; (with M. H. Shawkat and Robert Neilson) *Literary Terms,* Darel-Fikr, 1963; *The Theories of Literary Criticism from Aristotle to the Modern Age,* two volumes, Anglo-Egyptian Publishers, 1964; *T. S. Eliot: The Critic, the Poet and the Playwright,* El-Maaref, 1965; *The Mystical Philosophy of T. S. Eliot,* College & University Press, 1970. Contributor to *Forum, Orthodox Word, Cairo Theatre Magazine, Literary Review, Review of Contemporary Thought,* and education journals. Editor, *Teachers College Review* (Cairo), 1957-59; assistant editor, *Forum,* 1966-67; co-editor, *Art and Literary Review,* 1973—; member of editorial staff, *Coptologia.*

WORK IN PROGRESS: The Landmarks of Near and Far Eastern Mysticism; translating into English the Coptic Mass and the liturgy of St. Basil; research on paradoxical and sceptical elements in the poetry of John Donne, a philosophical reappraisal.

* * *

ISLAM, A(bul) K(hair) M(uhammed) Aminul 1933-

PERSONAL: Born December 21, 1933, in Dacca, East Pakistan (now Bangladesh); son of Sekander Ali and Safura (Khatoon) Islam; married Sarah Amin (a professor of psychology), December 16, 1966; children: Shahan and Salim (sons). *Education:* University of Dacca, B.A., 1952, M.A. (Bengali language and literature), 1954; University of London, graduate study, 1959-61; University of Toronto, M.A. (anthropology), 1964; McGill University, Ph.D., 1969. *Politics:* "Democracy." *Religion:* "Anthropology (Humanism)." *Home:* 1212 Mt. Vernon Ave., Dayton, Ohio 45405. *Office:* Department of Sociology-Anthropology-Social Work, Wright State University, Colonel Glenn Highway, Dayton, Ohio 45431.

CAREER: Gaffargaon College, Mymensingh, East Pakistan, professor of Bengali, 1954-55; Madan Mohan College, Sylhet, East Pakistan, professor of Bengali, 1955; University of Dacca, Dacca, East Pakistan, lecturer in Bengali, 1955-59; Bhuapur College, Bhuapur, East Pakistan, principal, 1962; St. Cloud State College, St. Cloud, Minn., assistant professor of sociology, 1967; State University of New York College at Plattsburgh, assistant professor of sociology, 1967-69, chairman of department of sociology and anthropology, 1968-69; Wright State University, Dayton, Ohio, associate professor of sociology, 1969-77, professor of anthropology, 1977—, and chairman of department of sociology-anthropology-social work, 1969-70. Maxwell Graduate School, Syracuse University, visiting assistant professor, summer, 1965, visiting professor, summer, 1969; visiting professor, Central State University, 1971. Life member, Linguistic Research Group of Pakistan; president, Bangladesh Association Incorporation—Midwest, 1971.

MEMBER: American Anthropological Association (fellow), Current Anthropology (associate), Royal Anthropological Society (Great Britain; fellow), Royal Philological Society (Great Britain; life member), Pakistan Sociological Association, Central State Anthropological Association, Northeastern Anthropological Association, Pakistan Students' Association (Montreal; president, 1965). *Awards, honors:* British Council scholarship, University of London, 1959-61; Vincent Massey fellowship, University of Toronto, 1962-64; Center for Developing Area Studies research fellowship, 1966-67.

WRITINGS: Jasim Uddin: Kavi O Kavva (a book about life and works of Jasim Uddin), Eden Press (Dacca), 1955, 2nd edition, 1969; *Bangle Shahitye Muslim Kavi O Kavva* (a critical study book of nineteenth-century Bengali Muslim writers), Book Stall (Dacca), 1959, 2nd edition, 1972; (contributor) Muhammad Fayaz, editor, *Pakistan Sociological Perspectives,* Punjab University Press, 1968; *A Bangladesh Village: Conflict and Cohesion,* Schenkman, 1973; *Introduction to Cultural Anthropology,* MSS Information, 1973; (editor) *Our Way—Their Way,* MSS Information, 1974; *Victorious Victims: Political Transformation in a Traditional Society,* Schenkman, 1978.

Contributor to symposia; translator from English into Bengali; former assistant editor of *Bengali Encyclopedia.* Contributor of articles and reviews to professional journals, including *Anthropological Quarterly* and *Pakistani Linguistics.* Associate editor, *Journal of Asian and African Studies,* 1966-68.

WORK IN PROGRESS: Research on an evaluation of network analysis, on national ideology versus the liberation movement (the Bengali case), and on certain cultural patterns of prehistoric Pakistan.†

* * *

IZZO, Herbert J(ohn)   1928-

PERSONAL: Born July 17, 1928, in Saginaw, Mich.; son of Joseph Anthony and Eleanor (Karau) Izzo; married Suzanne McLaughlin, September 22, 1958 (divorced, 1971); married Luisa Alexander (a college instructor), June 27, 1971; children: (first marriage) Victoria Sue, Alexander John; (second marriage) Sylvia Rachel, Daniel Stanley. *Education:* University of Michigan, B.A., 1950, M.A., 1951, B.S., 1953, Ph.D., 1965; graduate study at University of New Mexico, 1953-54, and University of Florence, 1959. *Politics:* Independent. *Home:* 4215 Brisebois Dr. N.W., Calgary, Alberta, Canada. *Office:* Department of Linguistics, University of Calgary, Calgary, Alberta, Canada.

CAREER: Stanford University, Stanford, Calif., instructor in Spanish, 1961-64; San Jose State College (now University), San Jose, Calif., assistant professor of linguistics, 1964-68; University of Calgary, Calgary, Alberta, associate professor, 1968-76, professor of linguistics, 1976—, head of department, 1970-72. Visiting lecturer at Hue University, 1958-59, and Babes-Bolyai University, 1966-67; visiting professor, University of Bucharest, 1975-76, and University of Michigan, 1977-78. *Member:* Linguistic Society of America, Canadian Linguistic Association, American Association of Teachers of Spanish and Portuguese, American Association of Teachers of Italian, Philological Association of the Pacific Coast, Phi Beta Kappa, Phi Kappa Phi. *Awards, honors:* America Council of Learned Societies grant, 1962-63; Fulbright-Hays Award, 1966-67, 1975-76.

WRITINGS: Tuscan and Etruscan: The Problem of Linguistic Substratum in Central Italy, University of Toronto Press, 1972. Also editor of *Studies in Honor of Ernst Pulgram.* Contributor to *Language Sciences, Modern Language Journal, Linguistics, Forum Italicum, General Linguistics,* and *Canadian Journal of Linguistics.*

WORK IN PROGRESS: Research on linguistic scholarship in the Renaissance.

SIDELIGHTS: Herbert Izzo has competence in Spanish, French, Italian, Portuguese, German, Romanian, and Latin. *Avocational interests:* Marathon running.

J

JACK, Homer A(lexander) 1916-

PERSONAL: Born May 19, 1916, in Rochester, N.Y.; son of Alexander (an artist) and Cecilia (Davis) Jack; married Esther Rhys Williams, November 23, 1939; married second wife, Ingeborg Kind, June 14, 1972; children: (first marriage) Alexander, Lucy. Education: Cornell University, B.S., 1936, M.S., 1937, Ph.D., 1940; Meadville Theological School, B.D., 1944. Politics: Independent. Home: 330 East 43rd St., New York, N.Y. 10017. Office: World Conference on Religion and Peace, 777 United Nations Plaza, New York, N.Y. 10017.

CAREER: Unitarian minister in Lawrence, Kan., 1942-43; Chicago Council Against Racial and Religious Discrimination, Chicago, Ill., executive director, 1943-48; Unitarian minister in Evanston, Ill., 1948-59; American Committee on Africa, New York City, founder and associate director, 1959-60; National Committee for a Sane Nuclear Policy, New York City, founder and executive director, 1960-64; Unitarian Universalist Association of the United States and Canada, Division of Social Responsibility, Boston, Mass., director, 1964-70; World Conference on Religion and Peace, New York City, secretary-general, 1970—. A founder of Congress of Racial Equality (CORE), 1942, and International Confederation for Disarmament and Peace. Awards, honors: Thomas H. Wright Award for better race relations, City of Chicago, 1949; D.D., Meadville Theological School, 1971.

WRITINGS—Editor: The Biological Field Stations of the World, Chronica Botanica, 1945; The Wit and Wisdom of Gandhi, Beacon Press, 1951; To Albert Schweitzer: A Festschrift, privately printed, 1955; The Gandhi Reader, Indiana University Press, 1956; Religion and Peace, Bobbs-Merrill, 1966; World Religions and World Peace, Beacon, 1968; Religion for Peace, Gandhi Peace Foundation, 1973. Contributor to Christian Century, Saturday Review, New York Times Magazine, Bulletin of Atomic Scientists, and other learned and popular journals. Editor, Africa Today, 1959-60.

SIDELIGHTS: Homer Jack first visited Albert Schweitzer in Africa in 1952, and he was present at Ghana's achievement of independence in 1957. He was an observer at the Asian-African Conference in Bandung, Indonesia, 1955, the All-African People's Conference in Ghana, 1958, and other international conferences. His work in race relations in the United States includes association with Martin Luther King, Jr., beginning in 1956.

JACKSON, John Howard 1932-

PERSONAL: Born April 6, 1932, in Kansas City, Mo.; son of Howard Clifford and Lucile (Deischer) Jackson; married Joan Leland, December 16, 1962; children: Jeanette, Lee Ann, Michele. Education: Princeton University, A.B. (magna cum laude), 1954; University of Michigan, LL.B., 1959. Home: 1 Heathridge, Ann Arbor, Mich. 48104. Office: School of Law, University of Michigan, Ann Arbor, Mich. 48109.

CAREER: Admitted to practice before the Bar in Missouri, 1959, Wisconsin, 1959, California, 1964, and Michigan, 1970; Executive Office of the President, Bureau of the Budget, Washington, D.C., management intern, summer, 1957; Foley, Sammond & Lardner, Milwaukee, Wis., attorney, 1959-61; University of California, Berkeley, associate professor, 1961-64, professor of law, 1964-66; University of Michigan, Ann Arbor, professor of law, 1966—, director of law research, 1967-71. Visiting professor of law, Delhi University, 1968-69, and University of Brussels, 1975; general counsel to U.S. Office of the Special Representative for Trade Negotiations, 1972-74. Consultant to U.S. State Department, General Agreement on Tariffs and Trade, U.S. Treasury, U.S. Special Trade Representative, and Ford Foundation. Military service: U.S. Army, Military Intelligence, 1954-56; served in Japan. Member: American Bar Association, American Society of International Law, Council on Foreign Relations, Phi Beta Kappa. Awards, honors: Rockefeller Foundation fellow, 1975-76.

WRITINGS: World Trade and the Law of GATT, Bobbs-Merrill, 1969; Contract Law in Modern Society: Cases and Materials, West Publishing, 1973; Legal Problems of International Economic Relations, West Publishing, 1977. Contributor of articles to law journals, including Modern Uses of Logic in Law, American Journal of International Law, and Journal of World Trade Law. Associate editor, Upper Staff (law review of University of Michigan); member of board of editors of Journal of World Trade Law and Journal of Law and Policy in International Business.

* * *

JACKSON, Miles M(errill) 1929-

PERSONAL: Born April 28, 1929, in Richmond, Va.; son of Miles Merrill and Thelma (Manning) Jackson; married Bernice Olivia Roane, January 7, 1954; children: Miles III,

Marsha, Muriel, Melia. *Education:* Attended University of New Mexico, 1949-59; Virginia Union University, B.A., 1955; Drexel University, M.S., 1956; Syracuse University, Ph.D., 1974. *Politics:* Democrat. *Home:* 6370 Hawaii Kai Dr., No. 18, Honolulu, Hawaii 96825. *Office:* Graduate School of Library Studies, University of Hawaii, Honolulu, Hawaii 96822.

CAREER: Free Library of Philadelphia, Philadelphia, Pa., librarian, 1956-58; Hampton Institute, C. P. Huntington Memorial Library, Hampton, Va., acting librarian, 1958-59, librarian, 1959-63, assistant professor of library science, 1958-62; Government of American Samoa, Pago Pago, territorial librarian, 1962-64; Atlanta University, Atlanta, Ga., library director, 1964-69; State University of New York College at Geneseo, associate professor of library science, 1969-75; University of Hawaii, Honolulu, professor of library studies, 1975—. Senior Fulbright lecturer at University of Tehran, 1968-69. Board member of We Shall Overcome Fund, 1965-68, and Martin Luther King Jr. Memorial Library, 1971-75. *Military service:* U.S. Navy, 1946-48. *Member:* American Library Association, Charles Sumner Literary Society (president, 1961-62), College Language Association. *Awards, honors:* American Philosophical Society grant, 1966; Ford Foundation area study award for travel in Africa, summer, 1969; Council on Library Resources, fellow, 1970; Ford Foundation research fellow, 1972-73; Beta Phi Mu Foreign Travel Award, 1976.

WRITINGS: (Editor) *Bibliography of Negro History and Culture,* University of Pittsburgh Press, 1968; (editor) *Comparative and International Librarianship,* Greenwood Press, 1970; *International Handbook of Contemporary Developments in World Librarianship,* Greenwood Press, 1980. Author of column, "Libraries Abroad," in *Journal of Library History,* 1965-69. Contributor to periodicals, including *Negro Digest, Black World, Freedomways, Phylon, Library Journal,* and *Wilson Library Bulletin.*

*   *   *

JACOBS, Robert D(urene)   1918-

PERSONAL: Born October 1, 1918, in Vicksburg, Miss.; son of Robert Durene (a teacher) and Buena (Andrews) Jacobs; married Mildred Simons, October 13, 1945; children: Bonnie. *Education:* University of Mississippi, B.A., 1937, M.A., 1938; Louisiana State University, graduate study, 1939-41; Johns Hopkins University, Ph.D., 1953. *Home:* 100 Hunters Glen Ct. N.E., Atlanta, Ga. 30328. *Office:* Department of English, Georgia State University, Atlanta, Ga. 30303.

CAREER: Johns Hopkins University, Baltimore, Md., instructor in creative writing, 1949-53; University of Kentucky, Lexington, assistant professor, 1953-58, associate professor, 1958-68, professor of English, 1968-71; Georgia State University, Atlanta, professor of English, 1971—, Calloway Professor of Literature and Language, 1976—. *Military service:* U.S. Marine Corps Reserve, 1941-68; became colonel. *Member:* Modern Language Association of America, American Studies Association, American Association of University Professors, National Council of Teachers of English, Marine Corps Reserve Officers Association, Sierra Club. *Awards, honors:* American Council of Learned Societies fellowship, 1960-61.

WRITINGS: (Editor with Louis D. Rubin, Jr.) *Southern Renascence,* Johns Hopkins Press, 1953; (editor with Rubin) *South: Modern Southern Literature in Its Cultural Setting,* Doubleday, 1961; *Poe: Journalist and Critic,* Louisiana State University Press, 1969.

WORK IN PROGRESS: Research in Southern literature, writings of Edgar Allan Poe, and nineteenth-century American literary criticism.

*   *   *

JACOBSON, Rodolfo   1915-

PERSONAL: Born November 10, 1915, in Berlin, Germany; naturalized U.S. citizen; son of Maxim (a musician) and Ilse (Immelmann) Jacobson; married Ema Rodriguez (a teacher of French), April 8, 1944; children: Rodolfo, Jr., Roy Francis, Irene E. (Mrs. Leonardo Soto Neri), Iyana M. *Education:* University of Panama, B.A., 1952; University of Michigan, M.A., 1963, Ph.D., 1966. *Home:* 14222 Golden Woods, San Antonio, Tex. 78249. *Office:* Department of Bicultural-Bilingual Studies and Foreign Languages, University of Texas, San Antonio, Tex. 78285.

CAREER: School principal in Panama City, Panama, 1949-52; high school teacher of English in Panama City, 1952-62; University of Michigan, Ann Arbor, lecturer in English as a second language, English Language Institute, 1962-66; State University of New York College at Cortland, associate professor, 1966-69, professor of English language and linguistics, 1969-74; University of Texas at San Antonio, professor of linguistics and bilingual education, 1974—. Sixth International Congress of Phonetic Sciences, Prague, Czechoslovakia, chairman of phonology and linguistic phonetics section, 1967, director of Title VII Bilingual Education Traineeship Program. Consultant to New York State Department of Education, 1970-71, and to United Independent School District, Laredo, Tex., 1975—. *Member:* International Sociological Association (member of research committee in sociolinguistics), National Association of Bilingual Education, Linguistic Society of America, Teachers of English to Speakers of Other Languages, Texas Association of Bilingual Education, San Antonio Area Association of Bilingual Education (chairperson of instructional services), Phi Kappa Phi.

WRITINGS: A New Course in American English, three volumes, Druckhaus Langenscheidt (Berlin), 1959-62; *The London Dialect of the Late Fourteenth Century,* Mouton, 1970, Humanities, 1971; (editor) *Studies in English to Speakers of Other Languages and Standard English to Speakers of a Non-Standard Dialect,* New York State English Council, 1971; *Introduction to Language: A Study Guide,* State University of New York Independent Study Program, 1973. Contributor of articles and reviews to language journals.

WORK IN PROGRESS: Codeswitching: Historical, Sociological, and Educational Perspectives.

SIDELIGHTS: Rodolfo Jacobson is fluent in Spanish, Italian, and French, in addition to German and English.

*   *   *

JACQUENEY, Mona G(raubart)

PERSONAL: Born in Detroit, Mich.; daughter of Alex (a restauranteur) and Leontina (Mahler) Graubart; married Theodore Jacqueney (a traffic manager); children: Theodore Robert, Joan Ruth, Stephanie Alice. *Education:* Nassau Community College, A.A., 1965; Hofstra University, B.A., 1967, M.A., 1971; New York University, doctoral candidate. *Home:* 233 East Beech St., Long Beach, N.Y. 11561.

CAREER: Sociologist, social scientist, writer and painter (work exhibited at Brooklyn Museum, and in other shows); former foreign trade executive. *Member:* International Bibliographical Centre, American Sociological Association, Sociologists for Women in Society, American Academy of Political and Social Science, Academy of Political Science, National Social Science Honor Society, Common Cause, Women's Equity Action League, Pi Gamma Mu.

WRITINGS: Radicalism on Campus: 1969-1971, Philosophical Library, 1972; *The Golden Age Society and Other Essays,* Philosophical Library, 1978.

BIOGRAPHICAL/CRITICAL SOURCES: Police Chief, May, 1972; *Annals* (of American Academy of Political and Social Science), July, 1972.

* * *

JAGER, Ronald (Albert) 1932-

PERSONAL: Born December 2, 1932, in McBain, Mich.; son of Jess (a farmer) and Kate (Scheppers) Jager; married Grace Otten (a teacher), June 4, 1957; children: Colin Lovell. *Education:* Calvin College, A.B., 1955; Indiana University, M.A., 1958; Harvard University, Ph.D., 1964. *Religion:* Protestant. *Home:* Half Moon Pond Rd., Washington, N.H. 03280.

CAREER: Northwestern University, Evanston, Ill., instructor in philosophy, 1961-63; Yale University, New Haven, Conn., assistant professor, 1965-70, associate professor of philosophy, 1970-77, executive secretary of humanities division of *Yale Review,* 1973-75. Associate director of National Humanities Institute, 1974-77. *Member:* American Philosophical Association, New Hampshire Maple Producers Association.

WRITINGS: (Editor) *Essays in Logic,* Prentice-Hall, 1963; *The Development of Bertrand Russell's Philosophy,* Allen & Unwin, 1972; *Historical Pillsbury,* Society for the Protection of New Hampshire Forests, 1976; (with wife, Grace Jager) *Portrait of a Hill Town,* Village Press, 1977. Contributor of articles to *Philosophical Review, Analysis, Journal of the History of Philosophy, Mind, Journal of Value Inquiry, Review of Metaphysics, New York Times, Country Journal, New Hampshire Profiles,* and *Country Gentleman.*

WORK IN PROGRESS: Three books, *A Philosophical Study of Perception, Nature and Aesthetics,* and *Essays from the Countryside.*

* * *

JAMES, Eleanor 1912-

PERSONAL: Born October 22, 1912, in Belton, Tex.; daughter of Robert Brown (a merchant) and Laura (Smith) James. *Education:* Mary Hardin-Baylor College, B.A., 1933; University of Texas, M.A., 1934; University of Wisconsin, Ph.D., 1942. *Politics:* Democrat. *Religion:* Baptist. *Home:* 717 Penelope St., Belton, Tex. 76513. *Office:* Department of English, Texas Woman's University, Denton, Tex. 76204.

CAREER: University of Texas, Main University (now University of Texas at Austin), instructor in English, 1942-45; Texas Woman's University, Denton, associate professor, 1945-62, professor of English, 1962-77. *Member:* American Association of University Women, American Association of University Professors, Modern Language Association of America, Renaissance Society of America, National Council of Teachers of English, College Conference of Teachers of English, South Central Modern Language Association, Texas Folklore Society, Texas Fine Arts Association.

WRITINGS: Roy Bedichek, Steck, 1970; (contributor) Evelyn M. Carrington, editor, *Women in Early Texas,* Jenkins Publishing, 1975. Contributor to *Studies in English* and *American West.*

* * *

JARAMILLO, Samuel 1925-

PERSONAL: Born October 25, 1925, in Manizales, Colombia; son of Manuel and Zoila Rosa (Giraldo) Jaramillo. *Education:* National University of Colombia, Doctor en Ciencias Politicas, 1950. *Home:* 271 Dartmouth St., Boston, Mass. 02116. *Office:* Department of Modern Languages, Northeastern University, Boston, Mass. 02115.

CAREER: Colombian Embassy, Mexico City, Mexico, first secretary, 1956-57; Northeastern University, Boston, Mass., assistant professor, 1962-65, associate professor of modern languages, 1965—.

WRITINGS: Morrogacho, Editorial Modelo, 1963; *Nadaismo diplomatico,* Ediciones Suramerica, 1965; *Gurropin,* Ediciones Suramerica, 1966; *Santos en elinfierno,* Ediciones Suramerica, 1967; *Voz en grito,* Editorial Colombia Nueva, 1970; *Un negro para mostrar,* Editorial Apolo, 1972; *America sin Norte,* Editorial Cosmos, 1976; *Los Cobardes,* Editorial Cosmos, 1978.

* * *

JARCHOW, Merrill E(arl) 1910-

PERSONAL: Surname pronounced "Jarko"; born September 25, 1910, in Stillwater, Minn.; son of Louis D. (a sheriff) and Elsie (Bruntlett) Jarchow; married Doris A. Vrenegor (a dance teacher), March 21, 1943; children: Barbara (Mrs. Keith Slater), Susan (Mrs. William Alrich). *Education:* University of Minnesota, B.A., 1930, M.A., 1933, Ph.D., 1941. *Politics:* Republican. *Religion:* Methodist. *Home:* 203 Oak, Northfield, Minn. 55057. *Office:* Carleton College, Northfield, Minn. 55057.

CAREER: South Dakota State College (now University), Brookings, instructor, 1935-37, assistant professor, 1937-40, associate professor of history, 1940-41; Carleton College, Northfield, Minn., associate professor, 1946-67, professor of history, 1967—, dean of men, 1946-67. Trustee, Shattuck School, Faribault, Minn., 1954-74. *Military service:* U.S. Navy, 1943-46; became lieutenant. *Member:* Organization of American Historians, American Historical Association, National Association of Deans and Advisers of Men (member of executive committee, 1948-50), National Association of Student Personnel Administrators, Minnesota Historical Society (member of council, 1954-62), Phi Beta Kappa, Northfield Golf Club (president, 1961).

WRITINGS: (With R. W. Murchie) *Population Trends in Minnesota,* University of Minnesota Press, 1936; (contributor) A. R. Buchanan, editor, *The Navy's Air War,* Harper, 1946; *The Earth Brought Forth,* Minnesota Historical Society, 1949, reprinted, [New York], 1970; (with L. A. Headley) *Carleton: The First Century,* Carleton College, 1966; *Minnesota's Private Liberal Arts Colleges: Their History and Contributions,* Minnesota Historical Society, 1973; *Donald J. Cowling,* Carleton College, 1974; *In Search of Fulfillment: Episodes in the Life of D. Blake Stewart,* North Central Publishing, 1974.

WORK IN PROGRESS: A biography of Amherst H. Wilder and the history of the Wilder Foundation, completion expected in 1979.

JARROTT, Mattie L.   1881(?)-1973

1881(?)—February 4, 1973; American educator and author of children's art books. Obituaries: *Washington Post,* February 6, 1973.

*   *   *

JAVITS, Benjamin A(braham)   1894-1973

October 21, 1894—May 18, 1973; American lawyer, economist, and philanthropist. Obituaries: *New York Times,* May 19, 1973.

*   *   *

JAYNES, Julian   1923-

PERSONAL: Born February 27, 1923, in West Newton, Mass.; son of Julian Clifford (a minister) and Clara (Bullard) Jaynes. *Education:* Attended Harvard University, 1940-42; McGill University, B.A., 1944; Yale University, M.A., 1948. *Religion:* Unitarian Universalist. *Office:* Department of Psychology, Princeton University, Princeton, N.J. 08540.

CAREER: Princeton University, Princeton, N.J., research associate, 1964-66, research psychologist and lecturer with status of associate professor of psychology, 1966—, master of Wilson College, 1965-69. Trustee of Mental Health Research Development Foundation, 1967—, Honor Studies in Man's Future, 1968—, and Archives of American Psychology, 1969—. *Member:* Cheiron (International Society for the History of the Behavioral and Social Sciences; founding chairman). *Awards, honors:* National Book Award nomination, 1978, for *The Origin of Consciousness in the Breakdown of the Bicameral Mind.*

WRITINGS: (Contributor) W. S. Dillon, editor, *Man and Beast: Comparative Social Behavior,* Smithsonian Institution, 1970; (contributor) C. C. Gillespie and others, editors, *Dictionary of Scientific Biography,* Scribner, 1970; *The Origin of Consciousness in the Breakdown of the Bicameral Mind,* Houghton, 1977; (editor with others) *The Lateralization of the Nervous System,* Academic Press, 1977. Contributor of over forty articles to psychology journals, including *Psychological Review, Journal of Comparative Physiology and Psychology, American Naturalist, American Scientist, Behavior, Contemporary Psychology,* and *Developmental Psychology.*

WORK IN PROGRESS: Research on aptic structures, the bicameral mind, and changes in memory and emotion with the advent of consciousness.

*   *   *

JEFFER, Marsha   1940-

PERSONAL: Born November 9, 1940, in Brooklyn, N.Y.; daughter of David (a carpenter) and Hilda (Schneider) Goldberg. *Education:* University of California, Los Angeles, B.A., 1962; California State College at Los Angeles (now California State University, Los Angeles), M.A., 1965. *Politics:* Democrat. *Religion:* Judaism. *Home:* 1714 Queens Rd., Los Angeles, Calif. 90069. *Office:* Department of English, Cypress College, 9200 Valley View, Cypress, Calif. 90630.

CAREER: English teacher in public high school, Los Angeles, Calif., 1963-66; Cypress College, Cypress, Calif., instructor in English, 1966—. *Member:* Academy of Television Arts and Sciences, National Council of Teachers of English, National Organization for Women, California Teachers Association, Pi Lambda Theta, Sierra Club.

WRITINGS: (With Nancy Rayl) *Reach Out,* with teacher's manual, Little, Brown, 1972.

WORK IN PROGRESS: A television drama about Mark Twain; a series of educational films on basic skills.

*   *   *

JEFFRIES, Ona (Griffin)   1893(?)-1973

1893(?)—February 4, 1973; American office manager and author of books on presidential families and other topics. Obituaries: *Washington Post,* February 19, 1973.

*   *   *

JELLEMA, Roderick   1927-

PERSONAL: Surname is accented on first syllable; born August 11, 1927, in Holland, Mich.; son of John Frank (a physician and teacher) and Betty M. (Hartigh) Jellema; married Matrona T. Van Zee, September 14, 1950 (divorced, 1967); married Mary Travis Todd (a drama teacher), December 18, 1971; children: (first marriage) John Frank II (deceased), David Moe, Michael Rory. *Education:* Calvin College, B.A., 1951; University of New Mexico, graduate study, 1951-52; University of Edinburgh, P.G. Diploma, 1954, Ph.D., 1962. *Politics:* Democrat. *Religion:* Christian Reformed. *Home:* 5 Hill Top Rd., Silver Spring, Md. 20910; summer address: Lost Valley, Montague, Mich. 49437. *Office:* Department of English, University of Maryland, College Park, Md. 20742.

CAREER: University of Maryland, College Park, instructor, 1956-63, assistant professor, 1964-67, associate professor of English and director of creative writing, 1967—. Consultant and talent scout, National Endowment for the Arts, 1969; director, Maryland Conference on Poetry and the National Conscience, 1968-71. *Military service:* U.S. Navy, 1945-47. *Member:* Academy of American Poets, Conference on Christianity and Literature, Washington Poets Workshop. *Awards, honors:* Annapolis Poetry Prize, 1967; Maryland Creative and Performing Arts grants, 1968, 1970, 1972, 1974, 1976; Hart Crane Award, 1969; National Endowment Prize for Poetry, 1970; Yaddo residence fellowships, 1970, 1971, 1972, 1974, 1975, 1976, 1978.

WRITINGS: *Peter De Vries,* Eerdmans, 1966; (author of introduction) Kenneth Hamilton, *In Search of Contemporary Man,* Eerdmans, 1968; (editor) Dorothy Sayers, *Christian Letters to a Post-Christian World,* Eerdmans, 1969; *Something Tugging the Line* (poems), Dryad, 1973; *The Lost Faces* (poems), Dryad, 1978. General editor, "Contemporary Writers in Christian Perspective" (critical booklets), Eerdmans, 1966-70. Author of "Curious Alice," a filmscript for National Institute of Mental Health, 1970. Contributor of poems to literary journals, including *Field, New Republic, Poetry Now, Poetry Northwest,* and *Dryad.*

WORK IN PROGRESS: Two books of poems, *Incarnality* and *Poems for the Left Hand;* a collection of essays on modern poetry, *Words Incarnate.*

SIDELIGHTS: Roderick Jellema told *CA:* "I started late. It took me forty years to find out that a poem is a process, a body of energy which discovers as it grows. I try very hard not to 'have my say' in poems; each poem has to be a finding out, a catching of something I cannot know in any other way. It begins by taking chances.

"This means that the words are not tools, but sources. The poem must be the process for all the words it gets to.

"Although poetry is a first cousin to myth and sleep and the unconscious, its gift is simply that it touches [and] pricks things wide alive.''

AVOCATIONAL INTERESTS: Traditional jazz music, summers among the sand dunes and on the waters of Lake Michigan, sailing, fresh water fishing, Friesland.

* * *

JENKINS, Marie M(agdalen) 1909-
(Sister Mary Scholastica; W. S. Markins, a pseudonym)

PERSONAL: Born September 26, 1909, in Eldorado, Ill.; daughter of B. Robert (a teacher and salesman) and Clara Ann (Rhine) Jenkins. *Education:* Phillips University, A.B., 1929; Catholic University of America, M.S., 1951; University of Oklahoma, Ph.D., 1961. *Politics:* Republican. *Religion:* Roman Catholic. *Home and office address:* Route 2, Box 19 B1, Strasburg, Va. 22657.

CAREER: Teacher in elementary and secondary schools of Oklahoma, 1931-42; St. Joseph's Convent, Tulsa, Okla., professed nun of Benedictine Order with religious name, Sister Mary Scholastica, 1942-57; taught in Catholic high school in Tulsa, Okla., 1944-48 and 1949-52; Benedictine Heights College, Tulsa, Okla., instructor, 1952-55, registrar, 1956-57; University of Oklahoma, Norman, instructor in zoology, 1960-62; James Madison University, Harrisonburg, Va., associate professor, 1962-67, professor of biology, 1967-75, professor emeritus, 1975—. *Member:* American Society of Zoologists, American Association for the Advancement of Science, Authors Guild, National Writers Club, Society of Children's Book Writers, Southwestern Association of Naturalists, Virginia Academy of Science, Sigma Xi, Phi Sigma, Skyline Kennel Club (charter member; former secretary). *Awards, honors:* Research grants from Virginia Academy of Science, 1963, Sigma Xi, 1964, 1966, and U.S. Public Health Service, 1966-69.

WRITINGS: (Contributor) William Corning and Stanley Ratner, editors, *Chemistry of Learning: Invertebrate Research*, Plenum, 1967; (contributor) Libbie H. Hyman, editor, *Biology of the Turbellaria*, McGraw, 1967.

Juveniles; all published by Holiday House: *Moon Jelly Swims through the Sea*, 1969; *Animals without Parents*, 1970; *The Curious Mollusks*, 1972; *Embryos and How They Develop*, 1975; *Kangaroos, Opossums, and Other Marsupials*, 1975; *Goats, Sheep, and How They Live*, 1978.

Contributor of articles to scientific journals, including *Biological Bulletin* and *Science;* contributor of reviews to *Science Books and Films* (quarterly publication of the American Association for the Advancement of Science).

WORK IN PROGRESS: A juvenile book on the deer family for Holiday House.

SIDELIGHTS: Marie Jenkins told *CA:* "I retired from both teaching and research at the close of the 1974-75 school term (mandatory—age discrimination) and moved to a small town in the northern part of the Shenandoah Valley. My home is just outside the town limits with woods, fields, and a small mountain nearby, and there is a big yard for my dogs.'' She raises, trains, and exhibits German shepherds, "but [I] also have two smaller dogs of the 'Heinz 57' variety. The Roman Catholic church is in another town; I attend regularly but find it impossible to continue taking an active part in church affairs. At present I am not engaged in research on planarians, but I still have two tanks of these interesting creatures. During the past year I was honored by an Italian scientist, Dr. Mario Benazzi, retired director of the Institute of Comparative Anatomy and Embryology at Pisa, Italy. Dr. Benazzi named a new species of planarian for me (I had sent him numerous specimens, collected in Texas), and the species will henceforth be known as *Dugesia jenkinsae*. Although I am officially retired, my days are full. I have begun work on a juvenile book on the deer family, and have several other books in mind on which I hope to work soon.'' Ms. Jenkins's reading preferences include teen-age adventure and mystery stories, stories about dogs and other animals, and archeology ("especially regarding prehistoric man . . . I have become fascinated by some of the remarkable discoveries'').

* * *

JESSOR, Richard 1924-

PERSONAL: Born November 24, 1924, in Brooklyn, N.Y.; son of Thomas (a seaman) and Clara (Merkin) Jessor; married Shirley Louise Glasser (a psychologist), September 13, 1948; children: Kim, Tom. *Education:* Attended College of the City of New York (now City College of the City University of New York), 1941-43; Yale University, B.A., 1946; Columbia University, M.A., 1947; Ohio State University, clinical psychology internship, 1947-50, Ph.D., 1951. *Home:* 595 Euclid, Boulder, Colo. 80302. *Office:* Department of Psychology, University of Colorado, Boulder, Colo. 80309.

CAREER: University of Colorado, Boulder, assistant professor, 1951-56, associate professor, 1956-61, professor of psychology, 1961—, director of research program on personal and social problem behavior at Institute of Behavioral Science, 1965—, member of board of institute, 1966—. Certified by Colorado Board of Psychologist Examiners. Co-chairman of task force on psychosocial deprivation and personality development and consultant, National Institute of Child Health and Human Development. Consultant to Federal Bureau of Prisons, National Institute on Alcohol Abuse and Alcoholism, and World Health Organization. *Military service:* U.S. Marine Corps, 1942-45; received Purple Heart.

MEMBER: American Psychological Association, American Sociological Association, Society for the Psychological Study of Social Issues, Society for the Study of Social Problems. *Awards, honors:* Social Science Research Council post-doctoral fellowship, University of California, Berkeley, 1956-57; National Institute of Mental Health special research fellowship, Harvard-Florence Research Project (Italy), 1965-66; National Institute of Mental Health research grants, 1959-64, 1964-65, 1968-74, and 1978-81; Licensed Beverage Industries research grant, 1967-68.

WRITINGS: (Editor with H. E. Gruber and K. R. Hammond) *Contemporary Approaches to Cognition,* Harvard University Press, 1957; (editor with Seymour Feshbach and contributor) *Cognition, Personality, and Clinical Psychology,* Jossey-Bass, 1967; (with wife, Shirley L. Jessor, T. D. Graves, and J. C. Hansen) *Society, Personality, and Deviant Behavior: A Study of a Tri-Ethnic Community,* Holt, 1968; (with S. L. Jessor) *Problem Behavior and Psychosocial Development: A Longitudinal Study of Youth,* Academic Press, 1977.

Contributor: A. E. Kuenzli, editor, *The Phenomenological Problem,* Harper, 1959; Thomas Gladwin and W. C. Sturtevant, editors, *Anthropology and Human Behavior,* Anthropological Society of Washington (D.C.), 1962; N. J. Smelser and W. T. Smelser, editors, *Personality and Social Systems,* Wiley, 1963; Martha T. Mednick and S. A. Mednick, editors, *Research in Personality,* Holt, 1963; M. H. Marx, editor, *Theories in Contemporary Psychology,* Macmillan,

1963; H. J. Peters and J. C. Hansen, editors, *Vocational Guidance and Career Development*, Macmillan, 1966; Mark Lefton, J. K. Skipper, and C. H. McCaghy, editors, *Approaches to Deviance: Theories, Concepts, and Research Findings*, Appleton, 1968; *Perspectives on Human Deprivation: Biological, Psychological, and Sociological*, U.S. Government Printing Office, 1969.

G. L. Maddox, editor, *The Domesticated Drug: Drinking among Collegians*, College and University Press, 1970; Edward Hart and William Sechrist, editors, *Dynamics of Wellness*, Wadsworth, 1970; J. B. Rotter, June E. Chance, and E. J. Phares, editors, *Applications of a Social Learning Theory of Personality*, Holt, 1972; C. D. Bryant, editor, *The Social Dimensions of Work*, Prentice-Hall, 1972; F. E. Seixas, editor, *Nature and Nurture in Alcoholism*, Annals of New York Academy of Sciences, 1972; M. E. Chafetz, editor, *Research on Alcoholism: Clinical Problems and Special Populations*, U.S. Government Printing Office, 1973; (with wife, Shirley L. Jessor) Chafetz, editor, *Psychological and Social Factors in Drinking*, U.S. Government Printing Office, 1973; (with S. L. Jessor) H. D. Thornburg, editor, *Contemporary Adolescence: Readings*, Brooks/Cole, 1975; (with S. L. Jessor) N. C. Kalt and S. S. Zalkind, *Urban Problems: Psychological Inquiries*, Oxford University Press, 1976; D. J. Lettieri, editor, *Predicting Adolescent Drug Abuse: A Review of Issues, Methods, and Correlates*, U.S. Government Printing Office, 1976; J. Fishman, editor, *The Bases of Addiction*, Dahlem Konferenzen (Berlin), 1978; (with S. L. Jessor) D. B. Kandel, editor, *Longitudinal Research on Drug Use: Empirical Findings and Methodological Issues*, Halsted, 1978; R. L. DuPont, A. Goldstein, and J. A. O'Donnell, editors, *Handbook on Drug Abuse*, U.S. Government Printing Office, 1978; (with S. L. Jessor) R. E. Muuss, editor, *Adolescent Behavior and Society: A Book of Readings*, 3rd edition (Jessor was not associated with earlier editions), Random House, 1979.

Also contributor to *Proceedings* of Conference on Normative Approaches to Alcoholism and Alcohol Problems, 1977, and to proceedings of other scholarly conferences. Contributor of over fifty articles and reviews to professional journals, including *American Behavioral Scientist, Public Opinion Quarterly, Journal of Personality and Social Psychology, Quarterly Journal of Studies on Alcohol, Psychotherapy, American Journal of Orthopsychiatry*, and *Contemporary Psychology. Sociometry*, consulting editor, 1964-66, associate editor, 1966-69; consulting editor, *Community Mental Health Journal*, 1974—, and *Journal of Consulting and Clinical Psychology*, 1975-77.

WORK IN PROGRESS: A research project on psychosocial development in young adults in their middle and late twenties.

AVOCATIONAL INTERESTS: Mountain climbing.

*   *   *

JINKS, William Howard, Jr. 1938-

PERSONAL: Born September 26, 1938, in New Castle, Pa.; son of William Howard and Georgia (Parker) Jinks; married Sandra Mae Clift, June 29, 1963; children: Devin Aric, Tarin Kathaleen. *Education:* Florida State University, B.A., 1963; San Francisco State College (now University), M.A., 1967. *Home:* 20911 Coral Sea Rd., Miami, Fla. 33157. *Office:* Department of English, Miami-Dade Community College, 11011 Southwest 104th St., Miami, Fla. 33176.

CAREER: Has worked as a clerk in San Francisco, Calif., 1963-64, and as a croupier in Stateline, Nev., 1964-65;

Miami-Dade Community College, Miami, Fla., 1967—, began as assistant professor, currently associate professor of English. *Military service:* U.S. Navy, 1957-59.

WRITINGS: The Celluloid Literature, Glencoe Press, 1971, 2nd edition, 1974. Author of monthly column of film criticism for *Village Post*. Contributor to *Tropic* magazine.

WORK IN PROGRESS: A novel.

*   *   *

JOERS, Lawrence E(ugene) C(laire) 1900-

PERSONAL: Born August 17, 1900, in Milwaukee, Wis.; son of August Julius (a farmer) and Ella Ann (Farrand) Joers; married Annetta Mae Peterson, June 15, 1948; children: Jeanne Marie Joers Bunker, Mary Lou Joers Sessums, Lawrence E. C., Jr., Linda Mae. *Education:* St. Helena Sanitarium, R.N., 1923; attended Auburn Academy, 1926; Walla Walla College, B.S., 1929; College of Medical Evangelists (now Loma Linda University), M.D., 1934. *Politics:* Republican. *Religion:* Seventh-day Adventist. *Home:* 547 Evergreen Loop, Reeds Port, Ore. 97467.

CAREER: Physician in private practice in Tacoma, Wash., 1934-41, 1945-51, and in Ardmore, Okla., 1955-65; Jay Memorial Hospital, Jay, Okla., chief of surgery and administrator, beginning 1965. Medical director, Ardmore Seventh-day Adventist Hospital, 1955-65; medical examiner and medical director of Delaware County. *Military service:* U.S. Navy, 1941-45, 1951-55; became captain; received Bronze Star Medal. *Member:* American Medical Association, American Academy of General Practice, Oklahoma State Medical Society, Craig County Medical Society, Delaware County Medical Society, Ottawa County Medical Society.

WRITINGS: God Is My Captain, Pacific Press Publishing Association, 1945; *Thou Art Peter*, Vantage, 1952; *Mercy Rides on Wings*, Southern Publishing, 1960; *The Journey: An Inside Look at the Human Body*, illustrations by Ronald Hester, Southern Publishing, 1972. Contributor to *U.S. Naval Bulletin*.

WORK IN PROGRESS: Writing about "quackery."

SIDELIGHTS: Joers has made a trip through Peru for medical purposes.†

*   *   *

JOHNS, Ray E(arl) 1900-

PERSONAL: Born September 5, 1900, in Ishpeming, Mich.; son of Samuel and Catherine (Rouse) Johns; married Florence Glasgow, October 21, 1923 (died April 10, 1967); married Rebecca Kittredge Hill, June 13, 1970; children: (first marriage) Robert E., Anne C. (Mrs. Allan E. Johns). *Education:* Young Men's Christian Association College (now George Williams College), B.S., 1924; University of Michigan, M.S.W., 1940; Columbia University, Ph.D., 1946. *Religion:* Congregationalist. *Home:* Flying Goose Farm, Hancock, N.H. 03449.

CAREER: Young Men's Christian Association, New York City, program executive of national council, 1938-41; National United Service Organizations, New York City, national director of operations, 1941-46; Young Men's Christian Association, Boston, Mass., general executive of greater Boston area, 1946-66; University of Toronto, Toronto, Ontario, visiting professor of social work, 1966-69; University of New Hampshire, Durham, visiting professor of organization and administration, 1970—. Member of board of directors of United Community Services and National Conference on Social Welfare; trustee of Northeastern University and Andover-Newton Theological School. *Member:* American Sociological Association (fellow), National Association of Social Welfare, American Association of Certified Social Workers, Association of Professional YMCA Directors.

WRITINGS: The Cooperative Process, Association Press, 1946; (with David F. DeMurche) *Community Planning and Agency Responsibility,* Association Press, 1951; *Executive Responsibility,* Association Press, 1952, revised edition, 1966; *Confronting Organizational Change,* Association Press, 1962; *Exploring Organizational Behavior,* University of Toronto Press, 1970.

WORK IN PROGRESS: The Impact of Environmental Forces on the American Business Firm.

SIDELIGHTS: Ray E. Johns has traveled in the Soviet Union, Europe, Scandinavia, Latin America, Canada, Africa, and the West Indies.

* * *

JOHNSON, Allison H(eartz)   1910-

PERSONAL: Born December 12, 1910, in Vancouver, British Columbia, Canada; son of Arthur Livingstone (a physician) and Lena (Heartz) Johnson; married Helen Margaret Bolender, July 1, 1935; children: Sandra (Mrs. Albert H. Oosterhoff), Sheila (Mrs. Hugh M. Kindred). *Education:* Mount Allison University, B.A. (honors), 1931; University of Toronto, M.A., 1932, Ph.D., 1937; research at University of Chicago, 1934-35, and Harvard University, 1936-37. *Home:* 1639 Richmond St. N., London, Ontario, Canada. *Office:* Department of Philosophy, University of Western Ontario, London, Ontario, Canada.

CAREER: University of Western Ontario, London, instructor, 1937-42, assistant professor, 1942-46, associate professor of philosophy and psychology, 1946-47, professor, 1947-64, senior professor of philosophy, 1964-76, professor emeritus, 1976—, head of department, 1948-64. *Member:* Royal Society of Canada (fellow), Canadian Philosophical Association (president, 1962-63), American Philosophical Association, Mind Association. *Awards, honors:* D.Litt., Mount Allison University, 1972.

WRITINGS: The Wit and Wisdom of Whitehead, Beacon Press, 1947; *The Wit and Wisdom of Dewey,* Beacon Press, 1949; (editor and author of introduction) *Whitehead and the Modern World,* Beacon Press, 1950; (editor and co-author with Charles Hartshorne and Victor Lowe) *Whitehead's Theory of Reality,* Beacon Press, 1952, revised edition, Dover, 1962; *Whitehead's Philosophy of Civilization,* Beacon Press, 1958; *Whitehead's American Essays in Social Philosophy,* Harper, 1959; (editor and author of introduction) *Alfred North Whitehead: The Interpretation of Science,* Bobbs-Merrill, 1961; (editor and author of introduction) *Experimental Realism,* Allen & Unwin, 1973; *Philosophers in Action,* C. E. Merrill, 1977; *Modes of Value,* Philosophical Library, 1978.

WORK IN PROGRESS: Studies in the Philosophy of A. N. Whitehead.

* * *

JOHNSON, Bertha French   1906-

PERSONAL: Born March 14, 1906, in Canon City, Colo.; daughter of John Aaron (a mining engineer) and Olive (Higgins) French; married Albert Franklin Johnson (a writer),

January 30, 1932; children: Christina. *Education:* University of Redlands, B.M., 1932; also studied at Yale University and University of Iowa. *Politics:* Independent. *Religion:* United Church of Christ. *Home:* 33551 Capstan Dr., Laguna Niguel, Calif. 92677.

CAREER: Cornell College, Mount Vernon, Iowa, instructor, 1933-40, assistant professor of drama, 1940-47; La Jolla Players, La Jolla, Calif., director, 1947-50; University of Redlands, Redlands, Calif., assistant professor of drama, 1950-70. Director, Redlands Bowl, 1950-56. Member of faculty, National Christian Writers Conference, 1956-61. *Member:* American Association of University Women.

WRITINGS—All with husband, Albert Johnson; all published by A. S. Barnes, except as noted: *Drama for Classroom and Stage,* 1969; *Directing Methods,* 1970; *Shakespeare Vignettes,* 1970; *Drama for Junior High,* 1971; *Oral Reading: Creative and Interpretive,* 1971; *To See a Play,* 1972; *Shakespeare at My Shoulder,* 1972; *Plays for Readers Theatre,* Baker's Plays, 1972; *Oh Rose of Sharon,* Baker's Plays, 1976; *Beloved Betrayer,* Baker's Plays, 1976; *Look Who's Playing God,* Baker's Plays, 1977; *John & Abigail Adams,* Pioneer Drama Service, 1977.

AVOCATIONAL INTERESTS: Travel, theater, hiking, swimming, music, cooking, preservation of California coastline and wild life.

* * *

JOHNSON, Diane   1934-

PERSONAL: Born April 28, 1934, in Moline, Ill.; daughter of Dolph and Frances (Elder) Lain; married B. Lamar Johnson, Jr., July, 1953; married second husband, John Frederic Murray (a professor of medicine), May 31, 1968; children: (first marriage) Kevin, Darcy, Amanda, Simon. *Education:* Attended Stephens College, 1951-53; University of Utah, B.A., 1957; University of California, M.A., 1966, Ph.D., 1968. *Home:* 46 El Camino Real, Berkeley, Calif. 90475. *Agent:* Helen Brann, Sterling Lord Agency, 660 Madison Ave., New York, N.Y. 10021. *Office:* Department of English, University of California, Davis, Calif. 95616.

CAREER: University of California, Davis, 1968—, began as assistant professor, currently professor of English. *Member:* International P.E.N., Modern Language Association of America. *Awards, honors:* National Book Award nomination, 1973, for *Lesser Lives;* Guggenheim fellow, 1977-78.

WRITINGS: Fair Game, Harcourt, 1965; *Loving Hands at Home,* Harcourt, 1968; *Burning,* Harcourt, 1971; *Lesser Lives,* Knopf, 1973; *The Shadow Knows,* Knopf, 1974; *Lying Low,* Knopf, 1978.

WORK IN PROGRESS: A biography of Dashiell Hammett, for Random House, completion expected in 1980.

SIDELIGHTS: In spite of the fact that her central characters are women, it would be wrong to label Diane Johnson a "feminist writer." According to Marjorie Ryan, she is "a contemporary writer with an interest in dehumanization, loss of personal identity, [and] rents in the social fabric. . . . She sees these conditions as affecting women perhaps even more acutely than men." Though her first two novels did not receive a great deal of attention, Johnson's subsequent work (*Burning, Lesser Lives, The Shadow Knows,* and *Lying Low*) has been carefully reviewed by a number of critics. In general, their negative comments center around Johnson's subject matter (or her approach to that subject matter) rather than her ability to write.

Speaking of *Burning,* for example, R. R. Davies points out: "Group therapy and the drug-induced self-analysis of depressed citizens have been done to death as satirical material." Another reviewer for *Best Sellers* writers: "A list of the characters of this slight novel would make one expect something quite hilarious. . . . It is astonishing how unfunny the result is." Or, as J. R. Frakes comments: "The literal holocaust threatens from page one, and when it finally roars . . . it comes almost as a relief." He goes on to admit, however, that Johnson "superintends this asylum with cool disdain and a remarkable neo-classic elegance of phrase, sentence, and chapter." Marjorie Ryan also praises Johnson's skills as a writer, "She has a sense of form that enables her to integrate symbolism, narrative, and characterization into a coherent whole."

With her next book, *Lesser Lives,* Johnson departed from her usual fiction and attempted a biography instead. Once again, she became a center of controversy, for her approach seemed to rely somewhat more on "creativity" than on historical fact. Piers Brendon claims: "She strays across the border of biography into the province of fiction. . . . The technique is a subtle one . . . and [the result] is supposed to do duty for material made out of solid fact. By a feat of biographical legerdemain 'artistic truth' has been substituted for literal." Catharine R. Stimpson, however, does not regard Johnson's approach as a deliberate attempt to deceive. "*Lesser Lives* is a brilliant book. . . . [Johnson] shows what she thinks to be true, what she thinks might be true, and what, in all candor, she thinks no one can prove to be either true or false. . . . Like a historian, she recovers pellets of the past. Like a psychologist, she applies theory and common sense to human behavior. Like a novelist, she takes imaginative liberties and worries about the internal coherence of her work of art. . . . *Lesser Lives* has the buoyant vitality of a book in which a writer has taken risks, and won."

Johnson's fifth book, *The Shadow Knows,* signaled a return to her previous style, aptly dubbed "California Gothic" by one critic. In spite of a plot which he finds to be "a bit too tricksy and modish," L. E. Sissman praises Johnson as "a fine writer with a fine ear [for dialogue]." Jonathan Yardley was more lavish in his praise: "The breadth and depth of Diane Johnson's accomplishment cannot be overstated. . . . [The heroine's] voyage through terror becomes that classic American story, the voyage to self-discovery, told with astonishing complexity and subtlety." Walter Clemons of *Newsweek* praises her efforts at characterization, but finds that Johnson is not quite as successful in bringing the story to a close. "The whodunit pattern imposes an expectation that obscurities will be clarified, and *The Shadow Knows* moves instead toward a shattering but highly ambiguous end." Sandra M. Gilbert attributed this uncertainty to her belief that the plot was "ultimately metaphorical [and therefore] hard to unravel. . . . The novelist herself, even while trying to finish the story on a hopeful note, recognized that there is no simple solution to the mystery, no easy way out of the mad tangle."

With the publication of *Lying Low,* Diane Johnson finally seems to have achieved that balance between style and content which the critics sought in her earlier work. "*Lying Low* seems to me a nearly flawless performance," writes Robert Towers in the *New York Times Book Review.* "[It is] a beautifully constructed, elegantly written book, delicate in its perceptions, powerful in its impact." Due to its abundance of "unfailingly correct" detail, Cyndi Meagher of the *Detroit News* calls it "a full book. Not busy: intellectually and emotionally full. The effect is rather like a literary snap-

shot, with more sense of detail than selective human perceptions usually registers. And because of that fullness, it is one of those increasingly rare books that a reader feels both obligated and willing to read more than once."

Regardless of their feelings about her subject matter, most critics agree that Johnson's greatest strength is her ability to breathe life into her characters and into the often bizarre situations in which they find themselves. "It is one of Diane Johnson's triumphs that she can capture and make interesting the sheer 'dailiness' of existence within a framework that could so easily lend itself to melodrama," comments Robert Towers in his review of *Lying Low.* Although referring specifically to *The Shadow Knows,* Pearl K. Bell echoed the opinion of many concerning all of Johnson's work with the following observation: "Miss Johnson . . . insists that her heroine[s] simply stand up and *be.* . . . [She] has an uncanny gift for infusing an evocative intensity into the here and now."

BIOGRAPHICAL/CRITICAL SOURCES: Book World, October 13, 1968, September 5, 1971, December 22, 1974, November 26, 1978; *New York Times Book Review,* October 27, 1968, November 19, 1978; *Best Sellers,* September 1, 1971; *New Statesman,* November 19, 1971; *Books and Bookmen,* September, 1973; *Critique: Studies in Modern Fiction,* Volume XVI, Number 1, 1974; *Ms.,* May, 1974; *Newsweek,* December 23, 1974; *New Leader,* January 20, 1975; *New Yorker,* March 10, 1975; *Nation,* June 14, 1975; *Contemporary Literary Criticism,* Volume V, Gale, 1976; *Chicago Tribune,* November 5, 1978; *Detroit News,* December 31, 1978.

* * *

JOHNSON, Kenneth G(ardner) 1922-

PERSONAL: Born July 25, 1922, in Iron Mountain, Mich.; son of Alex Gustaf (a superintendent) and Hulda Marie (Johnson) Johnson; married Carol Krause (a student counselor), September 15, 1946; children: Van Edwin, Susan Marie, Steven Alec. *Education:* University of Wisconsin, Ph.B. and M.S., 1947, Ph.D., 1961. *Home:* 1006 West Birch Ave., Milwaukee, Wis. 53209. *Office:* Department of Mass Communication, University of Wisconsin, Milwaukee, Wis. 53201.

CAREER: U.S. Forest Service, Columbus, Ohio, editor and science writer, 1951-52; U.S. Forest Products Laboratory, Madison, Wis., editor and science writer, 1952-55; University of Wisconsin Extension, Madison, assistant director of editorial services, 1955-61; University of Wisconsin—Milwaukee, assistant professor, 1961-63, associate professor, 1963-71, professor of mass communication, 1971—, chairman of department of journalism, 1963-70. Lecturer, Instutute of General Semantics, 1960—. *Military service:* U.S. Army Air Forces, 1943-45; became second lieutenant. *Member:* American Psychological Association, Association for Education in Journalism, International Society for General Semantics, International Communication Association.

WRITINGS: Needed: Trained Science Writers (monograph), University of Wisconsin News Service, 1949; *Reading Habits of Professional Research Workers at the U.S. Forest Products Laboratory* (monograph), U.S. Forest Products Laboratory, 1955; (contributor) *The Changing Nature of the Child in the Institution,* Extension Division, University of Wisconsin, 1960; (with Clifford Ewert) *Survey of Industrial Publications in Wisconsin: 1964* (monograph), Extension Division, University of Wisconsin, 1965; (editor with Lee Thayer, and contributor) *Communication: Perspectives from General Semantics,* Spartan, 1970; *General Semantics: An Outline Survey,* International Society for General Semantics, 1972; (editor and contributor) *Research Designs in General Semantics,* Gordon & Breach, 1974; (with John Senatore, Mark Liebig, and Gene Minor) *Nothing Never Happens: Exercises to Trigger Group Discussions and Promote Self Discovery,* Glencoe, 1974. Author of "Caution: Words at Work I and II," a film strip. Contributor to science, semantics, and other professional journals. Associate editor of *General Semantics Bulletin.*

WORK IN PROGRESS: Further research in general semantics.

AVOCATIONAL INTERESTS: Photography, camping, fishing, encounter groups.

* * *

JOHNSON, Lyndon Baines   1908-1973

August 27, 1908—January 22, 1973; American politician, statesman, and 36th President of the United States. Obituaries: *New York Times,* January 23, 1973; *Washington Post,* January 23, 1973; *L'Express,* January 29-February 4, 1973; *Newsweek,* February 5, 1973; *Time,* February 5, 1973; *Current Biography,* March, 1973.

* * *

JOHNSON, M. Glen   1936-

PERSONAL: Born November 18, 1936, in Pikeville, Ky.; son of Marvin Forrest (a civil engineer) and Norice (Wicker) Johnson; married Sipra Bose (an associate professor of anthropology); children: Denise Bose, Robert Alexander. *Education:* Georgetown College, Georgetown, Ky., A.B., 1958; University of North Carolina at Chapel Hill, M.A., 1961, Ph.D., 1966. *Home:* 9 Old Silvermine Pl., Vassar College, Poughkeepsie, N.Y. 12601. *Office:* Department of Political Science, Vassar College, Poughkeepsie, N.Y. 12601.

CAREER: University of Kentucky, Lexington, instructor in political science, 1963-64; Vassar College, Poughkeepsie, N.Y., instructor, 1964-66, assistant professor, 1966-72, associate professor, 1972-77, professor of political science, 1977—, dean of freshmen, 1968-69, assistant to president, 1968-72. Fulbright visiting professor of political science, University of Poona, India, 1977-78. *Member:* American Political Science Association, International Studies Association, New York State Political Science Association.

WRITINGS: (Editor with Howard Bliss) *Consensus at the Crossroads: Dialogues in American Foreign Policy,* Dodd, 1972; (with Bliss) *Beyond the Water's Edge: America's Foreign Policies,* Lippincott, 1975. Contributor of articles and reviews to *Mercurio, Man in Indian, Current History, Journal of Politics, American Political Science Review,* and other journals.

WORK IN PROGRESS: A study of human rights and U.S. foreign policy.

* * *

JOHNSON, Mauritz (Jr.)   1922-

PERSONAL: Born January 7, 1922, in New York, N.Y.; son of Mauritz (a machinist) and Alma (Hanson) Johnson; married Shirley Jane Busacker, June 29, 1945; children: William, David, Carl, Linnea, Elizabeth. *Education:* New York College for Teachers (now State University of New York at Albany), A.B., 1942, M.A., 1947; Cornell University,

Ph.D., 1952. *Religion:* Episcopalian. *Home:* 111 Berwick Rd., Delmar, N.Y. 12054. *Office:* School of Education, State University of New York, 1400 Washington Ave., Albany, N.Y. 12222.

CAREER: High school teacher and principal in New York, 1942-50; New York State Education Department, Albany, N.Y., research associate, 1952-53; State University College of Education (now State University of New York at Albany), associate professor, 1953-59, professor of education, 1959-60; Cornell University, Ithaca, N.Y., professor of education, 1960-68, dean of School of Education, 1960-68; State University of New York at Albany, professor of education, 1968—. *Military service:* U.S. Navy, 1944-46. U.S. Naval Reserve, 1946-60; became lieutenant. *Member:* American Educational Research Association, Association for Supervision and Curriculum Development, Northeast Education Research Association, Phi Delta Kappa, Phi Kappa Phi.

WRITINGS: (With William Busacker and Fred Bowman) *Junior High School Guidance,* Harper, 1961; (with Joseph Leese and Kenneth Frasure) *The Teacher in Curriculum Making,* Harper, 1961; *American Secondary Schools,* Harcourt, 1965; (with Morris Eson and Theodore Bayer) *Study Manual: Psychological Foundations of Education,* Holt, 1972; (editor with Philip Taylor) *Curriculum Development: A Comparative Study,* NFER Publishing, 1974; *Intentionality in Education,* Center for Curriculum Research, 1977. Contributor to *Saturday Review* and to journals in his field.

AVOCATIONAL INTERESTS: Camping.

* * *

JOHNSON, Niel M(elvin)   1931-

PERSONAL: Born July 28, 1931, in Galesburg, Ill.; son of Clarence H. and Frances (Nelson) Johnson; married Verna Gail Applegate (an elementary school teacher), May 1, 1952; children: Kristin, David. *Education:* Augustana College, Rock Island, Ill., B.A., 1953; University of Iowa, M.A., 1965, Ph.D., 1971. *Politics:* Democrat. *Religion:* Lutheran. *Home:* 15804 Kiger Cir., Independence, Mo. 64055. *Office:* Harry S Truman Library, Independence, Mo. 64050.

CAREER: U.S. Army Weapons Command Headquarters, Rock Island, Ill., historian, 1957-63; Augustana College, Rock Island, Ill., instructor in history, 1967-69; Dana College, Blair, Neb., assistant professor of history, 1969-74; University of Nebraska at Omaha, visiting assistant professor of history, 1975-76; Harry S Truman Library, Independence, Mo., historian, 1977—. *Member:* American Historical Association, Organization of American Historians, American Association of State and Local History, Society of American Archivists.

WRITINGS: George Sylvester Viereck: German-American Propagandist, University of Illinois Press, 1972; *Portal to the Plains,* Jacob North, Inc., 1974. Also author of *Johnsons and Nelsons: A Family History.* Contributor of articles to history journals, *Books at Iowa,* and *Psychoanalytic Review.*

WORK IN PROGRESS: Articles and essays on Harry S Truman and the Truman Library.

AVOCATIONAL INTERESTS: Art (paints landscapes), photography, choral music, spectator sports, politics.

* * *

JOHNSON, Pierce   1921-

PERSONAL: Born June 1, 1921, in Columbus, Ohio; son of

William M. (a merchant) and Valentine (Pierce) Johnson; married Nancy Crandall (an architect, designer, and planner), September 23, 1953; children: Mark Clayton, Valentine Crandall. *Education:* Harvard University, A.B., 1946; University of New Mexico, Ph.D., 1952; Union Theological Seminary, M.Div., 1957. *Home:* 3320 North Union, Tacoma, Wash. 98407. *Office:* Department of Religion, Tacoma Community College, Tacoma, Wash. 98465.

CAREER: Ordained United Methodist minister, 1944; Lambuth College, Jackson, Tenn., assistant professor of history and dean of men, 1953-54; Methodist minister in Maine, New Mexico, New York, and California, 1955-72; University of Puget Sound, Tacoma, Wash., associate professor of religion, and chaplain, 1972-76; United Church in University Place, Tacoma, minister, 1976—; Tacoma Community College, Tacoma, professor of religion and philosophy, 1976—. Speaker at religious retreats, teacher of zen, yoga, tai chi, and prayer meditation. Past president of Claremont Manor Board of Management, Claremont Intercultural Council, Claremont Coordinating Council, and Claremont Motion Picture Association. *Wartime service:* American Field Service Ambulance Corps, 1944-45; served in India. *Member:* American Academy of Religion, American Association of Marriage and Family Counselors, Phi Kappa Phi.

WRITINGS: Dying into Life: A Study in Christian Life Styles, Abingdon, 1972.

WORK IN PROGRESS: A book describing exercises that can be done in the car.†

* * *

JOHNSON, Richard B(righam) 1914-1977

PERSONAL: Born May 19, 1914, in Swampscott, Mass.; son of Francis Walker (an attorney) and Ruth (Brigham) Johnson; married Chloe Tyler Walker, October 12, 1946; children: Ruth B. (Mrs. Jonathan Dean), Sturart W., Chloe T. N., Anne C., Frances M. *Education:* Harvard University, A.B., 1936, J.D., 1939. *Home:* 42 Stanwood Rd., Swampscott, Mass. 01907. *Office:* 225 Franklin St., Boston, Mass. 02110.

CAREER: Admitted to the Bar of Massachusetts, 1939; Ropes & Gray, Boston, Mass., attorney, beginning 1941. Trustee, Charlestown Savings Bank; town moderator of Swampscott, Mass., beginning 1956; graduate trustee of Harvard *Lampoon,* beginning 1962. *Military service:* U.S. Army, 1942-45; became first lieutenant; received Bronze Star and Purple Heart. *Member:* American Bar Association, New England Historic Genealogical Society (recording secretary, beginning 1968), Massachusetts Bar Association, Massachusetts Moderators Association (president, 1963-65), Massachusetts Conveyancers Association (president, 1970-72), Essex County Bar Association, Boston Bar Association.

WRITINGS: (With Benjamin A. Trustman and Charles Y. Wadsworth) *Town Meeting Time: A Handbook of Parliamentary Law,* Little, Brown, 1962; *Mid-Atlantic Mountain Climbing,* Appalachian Mountain Club, 1973; *History of Swampscott in the 17th Century,* Essex Institute, 1973; (editor) *New Perspectives for Bank Directors,* Methodist University Press, 1977.†

(Died June 19, 1977)

* * *

JOHNSTON, Bruce F(oster) 1919-

PERSONAL: Born September 24, 1919, in Lincoln, Neb.; son of Homer K. and Ethel (Hockett) Johnston; married Harriet L. Pollins, March 31, 1944; children: Bruce C., Patricia C. *Education:* Cornell University, B.A., 1941; Stanford University, A.M., 1950, Ph.D., 1953. *Home:* 636 Alvarado Row, Stanford, Calif. 94305. *Office:* Food Research Institute, Stanford University, Stanford, Calif. 94305.

CAREER: U.S. Department of Agriculture, Milwaukee, Wis., field representative for Agricultural Marketing Administration, 1941-42; Supreme Commander of the Allied Powers in Japan, General Headquarters, Tokyo, chief of food branch of Economic and Scientific Section, 1945-48; U.S. Mission to North Atlantic Treaty Organization (NATO) and European Regional Organizations, Paris, France, agricultural economist in Food and Agriculture Division, 1952-54; Stanford University, Stanford, Calif., associate professor of agricultural economics and associate economist at Food Research Institute, 1954-59, professor and economist, 1959—. Member of committee on agricultural economics, Social Science Research Council, 1962-66; member of advisory board, Foreign Area Fellowship Program, 1963-66; member of advisory panel on development problems for Policy Planning Council, U.S. Department of State, 1966-68; consultant to World Bank, Pakistan Institute of Development Economics, Government of Ghana, and United Nations. *Military service:* U.S. Army, 1942-46; became captain.

MEMBER: American Economic Association, American Farm Economic Association, African Studies Association (fellow; member of board of directors, 1962-65), Western Economic Association, Western Farm Economic Association, Telluride Association, Phi Beta Kappa, Phi Kappa Phi. *Awards, honors:* Guggenheim fellowship for study of food economies in East Africa, 1962.

WRITINGS: (With Mosaburo Hosoda and Yoshio Kusumi) *Japan's Food Management During World War Two,* Stanford University Press, 1953; *The Staple Food Economies of Western Tropical Africa,* Stanford University Press, 1958; (contributor) M. J. Herskovits and Mitchell Harwitz, editors, *Economic Transition in Africa,* Northwestern University Press, 1964; (editor with H. M. Southworth) *Agricultural Development and Economic Growth,* Cornell University Press, 1967; (contributor) Erick Thorbecke, editor, *The Role of Agriculture in Economic Development,* National Bureau of Economic Research, 1969; (with Peter Greaves and others) *Manual on Food and Nutrition Policy,* Food and Agricultural Organization (of the United Nations), 1969; (editor with Kazuski Ohkawa and Hiromitsu Kaneda, and contributor) *Agriculture and Economic Growth: Japan's Experience,* Tokyo University Press, 1969; (contributor) Harrison Brown and Edward Hutchings, Jr., editors, *Are Our Descendants Doomed?: Technological Change and Population Growth,* Viking, 1972; (with Peter Kilby) *Agricultural Strategies, Rural Urban Interactions, and the Expansion of Income Opportunities,* Organization for Economic Co-operation and Development Centre, 1972; (with Kilby) *Agricultural and Structural Transformation: Economic Strategies in Late-Developing Countries,* Oxford University Press, 1975. Contributor to *Journal of Political Economy, American Economic Review, Food Research Institute Studies, Tropical Agriculture,* and *Journal of Economic Literature.*

WORK IN PROGRESS: Research on health, nutrition, and population in strategies for rural development.

JOHNSTON, H(ugh) J(ames) M(orton) 1939-

PERSONAL: Born January 20, 1939, in Woodstock, Ontario, Canada; son of W. Stafford (a journalist) and Jean (Morton) Johnston; married Patricia Wilson (an art instructor); children: Megan, Caitlin, Sian. *Education:* University of Toronto, B.A., 1961; University of Western Ontario, M.A., 1965; University of London, Ph.D., 1970. *Home:* 4985 Cliffridge Ave., North Vancouver, British Columbia, Canada. *Office:* Department of History, Simon Fraser University, Burnaby, British Columbia, Canada.

CAREER: Simon Fraser University, Burnaby, British Columbia, instructor, 1968-70, assistant professor, 1970-72, associate professor of history, 1972—, chairman of department, 1972-74.

WRITINGS: (With father, W. Stafford Johnston) *History of Perth to 1967,* Perth County Council, 1967; *British Emigration Policy, 1815-1830: Shovelling Out Paupers,* Clarendon Press, 1972.

* * *

JOHNSTON, Susan T. 1942-
(Tony Johnston)

PERSONAL: Born January 30, 1942, in Los Angeles, Calif; daughter of David L. (a golf professional) and Ruth (Hunter) Taylor; married Roger Johnston (a banker), June 25, 1966; children: Jennifer, Samantha. *Education:* Attended University of California, Berkeley, 1959-60; Stanford University, B.A., 1963, M.Ed., 1964. *Home:* Lazcano 44, San Angel Inn, Mexico 20, D.F. Mexico.

CAREER: Teacher in the public elementary schools, Pasadena, Calif., 1964-66; McGraw-Hill Publishing Co., New York, N.Y., editing supervisor, 1966-68; Harper & Row Publishers, Inc., New York, N.Y., copy editor of children's books, 1969.

WRITINGS—Under name Tony Johnston; all juveniles; published by Putnam, except as indicated: *The Adventures of Mole and Troll,* illustrations by Wallace Tripp, 1972; *Mole and Troll Trim the Tree,* illustrations by Tripp, 1974; *Fig Tale,* illustrations by Giulio Maestro, 1974; *Five Little Foxes and the Snow,* illustrations by Cyndy Szekeres, 1977; *Night Noises and Other Mole and Troll Stories,* illustrations by Szekeres, 1977; *Odd Jobs,* illustrations by Tomie de Paola, 1977; *Four Scary Stories,* illustrations by de Paola, 1978; *Happy Birthday Mole and Troll,* illustrations by Szekeres, 1979; *Little Mouse Nibbling,* illustrations by Diane Stanley, 1979; *Dedos de Luna* (title means "Moon Fingers"), Secretaria de Educacion Publica (Mexico City), 1979; *Odd Jobs II,* illustrations by de Paola, in press.

AVOCATIONAL INTERESTS: Cooking, tennis, archaeology; collecting dance masks and Latin American textiles.

* * *

JOLLY, Alison 1937-

PERSONAL: Born May 9, 1937, in Ithaca, N.Y.; daughter of Morris Gilbert (a professor and author) and Alison (an artist; maiden name, Kingsbury) Bishop; married Richard Jolly (an economist), October 12, 1963; children: Margaretta, Susan, Arthur Morris, Richard. *Education:* Cornell University, B.A., 1958; Yale University, Ph.D., 1962. *Home:* The Old Brewery House, Southover High St., Lewes, Sussex, England. *Office:* School of Biological Sciences, University of Sussex, Falmer, Sussex, England.

CAREER: New York Zoological Society, New York,

N.Y., research associate, 1962-64. *Member:* American Association for the Advancement of Science, Animal Behavior Society, American Society of Zoologists, American Society for Physical Anthropology, Zoological Society of London, Primate Society of Great Britain (treasurer, 1971-74), Sigma Xi.

WRITINGS: Lemur Behavior, University of Chicago Press, 1966; *The Evolution of Primate Behavior,* Macmillan, 1972, 2nd edition, in press; *Play: Its Role in Development and Evolution,* Basic Books, 1976. Contributor to journals in her field.

WORK IN PROGRESS: A World Like Our Own: Conservation in Madagascar.

* * *

JONASSEN, Christen T(onnes) 1912-

PERSONAL: Born September 5, 1912, in Farsund, Norway; U.S. citizen; son of Tonnes Omar (a sea captain) and Sigrid (Toennesen) Jonassen; married Lillian Alice Dolan (a teacher), December, 1938; children: Eric Demarest. *Education:* Brooklyn College (now Brooklyn College of the City University of New York), B.A., 1937; New York University, M.A., 1941, Ph.D., 1947. *Home:* 276 West Kenworth Rd., Columbus, Ohio 43214. *Office:* Department of Sociology, Ohio State University, Columbus, Ohio 43210.

CAREER: Ohio State University, Columbus, instructor, 1947-49, assistant professor, 1949-54, associate professor, 1954-60, professor of sociology, 1960—, chief investigator for research projects, 1952-62. Fulbright research professor, Oslo Institute for Social Research, 1962-63; chairman of research committee, Columbus United Community Council; consultant to National Science Foundation, National Institute for Mental Health, and Kellogg Foundation. *Military service:* U.S. Army, Infantry, 1944-46; served in Europe; became staff sergeant; received Bronze Star and Purple Heart.

MEMBER: International Studies Association, American Sociological Association, Society for the Advancement of Scandinavian Studies, American Association of University Professors, North Central Sociological Association. *Awards, honors:* National Research Council grant, 1952-54; Norwegian National Research Council grant, 1966-67; Social Science Research Council fellowship, 1970.

WRITINGS: The Suburban Shopping Center versus Downtown, Bureau of Business Research, Ohio State University, 1955; (with Sherwood H. Peres) *Interrelationships among Dimensions of Community Systems,* Ohio State University Press, 1960; *Community Conflict in School District Reorganization: A Cross-Cultural Study,* Norwegian Universities Press, 1968; *Values and Beliefs; A Study of American and Norwegian College Students,* Norwegian Universities Press, 1972. Contributor of over twenty articles to sociology journals, including *American Sociological Review, American Journal of Sociology, Social Forces, Acta Sociologica, American Scandinavian Review,* and *Journal of Marketing.* Editor, *Ohio Valley Sociologist.*

WORK IN PROGRESS: Studying central values of Norwegian culture and their significance for social structure and personality tendencies.

* * *

JONES, E(li) Stanley 1884-1973

January 3, 1884—January 25, 1973; American Methodist

missionary, diplomat, and writer on religious topics. Obituaries: *New York Times*, January 26, 1973; *Washington Post*, January 26, 1973; *Newsweek*, February 5, 1973; *Current Biography*, March, 1973.

*   *   *

JONES, (Max Him) Henri 1921- (Tristan Maxhim)

PERSONAL: Born October 5, 1921, in Neuville sur Oise, France; son of Frederick and Marsilia (Wattelier) Jones; married Paulette Bouchon-Desfougeres, October 18, 1947. *Education:* University of Toulouse, Doctorat (lettres) de l'Universite and Doctorat de 3e cycle, 1954. *Religion:* Roman Catholic. *Home:* 3425 Ridgewood Ave., Montreal 247, Quebec, Canada. *Office:* Department of French, McGill University, Montreal, Quebec, Canada H3C 3G1.

CAREER: Cleveland Museum of Art, Cleveland, Ohio, research scholar, 1958-59; McGill University, Montreal, Quebec, lecturer, 1959-63, assistant professor, 1963-66, associate professor of French, 1966—. Visiting professor of aesthetics at University of Montreal, 1963-65; visiting professor of philosophy at University of Toulouse-Le Mirail, 1974.

WRITINGS: (Under pseudonym Tristan Maxhim) *Recit Pudique*, Scorpion (Paris), 1964; *Le Surrealisme Ignore*, C.E.C. (Montreal), 1969; (editor) *Babelian Illustrations* (poems), CECF-McGill, Number 1, 1969, Number 2, 1970, Number 3, Cosmos, 1973; *De L'esthetique Classique*, C.E.C., 1971; *Mallarme Chez G. Seailles Toulouse*, A.P.U.T.L., 1975.

WORK IN PROGRESS: Essays on aesthetics; *Positivisme et Concretude*.

*   *   *

JORGENSEN, James D(ale) 1932-

PERSONAL: Born January 16, 1932, in Trent, S.D.; son of Lenius (a mason) and Bertha (Jensen) Jorgensen; married Joyce Parnell (a social worker), September 7, 1957 (divorced August 30, 1976); married Christine Turnbull, December 18, 1976; children: (first marriage) Catherine, Kirsten, John. *Education:* University of South Dakota, B.A., 1953; University of Denver, M.S.W., 1958. *Politics:* Democrat. *Home:* 2270 Albion St., Denver, Colo. 80207. *Office:* Graduate School of Social Work, University of Denver, Denver, Colo. 80210.

CAREER: South Dakota State Department of Public Welfare, child welfare worker in training in Pierre, 1956, child welfare worker in Huron and Sioux Falls, 1958-61; South Dakota State Training School, Plankinton, director of social services, 1961-64; University of Denver, Denver, Colo., 1964—, began as assistant professor, currently professor of social work. Member of board of directors of Volunteer Court Services, Inc., Denver Youth Services Bureau, and National Information Center on Volunteerism. Associate, Training Systems Design. *Military service:* U.S. Army, Cavalry Division, 1953-55; served in Japan. *Member:* National Association of Social Workers (Northern Colorado chapter), Academy of Certified Social Workers, Council on Social Work Education, Colorado Correctional Association.

WRITINGS: Volunteer Training Manual, State Judicial Department (Denver, Colo.), 1971; *Volunteer Training in Courts and Corrections*, Scarecrow, 1973; (with Timothy Fautsko) *Quid: How to Make the Best Decisions of Your Life*, Walker, 1978. Author of monographs for National In-

formation Center on Volunteerism and for Denver Research Institute. Contributor to conferences, symposia, and proceedings. Contributor to *Public Welfare, Federal Probation, Child Welfare, Volunteer Administration, Corrective Psychiatry*, and *Journal of Social Therapy*.

WORK IN PROGRESS: A book, *Solving Problems in Meetings*, for Nelson-Hall.

*   *   *

JORN, Asger 1914-1973

March 3, 1914—May 2, 1973; Danish painter and writer. Obituaries: *Washington Post*, May 3, 1973; *New York Times*, May 3, 1973.

*   *   *

JUDSON, Lewis Van Hagen 1893-1973

August 10, 1893—May 8, 1973; American physicist, author, and government expert on standards of length measurement. Obituaries: *Washington Post*, May 12, 1973.

*   *   *

JUDSON, Sylvia Shaw 1897-

PERSONAL: Born June 30, 1897, in Chicago, Ill.; daughter of Howard Van Doren (an architect) and Frances (a poet; maiden name, Wells) Shaw; married Clay Judson, 1922 (died, 1959); married Sidney Gatter Haskins, December 1, 1963; children: (first marriage) Alice (Mrs. Edward L. Ryerson, Jr.). *Education:* Attended Art Institute of Chicago, 1916-20, and Academe Grande Chaumiere, Paris, France, 1920-21.

CAREER: Sculptor. Work has been exhibited in one-man shows at Art Institute of Chicago, 1938, Arden Gallery, 1940, Illinois State Museum, 1948, Chicago Public Library, and Sculpture Center of New York, 1957; sculpture has also been exhibited at Philadelphia Museum of Art, Whitney Museum of Art, Museum of Modern Art, Metropolitan Museum, and at San Francisco World's Fair. Instructor of sculpture, American University, Cairo, Egypt, 1963. Sculpture on display in public parks and gardens. *Member:* National Academy of Design, National Sculpture Society (fellow), National Academy of Interior Decorators (honorary member), Art Club of Chicago, Cosmopolitan Club. *Awards, honors:* Logan Prize, 1929; Clyde Varr Prize, 1947; purchase prize, Philadelphia Museum International Sculpture Show, 1949; honorary Doctorate of Sculpture, Lake Forest College, 1952; honorary award in fine arts, Chicago Association of Commerce and Industry, 1956; Speyer Prize, American Academy of Design, 1957; medal from Garden Club of America, 1957; Municipal Art League prize, 1957.

WRITINGS: The Quiet Eye, Regnery, 1954; *For Gardens and Other Places: The Sculpture of Sylvia Shaw Judson*, Regnery, 1967. Also author of published lecture, *Universal or Particular?*, Society of Friends, 1963.

SIDELIGHTS: Sylvia Shaw Judson's sculpture is on display in such places as the Art Institute of Chicago, the National Academy of Design, and the First Lady's Garden at the White House. She has sculpted fountains and monuments for public parks and gardens in Philadelphia, Chicago, Boston, and Milwaukee. She is especially known for her sculptures which capture the quiet or thoughtful moments of children and animals. A writer for *National Sculpture Review* has said, "Simplified forms without refinement of surface intensify the quiet mood of Sylvia Shaw Judson's people and animals."

In *National Sculpture Review,* Judson describes a trip she made to China as "a continuing influence, especially the sculptured animals that I saw there." She cites Maillol, Seurat, and Gerhard Marcks as sculptors whose work she particularly admires.

"There is a thread which connects one generation and one country with another and which draws us close in a common humanity," she has written in *For Gardens and Other Places.* "This is the thread of authentic experience, simple, homely, fresh, and vivid as the parables."

BIOGRAPHICAL/CRITICAL SOURCES: Chicago Art Institute Bulletin, Volume XXXII, April, 1938; *Art News,* Volume XXXVIII, November 12, 1938; *Architectural Forum,* Volume LXXIII, July 12, 1940; *Art Digest,* Volume XV, April 1, 1941, Volume XXI, June, 1947; *National Sculpture Review,* Volume XVIII, Number 1, spring, 1969, Volume XXIV, Number 4, winter, 1975, Volume XXVI, Number 1, spring, 1977.†

* * *

JUERGENSMEYER, John Eli 1934-

PERSONAL: Born May 14, 1934, in Stewardson, Ill.; married Elizabeth Ann Bogart (a professor of biology), September 10, 1963; children: Margaret Ann, Frances Elizabeth. *Education:* University of Illinois, B.A. (with high honors), 1955, J.D., 1963; Princeton University, M.A., 1957, Ph.D., 1960. *Politics:* Republican. *Religion:* Methodist. *Home:* 401 Hazel Dr., Elgin, Ill. 60120. *Office:* Lawyers Building, Suite 500, 5 Douglas Ave., Elgin, Ill. 60120.

CAREER: University of Hawaii, Honolulu, instructor in American government, 1959-60; lecturer in political science, University of Illinois, Extension Division, 1962-63; Judson College, Elgin, Ill., 1963—, began as assistant professor, currently professor of constitutional law and political science. Admitted to Bar of State of Illinois, 1963; associate, Kirkland, Brady, McQueen, Martin, & Schnell, 1963-64; assistant to public defender, Kane County, 1964-67; attorney, Juergensmeyer, Zimmerman & Smith, Elgin, Ill., 1964—; assistant to state attorney, Kane County, 1977—. Lecturer, Northern Illinois University, 1969-70; Illinois Institute for Continuing Legal Education, 1972—. Field representative, People-to-People Program, 1961-63; field assistant, Committee for Modern Courts in Illinois, 1962; member of Illinois Governor's Advisory Council, 1969—; commissioner, City of Elgin Economic Development Commission, 1971—; hearing officer, Illinois Pollution Control Board, 1971—. *Military service:* U.S. Air Force Reserve, 1955—, active duty, 1958-60; served in Japan, Formosa, Asia, and Hawaii; present rank, captain.

MEMBER: American Bar Association, American Judicature Society, National Association of Defense Lawyers in Criminal Cases, American Trial Lawyers Association, Federal Bar Association, American Political Science Association, American Association of Public Opinion Researchers, American Economic Association, Seventh Circuit, Illinois Bar Association, Kane County Bar Association, Chicago Bar Association, Elgin Bar Association, Elgin Board of Realtors (affiliate), Phi Beta Kappa. *Awards, honors:* Award from Illinois Juvenile Officers Association, 1963; certificate of recognition, Illinois Youth Commission, 1967.

WRITINGS: The Campaign for the 1954 Reapportionment Amendment, Institute of Government, University of Illinois, 1956; *The President, the Foundations, and the People-to-People Program,* Bobbs-Merrill, 1965; *The Generation Gap,* Law and Order, 1969; (contributor) *Special Districts,*

Illinois Institute for Continuing Education, 1977. Contributor of articles to legal, academic, and popular journals.

WORK IN PROGRESS: Research on political parties and democratic theory.

AVOCATIONAL INTERESTS: Golf, hunting, skiing, skindiving, travel.

* * *

JULIARD, Pierre 1939-

PERSONAL: Born March 21, 1939, in Brussels, Belgium; son of Alex (a stamp dealer) and Andree (Freedman) Juliard; married Linda Jeffery, December 22, 1962 (died, 1968); married Christine White (a teacher), March 25, 1972; children: (first marriage) Jeffery, Wendy. *Education:* Franklin and Marshall College, A.B., 1961; Cornell University, M.A., 1964, Ph.D., 1966.

CAREER: Old Dominion College (now University), Norfolk, Va., assistant professor of history, 1966-68; University of Delaware, Newark, assistant professor of history, summer, 1968; Lehigh University, Bethlehem, Pa., assistant professor of history, beginning 1968. *Member:* American Historical Association, French Historical Studies, American Society for Eighteenth Century Study (president, 1971-72). *Awards, honors:* American Philosophical Society grant, 1971-72.

WRITINGS: Philosophies of Language in Eighteenth-Century France, Mouton, 1970.

WORK IN PROGRESS: Studying Louis Sebastien Mercier, prolific writer of eighteenth-century France.

AVOCATIONAL INTERESTS: Travel, photography.†

* * *

JULY, Robert W(illiam) 1918-

PERSONAL: Born May 11, 1918, in New York, N.Y.; married Jean Horne, September 27, 1958; children: Catherine, Richard. *Education:* Columbia University, B.A., 1938, M.A., 1939, Ph.D., 1951. *Office:* Department of History, Hunter College of the City University of New York, 695 Park Ave., New York, N.Y. 10021.

CAREER: Williston Academy, Easthampton, Mass., instructor in history, 1939-40; Columbia University, New York City, instructor in history, 1948; General Education Board, New York City, secretary and assistant director, 1948-55; Rockefeller Foundation, New York City, assistant director for humanities and social sciences, 1955-68; City University of New York, New York City, Hunter College, professor of history, 1968—, acting dean for graduate studies, 1971-72, Graduate School and University Center, professor of history, 1968—. Visiting research associate professor, University of Ibadan, Institute of African Studies, 1963-66; visiting senior lecturer and visiting professor of history, University College (Nairobi), 1966-68. *Military service:* U.S. Naval Reserve, active duty, 1941-45; became lieutenant. *Member:* American Historical Association, African Studies Association. *Awards, honors:* Anisfield-Wolf Award in Race Relations, 1970, for *A History of the African People.*

WRITINGS: (Contributor) A. R. Buchanan, editor, *The Navy's Air War,* Harper, 1946; *The Essential New Yorker: C. C. Verplanck,* Duke University Press, 1951; (contributor) H. U. Beier, editor, *Introduction to African Literature,* Longmans, Green, 1967; *The Origins of Modern African Thought,* Praeger, 1967; (contributor) E. D. Jones and

Christopher Fyfe, editors, *Freetown: A Symposium,* Oxford University Press, 1968; (author of introduction) A. B. C. Sibthorpe, *The History of Sierra Leone,* Frank Cass, 1970; *A History of the African People* (History Book Club selection), Scribner, 1970, 3rd edition, 1979; *Precolonial Africa: An Economic and Social History,* Scribner, 1975. Contributor to *Encyclopedia Americana* and *Dictionary of American Biography.* Contributor of articles and reviews to *Black Orpheus, Sierra Leone Studies, Journal of African History, American History Review, Ibadan, East Africa Journal, African Historical Studies,* and *New York Times Book Review.*

WORK IN PROGRESS: The Ideas of African Independence; Independent Africa: A History.

* * *

JURGENS, W(illiam) A(nthony) 1928-

PERSONAL: Born July 3, 1928, in Akron, Ohio; son of Charles Bernard and Ruth (Gardner) Jurgens. *Education:* Pontifical Gregorian University, H.E.D., 1959. *Home:* 4129 Superior Ave., Cleveland, Ohio 44108. *Office:* Chancery Building, Cathedral Square, Cleveland, Ohio 44108.

CAREER: Roman Catholic priest, ordained 1954; St. Michael Parish, Cleveland, Ohio, curate, 1955-56; St. Mary Seminary, Cleveland, professor of church music, 1959-69, instructor in patrology and professor of church history, 1959-74, professor emeritus, 1974—; secretary to Bishop C. G. Issenmann and diocesan research historian, Cleveland,

1974—. Instructor in church music, Borromeo Seminary, 1959-67; diocesan director of sacred music, 1963-69; tribunal translator for Diocese of Cleveland, beginning 1965. *Member:* American Catholic Historical Association.

WRITINGS—All published by Collegeville, except as indicated: (Translator) *The Priesthood: A Translation of the Peri Hierosynes of St. John Chrysostom,* Macmillan, 1955; *Gregorian Chant in Latin and in English,* Gregorian Institute of America, 1965; *Sung Vespers* (music), Liturgical Press, 1968; *The Faith of the Early Fathers,* Volume I, 1970, Volume II, in press, Volume III, in press; (translator) Karl Hermann Schelkle, *Theology of the New Testament: Creation,* 1971; (translator) Schelkle, *Theology of the New Testament: Morality,* 1973; *General Instruction on the Liturgy of the Hours,* 1975; (translator) Schelkle, *Theology of the New Testament: Salvation History-Revelation,* 1976; (translator) Cipriano Vagaggini, *Theological Dimensions of the Liturgy,* 1976; (translator) Schelkle, *Theology of the New Testment: The Rule of God: Church-Eschatology,* 1978. Numerous musical compositions have been published by Gregorian Institute of America, McLaughlin & Reilly, Liturgical Press, and J. Fischer & Brothers. Staff composer for Gregorian Institute of America and Liturgical Press. Contributor to *New Catholic Encyclopedia,* and to *Irish Ecclesiastical Record, Jurist, Emmanuel,* and *Harvard Theological Review.*

WORK IN PROGRESS: A five-volume history of the Catholic diocese of Cleveland, including a full biography of Bishop Amedeus Rappe.

K

KAHN, Alfred E(dward) 1917-

PERSONAL: Born October 17, 1917, in Paterson, N.J.; son of Jacob M. (a manufacturer) and Bertha (Orlean) Kahn; married Mary Simmons (an artist), October 10, 1943; children: Joel S., Rachel, Hannah. Education: New York University, A.B. (summa cum laude), 1936, M.A., 1937; University of Missouri, graduate study, 1937-38; Yale University, Ph.D., 1942. Home: R.D. 3, Trumansburg, N.Y. 14886. Office: Civil Aeronautics Board, Room 1810, 1825 Connecticut Ave. N.W., Washington, D.C. 20428; and College of Arts and Sciences, Cornell University, 136 Goldwin Smith Hall, Ithaca, N.Y. 14850.

CAREER: Brookings Institution, Washington, D.C., research fellow, 1939-40, junior member of staff, 1940; U.S. Department of Justice, Antitrust Division, Washington, D.C., economist, 1941-42; U.S. Department of Commerce, International Economics Section, Washington, D.C., economist, 1942; War Production Board, Washington, D.C., economist, 1943; Commission on Palestine Surveys, New York City, economist, 1944; Twentieth Century Fund, New York City, assistant to writers George W. Stocking and Myron W. Watkins, 1944-45; Ripon College, Ripon, Wis., assistant professor of economics and chairman of department, 1945-47; Cornell University, Ithaca, N.Y., assistant professor, 1947-50, associate professor, 1950-55, professor of economics, 1955—, Robert Julius Thorne Professor of Economics, 1967—, chairman of department, 1958-63, member of board of trustees of university, 1964-69, dean of College of Arts and Sciences, 1969-74; Civil Aeronautics Board, Washington, D.C., chairman, 1977—. Member of research staff, Brookings Institution, 1951-52; member of Attorney General's National Committee to Study the Antitrust Laws, 1953-55; senior staff member, U.S. Council of Economic Advisers (Office of the President), 1955-57; Chairman, New York Public Service Commission, 1974-77. Member of review committee on sulfur oxide emissions, National Academy of Sciences, 1974-75; member of Public Advisory Board, Electric Power Research Institute, 1974-77; member of National Commission for Review of Antitrust Laws, 1978—. Member of economic advisory committee, U.S. Chamber of Commerce, 1964-67; member of board of economic advisers, American Telephone & Telegraph, 1968-74; consultant to U.S. Tariff Commission, 1953-54, U.S. Foreign Agricultural Service (Israel), 1960-61, National Economic Research Associates, 1961-74, U.S. De-

partment of Justice, 1963-64, Federal Trade Commission, 1965, National Commission on Food Marketing, 1966, and Ford Foundation, 1967. Has testified before Federal Power Commission and before Congressional Committees. Military service: U.S. Army, 1943. Member: American Economic Association, National Association of Regulatory Utility Commissioners (chairman of committee on electrical energy, 1974-77; member of executive board, 1974—), American Academy of Arts and Sciences, Phi Beta Kappa. Awards, honors: Fulbright fellowship, Italy, 1954-55; Distinguished Alumni Award, New York University, 1976; LL.D., Colby College, 1978.

WRITINGS: Great Britain in the World Economy, Columbia University Press, 1946; (contributor) Walter Adams, editor, The Structure of the American Industry, Macmillan, 1948, 3rd edition, 1961; (with Joel B. Dirlam) Fair Competition: The Law and Economics of Antitrust Policy, Cornell University Press, 1954; (contributor) R. B. Heflebower and G. W. Stocking, editors, Readings in Industrial Organization and Public Policy, American Economic Association, 1958; (with Melvin G. DeChazeau) Integration and Competition in the Petroleum Industry (monograph), Yale University Press, 1959.

(Contributor) J. P. Miller, editor, Competition, Cartels and Their Regulation, North-Holland Publishing, 1962; (contributor) Harry Trebing, editor, Performance under Regulation, Michigan State University Press, 1968; The Economics of Regulation, Wiley, Volume I, 1970, Volume II, 1971. Contributor to bulletins and proceedings. Contributor to Encyclopedia of the Social Sciences, and to economic journals, including American Economic Review, Quarterly Journal of Economics, Journal of Political Economy, Fortune, as well as to law journals.

* * *

KAHN, Kathy 1945-

PERSONAL: Born April 2, 1945, in Seattle, Wash.; daughter of Robert (an engineer) and Donna (Green) Moody. Home: 1049 St. Paul St., Denver, Colo. 80206.
CAREER: Has performed as singer and banjo player.

WRITINGS: Hillbilly Women, Doubleday, 1973. Contributor of articles to New South, South Today, Mountain Life and Work, People's Appalachia, Off Our Backs, and Southern Patriot. Co-authored a series of pamphlets for poor and working people's groups.

SIDELIGHTS: Kathy Kahn is the vocalist on the LP record, "The Working Girl: Women's Songs of Mountains, Mines, and Mills," released by Voyager Records, 1972.

* * *

KAHN, Ludwig W(erner) 1910-

PERSONAL: Born October 18, 1910, in Berlin, Germany; came to United States in 1936, naturalized in 1943; son of Bernhard (a lawyer and social worker) and Dora (Frishberg) Kahn; married Tatyan Uffner, July 12, 1941; children: Andree (Mrs. James F. Blumstein), Miriam. *Education:* Attended University of Berlin, 1928-30, 1931-33 and University of Paris, 1931; University of Berne, Ph.D., 1934; University of London, M.A., 1936. *Politics:* Democrat. *Religion:* Jewish. *Home:* 9 Atherstone Rd., Scarsdale, N.Y. 10583. *Office:* Department of German, Columbia University, New York, N.Y. 10027.

CAREER: University of London, London, England, staff member, Warburg Institute, 1934-36, assistant lecturer in German, University College, 1935-36; University of Rochester, Rochester, N.Y., instructor in German, 1937-40; Bryn Mawr College, Bryn Mawr, Pa., instructor in German, 1940-42; Yale University, New Haven, Conn., editor, *Strategic Index of Latin America* (World War II research project), 1942-43; Vassar College, Poughkeepsie, N.Y., instructor, 1942-45, assistant professor of German, 1945-47; City College of the City University of New York, New York City, assistant professor, 1947-53, associate professor, 1953-62, professor of German, 1963-67, chairman of department of Germanic and Slavic languages, 1961-67; Columbia University, New York City, professor of German, Graduate Faculties, 1967-73, Gebhard Professor of German Language and Literature, 1973—. Goethe Bicentennial lecturer at Smith College, American International College, and Yeshiva University, 1949; guest professor and senior Fulbright lecturer at University of Stuttgart, 1959-60. Member of Woodrow Wilson fellowship election committee, 1961-66, and of screening committee, senior Fulbright-Hays program, 1970—.

MEMBER: American Association of Teachers of German, Modern Language Association of America (chairman of German IV section, 1955), American Association of University Professors, Wilhelm Busch Gesellschaft, Goethe Gesellschaft, Germanistic Society of America (member of board of directors, 1968—). *Awards, honors:* Faculty fellow, Fund for the Advancement of Education, 1951-52; Guggenheim fellow and Fulbright research fellow, 1969-70; Order of Merit (first class) from German Federal Republic.

WRITINGS: Shakespeares Sonette in Deutschland, Gotthelf Verlag, 1934; *Social Ideas in German Literature, 1770-1830,* Columbia University Press, 1938, reprinted, AMS Press, 1969; *Literature und Glaubenskrise,* Kohlhammer Verlag, 1964; *Letteratura E Crisi Della Fede,* Citta Nuova Editrice, 1978.

Contributor: Julius Petersen and Erich Trunz, editors, *Lyrische Weltdichtung in deutschen Uebertragungen,* Junker & Duennhaupt, 1933; Arno Schirokauer and Wolfgang Paulsen, editors, *Corona: Studies in Honor of S. Singer,* Duke University Press, 1941; Hans Joachim Stoerig, editor, *Das Problem des Uebersetzens,* Wissenschaftliche Buchgemeinschaft, 1963; Fritz Martini, editor, *Kaete Hamburger Festschrift,* Klett, 1971. Also contributor, W. Sokzl, editor, *A. von Gronicka Festschrift,* and Ralph Ley, editor, *Claude Hill Festschrift,* both 1978. Compiler of annual German bibliography on the Romantic movement published in *ELH,*

1949, and *Philological Quarterly,* 1950-54. Contributor of articles to *Collier's Encyclopedia, Encyclopedie Hebraica,* and to journals; more than fifty reviews have been published in language and education journals. Associate editor, *Germanic Review,* 1967—.

* * *

KALLEN, Laurence 1944-

PERSONAL: Born August 18, 1944, in Cleveland, Ohio; son of Edward S. (a salesman) and Ruth (Pearlman) Kallen; married Bonnie Venook, June 25, 1967; children: Jason. *Education:* University of Michigan, B.A., 1966, J.D., 1969; University of Wisconsin, additional study, summer, 1969. *Residence:* Chicago, Ill.

CAREER: Teacher in public schools in Ypsilanti, Mich., 1969-70; Walsh, Case & Coale, Chicago, Ill., attorney, 1970-71; Wexler, Kane, Rosenzweig & Shaw, Chicago, attorney, 1971-73; Hertz & Kallen, Chicago, attorney, beginning 1973. *Member:* American Bar Association, National Organization on Legal Problems of Education, Law and Society Association, Illinois State Bar Association, Chicago Bar Association, Chicago Council of Lawyers, Tau Epsilon Rho.

WRITINGS: Teachers' Rights and Liabilities under the Law, Arco, 1972. Contributor to *Trial Lawyers Guide.*††

* * *

KAMPELMAN, Max M. 1920-

PERSONAL: Born November 7, 1920, in New York, N.Y.; son of Joseph and Eva (Gottlieb) Kampelman; married Marjorie Buetow, August 21, 1948; children: Anne, Jeffrey, Julie, David, Sarah. *Education:* New York University, A.B., 1940, J.D., 1945; University of Minnesota, M.A., 1946, Ph.D., 1951. *Politics:* Democrat. *Religion:* Jewish. *Residence:* Washington, D.C. *Office:* Fried, Frank, Harris, Shriver & Kampelman, 600 New Hampshire Ave. N.W., Washington, D.C. 20037.

CAREER: Phillips, Nizer, Benjamin & Krim, New York, N.Y., law clerk, 1941-43; University of Minnesota, Minneapolis, instructor in political science, 1946-48; Bennington College, Bennington, Vt., member of faculty of political economy, 1948-50; legal counsel to U.S. Senator Hubert H. Humphrey, 1949-55; Fried, Frank, Harris, Shriver & Kampelman, Washington, D.C., attorney and partner, 1956—. Member of faculty, School for Workers, University of Wisconsin, summers, 1947-48; visiting lecturer, Howard University, 1954-56; visiting distinguished professor of political science, Claremont Graduate School and University Center (now Claremont Graduate School), summer, 1963. Alternate delegate to President's Commission on Intergovernmental Relations, 1954-55; senior adviser, U.S. Delegation to United Nations, 1966-67. Moderator of "Washington Week in Review," Eastern Educational Network, 1967-70. Chairman of executive committee, District of Columbia National Bank, 1962-66; member of Democratic National Committee Study on Vice-Presidential Selection, 1973-74; member of board of directors of Atlantic Council of the United States, 1965-70, and National Public Affairs Center for Television, 1971—. Vice-president, Helen Dwight Reid Educational Foundation, 1959—; member of board of advisors, Presidental Classroom for Young Americans, 1968-72, and Georgetown University Center for Strategic and International Studies. Member of national advisory council, Amnesty International, 1968-77; Anti-Defamation League of B'nai Brith, member of national commission, 1973-77, vice-chairman, 1977—; chairman, Martin Luther King, Jr.

Memorial Forest Committee, 1974; member of executive committee, Committee on the Present Danger, 1976—. Member of board of directors of Mount Vernon College, 1972—, Arena Stage, 1974-78, American Cultural Foundation, 1974—, American Friends of the Israeli Conservatory of Music, 1977—, and Georgetown University, 1978—; American Friends of Hebrew University, member of board of directors, 1972—, president, 1975-77, chairman, 1977—. Trustee of Institute for American Universities, 1959—, Federal City Council, 1965-75, Population Reference Bureau, 1966-67, American Histadrut Cultural Exchange Institute, 1968-72, Hebrew University of Jerusalem, 1973—, and Law Center Foundation of New York University, 1978—; Greater Washington Educational Telecommunication Association, Inc., chairman of board of trustees, 1963-70, honorary chairman of board of trustees, 1971-73; overseer, College of the Virgin Islands, 1963—. *Wartime service:* American Friends Service Committee, civilian public service, 1943-46. *Military service:* U.S. Marine Corps Reserve, 1955-62; became captain.

MEMBER: American Bar Association, Federal Bar Association, American Political Science Association, District of Columbia Bar Association, District of Columbia Political Science Association (president, 1955), Jewish Publication Society of America (vice-president, 1978—), Coalition for a Democratic Majority (vice-chairman, 1977—), American Peace Society (member of board of directors, 1978—), Friends of the National Zoo (president, 1958-60).

WRITINGS: (Contributor) *Interpreting the Labor Movement,* Industrial Relations Association, 1954; *The Communist Party vs. the C.I.O.: A Study in Power Politics,* Praeger, 1957; (with Jeane J. Kirkpatric) *The Strategy of Deception,* Farrar, Straus, 1963; (contributor) Donald G. Tacheron and Morris K. Udall, editors, *The Job of the Congressman,* Bobbs-Merrill, 1970. Contributor to proceedings and to *Annals* of the American Academy of Political and Social Science, 1954. Contributor to law and political science journals.

*   *   *

KANE, Dennis Cornelius 1918-

PERSONAL: Born September 24, 1918, in Boston, Mass.; son of Patrick Downey (a warehouseman) and Katherine (Murphy) Kane. *Education:* Providence College, A.B., 1941; Immaculate Conception College, S.T.L. and S.T.Lr., 1947; St. Thomas Aquinas Institute, River Forest, Ill., Ph.D., 1971. *Politics:* American. *Address:* Department of Philosophy, Providence College, Providence, R.I. 02918.

CAREER: Ordained Roman Catholic priest of Dominican Order (O.P.), 1946; University of Dayton, Dayton, Ohio, instructor in philosophy, 1947-48; Villa Madonna College (now St. Thomas More College), Covington, Ky., assistant professor of theology, 1948-51; Providence College, Providence, R.I., associate professor of philosophy and logic, 1955-64; St. Thomas Aquinas Seminary, Nairobi, Kenya, dean of students, 1964-67; Providence College, associate professor, 1967-74, professor of philosophy and logic, 1974—. *Military service:* U.S. Naval Reserve, chaplain, 1951-55; inactive status, 1955-65; became lieutenant. *Member:* American Philosophical Association, American Catholic Philosophical Association, Phi Sigma Tau.

WRITINGS: *Logic: The Art of Inference and Prediction,* Sheed, 1969; (contributor) *Readings in Early Greek and Roman Philosophies,* Providence College Press, 1977. Contributor to *Thomist.*

WORK IN PROGRESS: Researching logical studies of Vincent Ferrer.

AVOCATIONAL INTERESTS: Handball, vigorous walking, snow skiing, non-rock music.

*   *   *

KANE, Edward J(ames) 1935-

PERSONAL: Born June 30, 1935, in Washington, D.C.; son of Edward Anthony (a biochemist) and Mary Agnes (Kerwin) Kane; married Gloria N. Verdi (a dental hygienist), August 27, 1959; children: Laura, Stephen, Edward. *Education:* Georgetown University, B.S. (cum laude), 1957; Massachusetts Institute of Technology, Ph.D., 1960. *Religion:* Roman Catholic. *Home:* 2452 Tremont Rd., Columbus, Ohio 43221. *Office:* Department of Economics, Ohio State University, Columbus, Ohio 43210.

CAREER: Boston College, Chestnut Hill, Mass., lecturer in economics, summer, 1960; Iowa State University, Ames, assistant professor of economics, 1960-61; Princeton University, Princeton, N.J., assistant professor of economics, 1961-66; Boston College, associate professor, 1966-68, professor of economics, 1968-72; Ohio State University, Columbus, professor of economics, 1972, Everett D. Reese Professor of Banking and Monetary Economics, 1972—. UNESCO visiting professor, Institute of Economic Development, University of Istanbul, 1966; visiting professor, Simon Fraser University, summer, 1971; visiting scholar, San Francisco Federal Reserve Bank, 1975. Economist, Boston Federal Reserve Bank, 1967-72; senior financial economist, Federal Deposit Insurance Corp., 1975-76. Research assistant, Federal Reserve Board, summer, 1958-59; rapporteur, Merrill Center for Economics, summer, 1961. Consultant to Federal Aviation Administration, 1967, Federal Home Loan Bank Board, 1973-74, U.S. Department of Housing and Urban Development, 1978, and U.S. Congress Joint Economic Committee, 1978—. Member of New Jersey Fulbright-Hays scholarship committee, 1965-66, National Science Foundation panel to evaluate support proposals under Advanced Training Projects Program, 1966, 1969, National Research Council fellowship evaluation panel, 1971, and committee of examiners for graduate record examination in economics, Educational Testing Service, 1974-77. Trustee and member of finance committee, Teachers Insurance Annuity Association, 1975—.

MEMBER: American Economic Association, American Finance Association (president, 1979), Econometric Society, National Tax Association, American Association of University Professors. *Awards, honors:* Procter and Gamble fellowship, 1962-63; Bicentennial preceptorship, 1964-66; National Science Foundation research grants, 1965-66, 1967-69, 1971-72, 1972-73; Guggenheim fellowship, 1969-70; Georgetown University Phi Beta Kappa Alumni award, 1978.

WRITINGS: *Economic Statistics and Econometrics: An Introduction to Quantitative Economics,* Harper, 1968. Contributor to proceedings and compendiums. Contributor of about thirty articles to professional journals, including *Journal of Money, Credit and Banking, Journal of Political Economy, National Tax Journal,* and *Journal of Regional Science.* Associate editor, *Review of Social Economy,* 1966—; book review editor, *Journal of Finance,* 1967-70.

WORK IN PROGRESS: Research on econometric models of interest-rate forecasting, on investor habitats, interest-rate expectations, and term structure of interest rates, on effects of price expectations on nominal rates of interest, on effects of deposit-rate ceilings, on politics of Federal Reserve policy-making, and on direct cross-section tests of the pure expectations and Hicksian liquidity-premium theories of the term structure.

*   *   *

KANFER, Frederick H. 1925-

PERSONAL: Born December 6, 1925, in Vienna, Austria; naturalized U.S. citizen; son of Oscar and Ann (Schneier) Kanfer; married Ruby Weber, January 20, 1952; children: Ruth, Lawrence P. *Education:* Cooper Union, engineering student, 1942-44; Long Island University, B.S. (cum laude), 1948; Indiana University, M.A., 1952, Ph.D., 1953. *Residence:* Urbana, Ill. *Office:* Department of Psychology, University of Illinois, Urbana, Ill.

CAREER: Intern at Veterans Administration Hospital, 1951-52; Washington University, St. Louis, Mo., assistant professor of psychology and director of psychoeducational clinic, 1953-57; Purdue University, Lafayette, Ind., associate professor, 1957-62; University of Oregon, Portland, professor of psychiatry in Medical School, 1962-69, visiting professor of psychology in the university, Eugene, 1963, 1967-68; University of Cincinnati, Cincinnati, Ohio, professor of psychology, 1969-73; University of Illinois at Urbana-Champaign, professor of psychology, 1973—. Visiting professor, Louisiana State University, 1961; Fulbright lecturer, Ruhr University, 1968. Member of clinical and personality sciences fellowship review committee, National Institute of Mental Health, 1971—. Diplomate in clinical psychology, American Board of Examiners in Professional Psychology, 1969. *Military service:* U.S. Army, 1944-46.

MEMBER: American Psychological Association (fellow; member of executive council, Division 12), American Association for the Advancement of Science, Association for Advancement of the Behavioral Therapies (member of board of directors), Midwestern Psychological Association, Sigma Xi. *Awards, honors:* Research grants from U.S. Public Health Service, 1955—.

WRITINGS: (With J. S. Phillips) *Learning Foundations of Behavior Therapy*, Wiley, 1970; (with A. P. Goldstein) *Helping People Change*, Pergamon, 1975; (editor with Goldstein) *Maximizing Treatment Gains in Therapy*, Academic Press, 1979.

Contributor: Leonard Krasner and L. P. Ullmann, editors, *Research in Behavior Modification*, Holt, 1965; T. R. Dixon and D. L. Horton, editors, *Verbal Behavior and Its Relation to General S-R Theory*, Prentice-Hall, 1968; C. M. Franks, editor, *Behavior Therapy: Appraisal and Status*, McGraw, 1969; C. J. Frederick, editor, *The Future of Psychotherapy*, Little, Brown, 1969; Charles Neuringer and J. L. Michael, editors, *Behavior Modification in Clinical Psychology*, Appleton, 1970; Alfred Jacobs and Lewis B. Sachs, editors, *The Psychology of Private Events*, Academic Press, 1971; R. C. Johnson, P. R. Dokecki, and O. H. Mowrer, editors, *Conscience, Contract and Social Reality*, Holt, 1972; Carl E. Thoreson, editor, *Behavior Modification in Education*, National Society for the Study of Education, 1973.

Contributor of about one hundred articles to professional journals. Associate editor, *Psychological Reports*, 1961—; member of editorial board, *Behavior Therapy*, 1969-76; consulting editor, *Journal of Abnormal Psychology*, 1970-75.

WORK IN PROGRESS: Research on the socialization process and personality and on self control.

KANTAR, Edwin B(ruce) 1932-

PERSONAL: Born November 9, 1932, in Minneapolis, Minn.; son of Sigmund Saniel (a shoe salesman) and Alice (Brucker) Kantar; married Phyllis Morgenroth, 1967 (divorced, 1969). *Education:* University of Minnesota, B.A., 1955. *Religion:* Jewish. *Home:* 417 South Arnaz Dr., Los Angeles, Calif. 90048.

CAREER: Teacher of bridge, 1950—. Star of television show, "Master Bridge with Edwin Kantar."

WRITINGS: Introduction to Declarer's Play, Prentice-Hall, 1968; *Introduction to Defender's Play*, Prentice-Hall, 1968; *Bridge Bidding Made Easy*, Wilshire, 1972; *Bridge Conventions*, Wilshire, 1972; *Gamesman Bridge*, Liveright, 1972; *Defensive Bridge Play Complete*, Wilshire, 1975; *Bridge Humor*, Wilshire, 1977. Columnist, *Santa Monica Evening Outlook*, 1967-68. Contributor to *Bridge World*, *Popular Bridge*, *Bridge Bulletin*.

SIDELIGHTS: Edwin Kantar has won fifteen national bridge championships; he was the 1977 world bridge champion as well as a former table tennis champion. Several of his books have been translated into Spanish, Italian, and French.

*   *   *

KAPLAN, Fred 1937-

PERSONAL: Born November 4, 1937, in Bronx, N.Y.; son of Isaac (an attorney) and Bessie (Zwirn) Kaplan; married Gloria Taplin (a teacher), May 28, 1959; children: Benjamin, Noah, Julia. *Education:* Brooklyn College (now Brooklyn College of the City University of New York), B.A., 1959; Columbia University, M.A., 1961, Ph.D., 1966. *Home:* 42 Highland Place, Great Neck, N.Y. 11020. *Office:* Department of English, Queens College of the City University of New York, Flushing, N.Y. 11367.

CAREER: Lawrence University, Appleton, Wis., instructor in English, 1962-64; California State College (now University), Los Angeles, assistant professor of English, 1964-67; Queens College of the City University of New York, Flushing, N.Y., associate professor, 1967-71, professor of English, 1971—. Fulbright professor, University of Copenhagen, 1973-74. *Member:* Modern Language Association of America, Dickens Society, Tennyson Society. *Awards, honors:* City University of New York research grant, 1968-69, 1976-78; Guggenheim fellow, 1976-77.

WRITINGS: Miracles of Rare Device: The Poet's Sense of Self in Nineteenth-Century Poetry, Wayne State University Press, 1972; *The Hidden Springs of Fiction: Dickens and Mesmerism*, Princeton University Press, 1975. Contributor to *Media and Methods*, *Studies in English Literature*, *Nineteenth-Century Fiction*, *Victorian Poetry*, *Victorian Newsletter*, and *Journal of the History of Ideas*; contributor of poems and fiction to *New York Quarterly* and *Phoenix*.

WORK IN PROGRESS: Thomas Carlyle: A Centennial History.

*   *   *

KARSEN, Sonja (Petra) 1919-

PERSONAL: Born April 11, 1919, in Berlin, Germany; naturalized U.S. citizen, January 31, 1945; daughter of Fritz (a professor of education and author) and Erna H. F. (Heidermann) Karsen. *Education:* Ministerio de Educacion Nacional (Bogota), Titulo de Bachiller, 1937; Carleton College, B.A., 1939; Bryn Mawr College, M.A., 1941; Columbia

University, Ph.D., 1950. *Office:* Department of Modern Languages and Literatures, Skidmore College, Saratoga Springs, N.Y. 12866.

CAREER: Lake Erie College, Painesville, Ohio, instructor in Spanish, 1943-45; University of Puerto Rico, Rio Piedras, instructor in modern languages, 1945-46; Syracuse University, Syracuse, N.Y., instructor in Spanish, 1947-50; Brooklyn College (now Brooklyn College of the City University of New York), Brooklyn, N.Y., instructor in Spanish, 1950-51; UNESCO, Paris, France, personal assistant to deputy director-general, 1951-52, program officer in technical assistance department, 1952-53, member of technical assistance mission to Costa Rica, 1954; Sweet Briar College, Sweet Briar, Va., assistant professor of modern languages, 1955-57; Skidmore College, Saratoga Springs, N.Y., associate professor, 1957-61, professor of Spanish, 1961—, acting chairperson of department of Romance languages, 1957-58, chairperson, 1958-65, chairperson of department of modern languages and literatures, 1965—, director of Summer Language School, 1966-67. Fulbright lecturer, Free University of Berlin, 1968—. Liason officer, French Summer Language Institute, New York State Education Department, 1965. Fulbright-Hays awards, member of national screening committee, 1970, 1971, 1974, chairperson of American Republics area, 1971, 1974, member of planning committee for visiting scholars at State University of New York at Albany, 1976.

MEMBER: Instituto Internacional de Literature Iberoamericana, Asociacion Internacional de Hispanistas, Modern Language Association of America (member of delegate assembly, 1976-78), American Association of Teachers of Spanish and Portuguese, National Association of Self-Instructional Language Programs (treasurer, 1973-77), American Association of University Professors, American Association of University Women, United Nations Association, National Geographic Society, New England Council of Latin American Studies, New York State Association of Foreign Language Teachers (chairperson of standing committee on foreign language requirements and curriculum, 1969-73, co-chairperson, 1974; member of board of directors, 1972-73). *Awards, honors:* Buenos Aires convention grant, Bogota, Colombia, 1946-47; Skidmore College faculty research grants, 1959, 1961, 1963, 1964, 1967, 1969, 1970, and 1973; decorated Chevalier dans l'Ordre des Palmes Academiques, by French minister of national education, 1963; Leadership Award, New York State Association of Foreign Language Teachers, 1973.

WRITINGS: Guillermo Valencia: Colombian Poet, 1873-1943, Hispanic Institute in the United States, 1951; *Educational Development in Costa Rica with UNESCO's Technical Assistance: 1951-1954,* Ministerio de Educacion Publica (San Jose), 1954; *Jaime Torres Bodet: A Poet in a Changing World,* Skidmore College, 1963; (translator) *Selected Poems of Jaime Torres Bodet,* Indiana University Press, 1964; (editor) *Versos y prosas de Jaime Torres Bodet,* Ediciones Iberoamericanas (Madrid), 1966; *Jaime Torres Bodet,* Twayne, 1971. Also translator, Leopoldo Zea, *The Role of the Americas in History.* Contributor to *Encyclopedia of World Literature in the Twentieth Century;* contributor of over one hundred articles, reviews, and translations to *Brambler, World Literature Today, Antioch Review,* and Latin American studies journals. Member of editorial advisory board, *Modern Language Studies.*

WORK IN PROGRESS: Further research on Spanish-American literature and on Latin American culture.

KATZ, Daniel 1903-

PERSONAL: Born July 19, 1903, in Trenton, N.J.; son of Rudolph and Regina (Fleischer) Katz; married Christine Ross Braley, September 1, 1930; children: Joanna Braley, Jean Braley. *Education:* University of Buffalo (now State University of New York at Buffalo), B.A., 1925; Syracuse University, M.A., 1926, Ph.D., 1928. *Office:* Department of Psychology, University of Michigan, Ann Arbor, Mich. 48104.

CAREER: Princeton University, Princeton, N.J., instructor, 1928-31, assistant professor, 1931-40, associate professor of psychology, 1940-43; Brooklyn College (now Brooklyn College of the City University of New York), Brooklyn, N.Y., professor of psychology, and chairman of department, 1943-47; University of Michigan, Ann Arbor, professor of psychology, 1947-73, professor emeritus, 1973—, program director at Survey Research Center, 1947-50, research associate, 1950—. Visiting professor, Institute of Political Science, University of Aarhus, 1971-72; fellow, Center for Advanced Study in the Behavioral Sciences, 1960-61; member of Fulbright committee on international exchange of persons, 1950-53; member of American Council for Behavioral Sciences in Kibbutz Management and Social Research Center, 1969-71. Research director of Surveys Division, Office of War Information, 1943-44; senior analyst, U.S. Strategic Bombing Survey, War Department, 1945.

MEMBER: American Psychological Association (fellow; member of board of directors, 1960-63), Society for the Psychological Study of Social Issues (president, 1949-50), American Association of University Professors, Sigma Xi. *Awards, honors:* Fulbright fellowship, Norway, 1951-52; Social Science Research Council grant for Norwegian political studies, 1957-58; Kurt Lewin Memorial Award for integration of social research and social action, 1965; National Science Foundation fellowship, Greece and Yugoslavia, 1967-68; Gold Medal Award, American Psychological Foundation, 1973.

WRITINGS: (With Floyd Allport) *Students' Attitudes,* Craftsman Press, 1931; (contributor) L. L. Thurstone, editor, *The Measurement of Social Attitudes,* University of Chicago Press, 1931; (contributor) Edwin G. Boring, Herbert S. Langfeld and Harry P. Weld, editors, *Psychology: A Factual Textbook,* Wiley, 1935; (with Richard Schanck) *Social Psychology,* Wiley, 1938; (contributor) Boring, Langfeld, and Weld, editors, *Introduction to Psychology,* Wiley, 1939; (contributor) George Hartmann and Theodore Newcomb, editors, *Industrial Conflict: A Psychological Interpretation,* Gordon Co., 1939.

(Contributor) J. B. Botsford, editor, *Our Social World,* Delphian Society, 1940; (contributor) J. P. Guilford, editor, *Fields of Psychology,* Van Nostrand, 1940, 2nd edition, 1950; (contributor) Harwood Childs and John Whitton, editors, *Propaganda by Short Wave,* Princeton University Press, 1942; (contributor) Hadley Cantril, editor, *Gauging Public Opinion,* Princeton University Press, 1944; (contributor) Gardner Murphy, editor, *Human Nature and Enduring Peace,* Houghton, 1945; (contributor) Albert Blankenship, editor, *How to Conduct Consumer and Opinion Research,* Harper, 1946; (contributor) Theodore Newcomb and Eugene Hartley, editors, *Readings in Social Psychology,* Holt, 1947; (contributor) Wayne Dennis, editor, *Current Trends in Industrial Psychology,* University of Pittsburgh Press, 1949.

(Contributor) J. G. Miller, editor, *Experiments in Social*

Progress, University of Chicago Press, 1950; (with Nathan Maccoby and N. C. Morse) *Productivity, Supervision, and Morale in an Office Situation,* Survey Research Center, University of Michigan, 1950; (contributor) Harold Guetzkow, editor, *Groups, Leadership, and Men,* Carnegie Press Publishers, 1951; (contributor) Arthur Kornhauser, editor, *Industrial Productivity,* Industrial Relations Research Institute, 1951; (with Maccoby, Gerald Gurin, and Lucretia Floor) *Productivity, Supervision, and Morale among Railroad Workers,* Survey Research Center, University of Michigan, 1951; (contributor) G. E. Swanson, T. M. Newcomb, and E. L. Hartley, editors, *Readings in Social Psychology,* Holt, 1952; (editor with Leon Festinger, and contributor) *Research Methods in the Behavioral Sciences,* Dryden Press, 1953; (contributor) Dorwin Cartwright and Alvin Zander, editors, *Group Dynamics: Research and Theory,* Row, Peterson, 1953; (editor with Cartwright, S. Eldersveld, and A. McClung Lee) *Public Opinion and Propaganda,* Dryden Press, 1954; (contributor) Kornhauser, Robert Dubin, and Arthur M. Ross, editors, *Industrial Conflict,* McGraw, 1954; (contributor) Sigmund Koch, editor, *Psychology: A Study of a Science,* McGraw, 1959.

(Contributor) Sidney Malick and E. H. Van Ness, editors, *Concepts and Issues in Administrative Behavior,* Prentice-Hall, 1962; (with Henry Valen) *Political Parties in Norway,* Universitetsforlaget (Oslo), 1964; (contributor) E. B. McNeil, editor, *The Nature of Human Conflict,* Prentice-Hall, 1965; (contributor) H. C. Kelman, editor, *International Behavior,* Holt, 1965; (contributor) L. W. Kindred, editor, *Communications Research and School-Community Relations,* College of Education, Temple University, 1965; (with Robert Kahn) *The Social Psychology of Organizations,* Wiley, 1966, revised edition, 1978; (contributor) C. Y. Glock, editor, *Survey Research in the Social Sciences,* Russell Sage, 1967; (contributor) Lawrence C. Howard, editor, *Interinstitutional Cooperation in Higher Education,* Institute of Human Relations, University of Wisconsin, 1967; (contributor) Robert P. Abelson and others, editors, *Theories of Cognitive Consistency: A Sourcebook,* Rand McNally, 1968.

(With Robert Kuhn, Barbara Gutek, and Eugenia Barton) *Bureaucratic Encounters,* Institute of Social Research, University of Michigan, 1975.

Contributor to annals, proceedings, and to *Encyclopaedia Britannica* and *International Encyclopedia of the Social Sciences.* Contributor of about fifty articles to social science journals, including *Contemporary Psychology, Journal of Applied Behavioral Science, Peace Research Society Papers, Journal of Conflict Resolution, Organization and Administration,* and *Journal of Social Issues.* Former member of editorial board, *Human Relations, Journal of Social Issues, Public Opinion Quarterly, Personnel Psychology, Journal of Conflict Resolution,* and *Journal of Cross-Cultural Psychology;* editor, *Journal of Abnormal and Social Psychology,* 1962-64, and *Journal of Personality and Social Psychology,* 1964-67.

*   *   *

KAUFMAN, Bob   1925-
   (Bomkauf)

PERSONAL: Born April 18, 1925, in New Orleans, La.; married, June 23, 1958; wife's name, Eileen (a writer); children: Tony (daughter), Parker (son). *Education:* Attended public schools in New Orleans, La. *Religion:* Buddhist. *Residence:* San Francisco, Calif. *Agent:* Eileen Kaufman, 102 Mono, Fairfax, Calif. 94930.

CAREER: Poet; has worked as merchant seaman and has read poetry at Harvard University. *Awards, honors:* Nominated for Guinness Poetry Award, London, England, 1960-61.

WRITINGS: Does the Secret Mind Whisper, City Lights, 1959; *Second April,* City Lights, 1959; *Abomunist Manifesto,* City Lights, 1959; *Solitudes Crowded with Loneliness,* New Directions, 1965; *Golden Sardine,* City Lights, 1966; *Watch My Tracks,* Knopf, 1971. Work is represented in anthologies, including *City in All Directions,* edited by Arnold Adoff, Macmillan, 1969; *Mark in Time: Portraits and Poetry-San Francisco,* edited by Nick Harvey, Glide, 1971; *Making It New: American Poems and Songs,* edited by William M. Chace and Jo An E. Chace, Canfield, 1972. Founder with Allen Ginsberg, Bill Margolis, and John Kelley of *Beatitudes* (poetry magazine). Prepared the program "Coming from Bob Kaufman, Poet", which appeared on "Soul," a national hour-long broadcast by National Education Television, 1972, starring Ossie Davis and Ruby Dee.

SIDELIGHTS: Bob Kaufman's poems have been translated into German, French, Italian, Polish, Russian, Spanish, Arabic, and Danish.†

*   *   *

KAUFMAN, Jacob J(oseph)   1914-

PERSONAL: Born December 31, 1914, in New York, N.Y.; son of Frank E. (a businessman) and Sadie (Greenberg) Kaufman; married, wife's name, Thelma (a teacher), December 24, 1940; children: Frank E., Richard G. *Education:* Brooklyn College (now Brooklyn College of the City University of New York), A.B., 1934; Columbia University, M.S., 1935, Ph.D., 1952. *Home:* 534 Glenn Rd., State College, Pa. 16801. *Office:* 407 Graduate Bldg., Pennsylvania State University, University Park, Pa. 16802.

CAREER: U.S. Government, Washington, D.C., economist, 1936-47; University of Buffalo (now State University of New York at Buffalo), Buffalo, N.Y., assistant professor of economics, 1947-56; Pennsylvania State University, University Park, associate professor, 1956-58, professor of economics, 1958—, director of Institute for Research on Human Resources, 1964—. *Member:* American Economic Association, Industrial Relations Research Association, Operations Research Society of America, American Association for Higher Education.

WRITINGS: Collective Bargaining in the Railroad Industry, Columbia University Press, 1954; (with Carl J. Schaefer) *New Directions for Vocational Education,* Heath, 1971; (with Schaefer) *Vocational Education: Social and Behavioral Objectives,* Heath, 1971. Contributor to *Southern Economic Journal* and *Industrial and Labor Relations Review.*

WORK IN PROGRESS: Research in prison education and manpower.†

*   *   *

KAUFMANN, Henry William   1913-

PERSONAL: Born October 23, 1913, in Cambridge, Mass.; son of Otto (a salesman) and Mary (Korman) Kaufmann; married Helen Stewart Sanderson (a teacher), January 29, 1950. *Education:* Yale University, Mus.B., 1945, Mus.M., 1946; Harvard University, Ph.D., 1960. *Politics:* Democrat. *Home:* 3 Radio Court, Somerset, N.J. 08873. *Office:* Rutgers University, 25 Bishop Pl., New Brunswick, N.J. 08903.

CAREER: Rutgers University, New Brunswick, N.J., professor of music, 1964—, chairperson of department, 1964-73, director of Italian program, junior year abroad program, Florence, Italy, 1973-74. Episcopalian clergyman, St. Michael's Chapel, Piscataway, N.J., 1970, and Trinity Cathedral, Trenton, N.J., 1974—. *Member:* International Musicological Society, American Musicological Society, College Music Society (secretary, 1969-71), Renaissance Society, Medieval Society. *Awards, honors:* American Philosophical Society fellowship, 1969; certificate of merit from Yale School of Music Alumni Association, 1977, for distinguished contribution to the field of music.

WRITINGS: (Editor) *Nicola Vicentino Opera Omnia,* American Institute of Musicology, 1963; *The Life and Works of Nicola Vicentino,* American Institute of Musicology, 1966. Contributor to *Grove's Dictionary of Music and Musicians.* Contributor of articles and reviews to *Journal of the American Musicological Society* and *Musica Disciplina.*

WORK IN PROGRESS: Editio Medicaea, a study of the Medici edition of the chant in the early 17th century.

SIDELIGHTS: Henry Kaufmann has traveled in Italy and Germany, and speaks the languages of both countries.

* * *

KAUFMANN, U(rlin) Milo 1934-

PERSONAL: Born August 27, 1934, in Cleveland, Ohio; son of Albert Walter (a painter) and Wynona (Aiken) Kaufmann; married Helen Olson (a college teacher), September 1, 1956; children: Felice, Laurie, Andrew. *Education:* Greenville College, B.A., 1956; University of Illinois, M.A., 1957; Yale University, Ph.D., 1960. *Politics:* Democrat. *Religion:* Free Methodist. *Address:* Route 2, Urbana, Ill., 61801. *Office:* 100 English Building, University of Illinois, Urbana, Ill. 61801.

CAREER: Greenville College, Greenville, Ill., assistant professor of English, summer, 1961; North Park College, Chicago, Ill., instructor in English, 1961-62; University of Illinois at Urbana-Champaign, instructor, 1962-63, assistant professor, 1963-67, associate professor of English, 1967—. Member of board of directors, College of Christian Studies. *Member:* Conference on Christianity and Literature (member of board of directors, 1967-70).

WRITINGS: The Pilgrim's Progress and Traditions in Puritan Meditation, Yale University Press, 1966; *Paradise in the Age of Milton,* University of Victoria Press, 1978.

WORK IN PROGRESS: Far Other Worlds: Imaginative Literature and the Christian Hope, completion expected in 1981; a collection of poems, *Breaking the Light Barrier.*

* * *

KAY, Paul 1934-

PERSONAL: Born November 7, 1934, in New York, N.Y.; son of William de Young and Alice Sarah (Odenheimer) Kay; married Patricia Ann Boehm (a psychiatric social worker), August 15, 1956; children: Yvette, Suzanne. *Education:* Tulane University, B.A., 1955; Harvard University, Ph.D., 1962. *Residence:* Berkeley, Calif. *Office:* Department of Anthropology, University of California, Berkeley, Calif. 94720.

CAREER: Massachusetts Institute of Technology, Cambridge, assistant professor of political science, 1964-65; University of California, Berkeley, associate professor, 1966-69, professor of anthropology, 1970—. *Military service:* U.S. Army, 1958. *Member:* American Anthropological Associa-

tion, Linguistic Society of America, Phi Beta Kappa. *Awards, honors:* Center for Advanced Study in the Behavioral Sciences fellow, 1956; Guggenheim fellow, 1972-73.

WRITINGS: (With Brent Berlin) *Basic Color Terms: Their Universality and Evolution,* University of California Press, 1969; (editor) *Explorations in Mathematical Anthropology,* Massachusetts Institute of Technology, 1970. Contributor to *American Anthropologist, Language, Journal of the Polynesian Society, Southwestern Journal of Anthropology, Current Anthropology, Bulletin of the American Anthropological Association,* and other journals.

* * *

KEBSCHULL, Harvey G(ustav) 1932-

PERSONAL: Born April 9, 1932, in Eagle, Neb.; son of Gustav O. (a clergyman) and Estelle (Eicksteadt) Kebschull; married Georgia M. Grube, August 7, 1960; children: Susan Kim, Sharon Lynn. *Education:* University of Nebraska, B.A., 1955, M.A., 1956; University of Illinois, Ph.D., 1962. *Politics:* Democrat. *Religion:* Lutheran. *Home:* 1108 Bancroft Dr., Raleigh, N.C. 27612. *Office:* Department of Political Science, North Carolina State University, Raleigh, N.C.

CAREER: University of Montana, Missoula, assistant professor of politics, 1962-66; Vanderbilt University, Nashville, Tenn., visiting assistant professor, 1966-67; North Carolina State University at Raleigh, associate professor of politics, 1967—. *Military service:* U.S. Army, 1956-58. *Member:* International Studies Association, Southern Political Science Association, North Carolina Political Science Association.

WRITINGS: (Editor) *Politics in Transitional Societies,* Appleton, 1968, 2nd edition, 1973.

WORK IN PROGRESS: Politics of Military Regimes; The European Community.

AVOCATIONAL INTERESTS: Classical music, building exact-scale model railroad trains and equipment.

* * *

KEENEY, William (Echard) 1922-

PERSONAL: Born July 17, 1922, in Fayette County, Pa.; son of William Leroy (a coal miner and insurance agent) and Kathryn Olive (Echard) Keeney; married Willadene Hartzler, October 12, 1947; children: Lois Ruth, Carol Louise, William Leroy, Richard Lowell. *Education:* Attended Bethel College, 1947 (summer); Bluffton College, A.B., 1948; graduate study at Garrett Biblical Institute, 1951; Mennonite and Bethany Biblical Seminaries, B.D., 1953; Hartford Theological Seminary, S.T.M., 1957, Ph.D., 1959. *Home address:* P.O. Box 277, North Newton, Kan. 67117. *Office:* Bethel College, North Newton, Kan. 67117.

CAREER: National Mental Health Foundation, Philadelphia, Pa., community associate, 1946, acting director of Education Division, 1947; Mennonite Central Committee, Akron, Pa., relief worker in Germany, 1948-49, director in Netherlands, 1949-50; Bluffton College, Bluffton, Ohio, instructor, 1953-56, assistant professor, 1958-59, associate professor, 1959-65, professor of Bible, 1965-68, assistant to president, 1953-56; Bethel College, North Newton, Kan., professor of Bible and religion, 1968—, academic dean, 1968-72, provost, 1972-73, director of experimental learning, 1974-78, director of continuing education, 1975—. Executive director, Consortium on Peace Research, Education, and Development (COPRED), 1978—. *Member:* American Society of Church History, Kansas Association of Academic

Deans (chairman, 1971-72), Mennonite Central Committee (chairman of peace section, 1973), Kiwanis.

WRITINGS: (Contributor) Cornelius J. Dyck, editor, *A Legacy of Faith*, Faith & Life, 1962; (contributor) Dyck, editor, *An Introduction to Mennonite History*, Herald Press, 1967; *The Development of Dutch Anabaptist Thought and Practice from 1539-1564*, B. de Graaf, 1968; *Lordship as Servanthood: Thirteen Lessons on the Biblical Basis for Peacemaking*, Faith & Life, 1975, 2nd edition, 1977; (contributor) *Non-Traditional Study: Threat, Promise, or Necessity*, Drake University, 1975. Contributor to reports of general conferences. Contributor of more than fifty articles, reviews, and translations to church publications in the United States and abroad, including *Mennonite Life, Mennonite Quarterly Review, Mennonite, Mennonite Weekly Review, Canadian Mennonite*, and *Mennonite Historical Bulletin*.

WORK IN PROGRESS: Research on Dutch Anabaptism in the sixteenth century; continuing peace activities.

SIDELIGHTS: William Keeney traveled in Greece, Italy, Czechoslovakia, England, Vietnam, Japan, Thailand, and Israel. *Lordship as Servanthood* has been translated into Spanish and Hindi.

* * *

KEITH-SPIEGEL, Patricia 1939-

PERSONAL: Born March 16, 1939, in Glendale, Calif.; daughter of Boyd E. (a horticulturist) and Barbara (a teacher; maiden name, Halsey) Keith; married Don Spiegel (a psychologist), June 17, 1966; children: Gary Brian. *Education:* Occidental College, B.A., 1961; Claremont Graduate School, M.A., 1964, Ph.D., 1968. *Office:* Department of Psychology, California State University, Northridge, Calif. 91324.

CAREER: California State University, Northridge, assistant professor, 1966-69, associate professor, 1969-73, professor of psychology, 1973—. Member of San Fernando Valley Fair Housing Council. Free-lance civic and industrial consultant. *Member:* American Psychological Association, American Association for the Advancement of Science, Association for Women Psychologists, National Council on Graduate Education in Psychology, National Organization for Women, Western Psychological Association, California State Psychological Association, San Fernando Valley Psychological Association, Los Angeles County Psychological Association (member of board of directors, 1971-75), University of California at Los Angeles Medical School Auxiliary, Psi Chi. *Awards, honors:* National Institute of Mental Health grants, 1969-72; research award from Los Angeles County Psychological Association, 1972.

WRITINGS: (Contributor) J. Goldstein and P. McGhee, editors, *Psychology of Humor*, Academic Press, 1972; (editor with husband, Don Spiegel, and contributor) *Outsiders U.S.A.*, Holt, 1973; (contributor) Benjamin Wolman, editor, *Handbook of Psychology*, Prentice-Hall, 1973. Contributor of about forty articles to psychology journals.

WORK IN PROGRESS: *New Directions in Raising Female Children; The Ugly American Standards of Beauty*; research on sense of humor and correlated personality characteristics.

AVOCATIONAL INTERESTS: Glass sculpting, painting and drawing, wood-work, tie-dying, piano and guitar, reading and writing poetry, public speaking.†

KELLER, W(alter) D(avid) 1900-

PERSONAL: Born March 13, 1900, in Kansas City, Mo.; son of Theodore (a farmer) and Mary (Schulz) Keller; married Madge Jones, December, 1936 (deceased); children: David, Dwight. *Education:* University of Missouri, A.B., 1925, Ph.D., 1933; University of Missouri School of Mines and Metallurgy (now University of Missouri—Rolla), B.S., 1930; Harvard University, A.M., 1932. *Religion:* United Church of Christ. *Home:* 403 West Stewart Rd., Columbia, Mo. 65201. *Office:* 305 Geology Bldg., University of Missouri, Columbia, Mo. 65201.

CAREER: University of Missouri—Columbia, instructor, 1926-29, assistant professor, 1932-36, associate professor, 1936-42, professor of geology, 1942-70, professor emeritus, 1970—, head of department, 1941-45. Lecturer at U.S. Army University, Florence, Italy, 1945, and at American Geological Institute, 1959-60; professor of geology, University of South Florida, 1970-73; adjunct professor of geology, Texas Tech University, 1978. Distinguished lecturer, American Association of Petroleum Geologists. *Military service:* U.S. Army, 1918. *Member:* Association Internationale pour l'-Etude des Argiles, Geological Society of America (fellow), Clay Minerals Society (distinguished member), American Association of Petroleum Geologists, American Association for the Advancement of Science (fellow), Mineralogical Society of America (fellow), American Ceramic Society, British Mineral Society, American Institute of Mining and Metallurgical Engineers, Society of Economic Paleontologists and Mineralogists, American Geophysics Union, Phi Beta Kappa, Sigma Xi, Alpha Chi Sigma, Sigma Gamma Epsilon, Gamma Alpha. *Awards, honors:* Neil Miner Award from National Association of Geology Teachers, 1967; Faculty-Alumni Award, 1968, and Distinguished Faculty Member, 1969, from University of Missouri; citation from Missouri House of Representatives, 1970.

WRITINGS: *Common Rocks and Minerals of Missouri*, University of Missouri Press, 1948, revised edition, 1962; (with E. B. Branson and W. A. Tarr) *Introduction to Geology*, McGraw, 1952; *Principles of Chemical Weathering*, Lucas Brothers, 1967; *Chemistry in Introductory Geology*, Lucas Brothers, 1969. Contributor of 150 articles to journals.

WORK IN PROGRESS: Scanning election micrography of kaolin, bauxite, and chertl-1 novaculite.

* * *

KELLOGG, Alfred Latimer 1915-

PERSONAL: Born April 24, 1915, in Cleveland, Ohio; son of Alfred N. and Clara (Beck) Kellogg; married Ellen Cushman, June 7, 1941; children: Marion (Mrs. Lawrence L. Fisher), Alfred C. *Education:* Western Reserve University (now Case Western Reserve University), A.B., 1937; Yale University, Ph.D., 1941. *Home:* 224 Lawrence Ave., Highland Park, N.J. 08904. *Office:* Department of English, Rutgers University, New Brunswick, N.J. 08903.

CAREER: Yale University, New Haven, Conn., instructor in English, 1941-42, 1945-47; Cornell University, Ithaca, N.Y., instructor in English, 1942; Rutgers University, New Brunswick, N.J., assistant professor, 1947-51, associate professor, 1951-61, professor of English, 1961—. *Member:* Modern Language Association of America, Mediaeval Academy of America, Dante Society of America, Societe Internationale Arthurienne, Phi Beta Kappa. *Awards, honors:* Ford fellowship, 1951; Guggenheim fellowship,

1953; American Philosophical Society summer fellowship, 1965.

WRITINGS: Chaucer, Langland, Arthur, Rutgers University Press, 1972.

WORK IN PROGRESS: A book or books on Chaucer's *Troilus and Criseyde* and *Sir Gawain and the Green Knight.*

* * *

KELLY, Leo J. 1925-

PERSONAL: Born September 12, 1925, in Cambridge, Neb.; son of L. J. (a rancher) and Lillian Helen (Alcorn) Kelly; married Bonnie Ruth Brown, March 12, 1950; children: Rayann, Ava Jo, Stacey Sue, Lynn Rene. *Education:* Nebraska State Teachers College (now Chadron State College), B.S., 1950; University of Northern Colorado, M.A., 1951, Ed.D., 1960; Chico State College (now California State University, Chico), graduate study, 1954. *Politics:* Independent. *Religion:* Episcopalian. *Home address:* Route 8, Box 31, Lot 32, Valdosta, Ga. 31601. *Office:* Department of Special Education, Valdosta State College, Valdosta, Ga. 31601.

CAREER: Superintendent of Holstein Public Schools, Holstein, Neb., 1950-52, Eustis Public Schools, Eustis, Neb., 1952-55, and Axtell Community Schools, Axtell, Neb., 1955-60; Center of the Handicapped, Greeley, Colo., principal and teacher, 1959-60; Colorado State College (now University of Northern Colorado), Greeley, assistant professor of special education, 1960-65; Memphis State University, Memphis, Tenn., professor of special education and chairman of the department, 1965-69; Valdosta State College, Valdosta, Ga., Callaway Professor of Special Education, 1969—. Associate professor, Child Development Center, University of Tennessee Medical School, 1967-69; review panel member and field reader for the Bureau for the Education of the Handicapped, U.S. Office of Education, 1967—; advisor and executive board member, Work Activity Center for the Mentally Retarded, Valdosta, 1969—; chairman, Southwest Georgia Regional Mental Health and Mental Retardation Advisory Council, 1976—; program associate, Educational Resources Center and *Education Unlimited,* 1978—. *Military service:* U.S. Navy, 1943-46; served in Pacific; received Navy Unit Commendation, CVE Certificate of Commendation.

MEMBER: Council for Exceptional Children (life member; member of national governing board), National Education Association (life member), Georgia Association of Educators, Georgia Council for Administrators of Special Education (treasurer), Valdosta State College Association of Educators (president, 1972-73), Lowndes Association for Retarded Children, Phi Delta Kappa. *Awards, honors:* Memphis State University, Certificate of Merit, 1968; Georgia Association for the Mentally Retarded, Certificate of Award, 1971; South Georgia Council for Exceptional Children award, 1978, for developing outstanding special education programs.

WRITINGS: Dictionary of Exceptional Children, MSS Information Corp., 1971; *Sex through Affection,* Dorrance, 1976; (with Glen Vergason) *A Dictionary of Special Education and Rehabilitation,* Love Publishing, 1978. Contributor to *Exceptional Children, Pointer, TED Newsletter.*

AVOCATIONAL INTERESTS: Antiques, antique furniture restoration, reading, and gardening.

KELLY, Richard J(ohn) 1938-

PERSONAL: Born September 30, 1938, in Minneapolis, Minn.; son of James William Kelly (a salesman) and Constance (Flemming) Kelly Livermore; married Lois Saba (a secretary), May 30, 1957; children: Deborah. *Education:* University of Minnesota, B.A., 1966, M.A., 1968. *Home:* 1033 16th Ave. S.E., Minneapolis, Minn. 55414. *Office:* Library, University of Minnesota, Minneapolis, Minn. 55455.

CAREER: Minneapolis Star & Tribune, Minneapolis, Minn., clerk, 1958-68; University of Minnesota, Minneapolis, assistant professor and librarian, 1968—.

WRITINGS: John Berryman: A Checklist, Scarecrow, 1972. Also editor, with George E. Bogusch, of *Theatre Arts Library Resources: A Guide to Basic Materials in the University of Minnesota Libraries,* 1973. Contributor to *Minneapolis Sunday Tribune, Library Journal,* and *American Reference Books.* Contributing editor, *John Berryman Studies,* 1975-78.

SIDELIGHTS: Richard J. Kelly told *CA:* "My interest in Berryman dates back to my student days when, for a time, I was lucky enough to sit in his classes two or three times a week. Among my favorite writers are Ernest Hemingway, Graham Greene, Isak Dinesen, Joseph Conrad, Stephen Crane, and Edmund Wilson." *Avocational interests:* Libraries and bookstores, films, theater, travel, French Impressionists, long walks, fishing.

* * *

KENDRICK, Frank J(enness) 1928-

PERSONAL: Born October 18, 1928, in Fort Wayne, Ind.; son of Frank J. (a physician) and Dorothy (Gray) Kendrick; married Betty Grant, March 17, 1956; children: Ellen, Elizabeth, Grant, Emily. *Education:* Grinnell College, B.A., 1950; University of Chicago, M.A., 1956, Ph.D., 1962. *Politics:* Democrat. *Religion:* Protestant. *Home:* 2072 Braewick Dr., Akron, Ohio 44313. *Office:* Department of Political Science, University of Akron, Akron, Ohio 44325.

CAREER: Wofford College, Spartanburg, S.C., assistant professor of government, 1958-60; University of Evansville, Evansville, Ind., visiting instructor in political science, 1961-62; Drury College, Springfield, Mo., assistant professor of political science, 1962-63; Moorhead State College, Moorhead, Minn., associate professor of political science, 1963-69, chairman of department, 1965-67; Drury College, associate professor of political science and chairman of department, 1969-71; University of Akron, Akron, Ohio, associate professor of urban studies and political science, 1971—. *Military service:* U.S. Army, 1951-53; served in Korea. *Member:* American Political Science Association, American Association of University Professors, Southwestern Political Science Association, Southern Political Science Association.

WRITINGS: (Contributor) William O. Peterfi, editor, *The Prospects for Peace for the 1970's: Issues and Answers,* Minnesota World Affairs Center, 1970; (editor with James A. Burkhart) *The New Politics: Mood or Movement?,* Prentice-Hall, 1971; (with Burkhart, James Eisenstein, and Theodore Fleming) *Strategies for Political Participation,* Winthrop, 1972. Contributor to political science journals.

WORK IN PROGRESS: Editing *The Rule of the Majority: Rhetoric and Reality.*

KENNEBECK, Edwin 1924-

PERSONAL: Born 1924, in Denver, Colo. *Education:* Marquette University, B.A., 1948, M.A., 1951. *Office:* Viking Press, 625 Madison Ave., New York, N.Y. 10022.

CAREER: Viking Press, New York, N.Y., copy editor, 1955-71, editor, 1971—. *Military service:* U.S. Army Air Forces, 1942-45; became technical sergeant; received six air medals.

WRITINGS: Juror Number Four: The Trial of Thirteen Black Panthers as Seen from the Jury Box, Norton, 1973; (contributor) Rita James Simon, editor, *The Jury System in America*, Sage Publications, 1976. Contributor of articles and reviews to *Village Voice, Nation, Commonweal*, and *Semicolon.*

WORK IN PROGRESS: "An unserious novel"; two plays.

AVOCATIONAL INTERESTS: Movies, theatre, ballet, recordings by Billie Holiday, Duke Ellington, Mildred Bailey, Lee Wiley, and other jazz figures.

* * *

KENNEDY, Judith M(ary) 1935-

PERSONAL: Born April 17, 1935, in Kasauli, India; daughter of Lionel Roscoe and Norah (Cullum) Grundy; married Richard F. Kennedy (a professor of English), March 31, 1959; children: Robert Peter, James Edmund, Elizabeth Mary. *Education:* Somerville College, Oxford, B.A., 1957, M.A., 1961, B.Litt., 1965. *Religion:* Roman Catholic. *Residence:* Tracyville, New Brunswick, Canada E0G 3C0. *Office:* Department of English, St. Thomas University, Fredericton, New Brunswick, Canada.

CAREER: Goucher College, Baltimore, Md., instructor in English, 1957-58; St. Thomas More College, Saskatoon, Saskatchewan, lecturer in English, 1960-66; St. Thomas University, Fredericton, New Brunswick, associate professor, 1966-71, professor of English, 1971—. *Member:* Modern Language Association of America, Renaissance Society of America, Association of Canadian University Teachers of English, Spencer Society.

WRITINGS: (Editor) *A Critical Edition of Yong's Translation of George of Montemayer's 'Diana,' and Gil Polo's 'Enamoured Diana,'* Clarendon Press, 1968; (editor with James A. Reither) *A Theatre for Spenserians*, University of Toronto Press, 1973.

WORK IN PROGRESS: An edition of Barnabe Googe; research on Renaissance women, recusant literature, Chaucer, Shakespeare, and Spenser.

* * *

KENNY, Herbert Andrew 1912-

PERSONAL: Born December 22, 1912, in Boston, Mass.; son of Herbert A. (a lawyer) and Mary (Conroy) Kenny; married Teresa E. Flaherty (a social worker), September, 1939; children: Ann Gonzalez, Herbert A., Jr., Susan Kenny Carroll. *Education:* Boston College, A.B., 1934. *Politics:* Democrat. *Religion:* Roman Catholic. *Home:* 804 Summer St., Manchester, Mass. 01944. *Agent:* Collins-Knowlton-Wing, Inc., 60 East 56th St., New York, N.Y. 10022. *Office address:* Box 1472, Manchester, Mass. 01944.

CAREER: Worked as an arts editor, 1958-65; *Boston Globe*, Boston, Mass., book editor, 1965-75. Editor, X Press, Manchester, Mass. *Member:* Poetry Society of America. *Awards, honors:* Robert Frost fellow, Breadloaf Writers Conference, 1956.

WRITINGS: A Catholic Quiz Book, Macmillan, 1947; *Sonnets to the Virgin Mary,* Advance Publishing, 1956; *Dear Dolphin* (juvenile), Pantheon, 1962; *Alistare Owl* (juvenile), Harper, 1964; *Twelve Birds* (poems), University of Massachusetts Press, 1964; *Suburban Man* (poems), Monastine Press, 1965; *Cape Ann: Cape America,* Lippincott, 1968; *A Literary History of Dublin,* Taplinger, 1974; (with Barbara Westman) *A Boston Picture Book,* Houghton, 1974; *The Secret of the Rocks: The Boris Photographs,* X Press, 1978. Contributor to *Catholic Encyclopedia.* Editor, *National Book Critics Journal,* 1977—.

BIOGRAPHICAL/CRITICAL SOURCES: New York Times Book Review, November 5, 1967, January 4, 1970; *Commonweal,* November 10, 1967.

* * *

KENSHALO, Daniel R(alph) 1922-

PERSONAL: Born July 27, 1922, in West Frankfort, Ill.; son of Daniel Ralph and Edith C. (Shroeder) Kenshalo; married Janice Gordon, August 28, 1970; children: Daniel Ralph, Jr., Rebecca. *Education:* Washington University, St. Louis, Mo., B.A., 1947, Ph.D., 1953. *Politics:* Democratic Party. *Religion:* Christian Church. *Home:* 2414 Delgado, Tallahassee, Fla. 32304. *Office:* Department of Psychology, Florida State University, Tallahassee, Fla. 32306.

CAREER: Washington University, St. Louis, Mo., part-time instructor in psychology, 1948-49; Florida State University, Tallahassee, assistant professor, 1950-55, associate professor, 1955-59, professor of experimental psychology, 1959—. *Military service:* U.S. Naval Reserve, active duty, 1943-46; retired as commander. *Member:* American Physiological Society, American Psychological Association (fellow), American Association for the Advancement of Science, Psychonomic Society, New York Academy of Sciences, Southern Society of Philosophy and Psychology (secretary, 1959-62; president, 1963), Eastern Psychological Society, Florida Psychological Association, Sigma Xi, Psi Chi.

WRITINGS: (Editor) *The Skin Senses,* C. C Thomas, 1968.

Contributor: W. D. Neff, editor, *Contributions to Sensory Physiology,* Volume IV, Academic Press, 1970; J. D. Hardy, editor, *Physiological and Behavioral Temperature Regulation,* C. C Thomas, 1970; J. W. Kling and L. A. Riggs, editors, *Experimental Psychology,* Holt, 1971; R. N. Dubner and Y. Kawamura, editors, *Orial-Facial Sensory and Motor Mechanisms,* Appleton-Century-Croft, 1971; *Pain,* Georg Thieme Verlag, 1972; H. H. Kornhuber, editor, *The Somatosensory Systems,* Georg Thieme Verlag, 1975; Y. Zotterman, *Sensory Functions of the Skin,* Pergamon, 1976; A. Iggo and O. B. Illyinsky, editors, *Progress in Brain Research,* Volume XLIII: *Somatosensory and Visceral Receptor Mechanisms,* Elsevier, 1976; J. E. Birren and K. W. Schaie, editors, *Handbook of the Psychology of Aging,* Van Nostrand, 1977.

WORK IN PROGRESS: Contributing to *Biology of Special Senses in Aging,* edited by N. J. Moncrieff; *Sensory Systems and Aging in Man,* edited by J. M. Ordy; and *Handbook of Perception.*

* * *

KEPHART, William M. 1921-

PERSONAL: Born March 30, 1921, in Margate, N.J.; son of William J. (a salesman) and Reba (Criswell) Kephart; married Ann Kulousek, December 5, 1947; children: Janis.

Education: Franklin and Marshall College, A.B., 1941; University of Pennsylvania, M.A., 1948, Ph.D., 1950. *Home:* 111 South Thurlow, Margate, N.J. *Office:* Department of Sociology, University of Pennsylvania, Philadelphia, Pa. 19104.

CAREER: University of Pennsylvania, Philadelphia, assistant professor, 1952-56, associate professor, 1957-63, professor of sociology, 1964—. *Military service:* U.S. Army, 1941-46; became first lieutenant. *Member:* American Sociological Association, National Council of Family Relations, Pennsylvania Sociological Society (president, 1965-67), Phi Beta Kappa, Phi Gamma Mu.

WRITINGS: Family, Society and the Individual, Houghton, 1961, 4th edition, 1977; *Nursing Dynamics,* Pennsylvania Nurses Association, 1962; *Racial Factors and Law Enforcement,* University of Pennsylvania Press, 1965; *Liberal Education and Business,* Columbia University Press, 1968; *Extraordinary Groups,* St. Martin's, 1977.

One-act plays: *All-American Ape,* Samuel French, 1941; *Service Club,* Samuel French, 1942.

* * *

KERBY, Robert L(ee) 1934-

PERSONAL: Born June 26, 1934, in New York, N.Y.; son of Robert Lee (a realtor) and Sarah (Skehan) Kerby; married Mary Rose Corbett, June 7, 1957; children: Robert L., James S. *Education:* University of Notre Dame, B.A., 1955, M.A., 1956; Columbia University, Ph.D., 1969. *Politics:* Democrat. *Home:* 918 Simon Court, South Bend, Ind. 46615. *Office:* Department of History, University of Notre Dame, 347 O'Shaughnessy Hall, Notre Dame, Ind. 46556.

CAREER: Pilot in U.S. Air Force, 1956-63, became captain; Columbia University, New York, N.Y., assistant professor of history, 1966-72; University of Notre Dame, Notre Dame, Ind., assistant professor, 1972-75, associate professor of history, 1975—, director of graduate studies, 1976—. Priest of the Byzantine-Melkite Rite of the Roman Catholic Church, 1970—; parish priest of St. Ann's Parish, Paterson, N.J., 1970-72; administrator of St. John of Damascus Mission, 1978—. *Member:* Organization of American Historians.

WRITINGS: The Confederate Invasion of New Mexico and Arizona, Westernlore, 1958; *Kirby Smith's Confederacy: The Trans-Mississippi South, 1863-1865,* Columbia University Press, 1972. Contributor to history journals.

SIDELIGHTS: Robert L. Kerby has visited more than thirty-six countries, including prolonged periods of residence in Japan, France, and Viet Nam. He has reading ability in German, French, Dutch, Greek, and Latin.

* * *

KERSNOWSKI, Frank L. 1934-

PERSONAL: Born May 6, 1934; divorced; children: Maud Louise. *Education:* University of Tennessee, B.A., 1957, M.A., 1959; University of Kansas, Ph.D., 1963. *Politics:* "Vague." *Religion:* "Simple." *Home:* 522 West Lynwood, San Antonio, Tex. 78212. *Office:* Department of English, Trinity University, 715 Stadium, San Antonio, Tex. 78212.

CAREER: Trinity University, San Antonio, Tex., assistant professor, 1964-67, associate professor, 1967-74, professor of English, 1974—. *Member:* American Association of University Professors, American Committee for Irish Studies, South Central Modern Language Association. *Awards,*

honors: National Foundation for the Arts and Humanities research grant, 1968.

WRITINGS: To Adam (poems), Sisterdale, 1972; *John Montague,* Bucknell University Press, 1975; *The Outsiders: Poets of Contemporary Ireland,* Texas Christian University Press, 1975; (with C. W. Spinks and Laird Loomis) *A Bibliography of Modern Irish and Anglo-Irish Literature,* Trinity University Press, 1976.

WORK IN PROGRESS: Looking at Sound: Visual Poetry Inside/Outside.

* * *

KESTERSON, David B(ert) 1938-

PERSONAL: Born February 19, 1938, in Springfield, Mo.; son of Homer R. (a college administrator) and Dorothy (Mace) Kesterson; married Linda Marie Houston, April 12, 1963; children: A. Todd, Chad Russell. *Education:* Southwest Missouri State University, B.S.E. (cum laude), 1959; University of Arkansas, M.A., 1960, Ph.D., 1964. *Home:* 2719 Hartlee Ct., Denton, Tex. 76201. *Office:* Department of English, North Texas State University, Denton, Tex. 76203.

CAREER: North Carolina State University at Raleigh, assistant professor of English, 1964-68; North Texas State University, Denton, associate professor, 1969-74, professor of English, 1974—. *Military service:* U.S. Army Reserve, 1956-60. *Member:* Modern Language Association of America, College Conference of Teachers of English, Society for Study of Southern Literature, Nathaniel Hawthorne Society (co-founder; president, 1974-76), Melville Society, Poe Studies Association, South Atlantic Modern Language Association, South Central Modern Language Association, Southwestern American Literature Association.

WRITINGS: Studies in "The Marble Faun," C. E. Merrill, 1971; *Critics on Mark Twain,* University of Miami Press, 1973; *Critics on Poe,* University of Miami Press, 1973; *Josh Billings,* G. K. Hall, 1973; *Bill Nye: The Western Writings,* [Boise, Idaho], 1976. Contributor to journals, including *English Language Notes, Texas Studies in Literature and Language, Emerson Society Quarterly, Illinois Quarterly, Dickinson Review, South-Central Bulletin,* and *Studies in Short Fiction.* Associate editor, *Studies in the Novel,* 1969—, and *Nathaniel Hawthorne Journal,* 1978—; managing editor, *Southwestern American Literature,* 1970-72; editor, *Nathaniel Hawthorne Society Newsletter,* 1974—.

WORK IN PROGRESS: Bill Nye; The Hawthorne Handbook.

* * *

KESTERTON, Wilfred (Harold) 1914-

PERSONAL: Born July 22, 1914, in Regina, Saskatchewan, Canada; son of Ernest Harold and Eva (Hughes) Kesterton. *Education:* Queen's University, Kingston, Ontario, B.A., 1942; Carleton University, B.J., 1949. *Home:* 315 Holmwood Ave., Apt. 802, Ottawa, Ontario, Canada K1S 5B6. *Office:* Department of Journalism, Carleton University, Colonel By Dr., Ottawa, Ontario, Canada K1S 5B6.

CAREER: Carleton University, Ottawa, Ontario, lecturer, 1949-54, assistant professor, 1954-62, associate professor, 1962-69, professor of journalism, 1969—. *Military service:* Canadian Army, 1942-47; became captain. *Member:* Canadian Association of University Teachers. *Awards, honors:* Coronation Medal, 1953; Humanities Research Council grant, 1953.

WRITINGS: A History of Journalism in Canada, McClelland & Stewart, 1967; (editor with Lucien Brault, Jean-Louis Gagnon, D. C. McArthur, Frank Underhill, and Christopher Young) *A Century of Reporting: Un Siecle de Reportage,* Clarke, Irwin, 1967; *The Law and the Press in Canada,* McClelland & Stewart, 1976. Contributor to *Canadian Annual Review.*

* * *

KHAN, Zillur Rahman 1938-

PERSONAL: Born November 21, 1938, in Hoogly, West Bengal; son of Abdur Rahman (an educator) and Khadija Khatun (Choudhury) Khan; married Margaret Carol Noe, April 3, 1966; children: Tamiz, Kabir, Mary. *Education:* Dacca University, B.A. (honors), 1957, M.A., 1958, LL.B., 1959; Claremont Graduate School, M.A., 1965, Ph.D., 1967. *Office:* Department of Political Science, University of Wisconsin, Oshkosh, Wis. 54901.

CAREER: Dacca College, Dacca, Bangladesh, lecturer in political science, 1960-63; cantonment executive officer and magistrate of Jessore, Bangladesh, 1963-64; Sonoma State College (now California State College), Sonoma, Calif., assistant professor of anthropology, 1966-67; Dacca University, Dacca, associate professor of political science, 1969-71; University of Wisconsin—Oshkosh, assistant professor, 1967-69, 1971-72, associate professor of political science, 1973—. Director of the Bangladesh Foundation of the United States, 1973—. *Member:* American Political Science Association, American Society of Public Administration, Association of Muslim Social Scientists (chairman of political science group). *Awards, honors:* Fulbright fellowship, 1964-65; Asian Studies Award, 1965-66; Danforth Foundation award, 1966-67; National Science Foundation grant, 1967.

WRITINGS: (With A. T. R. Rahman) *Autonomy and Constitution Making: The Case for Bangladesh,* Green Book House, 1973. Contributor to *Western Political Quarterly, Indian Journal of Political Science, Canadian Review of Sociology and Anthropology, Pacific Affairs, Asian Affairs, Asian Forum,* and *Third World Review.* Member, editorial board, International Documentation Center, 1972—.

WORK IN PROGRESS: A Political History of Bangladesh; Bureaucracy in Bangladesh.

* * *

KIDDER, Barbara (Ann) 1933-

PERSONAL: Born January 29, 1933, in Minneapolis, Minn.; daughter of Ivan Link (a commercial artist) and Hazel (Muller) Kauffman; married M. Worden Kidder (a coordinator of health and physical education), September 3, 1953; children: Daniel, Dean, Kenneth. *Education:* Attended Augsburg College, 1950-51; Art Instruction, Inc., correspondence course diploma, 1956. *Religion:* Church of the Nazarene. *Home:* 15919 Tonkawood Dr., Minnetonka, Minn. 55343.

CAREER: Writer for children.

WRITINGS—All self-illustrated: (With Loraine Muller) *Little Sardine,* Denison, 1961; (with Muller) *The Brownie and the Green Elf,* Denison, 1961; *Mr. Wonderful,* Denison, 1964; (with husband, M. Worden Kidder) *Mr. Mighty,* Denison, 1964; *The Broken Vase,* Augsburg, 1964; *Juan and the Chameleon,* Augsburg, 1964; *The Red Bicycle,* Augsburg, 1964; *Little Corpuscle,* Denison, 1965; *Clancy Calcium,* Denison, 1965; *The Boy Preacher,* Augsburg, 1966; *Ato*

Finds a Friend, Augsburg, 1966; *The Long Night,* Augsburg, 1966; *Andy Oxygen,* Denison, 1966; *Heap Hungry Indian,* Denison, 1966; *Benny Bandage,* Denison, 1967; *Sammy's Railroad,* Denison, 1969. Writer of series of missionary lessons for Nazarene *Junior Topics,* 1968-69.

AVOCATIONAL INTERESTS: Painting in oils, needlework, gardening, traveling.††

* * *

KIDNER, (Frank) Derek 1913-

PERSONAL: Born September 22, 1913, in London, England; son of Frank (a business director) and Dora (Hatfield) Kidner; married Mary le Pelley Wheadon, February 14, 1942; children: James Frank, Faith Mary. *Education:* Royal College of Music, A.R.C.M., 1933; Christ's College, Cambridge, B.A., 1940, M.A., 1944. *Home:* 56 Manor Park, Histon, Cambridge CB4 4JT, England.

CAREER: Clergyman of Church of England; minister in Sevenoaks, England, 1941-47, and Felsted, England, 1947-51; Oak Hill Theological College, London, England, senior tutor, 1951-64; Tyndale House, Cambridge, England, warden, 1964-78. *Member:* Society for Old Testament Study, Tyndale Fellowship for Biblical Research.

WRITINGS: The Christian and the Arts (monograph), Tyndale Press, 1960; *Proverbs: An Introduction and Commentary,* Tyndale Press, 1964; *The Death Penalty* (monograph), Falcon Books, 1964; *Genesis: An Introduction and Commentary,* Tyndale Press, 1967; *Leviticus-Deuteronomy: Bible Study Book,* Scripture Union, 1971; *Hard Sayings: The Challenge of Old Testament Morals* (monograph), Tyndale Press, 1972; *Psalms 1-72,* Inter-Varsity Press, 1973; *Psalms 73-150,* Inter-Varsity Press, 1975; *A Time to Mourn and a Time to Dance: Ecclesiastes and the Way of the World,* Inter-Varsity Press, 1976; *Ezra and Nehemiah: An Introduction and Commentary,* Inter-Varsity Press, in press. Contributor to *New Bible Commentary Revised.* Music editor of *Christian Praise* (a hymn book), 1957.

* * *

KIMBALL, Arthur G(ustaf) 1927-

PERSONAL: Born July 2, 1927, in Minneapolis, Minn.; son of Arthur E. (a businessman) and Alice (Gustafson) Kimball; married Shirley Long, September 18, 1948; children: Arthur, Anton, Jess, Angela, Lenna. *Education:* Pacific Lutheran College, B.A., 1954; Chicago Lutheran Theological Seminary, B.D., 1957; Claremont Graduate School and University Center (now Claremont Graduate School), M.A., Ph.D., 1965. *Home:* 739 East 9th St., McMinnville, Ore. 97128. *Office:* Department of English, Linfield College, McMinnville, Ore. 97128.

CAREER: Willamette University, Salem, Ore., member of faculty, 1963-64; Linfield College, McMinnville, Ore., member of faculty, 1965—, currently chairman of English department. Former minister of the Lutheran Church. *Military service:* U.S. Navy, 1945-46; U.S. Naval Reserve, chaplain, 1961-65; became lieutenant. *Member:* Modern Language Association of America. *Awards, honors:* Fulbright grant for research in Japan, 1967-68; National Endowment for the Humanities grant to develop a course in Japanese literature and art, 1978.

WRITINGS: Rational Fictions: A Study of Charles Brockden Brown, Linfield Research Institute, 1968; *Crisis in Identity and Contemporary Japanese Novels,* Tuttle, 1973. Contributor of articles to *Critique, Studies in Romanticism,*

Japan Christian Quarterly, Pennsylvania Medicine, and *American Speech.*

WORK IN PROGRESS: Editing essays on contemporary Japanese fiction and writing short stories.

*   *   *

KIMBLE, Daniel Porter   1934-

PERSONAL: Born November 18, 1934, in Chicago, Ill.; son of Ralph A. (an Army officer, editor, personnel director, and writer) and Ruth (Hazen) Kimble; married Reeva Jacobson (a psychologist), July 14, 1963; children: Matthew Sidney, Evan Hazen, Sara Lynn. *Education:* Knox College, B.A. (magna cum laude), 1956; University of Michigan, Ph.D., 1961; postdoctoral study at Stanford University, 1961-63, and Oxford University, 1969-70. *Home:* 2352 Van Ness, Eugene, Ore. 97403. *Office:* Department of Psychology, University of Oregon, Eugene, Ore. 97403.

CAREER: University of Oregon, Eugene, assistant professor, 1963-66, associate professor, 1966-69, professor of psychology, 1969—, director of animal laboratories. *Member:* American Philatelic Society, Oregon Environmental Council, Phi Beta Kappa. *Awards, honors:* Woodrow Wilson fellowship, 1956-57; National Institute of Health postdoctoral fellowship for studying psychiatry, 1961-63; Ersted Award for distinguished teaching, University of Oregon, 1967; National Science Foundation science faculty fellowship, Oxford University, 1969-70.

WRITINGS: Physiological Psychology: A Unit for Introductory Psychology, Addison-Wesley, 1963; (editor) *The Anatomy of Memory: Proceedings of the First Conference on Learning, Remembering, and Forgetting,* Science & Behavior Books, 1965; (contributor) Jack Roy Strange and Ray Foster, editors, *Readings in Physiological Psychology,* Wadsworth, 1966; (contributor) T. K. Landauer, editor, *Readings in Physiological Psychology,* McGraw, 1966; (editor) *The Organization of Recall: Proceedings of the Second Conference on Learning, Remembering, and Forgetting,* Wiley, 1967; (editor) *Experience and Capacity: Proceedings of the Fourth Conference on Learning, Remembering and Forgetting,* New York Academy of Sciences, 1968; (editor) *Readiness to Remember: Proceedings of the Third Conference on Learning, Remembering, and Forgetting,* New York Academy of Sciences, 1970; *Psychology as a Biological Science,* Goodyear Publishing, 1973, 2nd edition, 1977; (editor) *Contrast and Controversey in Modern Psychology,* Goodyear Publishing, 1977. Contributor of about fifty articles to psychology journals, including *American Psychologist, Journal of Comparative Physiology and Psychology, Neuropsychologia, Psychonomic Science, Animal Behavior, Science, Physiology and Behavior, Physiological Psychology,* and *Behavioral Biology.*

*   *   *

KIMBROUGH, Richard B(enito)   1931-

PERSONAL: Born April 21, 1931, in Brule, Neb.; son of Orlan L. (a musician) and Irma (Allison) Kimbrough; married Beverly Hendrix (an interior decorator), September 23, 1951; children: Rick, Robin, Ed, Jim, Tom. *Education:* Kearney State College, B.A., 1955; San Francisco State College (now California State University), M.A., 1967; University of Maine, additional study, 1968. *Politics:* Democrat. *Religion:* Agnostic. *Office:* Department of Social Science, North Platte Junior College, North Platte, Neb. 69101.

CAREER: Teacher of history at high schools in Big Springs, Neb., 1955-58, Julesburg, Colo., 1958-61, and Pittsburg, Calif., 1961-68; North Platte Junior College, North Platte, Neb., chairman of social science department and athletic coach, 1968—. *Military service:* U.S. Army, 1951-53; received Presidential Unit Commendation, Korean Service Medal, and United Nations Medal. *Awards, honors:* Distinguished recognition award from Friends of American Writers, 1973, for *Cross Country Courage.*

WRITINGS: Cross Country Courage, Thomas Nelson, 1972.

WORK IN PROGRESS: Witch on the Court, a juvenile novel about basketball, drugs, and witchcraft; a novel, *The Spider Cave,* and *Black on the Green,* another juvenile novel.

SIDELIGHTS: Richard Kimbrough told *CA:* "I hold two world's records: (1) the most holes of golf ever played in 24 hours (364) . . . (2) the fastest 18 holes of golf ever played (30 min. 10 sec.). I run about 10 miles a day."†

*   *   *

KIMMEL, Arthur S(andor)   1930-

PERSONAL: Born September 1, 1930, in Brooklyn, N.Y.; son of Harry (a manufacturer) and Ruth (Weissberger) Kimmel; married Irene Pauzner (a librarian), October 17, 1955; children: Vivien Ruth, John Paul S. *Education:* Attended Franklin & Marshall College, 1947-51; University of Miami, Coral Gables, Fla., A.B., 1953, M.A., 1954; University of Aix-Marseille, graduate study, 1954-55; University of California, Berkeley, Ph.D., 1966. *Office:* Department of Foreign Languages and Literatures, Western Washington University, Bellingham, Wash. 98225.

CAREER: Sacramento State College (now California State University), Sacramento, Calif., instructor in French, 1959-62; University of South Carolina, Columbia, assistant professor of French, 1962-65; California State College (now University), Hayward, assistant professor, 1965-67, associate professor of French, 1967-68; Salem State College, Salem, Mass., associate professor of French, 1968-69; Western Washington University, Bellingham, associate professor of French, 1969—.

MEMBER: Modern Language Association of America, American Association of Teachers of French, American Council on the Teaching of Foreign Languages, International Arthurian Society, Societe Rencesvals, Centre d'-Etudes Superieures de Civilisation Medievale, National Association of Language Laboratory Directors, Philological Association of the Pacific Coast, Pacific Northwest Conference on Foreign Languages, Medieval Association of the Pacific, Pi Delta Phi, Sigma Delta Pi. *Awards, honors:* Boursier du Gouvernement Francais, 1954-55; Fulbright grant, 1954-55.

WRITINGS: A Critical Edition of the Old Provencal Epic Daurel et Beton, University of North Carolina Press, 1971. Contributor to language journals. Member of editorial committee, *Teaching Romance Philology Yearbook.*

WORK IN PROGRESS: Notes on the Dating of Late Twelfth Century Epics; The "Jongleur" as Hero in Epic.

*   *   *

KINDER, Marsha   1940-

PERSONAL: Born February 20, 1940, in Los Angeles, Calif.; daughter of Harry and Gertrude (Cohen) Jankofsky;

married Melvyn Kinder, June 20, 1959 (divorced, 1969). *Education:* University of California, Los Angeles, A.B., 1961, M.A., 1963, Ph.D., 1967. *Residence:* Los Angeles, Calif. *Office:* Department of English, Occidental College, Los Angeles, Calif. 90041.

CAREER: Occidental College, Los Angeles, Calif., instructor, 1965-71, assistant professor, 1971-75, associate professor of English, 1975—, director of Summer Institute on Film, 1968. *Member:* Modern Language Association of America, American Association of University Professors, University Film Association, Phi Beta Kappa.

WRITINGS: (Contributor) Roy Huss, editor, *Blow-Up: Critical Studies,* Prentice-Hall, 1971; (with Beverle Houston) *Close-Up: A Critical Perspective on Film,* Harcourt, 1972. Author, with Beverle Houston, of "The Life and Opinions of Tristram Shandy and Mary Wollstonecraft," a screenplay. Contributor to *Sight and Sound, Film Heritage, Literature/Film Quarterly,* and *Women and Film.* Member of editorial board, *Film Quarterly;* co-editor, *Dream Journal;* editor of a single issue of *Quarterly Review of Film Studies.*

WORK IN PROGRESS: Styles; The Self and the Cinema; Dreamwork.

* * *

KINDRED, Leslie W(ithrow) 1905-

PERSONAL: Born December 27, 1905, in Boston, Mass.; son of Leslie W. (an interior decorator) and Veronica (Vatter) Kindred; married Helen Parmenter, December 24, 1932; children: James W., Robert H. *Education:* Attended Clark University, 1924-26; University of Michigan, A.B., 1928, A.M., 1934, Ph.D., 1938. *Home:* 8 Carrizo Dr., Santa Barbara, Calif. 93105.

CAREER: Social studies teacher in Ann Arbor, Mich., 1928-38; Marsh Foundation, Van Wert, Ohio, director, 1938-39; State Department of Public Instruction, Lansing, Mich., consultant, 1939-40; Temple University, Philadelphia, Pa., assistant professor, 1940-43, associate professor, 1943-45, professor of educational administration, 1945-73. Past executive secretary, Public Education and Child Labor Association of Pennsylvania. *Member:* American Association of School Administrators, National School Public Relations Association, National Association of Secondary School Principals, Pennsylvania Schoolmen's Club, 75 Club of Pennsylvania, Phi Delta Kappa.

WRITINGS: (With others) *Helping Children Experience the Realities of the Social Order,* Ann Arbor Board of Education, 1933; *The Teacher and School Organization,* 2nd edition (Kindred was not associated with first edition), Prentice-Hall, 1949, 4th edition (with Leo M. Chamberlain), 1966; *School Public Relations,* Prentice-Hall, 1957; *Study Guide for School Public Relations,* Temple University Bookstore, 1957; (editor) *How to Tell the School Story,* Prentice-Hall, 1960; (with Prince B. Woodard) *Staff Welfare Practices in the Public Schools,* Center for Applied Research in Education, 1963; (contributor) Donald J. Leu and Herbert C. Rudman, editors, *Preparation Programs for School Administration,* College of Education, Michigan State University, 1963; (contributor) R. J. Corsini and D. D. Howard, editors, *Critical Incidents in Teaching,* Prentice-Hall, 1964; (assisted by George N. Fehr, Jr.) *Communications Research and School-Community Relations,* College of Education, Temple University, 1965; (editor) *The Intermediate Schools,* Prentice-Hall, 1968; *The Middle School Curriculum,* Prentice-Hall, 1976; *The School and Commu-*

nity Relations, Prentice-Hall, 1976. Contributor of about sixty-five articles to professional journals.

AVOCATIONAL INTERESTS: Travel, portrait painting, gardening.

* * *

KING, Algin B(raddy) 1927-

PERSONAL: Born January 19, 1927, in Latta, S.C.; son of Dewey Algin (a salesman) and Elisabeth (Braddy) King; married Drucilla Ratcliff, January 17, 1948 (divorced, 1970); married January 19, 1972; wife's name, Joyce; children: (first marriage) Drucilla Ratcliff, Martha Louise. *Education:* University of South Carolina, A.B. (cum laude), 1947; New York University, M.S., 1953; Ohio State University, Ph.D., 1966. *Politics:* Republican. *Religion:* Methodist. *Home:* 103 North Will Scarlet Lane, Williamsburg, Va. 23185. *Office:* Division of Business Administration and Economics, Christopher Newport College, P.O. Box 6070, Newport News, Va. 23606.

CAREER: Sears, Roebuck & Co., Columbia, S.C., executive trainee, 1947-48; University of South Carolina, Columbia, instructor in marketing, 1948-51; Texas A & M University, College Station, assistant professor of marketing, 1954-55; College of William and Mary, Williamsburg, Va., associate professor, 1955-59, professor of business administration, 1959-73, director of Bureau of Business Research, 1959-63, acting head of department, 1960-62, assistant dean of School of Business Adminsitration, 1968, associate dean, 1968-71; Madison College, Harrisonburg, Va., head of department of business and economics, 1973-74; Western Carolina University, Cullowhee, N.C., professor and dean of School of Business, 1974-76; College of William and Mary, Christopher Newport College, Newport News, Va., professor of marketing and management, 1976—, director, Division of Business Administration and Economics, 1977—. Professorial lecturer, George Washington University, 1965-67. Chief of Economic Analysis Branch of district office, Office of Price Stabilization, 1951-53. Partner and manager, Fine Virginia Foods, 1957-63, 1969-72. Consultant to business, banks, and government agencies; expert witness in federal and State of Virginia courts.

MEMBER: American Marketing Association, American Institute for Decision Sciences, International Council for Small Business, Academy of Management, Southern Marketing Association, Southern Management Association, Atlantic Economic Society, Phi Beta Kappa.

WRITINGS: (Contributor) *Principles of Retailing,* Pitman, 1955; (contributor) *Principles of Marketing,* Pitman, 1961; *A Comparative Analysis of Nine Selected Business and Economic Indicators in Thirteen Virginia Cities: 1956-60* (monograph), Bureau of Business Research, College of William and Mary, 1961; *Retailing and Wholesaling in Virginia* (monograph), Bureau of Business Research, College of William and Mary, 1962; *Selected Service Trades in Virginia* (monograph), Bureau of Business Research, College of William and Mary, 1965; (with others) *Hampton Waterfront Economic Study,* Administrative Research Associates, 1967; (with others) *The Seafood Industry,* City Planning Commission (Hampton, Va.), 1968; (editor with Leonard Schifrin, and contributor) *The Sourcebook of Economics,* Dushkin, 1973. Also author of several monographs.

Contributor to *Encyclopedia International.* Contributor of numerous articles to *Southern Business Journal, Life Advertiser,* and *Commonwealth Magazine of Virginia.* Editor, *Virginia Business Index Report,* 1959-63.

WORK IN PROGRESS: The American Automobile as a Status Symbol: Is It Declining?

AVOCATIONAL INTERESTS: Golf, swimming, travel, tennis.

*   *   *

KING, James Cecil   1924-

PERSONAL: Born September 14, 1924, in Uniontown, Pa.; son of Joseph Herbert and Eliza Ann (Kelley) King; divorced; children: Christopher Hanbury, Sheila Anne. Education: George Washington University, B.A., 1949, M.A., 1950, Ph.D., 1954. Home: 9296 Bailey Lane, Fairfax, Va. 22031. Office: 407 Rice Hall, George Washington University, Washington, D.C. 20052.

CAREER: St. Albans School for Boys, Washington, D.C., teacher of French, German, and Latin, 1952-55; George Washington University, Washington, D.C., assistant professor, 1955-60, associate professor, 1960-65, professor of German and Sanskrit, 1965—. Military service: U.S. Army, 1943-46. Member: American Association of Teachers of German, Linguistic Society of America, Modern Language Association of America, Mediaeval Academy of America, American Association of University Professors, Phi Beta Kappa. Awards, honors: German Academic Exchange service grant for research in Europe, 1963.

WRITINGS: (Editor) Arnold Littmann, Peter hat Pech!, Holt, 1961; (editor with F. A. Raven and W. K. Legner) Germanic Studies in Honor of Edward Henry Sehrt, University of Miami Press, 1968; (editor) Boethius' Bearbeitung der "Categoriae" des Aristoteles, Max Niemeyer, 1972.

WORK IN PROGRESS: "Die Werke Notkers des Deutschen," of which Boethius' Bearbeitung der "Categoriae" des Aristoteles is a part, with Petrus W. Tax.

*   *   *

KING, John L(afayette)   1917-

PERSONAL: Born October 16, 1917, in Douglas, Ariz.; son of William David (an attorney) and Lillian (Nolan) King; married Barbara Epps (a bridal consultant), July 14, 1942; children: Sherri King Dougan, William D. III, John L. Education: University of Pennsylvania, B.S.E., 1938. Religion: Episcopalian. Residence: Huntington Beach, Calif.

CAREER: Worked in advertising and marketing and in private business, 1946-59; Orange Coast College, Costa Mesa, Calif., instructor in adult education, 1960-64; California State College (now University), Fullerton, associate professor of marketing, 1968-69; Sawyer College, Los Angeles, Calif., professor of behavioral economics, 1968-72; Economic Behavior Institute, Huntington Beach, Calif., director, beginning 1972. Military service: U.S. Army, 1940-46; became captain. Member: American Council on Consumer Interests, Association for Social Economics, Union for Radical Political Economists.

WRITINGS: (Contributor) House and Garden Cookbook, Simon & Schuster, 1958; Human Behavior and Wall Street, Swallow Press, 1972; It Hit the Fan, Economic Behavior Institute, 1975.

WORK IN PROGRESS: A book on the economic behavior of the consumer, The Consumer Autopsy.†

*   *   *

KING, Winston L(ee)   1907-

PERSONAL: Born August 30, 1907, in Avilla, Ind.; son of

Alfred Hiram (a farmer) and Alberta (Bodenhafer) King; married Jocelyn A. Brownlee, June 2, 1931; children: Carroll A. (Mrs. Robert G. Heideman), Christopher R., Jonathan B. Education: Asbury College, A.B., 1929; Andover Newton Theological Seminary, B.D., 1936; Harvard University, S.T.M., 1938, Ph.D., 1940. Religion: Religious Society of Friends (Quakers).

CAREER: Minister in Methodist and Congregational churches in New England, 1930-43, 1945-49; Grinnell College, Grinnell, Iowa, chaplain, 1949-63, associate professor, 1949-54, professor of philosophy and religion, 1954-61, Rand Professor of Applied Christianity, 1961-64; Vanderbilt University, Nashville, Tenn., professor of history of religion, 1964-73; Colorado State University, Ft. Collins, Colo., special professor in department of philosophy, 1973-76. Visiting professor, International Institute of Advanced Buddhistic Studies (Rangoon), 1958-60, and Oberlin College, 1977; Fulbright lecturer in history and philosophy of religion, Kyoto University, 1965-66. Military service: U.S. Army, chaplain, 1943-45; served in European theater; became captain; received Bronze Star Medal with oak leaf cluster. Member: American Academy of Religion, American Association for the Study of Religion, Association for Asian Studies.

WRITINGS: The Holy Imperative, Harper, 1949; Introduction to Religion, Harper, 1954; Buddhism and Christianity, Westminster, 1962; In the Hope of Nibbana, Open Court, 1964; A Thousand Lives Away, Harvard University Press, 1964; Introduction to Religion: A Phenomenological Approach, Harper, 1968. Contributor to Buddhist and professional journals. Literary editor of Journal of American Academy of Religion, 1968-70.

WORK IN PROGRESS: Research on and a translation of the works of Suzuki Shosan for a book, tentatively entitled Suzuki Shosan: Wayfarer.

*   *   *

KINGHORN, Kenneth Cain   1930-

PERSONAL: Born June 23, 1930, in Albany, Okla.; son of Kenneth (a businessman) and Eloise (Rye) Kinghorn; married Hilda Hartzler, June 4, 1955; children: Kathleen, Kenneth, Kevin, Kent. Education: Ball State University, B.S., 1952; Asbury Theological Seminary, B.D., 1962; Emory University, Ph.D., 1965. Home: 419 Akers Dr., Wilmore, Ky. 40390. Office: Department of Church History, Asbury Theological Seminary, Wilmore, Ky. 40390.

CAREER: Ordained United Methodist minister, 1965; Asbury Theological Seminary, Wilmore, Ky., associate professor, 1965-70, professor of history of theology, 1970—.

WRITINGS: Contemporary Issues in Historical Perspective, Word Inc., 1970; Dynamic Discipleship, Revell, 1973; Fresh Wind of the Spirit, Abingdon, 1975; Gifts of the Spirit, Abingdon, 1976. Contributor of articles to periodicals.

WORK IN PROGRESS: A book, The New Humanity.

*   *   *

KIRK, Roger E(dward)   1930-

PERSONAL: Born February 23, 1930, in Princeton, Ind.; son of James D. (a businessman) and Janet (Kelner) Kirk. Education: Ohio State University, B.S., 1951, M.A., 1952, Ph.D., 1955. Religion: Presbyterian. Home: 5100 Hawthorne, No. 312, Waco, Tex. 76710. Office: Department of Psychology, Baylor University, Waco, Tex. 76703.

CAREER: Baldwin Piano Co., Cincinnati, Ohio, senior research engineer, 1955-58; Baylor University, Waco, Tex., assistant professor, 1958-60, associate professor, 1960-64, professor of psychology, 1964—, director of graduate studies, 1969-76, director of behavioral statistics program, 1976—. Consulting editor in statistics for Brooks/Cole, 1969—. *Member:* American Psychological Association, American Statistical Association, Psychometric Society, Human Factors Society, Southwestern Psychological Association, Texas Psychological Association.

WRITINGS: Experimental Design: Procedures for the Behavioral Sciences, Brooks/Cole, 1968; (editor) *Statistical Issues,* Brooks/Cole, 1972; *Introductory Statistics,* Brooks/ Cole, 1978. Contributor of articles to professional journals.

AVOCATIONAL INTERESTS: Sailing, music.

* * *

KIRKPATRICK, Donald L(ee) 1924-

PERSONAL: Born March 15, 1924, in Richland Center, Wis.; married Fern Abraham; children: four. *Education:* University of Wisconsin, B.B.A., 1948, M.B.A., 1949, Ph.D., 1954. *Home:* 1080 Lower Ridgeway, Elm Grove, Wis. 53122. *Office:* Department of Business and Management, University of Wisconsin Extension, 929 North 6th St., Milwaukee, Wis. 53203.

CAREER: University of Wisconsin—Madison, instructor, 1949-52, assistant professor, 1952-56, associate professor of management, 1956-60, assistant director of Management Institute, 1958-60; International Minerals & Chemical Corp., Skokie, Ill., corporate personnel development supervisor, 1960-62; Bendix Products, Aerospace Division, South Bend, Ind., personnel manager, 1962-64; University of Wisconsin Extension, Milwaukee, professor of management development, 1964—. Consultant to business and government. *Military service:* U.S. Army, Infantry, 1943-46; served in Europe and the Far East.

MEMBER: American Society for Personnel Administration (member of national board of directors, 1962-64; vice-president of Michiana chapter), American Society for Training and Development (national vice-president, 1969-73; president, 1975). *Awards, honors:* Research award from American Society for Personnel Administration, 1969; Distinguished Service Award, University of Wisconsin Extension, 1976.

WRITINGS: Selecting and Training Potential Foremen and Supervisors (booklet), University of Wisconsin, 1967; *Obtaining Maximum Benefit from Outside Management Development Programs* (booklet), University of Wisconsin, 1968; *Supervisory Training and Development,* Addison-Wesley, 1971; (contributor) L. R. Bittel and Robert L. Craig, editors, *ASTD Training Directors Handbook,* McGraw, 1976; *How to Plan and Conduct Productive Business Meetings,* Dartnell Corp., 1976; *No-Nonsense Communication,* KM Enterprises, 1978. Also author of tests used in training, "Supervisory Inventory on Human Relations," 1965, "Supervisory Inventory on Communication," 1965, "Supervisory Inventory on Safety," 1967, "Management Inventory on Leadership and Motivation," 1974, "Management Inventory on Time and Delegation," 1974, and "Management Inventory on Managing Change," 1978. Contributor to professional journals.

AVOCATIONAL INTERESTS: Golf, fishing, hunting, music, photography, tennis.

KIRKPATRICK, Samuel A(lexander) III 1943-

PERSONAL: Born October 24, 1943, in Harrisburg, Pa.; son of Samuel A. and Dorothy (MacFarlane) Kirkpatrick; married Pamela Richter, June 13, 1965; children: Shaun Alexander, Neal William. *Education:* Shippensburg State College, B.S. (cum laude), 1964; Pennsylvania State University, M.A., 1966, Ph.D., 1968. *Home:* 3703 Old Oaks, Bryan, Tex. 77801. *Office:* Department of Political Science, Texas A & M University, College Station, Tex. 77843.

CAREER: Commonwealth of Pennsylvania, Harrisburg, legal assistant to assistant attorney general, 1964; University of Oklahoma, Norman, assistant professor, 1968-71, associate professor, 1971-75, professor of political science, 1975-77, acting director of Bureau of Government Research, 1969-70, director, 1970-77; Texas A & M University, College Station, professor of political science and head of department, 1977—. Visiting assistant professor of political science and research associate at Survey Research Center of Institute for Social Research, University of Michigan, summer, 1970. State supervisor of National Broadcasting Corp. "Election Night Forecast," 1969-77.

MEMBER: American Political Science Association, American Sociological Association, American Association for Public Opinion Research, American Association of University Professors, Midwest Political Science Association, Southern Political Science Association, Southwestern Political Science Association (member of executive council, 1972; vice-president, 1973-74; president, 1975-76), Oklahomans for a Modern Constitution (charter member), Pi Sigma Alpha, Phi Sigma Pi, Kappa Delta Pi, Phi Kappa Phi. *Awards, honors:* American Political Science Association state legislative service fellow, 1971-73.

WRITINGS: (Contributor) Robert Wrinkle, editor, *Politics in the Urban Southwest,* University of New Mexico Press, 1971; (contributor) Allen Wilcox, editor, *Public Opinion and Political Attitudes,* Wiley, 1972; (contributor) Dan Nimmo and Charles Bonjean, editors, *Political Attitudes and Public Opinion,* McKay, 1972; (with David R. Morgan) *Urban Political Analysis: A Systems Approach,* Free Press, 1972; (editor with Lawrence K. Pettit, and contributor) *The Social Psychology of Political Life,* Duxbury, 1972; *Quantitative Analysis of Political Data,* C. E. Merrill, 1973; (contributor) C. Cotter, editor, *Political Science Annual,* Bobbs-Merrill, 1975; (editor) *American Electoral Behavior,* Sage Publications, Inc., 1976; (with Morgan and T. Kielhorn) *The Oklahoma Voter,* University of Oklahoma Press, 1977; (contributor) L. Maisel and J. Cooper, editors, *Electoral Studies Yearbook,* Sage Publications, Inc., 1977; *The Legislative Process in Oklahoma,* University of Oklahoma Press, 1978.

Monographs: (With Morgan) *State Constitutional Revision: Cases and Commentary,* Bureau of Government Research, University of Oklahoma, 1970; (with Morgan) *Oklahoma Voting Patterns: Congressional Elections,* Bureau of Government Research, University of Oklahoma, 1970; (with Morgan and Larry G. Edwards) *Oklahoma Voting Patterns: Presidential, Senatorial and Gubernatorial Elections,* Bureau of Government Research, University of Oklahoma, 1970; (with Gary L. Cathey) *Issues in Higher Education: Faculty Attitudes toward the University Community,* Bureau of Government Research, University of Oklahoma, 1971; (with Cathey) *The Legislative Process in Oklahoma: Preliminary Foundations for a Legislative Manual,* Bureau of Government Research, University of Oklahoma, 1972; (with Morgan) *Employee Training and Personnel Practices in Oklahoma Cities,* State of Oklahoma, Governor's Office,

Office of Community Affairs and Planning, 1972; (with Morgan) *Employee Training in Oklahoma Counties*, State of Oklahoma, Governor's Office, Office of Community Affairs and Planning, 1972; (with Morgan) *Oklahoma Organizations Active in Applied Local Government Training*, State of Oklahoma, Governor's Office, Office of Community Affairs and Planning, 1972.

Contributor of articles to *Social Science Quarterly, American Journal of Political Science, Western Political Quarterly, American Behavioral Scientist, Public Opinion Quarterly, Oklahoma Business Bulletin, Sociological Quarterly*, and other professional journals. Member of editorial board, *American Journal of Political Science*, 1971-72, 1973-76; editor, *American Politics Quarterly*, 1977—.

WORK IN PROGRESS: Research in the areas of psychological views of decision-making, political ideology and attitude constraint in elite and mass publics, and research methods in policy analysis.

* * *

KIRSHNER, Gloria Ifland

PERSONAL: Born in New York, N.Y.; children: Ralph. *Education:* Barnard College, A.B., 1953; Columbia University, M.A., 1958. *Residence:* New York, N.Y. *Office:* Teachers Guides to Television, 699 Madison Ave., New York, N.Y. 10021.

CAREER: Mademoiselle, New York City, guest editor, 1953; elementary school teacher in New York City, 1955-62; National Broadcasting Co. (NBC), New York City, educational consultant, 1962-65; Robert Saudek Associates, New York City, educational consultant, 1965-71; *Teachers Guides to Television*, New York City, editor and vice-president, 1968—. Educational supervisor and assistant to executive producer, "Animal Secrets on NBC," 1967-68; consultant to Ideal Toy Co. and others. Teacher of special course in television and film at Teachers College, Columbia University, 1970-72.

MEMBER: International Radio and Television Society, Education Writers Association, Educational Press Association, National Council for the Social Studies. *Awards, honors:* Brotherhood Award from National Conference of Christians and Jews, 1965, Freedoms Foundation Award, 1965, both for teachers's guides; Thomas Alva Edison Award, 1967, Cine Golden Eagle Award, 1967, Ohio State Award, 1967, Gran Primio International Tecnica Cinematografica, 1967, Special Award of Merit from National Society for Medical Research, all for film scripts.

WRITINGS: From Instinct to Intelligence: How Animals Learn, Grosset, 1969. Author of television filmscripts, "Exploring," 1964, "Animal Secrets," 1968, "When Children Search for Themselves," Robert Saudek Associates, 1971. Author of more than one thousand teacher's guides to television programs. Contributor to *Elementary English* and other publications.

WORK IN PROGRESS: "Growing Up in America," in development for National Broadcasting Co. (NBC).

* * *

KLEBERGER, Ilse 1921-

PERSONAL: Born March 22, 1921, in Potsdam, Germany; daughter of Wilhelm (a merchant) and Elisabeth (Fechner) Krahn; married Kurt Eberhard Kleberger (a professor of ophthalmology), May 20, 1949; children: Andrea. *Education:* Studied medicine at Universities of Berlin, Tuebingen, and Greifswald; qualified as physician, 1947, M.D., 1948. *Religion:* Evangelical. *Home and office:* Cimbernstrasse 16, Berlin, Germany.

CAREER: Doctor's assistant, Berlin, Germany, 1947-49; general practice of medicine, Berlin, 1949—. *Member:* Schriftstellerverband, Hartmannbund.

WRITINGS—Juvenile books; published by Erika Klopp, except as indicated: *Wolfgang mit dem Regenschirm*, Rascher, 1961; *Mit dem Leierkasten durch Berlin*, 1961; *Mit Dudelsack und Floete*, 1962; (with Orgel Koehne) *Piet und Ans leben in Holland*, 1962; (with Koehne) *Pierre und Anette leben in Frankreich*, 1962; (with Koehne) *Pietro und Anna leben in Italien*, 1963; *Unser Oma*, 1964, translation by Michael Heron published as *Grandmother Oma*, Bodley Head, 1966, Atheneum, 1967; *Jannis der Schwammtaucher*, 1965; *Ferien mit Oma*, 1967, translation by Belinda McGill published in England as *Grandmother Oma and the Green Caravan*, Bodley Head, 1969, and as *Traveling with Oma*, Atheneum, 1970; *Villa Oma*, 1972; *Keine Zeit fuer Langeweile*, Schaffstein Verlag, 1976. Also author of *Verliebt in Sardinien*, 1976.

Adult books: *Wein auf Lava* (novel), Erika Klopp, 1966; *Unser Kind wird gesund* (science), Schneider Verlag, 1966; *Wir sind alle Brueder: Im Zeichen des Roten Kreuzes* (science), Erika Klopp, 1969; *Berlin unterm Horrohr*, Arani Verlag, 1976. Also author of *Der grope Entschlub*, 1977.

Author of radio play, "Die Auswanderung," 1966, novelettes published in several newspapers, and of poems and short stories, some of them included in anthologies.

BIOGRAPHICAL/CRITICAL SOURCES: Horn Book, August, 1970.

* * *

KLEENE, Stephen Cole 1909-

PERSONAL: Born January 5, 1909, in Hartford, Conn.; son of Gustav Adolph and Alice Lena (Cole) Kleene; married Nancy Elliott, September 21, 1942 (died January 2, 1970); married Jeanne Steinmetz, March 19, 1978; children: (first marriage) Paul Elliott, Kenneth Cole, Bruce Metcalf, Pamela Lee. *Education:* Amherst College, A.B., 1930; Princeton University, Ph.D., 1934. *Home:* 1514 Wood Lane, Madison, Wis. 53705. *Office:* Department of Mathematics, University of Wisconsin, Madison, Wis. 53706.

CAREER: University of Wisconsin—Madison, instructor, 1935-37, assistant professor of mathematics, 1937-41; Amherst College, Amherst, Mass., associate professor of mathematics, 1941-42; University of Wisconsin—Madison, associate professor, 1946-48, professor, 1948-64, Cyrus C. MacDuffee Professor of Mathematics and Computer Sciences, 1964—, chairman of department of mathematics, 1957-58, 1960-62, chairman of department of numerical analysis, 1962-63, acting director of Mathematics Research Center, 1966-67, dean, College of Letters and Science, 1969-74. Member of Institute for Advanced Study, 1939-40, 1965-66; visiting professor, Princeton University, 1956-57; National Research Council, member of Division of Mathematical Sciences, 1956-58, chairman designate, 1969-72. *Military service:* U.S. Naval Reserve, active duty, 1942-46; became lieutenant commander.

MEMBER: International Union of the History and Philosophy of Science (president, 1961), Mathematical Association of America, American Mathematical Society, Association for Symbolic Logic (member of executive committee, 1939-41; vice-president, 1942, 1947-49; president, 1956-58),

National Academy of Sciences (elected, 1969), American Association for the Advancement of Science (fellow), Audubon Society, Nature Conservancy, Phi Beta Kappa, Sigma Xi (president of Wisconsin chapter, 1951-52). *Awards, honors:* Guggenheim fellowship, University of Amsterdam, 1950; National Science Foundation grant, University of Marburg, 1958-59; Sc. D., Amherst College, 1970.

WRITINGS: Introduction to Metamathematics, Van Nostrand, 1952, 7th edition, American Elsevier, 1974; (with Richard Eugene Vesley) *The Foundations of Intuitionistic Mathematics,* North-Holland Publishing, 1965; *Mathematical Logic,* Wiley, 1967. Contributor of articles on mathematical logic to scholarly journals. *Journal of Symbolic Logic,* consulting editor, 1936-42, 1946-49, editor, 1950-62.

SIDELIGHTS: Stephen Kleene's books have been issued in translation, including Russian, French, Spanish, and Japanese.

*   *   *

KLEIN, David Ballin   1897-

PERSONAL: Born April 15, 1897, in New York, N.Y.; son of Philip (a rabbi) and Julie (Hirsch) Klein; married Rose Schaffer, September 13, 1923 (died, 1958); married Anne Nurko Kaplan, February 5, 1959; children: (first marriage) Grace (Mrs. Henry Jameson), Philip, Stephen. *Education:* College of the City of New York (now City College of the City University of New York), A.B., 1918; Columbia University, M.A., 1921, Ph.D., 1930. *Religion:* Jewish. *Home:* 11901 Sunset Blvd., Los Angeles, Calif. 90049.

CAREER: University of Texas at Austin, assistant professor, 1923-27, associate professor, 1927-35, professor of psychology, 1935-47; University of Southern California, Los Angeles, lecturer, 1947-48, professor of psychology and director of psychology clinic, 1948-62, professor emeritus, 1962—. Diplomate in clinical psychology, American Board of Professional Psychology, 1948. Has lectured at Columbia University, City College of the City University of New York, University of New Mexico, Rutgers University, University of California, and University of Wyoming. *Member:* American Psychological Association, American Association for the Advancement of Science (fellow), Sigma Xi.

WRITINGS: (With F.A.C. Perrin) *Psychology: Its Facts and Principles,* Holt, 1926; *General Psychology,* Holt, 1936; *Mental Hygiene,* Holt, 1944; *Abnormal Psychology,* Holt, 1951; *A History of Scientific Psychology,* Basic Books, 1970; *The Unconscious: Invention or Discovery?—A Historico-Critical Inquiry,* Goodyear Publishing, 1977.

WORK IN PROGRESS: The Concept of Consciousness: A Historical and Contemporary Inquiry.

*   *   *

KLEIN, Norma   1938-

PERSONAL: Born May 13, 1938, in New York, N.Y.; daughter of Emanuel (a psychoanalyst) and Sadie (Frankel) Klein; married Erwin Fleissner (a biochemist), July 27, 1963; children: Jennifer Luise, Katherine Nicole. *Education:* Attended Cornell University, 1956-57; Barnard College, B.A. (cum laude), 1960; Columbia University, M.A., 1963. *Politics:* Democrat. *Religion:* None. *Home:* 29 West 96th St., New York, N.Y. 10025. *Agent:* Cyrilly Abels, 119 West 57th St., New York, N.Y. 10019, and Barbara Schiller, 180 Riverside Dr., New York, N.Y. 10024.

CAREER: Free-lance writer. *Member:* Phi Beta Kappa.

WRITINGS: Love and Other Euphemisms (a novel and five short stories), Putnam, 1972; *Mom, the Wolfman and Me* (juvenile novel), Pantheon, 1972; *Girls Can Be Anything* (Junior Literary Guild selection), Dutton, 1973; *It's Not What You Expect* (juvenile), Pantheon, 1973; *If I Had It My Way* (juvenile), Pantheon, 1973; *Dinosaur's Housewarming Party,* Crown, 1974; *Confessions of an Only Child,* illustrations by R. Cuffari, Pantheon, 1974; *Give Me One Good Reason,* Putnam, 1974; *Taking Sides,* Pantheon, 1974; *Coming to Life,* Simon and Schuster, 1974; *Naomi in the Middle,* Dial, 1974; *A Train for Jane,* illustrations by Miriam Schottland, Feminist Press, 1974; *Blue Trees, Red Sky,* illustrations by Pat Grant Porter, Pantheon, 1975; *Sunshine: A Novel,* Holt, 1975; *What It's All About,* Dial Press, 1975; *Coming to Life,* New American Library, 1976; *Girls Turn Wives,* Simon and Schuster, 1976; *Hiding,* Four Winds Press, 1976; *It's Ok If You Don't Love Me,* Dial, 1977; *Tomboy,* Four Winds Press, 1978; *Love Is One of the Choices,* Dial, 1979. Work has been anthologized in *Prize Stories: The O. Henry Awards,* 1963, 1968, and *The Best American Short Stories of 1969,* 1969. Contributor of about sixty short stories to magazines, including *Sewanee Review, Mademoiselle, Prairie Schooner,* and *Denver Quarterly.*

SIDELIGHTS: Norma Klein told *CA:* "What appeals to me in [juvenile fiction] is the opportunity to write for different age groups, from picture books to teenage novels. I find having children, observing them is invaluable in this regard. I also find that a 100-page manuscript, a length I find very congenial, is considered a novel in children's books and can be published on its own. What draws me most, however, is that I feel the children's book field has been and is still very weighed down by taboos on many subjects, on abortion, sex, the human body, etc. I feel one could write a book a year till one was just touching on each of these taboos. As a feminist, I especially want to write for girls, but girls who are active intellectually, who are strong, interesting people. I'd like parents and adults in general to be portrayed in children's book as they are, with faults, as children really see them. I'd like all this to be done nondidactically, humorously in books that are fun to read and I hope not just me but many others will make the same effort since it's so important. We need books where children masturbate, think about their parents sex lives, enjoy the physical sensations provided by their bodies. We need books that are non-punitive, open, honest. There aren't enough, not nearly."

BIOGRAPHICAL/CRITICAL SOURCES: Children's Literary Review, Volume II, Gale, 1976.

*   *   *

KLIMAS, Antanas   1924-

PERSONAL: Born April 17, 1924, in Pelekonys, Lithuania; came to United States, 1948, naturalized, 1959; son of Vincas (a farmer) and Marija (Siugzdinis) Klimas; married Dana Liormanas, May 19, 1954; children: A. Tadas, Ruta M. S., Paulius R., Lina V. *Education:* Studied at Teachers College, Kaunas, Lithuania, 1941-42, University of Kaunas, 1941-43, and Baltic University, 1946-67; University of Pennsylvania, M.A., 1950, Ph.D., 1956. *Religion:* Roman Catholic. *Residence:* Rochester, N.Y. *Office:* Department of Languages and Linguistics, University of Rochester, Rochester, N.Y. 14627.

CAREER: University of Pennsylvania, Philadelphia, assistant instructor, 1950-56, instructor in German, 1956-57; University of Rochester, Rochester, N.Y., assistant professor, 1957-62, associate professor, 1962-70, professor of

German and linguistics, 1970—, acting chairman of department of languages and linguistics, summers, 1964-65. *Member:* Linguistic Society of America, American Association of Teachers of German, Association for the Advancement of Baltic Studies, Institute of Lithuanian Studies, Lithuanian Catholic Academy of Sciences (member-scientist), Delta Phi Alpha.

WRITINGS: (With Leonardas Dambriunas and William R. Schmalstieg) *Introduction to Modern Lithuanian,* Franciscan Fathers Press, 1966, 2nd edition, 1972; (with Schmalstieg) *Lithuanian Reader for Self-Instruction,* Franciscan Fathers Press, 1967; (with Schmalstieg) *Lithuanian-English Glossary of Linguistic Terminology,* Department of Slavic Languages, Pennsylvania State University, 1971. Contributor to annals and proceedings. Contributor to *Encyclopedia Lituanica* and *Lietuviu Enciklopedija.* Contributor of about forty articles and reviews to linguistic journals, including *Slavonic and East European Review, English Record,* and *Baltic Linguistics.* Editor, *Lituanus.*

WORK IN PROGRESS: A Practical Guide and Reference Book for Teaching German Conversation and Composition; A Prehistory of Baltic, Germanic and Slavic; An Introduction to Indo-European Linguistics; research on historical linguistics.††

*   *   *

KLONGLAN, Gerald E(dward) 1936-

PERSONAL: Born April 1, 1936, in Nevada, Iowa; son of Bernie R. (a farmer) and Willene (Maland) Klonglan; married Donna Eileen Becvar (a teacher), June 29, 1960; children: Jason, Suzanne. *Education:* Iowa State University of Science and Technology, B.S., 1958, M.S., 1962, Ph.D., 1963. *Politics:* Democrat. *Religion:* Lutheran. *Home:* 2124 Duff, Ames, Iowa 50010. *Office:* Department of Sociology, 318 East Hall, Iowa State University of Science and Technology, Ames, Iowa 50010.

CAREER: Iowa State University of Science and Technology, Ames, research associate in sociology, 1962-63, assistant professor, 1963-66, associate professor, 1966-72, professor of sociology, 1972—. Sociological research consultant to government and private agencies and organizations, including Office of Economic Opportunity and American Cancer Society. *Military service:* U.S. Army Reserve, 1958-64; became sergeant. *Member:* American Sociological Association, American Association for the Advancement of Science, Rural Sociological Society (member of board of governors, 1969), Midwest Sociological Society, Common Cause, Alpha Kappa Delta, Phi Kappa Phi, Gamma Sigma Delta, Alpha Zeta.

WRITINGS: (With Leslie Wilcox, Ralph Brooks, and George Beal) *Annotated Bibliography on Social Indicators,* Elsevier, 1972.

Co-author of more than fifty monographs published by Department of Sociology and Anthropology, Iowa State University of Science and Technology, including: *Adoption of Public Fallout Shelters: A 1964 National Study,* 1966; *System Linkages among Women's Organizations,* 1967; *Communication Impact,* 1967; *Alcoholism Services: Client Characteristics and Treatment Outcomes,* 1969; *Coordinating Health Organizations: The Problem of Cigarette Smoking,* 1971.

Contributor: *Benefits and Burdens of Rural Development: Some Public Policy Viewpoints,* Iowa State University Press, 1970; Phillip Kantz and Merlin Brinkerhoff, editors,

Complex Organizations and Their Environments, W. C. Brown, 1972; David Horton Smith, Richard Reddy, and Burt R. Baldwin, editors, *Voluntary Action Research: 1972,* Heath, 1972; David Horton Smith, editor, *Voluntary Action Research: 1973,* Heath, 1973. Also author of numerous reports and government studies. Contributor to two research symposiums published by Institute for Defense Analysis, and to journals.

WORK IN PROGRESS: Research in social indicators, interorganizational relations, complex organizations, community change, and adoption and diffusion of innovations.†

*   *   *

KMOCH, Hans 1897(?)-1973

1897(?)—February 13, 1973; Austrian-born chess expert and author. Obituaries: *New York Times,* February 14, 1973.

*   *   *

KNAPP, David A(llan) 1938-

PERSONAL: Born February 25, 1938, in Cleveland, Ohio; son of Frederick Allan (an advertising executive) and Ethel (Ogden) Knapp; married Deanne Evander (a social psychologist), June 2, 1962; children: Wendy Kay. *Education:* Purdue University, B.S., 1960, M.S., 1962, Ph.D., 1965; postdoctoral study at University of Michigan, 1970-71, and Monarch University, Melbourne, Australia, 1974. *Home:* 11318 Cushman Rd., Rockville, Md. 20852. *Office:* Department of Pharmacy Administration, University of Maryland, 636 West Lombard St., Baltimore, Md. 21201.

CAREER: Ohio State University, Columbus, instructor, 1964, assistant professor, 1964-67, associate professor of pharmacy administration, 1967-70; University of Maryland, Baltimore, associate professor, 1971-72, professor of pharmacy administration, 1972—, chairperson of department, 1974—. Visiting scientist, American Association of Colleges of Pharmacy; member of review committee, Bureau of Health Manpower Education of National Institutes of Health, 1971-72; consultant to U.S. Department of Health, Education and Welfare. *Member:* American Association for the Advancement of Science (fellow), American Public Health Association (fellow), American Pharmaceutical Association, American Association of Colleges of Pharmacy, Sigma Xi, Rho Chi.

WRITINGS: (With wife, D. E. Knapp) *Perceived Occupational Roles of the Pharmacist: Relationship to Community Health,* Research Foundation, Ohio State University, 1968; (editor) *Bibliography of Theses and Dissertations Relevant to Pharmacy Administration,* American Association of Colleges of Pharmacy, 1970; (with M. C. Smith) *Pharmacy, Drugs, and Medical Care,* Williams & Wilkins, 1972, 3rd edition, 1979; (with F. B. Polumbo) *Containing Costs in Third-Party Drug Programs,* Drug Intelligence Publications, 1978. Contributor to proceedings. Contributor of over seventy articles to professional journals, including *Medical Care Review, American Journal of Pharmaceutical Education, Social Science and Medicine, Ohio Pharmacist,* and *Journal of Social Psychology.* Editorial reviewer, *American Journal of Hospital Pharmacy, Journal of the American Pharmaceutical Association,* and *American Journal of Pharmaceutical Education.*

WORK IN PROGRESS: Research on the qualify of antimicrobial use in hospitals.

KNAPP, Joseph G(eorge) 1924-

PERSONAL: Born March 5, 1924, in St. Louis, Mo.; son of Joseph Rudolph (a sales manager) and Kathryn (Zang) Knapp. *Education:* St. Louis University, B.A., 1948; Marquette University, M.A., 1952; University of Minnesota, Ph.D., 1962. *Office:* St. Louis University, 221 North Grand, St. Louis, Mo. 63103.

CAREER: St. Louis University, St. Louis, Mo., instructor, 1962-64, assistant professor, 1964-67, associate professor, 1967-73, professor of English and American studies, 1973—, director of interdisciplinary film program. Director, Fordyce House conference center. *Member:* Modern Language Association of America, American Studies Association, Conference on College Composition and Communication, American History Association, Council of Teachers of America, Mid Continent American Studies Association (president, 1969-70), Greater St. Louis Council of Teachers of English (president, 1968-70), Missouri Association of Teachers of English (member of board of directors). *Awards, honors:* Senior Fulbright lectureship, Rio de Janeiro, 1973-74, 1974-75.

WRITINGS: (Editor) *Rhetoric,* St. Louis University Press, 1963; *Tortured Synthesis: The Meaning of Melville's Clarel,* Philosophical Library, 1971; *Two Histories: The Beginnings of the Civil War in St. Louis,* National Endowment for the Humanities, in press. Contributor to *New Catholic Encyclopedia.* Contributor to academic journals, including *American Transcendental Quarterly* and *Manuscripta.* Co-editor, *Perspectiva Hispanica.*

WORK IN PROGRESS: Research on Herman Melville, Robert Penn Warren, and William Faulkner; research on relationship between literature and cinema.

SIDELIGHTS: Joseph G. Knapp has traveled in Europe, Japan, the Far East, and Brazil.

*   *   *

KNAUB, Richard K. 1928-

PERSONAL: Born July 7, 1928, in Springfield, Mo.; son of Norman K. (a teacher and insurance agent) and Bernice (Chesterson) Knaub; married Joan Slaker (a free-lance writer), December 20, 1953; children: Miranda, Richard S. *Education:* Indiana University, A.B., 1950, Ph.D., 1962; University of Iowa, M.F.A., 1955. *Politics:* "Free-thinking Republican." *Religion:* Presbyterian. *Home:* 4425 Osage Dr., Boulder, Colo. 80303. *Office:* University of Colorado Theatre, Boulder, Colo. 80309.

CAREER: Allegheny College, Meadville, Pa., technical director of theatre, 1955-57; Indiana University at Bloomington, technical director of theatre, 1957-62; University of Colorado, Boulder, assistant professor, 1962-67, associate professor, 1967-74, professor of theatre, 1974—, technical director of theatre, 1962-65, director, 1965-72. Fulbright professor, University of Wales, 1973-74; exchange professor, University of Lancaster, 1976-77. *Military service:* U.S. Army, 1950-52; became sergeant. *Member:* United States Institute of Theatre Technologists, American Theatre Association (member of national advisory council, 1972-73), Rocky Mountain Theatre Association (president, 1971-72), Boulder Rotary Club. *Awards, honors:* Medal of recognition from American Oil Company, 1973, for contributions to the American College Theatre Festival.

WRITINGS: (Editor) *On Shakespeare's Stage,* University of Colorado Press, 1967; (with John Dolman) *The Art of Play Production,* Harper, 1972. Editor of *Curtain Call,* 1967-71.

WORK IN PROGRESS: Let's Talk about Theatre, a series of monographs on all aspects of theatre.

*   *   *

KNIGHT, Arthur 1916-

PERSONAL: Surname legally changed, 1948; born September 6, 1916, in Philadelphia, Pa.; son of Arthur (a salesman) and Claudia (Oppenheimer) Rosenheimer; married Mary Ann Nyberg, April 23, 1965. *Education:* College of the City of New York (now City College of the City University of New York), B.A., 1940. *Home:* 22202 Pacific Coast Hwy., Malibu, Calif. 90265. *Agent:* (Literary) Roberta Pryor, International Creative Management, 40 West 57th St., New York, N.Y. 10019; (lectures) New Line Presentations, 853 Broadway, New York, N.Y. 10003. *Office:* Department of Cinema, University of Southern California, Los Angeles, Calif. 90007.

CAREER: Museum of Modern Art, Film Library, New York City, staff member, 1939-49; College of the City of New York (now City College of the City University of New York), New York City, instructor in cinema, 1950-60; University of Southern California, Los Angeles, professor of cinema, 1960—. Film critic, *Saturday Review,* 1949-73, and *Westways,* 1971—. Editorial advisor, *Encyclopaedia Britannica,* 1969—. Member of board of directors, Filmex; member of selection committee, New York Film Festival. Director of Benson & Hedges "100 Greatest Films" project, 1975—. Has participated in film festivals in Venice, Mar del Plato, Vancouver, New Delhi, New York, San Francisco, and elsewhere. *Military service:* U.S. Army, 1941-45; became first lieutenant; received Purple Heart.

MEMBER: Writers Guild of America, National Society of Film Critics, American Association of University Professors, Writers Guild Film Society (chairman). *Awards, honors:* Awards from Screen Directors Guild, 1958, and National Academy of Recording Arts and Sciences, 1970; named among Outstanding Educators of America, 1971.

WRITINGS: The Liveliest Art, Macmillan, 1957, revised edition, 1978; *The Hollywood Style* (illustrated with photographs), Macmillan, 1969. Contributor to *Encyclopaedia Britannica, World Encyclopedia,* and *Crowell-Collier Encyclopedia;* contributor to national magazines, including *Saturday Review* and *Theatre Arts,* and to major newspapers.

WORK IN PROGRESS: History of Sex in the Movies, with Hollis Alpert; revising *The Liveliest Art,* for New American Library.

BIOGRAPHICAL/CRITICAL SOURCES: Newsweek, December 15, 1969.

*   *   *

KNOLLENBERG, Bernhard 1892-1973

November 26, 1892—July 6, 1973; American historian, author, library director, lawyer, and government administrator. Obituaries: *New York Times,* July 17, 1973. (See index for *CA* sketch)

*   *   *

KNOWLTON, Edgar C(olby), Jr. 1921-

PERSONAL: Born September 14, 1921, in Delaware, Ohio; son of Edgar Colby (a teacher) and Mildred (a medical librarian; maiden name, Hunt) Knowlton. *Education:* Harvard University, A.B., 1941, A.M., 1942; Stanford University, Ph.D., 1959; also attended Middlebury College, summers, 1940, 1941. *Home:* 1026 Kalo Pl., Apt. 403, Honolulu, Hawaii 96826. *Office:* Department of European Languages, University of Hawaii, 1890 East-West Rd., Honolulu, Hawaii 96822.

CAREER: University of Hawaii, Honolulu, instructor, 1948-53, assistant professor, 1954-59, associate professor, 1959-65, professor of European languages, 1965—. Visiting professor of linguistics, University of Malaya, 1962-64, and Universidad Central de Venezuela, 1975. *Military service:* U.S. Naval Reserve, communications technician, active duty, 1944-46, 1951-52; served in Hawaii, Japan, and Korea. *Member:* Modern Language Association of America, Linguistic Society of America, American Association of Teachers of Spanish and Portuguese, Siam Society, Royal Asiatic Society, Phi Beta Kappa, Sigma Delta Pi. *Awards, honors:* Translation prize from secretary of information and tourism, Lisbon, Portugal, 1973.

WRITINGS: (Translator) Francisco de Sa de Meneses, *The Conquest of Malacca,* University of Malaya Press, 1971; (with A. Grove Day) *Vicente Blasco Ibanez,* Twayne, 1972; (translator) Almeida Garrett, *Camoens,* Imprensa Nacional (Macau), 1972; (translator) Casimiro de Abreu, *Camoens and the Man of Java,* Imprensa Nacional, 1972; (translator) Machado de Assis, *You, Love, and You Alone,* Imprensa Nacional, 1972; (contributor) *Atlas of Hawaii,* University Press of Hawaii, 1973; (contributor) John L. Cutler and Lawrence S. Thompson, editors, *Studies in English and American Literature: A Supplement to American Notes and Queries,* Whitston Publishing, 1978. Music reviewer, *Honolulu Advertiser,* 1957-61.

WORK IN PROGRESS: Research on words of Chinese, Japanese, and Korean origin found in the Romance languages; a study of Esteban Escheverria.

SIDELIGHTS: Edgar C. Knowlton has studied French, Italian, Spanish, Portuguese, German, Provencal, Russian, Polish, Romanian, Greek, Latin, Chinese, Japanese, Korean, Dutch, Ilokano, Thai, Indonesian-Malay, Cambodian, Vietnamese, Tamil, Hindi, Sanskrit, Tagalog, Hawaiian, Semai, and Samoan.

* * *

KNOX, David H., Jr. 1943-

PERSONAL: Born December 1, 1943, in Birmingham, Ala.; son of David H. (a salesman) and Jeanette (Gammill) Knox; married Frances Hayes (a teacher), August 30, 1969. *Education:* Auburn University, B.A., 1966; Florida State University, M.S., 1967, Ph.D., 1969; postdoctoral fellow, State University of New York at Stony Brook, 1971. *Religion:* Baptist. *Home:* 205 Hardee Circle, Greenville, N.C. 27834. *Office:* Department of Sociology, East Carolina University, Greenville, N.C. 27834.

CAREER: East Carolina University, Greenville, N.C., assistant professor of sociology, 1969-70, 1971—; The Nelson Clinic, Greenville, marriage counselor, 1972, 1973—. Consultant to Upward Bound Project, 1970, Learning Service Project at North Carolina Wesleyan College, 1970, and Behavior Modification Program for Youthful Offenders, Raleigh, 1972.

MEMBER: American Association of Marriage and Family Counselors, Association for the Advancement of Behavior Therapy, National Council on Family Relations, Southern Sociological Society, North Carolina Family Life Council.

WRITINGS: Marriage Happiness: A Behavioral Approach to Counseling, Research Press, 1971; *A Discussion Guide to*

Accompany the Love Attitude Inventory (manual), Family Life Publications, 1971; *Marriage: Who? When? Why?,* Prentice-Hall, 1975; *Marriage Exercise Book,* McKay, 1975; (with Sharryl Hawke) *One Child by Choice,* Prentice-Hall, 1977; *Exploring Marriage and the Family,* Scott, Foresman, 1979. Also author of *Keeping Happiness in Marriage: A Positive Approach,* Research Press. Contributor to *Sexology, Adolescence,* and other journals.

* * *

KNUTSON, Jeanne N(ickell) 1934-

PERSONAL: Born September 28, 1934, in Salt Lake City, Utah; daughter of Frank Andrew (a consulting geologist) and Mary (Oliver) Nickell; divorced; children: Leslie Kathleen, John Andrew, Stephen David, Anna-Marie Christina. *Education:* University of California, Berkeley, B.A. (with honors), 1955, M.A. (political science), 1956; University of Oregon, Ph.D. (political science), 1968; University of California, Los Angeles, M.A. (psychology), 1971, Ph.D. (psychology), 1972. *Home and office:* Wright Institute, 10837 Via Verona, Los Angeles, Calif. 90024.

CAREER: High school teacher in Modesto, Calif., 1959-61; Foothill College, Los Altos, Calif., instructor in literature, 1962; high school teacher in Los Altos, 1962-65; Wright Institute, Los Angeles and Berkeley, Calif., senior research associate in psychology and political science, 1968—; private practice of clinical psychology, 1978—. Research associate, Institute of Political Studies, Stanford University, 1968-69, and Center for Study of Instruction, Harcourt, Brace, Jovanovich, Inc., 1968—. Intern in clinical psychology, Cedars-Sinai Medical Hospital, 1970-71, and Los Angeles Psychiatric Service, 1972-73. Ross Loos Medical Group, staff psychologist, 1973—, chief psychologist, 1974-78.

MEMBER: International Neuropsychological Society, International Society of Political Psychology (founder), Society for Personality Assessment, American Psychological Association, American Political Science Association, Society for the Psychological Study of Social Issues, Phi Beta Kappa. *Awards, honors:* National Institute of Mental Health postdoctoral research fellowship, 1970-71; Society for the Psychological Study of Social Issues grant for research on black socialization, 1972.

WRITINGS: Outer Mongolia: A Study in Soviet Colonialism, Union Research Institute (Hong Kong), 1959; (with others) *The Social Sciences: Concepts and Values* (for grades kindergarten through eight), Harcourt, 1970, 1972, 1976; *The Human Basis of the Polity: A Psychological Study of Political Men,* Aldine, 1972; (contributor) Allen R. Wilcox, editor, *Public Opinion and Political Attitudes,* Wiley, 1973; (editor and contributor) *The Handbook of Political Psychology,* Jossey-Bass, 1973; (contributor) R. Niemi, editor, *The Politics of Future Citizens,* Jossey-Bass, 1974; *Psychological Variables in Political Recruitment: An Analysis of Party Politics,* Wright Institute, 1974; *Constraints on Political Learning: Pre-Political Ideology in Black and White Children,* Wright Institute, 1974; (contributor) R. Fitzgerald, editor, *Human Needs and Politics,* Pergamon, 1977. Contributor to professional journals.

WORK IN PROGRESS: Journeyings: A Social-Psychological Exploration of the Holocaust; The Differential Diagnosis of Schizophrenia and Brain Damage: The Rorschach vs. the Halstead-Reitan; The Critical Indices of Brain Damage: A Statistical Analysis of Psychological Test Data; The Mind of the Terrorist.

KNUTSON, Kent S(iguart)   1924-1973

August 7, 1924—March 12, 1973; American Lutheran minister and leader, educator, and writer. Obituaries: *Newsweek*, March 26, 1973. (See index for *CA* sketch)

*   *   *

KOBRIN, David   1941-

PERSONAL: Born April 13, 1941, in New York, N.Y.; son of Abraham and Ruth (Adelson) Kobrin; married Frances Engeman (a demographer), September, 1961; children: Sarah, Janet. *Education:* Brown University, B.A., 1962; University of Pennsylvania, M.A., 1964, Ph.D., 1968. *Residence:* Saratoga Springs, N.Y. *Office:* Department of History, State University of New York, Albany, N.Y. 12203.

CAREER: State University of New York at Albany, assistant professor of history, 1968—. *Member:* American Historical Association, Group on the Use of Psychology in History. *Awards, honors:* Faculty research fellowships, Research Foundation of the State University of New York, 1969, 1970; New York State Department of Mental Hygiene training grant, 1969-70.

WRITINGS: The Black Minority in Early New York, State University of New York Press, 1971. Contributor to *Church History.*

WORK IN PROGRESS: A book-length manuscript, *History and Group Process: The Historian as Participant Observer;* a work of fiction.††

*   *   *

KOHN, Melvin L(ester)   1928-

PERSONAL: Born October 19, 1928, in New York, N.Y.; son of Albert (a charter fishing boat captain) and Rose (Mickenberg) Kohn; married Janet Goldrich (an attorney), October 3, 1952. *Education:* Attended Deep Springs Junior College, 1944-46; Cornell University, B.A., 1948, Ph.D., 1952. *Residence:* Washington, D.C. *Office:* National Institute of Mental Health, Building 31, Room 4C 11, Bethesda, Md. 20014.

CAREER: National Institute of Mental Health, Bethesda, Md., research sociologist, 1952—, chief of Laboratory of Socio-environmental Studies, 1960—. *Member:* American Sociological Association, American Association for the Advancement of Science, Sociological Research Association. *Awards, honors:* Ernest W. Burgess Award from National Council on Family Relations, 1961.

WRITINGS: (Contributor) Benjamin Pasamanik, editor, *Epidemiology of Mental Disorder,* American Association for the Advancement of Science, 1959; (contributor) D. D. Jackson, editor, *The Etiology of Schizophrenia,* Basic Books, 1960; (contributor) Frederick Yu, editor, *Behavioral Science and the Mass Media,* Russell Sage, 1968; *Class and Conformity: A Study in Values,* Dorsey, 1969, 2nd edition, University of Chicago Press, 1977. Contributor to *Encyclopedia of Mental Health.* Contributor of about thirty articles and reviews to journals in the behavioral sciences, including *American Sociological Review, American Journal of Sociology, American Journal of Orthopsychiatry, Sociometry, Social Forces, Science, Schizophrenia Bulletin,* and *Journal of Psychiatric Research.* Member of board of editors, *American Sociological Review, American Journal of Sociology, Sociometry,* and *Schizophrenia Bulletin.*

WORK IN PROGRESS: Research on occupation and values.

KOHR, Louise Hannah   1903-

PERSONAL: Born June, 1903, in Dexter, Kan.; daughter of Will and Myrtle (Williamson) Hannah; married Harold Bowman Kohr, June 17, 1929; children: David, Thomas, Michael, Mary (Mrs. William Snyder). *Education:* Attended public schools in Kansas; studied at Kansas State University and Washington University. *Politics:* "Befuddled." *Religion:* Presbyterian.

WRITINGS: Fragrance of Geraniums (novel), Douglas-West, 1972. Contributor of more than eight hundred stories, articles, and photographs to religious magazines and newspapers.

WORK IN PROGRESS: Two books of Indian lore; a book on butterflies; story of a mission at Guadalupe.

AVOCATIONAL INTERESTS: Travel in Europe and the Middle East, and extensively in the United States.

*   *   *

KOILPILLAI, (Jesudas) Charles   (Das Koilpillai)

PERSONAL: Born in Madras, India. *Education:* Madras University, M.A., 1954; McGill University, Ph.D., 1958. *Home:* 147 Hogarth, Thunder Bay, Ontario, Canada. *Office:* Department of Economics, Lakehead University, Thunder Bay, Ontario, Canada.

CAREER: University of Manitoba, Winnipeg, assistant professor, 1959-65, associate professor of economics, 1965-66; Lakehead University, Thunder Bay, Ontario, professor of economics, 1966—, chairman of department, 1966-73. United Nations, economic affairs officer, 1967, 1968, 1970, social affairs officer, 1972-73; research economist, Canadian International Development Agency. *Member:* Canadian Economic Association, American Economic Association, Royal Economic Society, Indian Economic Association.

WRITINGS: Myth of Inflation, University of Manitoba, 1966, 2nd edition, 1968; *The Power of Negative Thinking and Other Parables from India,* Longmans, 1973; *Self-Knowledge,* Val Morin, 1974. Contributor to economic journals and literary publications, including poetry written under pseudonym, Das Koilpillai.

WORK IN PROGRESS: A book on economic development.

AVOCATIONAL INTERESTS: Indian philosophy, yoga, poetry, naturopathy.

*   *   *

KOLATCH, Jonathan   1943-

PERSONAL: Born September 2, 1943, in Hackensack, N.J.; son of Alfred Jacob (a publisher) and Thelma (Rubin) Kolatch. *Education:* Queens College of City University of New York, B.A., 1965; Harvard University, M.A., 1967; Columbia University, Ph.D., 1970. *Religion:* Jewish. *Home:* 72-08 Juno St., Forest Hills, N.Y. 11375. *Office:* Jonathan David Publishers, 68-22 Eliot Ave., Middle Village, N.Y. 11379.

CAREER: Massachusetts Institute of Technology, Cambridge, assistant baseball coach, 1966; Jonathan David Publishers, Middle Village, N.Y., vice-president, 1970—. *Member:* Association for Asian Studies, Phi Beta Kappa.

WRITINGS: Sports, Politics and Ideology in China, Jonathan David, 1972; (translator from the Hebrew) David Ben-Gurion, *Ben-Gurion Looks at the Bible,* Jonathan David, 1972.

KOLCHIN, Peter 1943-

PERSONAL: Born June 3, 1943, in Washington, D.C.; son of Ellis Robert (a mathematician) and Kate (Weil) Kolchin; married Anne M. Boylan (a historian), 1975. *Education:* Columbia University, A.B., 1964; Johns Hopkins University, Ph.D., 1970. *Home:* 3515 La Hacienda Pl. N.E., Albuquerque, N.M. 87106. *Office:* Department of History, University of New Mexico, Albuquerque, N.M. 87131.

CAREER: University of California, Davis, lecturer in history, 1968-69; University of Wisconsin—Madison, assistant professor of history, 1969-75; University of New Mexico, Albuquerque, associate professor of history, 1976—. *Member:* American Historical Association, Organization of American Historians, Southern Historical Association. *Awards, honors:* National Endowment for the Humanities fellowship in Afro-American history, 1971-72, fellowship for independent study and research, 1975-76; Charles Warren Center fellow, Harvard University, 1975-76.

WRITINGS: First Freedom: The Responses of Alabama's Blacks to Emancipation and Reconstruction, Greenwood Press, 1972. Contributor to *Journal of Southern History, Journal of Social History,* and *Reviews in American History.*

WORK IN PROGRESS: Research on a comparative study of American slavery and Russian serfdom.

*   *   *

KOLLAT, David T(ruman) 1938-

PERSONAL: Born July 7, 1938, in Elkhart, Ind.; son of Walter A. (a businessman) and Mildred E. (Good) Kollat; married Mary A. Maroon, January 2, 1965; children: Lisa, Andra. *Education:* Western Michigan University, B.B.A., 1960, M.B.A., 1962; Indiana University, D.B.A., 1966. *Office:* Management Horizons, Inc., 1651 Northwest Professional Plaza, Columbus, Ohio, 43220.

CAREER: Ohio State University, Columbus, assistant professor, 1965-68, associate professor, 1968-71, professor of marketing, 1971-72; Management Horizons, Inc., Columbus, Ohio, vice-president, 1968-72, executive vice-president and director of research, 1973—. *Member:* American Marketing Association, Association for Consumer Research, American Academy of Advertising, Beta Gamma Sigma, Omicron Delta Kappa.

WRITINGS: (With James F. Engel and Roger D. Blackwell) *Consumer Behavior,* Holt, 1968, 2nd edition, 1973; (with Engel and Blackwell) *Cases in Consumer Behavior,* Holt, 1969; (compiler with Engel and Blackwell) *Research in Consumer Behavior,* Holt, 1970; (with James Robeson and Blackwell) *Strategic Marketing,* Holt, 1972.†

*   *   *

KOOB, C(harles) Albert 1920-

PERSONAL: Born September 22, 1920, in Philadelphia, Pa. *Education:* St. Norbert College, B.A., 1942; Catholic University of America, M.A., 1948, Ph.D., 1978. *Home and office:* Daylesford Abbey, 220 South Valley Rd., Paoli, Pa. 19301.

CAREER: Roman Catholic priest; Southeast Catholic High School (now Bishop Neumann High School), Philadelphia, Pa., instructor, 1942-48, vice-principal, 1948-54, principal, 1954-61; National Catholic Education Association, Washington, D.C., associate secretary in secondary school department, 1961-66, interim executive secretary, 1966-67,

executive secretary, 1967-69, president, 1969—; Daylesford Abbey, Institute for Religion and Culture, Paoli, Pa., assistant director, 1978—. Instructor, St. John's Night School, 1951-53; prior, St. Norbert Priory, 1954-61; member of advisory committee, Educational Testing Service and National Assessment of Educational Progress; member of board of directors, National Merit Scholarship Corp. and Joint Council on Economic Education; member of board of trustees, St. Norbert College; member of commission on reform in secondary education, IDEA-Kettering Foundation; member of national advisory committee, Institute of Studies in Education (Notre Dame, Ind.); member of national advisory council, Scholastic Magazines, Inc. Project director, Program to Evaluate Catholic Education in Peru, 1965; delegate to Tenth Congress, Interamerican Catholic Education Association, Mexico City, 1969; participant in Seventh World Congress, World Union of Catholic Teachers, Montreal, 1970; participant in First National Conference on Administration of Catholic Education (Australia), 1972. Consultant to School of Education, Catholic University of America, 1974-78; adult education consultant to Cabrini College, 1978—.

MEMBER: Religious Education Association (member of board of directors), National Reading Council. *Awards, honors:* Ed.D., La Salle College, 1961; St. John Baptist de la Salle Medal for Leadership in Education, Manhattan College, 1968; D.H.L., Lewis College, 1970.

WRITINGS: (With Melvin P. Heller) *Catholic Secondary School Administration,* Bruce, 1968; (editor and contributor) *What Is Happening to Catholic Education?,* National Catholic Education Association, 1966; (editor with J. Lloyd Trump) *Shaping the Future,* National Catholic Education Association, 1967; (with Russell Shaw) *S.O.S. for Catholic Schools,* Holt, 1970. Editor, *Catholic High School Quarterly Bulletin,* 1961-66, *Pointers for Principals,* 1961-66, and *Alive,* 1969-74.

*   *   *

KOONTZ, Harold 1908-

PERSONAL: Born May 19, 1908, in Findlay, Ohio; son of Joseph Darius (a school principal) and Harriett (Dillinger) Koontz; married Mary Learey, June 16, 1935; children: Karen Kathryn Koontz Shair, Jeanne Carol Koontz Gullixson. *Education:* Oberlin College, A.B., 1930; Northwestern University, M.B.A., 1931; Yale University, Ph.D., 1935. *Politics:* Republican. *Religion:* Methodist. *Home:* 4838 Gloria Ave., Encino, Calif. 91316. *Office:* Graduate School of Business Administration, University of California, Los Angeles, Calif. 90024.

CAREER: Duke University, Durham, N.C., instructor in business administration, 1933-34; University of Toledo, Toledo, Ohio, instructor in accounting and transportation, 1934-35; Colgate University, Hamilton, N.Y., assistant professor of economics, 1935-42; War Production Board, Office of Civilian Requirements, Washington, D.C., chief of traffic branch, 1942-44; Association of American Railroads, Washington, D.C., assistant to vice-president in charge of research, 1944-45; Trans-World Airlines, Kansas City, Mo., assistant to president and director of planning, 1945-48; Consolidated Vultee Aircraft Corp., San Diego, Calif., director of commercial sales, 1948-50; University of California, Los Angeles, professor of business policy and transportation, 1950-62, Mead Johnson Professor of Management, 1962—. Cost analyst, New Haven & Hartford Railroad, 1936; president, Institute for Administrative Research, 1966-

70; chairman of board of directors, Genisco Technical Corp., 1960-72; member of board of directors, Farr Corp., Dust Control, Inc., Planning Dynamics, Inc., 1968-71, and Business Student Aid Foundation, Inc., 1978—. Consultant to government offices and prominent corporations, including Lockheed Aircraft Co., Metropolitan Life Insurance Co., Bank of America, Nippon Management Association (Tokyo), County of Los Angeles, and U.S. Internal Revenue Service.

MEMBER: International Academy of Management (fellow; member of board of governors, 1966-69; world chancellor, 1975—), Academy of Management (fellow; president, 1963), Society for the Advancement of Management, Institute of Management Sciences, American Society of Traffic and Transportation (founding member), Beta Gamma Sigma, Alpha Kappa Psi. *Awards, honors:* Distinguished service award from Society for Advancement of Management, 1957; Mead Johnson award, 1962; award from Academy of Management, for *The Board of Directors and Effective Management,* 1967; U.S. Air Force Air University award, 1971; Taylor Key award, Society for the Advancement of Management, 1974; Fort Findlay Award, 1975; Cowley award for best article on health care administration, 1976.

WRITINGS: Government Control of Business, Houghton, 1941; (with Cyril O'Donnell) *Principles of Management,* McGraw, 1955, 6th edition, 1976; (with R. W. Gable) *Public Control of Private Enterprise,* McGraw, 1956; (editor with O'Donnell) *Reading in Management,* McGraw, 1959; *Toward a Unified Theory of Management,* McGraw, 1964; (with O'Donnell) *Management: A Book of Readings,* McGraw, 1964, 4th edition, 1976; *Requirements for Basic and Professional Education for Scientific Management,* British Institute of Management, 1964; *The Board of Directors and Effective Management,* McGraw, 1967; *Appraising Managers as Managers,* McGraw, 1971; (with O'Donnell) *Essentials of Management,* McGraw, 1974, 2nd edition, 1978; (with R. M. Fulmer) *A Practical Introduction to Business,* Irwin, 1975, 2nd edition, 1978; *Management: A System of Continuing Analysis of Managerial Function,* McGraw, 1976.

Contributor of over seventy articles to management and economic journals, and to *Railway Age, Journal of Air Law and Commerce,* and *Public Utilities Fortnightly.* Member of board of editors: *California Management Review, Academy of Management Journal, Transportation Journal,* and *Journal of Economics and Business.*

*   *   *

KOPP, Harriet Green

PERSONAL: Born in New York, N.Y.; married George A. Kopp, June 19, 1948 (died, 1968); married Kurt Friedrich, November 22, 1972. *Education:* Brooklyn College (now Brooklyn College of the City University of New York), B.A., 1937, M.A., 1939; Lexington School for the Deaf, diploma, 1940; Columbia University, Ph.D., 1962. *Office:* Department of Speech Pathology and Audiology, San Diego State University, San Diego, Calif. 92115.

CAREER: Brooklyn College (now Brooklyn College of the City University of New York), Brooklyn, N.Y., instructor in phonetics and teacher in speech and hearing clinic, 1937-40; Indiana University at Bloomington, instructor in audiology and education of the deaf, 1941-42; Eastern Michigan University, Ypsilanti, assistant professor of speech correction and director of programs for speech correction and the deaf in demonstration school, 1946-48; director of

speech correction in Birmingham, Mich., 1948-55; Rehabilitation Institute of Metropolitan Detroit, Detroit, Mich., director of speech and hearing clinic, 1955-59; Detroit Day School for the Deaf, Detroit, principal, 1959-70; San Diego State University, San Diego, Calif., professor of speech pathology and audiology, 1970—, director of deaf program, 1970—. Teachers College, Columbia University, supervisor of speech and hearing clinic, 1939-40, 1941-43, research associate in clinical methods, 1940-41, 1942-43; member of adjunct faculty in deaf education and speech science, Wayne State University, 1949-70. Member of research staff at Bell Telephone Laboratories, 1943-46; member of advisory committee on establishment of National Technical Institute for the Deaf, 1965-66.

MEMBER: American Speech and Hearing Association (fellow; member of board of directors), National Advisory Council on Education of the Deaf (chairman, 1970-72), American Instructors of the Deaf, Council for Exceptional Children, Conference of Executives, Alexander Graham Bell Association for the Deaf (member of board of directors, 1962-70).

WRITINGS: Some Functional Applications of Basic Phonetic Principles, Edwards Letter Press, 1940, 4th edition, Neyensch, 1971; (with husband, George A. Kopp, and Ralph K. Potter) *Visible Speech,* Dover, 1966; (with G. A. Kopp and Angelo Angelucci) *Visible Speech for the Deaf,* Wayne State University Press, 1967; *Systems Concepts in the Education of the Deaf,* Annals of the Deaf, Gallaudet College, 1967; (editor and contributor) *Special Education and Programs for Disadvantaged Children and Youth,* Council for Exceptional Children, 1968; (editor) *Proceedings of the First Annual Forum,* Council of Organizations Serving the Deaf, 1968; (editor) *Curriculum, Cognition and Content* (monograph), Alexander Graham Bell Association for the Deaf, 1968. Contributor to proceedings. Contributor to *Volta Review.* Chairman of editorial policies board, *Volta Review;* associate editor of publications of American Speech and Hearing Association.

WORK IN PROGRESS: Research on physiologic phonetics in speech correction and development and on real-time spectrographic display; a book, *Physiologic Phonetics and Speech.*

*   *   *

KORNBLUM, Sylvan 1927-

PERSONAL: Born September 15, 1927, in Antwerp, Belgium; married Elizabeth Dorothea Humes (a concert singer), December 30, 1970; children: two. *Education:* Washington University, St. Louis, Mo., B.A., 1951; University of Michigan, M.A., 1953, Ph.D., 1960. *Home:* 3541 Daleview, Ann Arbor, Mich. 48105. *Office:* Mental Health Research Institute, University of Michigan, Ann Arbor, Mich. 48109.

CAREER: Currently research psychologist and professor of psychology, University of Michigan, Mental Health Research Institute, Ann Arbor. *Military service:* U.S. Army, 1945-47. *Member:* International Association for the Study of Attention and Performance (secretary/treasurer), American Psychological Association, American Association for the Advancement of Science, Psychonomic Society, Sigma Xi.

WRITINGS: Attention and Performance IV, Academic Press, 1973. Contributor to professional journals. Consulting editor, *Perception and Psychophysics* and *Acta Psychologica.*

KORNHAUSER, David H(enry) 1918-

PERSONAL: Born March 17, 1918, in Philadelphia, Pa.; son of David Emmanuel (an artist) and Mary Elizabeth (Parker) Kornhauser; married Kyoko Nakamura, February 12, 1948 (died April, 1963); married Michiko Usui, July 20, 1965; children: (second marriage) David Hajime. *Education:* Bucknell University, B.A., 1941; University of Michigan, M.A., 1951, Ph.D., 1956. *Home:* 5089 Maunalani Cir., Honolulu, Hawaii 96816. *Office:* Department of Geography, Room 415, 2424 Maile Way, University of Hawaii, Honolulu, Hawaii 96822.

CAREER: Member of headquarters in Osaka and Tokyo, Supreme Commander of Allied Powers in Japan, 1946-50; Pennsylvania State University, State College, assistant professor of geography, 1955-56; State University of New York College at New Paltz, associate professor of geography, 1956-63; University of Hawaii, Honolulu, professor of geography and Asian studies, 1963—. *Military service:* U.S. Army, 1943-47; became second lieutenant. *Member:* Association of American Geographers, American Geographical Association, Association of Japanese Geographers, Association for Asian Studies, Pacific Science Association. *Awards, honors:* Fulbright fellow, Tokyo Kyoiko University, Japan, 1959-60, University of Hawaii, 1964-65; Japan Society for Promotion of Science grant, summer, 1972.

WRITINGS: Urban Japan: Its Foundations and Growth, Longman, 1976. Also author of *Science Reports.* Contributor to *Encyclopedia Americana* and *Encyclopaedia Britannica;* contributor of articles to academic journals.

WORK IN PROGRESS: Research on growth and development of Japanese cities.

AVOCATIONAL INTERESTS: Music, photography.

*   *   *

KORTEN, David C(raig) 1937-

PERSONAL: Born July 30, 1937, in Longview, Wash.; son of Theodore Frederick (a corporation president) and Margaret (Heltzel) Korten; married Frances Fisher (a research psychologist), June 21, 1962; children: Diana Fisher, Alicia Margaret. *Education:* Stanford University, A.B., 1959, M.B.A., 1961, Ph.D., 1968. *Permanent home address:* 2327 Cascade Way, Longview, Wash. 98632. *Office:* Ford Foundation, MCC P.O. Box 740, Makati 3117, Metro Manila, Philippines.

CAREER: Haile Selassie I University, Addis Ababa, Ethiopia, Fulbright lecturer, assistant dean of College of Business Administration, and director of research, 1963-66; Instituto Centroamericano de Administracion de Empresas, Managua, Nicaragua, academic director, 1970-72, director of planning and institutional development, 1972-73; Harvard University, Cambridge, Mass., visiting associate professor of business administration, 1970-75, lecturer in population studies, 1976-78, associate of Institute for International Development, 1975-77; project specialist in population and social development management, Ford Foundation, 1977—. Visiting professor, Asian Institute of Management, 1976—. Member of board of directors, Technoserve, 1976-77. *Military service:* U.S. Air Force, 1967-70; became captain.

MEMBER: American Association for Humanistic Psychology, American Public Health Association, Common Cause, New Directions, Society for International Development, World Future Society, American Civil Liberties Union (chairman of Northwest Florida chapter, 1968).

WRITINGS: Planned Change in a Traditional Society:

Psychological Problems of Modernization in Ethiopia, Praeger, 1972. Also author of *Casebook for Family Planning Management: Motivating Effective Clinic Performance,* 1977, and *Population and Social Development Management: Challenge for Management Schools,* 1978.

Contributor: Dorwin Cartwright and Alvin Zander, editors, *Group Dynamics: Research and Theory,* 3rd edition (Korten was not associated with earlier editions), Harper, 1968; Glenn D. Paige, editor, *Political Leadership: Readings for an Emerging Field,* Free Press, 1972; Warren Ilchman, Harold Lasswell, John D. Montgomery, and Myron Weiner, editors, *Policy Studies and Population,* Heath, 1975; *A Study of Organizational Leadership,* Stackpole, 1976; Lawrence D. Stifel, James S. Coleman, and Joseph E. Black, editors, *Education and Training for Public Sector Management in Developing Countries,* Rockefeller Foundation, 1977. Also contributor, Montgomery and Joel Migda, editors, *Patterns in Policy.* Contributor of articles to journals, including *Studies in Family Planning, Journal of Applied Behavioral Science, Journal of Cross-Cultural Psychology,* and *Comparative Education Review.*

WORK IN PROGRESS: Editing a volume of Third World field research studies leading to a management technology for social development.

SIDELIGHTS: David C. Korten told *CA:* "In my earlier professional years, few of the things I wrote bore any evident relationship to one another, though most had to do with one or another aspect of development, culture, or organization. Over the past three years I have come to concentrate on a single theme, the creation of the management technologies required to achieve social development objectives in the Third World. Concerns for equity and the participation of the poor in decisions that affect their lives are not addressed adequately by the management models that have dominated thought and action in public management. A management technology more appropriate to these objectives is in the making by a group of major Third World management institutes. My current writing seeks to gain broader application of this work and to sharpen the definition of the conceptual frameworks which are emerging."

*   *   *

KORTEPETER, (Carl) Max 1928-

PERSONAL: Born May 27, 1928, in Indianapolis, Ind.; son of Carl F. (a civil engineer) and Olive (Derbyshire) Kortepeter; married Cynthia King, April 7, 1957; children: four sons, 2 daughters. *Education:* Harvard University, A.B., 1950; McGill University, M.A., 1954; University of Michigan, graduate study, 1956-57; University of London, Ph.D., 1962. *Home address:* R.D. 2, Box 166, Belle Meade, N.J. 08502. *Office:* Department of History, New York University, Washington Square, New York, N.Y. 10003.

CAREER: Robert College, Istanbul, Turkey, instructor in biology, 1950-53; University of Toronto, Toronto, Ontario, lecturer, 1961-63, assistant professor, 1963-66, associate professor of Islamic history, 1966-67, member of faculty council, 1964-66; New York University, New York, N.Y., associate professor of Near East history, 1967—, acting chairman of department of Near Eastern languages and literatures, 1968-70, acting director of Center for Near Eastern Studies, 1969-70. Visiting professor at Princeton University, 1969-70, and New Brunswick Seminary, 1977-78; special lecturer on Middle East, U.S. Department of State, 1977-78. Member of board of directors, Center for Slavonic and East European Studies (Toronto), 1964-66; secretary, American

Research Institute in Turkey, 1969-72; founder and director, Middle East Systems (consulting firm), 1975—. Consultant on subjects about the Middle East to television and radio. Member of Griggstown Voluntary Fire Co., 1968-77; member of board of directors, Mercer Symphonic Orchestra, 1976—. *Military service:* U.S. Marine Corps Reserve, 1947-54; became first lieutenant. U.S. Army Reserve, 1954-57; active duty, 1954-56; became master sergeant.

MEMBER: Middle East Institute, Middle East Studies Association (member of committee on research, 1968-70), American Association of University Professors (vice-president of humanities division, New York University chapter, 1972-73), Turkish Studies Association, American Historical Association, Society of Russian-American Scholars, Americans for Middle East Understanding (secretary, 1972, 1973-76). *Awards, honors:* Institute of Islamic Studies grant, McGill University, 1953; travel grant to Istanbul from University of London, 1960; American Research Institute in Turkey senior fellow, 1966-67; commendation from National Security Council of the United States, 1969; IREX travel grant, American Council of Learned Societies, 1973; American Research Institute in Egypt senior fellow, 1978-79.

WRITINGS: (Contributor) R. Schoeck, editor, *Editing Sixteenth Century Texts,* University of Toronto Press, 1967; (editor and contributor) *Modern Near East: Literature and Society,* Center for Near Eastern Studies, New York University, 1971; *Ottoman Imperialism During the Reformation: Europe and the Caucasus,* New York University Press, 1972; (contributor) Donald Little, editor, *Essays on Islamic Civilization Presented to Niyazi Berkes,* [Leiden], 1975; (contributor) Kemel Karpat, editor, *Institutions of the Ottoman Empire,* [Leiden], 1975; (contributor) *International Symposium on the Reforms of Atatruk,* [Istanbul], 1975. Consulting editor, United Nations children's series on the Middle East, 1968-69; history editor, "All-Color" series, Grosset, 1970-71. Contributor to proceedings of Association of Russian-American Scholars, *New World Encyclopedia, Encyclopedia of Islam,* and journals.

WORK IN PROGRESS: Two Centuries of American Experience in the Middle East, 1776-1976; A History of the Arabian Peninsula.

AVOCATIONAL INTERESTS: Athletics, folk dancing.

* * *

KOUMOULIDES, John (Thomas Anastassios) 1938-

PERSONAL: Born August 23, 1938, in Greece; naturalized U.S. citizen; son of Anastassios L. and Sophia (Theodossiadou) Koumoulides. *Education:* Montclair State College, A.B., 1960, M.A., 1961; Fitzwilliam College, Cambridge, graduate study, 1966-67; University of Maryland, Ph.D., 1968. *Religion:* Greek Orthodox. *Home:* 810 Wayne St., Muncie, Ind. 47303. *Office:* Department of History, Ball State University, Muncie, Ind. 47306.

CAREER: Austin Peay State University, Clarksville, Tenn., assistant professor of history, 1963-64; Ball State University, Muncie, Ind., assistant professor, 1968-70, associate professor, 1971-75, professor of history, 1975—. Visiting assistant professor, Vanderbilt University, summer, 1968; visiting fellow at Fitzwilliam College, Cambridge, 1971-72. *Member:* American Historical Association, Archaeological Institute of America, Society for the Promotion of Hellenic Studies, Modern Greek Studies Association, American Association of University Professors, British Historical Association, Cambridge Philological Society, Cambridge University Historical Society, Indiana Academy of

Social Sciences, Phi Alpha Theta. *Awards, honors:* Ball State University faculty research grants, 1969-70; American Council of Learned Societies travel grants, 1969, 1971, 1974; American Philosophical Society research grant, 1974; Fulbright-Hays senior scholar, 1977-78.

WRITINGS: Cyprus and the War of Greek Independence: 1821-1829, National Centre of Social Research (Athens), 1971, revised, enlarged edition, Zeno Publishers (London), 1974; (editor) *Summer in a Greek Village,* Ball State University, 1973; (editor with D. W. Hoover) *Focus on Biography,* Ball State University, 1975; (with Christopher Walter) *Byzantine and Post-Byzantine Monuments at Aghia in Thessaly, Greece,* Zeno Publishers, 1975.

AVOCATIONAL INTERESTS: Travel, photography, archaeology.

* * *

KOZIEBRODZKI, Leopold B(olesta) 1906-

PERSONAL: Born December 10, 1906, in Podhajczyki, Poland; naturalized U.S. citizen; son of Leopold B. (a count and diplomat) and Mary (Stillfried) Koziebrodzki; married Wladyslawa Brzezinska, December 13, 1955. *Education:* Attended University of Lwow, 1924-26; University of Warsaw, M.Law & Pol.Sci., 1928; University of Paris, D.Law, 1956; University of Texas, Main University (now University of Texas at Austin), postdoctoral study, 1958-59. *Religion:* Roman Catholic. *Home:* 1500 Oakview Dr., McLean, Va. 22101.

CAREER: Attached to Polish Ministry of Foreign Affairs, Warsaw, 1928-39, served as charge d'affaires in Spain, 1936-37, division head in exile in London, England, 1943-45; British Broadcasting Corp., London, England, program assistant and announcer in Polish section, 1941-43; United Nations Secretariat, Paris, France, conference officer, 1948, 1951-52; National Bureau of Economic Research, New York, N.Y., research assistant, 1957; St. Edward's University, Austin, Tex., assistant professor of economics, 1957-59; University of North Carolina at Chapel Hill, visiting lecturer, 1959-60, acting associate professor of economics and history, 1960-63; Research Analysis Corp., McLean, Va., senior member of professional staff, 1963-68. Vice-president, Brookhaven Civic Association, 1966-67; president, Lake Wilderness Property Owner's Association, 1971—. *Military service:* Polish Army, 1939-47; served in France and Great Britain; became major.

MEMBER: American Economic Association, American Society of International Law. *Awards, honors:* Knight, Polonia Restituta, 1936; Corona d'Italia award, 1939.

WRITINGS: Le Droit d'Asile, Sijthoff, 1962; (with Joseph T. Hart and others) *Strategic Analysis of Latin America, 1965-75* (monograph), Research Analysis Corp., 1966; (principal author) *Environmental Trends in Latin America* (monograph), Research Analysis Corp., 1968; (principal author) *Potential for Internal Conflict in Latin American Countries* (monograph), Research Analysis Corp., 1968; (principal author) *U.S. Strategic Interests in Latin American Countries* (monograph), Research Analysis Corp., 1969; (principal author) *Latin American Ties with Major Extra-Hemispheric Powers* (monograph), Research Analysis Corp., 1969; (principal author) *Third Country Military Assistance* (monograph), Research Analysis Corp., 1969; (with Dominik Lasok and others) *Polish Civil Law,* Sijthoff, Volume I, 1973. Contributor of articles and reviews to *American Journal of Comparative Law* and to political science journals.

WORK IN PROGRESS: The Glory and Misery of an Exchange Reserve Currency (tentative title).

SIDELIGHTS: Leopold Koziebrodzki's six monographs are classified as secret, although the titles are not similarly restricted. He speaks French, Polish, German, Spanish, Russian, and Rumanian, has lived in Austria, Poland, France, Czechoslovakia, Great Britain, Germany, Spain, and Rumania, and has traveled throughout Latin America.

* * *

KRAFT, Hy(man Solomon) 1899-1975

PERSONAL: Born April 30, 1899, in New York, N.Y.; son of Abraham (a tailor) and Yetta (Gellis) Kraft; married Reata Lautterstein (an interior decorator), May 17, 1938; children: Jill Kraft Herman (deceased). *Education:* Attended public schools in New York, N.Y. *Religion:* Jewish. *Home:* 221 West 82nd St., New York, N.Y. 10024.

CAREER: After early experience as a newspaperman and as assistant to Sigmund Spaeth (a musicologist), became a full-time writer. *Member:* Dramatists Guild, Authors League of America. *Awards, honors:* Citation from U.S. Treasury Dept., for "Treasury Parade" scripts, 1942.

WRITINGS—All plays, except as indicated: "Ten Per Cent," first produced on Broadway at George M. Cohan Theatre, September 13, 1927; (with Mark Hellinger, Lew Brown, and Ray Henderson) "Hot-Cha" (musical), first produced on Broadway at Ziegfeld Theatre, March 8, 1932; (with Edward Chodorov) *Cue for Passion* (first produced on Broadway at Royale Theatre, December 19, 1940), Samuel French, 1944; *Cafe Crown* (first produced on Broadway at Cort Theatre, January 23, 1942), Dramatists Play Service, 1952, author of book for musical version (first produced on Broadway at Martin Beck Theatre, April 17, 1964), Studio Duplicating Service, 1964; (with Eric Maschwitz) "Summer Song," first produced in London at Prince of Wales Theatre, February 16, 1956; (author of introduction) Borden Deal, *The Tobacco Men* (novel; based on notes by Kraft and Theodore Dreiser), Holt, 1965; *On My Way to the Theater* (autobiography), Macmillan, 1971.

Filmscripts: (Adapter with author of novel, Theodore Dreiser) "An American Tragedy," Paramount, 1932; (with Billy Wilder) "Champagne Waltz," Paramount, 1933; (with Oscar Hammerstein II) "Way of the River," MGM, 1938; "Stormy Weather," Fox, 1942; (with Dreiser) "Tobacco Story," Garrick Films, 1964 (script completed in 1933).

Television scripts: "Starlight Theater" productions, CBS, 1951; "Spectacular for Water Rats," BBC, 1956; "Robin Hood," Official Films, 1960; "Four Just Men," Official Films, 1960; "Gomer Pyle," 1963; "Hercules," TV pilot for Embassy.

(Writer and originator with Cy Howard) "Life with Luigi" (radio series) for CBS. Represented in *The Treasury Star Parade* (radio scripts), edited by William A. Bacher, Farrar & Rinehart, 1942. Contributor to *Variety, Screen Writers Guild Magazine, New Theatre League,* and other periodicals.

WORK IN PROGRESS: The Half Past Eight Curtain Will Positively Go up at Nine O'Clock Promptly, a story of the Yiddish Theatre in New York.

BIOGRAPHICAL/CRITICAL SOURCES: Variety, July 1, 1970; *Best Sellers,* August 15, 1971; *New York Times Book Review,* December 19, 1971.†

(Died July 29, 1975)

KRAFT, Leo 1922-

PERSONAL: Born July 24, 1922, in New York, N.Y.; son of Nathan (with U.S. Internal Revenue Service) and Yetta (Kaplowitz) Kraft; married Amy Lager (a psychologist), May 16, 1945; children: David, Evan. *Education:* Queens College of the City of New York (now Queens College of the City University of New York), B.A., 1945; Princeton University, M.F.A., 1947. *Home:* 9 Dunster Rd., Great Neck, N.Y. 11021. *Office:* Department of Music, Queens College of the City University of New York, Flushing, N.Y. 11367.

CAREER: Queens College of the City University of New York, Flushing, N.Y., 1947—, began as assistant professor, currently professor of music. President, American Music Center, 1976-78. *Military service:* U.S. Army Air Forces, 1943. *Member:* International Society for Contemporary Music (member of board of directors, 1970-78), Society for Music Theory (member of executive committee), American Society of University Composers, American Society of Composers, Authors and Publishers, College Music Society (second vice-president, 1970-71). *Awards, honors:* Fulbright fellow, 1954-55; National Endowment for the Arts fellowship, 1976.

WRITINGS: (With Sol Berkowitz and Gabriel Frontrier) *A New Approach to Sight Singing,* Norton, 1960, revised edition, 1976; *A New Approach to Ear Training: Book I, Melody,* Norton, 1967; *Gradus,* Norton, 1976. Also co-author of *A New Approach to Keyboard Harmony.*

Choral music: *Festival Song,* Mercury Music, 1951; *A Proverb for Solomon,* General Music, 1953; *Let Me Laugh,* Theodore Presser, 1954; *Thanksgiving,* Mercury Music, 1958; *When Israel Came Forth,* Theodore Presser, 1963; *I Waited Patiently,* Mercury Music, 1964; *A New Song,* Mercury Music, 1966; *Eight Choral Songs,* General Music, 1977. Also composer of "Psalm 114," 1961, "Four English Love Songs," 1961, and "Psalm 40," 1963.

Instrumental music: *Two's Company,* Boosey & Hawkes, 1957; *Partita #1* and *Partita #3,* General Music, 1969; *Five Pieces for Clarinet and Piano,* General Music, 1969; *Toccata for Band,* General Music, 1970; *Fantasy for Flute and Piano,* General Music, 1971; *Dualities,* General Music, 1971; *Short Sonata #1 for Harpsichord or Piano,* General Music, 1972; *Line Drawings,* General Music, 1972. Also composer of "Variations for Orchestra," 1958, "String Quartet 2," 1959, "Three Pieces for Orchestra," 1963, "Trios and Interludes," 1965, "Concerto Number 2," 1966, "Dialogues for Flute and Tape," 1967, "Concerto Number 3," 1969, "Sestina," 1971, "Music for Orchestra," 1975, "Partita 4," 1975, "Dialectica," and "Concerto for Piano and Fourteen Instruments."

SIDELIGHTS: Many of Leo Kraft's instrumental works have been recorded.

* * *

KRAMER, Jack 1923-

PERSONAL: Born February 24, 1923, in Lynn, Mass.; son of Charles and Sarah (Lipschitz) Kramer. *Education:* Attended School of the Museum of Fine Arts, Boston, Mass., 1941-43, 1945-49 and University of Reading, 1950; studied in Europe, 1950-53; Rhode Island School of Design, B.F.A., 1954; also studied privately with artist Oscar Kokoschka, 1950. *Home and studio:* 30 Ipswich St., Boston, Mass. 02215. *Office:* School for the Arts, Boston University, 855 Commonwealth Ave., Boston, Mass. 02215.

CAREER: University of Illinois at Urbana-Champaign, instructor in art, 1955-56; Boston University, Boston, Mass., assistant professor, 1957-64, associate professor, 1964-71, professor of art, 1971—. Assistant to Oscar Kokoschka in Salzburg, Austria, summers, 1955-58; collections exhibited at William Gurlitt Museum (Linz, Austria), Addison Gallery of American Art (Phillips Academy, Andover, Mass.), and private collections; has had numerous one-man shows. *Military service:* U.S. Army Air Forces, 1943-45.

WRITINGS: Human Anatomy and Figure Drawing, Van Nostrand, 1972; *The Jefferson Image,* Museum of Westward Expansion (St. Louis), 1978. Contributor of illustrations to *Audience, Drawing,* and *Liberal Context.*

*   *   *

KRAUS, Albert L(awson) 1920-

PERSONAL: Born October 8, 1920, in New York, N.Y.; son of Albert Frank (a civil engineer) and Marion (Lawson) Kraus; married Patricia Lou Bornman, June 12, 1948; children: Carla (Mrs. Richard Katz), Peter, Linda, Laura. *Education:* Queens College (now Queens College of the City University of New York), B.S., 1941; Columbia University, M.A., 1942; Harvard University, graduate study, 1954-55. *Politics:* Independent. *Religion:* Episcopalian. *Home:* 110 Ridge St., Cranford, N.J. 07016. *Office: Journal of Commerce,* 110 Wall St., Tenth Floor, New York, N.Y. 10005.

CAREER: Journal-Bulletin, Providence, R.I., financial writer, 1947-56; *New York Times,* New York City, assistant financial editor, 1956-72; *Money Manager* (financial weekly), New York City, editor, 1972-78; *Journal of Commerce,* New York City, editorial director, 1978—. *Military service:* U.S. Navy, 1942-46; became lieutenant. *Member:* New York Financial Writers Association, New York Business Economists Council, Sigma Delta Chi. *Awards, honors:* Wieman fellow, 1954-55.

WRITINGS: New York Times Guide to Business and Finance, Harper, 1972. Contributor to *Guardian* (London).

*   *   *

KRAUS, C(lyde) Norman 1924-

PERSONAL: Born February 20, 1924, in Denbigh, Va.; son of Clyde Henry and Phebe (Shenk) Kraus; married Ruth Elizabeth Smith, May, 1945; children: Yvonne, JoAnne, John, Bonnie and Robert (twins). *Education:* Goshen College, B.A., 1946, B.D., 1951; Princeton University, Th.M., 1954; Duke University, Ph.D., 1961. *Politics:* Independent. *Home:* 615 College Ave., Goshen, Ind. 46526. *Office:* Center for Discipleship, Goshen College, Goshen, Ind. 46526.

CAREER: High school social science teacher in Harrisonburg, Va., 1946-49; ordained minister of Mennonite church; Maple Grove Church, Topeka, Ind., pastor, 1950-54; Goshen College, Goshen, Ind., instructor, 1951-53, assistant professor, 1954-58, associate professor, 1961-62, professor of religion, 1962—, director of Center for Discipleship. Visiting professor, Serampore Theological College, Bengal, India, 1966-67; teacher on special mission to Africa and Asia, 1974-75. Mennonite Board of Missions, member of Health and Welfare Committee, 1967-74, member of Overseas Committee, 1976—. *Member:* American Academy of Religion, American Society of Church History, Mennonite Historical Society, Phi Beta Kappa.

WRITINGS: (Editor and contributor) *Bible Survey Course,* five volumes, Herald Press, 1956; *Integration: Who's Preju-*

diced, Herald Press, 1958, revised edition, 1964; *Dispensationalism in America: Its Rise and Development,* John Knox, 1958; (contributor) John A. Lapp, editor, *Peacemakers in a Broken World,* Herald Press, 1969; (contributor) H. Rapp Hernley, editor, *The Compassionate Community,* Association of Mennonite Aid Societies, 1970; *The Healing Christ: Social Services and the Evangelical Mission,* Herald Press, 1972; *The Community of the Spirit,* Eerdmans, 1974; (contributor) J. R. Burkholder and C. Redekop, editors, *Kingdom, Cross, and Community,* Herald Press, 1976; *The Authentic Witness,* Eerdmans, 1979; (editor and contributor) *Evangelism and Anabaptism,* Herald Press, 1979. Contributor of articles to *Mennonite Quarterly Review.*

*   *   *

KRAUSZ, Norman G(eorge) P(hilip) 1920-

PERSONAL: Born April 14, 1920, in New Baden, Ill.; son of Arthur A. (an insurance broker) and Irena (Schaubert) Krausz; married Bobby Bumann, September 21, 1941; children: Niky L. (Mrs. Ray Allen Compton), Linda L. (Mrs. Mark A. Mussatt). *Education:* University of Illinois, B.S., 1940, LL.B. (since converted to J.D.), 1948. *Politics:* Independent. *Religion:* Lutheran. *Home and office:* 1906 Maynard Dr., Champaign, Ill. 61820.

CAREER: University of Illinois at Urbana-Champaign, Institute of Government and Public Affairs and Agricultural Law, research assistant, 1948-51, research associate, 1951-53, assistant professor of government and law, 1953-55, College of Agriculture, associate professor, 1955-58, professor of agricultural law and head of program, 1958-77; currently engaged in specialized law practice and tax consultation. United Grain Corp., Champaign, legal counsel, 1957-60, consultant, 1960-62; member of board of directors, Farm Business Council, Urbana, 1959-70. Expert in Cyprus for United Nations Food and Agricultural Organization, 1961-62. Illinois Water Pollution and Water Resources Commission, public member and vice-chairman, 1965-69, consultant, 1969-73; chairman of finance committee, Illinois Small Community Problems Committee, 1972. *Military service:* U.S. Army, 1941-45; became major. *Member:* Illinois Bar Association, Phi Alpha Delta, Gamma Sigma Delta, Beta Sigma Psi.

WRITINGS: Handbook for Illinois Township Officers, Garrard, 1952, 4th edition, 1960; (with Thomas Page and Irving Howards) *Illinois Property Tax Procedures Manual,* Institute of Government and Public Affairs, University of Illinois, 1958; (with others) *Legal Handbook for Directors and Members of Illinois Co-ops,* Agricultural Experiment Station, University of Illinois, 1958; *Illinois Law and Court Decisions on Agriculture,* Stipes, 1960; (with Harold W. Hannah) *Illinois Water Use Law,* Agricultural Experiment Station, University of Illinois, 1964; (with Victor A. Hyde and others) *A Guide for County Zoning Administration,* Bureau of Community Planning, University of Illinois, 1965; (contributor) John Hembree, editor, *Agricultural Finance,* American Institute of Banking, 1969.

All published by the University of Illinois: *Water in Illinois,* 1970; *Intergovernmental Arrangements for Water Use Regulation in Illinois,* 1972; *Farm Property and Trusts,* 1972; *Law for the Illinois Farmer,* 1973; *Farm Tenancy Laws in Illinois,* 1974; *Partnerships in the Farm Business,* 1974; *Land Trusts for the Illinois Farmer,* 1975; *Corporations in the Farm Business,* 1975; *Developing Local Government Action Programs,* 1975; *Legal Aspects of Coal Leasing in Illinois,* 1976; *Installment Land Contracts for Farmland,*

1976. Also author of *The Farm Corporation*, 1977. Author or co-author of more than forty technical and research reports. Writer of "Law on the Farm" series, University of Illinois, 1946-48, and co-writer of "Congress on the Farm" series, 1960-61. Contributor to farming and other journals.

*   *   *

KREDEL, Fritz   1900-1973

February 8, 1900—June 10, 1973; German-born American illustrator and woodcut artist. Obituaries: *Publishers Weekly*, June 25, 1973.

*   *   *

KREGEL, J(an) A(llen)   1944-

PERSONAL: Born April 19, 1944, in Dallas, Tex.; son of M. J. (a professor) and Ellen (Hoefflin) Kregel. *Education:* Beloit College, B.A., 1966; Cambridge University, graduate study, 1968-70; Rutgers University, Ph.D., 1970. *Office:* Department of Economics, University of Southampton, Highfield, Southampton, England.

CAREER: Cambridge University, New Hall, Cambridge, England, supervisor in economics, 1968-70; University of Bristol, Bristol, England, lecturer in economics, 1969-72; University of Southampton, Highfield, Southampton, England, lecturer, 1973-77, senior lecturer in economics, 1977—. Institut des Sciences Economiques, Louvain, Belgium, visiting professor, 1972, research fellow, 1973; visiting professor, Instituto di Scienze Economiche, Universita di Bologna, 1973-74; professor of economics, Livingston College, Rutgers University, 1977—. *Member:* Royal Economic Society, American Economic Association.

WRITINGS: Rate of Profit, Distribution and Growth: Two Views, Aldine, 1971; *The Theory of Economic Growth*, Macmillan (England), 1972; *The Reconstruction of Political Economy: An Introduction to Post-Keynesian Economics*, Macmillan, 1973, 2nd edition, 1975; *Theory of Capital*, Macmillan, 1976.

*   *   *

KREIDER, Barbara   1942-

PERSONAL: Born February 16, 1942, in Old Fort, N.C.; daughter of Garland Stephen (a master carpenter) and Joyce (Sawyer) Byrd; married George van Dyck Kreider (an electrical engineer), July 14, 1962; children: Susan Patricia, Keith Allen. *Education:* Attended Mercer University, 1960-62; University of New Hampshire, B.A., 1965; San Jose State College (now University), M.A., 1971. *Politics:* Republican. *Religion:* Christian. *Home:* 1931 Crestmont Dr., San Jose, Calif. 95124.

CAREER: Kawananakoa Intermediate School, Honolulu, Hawaii, English teacher, 1965-66; San Jose Public Library System, San Jose, Calif., began as reference librarian in literature department of main branch, currently children's librarian at Rosegarden Branch Library. *Member:* Young Women's Christian Association (secretary, 1969-70), CSUSJ Librarianship Alumni Association.

WRITINGS: Index to Children's Plays in Collections, Scarecrow, 1972, enlarged edition, 1977.

SIDELIGHTS: Barbara Kreider told *CA* that she enjoys "meeting new people and helping them build a positive self-image." *Avocational interests:* Camping (with her family).

KREJCI, Jaroslav   1916-

PERSONAL: Surname rhymes with "Strachey"; born February 13, 1916, in Czechoslovakia; son of Jaroslav (a civil servant) and Zdenka (Dudova) Krejci; married Anna Cerna (a principal lecturer at Preston Polytechnic), May 11, 1940. *Education:* Charles University, Prague, Dr. Jur., 1945. *Office:* School of European Studies, University of Lancaster, Lancaster, England.

CAREER: State Planning Office, Prague, Czechoslovakia, secretary to chairman, 1945-48, head of department of national income, 1948-50; State Bank, Prague, research worker, 1950-53; Czechoslovak Academy of Sciences, Prague, research worker, 1968; University of Lancaster, Lancaster, England, lecturer in comparative social and cultural analysis, 1970-76, professor in School of European Studies, 1976—, head of a research unit on macrosociology, 1969-76. External associate professor at Graduate School of Political and Social Sciences, Prague, 1948-50, and at Technological University, Prague, 1950-52; member of advisory body for economic analysis for Deputy Prime Minister, Prague, 1968. *Member:* International P.E.N., National Association of Soviet and East European Studies, British Sociological Association. *Awards, honors:* Received award for participation in Czech resistance movement during World War II.

WRITINGS: Duchodove rozvrstveni (title means "Income Distribution"), [Prague], 1947; *Uvod do planovaneho hospodarstvi* (title means "Introduction into the Planned Economy"), [Prague], 1949; *Volkseinkommensvergleich Osterreich: CSSR* (title means "National Income Comparison: Austria-Czechoslovakia"), Verlag des Osterreichischen Gewerkschaftsbundes Wien, 1969; *Social Change and Stratification in Postwar Czechoslovakia*, Macmillan and Columbia University Press, 1972; *Social Structure in Divided Germany*, St. Martin's, 1976; (editor) *Sozialdemokratie und Systemwandel*, Dietz, 1978; (contributor) M. S. Archer and L. S. Giner, editors, *Ethnic Problems in Contemporary Europe*, Routledge & Kegan Paul, 1978. Contributor to *Review of Income and Wealth, Soviet Studies, Sociological Analysis, Journal of Religious History,* and *Systematics*.

WORK IN PROGRESS: National Income and Outlay in Different Types of Socialism.

SIDELIGHTS: Jaroslav Krejci spent the years from 1954-60 in a labor camp in Czechoslovakia.

*   *   *

KREMENTZ, Jill   1940-

PERSONAL: Born February 19, 1940, in New York, N.Y. *Education:* Attended Drew University, 1968-69, and Columbia University. *Home:* 971 First Ave., New York, N.Y. 10022.

CAREER: Free-lance photographer. *Harper's Bazaar,* New York City, secretary, 1959-60; *Glamour,* New York City, assistant to the features editor, 1960-61; *Show,* New York City, reporter and columnist, 1962-64; *New York Herald Tribune,* New York City, staff photographer (first woman to hold this position with a New York City newspaper since World War II), 1964-65; free-lance photographer in Viet Nam, 1965-66; *Status and Diplomat,* New York City, associate editor with status of staff photographer, 1966-67; *New York* (magazine), New York City, contributing editor, 1967-68; Time-Life, Inc., New York City, correspondent, 1969-70; *People* (magazine), Chicago, Ill., contributing photographer, 1975—. Public relations representative, Indian Industries Fair (New Delhi), 1961. Work has been exhibited at Madison Art Center (Wisconsin) and in permanent collection at Museum of Modern Art. Chosen to take the official photographs of four members of the U.S. Cabinet, 1978.

WRITINGS: The Face of South Vietnam (a book of photographs, with text by Dean Brelis), Houghton, 1968; *Sweet Pea: A Girl Growing Up in the Rural South* (a book of photographs with accompanying text), foreword by Margaret Mead, Harcourt, 1969; *Word People* (a book of photographs, with text by Israel Shenker), Doubleday, 1973; *A Very Young Dancer*, Knopf, 1976; *A Very Young Rider*, Knopf, 1977; *A Very Young Gymnast*, Knopf, 1978; *A Very Young Circus Flyer*, Knopf, 1979. Contributor to national and international magazines and newspapers, including *Vogue, Newsweek, Esquire, Holiday, Time, Life,* and *New York Times Book Review.*

WORK IN PROGRESS: A Very Young Skater.

SIDELIGHTS: Jill Krementz is best known for her photographic portraits of writers. Her work has appeared in *The New York Times, Newsweek, Time, Esquire, New York, People,* and *Ms.* as well as on many book jackets. Harvey V. Fondiller, writing in *Popular Photography* about her show at the Nikon House Gallery, said, "Her incisive portraits capture the spirit of their subjects." Krementz told the *Miami Herald,* "I really think of myself as a documentary photographer because I am basically documenting the lives of all these writers. The portraits are published with reviews and articles about the writers, but my real dream is that all of these photographs will one day be part of a university's archives available to anybody who wants to know how any of these writers lived."

Krementz is now concentrating her talents on a book series about young people in various athletic fields. These books have received high praise from the critics. Clive Barnes, writing in the *New York Times Book Review,* called her book *A Very Young Dancer* "the best ballet book ever written for children." Krementz has said of the series: "If children like these, I'll keep going. That's the ultimate payoff. It's not the reactions of adults that matter; it is how children respond."

AVOCATIONAL INTERESTS: Reading, tennis.

BIOGRAPHICAL/CRITICAL SOURCES: Newsweek, February 5, 1968; *Saturday Review,* February 17, 1968; *Mademoiselle,* March, 1968; *New York Times Book Review,* November 9, 1969, December 26, 1976; *Boston Sunday Globe,* December 28, 1969; *New Yorker,* December 23, 1974; *Detroit Free Press,* December 25, 1974; *Popular Photography,* April, 1975; *Miami Herald,* April 4, 1975; *Modern Photography,* January, 1976; *Publisher's Weekly,* November 15, 1976; *Esquire,* February, 1977.

*   *   *

KREVOLIN, Nathan   1927-

PERSONAL: Born November 21, 1927, in New Haven, Conn.; son of Abraham and Rebecca (Rich) Krevolin; married Lois Ann Silverman, July 3, 1955; children: Clay, Adam. *Education:* Quinnipiac College, A.S., 1948; Central Connecticut State College, B.S., 1950; Southern Connecticut State College, M.A., 1952; University of Connecticut, professional diploma, 1956, Ph.D., 1960. *Home:* 40 Osage Rd., West Hartford, Conn. 06117. *Office:* Maria Sanford Hall, Central Connecticut State College, New Britain, Conn. 06050.

CAREER: University of Connecticut, Storrs, instructor in business education, 1950-51; secondary school business education teacher in New Haven, Conn., 1951-55, and West Hartford, Conn., 1955-66; Central Connecticut State College, New Britain, associate professor, 1966-73, professor of business education, 1973—. Lecturer in business education for radio and television stations, including "Voice of America," 1967-68. *Military service:* U.S. Army, 1946-47.

MEMBER: National Education Association, National Business Education Association, American Association of University Professors, Eastern Business Education Association, Connecticut Education Association, Connecticut Business Education Association, Kappa Delta Pi, Phi Delta Kappa, Delta Pi Epsilon, Farmington Club.

WRITINGS: Art Typing, Pitman, 1962; (with Louis C. Nanassy) *Junior High Timed Writings,* Pitman, 1963, revised edition published as *Timed Writings for Teenagers,* 1968; (with Alan C. Lloyd) *You Learn to Type!,* with twenty record albums, McGraw, 1966; (with Nanassy and John E. Whitcraft) *Personal Typing,* with teacher's manual and key, Pitman, 1970; *The Gregg Office Job Training Program: Typist,* with training manual, resource materials, and teacher's manual, McGraw, 1972. Contributor to textbooks, magazines, handbooks, and yearbooks. Contributor of nineteen articles to education journals, including *Journal of Secondary Education, Education Digest, Business Education World, Journal of Business Education, Typewriting News,* and *Balance Sheet.*

AVOCATIONAL INTERESTS: Art, music, tennis, golf, swimming, and travel.

*   *   *

KRISLOV, Joseph   1927-

PERSONAL: Born August 14, 1927, in Cleveland, Ohio; son of Issack and Gussie (Hutner) Krislov; married Evelyn Moreida (a social worker), October 7, 1956; children: Marvin. *Education:* Ohio University, B.S.Ed., 1949; Western Reserve University (now Case Western Reserve University), M.A., 1950; University of Wisconsin, Ph.D., 1954. *Religion:* Jewish. *Home:* 1008 Gainesway Dr., Lexington, Ky. 40502. *Office:* Department of Economics, University of Kentucky, Lexington, Ky. 40506.

CAREER: AFL-CIO, American Federation of State, County and Municipal Employees, Columbus, Ohio, research director, 1953-58; Social Security Administration, Baltimore, Md., economist, 1958-64; University of Kentucky, Lexington, professor of economics, 1964—. Fulbright professor, Ireland, 1970-71; visiting professor, Israel, 1977-78. Arbitrator, 1965—. *Military service:* U.S. Army Air Forces, 1945-47. *Member:* Industrial Relations Research Association, National Academy of Arbitrators.

WRITINGS: State and Local Retirement Systems, U.S. Department of Health, Education and Welfare, 1962; (contributor) Thomas Weaver and Alvin Magid, editors, *Poverty,* Chandler Publishing, 1969; (contributor) Robert T. Woodworth and Richard P. Peterson, editors, *Collective Negotiation for Public and Professional Employees,* Scott, Foresman, 1969. Contributor to labor and arbitration journals.

WORK IN PROGRESS: Mediation in Israel: A Comparative Study of Mediation in the Western World.

*   *   *

KROCHMAL, Connie   1949-

PERSONAL: First syllable of surname rhymes with

"lock"; born August 17, 1949, in Cawood, Ky.; daughter of Marcum (a plantation owner) and Hestor (Gray) Brite; married Arnold Krochmal (a scientist and writer), November 30, 1970. *Education:* Attended Berea College, 1967-68, and University of North Carolina, 1971. *Residence:* Asheville, N.C.

CAREER: Extension lecturer, North Carolina Botanical Gardens and University of North Carolina Continuing Education Division at Chapel Hill; senior research fellow, department of tropical studies, Wageningen University, Netherlands. Visiting scholar, Jardin Botanico ''Uribe,'' Medellin, Colombia.

WRITINGS: A Guide to Natural Cosmetics, Quadrangle, 1973; (with Karen Snipes) *The Art of Woodburning,* Drake, 1974; *The Political Biography of Marshall Tito,* Nelson-Hall, 1978. Contributor to *Garden.*

With husband, Arnold Krochmal: *A Guide to the Medicinal Plants of the United States,* Quadrangle, 1973; *The Complete Illustrated Book of Dyes from Natural Sources,* Doubleday, 1974; *The Green Thumb Guide to Indoor Gardening,* Drake, 1974; *A Naturalist's Guide to Cooking with Wild Plants,* Quadrangle, 1975; *Caribbean Cookery,* Quadrangle, 1975; *Making It: How to Do It for Less,* Drake, 1975; *Gardening in the Carolinas,* Doubleday, 1975; (contributors) *Appalachian Ways,* Appalachian Regional Commission, 1976; *The Walker's Guide to Nature,* Drake, 1977; *Useful Plants of the Blue Ridge,* Forest Service, U.S. Department of Agriculture and National Park Service, U.S. Department of the Interior, 1977; *Some Notes about Nuts,* Forest Service, U.S. Department of Agriculture, 1977; (contributors) *Crop Resources,* Academic Press, 1977; *Interesting Plants of the Appalachian Trail in North Carolina,* Forest Service, U.S. Department of Agriculture, 1978; *Wild Nuts and Nut-Like Seeds of Use,* Forest Service, U.S. Department of Agriculture, 1978; *Useful Wild Nuts and Nut-Like Seeds of the World,* Forest Service, U.S. Department of Agriculture, in press; *A Manual of Economic Botany,* Garland, in press; *Handbook of Nursery Management,* Garland, in press. Contributing garden editors, *Tar-Heel,* 1977—.

*   *   *

KROTKI, Karol J(ozef)   1922-
(Jozef Krzywan)

PERSONAL: Born May 15, 1922, in Cieszyn, Poland; son of Karol S. (an industrialist) and Anna (Skrzywanek) Krotki; married Joanna Patkowska, July 12, 1947; children: Karol Peter, Jan Jozef, Filip Karol. *Education:* Cambridge University, B.A. (honors), 1948, M.A. 1952; Princeton University, M.A., 1959, Ph.D., 1960. *Religion:* Roman Catholic. *Home:* 10137 Clifton Pl., Edmonton, Alberta, Canada T5N 3H9. *Office:* Department of Sociology, University of Alberta, Edmonton, Alberta, Canada T6G 2E1.

CAREER: Sudanese Government, Khartoum, deputy director of statistics, 1949-58; Pakistan Institute of Development Economics, Karachi, research adviser, 1960-64; Dominion Bureau of Statistics, Ottawa, Ontario, assistant director of census research, 1964-68; University of Alberta, Edmonton, professor of demography, 1968—. Visiting professor of economics, University of California, Berkeley, 1967; visiting professor of biostatistics, University of North Carolina, 1970-72; visiting professor of sociology, University of Michigan, 1975. Research adviser in statistics, Kingdom of Morocco, 1971-72; program coordinator, Human Resources Research Council, province of Alberta.

Consultant to World Health Organization, governments of Algeria, Tunisia, Jordan, and others. *Military service:* Polish Army, 1939-45; served in France, Middle and Near East; mentioned in dispatches, received Cross of Valeur with bar, the 1939-1945 Star, Africa Star, Defence medal, War medal, Medaille Commemorative. Royal Air Force, pilot, 1943-46; became flight lieutenant; received Air Force medal, and ''green endorsement.''

MEMBER: American Statistical Association (fellow), Canadian Sociology and Anthropology Association, Philosophical Society for the Sudan (vice-president, 1956-58). *Awards, honors:* Achievement award from Government of Alberta, 1971, for work in sociology.

WRITINGS: The 1953 Population Pilot Census, Department of Statistics (Khartoum), 1955; *Twenty-One Facts About the Sudanese,* Population Census Office (Khartoum), 1958; (editor) *The Population of Sudan: Report on the Sixth Annual Conference,* Philosophical Society of Sudan, 1958; (with Sultan S. Hashmi and Masihur Rahman Khan) *The People of Karachi: Data from a Survey,* Pakistan Institute of Development Economics, 1964; (editor with Gwynn E. Nettler) *Social Science and Social Policy,* Human Resources Research Council (Alberta), 1971; (with Eli S. Marks and William Seltzer) *Population Growth Estimation: A Handbook of Vital Statistics Measurement,* Population Council (New York), 1974; (co-editor) *Issues in Demographic Data Collection in Pakistan,* Pakistan Government, 1977; (editor) *Developments in Dual System Estimation of Population Size and Growth,* University of Alberta Press, 1978. Also author, with Arthur A. Campbell, of *A Manual on Fertility Measurement and Analysis,* World Health Organization. Contributor of more than one hundred articles to professional journals; contributor to Polish literary journals under pseudonym Jozef Krzywan, 1943-45.

WORK IN PROGRESS: Causes and Consequences of Divergence between Age Pyramid and Opportunity Pyramid.

BIOGRAPHICAL/CRITICAL SOURCES: Edmonton Journal, January 2, 1970; *The American Statistician,* October, 1971.

*   *   *

KRUMPELMANN, John T(heodore)   1892-

PERSONAL: Born August 8, 1892, in New Orleans, La.; son of John (an office manager) and Marie (Bernard) Krumpelmann; married Catherine Dalton, June 15, 1929. *Education:* Tulane University, A.B., 1915, M.A., 1916; Harvard University, A.M., 1917, Ph.D., 1924; also studied at University of Munich and University of Berlin, 1924-25. *Politics:* Democrat. *Religion:* Roman Catholic. *Home:* 1708 Cloverdale Ave., Baton Rouge, La. 70808.

CAREER: Lehigh University, Bethlehem, Pa., instructor in Germanic philology, 1917-18; University of North Carolina at Chapel Hill, instructor, 1919-21, assistant professor of Germanic philology, 1925-27; St. Stephen's College, Columbia, Mo., associate professor of Germanic philology, 1927-33; West Virginia State Normal School (now Marshall College), Huntington, professor of Germanic philology, 1934-38, dean of men, 1936-38; Louisiana State University, Baton Rouge, 1938—, became professor of German and Russian, professor emeritus, 1962—. Visiting lecturer, University of Berlin, summer, 1933; Fulbright lecturer, University of Frankfurt-Main, 1954-55; visiting professor at Clark University, 1964; Tulane University, visiting professor, 1964-69, acting chairman of department of German, 1965-69. *Military service:* U.S. Army Infantry, 1918-19; became second lieutenant. Attache of U.S. Department of State, 1945-47.

MEMBER: Modern Language Association of America, American Association of Teachers of German, South Central Modern Language Association, Delta Phi Alpha. *Awards, honors:* Parker traveling fellowship, Harvard University, 1924-25; Schiller Sesquicentennial Medal, 1956; Verdienstkreuz, Erster Klasse, from German Federal Republic, 1972; LL. D., Louisiana State University, 1973.

WRITINGS: (Contributor) Carl Hammer, editor, *Goethe after Two Centuries,* Louisiana State University Press, 1952; *Mark Twain and the German Language* (monograph), Louisiana State University Press, 1953; *Bayard Taylor and German Letters* (monograph), de Gruyter, 1959; (translator) Friedrich Schiller, *The Maiden of Orleans,* University of North Carolina Press, 1959, revised edition, 1962; (contributor) Horst Oppel, editor, *Festschrift fuer Walther Fischer,* [Heidelberg], 1959; (translator) Heinrich von Kleist, *The Broken Jug,* Ungar, 1962; (contributor) Waldo Forest McNeir, editor, *Studies in Comparative Literature,* Louisiana State University Press, 1962; *Southern Scholars in Goethe's Germany* (monograph), University of North Carolina Press, 1965; *The American Students of Heidelberg University, 1830-1870,* Jahrbuch Ameri-Kastud (Berlin), 1969; (contributor) Siegfried Mews, editor, *Studies in German Literature of the Nineteenth and Twentieth Centuries: Festschrift fuer Frederic Coenen,* University of North Carolina Press, 1970; (editor) *The Indian Chief,* Volumes IV and V, Olms (Hildesheim, West Germany), 1972; (editor) *Der legitime und die Republikaner,* Olms, 1973; (contributor) Roger Johnson, Jr., editor, *Moliere and the Commonwealth of Letters,* University College Press, 1975. Contributor of about a hundred articles and reviews to professional journals. Editor, *South Central Modern Language Bulletin,* 1952.

WORK IN PROGRESS: Translating volumes four through seven of "The Complete Works of Charles Sealsfield," edited by Karl Arndt, and *Amphitryon Eine Lustspeil nach Moliere,* a comedy by Heinrich von Kleist.

BIOGRAPHICAL/CRITICAL SOURCES: Carl Hammer, Jr., editor, *Studies in German Literature,* Louisiana State University Press, 1963.†

*   *   *

KRUSCHKE, Earl R(oger) 1934-

PERSONAL: Born February 26, 1934, in Sheboygan, Wis.; son of Bernard G. and Louise (Kaesermann) Kruschke; married Marilyn Ann Reineking, August 26, 1956; children: Kari Lynn, John Kendall. *Education:* University of Wisconsin, B.A. (with honors), 1956, Ph.D., 1963; University of Wyoming, M.A. (with honors), 1957. *Politics:* Democrat. *Religion:* Protestant. *Home:* 4 Casita Ter., Chico, Calif. 95926. *Office:* Department of Political Science, California State University, Chico, Calif. 95929.

CAREER: WHBL-Radio, Sheboygan, Wis., continuity writer, 1957; *Sheboygan Press,* Sheboygan, editorial writer and columnist, 1958-59; University of Wisconsin—Madison, Extension Division, lecturer in political science, spring, 1961; lecturer in political science at Fort Lewis Army Base, Fort Lewis, Wash. and McChord Air Force Base, Tacoma, Wash., 1964-65; University of Wisconsin—Madison, instructor in political science, 1961-62; University of Puget Sound, Tacoma, Wash., assistant professor of political science, 1962-65; California State University, Chico, assistant professor, 1965-67, associate professor, 1967-72, professor of political science, 1972—, director of Institute of Commu-

nity and Regional Research, 1967-69. Visiting associate professor, University of Wisconsin—Milwaukee, summer, 1968; visiting scholar, Stanford University and University of Michigan, 1975. Member of board of directors of World Affairs Council of Tacoma, 1964-65, and Institute of Human Relations, 1967-68.

MEMBER: American Political Science Association, American Association of University Professors, American Institute of Parliamentarians, Western Political Science Association, Pi Gamma Mu, Mu Sigma Delta. *Awards, honors:* National Science Foundation grants to study student political protest movements, 1966, and to study impact of dissident groups on the American two-party system, 1968; grants from Stanford University to study voting behavior, political socialization, and the aging process, 1974, 1975, 1977; LL.B., University of Wyoming, 1977.

WRITINGS: *The Woman Voter* (monograph), Public Affairs Press, 1955; (editor with Charles Price, and contributor) *Consensus and Cleavage: Issues in California Politics,* Chandler Publishing, 1967; *An Introduction to the Constitution of the United States,* American Book Co., 1968. Contributor to political science, education, and social science journals. Associate editor, *Western Political Quarterly,* 1978-80.

WORK IN PROGRESS: The American Party Process in an Anti-Party Age.

*   *   *

KUGELMAN, Richard 1908-

PERSONAL: Born November 9, 1908, in Hoboken, N.J.; son of Emile Louis (a designer) and Madeline (Behr) Kugelman. *Education:* St. Michael's Monastic Seminary, A.B., 1930, M.A., 1934; St. Thomas University, Rome, Italy, S.T.L., 1936; Pontifical Biblical Institute, S.S.B., 1937, S.S.L., 1938. *Home:* Passionist Monastery, 178th St. and Wexford Ter., Jamaica, N.Y. 11432.

CAREER: Roman Catholic priest of Passionist Order (C.P.); St. Michael's Monastic Seminary, Union City, N.J., professor of New Testament and Hebrew, 1939-67; St. John's University, Jamaica, N.Y., adjunct professor, 1962-68, professor of New Testament, 1968-77, chairman of department of theology, 1969-74. Organized and for ten years carried on the Catholic apostolate among the Spanish-speaking in Union City, N.J. Member, Brooklyn Diocesan Commission on Justice, War, and Peace, 1972-78. *Member:* Catholic Biblical Association (vice-president, 1964; president, 1973), Society of Biblical Literature, American Schools of Oriental Research, Catholic Theological Society of America, Mariological Society of America, Columbia University Seminar on New Testament Studies.

WRITINGS: (Contributor) Juniper Carol, editor, *Mariology,* Volume I, Bruce, 1955; (contributor) J. M. Oesterreicher, editor, *The Bridge,* Volume I, Institute of Judaeo Christian Studies, Seton Hall University Press, 1955; (collaborator on English translation and adaptation) A. van den Born, *Encyclopedic Dictionary of the Bible,* edited by Louis Hartmann, McGraw, 1963; *The Use of Scripture in Preaching,* Catholic University of America Press, 1966; (contributor) *Maria in Sacra Scriptura,* Pontificia Academia Mariana Internationalis, 1967; (contributor) Raymond Brown, Joseph Fitzmeyer, and Roland Murphy, editors, *The Jerome Biblical Commentary,* Prentice-Hall, 1968; *A Commentary on the Letters of James and Jude,* W. Glazier (Wilmington, Del.), 1979. One of the translators of the New Testament from the original Greek for *The New American*

Bible. Contributor of about thirty articles to *Sign, Marian Studies,* and other journals.

SIDELIGHTS: Richard Kugelman is competent in Latin, Greek, Hebrew, French, German, Spanish, and Italian.

* * *

KUHL, Ernest Peter 1881-

PERSONAL: Born October 10, 1881, in Milan, Ohio; son of Henry P. and Elizabeth (Weichel) Kuhl; married Lucy Van Dyke Leech, September 9, 1909; children: Robert Wolfe, Elizabeth (Mrs. George Bemis Belting). *Education:* Indiana University at Bloomington, A.B., 1907; Harvard University, A.M., 1908, Ph.D., 1913. *Address:* Rochester Road Extended Care Center, Rochester Rd. and Scott Blvd., Iowa City, Iowa 52240.

CAREER: University of Michigan, Ann Arbor, instructor in English, 1908-12; Radcliffe College, Cambridge, Mass., instructor in English, 1913-14; Dartmouth College, Hanover, N.H., instructor in English, 1914-16; University of Minnesota, Minneapolis, instructor in English, 1916-18; Goucher College, Baltimore, Md., professor of English, 1918-26; University of Iowa, Iowa City, 1926—, began as professor of English, currently professor emeritus. Visiting faculty member at Radcliffe College, summers, 1914-15, extension department, Johns Hopkins University, 1919-26, University of Maine at Orono, 1925, University of Washington, 1929, and Stanford University, 1940. College Congress on English in Middle Atlantic States and Maryland, chairman, 1920-21, secretary-treasurer, 1923-26. *Member:* Modern Language Association of America, Research Club of the University of Iowa, Poe Society of Baltimore (president, 1926).

WRITINGS: Studies in Chaucer and Shakespeare, Belting Publications, 1971. Also author of *The Authorship of Shakespeare's "Taming of the Shrew."*

WORK IN PROGRESS: Two books, *Shakespeare, Soul of the Age* and *Chaucer Historical Studies.*

SIDELIGHTS: In 1924 Ernest Peter Kuhl discovered some important papers by Sidney Lanier, the American poet from the Civil War era.†

* * *

KUKLICK, Bruce 1941-

PERSONAL: Born March 13, 1941, in Philadelphia, Pa.; son of Emil and Emma (Roth) Kuklick; married Henrika Takiff (a teacher) May 5, 1965; children: Marya. *Education:* University of Pennsylvania, B.A. (with honors), 1963, M.A. (American civilization), 1966, Ph.D., 1968; attended St. John's College, Oxford, 1963-64; Bryn Mawr College, M.A. (philosophy), 1965. *Home:* 313 South 22nd St., Philadelphia, Pa. 19103. *Office:* Department of History, University of Pennsylvania, Philadelphia, Pa. 19104.

CAREER: Yale University, New Haven, Conn., instructor, 1968-69, assistant professor of philosophy and American studies, 1969-72; University of Pennsylvania, Philadelphia, associate professor, 1972-76, professor of history, 1976—. Co-director, National Endowment for the Humanities Institute, 1979. Television moderator, "Dateline Yesterday," WCAU, 1978. Consultant, Bobbs-Merrill Publishers, 1969-73. *Member:* American Historical Association, American Philosophical Association, American Studies Association (member of executive committee), Organization of American Historians, Social Science History Association (co-chairman, Network on the History and Epistemology of the

Sciences of Man), Society for the Advancement of American Philosophy, Society for Historians of American Foreign Relations, Intellectual History Group (member of executive committee), Center for Advanced Study in the Behavioral Sciences (fellow), Charles S. Peirce Society, Phi Beta Kappa, Pi Mu Epsilon. *Awards/honors:* Thouron fellowship, 1963-64; Woodrow Wilson fellow, 1964-65; Harrison fellowship, 1965-67; Penfield Traveling Fellowship in Diplomatic History, 1967-68; Penrose grants, American Philosophical Society, 1970, 1972; American Council of Learned Societies fellowship, 1973; Guggenheim fellow, 1976-77; Harry S Truman Library Institute grant, 1977.

WRITINGS: The United States and the Division of Germany, Cornell University Press, 1972; *Josiah Royce: An Intellectual Biography,* Bobbs-Merrill, 1972; *The Rise of American Philosophy,* Yale University Press, 1977; (contributor) Leila Zenderland, editor, *Recycling the Past,* University of Pennsylvania Press, 1978. Contributor to *Dictionary of American History, Encyclopedia Americana,* and *Encyclopedia of American Diplomacy.* Contributor of articles and reviews to over a dozen periodicals including *American Quarterly, American Historical Review, Nation, Progressive,* and *Journal of the History of Philosophy.* Editor, *American Quarterly,* 1974—.

* * *

KUNCE, Joseph T(yree) 1928-

PERSONAL: Born December 14, 1928, in St. Louis, Mo.; son of Ralph Waldo and Mabel (Warren) Kunce; married H. Joan Himebaugh, June 12, 1954; children: Jeffrey, Karen, Linda. *Education:* Washington University, St. Louis, Mo., A.B., 1950, M.A.Ed., 1954; University of Missouri—Columbia, Ph.D., 1959. *Religion:* Protestant. *Home:* 1002 South Greenwood, Columbia, Mo. 65201. *Office:* 5 Hill Hall, University of Missouri, Columbia, Mo. 65201.

CAREER: High school mathematics teacher in Webster Groves, Mo., 1953-56; Veterans Administration, St. Louis, Mo., counseling psychology trainee, 1956-57, 1958-59; Veterans Administration Hospital, Jefferson Barracks, Mo., counseling psychologist, 1959-63; University of Washington, Seattle, instructor in psychology and counseling psychologist at University Hospital, 1963-66, part-time lecturer in education, 1966-67; University of Missouri—Columbia, associate professor, 1967-71, professor of education, 1971—, director of Regional Rehabilitation Research Institute, 1967-74. Private practice of psychology, Seattle, Wash., 1966-67. Psychological consultant, 1964—. *Military service:* U.S. Army, 1951-52. *Member:* American Psychological Association (fellow), National Rehabilitation Association, American Personnel and Guidance Association, Society for Personality Assessment.

WRITINGS: (Editor with C. S. Cope, and contributor) *Rehabilitation and the Culturally Disadvantaged* (monograph), Regional Rehabilitation Research Institute, University of Missouri, 1969; (contributor) R. J. Mahoney, Cope, and R. R. Campbell, editors, *Rehabilitation and the Culturally Disadvantaged: A Digest* (monograph), Regional Rehabilitation Research Institute, 1969; (with Mahoney, Campbell and J. Finley) *Rehabilitation in the Concrete Jungle* (monograph), Regional Rehabilitation Research Institute, 1969; (with C. E. Block, Cope, and D. Harston) *The Badge of Poverty* (monograph), Regional Rehabilitation Research Institute, 1970.

Also author of technical reports. Contributor of over one hundred articles to professional journals, including *Journal of Rehabilitation, Personnel and Guidance Journal, Vocational Guidance Quarterly, Measurements and Evaluation in Guidance, Journal of Counseling Psychology,* and *Journal of Clinical Psychology.* Consulting editor, *Journal of Vocational Behavior,* 1970—, and *Rehabilitation Counseling Bulletin,* 1971-74.

WORK IN PROGRESS: Studies on vocational rehabilitation, counseling, and personality assessment.

AVOCATIONAL INTERESTS: Painting, composing music, nature, farming, horses, hiking.

* * *

KUNER, M(ildred) C(hristophe) 1922-

PERSONAL: Born February 10, 1922, in New York, N.Y.; daughter of Barnet and Diana (Kurz) Kuner. *Education:* Hunter College (now Hunter College of the City University of New York), B.A., 1943; Yale University, M.F.A., 1947; Columbia University, Ph.D., 1953. *Politics:* Independent. *Religion:* Roman Catholic. *Residence:* New York, N.Y. *Office:* Department of English, Hunter College of the City University of New York, 695 Park Ave., New York, N.Y., 10021.

CAREER: Yankton College, Yankton, S.D., instructor in English and drama, 1947-48; Hunter College of the City University of New York, New York, N.Y., lecturer, 1950-53, instructor, 1953-60, assistant professor, 1960-72, associate professor of English and theater arts, 1973—. Part-time instructor, New School for Social Research, 1955-56. *Member:* Modern Language Association of America, American Association of University Professors, American Educational Theatre Association, Dramatists Guild. *Awards, honors:* Fulbright research grant in theater history, University of Vienna, 1959-60.

WRITINGS: (Contributor) Klaus Jonas, editor, *The World of Somerset Maugham,* British Book Centre, 1960; (adaptor) Victoria Holt, *Mistress of Mellyn* (play), Dramatic Publishing Co., 1962; *Thornton Wilder,* Crowell, 1972.

Plays: "The Furnace of the World," first produced in Palo Alto, 1952; "Capacity for Wings," first produced in New York at Royal Theatre, 1956.

WORK IN PROGRESS: The World of James Thurber.

* * *

KUNITZ, Stanley (Jasspon) 1905-

PERSONAL: Born July 29, 1905, in Worcester, Mass.; son of Solomon Z. (a manufacturer) and Yetta Helen (Jasspon) Kunitz; married Helen Pearce, 1930 (divorced, 1937); married Eleanor Evans, November 21, 1939 (divorced, 1958); married Elise Asher (an artist), June 21, 1958; children: (second marriage) Gretchen. *Education:* Harvard University, A.B. (summa cum laude), 1926, A.M., 1927. *Home:* 37 West 12th St., New York, N.Y. 10011.

CAREER: Poet. *Wilson Library Bulletin,* New York City, editor, 1928-42; Bennington College, Bennington, Vt., professor of English, 1946-49; Potsdam State Teachers College (now State University of New York College at Potsdam), Potsdam, N.Y., professor of English, 1949-50; New School for Social Research, New York City, lecturer in English, 1950-58; Poetry Center of the Young Men's Hebrew Association, New York City, director of poetry workshop, 1958-62; Columbia University, New York City, lecturer, 1963-66, adjunct professor of writing in School of the Arts, 1967—. Member of staff of writing division, Fine Arts Work Center

in Provincetown, 1968—. Fellow, Yale University, 1969—; visiting senior fellow, Council of the Humanities, and Old Dominion Fellow in creative writing, Princeton University, 1978-79. Director of seminar, Potsdam Summer Workshop in Creative Arts, 1949-53; poet-in-residence, University of Washington, 1955-56, Queens College (now Queens College of the City University of New York), 1956-57, Brandeis University, 1958-59, and Princeton University, 1979. Danforth Visiting Lecturer at colleges and universities in the United States, 1961-63; visiting professor, Yale University, 1972, and Rutgers University, 1974. Lectured and gave poetry readings in USSR and Poland, 1967, and in Senegal and Ghana, under cultural exchange program. Library of Congress, Washington, D.C., consultant on poetry, 1974-76, honorary consultant in American letters, 1976—. *Military service:* U.S. Army, Air Transport Command, 1943-45; became staff sergeant.

MEMBER: American Academy and Institute of Arts and Letters, Academy of American Poets (chancellor, 1970—), Phi Beta Kappa. *Awards, honors:* Oscar Blumenthal Prize, 1941; John Simon Guggenheim Memorial fellowship, 1945-46; Amy Lowell travelling fellowship, 1953-54; Levinson Prize, *Poetry* Magazine, 1956; *Saturday Review* award, 1957; Ford Foundation grant, 1958-59; Harriet Monroe Poetry Award, University of Chicago, 1958; National Institute of Arts and Letters award, 1959; Pulitzer Prize, 1959, for *Selected Poems: 1928-1958;* Brandeis University creative arts award medal, 1965; Academy of American Poets fellowship, 1968; Litt.D., Anna Maria College, 1977, and Clark University.

WRITINGS: Intellectual Things (verse), Doubleday, Doran, 1930; *Passport to the War: A Selection of Poems,* Holt, 1944; *Selected Poems, 1928-1958,* Atlantic-Little, Brown, 1958; *The Testing Tree: Poems,* Atlantic-Little, Brown, 1971; (translator with Max Hayward) *Poems of Anna Akhmatova,* Atlantic-Little, Brown, 1973; *The Terrible Threshold* (verse), Secker & Warburg, 1974; (translator) Andrei Voznesensky, *Story under Full Sail,* Doubleday, 1974; *A Kind of Order, a Kind of Folly: Essays and Conversations,* Atlantic-Little, Brown, 1975; (editor and translator) Ivan Drach, *Orchard Lamps,* Sheep Meadow Press, 1978; *Poems of Stanley Kunitz: 1928-1978,* Atlantic-Little, Brown, 1979.

Editor; published by H. W. Wilson, except as indicated: *Living Authors: A Book of Biographies,* 1931; (with Howard Haycraft) *Authors Today and Yesterday: A Companion Volume to "Living Authors,"* 1933; (with Haycraft) *The Junior Book of Authors: An Introduction to the Lives of Writers and Illustrators for Younger Readers,* 1934, 2nd edition, revised, 1951; (with Haycraft) *British Authors of the Nineteenth Century,* 1936; (with Haycraft) *American Authors, 1600-1900: A Biographical Dictionary of American Literature,* 1938; (with Haycraft) *Twentieth Century Authors: A Biographical Dictionary,* 1942, first supplement, 1955; (with Haycraft) *British Authors before 1800: A Biographical Dictionary,* 1952; *Poems of John Keats,* Crowell, 1964; (with Vineta Colby) *European Authors, 1000-1900: A Biographical Dictionary of European Literature,* 1967. General editor, "Yale Series of Younger Poets," Yale University Press, 1969-77.

Contributor: John Fischer and Robert B. Silvers, editors, *Writing in America,* Rutgers University Press, 1960; Anthony J. Ostroff, editor, *The Contemporary Poet as Artist and Critic,* Little, Brown, 1964; Vineta Colby, editor, *American Culture in the Sixties,* H. W. Wilson, 1964; (of translations) Andrei Voznesensky, *Antiworlds,* Basic Books, 1966;

(of translations) Voznesensky, *Antiworlds and The Fifth Ace,* Anchor Books, 1967; Robert Lowell and others, editors, *Randall Jarrell, 1914-1965,* Farrar, Straus, 1967; (of translations) Yevgeny Yevtushenko, *Stolen Apples,* Doubleday, 1971.

Poetry represented in numerous anthologies, including: *War Poets: An Anthology of the War Poetry of the 20th Century,* edited by Oscar Williams, John Day, 1945; *The Criterion Book of Modern American Verse,* edited by W. H. Auden, Criterion, 1956; *How Does a Poem Mean?,* edited by John Ciardi, Houghton, 1959; *Modern American Poetry,* edited by Louis Untermeyer, Harcourt, 1962; *Poet's Choice,* edited by Paul Engle and Joseph Langland, Dial, 1962; *Anthology of Modern Poetry,* edited by John Wain, Hutchinson, 1963; *The Modern Poets,* edited by John Malcolm Brinnin and Bill Read, McGraw, 1963; *American Lyric Poems: From Colonial Times to the Present,* edited by Elder Olson, Appleton, 1964; *The Distinctive Voice,* edited by William J. Martz, Scott, Foresman, 1966; *Where Is Vietnam?: American Poets Respond,* edited by Walter Lowenfels, Doubleday-Anchor, 1967.

Contributor to many periodicals, including *Atlantic, New Republic, New Yorker, Poetry, Partisan Review, New York Review of Books, Nation, New American Review, Times Literary Supplement, Harper's,* and *New York Times Magazine.*

SIDELIGHTS: When *Intellectual Things* was first published, William Rose Benet wrote of Stanley Kunitz: "Here is a man immediately asserting his own fresh utterance, modern and yet very old, intricate and metaphysical and yet undeniably full of the sagacity of the true seer, the poet born.... First acquaintance with his words is an exciting adventure. They involve a great intricacy of meditation. His phrase can assume finality. After witnessing so much rambling experimentation it is profoundly pleasing to observe such agility. Mr. Kunitz has gained the front rank of contemporary verse in a single stride." Despite both initial and continuing critical acclaim, Kunitz's work has yet to achieve the wide readership many believe it merits. Aaron Kramer wrote that Kunitz's writing "has always been rich in vision and passion. But one could seldom ignore the technical virtuosity; matter seemed subordinate to manner; and this may in part account for his having remained a poet's poet, without readers." Kunitz told *CA,* however, that his supposed lack of readership is "fortunately not true!"

Kunitz's more recent work exhibits what Stanley Moss describes as "a new open style." Examining his development as a poet, Jean H. Hagstrum writes: "Stanley Kunitz provides his readers with the excitement, rarely encountered in modern poetry, of exploring both the guilty and joyful recesses of the personality. Of guilt alone, we have perhaps had more than our share, and the pilgrimage from sin to salvation has become ... almost fashionable. But relatively few have moved, as Mr. Kunitz has in his thirty-year poetic career, from the darkly morbid psychic interiors to a clean, well-lighted place, where personality is integrated through love and art—love that draws nourishment from the unabashedly physical and art that, though complex, rests on the honest simplifications of life." Moss also sees in the new work a separation of the "self," and states that Kunitz's "'I' poems usually deal with temporal material; he is the speaker and he tells of events that actually happened.... He pursues his own living and dying." Moss also observes "another self ... [in which Kunitz] is partly observer, partly the thing observed. He must be true to himself and, at the same time, he must speak within the confine of what the imagined

or actual character might say, feel and do. As this self, he deals with aging, dying, moral and spiritual survival. He reaches to become something 'beyond the merely human'—he prepares to die."

In a review of *The Testing Tree,* Kunitz's first book of poetry since the Pulitzer Prize winning *Selected Poems,* published in 1958, Robert Lowell writes: "One reads from cover to cover with the ease of reading good prose fiction, reads with such fresh confidence that even Kunitz's versions of Osip Mandelstam, darkest of the realistic masters, seem as open as Whitman. Kunitz's straight-forwardness is partly technical. His favorite meter is a four-beat line, or shorter; his measure is varied iambic.... His book looks back 60 years. I don't know of another in prose or verse that gives in a few pages the impression of a large autobiography." J. A. Avant feels that "Kunitz's poetry, with few flashy images and metaphors, is notably unspectacular; although when he likes he can dazzle.... His simplicity is not banal but has been arrived at out of complexity and suggests the unity in mazes that one finds in the fiction of Borges.... To read this volume, which includes some translations from the Russian, is to watch Kunitz work out his craft with seeming ease and to absorb the serenity which his discipline conveys." Jack Kroll says that Stanley Kunitz is "elegiac, tough, wistful, proud of having lived a life of sensibility, but manfully guilty of the domesticated havoc that any human life triggers. Like most poets his age, he has pulled the ripcord to end his youthful free fall and is floating to earth with the sun shining through his chute."

A writer for *Kirkus Reviews* calls Kunitz "our senior statesman of poetry. The careful editing and ordering of [*A Kind of Order, a Kind of Folly,* a] collection of critical essays, some dating from as early as the '40s, reflects his passionate discipline. It serves his reputation well. Two theoretical threads run through his approach to poetry: the participation of the individual in the style of the age (our own sensibility, as he proposes, corresponds to the physics of Einstein and Heisenberg—a poetry of process instead of fact) and the quest for selfhood." As Kunitz wrote in *A Kind of Order, a Kind of Folly:* "At the core of one's existence there is a pool of energy that has nothing to do with personal identity, but that falls away from self, blends into the natural universe. Man has only a bit part to play in the whole marvelous show of creation.... All poets want to believe in a transcendental harmony, a music of the spheres. Our poems can never satisfy us, since they are at best a diminished echo of a song that maybe once or twice in a lifetime we've heard and keep trying to recall." He says that he keeps "trying to improve my controls over language, so that I won't have to tell lies. And I keep reading the masters, because they infect me with human possibility. The vainest ambition is to want an art separated from its heritage, as though the tradition were a cistern full of toads instead of a life-giving fountain.... The fatal temptation for any poet is to become grandiose, to write only out of inflated emotional states. The way to achieve nobility in art is through the commonplace. Not to over-reach, not to strain for high-flown epithets or resolutions. But simply to be as true as one can to the grain of the life."

Kunitz has stated that, in his teaching, he tries "to help each person rediscover the poet within himself. I say 'rediscover' because I am convinced that it is a universal human attribute to want to play with words, to beat out rhythms, to fashion images, to tell a story, to construct forms.... The key is always in his possession: what prevents him from using it is mainly inertia, the stultification of the senses as a result of our one-sided educational conditioning and the fear of being made ridiculous or ashamed by the exposure of his feeling.'' Moss believes that Kunitz himself has achieved these goals. ''Kunitz . . . has found his way,'' Moss writes. ''His self, poetry and nature are worked with as one consubstantive stuff. This accomplishment . . . should occasion a national holiday. He has become a mulch, a protector locked into nature. He is 'a man with a leaf in his head.' The leaf is both growing and memorized.''

Kunitz has recorded his poetry for Yale University and the Library of Congress.

BIOGRAPHICAL/CRITICAL SOURCES—Books: M. L. Rosenthal, *The Modern Poets: A Critical Introduction,* Oxford University Press, 1960; Edward Hungerford, editor, *Poets in Progress,* Northwestern University Press, 1962, revised edition, 1967; Anthony J. Ostroff, editor, *The Contemporary Poet as Critic and Artist,* Little, Brown, 1964; Ralph J. Mills, Jr., *Contemporary American Poetry,* Random House, 1965; Stanley Kunitz, *A Kind of Order, a Kind of Folly: Essays and Conversations,* Atlantic-Little, Brown, 1975; *Contemporary Literary Criticism,* Volume VI, Gale, 1976.

Periodicals: *New York Quarterly,* fall, 1970; *Mediterranean Review,* winter, 1971; *New York Times Book Review,* March 21, 1971, November 16, 1975; *Newsweek,* April 12, 1971; *Library Journal,* May 1, 1971; *Malahat Review,* July, 1971; *Yale Review,* autumn, 1971; *Nation,* September 20, 1971; *Saturday Review,* December 18, 1971; *Kirkus Reviews,* May 1, 1975; *Agenda,* summer, 1975; *Choice,* November, 1975.

*   *   *

KUNJUFU, Johari M. Amini 1935-
(Johari M. Amini)

PERSONAL: Name legally changed; born February 13, 1935, in Philadelphia, Pa.; daughter of Vol William (a clergyman) and Alma Irene (Bazel) McLawler; married Jawanza Kunjufu; children: Marciana, Kim Allan (son), Shikamana (son). *Education:* Chicago City College, A.A., 1968; Chicago State College (now University); B.A., 1970; University of Chicago, M.A., 1972. *Office:* Third World Press, 7524 South Cottage Grove Ave., Chicago, Ill. 60619.

CAREER: Worked as secretary, 1956-66; Chicago City College, Chicago, Ill., instructor in psychology, 1970-72; University of Illinois at Chicago Circle, lecturer in black literature, 1972-76; currently an editor with Third World Press, Chicago. *Member:* Institute of Positive Education, African Heritage Studies Association, Organization of Black American Culture (treasurer, 1967-75).

WRITINGS—Under name Johari M. Amini; poems: *Images in Black,* Third World Press, 1967; *Black Essence,* Third World Press, 1968; *A Folk Fable for My People,* Third World Press, 1969; *Let's Go Some Where,* Third World Press, 1970; *A Hip Tale in the Death Style,* Broadside Press, 1972; *An African Frame of Reference,* Institute of Positive Education, 1972. Also author of *Re-Definition: Concept as Being* and *Commonsense Approach to Eating.* Work appears in thirteen anthologies. Contributor to *Black World* and *Negro Digest.* Assistant editor of *Black Books Bulletin,* 1970—.

SIDELIGHTS: Some of Johari Kunjufu's poetry is included on the recordings ''Black Spirits,'' Motown/Black Forum Records, 1972 and ''Spectrum in Black,'' Scott, Foresman, 1971.

KUNO, Susumu 1933-

PERSONAL: Born August 11, 1933, in Tokyo, Japan; son of Sakuro (a professor) and Sono (Ono) Kuno; married Sachiko Tomioka, April 8, 1957 (divorced, 1967); married Yoko Nakajima, August 30, 1967; children: (first marriage) Mayumi, Kanami; (second marriage) Alisa, Erika. *Education:* Tokyo University, A.B., 1956, A.M., 1958; Harvard University, Ph.D., 1964. *Home:* 47 Glendale Rd., Belmont, Mass. 02178. *Office:* Department of Linguistics, Harvard University, Science Center, Cambridge, Mass. 02138.

CAREER: Harvard University, Cambridge, Mass., research fellow in mathematical linguistics, 1960-63, instructor, 1964-65, assistant professor, 1965-68, associate professor, 1968-69, professor of linguistics, 1969—, chairman of department, 1972—. Trustee, Language Research Foundation. *Member:* Linguistic Society of America (member of executive committee, 1977-78), Association of Computation Linguistics (president, 1967-68), Association of the Japanese Teachers (member of executive committee, 1973-75), Linguistic Society of Japan. *Awards, honors:* Fulbright fellowship, 1960-63; Guggenheim fellowship, 1977-78.

WRITINGS: (Translator) Joshua Whatmough, *Gengo: Gendai ni okero Soogooteki Koosatsu* (title means ''Language: A Modern Synthesis''), Iwanami, 1960; *Nihonbunpoo Kenkyuu* (title means ''Studies in Japanese Grammar''), Taishukan, 1973; *The Structure of the Japanese Language,* M.I.T. Press, 1973; *Rules of Discourse,* Taishukan, 1978. Contributor to conferences, proceedings, seminars, and transactions. Contributor to linguistics journals in the United States and Japan. Associate editor, *Linguistic Inquiry,* 1970-77.

WORK IN PROGRESS: Studying English and Japanese syntax and semantics.

*   *   *

KURLAND, Gerald 1942-

PERSONAL: Born July 24, 1942, in Brooklyn, N.Y.; son of Carl (a pharmacist) and Sophia (Spar) Kurland. *Education:* Long Island University, B.A., 1963; Brooklyn College of the City University of New York, M.A., 1964; City University of New York, Ph.D., 1968. *Politics:* Generally conservative. *Religion:* None. *Office:* 6990 Southwest 30th St., Miramar, Fla. 33023.

CAREER: Brooklyn College of the City University of New York, Brooklyn, N.Y., lecturer in history, 1966-75; freelance writer and editor, mainly of textbooks and adult and juvenile historical works. *Member:* American Historical Association, Organization of American Historians.

WRITINGS—Published by Simon & Schuster, except as indicated: *Seth Low: The Reformer in an Urban and Industrial Age,* Twayne, 1971; *Western Civilization to 1500 A.D.,* 1971; *Western Civilization from 1500 A.D.,* 1971; *American History to Reconstruction,* 1971; (editor) *Misjudgment or Defense of Freedom: The United States in Vietnam,* 1975; (editor) *The Failure of Diplomacy: The Origins of the Cold War,* 1975.

Juvenile books; all published by StoryHouse: *Warren Harding,* 1971; *Thomas Dewey,* 1971; *Walt Disney,* 1971; *Nikita S. Khrushchev,* 1971; *Fidel Castro,* 1972; *George Wallace,* 1972; *Spiro Agnew,* 1972; *Fiorello LaGuardia,* 1972; *Alexander Hamilton,* 1972; *Benjamin Franklin,* 1972; *John D. Rockefeller,* 1972; *Samuel Gompers,* 1972; *Mao Tse Tung,* 1972; *Richard Daley,* 1972; *Clarence Darrow,* 1972; *Lyndon B. Johnson,* 1972; *Henry Ford,* 1972; *James R. Hoffa,* 1972; *Lucretia Mott,* 1972; *Thomas Edison,* 1972.

Andrew Carnegie, 1973; *John L. Lewis,* 1973; *Walter Reuther,* 1973; *The Arab-Israeli Conflict,* 1973; *The Cold War, 1945-1963,* 1973; *The Conflict in Vietnam,* 1973; *The Growth of Presidential Power,* 1973; *The Political Machine: What It Is, How It Works,* 1973; *The Supreme Court under Warren,* 1973; *The United States: Policeman of the World?,* 1973; *The Assassination of John F. Kennedy,* 1973; *The Assassination of Robert F. Kennedy,* 1973; *The Convention and the Crisis: Chicago, 1968,* 1973; *The Creation of Bangla Desh,* 1973; *The Cuban Missile Crisis,* 1973; *The Hiroshima Atomic Bomb Blast,* 1973; *The My Lai Massacre,* 1973; *The Suez Crisis, 1956,* 1973; *The Bay of Pigs Invasion,* 1974; *The Czechoslovakian Crisis of 1968,* 1974; *The Hungarian Rebellion of 1956,* 1974; *The Korean War,* 1974; *The Gulf of Tonkin Incident,* 1975; *Lindbergh Flies the Atlantic,* 1975.

General editor, *Outstanding Personalities of the American Revolution,* six volumes, Story House, 1973, and *Controversial Issues in United States History,* five volumes, Simon & Schuster, 1975. Contributor to *New York Historical Society Quarterly, New Jersey History, New York History, The Historian, America, History and Life,* and other journals.

*   *   *

KURTZ, David L(ee) 1941-

PERSONAL: Born February 19, 1941, in Riverside, N.J.; son of C. Reed and Catherine (Rohrbaugh) Kurtz; married Lynne Hambly (a teacher), July 23, 1968; children: Jennifer. *Education:* Davis and Elkins College, B.A., 1963; University of Arkansas, M.B.A., 1965, Ph.D., 1969. *Home:* 12975 LeBlanc Rd., Plymouth, Mich. 48170. *Office:* Department of Marketing, Eastern Michigan University, Ypsilanti, Mich. 48197.

CAREER: Davis and Elkins College, Elkins, W.Va., instructor in business and economics, 1966; University of Arkansas, Fayetteville, instructor in marketing, 1965-67; Eastern Michigan University, Ypsilanti, 1967—, began as assistant professor, currently professor of marketing. *Member:* American Marketing Association, Southern Marketing Association.

WRITINGS: (With C. W. Hubbard) *The Sales Function and Its Management,* General Learning Press, 1971; (with Louis E. Boone) *Sales Management Game,* General Learning Press, 1972; *Marketing: Concepts, Issues, and Viewpoints,* General Learning Press, 1972; (with Boone) *Contemporary Marketing,* Holt, 1974, 2nd edition, Dryden, 1977; (with H. R. Dodge and J. K. Lompmaker) *Professional Selling,* Business Publications, 1976; (with Boone) *Contemporary Business,* Dryden, 1976; (with Boone) *Foundations of Marketing,* Dryden, 1977.

WORK IN PROGRESS: Management, with Louis E. Boone, for Random House.

L

LABROCA, Mario 1897(?)-1973

1897(?)—July 1, 1973; Italian composer, conductor, writer, and critic. Obituaries: *New York Times*, July 2, 1973.

* * *

LACEY, Paul A. 1934-

PERSONAL: Born March 15, 1934, in Philadelphia, Pa.; married Margaret Smith; children: Mary, Patrick, James. *Education:* University of Pennsylvania, B.A., 1957; Harvard University, Ph.D., 1966. *Religion:* Society of Friends. *Office:* Department of English, Earlham College, Richmond, Ind.

CAREER: Earlham College, Richmond, Ind., instructor, 1960-62, assistant professor, 1962-67, associate professor, 1967-71, professor of English, 1971—, chairman of department, 1971-72, provost, 1972-75. Lecturer and seminar leader, Pendle Hill, 1961-62. *Member:* Modern Language Association of America, Society for Values in Higher Education, American Association of University Professors, Friends World Committee, Christians Associated for Relations with Eastern Europe, Phi Beta Kappa. *Awards, honors:* Woodrow Wilson fellow, 1958; Danforth fellow, 1966, Danforth associate, 1967; E. Harris Harbison Prize for Gifted Teaching, Danforth Foundation, 1970; Lilly Endowment open faculty fellowship, 1975-76.

WRITINGS: The Inner War, Fortress, 1972. Contributor to professional and religious periodicals.

WORK IN PROGRESS: Studying religious and political development of Samuel Taylor Coleridge.

* * *

LAEVASTU, Taivo 1923-

PERSONAL: Surname originally Granfeldt; name legally changed in 1940; born February 26, 1923, in Vihula, Estonia; came to United States in 1954, naturalized in 1967; son of Wilhelm and Martha (Vogt) Granfeldt; married Lahja Irene Marikanto, September 1, 1949; children: Eva-Kristina, Pia Margareta, Steve-Erich. *Education:* University of Lund, Fil. Kand., 1951; University of Washington, Seattle, M.S., 1954; University of Helsinki, Ph.D., 1960. *Home:* 10333 40th Ave. N.E., Seattle, Wash. 98125. *Office:* National Oceanic and Atmospheric Administration, National Marine Fish Service, 2725 Montlake Blvd. E., Seattle, Wash. 98112.

CAREER: Fisheries officer for Swedish National Commission on Migratory Fish, 1951-53; University of Washington, Seattle, research associate, 1954-55; Food and Agriculture Organization of the United Nations, Rome, Italy, fisheries oceanographer, 1955-62; University of Hawaii, Honolulu, associate professor of oceanography, 1962-64; Fleet Numerical Weather Central, Monterey, Calif., senior research oceanographer, 1964-71; U.S. Naval Postgraduate School, Environmental Prediction Research Facility, Monterey, Calif., head of department of oceanography, 1971-76; National Oceanic and Atmospheric Administration, National Marine Fish Service, Seattle, Wash., ecosystem modeling expert, 1976—. Member of panel on disposal of radioactive wastes, International Atomic Energy Agency; member of international expert panel on oceanic water balance, World Meteorological Organization. *Member:* American Geophysical Union, American Meteorological Society, American Association for the Advancement of Science, American Society of Limnology and Oceanography, Geochemical Society, Sigma Xi. *Awards, honors:* Military Oceanography Award, 1969; Naval Weather Service Special Contribution Award, 1971.

WRITINGS: Factors Affecting the Temperature of the Surface Layers of the Sea, Social Science Fannica (Helsinki), 1960; *Manual of Methods in Fisheries Biology,* United Nations Food and Agriculture Organization, 1962; (with Ilmo Hela) *Fisheries Hydrography,* Heighway, 1962; (with Hela) *Fisheries Oceanography,* Heighway, 1970. Contributor to scientific journals.

WORK IN PROGRESS: Research and reports on the results on hydrodynamical-numerical models in oceanography; research on sea air interactions and application of oceanographic forecasting to fisheries and other maritime use; manual of marine ecosystem modeling; results of ecosystem applications; fisheries resources evaluation.

SIDELIGHTS: Taivo Laevastu speaks Swedish, German, Estonian, Finnish, and Italian.

* * *

LAHR, Raymond M(errill) 1914-1973

June 27, 1914—June 14, 1973; American political reporter and author. Obituaries: *New York Times*, June 15, 1973.

LAIR, Jess K. 1926-

PERSONAL: Born October 11, 1926, in Bricelyn, Minn.; son of Merle T. and Bertha (Eggen) Lair; married Jacqueline Carey (a writer), July 7, 1949; children: Janet, Barbara (Mrs. Donald Richardson), Jess, Jr., Joseph, Michael. *Education:* University of Minnesota, B.A., 1948, M.A., 1964, Ph.D., 1965. *Home:* Route 2, Box 307, Bozeman, Mont. 59715. *Office:* Department of Education, Montana State University, Bozeman, Mont. 59715.

CAREER: Bruce B. Brewer Advertising Agency, Kansas City, Mo., and Minneapolis, Minn., assistant editor and copywriter, 1951-56; Leo Burnett Advertising Agency, Chicago, Ill., copywriter, 1956-57; owner of a marketing consultant company, Minneapolis, 1957-62; University of Minnesota, Minneapolis, assistant professor, 1963-66, associate professor of writing and speech, 1966-67; Montana State University, Bozeman, associate professor of writing, 1967-69, associate professor of educational psychology, 1968—. *Military service:* U.S. Army Air Forces, 1944-45. *Member:* American Psychological Association.

WRITINGS—All published by Doubleday: *I Ain't Much Baby, But I'm All I Got*, 1972; *Hey God, What Should I Do Now?*, 1974; *I Ain't Well but I Sure Am Better*, 1975; *Ain't I a Wonder and Ain't You a Wonder, Too!*, 1977; *Sex, If I Didn't Laugh, I'd Cry*, in press.

WORK IN PROGRESS: A book tentatively entitled *I Walk Most Safely When I Don't Know Where I Go.*

*   *   *

LAMBERT, B. Geraldine 1922-

PERSONAL: Born December 20, 1922, in Booneville, Ark.; daughter of Daniel Arthur (a locomotive engineer) and Bertha M. (Nicholls) Lambert. *Education:* Oklahoma College of Liberal Arts (now University of Science and Arts of Oklahoma), B.A., 1946; University of Oklahoma, M.Ed., 1958, Ph.D., 1966. *Religion:* Methodist. *Home and office address:* P.O. Box 41571, University of Southwestern Louisiana, Lafayette, La. 70504.

CAREER: Employed at various times as newspaperwoman, librarian, secretary, receptionist, and bookkeeper; teacher and counselor for Hobbs, N.M. schools, 1948-61, El Reno, Okla. schools, 1961-62, and Oklahoma City, Okla. schools, 1962-66; University of Southwestern Louisiana, Lafayette, assistant professor, 1966-69, associate professor, 1969-72, professor of psychology, 1972—, head of department, 1970—. Member of board of directors of Lafayette Juvenile and Young Adult Program, 1967-78, and Southwest Louisiana Rehabilitation Center, 1971—. *Member:* American Psychological Association, National Education Association, American Personnel and Guidance Association, American Association of University Women, Southwestern Psychological Association, Louisiana Pyschological Association, Louisiana Teachers Association, Louisiana Guidance Association, Phi Kappa Phi, Delta Kappa Gamma, Kappa Delta Pi, Order of Eastern Star.

WRITINGS: (With Barbara Rothschild, Richard Altman, and L. B. Greene) *Adolescence; Transition from Childhood to Maturity*, Brooks/Cole, 1972, 2nd edition, 1978. Editor of *Southwestern Psychological Newsletter*, 1967-69, 1975-76.

WORK IN PROGRESS: A counseling textbook.

*   *   *

LAMBERT, Janet 1895(?)-1973

1895(?)—March 16, 1973; American author of books for teen-age girls. Obituaries: *Publishers Weekly*, April 9, 1973.

*   *   *

LAMONT, Douglas Felix 1937-

PERSONAL: Born November 22, 1937, in Newark, N.J.; son of Felix Michael (an engineer) and Philomena (a grade school teacher; maiden name Verderosa) Italiano; married Janice Monk (a dietitian), January 20, 1965; children: Katherine Audrey, Kristine Andrea. *Education:* University of Pennsylvania, B.S., 1959; Tulane University, M.B.A., 1960; University of Alabama, Ph.D., 1964. *Home:* 414 Ozark Trail, Madison, Wis. 53705. *Office:* Walter E. Heller College of Business Administration, Roosevelt University, Chicago, Ill. 60605.

CAREER: University of Notre Dame, South Bend, Ind., assistant professor of marketing, 1966-67; University of Alabama, University, associate professor, 1967-70, professor of international business, 1970-73; University of Wisconsin—Madison, program coordinator for social sciences, 1973-78; Roosevelt University, Chicago, Ill., professor and dean of College of Business Administration, 1978—. *Military service:* U.S. Army, 1964-66; became captain. *Member:* American Marketing Association, Academy of International Business. *Awards, honors:* Fulbright commission lectureships in Ecuador, 1970, and Peru, 1972; American Council on Education fellow in academic administration, 1971-72.

WRITINGS: (Contributor) S. Hollander, editor, *Public Policy Toward Retailing: An International Study*, Heath, 1972; *Managing Foreign Investment in Southern Italy*, Praeger, 1973; *Foreign State Enterprises: A Threat to American Business*, Basic Books, 1979. Contributor to *Harvard Business Review, Journal of Marketing, Italian-American Business, Southern Journal of Business, Essays in International Business*, and *AACSE Bulletin*.

WORK IN PROGRESS: A book on international finance.

*   *   *

LAND, Aubrey C(hristian) 1912-

PERSONAL: Born September 2, 1912, in Panola County, Miss.; son of William Alexander and Lois (Christian) Land; married Helen Augusta Larrabee, December 21, 1941 (died, 1947); married Anne Wolfshohl (a librarian), January 31, 1949; children: (second marriage) Alison Christian, Alexandra Anne. *Education:* Southern Illinois Normal University (now Southern Illinois University at Carbondale), B.Ed., 1934; State University of Iowa, M.A., 1939, Ph.D., 1948. *Politics:* Democrat. *Religion:* Episcopalian. *Home:* 175 Homestead Dr., Athens, Ga. 30601. *Office:* Department of History, University of Georgia, Athens, Ga. 30601.

CAREER: Junior high school principal in Mound City, Ill., 1935-37; consultant on industrial relations, Commonwealth Edison, 1941-42; Carnegie Institute of Technolgy (now Carnegie-Mellon University), Pittsburgh, Pa., assistant professor of history, 1946-49; Princeton University, Princeton, N.J., visiting assistant professor of history, 1949-50; Vanderbilt University, Nashville, Tenn., assistant professor, 1950-54, associate professor of history, 1954-55; University of Nebraska, Lincoln, professor of history, 1955-58; University of Maryland, College Park, professor of history and chairman of department, 1958-68; University of Georgia, Athens, research professor of history, 1968—. Member of advisory board of American Bibliography Center, 1968—, Library of Congress's bicentennial on American Revolution, 1969—, and Historic Annapolis, Inc., 1976—.

Chairman of commemorations committee, American Revolution Bicentennial Commission, beginning 1972; member of board of directors, Loyalist Studies and Publications, 1974—. *Military service:* U.S. Army, 1942-46; became captain; received Bronze Star Medal with oak leaf cluster and Purple Heart. U.S. Army Reserve, 1946-55.

MEMBER: American Historical Association, Organization of American Historians, Economic History Association, American Association of University Professors, Southern Historical Association. *Awards, honors:* Fulbright senior fellowship, London School of Economics, 1957-58; Guggenheim fellowship, 1957-58; Huntington Library fellowship, 1970.

WRITINGS: The Dulanys of Maryland, Maryland Historical Society, 1955, 2nd edition, Johns Hopkins Press, 1968; (with Morris L. Radoff and others) *The Old Line State: A History of Maryland,* three volumes, Historical Record Association, 1956; (editor) *Bases of the Plantation Society,* Harper, 1969; (editor) William Eddis, *Letters from America,* Harvard University Press, 1969; (contributor) *The American Past,* Xerox College Publishing, 1971; (contributor) *Past Imperfect,* Knopf, 1973; (editor) *Law, Society and Politics in Early Maryland,* Johns Hopkins Press, 1977. Contributor to professional journals. Editor, *Archives of Maryland,* Volume LXXI, 1970; member of editorial board, *Georgia Review,* 1974—.

WORK IN PROGRESS: Merchants and Planters of the Chesapeake.

* * *

LANDY, Eugene E(llsworth) 1934-

PERSONAL: Born November 26, 1934, in Pittsburgh, Pa.; son of Jules C. (a physician) and Frieda Mae (Gordon) Landy; married Judy Kusknick (a writer), 1958 (divorced, 1959); married Elayne A. Bernstein (a social worker), November 7, 1961 (divorced, 1972); children: (second marriage) Evan Gordon. *Education:* Los Angeles City College, A.A., 1963; California State College (now University), Los Angeles, B.A., 1964; University of Oklahoma, M.S., 1967, Ph.D., 1968; also attended National University of Mexico. *Politics:* Non-partisan. *Religion:* "Born Jewish; currently areligious." *Office:* 303 South Robertson Blvd., Beverly Hills, Calif. 90211.

CAREER: Licensed by State of California as clinical psychologist, and as marriage, family, and child counselor; private practitioner of clinical psychology and psychotherapy, Beverly Hills, Calif.; University of Southern California, Los Angeles, lecturer, 1968, senior lecturer in psychology, 1969—, director of Youth Culture Seminar Center for Training and Development. Consultant to drug abuse training center, University of California, Los Angeles. Director of Foundation for Rechanneling of Emotions and Education, and Center for Adjunctive Therapeutic Activity; member of staff at Calabasas Hospital Neuropsychiatric Center; clinical staff psychologist and director of Adolescent Drug Abuse Program, Gateways Hospital. *Member:* American Psychological Association, American Association of University Professors, International Academy of Forensic Psychology (fellow), Western Psychological Association, California State Marriage Counseling Association, Group Psychotherapy Association of Southern California, Los Angeles County Psychological Association, Los Angeles Society of Clinical Psychologists.

WRITINGS: (With R. I. Gordon, S. L. Heavin, and W. R. Hood) *A Critical Analysis of Trans-Action* (monograph),

Institute of Group Relations, University of Oklahoma, 1968; (editor and contributor) *The Future of the University,* University of Oklahoma Press, 1969; *The Underground Dictionary* (Book-of-the-Month Club selection), Simon & Schuster, 1971. Contributor to psychology journals, including *Perceptual Motor Skills, Comparative Group Studies,* and *Psychological Reports.*

WORK IN PROGRESS: Marathon, a book of pictures and an explanation of the "marathon" psychotherapy experience; a book concerning the author's own methods of treatment for drug-abused adolescents and young adults.

* * *

LANE, Arthur (Ernest) 1937-

PERSONAL: Born March 13, 1937, in Middlesbrough, England; son of William Arthur (a machinist) and Minnie Potter (Greenhow) Lane; married Judy Frances Greenberg, December 30, 1971. *Education:* Royal Military College of Canada, B.A., 1959; University of Montreal, M.A., 1962; University of California, San Diego, Ph.D., 1967. *Home:* 4316 Camello Rd., Woodland Hills, Calif. 91364. *Office:* Department of English, California State University, Northridge, Calif. 91324.

CAREER: Royal Canadian Air Force, navigator, 1955-62, leaving service as a flying officer; California State University, Northridge, assistant professor, 1968-73, associate professor, 1973-77, professor of English, 1977—. *Member:* United Professors of California.

WRITINGS: An Adequate Response: The War Poetry of Wilfred Owen and Siegfried Sassoon, Wayne State University Press, 1972; *Dancing in the Dark* (poems), Kenmore Press, 1976; *Handing Over* (poems), Kenmore Press, 1979. Author of movie script: "Anthony, Anthony." Contributor of poetry to magazines.

WORK IN PROGRESS: The Poolsweep Murders, a book of poems.

* * *

LANE, Pinkie Gordon 1923-

PERSONAL: Born January 13, 1923, in Philadelphia, Pa.; married Ulysses S. Lane (deceased); children: Gordon Edward. *Education:* Spelman College, B.A. (magna cum laude), 1949; Atlanta University, M.A., 1956; Louisiana State University, Ph.D., 1967. *Home:* 2738 77th Ave., Baton Rouge, La. 70807. *Office:* Department of English, Southern University, Baton Rouge, La. 70813.

CAREER: High school English teacher in Georgia, 1949-55; Southern University, Baton Rouge, La., instructor, 1959-60, assistant professor, 1960-62, associate professor, 1963-67, professor of English, 1967—. Charter member, Mayor—President's Commission on the Needs of Women. Member of editorial board, South & West, Inc. Has given readings from her works in Arkansas, Tennessee, Oklahoma, New York, Mississippi, and Louisiana. *Member:* Modern Language Association of America, National Council of Teachers of English, Poetry Society of America, National Organization for Women, Louisiana Art and Artists' Guild, Delta Sigma Theta. *Awards, honors:* Awards from National Writer's Club, 1970, and Tulsa Poets, 1970; nominated for Pulitzer prize, 1978, for *Mystic Female.*

WRITINGS: Wind Thoughts (poems), South & West, 1972; (editor and contributor) *Discourses on Poetry* (an anthology of prose and poetry by black authors), South & West, 1972; (editor and contributor) *Poems by Blacks,* Volume III,

South & West, 1973; *Mystic Female* (poems), South & West, 1978.

Work in anthologized in *To Gwen with Love,* edited by Patricia L. Brown, Don L. Lee, and Francis Ward, Johnson Publishing Co., 1971; *Poems by Blacks,* edited by Sue Abbott Boyd, Volumes I and II, South & West, 1972. Contributor to literary journals, including *Phylon, Negro American Literary Forum, Journal of Black Poetry, Bardic Echoes, Personalist, South & West, Voices International, Energy West, Pembroke Magazine, Jeopardy, Poet: India, The Louisiana Review, The Last Cookie,* and *Hoo Doo.*

SIDELIGHTS: Pinkie Gordon Lane's works are included in the Beinecke Rare Book and Manuscript Library at Yale University in the James Weldon Johnson Collection of Negro Arts and Letters. Her avocational interests include art (has exhibited oil paintings).

* * *

LANE, Ronnie M(ack) 1949-

PERSONAL: Born August 13, 1949, in Blytheville, Ark.; son of Billy M. (an executive) and Myrtle (Robirds) Lane; married Jill A. Collins (an artist and poet); children: Sara Diane, Matthew William. *Education:* Attended Grand Rapids Junior College, 1967-70, and Grand Valley State College, 1970-72. *Home:* 1023 Chester S.E., Grand Rapids, Mich. 49508.

CAREER: Free-lance writer. *Awards, honors:* Dyer-Ives Poetry Award, 1971.

WRITINGS: Empty Cups, Metamorphosis, 1971; *Carnage,* Pilot Press, 1972; *Two Prose Poems,* Free Press (Grand Rapids, Mich.), 1972; (editor) *Face the Whirlwind: Anthology of Black Michigan Poets,* Pilot Press, 1973; *A Shephard Walks the Moon,* Pilot Press, 1973; *Under the Blood-Gorged Moon,* Free Press (Grand Rapids, Mich.), 1973; *The Greatest Show on Earth: Selected Poems, 1968-1975,* edited by Eric Greinke, Pilot Press, 1975. Fiction editor of *Amaranthus,* 1971—.

WORK IN PROGRESS: The Vestibules of Hell, a Civil War novel; *Frieda,* a novel; *The Pete Stories,* short stories; *Amnesty for the Unborn,* poetry; *Forest of Bones,* a science fiction novel.

* * *

LANFORD, H(orace) W(haley) 1919-

PERSONAL: Born May 25, 1919, in Atlanta, Ga.; son of Horace Whaley (a dentist) and Mattie (West) Lanford; married Joyce White, March 6, 1964; children: Michael Sean, Ward Fraser. *Education:* Attended Georgia Institute of Technology, 1938-40; University of Georgia, B.B.A., 1948; George Washington University, M.A., 1950; Ohio State University, Ph.D., 1964. *Politics:* Republican. *Religion:* Protestant. *Home:* 1825 Southlawn Dr., Fairborn, Ohio 45324. *Office:* Department of Management, Wright State University, Dayton, Ohio.

CAREER: U.S. Air Force, career officer, 1940-66, retired as colonel; Wright State University, Dayton, Ohio, associate professor, 1966-74, professor of management, 1974—, head of department, 1967-69. President, H. Lanford & Associates, Inc. (management consultants). Adjunct professor at U.S. Air Force Institute of Technology, 1965-68, and Wittenberg University, 1965-66. Member of board of directors of Dayton Honor Seminars, Inc., 1966—. *Member:* American Management Association, Academy of Management, Institute of Electrical and Electronic Engineers, Armed

Forces Management Association, Southern Management Association. *Awards, honors*—Military: Distinguished Flying Cross, Air Medal with three oak leaf clusters, Purple Heart.

WRITINGS: Coordinative Methods in Air Force Systems, Aeronautical Systems Division, Air Force Systems Command, 1965; *A Synthesis of Technological Forecasting Methodologies,* Foreign Technology Division, Air Force Systems Command, 1970; *Technological Forecasting Methodologies: A Synthesis,* American Management Association, 1972; *System Management: Planning and Control,* Kennikat, in press. Contributor to *Technological Forecasting and Social Change, Air University Review, Oklahoma Business Review, Business Horizons, Manage Magazine,* and *International Marketing Management.*

WORK IN PROGRESS: Research on technology assessment, systems management, and research and development management.

* * *

LANG, Berel 1933-

PERSONAL: Born November 13, 1933, in Norwich, Conn.; married. *Education:* Yale University, B.A. (magna cum laude), 1954; additional study at Hebrew University, 1954-55, and Indiana University, 1955-56; Columbia University, Ph.D., 1961. *Office:* Department of Philosophy, University of Colorado, Boulder, Colo. 80302.

CAREER: City College of New York (now City College of the City University of New York), New York, N.Y., lecturer in social sciences, 1958-61; University of Colorado, Boulder, assistant professor, 1961-66, associate professor, 1966-70, professor of philosophy and chairman of department, 1970—. Visiting associate professor, Long Island University, 1966-67; visiting professor, Hebrew University, 1971-72. *Military service:* U.S. Army, 1959-60. *Member:* American Philosophical Association, American Society of Aesthetics. *Awards, honors:* Lucius N. Littauer Foundation fellow, 1959, 1961; Rothschild fellow at Hebrew University, 1965; National Endowment for the Humanities fellow, 1967.

WRITINGS: (Editor with Forrest Williams) *Marxism and Art: Writings in Aesthetics and Criticism,* McKay, 1972; (editor with Charlotte Smokler) *Images of the Anti-Semite,* Sheed, 1973; *Art and Inquiry,* Wayne State University Press, 1975. Also contributor, P. A. French, editor, *Conscientious Action: The Revelation of the Pentagon Papers,* Schenkman; contributor to proceedings. Contributor to *Man and World, Personalist, Midstream, Judaism, Comment,* and to philosophy and aesthetics journals.†

* * *

LANG, Jovian Peter 1919-

PERSONAL: Born June 2, 1919, in Sioux City, Iowa; son of Peter (a cobbler) and Margaret (Horvath) Lang. *Education:* Quincy College, A.B., 1943; Case Western Reserve University, M.S. in L.S., 1950, M.A., 1955. *Home:* 37 South Ocean Ave., Freeport, N.Y. 11520. *Office:* Division of Library and Information Science, St. John's University, Grand Central and Utopia Parkway, Jamaica, N.Y. 11439.

CAREER: Ordained Roman Catholic priest of the Order of St. Francis (Franciscans), 1946; Quincy College, Quincy, Ill., assistant librarian, 1947-55, assistant professor of speech, 1950-55, associate professor of speech and librarian, 1960-71; St. Joseph Seminary, Oak Brook, Ill., assistant professor of speech and assistant librarian, 1955-57; Villa St.

Joseph, St. Louis, Mo., assistant professor of speech, 1957-60; University of South Florida, Tampa, assistant professor of library science, 1971-74; St. John's University, Jamaica, N.Y., associate professor of library science, 1974—. Assistant provincial librarian and archivist, St. Louis-Chicago Province O.F.M., St. Louis, Mo., 1955-68. Trustee, Free Public Library, Quincy, Ill., 1960-71; member, Tampa Book Fair Committee, 1971-74. Consultant to Order of Friars Minor Generalate, Rome, 1958—, and to Bishops Committee on Liturgy, Washington, 1968—.

MEMBER: North American Academy of Liturgy, American Franciscan Liturgical Conference, American Library Association (council member, 1964-68, 1972-76; chairman of Outstanding Reference Books Committee, 1978—), Catholic Library Association (vice-president, 1965-67; president, 1967-69; vice-chairman and chairman-elect, Library Education Section, 1977-79), Council for Exceptional Children, Beta Phi Mu.

WRITINGS: Guide for the Liturgy (published annually), Franciscan Press, 1957—; *Guide for Religious and the Laity,* Franciscan Press, 1957-68; *Guide for the Priest during Parish Services,* Franciscan Herald, 1964, 2nd edition, 1965; (editor of American edition) *Liturgy of Vatican II,* two volumes, Franciscan Herald, 1966; *Pray Together* (a monthly missal), Sunday Missal Service, 1970—; *Ordor for the Celebration of the Divine Office and the Mass* (published annually), Sunday Missal Service, 1972—; (editor) *St. Joseph Guide for the Liturgy of the Hours* (published annually), Catholic Book Publishing, 1975—; (editor) *St. Joseph Guide for Christian Prayer* (published annually), Catholic Book Publishing, 1976—; (editor) *St. Joseph Missal Guide* (published annually), Catholic Book Publishing, 1977—; (with others) *Reference Books for Small and Medium-sized Libraries,* American Library Association, 1979; *Your Key to L.C.,* Fordham Publishing, 1979. Contributor of articles to *American Libraries, Library Journal, Catholic Library World, The Library-College, Illinois Libraries, American Library Association, Education Division Newsletter,* and numerous other publications.

WORK IN PROGRESS: Research and constant writing and editing for annual guides and monthly missals; gathering material for a book proposing a new approach to the teaching and critical analysis of children's and young people's literature.

BIOGRAPHICAL/CRITICAL SOURCES: Life, December 19, 1955, May 13, 1957, April 7, 1958; *Time,* May 13, 1957; *Sports Illustrated,* May 13, 1957.

*   *   *

LANG, Robert (Peregrine) 1912-

PERSONAL: Born March 25, 1912, in Hope, N.D.; son of Fred Nathan (an accountant) and Hulda (a teacher of German; maiden name, Peregrine) Lang; married Elizabeth Whitehead (a bibliographer and lecturer in English literature), April 4, 1944; children: Pamela Elizabeth (Mrs. Allen Munro), Peter Alfred. *Education:* University of California, Los Angeles, A.B., 1933, M.A., 1934; Columbia University, B.S., 1935; Harvard University, graduate study, 1948-49. *Politics:* Democrat. *Religion:* Congregationalist. *Home:* 2008 Prince Albert Dr., Riverside, Calif. 92507.

CAREER: Henry E. Huntington Library and Art Gallery, San Marino, Calif., assistant in manuscripts, 1935; Oberlin College, Oberlin, Ohio, assistant reference librarian, 1935-41; Cornell University, Ithaca, N.Y., instructor, 1941-43, assistant professor of fine arts, 1946-51, librarian, 1941-43,

university curator of prints, 1946-51; State University of New York College at New Paltz, lecturer in art history and head librarian, 1951-63, director of Foreign Study Program in Art, 1955-57, head of World Study Center, 1959-63; University of California, Riverside, assistant university librarian, 1963-71, associate university librarian, 1971-78; City of Riverside, Cultural Heritage Board, member, 1976—, chairman, 1977—. Fulbright lecturer, University of the Panjab, Lahore, Pakistan, 1960-61. *Military service:* U.S. Army, Information and Education Division, 1942-46; became technical sergeant. *Member:* College Art Association, Society of Architectural Historians, National Trust for Historic Preservation, Californians for Preservation Action, Phi Beta Kappa.

WRITINGS: (With wife, Elizabeth Lang) *In a Valley Fair: A History of the State University of New York College at New Paltz,* American Book-Stratford Press, 1961; *The Land and People of Pakistan,* Lippincott, 1968, revised edition, 1974. Editor of art exhibition catalogs. Contributor of articles and reviews to professional publications. Editor of *Newsmap* and *Outfit* (military magazines), 1945-46.

WORK IN PROGRESS: A Victorian in Bengal: The Journal and Watercolors of William Dering Pratt, 1860-1868; The Land and People of Bangladesh; current research centers on architecture in the United States and Britain, especially garden ornament in England in the eighteenth century, and on Mission Revival and the origins of Spanish Colonial Revival in Southern California.

SIDELIGHTS: Robert Lang told *CA:* "I find the works of man more interesting than raw nature, and though I'm concerned with all the creative arts, my special interest is in architecture. In recent years, I've found it necessary to spend much of my time defending historic buildings threatened with destruction. It's a frustrating hobby, and I resent somewhat the political maneuvering required, as well as the large commitment of time. Saving a building is far more difficult than cherishing a painting or a musical score. Obviously an old house or church may not be of the same intrinsic worth as an opera or a novel, but 'Don Giovanni' and Barchester Towers aren't endangered in the same way; unlike old buildings, they don't occupy valuable real estate and hence aren't threatened with sudden death. Besides, there's a special satisfaction nowadays in preserving something good in our visual environment. If, as a result of my efforts, another fine old building survives to grace our urban scene, I'll be happy."

AVOCATIONAL INTERESTS: Rare books, typography, photography (especially of architecture).

*   *   *

LANGER, Susanne K(nauth) 1895-

PERSONAL: Born December 20, 1895, in New York, N.Y.; daughter of Antonio (a lawyer) and Else (Uhlich) Knauth; married William L. Langer, September 3, 1921 (divorced, 1942); children: Leonard C. R., Bertrand W. *Education:* Radcliffe College, A.B., 1920, A.M., 1924, Ph.D.,1926; University of Vienna, graduate study, 1921-22. *Religion:* None. *Home:* Neck Rd., Old Lyme, Conn. 06371. *Office:* Department of Philosophy, Connecticut College, New London, Conn. 06320.

CAREER: Radcliffe College, Cambridge, Mass., tutor in philosophy, 1927-42; University of Delaware, Newark, assistant professor of philosophy, 1943; Columbia University, New York, N.Y., lecturer in philosophy, 1945-50; Connecticut College, New London, professor, 1954-61, research scholar in philosophy, 1961—. Visiting professor of philosophy at New York University, 1945, Northwestern University, 1950, Ohio State University, 1950, University of Washington, 1952-53, and University of Michigan, 1954. *Member:* American Philosophical Association. *Awards, honors:* Radcliffe achievement medal, 1950; D.Litt. from Wilson College, 1954, Mt. Holyoke College, 1962, Western College for Women (now Western College), 1962, and Wheaton College, Norton, Mass., 1962; LL.D., Columbia University, 1964; D. Humane Letters, Clark University, 1968.

WRITINGS: The Practice of Philosophy, Holt, 1930; *Philosophy in a New Key,* Harvard University Press, 1942; *An Introduction to Symbolic Logic,* Houghton, 1953; *Feeling and Form,* Scribner, 1953; *Problems of Art,* Scribner, 1957; *Philosophical Sketches,* Johns Hopkins Press, 1962; *Mind: An Essay on Human Feeling,* Johns Hopkins Press, Volume I, 1967, Volume II, 1972.

WORK IN PROGRESS: Volume III of *Mind: An Essay on Human Feeling.*

SIDELIGHTS: In a *New York Times Book Review* article, James Lord writes that Susanne Langer has "vitally influenced not only other philosophers but artists and scientists as well in their concepts of function, and her theories are discussed with vivid concern in both studios and studies. Her works as well as her aspirations have remained serious and life-enhancing, and reflect a lively awareness of the 'state of the art' of the various disciplines from which she draws. This awareness and seriousness of purpose naturally dominate one's impression of her as a person." In an interview with Lord, Langer comments on her work: "'I am trying to tie together a number of disciplines into a structure that these disciplines—the arts, biology, neurology, psychology, language, anthropology, and others—won't themselves singly support. I am trying to develop basic concepts which underlie all these sciences or fields of study, and which can rule all such thought.'"

When asked about the satisfaction of her solitary intellectual pursuits, Langer, who has lived alone in an old New England farmhouse for many years, answered: "'Perhaps the ability to meet difficult problems is my ultimate satisfaction. All of a sudden a light dawns on something which I've been wrestling with for a long time. This happens every few weeks. Then I'm very excited. I know I should stay and work it out completely, but I can't. I get out my canoe or drive to Scarsdale to see my son and his family. I know I have the idea under control, but my excitement has to settle down before I can return to my desk. Whenever you know that you've broken through a difficult problem it gives you a great feeling of security. The greatest security in this tumultuous world is faith in your own mind.'"

BIOGRAPHICAL/CRITICAL SOURCES: New Yorker, August 12, 1967; *Listener,* November 30, 1967; *New York Times Book Review,* May 26, 1968.

* * *

LANGLEY, Stephen G(ould) 1938-

PERSONAL: Born December 25, 1938, in Gardner, Mass.; son of Delma Newkirk and Marjorie (Gould) Langley. *Education:* Central School of Speech and Drama, England, diploma, 1959; Emerson College, B.A., 1960, M.A., 1961; University of Illinois, Ph.D., 1966. *Home address:* Box 1527 GPO, Brooklyn, N.Y. 11202. *Office:* Department of Theatre, Brooklyn College of the City University of New York, Brooklyn, N.Y. 11210.

CAREER: Falmouth Playhouse, Falmouth, Mass., publicity director, 1959-64, general manager, 1965—; Brooklyn College of the City University of New York, Brooklyn, N.Y., instructor, 1963-67, assistant professor, 1967-73, associate professor of theatre administration, 1973-77, professor of performing arts management, 1977—, general manager of performing arts office, 1966-68, general manager of performing arts center, 1968-76, director of performing arts management division of department of theatre, 1976—, deputy chairman of department of theatre, 1978—. *Member:* United States Institute for Theatre Technology, Dramatists Guild, Business and Arts Council, American Theatre Association, Council of Stock Theatres.

WRITINGS: Theatre Management in America, Drama Book Specialists, 1973; *Producers on Producing,* Drama Book Specialists, 1975.

* * *

LAO, Kan 1907-

PERSONAL: Born January 13, 1907, in Shensi, China; son of Chung-wu and Ke-yu (Yen) Lao; married Yen-pu Chou, June 24, 1932; children: Yan-shuan, Yan-jeong, Yan-jing (Mrs. Floris Tsang), Yan-bing. *Education:* University of Peking, B.A., 1931; Academia Sinica, Taipei, China, Academician, 1958. *Religion:* Buddhism. *Home:* 1921 Holmby Ave., Los Angeles, Calif. 90025. *Office:* Department of Chinese Classics, University of California, Los Angeles, Calif. 90024.

CAREER: Academia Sinica, Naking, Peking, Taipei, research fellow in history, 1932-61; Taiwan University, Taipei, professor of history, 1948-61; University of California, Los Angeles, professor of Chinese classics, 1962—. *Member:* Association of Asian Studies. *Awards, honors:* Ph.D. from China Academy College of Chinese Culture (Taipei), 1968.

WRITINGS: A History of the Han Dynasty, Hua Kang Book Co. (Taipei), 1952; *Documents on Wooden Slips,* Academia Sinica (Taipei), 1960; *Tunhuang Arts,* Museum of History (Taipei), 1968; *A History of the Northern and Southern Dynasties,* Hua Kang Book Co., 1972. Contributor of more than one hundred and fifty articles to journals in his fields. Editor of *Bulletin* of Institute of History and Philology (Taipei), 1940-61.

WORK IN PROGRESS: Introduction to *A History of the Han Dynasty.*

* * *

LAPORTE, Jean 1924-

PERSONAL: Born July 18, 1924, in Saint-Satur, France. *Education:* Catholic Institute, Paris, France, Th.L., 1950, doctoral studies, 1956-57, Th.D. (maxima cum laude), 1972. *Office:* Department of Theology, University of Notre Dame, Notre Dame, Ind. 46556.

CAREER: Editions Bloud & Gay, Paris, France, editorial work as co-manager of twenty-volume collection, "Temoins de la Foi," 1956-66; University of Notre Dame, Notre Dame, Ind., associate professor of theology, 1966—.

WRITINGS: Sur les chemins de l'Evangile (description of the Holy Land), privately printed, 1954, second edition, 1960; (translator) J. Quasten, *Initiation aux Peres de l'Eglise,* Editions du Cerf, three volumes, 1956-62; *Lacordaire,* Bloud & Gay, 1961; (translator, and author of introduction and notes) Philo Judaeus, *De Iosepho,* Editions du Cerf, 1964; (contributor) *Kyriakon: Festschrift Johannes Quasten,* Verlag Aschendorff, 1970; *La doctrine Eucharistiaire chez Philon d'Alexandria* (doctoral thesis), Beauchesne, 1972; (contributor) R. L. Wilken, editor, *Aspects of Wisdom in Judaism and Early Christianity,* University of Notre Dame Press, 1975; (contributor) E. D. O'Connor, editor, *Perspectives on Charismatic Renewal,* University of Notre Dame Press, 1976. Contributor of articles to journals.

*   *   *

LaPORTE, Robert, Jr.   1940-

PERSONAL: Born February 12, 1940, in Detroit, Mich.; son of Robert (a barber) and Carrie (Logdon) LaPorte; married Beverley Jean Olson, June 16, 1962; children: Carrie Anne, Beverley Elizabeth. *Education:* Wayne State University, B.A., 1962, M.A., 1963; Syracuse University, Ph.D., 1967. *Home:* Kent Dr., Boalsburg, Pa. 16827. *Office:* Institute of Public Administration, Pennsylvania State University, University Park, Pa. 16802.

CAREER: Pennsylvania State University, University Park, assistant professor, 1966-70, associate professor of political science, 1970—. *Member:* American Society for Public Administration, Association for Asian Studies.

WRITINGS: (With James Petras) *Cultivating Revolution,* Random House, 1971; (with Petras) *Peru: Transformacion Revolucionaria O Modernizacion,* Amorrortu Editores, 1971; *Power and Privilege,* University of California Press, 1976. Contributor of articles to *Journal of Development Studies, Comparative Studies in Society and History, International Review of Administrative Sciences, Asian Survey,* and *Foreign Policy.*

WORK IN PROGRESS: A research project on the basic needs approach to socio-economic development, completion expected in 1980.

*   *   *

LAPP, John Allen   1933-

PERSONAL: Born March 15, 1933, in Landsdale, Pa.; son of John E. (a minister) and Edith (Nyce) Lapp; married Mary Alice Weber (a teacher), August 20, 1955; children: John Franklin, Jennifer, Jessica. *Education:* Eastern Mennonite College, B.A., 1954; Western Reserve University (now Case Western Reserve University), M.A., 1959; University of Pennsylvania, Ph.D., 1968. *Politics:* Independent. *Religion:* Mennonite. *Home:* 64859 Orchard Dr., Goshen, Ind. 46526. *Office:* Office of the Dean, Goshen College, Goshen, Ind. 46526.

CAREER: University Hospital, Cleveland Ohio, surgical assistant, 1954-56; Eastern Mennonite College, Harrisonburg, Va., associate professor, 1956-67, professor of history, 1968, chairman of department, 1962-69, coordinator of curriculum revision committee, 1966-68, chairman of committee on future planning, 1968-69; Mennonite Central Committee, Akron, Pa., executive secretary of peace section, 1969-72; Goshen College, Goshen, Ind., professor of history and dean of the College, 1972—. Member of advisory board, Harrisonburg (Va.) Salvation Army, 1962-69; member of Rockingham County Council on Human Relations, 1963-69; Virginia Council on Human Relations, member 1963-69, vice-president, 1965-69. Mennonite Central Committee, chairman of peace section, 1973-78, consultant for Middle East Program, 1978-79. Member of Conrad Grebel Lectureship Committee, 1967—, and Commission of Institutions of

Higher Education, North Central Association of Colleges and Schools, 1975—. *Member:* American Historical Association, American Association of Higher Education, American Conference of Academic Deans, Conference on Faith and History, Fellowship of Reconciliation. *Awards, honors:* Fulbright award to India, 1965; Danforth associate, 1966-69.

WRITINGS: (Editor) *Peacemakers in a Broken World,* Herald Press, 1969; (contributor) Frank Epp, editor, *I Would Like to Dodge the Draft Dodgers, but . . . ,* Conrad Press, 1970; *The Mennonite Church in India, 1897-1962,* Herald Press, 1972; *A Dream for America,* Herald Press, 1976; (contributor) J. R. Burkholder and Calvin Redekop, editors, *Kingdom, Cross, and Community,* Herald Press, 1976; (contributor) C. Norman Kraus, editor, *Evangelism and Anabaptism,* Herald Press, 1979. Contributor of articles and reviews to *Mennonite Quarterly Review, National Institute of Campus Ministries Journal, Mennonite Weekly Review, Provident Book Finder, Proceedings of Eastern Seaboard Strategy Conference,* and *Proceedings of the 14th Conference on Mennonite Education and Culture Problems.* Author of monthly column "Comments on the World News," in *Christian Living,* 1964—.

WORK IN PROGRESS: Research on the history of Christian missions; research on the church and its social-political milieu; higher education.

*   *   *

La RIVERS, Ira II   1915-1977

PERSONAL: Born May 1, 1915, in San Francisco, Calif.; son of Ira John (a teamster) and Yvonne (Groulx) La Rivers; married Marian Byrd Ballinger (a teacher), December 21, 1951; children: Ira III. *Education:* University of Nevada, B.S., 1937; North Carolina State College (now University), P.G., 1938; University of California, Berkeley, Ph.D., 1948. *Politics:* Republican. *Religion:* Methodist. *Home:* New Dog Valley Rd., Verdi, Nev. 89439. *Office:* Biological Society of Nevada, Box 267, Verdi, Nev. 89439.

CAREER: University of Nevada, Reno, entomologist, 1939-42; inspector, California Department of Agriculture, 1942; University of Nevada, assistant professor, 1948-54, associate professor, 1954-61, professor of biology, beginning 1961, head of department, 1953-63, director of the biological museum, 1953-63; Biological Society of Nevada, Verdi, field agent IV, beginning 1963. Field agent, U.S. Department of Agriculture, 1936, 1937, 1939, and 1942; field biologist, Nevada Fish and Game Commission, 1949; ecologist, Pacific Science Board, National Science Commission, Marshall Islands, 1950; worked in fire control, U.S. Forest Service, 1952, 1954, and 1955; fisheries biologist, U.S. Fish and Wildlife Service, 1953. Member of University of California tropical biogeographical expedition, Mexico, 1947. Consultant to Desert Research Institute, City of San Francisco, and National Lexicographic Board; consultant to several publications, including *Winston Encyclopedia, Handbook of Biology, Parent's Magazine Encyclopedia,* and *Reinhold Encyclopedia of Biology. Military service:* U.S. Navy, 1942-46; became lieutenant junior grade.

MEMBER: American Entomological Society, Paleontological Society, Society of Systemic Zoology, Ecological Society of America, American Association of University Professors, Coleopterists Society, Indian Academy of Zoology (fellow), Society of Vertebrate Paleontologists, Pacific Coast Entomological Society, Entomological Society of Washington, Nevada Wildlife Conservation Society, Nevada State Historical Society, Oahu Microscopical Society (fellow), Biological Society of Nevada (fellow), California Academy of Science, Alpha Epsilon Delta, Phi Kappa Phi, Sigma Xi. *Awards, honors:* National Science Foundation grant, 1968-70.

WRITINGS: General Zoology Laboratory Manual, Edwards Brothers, 1955; *Fishes and Fisheries of Nevada,* Nevada Fish and Game Commission, 1962; *Studies of Naucoridae (Hemiptera),* Biological Society of Nevada, 1971. Also author of *Freshwater Algae of Nevada,* University of Nevada Press; editor of occasional papers of the Biological Society of Nevada. Contributor to *Proceedings of the Entomological Society of Washington, Entomological News,* and *Bulletin of Southern California Academy of Science.*

WORK IN PROGRESS: Research on amphibians and reptiles of Nevada, limnology of Pyramid Lake, Nev., Naucoridae (Hemiptera) of the world, and Southwestern desert ecology.

AVOCATIONAL INTERESTS: Photography.†

(Died, 1977)

* * *

LARKIN, John A(lan) 1936-

PERSONAL: Born July 29, 1936, in Sharon, Conn.; son of E. Alan (a physician) and Yvette (Jutras) Larkin; married Judith Elaine Candib (assistant professor of psychology), September 1, 1961; children: Sean Michael, Sarah Bernadette, Emma Katherine. *Education:* Yale University, B.A., 1958, M.A., 1961; New York University, Ph.D., 1966. *Home:* 31 Brantford Pl., Buffalo, N.Y. 14222. *Office:* Departments of History and Anthropology, State University of New York, Buffalo, N.Y. 14214.

CAREER: Ford Foundation, New York, N.Y., research assistant and translator of Indonesian, 1961; University of the Philippines, Quezon City, associate lecturer, 1963-64, director of Institute of Asian Studies microfilm project, 1964; Yale University, New Haven, Conn., associate in research, 1965-66; State University of New York at Buffalo, lecturer, 1966, assistant professor, 1966, associate professor of history, 1972—. *Military service:* U.S. Army, 1958-60. *Member:* American Historical Association, American Council of Learned Societies (fellow), Association of Asian Studies (member of Inter-university Southeast Asia Committee, 1972—; member of Committee on Research Materials on Southeast Asia, 1971—; member of board of directors of the Philippine Studies Group, 1969—), American Anthropological Society. *Awards, honors:* Fulbright fellow, 1963-64; State University of New York research council grants, 1967, 1968, 1971; Department of Health, Education, and Welfare foreign area fellowship, 1969-70.

WRITINGS: (With Harry J. Benda) *The World of Southeast Asia,* Harper, 1967; *The Pampangans: Colonial Society in a Philippine Province,* University of California Press, 1972; (editor and author of historical introduction) *Perspectives on Philippine History: A Symposium* (monograph), Yale University Southeast Asia Studies, 1978; (contributor) *Southeast Asian Transitions,* Yale University Press, 1978. Contributor of articles and book reviews to *Journal of Asian Studies, Journal of Asian History, Journal of Southeast Asian Studies, Journal of Southeast Asian History, Pacific Affairs, Journal of Oriental Studies, Reviews in American History, American Historical Review,* and *Choice.*

WORK IN PROGRESS: A book tentatively entitled *The Sources of Poverty and Reasons for Revolt: The Philippine Sugar Industry, 1912-1941;* work with W. H. Scott and N.

Cushner to authenticate "The Will of Fernando Malang Balagtas," a document of importance to pre-Hispanic Philippine history.

* * *

LARROWE, Charles P(atrick) 1916-

PERSONAL: Surname is pronounced La-*Rue;* born May 1, 1916, in Portland, Ore.; son of Albertus and Helen (Maginnis) Larrowe; married Pat Fall, August 24, 1946 (divorced, 1970); children: Peter. *Education:* University of Washington, Seattle, B.A., 1946, M.A., 1948; Yale University, Ph.D., 1952. *Office:* Department of Economics, Michigan State University, East Lansing, Mich. 48823.

CAREER: Yale University, New Haven, Conn., assistant lecturer in economics, 1949-52; University of Utah, Salt Lake City, associate professor of economics, 1952-56; Michigan State University, East Lansing, assistant professor, 1956-57, associate professor, 1957-61, professor of economics, 1961—. Consultant to Bureau of Labor Statistics, 1957. *Military service:* American Field Service, ambulance driver, 1942-43; U.S. Army, 1943-45; received Silver Star and Purple Heart (with oak leaf cluster).

WRITINGS: Shape-Up and Hiring Hall, University of California Press, 1955; *Harry Bridges: The Rise and Fall of Radical Labor in the U.S.,* Lawrence Hill, 1972. Contributor to journals, including *Labor History* and *California Law Review.*

BIOGRAPHICAL/CRITICAL SOURCES: Michigan State News, January 30, 1970; *Lansing State Journal,* June 25, 1971; *Grand Rapids Press,* February 26, 1978; *Detroit News,* March 6, 1978.

* * *

LARSEN, Elyse 1957-

PERSONAL: Born March 16, 1957, in Brigham City, Utah; daughter of Jordan Lemoine (a teacher) and Joyce (Parson) Larsen. *Education:* Currently attending Oregon State University. *Home:* 335 North West 9th St., Corvallis, Ore. 97330. *Office:* Department of Agricultural Chemistry, Oregon State University, Corvallis, Ore.

CAREER: Logan Cold Storage, Logan, Utah, clerk, 1968-73; piano teacher, 1969-75; Cache Public Library, Logan, library assistant, 1973-75; production typist, Environmental Protection Agency, Corvallis, Ore., 1976-77, and Oregon State University, Corvallis, department of agricultural chemistry, 1977—. *Awards, honors:* First prize, League of Utah Writers, 1970, for "Fairyfoot," a radio play.

WRITINGS: (With sister, Kalee Larsen, and Ruth Harston) *Bradford and the Burglar* (juvenile), Young Scott Books, 1972. Author, with K. Larsen, of *Heart of Stone,* a juvenile book; also author, with K. Larsen and Harston, of a radio play, "Fairyfoot."

* * *

LARSEN, Erik 1911-

PERSONAL: Born October 10, 1911, in Vienna, Austria; naturalized U.S. citizen; son of Richard (an art dealer) and Adrienne (de Csepreg) Larsen; married Lucy Roman (an artist), October 4, 1932; children: Sigurd, Annik. *Education:* Attended Institut Superieur d'Histoire de l'Art et d'Archeologie, Brussels; Catholic University of Louvain, M.A., 1941, Ph.D. (magna cum laude), 1959; studied painting restoration under Jef Lammens of Ghent and Jules

Defort of Brussels. *Home:* 3103 Trail Rd., Lawrence, Kan. 66044. *Office:* Kress Foundation Department of Art History, University of Kansas, Lawrence, Kan. 66045.

CAREER: Lecturer, and director and editor-in-chief of *Pictura* (art magazine) in Belgium; visited Brazil on semi-official mission of Belgian Government, 1946-47; Manhattanville College of the Sacred Heart (now Manhattanville College), Purchase, N.Y., research professor of art, 1947-55; Georgetown University, Washington, D.C., lecturer, then visiting professor, 1955-58, associate professor, 1958-63, professor of fine arts, 1963-67, head of department, 1960-67; University of Kansas, Lawrence, professor of history of art, 1967—, director of Center for Flemish Art and Culture, 1970—. Instructor in Extension Division, City College of New York (now City College of the City University of New York), 1948-55. Free-lance art expert and appraiser. Member of Kansas Arts Advisory Council. *Military service:* Belgian Resistance, World War II.

MEMBER: Royal Society of Arts (London; fellow; corresponding member for Kansas), American Appraisers Association, American Association of University Professors, Schweizerisches Institut fuer Kunstwissenschaft (Zurich); correspondent member, academician, or associate of Academie d'Aix-en-Provence, Academie de Macon, Academie d'Alsace, Real Academia de Bellas Artes de San Telmo-Malaga, Accademia di Belle Arti "Pietro Vannucci," Real Academia de Bellas Artes de San Jorge, Accademia Tiberina.

AWARDS, HONORS: Knight's Cross, Order of the Belgian Crown, 1960; Prix Thorlet of Academie des Sciences morales et politiques, Institut de France, 1962, for *Frans Post, Interprete du Bresil;* Knight's Cross, Order of Leopold, 1971; Benjamin Franklin fellow, Royal Society of Arts, 1972.

WRITINGS: Peter Paul Rubens (with complete catalogue of his works in America), De Sikkel (Antwerp), 1952; *Les Primitifs flamands au Musee Metropolitain de New York,* Het Spectrum (Utrecht), 1960; *Hansegger: A Contribution to a Critical Study of His Art* (text in English, French, and German), Ascot-Verlag (Zurich), 1961; *Frans Post, Interprete du Bresil,* Colibris Editora (Amsterdam-Rio de Janeiro), 1962; *Catalogue of the Georgetown University Art Collection,* Georgetown University, 1963; *Flemish Painting 17th Century,* McGraw, 1967; *Rembrandt and the Dutch School,* Tudor, 1967; *El Greco and the Spanish Golden Age,* Tudor, 1969; (editor) *La vie, les ouvrages et les eleves de Van Dyck,* Academie Royale de Belgique, 1975. Writer of all entries on seventeenth-century Flemish painting for *Dictionary of Art,* five volumes, McGraw, 1969. Contributor of about one hundred articles, studies, reviews, and criticism to journals and magazines in Belgium, Netherlands, Switzerland, France, Canada, England, Italy, United States, and other countries. American editor, *Artis* and *Raggi* (both Switzerland).

WORK IN PROGRESS: The Paintings of Anthony Van Dyck, in three volumes, with a biography of Van Dyck included, completion expected in 1980.

* * *

LARSEN, Kalee 1952-

PERSONAL: Born September 28, 1952, in Logan, Utah; daughter of Jordan Lemoine (a teacher) and Joyce (Parson) Larsen. *Education:* Utah State University, B.A., 1975. *Home:* 335 Northwest Ninth St., Corvallis, Ore. 97330. *Office:* Division of Health and Physical Education, Oregon State University, Corvallis, Ore. 97331.

CAREER: Logan Cold Storage, Logan, Utah, clerk, 1966-69; Utah State University Publications Office, Logan, editorial assistant, 1970-71; Cache County Public Library, Logan, assistant, 1973-75; University of Utah Academic Advising Office, Salt Lake City, secretary, 1975-76; Oregon State University, Corvallis, administrative assistant of women's athletics, 1976—. Piano teacher, 1967—. *Member:* National Federation of Music Clubs, Phi Kappa Phi. *Awards, honors:* First place in Young Writers Division, League of Utah Writers, 1970, for "Spectre," a poem; first prize, League of Utah Writers, 1970, for "Fairyfoot," a radio play.

WRITINGS: (With sister, Elyse Larsen, and Ruth Harston) *Bradford and the Burglar* (juvenile), Young Scott Books, 1972. Also author of *Heart of Stone,* a juvenile novel, with E. Larsen, and "Fairyfoot," a radio play, with E. Larsen and R. Harston.

* * *

LARSEN, Ronald J(ames) 1948-

PERSONAL: Born April 27, 1948, in St. Paul, Minn.; son of Charles A. (a policeman) and Ruth (Maas) Larsen. *Education:* University of Minnesota, B.S., 1970. *Politics:* Independent liberal. *Home:* 2449 Harriet Ave. S., No. 3, Minneapolis, Minn. 55405. *Office:* Lerner Publications Co., 241 First Ave. N., Minneapolis, Minn. 55401.

CAREER: Lerner Publications Co., Minneapolis, Minn., editor and writer, 1971—. *Member:* Phi Beta Kappa.

WRITINGS—All published by Lerner: *The Puerto Ricans in America* (young adult book), 1973.

Editor: *Drag Racing,* 1973; *Ice Racing,* 1973; *Motorcycle Racing,* 1973; *Road Racing,* 1973; *Track Racing,* 1973; *Snowmobile Racing,* 1973; *American Assassins,* 1973.†

* * *

LARSON, Carl M. 1916-

PERSONAL: Born February 11, 1916, in Council Bluffs, Iowa; son of Carl E. (a contractor) and Anna (Fredrickson) Larson; married Mary Jane Jacobson, March 7, 1942; children: Deborah Rae (Mrs. Jeffrey Poat). *Education:* University of Illinois, B.S., 1939; Northwestern University, M.B.A., 1950. *Religion:* Lutheran. *Home:* 8 North Donald, Arlington Heights, Ill. 60004. *Office:* Department of Marketing, University of Illinois at Chicago Circle, Box 4348, Chicago, Ill. 60680.

CAREER: University of Illinois at Chicago Circle, assistant instructor, 1946-49, instructor, 1949-62, assistant professor, 1962-66, associate professor, 1966-70, professor of marketing, 1970—. Director, Paddock Publications, Inc., Arlington Heights, Ill. *Military service:* U.S. Army, 1941-45; became warrant officer junior grade; received Bronze Star Medal and Combat Infantryman's Badge with three battle stars. *Member:* American Marketing Association, National Council for Small Business Management Development, Small Business Institute, American Society of Marketing Associations, National Association of Management Educators (vice-president of research, 1976), Alpha Kappa Psi, Beta Gamma Sigma.

WRITINGS: (Co-author) *A Survey of Brand Preferences among Chicago Negro Families,* Stipes, 1967; (with James Engel and W. Wayne Talarzyk) *Cases in Promotional Strategy,* Irwin, 1971; (contributor) George Joyce and Norman A. P. Govani, editors, *The Black Consumer,* Random House, 1971; (with others) *Basic Retailing,* Prentice-Hall,

1976; (with R. Weigand) *Basic Retailing: Study Guide,* Prentice-Hall, 1976. Also author of research monographs; contributor to business journals.

WORK IN PROGRESS: Research on suburban newspapers and on black consumerism.†

* * *

LARSON, P(aul) Merville 1903-

PERSONAL: Born March 26, 1903, in Denmark, Kan.; son of Lauris Paul and Christina Larson; married Hazel Rebecca Popham, June 4, 1927; children: Shirley Jean (Mrs. Walter Cronan), David Paul, Carolyn Rebeca (Mrs. R. R. White). *Education:* Kansas State Agricultural College (now Kansas State University), B.S., 1927, M.S., 1930; Northwestern University, Ph.D., 1942. *Religion:* Episcopalian. *Home:* 3120 21st St., Lubbock, Tex. 79410.

CAREER: Worked as a teacher in Colorado public schools, 1921-24, and Kansas high schools, 1927-30; Hutchinson Community Junior College, Hutchinson, Kan., instructor in speech, 1930-39; North Park Junior College (now North Park College), Chicago, Ill., instructor in speech, 1939-42; Eastern Illinois State College (now University), Charleston, professor of speech, 1942-43, acting head of department, 1942-43; Southwest Texas State Teachers College (now Southwest Texas State University), San Marcos, professor of speech, 1943-45, acting head of department, 1943-45; Texas College of Arts and Industries (now Texas A & I University), Kingsville, professor of speech, 1945-46, head of department, 1945-46; Southern Illinois University at Carbondale, professor of speech, 1946-48, head of department, 1946-48; University of Denver, Denver, Colo., professor of speech, coordinator of forensics, 1948-50; Texas Tech University, Lubbock, professor of speech, 1950-73, head of department, 1950-69. Fulbright lecturer in Denmark, 1957-58. *Member:* National Education Association, Speech Communication Association, National Forensic League, Southern Speech Communication Association, Texas Speech Association (president, 1960-61; executive secretary, 1964-70), Delta Sigma Rho, Tau Kappa Alpha, Phi Rho Pi. *Awards, honors:* DSR-TKA Distinguished Alumni Award, 1970; Phi Rho Pi Distinguished Award, 1971, for forty years of service in forensics.

WRITINGS: Social Science and the Dalton Plan, Columbia University Press, 1937; (with Johnnye Akin, Al Williams, and Seth A. Fessenden) *Helping the Bible Speak,* Association Press, 1954, revised edition published as *How to Read the Bible Aloud,* 1964; (with Fessenden and Roy Ivan Johnson) *The Teacher Speaks,* Prentice-Hall, 1956; (with Keith Case, Cranell Tolliver, and George Vardaman) *Mastering Speech Skills,* Communications Ltd., 1956, revised edition published as *Communicating Effectively through Speech,* W. C. Brown, 1964; (with Paul Hibbs, Joseph Wagner, and Fessenden) *Speech for Today,* McGraw, 1965; (with Fessenden, Kaye Good, and Johnson) *Speech for the Creative Teacher,* W. C. Brown, 1968, revised edition, 1973.

WORK IN PROGRESS: Mediaeval and Renaissance Rhetoric and Oratory.

* * *

LARSON, Richard Francis 1931-

PERSONAL: Born April 2, 1931, in Yakima, Wash.; son of Renus Matthew (a retired farmer) and Helen (Snyder) Larson; married Celine M. Krupka (an inorganic chemist),

April 6, 1968. *Education:* Seattle University, B.A. (magna cum laude), 1957; University of Washington, Seattle, M.A., 1958; University of Notre Dame, Ph.D., 1961. *Religion:* Roman Catholic. *Home address:* Route 3, Box 469-B, Central, S.C. 29630. *Office:* Department of Sociology, Clemson University, Clemson, S.C. 29631.

CAREER: University of Alabama, University, assistant professor of sociology, 1961-62; University of Rhode Island, Kingston, assistant professor of sociology, 1962-64; Oklahoma State University, Stillwater, associate professor of sociology, 1964-67; University of Missouri—St. Louis, associate professor of sociology, 1967-68, chairman of department, 1968; University of Florida, Gainesville, associate professor, 1968-71, professor of sociology, 1971-73; California State University, Hayward, professor of sociology, 1973-78; Clemson University, Clemson, S.C., professor of sociology and chairman of department, 1978—. *Military service:* U.S. Navy, 1950-54. *Member:* American Sociological Association, Society for the Scientific Study of Religion, Society for the Study of Social Problems, National Council on Family Relations, American Association of University Professors, Midwest Sociological Society, Pacific Sociological Association, Southern Sociological Society, Alpha Kappa Delta.

WRITINGS: (Contributor) James K. Skipper, Jr. and Robert C. Leonard, editors, *Social Interaction and Patient Care,* Lippincott, 1965; (contributor) W. Richard Scott and Edmund H. Volkart, editors, *Medical Care,* Wiley, 1966; (with Gerald R. Leslie and Benjamin Gorman) *Order and Change: Introductory Sociology,* Oxford University Press, 1973; (with Bill Mendenhall and Lyman Ott) *Statistics: A Tool for the Social Sciences,* Duxbury, 1978. Contributor to sociology journals.

* * *

LASZLO, Ervin 1932-

PERSONAL: Born June 12, 1932, in Budapest, Hungary; lived in United States, 1948-56, in Europe, 1957-66; U.S. citizen; son of Stephen (an industrialist) and Mary (Kertesz) Laszlo; married Barbro Carita Marjorie Jagerhorn, November 16, 1957; children: Christopher Peter, Alexander Robert. *Education:* Franz Liszt National Academy of Music, Budapest, Artist Diploma, 1947; University of Fribourg, Graduate Certificate of Institute of East European Studies, 1967; Sorbonne, University of Paris, Dr. es Lettres, 1970. *Home:* 333 East 46th St., New York, N.Y. 10017. *Office:* United Nations Institute for Training and Research, 801 United Nations Plaza, New York, N.Y. 10017.

CAREER: Early activity was musical, chiefly as concert pianist, 1947-60; University of Fribourg, Fribourg, Switzerland, research associate, Institute of East European Studies, 1963-66; Yale University, New Haven, Conn., visiting fellow in philosophy, 1966-67; University of Akron, Akron, Ohio, associate professor of philosophy, 1967-68; State University of New York College at Geneseo, associate professor, 1968-69, professor of philosophy, 1969-77; United Nations Institute for Training and Research (UNITAR), New York, N.Y., director of research and special fellow, 1977—. Visiting professor of music at Indiana University, summer, 1967, of philosophy at Northwestern University, summer, 1968, and fall, 1970; visiting research fellow, Center of International Studies, Princeton University, 1973; lecturer at American universities and in ten countries of Europe. Still presents piano concerts occasionally; has recorded works of

Sibelius and Liszt for RCA Records. Member of council, Center for Integrative Education, 1969—, World Institute, 1970—, and Center for the Advanced Study of Religion and Science, 1972—.

MEMBER: American Philosophical Association, Metaphysical Society of America, American Association for the Advancement of Science, Society for General Systems Research (chairman of executive committee, Northeast division, 1972-75), American Society for Aesthetics, American Society for Value Inquiry, American Association of University Professors, Toronto Society for Social and Political Thought, Husserl Circle.

AWARDS, HONORS: Pro Arte Award of President of Hungary, 1947; second prize in International Music Competition, Geneva, 1947; award for exceptional achievement, Pedroso International Music Competition, Lisbon, 1959; associate fellow of Stillman College, Yale University, 1969-72; research grants from Center for Integrative Education, 1967-70, American Society for Aesthetics, 1968, American Council of Learned Societies—Social Science Research Council, 1968, Van Leer Jerusalem Foundation, 1968, 1969, World Institute, 1971, and John Parker Compton Fund of Princeton University, 1973; University Medal, Kyung Hee University (Seoul, Korea).

WRITINGS: Essential Society: An Ontological Reconstruction, Nijhoff, 1963; Individualism, Collectivism and Political Power: A Relational Analysis of Ideological Conflict, Nijhoff, 1963; Beyond Scepticism and Realism: A Constructive Exploration of Husserlian and Whiteheadian Methods of Inquiry, Nijhoff, 1966; The Communist Ideology in Hungary: Handbook for Basic Research, Humanities, 1966; System, Structure and Experience: Toward a Scientific Theory of Mind, Gordon & Breach, 1969; La Metaphysique de Whitehead: Recherche sur les prolongements anthropologiques, Nijhoff, 1970; Introduction to Systems Philosophy: Toward a New Paradigm of Contemporary Thought, Gordon & Breach, 1971, Harper, 1973; The Systems View of the World, Braziller, 1972; A Strategy for the Future, Braziller, 1974; Goals for Mankind, Dutton, 1977; The Objectives of the New International Economic Order, Pergamon, 1978; The Inner Limits of Mankind, Pergamon, 1978.

Editor: (And contributor) Philosophy in the Soviet Union: A Survey of the Mid-Sixties, Praeger, 1967; (with J. B. Wilbur) Human Values and Natural Science, Gordon & Breach, 1970; (with Rubin Gotesky, and contributor) Human Dignity: This Century and the Next, Gordon & Breach, 1970; (with Wilbur) Value Theory in Philosophy and the Social Sciences, Gordon & Breach, 1971; (with Wilbur) Human Values and the Mind of Man, Gordon & Breach, 1971; (with Julius Stulman, and contributor) Emergent Man: His Chances, Problems and Potentials, Gordon & Breach, 1971; (with Gotesky) Evolution and Revolution: Patterns of Development in Nature, Society, Culture and Man, Gordon & Breach, 1971; The World System, Braziller, 1973.

Contributor: Lee Thayer, editor, Communication: General Semantics Perspectives, Spartan, 1969; Henry Margenau, editor, Integrative Principles in Modern Thought, Gordon & Breach, 1971; Lee Thayer, editor, Communication: The Ethical Issues, Gordon & Breach, 1971; W. Gray and N. R. Rizzo, editors, Essays in Honor of L. von Bertalanffy, Gordon & Breach, 1973.

Contributor of more than one hundred articles, about thirty conference and research papers, reviews, and bibliographies to journals in America and abroad. Series editor, "Interna-

tional Library of Systems Theory and Philosophy," Braziller, "Systems Science and World Order Library," Pergamon; series co-editor, "Current Topics of Contemporary Thought," Gordon & Breach. Editor, Journal of Value Inquiry (The Hague), 1967; editor, Philosophy Forum, 1973; co-editor, Music and Man, 1973—; associate editor, Behavioral Science, 1973—, and Main Currents in Modern Thought, 1970; member of editorial advisory board, Process Studies, 1972.

SIDELIGHTS: Besides Hungarian and English, Ervin Laszlo is competent in French and German; less so in Italian, Swedish, and Russian. His work, he says, is directed at the "importance of bringing together contemporary science and philosophy for the benefit of mankind—resolution of current ethical, ecological, etc. crises and overcoming the 'meaninglessness' of contemporary existence." His books have been translated into a total of ten languages, and articles into five.

BIOGRAPHICAL/CRITICAL SOURCES: Book World, November 5, 1967; International Philosophical Quarterly, March, 1973.

*   *   *

LASZLO, Miklos   1904(?)-1973

1904(?)—April 19, 1973; Hungarian playwright. Obituaries: New York Times, April 20, 1973.

*   *   *

LAUREL, Alicia Bay   1949-

PERSONAL: Born May 14, 1949, in Los Angeles, Calif.; daughter of Paul Alan (a surgeon) and Verna (a sculptor; maiden surname, Lebow) Kaufman. Education: Attended public schools in Los Angeles. Agent: Leslie Elliot, 319 East 52nd St., New York, N.Y. 10019.

CAREER: Writer and illustrator. Awards, honors: Mademoiselle magazine's Woman of the Year award, 1971.

WRITINGS: Living on the Earth, Vintage, 1971; Earth-Time 1972 (illustrated astrological calendar), Random House, 1972; The Family of Families (coloring book), Harper, 1972; Sylvie Sunflower (coloring book), Harper, 1972; "Happy Day," Cried the Rainbow Lady, Full of Light (coloring book), Harper, 1972; (illustrator) Joe Pintauro, Earth Mass (poems), Harper, 1972; (with Ramon Sender) Being of the Sun, Harper, 1973; (illustrator and contributor) Home Comfort, New American Library, 1974; (illustrator) Mike Fleck, Shakespeare's "The Tempest," New Age Press, 1979.

WORK IN PROGRESS: Three children's books, The Goodnight Hug, How to Get What You Want from Grown-Ups, and The Talking Whale; a beauty book, Peach; with Radha Chesick and Krish Chesick, a compendium of self-help semantics, as yet untitled; Earth and Aetherias: A Fairy Tale from the 21st Century.

SIDELIGHTS: Alicia Bay Laurel, who uses that name because the bay laurel is her favorite tree, wrote to CA: "I am here to express compassion in an entertaining way." In a review Christopher Lehmann-Haupt describes Living on the Earth as "a manual for communal living . . . with notes on everything from building a kayak to curing meat to organic farming to childbirth at home. It is printed in the author's meandering longhand (entirely legible) and whimsically illustrated with line drawings in the style of Alexander Calder."

LAUTER, Geza Peter 1932-

PERSONAL: Born November 26, 1932, in Bad-Lauterberg, Germany; son of Eugene and Katherina (Kraus) Lauter; married Eva Maria Romeike (a registered nurse), August 9, 1959. *Education:* University of California, Los Angeles, B.A., 1962, M.B.A., 1964, Ph.D., 1968. *Office:* School of Government and Business Administration, George Washington University, Washington, D.C. 20006.

CAREER: Cornell University, Ithaca, N.Y., instructor, 1965-68; George Washington University, Washington, D.C., assistant professor, 1968-70, associate professor of management and marketing, 1970-75, professor of business administration, 1975—. *Member:* American Economic Association, Academy of International Business, American Marketing Association.

WRITINGS: The Manager and Economic Reform in Hungary, Praeger, 1972; (with Paul M. Dickie) *Multinational Corporations and East European Socialist Economies,* Praeger, 1975. Contributor to *Journal of the Academy of Management, Journal of Marketing, California Management Review, Management International Review, Quarterly Journal of Management Development,* and *Journal of International Business Studies.*

WORK IN PROGRESS: Research on the economic development of the Middle East, U.S.-Japanese trade relations, and East-West trade.

* * *

LAVE, Lester B(ernard) 1939-

PERSONAL: Born August 5, 1939; son of Israel and Esther (Axelrod) Lave; married Judith Rice (a professor), May 18, 1959; children: Tamara Rice, Jonathan Melville. *Education:* Reed College, B.A., 1960; Harvard University, Ph.D., 1963. *Home:* 1008 Devonshire Rd., Pittsburgh, Pa. 15213. *Office:* Department of Economics, Carnegie-Mellon University, Pittsburgh, Pa. 15213.

CAREER: Carnegie-Mellon University, Pittsburgh, Pa., assistant professor, 1963-68, associate professor, 1968-70, professor of economics, 1970—, head of department, 1971—. Visiting assistant professor, Northwestern University, 1965-66. Consultant to U.S. Department of Health, Education, and Welfare, Department of Defense, and Department of Transportation, to RAND Corp., Center for Naval Analysis, and General Motors Corp. Member of Pennsylvania Governor's Health Task Force, Pennsylvania Department of Health Data Task Force, and West Pennsylvania Regional Medical Program Advisory Committee.

MEMBER: American Economic Association, American Association for Advancement of Science, Econometric Society, Royal Economic Society, Operations Research Society of America, Industrial Management Society. *Awards, honors:* Research grants from National Institute of Mental Health, 1963, National Center for Health Services, 1967 and 1970, Resources for the Future, Inc., 1966, 1970, and 1972, and National Safety Council, 1967.

WRITINGS: Technological Change: Its Conception and Measurement, Prentice-Hall, 1967; (with Eugene P. Seskin) *Air Pollution and Health,* Johns Hopkins Press, 1977. Contributor to *American Economic Review, Econometrica, Journal of Political Economy, Quarterly Journal of Economics, Behavioral Science,* and other journals.

WORK IN PROGRESS: Research on the environment, on managing health resources, and on benefit-cost analysis.

LAVINE, Harold 1915-

PERSONAL: Surname rhymes with "divine"; born February 19, 1915, in New York, N.Y.; son of Elias and Pauline (Bershadsky) Lavine; married Violet Edwards (an educator), December 24, 1936; children: Cammie Caroline Edwards (Mrs. Atlee Stephan III). *Education:* Townsend Harris Hall, diploma, 1930. *Home:* 6505 North 12th Way, Phoenix, Ariz. 85014. *Office: Arizona Republic,* 120 East Van Buren St., Phoenix, Ariz. 85001.

CAREER: Reporter in New York City, for *New York American,* 1932-33, *New York Evening Journal,* 1933-34, and *New York Evening Post,* 1934-36; *PM* (newspaper), New York City, assistant managing editor, 1941-43; *Newsweek,* New York City, senior editor, 1946-63; *Forbes* (magazine), New York City, senior editor, 1963-74; *Arizona Republic,* Phoenix, columnist and editorial writer, 1974—. *Military service:* U.S. Army, News Service, 1943-46; became sergeant. *Member:* Lotos Club. *Awards, honors:* Page One Award, from New York Newspaper Guild, 1961, for feature magazine writing.

WRITINGS: Fifth Column in America, Doubleday, 1940; (with James A. Wechsler) *War Propaganda and the United States,* Yale University Press, 1940, 2nd edition, with new introduction by Leonard P. Riggio, Garland Publishing, 1972; (with the editors of *Life) Central America,* Time-Life, 1964; *Smoke-Filled Rooms: The Confidential Papers of Robert Humphreys,* Prentice-Hall, 1971.

Articles represented in anthologies, including: *A Matter of Choice,* edited by W. Royce Adams, Macmillan, 1968; *Deviance,* edited by Simon Dinitz, Russell R. Dynes, and Alfred C. Clarke, Oxford University Press, 1969; *America at Random,* edited by Herbert Mitgang, Coward, 1969.

BIOGRAPHICAL/CRITICAL SOURCES: National Review, June 30, 1970.

* * *

LAWHEAD, Victor B(ernard) 1919-

PERSONAL: Born February 26, 1919, in Vincennes, Ind.; son of William A. (a construction contractor) and Rilla Belle (Wood) Lawhead; married Doris J. Barber, July 11, 1953. *Education:* DePauw University, B.A., 1940; Ohio State University, M.A., 1947, Ph.D., 1950. *Home:* 1008 Neely Ave., Muncie, Ind. 47303. *Office:* AD 206D, Ball State University, Muncie, Ind. 47306.

CAREER: High school history teacher in Kokomo, Ind., 1940-48; Ball State University, Muncie, Ind., assistant professor, 1950-54, associate professor, 1954-59, professor of education, 1959—, acting dean, 1959-61, dean of undergraduate programs, 1963—. Visiting professor, Michigan State University, summer, 1952, and University of Maryland, summer, 1957. Member of Human Relations Council of Delaware County, 1962-69, member of board of directors, 1965-69; member of board of directors, Huffer Memorial Children's Center. *Military service:* U.S. Naval Reserve, active duty, 1943-46; became lieutenant. *Member:* Association for Supervision and Curriculum Development (member of board of directors, 1964-68; president of Indiana chapter, 1964), National Academy of Political and Social Science, National Society for the Study of Education, Common Cause, Kiwanis Club (Muncie, Ind.; president, 1971), Phi Delta Kappa, Lambda Chi Alpha.

WRITINGS: (With Harold Alberty and others) *Preparing Core Teachers for the Secondary Schools* (monograph), College of Education, Ohio State University, 1949; (with

Alberty and others) *Utilizing Subject Fields in High School Core-Program Development* (monograph), College of Education, Ohio State University, 1950; (contributor) Florence G. Robbins, *Educational Sociology,* Holt, 1952; (editor with Richard W. Burkhardt and Norman Bell) *Introduction to College Life: Meanings, Values and Commitment,* Houghton, 1962, revised edition, 1966; (with M. C. Beyerl and others) *Needs of Adolescent Youth,* Interstate, 1963; (editor and contributor) *Emerging Universities and National Concerns,* Ball State University, 1969; (editor) *Contemporary Perspectives on Higher Education: Proceedings of University Day,* Ball State University, 1975. Contributor to yearbooks and reports. Contributor of about twenty-five articles and reviews to education journals, including *Theory Into Practice, Educational Leadership, Indiana Teacher, Review of Educational Research, Teachers College Journal, Clearing House,* and *Thresholds in Secondary Education.* Editor, *Indiana Core Teacher,* 1954-58; member of editorial board, *Ball State Forum,* 1963-65.

WORK IN PROGRESS: General education models.

AVOCATIONAL INTERESTS: Travel (Western Europe and the Orient), sailing, fishing.

* * *

LAWRENCE, David 1888-1973

December 25, 1888—February 20, 1973; American magazine and news service founder, editor, columnist, and author. Obituaries: *New York Times,* February 21, 1973; *Washington Post,* February 21, 1973; *Time,* February 26, 1973; *Current Biography,* April, 1973.

* * *

LAWRENCE, Jerome 1915-
(Jerome Schwartz)

PERSONAL: Original name, Jerome Lawrence Schwartz; name legally changed in 1942; born July 14, 1915, in Cleveland, Ohio; son of Samuel (a printer) and Sarah (a poet; maiden name, Rogen) Schwartz. *Education:* Ohio State University, B.A., 1937; University of California, Los Angeles, graduate study, 1939-40. *Politics:* Democrat. *Religion:* Unity/transcendentalist. *Home and office:* 21056 Las Flores Mesa Dr., Malibu, Calif. 90265.

CAREER: Wilmington News Journal, Wilmington, Ohio, reporter and telegraph editor, 1937; *New Lexington Daily News,* New Lexington, Ohio, editor, 1937; Radio Station KMPC, Beverly Hills, Calif., continuity editor, 1937-39; Columbia Broadcasting System, New York, N.Y. and Los Angeles, Calif., senior staff writer, 1939-41; playwright and director with Robert E. Lee under partnership of Lawrence & Lee, 1942—, president of Lawrence & Lee, Inc., New York, N.Y., and Los Angeles, Calif., 1955—. Has directed numerous productions, including the premiere productions of *The Incomparable Max, The Crocodile Smile,* and "Jabberwock"; also staged the first arena production of *Mame* and the Dublin Theatre Festival production of *The Night Thoreau Spent in Jail.* Scenario writer, Paramount Studios, 1941, Samuel Goldwyn, 1946, Twentieth-Century Fox, 1965, and Hal Wallis Productions, 1971-72. Professor, Banff School of Fine Arts, University of Alberta, 1950-53; master playwright, New York University, 1967-69; professor, Salzburg Seminar in American Studies, 1972; professor of playwriting and criticism, Baylor University, 1977. Visiting professor and playwright-in-residence, Ohio State University, 1968-69; visiting professor, Squaw Valley (Calif.) Community of Writers, 1973. Lecturer at universities, including

University of California, Los Angeles, American University, Washington, D.C., Yale University, Tufts University, Villanova University, University of Southern California, California State University, Boston University, Kent State University, and Gorki Writers School (Leningrad). Has also lectured in Japan, Thailand, Egypt, Greece, France, and England. American Playwrights Theatre, Columbus, Ohio, president, 1968-69, founder and trustee; founder (with Lee), Armed Forces Radio Service; founder and judge (with Lee), Margo Jones Award. Expert consultant to Secretary of War, 1942-45; member of drama panel, U.S. State Department Cultural Exchange Program, 1963-71. Member of board of directors, National Repertory Theatre, American Conservatory Theatre, Eugene O'Neill Memorial Foundation, Board of Planning and Standards of the Living Theatre, U.S.D.A.N. Center for the Creative and Performing Arts, East-West Players; American National Theatre and Academy, member of board of directors, 1964-67, national vice-president, 1968-69. Member of advisory board, Ohio State University School of Journalism. *Military service:* U.S. Army, 1943-44; correspondent in North Africa and Italy; became staff sergeant; received Battle Star and special citation from Secretary of War.

MEMBER: American Society of Composers, Authors, and Publishers (ASCAP), American Guild of Authors and Composers, Academy of Motion Picture Arts and Sciences, National Academy of Television Arts and Sciences, Dramatists Guild (member of council, 1969-74), Authors League of America (member of council, 1972—), Writers Guild of America West (co-founder and member of board of trustees), Ohio State University Alumni Association (life member; member of board of directors), Phi Beta Kappa, Sigma Delta Chi, Zeta Beta Tau, Players Club (New York).

AWARDS, HONORS: New York Press Club award, 1942; City College of New York award, 1948; *Radio-TV Life* award, 1948, 1952; George Foster Peabody awards, 1948, 1950; *Radio-TV Mirror* awards, 1952, 1953; *Variety* Showmanship award, 1954; *Variety* New York Drama Critics Poll award for most promising new playwright, 1955, Outer Circle Critics award, 1955, and Donaldson Award for best new play, 1955, all for *Inherit the Wind;* Ohioana award, 1955; Ohio Press Club award, 1959; London Critics Poll award for best foreign play of the year, 1960, and British Drama Critics award for best foreign play, 1960, both for *Inherit the Wind;* named playwright of the year, Baldwin-Wallace College, 1960; D.H.L., Ohio State University, 1963; Moss Hart Memorial Award, 1967, for *Inherit the Wind;* selected "Man of the Year," Zeta Beta Tau, 1967; D.Litt., Fairleigh Dickinson University, 1968; U.S. State Department medal, 1968; D.F.A., Villanova University, 1969; Pegasus Award, 1970; centennial award medal, Ohio State University, 1970; Ohio governor's award, 1972.

WRITINGS: (Under name Jerome Schwartz) *Oscar the Ostrich* (juvenile), Random House, 1940; (editor) *Off Mike: Radio Writing by the Nation's Top Radio Writers,* Essential Books, 1944; (contributor) *The Spice of Variety,* Holt, 1952; (contributor) Sherman L. Sergel, editor, *The Language of Show Biz: A Dictionary,* Dramatic Publishing, 1973; *Actor: The Life and Times of Paul Muni,* Putnam, 1974.

Plays; all with Robert E. Lee, except as indicated: "Laugh, God!," published in *Six Anti-Nazi One-Act Plays,* Contemporary Play Publications, 1939; (with Budd Schulberg) "Tomorrow," published in *Free World Theatre,* edited by Arch Oboler and Stephen Longstreet, Random House, 1944; "Inside a Kid's Head," first published in *Radio Drama in Action,* edited by Erik Barnouw, Farrar & Rinehart, 1945;

"Look Ma, I'm Dancin'!," first produced on Broadway at Adelphi Theatre, January 29, 1948.

Inherit the Wind (three-act; first produced on Broadway at National Theatre [now Billy Rose Theatre], April 21, 1955), Random House, 1955, acting edition, Dramatists Play Service, 1958, revised acting edition, Dramatists Play Service, 1963; (with Lee and James Hilton) *Shangri-La* (musical; based on *Lost Horizon* by James Hilton; first produced on Broadway at Winter Garden Theatre, June 13, 1956), Morris Music, 1956; *Auntie Mame* (two-act; based on the novel by Patrick Dennis; first produced on Broadway at Broadhurst Theatre, October 31, 1956), Vanguard, 1957, acting edition, Dramatists Play Service, 1960 (also see below).

The Gang's All Here (three-act; first produced on Broadway at Ambassador Theatre, October 1, 1959), World Publishing, 1960, acting edition, Samuel French, 1961; *Only in America* (three-act; based on the book by Harry Golden; first produced on Broadway at Cort Theatre, November 19, 1959), Samuel French, 1960; *A Call on Kuprin* (three-act; based on the novel by Maurice Edelman; first produced on Broadway at Broadhurst Theatre, May 25, 1961), Samuel French, 1962; *Sparks Fly Upward* (first produced on Broadway as "Diamond Orchid" at Henry Miller's Theatre, February 10, 1965; rewritten and produced as "Sparks Fly Upward" in Dallas at McFarlin Auditorium, December 3, 1967), Dramatists Play Service, 1967; *Mame* (two-act musical comedy; based on the book *Auntie Mame* by Patrick Dennis and the play by Lawrence and Lee; first produced on Broadway at Winter Garden Theatre, May 24, 1966), Random House, 1967; "Dear World" (two-act musical comedy; based on Maurice Valency's adaptation of *The Madwoman of Chaillot* by Jean Giraudoux), first produced on Broadway at Mark Hellinger Theatre, February 6, 1969.

(Sole author) *Live Spelled Backwards: A Moral Immorality Play* (first produced in Beverly Hills, Calif., at Beverly Hills Playhouse, January 14, 1966), Dramatists Play Service, 1970; *The Night Thoreau Spent in Jail* (first produced in Columbus, Ohio at Ohio State University, April 21, 1970; produced in Washington, D.C. at Arena Theatre, October 28, 1970), Hill & Wang, 1971; *The Incomparable Max!* (based on Max Beerbohm's *Trips Beyond Reality;* Fireside Theatre Play-of-the-Month selection; first produced in Abingdon, Va., at Barter Theatre, 1969; produced on Broadway at Royale Theatre, October 19, 1971), Hill & Wang, 1972; *The Crocodile Smile* (first produced as "The Laugh Maker" in Los Angeles at Players Ring Theatre, August 1, 1952; rewritten and produced as "Turn on the Night" in Philadelphia at Playhouse-in-the-Park, August, 1961; rewritten and produced as "The Crocodile Smile" in Flat Rock, N.C. at State Theatre of North Carolina, August 12, 1970), Dramatists Play Service, 1972; *Jabberwock* (based on *My Life and Hard Times* by James Thurber; first produced in Columbus, Ohio at Thurber Theatre, November 18, 1972; produced in Dallas at Dallas Theatre Center, March 6, 1973), Samuel French, 1974; "First Monday in October," first produced in Cleveland, 1975, produced in Washington, D.C. at Kennedy Center, December 28, 1977, produced on Broadway at Majestic Theatre, October 3, 1978.

Unpublished and unproduced plays; all with Robert E. Lee: "Top of the Mark"; "Paris, France"; "Eclipse"; "Dilly"; "Some Say Ice"; "Houseboat in Kashmir"; "Short and Sweet"; "The Angels Weep."

One-act operas; with Robert E. Lee: *Annie Laurie,* Harms, Inc., 1954; *Roaring Camp,* Harms, Inc., 1955; *Familiar Strangers,* Harms, Inc., 1956.

Screenplays; with Robert E. Lee: "The New Yorkers"; "The Joyous Season"; "My Love Affair with the Human Race"; "Quintus"; "The Night Thoreau Spent in Jail"; "Whitewater."

Also writer, director, and producer with Lee of many television and radio programs, including "Hollywood Showcase," 1940-41, "I Was There," 1941-42, "They Live Forever," 1942, "Columbia Workshop," 1942-43, "Request Performance," 1945-46, "Orson Welles Theatre," 1945-46, "Favorite Story," 1945-48, "Frank Sinatra Show," 1947, "The Railroad Hour," 1948-54, "Hallmark Hall of Fame," 1949-51, "Halls of Ivy," 1950-51, "Date with Judy," "The Unexpected," "Times Square Playhouse," "Song of Norway," "West Point," "Lincoln: The Unwilling Warrior," as well as television adaptations of their plays "Shangri-La" and "Inherit the Wind," and of his book *Actor: The Life and Times of Paul Muni.* Also wrote and directed the official Army-Navy programs for D-Day, V.E. Day, and V.J. Day, as well as programs for "Mail Call," "Yarns for Yanks," "Command Performance," and "Globe Theatre." Writer and director of record album "One God" and of Decca dramatic albums ("Musi-plays"), including dramatizations of "Rip Van Winkle," "The Cask of Amontillado," and *A Tale of Two Cities.* Contributor of articles and short stories to *Saturday Evening Post,* New York *Herald Tribune, Variety,* and other publications.

WORK IN PROGRESS: A stage version of *Actor: The Life and Times of Paul Muni;* a musical version of George Bernard Shaw's *Major Barbara,* with Lee, Henry Mancini, and Leslie Bricusse; a play on John Donne.

SIDELIGHTS: In their collaboration, which began in 1942, Jerome Lawrence and Robert E. Lee have produced three particularly successful and very different plays. *Auntie Mame* and its musical adaptation, *Mame,* are two of the longer productions in Broadway history, the former also enjoying success as a motion picture. When *Auntie Mame* opened in New York, Wolcott Gibbs described it as "rich in situations whose comic effect I have no reason to suppose has been diminished by age; and the changes are that it will run forever." The stage version ran for almost seven hundred performances. The musical was even more successful, running well over four years and returning more than one million dollars on its original investment.

Inherit the Wind, a very different kind of theatre, is an example of what Richard Coe calls Lawrence's and Lee's "shared passion for individual freedom." The play concerns the famous Scopes "Monkey Trial," in which a young schoolteacher was tried in the 1920s for teaching Darwin's theory of evolution. Drawing from actual persons in the story, including William Jennings Bryan, the prosecutor, and Clarence Darrow, who represented the defendant, Lawrence and Lee brought to the stage what a *Newsweek* reviewer called "one of the best serious dramas to hit Broadway and one of the best rounded. Its dialogue moves easily, sometimes brilliantly...." A *Life* article described the play as "splashed together in bold colors like a circus poster, ... [and making] a vivid provocative piece of U.S. history." A more recent play, *The Night Thoreau Spent in Jail,* also attempts, in Richard Coe's words, "to see in the past striking parallels with the present." He describes it as "a stirring and a touching play ... [which] will prove hauntingly provocative." Gerald Colgan believes that it is "finely and vigorously written, with ... a true quality of revelation, a real insight into a mind that has left its stamp on the world's thought." Some critics were not as enthusiastic. A reviewer for *Variety* explained: "Thoreau without warts ... might still provide dramatic sparks if he had someone to clash with, but the invisible Establishment remains offstage, the reactionary Deacon Ball is mostly comic relief, and Emerson never disagrees. He just looks pained and inarticulately refused to come through in the clutch.'' Raymond Crinkley calls the play ''an idealization of comfortable dissent. . . . It's nice to sit around on the grass and be revolutionary. It is indicative of the poverty of our creative minds that Thoreau is well thought of.''

The response to Lawrence's book *Actor: The Life and Times of Paul Muni* was more favorable. A reviewer for *Publishers Weekly* writes: ''When better biographies of actors are written, they will be like this. Lawrence . . . approaches his subject with love and respect and comes up with a book that gives us a really three-dimensional portrait of a major performing artist.'' A reviewer for *Choice* agrees that the book is ''clearly a labor of love, but just as clearly an articulate, competent, remarkably objective, and sometimes moving accomplishment,'' and calls it ''one of the best and most evocative biographies of a major acting talent.''

Lawrence writes to *CA:* ''We like to be part of our national and international bloodstreams. We often use the past to help illuminate the present. We are pleased that our plays are performed on a larger Broadway than the few blocks of real estate in Manhattan.''

Auntie Mame was filmed by Warner Brothers in 1958, *Inherit the Wind* by United Artists in 1960. Both plays have been translated into more than thirty languages and have been produced throughout the world. *Mame* was filmed by Warner Brothers-Seven Arts in 1974. *The Night Thoreau Spent in Jail* has been performed more than two thousand times under the auspices of American Playwright's Theatre. 20th Century-Fox purchased the screen rights to ''Diamond Orchid,'' Hal Wallis the rights to *The Night Thoreau Spent in Jail.* A Lawrence and Lee Collection has been established at Lincoln Center in New York City.

BIOGRAPHICAL/CRITICAL SOURCES: New York Times, April 22, 1955, November 2, 1970, December 23, 1970; *Newsweek,* May 2, 1955; *Life,* May 9, 1955; *New Yorker,* November 10, 1956; *Variety,* January 1, 1969, February 12, 1969, November 4, 1970; *Cue,* February 15, 1969; *New York,* February 24, 1969, November 1, 1971; *Playbill,* May, 1969; *Washington Post,* May 8, 1970, October 30, 1970; *National Review,* January 12, 1971; *Irish Times,* March 18, 1972; *Evening Press* (Dublin), March 18, 1972; *Plays and Players,* May, 1972; *Dallas Morning News,* March 7, 1973; *Dallas Times Herald,* March 7, 1973; *Iconoclast,* March 9-16, 1973; *Publishers Weekly,* August 12, 1974; *Choice,* April, 1975.

*   *   *

LAWSON, Donna Roberta   1937-

PERSONAL: Born May 23, 1937, in Los Angeles, Calif.; daughter of Robert and Helen (McRuer) Lawson. *Education:* University of California, Los Angeles, B.A., 1959; attended New School for Social Research, City College of the City University of New York, and Art Student's League, 1961-67. *Politics:* Democrat. *Religion:* Protestant. *Agent:* Daniel M. O'Shea, 108 East 82nd St., New York, N.Y. 10016.

CAREER: Daily News, New York City, assistant fashion editor, 1961-63; *Suburbia Today,* New York City, associate editor, 1963-65; McCall Publishing Co., New York City, associate editor, Trade Book Division, 1965; Ohrbach's Department Store, New York City, fashion coordinator and

publicist, 1965-66; junior high school art teacher in New York City, 1966-67; fashion and beauty editor, *Eye* (magazine), 1967-69; free-lance writer, 1969—.

WRITINGS: Lola Montez, Chelsea House, 1969; (with Jean Conlon) *Beauty Is No Big Deal: The Commonsense Beauty Book,* Geis, 1971; *Brothers and Sisters All over This Land: America's First Communes,* Praeger, 1972; *Mother Nature's Beauty Cupboard,* Crowell, 1973; *If You Can't Go Naked, Here Are Clothes to Sew On Fast,* self-illustrated, Grosset, 1973; (with Conlon) *Superbaby Cookbook,* Macmillan, 1974; *Superjeans: Easy Ways to Recycle and Decorate Your Jeans,* Scholastic Book Services, 1975; *Yesterday's Clothing and Castoffs into Exciting New Fashions for Today,* Butterick, 1977; *Kid's Clothes for under Five Dollars,* Music Sales Corp., 1978; *Thinking Your Way Thin,* Bantam, 1978; *The Vegetarian Diet,* Bantam, 1978.

Also author of syndicated column, ''In Gear,'' for North American Newspaper Alliance (NANA), and of column, ''The Happy Body,'' for *Natural Living* magazine. Contributor to *New York, Craft Horizons, Rags,* and *Charlie.*†

*   *   *

LAZARUS, Arnold A(llan)   1932-

PERSONAL: Born January 27, 1932, in Johannesburg, South Africa; son of Benjamin and Rachel (Mosselson) Lazarus; married Daphne Ann Kessel, June 10, 1956; children: Linda Sue, Clifford Neil. *Education:* University of the Witwatersrand, B.A. (honors), 1956, M.A., 1957, Ph.D., 1960. *Politics:* Semi-Liberal. *Religion:* Agnostic. *Home:* 56 Herrontown Cir., Princeton, N.J. 08540. *Agent:* Mary Yost, 141 East 55th St., New York, N.Y. 10022. *Office:* Graduate School of Applied and Professional Psychology, Rutgers University, P.O. Box 819, Piscataway, N.J. 08854.

CAREER: Private psychotherapy practice, Johannesburg, South Africa, 1959-63; Stanford University, Stanford, Calif., visiting assistant professor of psychology, 1963-64; Behavior Therapy Institute, Sausalito, Calif., director, 1966-67; Temple University Medical School, Philadelphia, Pa., professor of psychology, 1967-70; Yale University, New Haven, Conn., director of clinical training, 1970-72; Rutgers University, New Brunswick, N.J. and Piscataway, N.J., professor of psychology and chairman of department, 1972-74, professor, Graduate School of Applied and Professional Psychology, 1974—; Multimodal Therapy Institute, Kingston, N.J., director, 1976—. Diplomate in clinical psychology awarded by American Board of Professional Psychology, 1972. Vice-president of Transvaal Workers Association, Johannesburg, South Africa, 1960. *Member:* American Psychological Association (fellow), American Group Therapy Association, American Academy of Psychotherapists, Association for Advancement of Behavior Therapy (president, 1968), New Jersey Psychological Association.

WRITINGS: (With Joseph Wolpe) *Behavior Therapy Techniques,* Pergamon, 1966; *Behavior Therapy and Beyond,* McGraw, 1971; (editor with Richard Rubin, Herbert Fensterheim, and Cyril Franks) *Advances in Behavior Therapy,* Academic Press, 1971; *Clinical Behavior Therapy,* Brunner, 1972; (with Allen Fay) *I Can if I Want To,* Morrow, 1975; *Multimodal Behavior Therapy,* Springer Publishing, 1976; *In the Mind's Eye,* Rawson Associates, 1978. Contributor of over one hundred papers, articles, and chapters; member of editorial panel, *Behavior Research and Therapy,* 1963, *Behavior Therapy,* 1970, *Psychotherapy: Theory, Research, and Practice,* 1970, *Journal of Individual Psychology,* 1976, *Cognitive Therapy and Research,* 1977, *Comprehensive Psychotherapy,* 1979.

WORK IN PROGRESS: Multimodal Therapy: Comprehensive and Effective Psychotherapy.

SIDELIGHTS: Arnold Lazarus told *CA:* "As a professional psychologist in academe and in clinical practice, I used to denigrate psychologists and psychiatrists who wrote 'popular' books, especially those of the 'self-help' variety. Gradually, I have come to change my mind. A picture may be worth a thousand words, and a good self-help book can be worth dozens of psychotherapy sessions. Thus, in 1975 I wrote *I Can if I Want To* with my friend and colleague, Dr. Allen Fay. I am continuing to write clinical textbooks and scientific papers for professional journals, but I am now a firm believer in trying to reach [lay] people . . . about useful methods and techniques, rather than only writing for other psychologists."

AVOCATIONAL INTERESTS: Cultivation of deep and special friendships, music, theatre, good food.

* * *

LAZARUS, Keo Felker   1913-

PERSONAL: Born October 22, 1913, in Callaway, Neb.; daughter of John Edwin (a rancher and jeweler) and Nola (Smith) Felker; married Arnold Leslie Lazarus (a professor of English), July 24, 1938; children: Kearvelle (Mrs. John B. Friedman), Dianne (Mrs. James Runnels), J. David, Peter D. *Education:* University of California, Los Angeles, B.E., 1938. *Home:* 945 Ward Dr. No. 69, Santa Barbara, Calif. 93111.

CAREER: Physical education teacher in Los Angeles, Calif., 1939-41, 1955-59. *Member:* Authors Guild, Society of Children's Book Writers, Chicago Children's Reading Round Table, Purdue University Writer's Group, Tippecanoe County Historical Association.

WRITINGS—Juvenile: Rattlesnake Run, Follett, 1968; *The Gismo,* Follett, 1970; *Tadpole Taylor,* Steck, 1970; *The Billy Goat in the Chili Patch,* Steck, 1972; *The Shark in the Window,* Morrow, 1972; *A Totem for Ti-Jacques,* Waveland Press, 1977. Contributor of stories and poems to *Jack and Jill, Cricket,* and *Highlights for Children.*

WORK IN PROGRESS: A story about a theatre family and their misadventures, tentatively entitled *Secret of the Lucky Blue; You've Got a Pet What?,* the humorous coping of a family with a series of exotic pets.

SIDELIGHTS: Keo Lazarus told *CA:* "Each time I talk to children in the schools, I come away re-dedicated to writing for these clear-eyed, enthusiastic, probing, young people. They want fact, fancy, and fun—three ingredients an author needs to combine in the right amounts to make a book good reading. The addition of moral integrity stirred into the plot strengthens the result, and makes writing for the young a rewarding and worthy profession."

BIOGRAPHICAL/CRITICAL SOURCES: Book World, May 5, 1968.

* * *

LEACH, (Richard) Max(well)   1909-

PERSONAL: Born February 10, 1909, in Childress, Tex.; son of John Reuben (a merchant) and Cora (Curd) Leach; married Lelia Page, January 17, 1931 (died September 24, 1976); married Lavoy Miller, July 10, 1977; children: (first marriage) Beth (Mrs. Ray Tatum), Max, Jr., Leslie (Mrs. Jack Prather). *Education:* Abilene Christian College (now University), B.A., 1931; University of Denver, M.A., 1939;

University of Colorado, Ed.D., 1950. *Politics:* Democrat. *Religion:* Church of Christ. *Home and office:* 1011 North 13th, Lamesa, Tex. 79331.

CAREER: Abilene Christian College (now University), Abilene, Tex., instructor in chemistry and psychology, 1942-48, associate professor, 1948-50, professor of psychology, 1950-74, head of department, 1953-66. Part-time private practice in psychology, Abilene, 1950—. Visiting instructor, University of Connecticut, 1953, University of Colorado, Pepperdine University, Stephen F. Austin State University, and Midwestern University. *Member:* American Psychological Association, American Academy of Psychotherapists, International Institute of Arts and Letters (fellow).

WRITINGS: Like Stars Shining Brightly, Abilene Christian Press, 1951; (with Orval Filbeck) *College, Classroom, Campus, and You,* W. C. Brown, 1953; *Christianity and Mental Health,* W. C. Brown, 1957; *His Way in His Words,* Christian Life Publishing, 1963; *Sex and the Christian,* Christian Life Publishing, 1971. Also author of *Space Ship of Fools* and *The Way.* Contributor of more than twenty articles to journals in his field.

SIDELIGHTS: Max Leach told *CA:* "I have been writing for most of my life, for newspapers, magazines, and wire services. I have the Great American Novel, written forty years ago, stored safely away. It will stay there. I'm a writer because I like to write. If it's published, fine. If it's not, the fineness is blunted a little bit. But not enough to bother much, for writing has always been an avocation—probably a spinoff of my vocation, teaching and counseling. Since retiring from college teaching I am more a writer than anything else—unless it's yard man—and have finished two books."

* * *

LEADBITTER, Mike   1942-

PERSONAL: Born March 12, 1942, in Simla, India; son of Nicholas Andrew and Joyce (Von Goldstein) Leadbitter; married Rosemary Davis, October 23, 1967. *Education:* Bexhill-on-Sea Grammar School, general certificate of education, 1956. *Politics:* None. *Religion:* None. *Office:* Hanover Books, 4 Mill St., London W.1, England.

CAREER: Hanover Books, London, England, member of editorial and advertising staffs, 1970—.

WRITINGS: (With Neil Slaven) *Blues Records* (discography), Hanover Books, 1968; (editor) *Nothing But the Blues,* Hanover Books, 1970. Also author of several short musical histories. Contributor to *Old Time Music.* Co-editor and publisher of *Blues Unlimited,* 1963—; contributing editor, *Let It Rock,* 1972.

WORK IN PROGRESS: A discography covering all rhythm and blues recordings, 1943-1970.†

* * *

LEBLON, Jean (Marcel Jules)   1928-

PERSONAL: Born June 7, 1928, in St. Remy-lez-Chimay, Belgium; son of Alfred and Marcelle (Lefevre) Leblon; married Mary Lorraine Hovorka (a teacher), June 3, 1952; children: Annette Marie Lee, Simone Marie Jeanne. *Education:* Kansas State Teachers College (now Emporia State University), B.S.Ed., 1951; Yale University, Ph.D., 1960. *Religion:* Roman Catholic. *Home:* 1816 Cedar Lane, Nashville, Tenn. 37212. *Office:* Department of French and Italian, Vanderbilt University, Nashville, Tenn. 37235.

CAREER: Connecticut College, New London, instructor in

French, 1953-59; City College of the City University of New York, New York, N.Y., instructor in French, 1959-62; Hollins College, Hollins, Va., associate professor of French, 1962-65, chairman of modern language department, 1962-65; Vanderbilt University, Nashville, Tenn., associate professor, 1966-74, professor of French, 1974—, chairman of department of French and Italian, 1971—, director of Vanderbilt-in-France Program, 1969-71, summers, 1973—. *Member:* Modern Language Association of America, American Association of Teachers of French, American Association of University Professors, Association for the Study of Dada and Surrealism, Association des Parents d'Eleves de Ecoles Publiques, Societe des Professeurs Francais en Amerique, Les Amis de Sainte-Victoire, South Atlantic Modern Language Association.

WRITINGS: (Translator) Marc Bernard, *Zola,* Grove, 1960; (with M. M. Miller and J. R. Nelson) *Precis de Civilisation francaise,* Appleton, 1966; (author of introduction and notes) Georges Perec, *Les Choses,* Appleton, 1969.

WORK IN PROGRESS: Le Theatre d'Henri de Montherlant; Le moralisme dans le theatre francais contemporain.

AVOCATIONAL INTERESTS: Hiking, mountain climbing, acting, history of architecture.

* * *

LEBRUN, Richard Allen 1931-

PERSONAL: Born October 1, 1931, in Milton, N.D.; son of Jules Emile (a farmer) and Marie (Pelletier) Lebrun; married Constance Marjorie Olsen (a piano teacher), June 22, 1954; children: Constance Marie, Paul Richard, Mary Teresa, Jeanne Marie, Mark Joseph, John Benedict. *Education:* St. John's University, B.A., 1953; University of Minnesota, M.A., 1957, Ph.D., 1963. *Religion:* Roman Catholic. *Home:* 195 Elm St., Winnipeg, Manitoba, Canada R3M 3N5. *Office:* Department of History, University of Manitoba, Winnipeg, Manitoba, Canada.

CAREER: University of Ottawa, Ottawa, Ontario, lecturer, 1960-62, assistant professor, 1962-65, associate professor of history, 1965-66; University of Manitoba, Winnipeg, associate professor, 1966-72, professor of history, 1972—, associate dean of graduate studies, 1971-73, executive assistant to the president, 1973-77. *Military service:* U.S. Navy, 1953-56; became lieutenant. *Member:* American Historical Association, Canadian Historical Association, Canadian Catholic Historical Association (president, 1969-70). *Awards, honors:* Woodrow Wilson fellow, 1956.

WRITINGS: Throne and Altar: The Political and Religious Thought of Joseph de Maistre, University of Ottawa Press, 1965; (translator, and author of introduction and notes) Joseph de Maistre, *Considerations on France,* McGill-Queen's University Press, 1974. Contributor of articles and book reviews to *French Historical Studies, Studies on Voltaire and the Eighteenth Century, Journal of Modern History, Catholic Historical Review, Canadian Journal of History,* and *American Historical Review.*

WORK IN PROGRESS: Research on a biography of Joseph de Maistre; articles for *Revue des Etudes Maistriennes.*

* * *

LECLAVELE, Roland 1886-1973
(Roland Dorgeles)

June 15, 1886—March 18, 1973; French author of books on war, travel, and other topics. Obituaries: *New York Times,* March 20, 1973; *Publishers Weekly,* April 2, 1973.

LeCROY, Anne K(ingsbury) 1930-

PERSONAL: Born January 21, 1930, in Summit, N.J.; daughter of Arthur Howard and Anne (Johnston) Kingsbury; married William H. LeCroy, February 9, 1956 (divorced, 1965); children: Bobbi Lynn, Lyman Philip, Kathi Anne. *Education:* Bryn Mawr College, A.B., 1947, A.M., 1948; University of Cincinnati, Ph.D., 1952; also studied at Johns Hopkins University and Syracuse University. *Politics:* Democrat. *Religion:* Anglo-Catholic. *Home:* 1105 Cherokee St., Johnson City, Tenn. 37601. *Office:* Department of English, East Tennessee State University, Johnson City, Tenn. 37601.

CAREER: Girls Latin School, Baltimore, Md., teacher of history and Latin, 1950-51; Western Reserve University (now Case Western Reserve University), Cleveland, Ohio, instructor in classics, 1952-55; University of New Mexico, Albuquerque, assistant professor of classics, 1955-56; Endicott Junior College, Beverly, Mass., assistant dean, 1956-57; East Tennessee State University, Johnson City, assistant professor of English, 1959-63, associate professor of English and Greek, 1963-67, professor of English, 1967—. Lay consultant, National Standing Liturgical Commission of Episcopal Church, 1971-73; Diocesan coordinator, 1972; committee member for revision of the Eucharist, 1973. Member of FISH (a voluntary aid association); delegate to state Democratic convention.

MEMBER: National Council of Teachers of English, College English Association, Conference on College Composition and Communication, American Association of University Professors, American Civil Liberties Union (local president), Southeastern Institute of Renaissance and Mediaeval Studies (fellow, Duke University) Tennessee English Association, Tennessee Philosophical Association, Mental Health Association of Washington County. *Awards, honors:* Fulbright award to Athens, Greece, 1952.

WRITINGS: Footnote to Thucydides, American Philological Association, 1956; *Liturgical Structure of "Murder in the Cathedral,"* East Tennessee State University Press, 1969; *Semantic Analysis of the Liturgy of 1967,* privately printed, 1970. Contributor to *Tennessee Churchman, American Church News,* and classics journals.

WORK IN PROGRESS: A history of the Episcopal church in upper eastern Tennessee.†

* * *

LEE, Arthur M(atthias) 1918-

PERSONAL: Born May 22, 1918, in Superior, Wis.; son of Charles Chrest (a farmer) and Julia (Blochar) Lee; married Alice Edna Gentry (a teacher), April 16, 1939; children: Linda (Mrs. Dennis Anderson), David John, Elizabeth Ann (Mrs. Carl Nelson). *Education:* University of Kansas City (now University of Missouri—Kansas City), B.A., 1947, M.A., 1948; Syracuse University, Ph.D., 1953. *Politics:* Republican. *Religion:* Baptist. *Home:* 254 Buffalo Trail, Flagstaff, Ariz. 86001. *Office:* Northern Arizona University, Box 15015, Flagstaff, Ariz. 86001.

CAREER: Syracuse University, Syracuse, N.Y., instructor in history, 1950-51; Grand Canyon College, Phoenix, Ariz., associate professor, 1951-53, professor of history and government, 1953-59, head of department of social studies, 1953-59; administrative assistant to U.S. Congressman John J. Rhodes of Arizona, Washington, D.C., 1959-61; executive secretary to Governor Paul J. Fannin, Phoenix, 1961-65; Northern Arizona University, Flagstaff, director of Arizona Research Coordinating Unit, 1965-71, director of research and grants, 1971-73, director of Project Baseline, 1971—, academic advisor, American Enterprise Program, 1972-73. Visiting lecturer at University of Kansas City (now University of Missouri—Kansas City), 1951, University of Arizona, 1956-59, and University of Maryland, 1960-61; member of president's advisory council of Grand Canyon College, National Advisory Council on Vocational Education, 1972-74, and National Council on Educational Research, 1974-78; consultant to U.S. Secretary of the Interior, summer, 1958. *Military service:* U.S. Army, Infantry, 1943-46; became sergeant; received Purple Heart.

MEMBER: American Educational Research Association, American Vocational Education Research Association (president, 1971), Association for Educational Data Systems, American Technological Association, American Association for the Advancement of Science, Phi Delta Kappa, Arizona Academy, Kiwanis, Red Red Rose.

WRITINGS—All published by Northern Arizona University: *Research for Career Education,* 1966; *Engineering and Technology in Arizona,* 1968; *Learning a Living,* 1970; *Learning a Living across the Nation,* 1973. Contributor to professional journals.

WORK IN PROGRESS: Continuing national research on vocational education for U.S. Office of Education, National Institute of Education, and National Center for Research in Vocational Education.

SIDELIGHTS: Arthur Lee told *CA:* "My writing for many years has been focused on a group of students in our schools—sometimes tolerated, sometimes scorned, and occasionally praised—the 'vokies.' Their claim to respectability in the educational system has been under attack by academic purists for more than a century. For the past fifteen years, vocational education has been a battleground in Washington and many state capitols. My interest is in the kids themselves—who they are, where they come from, what they get out of their vocational training, what happens to them afterward, and if it is really very expensive to give them job skills in school while they're also studying mathematics, English, and all of the other academic subjects available to them.

"The National Advisory Council on Vocational Education once referred to them as 'other people's children.' My interest and my efforts in writing are to remove them from the shadows of our educational programs, to bring them into the mainstream of public awareness, and to bring a little human understanding into a segment of public policy too often left to theorists and critics."

* * *

LEE, Chong-Sik 1931-

PERSONAL: Born July 30, 1931, in Korea; came to United States, 1954; married; children: three. *Education:* University of California, Los Angeles, A.B., 1956, M.A., 1957; University of California, Berkeley, Ph.D., 1961. *Office:* Department of Political Science, University of Pennsylvania, Philadelphia, Pa. 19104.

CAREER: University of Colorado, Boulder, instructor in political science, 1960-61; Dartmouth College, Hanover, N.H., instructor in great issues, 1961-63; University of Pennsylvania, Philadelphia, assistant professor, 1963-65, associate professor, 1965-73, professor of political science, 1973—. Chairman of Joint Committee on Korean Studies of Social Science Research Council and American Council of Learned Societies, 1970-76. *Awards, honors:* Social Science Research Council grants, 1963, 1966-67, 1972; Rockefeller Foundation grant, 1965-66; Ford Foundation faculty fellowship, 1969-70; Woodrow Wilson Award for best book of 1973, American Political Science Association, 1974.

WRITINGS: The Politics of Korean Nationalism, University of California Press, 1963; (contributor) Robert A. Scalapino, editor, *North Korea Today,* Praeger, 1963; (contributor) Thomas T. Hammond, editor, *Soviet Foreign Relations and World Communism,* Princeton University Press, 1965; (contributor) Scalapino, editor, *Communist Revolution in Asia,* Prentice-Hall, 1965, revised edition, 1969; (contributor) Guy Wint, editor, *Asia: A Handbook to the Continent,* Praeger, 1966; (editor and translator) *Counterinsurgency in Manchuria: The Japanese Experience, 1931-1940,* RAND Corp., 1967; (contributor) Yi Pyong-du, editor, *Ch'ilsipnyon-dae wa Hanguk ui anjon pojang* (title means "1970's and the Security of Korea"), Shin-a-gak, 1970; *Usa Kim Kyu-sik* (political biography of Kim Kyu-sik), Shin-gu Munhwasa, 1973; (with Scalapino) *Communism in Korea,* two volumes, University of California Press, 1973; (contributor) Gene T. Hsiao, editor, *Sino-American Detente and Its Policy Implications,* Praeger, 1974; (contributor) William E. Griffith, editor, *The World and the Great Power Triangles,* M. I. T. Press, 1975; (contributor) Dae-Sook Suh and Chae-Jin Lee, editors, *Political Leadership in Korea,* University of Washington Press, 1976; (editor and translator) *Materials on Korean Communism, 1945-1947,* Center for Korean Studies, University of Hawaii, 1977; *Korean Workers' Party: A Short History,* Hoover Institution, 1978.

Author of monographs. Contributor to Japanese edition of *Encyclopaedia Britannica.* Contributor of about twenty-five articles to professional journals in the United States and abroad, including *Journal of Asian Studies, China Quarterly, Asian Survey, Pacific Affairs,* and *Journal of Korean Affairs.*

* * *

LEE, Joe Won 1921-

PERSONAL: Born April 19, 1921, in Pusan, Korea; son of Sun Jae and Yichoon (Kim) Lee; married Rosa Zung Za (a physician), June 29, 1964; children: Melissa Ann, Steven Joseph. *Education:* Pusan National University, Korea, B.A., 1952, M.B.A., 1956; Ball State University, M.A., 1957; Indiana University, D.B.A., 1962. *Religion:* Roman Catholic. *Office:* Applied Systems Institute, 918 16th St. N.W., Washington, D.C. 20006.

CAREER: Pusan National University, Pusan, Korea, instructor, 1952-56, assistant professor of business, 1956-58; National Planning Association, Washington, D.C., economist, 1961-63; Indiana University International Development Research Center, Bloomington, Ind., research associate, 1963-64; Cambridge University, Cambridge, England, research associate, 1964-65; National Planning Association, Washington, D.C., senior economist, 1965-69, associate director, 1969-71, director for regional projections, 1971-77; Applied Systems Institute (consulting firm), Washington, D.C., president, 1977—. Instructor, Howard University. *Member:* American Economic Association, Korean Economic Society (president, 1968-69).

WRITINGS—All published by National Planning Association: *Projection of Income Size Class Distribution of Consumer Units, by State,* 1964; *Economic and Demographic Projections for Eighty-Two Metropolitan Areas,* 1966; *Eco-*

nomic and Demographic Projections for 224 Metropolitan Areas, 1967; *Economic and Demographic Projections for States and Metropolitan Areas,* 1969; (with William Hong) *State Economic and Demographic Projections to 1975 and 1980: Population, Income, Industry, Employment, and Consumption Expenditures,* 1970; (with Hong) *Metropolitan Area Growth Patterns for the Coming Decade,* 1970; (with Hong) *Income, Saving and Consumption Patterns for Regions, States, and Metropolitan Areas, 1960-80,* 1971; (with Hong) *Regional Demographic Projections–1960-1985: Population, Labor Force, Migration, and Households for Regions and States,* 1972; (with Hong) *Regional Economic Projections, 1960-85,* 1973. Also author of annual reports for National Planning Association. Contributor of articles to *Metropolitan Area Annual, Looking Ahead, Proceedings* of the American Statistical Association, and other professional publications.

WORK IN PROGRESS: Economic analyses of transportation and education.

SIDELIGHTS: In addition to English and Korean, Joe Won Lee speaks Japanese and reads French, German, and classical and modern Chinese.

*   *   *

LEE, Oliver M(inseem) 1927-

PERSONAL: Born December 7, 1927, in Shanghai, China; son of Ginffa and Gerta (Scheuermann) Lee; married May Yee, July 8, 1950; children: Vivien, Steven, Anthony. *Education:* Harvard University, A.B., 1951; University of Chicago, M.A., 1955, Ph.D., 1962. *Home:* 1355 Frank St., Honolulu, Hawaii 96816. *Office:* Department of Political Science, University of Hawaii, 2500 Campus Rd., Honolulu, Hawaii 96822.

CAREER: University of Maryland at College Park, instructor in politics, 1958-62; Library of Congress, Washington, D.C., Far East analyst, 1962-63; University of Hawaii, Honolulu, assistant professor, 1963-73, associate professor of political science, 1973—. Co-chairman, Hawaii Committee to End the War in Vietnam, 1965-68. Peace and Freedom Party candidate for U.S. Senate from Hawaii, 1968. *Military service:* U.S. Army Reserve, 1957-58. *Member:* American Association of University Professors, American Civil Liberties Union, Committee of Concerned Asian Scholars.

WRITINGS: (Contributor) Arthur Stahnke, editor, *China's Trade with the West,* Praeger, 1972. Contributor of articles to *Current History, East-West Center Review, Nation, Salmagundi,* and *Impulse.*

WORK IN PROGRESS: A book on U.S. relations with China; a book concerning the origins of the Korean War; a book on the history of the Hakka people.

BIOGRAPHICAL/CRITICAL SOURCES: Bulletin of Atomic Scientists, September, 1968; *American Association of University Professors Bulletin,* spring, 1969.

*   *   *

LEE, Raymond L(awrence) 1911-

PERSONAL: Born May 27, 1911, in Deckerville, Mich.; son of George J. (a farmer) and Mildred (Cleland) Lee; married Virginia Horton, August 19, 1939; children: Richard H., Robert H., Raymond L., Jr. *Education:* Eastern Michigan University, A.B., 1937; University of Michigan, M.A., 1939, Ph.D., 1946. *Politics:* Democrat. *Home:* Route 2, Marion Center, Pa., 15759. *Office:* John Sutton Hall, Indiana University of Pennsylvania, Indiana, Pa. 15705.

CAREER: Teacher in Michigan public schools, 1932-35, 1937-40; Stephens College, Columbia, Mo., instructor in political science, 1946-53; Indiana University of Pennsylvania, Indiana, professor of political science, 1953-76, director of Social Science Division, 1953-72, associate dean of arts and sciences, 1973-76, dean emeritus, 1976—. Visiting summer professor at Wisconsin State Teachers College (now University of Wisconsin), Whitewater, 1947, and University of Missouri, 1952. Merchant seaman, 1929-31, and 1942-45. *Member:* American Political Science Association, American Academy of Political and Social Science, Midwest Political Science Association, Northeastern Political Science Association.

WRITINGS: (Editor with James A. Burkhart and Van B. Shaw) *Contemporary Social Issues,* Crowell, 1954; (editor with Burkhart and Samuel Krislov) *American Government: The Clash of Issues,* Prentice-Hall, 1960; *Guide to American Government,* Prentice-Hall, 1963; (editor with Dorothy A. Palmer) *America in Crisis: Contemporary Political Dilemmas,* Winthrop, 1972. Contributor to *Journal of Modern History, Revista de historia de America,* and *Hispanic American Historical Review.*

WORK IN PROGRESS: The Mass Media in the American Political Process.

SIDELIGHTS: Raymond L. Lee lives on and operates a 115 acre sheep farm, and raises Christmas trees for market. He travels extensively in the Caribbean area, Scotland, Wales, and the Shetland and Orkney Islands.

*   *   *

LEFRANC, Pierre 1927-

PERSONAL: Born November 30, 1927, in Aulnay Sous Bois, France; son of Georges (a professor) and Emilie (a professor; maiden name, Lamare) Lefranc; married Yane Guichard, July 4, 1958. *Education:* Sorbonne, University of Paris, Licence Libre, 1950, Licence d'Anglais, 1950, D.E.S. d'Anglais, 1951, Agregation d'Anglais, 1952, Doctorat es Lettres, 1968. *Home:* 185 bis Avenue de Fabron, 06200 Nice, France. *Office:* Universite de Nice, Parc Valrase, 06034 Nice Cedex, France.

CAREER: Ecole Normale Superieure, Paris, France, reader in English, 1953-60; University of Mohammed V, Rabat, Morocco, head of department of English, 1960-64; University of Laval, Laval, Quebec, visiting professor, 1964-65, associate professor, 1965-68, professor of English, 1968-72, head of department, 1964-68; Centre Universitaire de la Reunion, St. Denis, France, professor of English, 1972-75; currently affiliated with Universite de Nice, Nice, France. *Military service:* French Air Force, 1952-53; became lieutenant. *Member:* Hakluyt Society, Societe des Anglicistes de l'Enseignement superieur.

WRITINGS: Sir Walter Ralegh ecrivain: L'oeuvre et les Idees, Librairie Armand Colin, 1968. Contributor of articles and reviews to literature journals.

WORK IN PROGRESS: An edition of the poems of Sir Walter Ralegh, for Clarendon Press; research on the life and career of Sir Walter Ralegh.

AVOCATIONAL INTERESTS: Gypsies of Lower Andalusia and their songs; travel.

*   *   *

LEFTWICH, James (Adolf) 1902-

PERSONAL: Born July 23, 1902, in Newport News, Va.;

son of David (a distiller and land developer) and Eugenia (Mihalovics) Leftwich; married Ilka Renwick, March 4, 1947 (divorced, 1958); married Merry Ann Ottosen (director of a pathology laboratory), March 12, 1963; children: (first marriage) Jeannie Renwick (Mrs. Tom Bushnell). *Education:* Studied at University of Virginia, 1925. *Politics:* Republican. *Religion:* Episcopalian. *Home:* 2056 Torrey Pines Rd., La Jolla, Calif. 92037. *Office address:* P.O. Box 2206, La Jolla, Calif. 92038.

CAREER: Miami Daily Tab, Miami, Fla., feature writer, 1926; *New York Sun,* New York City, reporter and rewriter, 1926-30; member of book review staff, *New York American,* 1931-33; news editor, National Radio Press Syndicate, 1933-34; *Newport News Times-Herald,* Newport News, Va., columnist, 1934; member of public relations staff for Admiral Byrd's second Antarctic expedition, 1934-36; freelance writer, 1934—. New York Board of Trade, New City, public relations counsel, 1943-50, vice-chairman of aviation section, 1947; member of Leftwich & Barkley (public relations consultants), New York City, 1951-56; member of public relations staff, Ryan Aeronautics Co., 1957; advertising director and public relations counsel for La Jolla Federal Savings & Loan Association, La Jolla Town Council, and Decent Literature Commission of La Jolla. Public relations director for U.S. Congressional Committee investigating the Federal Communications Commission, 1943; public relations associate for Committee for International Economic Policy's reciprocal trade agreements act, 1944, and loan agreement to Great Britain, 1946. Established La Jolla Press, 1968. *Military service:* U.S. Army, athletic director in 111th Virginia Field Artillery, 1926.

MEMBER: National Press Club, U.S. Olympians (vice-president, 1954; member of board of directors, 1956), Society of Professional Journalists, Thomas Jefferson Society of Alumni (University of Virginia), University of Virginia Club of Southern California (founder and president, 1957), La Jolla Executive Club (member of board of directors), La Jolla Sportsmans Club, La Jolla Beach and Tennis Club, John Ericsson Society of New York City, Press and Union League Club (San Francisco), Sigma Delta Chi. *Awards, honors:* Named honorary police commissioner of Lambertville, N.J., 1949-56; honorary alumnus, University of California, San Diego; citation from John Ericsson Society of New York City for distinguished writing about the Merrimack and Monitor.

WRITINGS: Biography of Frank Forester, Derrydale, 1930; *O'Malley Loves Josephine,* Huffnagle, 1940; *The Renwicks* (a family biography), privately printed, 1946; *Meet Sir George Carteret,* [Lambertville, N.J.], 1953; *La Jolla's House of Many Legends,* La Jolla Press, 1960, revised edition, 1978; *Record and Legend of the Ancient Aztec Calendar,* La Jolla Press, 1967; (editor and contributor) *Duel of the Ironclads,* Time-Life, 1969; (with wife, Merry Ann Leftwich) *Pathology Laboratory Careers for Tissue Technicians,* La Jolla Press, 1971. Editor, *Bulletin* of American Society of Swedish Engineers, 1939-48.

WORK IN PROGRESS: Aunt Matt's House, a biography of a former slave woman who ran a bawdy house in Charlottesville, Va., 1890-1920.

SIDELIGHTS: James Leftwich has won U.S. Intercollegiate and Amateur Athletic Union middleweight boxing titles; he was a member of U.S. Olympic boxing team performing in Paris in 1924. *Avocational interests:* Collecting antique and modern firearms, collecting literature on, and studying circumstances relating to the battle of the Merrimack and the Monitor.

LEHMANN, Theo   1934-

PERSONAL: Born May 29, 1934, in Dresden, Germany; son of Arno (a professor, writer, and editor) and Gertrud (a writer; maiden name, Harstall) Lehmann; married Elke Weidlich, June 6, 1959; children: Constantia, Mirjam, Camilla. *Education:* Studied at Theological Seminary, Leipzig, 1952-54, and University of Leipzig, 1954-59; University of Halle-Wittenberg, Dr.theol., 1963. *Home:* Schlossplatz 7, Karl-Marx-Stadt, East Germany.

CAREER: University of Halle-Wittenberg, Halle, Germany, scientific assistant, 1960-64; Lutheran pastor in Karl-Marx-Stadt, 1965-75; evangelist, 1976—. *Member:* International Fellowship for Hymnology.

WRITINGS: Nobody Knows: Negro Spirituals (in English and German), Koehler & Amelang, 1961, 2nd edition, 1963; *Negro Spirituals: Geschichte und Theologie* (in English and German), Eckart-Verlag and Evangelische Verlagsanstalt, 1965; *Blues and Trouble* (in English and German), Henschel-Verlag, 1966, 2nd revised edition, 1979; *Gospelmusik ist mein Leben–Mahalia Jackson,* Union-Verlag, 1974, 2nd edition, 1976.

Contributor: G. Hegele, *Warum neue religiose Lieder?,* Bosse Verlag, 1964; *Calendarium spirituale,* Evangelische Verlagsanstalt, 1965; V. Vajta, *The Gospel and the Ambiguity of the Church,* Fortress, 1974; P. Grunow, *Eine Prise Froehlichkeit,* Evangelische Verlagsanstalt, 1976; Grunow, *Lockrui zum Leben,* Evangelische Verlagsanstalt, 1977. Contributor of articles and reviews to journals and newspapers.

WORK IN PROGRESS: A collection of songs for young Christians, for Evangelische Verlagsanstalt.

SIDELIGHTS: Theo Lehmann told *CA:* "My father has translated religious hymns from Tamil (India) into German. I have translated religious hymns of the American Negroes into German. Under such influences I became a songwriter, writing songs for young Christians."

*   *   *

LEHNERT, Herbert (Hermann)   1925-

PERSONAL: Born January 19, 1925, in Luebeck, Germany; son of Bernhard and Elisabeth (Doemel) Lehnert; married Ingeborg Poth, August 13, 1952; children: Bernard (deceased), Brigitte, Bettina. *Education:* University of Kiel, Germany, Ph.D., 1952. *Politics:* Democratic. *Home:* 10 Aspen Tree Lane, Irvine, Calif. 92715. *Office:* Department of German, University of California, Irvine, Calif. 92717.

CAREER: Teacher in German secondary schools, 1952-57; University of Western Ontario, London, lecturer in German, 1957-58; Rice University, Houston, Tex., lecturer, 1958-59, assistant professor, 1959-63, associate professor, 1963-66, professor of German, 1966-68; University of Kansas, Lawrence, professor of German, 1968-69; University of California, Irvine, professor of German, 1969—. *Member:* International Association for Germanic Research, Modern Language Association of America, American Association of Teachers of German, Thomas Mann Society, Hofmannsthal Society.

WRITINGS: Thomas Mann: Fiktion, Mythos, Religion, Kohlhammer (Stuttgart), 1965, 2nd edition, 1968; *Struktur und Sprachmagie,* Kohlhammer, 1966, 2nd edition, 1972; *Thomas Mann Forschung,* Metzler (Stuttgart), 1969; *Geschichte der deutschen Literatur: Vom Jugendstil zum Expressionismus,* Reclam (Stuttgart), 1978. Contributor of articles to journals in his field.

WORK IN PROGRESS: A history of German literature from 1890 to the present.

* * *

LEICHTER, Otto 1898(?)-1973

1898(?)—February 14, 1973; Austrian-born politician, journalist, and author. Obituaries: *New York Times,* February 15, 1973.

* * *

LEIGHTON, Alexander H(amilton) 1908-

PERSONAL: Born July 17, 1908, in Philadelphia, Pa.; son of Archibald O. and Gertrude (Hamilton) Leighton; married Dorothea Cross, August 17, 1937 (divorced October, 1965); married Jane Murphy (an anthropologist and educator), July 30, 1966; children: (first marriage) Dorothea Gertrude Leighton Uehara, Frederick A. *Education:* Princeton University, B.A., 1932; Cambridge University, M.A., 1934; Johns Hopkins University, M.D., 1936. *Home address:* Box 314, Digby, Nova Scotia, Canada B0V 1A0. *Office:* Department of Preventive Medicine, Dalhousie University, Halifax, Nova Scotia, Canada B3H 4H6.

CAREER: Johns Hopkins Hospital, Baltimore, Md., intern, 1936-37, chief resident in psychiatry, 1940-41, instructor in psychiatry, 1940-41; Cornell University, Ithaca, N.Y., professor of sociology and anthropology, 1947-66, professor of social psychiatry and director of program, 1956-66; Harvard University, Boston, Mass., professor of social psychiatry, 1966-75, professor emeritus, 1975—, head of department of behavioral sciences, 1966-75; Dalhousie University, Halifax, Nova Scotia, professor of psychiatry and preventive medicine, 1975—. Fellow, Center for Advanced Study in the Behavioral Sciences, 1957-58; Thomas W. Salmon Lecturer, New York Academy of Medicine, 1958; visiting lecturer, Catholic University of Louvain, 1971. Director of Cornell Southwest Project, 1948-53, and Stirling County Project, 1948—. Member of board of directors, Social Science Research Council, 1948-58; technical adviser, Milbank Memorial Fund, 1956-63; member of expert advisory panel on mental health, World Health Organization, 1957-76. Consultant to Bureau of Indian Affairs, U.S. Department of the Interior, 1948-50, U.S. Surgeon General, 1956-59, President's Scientific Advisory Committee, 1961-62, and Peace Corps, 1961-63. National health scientist (Canada), 1975—. *Military service:* U.S. Naval Reserve, Medical Corps, active duty, 1941-46; became commander.

MEMBER: American Psychiatric Association (life fellow), American College of Psychiatrists (fellow), American Psychopathological Association, American Association for the Advancement of Science (fellow), American Anthropological Association (fellow), Society for Applied Anthropology, Sociological Research Association, American Philosophical Society, Association on American Indian Affairs (member of board of directors), Polish Psychiatric Association (corresponding fellow), Atlantic Provinces Psychiatric Association (honorary member), Societe de Psychopathologie et d'Hygiene Mentale de Dakar, Canadian Psychiatric Association, Sigma Xi, Phi Beta Kappa, Alpha Omega Alpha. *Awards, honors:* Social Science Research Council research fellowship, 1939-40, for anthropological field work among Navaho Indians and Eskimos; Human Relations Award from American Association for the Advancement of Management, 1946; Guggenheim fellow, 1946-47; Carnegie fellow, 1962-63; A.M., Harvard University, 1966; D.S., Acadia University, 1974; Rema Lapouse Award from Amer-

ican Public Health Association, 1975; McAlpin Award from American Association for Mental Health, 1975.

WRITINGS: (With wife, Dorothea C. Leighton) *The Navaho Door,* Harvard University Press, 1944; *The Governing of Men,* Princeton University Press, 1945; (contributor) *Learning and World Peace,* Harper, 1948; (with D. C. Leighton) *Gregorio: The Hand-Trembler,* Harvard University Press, 1949; *Human Relations in a Changing World,* Dutton, 1949.

(Contributor) *Epidemiology of Mental Disorder,* Milbank Memorial Fund, 1950; (contributor) *The Interrelations Between the Social Environment and Psychiatric Disorders,* Milbank Memorial Fund, 1952; (contributor) Edward Spicer, editor, *Human Problems in Technological Change,* Russell Sage, 1952; (contributor) *Programs for Community Mental Health,* Milbank Memorial Fund, 1956; (editor with Robert N. Wilson and John S. Clausen, and contributor) *Explorations in Social Psychiatry,* Basic Books, 1957; (contributor) Iago Galdston, editor, *Medicine and Anthropology,* International Universities Press, 1959; *My Name Is Legion: Foundations for a Theory of Man in Relation to Culture,* Basic Books, 1959.

An Introduction to Social Psychiatry, C. C Thomas, 1960; (with Charles C. Hughes, Marc Adelard Tremblay, and Robert N. Rapoport) *People of Cove and Woodlot: Communities from the Viewpoint of Social Psychiatry,* Basic Books, 1960; (contributor) Clarence Morris, editor, *Trends in Modern American Society,* University of Pennsylvania Press, 1962; (contributor) *Health and Nutrition,* Volume V: *Science, Technology and Development,* U.S. Government Printing Office, 1963; (with D. C. Leighton, John S. Harding, David B. Macklin, and Allister M. Macmillan) *The Character of Danger: Psychiatric Symptoms in Selected Communities,* Basic Books, 1963; (contributor) T. A. Lambo, editor, *First Pan-African Psychiatric Conference,* Government Printer (Ibadan), 1963; (with D. C. Leighton, Lambo, Hughes, Macklin, and Jane M. Murphy) *Psychiatric Disorder among the Yoruba: A Report from the Cornell-Aro Mental Health Research Project,* Cornell University Press, 1963; (contributor) Leopold Bellak, editor, *Handbook of Community Psychiatry and Community Mental Health,* Grune, 1964; (contributor) *Concepts of Community Psychiatry: A Framework for Training,* U.S. Department of Health, Education and Welfare, 1965; (editor with Murphy) *Approaches to Cross-Cultural Psychiatry,* Cornell University Press, 1965; (contributor) Bernard J. Bergen and Claudewell Thomas, editors, *Issues and Problems in Social Psychiatry: A Book of Readings,* C. C Thomas, 1966; (contributor) Leo Fishman, editor, *Poverty amid Affluence,* Yale University Press, 1966; (contributor) R. F. Monroe, G. D. Klee, and E. B. Brody, editors, *Psychiatric Epidemiology and Mental Health Planning,* American Psychiatric Association, 1967; (contributor) Alfred M. Freedman and Harold I. Kaplan, editors, *Comprehensive Textbook of Psychiatry,* Williams & Wilkins, 1967; (contributor) Galdston, editor, *Historic Derivations of Modern Psychiatry,* McGraw, 1967; (contributor) Platt and Parkes, editors, *Social and Genetic Influences on Life and Death,* Oliver & Boyd, 1967; (contributor) William Caudill and Tsung-Yi Lin, editors, *Mental Health Research in Asia and the Pacific,* East-West Center, 1969; (contributor) Stanley C. Plog and Robert B. Edgerton, editors, *Changing Perspectives in Mental Illness,* Holt, 1969.

(Collaborator and contributor) B. H. Kaplan, editor, *Psychiatric Disorder and the Urban Environment,* Behavioral Publications, 1971; *Come Near* (novel), Norton, 1971; (contributor) *The Future Role of University-Based Metropolitan Medical Centers,* Josiah Macy, Jr. Foundation, 1972; (with Murphy and others) *The Effects of Herbicides in South Vietnam,* National Academy of Sciences, 1974; (editor with B. H. Kaplan and Wilson, and contributor) *Further Explorations in Social Psychiatry,* Basic Books, 1976. Also contributor to *The Community as an Epidemiologic Laboratory: A Casebook of Community Studies,* 1969, and *Social Science and Medicine,* Volume V, 1971.

Contributor to *International Encyclopedia of the Social Sciences;* contributor of about fifty scientific articles to anthropology, biology, psychiatry, public opinion, philosophy, personnel administration, and medical journals. Associate editor of *American Journal of Psychiatry,* 1964-66; member of editorial board, *Journal of Psychiatric Education.*

WORK IN PROGRESS: Research on mental health and social environment.

SIDELIGHTS: Alexander Leighton told *CA:* "For me, the struggle to write is a struggle to express what I discover about life. [My] driving force is an enormous curiosity ... directed through the channels provided by the social and psychological sciences.... [I moved from] bird and animal behavior ... to physiological studies of the central nervous system, and then back again to behavior, limited now to just one species—man. My approach has been through comparative work on health and illness, and on sanity and insanity; it has been across a variety of cultures from African to Eskimo, and across a variety of situations as different as living in peace and living in the disasters of Hiroshima and Vietnam.

"In the course of this, the original, omnivorous curiosity has been transmuted to a concern with whether the social and behavioral sciences can help man to enrich his life and avoid cataclysm; in short, to a commitment to science that sits in a broad humanistic context.

"[My] writing falls into two categories: one aims to present the results of fact-finding, calculations, and orderly inference in a form that is both intelligible and accurate. This is difficult since nature's complexity easily leads to author [verbosity]. On the other hand, author simplicity is liable to be achieved at a heavy cost of truth.

"The other category strives to create feeling as well as intellectual grasp in the reader. I see this as an effort to communicate a wider and deeper kind of knowing through painting with symbols. My aim is to set before readers materials which will move them to their own creative thinking and so to an increased wisdom that is intellectual, aesthetic, and moral."

*   *   *

LEISS, William 1939-

PERSONAL: Born December 28, 1939, in New York, N.Y.; son of William and Ethel (Walter) Leiss. *Education:* Fairleigh Dickinson University, B.A. (summa cum laude), 1960; Brandeis University, M.A., 1963; University of California, San Diego, Ph.D., 1969. *Office:* Faculty of Environmental Studies, York University, Downsview, Ontario, Canada M3J 1P3.

CAREER: University of Saskatchewan, Regina, assistant professor, 1968-72, associate professor of political science, 1972-74; University of Toronto, Toronto, Ontario, associate professor of sociology, 1974-76; York University, Downsview, Ontario, professor of environmental studies and political science, 1976—. *Awards, honors:* Woodrow Wilson fellow, 1960; Canada Council research grants, 1969, 1971, 1973, 1976; nominated for U.S. National Book Award, 1973.

WRITINGS: The Domination of Nature, Braziller, 1972; *The Limits to Satisfaction,* University of Toronto Press, 1976; (editor) *Ecology versus Politics in Canada,* University of Toronto Press, 1979. Contributor of fifteen articles to journals.

WORK IN PROGRESS: A research project on advertising imagery.

*   *   *

LEMANN, Bernard 1905-

PERSONAL: Born September 7, 1905, in Donaldsonville, La.; son of Ferdinand Bernard (a merchant and sugar planter) and Mathile Madeleine (Frank) Lemann; married Elinor Jane Terhune, March 4, 1945; children: John Ferdinand, Jeremy. *Education:* Tulane University, B.Arch., 1926; Columbia University, B.S., 1930; Harvard University, M.A., 1931, Ph.D., 1936; also studied at Institut d'Art et d'Archeologie, University of Paris, summers, 1930-1932. *Residence:* New Orleans, La.

CAREER: University of Kentucky, Lexington, instructor in history of art, 1933-34; Tulane University, New Orleans, La., Newcomb College, instructor, 1941-42, 1946, assistant professor of history of art and architecture, 1946-48, School of Architecture, associate professor, 1948-60, professor of history of architecture and town planning, 1960-76. Member of board of directors of Louisiana Historical Preservation and Cultural Commission and Citizens Housing Council of Greater New Orleans Area. *Wartime service:* Civilian public service with National Parks and a mental hospital, 1943-46.

MEMBER: American Institute of Architects (New Orleans chapter), College Art Association, Society of Architectural Historians (member of board of directors, 1970-73), Louisiana Landmarks Society (former member of board of directors), Art Association of New Orleans (member of executive committee, 1942), Arts and Crafts Club (New Orleans; member of board of directors, 1948-51), Carrollton Civic Association (president, 1956-60), Tulane Cinema Guild (president, 1948-49), Friends of the Cabildo (member of board of directors, 1956—; vice-president, 1960). *Awards, honors:* Carnegie Foundation fellowships, Paris, France, 1930, 1932.

WRITINGS: Honore Daumier, Reynal, 1947; *The Vieux Carre: A General Statement,* School of Architecture, Tulane University, 1966; *New Orleans Architecture,* Pelican, (with Samuel Wilson, Jr.) Volume I: *The Lower Garden District,* 1971, (with others) Volume II: *The American Sector,* 1972, (with others) Volume III: *The Cemeteries,* 1974; (with Russell Wright and others) *A Guide to Delineating Edges of Historical Districts,* National Trust for Historic Preservation, 1976. Author of reports. Contributor to *World Book Encyclopedia* and *Books in Literature and the Arts.* Contributor to art journals and to *Politics, Juilliard Review,* and *New Orleans.*

*   *   *

LEMIEUX, Lucien 1934-

PERSONAL: Born April 30, 1934, in St. Remi, Quebec, Canada; son of Isidore (a merchant) and Yvonne (Beaudin) Lemieux. *Education:* Seminaire St. Jean, B.A., 1954; Universite de Montreal, L.Th., 1958; Universita Gregoriana, D.Hist., 1965. *Home:* 601 Front, Longueuil, Quebec,

Canada. *Office:* Faculty of Theology, Universite de Montreal, C.P. 6128, Montreal 3, Quebec, Canada.

CAREER: Ordained Roman Catholic diocesan priest of St. Jean, 1958; Seminaire St. Jean, St. Jean, Quebec, professor of contemporary history, 1965-68; Universite de Montreal, Montreal, Quebec, professor of church history, 1965—. Consultant to Centre de Recherches en histoire religieuse du Canada, 1968—. *Member:* Societe Canadienne de Theologie.

WRITINGS: L'Etablissement de la premiere province ecclesiastique au Canada (1783-1844), Fides (Montreal), 1968.

WORK IN PROGRESS: Histoire socio-religieuse du peuple quebecois, 1760-1840 (dynamismes pastoraux).

* * *

LE MIRE, Eugene D(ennis) 1929-

PERSONAL: Born May 18, 1929, in Flint, Mich.; son of Louis Emmanuel (a farmer) and Mary (Zinsli) Le Mire; married Margaret Mary Robin Niall (a biochemist), June 27, 1964; children: Marc Francis, Suzanne Mary, David Andre. *Education:* University of Detroit, Ph.B., 1951, M.A., 1954; Wayne State University, Ph.D., 1962. *Religion:* Roman Catholic. *Home:* 6 Deepdene Ave., Westbourne Park, South Australia. *Office:* Department of English, Flinders University, Bedford Park, South Australia 5042.

CAREER: University of Detroit, Detroit, Mich., instructor in English, 1954-56; Wayne State University, Detroit, instructor in English, 1959-61; University of Detroit, assistant professor of English, 1961-62; University of Windsor, Windsor, Ontario, assistant professor, 1962-64, associate professor, 1964-68, professor of English, 1968-70; Flinders University, Bedford Park, South Australia, senior lecturer, 1970-71, reader, 1972-74, professor of English, 1974—. Great Lakes seaman, seasonally, 1947-61, wheelsman, 1951-61. *Member:* English Association, Australian Universities Language and Literature Association, Federation of Australian University Staff Associations, Australasian Victorian Studies Association, William Morris Society. *Awards, honors:* Canada Council fellow, 1968-69.

WRITINGS: (Editor) *The Unpublished Lecturers of William Morris,* Wayne State University Press, 1969. Writer of programs for education stations in Detroit and Windsor, for the Canadian Broadcasting Corporation, and the Australian Broadcasting Commission. Contributor of articles to *Southern Review.* Co-editor, *Southern Review,* 1977—.

WORK IN PROGRESS: A critical study of Jane Austen emphasizing the importance of her religious belief.

* * *

LENNON, Sister M. Isidore 1901-

PERSONAL: Born August 6, 1901, in Ireland; daughter of John (a farmer) and Brigid (Phelan) Lennon. *Education:* Doctor Steeven's Hospital, Dublin, Ireland, R.N., 1925; St. Louis University, B.S., 1933, M.A., 1934, M.S.W., 1949, certificate in hospital administration, 1967. *Home and office:* St. John's Mercy Medical Center, 615 South New Ballas Rd., St. Louis, Mo. 63141.

CAREER: Roman Catholic nun of Order of Religious Sisters of Mercy; St. John's Hospital, St. Louis, Mo., supervisor of medical and surgical departments, 1934-39, director of nurses, 1939-45, director of outpatient and social services departments, 1945-61, assistant administrator and member of board of directors, 1961-64, administrator of St. John's

Mercy Hospital, 1964-69, president of board of directors at St. John's Mercy Medical Center, 1964-69, director of community relations and development, 1969—, instructor in sociology at School of Nursing, 1939-64. St. Louis University, instructor in nursing, 1935-39, guest lecturer in hospital administration, 1949-62, chairman of planning committee for Institute of Hospital Administration, 1949; instructor in sociology, Mercy Junior College—Frontenac, 1962-64; guest lecturer in hospital administration, Washington University, 1968-70. Member of board of directors, Child Center of Our Lady of Grace, 1947-60; member of board of governors, Catholic Charities of St. Louis (now Cardinal Ritter Institute), 1940—; member of corporate board of St. Louis Blue Cross, 1964-72; member of advisory board of Forest Park Community College and Life Seekers, 1965—; member of Missouri State Board of Nursing, 1966-71; chairman of board of directors, St. Elizabeth's Hospital. Member of planning committee: Institute on Hospital Administration at Our Lady of Cincinnati College (now Edgecliffe College), 1950; Institute on Operating Room and Dietary Service Administration at Mount St. Agnes College (now Loyola College), 1951; Mid-Continent Regional Institute, 1962-63; member of committee on functions of social work section in Health and Hospital Division of St. Louis Social Planning Council, 1956-57; member of advisory committee on care of the indigent of Missouri Division of Health, 1959-75; member of generalate commission on health and welfare of Sisters of Mercy of the Union, 1967-71; member of advisory committee, Forest Park Community College, 1964—, and Gordon A. Friesen International Associates, 1966-70; member of nominating committee, St. Louis League for Nursing, 1964-65.

MEMBER: Association of American Medical Colleges Public Relations Group, National League of Nursing, American College of Hospital Administrators (fellow), Public Relations Society of America, Royal Society for the Promotion of Health, Missouri Association of Social Welfare, Hospital Association of Metropolitan St. Louis (member of board of directors, 1964-69). *Awards, honors:* Missouri Federation of Business and Professional Women's Club award, 1966, for outstanding work in the health field; community service award from Hospital Association of Metropolitan St. Louis for outstanding success in meeting emergency treatment needs of St. Louis county residents in the tornado of January 24, 1967; Creve Coeur Squires membership, 1971, for community service in the health field.

WRITINGS: Professional Adjustments for Students of Nursing, Mosby, 1946, 3rd edition, 1959; *Sociology and Social Problems in Nursing,* Mosby, 1951, 3rd edition, 1959; *Teaching in the Outpatient Department,* Putnam, 1954; *Mother Catherine McAuley: A Great Social Worker,* Mulligan, 1954; *Milestones of Mercy: A Story of the Sisters of Mercy in St. Louis—1956,* Bruce, 1957; *St. John's Mercy: The Evolution of a Medical Center in St. Louis, 1871-1971,* Khoury Press, 1972; *Prayers and Reflections for Patients and Personnel in Burn Centers,* St. Charles, 1977.

Contributor to *New Catholic Encyclopedia* and to nursing and church publications, including *Hospital Topics, Modern Hospital, Hospitals, Hospital Management, Hospital Progress,* and *Catholic Nurse.* Member of editorial board, *Davis Nursing Survey,* 1935-36.

BIOGRAPHICAL/CRITICAL SOURCES: St. Louis Review, July 31, 1964; *St. Louis Post Dispatch,* February 13, 1968, March 3, 1971; *Community Press* (Creve Coeur), May 19, 1971.

LERNER, I. Michael 1910-

PERSONAL: Born May 15, 1910, in Harbin, China; came to United States in 1933; naturalized, 1942; son of Michael (a merchant) and Cecelia (Sudja) Lerner; married Ruth Stuart, June 9, 1937. *Education:* University of British Columbia, B.S.A., 1931, M.S.A., 1932; University of California, Ph.D., 1936. *Politics:* Democrat. *Home:* 2507 Rose Walk, Berkeley, Calif. 94708.

CAREER: University of California, Berkeley, instructor, 1936-41, assistant professor, 1941-46, associate professor, 1946-51, professor of poultry husbandry, 1951-58, professor of genetics, 1958-73, professor emeritus, 1973—, chairman of genetics department, 1958-63. Research geneticist, Institute for Personality Assessment and Research, 1970-76. *Member:* National Academy of Science, American Philosophical Society, American Academy of Arts and Sciences (fellow), Permanent International Committee on Genetics (secretary, 1953-58), Genetics Society of America, Eugenics Society (fellow), American Genetic Association, Society for Behavior Genetics, Evolution Society, American Society of Naturalists (vice president, 1957). *Awards, honors:* Belling Prize of University of California, 1940; Borden Award, 1951; Weldon Medal of Oxford University, 1969; Mendel Medal of Czechoslavakia Academy of Science, 1965; honorary D.Sc. from University of British Columbia, 1962, University of Edinburgh, 1973; recipient of three Guggenheim fellowships; fellow of Center for Study in Behavioral Sciences, Stanford University.

WRITINGS: Population Genetics and Animal Improvement, Cambridge University Press, 1950; *Genetic Homeostasis,* Oliver & Boyd, 1954; *Genetic Basis of Selection,* Wiley, 1958; (with Hugh P. Donald) *Modern Developments in Animal Breeding,* Academic Press, 1966; *Heredity, Evolution, and Society,* W. H. Freeman, 1968, 2nd edition (with W. J. Libby), 1976; (translator and editor) *Rh. A. Medvedev: The Rise and Fall of T. D. Lysenko,* Columbia University Press, 1969. Editor of *Evolution,* 1959-61.

WORK IN PROGRESS: A primer of human behavior genetics.†

*   *   *

LESLIE, Roy F. 1922-

PERSONAL: Born May 9, 1922, in Milngavie, Dumbartonshire, Scotland; married Erika Froehlich, June, 1946; children: Adrian, Malcolm. *Education:* University of Manchester, B.A. (first class honors), 1949, M.A., 1951, Ph.D., 1955. *Office:* Department of English, University of Victoria, Victoria, British Columbia, Canada.

CAREER: University of Manchester, Manchester, England, assistant lecturer, 1950-53, lecturer, 1953-60, senior lecturer in English, 1960-64; University of Wisconsin—Madison, visiting professor of English, 1964-65, professor of English, 1965-68; University of Victoria, Victoria, British Columbia, professor of English, 1968—, head of department, 1968-73. *Military service:* Royal Air Force, 1940-46. *Member:* Modern Language Association of America, Modern Humanities Research Association, Association of Canadian University Teachers of English, Humanities Association of Canada, International Platform Association, Philological Society, International Arthurian Society, Mediaeval Academy of America, American Association of University Professors, Association of Departments of English, Canadian Association of University Teachers, Early English Text Society, Lancashire Dialect Society, Mediaeval Association of the Pacific, National Geographic Society, National Travel Club. *Awards, honors:* Canada Council fellow, 1973-74.

WRITINGS: Three Old English Elegies: The Wife's Lament, The Husband's Message, and The Ruin, Barnes & Noble, 1961, revised edition, 1966; (with G. L. Brook) *Layamon's Brut,* Early English Text Society, 1963; *The Wanderer: An Edition of an Old English Elegiac Poem,* Barnes & Noble, 1966, revised edition, 1969. Contributor to academic journals.

WORK IN PROGRESS: Volume II of *Layamon's Brut,* for Early English Text Society; editions of Old English shorter poems and of the epic poem, ''Beowulf''; a contribution to a collection of articles on medieval English literature, to be edited by Beryl Rowland, and one for a volume of medieval studies in English to be published by Medieval Institute, Toronto.†

*   *   *

LESNOFF-CARAVAGLIA, Gari

PERSONAL: Born in Russellton, Pa.; daughter of Igor and Mavra (Sashilkina) Lesnoff; divorced; children: D. Alexander, Silvana Alexandra. *Education:* University of California, Los Angeles, Ph.D., 1970. *Office:* Gerontology Program, Sangamon State University, Springfield, Ill. 62708.

CAREER: Sangamon State University, Springfield, Ill., assistant professor of philosophy and education, 1970-76, associate professor of gerontology, 1976—, director of gerontology program, 1977—. Adjunct professor, Southern Illinois University School of Medicine, 1977. *Member:* Philosophy of Education Society, American Association of University Professors, Midwest Philosophy of Education Society, Foundation of Thanatology, Institute of Society, Ethics, and the Life Sciences, Geriatrics Society, Gerontological Society, Pi Lambda Theta.

WRITINGS: Education as Existential Possibility, Philosophical Library, 1972; *Perspectives on Aging,* Whitehall, 1976; *Health Care of the Elderly: Strategies for Prevention and Intervention,* Human Sciences Press, 1979. Contributor of articles to *School and Community, Educational Forum, U.C.L.A. Educator, Gerontologist, International Journal of Aging and Human Development, Clearinghouse, Journal of Thought,* and other periodicals in her field.

*   *   *

LEV, Daniel S(aul) 1933-

PERSONAL: Born October 23, 1933, in Youngstown, Ohio; son of Louis (a carpenter) and Bessie (Gessen) Lev; married Arlene Offenhender (a painter), March 22, 1958; children: Claire Ellen, Louis Benjamin George. *Education:* Miami University, Oxford, Ohio, B.A., 1955; Cornell University, Ph.D., 1964. *Home:* 936 12th Ave. E., Seattle, Wash. 98102. *Office:* Department of Political Science, University of Washington, Seattle, Wash. 98105.

CAREER: Ford Foundation in Djakarta, Indonesia, assistant to representative, 1961; Cornell University, Ithaca, N.Y., lecturer in political science, 1963; University of California, Berkeley, assistant professor of political science, 1965-70; University of Washington, Seattle, associate professor, 1970-74, professor of political science, 1974—. Conducted field research in Indonesia and Southeast Asia, 1959-61, 1964, 1967, 1968, 1971-72. *Member:* American Political Science Association, Association for Asian Studies.

WRITINGS: The Transition to Guided Democracy (monograph), Modern Indonesia Project, Cornell University,

1966; (contributor) P. Seabury and A. Wildavsky, editors, *U.S. Foreign Policy Perspectives and Proposals for the 1970's*, McGraw, 1969; *Islamic Courts in Indonesia: A Study in the Political Bases of Legal Institutions*, University of California Press, 1972; (contributor) Claire Holt, editor, *Culture and Politics in Indonesia*, Cornell University Press, 1972. Contributor of about ten articles to professional journals, including *American Journal of Comparative Law, Comparative Studies in Society and History, United Asia, Asian Survey, Foreign Service Bulletin, Asia, Journal of Southeast Asian History,* and *Pacific Affairs*.

WORK IN PROGRESS: Research on social and political bases of legal systems and comparative political systems.

*   *   *

LEVEN, Charles L(ouis) 1928-

PERSONAL: Born May 2, 1928, in Chicago, Ill.; son of Elie H. (an insurance salesman) and Ruth (Reinach) Leven; married Judith Danoff, September 10, 1950 (divorced, 1968); married Dorothy Wish, December 31, 1970; children: (first marriage) Ronald L., Robert M., Carol E.; (second marriage) Philip W., Alice S. *Education:* Attended Illinois Institute of Technology, 1945, 1946-47, and University of Illinois, 1947-48; Northwestern University, B.S. (with honors), 1950, M.A., 1957, Ph.D., 1958. *Home:* 7042 Delmar, St. Louis, Mo. 63130. *Office:* Department of Economics, Washington University, St. Louis, Mo. 63130.

CAREER: Federal Reserve Bank of Chicago, Chicago, Ill., research assistant, 1949-51, economist, 1951-56; Iowa State University of Science and Technology, Ames, assistant professor of economics, 1957-59; University of Pennsylvania, Philadelphia, assistant professor of economics and regional science, 1959-62; University of Pittsburgh, Pittsburgh, Pa., associate professor of economics, 1962-65, associate director of Center for Regional Economic Studies, 1963-65; Washington University, St. Louis, Mo., professor of economics, 1965—, chairman of faculty of urban and regional science, 1965-69, director of Institute for Urban and Regional Studies, 1965—, chairman of economics department, 1975—. Visiting professor, University of California, Los Angeles, 1961; special lecturer, Brookings Institution, 1966-76. Member of regional economics advisory committee, U.S. Department of Commerce, 1963; member of advisory committee on small area data, U.S. Bureau of Census, 1965-70; member of research advisory group, Regional Economic Development Institute, 1965-68; chairman of economic advisory committee, St. Louis Regional Industrial Development Corp., 1969-74. Consultant to industry and to public and private groups, including Army Corps of Engineers, 1967—, Planning and Development Cooperative International, 1970, Puerto Rico Planning Board, 1970, and Municipality of Anchorage, 1977. *Military service:* U.S. Navy, 1945-46.

MEMBER: American Economic Association, Regional Science Association (president, 1963-64), Southern Economic Association, Western Regional Science Association (councillor, 1969-72; president, 1973-74), Mid-Continent Regional Science Association. *Awards, honors:* Social Science Research Council grant, 1960; Committee on Urban Economics grants, 1965, 1966; National Science Foundation grants, 1968, 1975.

WRITINGS: Theory and Method of Income and Product Accounts for Metropolitan Area: Including the Elgin-Dundee Area as a Case Study, Center for Regional Economic Studies, University of Pittsburgh, 1963; *Development Benefits of Water Resource Investments,* Institute for Water

Resources, U.S. Army Corps of Engineers, 1969; (with John Legler and Perry Shapiro) *An Analytical Framework for Regional Development Policy,* M.I.T. Press, 1970; (editor with M. Perlman and B. Chinitz) *Spatial, Regional, and Population Economics: Essays in Honor of Edgar M. Hoover,* Gordon & Breach, 1972; (with J. Little, H. Nourse, and R. Read) *Neighborhood Change: Lessons in the Dynamics of Urban Decay,* Praeger, 1976; (editor) *The Mature Metropolis,* Heath, 1978.

Contributor: Werner Hochwald, editor, *Design of Regional Accounts,* Johns Hopkins Press, 1961; *Economic Study of the Pittsburgh Region,* Volume III: *Region with a Future,* University of Pittsburgh Press, 1963; John Friedmann and William Alonso, editors, *Regional Development and Planning,* M.I.T. Press, 1964; Werner Hirsch, editor, *Studies in Regional Accounts,* Johns Hopkins Press, 1964; Paul Davidson and Eugene Smolensky, editors, *Aggregate Demand and Supply Analysis,* Harper, 1964; Earl Heady, editor, *Research and Education for Regional and Area Development,* Iowa State University Press, 1965; *Lectures on Water Management,* Johns Hopkins University Press, 1965; *Urban Development Models,* Highway Research Board, National Academy of Science, 1968; Lionel Needleman, editor, *Regional Economics,* Penguin, 1968; R. P. Misra, editor, *Regional Planning,* University of Mysore (India), 1969; *Information Systems for Regional Development,* Lund Studies in Geography, 1971; *Urban and Social Economics in Market and Planned Economies,* Praeger, 1974; *Regional Sociology and Regional Planning,* Mouton, 1977; *Internal Migrations: A Comparative Perspective,* Academic Press, 1977. Contributor of about twenty articles to scholarly journals.

WORK IN PROGRESS: Dynamics of Neighborhood Change; Metropolitan Change and Development.

SIDELIGHTS: Charles Leven told *CA:* "Most of what I have to write is fairly technical. At the same time, I try to make what I have to say as clear as possible to non-professionals since I believe that academic scholarship . . . [has] something of importance to contribute to practical problems of today. It should be conceded that professional economists . . . are probably much better at asking than [at] answering questions, but perhaps taking the question in the right way may be more of a practical contribution than is commonly supposed."

*   *   *

LEVI, Hans 1935-

PERSONAL: Born July 20, 1935, in Mainz, Germany; son of Curt Bruno (a shoe manufacturer) and Edith (Isselbacher) Levi; married Jane Goralnik, August 23, 1963; children: Margaret Alexandra. *Education:* Washington University, St. Louis, Mo., B.S.B.A., 1957; California College of Arts and Crafts, graduate study, 1969-70; California State University, San Francisco (now San Francisco State University), M.A., 1972. *Home:* 3 Cardigan Lane, St. Louis, Mo. 63135. *Office:* St. Louis Community College at Florissant Valley, 3400 Pershall Rd., St. Louis, Mo. 63137.

CAREER: Krone Business Systems, St. Louis, Mo., president, 1963-68; St. Louis Community College at Meramic, St. Louis, instructor in photography, beginning 1972; currently affiliated with St. Louis Community College at Florissant Valley, St. Louis. *Military service:* U.S. Army, 1957.

WRITINGS: Street Jesus (photographs and text), Scrimshaw Press, 1972.

WORK IN PROGRESS: Photographing American mammals as they exist in the 1970's (including humans).

BIOGRAPHICAL/CRITICAL SOURCES: St. Louis Post Dispatch, November 21, 1971.

* * *

LEVINE, Isidore N. 1909-1972

PERSONAL: Born January 19, 1909, in Odessa, Russia; naturalized U.S. citizen; son of Aaron (a salesman) and Yetta (Nicholsberg) Levine; married Rose Goodman, October 11, 1932; children: Frances, Marian. *Education:* City College of New York (now City College of the City University of New York), B.S., 1930, M.S., 1932; graduate study at Columbia University and Brooklyn College of the City University of New York. *Home:* 33-47 14th St., Long Island City, N.Y. 11106. *Office:* Department of English, Bryant High School, 48-10 31st Ave., Long Island City, N.Y. 11103.

CAREER: Bushey Shipyards, Brooklyn, N.Y., welder, 1942-46; teacher of English in New York public schools, 1946-72, Bryant High School, Long Island City, N.Y., teacher of English, 1958-72. *Member:* International Reading Association, National Council of Teachers of English, Modern Language Association of America, Conference on College Composition and Communication, American Studies Association, New York State English Council, New York Society for the Experimental Study of Education, New York City Association of Teachers of English, Queensborough Council of Reading (president, 1967-69).

WRITINGS: (With Rinaldo C. Simonini, Jr. and Lionel R. Sharp) *English 11- Composition and Language,* Ginn, 1968; (contributor) Walter Petty, editor, *Issues and Problems in Elementary School Language Arts,* Allyn & Bacon, 1968; (contributor) Robert Karlin, editor, *Teaching Reading in High Schools: Selected Articles,* Bobbs-Merrill, 1969; (contributor) Arthur Olson and Walter Ames, editors, *Teaching Reading Skills in Secondary Schools: Readings,* Intext, 1970; (contributor) Roger Cayer, Jerome Green, and Elmer Baker, Jr. editors, *Listening and Speaking in the English Classroom: A Collection of Readings,* Macmillan, 1971; (contributor) Esther Hamon, editor, *Rhetorical Tactics,* Wiley, 1972. Contributor to *Elementary English, High Points, Journal of Reading, Education Digest, Minnesota Reading Quarterly,* and *English Record.* Editor of *N.Y.C.A.T.E. Newsletter,* 1967-70, 1972, and *Queensborough Council of Reading Newsletter,* 1964-72.

WORK IN PROGRESS: Quantity Reading; History of Education in the Classroom.††

(Died November 12, 1972)

* * *

LEVIS, Donald J(ames) 1936-

PERSONAL: Born September 19, 1936, in Cleveland, Ohio; married Jean Chambers, June 19, 1965; children: Brian. *Education:* John Carroll University, B.S.S., 1958; Kent State University, M.A., 1960; Emory University, Ph.D., 1964. *Office:* Department of Psychology, State University of New York, Binghamton, N.Y. 13901.

CAREER: Lafayette Clinic, Laboratory of Psychobiology, Detroit, Mich., research psychologist, 1965-66; University of Iowa, Iowa City, assistant professor, 1966-70, associate professor of psychology, 1970-72, director of research and training clinic, 1970-72; State University of New York at Binghamton, professor of psychology and director of clinical

training, 1972—. *Military service:* U.S. Army Reserve, Medical Specialists Corps, 1958-66; became captain. *Member:* American Psychological Association, American Association for the Advancement of Science, Psychonomic Society, Association for the Advancement of the Behavioral Therapies, Corresponding Committee of Fifty, Midwestern Psychological Association, Sigma Xi.

WRITINGS: Learning Approaches to Therapeutic Behavior Modification, Aldine, 1970; (with T. G. Stampfl) *Implosive Therapy,* General Learning Press, 1973. Author of "Fighting Fear with Fear," a film for Columbia Broadcasting System, 1968.

* * *

LEVITINE, George 1916-

PERSONAL: Name legally changed; born March 17, 1916, in Kharkov, Russia; came to United States in 1942, naturalized in 1943; son of Joseph and Maria (Arlozorof) Levitin; married Eda Mezer (a professor of French), December 2, 1944; children: Elizabeth M. Bucuvalas, Denise Y., Annette M. *Education:* University of Paris, Baccalaureat (lettres), 1936, P.C.B., 1938; Boston University, M.A., 1946; Harvard University, Ph.D., 1952. *Home:* 420 Pershing Dr., Silver Spring, Md. 20910. *Office:* Department of Art, University of Maryland, College Park, Md. 20742.

CAREER: Boston University, Boston, Mass., instructor, 1949-53, assistant professor, 1953-56, associate professor, 1956-59, professor of art, 1959-1964; University of Maryland, College Park, professor of art, 1964—, head of department, 1964—. Member of faculty of Harvard University Extension, 1959-64; member, Maryland Governor's Council of Arts, 1967—. *Military service:* French Army, 1939-41; U.S. Army, 1942-45; became second lieutenant. *Member:* College Art Association, American Society for Aesthetics, National Society for Literature and the Arts. *Awards, honors:* American Council of Learned Societies grant, 1961; American Philosophical Society grant, 1974; National Endowment for the Humanities fellow at Institute for Advanced Study, 1977-78.

WRITINGS: The Sculpture of Falconet, New York Graphic Society, 1972; (with Melinda Curtis) *Search for Innocence* (essay by Levitine, text and catalogue by Curtis), University of Maryland Art Gallery, 1975; *Girodet-Trioson: An Iconographical Study,* Garland Publishing, 1978; *The Dawn of Bohemianism,* Pennsylvania State University Press, 1978. Contributor of articles to *Warburg Journal, Art Bulletin, Gazette des Beaux-Arts, Burlington Magazine.* Editor-in-chief, Art Gallery publications of University of Maryland. Guest editor of *Comparative Literature Studies,* 1968; book review editor of *College Art Journal,* 1971—.

WORK IN PROGRESS: French Pre-Romanticism.

* * *

LEVITT, Morris J(acob) 1938-

PERSONAL: Born June 11, 1938, in New York, N.Y.; son of Harold and Mary (Rosenblatt) Levitt. *Education:* Pace College (now University), B.A., 1960; University of North Carolina, M.A., 1962; University of Maryland, Ph.D., 1965. *Residence:* College Park, Md. *Office:* Department of Political Science, Howard University, Washington, D.C. 20059.

CAREER: University of Maryland, College Park, lecturer in political science, 1965; Howard University, Washington, D.C., assistant professor, 1965-70, associate professor, 1970-74, professor of political science, 1974—, director of

Citizenship Project, 1965-66. *Member:* American Political Science Association, National Municipal League, Southern Political Science Association, National Capital Area Political Science Association (secretary-treasurer, 1967-69; vice-president, 1970-72; president, 1972-74).

WRITINGS: (With Eleanor Feldbaum) *State and Local Government and Politics,* Dryden Press, 1973. Editor, *CAPSULE* (of National Capitol Area Political Science Association), 1975—. Contributor to *Encyclopedia Americana Annual.* Contributor to *American Political Science Review, Journal of Politics, Social Forces, Journal of Human Relations, Journal of Voluntary Action Research, Teaching Political Science, Social Studies,* and *Simulations and Games.*

* * *

LEVY, David W(illiam) 1937-

PERSONAL: Born May 6, 1937, in Chicago, Ill.; son of Roy A. (a newspaperman) and Helen (Loeffler) Levy; married Lynne Hunt, September 7, 1969; children: Beth Ellen, Benjamin Robert. *Education:* University of Illinois, A.B., 1959; University of Chicago, M.A., 1961; University of Wisconsin, Ph.D., 1967. *Politics:* Democrat. *Religion:* Jewish. *Home:* 914 Hoover St., Norman, Okla. 73069. *Office:* Department of History, University of Oklahoma, Norman, Okla. 73019.

CAREER: Ohio State University, Columbus, instructor in history, 1964-67; University of Oklahoma, Norman, assistant professor, 1967-71, associate professor of history, 1971—. *Member:* Organization of American Historians, American Studies Association, Phi Alpha Theta, Phi Beta Kappa. *Awards, honors:* Danforth teaching associate, 1971.

WRITINGS: (Editor with Melvin I. Urofsky) *The Letters of Louis D. Brandeis,* State University of New York Press, Volume I, 1971, Volume II, 1972, Volume III, 1973, Volume IV, 1975, Volume V, 1978. Contributor of articles and reviews to *Phylon, Journal of Thought, New Republic, Oklahoma Law Review, Wisconsin Magazine of History, Mid-America, Indiana Magazine of History,* and other journals.

WORK IN PROGRESS: The Life and Thought of Herbert Croly, completion expected in 1979.

* * *

LEVY, Isaac Jack 1928-

PERSONAL: Born December 21, 1928, in Rhodes, Italy (island now Greek territory); son of Jack (a merchant) and Catherine (Musafir) Levy; married Judy Ann Bearsch (an elementary teacher), 1960; children: Catherine Ann, Michael Jack. *Education:* Attended Brooklyn College (now Brooklyn College of the City University of New York), 1948; Emory University, B.A., 1957; University of Iowa, M.A., 1959; University of Michigan, Ph.D., 1966. *Religion:* Jewish. *Home:* 4040 Rockbridge Rd., Columbia, S.C. 29206. *Office:* Department of Foreign Languages and Literatures, University of South Carolina, Columbia, S.C. 29208.

CAREER: University of South Carolina, Columbia, assistant professor, 1963-68, associate professor, 1968-73, professor of Spanish, 1973—, chairman of Division of Spanish and Portuguese, 1972-74, head of department of foreign languages and literatures, 1975-77. Visiting instructor at Purdue University, summer, 1961, and Texas Technological College (now Texas Tech University), summer, 1963. *Military service:* U.S. Army, Signal Corps, 1948-49, 1950-52.

MEMBER: American Association of Teachers of Spanish and Portuguese, Modern Language Association of America (secretary, Sephardic studies section, 1972), American Society of Sephardic Studies (founder; executive secretary-treasurer, 1967-72), American Association of University Professors, South Atlantic Modern Language Association, Southeastern Conference on Latin American Studies, South Carolina Conference of Foreign Language Teachers (founder; president, 1970-71), Phi Sigma Iota, Sigma Delta Pi, Alpha Mu Gamma. *Awards, honors:* Research grant from Lucius N. Littauer Foundation for travel in Turkey and Israel, 1968; Order of Don Quixote, Sigma Delta Pi, 1968.

WRITINGS: Sephardic Ballads and Songs in the United States, limited edition, privately printed, 1959; *Prolegomena to the Study of the "Refranero Sefardi,"* Las Americas, 1969. Co-author of elementary Spanish text for Columbia schools, *Entre amigos.* Contributor of articles and reviews to *Southern Israelite* and to language and education journals. Editor and contributor, "American Society of Sephardic Studies" Series I, 1969, Series II, 1973. Director and editor, *Hispanic Studies,* 1974—.

WORK IN PROGRESS: Two books, *The Music of the Spanish Jews* and *The "Romancero" Sephardi;* a series of articles on folklore and the Spanish Jews.

SIDELIGHTS: Isaac Jack Levy has traveled extensively and lived in Tangiers for five years.

* * *

LEWIS, David 1922-

PERSONAL: Born January 24, 1922, in Southampton, England; came to United States in 1963; son of Neville (a painter) and Theodosia (Townshend) Lewis; married Patricia Ann Mills, December, 1968; children: An, Sam. *Education:* Attended University of Capetown, 1940-42; University of Leeds, D.A. (distinction), 1961. *Office:* Urban Design Associates, 249 North Craig St., Pittsburgh, Pa. 15213.

CAREER: Chartered architect in Great Britain; registered architect in Pennsylvania, Indiana, New York, Ohio, and Massachusetts; co-founder and partner of Neo-Vision, 1956, and Design Collaborative, 1956-64; Urban Design Associates, Pittsburgh, Pa., founder and partner, 1964—. Lecturer at British universities in Cambridge, Exeter, Durham, Sheffield, Leeds, and Liverpool, 1954-60, and at universities and schools throughout the United States; senior architect, City of Leeds, 1962-63; Andrew Mellon Professor of Architecture and Urban Design, Carnegie-Mellon University, 1963-68; Yale University, visiting critic in urban design and architecture, 1968-70, William Henry Bishop Visiting Professor, 1975, 1977; visiting professor of urban design, Ohio State University, 1978. Exhibitor, International Union of Architects (London), 1962; American correspondent, *Architectural Design,* 1963-70; director, Leadership Training Institute on School Administration, 1968-70. Member of board of directors of Pittsburgh History and Landmarks Foundation, 1967—; Pittsburgh Council for the Arts, 1968-70, and Gallery for Contemporary Arts (Pittsburgh), 1969-70. *Military service:* South African Naval Forces, 1942-44.

MEMBER: American Institute of Architects (corporate member; chairman of national committee for urban planning and design), American Institute of Planners, Royal Institute of British Architects (associate), Architectural Association (London), Royal Society of the Arts (London; fellow), Penwith Society of the Arts (England; founding member and director, 1951), South African Association of Art (national secretary, 1944). *Awards, honors:* Gertrude Page Award from Society of Authors, 1952; Louis Aaron fellowship in architecture, 1961-63; first national award, *House and Home*, 1963.

WRITINGS: End and Beginning, Constantia, 1945; *The Naked Eye*, Paul Keston, 1946; *Piet Mondrian*, Faber, 1956; (contributor) F. Felice, coordinator, *The Schoolhouse in the City*, School Planning Laboratory, Stanford University, 1956; *Constantin Brancusi*, Alex Tiranti, 1957, revised edition, St. Martin's, 1975.

(With Hansmartin Bruckmann) *New Housing in Great Britain*, Universe Books, 1961; *The Pedestrian in the City*, Van Nostrand, 1966; *Urban Structure*, Wiley, 1968; (contributor) Sol Tax, editor, *The People versus the System*, Acme Press, 1968; (contributor) R. F. Campbell, L. A. Marx, and R. L. Nystrand, editors, *Education and Urban Renaissance*, Wiley, 1968; (contributor) Kurt Baier and Nicholas Rescher, editors, *Values and the Future*, Free Press, 1969; *The Growth of Cities*, Elek Books, 1971; (with Jules Gregory) *Community Design: By the People*, Process Architecture (Tokyo), 1977; (with Raymond L. Gindroz) *The Olden Triangle*, Pittsburgh History and Landmarks Foundation, 1977. Contributor to *eye: the magazine of the Yale Arts Association, Carnegie Magazine, A I A Journal, Architectural Record*, and other art and architecture journals. Editor of British journals, *Politics and Letters* and *Critic*, 1947-49; editor, *Accent*, 1956.

SIDELIGHTS: David Lewis comments: "I am one of those crazy people who think that aesthetic appreciation is something that every living person has, and that it's not the private property of a self-appointed elite. Not to be pompous about it, but the thrust of my writings, teaching, and my architectural and environmental work—and of those I associate so happily with—is to make sophisticated aesthetic experience part of everyday life, and to release the spontaneous creativeness and sensuous enjoyment of every man."

*   *   *

LEWIS, Peirce F(ee)   1927-

PERSONAL: Born October 26, 1927, in Detroit, Mich.; son of Peirce and Amy (Fee) Lewis; married Felicia Stegeman, February 2, 1952; children: Hugh Gilchrist. *Education:* Albion College, B.A., 1950; University of Michigan, M.A., 1952, Ph.D., 1958; postdoctoral study at University of Washington, Seattle, 1957-58, and Northwestern University, summer, 1962. *Office:* Department of Geography, Pennsylvania State University, 403 Deike Building, University Park, Pa. 16802.

CAREER: University of Michigan, Ann Arbor, map custodian, 1952-53, metropolitan community fellow in urban political geography, 1956-57; U.S. Army Intelligence, Tokyo, geographer, 1953-55; Pennsylvania State University, University Park, assistant professor, 1958-62, professor of geography, 1962—. Visiting lecturer in geography, University of Michigan (extension), summer, 1958, University of Oregon, summer, 1967; research associate with field study of folk architecture of St. Lawrence estuary and Canadian maritime provinces, University of Montreal, summer, 1970; visiting scientist, Association of American Geographers and National Science Foundation, 1969, 1970, 1971; visiting professor, Concordia University, summer, 1976, University of California, Berkeley, 1976-77. Member of traffic commission (State College, Pa.), 1968-70, and planning commission, 1969—; member of board of directors of Pennsylvania Roadside Council, 1969-74; member of Centre Regional Planning

Commission (Centre County), 1972—. *Military service:* U.S. Army, 1945-47; served in U.S.

MEMBER: International Geographical Union, American Geographical Society, Association of American Geographers, Pioneer America Society, State College Literary Club, Phi Beta Kappa, Sigma Xi, Phi Kappa Phi, Omicron Delta Kappa. *Awards, honors:* Fellowships from National Science Foundation, 1957-58, 1960, summer, 1962, all for geological and geographical studies; award from Association of American Geographers, 1960, for presentation of a paper; grants from U.S. Office of Education, 1967-68, 1969, for teacher programs; grant from Association of American Geographers, 1968-69, for studies on diffusion of folk architecture from New England through New York State, 1976-77, for study of the American vernacular landscape; Pennsylvania State University faculty research grants, 1960-73, for geological and geographical studies; national honors award from Association of American Geographers, 1977, for "truly perceptive and eloquent studies of the evolving human scene in America."

WRITINGS: (Contributor) Fred E. Dohrs and Lawrence M. Sommers, editors, *Physical Geography: Selected Readings*, Crowell, 1967; (contributor) John Fraser Hart, editor, *Field Training in Geography* (technical paper), Commission on College Geography, Association of American Geographers, 1968; (contributor) Roger E. Kasperson and Julian Minghi, editors, *The Structure of Political Geography*, Aldine, 1969; (with Kenneth Corey, George Demko, George Schnell, Harold Meyer, and Hart) *The Local Community: A Handbook for Teachers*, Association of American Geographers and Macmillan, 1971; (contributor) Hart, editor, *Regions of the United States*, Harper, 1973; (editor and contributor) *Visual Blight in America*, Association of American Geographers, 1973; (contributor) Robert Secor and others, editors, *Pennsylvania 1776*, Pennsylvania State University Press, 1975; *New Orleans: The Makings*, Ballinger, 1976. Contributor to *Annals of the Association of American Geographers*, and to *Encyclopaedia Britannica*. Contributor of articles and reviews to *Landscape, Smithsonian, Pioneer American, Journal of Architechtural Education, Geographical Review, Public Management, Earth and Mineral Sciences, Pennsylvania Junior Geographer*, and *Professional Geographer*.

*   *   *

LEWIS, Stephen Richmond, Jr.   1939-

PERSONAL: Born February 11, 1939, in Englewood, N.J.; son of Stephen Richmond (a business analyst) and Esther (Magan) Lewis; married Gayle Elizabeth Foster, June 24, 1961; children: Virginia R., Deborah E., Mark S. *Education:* Williams College, B.A., 1960; Stanford University, M.A., 1962, Ph.D., 1963. *Home:* 410 Petersberg Rd., Williamstown, Mass. 01267. *Office:* Department of Economics, Williams College, Williamstown, Mass. 01267.

CAREER: Stanford University, Stanford, Calif., instructor in economics, 1962-63; Pakistan Institute of Development Economics, Karachi, Pakistan, research advisor, 1963-65; Harvard University, Cambridge, Mass., assistant professor of economics, 1965-66; Williams College, Williamstown, Mass., assistant professor, 1966-68, associate professor, 1968-73, professor of economics, 1973-76, Herbert H. Lehman Professor, 1976—, provost of the college, 1968-71, 1973-76. Visiting senior research fellow, Institute for Development Studies, Nairobi, Kenya, 1971-73; economic consultant, Ministry of Finance and Development Planning, government of Botswana, 1977-78. *Member:* American Economic Association, National Tax Association, Phi Beta Kappa. *Awards, honors:* Ford Foundation dissertation fellow, 1962-63.

WRITINGS: (With S. M. Hussain) *Industrialization and Relative Price Changes in Pakistan,* Pakistan Institute of Development Economics, 1966; (contributor) H. M. Southworth and B. F. Johnston, editors, *Agricultural Development and Economic Growth,* Cornell University Press, 1967; *Economic Policy and Industrial Growth in Pakistan,* M.I.T. Press, 1969; *Pakistan: Industrialization and Trade Policy,* Oxford University Press, 1970; (contributor) Bela Balassa and others, editors, *The Structure of Protection in Developing Countries,* Johns Hopkins Press, 1971; *Taxation for Development,* Oxford University Press, 1979. Contributor to *American Economic Review, Journal of Political Economy, Manchester School, Pakistan Development Review,* and *Food Research Institute Studies.*

WORK IN PROGRESS: Research on industrialization and international trade in East Africa; research on economic development in Kenya and Botswana since independence.

*   *   *

LEY, Ralph 1929-

PERSONAL: Born June 17, 1929, in New York, N.Y.; son of William (a paper-maker) and Katharine (Jaeger) Ley; married Teresa Appezzato, March 20, 1966; children: Mary Virginia, John Matthew. *Education:* Attended Cathedral College of the Immaculate Conception, 1947-49; St. Joseph's Seminary and College, Yonkers, N.Y., A.B., 1951; Rutgers University, A.M., 1958, Ph.D., 1963. *Politics:* Democrat. *Religion:* Roman Catholic. *Home:* 207 Elizabeth St., South Bound Brook, N.J. 08880. *Office:* Department of Germanic Languages and Literatures, Rutgers University, 64 College Ave., New Brunswick, N.J. 08903.

CAREER: Rutgers University, New Brunswick, N.J., instructor, 1959-63, assistant professor, 1963-68, associate professor of German, 1968—. *Military service:* U.S. Army, 1953-55. *Member:* International Brecht Society, American Association of University Professors, American Association of Teachers of German, Modern Language Association of America.

WRITINGS: (With Claude Hill) *The Drama of German Expressionism,* University of North Carolina Press, 1960; (editor) *Boell Fuer Zeitgenossen,* Harper, 1970; (contributor) Siegfried Mews, editor, *Studies in German Literature of the Nineteenth and Twentieth Centuries: Festschrift for Frederic E. Coenen,* University of North Carolina Press, 1971; (contributor) Mews and Herbert Knust, editors, *Essays on Brecht: Theatre and Politics,* University of North Carolina Press, 1974; (co-editor and contributor) *Perspectives and Personalities: Studies in Modern German Literature* (honoring Claude Hill), Carl Winter Universitatsverlag (Heidelberg), 1978; *Brecht as Thinker: Studies in Literary Existentialism and Marxism,* Applied Literature Press, in press. Contributor of articles and reviews to *Comparative Literature, Germanic Review, German Quarterly,* and *University of Dayton Review.*

*   *   *

LI, Tze-chung 1927-

PERSONAL: Born February 17, 1927, in China; son of Ken-hsiang (a lawyer) and Yu-hsien (Chang) Li; married In-lan Wang (a librarian), October 21, 1961; children: Lily,

Rose. *Education:* Soochow University, LL.B., 1948; Southern Methodist University, M.C.L., 1957; Harvard University, LL.M., 1958; Columbia University, M.S., 1965; New School for Social Research, Ph.D., 1963. *Home:* 1104 Greenfield, Oak Park, Ill. 60305. *Office:* Graduate School of Library Science, Rosary College, River Forest, Ill. 60305.

CAREER: Ministry of Justice, Taiwan, China, district judge, 1949-51; Ministry of Defence, Taiwan, China, section head, 1951-56; Atlantic Fiscal Corp., New York, N.Y., vice-president, 1960-64; Illinois State University, Normal, assistant professor of library science and assistant librarian, 1965-66; Rosary College, River Forest, Ill., associate professor, 1966-74, professor of library science, 1974—. Visiting professor, National Taiwan University, and Soochow University, 1969; director, National Central Library (Taiwan), 1970-72; chairman, Graduate Institute of Library Science (Taiwan), 1971-72; member of board of directors, Center for American Studies (Taiwan), 1971; president, Chinese-American Educational Foundation, 1969-70.

MEMBER: International Association of Orientalist Librarians (area representative, 1971-76), American Library Association, National Librarians Association, Chinese-American Librarians Association (president, 1974-76; executive director, 1976—), American Association for Chinese Studies, Association of Asian Studies, Organization of Chinese Americans, Chinese Library Association (convenor, 1971-72), American Association of Library Schools. *Awards, honors:* Chinese Government citations, 1963, 1972; Elsie O. and Philip D. Sang award from Rosary College, 1971, for excellence in teaching.

WRITINGS: *Lu-hai-k'ung-chun hsing-fa kai-lun* (title means "A Treatise on Military Criminal Law") Far East, 1955; *A List of Doctoral Dissertations by Chinese Students in the United States: 1961-1964,* Chinese American Educational Foundation, 1969; *Mei-kuo tushu-kuan yeh-wu* (title means "American Librarianship"), Far East, 1972; (with In-lan Wang) *Chung-wen ts'an-k'ao yung-shu* (title means "A Guide to Chinese Reference Books"), Cheng-chung, 1972. Contributor to law and library journals. Executive editor, *Journal of Library and Information Science,* 1975—.

WORK IN PROGRESS: A Guide to the Sources of Information in the Social Sciences.

*   *   *

LIAO, David C. E. 1925-

PERSONAL: Born October 30, 1925, in Foochow, Fukien, China; son of Teng-Chu and Yu-Ping (Wen) Liao; married Margaret Cheng-Cheng Loh, December 27, 1955; children: Peggy En-Tse, Freddy En-Huei, Teddy En-Kuan. *Education:* Fukien Christian University, Foochow, China, B.S., 1946; Fuller Theological Seminary, M.A., 1969, D.Miss., 1977. *Home:* 8826 Woodley Ave., Sepulveda, Calif. 91343. *Office:* Overseas Crusades, Inc., 3033 Scott Blvd., Santa Clara, Calif. 95043.

CAREER: Worked as a national missionary in the Republic of China, 1955-69; Overseas Crusades, Inc., Taipei, Taiwan, national director, 1969-73, missionary, 1974—. Part-time lecturer with China Evangelical Seminary, Taipei, Taiwan, 1971-72. Consultant to Thailand Church Growth Committee, 1977-78. *Member:* Asian Church Growth Society.

WRITINGS: The Unresponsive: Resistant or Neglected?, Moody, 1972; (editor and translator into Chinese) Donald A. McGavran, *Into His Harvest,* Christian Communications

(Hong Kong), 1973; (editor and translator into Chinese) *Every Believer A Noble Vessel,* Christian Communications, 1973. Editor of *T'ung Kung Yueh K'an,* 1966-73.

* * *

LIBRACH, Jan 1904(?)-1973

1904(?)—March 14, 1973; Polish politician, diplomat, and author. Obituaries: *New York Times,* March 16, 1973.

* * *

LICHTHEIM, George 1912-1973
(G. L. Arnold)

1912—April 22, 1973; German-born social historian, authority on Marx, and author. Obituaries: *New York Times,* April 26, 1973.

* * *

LICHTMAN, Celia S(chmukler) 1932-

PERSONAL: Born May 9, 1932, in Brooklyn, N.Y.; daughter of Harry and Rose (Farvelevitch) Schmukler; married Arthur Lichtman (an attorney), February 21, 1965; children: Adam David, Sarah Ann. *Education:* Brooklyn College (now Brooklyn College of the City University of New York), B.A., 1952; New York University, M.A., 1955, Ph.D., 1965. *Religion:* Hebrew. *Home:* 401 Union St., Brooklyn, N.Y. 11231. *Office:* Department of Modern Languages, Long Island University, Brooklyn Center, Brooklyn, N.Y. 11201.

CAREER: Rutgers University, Newark, N.J., instructor in Spanish, 1960-65; Long Island University, Brooklyn, N.Y., assistant professor, 1965-70, associate professor, 1970-77, professor of modern languages, 1977—. Lecturer in School of General Studies, Hunter College of the City University of New York, 1960-67. *Member:* Modern Language Association of America.

WRITINGS: (With Mary Plevich) *Hojas literarias,* three volumes, Litton Educational Publishing, 1972. Contributor to *Garcia Lorca Review.*

WORK IN PROGRESS: Malcolm Lowry and Federico Garcia Lorca: Two Descents into Hell; myth and symbolism section of the complete Federico Garcia Lorca bibliography.

AVOCATIONAL INTERESTS: Foreign travel, classical piano, opera.

* * *

LIEBERMAN, Morton A(lexander) 1931-

PERSONAL: Born May 23, 1931, in New York, N.Y.; son of Samuel Z. and Eva (Yampol) Lieberman; married Grace Levit (a research analyst), February 19, 1956; children: Leslie (a daughter), Daniel, David. *Education:* University of Chicago, Ph.D., 1957. *Religion:* Jewish. *Office:* Department of Psychology, University of Chicago, Chicago, Ill. 60657.

CAREER: University of Chicago, Chicago, Ill., instructor, 1957-58, assistant professor, 1958-64, associate professor, 1964-72, professor of psychiatry and human development, 1973—.

WRITINGS: (With Dorothy Stock Whitaker) *Psychotherapy through the Group Process,* Atherton, 1964; (with Irving D. Yalom and Matthew L. Miles) *Encounter Groups: First Facts,* Basic Books, 1973; (with Sheldon S. Tobin)

Last Home for the Aged: Institutionalization Effects and Their Causes, Jossey-Bass, 1976. Also author of *Crisis and Survival in Old Age,* with Tobin.

WORK IN PROGRESS: Research on aging, group psychotherapy, and on use of groups for personal change.

* * *

LIEBERT, Robert M. 1942-

PERSONAL: Born January 22, 1942, in New York, N.Y. *Education:* Studied at University College, London, 1961-62; Tulane University, B.S., 1963; Stanford University, Ph.D., 1966. *Office:* Department of Psychology, State University of New York, Stony Brook, N.Y. 11790.

CAREER: Vanderbilt University, Nashville, Tenn., assistant professor of psychology, 1966-69; Antioch College, Yellow Springs, Ohio, associate professor of psychology, 1969-70; State University of New York at Stony Brook, associate professor, 1970-73, professor of psychology, 1973—. Senior investigator at Fels Research Institute, 1969-70; visiting lecturer at University of Minnesota, summer, 1970. *Member:* American Psychological Association (fellow), Society for Research in Child Development, Southeastern Psychological Association, Midwestern Psychological Association, Western Psychological Association, Phi Beta Kappa. *Awards, honors:* Woodrow Wilson fellow, 1963-64.

WRITINGS: (With Michael D. Spiegler) *Personality: An Introduction to Theory and Research,* Dorsey, 1970; (editor with Robert A. Baron) *Human Social Behavior: A Contemporary View,* Dorsey, 1971; (with John M. Neale) *Science and Behavior,* Prentice-Hall, 1973; (with Neale and Emily S. Davidson) *The Early Window: Effects of TV on Children and Youth,* Pergamon, 1973; (with R. W. Povlos and G. S. Marmor) *Developmental Psychology,* Prentice-Hall, 1977; (with M. D. Spiegler) *Personality: Strategies and Issues,* Dorsey, 1978.

* * *

LIEDHOLM, Carl (Edward) 1940-

PERSONAL: Born July 22, 1940, in Long Beach, Calif.; son of George and Marian Liedholm. *Education:* Pomona College, B.A., 1961; University of Michigan, Ph.D., 1965. *Home:* 830 Wildwood, East Lansing, Mich. 48823. *Office:* Department of Economics, Michigan State University, East Lansing, Mich. 48823.

CAREER: Michigan State University, East Lansing, assistant professor, 1965-69, associate professor, 1969-72, professor of economics, 1972—, chairman of department, 1970—. Fellow, Economic Growth Center, 1974, and visiting fellow, Sussex University, 1975. Member of Governor's Economic Outlook Panel. *Member:* Nigerian Economic Association, American Economic Association, African Studies Association, Michigan Economic Society, Phi Beta Kappa.

WRITINGS: (With Carl Eicher) *Growth and Development of the Nigerian Economy,* Michigan State University Press, 1970; *The Indian Iron and Steel Industry: An Analysis of Comparative Advantage,* Michigan State University Business and Economic Studies, 1972.

* * *

LINDER, Leslie (?)-1973

(?)—April 4, 1973; British engineer and mathematician, authority and writer on the works of Beatrix Potter. Obituaries: *Publishers Weekly,* June 4, 1973.

LINDER, Robert D(ean) 1933-

PERSONAL: Born October 6, 1933, in Salina, Kan.; son of Orel Andrew and Minnie (Bickel) Linder; married Jean Ann Burch, August 5, 1957; children: Whitney Allison, Gretchen Kassel, Inge Erika, Lincoln Jefferson. *Education:* Kansas State Teachers College, B.S., 1956; Central Baptist Theological Seminary, M.Div., 1958, M.R.E., 1958; University of Iowa, M.A., 1960, Ph.D., 1963; additional study at University of Geneva, 1961, and Oxford University, 1974. *Politics:* Republican. *Home:* 321 North 17th St., Manhattan, Kan. 66502. *Office:* Department of History, Kansas State University, Manhattan, Kan. 66506.

CAREER: William Jewell College, Liberty, Mo., assistant professor of history, 1963-65; Kansas State University, Manhattan, associate professor, 1965-73, professor of history, 1973—. City commissioner of Manhattan, Kan., 1969-73, 1973-79, mayor, 1971-72, 1978-79; member of Riley County (Kansas) Law Enforcement Agency, 1973-75. Member of board of directors of Midwestern Baptist Theological Seminary, 1969—. *Military service:* U.S. Army Reserve, 1957-65, active duty, 1960, 1961-62; became captain.

MEMBER: American Historical Association, Renaissance Society of America, American Society for Reformation Research (member of executive council, 1972—), American Society of Church History, Rocky Mountain Social Science Association, Conference on Faith and History (member of executive committee, 1968-78), Kansas History Teachers Association (member of executive committee, 1971-74), Kiwanis (member, board of directors, 1968-70).

WRITINGS: The Political Ideas of Pierre Viret, Droz, 1964; (editor with R. G. Clouse and R. V. Pierard) *Protest and Politics,* Attic Press, 1968; (with Robert M. Kingdon) *Calvin and Calvinism: Sources of Democracy?,* Heath, 1970; (editor) *God and Caesar: Case Studies in the Relationship between Christianity and the State,* Conference on Faith and History, 1971; (contributor) Jerald C. Brauer, editor, *The Westminster Dictionary of Church History,* Westminster, 1971; (editor with Clouse and Pierard) *The Cross and the Flag,* Creation House, 1972; (contributor) Carl F. Henry, editor, *A Dictionary of Christian Ethics,* Baker Book, 1973; (consulting editor and contributor) Timothy Dowley, editor, *The Eerdmans' Handbook to the History of Christianity,* Eerdmans, 1977; (with Pierard) *Twilight of the Saints: Biblical Christianity and Civil Religion in America,* IV Press, 1978. Contributor to *The New International Dictionary of the Christian Church,* and *Christianity and Politics.* Also contributor of articles to history and religion journals in the United States and abroad. Editor, *Fides et Historia,* 1968-78.

WORK IN PROGRESS: A bibliographical study of works of Pierre Viret; a biography of Pierre Viret; a study of the role of the clergy in politics in Northern Ireland.

AVOCATIONAL INTERESTS: Softball, racquetball, tennis, and travel.

*   *   *

LINDQUIST, John H(enry) 1931-

PERSONAL: Born in 1931, in Chicago, Ill.; son of Andrew R. and Margaret (Edstrom) Lindquist; children: Lynne, Diane, Lorraine, Kathryn. *Education:* Northern Arizona University, B.S., 1956, M.A., 1957; Syracuse University, D.Soc.Sc., 1961. *Home:* 7326 Leading Oaks, San Antonio, Tex. 78233. *Office:* Department of Sociology, Trinity University, San Antonio, Tex. 78284.

CAREER: Teacher of English and social studies in junior and senior high schools, 1956-58; Syracuse University, Syracuse, N.Y., instructor in social sciences, 1960-61; Northern Arizona University, Flagstaff, assistant professor of social science, 1961-65; University of Akron, Akron, Ohio, associate professor of sociology and course director/TV teacher, 1965-70; Trinity University, San Antonio, Tex., associate professor of sociology, 1970—. *Military service:* U.S. Air Force, 1951-53. *Member:* American Sociological Association, National Education Association, American Association of University Professors (past president of Arizona conference; past secretary-treasurer of Ohio conference), Ohio Valley Sociological Association, Phi Kappa Phi, Alpha Kappa Delta, Kappa Delta Phi.

WRITINGS: (Editor with Edward E. Walker, Roy D. Morey, and Donald E. Walker) *Readings in American Public Opinion,* American Book Co., 1968. Contributor to social science, political science, history, education, and law journals. Associate editor of *Sociological Forces,* 1968-69, editor, 1969-73; editorial consultant, Macmillan Co. and Prentice-Hall, Inc.

*   *   *

LINDSEY, Alfred J. 1931-

PERSONAL: Born July 7, 1931, in Macomb, Ill.; son of Alfred and Dorothy Louise (Crain) Lindsey; married Joan Marie, July 22, 1951; children: Alan Lee. *Education:* Western Illinois University, B.S.Ed., 1955, M.S.Ed., 1961; University of Illinois, Ed.D., 1968. *Home:* 236 Jana Rd., Macomb, Ill. 61455. *Office:* Stripes Hall 451, Western Illinois University, Macomb, Ill. 61455.

CAREER: High school teacher in Illinois, 1955-57; automobile dealer in Robinson, Ill., 1957-59; high school and junior college teacher in Illinois, 1960-63; Western Illinois University, Macomb, instructor, 1963-65, assistant professor, 1965-68, associate professor, beginning 1968, currently professor of educational foundations. *Member:* National Council of Teachers of English, Conference on English Education, Illinois Association of Teachers of English, Illinois Conference on English Education.

WRITINGS: (With Arthur Donart) *The Student Speaks Out: A Rhetorical View of Student Writing,* W. C. Brown, 1972. Contributor to project reports, and to education journals, including *Illinois School Research, Illinois Education Review,* and *English Education.*

WORK IN PROGRESS: Teaching High School Youth English; Diagnosis–Prescription–Cure: Teaching Skills to All Children; research on strengths and weaknesses of freshmen writers.†

*   *   *

LINGARD, Joan

PERSONAL: Born in Edinburgh, Scotland. *Education:* Moray House Training College, general teaching diploma. *Home:* 72 Gt. King St., Edinburgh EH3 6QU, Scotland.

CAREER: Teacher and writer.

WRITINGS—Novels; all published by Hodder & Stoughton: *Liam's Daughter,* 1963; *The Prevailing Wind,* 1964; *The Tide Comes In,* 1966; *The Headmaster,* 1967; *A Sort of Freedom,* 1969; *The Lord on Our Side,* 1970.

All published by Nelson, except as indicated: *The Twelfth Day of July,* Hamish Hamilton, 1970; *Across the Barricades,* Hamish Hamilton, 1972; *Into Exile,* 1973; *Frying as*

Usual, 1973; The Clearance, 1974; A Proper Place, 1975; The Resettling, 1976; No Place for Love, Scholastic Book Services, 1976; Hostages to Fortune, 1977; Snake among the Sunflowers, 1977; The Pilgrimage, 1977; The Reunion, 1978. Author of television scripts for Scottish television and British Broadcasting Corp. (Scotland).

WORK IN PROGRESS: An adult novel set in contemporary Edinburgh.

SIDELIGHTS: Joan Lingard and her family moved to Belfast, Northern Ireland when she was very young. She lived in Belfast until she turned eighteen. Lingard told CA: "I began to write because I couldn't get enough to read and I was an avid reader. I was eleven years old and living in Belfast. The choice of books at my local library was poor and the books themselves were in pretty bad shape though I read them, regardless of dirt and smell, until the day came when I had nothing to read at all and so I sat down and wrote my own book, my first book."

*   *   *

LINLEY, John (William)   1916-

PERSONAL: Born June 23, 1916, in Anderson, S.C.; son of John William and Annie (Farmer) Linley. Education: Clemson College (now University), B.S., 1938; Princeton University, M.F.A., 1945. Religion: Presbyterian. Home: 530 Pulaski St., Athens, Ga. 30601. Office: School of Environmental Design, University of Georgia, Athens, Ga. 30601.

CAREER: Architect, in private practice, 1950-51; Linley and Watkins (architects), partner, 1952-63; University of Georgia, Athens, assistant professor, 1963-67, associate professor of architecture, 1967—. Architectural consultant for restoration and preservation of important structures. Member: American Institute of Architects, American Association of University Professors, Association of Collegiate Schools of Architecture. Awards, honors: Chicago Book Clinic Award for general excellence in the bookmaking art, 1972, for Architecture of Middle Georgia: The Oconee Area.

WRITINGS: Architecture of Middle Georgia: The Oconee Area, University of Georgia Press, 1972.

WORK IN PROGRESS: Georgia: Historic American Buildings Survey.

*   *   *

LINTON, Ron(ald) M.   1929-

PERSONAL: Born May 7, 1929, in Detroit, Mich.; son of Louis D. and Lillian (Gordon) Linton; married Nancy Gault, November 5, 1955; children: Cynthia, Victoria. Education: Michigan State University, B.A., 1951. Politics: Democrat. Religion: Unitarian Universalist. Home: 2029 Connecticut N.W., Washington, D.C. 20008. Office: Linton, Mields, Reisler & Cottone, Ltd., 1015 18th St. N.W., Washington, D.C. 20036.

CAREER: Entered newspaper work in 1951, working for United Press in Michigan and Iowa, with papers in Texas, and as labor editor of Courier-Journal, Louisville, Ky.; State of Michigan, Department of Economic Development, Lansing, staff member, 1954-55; State of Michigan, Department of Workmen's Compensation, Lansing, secretary of department, 1955-56; joined the campaign staff of Senator John F. Kennedy in 1960; U.S. Department of Defense, Washington, D.C., director of economic utilization policy, 1961-63; U.S. Senate, Washington, D.C., chief clerk and staff director of Committee on Public Works, 1963-67; U.S. Department of Health, Education and Welfare, Washington, D.C., chairman of secretary's Task Force on Environmental Health and Related Problems, 1966-67; Urban American, Inc., Washington, D.C., director of special projects, 1966-67; National Urban Coalition, Washington, D.C., national coordinator, 1967-68; Linton & Co., Inc., (environmental and urban consultants), Washington, D.C., president, 1968-75, chairman, 1976—; Linton, Mields, Reisler & Cottone, Ltd., Washington, D.C., managing associate, 1976—. Visiting professor, Rensselaer Polytechnic Institute, 1960-70. Executive director, Association of Metropolitan Sewerage Agencies, 1976, and National Association of Urban Flood Management Agencies, 1977.

MEMBER: American Public Health Association, National Urban Coalition (co-founder). Awards, honors: American Political Science Association fellow in Washington, 1959-60.

WRITINGS: Terracide: America's Destruction of Her Living Environment, Little, Brown, 1970. Writer of government research reports.

BIOGRAPHICAL/CRITICAL SOURCES: Saturday Review, May 2, 1970; Smithsonian, June, 1970.

*   *   *

LIPKING, Lawrence (Irwin)   1934-

PERSONAL: Born April 28, 1934, in New York, N.Y.; son of Irving (a prizefighter) and Jean (Hirsohn) Lipking; married Joanna Brizdle, May 23, 1965. Education: Attended Columbia University, 1951-52; Western Reserve University (now Case Western Reserve University), B.A., 1955; Cornell University, M.A., 1956, Ph.D., 1962. Home: 185 Prospect Ave., Princeton, N.J. 08540. Office: Department of English, Princeton University, Princeton, N.J. 08540.

CAREER: Princeton University, Princeton, N.J., 1960—, began as instructor, currently professor of English and comparative literature. Member: Modern Language Association of America, English Institute. Awards, honors: American Philosophical Society grant, 1967; Weslyan Center for the Humanities fellow, 1972; American Council of Learned Societies fellowship, 1972-73; National Endowment for the Humanities fellowship, 1976-77.

WRITINGS: The Ordering of the Arts in Eighteenth-Century England, Princeton, 1970; (editor with A. Walton Litz) Modern Literary Criticism 1900-1970, Atheneum, 1972; (editor) The Norton Anthology of English Literature: 1660-1798, 3rd edition (Lipking was not associated with earlier editions), Norton, 1974, 4th edition, 1979.

WORK IN PROGRESS: The Poet-Critics, a study of relations between poetry and criticism from Horace to the present; The Life of the Poet, a study of poetic careers.

AVOCATIONAL INTERESTS: Chess, writing poetry.

*   *   *

LIPSCHUTZ, Ilse Hempel   1923-

PERSONAL: Born August 19, 1923, in Boennigheim, Germany; naturalized U.S. citizen; daughter of Joseph Martin Paul and Fanny (Wuerzburger) Hempel; married Lewis D. Lipschutz (a research engineer), February 5, 1952; children: Elizabeth, Marion, Marc, Margaret. Education: Sorbonne, University of Paris, IPPFE, 1942, Licence es Lettres, 1943, Diplome d'Etudes Superieures, 1944; Universidad Central (Madrid), Diploma de Estudios Hispanicas, 1945; Harvard University, M.A., 1949, Ph.D., 1958. Politics: Democrat.

Home: 11 Park Ave., Poughkeepsie, N.Y. 12603. *Office:* Department of French, Vassar College, Poughkeepsie, N.Y. 12601.

CAREER: Vassar College, Poughkeepsie, N.Y., instructor, 1951-58, assistant professor, 1958-63, associate professor, 1963-72, professor of French, 1972—, chairman of department, 1975—. Ann Radcliffe fellow, 1950-51. *Member:* American Association of University Professors, American Association of University Women, Societe des Etudes romantiques, Association internationale des Etudes francaises. *Awards, honors:* Fellowship from American Association of University Women, 1950-51.

WRITINGS: Spanish Painting and the French Romantics, Harvard University Press, 1972. Contributor to *Arte Espanol, Nineteenth-Century French Studies,* and *Revista de Occidente.*

WORK IN PROGRESS: Theophile Gautier and Spanish Painting; Goya and Baudelaire.

* * *

LISS, Peggy K(orn) 1927-
(Peggy Korn)

PERSONAL: Born October 3, 1927, in Philadelphia, Pa.; daughter of Joseph (a manufacturer) and Reta (Sickles) Karr; married Stephen J. Korn, June 12, 1949 (divorced, 1971); married Sheldon B. Liss (a professor of history), August 14, 1971; children: (first marriage) Peter David, Margaret Rita. *Education:* Beaver College, B.A., 1961; University of Pennsylvania, M.A., 1962, Ph.D., 1965. *Home:* 134 North Revere Rd., Akron, Ohio 44313.

CAREER: Has worked as a feature writer and public relations representative; Swarthmore College, Swarthmore, Pa., lecturer in history, 1966-70. Visiting lecturer in history, University of Pennsylvania, 1967. Board member, Conference on Latin American History, 1978—. *Member:* American Historical Association, Latin American Studies Association, Committee on Mexican Studies, Conference of Latin American History (executive secretary, 1969-70). *Awards, honors:* Carnegie-Ford Foundation fellowship, 1963-64, to study Latin American nationalism; American Philosophical Society grant, 1970, 1975.

WRITINGS: (Contributor, under name Peggy Korn) Fredrick B. Pike, editor, *Problems in Latin American History,* Harcourt, 1970; (editor with husband, Sheldon B. Liss) *Man, State, and Society in Latin American History,* Praeger, 1972; *Mexico under Spain: Society and the Origins of Nationality, 1521-1556,* University of Chicago Press, 1975. Contributor to *American Historical Review, Hispanic American Historical Review, Americas, Historia Mexicana,* and other journals.

WORK IN PROGRESS: A book on Latin American-United States relations, 1713-1826; a biography of Isabel I.

* * *

LITCHFIELD, Harry R(obert) 1898-1973

1898—May 27, 1973; American pediatrician, educator, and author of books on child and infant care. Obituaries: *New York Times,* May 30, 1973.

* * *

LITTLEFIELD, David Joseph 1928-

PERSONAL: Born August 22, 1928, in Tupper Lake, N.Y.; son of J. Herbert and Julia Grace (Hayes) Littlefield; mar-

ried Jean Johnston, August 25, 1953; children: James Patrick, David J., Jr., Thomas Mark, Christopher Johnston. *Education:* Spring Hill College, A.B., 1951; Yale University, M.A., 1953, Ph.D., 1961. *Home:* R.D. 2, Middlebury, Vt. 05753. *Office:* Department of English, Middlebury College, Middlebury, Vt. 05753.

CAREER: Middlebury College, Middlebury, Vt., instructor, 1953-56, 1959-61, assistant professor, 1961-65, associate professor, 1966-69, professor of English, 1969—, Philip Battell Stewart and Frances Cowles Stewart Professor of English, 1972—. Visiting fellow, Princeton University, 1965-66. Visiting professor, Antioch School of Law, summer, 1976, fall, 1978. *Military service:* U.S. Air Force, 1951-52; became sergeant. *Member:* Modern Language Association of America, American Philosophical Association, Classical Association of New England, Vermont Council on the Humanities and Public Issues (chairman, 1972-76). *Awards, honors:* National Endowment for the Humanities summer seminar fellowship, 1975.

WRITINGS: (Editor) *Twentieth Century Interpretations of "The Frogs": A Collection of Critical Essays,* Prentice-Hall, 1968.

WORK IN PROGRESS: A book on law and drama.

* * *

LITTLEJOHN, David 1937-

PERSONAL: Born May 8, 1937, in San Francisco, Calif.; son of George T. and Josephine (Cullen) Littlejohn; married Sheila Hageman, June 10, 1963; children: Victoria, Gregory David. *Education:* University of California, Berkeley, B.A., 1959; Harvard University, M.A., 1961, Ph.D., 1963. *Home:* 719 Coventry Rd., Kensington, Calif. 94707. *Office:* School of Journalism, University of California, Berkeley, Calif. 94720.

CAREER: University of California, Berkeley, assistant professor of English and journalism, 1963-70, associate professor, 1970-76, professor of journalism, 1976—, associate dean, 1974-78. Critic for KQED, San Francisco, 1965—, and Public Broadcasting Service, 1971-72; Fulbright professor in France, 1966-67. Consultant to Aspen program on communications and society, 1973-75. *Awards, honors:* American Council of Learned Societies fellow in England and France, 1972-73.

WRITINGS: (Editor) *Dr. Johnson: His Life in Letters,* Prentice-Hall, 1965; *Black on White: A Critical Survey of Writing by American Negroes,* Grossman, 1966; *Interruptions* (essays), Viking, 1969; (editor) *Gide: A Collection of Critical Essays,* Prentice-Hall, 1970; (editor) *The Andre Gide Reader,* Knopf, 1971; *Dr. Johnson and Noah Webster: Two Men and Their Dictionaries,* Book Club of California, 1972; *Three California Families,* privately printed, 1976; *The Man Who Killed Mick Jagger* (fiction), Little, Brown, 1977. Author of approximately two hundred TV scripts for Public Broadcasting Service programs. Contributor of over eighty articles and book reviews to journals.

WORK IN PROGRESS: Fiction, journalism, and criticism; miscellaneous articles; two novels on Michelangelo.

* * *

LITVINOFF, Saul 1925-

PERSONAL: Born March 15, 1925, in Buenos Aires, Argentina; son of Abraham and Sara (Lificir) Litvinoff; married Ana Di Chiara (a librarian), August 29, 1955; children: Ana Alejandra. *Education:* University of Buenos Aires,

LL.B., 1949, LL.D., 1956; Yale University, LL.M., 1964. *Home:* 4022 South Ramsey, Baton Rouge, La. 70808. *Office:* Department of Law, Louisiana State University, Baton Rouge, La. 70803.

CAREER: Louisiana State University, Baton Rouge, visiting professor, 1963, associate professor, 1967-70, professor of law, 1970—, director of law center, 1977—. Visiting professor, University of Puerto Rico, 1963. Dean of the Central American Graduate School of Banking, 1974. *Member:* Louisiana State Law Institute.

WRITINGS: Las ventas a plazos en Puerto Rico, Equity de Puerto Rico, 1965; *Obligations,* Volume I, West Publishing, 1969, Volume II, 1975; *Louisiana Legal Transactions,* Claitors, 1969. Also author of "Banking Laws" series, 1973-75.

WORK IN PROGRESS: Third volume of *Obligations.*

* * *

LIU, Leo Yueh-yun 1940-

PERSONAL: Born April 3, 1940, in Canton, China; became Canadian citizen; son of Wei Liu (an army general); married Shirley H. C. Chu, September 23, 1965. *Education:* Law College, National Taiwan University, B.A., 1962; attended New York University, 1964; University of Hawaii, M.A., 1965; University of Western Ontario, M.L.S., 1968; University of Alberta, Ph.D., 1970. *Home:* 16 Lily Bay, Brandon, Manitoba, Canada. *Office:* Department of Political Science, Brandon University, Brandon, Manitoba, Canada.

CAREER: University of Alberta, Edmonton, lecturer in political science, 1970-71; Brandon University, Brandon, Manitoba, assistant professor, 1971-76, associate professor of political science, 1976—.

WRITINGS: China as a Nuclear Power in World Politics, Macmillan (London), 1972; *Wheat Board Advisory Committee Election: A Study of Canada's Participatory Democracy,* Government of Canada, 1976. Contributor of articles to *Asian Affairs, Current History,* and other journals.

WORK IN PROGRESS: Voting Behaviors in Canada and the Military in China.

* * *

LIVELY, Penelope 1933-

PERSONAL: Born March 17, 1933, in Cairo, Egypt; married Jack Lively (a university teacher), June 27, 1957; children: Josephine, Adam. *Education:* St. Anne's College, B.A., 1956. *Home and office:* Duck End, Great Rollright Chipping Norton, Oxfordshire OX7 55B, England. *Agent:* Murray Pollinger, 4 Garrick St., London WC2E 9BH, England.

CAREER: Free-lance writer. *Member:* Society of Authors. *Awards, honors:* Children's Spring Book Festival Award, *Book World,* 1973, for *The Driftway;* Carnegie Medal, 1973, for *The Ghost of Thomas Kempe.*

WRITINGS—Juvenile; all published by Heinemann, except as indicated: *Astercote,* 1970, Dutton, 1971; *The Whispering Knights,* 1971; *The Wild Hunt of the Ghost Hounds,* 1971, Dutton, 1972; *The Driftway,* 1972, Dutton, 1973; *The Ghost of Thomas Kempe* (Junior Literary Guild selection), 1973; (contributor) *My England,* 1973; *The House in Norham Gardens,* Dutton, 1974; *Going Back,* 1975, Dutton, 1976; *A Stitch in Time,* 1976, Dutton, 1977; *Boy Without a Name,* 1976, Parnassus Press, 1977; *The Voyage of QV66,* 1977, Dutton, 1978; *Fanny's Sister,* 1977, Dutton, 1978; *The Road to Lichfield,* 1977; *Nothing Missing but the Samovar,* 1978.

BIOGRAPHICAL/CRITICAL SOURCES: Times Literary Supplement, April 4, 1970; *Spectator,* May 9, 1970; *Books and Bookmen,* May, 1970.

* * *

LOCK, Dennis (Laurence) 1929-

PERSONAL: Born September 15, 1929, in London, England; son of Douglas Leonard and Marjorie (Rouledge) Lock; married Gladys Nancie Shilling, July 11, 1953. *Education:* Acton Technical College, Higher National Certificate in applied physics, 1955. *Politics:* Conservative. *Religion:* Church of England. *Home:* 29 Burston Dr., Park St., St. Albans, Hertfordshire, England. *Office:* Seltrust Engineering Ltd., 57/61 Clerkenwell Rd., London EC1M 5SP, England.

CAREER: General Electric Co., Wembley and Stanmore, England, physicist, 1945-48 and 1950-62; Honeywell Controls Ltd., Hemel Hempstead, England, contracts control manager, 1963-68; Herbert-Ingersoll Ltd., Daventry, England, manager of engineering administrative services, 1968-71; Seltrust Engineering Ltd., London, England, office services manager, 1971—. Consultant. *Military service:* Royal Air Force, 1948-50. *Member:* British Institute of Management, Physical Society (fellow), Writers Guild of Great Britain.

WRITINGS—All published by Gower Press, except as indicated: *Project Management,* Canner, 1968, revised edition, 1977; (editor) *Directors' Guide to Management Techniques,* 1970, revised edition, 1972; *Industrial Scheduling Techniques,* 1971; (editor) *Engineers' Handbook of Management Techniques,* 1973; (editor) *Financial Management Production,* 1975; *Factory Administration Handbook,* 1976.

WORK IN PROGRESS: A book on automation.

AVOCATIONAL INTERESTS: Music, opera, mountain walking.

* * *

LOCKE, David M(illard) 1929-

PERSONAL: Born April 7, 1929, in Escanaba, Mich.; son of Millard Carleton and Catherine (Stephenson) Locke. *Education:* University of Michigan, B.S. (with honors), 1951; University of Illinois, M.S., 1952, Ph.D., 1954; Birkbeck College, London, postdoctoral study, 1954-55. *Home:* 205 Southeast 16th Ave., No. 29F, Gainesville, Fla. 32601. *Office:* Department of English, University of Florida, Gainesville, Fla. 32611.

CAREER: Rockefeller Institute (now Rockefeller University), New York City, research associate in biochemistry, 1956-61; American Chemical Society News Service, New York City, staff writer, 1961-65; University of Chicago, Chicago, Ill., assistant director of public relations, 1965-67; *Encyclopaedia Britannica,* Chicago, associate editor, 1967-71; Illinois Institute of Technology, Chicago, assistant professor of English and assistant director of science information program, 1971-77; University of Florida, Gainesville, assistant professor of English, 1977—.

MEMBER: Modern Language Association of America, American Association for the Advancement of Science, National Association of Science Writers, Society for Technical Communication, National Council of Teachers of English, American Business Communication Association, Phi Beta Kappa, Sigma Xi, Phi Eta Sigma, Phi Kappa Phi, Phi Lambda Upsilon, Alpha Chi Sigma. *Awards, honors:* Fulbright fellowship, University of London, 1954-55.

WRITINGS: (Contributor) Mario Pei, editor, *Language of the Specialists,* Funk, 1966; *Enzymes: The Agents of Life,* Crown, 1969; *Viruses: The Smallest Enemy,* Crown, 1974; *Virus Diseases: A Layman's Handbook,* Crown, 1978. Author of "As of This Day," a three-part television filmscript, for NBC-Television (Chicago). Contributor to *New International Yearbook,* 1962-64. Contributor to chemistry journals and to *Saturday Review.*

* * *

LOEMKER, Leroy E(arl) 1900-

PERSONAL: Born December 28, 1900, in Platteville, Wis.; son of Herman J. (a clergyman) and Sophia (Bergman) Loemker; married Priscilla Warren, October 13, 1928; children: Katharine Warren Loemker Kokomoor, Nancy Sargeant Loemker Isear, Elsa Bergman Loemker Mauger. *Education:* University of Dubuque, A.B., 1921; attended Columbia University, 1921, University of Chicago, 1922, and University of Berlin, 1927-28; Boston University, S.T.B., 1927, Ph.D., 1931. *Politics:* Independent. *Religion:* Christian (Methodist). *Home:* 2925 Willow St., Lakeland, Fla. 33803.

CAREER: University of Dubuque, Dubuque, Iowa, instructor in mathematics, 1921-24; minister of Congregational church in Lowell, Mass., 1928-29; Emory University, Atlanta, Ga., assistant professor, 1929-32, associate professor, 1932-36, professor of philosophy, 1936-55, C. H. Candler Professor, 1955-69, professor emeritus, 1969—, chairman of department, 1940-61, dean of graduate school, 1946-52. Consultant to Division of Education and Cultural Affairs, United States Office of Military Government, Germany, 1948. *Member:* American Philosophical Association, Metaphysical Society of America, Symposium, Southern Society for Philosophy and Psychology (president, 1963), Southern Society for Philosophy of Religion (president, 1961), Phi Beta Kappa, Omicron Delta Kappa. *Awards, honors:* Rosenwald fellow, 1938-39; Guggenheim fellowship, 1958-59; Fulbright research fellowship, 1959.

WRITINGS: (Translator and editor) *The Philosophical Papers and Letters of G. W. Leibniz,* two volumes, University of Chicago Press, 1956, revised edition, D. Reidel (Dordrecht), 1969; (contributor) Paul Edwards, editor, *The Encyclopedia of Philosophy,* Crowell Collier, 1967; *Struggle for Synthesis,* Harvard University Press, 1972; (contributor) Ivor Leclerc, editor, *Leibniz and the Modern World,* Vanderbilt University Press, 1973. Contributor of papers to philosophical and literary journals. Contributing editor of several philosophical journals.

WORK IN PROGRESS: A collection of papers on Leibniz's thought; a developmental analysis of the thought of Leibniz.

* * *

LOEVINGER, Jane 1918-

PERSONAL: Surname is pronounced Lev-in-jer; born February 6, 1918, in St. Paul, Minn.; daughter of Gustavus (a lawyer and judge) and Millie (Strouse) Loevinger; married Sam I. Weissman (a professor of chemistry), July 13, 1943; children: Judith, Michael Benjamin. *Education:* University of Minnesota, B.A. (magna cum laude), 1937, M.S., 1938; University of California, Berkeley, Ph.D., 1944. *Politics:* Democrat. *Religion:* None. *Home:* 6926 Princeton Ave., University City, Mo. 63130. *Office:* Department of Psychology, Washington University, St. Louis, Mo. 63130.

CAREER: Stanford University, Stanford, Calif., acting instructor, 1942; University of California, Berkeley, lecturer in psychology, 1942-43; Washington University, St. Louis, Mo., instructor in statistics, 1946-47, research psychologist, 1950-53; Jewish Hospital, St. Louis, research associate, 1954-60; Washington University, research associate professor of medical psychology, School of Medicine, 1960-64, research associate professor, Graduate Institute of Education, 1964-71, professor of psychology, 1971—, research associate, Social Science Institute, 1964—. Visiting lecturer, University of Colorado, summer, 1957; distinguished visiting scholar, Educational Testing Service, 1969. *Member:* American Psychological Association (fellow; president, Division of Evaluation and Measurement, 1962-63), Phi Beta Kappa. *Awards, honors:* Margaret M. Justin fellow of American Association of University Women, 1955-56.

WRITINGS: Measuring Ego Development, Jossey-Bass, Volume I (with Ruth Wessler), 1970, Volume II (with Wessler and Carolyn Redmore), 1970; *Ego Development: Conceptions and Theories,* Jossey-Bass, 1976; *Scientific Ways in the Study of Ego Development,* Clark University Press, 1979.

Contributor: H. Helson, editor, *Theoretical Foundations of Psychology,* Van Nostrand, 1951; J. C. Glidewell, editor, *Parental Attitudes and Child Behavior,* C. C Thomas, 1961; B. B. Wolman, editor, *Handbook of Clinical Psychology,* McGraw, 1965; Kenneth Hammond, editor, *The Psychology of Egon Brunswik,* Holt, 1966; Anne Anastasi, editor, *Testing Problems in Perspective,* American Council on Education, 1966; D. N. Jackson and S. J. Messick, editors, *Problems in Human Assessment,* McGraw, 1967; S. B. Sells, editor, *The Definition and Measurement of Mental Health,* National Center for Health Statistics, U.S. Department of Health, Education, and Welfare, 1968; Louis Breger, *Clinical-Cognitive Psychology: Models and Integrations,* Prentice-Hall, 1969; J. N. Butcher, editor, *Objective Personality Assessment: Changing Perspectives,* Academic Press, 1972; P. Holzman and M. Gill, editors, *Psychology versus Metapsychology: Psychoanalytic Essays in Memory of George S. Klein,* International Universities Press, 1976. Contributor of about twenty papers to professional journals.

* * *

LOEWENSTEIN, Karl 1891-1973

November 9, 1891—July 10, 1973; German-born lawyer, educator, and writer on politics, constitutional law, and other topics. Obituaries: *New York Times,* July 17, 1973.

* * *

LOGAN, Frank A(nderson) 1924-

PERSONAL: Born July 22, 1924, in Palatka, Fla.; son of Frank Anderson and Bernice (Hilty) Logan; married Julia Bingham Allen, July 1, 1948; children: Frank Anderson III, Nancy Allen. *Education:* University of Iowa, B.A., 1948, M.A., 1950, Ph.D., 1951. *Home:* 1300 Stagecoach Rd. S.E., Albuquerque, N.M. 87123. *Office:* Department of Psychology, University of New Mexico, Albuquerque, N.M. 87106.

CAREER: Instructor in psychology at University of Missouri—Columbia, summer, 1950, and University of Iowa, Iowa City, 1950-51; Yale University, New Haven, Conn., assistant professor, 1952-58, associate professor of psychology, 1958-64; University of New Mexico, Albuquerque, professor of psychology and chairman of department, 1964—. National Institutes of Health, member of experimental psychology study section, 1962-66. *Member:* American Psychological Association (fellow; member of executive committee and secretary-treasurer, Division 3, 1969-72), Psychonomic Society (member of executive committee, 1970—), American Association for the Advancement of Science, Southwestern Psychological Association (president, 1973), Midwestern Psychological Association, Rocky Mountain Psychological Association, Sigma Xi.

WRITINGS: (With others) *Behavior Theory and Social Science,* Yale University Press, 1955; *Incentive: How the Conditions of Reinforcement Affect the Performance of Rats,* Yale University Press, 1960; (with A. R. Wagner) *Reward and Punishment,* Allyn & Bacon, 1965; *Fundamentals of Learning and Motivation,* W. C. Brown, 1970, revised edition, 1976; (with D. P. Ferraro) *Systematic Analyses of Learning and Motivation,* Wiley, 1978.

Contributor: Sigmund Koch, editor, *Psychology: A Study of a Science,* Volume II, McGraw, 1959; K. W. Spence and J. A. Spence, editors, *The Psychology of Learning and Motivation,* Volume II, Academic Press, 1968; B. A. Campbell and R. M. Church, editors, *Punishment and Aversive Behavior,* Appleton, 1969; William N. Schoenfeld, editor, *Theory of Reinforcement Schedules,* Appleton, 1970; W. A. Hunt, editor, *Learning Mechanisms in Smoking,* Aldine, 1970; H. H. Kendler and J. T. Spence, editors, *Essays in Neobehaviorism,* Appleton, 1971; H. D. Kimmel, editor, *Experimental Psychopathology,* Academic Press, 1971; Robert Glaser, editor, *The Nature of Reinforcement,* Academic Press, 1971.

Contributor to *International Encyclopedia of the Social Sciences,* and of about forty articles to journals. Member of editorial advisory board, *Journal of Comparative and Physiological Psychology,* 1956-74, *Psychological Review,* 1958-64, *Journal of Experimental Psychology,* 1963-74, *Psychological Bulletin,* 1964-66, *Psychological Monographs,* 1964-66, and *Psychonomic Science,* 1971-74; associate editor, *Psychological Bulletin,* 1966-68, and *Animal Learning and Behavior,* 1973—.

* * *

LOMAX, Pearl Cleage 1948-

PERSONAL: Maiden name is pronounced Clegg; born December 7, 1948, in Springfield, Mass.; daughter of Albert Buford (a minister) and Doris (Graham) Cleage; married Michael Lucius Lomax (an elected official of Fulton County, Ga.), October 31, 1969; children: Deignan Njero. *Education:* Attended Howard University, 1966-69, Yale University, 1969, and University of the West Indies, 1971; Spelman College, B.A., 1971; Atlanta University, graduate study, 1972—. *Religion:* Black Christian Nationalism. *Home:* 1478 Willis Mill Rd. S.W., Atlanta, Ga. 30311.

CAREER: Martin Luther King, Jr. Archival Library, Atlanta, Ga., member of field staff, 1969-70; Southern Education Program, Inc., Atlanta, assistant director, 1970-72; WQXI, Atlanta, writer and associate producer, 1972-73; City of Atlanta, director of communications, 1974-76; Brown/Gray Ltd., Atlanta, writer, 1976—. Hostess/interviewer, "Black Viewpoints," produced by Clark College, WETV, Atlanta, 1970-71; staff writer, *Ebony Beat Journal,* WQXI, Atlanta, 1972; executive producer, WXIA, Atlanta, 1972-73. Instructor, Emory University, 1978. Member of board of directors, Atlanta Center for Black Art, 1970-71. *Member:* Writers Guild of America, East, Southern Collective of African American Writers.

WRITINGS: "Hymn for the Rebels" (one-act play), first produced in Washington, D.C. at Howard University, 1968;

"Duet for Three Voices" (one-act play), first produced in Washington, D.C. at Howard University, 1969; *We Don't Need No Music* (poems), Broadside Press, 1971; "The Sale" (one-act play), first produced in Atlanta, Ga., at Spelman College, 1972. Poetry anthologized in *The Insistent Present,* edited by John Mahoney and John Schmittroh, Houghton, 1970, *We Speak as Liberators: Young Black Poets,* edited by Orde Coombs, Dodd, 1970, and *A Rock against the Wind,* edited by Lindsay Patterson, Dodd, 1973. Columnist for *Atlanta Gazette,* 1976—, and *Atlanta Constitution,* 1977. Contributor to various periodicals and journals, including *Readers and Writers, Promethean, Afro-American Review, Journal of Black Poetry, Dues, Essence, Pride, Black World, Ms., Atlanta Magazine, New York Times Book Review, Southern Voices,* and *Black Collegian.*

WORK IN PROGRESS: Dolly Dimple Is Dead, a book of poems; a novel.

SIDELIGHTS: Pearl Cleage Lomax told *CA:* "As a black female writer living and working in the United States, my writing of necessity reflects my blackness and my femaleness. I am convinced that this condition of double-oppression based on race and sex gives me a unique perspective that, hopefully, adds energy and a certain creative tension to my work. Here's hoping...." Lomax has sold an original screenplay entitled "Cat's Song," to Pinebloom Productions.

* * *

LOMMASSON, Robert C(urtis) 1917-

PERSONAL: Born January 4, 1917, in Topeka, Kan.; son of Charles Curtis (a postal clerk) and M. Estella (Darby) Lommasson; married Helen Elizabeth Chamberlin (a nurse), November 25, 1943; children: Elizabeth Ann (Mrs. Gerald M. Hodgson), Paul Alfred, Carol Jeanne Meyer, Timothy Charles. *Education:* University of Kansas, A.B., 1938, M.A., 1940; University of Iowa, Ph.D., 1948. *Religion:* Methodist. *Home:* 4301 Holdrege, Lincoln, Neb. 68503. *Office:* School of Life Sciences, University of Nebraska, Lincoln, Neb. 68588.

CAREER: University of Iowa, Iowa City, instructor in botany, 1946-48; University of Nebraska, Lincoln, assistant professor, 1948-58, associate professor, 1958-63, professor of botany, 1963—. *Military service:* U.S. Naval Reserve, 1942-45; became lieutenant commander. *Member:* International Society of Plant Morphologists, International Phycological Society, American Fern Society (president, 1962-63), Botanical Society of America, National Association of Biology Teachers, National Forage and Grasslands Council, Association of Midwest College Biology Teachers, Midwest Biosystematists, Nebraska Academy of Science, Iowa Academy of Science.

WRITINGS: Nebraska Wild Flowers, University of Nebraska Press, 1973. Contributor to *American Fern Journal, Phytomorphology, Transactions of the Nebraska Academy of Sciences,* and *Proceedings of the Iowa Academy of Science.*

WORK IN PROGRESS: Research on tissue organization of grass leaves and fern leaves, on venation of grass leaves, and on leaf anatomy of grass subfamilies.

* * *

LONGLEY, Lawrence D(ouglas) 1939-

PERSONAL: Born November 12, 1939, in Bronxville, N.Y.; son of Henry N. (a lawyer) and Effie P. Longley; divorced; children: Rebecca Jane. *Education:* Oberlin College, B.A., 1962; Vanderbilt University, M.A., 1964, Ph.D., 1969. *Religion:* Congregationalist. *Home:* 35 Woodmere Ct., Appleton, Wis. 54911. *Office:* Department of Government, Lawrence University, Appleton, Wis. 54912.

CAREER: Lawrence University, Appleton, Wis., instructor, 1966-69, assistant professor, 1969-77, associate professor of government, 1977—. Active in state and local Democratic Party activities. *Member:* American Political Science Association, Midwest Political Science Association, Southern Political Science Association, Wisconsin Political Science Association (member of executive committee, 1966—; secretary, 1967-68; vice-president, 1968-69; president, 1969-70). *Awards, honors:* National Science Foundation College Science Improvement Program grants, summers, 1970, 1971.

WRITINGS: (With Alan G. Braun) *The Politics of Electoral College Reform,* Yale University Press, 1972, 2nd edition, 1975; (contributor) Donald R. Matthews, editor, *Perspectives on Presidential Selection,* Brookings Institution, 1973; (with Erwin G. Krasnow) *The Politics of Broadcast Regulation,* St. Martin's, 1973, 2nd edition, 1978; (with John H. Yunker) *The Electoral College: Its Biases Newly Measured for the 1960's and 1970's,* Sage, 1976; (contributor) William J. Crotty, editor, *Paths to Political Reform,* Heath, 1979. Author of community research reports. Contributor to *Encyclopedia Americana.* Contributor to *Forum on Public Affairs, Journal of Broadcasting, Journal of Politics,* and *Tennessee Historical Quarterly.*

WORK IN PROGRESS: Research on congressional politics, on politics of the regulatory process, on interest group behavior, on election laws and systems, and on British politics.

*   *   *

LOPUKHOV, Fyodor V(asilevich)   1886-1973

1886—February (?), 1973; Russian ballet master and innovator, and author of books on the dance. Obituaries: *New York Times,* February 7, 1973.

*   *   *

LORA, Ronald   1938-

PERSONAL: Born August 10, 1938, in Bluffton, Ohio; son of Milo August (a farmer) and Mabel (Luginbuhl) Lora; children: Jacqueline, Cynthia. *Education:* Bluffton College, B.S., 1960; Ohio State University, Ph.D., 1967. *Home:* 3425 Brantford Rd., Toledo, Ohio 43606. *Office:* Department of History, University of Toledo, West Bancroft, Toledo, Ohio 43606.

CAREER: Bluffton College, Bluffton, Ohio, instructor in history, 1964-66; University of Toledo, Toledo, Ohio, assistant professor, 1967-71, associate professor, 1971-75, professor of history, 1975—. *Member:* Organization of American Historians, American Historical Association, Southern Historical Association, Ohio Academy of History, Phi Alpha Theta. *Awards, honors:* Huntington Library fellow, summer, 1973; Outstanding Teacher award, University of Toledo, 1976.

WRITINGS: (Contributor) Duane Leach and Monroe Billington, editors, *American Democracy on Trial,* McCutchan, 1968; *Conservative Minds in America.* Rand McNally, 1972; (contributor) Lyle E. Meyer, editor, *Historical Papers: Selected Proceedings of the Northern Great Plains History Conference,* Moorhead State College, 1973;

(editor) *America in the 1960s: Cultural Authorities in Transition,* Wiley, 1974; (contributor) Robert Griffith and Athan Theoharis, editors, *The Specter: Original Essays on the Cold War,* New Viewpoints, 1974; (contributor) Louis Filler, editor, *A Question of Quality,* Popular Press, 1976. Contributor to *Menckeniana Quarterly.*

WORK IN PROGRESS: A study of the sixties; with William H. Longton, *The American Conservative Press.*

*   *   *

LORAYNE, Harry   1926-

PERSONAL: Born May 4, 1926, in New York, N.Y.; married Renee Lefkowitz, January 31, 1948; children: Robert Emery. *Education:* Attended high school in New York, N.Y. *Home:* 62 Jane St., New York, N.Y. 10014. *Agent:* William Morris Agency, 1350 Avenue of Americas, New York, N.Y. 10019. *Office:* Cogan, Bell & Co., 350 Fifth Ave., New York, N.Y. 10001.

CAREER: Began as a professional magician, currently a memory training expert; Harry Lorayne School of Memory, New York, N.Y., founder and president. Gives executive programs in memory-training for industrial firms. Has appeared frequently on national television talk shows and special programs. *Military service:* U.S. Army, 1943.

WRITINGS: How to Develop a Super-Power Memory, Fell, 1956; *Secrets of Mind Power,* Fell, 1961; *Miracle Math,* Executive Research Institute, 1966; *Instant Mind Power,* Executive Research Institute, 1967; *Memory Isometrics Course,* Information, Inc., 1968; *Mental Magnetism Course,* Information, Inc., 1969; *Good Memory—Good Student!* (grades 5-9), Nelson, 1972; *Good Memory—Successful Student!* (grades 9-12), Nelson, 1973; (with Jerry Lucas) *The Memory Book,* Stein & Day, 1974; *Remembering People,* Stein & Day, 1975; *The Magic Book,* Putnam, 1977; (contributor) *Introductory Psychology,* Addison-Wesley, 1978. Author of thirteen books on card magic; contributor to magazines and newspapers.

*   *   *

LORD, Edith Elizabeth   1907-

PERSONAL: Born August 4, 1907, in Newark, N.J. *Education:* University of Houston, B.S., 1935; University of Texas, Main University (now University of Texas at Austin), M.A., 1938; University of Southern California, Ph.D., 1948; New York University, M.A. (public health education), 1954. *Home:* 880 Northeast 69th St., Apt. 1-A, Miami, Fla. 33138.

CAREER: University of Houston, Houston, Tex., 1934-44, began as instructor, became associate professor of psychology, University of Southern California, Los Angeles, lecturer in psychology, 1946-48; Hawaii Department of Public Health, Division of Mental Health, clinical psychologist, 1948-49; Arizona State Department of Public Health, Phoenix, state supervisor of mental hygiene, 1949-51; U.S. Veterans Administration, New York, N.Y., chief of psychology training program, 1952-54; U.S. Department of State, Washington, D.C., human resources development officer (held position in Ethiopia, the Philippines, Nigeria, Liberia, and Ghana), 1954-68; University of Miami, Coral Gables, Fla., professor of psychology and adjunct professor of psychiatry in School of Medicine, 1968-76. Certified psychologist in State of New York and licensed in State of Florida; diplomate in clinical psychology, American Board of Professional Psychology. *Military service:* U.S. Army, WAC, 1944-46;

became lieutenant. *Awards, honors:* National Science Foundation fellowship, summer, 1971, to study African Muslim culture.

WRITINGS: Experimentally Induced Variations in Rorschach Performance, Psychological Monographs, 1950; (with Wolde Christos Bekele) *A Brief Introduction to the Amharic Language,* EUSCEP Press (Ethiopia), 1955, 3rd edition, 1958; *Cultural Facts and Fancies,* University of Miami (Coral Gables), 3rd edition, 1970; *Ghana-United States Participant Training Evaluation Survey: 1957-1967,* Liberty Press, 1968; (contributor) Georgene H. Seward and Robert C. Williamson, editors, *Sex Roles in Changing Society,* Random House, 1970; *Queen of Sheba's Heirs: Cultural Patterns of Ethiopia,* Acropolis Books, 1970; *Fragments* (poems), University of Miami (Coral Gables), 1971; (contributor) Albert R. Roberts, editor, *Childhood Deprivation,* C. C Thomas, 1974. Contributor to a variety of journals, including *American Psychologist, Journal of Social Psychology, Catholic Digest, International Journal of Social Psychiatry, Journal of Projective Techniques, Journal of Consulting Psychology, Human Organization, Research in Education,* and *International Psychologist.*

SIDELIGHTS: Edith Lord told *CA* that of all the honors and awards she's received, her most cherished is the one given her by her graduate students upon her retirement from the University of Miami. The engraved plaque read: "As a teacher and friend, you have enriched both our professional and personal lives. Thanks for sharing your wisdom—we will do our best to pass it on."

* * *

LOSHAK, David (Leslie Ivor) 1933-

PERSONAL: Surname is pronounced *Low*-shak; born April 16, 1933, in London, England; son of Harry and Judith (Katz) Loshak; married Mollie Powell, May 12, 1961; children: Stephanie, Daniel. *Education:* Brasenose College, Oxford, B.A. (honors), 1955. *Home:* 164 Burbage Rd., London SE21 7AG, England. *Agent:* Nicholas Thompson, 23 Pont St., London S.W.1, England. *Office: Daily Telegraph,* 135 Fleet St., London E.C.4, England.

CAREER: Daily Telegraph and *Sunday Telegraph,* London, England, 1963—, former foreign correspondent based in Capetown, South Africa, currently health correspondent based in London.

WRITINGS: Pakistan Crisis, Heinemann, 1971, McGraw, 1972. Also author of *Daily Telegraph Guide to Retirement,* 1978.

* * *

LOUGHARY, John W(illiam) 1930-

PERSONAL: November 6, 1930, in Omak, Wash.; son of William E. and Margaret (Bagen) Loughary; married Josephine Caughell (a librarian), April 23, 1952; children: Kathleen, Kevin, Patrick, Rebecca, Kelly, Keenan. *Education:* University of Oregon, B.A., 1952; State University of Iowa, M.A., 1956, Ph.D., 1958. *Home:* 3255 Olive St., Eugene, Ore. 97405. *Office:* 1618 Columbia St., University of Oregon, Eugene, Ore. 97403.

CAREER: Teacher and principal in high school in Oregon, 1953-58; director of guidance in high school in Iowa, 1955-58; University of California, Berkeley, acting assistant professor of education, 1958-59; supervisor of guidance and research in San Bernadino, California, 1959-61; owner of instructional systems company in Los Gatos, Calif., 1961-62;

University of Oregon, Eugene, associate professor, 1962-66, professor of counseling, 1966—, chairman of department, 1968-74, associate dean, College of Education, 1974-78. President, United Learning Corp. *Member:* American Psychological Association.

WRITINGS: Counseling in Secondary Schools, Harper, 1961; *Counseling: A Growing Profession,* American Personnel and Guidance Association, 1965; (editor and contributor) *Man Machine Systems in Education,* Harper, 1966; (with Murray Tondow, William Yarbroff, and C. W. Bowman) *Counseling Information System,* Follett, 1967; (editor with Tondow) *Requirements of Educational Information Systems During the Next Two Decades,* College of Education, University of Oregon, 1968; (with T. M. Ripley) *Career Survival Skills,* Merrill, 1974; (with Ripley) *This Isn't Quite What I Had in Mind,* Follett, 1974; (with Ripley) *Career and Life Planning Guide,* Follett, 1976; (with Ripley) *Helping Others Help Themselves,* McGraw, 1979; (with Barrie Hopson) *Trainers Handbook,* Follett, 1979.

* * *

LOVESEY, Peter 1936-
(Peter Lear)

PERSONAL: Born September 10, 1936, in Whitton, Middlesex, England; son of Richard Lear (a bank official) and Amy (Strank) Lovesey; married Jacqueline Ruth Lewis, May 30, 1959; children: Kathleen Ruth, Philip Lear. *Education:* University of Reading, B.A. (honors), 1958. *Home:* 47 West Dr., Cheam, Surrey, England.

CAREER: Thurrock Technical College, Grays, Essex, England, senior lecturer, 1961-69; Hammersmith College for Further Education, London, England, head of general education department, 1969-75; currently full-time writer. *Military service:* Royal Air Force, 1958-61; became a flying officer. *Member:* Crime Writers' Association, Detection Club. *Awards, honors:* Macmillan/Panther First Crime Novel Award for *Wobble to Death,* 1970.

WRITINGS—All published by Dodd, except as indicated: *The Kings of Distance,* Eyre & Spottiswoode, 1968; *Wobble to Death,* 1970; *The Detective Wore Silk Drawers,* 1971; *Abracadaver,* 1972; *Mad Hatter's Holiday,* 1973; *The Tick of Death,* 1974; *A Case of Spirits,* 1975; *Swing, Swing Together,* 1976; *Waxwork,* Pantheon, 1978; (under pseudonym Peter Lear) *Goldengirl,* Doubleday, 1978.

WORK IN PROGRESS: Crime novels in Victorian English settings.

SIDELIGHTS: Cyril Ray said of Peter Lovesey's book *Wobble to Death:* "[It is] a novel brilliantly evocative of the sporting London of 1879, and fascinating in its description of one of the six-day pedestrian contests—'wobbles'—of the period. The murder arises out of the contest, and it is long since I came across so original a setting for a novel of mystery, or one in which the plot is so firmly fixed; nothing is dragged in merely to parade the author's special knowledge. So one pays the author the compliment of judging by the highest standards, and observes that one clue, perhaps, is not quite fairly withheld, and that there are half a dozen anachronistic turns of phrase.... Mercurius Oxoniensis should offer a series of tutorials on period pastiche for crime-writers."

BIOGRAPHICAL/CRITICAL SOURCES: Spectator, March 28, 1970.

LU, Paul Hsien 1926-

PERSONAL: Middle name sounds like "shin"; born November 3, 1926, in Foochow, China; son of Lang and Ruo-Fen (Chou) Lu; married Mary Chao (a college teacher), June 17, 1961; children: William Yuan-Hai, Henry Yuan-Huang. *Education:* National Taiwan Normal University, B.A., 1953; National Chengchi University, M.A., 1956; University of Chicago, M.A., 1957; University of Illinois, graduate study, 1957-58; Columbia University, Ed.D., 1963. *Home address:* Route 7, Box 693, Morristown, Tenn. *Office:* Department of Psychology, Walters State Community College, Morristown, Tenn. 37814.

CAREER: U.S. Department of State, Washington, D.C., interpreter, 1961; Morris College, Sumter, S.C., professor of education and psychology, 1963-64; Johnson C. Smith University, Charlotte, N.C., professor of psychology, 1964; Lincoln Memorial University, Harrogate, Tenn., professor of psychology, 1964-77, head of department, 1964-77; Walters State Community College, Morristown, Tenn., professor of psychology, 1978—. *Military service:* Chinese Military Academy, 1953-54; became second lieutenant.

MEMBER: American Association for Humanistic Psychology, American Psychology-Law Society, American Association for the Advancement of Science, National Education Association, American Association of University Professors, National Association of School Psychologists, Tennessee Association for Psychology in the Schools, Tennessee Psychological Association, Alpha Chi (honorary member). *Awards, honors:* China Academy fellow, 1969-70.

WRITINGS: (Editor) *Directory of Chinese Students and Alumni in Greater New York,* Chinese Student Association in New York, 1962; *Federal Role in Education,* American Press, 1965; (editor) *Scientific Studies in Behavioral Development,* MSS Educational Publishing, 1971; (editor) *Behavioral Modification and Conative, Affective Processes,* MSS Educational Publishing, 1971; (editor) *Personality and Adjustment,* MSS Information Corp., 1972. Contributor to Chinese journals and to *Journal of Teaching of Psychology* and *Resources in Education.* Editor-in-chief, *Chinese Student Weekly, Ren-Wen Hsueh-Pao, Chinese Intellectuals Quarterly.*

WORK IN PROGRESS: Conducting a survey on emotional problems of college students.

SIDELIGHTS: Paul Hsien Lu told *CA* that his interest in writing started in the elementary grades "when I fortunately won the first prize in a country-wide essay contest. Thereafter, it almost became my semi-career to participate in any essay contest. Especially during my college years, I won contest after contest in either school-wide or nation-wide competitions with sizable material and spiritual rewards. Thus, I have been 'behavior-modified' by the continuous or intermittent positive reinforcements like a pigeon or chimpanzee bustling in the psychology lab. Who says my later and recent professional writings have not been the same sort of operant-conditioning responses (e.g., 'discriminative' behavior conditioned to the 'publish or perish' principle and 'generalized' from the Chinese language to the English language)?"

AVOCATIONAL INTERESTS: Photography, collecting, fishing.

BIOGRAPHICAL/CRITICAL SOURCES: Lincoln Memorial University Alumnus, winter, 1969.

LUBIN, Ernest 1916-1977

PERSONAL: Born May 2, 1916, in New York, N.Y.; son of Harry (an actuary) and Anna (Saltzman) Lubin; married Eleanore Casseen (a psychologist), August 27, 1955; children: Miriam Elise, Robert Thor and Daniel Casseen (twins). *Education:* Attended Manhattan School of Music, 1932-35; Columbia University, B.S., 1937, M.S., 1938. *Politics:* Democrat. *Religion:* Agnostic. *Home:* 336 Fort Washington Ave., New York, N.Y. 10033.

CAREER: New York Times, New York City, music critic, 1945 and 1949-50; High School of Performing Arts, New York City, teacher, beginning 1959. Composer member of the MacDowell Colony, 1948. *Member:* American Society of Composers, Authors, and Publishers. *Awards, honors:* Bearns Prize in musical composition, 1938.

WRITINGS: A Start at The Piano, Amsco Music Corp., 1969; *The Piano Duet,* Grossman, 1970; *The Pianist's Chord Manual,* Amsco Music Corp., 1972; (compiler and editor) *Piano Pieces by Children,* Amsco Music Corp., 1974; (compiler) *Beethoven and His Circle: An Anthology of Music by Beethoven and His Contemporaries,* Amsco Music Corp., 1974; (compiler) *Chopin and His Circle: An Anthology of Music,* Amsco Music Corp., 1975.

Composer: "Variations for Orchestra on a Theme of Stephen Foster," 1942; "Songs of Innocence," 1944; "Quartet Number 1," 1952; "Quartet Number 2," 1956; "The Pardoners Tale" (one-act opera), 1958; "Variations on a Pastoral Theme," 1959; "First Perf," 1960; "Sonata for Violin and Piano," 1966. Also composer of "Suite in Olden Style," "Wayfaring Stranger," "Three Piano Pieces," and "Pavane for Flute, Strings." Arranger of score for the Broadway musical, "Sing Out, Sweet Land." Contributor of articles to *New York Times* and to musical and chess magazines.

WORK IN PROGRESS: Research on the harpsichord and its literature; a chess book devoted to the subject of queen sacrifices.

SIDELIGHTS: Ernest Lubin studied with Roger Sessions, Ernest Bloch, and Darius Milhaud. *Avocational interests:* Chess.†

(Died March 15, 1977)

*   *   *

LUGO, Ariel E(milio) 1943-

PERSONAL: Born April 28, 1943, in Mayaguez, Puerto Rico; son of Herminio (a professor) and Ramonita (Alvarez) Lugo; married Alma L. Guzman (an artist), May 23, 1964; children: Alma Veronica, Ariel Alexei. *Education:* University of Puerto Rico, B.S., 1963, M.S., 1965; University of North Carolina, Ph.D., 1969. *Politics:* Independent. *Religion:* Presbyterian. *Home:* 2115 Southwest First Ave., Gainesville, Fla. 32601. *Office:* Department of Botany, University of Florida, Gainesville, Fla. 32611.

CAREER: University of Florida, Gainesville, assistant professor of ecology, 1969-73; Puerto Rican Department of Natural Resources, assistant secretary for planning and resource analysis, 1973-74, and for science and technology, 1974-75; University of Florida, assistant professor, 1975-76, associate professor of ecology, 1976—, acting director of Center for Wetlands, 1977—; U.S. Council on Environmental Quality, Washington, D.C., staff member (on leave from University of Florida), 1977-79. Has taught short courses on ecology for U.S. Forest Service and at institutes and universities in the Netherlands, Costa Rica, Venezuela,

Puerto Rico, and Dominican Republic. Consultant to numerous environmental, governmental, and business organizations. Ad honorem lecturer, University of Puerto Rico, 1974-76. *Member:* International Association for Ecology, International Society for Tropical Ecology, Ecological Society of America, Association of Tropical Biologists, Botanical Society of America, American Forestry Association, Society of Limnology and Oceanography, Institute of Caribbean Studies, Florida Academy of Sciences, Florida Defenders of the Environment, Sigma Xi. *Awards, honors:* Grants from University of Florida Graduate School, 1969, Florida Department of Natural Resources, 1972-75, H. W. Lochner, Inc., 1972, U.S. Environmental Protection Agency, 1977, National Science Foundation, Conservation Foundation, and U.S. Department of Energy; contracts for environmental studies from U.S. Forest Service, 1970, U.S. Department of the Interior, 1971, Bureau of Sport Fisheries and Wildlife, 1971-73 and 1973-76, American Oil Co., 1972, and U.S. Department of the Interior and State of Florida, 1972-74; award from Institute of Food and Agricultural Sciences, University of Florida, 1973, for graduate research excellence; Fulbright fellow, University of La Plata, 1978.

WRITINGS: (With S. C. Snedaker and others) *The Ecology of the Oscar Scherer State Park: The Effects of Man on Its Structure and Function,* Save Our Bays Association, 1970; (contributor and editor with Snedaker) *Readings on Ecological Systems: Their Function and Relation to Man,* MSS Educational Publishing, 1971; (with Susan Bayley, Snedaker, and H. T. Odum) *Models for Planning and Research for the South Florida Environmental Study,* U.S. Department of the Interior, 1971; (with Snedaker) *The Ecology of the Ocala National Forest,* U.S. Government Printing Office, 1972; (with others) *Towards a General Theory of Planning Design,* Department of Architecture, University of Florida, 1972; (editor with H.G.T. Van Raay and contributor) *Man and Environment LTD,* Rotterdam University Press, 1974; (co-author) *Habitat Evaluation of a Dry Coastal Forest,* two volumes, Puerto Rican Department of Natural Resources, 1976; (with C. Carrera) *Los Sistemas de Mangles de Puerto Rico,* Puerto Rican Department of Natural Resources, 1978.

Contributor: R. F. Pigeon and Odum, editors, *A Tropical Rain Forest,* U.S. Atomic Energy Commission Division of Technical Information, 1970; *Range Resources of the Southeastern United States,* American Society of Agronomy and Crop Science Society of America, 1973; B. Strain and W. D. Billings, editors, *Vegetation and Environment,* [The Hague], 1974; E. G. Farnworth and F. B. Golley, editors, *Fragile Ecosystems: Evaluation of Research and Applications in the Neotropics,* Springer-Verlag, 1974; E. Medina and Golley, editors, *Tropical Ecological Systems,* Springer-Verlag, 1975; F. G. Howell, J. B. Gentry, and M. H. Smith, editors, *Mineral Cycling in Southeastern Ecosystems,* ERDA Symposium Series, 1975; B. C. Patton, editor, *Systems Analysis and Simulation Ecology,* Volume IV, Academic Press, 1976; C. H. Wharton and others, editors, *Forested Wetlands of Florida: Their Management and Use,* Center for Wetlands, University of Florida, 1976; L. F. Seatz, editor, *Ecology and Agricultural Production,* University of Tennessee Press, 1977. Also author of environmental impact reports for various governmental agencies. Contributor to proceedings and symposia. Contributor of book reviews and about fifty articles to professional journals including *Ecology, Bulletin of Marine Science, Biotropica, Tropical Ecology, Bulletin of the Ecological Society of America, Science Education, Plant Science Bulletin,* and *Caribbean Science Journal.*

WORK IN PROGRESS: A tropical ecology book for Spanish-speaking people; a book on forested wetlands of the world.

SIDELIGHTS: Ariel Lugo told *CA:* "To me, writing is an extremely painful exercise, but I do a lot of writing for two simple reasons. First, I believe that there is an urgent need to inform people about the current ecological and energy crisis facing our civilization. The second reason is the selfish feeling of satisfaction that one gets with the knowledge that writing, like sexual reproduction is one way for us humans to leave a legacy to other generations." *Avocational interests:* Basketball, collecting stamps and coins.

* * *

LUNN, John Edward 1930-

PERSONAL: Born October 30, 1930, in Preston, England; son of Reginald William and Carrie (Kean) Lunn; married Marion McKissock (a medical practitioner); children: one daughter. *Education:* University of Glasgow, M.B.Ch.B., 1955, D.P.H., 1958, D.P.A., 1959, M.D., 1960; University of Sheffield, Ph.D., 1967. *Office:* Department of Community Medicine, University of Sheffield, Sheffield, England.

CAREER: University of Sheffield, Sheffield, England, lecturer, 1962-72, senior lecturer in community medicine, 1972—.

WRITINGS: (With Ursula Vaughan Williams) *Ralph Vaughan Williams: A Pictorial Biography,* Oxford University Press, 1971. Contributor of medical articles to technical journals.

* * *

LUPO, Alan 1938-

PERSONAL: Born May 4, 1938, in Boston, Mass.; son of Max (a salesman) and Esther (Sacon) Lupo; married Caryl Rivers (a writer), May 20, 1962; children: Steven, Alyssa. *Education:* University of Massachusetts, B.A., 1959; Columbia University, M.S., 1960. *Politics:* Generally Democrat. *Religion:* Jewish. *Home:* 54 Johnson Ave., Winthrop, Mass. 02152.

CAREER: Middletown Times Herald Record, Middletown, N.Y., reporter, bureau chief, and photographer, 1961-63; *Baltimore Evening Sun,* Baltimore, Md., reporter, 1963-66; *Boston Globe,* Boston, Mass., reporter and director of "city team", 1966-70; WGBH-TV, Boston, co-founder and editor "The Reporters" program, 1970-73; *Boston Magazine,* Boston, executive editor, 1973-74; *Boston Globe,* columnist, 1976-77; WBZ-TV, Boston, on-the-air investigative reporter, 1977-78. Affiliated with *East Boston Community News,* a non-profit newspaper. Free-lance writer and lecturer. *Military service:* U.S. Army, 1960-61; became first lieutenant. *Member:* Phi Eta Sigma. *Awards, honors:* American Newspaper Guild second place award, 1965, for feature writing; United Press International award, 1967, for writing, editing, and directing neighborhood series for *Boston Globe;* Boston Press Club Amassa Howe award, 1968, for news coverage; American Bar Association Gavel award, 1970, for series on lawyers aiding the poor; Corporation for Public Broadcasting fellowship, 1970; co-recipient of United Press International investigative award, 1978, for broadcasting.

WRITINGS: (With Edmund Fowler and Frank Colcord) *Rites of Way: The Politics of Transportation in Boston and the U.S. City,* Little, Brown, 1971; *Liberty's Chosen Home: The Politics of Violence in Boston,* Little, Brown, 1977.

LURIE, Harry L.   1892(?)-1973

1892(?)—June 25, 1973; American social work leader, educator, author, organizer and director of Jewish philanthropic foundations. Obituaries: *New York Times*, June 27, 1973.

* * *

LUSCOMBE, David Edward   1938-

PERSONAL: Born July 22, 1938, in London, England; son of Edward Dominic (a schoolmaster) and Nora (Cowell) Luscombe; married Megan Phillips, August 20, 1960; children: Nicholas, Mark, Philip, Amanda. *Education:* King's College, Cambridge, B.A., 1959, M.A., 1963, Ph.D., 1964. *Religion:* Roman Catholic. *Home:* 129 Prospect Rd., Totley Rise, Sheffield S17 4HX, England. *Office:* Department of History, University of Sheffield, Sheffield, England.

CAREER: Cambridge University, Churchill College, Cambridge, England, lecturer, 1964-72, director of studies in history, 1964-72; University of Sheffield, Sheffield, England, professor of medieval history, 1972—. *Member:* Royal Historical Society (fellow).

WRITINGS: The School of Peter Abelard, Cambridge University Press, 1969; (editor and translator) *Peter Abelard's Ethics*, Clarendon Press, 1971; (editor with C.N.L. Brooke, G. H. Martin, and Dorothy Owen) *Church and Government in the Middle Ages: Essays presented to C. R. Cheney on his 70th Birthday*, Cambridge University Press, 1976, reprinted with corrections, 1977.

WORK IN PROGRESS: Pseudo-Denys the Areopagite in the Medieval West; editing the letters of Peter Abelard and Heloise.

* * *

LUTWACK, Leonard   1917-

PERSONAL: Born April 18, 1917, in Hartford, Conn.; son of Morris and Augusta (Zerwitz) Lutwack; married Ruth Taylor, February 23, 1956; children: Penelope Mae. *Education:* Wesleyan University, B.A., 1939, M.A., 1940; Ohio State University, Ph.D., 1950. *Politics:* Democrat. *Religion:* None. *Home:* 4308 East-West Highway, Hyattsville, Md. 20782. *Office:* Department of English, University of Maryland, College Park, Md. 20742.

CAREER: University of Maine at Orono, instructor in English, 1946; University of Maryland at College Park, instructor, 1950-54, assistant professor, 1955-61, associate professor, 1962-70, professor of English, 1970—. Fulbright lecturer at University of Oslo, 1954-55. *Military service:* U.S. Army, 1943-46. *Member:* Modern Language Associate of America, American Association of University Professors.

WRITINGS: Heroic Fiction: The Epic Tradition and American Novels of the Twentieth Century, Southern Illinois University Press, 1971. Contributor of articles on prose style to *Journal of Aesthetics and Art Criticism*.

WORK IN PROGRESS: Place and Motion in Literature, a study of the formal uses of place and motion in narrative literature emphasizing late 19th- and 20th-century fiction, completion expected in 1979.

* * *

LUX, Thomas   1946-

PERSONAL: Born December 10, 1946, in Northampton, Mass.; son of N. O. (a milkman) and Eleanor (Healey) Lux. *Education:* Emerson College, B.A., 1970; University of Iowa, graduate study, 1971. *Office:* Department of English, Sarah Lawrence College, Bronxville, N.Y.

CAREER: Emerson College, Boston, Mass., poet-in-residence, 1972-75; Sarah Lawrence College, Bronxville, N.Y., member of faculty, 1975—. Editor, Born Dream Press. *Awards, honors:* Bread Loaf scholarship, 1970; MacDowell Colony fellowship, 1973.

WRITINGS: The Land Sighted, Pym-Randall, 1970; *Memory's Handgrenade*, Pym-Randall, 1972; *Poems: The Glassblower's Breath*, Cleveland State University, 1976. Managing editor, *Iowa Review*, 1971-72, *Ploughshares*, 1973.

WORK IN PROGRESS: The Body of the Dreamer (tentative title), a book of poems.†

* * *

LUXENBURG, Norman   1927-

PERSONAL: Born April 15, 1927, in Cleveland, Ohio; son of Louis (a builder) and Anna (Zieve) Luxenburg; married Lucille Tomb, June 26, 1965; children: Laura Lynn, Wendy Jean. *Education:* University of Michigan, B.A., 1949, M.A., 1951, Ph.D., 1956; University of Zuerich, M.A., 1950. *Office:* Department of Russian, University of Iowa, Iowa City, Iowa 52240.

CAREER: Illinois State University, Normal, associate professor of Russian, 1959-65; Purdue University, Lafayette, Ind., associate professor of Russian history, 1965-67; University of Iowa, Iowa City, professor of Russian, 1967—, head of department, 1967—. *Military service:* U.S. Army, 1944-47. *Member:* American Historical Association, Modern Language Association of America.

WRITINGS: (With Helene Scriabine) *Siege and Survival*, Southern Illinois University Press, 1971; *Twentieth Century Europe: The Big Change*, Southern Illinois University Press, 1972; (with Scriabine) *After Leningrad: From the Caucasus to the Rhine*, Southern Illinois University Press, 1978. Contributor to journals in his field.

WORK IN PROGRESS: Let's Set the Record Straight, a book in defense of the United States against unwarranted criticism; *Twentieth Century Russia.*

* * *

LYMAN, Howard B(urbeck)   1920-

PERSONAL: Born February 12, 1920, in Athol, Mass.; son of Stanley Burbeck (a florist) and Ruth Mary (Gray) Lyman; married Zoe Elizabeth Neale, November 3, 1944 (divorced, 1960); married Patricia Ann Malone (an artist), May 4, 1966; children: (first marriage) David Stanley, Nancy Moya, Dorothy Jane; (second marriage) Richard Putney Taylor, Martha Carol Taylor, Robert Malone Taylor, David Patrick Taylor. *Education:* Brown University, A.B., 1942; University of Minnesota, M.A., 1948; University of Kentucky, Ph.D., 1951. *Religion:* Protestant. *Home:* 3422 Whitfield Ave., Cincinnati, Ohio 45220. *Office:* Department of Psychology, University of Cincinnati, Cincinnati, Ohio 45221.

CAREER: University of Cincinnati, Cincinnati, Ohio, assistant professor, 1951-56, associate professor of psychology, 1956—. *Military service:* U.S. Army, 1942-46. *Member:* American Psychological Association, American Personnel and Guidance Association, American College Personnel Association, Association for Measurement and Evaluation in Guidance, National Vocational Guidance Association, Psychometric Society, National Council for Measurement in Education, Authors Guild, Midwestern Psychological Association, Ohio Psychological Association (former president), Cincinnati Psychological Association (former president), Psi Chi (vice-president, 1959-65, 1970-74).

WRITINGS: Test Scores and What They Mean, Prentice-Hall, 1963, 3rd edition, 1978; *Intelligence, Aptitude, and Achievement Testing,* Houghton, 1968; *Single Again,* McKay, 1971. Has written ten audio tapes for McGraw.

WORK IN PROGRESS: Research on differences in vocabulary between black and white people; research on alternatives to marriage; research on today's children.†

* * *

LYON, Harold C(lifford), Jr. 1935-

PERSONAL: Born April 26, 1935, in New Brunswick, N.J.; son of Harold Clifford (an army officer and teacher) and Toni Marie (Briggs) Lyon; married Cynthia Smith, August 26, 1959 (divorced January, 1970); married Edith Ann Gosnell, March 16, 1972; children: (first marriage) Eric C., Gregg L.; stepchildren: Dian Gosnell, Rita Gosnell, Roy Gosnell, John Gosnell. *Education:* U.S. Military Academy at West Point, B.S., 1958; George Washington University, M.A., 1965; University of Massachusetts—Amherst, Ed.D., 1970. *Politics:* Democrat. *Home:* 4217 Van Ness St. N.W., Washington, D.C. 20016. *Office:* Department of Health, Education, and Welfare, 330 Independence Ave., Washington, D.C. 20201. *Agent:* John Brockman, Box 376, New York, N.Y. 10024.

CAREER: U.S. Army, commissioned Ranger-Airborne officer, 1958-65, became captain; Ohio University, Athens, special assistant to the president, 1965-67; U.S. Office of Education, Washington, D.C., assistant deputy commissioner of education, 1967-69; University of Massachusetts—Amherst, Horace Mann Lecturer at School of Education, 1969-70; U.S. Office of Education, Washington, D.C., deputy associate commissioner of education for libraries and educational technology, 1970-72, director of education for the gifted and talented, 1972-76; Antioch College, Columbia, Md., Abraham Maslow Professor, 1976-78; currently affiliated with the U.S. Department of Health, Education and Welfare, Washington, D.C. Visiting scholar in department of psychology, Georgetown University, 1976-78. Consultant for White House Task Force on Education of the Gifted, 1968. Chairman of board of trustees, American Excellence, Inc.; member of national advisory board of Erhard Seminars Training (EST). Has lectured at twenty-five universities and on radio and television.

MEMBER: Association for Humanistic Psychology, American Psychological Association, Association for the Gifted, World Council for Gifted and Talented Children (founder and U.S. delegate), Society for General Semantics, National Association for Gifted Children, Mensa. *Awards, honors*—Military: Army Commendation Medal, 1961; Defense Commendation Medal, 1963. Other: Winner of American College Public Relations Association's national honors competition, 1967, for federal relations program; Horace Mann Award of University of Massachusetts for educational leadership, 1968; named one of the Outstanding Young Men of the Year by the Secretary of Health, Education, and Welfare, 1968; nominated for the Arthur S. Flemming Award, 1968; citation of merit, National Association for Gifted Children, 1973; National Award of Merit from Association for the Gifted, 1974.

WRITINGS: (Contributor) Asa Knowles, editor, *College and University Administration,* McGraw, 1970; *Learning to Feel-Feeling to Learn,* C. E. Merrill, 1971; *It's Me and I'm Here!,* Delacorte, 1974; *Tenderness Is Strength,* Harper, 1978. Also author of an unpublished children's book, "The Adventures of Buba and Jude; a Busy Father's Bedtime Story Book," written with his sons, Eric and Gregg. Contributor to *Education for the Seventies,* U.S. Congress, 1971; contributor of about fifty articles on leadership and new educational concepts to magazines, newspapers, and professional journals.

WORK IN PROGRESS: A novel, tentatively entitled *Behind the Lilac Bushes; Tales of Tender Men;* a book on second marriages, with wife, Edith Lyon.

SIDELIGHTS: In the course of Harold Lyon's widely varied career, he has been an Army officer, a government official, an academic administrator, and a licensed therapist. He also played a part in the integration of James Meredith into the University of Mississippi. He has worked closely with the Children's Television Workshop (producers of "Sesame Street" and "The Electric Company") and with a project to bring educational programming to isolated Alaskan villages by satellite. Most recently he has taken a two-year sabbatical to help develop an international olympiad for gifted youths while teaching humanistic psychology at Georgetown University and Antioch College. He is also the founder of American Excellence, Inc., an organization dedicated to planning these olympics and to renewing American values of excellence.

Learning to Feel-Feeling to Learn, his first book, has proved to be a controversial and comprehensive text. It has been used on over four hundred college campuses and translated into several languages. *It's Me and I'm Here!* is an autobiographical work about Lyon's own therapy, work, and practice as a therapist. He is a leader in the human potential movement and has conducted sessions at Esalen Institute and other "growth centers" around the country. He is interested in "applying the ideas behind the human potential movement to education, management, and living" and has tried to encourage a humanistic approach to the management of U.S. Office of Education programs.

Harold Lyon told *CA:* "My need to express myself in writing springs from an inner conflict which I am struggling to resolve in action. I do not write at having found the answer to a problem but rather out of my having found a problem and wanting an answer. It's an inner experience something within me trying to work.... My art is the process of sharing my search and struggle."

AVOCATIONAL INTERESTS: Fishing, hunting, ecology, "creative and erotic energy."

BIOGRAPHICAL/CRITICAL SOURCES: Harold C. Lyon, Jr., *It's Me and I'm Here* (autobiographical), Delacorte, 1974.

* * *

LYON, John 1932-

PERSONAL: Born September 18, 1932, in Chicago, Ill.; son of William B. (an optical engineer) and Mary C. (Sullivan) Lyon; married Jacqueline T. Woods, September 3, 1955; children: Thomas, Siobhan, Nora, Matthew, Geoffrey, Mark, Arthur, Kathleen. *Education:* University of Notre Dame, B.A., 1954, M.A., 1955; University of Pittsburgh, Ph.D., 1966. *Religion:* Roman Catholic. *Office:* General Program of Liberal Studies, University of Notre Dame, Notre Dame, Ind. 46556.

CAREER: Has worked as a farm laborer and a high school teacher; Duquesne University, Pittsburgh, Pa., instructor, 1960-62, assistant professor, 1962-66, associate professor of history, 1966-67; University of Notre Dame, Notre Dame, Ind., assistant professor, 1967-70, associate professor of liberal studies, 1970—. *Member:* American Historical Association, History of Science Society, American Association of University Professors. *Awards, honors:* Danforth grant, 1965-66; National Endowment for the Humanities grant, 1971-72.

WRITINGS: (With Robert Burns, Philip Gleason, Lee Boyer, James Felton, James O'Neill, and Charles Tull) *Episodes in American History,* Ginn, 1973. Contributor to *Westminster Dictionary of Church History;* contributor to *Isis, Church History, Duquesne Review, Journal of the History of Biology, Review of Politics,* and other history and politics journals.

WORK IN PROGRESS: Research on idea of progress, on concept of species, and on the meaning of metamorphosis; preparing a world history course and text.

AVOCATIONAL INTERESTS: Gardening, photography, canoeing.

*   *   *

LYONS, Daniel   1920-

PERSONAL: Born August 13, 1920, in Seattle, Wash.; son of Patrick and Alice (Linnell) Lyons. *Education:* Gonzaga University, M.A., 1945; St. Louis University, M.A., 1947; Milltown Park, Dublin, Ireland, S.T.L., 1952. *Home and office:* 86 Riverside Dr., New York, N.Y. 10024.

CAREER: Roman Catholic priest of Society of Jesus (Jesuits; S.J.); Seattle University, Seattle, Wash., director of forensics and professor of speech, 1960-61; Gonzaga University, Spokane, Wash., professor of sociology, 1961-62, dean of students, 1962-64. Twin Circle Publishing Co., Inc., New York, N.Y., founder; currently editor at large and columnist for *Twin Circle, National Catholic Press,* and *National Register.* Conducted a daily radio program, 1970-71, and a weekly television program, 1969-71; columnist, *Our Sunday Visitor,* 1965-67. Has served as a federal labor arbi-

trator. *Awards, honors:* Medal from Freedoms Foundation, 1966, from American Legion, 1967, and from Republic of China, 1967.

WRITINGS: (With Stephen C.Y. Pan) *Vietnam Crisis,* Twin Circle, 1966; (author of introduction) Anthony Bouscaren, *Tshombe,* Twin Circle, 1967; (with Suzanne Labin) *Fifty Years: USSR vs. USA,* Twin Circle, 1967; (editor with Pan) *Voice of Peking,* Twin Circle, 1968; (with Bouscaren) *Left of Liberal,* Twin Circle, 1969, revised edition, 1971.

BIOGRAPHICAL/CRITICAL SOURCES: John D. McCallum, *The Story of Dan Lyons, S.J.,* Twin Circle, 1972.†

*   *   *

LYONS, Grant   1941-

PERSONAL: Born August 19, 1941, in Butler, Pa.; son of Grant Maxwell and Irene (Meermans) Lyons; married Bonnie Kaplan, September 1, 1965. *Education:* Tulane University, B.A., 1963; Louisiana State University, M.A., 1973.

CAREER: Port Arthur News, Port Arthur, Tex., reporter, 1964-65; *Austin American-Statesman,* Austin, Tex., reporter, 1965; Travis County Child Welfare, Austin, social worker, 1965; *Stockton Record,* Stockton, Calif., reporter, 1965-67; English teacher in Sherut La'am, Israel, 1967-68; Loyola University, City College, New Orleans, La., instructor in philosophy, 1970. Writer. *Member:* Phi Eta Sigma, Phi Beta Kappa.

WRITINGS—All juvenile: *Tales the People Tell in Mexico,* Messner, 1972; *Andy Jackson and the Battles for New Orleans,* Messner, 1976; *The Creek Indians,* Messner, 1978. Contributor of short fiction to *Nunc Dimittis* and *Occident.* Editor of *Austin Chamber of Commerce Magazine,* 1965.

WORK IN PROGRESS: A novel; two collections of short stories; *Tales the People Tell of the Supernatural.*†

M

MacCURDY, Raymond R(alph, Jr.) 1916-

PERSONAL: Born May 12, 1916, in Oklahoma City, Okla.; son of Raymond R. (an auditor) and Ada May (Eastland) MacCurdy; married Blanche Hermine Wolf, June 2, 1939; children: George Grant II, William Douglas. *Education:* Louisiana State University, B.A., 1939, M.A., 1941; University of North Carolina, Ph.D., 1948. *Politics:* Democrat. *Religion:* Christian. *Home:* 1804 Newton Pl. N.E., Albuquerque, N.M. 87106. *Office:* Department of Modern and Classical Languages, University of New Mexico, Albuquerque, N.M. 87106.

CAREER: University of Georgia, Athens, associate professor of modern languages, 1948-49; University of New Mexico, Albuquerque, associate professor, 1949-53, professor of Spanish literature, 1953—, chairman of department of modern and classical languages, 1963—. Coordinator of language programs, National Defense Education Act. Consultant to National Foundation for the Humanities. *Military service:* U.S. Army, 1942-46; became major.

MEMBER: Modern Language Association of America, American Association of Teachers of Spanish and Portuguese (vice-president, 1959-62), Hispanic Society of America (corresponding member), Rocky Mountain Modern Language Association (president, 1957). *Awards, honors:* Fund for the Advancement of Education fellow, 1954-55; Fulbright research scholar in Spain, 1960-61.

WRITINGS: The Spanish Dialect in St. Bernard Parish Louisiana, University of New Mexico Press, 1950; *Francisco de Rojas Zorrilla and the Tragedy,* University of New Mexico Press, 1958; (editor) Francisco de Rojas Zorrilla, *Morir Pensando Matar,* Espasa-Calpe, 1961; (editor) Rojas Zorrilla, *La Vida en la Ataud,* Espasa-Calpe, 1961; (editor) Rojas Zorrilla, *Lucrecia y Tarquino,* University of New Mexico Press, 1963; *Francisco de Rojas Zorrilla,* Twayne, 1969; (editor) *Spanish Drama of the Golden Age: Twelve Plays,* Appleton, 1971; *The Tragic Fall: Don Alvaro de Luna and Other Favorites in Spanish Golden Age Drama,* University of North Carolina, 1978.

BIOGRAPHICAL/CRITICAL SOURCES: La Estafeta Literaria, April 1, 1973.

*   *   *

MacDONALD, Edwin A(nderson) 1907-

PERSONAL: Born November 23, 1907, in Hazel Creek, Calif.; son of Orion (a lumberman) and Edith (Anderson) Mac Donald; married Jessie Bell MacKenzie, April 11, 1964. *Education:* U.S. Naval Academy, B.S., 1931; Naval Bureau of Ordnance, ordnance engineering degree, 1956. *Politics:* Republican. *Religion:* Episcopalian.

CAREER: U.S. Navy, 1931-62, leaving service as captain. Commanding officer on icebreaker in Antarctic expedition, 1947-48, participated in six other Arctic expeditions as commanding officer, ice expert, or task unit commander, 1948-53; led task group to construct Ellsworth Station for Deep Freeze II and III in Weddell Sea, 1956-58, commanded eight ships in Antarctic supply stations for Deep Freeze IV, 1958-59, and other Deep Freeze operations, 1959-60, 1961-62; deputy commander of U.S. Naval Support Force in Antarctic, 1958-61, penetrated coast of Bellingshausen Sea with icebreaker task unit, 1959-60, penetrated Amundsen Sea coast in Antarctic; Arctic Institute of North America, Washington, D.C., polar consultant, 1962-66; Raytheon, Waltham, Mass., technical writer, 1965-66; Alpine Geophysical Association, Inc., Norwood, N.J., director of polar operations, 1966-67; Lindblad Travel, New York, N.Y., director of ships and polar operations, 1967-72. National Science Foundation, writer and ship operations consultant, 1962-65.

MEMBER: Explorers Club, Scott Polar Research, U.S. Naval Institute, Arctic Institute of North America, Royal Geographic Society, Retired Officers Association, Audubon Society, Jackson County Historical Society. *Awards, honors*—Military: Silver Star Medal, two Legions of Merit, three Bronze Star Medals, Antarctic Medal, fourteen battle stars, Leopold Medal (Belgium), Queen's Gold Patrons Medal (Great Britain).

WRITINGS: (Contributor) R. S. Crenshaw, Jr., editor, *Naval Shiphandling,* U.S. Naval Institute, 1960; *Polar Shiphandling,* Arctic Institute of North America, 1965; *Polar Operations,* U.S. Naval Institute, 1969; (contributor) John V. Noel, Jr., editor, *Knight's Seamanship,* Van Nostrand, 15th edition (Mac Donald was not associated with earlier editions), 1972. Contributor of articles and papers on hydrographic and polar research to national magazines, scientific journals, and newspapers.

WORK IN PROGRESS: A history of the U.S. Navy and Coast Guard in polar exploration, tentatively entitled *Beyond the Frozen Seas.*††

MacDONALD, Malcolm M(urdoch) 1935-

PERSONAL: Born June 15, 1935, in Uniontown, Pa.; son of Morgan Bowman and Ruth (Greene) MacDonald; married Constance Marsh (a free-lance editor), June 13, 1959; children: Randall, Alison, Ellen. Education: Trinity College, Hartford, Conn., A.B., 1957. Office: University of Alabama Press, Box 2877, University, Ala. 35486.

CAREER: D. Van Nostrand Company, Inc., Princeton, N.J., college representative, 1958-62, science editor, 1962-68; Van Nostrand Reinhold Company, New York, N.Y., science editor, 1968-70; Pennsylvania State University Press, University Park, editor, 1970-72; University of North Carolina Press, Chapel Hill, chief editor, 1972-76; University of Georgia Press, Athens, assistant director, 1976-78; University of Alabama Press, University, director, 1978—. A free-lance editor with wife in home-based Editorial Associates. Military service: U.S. Army Reserve, 1957-62.

WRITINGS: (With Cecil E. Johnson) Society and the Environment, Van Nostrand, 1971; (with Robert E. Davis) Chemistry and Society, Willard Grant Press, 1972.

*   *   *

MACE, Carroll Edward 1926-

PERSONAL: Born December 5, 1926, in Neosho, Mo.; son of Rector Tolle (in U.S. Army) and Beatrice (Dunkeson) Mace. Education: Drury College, B.A., 1949; Tulane University, M.A., 1952, Ph.D., 1965. Religion: Catholic. Office: Department of Languages, Xavier University of Louisiana, New Orleans, La. 70125.

CAREER: University of South Carolina, Columbia, instructor, 1960-62, assistant professor of Spanish, 1962-63; Tulane University, New Orleans, La., instructor in Spanish, 1963-65; Xavier University of Louisiana, New Orleans, assistant professor, 1965-68, associate professor, 1968-71, professor of Spanish, 1971—. Member: American Association of University Professors, American Association of Teachers of Spanish.

WRITINGS: Two Spanish-Quiche Dance-Dramas of Rabinal, Tulane Studies in Romance Languages and Literature, 1971.

WORK IN PROGRESS: The Black Magi: Maya Christmas Satires of Rabinal, completion expected in 1979.

*   *   *

MacEWAN, J(ohn) W(alter) Grant 1902-

PERSONAL: Born August 12, 1902, in Brandon, Manitoba, Canada; son of Alexander H. (a farmer) and Bertha (Grant) MacEwan; married Phyllis Cline, 1935; children: Heather (Mrs. Maxwell Foran). Education: Ontario Agricultural College, University of Toronto, B.S.A., 1926; Iowa State College of Agriculture and Mechanic Arts (now Iowa State University of Science and Technology), M.S., 1928. Home: 132 Hallbrook Dr. S.W., Calgary, Alberta, Canada.

CAREER: University of Saskatchewan, Saskatoon, assistant professor, 1928-35, professor of animal husbandry and farm superintendent, 1935-46; University of Manitoba, Winnipeg, dean of agriculture, 1946-51; member of city council of Calgary, Alberta (serving as mayor for three years), 1951-63; member of provincial legislature of Alberta, 1955-59; lieutenant-governor of province of Alberta, 1966-74. Awards, honors: LL.D. from University of Alberta, 1966, University of Brandon, 1969, and University of Guelph, 1972; D.U.C., University of Calgary, 1967, and University of Saskatchewan, 1973.

WRITINGS: (With A. H. Ewen) The Science and Practice of Canadian Animal Husbandry, Nelson, 1936; (with Ewen) General Agriculture, Nelson, 1939; Breeds of Livestock in Canada, Nelson, 1941; Feeding Farm Animals, Nelson, 1945; The Sodbusters, Nelson, 1946.

Agriculture on Parade, Nelson, 1950; Between the Red and the Rockies, University of Toronto Press, 1952; Eye Opener Bob, Institute of Applied Art (Edmonton), 1957; Calgary Cavalcade, Institute of Applied Art (Edmonton), 1958; Fifty Mighty Men, Modern Press, 1958; John Ware's Cow Country, Institute of Applied Art, 1960; Blazing the Old Cattle Trails, Modern Press, 1962; Hoofprints and Hitchingposts, Modern Press, 1964; Entrusted to My Care, Modern Press, 1966; Poking into Politics, Institute of Applied Art, 1966; (with son-in-law, Maxwell Foran) West to the Sea, McGraw (Ontario), 1968; Tatanga Mani, Mel Hurtig, 1969; Harvest of Bread, Modern Press, 1969.

Portraits from the Plains, McGraw, 1971; Power for Prairie Plows, Modern Press, 1971; Sitting Bull–The Years in Canada, Hurtig, 1971; And Mighty Women, Too, Modern Press, 1974; Memory Meadows, Modern Press, 1976; Cornerstone Colony, Modern Press, 1977; The Rhyming Horseman, Modern Press, 1978. Contributor to farm magazines and newspapers.

AVOCATIONAL INTERESTS: Farming, conservation, youth work.

*   *   *

MacINNIS, Donald E(arl) 1920-

PERSONAL: Born October 8, 1920, in Jefferson, Wis.; son of Earl Carlyle and May (Williams) MacInnis; married Helen Paulsen (a teacher), January 23, 1944; children: Donald Bruce, Peter, Kristin, Martha. Education: University of California, Los Angeles, B.A., 1942; Stanford University, graduate study, 1946-47; Yale University, B.D., 1953, S.T.M., 1959. Religion: Methodist. Home: 2298 Doswell Ave., St. Paul, Minn. 55108. Office: Midwest China Study Resource Center, 2375 Como Ave., St. Paul, Minn. 55108.

CAREER: Clergyman of Methodist Church; affiliated with Methodist Church Board of World Missions, 1953-66; National Council of Churches, New York, N.Y., director of China program, 1966-75; Midwest China Study Resource Center, St. Paul, Minn., director, 1975—. Military service: U.S. Army, 1942-46; became staff sergeant. Awards, honors: D.D., Ohio Northern University, 1965.

WRITINGS: Religious Policy and Practice in Communist China: A Documentary History, Macmillan, 1972.

Contributor: The Religious Situation, Beacon Press, 1969; China Today, Maryknoll, 1969; Det Ny Kina, [Denmark], 1971; China and the Peasant Revolution, World Student Christian Federation, 1972; Gerald H. Anderson and Thomas F. Stransky, editors, Mission Trends, Paulist/Newman, Volume I: Crucial Issues in Mission Today, 1974, Volume II: Evangelization, 1976; People and Systems: China, Friendship, 1975; Christianity and the New China, Ecclesia Publications, 1976; China: Search for Community, Friendship, 1978. Editor, China Notes, 1966—.

WORK IN PROGRESS: The Maoist Vision for New Man and New Society; contributing to China: The Religious Dimensions, for University of Notre Dame Press.

*   *   *

MACKIE, (Benjamin) James 1932-

PERSONAL: Born May 21, 1932, in Salt Lake City, Utah;

son of Albert V. (a businessman) and Cleo (Holdaway) Mackie; married L. Benita Johnson (a college professor), September 10, 1955 (divorced, August 11, 1969); children: James Benjamin III, Erin Skye, Palmer Johnson. *Education:* University of Utah, B.A., 1955, M.A., 1957, Ph.D., 1963. *Home address:* R.R. 4, Box 665, Duncannon, Pa., 17020.

CAREER: Institute of Psychiatry and Human Behavior at University of Maryland Medical School, Baltimore, chief psychologist in division of child psychiatry, 1963-69, assistant professor, 1963-69, associate professor of psychiatry, 1969-78, chief of clinical psychology, 1969-78. Chief investigator in studies sponsored by W. T. Grant Foundation, 1967-71. Consultant to Peace Corps, 1965-67. *Member:* American Psychological Association, American Association of University Professors, New York Academy of Science, Maryland Academy of Science, Maryland Psychological Association (member of executive council, 1968-70). *Awards, honors:* National Institute of Mental Health grant, 1969.

WRITINGS: (With Robert Geertsma) *Studies in Self Cognition*, Williams & Wilkins, 1969. Contributor to professional journals. *Journal of Nervous and Mental Disease*, managing editor, 1968-70, associate editor, 1971.

WORK IN PROGRESS: Writing on the effects of preschool education on the academic achievement of black ghetto children, and on the effect of black dialect on the intellectual development of its speakers; work on child development, especially autistic children, on sensory changes in brain injury, and on the effects of gender change.

* * *

MACKIN, Cooper R(icherson) 1933-

PERSONAL: Born April 26, 1933, in Selma, Ala.; son of Thomas R. (a veterans' service officer) and Muriel (Green) Mackin; married Catherine Barragy (a teacher), February 15, 1958; children: Michele, Patrick, Daniel. *Education:* Troy State University, B.A., 1956; Tulane University, M.A., 1958; Rice University, Ph.D., 1962. *Religion:* Roman Catholic. *Home:* 18 Charlotte Dr., New Orleans, La. 70122. *Office:* College of Liberal Arts, University of New Orleans, New Orleans, La. 70122.

CAREER: Texas Southern University, Houston, instructor in English, 1958-59; North Texas State University, Denton, assistant professor of English, 1962-63; University of New Orleans, New Orleans, La., assistant professor, 1963-66, associate professor and chairman of department, 1966-69, professor of English and dean of College of Liberal Arts, 1969—. Member of board of directors of New Orleans Chapter of National Conference of Christians and Jews. *Military service:* U.S. Army, 1953-55. *Member:* Milton Society of America, Renaissance Society of America, South Central Modern Language Association, South Central Renaissance Conference, Louisiana Folklore Society. *Awards, honors:* American Philosophical Society grant, 1972.

WRITINGS: (With Rima Drell Reck and others) *Explorations of Literature*, Louisiana State University Press, 1966; *William Styron*, Steck, 1969.

WORK IN PROGRESS: Poetry of John Oldham.

* * *

MacLEISH, Rod(erick) 1926-

PERSONAL: Born January 15, 1926, in Bryn Mawr, Pa.; son of Norman Hillard (an artist) and Lenore (McCall) MacLeish; married Diana Chapin, May 20, 1950 (divorced, 1968); married Doris Ethel Inch, April 20, 1970; children: (first marriage) Eric, Cynthia. *Education:* Attended University of Chicago and Art Institute of Chicago. *Politics:* Independent. *Religion:* Anglican.

CAREER: United Press International, New York City member of staff, 1946-47; American Broadcasting Co., New York City, member of staff, 1947-50; WLAW-Radio, Boston, Mass., news director, 1950-55; WBZ-Radio, Boston, news commentator, 1955-57; Westinghouse Broadcasting Co., Washington, D.C., bureau chief, 1957-59, chief of Foreign Service in London, England, 1959-66, chief commentator, Washington, D.C., 1966-68, senior commentator, beginning 1968. *Member:* Association of American Correspondants (president, 1965), Reform Club (London), Federal City Club (Washington, D.C.).

WRITINGS: A Time of Fear, Viking, 1957; *The Sun Stood Still* (a first-person account of the Arab-Israeli War in 1967), Atheneum, 1967; *The Guilty Bystander*, Fortress, 1971; *A City on the River*, Dutton, 1973; *Carnaby Rex*, Weidenfeld & Nicolson, 1976; *The Man Who Wasn't There*, Random House, 1976. Author of documentary programs for British Broadcasting Corp. Columnist for *Christian Science Monitor*. Contributor of articles and short stories to *Saturday Evening Post*, *Reader's Digest*, and *China Quarterly*.

BIOGRAPHICAL/CRITICAL SOURCES: Christian Science Monitor, November 2, 1967; *New York Times Book Review*, December 31, 1967; *New York Magazine*, November 22, 1971.†

* * *

MacMAHON, Bryan (Michael) 1909-

PERSONAL: Born September 29, 1909, in Listowel, County Kerry, Ireland; son of Patrick Mary (a land clerk) and Joanna (a teacher; maiden name, Caughlin) MacMahon; married Kathleen Ryan, November 4, 1936; children: Patrick Gerald, James, Bryan, Maurice, Owen. *Education:* Attended St. Michael's College, Listowel, 1921-28, and St. Patrick's College, Drumcondra, 1928-30; qualified as national teacher, 1930. *Politics:* Eclectic. *Religion:* Roman Catholic. *Home:* 38 Ashe St., Listowel, County Kerry, Ireland. *Agent:* Curtis Brown Ltd., 575 Madison Ave., New York, N.Y. 10022; and A. P. Watt & Son, 26-28 Bedford Row, London WC1R 4HL, England. *Office:* 38 Church St., Listowel, County Kerry, Ireland.

CAREER: Writer, folklorist, and lecturer; teacher at parochial primary school in Dublin, Ireland, 1930-31; Scoil Realta na Maidine 2 (name in English, Morning Star School No. 2), Listowel, County Kerry, Ireland, 1942-75, began as teacher, became principal teacher. With his wife ran a bookstore for a time; producer as well as author of plays and pageants, and shareholder (appointed) of Abbey Theatre; initiated series, "The Balladmaker's Saturday Night," for Radio Eireann and has done other broadcasting for Radio Eireann and British Broadcasting Corp. Represented Ireland in the humanities at Harvard International Seminar, 1963; lectured at Writers' Workshop at University of Iowa, 1965; opening speaker at National Council of Teachers of English conference in Colorado Springs, Colo., 1968; founded first Irish Short Story Workshop, in conjunction with Writers' Week in Listowel, 1972; also has lectured in Germany and throughout Ireland.

MEMBER: Irish Academy of Letters, Irish P.E.N. (president, 1972), Listowel Drama Group (founding member). *Awards, honors: Bell* Award for best short story published in the magazine, 1945; Catholic Press Award for best short story in a Catholic Magazine in the United States, 1961, and runner-up (to Flannery O'Connor), 1962; LL.D., National University of Ireland, 1972, for services to Irish literature.

WRITINGS—Adult books: *The Lion Tamer and Other Stories,* Macmillan (London), 1948, Dutton, 1949; *Children of the Rainbow* (novel), Dutton, 1952; *The Red Petticoat and Other Stories,* Dutton, 1955; *The Honey Spike* (novel), Dutton, 1967; *Here's Ireland* (nonfiction), Dutton, 1971; (translator from the Irish) Peig Sayers, *Peig,* Syracuse University Press, 1973; *The End of the World and Other Stories,* Poolberg (Dublin), 1976.

Juvenile books: *Jackomoora and the King of Ireland's Son,* Dutton, 1950; *Brendan of Ireland* (photographs by W. Suschitzky), Hastings House, 1967; *Patsy-O and His Wonderful Pets,* Dutton, 1970.

Plays: "The Bugle in the Blood," first produced in Dublin at Abbey Theatre, March, 1949, and still widely performed; "Song of the Anvil" (first produced in Dublin at Abbey Theatre for International Theatre Festival, 1960; later produced in California by Ria Mooney of Abbey Theatre), published in *Seven Irish Plays, 1946-1964,* edited by Robert Hogan, University of Minnesota Press, 1967; "The Honey Spike," first produced in Dublin at Abbey Theatre, 1961; "The Gap of Life," first produced in Dublin at Peacock Theatre by Society of Irish Playwrights, October, 1972.

Author of other plays for Listowel Drama Group and of historical pageants for national occasions in Ireland, including "Seachtar Fear, Seacht La," first produced in Croke Park, Dublin, in commemoration of the 1916 Easter Rebellion and later televised. Writer of radio and television plays for children and adults, stories, and features. His stories and poems have been published in magazines in Ireland, England, United States, and Germany, and included in most anthologies of modern Irish writing. Some of his work has appeared under undivulged pseudonyms.

WORK IN PROGRESS: Short stories, national pageants and a longer untitled experimental work.

SIDELIGHTS: Initial recognition of Bryan MacMahon's work came in the magazine *The Bell,* where he was welcomed as a poet of merit by Frank O'Connor and as a short story writer by editor Sean O'Faolain. His first published collection, *The Lion Tamer and Other Stories,* received a cover note in the *Saturday Review* and such a cordial reception from American critics that it quickly went through four printings. When *Children of the Rainbow* appeared, Henry Seidel Canby called it "the richest and raciest book that has come out of Ireland for many years." It was serialized for radio-television presentation in 1973, and, like most of MacMahon's books, was also published in England. The novel and many of his stories have been translated into German.

MacMahon likes "people, people, people," and lives in a small town because it affords him an unique opportunity of meeting neighbors in all their moods. He credits the tradesmen of the town for his most valuable education and "reckons a visit to the saddler's shop essential in every day."

A life-long collector of native music, MacMahon's work on the Radio Eireann series, "The Balladmaker's Saturday Night," helped pave the way for the current revival of native balladry. As a relief from serious work, he "often writes ballads which are published in his native town by his friend the printer and are sung later in the pubs of Ireland." He is a "fluent speaker of Irish" and says that he "draw[s] much sustenance from a Gaelic background." One of the few "outsiders" who can speak Shelta, the secret language of the Irish traveling people, he considers these people the "final free" and the "outer palisades of human liberty." An article by him on the lives of the Irish travelers appeared in *Natural History* and *Merian.*

According to MacMahon, Ireland is one of the last places where a human being is valued and is an excellent place to return to after a stint of lecturing in America. He prefers to read short stories and novels in translation from other languages and cultures, chiefly those of Africa, the Philippines, and South America. He finds life exciting and the day too short for his many interests and activities, which include beagling, fishing, and wandering in Ireland.

BIOGRAPHICAL/CRITICAL SOURCES: *Library Journal,* January 1, 1952, January 1, 1955, January 1, 1967; *New Yorker,* March 15, 1952, March 12, 1955; *Atlantic,* May, 1952; *Times Literary Supplement,* May 23, 1952; *New York Times,* January 30, 1955, February 26, 1967; *Best Sellers,* March 1, 1967; *Saturday Review,* March 25, 1967; *New Statesman,* September 15, 1967; *Journal of Irish Literature,* Proscenium Press, 1971.

* * *

MacPEEK, Walter G. 1902-1973
(Hugo Jumpp)

March 14, 1902—January 31, 1973; American writer and editor. Obituaries: *Publishers Weekly,* February 26, 1973. (See index for *CA* sketch)

* * *

MACQUARRIE, Heath Nelson 1919-

PERSONAL: Born September 18, 1919, in Victoria, Prince Edward Island, Canada; son of Wilfred and Mary (Mallard) Macquarrie; married Jean Isabel Stewart, December 27, 1949; children: Heather Jean, Flora Mary, Iain Heath. *Education:* Attended Prince of Wales College, 1933-35; University of Manitoba, B.A., 1947; University of New Brunswick, M.A., 1949; McGill University, graduate study, 1949-51. *Politics:* Progressive Conservative. *Religion:* Presbyterian. *Residence:* Victoria, Prince Edward Island, Canada. *Office:* House of Commons, Ottawa, Ontario, Canada.

CAREER: High school teacher in Prince Edward Island, 1936-43; University of New Brunswick, Fredericton, assistant professor of economics and political science, 1947-49; McGill University, Montreal, Quebec, lecturer, 1949-51, professor of political science and international relations, 1952; Brandon University, Brandon, Manitoba, instructor, 1951-52, assistant professor, 1952-53, professor of political science and international relations, 1953-55; elected member of the Canadian House of Commons, 1957—; Canadian delegate to United Nations General Assemblies, 12th, 1957, 13th, 1958, 14th, 1959, 18th, 1963, 25th, 1970. National vice-president of Progressive Conservative Party of Canada, 1953-55; news analyst, Radio Station CKX, 1952-55; instructor in international relations, Carleton University, 1963-64; summer instructor at Acadia University, University of Manitoba, and other institutions, 1948—; associate professor of political science, Mount Allison University, 1978—. Member of committee on international affairs, Presbyterian Church in Canada.

MEMBER: Amnesty International, Canadian Political Science Association, American Political Science Association,

Canadian Institute of International Affairs, United Nations Association of Canada, Commonwealth Parliamentary Association, Inter-Parliamentary Union, Canadian Historical Association, Canadian Foundation for Human Rights (honorary member), Oxford Committee for Famine Relief (honorary officer), Scottish Historical Society, Prince Edward Island Historical Society. *Awards, honors:* John S. Ewart Foundation grant, 1955-56; L.L.D., University of Prince Edward Island, 1978; honorary member, UNICEF of Canada.

WRITINGS: The Conservative Party, McClelland & Stewart, 1965; (editor) *Robert Laird Borden, His Memoirs*, Carleton Library Series, 1969. Contributor of articles to *Dalhousie Review, Canadian Journal of Economic and Political Science, International Journal, School Trustee, Canadian Forum, Western Political Quarterly, Christian Science Monitor, Atlantic Advocate, Queen's Quarterly*, and *Globe Magazine*. Contributing editor of *Brandon Daily Sun*, 1952-55.

WORK IN PROGRESS: Canada and the Commonwealth Caribbean, for Chateau Press; research on Sir Robert Borden; *Canada and the Middle East*, for Source Publishers.

*　　*　　*

MACRAE, Marjorie Knight   (?)-1973

(?)—July 10, 1973; American publisher, columnist, and author of children's books. Obituaries: *New York Times*, July 12, 1973; *Publisher's Weekly*, July 30, 1973.

*　　*　　*

MADAY, Bela C(harles)   1912-

PERSONAL: Born November 3, 1912, in Prague, Austria; son of Stephan (a psychiatrist) and Viktoria (Maxa) Maday; married Maria Szollosy (a secretary), January 4, 1940; children: Kathryn (Mrs. James Fairbairn), Steven Z. *Education:* Pazmany University, Ph.D., 1937; Springfield College, post-doctoral study, 1947-48. *Home:* 4528 49th St. N.W., Washington, D.C. 20016. *Office:* Department of Anthropology, American University, Washington, D.C. 20016.

CAREER: International Red Cross, Western Europe chief of mission, 1945-47; Defense Language Institute, Monterey, Calif., assistant professor, 1948-49, associate professor, 1949-52, professor of Hungarian, 1952-57; American University, Washington, D.C., professor of research, anthropology, and East European studies, 1958-66, adjunct professor, 1966—; National Institute of Mental Health, Washington, D.C., anthropologist and program director, 1966-77. *Member:* American Anthropological Association (fellow), American Association for the Advancement of Science, Anthropological Society of Washington (president, 1972-73), American Hungarian Foundation (vice-president).

WRITINGS: (With G. A. Lipsky) *Ethiopia, Its Land, Its Culture, Its Society*, Human Relations Area File Press, 1961; (editor) *United States Area Handbook for Brazil*, U.S. Government Printing Office, 1965; *Bibliography for the Study of East-Central and Southeast Europe*, American University, 1971; *Anthropology and Society*, Anthropological Society of Washington, 1975. Also author of nine other handbooks on the languages and cultures of various countries. Contributor of articles to journals in his field. Founder and editor, *Hungarian Studies Newsletter*, 1973—.

WORK IN PROGRESS: Research in cognitive process of acculturation among Hungarian emigrants.

SIDELIGHTS: Bela Maday told *CA*, "The greatest satisfaction that I get out of writing (not unlike teaching) comes from sharing thoughts, knowledge, and emotions with others." He traces his writing career back to 1933, the year in which he won a national journalism competition sponsored by a Hungarian daily with the largest circulation. He subsequently was invited to become a regular contributor to the paper, an event which, Maday says, "certainly increased [my] self-confidence and constituted a strong drive to write."

*　　*　　*

MADDEN, Carl H(alford)   1920-1978

PERSONAL: Born February 14, 1920, in Baltimore, Md.; son of John Thomas and Russell (Morrissett) Madden; married Joan L. Clarke (an administrative aide at the Smithsonian Institution), December 26, 1944; children: John T., James M., Martin C., Corey Beth. *Education:* University of Virginia, Charlottesville, B.A. (with honors), 1942, M.A., 1951, Ph.D., 1954; Harvard University, graduate study, 1947-48. *Residence:* Alexandria, Va. *Office:* School of Business Administration, American University, Washington, D.C. 20016.

CAREER: Virginia Polytechnic Institute (now Virginia Polytechnic Institute and State University), Blacksburg, instructor in English, 1946-48; Federal Reserve Bank of New York, New York, N.Y., public information officer, 1954, chief of Public Information Division, 1954-57, manager of public information department, 1957-60; Lehigh University, Bethlehem, Pa., professor of economics and dean of College of Business Administration, 1960-63; Chamber of Commerce of the United States, Washington, D.C., director of economic research, 1963-65, chief economist, 1965-76; American University, Washington, D.C., professor of business, 1976-78. Instructor at Rutgers University, 1954, American Institute of Banking, 1954-58, and New York University, 1958-60. *Military service:* U.S. Coast Guard Reserve, 1942-46; became lieutenant commander. *Member:* American Economic Association, American Statistical Association, World Future Society.

WRITINGS: The Money Side of the Street, Federal Reserve Bank of New York, 1959; *Understanding Economics*, Chamber of Commerce of the United States, 1968; *The Economic Process*, Scott, Foresman, 1970; *Clash of Culture*, National Planning Association, 1972. Contributor of articles to industry trade association journals.

WORK IN PROGRESS: A New Concept of Growth.

AVOCATIONAL INTERESTS: Tennis.

(Died October 8, 1978)

*　　*　　*

MAHONEY, John (Francis)   1929-

PERSONAL: Born May 19, 1929, in Detroit, Mich.; son of J. Frank and Rosine (Mulreney) Mahoney; children: Penelope (Mrs. Charles Goergen), Thomas, Brendan, Mildred. *Education:* Studied at Sacred Heart Seminary; University of Detroit, B.A., 1950, M.A., 1952; University of North Carolina, Ph.D., 1956. *Home:* 895 High Mountain Rd., North Haledon, N.J. 07508. *Office:* Morrison Hall, William Paterson College, Wayne, N.J. 07470.

CAREER: University of North Carolina at Chapel Hill, instructor in English, 1953-56; Duke University, Durham, N.C., instructor in Latin, 1954-56; Duquesne University, Pittsburgh, Pa., assistant professor, 1956-59, associate professor of English, 1959-61; University of Detroit, Detroit, Mich., associate professor, 1961-63, professor of English and comparative literature and chairman of department of English, 1963-69, dean of College of Arts and Sciences, 1969-73; Walden University, Naples, Fla., dean, 1973-74; William Paterson College of New Jersey, Wayne, vice-president for academic affairs, 1974—. *Member:* Modern Language Association of America, Mediaeval Academy of America, Dante Society of America, International Federation of Comparative Literature, South Atlantic Modern Language Association.

WRITINGS: Parousia (poems), Harlo Pocket Books, 1955; (editor with John Schmittroth) *The Insistent Present* (textbook), Houghton, 1970; (compiler with Schmittroth) *New Poets, New Music,* Winthrop, 1970; (compiler with Schmittroth) *New Fiction, Non-Fiction,* Winthrop, 1971. General editor, "American Authors and Critics" series, 12 volumes, Holt, 1962—. Contributor to and reviewer for literary quarterlies. Editor, *Annuale Mediaevale,* 1957-64.

WORK IN PROGRESS: A book, *On Learning Depots; A Second Life,* a collection of poems.

* * *

MAHONY, Elizabeth Winthrop   1948-
(Elizabeth Winthrop)

PERSONAL: Born September 14, 1948, in Washington, D.C.; daughter of Stewart J. O. (a writer and editor) and Patricia (Hankey) Alsop; married Walter B. Mahony III (an architect and urban planner), June 13, 1970. *Education:* Sarah Lawrence College, B.A., 1970. *Residence:* New York, N.Y.

CAREER: Berkshire Eagle, Pittsfield, Mass., reporter, 1969; Harper & Row Publishers, Inc., New York, N.Y., assistant editor of "Harper Junior Books," 1971-73.

WRITINGS—Juveniles; under name Elizabeth Winthrop: *Bunk Beds,* Harper, 1972; *Walking Away,* Harper, 1973; *A Little Demonstration of Affection,* Harper, 1975; *Potbellied Possums,* Holiday House, 1977; *That's Mine!,* Holiday House, 1977; *Knock, Knock, Who's There?,* Holiday House, 1978. Contributor to *New England Review.*

WORK IN PROGRESS: Journey to the Bright Kingdom, for Holiday House; *Maybe That Will Make You Happy* and *He Just Wants to Play with Me,* for Harper.

* * *

MALAN, Roy Mark   1911-
(Roy Mark-Alan)

PERSONAL: Original name, Renato Marco Malan; name legally changed upon receiving U.S. citizenship; born December 15, 1911, in Turin, Italy; son of Guido (a physician) and Augusta (Peyrot) Malan; children: one son, one daughter. *Education:* Turin University, M.D., 1935; London University, D.P.H., 1950, D.I.H., 1954. *Home:* 10 Park Ave., New York, N.Y. 10016.

CAREER: Assistant in hospital surgical departments, Turin, Italy, 1937-40; Ministry of Health, Rome, Italy, provincial medical inspector of health, 1948-52; United Nations, World Health Organization, serving as regional health officer in various countries, as country representative, then medical liaison officer at United Nations Headquarters, 1952-74; U.S. Department of State, Agency for International Development, Washington, D.C., medical consultant and team leader in African countries, 1977. *Military service:* Italian Army, 1940-43; became lieutenant; received Military

Cross for bravery. Allied Military Government, Public Health and Welfare Division, 1945-46.

WRITINGS—Under pseudonym Roy Mark-Alan: *Whitecoats under Fire,* Helios, 1972. Also author of about twenty-five articles and scientific publications.

WORK IN PROGRESS: The Vatican Edict; A Waldensian Saga: The Story of the Martins.

* * *

MALECKI, Edward S(tanley)   1938-

PERSONAL: Born November 16, 1938, in Chicago, Ill.; son of Edward Stanley (a business executive) and Lucele (May) Malecki; married Judith Sobczak (a teacher); children: Stephen. *Education:* University of Illinois, A.B., 1961, LL.B., 1963, M.A., 1965, Ph.D., 1969. *Politics:* "Left." *Home:* 2225 Midwick Dr., Altadena, Calif. 91001. *Office:* Department of Political Science, California State University, Los Angeles, Calif. 90032.

CAREER: Variously employed as a factory worker, salesman, bar and grill man, and traffic expediter; California State University, Los Angeles, assistant professor, 1967-71, associate professor, 1971-75, professor of political science, 1975—. *Member:* American Sociological Association, American Political Science Association, Caucus for a New Political Science (chairman, 1970-71; member of executive committee, 1970-72, 1976-77), Phi Kappa Phi.

WRITINGS: (Editor with H. R. Mahood) *Group Politics: A New Emphasis,* Scribner, 1972. Contributor to *Journal of Politics, Caucus Cable, Caucus Newsletter, Dictionary of American History, Western Political Quarterly,* and *Radical Politics.*

WORK IN PROGRESS: Radical Change and the Liberal State.

* * *

MALTZ, Albert   1908-

PERSONAL: Born October 28, 1908, in Brooklyn, N.Y.; son of Bernard (a builder) and Lena (Sherry) Maltz; married Margaret Larkin, 1937 (divorced, 1963); married Rosemary Wylde, 1964 (died, 1968); married Esther Engelberg, 1969; children: (first marriage) Peter, Katherine. *Education:* Columbia University, A.B. (honors), 1930; Yale University, graduate study, 1930-32. *Agent:* Roslyn Targ Agency, 325 East 57th St., New York, N.Y. 10022. *Office:* c/o Author's League of America, 234 West 44th St., New York, N.Y. 10036.

CAREER: Novelist, playwright, and film writer; began as a dramatist, collaborating on first Broadway play while still at Yale University. Member of executive board, Theatre Union, Inc., 1933-37; teacher of playwriting at New York University School of Adult Education, 1937-41, and at Rocky Mountain Writers' Conference, 1939, 1940; became writer for films in Hollywood in 1941. In 1947 Maltz was one of the prominent film writers indicted for contempt of Congress after refusing to tell the House Un-American Activities Committee whether or not he was a Communist; he served a prison term from June, 1950 to April, 1951. *Member:* Authors League of America (member of executive board, 1936-41), Authors Guild, American Arbitration Association (arbitrator, 1936-41), Writers Guild of America West (president, 1946-48), Phi Beta Kappa. *Awards, honors:* First prize, New Theatre League contest, 1935, for play, "Private Hicks"; O. Henry Memorial Award, 1938, for short story, "The Happiest Man on Earth"; Academy of

Motion Picture Arts and Sciences awards, 1943, for "Moscow Strikes Back," and 1945, for "The House I Live In"; Silver Medal of Commonwealth Club, 1950, for *The Journey of Simon McKeever;* Normandy Pen Award, 1952.

WRITINGS: (With George Sklar) "Merry Go Round" (play), first produced Off-Broadway at Provincetown Playhouse, April 22, 1932; (with Sklar) *Peace on Earth* (play; first produced in New York at Civic Repertory Theatre, November 29, 1933), Samuel French, 1934; *Black Pit* (play; first produced in New York at Civic Repertory Theatre, March 20, 1935), Putnam, 1935; *The Way Things Are and Other Stories,* International Publishers, 1938; *The Underground Stream: An Historical Novel of a Moment in the American Winter,* Little, Brown, 1940; *The Cross and the Arrow* (novel), Little, Brown, 1944; *The Journey of Simon McKeever* (novel), Little, Brown, 1949; *The Citizen Writer* (essays), International Publishers, 1950; *Off-Broadway* (short stories), Aufbau Verlag (Berlin), 1960; *A Tale of One January: A Novel,* Calder & Boyars, 1966; *Afternoon in the Jungle: The Selected Short Stories of Albert Maltz,* Liveright, 1970, new edition, 1971.

Screenplays: (With W. R. Burnett) "This Gun for Hire," Paramount, 1941; (with Delmar Daves) "Destination Tokyo," Warner Brothers, 1943; (writer of English commentary) "Moscow Strikes Back," Republic, 1943; "Pride of the Marines," Warner Brothers, 1945; "The House I Live In," Paramount, 1945; (with Ring Lardner, Jr.) "Cloak and Dagger," Warner Brothers, 1946; (with Marvin Wald) "The Naked City," Universal, 1948; "Two Mules for Sister Sara," Universal, 1970; (with Sidney Fleishman) "Scalawag," Paramount, 1973.

Author of radio script, "Red Head Baker" (produced by CBS, 1937), published in *One Hundred Non-Royalty Radio Plays,* Greenberg, 1941. One-act plays and short stories have appeared in anthologies, including *Best Short Stories,* 1936, 1939, 1941, *O. Henry Memorial Award Prize Stories,* 1938, 1941, *Best Short Plays of the Social Theatre,* 1939, and *Best American Short Stories.* Contributor to *New Yorker, Saturday Evening Post, Harper's, Southern Review,* and other periodicals. Editor, *Equality,* 1939-40.

AVOCATIONAL INTERESTS: Swimming, walking, chess, American history.

BIOGRAPHICAL/CRITICAL SOURCES: Scholastic, March 5, 1938; *Wilson Library Bulletin,* September, 1939; *New Republic,* April 29, 1946, May 13, 1946.

*   *   *

MANDELBAUM, David G(oodman) 1911-

PERSONAL: Born August 22, 1911, in Chicago, Ill.; son of Samuel and Lena (Goodman) Mandelbaum; married Ruth Weiss (an educator), May 23, 1943; children: Michael, Susan, Jonathan (deceased). *Education:* Northwestern University, B.A., 1932; Yale University, Ph.D., 1936. *Religion:* Jewish. *Residence:* Berkeley, Calif. *Office:* Department of Anthropology, University of California, Berkeley, Calif. 94720.

CAREER: National Research Council fellow in India, 1937-38; University of Minnesota, Minneapolis, 1938-46, began as instructor, became assistant professor of anthropology; University of California, Berkeley, associate professor, 1946-48, professor of anthropology, 1948—, chairman of department, 1955-57, chairman of Center for South Asia Studies, 1965-68. Research analyst, U.S. Government, Washington, D.C., 1942-43; chief of Indian-Ceylon section,

Office of Research and Intelligence, U.S. Department of State, 1945-46. U.S. National Commission for UNESCO, member, 1957-62, chairman of social sciences committee, 1960-62; trustee and member of executive committee, American Institute of Indian Studies, 1965-70. Did field work in South India, 1937-38, 1949-50, 1958, 1969-70, 1973, 1977, 1978, Burma, 1945, North India, 1963-64, and among San Carlos Apache, Plains Cree, and Chippewa. *Military service:* U.S. Army, 1943-45; became major.

MEMBER: American Anthropological Association (member of executive board, 1955-58), Association for Asian Studies, Society for Applied Anthropology (member of executive committee, 1954-56), Royal Anthropological Institute of Great Britain and Ireland (fellow), Sigma Xi. *Awards, honors:* Fellowships of Carnegie Foundation, 1941-42, Guggenheim Foundation, 1949-50; Fulbright research professor at Cambridge University, 1953; fellow, Center for Advanced Studies in the Behavioral Sciences, 1957-58; senior fellow, American Institute of Indian Studies, 1963-64.

WRITINGS: The Plains Cree, American Museum of Natural History, 1940, reprinted, AMS Press, 1977, enlarged edition, University of Regina, 1978; (editor) *Selected Writings of Edward Sapir,* University of California Press, 1949; *Soldier Groups and Negro Soldiers,* University of California Press, 1952; *Change and Continuity in Jewish Life* (booklet), North Shore Congregation Israel (Glencoe, Ill.), 1955; (editor) Edward Sapir, *Culture, Language, and Personality,* University of California Press, 1956; (editor with Ethel Albert and Gabriel W. Lasker, and contributor) *The Teaching of Anthropology,* University of California Press, 1963, abridged edition, 1967; (editor with Albert and Lasker) *Resources for the Teaching of Anthropology,* University of California Press, 1963; *Anthropology and People: The World of the Plains Cree* (university lecture), University of Saskatchewan, 1967; *Society in India,* University of California Press, Volume I: *Continuity and Change,* 1970, Volume II: *Change and Continuity,* 1970; *Human Fertility in India,* University of California Press, 1973.

Contributor: *Primite Art,* Art Gallery, University of Minnesota, 1940; Leslie Spier, A. I. Hallowell, and S. S. Newman, editors, *Language, Culture and Personality,* [Wisconsin], 1941; R. N. Anshen, editor, *The Family: Its Function and Destiny,* Harper, 1949; R. F. Spencer, editor, *Method and Perspective in Anthropology,* University of Minnesota Press, 1954; *Ghurye Felicitation Volume,* Popular Book Depot (Bombay), 1954; McKim Marriott, editor, *Village India,* University of Chicago Press, 1955; R. L. Lee and others, editors, *Contemporary Social Issues,* Crowell, 1955; H. L. Shapiro, editor, *Man, Culture, and Society,* Oxford University Press, 1956; W. L. Thomas, editor, *Current Anthropology,* University of Chicago Press, 1956; Marshall Sklare, editor, *The Jews: Social Patterns of an American Group,* Free Press, 1958; Herman Feifel, editor, *The Meaning of Death,* McGraw, 1959; Joseph B. Casagrande, editor, *In the Company of Man,* Harper, 1960; Charles M. Leslie, editor, *Anthropology of Folk Religion,* Vintage Books, 1960; Stanley Diamond, editor, *Culture and History,* Columbia University Press, 1960; T. N. Madan and G. Sarana, editors, *Indian Anthropology,* Asia Publishing House (Bombay), 1962; S. M. Farber and R.H.L. Wilson, editors, *Conflict and Creativity,* McGraw, 1962; S. P. Lucia, editor, *Alcohol and Civilization,* McGraw, 1964; Albert Love and J. S. Childers, editors, *Listen to Leaders in Science,* McKay, 1965; Robert L. Fulton, editor, *Death and Identity,* Wiley, 1965; C. L. Riley and W. W. Taylor, editors, *American Historical Anthropology,* Southern Illinois University

Press, 1967; Bernard S. Cohen and Milton Singer, editors, *Structure and Change in Indian Society,* Aldine, 1968; R. L. Breeden, editor, *Vanishing Peoples of the Earth,* National Geographic Society, 1968.

Author of foreword or introduction: "Civilization of India Series," University of Chicago, 1956; W. H. and C. V. Wiser, *Behind Mud Walls,* University of California Press, 1963.

Writer of book-length course materials, including "Materials for a Bibliography of the Ethnology of India" and "The System of Caste in India," Parts I-II. Contributor to *New Century Cyclopedia of Names, Encyclopaedia Britannica, Collier's Encyclopedia, Dictionary of American Biography, International Encyclopedia of the Social Sciences,* and year-books. About one hundred articles and reviews have been published in a variety of journals.

WORK IN PROGRESS: Manuscripts on religion, on social organization, and on the Todas, a tribe of South India.

* * *

MANDELL, Mel 1926-

PERSONAL: Born March 19, 1926, in Boston, Mass.; son of Maurice Sylvester (a businessman) and Sylvia (Burg) Mandell; children: Matthew Isaak. *Education:* Columbia University, B.S.E.E., 1945, M.A., 1950. *Home:* 3206 Fairfield Ave., Riverdale, N.Y. 10463. *Office:* Editor, *Computer Decisions* Magazine, 50 Essex St., Rochelle Park, N.J. 07662. *Lecture agent:* Lecture Consultants, 190 Mineola Ave., Mineola, N.Y.

CAREER: Electronic Design, New York City, associate editor, 1954-55; *Research & Engineering,* Stamford, Conn., editor, 1955-57; *Dun's Review & Modern Industry,* New York City, senior editor, 1957-61; United Technical Publications, Garden City, N.Y., editorial director, 1964-69; *Data Product News,* New York City, editorial adviser, 1969-72; *Electronic Business,* Boston, Mass., consulting editor, 1977-78; *Computer Decisions,* Rochelle Park, N.J., editor, 1978—. Contributing editor, *Innovation,* 1971-72. Lecturer on television and radio programs on subject of personal security. *Military service:* U.S. Navy, 1944-46, 1950-52; became lieutenant.

WRITINGS: Being Safe, Saturday Review Press, 1972; *The Handbook of Business and Industrial Security and Protection,* Prentice-Hall, 1973; *1001 Ways to Operate Your Business More Profitably,* Dow-Jones Irwin, 1975; *Handbook of Home Security,* Dell, 1978. Contributor to *Ladies Home Journal, Publishers Weekly, New York Magazine, New York Times, Apartment Life, Money,* and *Family Circle.*

* * *

MANDELSTAMM, Allan B(eryle) 1928-

PERSONAL: Born October 18, 1928, in Saginaw, Mich.; son of Jonas (a pharmacist) and Helen (Weinberg) Mandelstamm; married Marie Buhlmeyer (a physician), September 1, 1967. *Education:* University of Michigan, A.B. (with great distinction), 1950, A.M. (with great distinction), 1951, Ph.D., 1962. *Home:* 600 Landsdowne Dr. S.E., Blacksburg, Va. 24060. *Office:* Department of Economics, Virginia Polytechnic Institute and State University, Blacksburg, Va. 24061.

CAREER: University of Michigan, Ann Arbor, instructor in economics, 1954-56; Northwestern University, Evanston, Ill., instructor in economics, 1957-59; Vanderbilt Univer-

sity, Nashville, Tenn., assistant professor of economics and business administration, 1959-63; Michigan State University, East Lansing, associate professor, 1963-67, professor of economics, 1967-74; Virginia Polytechnic Institute and State University, Blacksburg, professor of economics, 1974—. Visiting professor of business administration, Dartmouth College, 1970; visiting professor of economics and business administration, University of Florida, 1972; lecturer at National Student Conference on Social Problems, 1971. Adviser on manpower problems to Government of Thailand, 1965; consultant to Council of Economic Education, 1965-66, and Bank of Ghana, 1971.

MEMBER: American Economic Association, Industrial Relations Research Association, Associated Appraisers of Impaired Earning Capacity, American Association of University Professors, Midwest Economic Association, Phi Beta Kappa, Phi Kappa Phi, Phi Eta Sigma, Sigma Delta Pi. *Awards, honors:* Ford Foundation fellowship, 1962.

WRITINGS: (With William Haber and Harold M. Levinson) *Labor Relations and Productivity in the Building Trades,* Ann Arbor Bureau of Industrial Relations, University of Michigan, 1956; (contributor) *1963 Proceedings of the Annual Seminar for Manpower in Developing Countries,* U.S. Department of State, 1964; (contributor) K. S. Panich, editor, *Current and Projected Secondary Education Programs for Thailand: A Manpower and Educational Development Planning Project,* Educational Planning Office, Ministry of Education (Bangkok, Thailand), 1966. Also editor of *Readings in Economics.* Contributor to *Groliers International Encyclopedia* and *Dushkin Encyclopedia of Economics.* Contributor of articles to *Industrial Relations, Industrial and Labor Relations Review,* and *Journal of Economic Education* and of music reviews to various publications.

WORK IN PROGRESS: Principles of Economics, for Wiley; *Attitudes of Economists toward the Sub-Disciplines.*

AVOCATIONAL INTERESTS: Photography, high fidelity, collecting phonograph albums.

* * *

MANLEY, Ruth Rodney King 1907(?)-1973 (Ruth Rodney King)

1907(?)—April 3, 1973; American poet and short story writer. Obituaries: *Washington Post,* April 10, 1973; *New York Times,* April 11, 1973.

* * *

MANN, Charles W., Jr. 1929-

PERSONAL: Born December 29, 1929, in Altoona, Pa.; son of Charles W. and Elizabeth (Warner) Mann; married Nan Gullo, July 9, 1960 (divorced, 1970); married Nancy McCall, November 23, 1977; children: (first marriage) Molly. *Education:* Pennsylvania State University, B.A., 1952, M.A., 1954; Rutgers University, M.L.S., 1961. *Home:* 416 South Allen St., State College, Pa. 16801. *Agent:* Robert Lescher, 155 East 71st St., New York, N.Y. 10021. *Office:* W342 Pattee Library, Pennsylvania State University, University Park, Pa. 16802.

CAREER: Pennsylvania State University, University Park, 1954—, currently professor of English and chief of rare books and special collections. *Member:* Grolier Club. *Awards, honors:* Cited for outstanding contributions to the Pennsylvania State University libraries.

WRITINGS: (With P. Young) *The Hemingway Manu-*

scripts, Pennsylvania State University Press, 1969. Contributor to *Fitzgerald/Hemingway Annual, American Reference Books Annual, Library Journal, History of Photography,* and *Literature East and West.*

* * *

MANSOOR, Menahem 1911-

PERSONAL: Born August 4, 1911, in Port Said, Egypt; came to United States in 1954, naturalized in 1963; son of Asher S. and Yonah H. (Shalom) Mansoor; married Claire Kramer, 1951; children: Yardena, Daniel. *Education:* Attended London School of Oriental Studies, 1936-39; Kings College, London, B.A. (with honors), 1941; Trinity College, Dublin, M.A. (Oriental languages), 1942, Ph.D., 1944. *Home:* 1225 Sweet Briar Rd., Madison, Wis. 53715. *Office:* University of Wisconsin, 1220 Linden Dr., Madison, Wis. 53706.

CAREER: Teacher in secondary schools in United Kingdom and Ireland, 1932-42, 1944-46; Ministry of Information, London, England, reader in Arabic and Hebrew, 1942-44; Department of Education, Palestine Government, Jerusalem, senior education officer, 1946-49; British Embassy, Tel Aviv, Israel, chief interpreter and assistant press attache, 1949-54; Johns Hopkins University, Baltimore, Md., lecturer in modern and classical Arabic and research associate, 1954-55; University of Wisconsin—Madison, assistant professor, 1955, associate professor, 1955-61, professor of Hebrew and Semitic studies, 1961—, Joseph L. Baron Professor in Semitic Studies, 1974, chairman of department, 1955-77. Member of College Entrance Examination Board in Hebrew for College Testing Service, 1962-64, chairman, 1964-69.

MEMBER: International Studies Association, National Association of Professors of Hebrew (member of executive board, 1975—), Association for Jewish Studies, American Oriental Society (president of Midwest branch, 1971), Society of Biblical Literature (president of Midwest branch, 1969-70), Middle East Institute, Middle East Studies Association, Wisconsin Council of Writers (member of advisory board). *Awards, honors:* Fulbright grant, 1953-54; Kohut research grant, Yale University, 1954-55; National Association of Educational Broadcasters grant, 1956; American Philosophical Society grant, 1958; National Association of Educational Broadcasters grant, 1956; American Council of Learned Societies grant, 1958-59; research fellowship, Harvard University, 1962, 1965; awards from Wisconsin Society for Jewish Learning, 1967, 1975; Myrtle Wreath Award from Hadassah, 1969.

WRITINGS—Textbooks; all published by Extension Division, University of Wisconsin, except as indicated: *First Semester Hebrew,* 1957, 6th edition, 1969; *Second Semester Modern Hebrew,* 1958, 4th edition, 1964; *Second Semester Biblical Hebrew,* 1959, revised edition, 1973; (with Lucian Meysels) *General Survey of Hebrew Literature in Translation: The Biblical Period,* 1959, 3rd edition, 1966; *First Semester Arabic,* 1959, revised edition, 1964; *Say It Correctly in Arabic (Egyptian Dialect),* Dover, 1961; *Say it Correctly in Hebrew,* Dover, 1962; *Listen and Learn Modern Hebrew,* Dover, 1962; *Second Semester Arabic,* 1964; *Legal and Documentary Arabic Reader,* two volumes, E. J. Brill, 1964; *The Dead Sea Scrolls: A College Textbook and a Study Guide,* Eerdmans, 1964; *Biblical Archaeology,* 1964; *Selections from Exodus and Leviticus,* 1964; *Intermediate Modern Hebrew Reader,* 1967; *The Book of Esther,* 1968; *Newspaper Hebrew Reader,* Ktav, Volume I, 1971, Volume

II, 1972, Volume III, 1972; *Modern Hebrew Literature Reader for Advanced Students,* two volumes, Ktav, 1971; *Modern Hebrew Course,* three volumes, Linguaphone Language Institute, 1972; *Basic Course in Standard Spoken Hebrew,* Linguaphone Language Institute, 1973; *Modern Arabic Course,* three volumes, Linguaphone Language Institute, 1978; *Biblical Hebrew Step by Step,* Baker Book, 1978.

Other: (Translator and author of introduction) *The Scroll of the Thanksgiving Hymns,* E. J. Brill, 1961, published as *The Thanksgiving Hymns,* Eerdmans, 1961; *English-Arabic Dictionary of Political, Diplomatic and Conference Terms,* McGraw, 1961; *The Book and the Spade,* Departments of Anthropology and Hebrew Studies and Committee on Religious Activities of University of Wisconsin, 1964, revised edition, 1968; *Political and Diplomatic History of the Arab World: 1900-1967,* Volumes I-V: *A Chronological Study,* Microcard Editions, 1972, Volumes VI-VII: *Index,* Microcard Editions, 1972, Volume VIII: *Biographical Dictionary,* Information Handling Services, 1974, Volumes IX-XVI: *Guide to Documents,* Informational Handling Services, 1976; (translator) Ibn Pakuda, *Duties of the Heart,* Routledge & Kegan Paul, 1973. Contributor to *Encyclopaedia Judaica, Enclyclopaedia Britannica,* and *American Oxford Encyclopedia;* contributor of articles to professional journals. Associate editor of *Hebrew Studies,* 1976—.

WORK IN PROGRESS: A textbook, *Contemporary Hebrew-I,* for Behrman.

* * *

MARCELL, David Wyburn 1937-

PERSONAL: Born January 13, 1937, in Yonkers, N.Y.; son of Joseph Henry and Louise (Hellis) Marcell; married Gretchen Anne Kellerhouse (a teacher), July 31, 1971; children: Mary Louise, Elizabeth Anne. *Education:* Stetson University, A.B., 1958; Yale University, M.A., 1959, Ph.D., 1964; University of St., Andrews, graduate study, 1959-60. *Religion:* Episcopalian. *Home:* 116 State St., Saratoga Springs, N.Y. 12866. *Office:* Department of American Studies, Skidmore College, Saratoga Springs, N.Y. 12866.

CAREER: Skidmore College, Saratoga Springs, N.Y., assistant professor, 1964-68, associate professor, 1968-71, professor of American studies, 1971—, chairman of department, 1968-77, provost, 1977—. Union College, visiting assistant professor of American studies, 1967, visiting assistant professor, Graduate History Institute, summer, 1968, visiting professor of political science, 1972. Member of selection committee, Woodrow Wilson Foundation Fellowships, 1970. *Member:* American Historical Association, Organization of American Historians, American Studies Association, New York State American Studies Association (vice-president, 1971-72; president, 1972—). *Awards, honors:* Woodrow Wilson fellow, 1958; Danforth fellow, 1958-63; American Philosophical Society research grant, 1967; Yale University post-doctoral research fellow, 1970-71.

WRITINGS: (Contributor) Richard E. Langford, editor, *Essays in Modern American Literature,* Stetson University Press, 1963; (contributor) Ray Browne, editor, *Challenges in American Culture,* Bowling Green University Press, 1970; (contributor) Robert Skotheim and Michael McGiffert, editors, *Social Thought in America,* Volume II, Addison-Wesley, 1971; *Progress and Pragmatism: A Study of the Idea of Progress in the Writings of William James, John Dewey, and Charles Beard,* Greenwood Press, 1974. Contributor to history and American studies journals.

WORK IN PROGRESS: A volume on American studies for "Gale Information Guide Series," completion expected in 1979.

* * *

MARCUS, Ruth Barcan 1921-

PERSONAL: Born August 2, 1921, in New York, N.Y.; daughter of Samuel and Rose (Post) Barcan; children: James S., Peter W., Katherine H., Elizabeth P. *Education:* New York University, B.A., 1941; Yale University, M.A., 1942, Ph.D., 1946. *Office:* Department of Philosophy, Yale University, New Haven, Conn. 06520.

CAREER: Roosevelt University, Chicago, Ill., assistant professor, 1957-59, associate professor of philosophy, 1959-63; University of Illinois at Chicago Circle, professor of philosophy and head of department, 1964-70; Northwestern University, Evanston, Ill., professor of philosophy, 1970-73; Yale University, New Haven, Conn., professor of philosophy, 1973—. *Member:* American Philosophical Association (member of national board of officers, 1967—, currently chairman), Association for Symbolic Logic (member of executive council, 1961-63), Society for Philosophy and Public Affairs (member of executive committee, 1968—). *Awards, honors:* Guggenheim fellow, 1954; National Science Foundation fellow, 1963-64; fellow of Center for Advanced Study, University of Illinois, 1968-69.

WRITINGS: (Contributor) M. Wartofsky, editor, *Boston Studies in the Philosophy of Science,* Holland, 1963; (contributor) Irving Copi and James Gould, editors, *Contemporary Readings in Logical Theory,* Macmillan, 1967; (contributor) Raymond Klibansky, editor, *Contemporary Philosophy,* Casalini, 1968; (contributor) Leonard Linsky, editor, *Reference and Modality,* Clarendon Press, 1971; (editor and contributor) *The Logical Enterprise,* Yale Univeristy Press, 1975. Contributor to philosophy journals. Member of editorial board, *Monist, Journal of Philosophical Logic.*

* * *

MARCUS, Steven 1928-

PERSONAL: Born December 13, 1928, in New York, N.Y.; son of Nathan (an accountant) and Adeline (Gordon) Marcus; married Gertrud Lenzer (a sociologist), January 20, 1966. *Education:* Columbia University, A.B., 1948, A.M., 1949, Ph.D., 1961. *Agent:* Georges Borchardt, Inc., 136 East 57th St., New York, N.Y. 10022. *Office:* Department of English, Columbia University, New York, N.Y. 10027.

CAREER: Indiana University at Bloomington, teaching fellow, 1949-50; City College (now City College of the City University of New York), New York City, lecturer in English, 1950-52; Columbia University, New York City, instructor, 1956-61, assistant professor, 1961-63, associate professor, 1963-66, professor of English, 1966—. *Military service:* U.S. Army, 1954-56. *Awards, honors:* Fulbright fellowship, Pembroke College, Cambridge University, 1952-54; Guggenheim fellowship, 1967-68; Center for Advanced Study in the Behavioral Sciences fellowship, 1972-73.

WRITINGS: (Editor with Lionel Trilling and Ernest Jones) *The Life and Work of Sigmund Freud,* Basic Books, 1961; *Dickens from Pickwick to Dombey,* Basic Books, 1965; *The Other Victorians,* Basic Books, 1966; (editor) *The World of Modern Fiction,* two volumes, Simon & Schuster, 1967; *Engels, Manchester and the Working Class,* Random House, 1974; *Representations: Essays on Literature and*

Society, Random House, 1976; (with W. Gaylin and others) *Doing Good,* Pantheon, 1978. Associate editor of *Partisan Review.*

BIOGRAPHICAL/CRITICAL SOURCES: Kenyon Review, November, 1966; *Listener,* January 19, 1967; *Times Literary Supplement,* January 19, 1967; *Punch,* January 25, 1967; *Criticism,* winter, 1968; *New York Times Book Review,* May 21, 1978.

* * *

MARINELLI, Peter V(incent) 1933-

PERSONAL: Born July 30, 1933, in New York, N.Y.; son of Mario and Lena (Leone) Marinelli. *Education:* Fordham University, B.A., 1955, M.A., 1960; Princeton University, Ph.D., 1964. *Office:* Department of English, University College, University of Toronto, Toronto 5, Ontario, Canada.

CAREER: University of Toronto, Ontario, 1963—, currently professor of English.

WRITINGS: Pastoral, Methuen, 1971; (contributor) Paul A. Ruggiers, editor, *Versions of Medieval Comedy,* University of Oklahoma Press, 1977.

WORK IN PROGRESS: A book on the Renaissance Italian and English epic with emphasis on Boiardo, Ariosto, and Spenser.

* * *

MARION, Frances 1886-1973

1886—May 12, 1973; American reporter, screenwriter, and author. Obituaries: *Washington Post,* May 15, 1973; *Newsweek,* May 28, 1973; *Time,* May 28, 1973.

* * *

MARITAIN, Jacques 1882-1973

November 18, 1882—April 28, 1973; French Roman Catholic philosopher, educator, diplomat, papal counselor, and author. Obituaries: *New York Times,* April 29, 1973; *Newsweek,* May 7, 1973; *Time,* May 7, 1973.

* * *

MARKER, Frederick (Joseph, Jr.) 1936-

PERSONAL: Born October 28, 1936, in Medford, Mass.; son of Frederick J. and Grace (McNamara) Marker; married Lise-Lone Christensen (a professor), November 27, 1959. *Education:* Harvard University, A.B. (magna cum laude), 1958; University of Copenhagen, graduate study, 1958-63; Yale University, D.F.A., 1967. *Home:* 144 Banbury Rd., Don Mills, Ontario, Canada M3B 2L3. *Agent:* Kurt Hellmer, 52 Vanderbilt Ave., New York, N.Y. 10017. *Office:* Department of English, University College 314, University of Toronto, Toronto, Ontario, Canada.

CAREER: IBM Denmark A/S, Copenhagen and IBM World Trade Corp., New York, N.Y., executive of DP sales and policy administration, 1959-65; University of Toronto, Toronto, Ontario, assistant professor, 1967-70, associate professor, 1970-75, professor of English and drama, 1975—, graduate secretary of Drama Centre, 1971-72, director of technical training of Drama Centre, 1972-73. *Member:* International Federation for Theatre Research, American Society of Theatre Research, Society for Advancement of Scandinavian Study, Canadian Association of University Teachers. *Awards, honors:* Fulbright fellowship, 1958-59; Salzburg Seminar in American Studies, fellow,

1959; research and publication grants from Rask-Orsted Foundation, 1968, Humanities Research Council, 1970, and Canada Council, 1970, 1971, 1972; Canada Council leave fellowship, 1974-75; Nordisk Kulturfond, 1974, 1975, 1978.

WRITINGS: (Translator) Johannes Allen, *Tumult,* Hogarth Press, 1968, published as *Relations,* New American Library, 1970; (editor and translator) *The Heibergs,* Twayne, 1971; *Hans Christian Andersen and the Romantic Theatre,* University of Toronto Press, 1971; (with others) *The Revels History of Drama in English, 1750-1880,* Harper, 1975; (editor) Hans Christian Andersen, *Den nye Barselstue,* N. Olaf Moeller, 1975; *Kjeld Abell,* Twayne, 1976; (with wife, Lise-Lone Marker) *The Scandinavian Theatre: A Short History,* Basil Blackwell, 1975, Rowman & Littlefield, 1976.

Unpublished translations; plays: (With L.-L. Marker) H. C. Branner, "Gates of Courage," 1959; Einer Plesner, "The Judgment of Albert Small," 1960; J. D. Jacobsen, "The Questioning," 1960; Preben Thomsen, "The Dark and the Morning," 1961; Finn Methling, "Parade," 1962; Finn Methling, "Little Man, You've Had It," 1964; Johannes Allen, "Project Charlie," 1965; Jens August Schade, "To Save the Night," 1966; (with L.-L. Marker) Henrik Ibsen, "Rosmersholm," produced at Hart House Theatre, Toronto, 1972.

Contributor to *Encyclopedia of Distinguished Americans* and *Das Theater und sein Publikum.* Contributor of articles to *Theatre Survey, Theatre Notebook, Scandinavian Review, Nineteenth Century Theatre Research, Scandinavica, Modern Drama, Quarterly Journal of Speech, Educational Theatre Journal, Anderseniana,* and *Ibsen Yearbook.* Editor, *Modern Drama,* 1972-76.

WORK IN PROGRESS: With wife, Lise-Lone Marker, *The Theatre of Ingmar Bergman,* for Cambridge University Press; a monograph, *Edward Gordon Craig and "The Pretenders": A Production Revisited,* for American Society for Theatre Research.

SIDELIGHTS: Frederick Marker told *CA* that he "maintains a keen interest in the practical theatre and has directed numerous productions." As a playwright, he has had a handful of short works performed.

*   *   *

MARLEY, Augusta Anne   (?)-1973

(?)—July 30, 1973; American composer and poet. Obituaries: *Washington Post,* August 2, 1973.

*   *   *

MARSHALL, Hermine H(alprin)   1935-

PERSONAL: Born April 21, 1935, in Newark, N.J.; daughter of Hyman H. (a businessman) and Anita (Ackerman) Halprin; married Sumner Marshall (a physician), August, 1956; children: Randolph, Gregory, Bradley. *Education:* Wellesley College, B.A., 1957; Bank Street College of Education, M.S., 1959; Syracuse University, graduate study, 1959-61; University of California, Berkeley, Ph.D., 1967. *Home:* 27 Norwood Ave., Kensington, Calif. 94707. *Office:* Department of Education, University of California, Berkeley, Calif. 94720.

CAREER: Worked as a kindergarten teacher in New York, 1958-60; California State College (now University), Hayward, assistant professor of education, 1967-68; University of California, Berkeley Education Extension, instructor in education, 1965—; University of California, Berkeley, lec-

turer in education, 1969-77, assistant research educator, 1973-77; California State College, Sonoma, lecturer, 1977-78. Visiting lecturer at San Francisco State College (now University), 1967. *Member:* American Psychological Association, American Educational Research Association, National Association for the Education of Young Children, Phi Beta Kappa, Pi Lambda Theta, Phi Delta Kappa.

WRITINGS: (Contributor) E. D. Evans, editor, *Children: Readings in Behavior and Development,* Holt, 1968; *Positive Discipline and Classroom Interaction: A Part of the Teaching-Learning Process,* C. C Thomas, 1972; *Dimensional Occurrence Scale: Manual,* School of Education, University of California, 1976; *Manual for Revised Reciprocal Category System,* School of Education, University of California, 1976; *Task Involvement Scan,* School of Education, University of California, 1976. Also author of *Self-Evaluation of Openness.* Contributor to *Child Development, Journal of Genetic Psychology, Psychological Reports, Journal of Educational Psychology, Early Childhood Education, Young Children, California Journal of Teacher Education,* and *Journal of Educational Research.*

*   *   *

MARSHALL, James   1896-

PERSONAL: Born May 12, 1896, in New York, N.Y.; son of Louis and Florence (Lowenstein) Marshall; married Lenore K. Guinzberg, August 20, 1919 (died September, 1971); married Eva Garson Levy, May, 1974; children: (first marriage) Ellen Marshall Scholle, Jonathan. *Education:* Columbia University, LL.B., 1920. *Politics:* Republican. *Religion:* Jewish. *Office:* 430 Park Ave., New York, N.Y. 10022.

CAREER: Admitted to New York Bar, 1921, to U.S. Supreme Court Bar, 1924; Guggenheim, Untermyer & Marshall, New York City, associate, 1929-30; attorney in private practice, 1930-34; Marshall, Bratter, Seligson & Klein, New York City, member of firm, 1934-37; Marshall, Bratter, Greene, Allison & Tucker, New York City, counsel, 1937—. New York University, lecturer, 1953-59, adjunct professor of public administration, 1959-65. New York City Board of Education, member, 1935-52, president, 1938-42. Member of U.S. delegations to UNESCO, 1946, 1947, 1950; member of U.S. National Committee for UNESCO, 1946-51; raporteur, NGO Conference, Geneva, 1949; training associate, Human Relations Center, Boston, Mass., 1966-70. Member, New York City Charter Commission, 1934; New York Training School for Boys, member of board of directors, 1933, president of board, 1934-35; American Jewish Committee, vice-president, 1959-62, honorary vice-president, 1962—; member of executive committee, American Jewish Joint Distribution Committee; governor, Hebrew University. Vice-president, Natural Resources Defense Council, Inc.; member of board of directors, P.E.N. American Center and Citizen's Committee for Children, Inc. *Military service:* U.S. Army, 1917-19; became second lieutenant.

MEMBER: American Bar Association, Wilderness Society (member of council), Council of New York Law Associates, New York County Lawyers Association, Association of the Bar of the City of New York. *Awards, honors:* Butler Silver Medal from Columbia University, 1941, for contributions to political philosophy and education; distinguished public service award from B'nai B'rith, 1946; Public Education Association gold medal, 1952, for distinguished service to New York City public schools; American Veterans Committee public service award, New York region, 1952.

WRITINGS: *Ordeal by Glory*, McBride, 1927; *Swords and Symbols: The Technique of Sovereignty*, Oxford University Press, 1939, revised edition, Funk, 1969; *The Freedom to Be Free*, John Day, 1943; *Law and Psychology in Conflict*, Bobbs-Merrill, 1966; *Intention in Law and Society*, Funk, 1968. Contributor to law and political science journals, and to *Harper's, Atlantic, Saturday Review, Psychology Today*, and *American Scholar*.

WORK IN PROGRESS: Preparing a revised edition of *Law and Psychology in Conflict*, for Michie Co.

* * *

MARSHALL, James 1942-

PERSONAL: Born October 10, 1942, in San Antonio, Tex.; son of George E. (an insurance salesman) and Cecille (Harrison) Marshall. *Education:* Attended New England Conservatory of Music, 1960-61; Southern Connecticut State College, B.A., 1967. *Home:* 300 West 23rd St., New York, N.Y. 10011.

CAREER: Cathedral High School, Boston, Mass., French and Spanish teacher, 1968-70; writer and illustrator. *Awards, honors:* New York Times award for one of ten best illustrated books of the year, 1972, for *George and Martha*, 1973, for *George and Martha Encore*; Children's Book Showcase Title, 1973, for *George and Martha*, 1974, for *All the Way Home*.

WRITINGS—All self-illustrated juveniles; all published by Houghton, except as indicated: *Air We Live In: Air Pollution, What We Must Do about It*, Coward, 1969; *Going to Waste: Where Will All the Garbage Go?*, Coward, 1972; *George and Martha*, 1972; *What's the Matter with Carruthers?*, 1972; *Yummers!*, 1973; *George and Martha Encore*, 1973; *Miss Dog's Christmas Treat*, 1973; *Willis*, 1974; (with Harry Allard) *The Stupids Step Out*, 1974; *The Guest*, 1975; *Four Little Troubles*, 1975, Volume I: *Eugene*, Volume II: *Someone Is Talking about Hortense*, Volume III: *Sing Out Irene*, Volume IV: *Snake–His Story; Going, Going, Gone? The Waste of Our Energy Resources*, Coward, 1976; *Speedboat*, 1976; *George and Martha Rise and Shine*, 1976; (with Allard) *Miss Nelson Is Missing!*, 1977; *A Summer in the South*, 1977; *The Stupids Have a Ball*, 1978; *George and Martha One Fine Day*, 1978.

Illustrator: Byrd Baylor, *Plink, Plink, Plink*, Houghton, 1971; Lore Segal, *All the Way Home*, Farrar, Straus, 1973; Norma Klein, *Dinosaur's Housewarming Party*, Crown, 1974; Charlotte Pomerantz, *The Piggy in the Puddle*, Macmillan, 1974; Jan Wahl, *Carrot Nose*, Farrar, Straus, 1974; Allard, *Tutti-Frutti Case*, Prentice-Hall, 1975; Allard, *It's So Nice to Have a Wolf around the House*, Doubleday, 1977.

* * *

MARSHALL, Natalie J(unemann) 1929-

PERSONAL: Born June 13, 1929, in Milwaukee, Wis.; daughter of Harold E. (an accountant) and Myrtle (Findlay) Junemann; married Howard D. Marshall (a professor), August 7, 1954 (died, 1972); children: Frederick S., Alison B. *Education:* Vassar College, A.B., 1951; Columbia University, M.A., 1952, Ph.D., 1963. *Home:* 17 Thelberg Rd., Poughkeepsie, N.Y. 12601. *Office:* Vice-President of Student Affairs, Vassar College, Poughkeepsie, N.Y. 12601.

CAREER: Vassar College, Poughkeepsie, N.Y., instructor in economics, 1952-54, 1959-60, 1963; Wesleyan University, Middletown, Conn., teaching fellow, 1955-56; State Univer-

sity of New York College at New Paltz, assistant professor, 1964-67, associate professor, 1967-69, professor of economics, 1969-73; Vassar College, Poughkeepsie, N.Y., professor of economics, 1973—, dean of studies, 1973-75, vice-president of student affairs, 1975—. Member of board of managers, Children's Home (Poughkeepsie), 1968-71. *Member:* American Association of University Women (Poughkeepsie branch president, 1961-63; New York State Division vice-president, 1964-66), American Association of University Professors, American Economic Association.

WRITINGS: (Editor with husband, Howard D. Marshall) *The History of Economic Thought*, Pitman, 1968; (editor and author of introduction) *Keynes: Updated or Outdated?*, Heath, 1970; (with H. D. Marshall) *Collective Bargaining*, Random House, 1971. Contributor of articles to *National Tax Journal, Labor Law Journal*, and *Current Economic Comment*.

WORK IN PROGRESS: *Economics of Consumer Problems; Works of Thomas Edward Cliffe Leslie.*

* * *

MARTIN, R(ichard) M(ilton) 1916-

PERSONAL: Born January 12, 1916, in Cleveland, Ohio; son of Frank Wade and Lena (Bieder) Martin; married Marianne Winter (a professor), October 23, 1948. *Education:* Harvard University, A.B., 1938; Columbia University, M.A., 1939; Yale University, Ph.D., 1941. *Home:* 582 Blue Hill Ave., Milton, Mass. 02186. *Office:* Department of Philosophy, Northwestern University, Evanston, Ill.

CAREER: Princeton University, Princeton, N.J., instructor in mathematics, 1942-44; University of Chicago, Chicago, Ill., instructor in mathematics, 1944-46; Bryn Mawr College, Bryn Mawr, Pa., assistant professor of philosophy, 1946-48; University of Pennsylvania, Philadelphia, assistant professor, 1948-53, associate professor of philosophy, 1953-59; University of Texas, Main University (now University of Texas at Austin), professor of philosophy, 1959-63; New York University, New York, N.Y., professor of philosophy, 1963-73; Northwestern University, Evanston, Ill., professor of philosophy, 1973—. Visiting professor at Universitaet Bonn, 1960-61, Yale University, 1964-65, Universitaet Hamburg, 1970-71, New School for Social Research, graduate faculty, 1972-73, and Temple University, 1973. Associate fellow, Clare Hall, Cambridge University, 1971. Member, Institute for Advanced Study, Princeton, 1975-76. Member of advisory board, Peirce edition project, 1976—.

MEMBER: Association for Symbolic Logic (member of executive committee and council, 1950-53), American Philosophical Association (member of executive committee of Eastern Division, 1964-67). *Awards, honors:* Guggenheim Memorial Foundation fellow, 1951-52; fellow of the Fund for the Advancement of Education, 1955-56; National Science Foundation research grants, 1958-74; fellow of the American Council of Learned Societies, 1961; Vaughn Foundation research grant, 1970.

WRITINGS: *Truth and Denotation*, University of Chicago Press, 1958; *The Notion of Analytic Truth*, University of Pennslyvania Press, 1959; *Towards a Systematic Pragmatics*, North-Holland Publishing, 1959; *Intension and Decision*, Prentice-Hall, 1963; *Belief, Existence, and Meaning*, New York University Press, 1969; *Logic, Language, and Metaphysics*, New York University Press, 1971; *Whitehead's Categoreal Scheme and Other Papers*, Nijhoff, 1974; (editor with Alan Anderson and Ruth Marcus) *The Logical*

Enterprise, Yale University Press, 1975; *Events, Reference, and Logical Form,* Catholic University of America Press, 1978; *Semiotics and Linguistic Structure,* State University of New York Press, 1978; *Peirce's Logic of Relations and Other Studies,* Peter de Ridder, 1978.

Contributor: Sidney Hook, editor, *Dimensions of Mind,* New York University Press, 1960; Mario Bunge, editor, *Antologia semantica,* Ediciones Nueva Vision, 1960; William L. Reese and Eugene Freeman, editors, *Process and Divinity, the Hartshorne Festschrift,* Open Court, 1964; *Form and Strategy in Science,* D. Reidel, 1964; P. A. Schilpp, editor, *The Philosophy of Rudolf Carnap,* Open Court, 1964; Wroe Alderson, Reavis Cox, and Stanley Shapiro, editors, *Theory in Marketing,* Irwin, 1964; E. C. Moore and R. Robin, editors, *Studies in the Philosophy of Charles Sanders Peirce,* University of Massachusetts Press, 1964; *Contributions to Logic Methodology, and the Philosophy of Science; Festschrift for J. M. Bochenski,* North-Holland Publishing, 1965; S. Hook, editor, *Law and Philosophy,* New York University Press, 1966; P. Kurtz, editor, *Sidney Hook and the Contemporary World, Essays on the Pragmatic Intelligence,* John Day, 1968; J. Margolis, editor, *Fact and Existence,* Basis Blackwell, 1969; S. Morgenbesser, P. Suppes, and M. White, editors, *Philosophy, Science, and Method,* St. Martin's, 1969; R. Klibansky, editor, *Contemporary Philosophy, A. Survey,* La Nuove Editrice Italia, 1969; K. Lambert, editor, *The Logical Way of Doing Things,* Yale University Press, 1969; Hook, editor, *Language and Philosophy,* New York University Press, 1969; R. E. Wood, editor, *The Future of Metaphysics,* Quadrangle, 1970; R. Rudner and I. Scheffler, editors, *Logic and Art: Essays in Honor of Nelson Goodman,* Bobbs-Merrill, 1971; Asa Kasher, editor, *Language in Focus: Foundations, Methods, and Systems: Essays in Memory of Yehoshua Bar-Hillel,* D. Reidel, 1976; K. Lorenz, editor, *Konstruktionen Versus Positionen Beitrage Zur Wissenschaftstheoretishen Diskussion Zum 60 Geburtstag Von Paul Lorezen,* two volumes, De Gruyter, 1977; Paul Weiss, *First Considerations: An Examination of Philosophical Evidence,* Illinois University Press, 1977.

Contributor to proceedings. Contributor of articles to *Journal of Symbolic Logic, Philosophy and Phenomenological Research, Methodos, Philosophical Studies, Review of Metaphysics, Philosophy of Science, Kant-Studien, Methodology and Science, International Philosophical Quarterly, Monist,* and other journals in his field. Member of the editorial board of *Monist,* 1961—, *Philosophy and Phenomenological Research,* 1966—, *Encyclopedia of Philosophy,* 1967, *Transactions of the Charles S. Peirce Society,* 1969—, *Philosophia,* 1969—, *Kant-Studien,* 1971—, and *Philosophical Studies,* 1971—; member of board of referees of *Philosophy Research Archives,* 1974—.

WORK IN PROGRESS: Primordiality and Philosophical Theology and *Semantics and Ontology.*

*   *   *

MARTIN, Warren Bryan 1925-

PERSONAL: Born September 8, 1925, in Connellsville, Pa.; son of Edwin C. (a clergyman) and Betty (Neff) Martin; married M. Elizabeth Hart, September 4, 1949. *Education:* Asbury College, B.A., 1947; Nazarene Theological Seminary, B.D., 1950; Boston University, Ph.D., 1954. *Religion:* Protestant. *Office:* Danforth Foundation, 222 S. Central Ave., St. Louis, Mo. 63119.

CAREER: Pasadena College, Pasadena, Calif., assistant

professor of church history, 1954-58; Cornell College, Mt. Vernon, Iowa, associate professor of church history, 1958-62; University of the Pacific, Raymond College, Stockton, Calif., professor of church history, 1962-66, provost, 1962-66; University of California, Berkeley, Center for the Study of Higher Education, visiting research educator, 1966, Center for Research and Development in Higher Education, lecturer in education and specialist, 1966-69, research educator and coordinator of development, 1969-72; California State College, Sonoma, provost and professor of history, 1972-73; Danforth Foundation, St. Louis, Mo., vice-president, 1974—.

MEMBER: Association for General and Liberal Studies, American Historical Association, American Association of Higher Education, Western Association of Schools and Colleges (member of senior commission), Kappa Phi Kappa, Phi Eta Sigma, Phi Kappa Phi. *Awards, honors:* H.D.L., Westminster College, Salt Lake City, Utah, 1971; National Endowment for the Humanities grant, 1971; Hazen Foundation grant for series of seminars on national purpose and educational responsibilities, 1971-72; Fulbright research award, 1972-73.

WRITINGS: Alternative to Irrelevance: A Strategy for Reform in Higher Education, Abingdon, 1968; (with Dale M. Heckman) *Inventory of Current Research on Higher Education,* McGraw, 1968; (contributor) Joseph Axelrod, editor, *Agony and Promise,* American Association for Higher Education, 1969; *Conformity: Standards and Change in Higher Education,* Jossey-Bass, 1969; (contributor) Jerry Gaff, editor, *The Cluster College,* Jossey-Bass, 1970; (contributor) Paul Dressel, editor, *The New Colleges: Toward an Appraisal,* American College Testing, 1971; (contributor) Lloyd Averill and William Jellema, editors, *Colleges and Commitments,* Westminster, 1971; *To Whom Is the University Accountable: And for What?* (monograph), Florida State University Press, 1972; (editor) *Redefining Service, Research, and Teaching,* Jossey-Bass, 1977.

Author of reports. Contributor to *Encyclopedia of Education.* Contributor of nearly fifty articles and reviews to education journals, including *Humanities, Educational Researcher, Change, Research Reporter, Liberal Education, Teachers College, Journal of Higher Education, Improving College and University Teaching, Ethics,* and *Christian Century.*

WORK IN PROGRESS: Colleges for a New Culture, for Jossey-Bass; writing on change in graduate education.

*   *   *

MARTINS, Maria 1898(?)-1973

1898(?)—March 26, 1973; Brazilian sculptress, poet, and biographer. Obituaries: *Washington Post,* March 28, 1973.

*   *   *

MARTINSON, Robert M. 1927-

PERSONAL: Born May 19, 1927, in Minneapolis, Minn.; son of Magnus Constantine (an office manager) and Gwynne (Gagnon) Martinson; divorced; children: Michael S. *Education:* University of California, Berkeley, B.A., 1949, M.A., 1953, Ph.D., 1968. *Office:* Department of Sociology, Room 901, City College of the City University of New York, 33 West 42nd St., New York, N.Y. 10006.

CAREER: California State Department of Public Health, Division of Alcoholic Rehabilitation, Berkeley, statistician, 1962-63; Los Angeles State College (now California State

University, Los Angeles), assistant professor of sociology, 1963; University of California, Los Angeles, research specialist in School of Public Health, 1963-64; University of California, Berkeley, research sociologist in School of Criminology, 1964-67, research fellow at Center for the Study of Law and Society, 1966-67; University of California, Davis, lecturer in sociology, 1967; City College of the City University of New York, New York, N.Y., lecturer, 1967-69, assistant professor, 1969-71, associate professor of sociology, 1972—, chairman of department, 1970—. Lecturer in sociology, Sacramento State College (now California State University), 1965. Consultant to Governor's Special Committee on Criminal Offenders, 1967-68, and Office of Crime Control Planning, 1969-70. Testified before President's task force on prisoner rehabilitation, 1969. *Military service:* U.S. Navy, 1945-46. U.S. Army, 1953-55. *Member:* American Sociological Association, Society for the Study of Social Problems.

WRITINGS: (Contributor) R. M. Carter and L. T. Wilkins, editors, *Probation and Parole: Selected Readings,* Wiley, 1970; (contributor) Jerome H. Skolnick and Elliott Currie, editors, *Crisis in American Institutions,* Little, Brown, 1970; (contributor) Gertrude Ezorsky, editor, *The Philosophy of Punishment,* State University of New York Press, 1972; (with Douglas Lipton and Judith Wilks) *Treatment Evaluation Survey,* State of New York, 1973; (with Lipton and Wilks) *The Effectiveness of Correctional Treatment: A Survey of Treatment Evaluation Studies,* Praeger, 1975. Author of research reports for University of California, Berkeley, and California State Department of Public Health. Contributor to proceedings. Contributor of articles and reviews to professional journals and to *Liberation, Anvil, Nation, New America, Liberal Democrat, New Republic,* and *Dissent.*

* * *

MARWELL, Gerald 1937-

PERSONAL: Born February 12, 1937, in New York, N.Y.; son of Hilton and Pearl (Berman) Marwell; married Barbara Epstein (a school psychologist), June 16, 1957; children: Evan, Nicole. *Education:* Massachusetts Institute of Technology, B.S., 1957; New York University, M.A., 1959, Ph.D., 1964. *Home:* 3509 Blackhawk Dr., Madison, Wis. 53705. *Office:* Department of Sociology, University of Wisconsin, Madison, Wis. 53706.

CAREER: New York University, New York, N.Y., instructor in sociology and anthropology, 1959-61; Bard College, Annandale, N.Y., instructor in sociology, 1961-62; University of Wisconsin—Madison, instructor, 1962-63, assistant professor, 1963-68, associate professor, 1968-71, professor of sociology, 1971—. Research associate, International Peace Research Institute, Oslo, Norway, 1969-70; visiting professor at University of Oslo, 1970, and University of Essex, 1978-79. *Member:* American Sociological Association, Society for the Study of Social Problems.

WRITINGS: (With N. J. Demerath III and Michael Aiken) *Dynamics of Idealism: White Activists in a Black Movement,* Jossey-Bass, 1971; (with David R. Schmitt) *Cooperation: An Experimental Analysis,* Academic Press, 1975; (with Demerath) *Sociology: Perspectives and Applications,* Harper, 1976; (with L. Edward Wells) *Self-Esteem: Its Conceptualization and Measurement,* Sage Publications, 1976. Contributor of about forty articles and reviews to professional journals, including *American Sociological Review, Journal of Experimental Analysis of Behavior, Journal of*

Personality and Social Psychology, Sociometry, Social Problems, American Journal of Sociology, Science, and *Behavioral Science.*

WORK IN PROGRESS: Experiments on the provision of public goods; a series of research articles, the first to be published in *American Journal of Sociology;* research on entrepreneurship among immigrant groups in England.

* * *

MASOTTI, Louis H(enry) 1934-

PERSONAL: Born May 16, 1934, in New York, N.Y.; married Iris P. Leonard, August 23, 1958; children: Laura, Andrea. *Education:* Princeton University, A.B., 1956; Northwestern University, M.A., 1961, Ph.D., 1964. *Home:* 2700 Grant St., Evanston, Ill. 60201. *Office:* Center for Urban Affairs, Northwestern University, Evanston, Ill. 60201.

CAREER: Case Western Reserve University, Cleveland, Ohio, assistant professor, 1963-67, associate professor of political science, 1967-69, director of Civil Violence Research Center, 1968-69; Johns Hopkins University, School for Advanced International Studies, Bologna, Italy, senior lecturer in political science, 1969-70; Northwestern University, Evanston, Ill., professor of political science, 1970—, director of Center for Urban Affairs, 1971—. Visiting associate professor, University of Washington, 1969. Assistant state director, National Center for Education in Politics (Ohio affiliate), 1963-66; trustee and member of executive committee, Plan of Action for Tomorrow's Housing, Cleveland, 1967-69. Member of local planning commission, 1965-67, and local board of education, 1967-69. Consultant to Kerner Commission, National Commission on the Causes and Prevention of Violence, New York RAND Institute, United Nations Social Defense Research Institute (Rome), *Newsweek, Time,* and others. *Military service:* U.S. Naval Reserve, active duty, 1956-59; became lieutenant.

MEMBER: American Political Science Association, Society for the Study of Social Problems, Comparative Community Research Committee, American Sociological Association, International Studies Association, Midwest Political Science Association, Chicago Association of Commerce and Industry. *Awards, honors:* Senior Fulbright fellow, School for Advanced International Studies (Bologna), 1969-70.

WRITINGS: Education and Politics in Suburbia: The New Trier Experience, Press of Case Western Reserve University, 1967; (contributor) Marilyn Gittel, editor, *Educating an Urban Population: Implications for Public Policy,* Sage Publications, 1967; (editor with Jeffrey K. Hadden and Calvin Larsen) *Metropolis in Crisis: Social and Political Perspectives* (Library of Urban Affairs book-of-the-month selection), F. E. Peacock, 1968, 2nd edition, 1971; (editor with Don R. Bowen) *Riots and Rebellion: Civil Violence in the Urban Community,* Sage Publications, 1968; (contributor) Scott Greer, David Minnar, Dennis McElrath, and Peter Orleans, editors, *The New Urbanization,* St. Martin's, 1968; (with John Krause, Jr. and Sheldon Gawiser) *Race and Representation in Detroit,* New Detroit, Inc., 1969; (with Hadden, Kenneth Seminatore, and Jerome Corsi) *A Time to Burn? An Evaluation of the Crisis in Race Relations,* Rand McNally, 1969; (with Corsi) *Shootout in Cleveland: Black Militants and the Police,* U.S. Government Printing Office, 1969; (contributor) Henry J. Schmandt and Warner Bloomberg, editors, *The Quality of Urban Life,* Sage Publications, 1969; (contributor) Clyde C. Wooten and Edward Sofen, editors, *Psychological Dynamics in Miami,*

Center for Advanced International Studies, University of Miami, Coral Gables, Fla., 1969.

(Contributor) Samuel A. Kirkpatrick and David Morgan, editors, *Urban Political Analysis: A Systems Approach,* Free Press, 1970; (with Hadden) *Suburbs, Suburbia, and Suburbanization,* Exchange Bibliography, 1972; (contributor) Ekkehardt Krippendorf, editor, *Studies in International Relations: Festschrift in Honor of C. Grove Haines,* School of Advanced International Studies, Johns Hopkins University, 1972; (editor with Hadden) *Suburbia in Transition,* Quadrangle, 1973; (with Hadden) *The Urbanization of the Suburbs,* Sage Publications, 1974; (with Robert Lineberry) *Urban Policy Problems,* Policy Studies Organization, 1975; (editor with Richard D. Lambert) *The Suburban Seventies,* American Academy of Political and Social Science, 1975; (editor with John Walton) *Cities in Comparative Perspective,* Halsted, 1976; (editor with Robert Lineberry) *Politics and Public Policy,* Heath, 1976; (editor with Lineberry) *The New Urban Politics,* Ballinger, 1977.

Contributor to proceedings; contributor to *Enciclopedia della Scienza e della Tecnica* and *Dictionary of American History.* Contributor to *Journal of Urban Law, National Civic Review, Trans-Action, American Behavioral Scientist, Urban Affairs Quarterly, Real Estate Today,* and other professional journals. Book review editor, *Urban Affairs Quarterly,* 1966-69; editor-in-chief, *Education and Urban Society,* 1968-71, and *Urban Affairs Quarterly,* 1974—; member of editorial board, *Midwest Journal of Political Science,* 1971-74, *Comparative Urban Research,* 1971—, and *Sage Urban Studies Abstracts,* 1972—.

* * *

MASSY, William F(rancis) 1934-

PERSONAL: Born March 26, 1934, in Milwaukee, Wis.; son of Willard Francis (an executive) and Ardys (Digman) Massy; married June A. Oelschlaeger, September 1, 1956; children: Willard Francis, June Elizabeth. *Education:* Yale University, B.S. (with high honors), 1956; Massachusetts Institute of Technology, M.S., 1958, Ph.D., 1960. *Politics:* Republican. *Religion:* Episcopalian. *Home:* 927 Cottrell Way, Stanford, Calif. 94305. *Office:* 105 Encina Hall, Stanford University, Stanford, Calif. 94305.

CAREER: Massachusetts Institute of Technology, Cambridge, instructor, 1958-60, assistant professor of industrial management, 1960-62; Stanford University, Stanford, Calif., assistant professor, 1962-64, associate professor, 1964-68, professor of business administration, 1968—, director of research, 1969-71, area coordinator for Computer and Information Systems Area Group, 1968-71, associate dean of Graduate School of Business, 1971, vice provost for research, 1971-77, acting vice-president and provost, 1976, vice-president for business and finance, 1977—. Member of editorial board, Harcourt Brace Jovanovich, Inc., 1963—. Ford Foundation Distinguished Associate Professor of Research at Carnegie Institute of Technology (now Carnegie-Mellon University), 1966-67. Member of Yale University Council, 1978—. Principal and member of board of directors of Management Analysis Center (consultants). Has taught seminars in Iran, Peru, Denmark, England, and France. *Member:* American Marketing Association (director, 1971-72; vice-president for education, 1976-77), Institute of Management Sciences (chairman of Marketing College, 1967-68), Sigma Xi, Tau Beta Pi.

WRITINGS: (Editor with R. E. Frank and A. A. Kuehn and contributor) *Quantitative Techniques in Marketing Analysis: Text and Readings,* Irwin, 1962; (contributor) Wroe Alderson and Stanley Shapiro, editors, *Marketing and the Computer,* Prentice-Hall, 1963; (with Frank) *Computer Programs for the Analysis of Consumer Panel Data,* Graduate School of Business, Stanford University, 1965; *Planning in Marketing: A Selected Bibliography,* M.I.T. Press, 1966; (with James Becknell, Jr., Frank, Paul Green, Charles Hinkle, Kuehn, Patrick Robinson, Alfred Rohloff, and Henry Sieber, Jr.) *Promotional Decisions Using Mathematical Models,* Allyn & Bacon, 1967; (with Frank and T. M. Lodahl) *Purchasing Behavior and Personal Attributes,* University of Pennsylvania Press, 1968; (contributor) Frank Bass, Charles King, and Edgar Pessemier, editors, *Applications of the Sciences in Marketing Management,* Wiley, 1968.

(With D. B. Montgomery and D. G. Morrison) *Stochastic Models of Buying Behavior,* M.I.T. Press, 1970; (with Frank) *An Econometric Approach to a Marketing Decision Model,* M.I.T. Press, 1971; (with Frank and Yoram Wind) *Marketing Segmentation,* Prentice-Hall, 1971; (with H. W. Boyd, Jr.) *Marketing Management,* Harcourt, 1972; (editor with M. Greenberger, J. Aronofsky, and J. McKenney) *Networks for Research and Education: Sharing Computer and Information Sources Nationwide,* M.I.T. Press, 1974. Contributor to proceedings. Contributor of about forty articles and reviews to business journals, including *Metroeconomica, Journal of the American Statistical Association, Management Science, Journal of Marketing Research, Journal of Advertising Research, Journal of Marketing, Computer Operations,* and *Journal of Business,* and to *Journal of Applied Psychology* and *New England Architect and Builder.* Member of editorial board, *Journal of Marketing Research,* 1965-71; associate editor, *Management Science,* 1967-72, and *Decision Sciences,* 1969-72; member of advisory committee, *Marketing Research Handbook,* 1969-73.

WORK IN PROGRESS: Research on microeconomic theory and planning systems for colleges and universities; writing a book with D. S. P. Hopkins, *Planning Models for Colleges and Universities,* for Stanford University Press.

* * *

MATHIS, Sharon Bell 1937-

PERSONAL: Born February 26, 1937, in Atlantic City, N.J.; daughter of John Willie and Alice Mary (Frazier) Bell; married Leroy Franklin Mathis, July 11, 1957 (divorced, January 24, 1979); children: Sherie, Stacy, Stephanie. *Education:* Morgan State College, B.A., 1958; Catholic University of America, M.S. in L.S., 1975. *Religion:* Roman Catholic. *Home:* 1274 Palmer Rd., Oxon Hill, Md. 20022. *Agent:* Marilyn Marlow, Curtis Brown Ltd., 60 East 56th St., New York, N.Y. 10022.

CAREER: Children's Hospital of District of Columbia, Washington, interviewer, 1958-59; teacher in parochial elementary school in Washington, D.C., 1959-65; Stuart Junior High School, Washington, D.C., special education teacher, 1965-75; Benning Elementary School, Washington, D.C., librarian, 1975-76; Friendship Educational Center, Washington, D.C., librarian, 1976—. Writer-in-residence, Howard University, 1972—. Writer in charge of children's literature division, Washington, D.C. Black Writers Workshop, 1970-73. Member of board of advisers of lawyers committee of District of Columbia Commission on the Arts, 1972-76; member of Black Women's Community Development Foundation, 1973—. *Awards, honors:* Award from Council on

Interracial Books for Children, 1970, for *Sidewalk Story;* awards from *New York Times* and American Library Association, 1972, for *Teacup Full of Roses;* fellowship from Wesleyan University and Weekly Readers Book Club, awarded at Bread Loaf Writer's Conference, 1970; Coretta Scott King Award, 1974, for *Ray Charles;* Newbery Honor Book award, 1976, for *The Hundred Penny Box;* Arts and Humanities award from Archdiocese of Washington Black Secretariat, 1978; fellowship, MacDowell Colony, 1978.

WRITINGS—For children: *Brooklyn Story,* Hill & Wang, 1970; *Sidewalk Story,* Viking, 1971; *Teacup Full of Roses,* Viking, 1972; *Ray Charles,* Crowell, 1973; *Listen for the Fig Tree,* Viking, 1973; *The Hundred Penny Box,* Viking, 1975; *Cartwheels,* Scholastic Book Services, 1977. Author of "Ebony Juniors Speak!," a monthly column in *Ebony, Jr!* and "Society and Youth," a bi-weekly column in *Liteside.*

WORK IN PROGRESS: A novel for young adults.

SIDELIGHTS: With the publication of her books *Brooklyn Story, Sidewalk Story, Teacup Full of Roses, Listen for the Fig Tree,* and *The Hundred Penny Box,* Sharon Bell Mathis established herself as a leader of the current trend in children's literature which advocates portraying people and events in a starkly realistic light. "There are people in [Mathis' books]," writes Eloise Greenfield, "real, live people that every black reader will recognize. With every word, [the author] reveals . . . a profound knowledge of people and an infinite love and respect for black children. . . . [However,] these books will not be a comfort to those escapist adults who refuse to acknowledge that our children do not live carefree, Dick and Jane lives."

The basis of this latter observation becomes clear after scanning the contents of the books, for the predominant themes include drug addiction, alcoholism, senility, and death. Nevertheless, continues Greenfield, "every young person trying to grow up and survive physically, emotionally, mentally and spiritually will recognize them as truth."

Carol T. Gallagher also applauds Mathis' willingness to break the "last taboo" in children's books by realistically discussing such subjects as aging, senility, and death (specifically in *The Hundred Penny Box*), but she questions the ability of young children to respond to and understand what they are reading in the way in which the author intended (at least without the benefit of adult guidance). In general, though, she praises Mathis for illustrating the strong bond of affection and respect which can exist between the very young and the very old, and also for her attempts to explore the "day-to-day effects of an older person living with a young family . . . , very different from the 'holiday visit from grandma' syndrome."

Annie Gottlieb disagrees with Gallagher's contention that young children could not understand the subtleties of such a book: "The story makes you think of whoever has been old and dear in your life. . . . The experience is universal. . . . What is so fine about this book is that it does not set out in that kind, condescending, nervous way to acquaint its young readers with the concepts of Old Age and Death. . . . It is a quiet work of art, not an educational project."

Hazel Copeland, however, feels that *The Hundred Penny Box* successfully blends both artistic and educational elements: "[It] is an excellent story of the family life and love that transcends generations and paints a very warm picture of human interactions. . . . [It] is definitely a step in the right direction toward literature that entertains and provides some positive direction for our children."

However "negative" the theme, though, Mathis never allows it to overwhelm the reader. For at the base of each story is a wellspring of hope, pride, love, and a will to survive. Although she is speaking primarily of *Teacup Full of Roses,* Greenfield's observation holds true for Mathis' other books as well: "Black strength is what this book is all about. . . . The story is told in words and symbols that confirm, without slogans, the strength and beauty of Blackness. . . . [It is] a book to grow on."

BIOGRAPHICAL/CRITICAL SOURCES: New York Times, March 27, 1970; *Jet,* April 23, 1970, May 2, 1974; *Washington Post,* March 21, 1971; *Black World,* August, 1971, May, 1973, August, 1973, May, 1974; *Redbook,* August, 1972; *New York Times Book Review,* September 10, 1972, May 4, 1975; *Ebony,* December, 1972; *Essence,* April, 1973; *Journal of Negro Education,* summer, 1974; *Black Books Bulletin,* winter, 1975; *Catholic Library World,* October, 1977; *Children's Literature Review,* Volume III, Gale, 1978.

*   *   *

MATHUR, Dinesh C(handra)   1918-

PERSONAL: Born December 9, 1918, in Jodhpur, India; son of Fateh C. and Ba Mathur; married Savitri Shankar, May 19, 1943; children: Shobha, Usha, Avinash, Vandana. *Education:* Agra University, M.A., 1941, LL.B., 1942; Columbia University, A.M., 1954, Ph.D., 1955. *Religion:* Hindu. *Home:* 24 Trefoil Lane, Brockport, N.Y. 14420. *Office:* Department of Philosophy, State University of New York College, Brockport, N.Y. 14420.

CAREER: Jaswant College, Jodhpur, India, lecturer, 1942-50, senior lecturer in philosophy, 1951-53; Maharaja's College, Jaipur, India, senior lecturer in philosophy, 1950-51; M.S.J. College, Bharatpur, India, professor of philosophy, 1956; S.M.K. College, Jodhpur, professor of philospophy, 1956-57; Rajasthan College, Jaipur, professor of philosophy, 1957-60; University of Rajasthan, Jaipur, reader in philosophy, 1960-67; State University of New York College at Brockport, professor of philosophy, 1968—. *Member:* All India Philosophical Congress (former member of executive committee), American Philosophical Association.

WRITINGS: (With Krishna Daya and A. P. Rao) *Modern Logic: Its Relevance to Philosophy,* Impex India (New Delhi), 1969; *Naturalistic Philosophies of Experience,* Warren H. Green, 1971; (contributor) Dale Riepe, editor, *Phenomenology and Natural Existence,* State University of New York Press, 1973. Contributor to *Indian Journal of Political Science, Philosophical Quarterly, Journal of Philosophy and Phenomenological Research, Quest, Philosophy: East and West,* and other publications. Member of editorial board, *Journal of Philosophy and Phenomenological Research.*

WORK IN PROGRESS: India's Philosophies of Action and Their Relevance to Social Change.

*   *   *

MATSUI, Tadashi   1926-

PERSONAL: Born October 5, 1926, in Kyoto, Japan; son of Yoshifumi and Sumi Matsui; married Mikiko Sato (a crafts artist), May 5, 1952; children: Tomo (son), Kazu (son), Sachi (daughter). *Education:* Dohshisha University, LL.D., 1951. *Home:* 1-5 Kugayama 1-chome, Suginami-ku, Tokyo 168, Japan. *Office:* Fukuinkan Shoten Publishers, 1-9 Misaki-cho 1-chome, Chiyoda-ku, Tokyo 101, Japan.

CAREER: Fukuinkan Shoten Publishers, Tokyo, Japan, president, 1968—. Biennale of Illustrations Bratislava, member of international committee, 1968-69, organizer of Japan committee, 1968—; member of council, Asian Cultural Centre for UNESCO. *Member:* Japan Book Publishers' Association (member of board, 1969—).

WRITINGS—Mostly Japanese folktales retold, for children: *Yama no Kikansha* (title means "The Train in the Mountain"), Fukuinkan, 1958; *Daiku to Oniroku,* Fukuinkan, 1962, translation by Masako Matsuno published as *Oniroku and the Carpenter,* Prentice-Hall, 1963; *Kobu Jiisama* (title means "The Old Men and Their Wens"), Fukuinkan, 1964; *Momotaro,* Fukuinkan, 1965; *Pika-kun Me o Mawasu,* Fukuinkan, 1965, translation by M. Weatherby published as *Peeka, the Traffic Light,* Walker/Weatherhill, 1970; *What Is a Picture Book?,* Editors Library, 1973; *Eyes to Look Picture Books,* Editors Library, 1978. Editor of several reference books on children's literature published by Fukuinkan.

* * *

MATSUNAGA, Daigan Lee 1941-

PERSONAL: Born June 22, 1941, in Tadoshi, Hokkaido, Japan; son of Taie and Kei (Teramoto) Matsunaga; married Alicia Orloff (a writer), April 14, 1964. *Education:* Otani University, A.B., 1964; Claremont Graduate School, M.A., 1967, Ph.D., 1970. *Religion:* Buddhist. *Office:* Department of History, California State University, Northridge, Calif. 91324.

CAREER: California State University, Northridge, associate professor of history, 1969—. Eikyoji Temple, Hokkaido, Japan, Buddhist priest, 1964—, temple master, 1976—.

WRITINGS: (With wife, Alicia Matsunaga) *The Buddhist Concept of Hell,* Philosophical Library, 1971; *Foundation of Japanese Buddhism,* Buddhist Books International, Volume I: *The Aristocratic Age,* 1974, Volume II: *The Mass Movement,* 1976.

WORK IN PROGRESS: A book, *Shinran and His Theology.*

* * *

MATTES, Merrill J(ohn) 1910-

PERSONAL: Born November 16, 1910, in Congress Park, Ill.; son of Edgar Merrill and Pauline Catherine (Neumann) Mattes; married Eleanor Lois Shutt, September 11, 1937 (died, 1941); married Clara Ritschard, September 19, 1942; children: (first marriage) David; (second marriage) Warren, John. *Education:* University of Missouri, B.A., 1931; University of Kansas, M.A., 1933; Yale University, graduate study, 1938-39. *Politics:* Republican. *Religion:* Protestant. *Home:* 5800 West Plymouth Dr., Littleton, Colo. 80123.

CAREER: National Park Service, park superintendent in Scottsbluff, Neb., 1935-46, regional historian in Omaha, Neb., 1946-66, chief of history and historic architecture in San Francisco, Calif., 1966-71, and manager of Historic Preservation of the United States in Denver, Colo., 1971-75; self-employed historical consultant, 1975—. *Member:* Western History Association, Society for Historical Archaeology, Nebraska State Historical Society, South Dakota State Historical Society, Colorado State Historical Society, Denver Westerners, Omaha Westerners, Council on Abandoned Military Posts. *Awards, honors:* Nebraska Civil Servant of the Year, 1958; Distinguished service award from U.S. Department of the Interior, 1959; best western

non-fiction award from National Cowboy Hall of Fame, merit award from American Association of State and Local History, and Silver Spur Award from Western Writers of America, all 1969, for *Great Platte River Road.*

WRITINGS: Indians, Infants, and Infantry, Old West, 1960; *Colter's Hell and Jackson's Hole,* Yellowstone Library Association, 1961; (contributor) LeRoy R. Hafen, editor, *Mountain Men and the Fur Trade,* ten volumes, Arthur Clark, 1965-72; (with John F. McDermott) *Frontier Reexamined,* University of Illinois Press, 1966; *Great Platte River Road,* Nebraska State Historical Society, 1969; *The Missouri Valley,* Teachers College Press, 1971. Contributor to *Colorado Magazine, Nebraska History, Pacific Northwest Quarterly, American West, Journal of the West, Holiday, Montana Magazine, California Historical Society Quarterly, Omaha World-Herald, Military Engineer, South Dakota Collections, Kansas Historical Quarterly, Indiana Magazine of History,* and *Annals of Wyoming.*

WORK IN PROGRESS: Research on central overland migrations and Western military posts; fur trader biographies.

* * *

MAXWELL, Richard C(allender) 1919-

PERSONAL: Born October 7, 1919, in Minneapolis, Minn.; son of Bertram Wayburn and Blossom (Callender) Maxwell; married Frances Lida McKay, January 27, 1942; children: Richard Callender, John McKay. *Education:* University of Minnesota, B.S.L., 1941, LL.B., 1947. *Home:* 18083 Sandycape Dr., Pacific Palisades, Calif. 90272. *Office:* School of Law, University of California, Los Angeles, Calif. 99024.

CAREER: Admitted to Minnesota Bar, 1947; University of North Dakota, Grand Forks, associate professor of law, 1947-49; University of Texas, Main University (now University of Texas at Austin), associate professor, 1949-51, professor of law, 1951-53; University of California, School of Law, Los Angeles, professor of law, 1953—, acting dean, 1958-59, dean, 1959-69. Fulbright lecturer, Queen's University of Belfast, 1970; visiting alumni professor, University of Minnesota, 1970-71; Ford Foundation professor, University of Singapore, summer, 1971. Staff attorney, Amerada Petroleum Corp., 1952-53; arbitrator for Writers Guild of America, Alliance of Television Film Producers, United Shoe Works of America, and Southern California Shoe Manufacturers Association; consultant to California Law Revision Commission. Member of board of directors of Los Angeles Constitutional Rights Foundation; member of Los Angeles Employee Rights Commission; former chairman of research committee, American Bar Foundation; past chairman, Council on Legal Educational Opportunities; president, Association of American Law Schools, 1972. *Military service:* U.S. Naval Reserve, active duty, 1941-45; became lieutenant commander. *Member:* American Bar Association, American Association of University Professors. *Awards, honors:* Distinguished Teaching Award, University of California, Los Angeles, 1977.

WRITINGS: (With Stefan A. Riesenfeld) *Cases and Materials on Modern Social Legislation,* Foundation Press, 1950; (with H. R. Williams and C. J. Meyers) *Cases and Materials on the Law of Oil and Gas,* Foundation Press, 1956, 3rd edition, 1974; (with Riesenfeld) *California Cases on Security Transactions,* West Publishing, 1957, 2nd edition, 1976. Contributor to *Encyclopaedia Britannica;* contributor of articles and reviews to legal periodicals. West Coast editor, *Oil and Gas Reporter.*

WORK IN PROGRESS: Revising *Cases and Materials on the Law of Oil and Gas.*

* * *

MAY, William E(ugene) 1928-

PERSONAL: Born May 27, 1928, in St. Louis, Mo.; son of Robert William (an oil company executive) and Katherine (Armstrong) May; married Patricia Ann Keck, October 4, 1958; children: Michael, Mary Patricia, Thomas, Timothy, Patrick, Susan, Kathleen. *Education:* Catholic University of America, B.A., 1950, M.A., 1951; Marquette University, Ph.D., 1968. *Politics:* "Independent, with more democratic than republican leanings." *Religion:* Roman Catholic. *Home:* 4412 Saul Rd., Kensington, Md. 20795. *Office:* Department of Theology, Catholic University of America, Washington, D.C. 20064.

CAREER: Newman Press, Westminster, Md., associate editor, 1954-55; Bruce Publishing Co., Milwaukee, Wis., associate editor, 1955-66, trade book editor-in-chief, 1966-68; Corpus Instrumentorum, Inc., Washington, D.C., editor-in-chief of Corpus Books, 1969-70; Catholic University of America, Washington, D.C., assistant professor of religion, 1971—. *Member:* American Philosophical Association, American Catholic Philosophical Association, American Society for Christian Ethics, College Theology Society (chairman of Chicago region, 1968), American Academy of Religion. *Awards, honors:* College Theology Society award, 1971, for best work published by a member, *Christ in Contemporary Thought.*

WRITINGS: Christ in Contemporary Thought, Pflaum, 1970; (editor) Jopseh Fletcher and Thomas Wassmer, *Hello, Lovers!,* Corpus Publications, 1970; *Becoming Human: An Invitation to Christian Ethics,* Pflaum, 1975; *The Meaning and Nature of Chastity,* Franciscan Herald, 1976; *Human Existence, Medicine, and Ethics,* Franciscan Herald, 1977; *Sex, Love, and Procreation,* Franciscan Herald, 1977; *The Unity of the Moral and Spiritual Life,* Franciscan Herald, 1978. Contributor to *American Journal of Jurisprudence, Homilectic and Pastoral Review, Communio,* and *Linacre Quarterly.*

WORK IN PROGRESS: A Christian Understanding of Sex.

* * *

MAYER, Harold M(elvin) 1916-

PERSONAL: Born March 27, 1916, in New York, N.Y.; son of Alexander and Rose (Kreiss) Mayer; married Florence Schulson, March 23, 1952; children: Jonathan D., Judee H. *Education:* Northwestern University, B.S., 1936; Washington University, M.S., 1937; University of Chicago, Ph.D., 1943. *Home:* 3488 Murray Ave., Milwaukee, Wis. 53211. *Office:* Department of Geography, University of Wisconsin, Milwaukee, Wis. 53201.

CAREER: Chicago Plan Commission, Chicago, Ill., research planner, 1940-43; Philadelphia City Planning Division, Philadelphia, Pa., chief of division of planning analysis, 1944-48; U.S. Office of Strategic Services, Washington, D.C., civilian geographer, 1943-44; Chicago Plan Commission, director of research, 1948-50; University of Chicago, Chicago, Ill., assistant professor, 1950-56, associate professor, 1956-58, professor of geography, 1958-68; Kent State University, Kent, Ohio, university professor of geography, 1968-74; University of Wisconsin—Milwaukee, professor of geography, 1974—, associate director of Center for Great

Lakes Studies, 1974—. Fulbright professor, University of Auckland, 1961. Consultant in city and metropolitan planning, 1950—. Member, Chicago Regional Port District Board, 1951-53; member of board of directors, Community Renewal Foundation, 1964-68; commissioner, Northeastern Illinois Planning Commission, 1966-68, and Milwaukee Board of Harbor Commissioners, 1978—.

MEMBER: World Future Society, Association of American Geographers (councilor, 1965-68), American Geographical Society, National Council for Geography Education, American Institute of Planners (president of Western Great Lakes chapter, 1956-58), American Society of Planning Officials, Transportation Research Forum, Regional Science Association, Steamship Historical Society of America, Great Lakes Historical Society, Wisconsin Council for Geographic Education, Wisconsin Association of Planners, Wisconsin Marine Historical Society, Research Clearing House of Metropolitan Milwaukee (president, 1978-79), Geographic Society of Chicago (member of board of directors, 1960-68), Phi Beta Kappa, Sigma Xi, Lambda Alpha. *Awards, honors:* Publication award, Geographical Society of Chicago, 1970; Content award, National Council for Geography Education, 1970.

WRITINGS: Railway Pattern of Metropolitan Chicago, Department of Geography, University of Chicago, 1943; *Chicago: City of Decisions,* Geographic Society of Chicago, 1955; *The Port of Chicago and the St. Lawrence Seaway,* University of Chicago Press, 1957; (editor with Clyde F. Kohn) *Readings in Urban Geography,* University of Chicago Press, 1959; (with Richard C. Wade) *Chicago: Growth of a Metropolis,* University of Chicago Press, 1969; (with others) *A Modern City: Its Geography,* National Council for Geographic Education, 1970; (contributor) William Claire, editor, *Handbook on Urban Planning,* Van Nostrand, 1973; *Freight Transportation and Metropolitan Land Use,* Northeastern Illinois Planning Commission, 1975. Contributor of about one hundred articles on city planning, urban and regional geography, transportation, and related topics to technical journals.

WORK IN PROGRESS: A new book of readings in urban geography; a book on urban land use; chapters for an urban planning handbook.

SIDELIGHTS: Although he has successfully combined careers in teaching, writing, *and* active planning, Harold M. Mayer told *CA* that he is "especially interested in [the] applications of geography to city and metropolitan planning."

* * *

MAYER, Herbert Carleton 1893-1978

PERSONAL: Born November 6, 1893, in Chicago, Illinois; son of Frank E. (an executive) and Ella (Knecht) Mayer; married Elsie Hauser, March 19, 1919 (died December 25, 1965); married Muriel L. Howard (a concert pianist), November 6, 1968; children: (first marriage) Jane Mayer Shovell, Herbert C., Jr., Ann Mayer Wattman. *Education:* Oberlin College, A.B., 1915; Boston University, A.M., 1923, Harvard University, Ed.D., 1941. *Religion:* Presbyterian. *Home:* 133 Sumner Ave., Springfield, Mass. 01108.

CAREER: Cleveland Press, Cleveland, Ohio, reporter, 1914-15; superintendent of secondary division, Chicago Council of Religious Education, 1916-17, and Ohio Council of Religious Education, 1919-20; Boston University, Boston, Mass., professor of secondary education, 1920-29; Northeastern University, Boston, instructor in aeronautical engineering, 1931-39; Bentley School of Accounting, Boston, guidance director, 1939-40; Parsons College, Fairfield, Iowa, president, 1941-47; U.S. Office of Education, Washington, D.C., specialist in higher education, 1947; Office of Military Government, U.S. and West Berlin, Germany, quadri-partite policy officer, 1947-48; American Viewpoint, Inc. (educational research firm), New York, N.Y., president, 1949-73, consultant, 1973-78. Director of training, Curtiss-Wright Flying Service, New York and Boston, 1928-30. President, Aeronautical Service, Inc., 1930-34, A.D.M. Corp., 1931-45, and Avite Products, Inc., 1932-37. Former member of advisory council, National Planning Association. Vice-president, Council for Democracy, New York, N.Y., 1940-42. Founder and director of Summer Camp Conference, 1915-23, International Sunday School Association, and American Youth Foundation, 1924-41. Member of youth board, Manhattan Borough Committee, 1959-64. Honorary marshall, Oberlin College, 1965. Director of Lincoln Educational Foundation, 1969. Co-chairman, Allied German-American Heritage Conference, 1970; former chairman of board of directors, German-American Council. *Military service:* U.S. Army Air Service, 1917-18; served as pursuit pilot; became second lieutenant. *Member:* National Council for the Social Studies, Adult Education Association, National Educational Association, Phi Delta Kappa, Rotary (president, 1945-46), American Legion, Phi Kappa Phi. *Awards, honors:* Medallion of Space and Rocketry, 1970, from the German-American National Congress for most outstanding German-American in the post-war era.

WRITINGS: The Church's Program for Young People, Century Co., 1925; (editor) *Flying Instructor's Manual,* Curtis Books, 1928; *Mechanic's Handbook,* Curtis Books, 1928; *New Footprints of the Trojan Horse,* Farrar, Straus, 1950; *Young People in Your Church,* Revell, 1953; *Toward the Prevention of Juvenile Crime,* American Viewpoint, 1954; *Who? ... Me?,* American Viewpoint, 1954; *The Teacher's Guide to Teaching Ethical and Moral Values,* American Viewpoint, 1960; *Germany and the Marshall Plan: 1948-52,* Atlantic Press, 1970. Also author of *Community Youth Councils,* 1927, *Introduction to Aeronautics,* 1930, *Diplomacy and World Security,* 1960, and *The Good American Program—The Direct Teaching of Citizenship Values in the Elementary Grades,* with Ruth F. Towne. Contributor to aviation and education journals.

WORK IN PROGRESS: Research for a book on the new Germany; research on teaching ethical and moral values.†

(Died February 7, 1978)

*   *   *

MAYERS, Marvin K(eene)   1927-

PERSONAL: Born October 25, 1927, in Canton, Ohio; son of Homer D. (a salesman) and Irma Hope (Kean) Mayers; married Marilyn A. Peipgrass (a secretary), May 24, 1952; children: Margaret Lynn (Mrs. Richard A. New), Donna Grace. *Education:* Wheaton College, Wheaton, Ill., B.A., 1949; Fuller Theological Seminary, B.D., 1952; University of Chicago, M.A., 1958, Ph.D., 1960. *Religion:* Evangelical. *Home:* 210 Timothy Tr., Duncanville, Tex. 75137. *Office:* International Linguistics Center, Dallas, Tex. 75211; and Department of Linguistics, University of Texas, Arlington, Tex. 76019.

CAREER: Summer Institute of Linguistics, Santa Ana, Calif., field researcher and translator, 1952-65; Wheaton College, Wheaton, Ill., associate professor, 1965-70, professor of anthropology, 1970-74; University of Texas at Arlington, professor of linguistics, 1974—; Texas Summer In-

stitute of Linguistics, Dallas, director, 1976—. Visiting professor of linguistics, University of Washington, summers, 1958-67. *Member:* American Anthropological Association. *Awards, honors:* Organization of American States fellowship, 1958-59; Tyndale Foundation fellowship for Philippine studies, 1969.

WRITINGS: (Editor) *Pocomchi Texts,* University of Oklahoma Press, 1958; (editor) *Languages of Guatemala,* Mouton, 1966; *Notes on Christian Outreach in the Philippines,* William Carey Library, 1970; (with others) *Reshaping Evangelical Higher Education,* Zondervan, 1972; (compiler, with David D. Koechel, designer) *Love Goes On Forever,* Zondervan, 1972; *Christianity Confronts Culture,* Zondervan, 1973; *A Look at Latin American Lifestyles,* Summer Institute of Linguistics, 1976; (with Stephen Grunlan) *Cultural Anthropology, A Christian Perspective,* Zondervan, 1978. Contributor to *Anthropological Linguistics, International Journal of Applied Linguistics,* and *Linguistics.*

WORK IN PROGRESS: Latin American Culture; Bicultural Evangelism: Philippine Focus.

*   *   *

MAYERSON, Philip   1918-

PERSONAL: Born May 20, 1918, in New York, N.Y.; son of David and Clara (Fader) Mayerson; married Ann Barkow, November 28, 1957 (deceased); children: Miriam, Clare. *Education:* New York University, A.B., 1947, Ph.D., 1956. *Office:* Office of the Dean, Washington Square College, New York University, New York, N.Y. 10003.

CAREER: New York University, New York, N.Y., instructor, 1948-56, assistant professor, 1956-60, associate professor, 1960-66, professor of classics, 1966—, vice-dean, 1970-71, acting dean, 1971-73, dean of Washington Square College and University College, 1973—. *Military service:* U.S. Navy, 1942-45. *Member:* Association Internationale de papyrologues, American Philological Association, Archaeological Institute of America, American Oriental Society, American School of Oriental Research, Colt Archaeological Institute. *Awards, honors:* Grant-in-aid, Rockefeller Foundation, 1956-57; American Council of Learned Societies fellow, 1961-62.

WRITINGS: The Ancient Agricultural Regime of Nessana and the Central Negeb (monograph), British School of Archaeology in Jerusalem and Colt Archaeological Institute, 1961; (contributor) N. Dunscombe Colt, editor, *Excavations at Nessana,* Volume I, British School of Archaeology in Jerusalem, 1962; *Classical Mythology in Literature, Art, and Music,* Xerox College Publishing, 1971. Advisory editor, *Journal of American Research Center in Egypt,* 1969—.†

*   *   *

McALLISTER, Lester G(rover)   1919-

PERSONAL: Born October 12, 1919, in Little Rock, Ark.; son of Lester G. (an insurance agent) and Clara (Brown) McAllister. *Education:* Attended Little Rock Junior College (now University of Arkansas at Little Rock), 1937-39; Transylvania University, A.B. (with honors), 1941; Lexington Theological Seminary, B.D., 1944; University of California, graduate study, 1950; Pacific School of Religion, Th.D., 1953. *Home:* 5937 Deerwood Ct., Indianapolis, Ind. 46254. *Office:* Christian Theological Seminary, Box 88267, Indianapolis, Ind. 46208.

CAREER: Minister of Christian Church (Disciples of

Christ) in Berkeley, Calif., 1950-53; Bethany College, Bethany, W.Va., associate professor, 1953-54, professor of religion and provost, 1954-62; Christian Theological Seminary, Indianapolis, Ind., professor of church history, 1962—. Visiting professor, Overdale College, Birmingham (England), 1959-60. *Member:* American Academy of Religion, American Society of Church History, American Historical Association, Disciples of Christ Historical Society, Royal Scottish Auto Club (Glasgow), Author's Club (London), Theta Phi.

WRITINGS: Our Church at Work around the World, Christian Board of Publications, 1947; *Thomas Campbell: Man of the Book,* Bethany Press, 1954; *Z. T. Sweeney: Preacher and Peacemaker,* Christian Board of Publications, 1968; *Alexander Campbell at Glasgow University,* Disciples of Christ Historical Society, 1971; (with William Tucker) *A History of the Christian Church (Disciples of Christ),* Bethany Press, 1975.

WORK IN PROGRESS: A research project on religious contributions of Robert Richardson (1806-1876).

AVOCATIONAL INTERESTS: Reading biography, collecting stamps.

* * *

McARTHUR, Charles C(ampbell) 1920-

PERSONAL: Born May 14, 1920, in Quincy, Mass.; son of Charles Melvin (a minister) and Violet (Finn) McArthur; married Nancy Elizabeth Mercer, December 19, 1946; children: Bonnie Anne. *Education:* Harvard University, A.B., 1946, M.A., 1948, Ph.D., 1950. *Religion:* Gnostic. *Office:* Career Ventures, Room 45, 51 Brattle St., Cambridge, Mass. 02138.

CAREER: Harvard University, Cambridge, Mass., University Health Services, psychologist, 1949-73, Graduate School of Business Administration, consultant for careers, 1973-75. Management consultant and career counselor. *Awards, honors:* Exxon Award, 1976-77, for innovation in management education.

WRITINGS: (Editor with Graham Burt Blaine) *Emotional Problems of the Student,* Appleton, 1961, 2nd edition, 1971; (contributor) Paul Stern, *In Praise of Madness: Realness Therapy—The Self Reclaimed,* Norton, 1972; (with John P. Kotter and Victor A. Faux) *Self-Assessment and Career Development,* Prentice-Hall, 1978. Consulting editor, *Journal of Counseling Psychology.*

WORK IN PROGRESS: Books on career counseling, on the interview, and on the Rorschach experiment.

BIOGRAPHICAL/CRITICAL SOURCES: Adam Smith, *The Money Game,* Random House, 1967.

* * *

McBAIN, John M(aurice) 1921-

PERSONAL: Born November 30, 1921, in Bottineau, N.D.; son of I.D. (a pioneer Baptist preacher) and Ada (Wasson) McBain; married Dorothy Hunt, May 30, 1943; children: Jerry, Daniel, Michael. *Education:* William Jewell College, B.A., 1944; Central Baptist Theological Seminary, additional study, 1951; University of Corpus Christi, D.D., 1969; Luther Rice Seminary, M.Div., 1977. *Office:* Staff of Stewardship Commission, Southern Baptist Convention, 460 James Robertson Pkwy., Nashville, Tenn.

CAREER: Ordained minister of Southern Baptist Church, 1941; minister in King City, Mo., 1943-46, St. Joseph, Mo.,

1946-54, Coffeyville, Kan., 1954-56, Kansas City, Kan., 1956-63, and Harlingen, Tex., 1963-72; First Southern Baptist Church, Tucson, Ariz., minister, 1972-77; Southern Baptist Convention, Nashville, Tenn., assistant director, Stewardship Commission, 1977—. Minister of televised Sunday morning worship service, 1965-72. Former member of Southern Baptist Home Mission Board; member of executive boards of Kansas and Missouri Southern Baptist State Convention Service; vice-president of Kansas Convention of Southern Baptists; member of Texas Southern Baptist State Convention Service Missions Commission; trustee of Valley Baptist Hospital, 1964-72, of Valley Baptist Academy, 1970-72. Member of Mayor's Committee on Housing, Harlingen, Tex.; member of board of Cameron County (Tex.) Cancer Society; chaplain of Cameron County Sheriffs' Posse.

WRITINGS: It Is Required of Stewards, Broadman, 1972; *The Ten Commandments in the New Testament,* Broadman, 1977.

SIDELIGHTS: John M. McBain told *CA:* "I believe the hope for the future of America is to get 'back to the basics.' This is the common cry across our nation concerning education. I believe that survival in the jungle of society created by permissiveness, materialism, and hopelessness of youth, is to be found in getting back to the basics in terms of morals."

* * *

McBRIDE, Joseph (Pierce) 1947-

PERSONAL: Born August 9, 1947, in Milwaukee, Wis.; son of Raymond Edward (a newspaper reporter) and Marian (Dunne) McBride; married Linda Mary Detra, November 15, 1969 (divorced, 1973); children: Jessica. *Education:* Attended University of Wisconsin, 1965-68. *Home and office:* 1004 North Alfred St., Los Angeles, Calif. 90069.

CAREER: Daily Cardinal (of University of Wisconsin), Madison, staff writer, 1965-69; *Wisconsin State Journal,* Madison, reporter, 1969-73; *Riverside Press and Daily Enterprise,* Riverside, Calif., reporter, 1973-74; reporter and critic, *Daily Variety,* Hollywood, Calif., and *Variety,* New York, N.Y., 1974-77; full-time screenwriter, 1977—. *Member:* Wisconsin Film Society (president, 1967-69), Writers Guild of America. *Awards, honors:* Best nonfiction book award from Wisconsin Council for Creative Writers, 1972, for *Orson Welles;* best screenplay nomination from Canadian Film Awards, 1978, for "Blood and Guts."

WRITINGS: (Editor) *Persistence of Vision: A Collection of Film Criticism,* Wisconsin Film Society Press, 1968; *Orson Welles,* Viking, 1972; (editor) *Focus on Howard Hawks,* Prentice-Hall, 1972; (contributor) *Favorite Movies,* Macmillan, 1973; (with Michael Wilmington) *John Ford,* Secker & Warburg, 1974, Da Capo Press, 1975; (contributor) *International Film Guide Annual,* Tantivy Press, 1975; (contributor) *Focus on Orson Welles,* Prentice-Hall, 1976; *Kirk Douglas,* Harcourt, 1976; *Orson Welles: Actor and Director,* Harcourt, 1977; (contributor) *Federico Fellini: Essays in Criticism,* Oxford University Press, 1978; (contributor) *Great Film Directors,* Oxford University Press, 1978; (author of preface) *The Late Great Planet Earth,* movie edition, Zondervan, 1978. Contributor to numerous journals, magazines, and newspapers, including *Life, Rolling Stone, Film Comment, Sight and Sound, American Film Gallery, Film Quarterly, Film Heritage, AFI Report, New Times, Montage, Milwaukee Journal,* and *Capital Times.*

WORK IN PROGRESS: Speaking of Baseball.

SIDELIGHTS: Joseph McBride began a full-time career as a screenwriter in 1977. He has written the scripts for several films, including "Blood and Guts," "Rock 'n' Roll High School," "Hard Time Aces," and "Big Money." He has also acted in "The Other Side of the Wind," a film directed by Orson Welles, as well as in "The Wild Party," "Hollywood Boulevard," "Cannonball," "Olly Olly Oxen Free," "Blood and Guts," and "Rock 'n' Roll High School."

* * *

McCARTHY, Charlene B(arbara) 1929-

PERSONAL: Born July 22, 1929, in San Francisco, Calif.; daughter of Charles Henry (a civil engineer) and Imogene (Peyer) McCarthy. *Education:* Marquette University, M.A., 1966, Ph.D., 1968; University of Chicago, graduate study, 1967-68. *Residence:* San Francisco, Calif. *Office:* Department of Religion, University of San Francisco, San Francisco, Calif. 94117.

CAREER: University of San Francisco, San Francisco, Calif., associate professor of biblical studies and religion, 1968—. Visiting lecturer at Gonzaga University, 1966-68, and Institute of Lay Theology, Berkeley, Calif., 1968—. *Member:* Society of Biblical Literature, Catholic Biblical Society, American Academy of Religion, Society for Values in Higher Education, College Theological Society, American Society for Oriental Research. *Awards, honors:* Johnson Foundation Award for teaching religious studies in higher education, 1972.

WRITINGS: Set My People Free, Glencoe Press, 1976. Contributor to *Catholic Biblical Quarterly* and *Journal of Biblical Literature.*

WORK IN PROGRESS: Research on the correlation between Jungian principles and biblical studies.

* * *

McCARTHY, James J(erome) 1927-

PERSONAL: Born May 20, 1927, in Gary, Ind.; son of James Patrick (a shoe store manager) and Faye Irene (Kapelka) McCarthy; married Joan Frances Cerny, August 8, 1953; children: Peggy Ann, Patricia, James. *Education:* Marquette University, Ph.B., 1950; University of Wisconsin—Milwaukee, M.Ed., 1954; University of Illinois, Ph.D., 1957. *Religion:* Roman Catholic. *Home:* 5925 South Hill Dr., Madison, Wis. 53705. *Office:* Department of Special Education, University of Wisconsin, 2605 Marsh Lane, Madison, Wis. 53706.

CAREER: Teacher of mentally retarded children in Milwaukee, Wis., 1952-54; University of Illinois at Urbana-Champaign, research assistant, 1958-61; University of Wisconsin—Madison, assistant professor, 1961-64, associate professor, 1964-68, professor of special education, 1968—, head of department of studies in behavioral disabilities, 1966-68. *Military service:* U.S. Navy, 1945-46. U.S. Naval Reserve, 1950-54. *Member:* American Association on Mental Deficiency, Council for Exceptional Children (chairman of publications committee, 1969-72), American Psychological Association, American Association of University Professors.

WRITINGS: (With S. A. Kirk and Winifred Kirk) *The Illinois Test of Psycholinguistic Abilities,* University of Illinois Press, 1968; (with wife, Joan McCarthy) *Learning Disabilities,* Allyn & Bacon, 1969. Author of *Exceptional Children,* a correspondence course at the University of Wisconsin, 1968, and "As the Twig Is Bent," a documentary film con-

cerning a three year study of severely retarded infants and children, 1969.

AVOCATIONAL INTERESTS: Sailing.

* * *

McCARTHY, Richard D(ean Max) 1927-
(Max McCarthy)

PERSONAL: Born September 24, 1927, in Buffalo, N.Y.; son of Ignatius D. (an attorney) and Kathleen (Walsh) McCarthy; married Gail E. Coughlin, February 2, 1957; children: Richard, Jr., Barry, Brendan, Maura, Deirdre. *Education:* Canisius College, B.A., 1950. *Politics:* Democrat. *Religion:* Roman Catholic.

CAREER: Buffalo Evening News, Buffalo, N.Y., reporter, 1952-53; National Gypsum Company, Buffalo, N.Y., director of public relations, 1953-64; U.S. House of Representatives, Washington, D.C., congressman from New York 39th district, 1965-71. Chubb fellow, Yale University, 1969. Visiting professor, Harvard University, 1971, Niagara University and Canisius College, 1972-73. *Military service:* U.S. Navy, 1945-46; U.S. Army, 1950-52. *Member:* Public Relations Society of America (president of Niagra Frontier chapter), American Legion, Central Park Association, Buffalo Philharmonic Orchestra Society, Frontier Press Club, Buffalo and Erie County Historical Society. *Awards, honors:* LL. D., Brandeis University, 1970.

WRITINGS: The Ultimate Folly: War by Pestilence, Asphyxiation, and Defoliation, Knopf, 1969; (under name Max McCarthy) *Elections For Sale,* Houghton, 1972.

SIDELIGHTS: While watching a short television news documentary on the U.S. government's chemical and biological warfare program, a horrified Gail McCarthy asked her then-congressman husband what he knew about the subject. Richard D. McCarthy admitted that he knew nothing, but after making several phone calls and holding a few meetings, he soon discovered that he was not alone among his colleagues in the House and Senate. The investigation which followed led to the writing of his first book, *The Ultimate Folly.*

Kenneth Boulding in the *New Republic* refers to it as a "terrifying case study in non-decision." He writes: "Even the most modest appraisal of this little volume would sound fulsome. It covers a subject of enormous importance. It does this without a wasted word, without an unnecessary epithet, and without hysteria. . . . It documents how a technological process can take control and by a series of small steps carry a society to a position utterly at variance with its ideals, with its interests, or its image of itself."

While Donald Gropman feels that the book is somewhat "hastily written [and] in need of editing and proofreading, . . . clearer thinking and more cogent reasoning," he admits that its shortcomings can be overlooked in light of the importance of its message. Aaron L. Fessler also believes that *The Ultimate Folly* serves its main purpose well: "Congressman McCarthy . . . has, almost singlehandedly, done more to awaken the public to the sinister, cancerous growth of chemical and biological weapons in our midst than anyone else in recent history. . . . Stories about these weapons have appeared in print with increasing frequency since McCarthy interested himself in the matter in 1968. It is also due to his persistence that the whole matter of U.S. participation in steps to ban chemical-biological warfare has at last come under official review at the highest levels. His book forthrightly states and documents his case. It should be read by everyone."

BIOGRAPHICAL/CRITICAL SOURCES: Christian Science Monitor, November 25, 1969; *New Republic,* November 29, 1969; *Library Journal,* January 1, 1970.†

*   *   *

McCLELLAND, Doug 1934-

PERSONAL: Born July 16, 1934, in Plainfield, N.J.; son of William Vincent and Elna (Whitlock) McClelland. *Education:* Attended Newark, N.J. public schools. *Home:* 704 Madison Ave., Bradley Beach, N.J. 07720.

CAREER: Office boy for *Newark Star-Ledger,* Newark, N.J., during late 1940s; *Newark Evening News,* Newark, assistant theater editor, 1953-56; *Record World Magazine,* New York, N.Y., editor, 1961-72. Lecturer on motion pictures.

WRITINGS: The Unkindest Cuts, A. S. Barnes, 1972; (contributor) *The Real Stars,* Curtis Publishing, 1973; *Susan Hayward: The Divine Bitch,* Pinnacle, 1973; *Down the Yellow Brick Road,* Pyramid Publications, 1976; *The Golden Age of "B" Movies,* Charterhouse, 1978; (contributor) *Hollywood Kids,* Popular Library, 1978. Contributor to *Encyclopedia Year Book 1969.* Contributor of articles to *After Dark, Films and Filming, Films in Review, Filmograph, Film Fan Monthly, Screen Facts,* and *The Many Worlds of Music.* Writer of jacket notes for record albums.

*   *   *

McCORMAC, John W. 1926-

PERSONAL: Born February 8, 1926, in Zanesville, Ohio; son of Samuel D. (a barber) and Phyllis (Murray) McCormac; married Martha Cunningham, June 22, 1952; children: Michael, John, James. *Education:* Muskingum College, B.S., 1951; Capital University, J.D., 1961. *Politics:* Republican. *Religion:* Methodist. *Home:* 395 Longfellow Ave., Worthington, Ohio 43085. *Office:* Franklin County Hall of Justice, 369 South High St., Columbus, Ohio 43215.

CAREER: Ohio Inspection Bureau, Columbus, Ohio, fire protection engineer, 1951-60; Schwenker, Teaford, Brothers & Bernard (law firm), Columbus, attorney, 1961-65; Capital University, Franklin Law School, Columbus, professor of law, 1965-74, dean, 1966-71; judge, Tenth District Court of Appeals, Columbus, 1975—. Admitted to Ohio and Federal Bars; consultant on civil procedure and member of rules advisory committee of Ohio Supreme Court. Senior vice-chairman, Ohio Judicial Conference, 1978. *Military service:* U.S. Navy, 1943-46. *Member:* American Bar Association, American Judicature Society, American Arbitration Association, League of Ohio Law Schools (president, 1969-70), Ohio Bar Association, Ohio State Bar Association Foundation (fellow), Columbus Bar Association (member of board of governors, 1968-72; secretary-treasurer, 1973-74; president-elect, 1974-75; president, 1975-76), Sigma Pi Sigma, Order of Curia, Masons, American Legion.

WRITINGS: Ohio Civil Rules Practice, W. H. Anderson, 1970, supplement I, 1972, supplement II, 1973, supplement III, 1977; *Anderson's Ohio Civil Practice,* W. H. Anderson, Volume I, 1971, Volume II, 1972, Volume III, 1977.

SIDELIGHTS: John McCormac is an eight-gallon Red Cross blood donor.

*   *   *

McCULLOUGH, Frances Monson 1938-

PERSONAL: Born October 23, 1938, in Quantico, Va.; daughter of George Edward (a career officer in the Marine Corps) and Frances (Fouche) Monson; married David McCullough (a book critic), November 20, 1965; children: Benjamin, Katy. *Education:* Stanford University, B.A., 1960; Brandeis University, graduate study, 1960-61. *Politics:* Democrat. *Residence:* Brooklyn, N.Y. *Office:* Harper & Row Publishers, Inc., 10 East 53rd St., New York, N.Y. 10016.

CAREER: Harper & Row Publishers, Inc., New York, N.Y., editor, 1963—. Member of National Endowment for the Arts literature panel, 1977—. *Awards, honors:* Roger Klein Award for creative writing, 1971.

WRITINGS: (Editor) *Earth, Air, Fire and Water* (poetry anthology for young people), Coward, 1971.

WORK IN PROGRESS: Love Is Like the Lion's Tooth, an anthology of love poems for teenagers, for Harper.

*   *   *

McCURDY, Frances Lea 1906-

PERSONAL: Born January 12, 1906, in Clifton Hill, Mo.; daughter of Ashley G. (a farmer) and Lillian A. (Pollard) Lea; married William E. McCurdy, June 6, 1944; children: (stepdaughters) Patricia, Mignon (Mrs. John Joseph Millin). *Education:* Stephens College, A.A., 1925; University of Missouri, B.S., 1936, M.A., 1944, Ph.D., 1957. *Politics:* Democrat. *Religion:* Christian. *Home:* Candlelight Lodge, Columbia, Mo. 65201. *Office:* Department of Speech and Dramatic Arts, University of Missouri, Columbia, Mo. 65201.

CAREER: High school English and speech teacher in Missouri and Oklahoma, 1925-52; University of Missouri—Columbia, instructor, 1952-57, assistant professor, 1957-60, associate professor, 1960-66, professor of speech and dramatic art, 1966-73, professor emerita, 1973—, chairman of department, 1968-70. Visiting professor at University of Hawaii, 1967, University of Colorado, summer, 1972, and Northwestern University, spring, 1974. *Member:* American Association of University Professors, Speech Communication Association (chairman of interpretive division, 1970), Central States Speech Association, Speech Association of Missouri (president, 1960), Phi Lambda Theta.

WRITINGS: (Contributor) Ronald Reid, editor, *Introductions to the Field of Speech,* Scott, Foresman, 1965; *Stump, Bar, Pulpit: Speechmaking on the Missouri Frontier,* University of Missouri Press, 1969. Also author of *A Guide for Speech, Dramatics, Radio and Television* and *Frontier Rhetoric;* co-author of *The People's Rhetoric.* Contributor of articles to *Missouri Historical Review, Quarterly Journal of Speech,* and *The Speech Teacher.*

WORK IN PROGRESS: Monographs on women suffragists of the 19th century and the ethos of frontier lawyers.

*   *   *

McCUTCHEON, W(illiam) J(ohn) 1928-

PERSONAL: Born December 16, 1928, in Oak Park, Ill.; son of William M. (a postal clerk) and Eva (Schlitz) McCutcheon; married Kathryn Trembly, August 19, 1950; children: Gwen, Nan, Mike, Matt. *Education:* Simpson College, B.A., 1952; Garrett Theological Seminary, B.D., 1955; Yale University, Ph.D., 1960. *Home:* 129 Roosevelt Dr., Beaver Dam, Wis. 53916. *Office:* Chaplain, Wayland Academy, Beaver Dam, Wis. 53916.

CAREER: Christian clergyman. Beloit College, Beloit, Wis., dean of chapel, 1960-63, assistant professor, 1963-66, associate professor, 1967-73, professor of religious studies, 1973-76, chairman of department, 1963-76; Wayland Academy, Beaver Dam, Wis., chaplain, 1977—, associate academic dean, 1978—. Visiting lecturer in American church history and religious thought at Garrett Theological Seminary, 1961-64; member of faculty at Camp Miniwanca Christian Leadership Training, 1966—; Protestant theologian-in-residence at College of Great Falls, 1969. Convened and directed Ecumenical Task Force (Beloit), 1966-68; member of board of directors of Beloit Cooperative Ministry, 1968-70; chairman of local inter-racial inter-church committee. Volunteer elementary school teacher in Beloit, 1970-71, and teacher in high school in Clinton, Wis., 1972. *Military service:* U.S. Army, 1946-48. *Member:* American Academy of Religion.

WRITINGS: (Contributor) Emory Stevens Bucke, editor, *History of American Methodism*, Volume III, Abingdon, 1964; (contributor) Albea Godbold, editor, *Forever Beginning*, Association of Methodist Historical Societies, 1967; (contributor) Edward T. James, editor, *Notable American Women: A Biographical Dictionary, 1607-1950*, Radcliffe College, 1971; *Essays in American Theology: The Life and Thought of Harris Franklin Rall*, Philosophical Library, 1972. Contributor of articles and reviews to theology and education journals, including *Christian Advocate, Council Journal, Criterion, Adult Teacher, Church History, Wesleyan Quarterly Review,* and *Christian Century.*

WORK IN PROGRESS: How High the Moon: An Introduction to Theology; an analysis of American religion in the 1920's and the 1930's; research on contemporary theological methodologies.

* * *

McDAVID, John W(alter, Jr.) 1933-

PERSONAL: Born May 27, 1933, in Longview, Tex.; son of John Walter (a banker) and Lula Mae (Lacey) McDavid; married Marilyn Vreugde (a social worker), May 31, 1956 (divorced, 1971); children: John Christopher, Bruce Alan. *Education:* Rice University, A.B., 1953; attended University of Texas, Main University (now University of Texas at Austin), 1953-54; Princeton University, A.M., 1956, Ph.D., 1957. *Address:* P.O. Box 54031, Atlanta, Ga. 30308. *Office:* Department of Counseling and Psychological Services, Georgia State University, 33 Gilmer St. S.E., Atlanta, Ga. 30303.

CAREER: University of Iowa, Iowa City, assistant professor of child psychology, 1957-60; University of Miami, Coral Gables, Fla., assistant professor, 1960-63, associate professor, 1963-67, professor of psychology, 1968-71, chairman of department, 1962-63; Georgia State University, Atlanta, visiting professor of counseling and educational psychology, 1970, professor of school psychology, 1971—. Director of research and evaluation, Project Head Start, 1967-68. Consultant to numerous organizations. *Member:* American Psychological Association, American Educational Research Association, American Association for the Advancement of Science, American Association of University Professors, Society for Research in Child Development, Psychonomic Society, Sigma Xi.

WRITINGS: (With Herbert Harari) *Social Psychology: Individuals, Groups, Societies,* Harper, 1968; (with Harari) *Psychology and Social Behavior,* Harper, 1974; (with S. Gray Garwood) *Understanding Children,* Heath, 1978.

Contributor to *Collier's Encyclopedia,* and to *American Psychologist, Journal of Personality, Journal of Consulting Psychology, Journal of Educational Psychology,* and *International Journal of Psychology.*

* * *

McDAVID, Raven I(oor), Jr. 1911-
(M. B. Darwin, Owen Hatteras III, Aitken Pyles)

PERSONAL: Born October 16, 1911, in Greenville, S.C.; son of Raven Ioor (a lobbyist) and Marie Louise (Henderson) McDavid; married Elizabeth Lee Harris, March 7, 1942 (divorced, 1945); married Virginia Ann Glenn (a university professor), June 7, 1950; children: (first marriage) Bettie McClain (Mrs. James David Mason); (second marriage) Glenn Truxtun, Raven Ioor III, Thomas Inglesby, Ann Hamilton. *Education:* Furman University, B.A., 1931; Duke University, M.A., 1933, Ph.D., 1935; additional study at University of Michigan, 1937-58, University of North Carolina, 1941, and Yale University, 1942-43. *Politics:* Conservative Democrat. *Religion:* Episcopalian. *Home:* 5736 South Blackstone Ave., Chicago, Ill. 60637. *Agent:* Howard Battles, 220 East 57th St., New York, N.Y. 10022. *Office:* 403 Wiebolt, University of Chicago, 1050 East 59th St., Chicago, Ill. 60637.

CAREER: The Citadel, Charleston, S.C., instructor in English, 1935-38; Michigan State University, East Lansing, instructor in English, 1939-40; Southwestern Louisiana Institute (now University of Southwestern Louisiana), Lafayette, assistant professor of English, 1940-42; Cornell University, Ithaca, N.Y., assistant professor of modern languages, 1950-51; University of Illinois at Urbana-Champaign, assistant professor of English, 1949-50; Western Reserve University (now Case Western Reserve University), Cleveland, Ohio, assistant professor of English, 1952-57; University of Chicago, Chicago, Ill., associate professor, 1957-64, professor of English and linguistics, 1964—. Has also taught at University of Colorado, Montana State College (now University), University of Michigan, University of New Brunswick, West Virginia State College, Illinois Institute of Technology, University of South Carolina, and Louisiana State University. Partner, Language Research Services (consultants). Linguist, U.S. Army, Language Section, 1943-45; linguist for U.S. Board on Geographical Names, 1947; consultant, U.S. Office of Education, 1966-68.

MEMBER: Modern Language Association of America, Linguistic Society of America, American Dialect Society (president, 1967-68), American Studies Association, National Council of Teachers of English, American Name Society, American Association for the Advancement of Science (fellow), American Anthropological Association (fellow), American Oriental Society, International Association of University Professors of English, International Centre for General Dialectology, Midwest Modern Language Association, Quadrangle Club, Phi Beta Kappa, City Club. *Awards, honors:* American Council of Learned Societies fellowship, 1942-44, 1945, 1950-51; Rosenwald fellowship, 1947; Fulbright fellowship to Germany, 1965; Litt.D., Furman University, 1966, and Duke University, 1972; David Russell Award from National Council of Teachers of English, 1969.

WRITINGS: (With W. N. Francis) *Structure of American English,* Ronald, 1958; (with Hans Kaurth) *Pronunciation of English in the Atlantic States,* University of Michigan Press, 1961; (editor with D. W. Maurer) *H. L. Mencken, The*

American Language, Knopf, 1963; (with Guy J. Forgue) *La langue des Americains,* Aubier-Montaigne, 1972; (editor with Audrey Pickert) *Lexicography in English,* New York Academy of Sciences, 1973. Contributor of articles and reviews to *Language, American Speech, Names, Orbis,* and other journals, and to newspapers. Contributor, under pseudonyms M. B. Darwin and Owen Hatteras III, of articles to linguistic journals. Editor, *Linguistic Atlas of the Middle and South Atlantic States,* 1964—; editor, *Linguistic Atlas of the North Central States,* 1952—.

WORK IN PROGRESS: Varieties of American English; Dialects in Culture, with Walter Blur; *The Mirth of a Nation.*

* * *

McDONALD, James Robert 1934-

PERSONAL: Born January 28, 1934, in San Francisco, Calif.; married; children: two. *Education:* Antioch College, A.B., 1955; University of Illinois, M.A., 1956, Ph.D., 1964. *Office:* Department of Geography and Geology, Eastern Michigan University, Ypsilanti, Mich. 48197.

CAREER: Eastern Michigan University, Ypsilanti, assistant professor of geography, summer, 1963; University of California, Los Angeles, assistant professor of geography, 1963-65; Eastern Michigan University, associate professor, 1965-68, professor of geography and geology, 1968—. Corresponding member for the United States on Commission on History of Geographic Thought, International Geographical Union, 1970—. *Military service:* U.S. Army, Counter-intelligence, 1956-59; served in France.

MEMBER: Association of American Geographers, American Association for the Advancement of Science, Michigan Academy of Sciences, Arts and Letters, Sigma Xi. *Awards, honors:* National Science Foundation fellowships, 1966-67, (India) 1968, 1970-71; Social Science Research Council grant, 1967-68.

WRITINGS: A Geography of Regions, W. C. Brown, 1972. Contributor to annals and author of abstracts. Contributor of articles and reviews to professional journals, including *Professional Geographer, International Migration, Economic Geography, Journal of Geography, Elan,* and *Michigan Academician.*

BIOGRAPHICAL/CRITICAL SOURCES: Norois, winter, 1965.

* * *

McDONALD, William Andrew 1913-

PERSONAL: Born April 26, 1913, in Warkworth, Ontario, Canada; came to U.S. in 1936, naturalized citizen, 1943; son of William Douglas (a clergyman) and Jean (Lane) McDonald; married Elizabeth Jackson Anderson, June 28, 1941; children: Susan Jane (Mrs. Gerald DePerry), Elizabeth Anne. *Education:* University of Toronto, B.A., 1935, M.A., 1936; Johns Hopkins University, Ph.D., 1940; also studied at American School of Classical Studies, Athens, Greece, 1938-39. *Politics:* Independent. *Religion:* Episcopalian. *Home:* 1707 Lindig, Apt. 5, St. Paul, Minn. 55113. *Office:* 312 Folwell Hall, University of Minnesota, Minneapolis, Minn. 55455.

CAREER: Lehigh University, Bethlehem, Pa., instructor, 1939-41, assistant professor of classics, 1941-43; Consolidated Vultee Aircraft, Allentown, Pa., editor of technical publications, 1943-45; University of Texas, Main University (now University of Texas at Austin), visiting associate pro-

fessor of classics, 1945-46; Moravian College, Bethlehem, Pa., professor of classics and chairman of department, 1946-48; University of Minnesota, Minneapolis, assistant professor, 1948-49, associate professor, 1949-54, professor of classics, 1954-73, Regents' Professor of Classical Studies, 1973—, director of Honors Division, College of Liberal Arts, 1964-67, director of Minnesota Messenia expedition in southwest Greece, 1961—, director of Center for Ancient Studies, 1973-78. Member of excavation teams in Olynthos, 1938, Pylos, 1939, 1953; director of excavation team in Nichoria, 1969—.

MEMBER: Archaeological Institute of America, American Philological Association, Association for Field Archaeology, Society of Professional Archaeologists. *Awards, honors:* Guggenheim fellowship, 1958-59, 1967-68; Horace T. Morse Award, Standard Oil Co., 1967; research award from National Geographic Society and American Council of Learned Societies, 1972-73.

WRITINGS: The Political Meeting Places of the Greeks, Johns Hopkins Press, 1943; *Progress into the Past: The Rediscovery of Mycenaean Civilization,* Macmillan, 1967 (published in England as *The Discovery of Homeric Greece,* Elek, 1968); (with D. J. Georgacas) *Place Names of the Southwest Peloponnesus,* University of Minnesota Press, 1969; (editor with George Rapp, Jr.) *Minnesota Messenia Expedition: Reconstructing a Bronze Age Regional Environment,* University of Minnesota Press, 1972. Editor, "Excavations at Nichoria" series, University of Minnesota Press, 1978—.

Contributor to *Grolier Encyclopedia.* Contributor of articles and reviews to *Classical Journal, American Journal of Archaeology, Journal of the American Name Society, Hesperia, Nestor, Biblical Archaeologist,* and other professional publications.

WORK IN PROGRESS: Study of domestic architecture and village layout in mainland Greece (2000-800 B.C.); writing and editing the last book of "Excavations at Nichoria" series.

* * *

McDONOUGH, George Edward 1924-

PERSONAL: Born March 25, 1924, in Bridgeport, Conn.; married Roxy Elizabeth Jensen (a nurse), October 17, 1948; children: Tina-Christi, Mark Andrew. *Education:* University of California, Berkeley, B.A., 1949; Johns Hopkins University, M.A., 1950; University of Washington, Seattle, M.Libr., 1963. *Office:* Weter Memorial Library, Seattle Pacific University, 3307 Third Ave. West, Seattle, Wash. 98119.

CAREER: Cascade College, Portland, Ore., associate professor of English, 1957-62; Seattle Pacific College (now University), Seattle, Wash., assistant professor of English, 1962-65; Chicago State College (now University), Chicago, Ill., assistant professor of library science, 1965-66; University of Maryland, Graduate School of Library and Information Services, College Park, director of admissions and student affairs, 1966-67; University of Washington, Seattle, assistant professor of library science, 1967-68; Seattle Pacific University, associate professor, 1968-69, professor of English, 1970-71, librarian, 1968-71; Hamline University, St. Paul, Minn., professor and university librarian, 1971-73; Seattle Pacific University, professor of English and director of learning resources, 1973—. Lilly fellow, Stanford University, 1976. *Military service:* U.S. Army, 1942-46; became sergeant. *Member:* American Library Association, American Association of University Professors, Washington Library Association. *Awards, honors:* Middlebury College Bread Loaf School of English fellowship, 1942; Emily Chamberlain Cook Prize in Poetry, University of California, 1948; Johns Hopkins University fellowship in writing, 1949-50; University of Chicago fellowship, 1965-66.

WRITINGS: Collected Poems, University of California Press, 1948; (with James P. Spradley) *Anthropology Through Literature: Cross-Cultural Perspectives,* Little, Brown, 1973. Contributor to *Saturday Review, Johns Hopkins Review, Poetry Australia, Catholic Library World, Pacific Search, Christian Century, Christianity Today,* and *Catholic Educational Review.* Editor, *Journal of the Institute of Research* (Seattle Pacific College).

WORK IN PROGRESS: The literature of anthropology; new poems.

* * *

McFARLAND, Thomas (Alfred, Jr.) 1926-

PERSONAL: Born September 13, 1926, in Birmingham, Ala.; son of Thomas Alfred (a lawyer) and Lucile (a teacher; maiden name Sylvester) McFarland. *Education:* Harvard University, A.B., 1949; Yale University, M.A., 1951, Ph.D., 1953; University of Tuebingen, additional study, 1953-54. *Home:* 33 Greenwich Ave., New York, N.Y. 10014. *Office:* McCosh Hall 22, Princeton University, Princeton, N.J. 08540.

CAREER: Oberlin College, Oberlin, Ohio, instructor in English, 1954-56; University of Virginia, Charlottesville, instructor in English, 1956-58; Western Reserve University (now Case Western Reserve University), Cleveland, Ohio, assistant professor, 1958-62, associate professor, 1962-64, professor of English, 1964-67; Graduate School and University Center of the City University of New York, New York, N.Y., professor of English literature, 1967-73, Distinguished Professor of English Literature, 1973-78; Princeton University, Princeton, N.J., professor of English, 1978—. Visiting professor at University of Colorado, summer, 1968, University of Virginia, spring, 1972, Yale University, spring, 1975. Consultant on Shakespeare, Coleridge, and Romantic literature to Clarendon Press, Cambridge University Press, Harvard University Press, Columbia University Press, Cornell University Press, Princeton University Press, University of California Press, and Case Western Reserve University Press. Columbia University, member of Seminar on the Romantic Movement and the Nineteenth Century, 1971—, and Seminar on the Theory of Literature, 1976—. *Military service:* U.S. Naval Reserve, 1944-46. *Member:* Modern Language Association of America (member of executive committee, 1970-73), English Institute (member of supervising committee, 1971-74; chairman, 1974). *Awards, honors:* Fulbright scholarship, 1953-54; Guggenheim fellowships, 1964-65, 1974-75; American Council of Learned Societies fellowship, 1973-74.

WRITINGS: Tragic Meanings in Shakespeare, Random House, 1966; *Coleridge and the Pantheist Tradition,* Clarendon Press, 1969; *Shakespeare's Pastoral Comedy,* University of North Carolina Press, 1972; (contributor) Geoffrey H. Hartman, editor, *New Perspectives on Coleridge and Wordsworth: Selected Papers from the English Institute,* Columbia University Press, 1972; (contributor) Frank Brady, John Palmer, and Martin Price, editors, *Literary Theory and Structure: Studies in Honor of W. K. Wimsatt,* Yale University Press, 1973; (contributor) John Beer, editor, *Coleridge's Variety: Bicentenary Studies,* Macmillan,

1974. Contributor of articles and reviews to *Halcyon, Yale Review, Polemic: A Journal of Contemporary Ideas, Studies in Romanticism, College English, Journal of Aesthetics and Art Criticism, English Language Notes, Wordsworth Circle, Commonweal, Journal of English and Germanic Philology, Modern Philology,* and *New Literary History.*

WORK IN PROGRESS: Editing *The Opus Maximum of Samuel Taylor Coleridge,* and *The Philosophical Lectures of Samuel Taylor Coleridge* for "The Collected Works of Samuel Taylor Coleridge," for Princeton University Press.

* * *

McGEE, Victor (Errol) 1935-

PERSONAL: Born October 31, 1935, in Pietermaritzburg, South Africa; son of A. Victor (a printer) and Winifred M. (Barton) McGee; married Marie Lambert, February 3, 1962; children: Elizabeth, William V., Edward A. *Education:* Natal University, B.Sc., 1956; Cambridge University, B.A., 1958, M.A., 1962; Princeton University, Ph.D., 1962. *Home:* 6 Wyeth Rd., Hanover, N.H. 03755. *Office:* Amos Tuck School of Business Administration, Dartmouth College, Hanover, N.H. 03755.

CAREER: High school mathematics teacher in Estcourt, South Africa, 1958-59; University of Illinois at Urbana-Champaign, research associate, 1961-62; Dartmouth College, Hanover, N.H., assistant professor, 1962-68, associate professor of psychology, 1968-69, Tuck School of Business Administration, associate professor, 1969-72, professor of applied statistics, 1972—. Consultant to the State of Vermont on real property taxation and aid to education, also consultant to various organizations. *Member:* American Statistical Association, Classification Society.

WRITINGS: Principles of Statistics: Traditional and Bayesian, Appleton, 1971. Contributor of articles to *Spectrum, Journal of Speech & Hearing Research, Perceptual and Motor Skills, British Journal of Mathematical and Statistical Psychology, Multivariate Behavioral Research, Journal of Marketing Research, International Journal of Psychology, Journal of the Franklin Institute,* and *Journal of the American Statistical Association.*

WORK IN PROGRESS: Computer programs for multivariate analysis; a textbook on the use of multivariate methods.

* * *

McGLADE, Francis S(tanley) 1930-

PERSONAL: Born June 6, 1930, in Bethlehem, Pa.; son of William and Elda (Keck) McGlade; married Sue Nosal, October 14, 1952; children: Michele, Matthew, Marc. *Education:* East Stroudsbury State College, B.S., 1952; New York University, Ph.D., 1960. *Home:* 6540 Chesterfield Ave., McLean, Va. 22101. *Agent:* A. L. Fierst, 630 Ninth Ave., New York, N.Y. 10036. *Office:* U.S. Department of the Army, Pentagon, Washington, D.C. 20310.

CAREER: Currently director of safety, U.S. Department of the Army, Pentagon, Washington, D.C.

WRITINGS: Adjustive Behavior & Safe Performance, C. C Thomas, 1970.

* * *

McGLASHAN, Alan (Fleming) 1898-

PERSONAL: Born October 20, 1898, in Nottingham, England; son of James (a physician) and Marian (Fleming)

McGlashan; married Hylda Cameron-Smith, November 4, 1934; children: Ian Purvis (stepson). *Education:* Attended Epsom College, Surrey, England, 1910-16; Clare College, Cambridge, B.A., 1921; St. George's Hospital, London, England, M.R.C.S. and L.R.C.P., 1924; Maudsley Hospital and Tavistock Clinic, D.P.M. 1940. *Home:* 6 Dorchester Court, Sloane St., London S.W.1, England. *Office:* 21 Wimpole St., London W.1, England.

CAREER: London Observer, London, England, drama critic, 1923-24; ship's surgeon on tramp steamer, 1924-25; general practice of medicine in Surrey, England, 1925-37; consulting psychiatrist in London, 1939—. Consulting psychiatrist, War Office Selection Board, 1941-45 and National Health Service, 1950-53. Member of psychiatric staff at St. George's Hospital, Maudseley Hospital, and West End Hospital. *Military service:* Royal Flying Corps (now Royal Air Force), pilot-officer, 1916-18; received Military Cross and Croix de Guerre avec Palmes. Royal Army Medical Corps, 1940-45; became major. *Member:* Royal Society of Medicine (fellow), British Psychological Society, Analytical Psychology Club (London), Boodles Club, Hurlingham Club.

WRITINGS: St. George and the Dragon, Selwyn Blount, 1931; (contributor) Arthur Koestler, editor, *Suicide of a Nation,* Hutchinson, 1963; *The Savage and Beautiful Country,* Chatto & Windus, 1966, Houghton, 1967; *Gravity and Levity,* Houghton, 1976. Work included in collection published in Japan by Orion Press, 1969. Contributor to *Lancet, Listener, Encounter, Realites, London,* and other European magazines.

WORK IN PROGRESS: Time Is a Monster, a fresh look at an old enemy.

AVOCATIONAL INTERESTS: Flying gliders and balloons, tennis, bridge.

BIOGRAPHICAL/CRITICAL SOURCES: Atlantic, July, 1967.

* * *

McGUIRE, Michael Terrance 1929-

PERSONAL: Born May 17, 1929, in Berkeley, Calif.; son of Raymond Albert (an insurance man) and Elain (Carroll), McGuire; married; children: Marsden, Stuart, Terrance, Katherine, Colleen. *Education:* University of California, Berkeley, B.S., 1952; University of Rochester, M.D., 1960. *Home:* 1930 Parnell Ave., Los Angeles, Calif. 90025. *Office:* Neuropsychiatric Institute, University of California, Los Angeles, Calif. 90024.

CAREER: Harvard University Medical School, Cambridge, Mass., assistant professor of psychiatry, 1968-71; University of California, Los Angeles, associate professor, 1971-73, professor of psychiatry, 1973—. *Member:* Boston Psychoanalytic Society. *Awards, honors:* Felix and Helena Deutsch Prize, 1967, 1969.

WRITINGS: Reconstructions in Psychoanalysis, Appleton, 1971; *The St. Kitts Vervet,* Karger, 1974; *Ethological Psychiatry,* Grune, 1977.

WORK IN PROGRESS: Research on non-human primates.

* * *

McINTYRE, Michael P(erry) 1921-

PERSONAL: Born May 16, 1921, in Seattle, Wash.; son of Harry J. (a professor) and Florence (Armin) McIntyre; married Elizabeth Woodson (a receptionist), December 23, 1945; children: Maureen (Mrs. Donald Alexander), Kathleen (Mrs. Robert Rodgers), Patricia. *Education:* University of Washington, Seattle, B.A., 1943, M.A., 1947; Ohio State University, Ph.D., 1951. *Politics:* Independent. *Home:* 340 South 15th St., San Jose, Calif. 95112. *Office:* Department of Geography, San Jose State University, San Jose, Calif. 95192.

CAREER: Kent State University, Kent, Ohio, assistant professor of geography, 1949-52; Wayne State University, Detroit, Mich., assistant professor of geography, 1952-56; San Jose State University, San Jose, Calif., assistant professor, 1956-60, associate professor, 1960-65, professor of geography, 1965—, chairman of department, 1965-73. *Military service:* U.S. Marine Corps, 1943-46; became first lieutenant. *Member:* American Association for the Advancement of Science, Association of American Geographers, Association of Pacific Coast Geographers, Philippine Geographical Society, California Council of Geographers in Education. *Awards, honors:* California State Colleges, distinguished teaching award, 1966-67.

WRITINGS: (Contributor) Everett Jones and Philip Durham, editors, *Readings in Science and Engineering,* Holt, 1961; *Physical Geography,* Ronald, 1966, 2nd edition, 1973. Contributor to *Yearbook Association of Pacific Coast Geographers, Ohio State University Graduate Record, Philippine Geographical Journal, Journal of Geography, Science,* and *Science Press.*†

* * *

McKEE, John DeWitt 1919-

PERSONAL: Born December 22, 1919, in Emporia, Kan.; son of L(ewis) D(eWitt) (a lapidarist) and Mary (Machen) McKee; married Jeannette Marie Hervin, April 23, 1956. *Education:* Kansas Wesleyan University, A.B., 1943; University of New Mexico, M.A., 1952, Ph.D., 1959. *Politics:* Independent. *Religion:* Christian. *Home:* 1302 Vista Dr. N.W., Socorro, N.M. 87801. *Office:* Department of Humanities, New Mexico Institute of Mining and Technology, Socorro, N.M. 87801.

CAREER: Raton Daily Range, Raton, N.M., reporter, sports editor, editorial columnist, 1943-45; *Albuquerque Tribune,* Albuquerque, N.M., reporter, 1945-46; University of New Mexico, Albuquerque, sports information director and magazine editor, 1946-50, instructor in English, 1958; New Mexico Institute of Mining and Technology, Socorro, assistant professor, 1959-66, associate professor, 1966-70, professor of English, 1970—. Chairman, New Mexico Development Disabilities Advisory Council, 1973. Member, New Mexico Developmental Disabilities Planning Council, 1971, New Mexico Developmental Disabilities Protection and Advocacy Services Council, 1977—. Member of board, Socorro County Services for the Handicapped, 1977—. *Member:* American Association of University Professors (president of local chapter, 1962), American Studies Association, Rocky Mountain Modern Language Association, Western American Literature Association (member of board of directors, 1973-76), New Mexico Folklore Association (vice-president, 1969; president, 1970), Socorro County Historical Society (member of board, 1967-69), Sigma Delta Chi. *Awards, honors:* "Who's Crippled?" Award, National Society for Crippled Children and Adults, 1954; Frank Luther Mott Research Award, 1976, for *William Allen White.*

WRITINGS: Two Legs to Stand On: My Battle With Cerebral Palsy, Appleton, 1955; (contributor) E. D. Henrick, editor, *Experiments in Survival,* Association for the Aid of Crippled Children, 1961; (contributor) Golden Taylor, editor, *The Literature of the American West,* Houghton, 1971; (co-editor) *Spanish Times and Boom Times: Toward An Architectural History of Socorro, New Mexico,* Socorro County Historical Society, 1972; (co-editor) *Socorro Photographer: Joseph Edward Smith, 1858-1936,* Socorro County Historical Society, 1974; *William Allen White: Maverick on Main Street,* Greenwood Press, 1975; (contributor) Emil Hurtik, editor, *Insight: A Rhetoric Reader,* 3rd edition, Lippincott, 1976. Contributor to *The Writer's Digest Handbook of Article Writing,* Writer's Digest, 1961. Contributor of short stories, poems, articles, and reviews to *Scimitar and Song, Extension, Social Science, Today's Health, Quill, New Mexico Sun Trails, Tell-n-It to the Marines, Atlantic Monthly, Faith Today, Democracy in Action, Crippled Child, New Mexico School Review, Bulletin of the Rocky Mountain Modern Language Association, New Mexico Humanities Review, Freshman English Research Notes, New Mexico Architecture, Crosier Family Monthly, New Mexico Quarterly, Daily Meditations, New Mexico Magazine, Mark Twain Journal, Target, Author and Journalist, Writer's Digest, Times* (El Paso), *Colorado Quarterly, Western Review, Western American Literature, College Composition and Communication, Mondo Occidentale* (Rome), *American Journal* (Manila), and *Hyacinths and Biscuits.*

WORK IN PROGRESS: With G. W. Gross, *A Literature of Science; How to Teach Writing; Prayers for the Earth,* a book of poems.

SIDELIGHTS: John DeWitt McKee wrote *CA* about his advice to aspiring writers: "Keep your mental and spiritual pores open. Absorb the world and put it through your own private mixmaster. And don't write until you do. Read everything you can get your hands on. That's an extension of the world, and it also lets you know about varieties of style and outlook. Then write. And write. And write. And be prepared to be uncomfortable—uncomfortable when you are not writing because the urge and the pressure are always dimmer than the vision."

AVOCATIONAL INTERESTS: Travel, sports, music.

* * *

McKENZIE, Garry D(onald) 1941-

PERSONAL: Born June 8, 1941, in Niagara Falls, Ontario, Canada; son of Donald F. (a businessman) and Audrey C. (Hall) McKenzie; married Dianne E. Hohmann, September 11, 1965; children: Keith Fraser Keewatin. *Education:* University of Western Ontario, B.Sc., 1963, M.Sc., 1964; Ohio State University, Ph.D., 1968. *Home:* 225 East Longview Ave., Columbus, Ohio 43202. *Office:* Department of Geology and Mineralogy, Ohio State University, Columbus, Ohio 43210.

CAREER: Ohio State University, Columbus, assistant professor, 1969-75, associate professor of geology, 1975—. *Member:* Geological Society of America, American Association for the Advancement of Science, Society for Environmental Geochemistry and Health, Sigma Xi.

WRITINGS—All published by Burgess: (Editor with R. O. Utgard) *Man and His Physical Environment: Readings in Environmental Geology,* 1972, 2nd edition, 1975; (editor with Utgard, and contributor) *Man's Finite Earth,* 1974; (editor with Utgard and W. A. Pettyjohn, and contributor) *Investigations in Environmental Geoscience,* 1975; (editor with Utgard and D. Foley) *Geology in the Urban Environment,* 1978.

McKINNEY, H(enry) Lewis 1935-

PERSONAL: Born December 20, 1935, in Oklahoma City, Okla.; son of James Raymond (an assistant district attorney) and Edith (an attorney; maiden name, Goddard) McKinney; married Lillie Marie Cooper, August 30, 1957; children: David, Debra, Christopher, Sean. *Education:* University of Oklahoma, B.A. (with distinction), 1958; Cornell University, Ph.D., 1967; Yale University, post-doctoral study, 1967-68. *Home:* 1230 West 28th Ct., Lawrence, Kan. 66044. *Office:* Department of History, University of Kansas, Lawrence, Kan. 66045.

CAREER: Teacher of Latin and English in public schools of Wichita, Kan., 1961-62; Yale University, New Haven, Conn., visiting instructor in department of history of science and medicine, 1966-67; University of Kansas, Lawrence, assistant professor, 1968-72, associate professor, 1972-78, professor of history, 1978—. *Member:* American Association for the History of Medicine, British Society for the History of Science, History of Science Society, Society for the Bibliography of Natural History, Phi Beta Kappa, Kappa Delta Pi. *Awards, honors:* Woodrow Wilson fellow, 1959-60; U.S. Public Health Service post-doctoral fellow, 1967-68; American Philosophical Society Penrose Fund grant, 1968; Watkins fellow, University of Kansas, 1969; American Council of Learned Societies fellow, 1972-73; National Book Award runner-up (science), 1973, for *Wallace and Natural Selection.*

WRITINGS: (Editor and translator) *Lamarck to Darwin: Contributions to Evolutionary Biology, 1809-1859,* Coronado Press, 1971; (author of introduction) Alfred Russel Wallace, *A Narrative of Travels on the Amazon and Rio Negro,* Dover, 1972; *Wallace and Natural Selection,* Yale University Press, 1972; (co-author) *Fluoridation: The Great Dilemma,* Coronado Press, 1978. Contributor to encyclopedias. Contributor of about fifteen articles to scholarly journals.

WORK IN PROGRESS: Wallace and Evolution: Notebooks and Journals of A. R. Wallace; Alfred Russel Wallace: A Biography.

SIDELIGHTS: H. Lewis McKinney has studied voice and has made many choral and solo appearances, including ones on television and radio, at the Cornell Opera Workshop, the Oklahoma City Municipal Auditorium, and at churches.

* * *

McKOWEN, Clark 1929-

PERSONAL: Born April 24, 1929, in Derry, Pa.; son of Clark Welty (a railroad freight conductor) and Inez Marie (Talbot) McKowen; married Mary Ruth Luttner (a registered nurse), December 18, 1953; children: Mary Patricia, Kathleen Ann. *Education:* Indiana State University, B.S., 1951; Bucknell University, M.S., 1957. *Home:* 717 Arlington Way, Martinez, Calif. 94553.

CAREER: High school English teacher and chairman of department in Stockton, Calif., 1957-63; Diablo Valley College, Pleasant Hill, Calif., English teacher, 1963-72, chairman of English Division, 1972-75. *Military service:* U.S. Navy, 1951-55; became lieutenant. *Member:* National Council of Teachers of English, American Federation of Teachers, California Teachers Association.

WRITINGS: Montage: Investigations in Language, Macmillan, 1970; *It's Only a Move,* Prentice-Hall, 1971; *Image: Reflections on Language,* Macmillan, 1973. Contributor to *English Journal, Journal of Secondary Education,* and *Junior College Journal.*

WORK IN PROGRESS: Aggressive Grade Getting for College Students.

* * *

McKUEN, Rod 1933-

PERSONAL: Born April 29, 1933, in Oakland, Calif.; children: one son. Education: Less than four years, mostly in one-room schoolhouses and rural country schools in Nevada, California, Washington, and Oregon; attended high school in Oakland, Calif. Address: P.O. Box G, Beverly Hills, Calif. 90213. Office: 8440 Santa Monica Blvd., Los Angeles, Calif. 90069.

CAREER: Poet, author, composer, singer, songwriter. Has appeared in films, on television, and in concerts. President of Stanyan Records, Discus Records, Mr. Kelly Productions, Montcalm Productions, Stanyan Books, Cheval Books, Biplane Books, and Rod McKuen Enterprises; vice-president of Tamarack Books. Member of board of directors of Animal Concern and American National Theatre of Ballet; member of advisory board of International Education and Fund for Animals. Military service: U.S. Army, 1953-57; served in Korea; was Psychological Warfare script writer and military assistant to Korean Civil Assistance Command; decorated by Syngman Rhee for bringing friendship and understanding to the Korean people.

MEMBER: American Society of Composers, Authors and Publishers, American Federation of Television and Radio Artists, National Academy of Recording Arts and Sciences (member of board of directors; vice-president), American Guild of Variety Artists, Modern Poetry Association, Writers Guild, New Gramophone Society (president), American Human Society (member of board of directors). Awards, honors: Grand Prix du Disc (Paris), 1966; received eleven nominations from National Academy of Recording Arts and Sciences, won Grammy for "Lonesome Cities," 1969; received Motion Picture Academy Award nominations for musical score for the films, "Jean," 1969, and "A Boy Named Charlie Brown," 1970; Golden Globe Award, 1969; Motion Picture Daily Award, 1969; received Emmy, Academy of Television Arts and Sciences, for musical scores, "Say Goodbye," 1970, and "Hello Again," 1977; nominated for Pulitzer Prize in classical music, 1973, for the composition, "The City"; Freedom Foundation award, 1975; recipient, Man of the Year award, Menninger Foundation, 1975; named Entertainer of the Year, Shriners Club of Los Angeles, 1975; Horatio Alger Award, 1976; Humanitarian Award, First Amendment Society, 1977; Carl Sandburg Award, International Platform Association, 1978.

WRITINGS—Poetry: And Autumn Came, Pageant, 1954; Stanyan Street and Other Sorrows (also see below), Stanyan Music Co., 1966; Listen to the Warm (also see below), Random House, 1967; Twelve Years of Christmas, Stanyan/Cheval, 1968; Lonesome Cities (also see below), Random House, 1968; Sea Cycle, Montcalm Productions, 1969; In Someone's Shadow, Stanyan/Cheval, 1969; With Love, Random House, 1970; Caught in the Quiet, Random House, 1970; New Ballads, Random House, 1970; Rod McKuen at Carnegie Hall, Grosset, 1970; Moment to Moment, Stanyan/Cheval, 1971; The Carols of Christmas, Random House, 1971; So My Sheep Can Safely Graze, Random House, 1971; Pastorale: A Collection of Lyrics, Random House, 1971; And to Each Season, Simon & Schuster, 1972; Grand Tour, Random House, 1972; Beyond the Boardwalk, Stanyan/Cheval, 1972; Grand Tour, Stanyan/Cheval, 1972; Come to Me in Silence, Simon &

Schuster, 1973; Seasons in the Sun, Pocket Books, 1974; Celebrations of the Heart, Simon & Schuster, 1975; Hand in Hand, Pocket Books, 1976; The Sea Around Me . . . , Simon & Schuster, 1977; Coming Close to the Earth, Simon & Schuster, 1978.

Other: The World of Rod McKuen (illustrated songbook), Random House, 1968; (compiler) Robert Allen, editor, Here's Another Book, My Friend, Stanyan/Cheval, 1971; (contributor) Never Let the Sun Set on a Quarrel, Stanyan/Cheval, 1971; (editor and compiler) The Will to Win, Stanyan/Cheval, 1971; The Rod McKuen Omnibus (including Stanyan Street and Other Sorrows, Listen to the Warm, and Lonesome Cities, and fourteen new poems), W. H. Allen, 1975; Finding My Father: One Man's Search for Identity, Stanyan/Cheval, 1976.

Composer of musical scores for films including "Joanna," 1968, "The Prime of Miss Jean Brodie," 1969, "Me, Natalie," 1969, "A Boy Named Charlie Brown," 1970, "Come to Your Senses," 1971, "Scandalous John," 1971, "Wildflowers," 1971, "The Seagull," 1972, "Lisa, Bright and Dark," 1973, "Big Mo," 1973, and "The Borrowers," 1973.

Composer of more than a thousand songs, including "Jean," "If You Go Away," "Seasons in the Sun," "I Think of You," "The World I Used to Know," "Doesn't Anybody Know My Name," "I'm Not Afraid," "The Lovers," "Love's Been Good to Me," "A Man Alone," "Stanyan Street," "The Single Man," "We," "Natalie," "I'll Catch the Sun," "Kaleidoscope," "Soldiers Who Want to Be Heroes," "Everybody's Rich But Us," "The Beautiful Stranger," "Champion Charlie Brown," "Bend Down and Touch Me," and "The Ever Constant Sea."

Classical compositions include "Symphony Number One," "Concerto for Guitar and Orchestra," "Concerto for Four Harpsichords," "Ballad of Distances," "Suite for Orchestra," "I Hear America Singing," "Concerto Number Three for Piano and Orchestra," "Adagio for Harp and Strings," "The City," and "Piano Variations." Co-author and composer of music, for television documentary, "The Unknown War," 1978. Author of monthly poetry column in Cosmopolitan, 1970-71. Also author of annual datebook and calendar.

SIDELIGHTS: The name Rod McKuen triggers various thoughts: To some he's a sensitive poet, to others he is a composer with several Academy Award nominations to his credit, many think of him as a jetsetter and frequent talk-show guest, and still others remember his earlier career as an actor and singer.

McKuen runs a business empire consisting of four record labels, three book publishers, two music-publishing companies, a mail-order venture, and a clothing outfit named, "Rod McKuen Casuals." Discussing his business involvements, McKuen remarks: "I never meant to be a conglomerate, but my interests are varied. When anyone suggests I cut back on some of my activity, it would be like cutting off my arm. . . . I want to work. Without working, you go bananas."

McKuen told an interviewer for Esquire: "I paved the way for Erich Segal. It's been my strange lot to have preceded all sorts of things for some time now. I told everybody that folk music was going to come in very big three years before it happened and nobody believed me and of course it did happen. And I went around telling people there was going to be a romantic revival and nobody believed that either. I think it's a reaction people are having against so much insanity in the world. I mean, people are really all we've got. You know it sounds kind of corny and I suppose it's a cliche, but it's really true, that's just the way it is."

McKuen is one of the best-selling poets of this century and perhaps, according to the *New York Times,* of all time. McKuen believes the reason he has been so well received by the public is "because I've been honest. I've had little formal education, and I taught myself to write music." McKuen continues: "I didn't know that there were defenses you could throw up to keep yourself hidden. I just wrote straight ahead. By the time I learned about these defenses, I was too old to do otherwise.

"I think I'm a great poet. I'm writing because I have something to say and people are responding to it, and what better measure is there? Those writers who say they're only writing for themselves ... well it's true if what they write ends up in a filing cabinet, but most everyone needs an audience.... The people who find it easy to criticize my work more often than not haven't even read it. That's snobbery. It's become fashionable to dismiss me, and I would be dishonest if I said it didn't bother me.

"There's something criminal, apparently, about being a successful poet. Too many writers take umbrage at that. It's not fair. I don't think poets should starve. I don't think anyone should starve. That's another problem we have in this country that should be changed."

McKuen's critics are fairly evenly divided as to his talent or lack of talent. As one of McKuen's more favorable critics, Marilyn Beck writes, McKuen's "talent for writing and composing is obvious, but beyond that there is a quality, deeper and more profound, that has been responsible for making Rod McKuen America's unofficial poet laureate, with an international cult of worshippers that grows with each passing day."

According to Bill Hutchinson, McKuen "developed more than a cultist following. Gradually, with the phenomenal sales volumes like *Stanyan Street and Other Sorrows* and *Listen to the Warm* he received both material affirmation of his ability and the kind of criticism that often falls to people whose words are too accessible and whose success is too great."

Nora Ephron writes that McKuen has "hit on a formula so slick that it makes mere sentimentality have the force of emotion. [His] work is instantly accessible and comprehensible; and when the reader is moved by it, he assumes that it must be art. As a result, ... McKuen, who started out rather modest about his achievement, [has] become convinced that [he] must be doing something not just right but important. Can you blame [him]? The money rolls in. The mail arrives by the truckload. The critics outside New York are enthusiastic. And to those who aren't, ... McKuen falls back on sheer numbers. Millions of people have read and loved his work."

A much stronger point of view is held by Pulitzer prize-winning poet Karl Shapiro who remarked, "It is irrelevant to speak of McKuen as a poet. His poetry is not even trash." To which McKuen replied in 1971, "I don't think it's irrelevant to speak of me as a poet. If I can sell five million books of poetry, I must be a poet."

Andrew J. Hirt writes: "few poets who have said so little have sold so much. Perhaps the answer can only be guessed at. Maybe great masses have latched on to his poetry because it satisfies a desire in them to feel intellectual. His allusions and imagery are so simple, so blandly elementary, that they can be easily understood; these thin thoughts spun in the 'form' of poetry make the reader feel that he has probed intellectual depths when in fact he has only been fooled by a shadow of the real thing. Certainly symbol with depth is painfully lacking in McKuen's poetry. Perhaps his followers are not applauding his poetry but themselves for recognizing a 'form' and being able to digest it without realizing that what they are eating is as substantial as cotton candy...."

An interesting point is raised by Donald Hall who writes: "It's a good thing the way high school students read Rod McKuen. Of course he can't write a decent line; it's his narcissism that turns people on. But if a hundred people get thrills from Rod McKuen when they are fifteen, twelve of them will read William Blake when they are twenty. He gets them started."

BIOGRAPHICAL/CRITICAL SOURCES: Time, November 24, 1967, May 16, 1969; *Life,* February 9, 1968; *Book World,* November 24, 1968; *New York Times,* May 1, 1969; *Detroit News,* May 1, 1969; *Journal of Popular Culture,* spring, 1970; *Esquire,* June, 1971; *Writer's Digest,* October, 1972; *American Poetry Review,* May/June, 1973; *Contemporary Literary Criticism,* Gale, Volume I, 1973, Volume III, 1975; *Denver Post,* August 14, 1974; *Miami Herald,* January 10, 1975.

*   *   *

McLELLAN, Robert   1907-

PERSONAL: Born January 28, 1907, in Lanark, Scotland; son of John (a printer) and Elizabeth (Hannah) McLellan; married Kathleen Heys, October 1, 1938; children: Kathleen, John. *Education:* Attended Glasgow University, 1925-29. *Home:* High Corrie, Isle of Arran, Scotland.

CAREER: Writer. President of District Councils' Association for Scotland, 1962-64. *Military service:* Royal Artillery, 1944-46; became lieutenant. *Member:* League of Dramatists, Society of Authors, Scottish Society of Playwrights (president). *Awards, honors:* Scottish Arts Council Poetry Prize, 1956, for "Sweet Largie Bay"; Scottish Arts Council, drama bursary, 1968, special drama award, 1976.

WRITINGS: The Isle of Arran (history), Praeger, 1970; *Ancient Monuments of Arran,* H.M.S.O., 1977.

Plays: *Jeddart Justice* (one-act comedy), Bone & Hulley, 1934; *The Changeling* (one-act comedy), Porpoise Press, 1938 (first published in *Scottish One-Act Plays,* edited by J. M. Reid, Porpoise Press, 1935); *Toom Byres* (three-act comedy), William Maclellan, 1947; *Torwatlie* (three-act comedy), William Maclellan, 1950; *The Hypocrite* (five-act comedy), Calder & Boyars, 1970; *Jamie the Saxt: A Historical Comedy* (four-acts), edited by Ian Campbell and Ronald D. S. Jack, Calder & Boyars, 1970; *Linmill,* Akros, 1977; *Sweet Largie Bay,* Akros, 1977; *Arran Burn,* Akros, 1977.

Unpublished plays: "Tarfessock," 1933; "Cian and Ethne," 1935; "Portrait of an Artist," 1939; "Mary Stewart," 1951; "The Road to the Isles," 1954.

Television and radio productions: "As Ithers [sic] See Us," 1956; "Rab Mossgiel," commissioned by BBC radio for the Burns Bicentenary, 1959, adapted for television, 1960; "Balloon Tytler," 1962; "The Old Byre at Clashmore," 1965; "Island Burn," 1965.

Also author of stage productions for Edinburgh International Festival, "The Flouers o Edinburgh," 1957, and "Young Auchinleck," 1962 (produced on television, 1963). Plays, short stories, and poems represented in anthologies, including *Scottish Short Stories,* Faber, 1932, new edition, 1942, *Fifty One-Act Plays,* Gollancz, 1940, *Best Broadcast Stories,* Faber, 1944, *Modern Scottish Poetry,* Faber, 1946, 1966, *No Scottish Twilight* (short stories), William Maclellan, 1947, *North Light,* William Maclellan, 1947, *Scottish*

Verse, 1851-1951, Nelson, 1952, *Oxford Book of Scottish Verse*, Oxford University Press, 1966, and *Scottish Love Poems*, Canongate, 1975. Contributor to *The New Alliance*, *Poetry Scotland*, *Scottish Art and Letters*, *The Saltire Review*, *Lallaus*, and *The Scotia Review*.

WORK IN PROGRESS: Adapting his short stories for film and television.

BIOGRAPHICAL/CRITICAL SOURCES: Scottish Field, December, 1956; *Scotland's Magazine*, January, 1959; *Library Review*, spring, 1971; *Lallaus*, spring, 1978.

* * *

McLENDON, James (Nelson) 1942-

PERSONAL: Born March 7, 1942, in Gainesville, Fla.; son of Robert Paul (a prison official) and Frances Hellena (Cogdill) McLendon; married Rebecca Ann Rash (a photographer), August 24, 1964; children: Stacey Heather, Ian Stefan, Caitlin Laurel. *Education:* Studied at Florida State University, 1960-61, East Tennessee State University, 1962-64, and Florida Atlantic University, 1966-67. *Politics:* Democrat. *Religion:* Catholic. *Home and office address:* P.O. Box 147, Blowing Rock, N.C. 28605. *Agent:* Gerard F. McCauley, P.O. Box 456, Cranbury, N.J. 08512.

CAREER: Elementary school teacher in Pasadena, Md., 1964-65; junior high school algebra teacher in Pasadena, 1966; Winslow, Cohu & Stetson, Inc., Baltimore, Md., stockbroker trainee, 1966; WPUV-Radio, Pulaski, Va., news director, 1967; *St. Augustine Record*, St. Augustine, Fla., reporter, 1968-69; *Key West Citizen*, Key West, Fla., author of column "On the Keys," 1969-72; free-lance writer, 1972—. Instructor in creative writing in public schools in St. Johns County and St. Augustine, Fla., 1968-69; news writer for United Press International (UPI) in Miami, Fla., 1969-72. *Military service:* U.S. Marine Corps Reserve, 1960-66. *Awards, honors:* Won short story contest sponsored by *Writer's Digest*, 1967.

WRITINGS: Papa: Hemingway in Key West, E. A. Seemann, 1972; *Pioneer in the Florida Keys*, E. A. Seemann, 1976; *Deathwork* (Literary Guild alternate selection), Lippincott, 1977; *Eddie Macon's Run*, Lippincott, 1979. Also author of original screenplays, "Pursuit," 1979, and "Last Shot," 1979. Contributor to *Holiday, Writer's Digest, Tropic, Florida Sportsman, Town and Country*, and *Christian Science Monitor*.

WORK IN PROGRESS: A television mini-series, "The Grandees."

SIDELIGHTS: At the age of 17, James McLendon accompanied his father, the chief inspector for Florida prisons, to Raiford Prison in Starke, Florida. There they watched as three men were electrocuted in the prison's death chamber. The horrifying event is the basis for McLendon's novel *Deathwork*, the story of the resumption of executions at Raiford Prison. It took McLendon five years to sell the book because the Supreme Court had declared capital punishment unconstitutional. "When the publishing company took it [the novel]," he told the *Atlanta Journal and Constitution*, "nobody believed there would ever be another execution." But shortly before the book was published, the Supreme Court reversed itself and ruled in favor of capital punishment. Suddenly, *Deathwork* was no longer fantasy.

A reviewer for the *New York Times Book Review* called *Deathwork* "a graphic look at Florida's death row." *Library Journal*'s reviewer thought the novel's execution scene so dramatic "that readers may feel that some of those 2,250 volts are passing through their own heads."

McLendon favors capital punishment. "Capital criminals practice capital punishment on their victims," he has said, "why should society not practice capital punishment on them?"

Deathwork is the first in a planned series of four novels concerning human freedom. The second, *Eddie Macon's Run*, tells the story of a Texas prisoner's escape across a desert. Movie rights to both books have been sold.

BIOGRAPHICAL/CRITICAL SOURCES: Publisher's Weekly, July 18, 1977; *Library Journal*, September 15, 1977; *Christian Science Monitor*, October 12, 1977; *New York Times Book Review*, October 16, 1977; *Atlanta Journal and Constitution*, September 10, 1978.

* * *

McLEOD, James R(ichard) 1942-

PERSONAL: Born January 8, 1942, in Spokane, Wash.; married Ellen Gay Brockman, August 1, 1964 (divorced January 2, 1978); children: James Brock, Rory Richard. *Education:* University of Washington, Seattle, B.A., 1966; Eastern Washington State College (now University), M.A., 1969. *Home:* South 311 Whipple Rd., #6, Spokane, Wash. 99206. *Office:* Department of English, North Idaho Junior College, Coeur d'Alene, Idaho 83814.

CAREER: Ryther Center for Emotionally Disturbed Children, Seattle, Wash., psychiatric group worker, 1961-63; high school teacher of English and geography in Spokane, Wash., 1966-69; elementary school teacher in Mukilteo, Wash., 1969-70; North Idaho Junior College, Coeur d'Alene, instructor in English, 1970—. Counselor, Morningstar Boys' Ranch, summer, 1966. President, Coeur d'Alene Citizens Council for the Arts, 1971-72; chairman of youth committee, Kootenai County Interagency Council, 1972-73. Poetry judge, Idaho Writers League State Contest, 1972.

WRITINGS: Theodore Roethke: A Manuscript Checklist, Kent State University Press, 1971; *Theodore Roethke: A Bibliography*, Kent State University Press, 1973. Contributor to *Northwest Review, Mirror Northwest*, and *Slackwater Review*.

WORK IN PROGRESS: The Fourth Face, a novel; a book of poems.

* * *

McMILLAN, Priscilla Johnson 1928-

PERSONAL: Born July 19, 1928, in Glen Cove, N.Y.; daughter of Stuart Holmes (a businessman) and Mary Eunice (Clapp) Johnson; married George E. McMillan (a writer), December 30, 1966. *Education:* Bryn Mawr College, A.B., 1950; Radcliffe College, M.A., 1953. *Politics:* Democratic. *Religion:* Episcopalian. *Home:* 12 Hilliard St., Cambridge, Mass. 02138. *Agent:* Perry Knowlton, Curtis Brown, Ltd., 575 Madison Ave., New York, N.Y. 10022. *Office:* Russian Research Center, Harvard University, Cambridge, Mass. 02138.

CAREER: Current Digest of Soviet Press, New York, N.Y., translator and editor, 1953-56; North American Newspaper Alliance, correspondent in Moscow, 1958-60; Harvard University, Russian Research Center, Cambridge, Mass., visiting scholar, 1961-67, associate, 1970—.

WRITINGS: Khrushchev and the Arts: The Politics of Soviet Culture 1962-64, M.I.T. Press, 1965; (translator) Svetlana Alliluyeva, *Twenty Letters to a Friend*, Harper, 1967;

Marina and Lee (a book on John F. Kennedy's assassination, authorized by Marina Oswald Porter), Harper, 1977. Contributor of articles to newspapers, magazines, and journals, including *Saturday Review, Nation, Harper's, Progressive, Reporter,* and *Virginia Quarterly Review.*

* * *

McMURRAY, Nancy A(rmistead) 1936-
(Yowa)

PERSONAL: Born June 5, 1936, near Kananga, Belgian Congo (now Zaire); daughter of Louis Armistead (a Presbyterian missionary) and Jean (a teacher; maiden name Harlan) McMurray. *Education:* Mary Baldwin College, B.A., 1959; Harvard University, M.A.T., 1961; further study at George Washington University, 1966, 1967-68, and Hebrew University of Jerusalem, summer, 1972. *Religion:* Jewish.

CAREER: Mary Baldwin College, Staunton, Va., assistant to director of admissions, 1959-60; art teacher in public schools in Washington, D.C., 1961-66; Central High School, Seat Pleasant, Md., art teacher, beginning 1966. *Member:* Maryland State Teachers Association, Prince George's County Educators' Association.

WRITINGS: When Man Is an Artist, CLC Press, 1966; (under name Yowa; self-illustrated) *The Becoming of Ruth,* Crown, 1972. Contributor to *Jewish Spectator.*

WORK IN PROGRESS: A book tentatively entitled *Uh Oh, Here Come the Grown-Ups;* writing and illustrating a children's book.††

* * *

McNAMARA, John J(oseph), Jr. 1932-

PERSONAL: Born February 7, 1932, in Boston, Mass.; son of John J. and Kathleen (Tobin) McNamara; married Ann Louise Greep (an author), Dec. 28, 1964; children: Lisa, Emily, Sarah. *Education:* Harvard University, A.B., 1953. *Home and office:* 6 Hill Top Dr., Wenham, Mass. 01984.

CAREER: Registered representative for a Boston firm, 1957-62; vice president of King Resources Co., 1967-70; free-lance writer, 1970-71; ship broker, 1971—. *Military service:* U.S. Army, Counter-Intelligence Corps, 1953-57; special agent.

WRITINGS: White Sails, Black Clouds, Burdette, 1967; *The Money Maker,* Crowell, 1972.

* * *

McNAUGHTON, William (Frank) 1933-

PERSONAL: Born May 21, 1933, in Westboro, Mo.; son of Frank (a writer) and Ruth (Flanders) McNaughton; married Margaret Orminski, April 6, 1957 (divorced, 1971); children: Dorothy Ellen. *Education:* Attended University of Missouri, 1951-53, and Georgetown University, 1953-54; Brooklyn College of the City University of New York, B.A., 1961; Yale University, Ph.D., 1965. *Politics:* Jeffersonian Democrat. *Home:* 172 Shipherd Cir., Oberlin, Ohio 44074.

CAREER: Oberlin College, Oberlin, Ohio, assistant professor of Chinese, 1965-70; Experimental College, Oberlin, Ohio, lecturer on Ezra Pound and on guerilla war, 1970-71; Bowling Green State University, Bowling Green, Ohio, lecturer on Chinese language, 1973-75; Denison University, Granville, Ohio, visiting lecturer in classics, 1972-76, visiting lecturer in Chinese, 1976—. Lecturer, U.S. Navy's PACE program, Old Dominion University, 1978. Arts and

Letters, a Center for Classical Studies, co-founder and trustee, 1975-77, president, 1977. Consultant to Great Lakes Colleges Association Chinese language project and to National Translation Center, 1965-68. *Member:* Modern Language Association of America, Association for Asian Studies, American Oriental Society, Chinese Language Teachers Association. *Awards, honors:* Woodrow Wilson fellow, 1961-62; National Translation Center grant, 1967; Fulbright center faculty fellow, 1968-69; Asia Society Chinese translations project grant, 1971-72.

WRITINGS: The Taoist Vision, University of Michigan Press, 1971; *The Book of Songs,* Twayne, 1971; (translator with Lenore Mayhew) *A Gold Orchid: Love Poems of Tzu Yeh,* Tuttle, 1972; (editor) *Chinese Literature: An Anthology,* Tuttle, 1973; *The Confucian Vision,* University of Michigan Press, 1974; (translator with Mayhew) *As Though Dreaming: The Tz'u of Li Ching-Chao,* Mushinsha, 1977; *A Guide to Reading and Writing Chinese,* Tuttle, in press; *Light from the East,* Dell, in press. Contributor to *Texas Quarterly, Hudson Review, Kulchur,* and other journals.

WORK IN PROGRESS: Ezra Pound and His Masks, an intellectual biography; a book based on ancient Chinese folk and literary tales, *Lives of the Taoists; Imaginary Dialogues.*

SIDELIGHTS: William McNaughton lived in Taiwan in 1968-69 and the summers of 1966 and 1967, in Japan the summers of 1966-68, and in Italy, summers, 1969, and 1974-77.

* * *

McNEELY, Jeannette 1918-
(Maron Mackie, Janet Macneill)

PERSONAL: Born December 12, 1918, in San Francisco, Calif.; daughter of Loren Goodell (a railway postal clerk) and Marjorie (Wood) Mackie; married William H. McNeely (a research organic chemist), August 9, 1940 (divorced, 1967); children: Craig Warren, Kathleen Bernice McNeely Walker, Loretta Jean, Linda Darlene. *Education:* University of California, Berkeley, A.B., 1940; San Diego State College (now University), elementary teaching credential, 1961; United States International University, M.A., 1976. *Religion:* Protestant. *Home:* 5343 West Falls View Dr., San Diego, Calif. 92115.

`CAREER:* San Diego Unified School District, San Diego, Calif., teacher of the second grade, 1960—. *Member:* National Educational Association, Society of Children's Book Writers, California Teachers Association, San Diego Teachers Association, San Diego Professional Writers Workshop, Pi Delta Phi.

WRITINGS: Where's Izzy? (juvenile picture book), Follett, 1972; *Led by a Star* (juvenile picture book), Concordia, 1977. Contributor of juvenile fiction and adult non-fiction to *Christian Standard, Our Little Friend, One/Two, Young World,* and to other publications; one article appeared under pseudonym Janet Macneill.

WORK IN PROGRESS: Two books for young people, *River Cradle* and *Foggy Ideas.*

* * *

McTEER, Wilson 1905-

PERSONAL: Born July 25, 1905, in Maryville, Tenn.; son of Will A. (a lawyer) and Lucy Wilson (Tilden) McTeer; married Frances Coon Davis (a genealogist), July 3, 1931; children: Lucy Frances (Mrs. Robert M. Brusic), Mary

Margaret (Mrs. Joseph K. Ullmer), William Davis. *Education:* Maryville College, B.A., 1925; University of Chicago, Ph.D., 1930. *Politics:* Republican. *Religion:* Protestant. *Home and office:* 1712 Cherrywood Dr., Holiday, Fla. 33590.

CAREER: Maryville College, Maryville, Tenn., instructor in psychology, 1925-27; College of the City of Detroit (now Wayne State University), Detroit, Mich., instructor, 1930-36, assistant professor, 1936-43, associate professor, 1943-52, professor of psychology, 1952-71, professor emeritus, 1975—, acting head of department, 1947-52, 1953-54, 1956-57, 1962-63, associate chairman of department, 1960-62, 1963-75. *Member:* American Psychological Association, American Association for the Advancement of Science, American Association of University Professors, Midwestern Psychological Association, Michigan Academy of Science, Arts and Letters, Sigma Xi, Phi Beta Kappa.

WRITINGS: *The Scope of Motivation,* Brooks-Cole, 1972. Contributor to psychological journals.

* * *

McWILLIAMS, Peter 1949-

PERSONAL: Born August 5, 1949, in Detroit, Mich.; son of Henry G. and Mary (Toarmina) McWilliams. *Education:* Attended Eastern Michigan University and studied under Maharishi Mahesh Yogi at Maharishi International University. *Office:* Leo Press, 84 Washington St., Hoboken, N.J. 07030.

CAREER: Teacher of transcendental meditation, International Meditation Society, Los Angeles, Calif.; co-founder, Three Rivers Press; publisher, Versemonger Press and Lion Press; currently owner of Leo Press, Hoboken, N.J. Poet laureate, Maharishi International University.

WRITINGS—Poetry, except as indicated; all published by Versemonger Press, except as indicated: *Come Love with Me and Be My Life,* 1967; *I Have Loved* (formerly entitled "Love Two"), 1968; *For Lovers and No Others,* 1968; *I Love Therefore I Am,* 1969; *The Hard Stuff: Love,* 1969; *Evolving at the Speed of Love,* 1971; *Surviving the Loss of a Love,* 1971; *Love: An Experience Of,* Doubleday, 1972; *Love and All the Other Verbs of Life,* Doubleday, 1973; *Love Is Yes,* 1973; *This Longing May Shorten My Life,* 1974; (with Denise Denniston) *The TM Book: How to Enjoy the Rest of Your Life* (prose), Warner Books, 1975; (with Melba Colgrove and Harold Bloomfield) *How to Survive the Loss of a Love: 58 Things to Do When There Is Nothing to Be Done* (prose), Lion Press, 1976; *Catch Me with Your Smile,* edited by Susan P. Schutz, Blue Mountain Publishing, 1976.

AVOCATIONAL INTERESTS: Beethoven and Mozart, making color sound films, driving a Volkswagen.†

* * *

MEAD, Robert Douglas 1928-

PERSONAL: Born July 22, 1928, in Birmingham, England; son of James Enoch (a businessman) and Madge (Parker) Mead; married Thulia McKee (an editor), September 21, 1951; children: James Enoch II, Vance Mark Rutherford, Andrew Grant Parker, Matthew John. *Education:* Princeton University, A.B., 1950; Cambridge University, B.A., 1952. *Politics:* Independent Liberal. *Religion:* Anglo-Catholic. *Address:* P.O. Box 603, Paoli, Pa. 19301.

CAREER: Seabury Press, Greenwich, Conn., assistant production manager, 1952-56; American Library Associa-

tion, Chicago, Ill., sales manager, 1956-59; Harcourt, Brace & World, Inc., New York City, editor, 1959-63; J. B. Lippincott Co., Philadelphia, Pa., editor, 1963-69; Holt, Rinehart & Winston, Inc., New York City, editor, 1969-70; Media Systems Corp., Moorestown, N.J., editor, 1970-71. *Member:* American Recorder Society (president of Philadelphia chapter, 1969-70), Princeton Club of New York, Dolmetsch Society, Phi Beta Kappa.

WRITINGS: *Paradise Lost,* American RDM Corp., 1965; *Hellas and Rome: The Story of Greco-Roman Civilization,* New American Library, 1972; *Reunion: Twenty-Five Years Out of School,* Saturday Review Press, 1973; *New Promised Land: The Story of American Civilization,* New American Library, 1974; *Europe Reborn: The Story of Renaissance Civilization,* New American Library, 1975; *Colonial American Literature: From Wilderness to Independence,* New American Library, 1976; *Literature of the American Nation: From Independence to the Gilded Age,* New American Library, 1976; *The Canoer's Bible,* Doubleday, 1976; *Ultimate North: Canoeing Mackenzie's Great River,* Doubleday, 1976; *You'll Never Take Me* (novel), Doubleday, 1978; *Journeys Down the Line: Building the Trans-Alaska Pipeline,* Doubleday, 1978. Contributor to short stories, articles, and poems to periodicals, including *Harper's, Kansas Quarterly,* and *New York Times.*

WORK IN PROGRESS: A three-volume historical narrative of the Midwest; "and, probably in intervals . . . , one or more short novels."

SIDELIGHTS: Robert Douglas Mead, who has traveled or lived in France, Austria, and the American Arctic, told *CA:* "I resist the temptation to talk about motives—beyond the fundamental motive of putting truthfully what one has seen, felt, thought, and learned into literary forms that will be intelligible to one's audience and [hopefully] transforming. The particular motives that shape particular works, on the other hand, must be evident in the work, and if not, there is no value in talking about them. Apart from the 'personality' of one's work, the ways in which one is necessarily present in it, one aspires to anonymity."

AVOCATIONAL INTERESTS: Baroque music, hiking, skiing, canoeing, vegetable gardening, tennis.

* * *

MEADOWS, Paul 1913-

PERSONAL: Born June 19, 1913, in Herrin, Ill.; son of William C. and Mae (McCree) Meadows; married Mary Nell Gouldin, August 17, 1940; children: Michael M., Peter J. *Education:* McKendree College, A.B., 1935; Washington University, M.A., 1936; Northwestern University, Ph.D., 1940. *Politics:* Democratic. *Religion:* Unitarian. *Home:* 2016 Debutante Manor, Schnectady, N.Y. 12303; and P.O. Box 208, Guilderland, N.Y. 12084. *Office:* Department of Sociology, State University of New York, 1400 Washington Ave., Albany, N.Y. 12222.

CAREER: Western Michigan University, Kalamazoo, instructor in sociology, 1940-41; Northwestern University, Evanston, Ill., instructor in sociology, 1941-44; Montana State University, Missoula, assistant professor of sociology, 1944-47; University of Nebraska at Lincoln, professor of sociology, 1947-59; Syracuse University, Syracuse, N.Y., professor of sociology and chairman of the department, 1959-68; State University of New York at Albany, chairman of department of sociology, 1968-71, research professor of sociology, 1971—. President, Family Welfare Association, Lincoln, Neb., 1951-53. Acting director of research, Episcopal Diocese of Albany, 1970—. Senior staff consultant, Institute on Man and Science, 1973—. *Member:* American Sociological Association, Midwest Sociological Society (president, 1957-58), Eastern Sociological Society, Phi Beta Kappa. *Awards, honors:* Co-recipient, Weatherly Award, American Unitarian Association, 1957; Brotherhood Award, National Conference of Christians and Jews, 1959.

WRITINGS: (With C. E. Howell) *Students' Manual for Introductory Sociology,* American Book Co., 1939; *The Culture of Industrial Man,* University of Nebraska Press, 1950; (with James Melvin Reinhardt and J. M. Gillette) *Social Problems and Social Policy,* American Book Co., 1950; *John Wesley Powell: Frontiersman of Science,* University of Nebraska, 1952; (with Reinhardt) *Society and the Nursing Profession,* American Book Co., 1953; *La Technologia y el orden social,* Universidad de Mexico, 1957; *El Proceso social de la revolucion,* Universidad de Mexico, 1958.

Marcos para el estudio de los movimentos sociales, Universidad de Mexico, 1961; (editor with Donn V. Hart) *Selected Abstracts in Development Administration,* Syracuse University Press, 1962; (editor with others) *A World of Cities,* Maxwell Graduate School, Syracuse University, 1963; (contributor) I. Swerdlow, editor, *Development Administration,* Syracuse University Press, 1963; (contributor) E. W. Count and G. T. Bowles, editors, *Fact and Theory in Social Science,* Syracuse University Press, 1964; (contributor) I. L. Horowitz, editor, *The New Sociology,* Oxford University Press (New York), 1964; *Industrial Man: Profiles of Developmental Society,* Center for Overseas Operations and Research, Syracuse University, 1965; *The Rhetoric of Sociology,* Syracuse Book Center, 1966; (contributor) L. Gross, editor, *Sociological Theory: Inquiries and Paradigms,* Harper, 1967; (contributor) E. H. Mizruchi, editor, *The Substance of Sociology,* Appleton, 1968; (contributor) I. Deutscher and E. J. Thompson, editors, *Among the People: Encounters with the Poor,* Basic Books, 1968; (editor with Mizruchi) *Urbanism, Urbanization and Change,* Addison-Wesley, 1969, revised edition, 1975.

The Many Faces of Change, Schenckman, 1971; (contributor) *Alienation: Concepts and Theories,* Academic Press, 1973; *Alienation in Contemporary Society,* Praeger, 1977; (contributor) G. C. Hallen, editor, *Essays on the Sociology of Talcott Parsons,* Indian Journal of Social Research, 1977; *The New Immigration,* Transaction Books, 1978; *The Theory of Revolution: A Study in Social Change and Conflict,* Nelson-Hall, 1979. Editor, *Midwest Sociologist,* 1955-56.

WORK IN PROGRESS: Social Movements: Action, Structure and Process.

* * *

MEAGHER, Robert F. 1927-

PERSONAL: Surname is pronounced Mar; born May 13, 1927, in Brooklyn, N.Y.; son of Francis X. and Marie J. (Tallent) Meagher. *Education:* College of the City of New York (now City College of the City University of New York), B.S.S., 1949; Yale University, J.D., 1952; Bombay University, graduate study, 1952-53. *Home:* 61 Talbot Ave., Somerville, Mass. 02155. *Office:* Fletcher School of Law and Diplomacy, Tufts University, Medford, Mass. 02155.

CAREER: U.S. Department of State, sponsored lecturer in India and Pakistan, 1953-54; Winthrop, Stimson, Putnam & Roberts (law firm), New York City, lawyer, 1954-58; United Nations Relief and Works Agency, Beirut, Lebanon, lawyer, 1958-60; Columbia University, Law School, New York

City, assistant director of public international development financing project, 1961-65, associate director of international legal research, adjunct professor of law, 1972-73; Tufts University, Fletcher School of Law and Diplomacy, Medford, Mass., professor of international law, 1967—. Consultant and adviser to governments, international organizations, and private groups on foreign aid and foreign investment in Asia and Africa; legal advisor to India committee, Business Council for International Understanding, 1964-68. Teacher in seminar for senior government officials of East and Central Africa, University of East Africa, summers, 1964-66. *Military service:* U.S. Army, 1945-46; served in Europe.

MEMBER: American Bar Association, African Studies Association, American Foreign Law Association, African Law Association in America (president, 1967-69), American Society of International Law, Asia Society, Association for Asian Studies, Council on Foreign Relations, International Law Association, Society for International Development, World Peace Through Law Center, Southeast Asia Development Advisory Group, African-American Institute (member of council), Harvard/M.I.T. Seminar on Political Development, Association of the Bar of the City of New York. *Awards, honors:* Fulbright scholar in Bombay, India, 1952-53.

WRITINGS: (With Wolfgang Friedmann and George Kalmanoff) *International Financial Aid: A Comparative Study of Policies, Institutions, and Methods,* Columbia University Press, 1966. Contributor to legal journals and to journals of African and Asian affairs.

WORK IN PROGRESS: An International Redistribution of Wealth and Power: A Study of the Charter of Economic Rights and Duties of States, for Pergamon.

SIDELIGHTS: Robert Meagher has traveled throughout Asia and the Pacific, Africa, the Middle East, and Europe, and lived abroad in 1952-54, 1958-60, and 1961-63.

* * *

MEIER, Matt S(ebastian) 1917-

PERSONAL: Born June 4, 1917, in Covington, Ky.; son of Matthias John (a barber) and Mary (Berberich) Meier; married Bettie C. Beckman (a secretary), September 21, 1946; children: Gary Peter, Guy Patrick, G. Paul, G. Philip, Pepe. *Education:* University of Miami, Coral Gables, Fla., A.B. (magna cum laude), 1948; University of the Americas, Mexico City, Mexico, M.A. (magna cum laude), 1949; University of California, Berkeley, Ph.D., 1954. *Politics:* Democrat. *Religion:* Roman Catholic. *Home:* 603 Glen Alto Dr., Los Altos, Calif. 94022. *Office:* Department of History, University of Santa Clara, Santa Clara, Calif. 95053.

CAREER: High school teacher in Oroville, Calif., 1954-55; Bakersfield College, Bakersfield, Calif., instructor in Latin American history, 1955-63; University of Santa Clara, Santa Clara, Calif., 1963—, began as assistant professor, currently professor of Latin American history, chairman of the department, 1968-71, 1976—. Fulbright professor in Argentina, 1958-59. *Military service:* U.S. Army, Signal Corps, 1943-46; became technical sergeant. *Member:* American Historical Association, American Association of University Professors (local president, 1962-63, 1970-71), Pacific Coast Council on Latin American Studies (president, 1964-65).

*WRITINGS—*With Feliciano Rivera: *The Chicanos: A History of Mexican Americans,* Hill & Wang, 1972; *A Bibliography for Chicano History,* R. & E. Research Associates, 1972; (editors) *Readings on La Raza: The Twentieth Century,* Hill & Wang, 1973.

WORK IN PROGRESS: Chicano Lives, a collection of about ninety biographies telling the history of the Mexican Americans; Dictionary of Mexican American History, for Greenwood Press.

SIDELIGHTS: "I believe very strongly," Matt Meier told CA, "in the importance of a maximum number of Americans, both Anglo and Chicano, expanding their understanding of the historical reasons for the current position of Chicanos, social, political, and economic. Only with knowledge and deeper understanding can come progress." Ralph Guzman believes Meier and Rivera's book, The Chicanos: A History of Mexican Americans, "may provide a useful bridge between Anglo scholarly apprehension and Chicano aspiration. . . . It is a carefully written, important contribution to the literature in Chicano studies." The New Republic reviewer calls the book "especially good; it is not long or pretentious, nor is it especially polemical. Rather the authors in a quiet but determined way want to educate their readers, presumably the Anglos. . . . It would be nice if a few Texas Rangers, so exclusively Anglo, so powerful and sure of themselves, so willing to use force to keep 'them' in line, were to read what Meier and Rivera have to say, and even nicer if senators like John Tower or Barry Goldwater, or Peter Dominick, who represent so many Chicanos, also dipped into these pages. But those strong and influential senators have limited time, and have long ago learned whose voices to heed, the voices of the owners of factory-farms rather than of men and women who without exaggeration can simply be called subjects."

BIOGRAPHICAL/CRITICAL SOURCES: New Republic, August 19, 1972; New York Review of Books, August 31, 1972; Congressional Record, October 25, 1972; California Historical Quarterly, summer, 1973.

*   *   *

MEIERHENRY, Wesley Carl 1915-

PERSONAL: Born November 12, 1915, in Arlington, Neb.; son of Carl and Anna (Niederdeppe) Meierhenry; married Delsie Boschult, 1936; children: Dwight, Kent, Redge. Education: Midland College, B.Sc., 1936; University of Nebraska, M.A., 1941, Ph.D., 1946. Home: 2920 William, Lincoln, Neb. Office: Department of Adult and Continuing Education, University of Nebraska, 61 Henzlik Hall, Lincoln, Neb. 68508.

CAREER: University of Nebraska, Lincoln, assistant professor, 1946-52, associate professor, 1952-57, professor of education administration and history and philosophy of education, 1957-68, professor of adult and continuing education and head of department, 1968—, coordinator of teacher placement division, 1953-68, director of advanced professional division, Teachers College, 1958-68, assistant dean of Teachers College, 1959-68. Member: National Education Association, American Educational Research Association, National Association of Educational Broadcasters, Association of Educational Communications and Technology (president, 1967-68), Phi Delta Kappa, Nebraska Schoolmaster's Club.

WRITINGS: Enriching the Curriculum through Motion Pictures, University of Nebraska Press, 1952; Teaching in the Northern Midwest, Howard Chandler, 1958; (with G. D. Ofiesh) Trends in Programmed Instruction, Department of Audiovisual Instruction Instruction, National Education Association, 1964; Media and Educational Innovation, University of Nebraska Press, 1966; (with Raymond Wiman) Educational Media: Theory and Practices, C. E.

Merrill, 1969; Compendium of Non-Print Materials for Staff Development, ERIC Teacher Education Center (Washington, D.C.), 1974; (contributor) Open Learning, UNESCO Press (Paris), 1975; (contributor) Media in Higher Education, Information Futures (Pullman, Wash.), 1976.

WORK IN PROGRESS: Research in media, technology, and continuing education.

*   *   *

MELNYK, Z(inowij) Lew 1928-

PERSONAL: Born October 7, 1928, in Ukraine; naturalized U.S. citizen; son of Iwan and Anna (Hluszko) Melnyk; married Oksana A. Muszynsky, August 31, 1957; children: Orest M., Ihor R., Nestor L. Education: Fort Hays Kansas State College, A.B., 1951; University of Michigan, M.B.A., 1953; Michigan State University, Ph.D., 1961. Home: 1000 Tahoe Ter., Cincinnati, Ohio 45238. Office: Department of Finance, University of Cincinnati, Cincinnati, Ohio 45221.

CAREER: Ferry-Morse Seed Co., Detroit, Mich., accountant, 1953-56; Ford Motor Co., Lincoln-Mercury Division, Dearborn, Mich., cost accountant, 1956-57; Michigan State University, East Lansing, instructor in finance, 1958-61; Purdue University, Lafayette, Ind., assistant professor of industrial management, 1961-64; University of Cincinnati, Cincinnati, Ohio, associate professor, 1964-67, professor of finance, 1967—, head of department, 1972—. Visiting associate professor, Michigan State University, summer, 1963; visiting professor, University of Michigan, summer, 1978. Member: American Finance Association, American Institute for Decision Sciences, Financial Management Association, Ukrainian Academy of Arts and Sciences in the U.S., Midwest Finance Association (member of board of directors, 1972-75), Western Finance Association.

WRITINGS: Soviet Capital Formation: Ukraine, 1928/29-1932 (English text, with resumes in German and Ukrainian), Ukrainian Free University Press (Munich), 1965; (editor with Richard E. Ball, and contributor) Theory of Managerial Finance: Selected Readings, Allyn & Bacon, 1967; (with Charles L. Barngrover) Cases in Business Finance, Irwin, 1971; (editor with V. N. Bandera, and contributor) The Soviet Economy in Regional Perspective, Praeger, 1973. Contributing editor, The Financial Handbook, 4th edition. Contributor to professional journals in Germany, Italy, Australia, and United States. Associate editor, Financial Management, 1971-75.

WORK IN PROGRESS: With Charles L. Barngrover, Business Finance: Text and Cases; also working on defining and measuring risk, analysis of asset structure, analysis and testing of capital structure, and on the application of multivariate techniques to financial problems and investments.

*   *   *

MELVILLE, Keith 1945-

PERSONAL: Born January 4, 1945, in Cleveland, Ohio; son of Clyde and Margaret Melville. Education: Colgate University, B.A., 1967; Columbia University, M.A., 1971. Office: Department of Social Sciences, Bronx Community College, University Ave. and 181st St., Bronx, N.Y. 10453. Agent: Oliver Swan, Paul R. Reynolds, Inc., 12 East 41st St., New York, N.Y. 10017.

CAREER: City University of New York, New York City, assistant professor of social sciences, beginning 1971; Center for Understanding Media, New York City, instructor in media and social sciences, beginning 1972; currently teaching in department of social sciences at Bronx Community College of the City University of New York, Bronx, N.Y.

WRITINGS: (Program analyst) *School Desegreation Plan, Berkeley, California: A Report by the Program Reference Service,* Center for Urban Education, 1970; *Communes in the Counter Culture: Origins, Theories, Styles of Life* (Book-of-the-Month Club alternate selection), Morrow, 1972; *Marriage and Family Today,* Random House, 1977. Consulting editor, *The Sciences,* of New York Academy of Sciences.

WORK IN PROGRESS: A film on alternative marriage styles; monthly articles for *The Sciences;* a book on anthropology and contemporary American culture.†

*   *   *

MELZACK, Ronald 1929-

PERSONAL: Born July 19, 1929; son of Joseph (a bookseller) and Annie (Mandel) Melzack; married Lucy Birch (a teacher), August 2, 1960; children: Lauren Marsha, Joel David. *Education:* McGill University, B.Sc., 1950, M.Sc., 1951, Ph.D., 1954. *Politics:* Liberal. *Religion:* Jewish. *Home:* 51 Banstead Rd., Montreal, Quebec, Canada. *Office:* Department of Psychology, McGill University, Montreal, Quebec, Canada H3C 3GI.

CAREER: University of Oregon, Portland, research fellow in Medical School, 1954-57; University of London, University College, London, England, visiting lecturer, 1957-58; University of Pisa, Pisa, Italy, research associate, 1958-59; Massachusetts Institute of Technology, Cambridge, associate professor of psychology, 1959-63; McGill University, Montreal, Quebec, professor of psychology, 1963—.

WRITINGS: The Day Tuk Became a Hunter and Other Eskimo Stories (retold), Dodd, 1967; *Raven, Creator of the World* (Eskimo legends retold), Little, Brown, 1970; *The Puzzle of Pain* (adult nonfiction), Penguin, 1973; *Why the Man in the Moon Is Happy, and Other Eskimo Creation Stories* (retold), McClelland & Stewart, 1977.

WORK IN PROGRESS: A book on the psychology of aggression and war; a book of Eskimo stories for children; a baseball story, also for children.

BIOGRAPHICAL/CRITICAL SOURCES: New York Times Book Review, March 10, 1968; *Young Readers' Review,* April, 1968; *Book World,* May 5, 1968.

*   *   *

MENACKER, Julius 1933-

PERSONAL: Born June 4, 1933, in Chicago, Ill.; son of Maurice (a tailor) and Anna (Silverberg) Menacker; married Nadine Bloom, August 10, 1958; children: Mark, Terri, Rebecca. *Education:* Roosevelt University, B.A., 1956, M.A., 1958; Loyola University, Chicago, Ill., M.Ed., 1961; University of Illinois, Ed.D., 1965. *Home:* 500 Indian Hill Rd., Deerfield, Ill. 60015. *Office:* Department of Education, University of Illinois at Chicago Circle, Box 4348, Chicago, Ill. 60680.

CAREER: Worked as a history teacher, 1956-60, and as a counselor, 1961-64, in Chicago, Ill.; University of Illinois at Chicago Circle, Chicago, assistant director, 1965-68, associate director of admissions, 1965-71, assistant professor, 1965-70, associate professor, 1971-75, professor of education, 1976—. *Military service:* U.S. Army, 1954-56. *Member:* American Personnel and Guidance Association, American College Personnel Association, Phi Delta Kappa.

WRITINGS: Urban Poor Students and Guidance, Houghton, 1971; (with Erwin W. Pollack) *Spanish Speaking Students and Guidance,* Houghton, 1971; *Vitalizing Guidance in Urban Schools,* Harper, 1974; *From School to College: Articulation and Transfer,* American Council on Education, 1975. Contributor to *Phi Delta Kappan, Personnel and Guidance Journal, Educational Record, College and University, National ACAC Journal, Clearing House, High School Journal, Improving College and University Teaching, Social Studies, Journal of Business Education, Chicago Schools Journal,* and *Education Digest.*

WORK IN PROGRESS: A book tentatively entitled *Foundations of Education.*

*   *   *

MENDEL, Arthur 1905-

PERSONAL: Born June 6, 1905, in Boston, Mass.; son of Philip (a businessman) and Gertrude (Newman) Mendel; married Elsa M. Wissell, August 23, 1934. *Education:* Harvard University, B.A., 1925; study with Nadia Boulanger, Paris, France, 1925-27. *Politics:* Independent. *Religion:* None. *Residence:* Princeton, N.J. *Office:* Woolworth Center, Princeton University, Princeton, N.J. 08540.

CAREER: Worked for Columbia Broadcasting System and for *Musical America,* New York City, 1927-30; G. Schirmer, Inc. (music publishers), New York City, literary editor, 1930-38; free-lance editor, teacher, conductor, and scholar in New York City, 1938-52, including posts as teacher at Diller-Quaile School of Music, teacher and president at Dalcroze School of Music; lecturer in music history at Columbia University, New York City, and University of California, Berkeley, 1950-51; Princeton University, Princeton, N.J., professor of music, 1952-69, Henry Putnam University Professor of Music, 1969-73, professor emeritus, 1973—, chairman of department, 1952-57. Music critic, *Nation,* 1930-33. Conductor of Cantata Singers; editor during World War II of Associated Music Publishers, Inc.; authority on the works of Johann Sebastian Bach, and scholar in the field of sixteenth through eighteenth century music.

MEMBER: American Musicological Society (editor, 1941-44; vice-president, 1962-63; honorary member, 1975—); member of several foreign and international learned societies. *Awards, honors:* J. K. Paine Traveling Fellow in Paris, 1925-27; Guggenheim fellow, 1949-50; American Council of Learned Societies fellow, 1962-63; National Endowment for the Humanities senior fellow, 1967-68; American Academy of Arts and Sciences fellow, 1973; Mus.Doc., Rutgers University, 1973; Dr. Humane Letters, Brandeis University, 1976.

WRITINGS: (Translator) Paul Bekker, *The Changing Opera,* Norton, 1935; (translator) Paul Hindemith, *The Craft of Musical Composition: Theoretical Part,* Associated Music Publishers, 1942; (translator with Nathan Broder) Alfred Einstein, *Mozart: His Character, His Work,* Oxford University Press, 1945; (editor with Hans T. David) *The Bach Reader,* Norton, 1945, revised edition, with supplements, 1966; (editor) Heinrich Schuetz, *The Christmas Story,* G. Schirmer, 1949; (editor) J. S. Bach, *The St. John Passion* (vocal score), G. Schirmer, 1951; (editor) Mozart, *Missa Brevis,* G. Schirmer, 1954; (editor) Schuetz, *A German Requiem,* G. Schirmer, 1955; (with A. J. Ellis) *Studies in the History of Musical Pitch,* Frits Knuf, 1968; (editor) Bach, *Passion nach dem Evangelisten Johannes,* Neue Bach-Ausgabe, 1973-74. Member of international editorial board for *Neue Bach Ausgabe,* a new critical edition of the collected works of Bach, 1950—. Contributor to musicological journals.

WORK IN PROGRESS: Research on the masses and motets of Joaquin Desprez (c. 1440-1521), including a search for objective criteria of their style, chronology, and authenticity; further research on Bach.

* * *

MENNIS, Bernard 1938-

PERSONAL: Born February 5, 1938, in New York City; son of Saul and Edith (Skolnick) Mennis; married Marilyn M. Broida (a mental health/mental retardation planner), 1964; children: Jeremy, Shannan. *Education:* College of the City of New York (now City College of the City University of New York), B.A., 1959; University of Michigan, M.A., 1962, Ph.D., 1967. *Home:* 401 Hemlock Rd., Flourtown, Pa. 19031. *Office:* Department of Political Science, Temple University, Philadelphia, Pa. 19122.

CAREER: University of Michigan, Ann Arbor, instructor in political science, 1965-66; New York University, New York, N.Y., instructor in political science, 1966-67; University of Pennsylvania, Philadelphia, assistant professor of political science, 1968-74; Temple University, Philadelphia, associate professor of political science, 1974—. *Military service:* U.S. Army Reserve, 1959-65.

WRITINGS: American Foreign Policy Officials, Ohio State University Press, 1971; (with Karl P. Sauvant) *Emerging Forms of Transnational Community: Transnational Business Enterprises and Regional Integration,* Lexington Books, 1976. Contributor to proceedings and to scholarly journals.

WORK IN PROGRESS: Research on transnational corporations and investment in the United States.

* * *

MERAS, Phyllis 1931-

PERSONAL: Surname is pronounced *Mer*-a; born May 10, 1931, in Brooklyn, N.Y.; daughter of Edmond Albert (a teacher) and Leslie (a teacher; maiden name, Ross) Meras; married Thomas Cocroft (an artist), November 3, 1968. *Education:* Wellesley College, B.A., 1953; Columbia University, M.S., 1954; also studied at Institut des Hautes Etudes Internationales, Geneva, Switzerland. *Politics:* Democrat. *Religion:* Congregationalist. *Home:* Sunnyside Ave., Vineyard Haven, Mass. *Office: Vineyard Gazette,* Edgartown, Mass. 02539.

CAREER: Providence Journal, Providence, R.I., copy editor and reporter, 1954-57; *Ladies Home Journal,* Philadelphia, Pa., writer, 1958-59; *Providence Journal,* copy editor and reporter, 1959-61; *Weekly Tribune,* Geneva, Switzerland, editor-in-chief, 1961-62; *New York Times,* New York, N.Y., reporter and copy editor for travel section, 1962-68; *Vineyard Gazette,* Edgartown, Mass., managing editor, 1968-74, contributing editor, 1974—; *Providence Journal,* travel editor, 1976—. *Awards, honors:* Exchange fellow, Government of Switzerland, 1957; Pulitzer fellow in critical writing, 1966.

WRITINGS: First Spring: A Journal of Martha's Vineyard, Chatham Press, 1972; *A Yankee Way with Wood,* Houghton, 1975; *Miniatures: How to Make, Use and Sell Them,* Houghton, 1976; *Vacation Crafts,* Houghton, 1978. Contributor to *Saturday Review, Nation,* and various travel guides.

WORK IN PROGRESS: A children's book and a Christmas crafts book.

MERCATANTE, Anthony Stephen 1940-

PERSONAL: Born January 29, 1940, in New York, N.Y.; son of Stephen S. (a carpenter) and Carmela (La Tempa) Mercatante. *Education:* Attended St. Peter's College, Oxford, summer, 1974, and School of Visual Arts; City University of New York, B.A., 1975. *Religion:* Christian. *Home:* 15 Abingdon Sq., New York, N.Y. 10014. *Office:* Passaic County Community College, Paterson, N.J. 07505.

CAREER: Fairchild Publications, New York City, editor, 1960-63; Maco Publishing Co., New York City, editor, 1963-66; Copylab Publishing Co., New York City, editor of *The United States Encyclopedia of History,* 1966-67; Harper & Row Publishers, Inc., New York City, editor, 1967-72; Grosset & Dunlap, Inc., New York City, senior editor, 1972-74; J. Montoya Design, Inc., New York City, involved in public relations, 1974—; Passaic County Community College, Paterson, N.J., teacher of writing and anthropology, 1976—. Graphics and paintings have been exhibited in one-man shows in New York City.

WRITINGS: (Illustrator) Fulton J. Sheen, *Walk with God,* Maco, 1965; (illustrator) Sheen, *Guide to Contentment,* Maco, 1967; (editor and author of introduction) *The Harper Book of Christian Poetry,* Harper, 1972; *Zoo of the Gods: Animals in Myth, Legend and Fable,* Harper, 1974; *The Magic Garden: Myths and Folklore of Flowers, Plants, Trees and Herbs,* Harper, 1976; *Good and Evil: Mythology and Folklore,* Harper, 1978. Contributor of numerous articles to magazines, including *Budget Decorating, Easy to Do Decorating, Gentlemen's Quarterly,* and *Budget Travel.*

* * *

MERK, Frederick 1887-1977

PERSONAL: Born August 15, 1887, in Milwaukee, Wis.; son of Frederick (an artist) and Katharine (Klein) Merk; married Lois A. Bannister (an associate in historical research), June 21, 1931; children: Katharine (Mrs. James G. McNally, Jr.), Frederick Bannister. *Education:* University of Wisconsin, A.B., 1911; Harvard University, Ph.D., 1920. *Home:* 10 Village Rd., Belmont, Mass. 02178.

CAREER: State Historical Society of Wisconsin, Madison, member of editorial staff, 1911-16; Harvard University, Cambridge, Mass., tutor in history, government, and economics, 1918-20, instructor in American history, 1921-24, assistant professor, 1924-30, associate professor, 1930-36, professor, 1936-46, Gurney Professor of History and Political Science, 1946-57, professor emeritus, 1957-77, head of department, 1941-46. Exchange professor at Carleton, Grinnell, and Pomona Colleges, 1927-28. *Member:* American Historical Association, Organization of American Historians (president, 1959), Agricultural History Society (president, 1948), American Antiquarian Society, American Academy of Arts and Sciences (fellow), Massachusetts Historical Society, Phi Beta Kappa, Delta Sigma Rho. *Awards, honors:* Harvard University, Edward Austin fellow, 1916-18, Toppan prize, 1920, Sheldon traveling fellow, 1920-21, Litt. D., 1958; L.H.D., University of Wisconsin, 1971, and Clark University, 1977.

WRITINGS: (Editor) *Civil War Messages and Proclamations of Wisconsin War Governors,* Wisconsin History Commission, 1912; *Economic History of Wisconsin During the Civil War Decade,* State Historical Society of Wisconsin, 1916, revised edition, 1971; (with Frederick J. Turner) *List of References on the History of the West,* Harvard University Press, 1922; (editor) George Simpson, *Fur Trade and Empire: George Simpson's Journal, 1824-1825,* Harvard University Press, 1931, revised edition, 1968; *Albert Gallatin and the Oregon Problem*, Harvard University Press, 1950; (with Oscar Handlin, A. M. Schlesinger, S. E. Morison, A. M. Schlesinger, Jr., and Paul H. Buck) *Harvard Guide to American History*, Harvard University Press, 1954, revised edition, 1974; *Manifest Destiny and Mission in American History: A Reinterpretation*, Knopf, 1963; *The Monroe Doctrine and American Expansionism: 1843-49*, Knopf, 1966; *The Oregon Question: Essays in Anglo-American Diplomacy and Politics*, Harvard University Press, 1967; (with Samuel Eliot Morison and Frank Freidel) *Dissent in Three American Wars*, Harvard University Press, 1970; (with wife, Lois A. Merk) *The Fruits of Propaganda in the Tyler Administration*, Harvard University Press, 1971; *Slavery and the Annexation of Texas*, Knopf, 1972; *History of the Westward Movement*, Knopf, 1978. Contributor to history journals including *Agricultural History* and *Mississippi Valley Historical Review*.

SIDELIGHTS: Frederick Merk, an historian the *New York Times* called "a leading scholar in the field," was perhaps best known for his course "The Westward Movement," which students affectionately nicknamed "Wagon Wheels." The course has influenced several generations of Harvard students, a number of whom have gone on to become historians in their own right.

Historian John Morton Blum, a former Merk student, remembers that "to the first meeting of his graduate seminar [Merk] always put the same question: 'Why do you want to study history?'"; after hearing his students answer, "Fred has the last word, the only good answer to his own query: 'I study history because I like to.'"

Merk became fascinated with the American West as a student of Frederick Jackson Turner, one of the first historians to seriously study the American frontier. During his years of teaching at Harvard, Merk found time to write a number of books containing what the *New York Times* described as "extensive research and penetrating analysis." After his retirement in 1957, he devoted most of his time to research and writing. His last book, *History of the Westward Movement*, is based on the lectures he delivered during his "Wagon Wheels" course.

BIOGRAPHICAL/CRITICAL SOURCES: American Historical Review, Volume LXXII, October, 1972; *Times Literary Supplement*, March 2, 1973; *Journal of American History*, Volume LX, June, 1973; *New York Times*, September 27, 1977, September 28, 1977; *Western Historical Quarterly*, Volume IX, April, 1978; *Virginia Quarterly Review*, Volume LIV, summer, 1978.†

(Died September 24, 1977)

* * *

MERRILL, M. David 1937-

PERSONAL: Born March 27, 1937, in Ogden, Utah; son of David M. and Leola D. (Green) Merrill; married Dixie Rogers, May 10, 1959; children: Roger, Mardi, Mondi, Misti, MiKelle, Mariner. *Education:* Brigham Young University, B.A., 1961; University of Illinois, M.A. and Ph.D., 1964. *Religion:* Church of Jesus Christ of Latter-day Saints (Mormon). *Home:* 1970 South 50th St. E., Orem, Utah 84057. *Office:* Courseware, Inc., Brigham Young University, B-30, Provo, Utah 84601.

CAREER: George Peabody College for Teachers, Nashville, Tenn., assistant professor of educational psychology and research associate of Institute for School Learning,

1964-66; Brigham Young University, Provo, Utah, assistant professor, 1966-67, associate professor of educational psychology, 1968-78, director of Laboratory for Experimental Study of Instruction, 1968-69, director of department of instructional research and development, 1969-78, vice-president for research, Courseware, Inc. and adjunct professor, 1978—. Visiting assistant professor of educational psychology and research associate, Stanford Center for Research and Development in Teaching, Stanford University. *Member:* American Educational Research Association, American Psychological Association, Association of Educational Communications and Technology, Phi Delta Kappa, Phi Kappa Phi.

WRITINGS: (Editor and contributor) *Instructional Design: Readings*, Prentice-Hall, 1971; *Education 560X, Educational Tests and Measurement*, Brigham Young University Press, 1971; (contributor) Robert N. Singer, editor, *The Psychomotor Domain: Movement and Behavior*, Lea and Febiger, 1972; (with R. Irwin Goodman) *Selecting Instructional Strategies and Media: A Place to Begin*, National Special Media Institutes, 1972; (with B. Lee) *Writing Complete Affective Objectives*, Wadsworth, 1972; (contributor with R. C. Boutwell) T. H. Kerlinger, editor, *Review of Research in Education*, F. E. Peacock, 1973; (with N. D. Wood) *Instructional Strategies: A Preliminary Taxonomy*, Ohio State University, 1974; (contributor with Wood) F. S. Cook and R. C. Richey, editors, *Humanizing Education through Competency-Based Teacher Education*, College of Education, Wayne State University, 1974; (with R. D. Tennyson) *Teaching Concepts: An Instructional Design Guide*, Educational Technology, 1977. Also author of *Technical Specifications for a Learner Controlled Computer Assisted Courseware System*, 1973. Contributor of numerous articles to educational journals. Editor, *AV Communications Review*.

WORK IN PROGRESS: Research under a multimillion dollar grant from Mitre Corp.

* * *

MERRITT, Richard L(awrence) 1933-

PERSONAL: Born August 8, 1933, in Portland, Ore.; son of Raymond A. (a store manager) and Sarah Elizabeth (Cook) Merritt; married Anna Johanna Gode-von Aesch (an editor-translator), August 9, 1958; children: Christopher Eugene, Geoffrey Andreas, Theodore Aleyn. *Education:* University of Southern California, B.A., 1955; University of Virginia, M.A., 1956; Free University of Berlin, graduate study, 1956-57; Yale University, Ph.D., 1962. *Politics:* Democratic. *Home:* 715 West Indiana Ave., Urbana, Ill. 61801. *Office:* Department of Political Science, University of Illinois, Urbana, Ill. 61801.

CAREER: Yale University, New Haven, Conn., instructor, 1962-63, assistant professor of political science, 1963-67; University of Illinois at Urbana-Champaign, associate professor and research associate professor, 1967-69, professor of political science and research professor in communications, 1969—, head of political science department, 1978—. Chairperson, International Political Science Association meeting in Munich, Germany, 1979. *Member:* American Political Science Association, International Political Science Association, International Studies Association, Peace Research Society, University of Illinois Film Society (president, 1971), Phi Beta Kappa. *Awards, honors:* Woodrow Wilson fellow, 1955-56; Fulbright student, 1956-57, and research professor, 1966-67, at Free University of Berlin; Social Science Research Council grant for study in West Berlin, 1960-61, summer research grant, 1962.

WRITINGS: Symbols of American Community, 1735-1775, Yale University Press, 1966; (editor with Stein Rokkan, and contributor) *Comparing Nations: The Use of Quantitative Data in Cross-National Research,* Yale University Press, 1966; (with Ellen B. Pirro) *Press Attitudes to Arms Control in Four Countries, 1946-1963,* Political Science Research Library, Yale University, 1966; (editor with Donald J. Puchala) *Western European Attitudes on Arms Control, Defense, and European Unity, 1952-1963,* Political Science Research Library, Yale University, 1966; (with Karl W. Deutsch, Lewis J. Edinger, and Roy C. Macridis) *France, Germany, and the Western Alliance: A Study of Elite Attitudes on European Integration and World Politics,* Scribner, 1967; (editor with Donald J. Puchala, and contributor) *Western European Perspectives on International Affairs: Public Opinion Studies and Evaluations,* Praeger, 1968; (with Gloria J. Pyska) *The Student Political Scientist's Handbook,* Schenkman, 1969.

Systematic Approaches to Comparative Politics, Rand McNally, 1970; (editor with wife, Anna J. Merritt, and contributor) *Public Opinion in Occupied Germany: The OMGUS Surveys, 1945-1949,* University of Illinois Press, 1970; (editor with Deutsch) *Nationalism and National Development: An Interdisciplinary Bibliography,* M.I.T. Press, 1970; (with A. J. Merritt) *West Germany Enters the Seventies,* Foreign Policy Association, 1971; (editor) *Political Science Enters the 1970s,* American Political Science Association, 1971; (editor and contributor) *Communication in International Politics,* University of Illinois Press, 1972; (editor) *Growth and Change in the Global System,* International Studies Association, 1973; (editor) *Foreign Policy Analysis,* Lexington Books, 1975; (editor with David G. Warren) *A Legislator's Guide to the Medical Malpractice Issue,* Health Policy Center, Georgetown University, 1976; (editor with A. J. Merritt) *Politics, Economics, and Society in the Two Germanies, 1945-75: A Bibliography of English Language Works,* University of Illinois Press, 1978.

Contributor: Karl W. Deutsch and William J. Foltz, editors, *Nation-Building,* Aldine-Atherton, 1963; Ludwig von Bertalanffy and Anatol Rapoport, editors, *General Systems: Yearbook of the Society for General Systems Research, 1963,* Society for General Systems Research, 1964; Herbert C. Kelman, editor, *International Behavior: A Social-Psychological Analysis,* Holt, 1965; Joseph L. Bernd, editor, *Mathematical Applications in Political Science,* Southern Methodist University Press, Volume II, 1966, Volume III, 1967; Edmund A. Bowles, editor, *Computers in Humanistic Research: Readings and Perspectives,* Prentice-Hall, 1967; Roy C. Macridis, editor, *Major European Governments: Case Studies in Policy-Making,* Prentice-Hall, 1968; John D. Montgomery and Albert O. Hirschman, *Public Policy,* Volume XVII, Harvard University Press, 1968; Hennig Cohen, editor, *The American Experience: Approaches to the Study of the United States,* Houghton, 1968; Seymour Martin Lipset and Richard Hofstadter, editors, *Sociology and History: Methods,* Basic Books, 1968; James N. Rosenau, editor, *Linkage Politics: Essays on the Convergence of National and International Systems,* Free Press, 1969; Wolfgang Zapf, editor, *Theorien des sozialen Wandels,* Kiepenheuer & Witsch, 1969; Roger E. Kasperson and Julian V. Minghi, editors *The Structure of Political Geography,* Aldine-Atherton, 1969.

Melvin Small, editor, *Public Opinion and Historians,* Wayne State University Press, 1970; Naomi Rosenbaum,

editor, *Readings on the International Political System,* Prentice-Hall, 1970; Robert P. Swierenga, editor, *Quantification in American History: Theory and Research,* Atheneum, 1970; Oliver Walter, editor, *Political Scientists at Work,* Duxbury Press, 1971; Robert J. Jackson and Michael Stein, editors, *Issues in Comparative Politics: A Text with Readings,* St. Martin's, 1971; Robert D. Marcus and David Burner, editors, *The American Scene: Varieties of American History,* Appleton, 1971; Bruce L. Sanders and Alan C. Durbin, editors, *Contemporary International Politics: Introductory Readings,* Wiley, 1971; Kevin R. Cox, David R. Reynolds, and Stein Rokkan, editors, *Locational Approaches to Power and Conflict,* Sage Publications, 1972; Richard W. Budd and Brent D. Ruben, editors, *Approaches to Human Communication,* Spartan, 1972; Martin O. Heisler, editor, *Politics in Europe: Structures and Processes,* McKay, 1972; Norman J. Vig and Rodney P. Stiefbold, editors, *Politics in Advanced Nations,* Appleton, 1972.

Contributor of more than sixty articles and reviews to political affairs journals in the United States and Europe. Member of editorial board of *American Political Science Review,* 1963-66, *Midwest Journal of Political Science,* 1971-73, *Comparative Political Studies,* 1972—, and *Policy Studies Journal,* 1972—.

WORK IN PROGRESS: Editing and contributing to *Cross-System Approaches to Political Integration; The End of Community: Political Division in Postwar Berlin;* with Karl W. Deutsch, *The Process of World Politics,* for McGraw; with wife, Anna J. Merritt, *Public Opinion in Semisovereign Germany: The HICOG Surveys, 1949-1955,* for University of Illinois Press; *The Extended Community: Postwar West Berlin and West Germany; Communications and International Politics,* for St. Martin's; *Systematic Approaches to International Politics,* for Schenkman.†

*   *   *

MERTINS, Herman, Jr.   1931-

PERSONAL: Born December 29, 1931, in Paterson, N.J.; son of Herman Frederick and Nora (Enright) Mertins; married Barbara Jordan (an assistant professor of library science), July 11, 1953; children: Glenn, Gary. *Education:* Drew University, B.A. (magna cum laude), 1953; Syracuse University, M.P.A., 1954, Ph.D., 1969. *Home:* 717 South Hills Dr., Morgantown, W.Va. 26505. *Office:* West Virginia University, 208 Woodburn Hall, Morgantown, W.Va. 26506.

CAREER: Port of New York Authority, New York, N.Y., executive training program trainee, 1954, junior administrative assistant of operations services department, 1956-58, staff assistant of purchase and administrative services department, 1958-60, assistant to director of planning and development, 1960-66, assistant manager of New Jersey Marine Terminals, 1966-67, executive assistant to the chief of central planning, 1967; Syracuse University, Syracuse, N.Y., assistant to director of Public Administration Programs, 1967-68, research associate, 1968-69; West Virginia University, Morgantown, associate professor, 1969-73, professor of public administration, 1973—, chairman of department, 1969—. Consultant to Department of Welfare, W.Va.; former member of New York Port Authority Speakers Bureau and Little Falls (N.J.) Board of Education. *Military service:* U.S. Army, 1954-56. *Member:* International City Managers Association, American Society of Public Administration, National Academy of Public Administration, National Association of Schools of Public Affairs and Administration (West Virginia University representative, 1972—; member of executive council, 1978—), Public Personnel Association.

WRITINGS: (Contributor) Frank Marini, editor, *Toward a New Public Administration: The Minnowbrook Perspective*, Chandler Publishing, 1971; *National Transportation Policy in Transition*, Heath, 1972; (contributor) David R. Miller, editor, *Urban Transportation Policy: New Perspectives*, Heath, 1973; (editor) *Professional Standards and Ethics*, American Society of Public Administration, 1978. Editor of special symposia and member of board of editors, *Public Administration Review*.

WORK IN PROGRESS: Research on transportation and public policymaking and on the future development of higher education for public administrators.

* * *

MERTINS, (Marshall) Louis 1885-1973

PERSONAL: Born December 7, 1885, in Jackson County, Mo.; son of Carl Henry (a farmer) and Mary E. (Koger) Mertins; married Lena Lee Holman, September 28, 1907 (divorced, 1936); married Esther Pedersen Erickson (an adviser to foreign students), May 12, 1939; children: (first marriage) Blanche (Mrs. Louis Garcia), Virginia (deceased), Sara (Mrs. Malcolm Dewees), Ellis Holman. *Education:* Attended William Jewell College, 1905-10, and Kansas City Seminary, 1906-07. *Politics:* Democrat. *Home:* 554 Terracina Blvd., Redlands, Calif. 92373.

CAREER: Baptist minister in Missouri, 1911-16; lecturer at chautauquas and lyceums, 1916-26; columnist and radio commentator in California, 1926-56; San Bernardino Valley College, San Bernardino, Calif., lecturer in world literature, 1956-63. *Member:* International P.E.N. (president of Los Angeles center, 1964-66), American Schools of Oriental Research, California Writers Guild (co-founder). *Awards, honors:* LL.D., William Jewell College, 1939.

*WRITINGS—*All published by Hunt & Co. Ltd., except as indicated: *The Wishing Gate* (poems), 1918; *The Sumac Trail* (poems), 1919; *The Covered Wagon* (poems), 1921; *The Mail Cart Man* (poems), 1921; *A Voice Crying in the Wilderness* (poems), 1923; *Tales of Kettles Shop* (poems), 1923; *The Baratarians* (poems), 1924; (with wife, Esther Mertins) *The Intervals of Robert Frost*, University of California Press, 1947, reprinted, Russell, 1976; *Robert Frost: Life and Talks–Walking*, University of Oklahoma, 1965; *The Blue God: An Epic of Mesa Verde*, Richie, 1968. Contributor of articles and poems to magazines.

AVOCATIONAL INTERESTS: Collecting signed books, manuscripts, and silhouettes of notable people, archaeology, travel.†

(Died January 17, 1973)

* * *

MERTON, Robert K(ing) 1910-

PERSONAL: Born July 5, 1910, in Philadelphia, Pa.; son of Jewish, working–class, immigrant parents from eastern Europe; married Suzanne M. Carhart (a social worker), September 8, 1934; children: Stephanie (Mrs. Thomas A. Tombrello, Jr.), Robert C., Vanessa H. (Mrs. John Carroll). *Education:* Temple University, A.B., 1931; Harvard University, M.A., 1932, Ph.D., 1936. *Home:* 450 Riverside Dr., New York, N.Y. 10027. *Office:* Fayerweather Hall, Columbia University, New York, N.Y. 10027.

CAREER: Harvard University, Cambridge, Mass., tutor and instructor in sociology, 1936-39; Tulane University, New Orleans, La., associate professor, 1939-40, professor of sociology and chairman of department, 1940-41; Columbia University, New York, N.Y., assistant professor, 1941-44, associate professor, 1944-47, professor, 1947-63, Giddings Professor of Sociology, 1963-74, University Professor, 1974—, associate director, Bureau of Applied Social Research, 1942-71. Distinguished or special lecturer at universities across the country, including Princeton University, 1946, Claremont College (now Claremont Graduate School), 1960, University of Pennsylvania, 1961, Johns Hopkins University, Baylor University, and University of California, Los Angeles, 1962, Economic and Social Research Institute, Dublin, Ireland, Cornell University Medical School, and Smith College, 1975, and Yale University, and Washington University, 1976. National Institutes of Health lecturer, 1964; Fulbright lecturer at University of Kyoto, 1967; Phi Beta Kappa-Sigma Xi lecturer, 1968. Member of first official delegation of behavioral scientists to U.S.S.R. Academy of Sciences, 1961; vice-president, National Commission for the Study of Nursing and Nursing Education, 1967-69; chairman of committee on the social organization of science, Social Science Research Council, 1968-70. Trustee of Center for Advanced Study in the Behavioral Sciences, 1953-75, Institute for Scientific Information, 1969—, and American Nurses Foundation, 1969-71; Guggenheim Foundation Educational Advisory Board, trustee, 1963—, chairman, 1971. Consulting editor on sociology, Harcourt, Brace & Jovanovich.

MEMBER: National Academy of Sciences, National Academy of Education, American Philosophical Society, American Academy of Arts and Sciences, World Academy of Art and Science, American Sociological Association (president, 1957), Sociological Research Association (president, 1968), History of Science Society, Society for the Study of Social Problems, History of Technology Society, American Association for the Advancement of Science, American Association of University Professors, Society for Social Studies of Science (president, 1975-76), Royal Swedish Academy of Sciences (foreign member), Authors Guild (member of council, 1974-77), Eastern Sociological Society (president, 1969), Century Association.

AWARDS, HONORS: LL.D. from Temple University, 1956, Western Reserve University (now Case Western Reserve University), 1966, University of Chicago, 1968, and Tulane University, 1971; Lit.D. from Emory University, 1965, Loyola University, Chicago, 1970, Kalamazoo College, 1970, and Cleveland State University, 1977; Dr. honoris causa from University of Leyden, 1965; Litt.D. from Colgate University, 1967; Dr. Social Sci. from Yale University, 1968; D.Sc. in Econ. from University of Wales, 1968. American Council of Learned Societies Prize for Distinguished Scholarship in the Humanities, 1962; Guggenheim fellow, 1962; Distinguished Alumni Award, Temple University, 1964; fellow of Center for Advanced Study in the Behavioral Sciences, 1973, and Institute of Medicine, National Academy of Sciences, 1973.

WRITINGS: *Science, Technology and Society in Seventeenth-Century England* (doctoral thesis), first published in *Osiris: Studies on the History and Philosophy of Science, and on the History of Learning and Culture*, edited by George Sarton, St. Catherine Press (Brussels), 1938, published under original title with new introduction, Harper, 1970; (with Marjorie Fiske and Alberta Curtis) *Mass Persuasion*, Harper, 1946, reprinted, Greenwood Press, 1971;

Social Theory and Social Structure, Free Press, 1949, 3rd edition, enlarged, 1968; (with Fiske and Patricia M. Kendall) *The Focused Interview: A Manual of Problems and Procedures,* Free Press, 1956; (with R. P. McKeon and Walter Gellhorn) *The Freedom to Read: Perspective and Program,* Bowker, 1957; *On the Shoulders of Giants: A Shandean Postscript,* Free Press, 1965; *On Theoretical Sociology: Five Essays, Old and New,* Free Press, 1967; *Social Theory and Functional Analysis,* translation by Togo Mori, Yoshio Mori, and Kanazawa Minoru, Aoki Shoten (Tokyo), 1969; (with Howard S. Becker, Seymour M. Lipset, and others) *Varieties of Political Expression in Sociology,* University of Chicago Press, 1972; *The Sociology of Science: Theoretical and Empirical Investigations,* University of Chicago Press, 1973; *Sociological Ambivalence and Other Essays,* Free Press, 1976.

Editor: (With Paul F. Lazarsfeld) *Continuities in Social Research: Studies in the Scope and Methods of the American Soldier,* Free Press, 1950; (with P. S. West, Marie Jahoda, and Hanan C. Selvin) *Social Policy and Social Research in Housing,* published as issues of *Journal of Social Issues,* Volume VIII, number 1 and 2, 1951; (with A. P. Gray, Barbara Hockey, and Selvin) *Reader in Bureaucracy,* Free Press, 1952; (with G. G. Reader and P. L. Kendall) *The Student Physician: Introductory Studies in the Sociology of Medical Education,* Harvard University Press, 1957; (with Leonard Broom and L. S. Cottrell, Jr.) *Sociology Today: Problems and Prospects,* Basic Books, 1959; (with Robert A. Nisbet) *Contemporary Social Problems,* Harcourt, 1961, 4th edition, 1976; (with Jerry Gaston) *The Sociology of Science in Europe,* University of Southern Illinois Press, 1977; (with others) *Toward a Metric of Science,* Wiley, 1978; (with J. S. Coleman and P. H. Rossi) *Qualitative and Quantitative Social Research: Essays in Honor of Paul F. Lazarsfeld,* Free Press, in press.

Compiler: (With Aron Halberstam) *Perspectives in Social Inquiry: Classics, Staples, and Precursors in Sociology,* forty volumes, Arno, 1974; (with Y. Elkana, A. Thackray, and H. Zuckerman) *History, Philosophy, and Sociology of Science,* sixty volumes, Arno, 1975.

Contributor of articles to journals. Member of editorial council, *International Encyclopedia of the Social Sciences;* consulting editor on sociology, *Webster's International Unabridged Dictionary* and *World Book Encyclopedia.* Former or present member of board of editors, *American Sociological Review, Sociological Abstracts, Social and Economic Studies, Social Problems, Human Relations, Isis: Review of the History of Science, Journal of Health and Human Behavior, Inquiry, Natural Philosopher, Journal of the History of the Behavioral Sciences, Transaction: Social Science and Modern Society, Estudios de Sociologia, Journal of Applied Behavioral Science, International Journal of Contemporary Sociology, Sociological Focus, Inquiry, Theory of Society,* and *Journal of Medicine and Philosophy.*

SIDELIGHTS: Robert K. Merton, who began as a philosophy major at Temple University but converted to the study of sociology, is an articulate and well-known defender of sociology as a genuine science. Reviewing *The Sociology of Science: Theoretical and Empirical Investigations,* Joseph Ben-David comments that Merton "shows that sociology can only do what science can do, namely reduce a subject to its logical components, where emotions disappear, and the problem becomes amenable to analysis in the light of empirical evidence. This requires the renouncement of immediate practical solutions, and the willingness to follow unexpected

leads. But it is the only way in which social science can ever become really useful. There are very few other books in sociology that teach this lesson as well as the present one. And none that teaches it with such meticulous scholarship, or in so elegant a style."

Alden Whitman, writing on *Sociological Ambivalence and Other Essays,* finds that Merton "has a knack for straightforward English and a fondness for the witty, illuminating phrase, as this collection of his occasional essays over almost 40 years attests. He has a tart mind, too. . . . Dr. Merton's book will profit almost anyone who troubles to peruse it with a modicum of interest and intelligence. It will help to give sociology the good name it deserves."

Merton's *Social Theory and Social Structure* has been translated into French, Italian, Japanese, Spanish, Hebrew, German, Russian, Portuguese, and Czechoslovakian. There have been Russian, Rumanian, and Spanish editions of *Sociology Today,* which he co-edited, and Italian and Spanish editions of his doctoral thesis, *Science, Technology and Society in Seventeenth-Century England.*

BIOGRAPHICAL/CRITICAL SOURCES: *New Yorker,* January 28, 1961; *Times Literary Supplement,* April 16, 1971, April 26, 1974; *New York Review of Books,* May 6, 1971; *New York Times Book Review,* November 11, 1973; Lewis A. Coser, editor, *The Ideas of Social Structure: Papers in Honor of Robert K. Merton,* Harcourt, 1975; *New York Times,* March 4, 1977.

*   *   *

MESSERLI, Jonathan C. 1926-

PERSONAL: Born February 14, 1926, in Albany, Ore.; son of Henry Conrad (a minister) and Lilly (Rietz) Messerli; married Vi L. Rabey, August 15, 1948; children: Timothy, Martha, Hannah. *Education:* Concordia Teachers College, River Forest, Ill., B.S., 1947; Washington University, St. Louis, Mo., M.A., 1952; Harvard University, Ph.D., 1963. *Religion:* Lutheran. *Home:* 501 University Ave., Selinsgrove, Pa. 17870. *Office:* Susquehanna University, Selinsgrove, Pa. 17870.

CAREER: High school biology teacher, 1947-52, and general science teacher, 1952-57, in St. Louis, Mo.; Harvard University, Cambridge, Mass., coordinator of international teacher development program, 1960-61; University of Washington, Seattle, assistant professor of history and education, 1963-64; Columbia University, New York City, assistant professor, 1964-66, associate professor of history and education, 1966-68; Hofstra University, Hempstead, N.Y., dean of School of Education, 1968-72; Fordham University, New York City, dean of School of Education, 1972-77; Susquehanna University, Selinsgrove, Pa., president, 1977—. Visiting professor, Sarah Lawrence College, 1967; visiting summer professor at Yale University, 1967, University of Hawaii, 1968, and New York University, 1970, 1971. Ford Foundation lecturer in Japan, 1966; lecturer at Johns Hopkins University, State University of New York at Albany, Kent State University, and University of Massachusetts. *Member:* American Association of Colleges of Teacher Education. *Awards, honors:* Fund for the Advancement of Education fellow, 1963.

WRITINGS: (Editor) *Readings in the History of Education,* Beaver Island Publishing, 1967; *Horace Mann,* Knopf, 1972. Contributor of about thirty articles to scholarly journals. *Harvard Educational Review,* member of editorial board, 1958-61, editorial chairman, 1960-61.

MICHAEL, George 1919-

PERSONAL: Born August 29, 1919, in Rochester, N.H.; son of Joseph (a merchant) and Antoinette (Arooth) Michael; married Elizabeth Palmer, October 17, 1946; children: Gregory, Glenn, Geoffrey, Gary, Gerald. *Education:* Attended Emerson College. *Politics:* Republican. *Religion:* Episcopalian. *Home:* 12 Evergreen Dr., Merrimack, N.H. 03054. *Agent:* (Literary) Toni Mendez, Inc., 140 East 56th St., New York, N.Y. 10022; (lectures) Lordly & Dame, Boston, Mass.

CAREER: Operator of auction gallery in Rochester, N.H., 1950-67, conducting more than 3,150 auctions of estates; host of television program, "Antiques," 1963—, and of color television series, "Commonwealth," produced for Pennsylvania Historical and Museum Commission, 1970; professional lecturer on antiques throughout the country, 1964—; president of National Antiques Industries, Portland, Me., 1969, and editor of *National Antiques Review,* 1969-72; antiques editor, columnist, or writer for *Christian Science Monitor,* 1967-69, *New England Homestead* (magazine), 1967-69, *New Hampshire Sunday News,* 1969-72, *Yankee* (magazine), 1972—, and *Boston Sunday Globe,* 1972-76. Instructor in antiques courses at University of Maine, University of New Hampshire, Boston Adult Evening Education Center, and elsewhere; conductor of antiques buying tours in Europe, 1971—; antiques consultant, Wistariahurst Museum, Holyoke, Mass. Councilman, Rochester, N.H., 1956-60; town moderator, Merrimack, N.H., 1972—. *Military service:* U.S. Army, 1942-43; U.S. Merchant Marine, 1943-44; Canadian Army, Royal Canadian engineers, 1944-45. *Member:* Washington Crossing Foundation, Merrimack Historical Society, Canterbury Shakers, Inc.

WRITINGS: Antiquing with George Michael, Stephan Greene Press, 1967; *The Treasury of New England Antiques,* Hawthorn, 1969; *The Treasury of Antiques of the Federal Period,* Hawthorn, 1972; *Basic Book of Antiques,* Arco, 1974. Contributor to *New Hampshire Profiles Magazine, American Antiques,* and *Early American Life.*

WORK IN PROGRESS: An untitled novel.

* * *

MICHAEL, Wolfgang F(riedrich) 1909-

PERSONAL: Born February 23, 1909, in Freiburg, Germany; naturalized U.S. citizen; son of Wolfgang W. (a university professor) and Else (Wehrenpfennig) Michael; married Hadassah Posey, December, 1937 (divorced, 1948); married Marian Pendergrass (a journalism teacher), 1952; children: (first marriage) Hadassah H., Michael Hiscott, Dorothea F., Felton P. *Education:* Attended University of Freiburg, University of Berlin, and University of Marburg; University of Munich, Ph.D., 1934. *Home:* 405 West 37th St., Austin, Tex. 78705. *Office:* Department of German, University of Texas, Austin, Tex. 78712.

CAREER: Bryn Mawr College, Bryn Mawr, Pa., instructor in German, 1939; Chestnut Hill College, Philadelphia, Pa., assistant professor of German, 1939-47; University of Texas at Austin, assistant professor, 1946-51, associate professor, 1951-61, professor of German, 1961—. *Member:* Modern Language Association of America, American Association of Teachers of German, Mediaeval Academy of America, Internationale Vereinigung der Germanisten.

WRITINGS: Die Anfaenge des Theaters zu Freiburg in Breisgau, Joseph Wait al, 1934; *Die geistlichen Prozessionsspiele in Deutschland,* Johns Hopkins Press, 1947; *Frueh-*

formen der deutschen Buehne, Gesellschaft fuer Theatergeschichte, 1963; *Das deutsche Drama des Mittelalter,* Walter De Gruyter, 1971; (editor) Thomas Brunner, *Tobias,* Peter Lang, 1978. Contributor to language journals.

WORK IN PROGRESS: Critical Bibliography of German Medieval Drama.

* * *

MICHAUX, William W(hitehead) 1919-

PERSONAL: Born September 12, 1919, in Wilson, N.C.; son of William Walthall, Jr. (a tobacco manufacturing executive) and Nolia (Whitehead) Michaux; married Kathleen Muriel Capps, March 28, 1942 (divorced, 1961); married Maru Helen Tatom (a psychologist), March 18, 1961; children: (first marriage) William W., Jr. *Education:* Attended Atlantic Christian College, 1934-36; University of North Carolina, A.B., 1939; University of Pittsburgh, M.Litt., 1949; Duke University, Ph.D., 1952. *Home:* 501 Colleen Rd., Baltimore, Md. 21229. *Office:* Epoch House, 38 Bloomsbury Ave., Baltimore, Md. 21228.

CAREER: Employed in tobacco manufacturing industry and with U.S. Government, 1939-42; Veterans Administration Subregional Office, Charlotte, N.C., vocational adviser, 1946-48; Veterans Administration Mental Hygiene Clinic, Washington, D.C., clinical psychologist, 1952-58; Veterans Administration, Washington, D.C., assistant chief of Outpatient Psychiatric Research Laboratory and research psychologist, 1958-61; Spring Grove State Hospital, Baltimore, Md., research psychologist and project director, 1961-67; State of Maryland Department of Mental Hygiene, Maryland House of Correction at Jessup, member of narcotic addict treatment team, 1968-69; Johns Hopkins University, School of Medicine, Baltimore, assistant professor of medical psychology, 1969—; Johns Hopkins Hospital, director of research and evaluation at Drug Abuse Center, 1969-73; Epoch House, Baltimore, senior staff psychologist, 1973—. Diplomate in clinical psychology from American Board of Professional Psychology, 1956; certified psychologist in State of Maryland, 1964. Vocational consultant, U.S. Social Security Administration, 1963—; research consultant, Maryland Commission to Study Problems of Drug Addiction, 1968-69. *Military service:* U.S. Army Air Forces, 1942-45. *Member:* American Psychological Association, Maryland Psychological Association (fellow), New York Academy of Sciences, Sigma Xi.

WRITINGS: (With M. M. Katz, A. A. Kurland, and Kathleen H. Gansereit) *The First Year Out: Mental Patients after Hospitalization,* Johns Hopkins Press, 1969. Contributor of more than thirty articles to psychology journals, including *Community Mental Health Journal* and *Journal of Abnormal Social Psychology.*

WORK IN PROGRESS: Psychological research on outpatient treatment of narcotic addicts.

AVOCATIONAL INTERESTS: His workshop, music, Scrabble, bowling, chess, home movies, swimming, travel, homemade beer.†

* * *

MIDDLETON, Bernard C(hester) 1924-

PERSONAL: Born October 29, 1924, in London, England; son of Regent Marcus Geoffry (a bookbinder) and Doris Hilda (Webster) Middleton; married Dora Davies (assistant to husband in book restoring business), June 2, 1951. *Education:* Attended Central School of Arts and Crafts, London,

England, 1938-40. *Politics:* Conservative. *Home and office:* 3 Gauden Rd., Clapham, London SW4 6LR, England.

CAREER: British Museum Bindery, London, England, apprentice and journeyman bookbinder, 1940-49; Royal College of Art, London, craftsman demonstrator, 1949-51; Zaehnsdorf Ltd., London, manager, 1952-53; owner of a book restoring business, London, 1953—. Chief examiner in general bookbinding at City and Guilds of London Institute, 1957-63. *Military service:* Royal Navy, 1943-46. *Member:* Royal Society of Arts (fellow), Art Workers' Guild, Designer Bookbinders (president, 1973-75), Society of Antiquaries (fellow). *Awards, honors:* City and Guilds of London Institute, Silver Medal for Bookbinding, 1943.

WRITINGS: A History of English Craft Bookbinding Technique, Hafner, 1963, 2nd supplemented edition, Holland Press, 1978; *The Restoration of Leather Bindings,* American Library Association, 1972. Contributor to trade journals.

* * *

MIDGLEY, Louis C(asper) 1931-

PERSONAL: Born March 12, 1931, in Salt Lake City, Utah; son of Rushby C. (an engineer) and Mary Alice (Shaw) Midgley; married Ireta Troth, September 16, 1955; children: Matthew, Martin, Sara Louise. *Education:* University of Utah, B.S., 1954, M.S., 1957; Brown University, Ph.D., 1965. *Religion:* Mormon. *Home:* 385 East 4300 North, Provo, Utah 84601. *Office:* Department of Government, Brigham Young University, Provo, Utah 84602.

CAREER: Weber State College, Ogden, Utah, instructor in political science, 1957-58; Brigham Young University, Provo, Utah, instructor, 1960-61, assistant professor, 1963-66, associate professor, 1966-70, professor of political philosophy, 1970—. Visiting professor at University of Utah, 1965. *Military service:* U.S. Army, 1954-56. *Member:* Conference for the Study of Political Thought, American Political Science Association, Tillich Gesellschaft, Western Political Science Association (member of executive council, 1970-73).

WRITINGS: Beyond Human Nature: The Contemporary Debate over Moral Natural Law, Brigham Young University Press, 1968. Contributor to *Dialogue, Improvement Era, BYU Studies, American Journal of Jurisprudence, Natural Law Forum, Proceedings of the Utah Academy of Sciences, Arts, and Letters, Western Political Quarterly,* and *American Political Science Review.*

WORK IN PROGRESS: Essays on the political thought of Lee Strauss and on the idea of progress as a religious symbol; a book of essays on political theology (an examination of the arguments about God in political philosophy).

* * *

MIHAILOVICH, Vasa D. 1926-

PERSONAL: Born August 12, 1926, in Prokuplje, Yugoslavia; son of Dragutin V. (a postmaster) and Vidosava (Petkovic) Mihailovich; married Branka Jancetovic, 1957; children: Draggan Paul, Zoran Mark. *Education:* Wayne State University, B.A., 1956, M.A., 1957; University of California, Berkeley, Ph.D., 1966. *Politics:* Democrat. *Religion:* Serbian Orthodox. *Home:* 821 Emory Dr., Chapel Hill, N.C. 27514. *Office:* Department of Slavic Languages, University of North Carolina, Chapel Hill, N.C. 27514.

CAREER: University of North Carolina at Chapel Hill, instructor, 1961-63, assistant professor, 1963-68, associate professor, 1968-75, professor of Slavic languages, 1975—. *Member:* Modern Language Association of America, American Association of Teachers of Slavic and East European Languages (vice-president, 1969-71), American Association for the Advancement of Slavic Studies, Southern Conference on Slavic Studies.

WRITINGS: (Editor) *Modern Slavic Literatures,* Volume I, Ungar, 1972; (editor) *Introduction to Yugoslav Literature,* Twayne, 1973; (editor) *Modern Slavic Literatures,* Volume II, Ungar, 1976; (editor) *Yugoslav Literature in English: A Bibliography of Translations and Criticisms, 1821-1975,* Slavica, 1976; (editor) *White Stones and Fir Trees: An Anthology of Contemporary Slavic Literature,* Fairleigh Dickinson University Press, 1977; (editor) *Contemporary Yugoslav Poetry,* University of Iowa Press, 1977; *Stari i novi vilajet* (poems in prose), Kosovo, 1977; *Bibliography and Guide to Slavic Literatures,* Ungar, 1978; *Learn Serbian,* Kosovo, 1979. Guest editor of Yugoslav and Russian issues of *Literary Review,* 1968, 1970. Contributor of articles to *Books Abroad, Saturday Review, Slavic and East European Journal, Slavic Review,* and *Encyclopedia Americana.*

WORK IN PROGRESS: Landmarks in Serbian Culture and History; translating Njego's *Gorski vijenac* into English.

* * *

MILLER, Clement (Albin) 1915-

PERSONAL: Born January 29, 1915, in Cleveland, Ohio; son of Oscar C. and Rose (Mueller) Miller; married Jean Meagher, August 5, 1937; children: Neil, Paul, Karen (Mrs. Richard N. Goodwin). *Education:* Cleveland Institute of Music, Mus.B., 1936, Mus.M., 1937; Western Reserve University (now Case Western Reserve University), M.A., 1942; University of Michigan, Ph.D., 1950. *Politics:* Independent. *Religion:* Catholic. *Home:* 18975 Van Aken Blvd., Apt. 411, Shaker Heights, Ohio 44122. *Office:* Department of Fine Arts, John Carroll University, University Heights, Cleveland, Ohio 44118.

CAREER: Cleveland Institute of Music, Cleveland, Ohio, instructor in music theory, 1937-50, head of department of music history, 1951-65, dean, 1955-65; John Carroll University, Cleveland, professor of music, 1966—. *Member:* Royal Musical Association, Renaissance Society of America, Mediaeval Academy of America, American Musicological Society, Dolmetsch Foundation, Lute Society of America, American Recorder Society. *Awards, honors:* Guggenheim fellowship, 1974-75.

WRITINGS—Translator: (And editor) Heinrich Glarean, *Dodecachordon,* American Institute of Musicology, 1966; Franchinus Gaffurius, *Practica Musicae,* American Institute of Musicology, 1968; Johannes Cochlaeus, *Tetrachordum Musices,* American Institute of Musicology, 1970; Sebald Heyden, *De Arte Canendi,* American Institute of Musicology, 1972; (and editor) *The Musical Writings of Jerome Cardan,* American Institute of Musicology, 1973; Franchinus Gaffurius, *De Harmonia Musicorum Instrumentorum Opus,* American Institute of Musicology, 1977. Contributor to music journals.

WORK IN PROGRESS: Continuing research on the relation of renowned men of the Renaissance to music.

* * *

MILLER, Paul William 1926-

PERSONAL: Born June 6, 1926, in Welland, Ontario,

Canada; son of William J. (a farmer) and Aurelia (Sauer) Miller; married Mary Joan Cooper (a realtor), August 18, 1951; children: Gary William, Cynthia Anne, Mark Warren. *Education:* McMaster University, B.A., 1947; Brown University, M.A., 1948; University of Michigan, Ph.D., 1955. *Politics:* Democrat. *Religion:* Lutheran. *Home:* 1122 Garfield Ave., Springfield, Ohio 45504. *Office:* Department of English, Wittenberg University, Springfield, Ohio 45501.

CAREER: University of Wisconsin—Madison, instructor in English, 1955-58; King College, Bristol, Tenn., associate professor of English, 1958-61; Wittenberg University, Springfield, Ohio, associate professor, 1961-67, professor of English, 1967—. *Member:* Modern Language Association of America, American Association of University Professors.

WRITINGS: (Editor) *Seven Minor Epics of the English Renaissance,* Scholar's Facsimiles & Reprints, 1967; (contributor) Thomas Connolly, editor, *Nathaniel Hawthorne: Young Goodman Brown,* Bobbs-Merrill, 1968; (editor) Brand Whitlock, *The Buckeyes: A Story of Politics and Abolitionism in an Ohio Town, 1836-1845,* Ohio University Press, 1977; (editor) *The Plays of William Mountford,* Scholar's Facsimiles & Reprints, 1977. Contributor of articles to *Studies in Philology, Notes and Queries, Nineteenth Century Fiction, Criticism, Psychoanalytic Review,* and other professional journals.

WORK IN PROGRESS: Study of James Purdy; Brand Whitlock's Belgian writings.

SIDELIGHTS: Paul W. Miller writes, "Autobiographical tracings in an author's work, and his sense of place, whether English, Midwestern, or Canadian, continue to provide me with fascinating and useful interpretive insights." *Avocational interests:* Travel, cottage building, collecting, fishing, swimming.

*　*　*

MILLER, Richard I(rwin)   1924-

PERSONAL: Born February 1, 1924, in Fairbury, Neb.; married Peggy McLaren, 1955; children: three daughters. *Education:* University of Nebraska, B.S. (with distinction), 1947; Springfield College, M.Ed., 1948; University of Illinois, additional graduate study, 1949-52; Columbia University, Ed.D., 1958. *Home:* 6 Old Elm Dr., Brockport, N.Y. 14420. *Office:* State University of New York College, Brockport, N.Y. 14420.

CAREER: University of Illinois at Urbana-Champaign, instructor in education and physical education, 1948-53; American Community School, Beirut, Lebanon, teacher, 1954-55; part-time instructor at Adelphi University, Garden City, N.Y., Teachers College, Columbia University, New York, N.Y., and Pennsylvania State University, University Park, 1955-58; National Education Association, Washington, D.C., observer to United Nations, 1958-60, associate director of Center for the Study of Instruction, 1960-64; University of Kentucky, Lexington, associate professor, 1964-66, professor of education, 1966-69, chairman of department of social and philosophical studies in education, 1967-69, director of program on educational change, 1964-69; Baldwin-Wallace College, Berea, Ohio, vice-president for academic affairs and dean of college, 1970-72; Illinois Board of Higher Education, Chicago, associate director of programs and planning, 1972-77; State University of New York College at Brockport, vice-president for educational services, 1977—. Coordinator of special educational seminars, Mead Educational Services, Inc., 1965-69; member of board of directors, Center for Information on America, 1966—;

member of national committee, Kettering Diffusion Project, 1967-69; member of executive committee and board of directors, Regional Council for International Education, 1971-72; member of research committee, National Council for the Social Sciences, 1967-70; member of National Committee on Citizenship Education, 1965-67; executive secretary, President's National Advisory Council on Supplementary Centers and Services, 1968-69.

MEMBER: American Association of University Administrators (member of board of directors and chairman of national assembly, 1972), American Association for Higher Education, American Association of Colleges for Teacher Education, American Educational Research Association, National Society for the Study of Education, American Association for the Advancement of Science, American Political Science Association, American Association of University Professors, Phi Delta Kappa, Cosmos Club (Washington, D.C.), Rotary Club. *Awards, honors:* Smith-Mundt grant, American Community School (Beirut), 1954-55; Richardson Foundation grant, 1964; Kettering Foundation grant, 1967; grants from General Learning Corp., Xerox, and Fund for Media Research, 1967-70.

WRITINGS: Dag Hammarskjold and Crisis Diplomacy, Oceana, 1961; (contributor) *Democracy and Communism in World Affairs,* American Bar Association, 1963; (with Ole Sand) *Schools of the Sixties,* McGraw, 1963; *Education in a Changing Society,* National Education Association, 1963; (editor and contributor) *A Multidisciplinary Focus on Educational Change,* Bureau of School Services, University of Kentucky, 1965; (with associates of Center on Innovation, New York State Department of Education) *A Selected and Annotated Bibliography on the Process of Change,* Center on Innovation, New York State Department of Education, 1966; (editor and contributor) *Humanities and the Schools,* Mead Educational Services, 1966; *Teaching about Communism,* McGraw, 1966; (editor) *A Directory of Individuals, Programs, and Agencies Engaged in the Study of Change,* National Institute for the Study of Educational Change, 1967; (editor and contributor) *The Thrill of Learning,* Mead Educational Services, 1967; (editor and contributor) *Perspectives on Educational Change,* Appleton, 1967; (editor and contributor) *The Nongraded School,* Harper, 1967; (editor and contributor) *Notes and Working Papers concerning the Administration of Programs Authorized Under Title III as Prepared for the Subcommittee on Education of the Committee on Labor and Public Welfare,* U.S. Government Printing Office, 1967; (editor and contributor) *Those Who Teach Children,* Mead Educational Services, 1968; (with William Diamond and Charles Martin) *Quality Rankings of Kentucky School Districts,* Bureau of School Services, University of Kentucky, 1968; (with Drummond and Martin) *Methodology for Assessing the Quality of Public Education,* Bureau of School of Services, University of Kentucky, 1969; (editor and contributor) *Frontiers of Learning,* Mead Educational Services, 1969.

(Editor and contributor) *The Seat of Heat,* Mead Educational Services, 1970; *Evaluating Faculty Performance,* Jossey-Bass, 1972; *Developing Programs for Faculty Education,* Jossey-Bass, 1974; *Evaluating and Improving Colleges and Universities,* Jossey-Bass, 1979. Also author of special studies and reports; contributor to yearbooks and proceedings of professional associations; contributor to *World Book Encyclopedia* and *Encyclopaedia Britannica;* contributor of numerous articles to education, linguistics, and science journals. Contributing editor, *Educational Technology,* 1968—.

WORK IN PROGRESS: Further research on faculty, administrative, and institutional evaluation; studying "methods of delivery of non-traditional education" at the post-secondary school level.

AVOCATIONAL INTERESTS: Tennis.

*   *   *

MILLER, Richard Ulric 1932-

PERSONAL: Born September 6, 1932, in New York, N.Y.; son of Luther C. (a publicist) and Frances (Wells) Miller; married Louise O'Donnell, January 6, 1954; children: Elizabeth Louise, Richard Christopher. *Education:* University of Miami, B.B.A. (cum laude), 1958; Cornell University, M.S., 1960, Ph.D., 1966. *Home:* 11 Glenway St., Madison, Wis. 53705. *Office:* Graduate School of Business, University of Wisconsin, Madison, Wis. 53706.

CAREER: University of Miami, Coral Gables, Fla., employment interviewer for placement service, 1957-58; University of Arizona, Tucson, instructor in economics and business administration, 1960-62; State University of New York at Buffalo, assistant professor of industrial relations, 1965-66; University of Wisconsin—Madison, assistant professor, 1966-68, associate professor, 1968-71, professor of business administration, 1971—, assistant director of Center for International Business Research, 1966-71, associate director of Industrial Relations Research Institute, 1968-71, director, 1973-77. Visiting professor of business administration, Institute of Latin American Studies at University of Texas, 1971-72. *Military service:* U.S. Navy, 1951-55.

MEMBER: American Economic Association, Industrial Relations Research Association (president of Wisconsin chapter, 1970-71; national secretary-treasurer, 1973-77), Academy of Management, Latin American Studies Association, Phi Kappa Phi, Beta Gamma Sigma, Delta Sigma Pi. *Awards, honors:* Doherty fellowship for study in Latin America, 1964-65.

WRITINGS: (Editor with A. F. Isbester, and contributor) *Canadian Labour in Transition,* Prentice-Hall, 1971; (contributor) David Chaplin, editor, *Population Policies and Growth in Latin America,* Heath, 1972. Contributor of articles and reviews to business journals, including *Industrial Relations, Arbitration Journal, Industrial and Labor Relations Review, Labor Law Journal, Employee Relations Law Journal, Labor History,* and *Arizona Review of Business and Public Administration.*

WORK IN PROGRESS: Collective Bargaining in Hospitals, with Brian Becker and Glen Cain; *Occupational Mobility in Economic Development,* with Mahmood Zaidi.

SIDELIGHTS: Richard Ulric Miller has resided and studied in Cuba, Mexico, Chile, Peru, Barbados, Canada, and Switzerland.

*   *   *

MILLER, Robert Ryal 1923-

PERSONAL: Born October 3, 1923, in Lake Andes, S.D.; son of John Carroll and Hazel (Peck) Miller; married Penelope Handsaker (a teacher), June 12, 1955. *Education:* Attended University of Mexico, 1947-48; University of California, Berkeley, A.B., 1948, M.A., 1951, Ph.D., 1960. *Home:* 1636 La Loma Ave., Berkeley, Calif. 94709. *Office:* Department of History, California State University, Hayward, Calif. 94542.

CAREER: Southwestern Louisiana University, Lafayette,

assistant professor of history, 1959-60; New Mexico State University, Las Cruces, assistant professor, 1960-65, associate professor of history, 1965-68; Indiana University Southeast, Jeffersonville, professor of history, 1970; California State University, Hayward, professor of history, 1970—. Visiting professor at San Marcos University (Lima, Peru), 1966. Consultant to Oakland Museum, Oakland, Calif., 1969. *Military service:* U.S. Army Air Forces, 1942-45; received Air Medal with ten oak leaf clusters. *Member:* Latin American Studies Association, Conference on Latin American History. *Awards, honors:* American Philosophical Society grant, 1964; research grants from California State University, Hayward, 1973, 1975.

WRITINGS: For Science and National Glory: The Spanish Scientific Expedition to America, 1862-1866, University of Oklahoma Press, 1968; *Arms across the Border: United States Aid to Juarez during the French Intervention in Mexico,* American Philosophical Society, 1973; *Chronicle of Colonial Lima, Peru,* University of Oklahoma Press, 1975; (with John Francis Bannon) *Latin America,* Glencoe Press, 1977. Contributor to professional historical journals.

*   *   *

MILLER, Stuart 1937-

PERSONAL: Born December 28, 1937, in New York, N.Y.; son of Irving and Annette (Freedman) Miller; married Gay Sweet, May 18, 1962 (divorced December, 1964); married Sara Unobskey, December 25, 1968 (divorced February, 1978); children: (first marriage) Antony Gordon. *Education:* Oberlin College, A.B., 1958; Yale University, M.A., 1961, Ph.D., 1963. *Home:* 3847 21st St., San Francisco, Calif. 94114. *Agent:* Sterling Lord, 660 Madison Ave., New York, N.Y. 10021.

CAREER: University of California, Berkeley, instructor, 1963-64, assistant professor of English and comparative literature, 1964-66, assistant to dean of Graduate Division, 1965-66; Rutgers University, Livingston College, New Brunswick, N.J., assistant professor of English, 1966-67, coordinator of curriculum planning, 1966-67; State University of New York College at Old Westbury, associate professor of English, 1967-69; Esalen Institute, Big Sur and San Francisco, Calif., director of development, 1969-72; president, Institute for the Study of Humanistic Medicine, 1972-77, consultant, 1977—. *Member:* American Association of University Professors, Modern Language Association of America, American Comparative Literature Association, Association of Humanistic Psychology, Phi Beta Kappa. *Awards, honors:* Fulbright fellow, 1958-59; Woodrow Wilson fellow, 1959-60.

WRITINGS: The Picaresque Novel, Press of Case Western Reserve University, 1967; *Measure, Number and Weight: A Polemical Study of the College Grading Problem* (pamphlet), Center for Research on Learning and Teaching (University of Michigan) and Learning Resources Center (University of Tennessee), 1967; *Hot Springs: The True Adventures of the First New York Jewish Literary Intellectual in the Human Potential Movement* (autobiography), Viking, 1971; *Dimensions of Humanistic Medicine,* Institute for the Study of Humanistic Medicine, 1975.

WORK IN PROGRESS: Europe: A California Perspective; Why Educational Experiments Fail; Love God Rages.

SIDELIGHTS: On the surface, it would appear that Stuart Miller's first book, *The Picaresque Novel,* and his second, *Hot Springs: The True Adventures of the First New York Jewish Literary Intellectual in the Human Potential Move-*

ment, do not have anything in common. Both, however, deal with basically the same theme approached from two entirely different directions. *The Picaresque Novel* is a scholarly work which examines the role of rogues in sixteenth- and seventeenth-century literature. *Hot Springs,* on the other hand, is an account of the experiences of a modern-day rogue (namely Miller himself).

Although its complete title suggests that it is not your average autobiography, John Seelye in *New Republic* claims that *Hot Springs* is not all that unique. "From its most remote beginnings," he writes, "American literature has been evangelical and autobiographical, reflecting its Puritan heritage.... *Hot Springs* springs hotly from the American vein, in a gush of red-blooded zeal." He goes on to explain that "the emphasis in all these books is on transformation, awakening, the sloughing off of a former (stupid, blind, selfish) identity, the discovery of a new, true (perceptive, generous, open) self. Travel is often involved, ... a symbolic *rite de passage.*" These "auricular confessions," as Seelye dubs them, can all be grouped together and given a general title: "Spiritual Autobiography, or, 'How I Blah, Blah, Blah, And Found God'."

Having established its genre, Seelye delves into *Hot Springs* cautiously, suspicious of Miller and of California's Esalen Institute with its "packaged, instant salvation.... What [Miller] is selling is not Esalen, but Miller himself, who turns out to be less a gay blade than a whole Swiss Army Knife full of sharp, screwy, smooth, and spoony identities, all of which he tries out on himself, on his various encounters, ... on the reader, and when we leave him, he seems to be pulling yet another identity out of his vasty kit of tools, ... leaving us wondering whether he is a knave or a fool, a saint or a devil."

S. K. Overbeck agrees that one is left with some uncertainty after reading *Hot Springs:* "Miller can be sharp, delicate, funny, even wise but also giddily indulgent, resorting to *ipso facto* self-mockery that really functions as a great big pat on the back.... Yet despite his narrative facility, despite his 'confessions,' I never got the feeling from his book that he has really opened up, nor gone back far enough to find out where his life went wrong. His subtitle certainly does not ring with humility, nor reflect the notion that behind the stereotype is a unique human being waiting for his cue to emerge."

Writing in *Best Sellers,* Nicholas J. Loprete, Jr. admits that he, too, was prepared to dislike *Hot Springs,* primarily for its propaganda aspects and for the character of Miller himself ("such a sad little boy assuming a variety of roles"). However, Loprete continues, he soon discovered that he was beginning to like Miller more and more as he read the "painful, ... hilarious, ... moving report of his psychological crisis." This report, he says, "is as honest and as painful as an open wound. It is a searing appraisal of himself that Stuart Miller has written with all the skill of a novelist. [It] is a fascinating psychological journey towards peace, humility, understanding, and the fulfillment of the desire to be loved, to be good."

BIOGRAPHICAL/CRITICAL SOURCES: Time, July 26, 1971; *Book World,* August 22, 1971; *New York Times Book Review,* August 29, 1971; *Best Sellers,* October 1, 1971; *New Republic,* October 16, 1971.

*   *   *

MILLIGAN, Edward Archibald   1903-1977

PERSONAL: Born June 14, 1903, in Michigan, N.D.; son of Robert Hickorty (a farmer) and Emma Clara (von Evers Gennamt Behme) Milligan. *Education:* Attended State Teachers College (now Mayville State College), 1927; University of North Dakota, B.S., 1947, M.S., 1948. *Politics:* Independent Democrat. *Religion:* Roman Catholic. *Home address:* Lake Metigoshe, Bottineau, N.D. 58318. *Office:* Turtle Mountain School of Paramedical Technology, Bottineau, N.D. 58318.

CAREER: North Dakota School of Forestry, Bottineau, teacher of history and anthropology, 1927-34; conducted archaeological and ethnological research among American Indians in North Dakota, 1934-40; North Dakota State University—Bottineau, instructor and head of social sciences, 1948-72, professor emeritus, 1972-77; Turtle Mountain School of Paramedical Technology, Bottineau, N.D., curriculum coordinator, 1972-77. Consultant to Secretary of Interior, 1951. Member of archaeological expedition from Columbia University, summer, 1938; member of Smithsonian expedition in Fort Yates, N.D., 1947. Lecturer on Plains Indians in high schools and colleges, 1940-42. Executive director, North Dakota Indian Affairs Commission, 1959-63; member of North Dakota Governor's conference on aging; member of North Dakota Heritage Commission, North Dakota Arts and Humanities Board, and North Dakota Beautification Commission. Member of advisory board, Assumption College. *Military service:* U.S. Army, Infantry, 1942-45; served in European theater; became sergeant; received Bronze Star.

MEMBER: International Platform Association (president), Society for American Archaeology (life member), Society for Applied Anthropology, National Timberwolf Association (president, 1950), Western History Society, Red River Valley Historical Society, North Dakota Historical Society (life member; president, 1960-66), Ulster Society of North Dakota (president), Alpha Pi Zeta, Phi Alpha Theta, Phi Delta Kappa, Alpha Psi Omega, American Legion, Disabled American Veterans, Veterans of Foreign Wars, Knights of Columbus.

WRITINGS: Petroglyphs, Pictographs and Prehistoric Art, Bottineau Courant, 1968; *Known Migrations of Historic Indian Tribes,* Bottineau Courant, 1969; *Sun Dance of the Sioux,* Bottineau Courant, 1969; *High Noon on the Greasy Grass,* Bottineau Courant, 1972; *Wounded Knee and the Fort Laramie Treaty of 1868,* Bottineau Courant, 1973; *Dakota Twilight: The Standing Rock Sioux, 1874-1890,* Exposition Press, 1976. Also author of *Indians on the North Plains.* Author of column in *Leader* and *Timberwolf.* Contributor to *Red River Valley Historian.*

WORK IN PROGRESS: Ben Hur Lampmann: Naturalist, Poet, Writer; Cultural Contributions of the American Indian.

SIDELIGHTS: Edward Milligan was adopted by Indians of more than thirty tribes and participated in many rare Indian ceremonies.

BIOGRAPHICAL/CRITICAL SOURCES: Red River Valley Historian, winter, 1969-70.†

(Died March 19, 1977)

*   *   *

MILLION, Elmer M(ayse)   1912-

PERSONAL: Born December 10, 1912, in Pond Creek, Okla.; son of Elmer Joseph and Jozie (Mayse) Million; married Zenna Belle Clark, September 7, 1937 (divorced, 1956); married Angela de Carteret, September 27, 1958; children:

(first marriage) Elmer Z., Kenneth M., Earl C., Tedder R.; (second marriage) Heather C., Stephen M. *Education:* University of Oklahoma, LL.B., 1935; Southwestern State Teachers College (now Southwestern State College), A.B. (magna cum laude), 1936; Yale University, J.S.D., 1938. *Politics:* Democrat. *Religion:* Episcopal. *Home:* 2530 Beaurue Dr., Norman, Okla. 73069. *Office:* College of Law, University of Oklahoma, 300 West Timberdell Rd., Norman, Okla. 73019.

CAREER: Attorney in Weatherford and Norman, Okla., 1935-36; Southern Methodist University, Dallas, Tex., instructor in law, 1937-38; University of Idaho, Moscow, assistant professor, 1938-44, associate professor of law, 1944-46; West Virginia University, Morgantown, associate professor of law, 1946-47; New York University, New York, N.Y., assistant professor, 1947-48, associate professor, 1948-53, professor of law, 1953-70; University of Oklahoma, Norman, professor of law, 1970—. Senior attorney, U.S. Department of Justice, 1943-46; custodian, Office of Alien Property, 1946. Professorial lecturer, George Washington University, summer, 1946; visiting professor, University of Oklahoma, summer, 1947, University of Southern California, summer, 1961, University of Michigan, 1964-65, and Washington University, summer, 1972. Member of board of directors, Greenwich Village Montessori School, 1965-69. *Military service:* Idaho State Guard, 1942-43. *Member:* American Bar Assocication, Oklahoma Bar Association.

WRITINGS: (With R. D. Niles) *Cases on Property,* 2nd edition (Million was not associated with first edition), Bobbs-Merrill, Volume I, 1951, Volume II, 1953, Volume III, 1957; (contributor) Ray D. Henson, editor, *Landmarks of Law,* Harper, 1960; (contributor) Alfred Avins, editor, *Open Occupancy vs. Forced Housing under the Fourteenth Amendment,* Bookmailer, 1963. Also general editor of and contributor to *Oklahoma Practice Methods* supplements, 1975, 1978. Contributor to *Annual Survey of American Law,* 1948-69; contributor of about thirty-five articles to legal publications. Chief editor, *New York University Intramural Law Review,* 1954-64.

AVOCATIONAL INTERESTS: English history and American history, legal history, genealogy, travel (study trips to England, Italy, Switzerland, France, and Holland).

*   *   *

MILNER, Murray, Jr. 1935-

PERSONAL: Born July 21, 1935, in Dallas, Tex.; son of Murray and Mary F. (Brownfield) Milner; married Sylvia Jane Shelton (a musician), September 8, 1957; children: Helene, Catherine. *Education:* Agricultural and Mechanical College of Texas (now Texas A & M University), B.Sc., 1957; Union Theological Seminary, New York, N.Y., B.D., 1960; University of Texas, Main University (now University of Texas at Austin), M.A., 1965; Columbia University, Ph.D., 1970. *Religion:* Protestant. *Home:* 2415 Jefferson Park Ave., Charlottesville, Va. 22903. *Office:* Department of Sociology, University of Virginia, Charlottesville, Va. 22903.

CAREER: Church World Service-National Council of Churches, Dacca, East Pakistan (now Bangladesh), director of relief and rehabilitation program, 1960-63; Bureau of Social Science Research, Washington, D.C., research analyst, 1968-69; New York University, New York City, assistant professor of sociology, 1969-72; University of Virginia, Charlottesville, associate professor of sociology, 1972—. Center for Policy Research, New York City, research asso-

ciate, 1968-72, senior research associate, 1972—; visiting Fulbright professor, Patna University, 1976-77. *Member:* American Sociological Association, American Association of University Professors, American Association for the Advancement of Science, American Civil Liberties Union, Eastern Sociological Association.

WRITINGS: (With Michael Baker, Bradley Brewer, Raymond DeBuse, Sally Hillsman, and David Soeiro) *Police on Campus: The Mass Police Action at Columbia University, Spring 1968,* New York Civil Liberties Union, 1969; *Effects of Federal Aid to Higher Education on Social and Educational Inequality,* Center for Policy Research, 1970; *The Illusion of Equality: The Effect of Education on Opportunity, Inequality, and Social Conflict,* Jossey-Bass, 1972. Also author of *Interorganizational Inequality and Cooperation: Health Care in an Urban Neighborhood,* 1973. Contributor of articles to *Columbia Forum, Intellectual Digest,* and *Sociology of Education.*

SIDELIGHTS: Murray Milner, Jr's. book *The Illusion of Equality* has been published in Japanese.†

*   *   *

MINDEL, Eugene D. 1934-

PERSONAL: Surname is pronounced Min-*dell*; born June 29, 1934, in Washington, D.C.; son of Sidney (an insurance salesman) and Esther (Marlieb) Mindel; married Ileane Charlotte Epstein (a travel agent), December 24, 1961; children: Jannis, Jennifer, Seth. *Education:* University of Maryland, B.S., 1956; George Washington University, M.D., 1960. *Residence:* Evanston, Ill. *Office:* 636 Church, Room 602, Evanston, Ill. 60201.

CAREER: Michael Reese Hospital, Chicago, Ill., internship and training in general and child psychiatry, 1960-64, 1966-68, director of child psychiatry services, 1969-75; University of Chicago, Chicago, Ill., clinical assistant professor, 1972—. Consultant to David T. Siegel Institute for Communicative Disorders, Michael Reese Hospital, 1968—, Chicago Lighthouse for the Blind, 1970—, Northern Suburban Special Education District, Highland Park, 1971-75, and the Illinois State Psychiatric Unit for the emotionally disturbed deaf. Director at large, Council of Organizations Serving the Deaf, 1970-73. Member of attending staff, Evanston Hospital, 1975—; staff psychiatrist, North Communities Health Plan, 1975—; medical associate, Northwestern University Medical School, 1977—. *Military service:* U.S. Naval Reserve, 1957-67, active duty, 1964-66; resigned as lieutenant commander. *Member:* American Psychiatric Association (fellow), Illinois Psychiatric Society, Chicago Council of Child Psychiatry (member of board, 1971-75), Chicago Society for Adolescent Society, Film Review Board, Midwest Film Conference.

WRITINGS: (With McCay Vernon) *They Grow in Silence: The Deaf Child and His Family,* National Association of the Deaf, 1971; (co-editor) *Deafness and Mental Health,* Grune, 1979. Also co-author and producer of a film, "It's Okay to Be Deaf, Denise," for Siegel Institute, 1975. Contributor of articles on deafness and other handicaps in children to journals. Member of editorial board, *American Annals of the Deaf,* 1970-71.

WORK IN PROGRESS: A mystery thriller with a psychiatrist as narrator.

*   *   *

MINTZ, Norman N(elson) 1934-

PERSONAL: Born September 18, 1934, in New York.

N.Y.; son of Alexander (a businessman) and Rebecca (Nelson) Mintz; married Marcia Belford (a professor of education), August 27, 1960; children: Geoffrey B., Douglas N. *Education:* Bucknell University, A.B., 1955; New York University, Ph.D., 1966. *Home:* 35 Claremont Ave., New York, N.Y. 10027. *Office:* 205 Low, Columbia University, New York, N.Y. 10027.

CAREER: Syracuse University, Syracuse, N.Y., assistant professor of finance, 1965-68; Columbia University, New York, N.Y., assistant professor of economics, 1968—, associate dean of Graduate School of Arts and Sciences, 1972-77, deputy provost, 1977—. *Military service:* U.S. Army, Signal Corps, 1955-57; became first lieutenant. *Member:* American Economic Association, American Finance Association, Royal Economic Association.

WRITINGS: Monetary Union and Economic Integration, New York University Press, 1970. Contributor to professional journals.

WORK IN PROGRESS: Research on expropriation of American-owned property abroad and the economics of higher education.

*   *   *

MITCHELL, Jeremy 1929-

PERSONAL: Born May 25, 1929, in Manchester, England; son of G. O. and Josephine (Garner) Mitchell; married Margaret Ayres, July 18, 1956; children: Laurence, Veronica, Dominic, Alcuin. *Education:* Brasenose College and Nuffield College, Oxford, M.A., 1953. *Home:* 32 Brookfield Park, London NW5, England.

CAREER: Consumers' Association, London, England, deputy research director and director of information, 1958-65; National Economic Development Office, London, section head, 1965-66; Social Science Research Council, London, secretary and chief executive, 1966-73; Office of Fair Trading, London, director of consumer affairs, 1973-77; National Consumer Council, London, director, 1977—. *Military service:* British Army, 1947-49.

WRITINGS: (Editor with A.T.M. Wilson and A. B. Cherns) *Social Science Research and Industry,* Harrap, 1971; *Betting,* Pelham Books, 1972; (editor) *Marketing and the Consumer Movement,* McGraw, 1978. Contributor of articles to *Yale French Studies, NAS-NRC Highway Research Record, Applied Statistics, Social Science Information, Journal of General Management, Journal of Consumer Studies, Journal of Consumer Policy,* and *International Social Science Journal.* Editor of *Social Science Research Council Reviews of Research,* 1967-73.

*   *   *

MITTRA, S(id) 1930-

PERSONAL: Born May 13, 1930, in India; son of Kashi Nath (a banker) and Taru (Dutt) Mittra; married Bani Sarkar, January 31, 1961; children: Rita, Ajit. *Education:* Agra University, B.Com., 1949, M.Com., 1951; Bookkeepers' Institute, London, England, Certified Associate Diploma, 1950; Indian Institute of Bankers, Certified Associate Diploma, 1954; University of Florida, Ph.D., 1961. *Home:* 721 McGill Dr., Rochester, Mich. 48063. *Office:* Department of Economics, Oakland University, Rochester, Mich. 48063.

CAREER: Reserve Bank of India, Bombay, research associate, 1951-57; Stetson University, DeLand, Fla., assistant professor of economics, 1960-62; University of Detroit, Detroit, Mich., assistant professor of economics, 1962-63,

1965-66; Oakland University, Rochester, Mich., associate professor, 1966-69, professor of economics and chairman of department, 1969-72, professor of economics and management, 1972—. Joint economic advisor to Planning Commission, Government of Venezuela, 1963-65; consultant, United Nations, 1965—. Lecturer at University of California, Berkeley, Chulalongkorn University, Indian Institute of Growth, and other public and private groups. *Member:* American Economic Association, Phi Kappa Phi. *Awards, honors:* Ford Foundation faculty fellow, 1962; Social Science Research Council fellowship, 1966.

WRITINGS: (Co-author) *Dynamic Models for Simulating the Venezuelan Economy,* Simulmatics Corp., 1966; *Simulatrics and Development Planning,* United Nations (Bangkok), 1967; *A New Horizon in Central Banking,* Asia Publishing House, 1967; *Money and Banking: Theory, Analysis, Policy,* Random House, 1970; (editor) *Dimensions in Macroeconomics: A Book of Readings,* Random House, 1971; *Inside Wall Street,* Dow Jones-Irwin, 1971; *Monetary Politics in India,* Vora & Co., 1972; *C.P.A. Review Study Manual: Economics,* Oakland University, 1975; *Personal Finance: Lifetime Management by Objectives,* with study guide, Harper, 1977; *Central Bank versus Treasury: An International Study,* University Press of America, 1977. Contributor of more than fifty articles to journals in United States, Europe, Thailand, Japan, India, and Venezuela. Joint editor of *Economic Affairs.*

WORK IN PROGRESS: Investment Principles and Portfolio Management.

*   *   *

MIXTER, Keith Eugene 1922-

PERSONAL: Born May 22, 1922, in Lansing, Mich.; son of Herbert Leigh and Thelma (Chamberlain) Mixter; married Beatrice Ruf, June 30, 1950; children: Christian John, Constance Anne, Thomas Keith, Stephen Charles. *Education:* Michigan State University, Mus.B., 1947; University of Basle, graduate study, 1947-49, 1952-53; University of Chicago, M.A., 1951; University of North Carolina at Chapel Hill, Ph.D., 1961. *Religion:* Episcopalian. *Home:* 4455 Shields Pl., Columbus, Ohio 43214. *Office:* Department of Music, Ohio State University, Columbus, Ohio 43210.

CAREER: University of North Carolina at Chapel Hill, music librarian, 1953-61; Ohio State University, Columbus, assistant professor, 1961-65, associate professor, 1965-74, professor of music, 1974—, chairman of graduate studies in music, 1977—. *Military service:* U.S. Army, 1943-46. *Member:* American Musicological Society (chairman of Southeast chapter, 1955-57), Music Library Association (member of executive board, 1961-63), International Association of Music Libraries, International Musicological Society, Pi Kappa Lambda, Phi Mu Alpha, Sinfonia.

WRITINGS: (Editor) Johannes Brassart, *Sechs Motetten,* Akademische Druck und Verlagsanstalt, 1960; *General Bibliography for Music Research,* Information Coordinators, 1962, 2nd edition, 1975; *An Introduction to Library Resources for Music Research,* Ohio State University, 1963; (editor) Brassart, *Opera Omnia,* two volumes, American Institute of Musicology (Rome), 1965-71; (contributor) James W. Pruett, editor, *Studies in Musicology: Essays in the History, Style, and Bibliography of Music in Honor of Glen Haydon,* University of North Carolina Press, 1968. Contributor to *Encyclopedia della Musica;* contributor to music journals, including *Musica Disciplina, Current Musicology,* and *College Music Symposium.*

WORK IN PROGRESS: Guide to European Music Libraries; articles for Grove's Dictionary of Music and Musicians, 6th edition, edited by Stanley Sadie; a second edition of An Introduction to Library Resources for Music Research.

* * *

MIZRUCHI, Ephraim H(arold) 1926-

PERSONAL: Born March 24, 1926, in Chicago, Ill.; married, 1952; wife's name, Ruth; children: Mark, David, Susan. Education: Roosevelt College (now University), B.A., 1951; Yale University, M.A., 1955; Purdue University, Ph.D., 1961. Home: 109 Harrington Rd., Syracuse, N.Y. 13224. Office: Department of Sociology, Syracuse University, Syracuse, N.Y. 13210.

CAREER: Yale University, Center of Alcohol Studies, New Haven, Conn., research assistant, 1953-55; State University of New York College at Cortland, assistant professor, 1955-60, associate professor of sociology, 1961-64; New York State Department of Health, Albany, director of rural phase of research on poliomyelitis vaccine, 1956-58; director of community survey in Cortland, N.Y., 1958-64; Syracuse University, Syracuse, N.Y., associate professor, 1964-67, professor of sociology, 1967—, director of Urban Social Problems Project, 1968-72, and Maxwell Policy Center on Aging, 1975—. Danforth Foundation teacher at Purdue University, 1960-61; consultant to Economics Consultants Organization, Inc. Consulting editor, Addison-Wesley Publishing Co., 1969-70. Member: American Sociological Association (fellow). Awards, honors: Research grants from State University of New York College at Cortland, 1962-64; grant from National Institute of Mental Health, 1963, 1969-72.

WRITINGS: Success and Opportunity: A Study of Anomie, Free Press, 1964; (contributor) Irving L. Horowitz, editor, The New Sociology, Oxford University Press (Toronto), 1964; (editor) The Substance of Sociology: Codes, Conduct and Consequences, Appleton, 1967, revised edition, 1973; (contributor) Celia Heller, editor, Structured Social Inequality, Macmillan, 1969; (contributor) Lewis Coser and Bernard Rosenberg, editors, Sociological Theory, Macmillan, 1969; (editor with Paul Meadows and contributor) Urbanism, Urbanization and Change: Comparative Perspectives, Addison-Wesley, 1969, revised edition, 1976; (contributor) George Maddox, editor, The Domesticated Drug, College & University Press, 1970; (contributor) Frank Johnson, editor, The Concept and Meaning of Alienation, Seminar Press, 1973; (co-author) Stratification and Mobility, Macmillan, 1976. Contributor to professional journals, including Sociological Quarterly, American Sociological Review, Social Forces, and Journal of Human Relations.

WORK IN PROGRESS: Regulating Society: Sociological and Historical Perspectives, for Free Press.

* * *

MOE, Christian (Hollis) 1929-

PERSONAL: Born July 6, 1929, in New York, N.Y.; son of Henry Allen (a foundation executive) and Edith (Monroe) Moe; married Carolyn Forman, May 7, 1952; children: Eric Henry, Keith Van Doren. Education: College of William and Mary, A.B., 1951; University of North Carolina, M.A., 1955; Cornell University, Ph.D., 1958. Politics: Democrat. Religion: Unitarian Universalist. Home: 603 South Curtis Pl., Carbondale, Ill. 62901. Office: Department of Theatre, Southern Illinois University, Carbondale, Ill. 62901.

CAREER: Actor in Colonial Williamsburg series of Restoration plays, 1949, 1950, and outdoor productions, "The Common Glory, " 1949, 1950, 1956, and "Unto These Hills," 1954, 1955; Cornell University Theatre, Ithaca, N.Y., publicist, 1956-58; Southern Illinois University at Carbondale, assistant professor, 1958-60, associate professor, 1960-68, professor of theater, 1968—, assistant dean, School of Communications, 1961-68, director of Southern Players Summer (stock) Theatre, 1971—. Co-director of historical drama seminar, Seminars on American Culture, Cooperstown, N.Y., 1958; visiting lecturer, Vita International Study Center, Luxembourg, 1970; Fulbright lectureship, Flinders University, Australia, 1975. Member of advisory board, Institute of Outdoor Drama, 1965—, and Illinois Arts Council, 1967-68, 1977—; member of performing arts committee, Illinois Sesquicentennial Commission, 1967-68. Military service: U.S. Navy, 1951-53.

MEMBER: American Theatre Association, American Film Institute, Federation of University Teachers, Southeastern Theatre Conference, Illinois Theatre Association, Illinois State Speech and Theatre Association, Phi Beta Kappa. Awards, honors: Awards in Samuel French National Collegiate Playwriting Contest, 1956, 1957; first prize in Encore Players' National Playwriting Contest, 1957; Joseph D. Feldman Award in Playwriting, University of North Carolina, 1957; first prize in Humboldt State College National Children's Play Contest, 1966; Silver Sesquicentennial Medallion, State of Illinois, 1968; Amoco-American College Theatre Festival Gold Medallion Award of Excellence, 1976.

WRITINGS: (With George McCalmon) Creating Historical Drama, Southern Illinois University Press, 1965; (contributor) G. K. Plochmann, editor, Introduction to Western Humanities: A Syllabus, Stipes, 1966; (contributor) Althea Hunt, editor, The William and Mary Theatre: A Chronicle, 1926-56, Dietz, 1968; (editor with Darwin Reid Payne, and contributor) Six New Plays for Children, Southern Illinois University Press, 1971; (contributor) Contemporary Dramatists, St. James Press, 1974, 2nd edition, 1976; (contributor) Guide to Play Selection, 3rd edition (Moe was not associated with earlier editions), Bowker, 1975; (contributor) Twentieth-Century Children's Writers, St. Martin's, 1978.

Plays: "Gomennasi" (one-act), first produced in Chapel Hill at University of North Carolina, January 12-13, 1955, produced in Ithaca at Cornell University, May 26, 1957; "The Finer Performance" (one-act), first produced in Chapel Hill at University of North Carolina, May 18-19, 1955; "Stranger in the Land" (three-act), first produced in Chapel Hill at University of North Carolina, March 27-31, 1957, produced Off-Broadway at St. Felix Street Playhouse, November 15-16, 1957; "Hark Upon the Gale" (historical drama commissioned in connection with Jamestown's 350th anniversary celebration), first produced in Williamsburg at College of William and Mary, October 23-25, 1957; (with Darwin Reid Payne) "The Strolling Players" (children's play), first produced in Carbondale at Southern Illinois University, November, 1962; "Make Her Wilderness Like Eden" (officially commissioned Illinois Sesquicentennial drama), first produced in Chicago at Museum of Science and Industry, 1967; "Between the Tower and the Town" (for Mississippi River Tricentennial), first produced in Grand Tower, Ill., 1973; (with Cameron Garbutt) How Santa Claus Came to Simpson's Crossing, I. E. Clark, 1975; "Three Rabbits White" (children's play), first produced in Carbondale at Southern Illinois University, 1975; "Tom

Sawyer" (children's play), first produced in Carbondale at Southern Illinois University, 1978.

Contributor to speech and theater journals. American Educational Theatre Association, chairman of publications committee, 1966-71, bibliographer, 1972-76; associate editor, *Bibliographie Annual of Speech Communication,* 1973-76.

WORK IN PROGRESS: With Cameron Garbutt, a children's play dealing with science fiction and a new collection of children's plays; an adult comedy suggested by a Ben Jonson play.

* * *

MOHAN, Robert Paul 1920-

PERSONAL: Born October 25, 1920, in Wilkes Barre, Pa.; son of John Augustus (a safety supervisor) and Lucy (Riley) Mohan. *Education:* Attended St. Charles College, 1941-42; Catholic University of America, A.B., 1942, M.A., 1943, Ph.D., 1947, S.T.L., 1953. *Politics:* Independent. *Office:* School of Philosophy, Catholic University of America, Washington, D.C. 20017.

CAREER: Ordained Roman Catholic priest, 1946; Catholic University of America, Washington, D.C., instructor, 1950-53, assistant professor, 1953-57, associate professor, 1957-60, professor of philosophy, 1960—, dean of summer session and director of workshops, 1960-72, member of academic senate, 1963-72, marshal of the university, 1969—.

WRITINGS: Philosophy of History, Bruce Publishing, 1970. Associate editor, *American Ecclesiastical Review,* 1956-62.

WORK IN PROGRESS: Research on G. B. Vico (an Italian philosopher), and for a book on social and political philosophy.

* * *

MOIR, John S(argent) 1926-

PERSONAL: Born February 14, 1926, in Toronto, Ontario, Canada; son of Richard Eldon (a salesman) and Hazel (Fieldhouse) Moir; married Jacqueline R. Heyland, June 7, 1952; children: Christine, Sheila, Alison, Ian, Gillian, David, Andrew, Michael. *Education:* University of Toronto, B.A., 1948, M.A., 1949, Ph.D., 1954. *Home:* 167 Main St., Markham, Ontario, Canada. *Office:* Scarborough College, University of Toronto, 1265 Military Trail, West Hill, Ontario, Canada.

CAREER: Ontario Provincial Archives, Toronto, assistant archivist, 1950-52; Queen's University, Kingston, Ontario, documents librarian, 1954-55; Carleton University, Ottawa, Ontario, lecturer, 1956-58, assistant professor, 1959-63, associate professor of history, 1963-65; University of Toronto, Scarborough College, West Hill, Ontario, associate professor, 1965-67, professor of history, 1967—. *Member:* Canadian Historical Association, Canadian Society of Church History, Ontario Historical Society (president, 1967-68). *Awards, honors:* Canadian Council fellow, 1964-65, 1971-72, 1978-79.

WRITINGS: Church and State in Canada West, University of Toronto Press, 1959; *The Cross in Canada,* Ryerson, 1966; *Church and State in Canada: Basic Documents,* McClelland & Stewart, 1967; (with Robert Saunders) *Northern Destiny,* Dent, 1970; *The Church in the British Era,* McGraw-Ryerson, 1972; *Enduring Witness,* Presbyterian Publications, 1974. Editor of *Ontario History,* 1960-62.

WORK IN PROGRESS: A biography of John Strachan, first Anglican bishop of Toronto; a history of biblical studies in Canada.

AVOCATIONAL INTERESTS: Travel.

* * *

MOLINARO, Julius A(rthur) 1918-

PERSONAL: Born June 13, 1918, in Toronto, Ontario, Canada; son of Pasquale and Maria (Formoso) Molinaro; married Matie Armstrong (a literary agent), 1945; children: Juliette, Paul. *Education:* University of Toronto, B.A., 1939, M.A., 1941, Ph.D., 1954. *Religion:* Roman Catholic. *Home:* 44 Douglas Crescent, Toronto 5, Ontario, Canada. *Office:* Department of Italian Studies, University of Toronto, Sussex Court, Toronto, Ontario, Canada.

CAREER: University of Toronto, Tortonto, Ontario, instructor, 1946-49, lecturer in Italian and Spanish, 1949-55, assistant professor of Italian, 1955-62, associate professor, 1962-67, professor of Italian, 1967—. *Military service:* Allied Forces Headquarters, Psychological Warfare Branch, 1944-46. *Member:* Renaissance Society of America, Canadian Society of Italian Studies, Canadian Society of Renaissance Studies, Royal Society of Canada (fellow), Modern Language Association of America, American Association of Teachers of Italian, American Association of Teachers of Spanish and Portuguese, Dante Society of America (council associate, 1963-65; council member, 1974-77).

WRITINGS: (With J. H. Parker and Evelyn Rugg) *Comedias Sueltas* (a bibliography), University of Toronto Press, 1959; (with Warren T. McCready) *Angelica y Medoro: Zarzuela inedita de Jose de Canizares—Con su loa y entremes, Edicion critica,* Quaderni Ibero-Americani, 1958; (translator and editor with Beatrice Corrigan) *Vittorio Alfieri: Of Tyranny,* University of Toronto Press, 1961; (editor with S. B. Chandler) *The World of Dante: Six Studies in Language and Thought,* University of Toronto Press, 1966; *A Bibliography of Sixteenth-Century Italian Verse Collections in the University of Toronto Library,* University of Toronto Press, 1969; (with Corrigan) *Vittorio Alfieri: The Prince and Letters,* University of Toronto Press, 1972; (editor) *Petrarch to Pirandello: Studies in Italian Literature in Honour of Beatrice Corrigan,* University of Toronto Press, 1973. Author of abstracts and bulletins. Contributor to language journals, including *Italica, Studies in Philology, Forum Italicum, Esperienze Letterarie,* and *Romance Notes.* Editor of *Renaissance and Reformation,* 1969-76.

WORK IN PROGRESS: Research on Ludovico Ariosto.

* * *

MOLOTCH, Harvey L(uskin) 1940-

PERSONAL: Born January 3, 1940, in Baltimore, Md. *Education:* University of Michigan, B.A. (with honors), 1963; University of Chicago, M.A., 1966, Ph.D., 1968; also studied at University of California, Berkeley, and University of Vienna. *Office:* Department of Sociology, University of California, Santa Barbara, Calif. 93106.

CAREER: University of California, Santa Barbara, assistant professor, 1967-71, associate professor, 1971-78, professor of sociology, 1978—. Instructor in social science at Indiana University at Gary, summer, 1964, University of Illinois at Chicago Circle, spring, 1966, University of Chicago, summer, 1966, and winter, 1967; visiting associate professor, State University of New York at Stony Brook, 1971-72; visiting professor, University of Essex, 1975-76. *Military service:* U.S. Army, aide to regimental commander, 1961-62. *Awards, honors:* Ford Foundation grant for research on urban crisis, 1970.

WRITINGS: (Contributor) Paul B. Downing, editor, *The Contribution of the Social Sciences to the Solution of the Air Pollution Problem,* Project Clean-Air, University of California, Riverside, 1970; (contributor) Eugene C. Lee, editor, *The Challenge of California,* Little, Brown, 1970; (contributor) Peter Orleans and William Russell Ellis, Jr., editors, *Race, Change, and Urban Society,* Sage Publications, 1971; (contributor) Jack D. Douglas, editor, *Introduction to Sociology: Situations and Structures,* Free Press, 1972; (contributor) Downing, editor, *Air Pollution and the Social Sciences,* Praeger, 1972; *Doing Good in the City: Dilemmas of Intervention for Integration,* University of California Press, 1972; (contributor) Douglas, editor, *Social Problems in a Revolutionary Age,* Random House, 1973; *The Effects of Urban Growth,* Praeger, 1977. Also contributor to *Racial and Ethnic Relations: A Survey,* edited by B. Eugene Griessman, and *The City in the Seventies,* edited by Robert K. Yin. Contributor of articles and reviews to professional journals, including *Land Economics, American Sociologist, Ramparts, American Sociological Review, American Journal of Sociology,* and *Sociological Inquiry.* Editor, *Bulletin of Sociology for Social Research,* 1966-67; member of advisory board, *American Journal of Sociology,* 1972.

*   *   *

MONAGHAN, (James) Jay (IV)   1891-

PERSONAL: Born March 19, 1891, in West Chester, Pa.; son of James (a lawyer) and Anna (Jackson) Monaghan; married Mildred Eversole, December 15, 1941. *Education:* Received early education in Vevey, Switzerland; Swarthmore College, A.B., 1913; University of Pennsylvania, M.A., 1918. *Home:* The Samarkand, N-188, 2663 Tallant Rd., Santa Barbara, Calif. 93105. *Office:* Library, University of California, Santa Barbara, Calif. 93106.

CAREER: Cowboy in Wyoming, 1908-09; owner and operator of cattle and sheep ranches in Utah and Colorado, 1913-34; Colorado Historical Society, Denver, located early trapper forts and interviewed Indians, 1935; Works Progress Administration, Chicago, Ill., superintendent of project to analyze foreign language press and index English press, 1938; Illinois State Historical Library, Springfield, historical research editor, 1939-45, state historian in charge of library, 1946-49; University of California, Santa Barbara, Wyles Collection of Lincolniana and Western Americana, special consultant, 1952—. Teacher, Uintah Indian Reservation, Utah, 1914-15; president, Rio Blanco Wool Growers Association, 1927-34; director, Colorado State Wool Growers Association, 1929-34, and Colorado Cooperative Wool Marketing Association, 1930-33. Lecturer on Abraham Lincoln in South America and Caribbean, U.S. Department of State, 1959. *Military service:* U.S. Aviation Service, Signal Corps, instructor in aerial photography, 1918.

MEMBER: American Historical Association, Organization of American Historians, National Historical Society, Western History Association, Illinois State Historical Society, Phi Beta Kappa. *Awards, honors:* Diploma of honor, Lincoln Memorial University, 1944; Rockefeller Foundation fellow, Newberry Library (Chicago), 1944-45; Litt. D., Monmouth College, Monmouth, Ill., 1947; American Philosophical Society fellow, 1950, 1967; Huntington Library fellow, 1951-52; Fulbright fellow, University of Sydney, 1954-55.

WRITINGS: Lincoln Bibliography, Illinois State Historical Library, 1945; *Diplomat in Carpet Slippers: Lincoln Deals with Foreign Affairs,* Bobbs-Merrill, 1945; *Last of the Bad Men: Legend of Tom Horn,* Bobbs-Merrill, 1946; *Overland Trail,* Bobbs-Merrill, 1947; *This Is Illinois,* University of Chicago Press, 1949; *The Great Rascal: The Life and Adventures of Ned Buntline,* Little, Brown, 1952; *Civil War on the Western Border,* Little, Brown, 1955; *The Man Who Elected Lincoln,* Bobbs-Merrill, 1956; *Swamp Fox of the Confederacy,* Confederate Publishing, 1956; *Custer: The Life of General George Armstrong Custer,* Little, Brown, 1959; *Australians and the Gold Rush,* University of California Press, 1966; *Chile, Peru and the California Gold Rush,* University of California Press, 1972; *Schoolboy, Cowboy, Mexican Spy* (autobiography), University of California Press, 1977.

Editor: John Hope Franklin, *Civil War Diary of James T. Ayres,* Illinois State Historical Society, 1947; Robert L. Kincaid, *Wilderness Road,* Bobbs-Merrill, 1947; Philip D. Jordan, *The National Road,* Bobbs-Merrill, 1948; John Drury, *Old Illinois Houses,* Illinois State Historical Society, 1948; Theodore Calvin Pease, *Story of Illinois,* University of Chicago Press, 1949; Francis Philbrick, *Laws of Illinois Territory, 1809-1818,* Illinois State Historical Library, 1950; Mary Waters, *Illinois in the Second World War,* Illinois State Historical Library, 1951; *The Book of the American West,* Messner, 1963; R. B. Townshend, *A Tenderfoot in Colorado,* University of Oklahoma Press, 1968; *The Private Journal of Louis McLane, U.S.N., 1844-1848,* Dawson's Book Shop, 1971.

Contributor to *Dictionary of American History* and *Atlas of American History;* contributor of articles to history journals. Editor, "American Trails" series, 1947.

SIDELIGHTS: It was Jay Monaghan who opened the northwest cattle ranges of Colorado for sheep grazing; he also discovered the cliff-house village which is now Yampa National Monument. In 1911, he participated in Madero's revolution in Mexico. In his book, *Schoolboy, Cowboy, Mexican Spy,* Monaghan gives a lively account of his experiences in the West from 1908 to 1913. A *Choice* reviewer writes: "Historians who have witnessed the events about which they write rather than writing about events witnessed through the eyes of others are becoming increasingly rare. Even rarer among those historians are writers who vividly express a 'feel' for the times about which they write. Such a historian is Jay Monaghan." He was also a guest of President Tubman in conference with Liberian paramount chiefs.

BIOGRAPHICAL/CRITICAL SOURCES: Jay Monaghan, *Schoolboy, Cowboy, Mexican Spy,* University of California Press, 1977; *Choice,* May, 1978.

*   *   *

MONDALE, Joan Adams   1930-

PERSONAL: Born August 8, 1930, in Eugene, Ore.; daughter of John Maxwell (a minister and college professor) and Eleanor Jane (Hall) Adams; married Walter Frederick Mondale (vice-president of the United States), December 27, 1955; children: Teddy, Eleanor Jane, William. *Education:* Macalester College, B.A., 1952. *Politics:* Democratic. *Religion:* Presbyterian. *Home:* Vice-President's House, Washington, D.C. 20501.

CAREER: Boston Museum of Fine Arts, Boston, Mass., assistant slide librarian, 1952-53; Minneapolis Institute of Arts, Minneapolis, Minn., assistant in education, 1953-57. Member of the board, Institute of Museum Services. Honorary chairperson, Federal Council on the Arts and the Humanities. *Member:* Junior League of Washington, D.C., Women's National Democratic Club of Washington, D.C. (board member, 1967-71).

WRITINGS: Politics in Art, Lerner, 1972.

SIDELIGHTS: As the wife of the vice-president of the United States, Joan Mondale finds herself in an ideal position to serve as a champion of the visual arts. A trained art historian and ceramicist, she has become "a kind of unofficial ombudswoman, mediating between the art world and government," writes Barbara Rose in *Vogue.* "Politicians passing through Joan Mondale's house, which is radiant with shining color and beautiful forms, are slowly absorbing the idea that modern art is a normal part of modern life, rather than the expression of a lunatic fringe."

In her days as a senator's wife, she gave guided tours once a week at the National Gallery of Art for District of Columbia schoolchildren. Now, however, Mondale's efforts to incorporate art into American life have taken on a nationwide aspect. She is, for example, firmly committed to establishing a vital role for art in the core curriculum of educational systems throughout the country. "There's no question that when the arts are combined with other subjects in a general curriculum the arts improve perceptions, attitudes, understandings, and motivation of schoolchildren," she insists. "They break down not only the barriers to learning but the barriers raised by our own society in a racial and economic and social way. In this atmosphere children learn to share, to experience, and to create together."

At the legislative level, Mondale is actively seeking support for a measure which would require that one percent of all construction costs of federal buildings be set aside for the purchase of works of art. In addition, she hopes to reverse a decision made during the Nixon administration which ended tax benefits to artists (or their heirs) who wanted to donate works to museums. She is also encouraging federal government departments to commission and buy works of art by contemporary American artists.

In spite of her busy public schedule, Mondale manages to make time to follow her own artistic bent—ceramics. "What pottery means to me is serenity," she says. "It takes all your concentration. . . . It is important to me to be able to draw inward. Everything else I enjoy immensely—lecturing on art, setting up programs—all my volunteer activities are ultimately *for* others. My pottery classes are not for anybody but myself."

BIOGRAPHICAL/CRITICAL SOURCES: Time, July 26, 1976; *Newsweek,* July 26, 1976; *Design,* January-February, 1978; *Vogue,* March, 1978; *New York Times Book Review,* June 18, 1978.

* * *

MONTGOMERY, Elizabeth Wakefield 1891-

PERSONAL: Born April 18, 1891, in Seattle, Wash.; daughter of Theron A. (a farmer) and Flora (Taylor) Wakefield; married Edward E. Montgomery (a chiropractor), June 21, 1930 (deceased); children: Lowell A. *Education:* Private study in music and music teaching; Chiropractic College Hospital, Minneapolis, Minn., training in practical nursing. *Religion:* Seventh-day Adventist.

CAREER: Has worked as a piano teacher and a practical nurse.

WRITINGS: James Jays Takes a Case, Southern Publishing Association, 1972. Contributor to *Listen, Youth's*

Instructor, Guide, Braille, Review and Herald, and *M. V. Program Notes.*

WORK IN PROGRESS: Nothing New under the Sun; collecting material for *Suggestive Causes and Cures for Arthritis.*††

* * *

MOON, Rexford G(eorge), Jr. 1922-

PERSONAL: Born June 8, 1922, in Schenectady, N.Y.; son of Rexford G. (an accountant) and Ruby (Rounds) Moon; married Margaret Merriam (a teacher), January 4, 1944; children: Rexford III, Wayne M., Timothy C., Peter M. *Education:* Attended Alabama Polytechnic Institute (now Auburn University), 1943-44; Union College, Schenectady, N.Y., B.S., 1947; University of Maryland, M.A., 1950. *Politics:* Republican. *Religion:* Episcopalian. *Home:* 90 Columbus Ave., Closter, N.J. 07624. *Office:* College Board, 888 Seventh Ave., New York, N.Y. 10019.

CAREER: University of Maryland, College Park, instructor in psychology and vocational counselor, 1947-50; American University, Washington, D.C., instructor in psychology, 1950; Union College and University, Union College, Schenectady, N.Y., associate director of admissions, 1950-55; College Entrance Examination Board, New York City, assistant director, 1955-57; College Scholarship Service, New York City, director, 1957-65; Academy for Educational Development, New York City, consultant, 1965, director of studies, 1966—, senior vice-president, 1968—; Future Development and Resources, Inc., New York City, vice-president, 1969—; College Board, New York City, managing director of Future Directions for a Learning Society, 1977—. Consultant to U.S. Office of Education, Superior Educational Council, Fund for Advancement of Education, and Ford Foundation. Member of New York Governor's Committee on Scholastic Achievement, 1957—; member of board of directors of Citizens Scholarship Foundation of America, 1957—; member of Committee on Equality of Opportunity in Higher Education, American Council of Education, 1957-60; member of advisory committee, Pennsylvania Higher Education Assistance Agency, 1967-70; district vice-chairman, North Bergen County Council of Boy Scouts of America, 1960-63. Member of board of directors of American Council for Emigres in Professions, 1965-68, and Educational Advisory Corp., 1965-67. *Military service:* U.S. Army, Infantry, 1942-45; became staff sergeant; received Silver Star and four battle stars. *Member:* American Psychological Association, American Personnel and Guidance Association, Society for College and University Planning, National Association for Higher Education, American College Personnel Association, Sigma Xi.

WRITINGS: Student Financial Aid in the United States, College Entrance Examination Board, 1961; *National Planning for Education,* Academy for Educational Development, 1970. Contributor to *Saturday Review, College Board Review,* and *Current Issues in Higher Education.* Columnist, *College Management,* 1973-75. Editor, *Financial Aid News,* 1960-63.

WORK IN PROGRESS: Research and program development on future needs of adult learners in the United States.

* * *

MOORE, L. Silas (Jr.) 1936-

PERSONAL: Born August 24, 1936, in Hodge, La.; son of L. Silas (a civil engineer) and Sallie (Durbin) Moore; married Ann Lee Kinner, August 19, 1967; children: Logan Kinner, Merrill Ann. *Education:* Attended Georgia Institute of Technology, 1954-58, and Pasadena Playhouse College of Theater Arts, 1958-59; Oglethorpe University, B.A., 1961. *Politics:* Right-wing libertarian independent. *Religion:* Protestant Christian. *Home:* 313 Lakeshore Dr., Marietta, Ga. 30067. *Office:* Georgia State Board of Pardons and Paroles, 800 Peachtree St. N.E., Atlanta, Ga. 30308.

CAREER: Editor of weekly newspapers in metropolitan Altanta, Ga., 1964-65; W.R.C. Smith Publishing Company, Atlanta, associate editor, 1965-71; Harrison Public Relations, Atlanta, news director, 1971; Georgia State Board of Pardons and Paroles, Atlanta, hearing examiner, 1972—. *Military service:* U.S. Army Reserve, 1959-65; became sergeant. *Member:* Georgia Probation and Parole Association.

WRITINGS: Scarlet Arena 30303, Oddo, 1972. Contributor to *Prospect.*

*   *   *

MOORE, Vardine (Russell) 1906-

PERSONAL: Born September 25, 1906, in Uniontown, Ky.; daughter of Jerome S. (a salesman) and Annabelle (Yewell) Russell; married Robert Bruce Moore, October 7, 1933 (deceased); children: Melinda (Mrs. Daniel Malcom Martyn). *Education:* Attended Evansville College (now University of Evansville), 1925-27, 1945-46, National College of Education, 1927-28, and Indiana University, summer 1956. *Home:* 434 Roosevelt Dr., Evansville, Ind. 47714.

CAREER: Storyteller on the WGBF radio show, "Bedtime Story Hour," Evansville, Ind., 1920-30; worked as a teacher in kindergartens in Evansville, 1928-53; Evansville Printing Corp., Evansville, newspaper advertising writer, 1961-69. Lecturer in creative writing for children, University of Evansville Community College, Evansville, 1956—.

WRITINGS: (With Fleur Conkling) *Billy Between,* Westminster, 1951; (with Conkling) *The House Next Door,* Westminster, 1954; *Mystery of the Bells,* Westminster, 1955; *Picnic Pony,* Lothrop, 1956; *Developmental Reading Textbooks,* grades 4, 5, and 6, Bobbs-Merrill, 1961; *Pre-School Story Hour,* Scarecrow, 1966, revised edition, 1972.

WORK IN PROGRESS: Old Fly, a Civil War House, a book for young people; a revision of *Developmental Reading Textbooks; The Creative Spark Needs Fanning.*†

*   *   *

MORDVINOFF, Nicolas 1911-1973
(Nicolas)

September 27, 1911—May 5, 1973; Russian-born American painter, graphic artist, and illustrator of children's books. Obituaries: *Publishers Weekly,* May 28, 1973. (See index for CA sketch)

*   *   *

MORGAN, Elaine (Neville) 1920-

PERSONAL: Born November 7, 1920, in Pontypridd, Wales; daughter of William Mansel (a colliery pumpsman) and Olive (Neville) Floyd; married Morien Morgan (a schoolmaster), April 11, 1945; children: John Dylan, Gareth Floyd, Morien Huw (adopted). *Education:* Lady Margaret Hall, Oxford, B.A., 1942. *Politics:* Labour Party. *Religion:* Humanist. *Home:* 24 Aberffrwd Rd., Mountain Ash CF45 4AR, Glamorganshire, Wales. *Agent:* Harvey Unna Ltd., 14, Beaumont Mews, Marylebone High St., London W1N 2HE, England.

CAREER: Writer. Has been employed as a supply teacher and as a lecturer in adult education courses. *Member:* Writers' Guild of Great Britain. *Awards, honors:* M.A., Oxford University, 1948; Italia Prize, for "Joey"; Writers' Guild award, 1973, for "A Pin to See the Peepshow"; Christopher Award, 1976, for "How Green Was My Valley"; BFTA award, 1978, for "Marie Curie."

WRITINGS: (With Jean Scott Rogers) *Teli'r teulu* (Welsh translation of her television script, "Without Vision"), Gwasg Aberystwyth, 1960; *The Descent of Woman* (nonfiction; Book-of-the-Month Club selection), Stein & Day, 1972; *Falling Apart* (nonfiction), Stein & Day, 1977.

Plays: *The Waiting Room* (one-act; first produced for BBC television, 1959), Samuel French, 1958; *Rest You Merry* (two-act; first produced for BBC television, 1958), Samuel French, 1959; *The Soldier and the Woman* (one-act; first produced for BBC television, 1960), Samuel French, 1961; *A Chance to Shine* (two-act; first produced for BBC television, 1962), Samuel French, 1963; *License to Murder* (two-act; first produced in London at Vaudeville Theatre, 1963), Samuel French, 1963; *Love from Liz* (two-act; first produced in Windsor at Theatre Royal, 1966), Samuel French, 1967.

Television scripts; all produced on BBC, except as noted: "Mirror, Mirror," 1954; "The Tamer Tamed," 1955; "Wilde West," "Without Vision," "Eleven Plus" (documentary), and "FSU" (documentary), all 1956-57; "Do It Yourself," "Cuckoo," "Black Furrow" (documentary), and "You're a Long Time Dead," 1957-58; "A Matter of Degree" (six-part serial), 1961. Also author of three serials, "A Pin to See the Peepshow," "How Green Was My Valley," and "Marie Curie," and a documentary, "Joey." Author of additional television scripts, and contributor to numerous programs and series for BBC and commercial television, 1962—.

WORK IN PROGRESS: Writing television scripts; research in sociology.

SIDELIGHTS: The Descent of Woman, a challenge to the "man the hunter" school of evolutionary thought, created controversy among its reviewers. Elaine Morgan's thesis is based on the theory that the peculiarities of human anatomy and behavior, as opposed to those of other primates, are the result of an aquatic period in primate development which took place in the Pliocene Age and lasted twelve million years. Morgan believes, based on a paper presented by Alister Hardy in 1960, that it was the female's need for protection for herself and her young that drove the apes to the sea-coasts of Africa and resulted in such characteristics as hairlessness, erect posture, front-to-front sex, and the origin of speech.

Her theory has created both enthusiasm and disdain. Anthropologist Ian Tattersall refutes her thesis by pointing out that homo sapiens never made the adaptation for underwater breathing characteristic of aquatic mammals and claims that there is evidence that man has been a land-based creature for at least fifteen million years. The *Time* reviewer described Morgan's ideas as "fanciful notions." Other critics take her work more seriously. Carolyn Riley states: "Never, I think, will the reader have encountered before a theory which is so thrillingly convincing, which 'feels so right' when applied to conditions and characteristics observable in the twentieth century." Anthony Storr describes the book as "brimful of stimulating ideas" and the author as "formidably intelligent, extremely well-informed, provocative, and original."

Morgan acknowledges that she has considered the ramifications of her attack upon the widely accepted theory.

"Writing the book, I did have periods of feeling that it was the most outrageous cheek," she says. "Perhaps it was easier for me because I had nothing to lose, no high academic position to think of. If you talk about flying saucers, you're branded as a kook. I don't believe in flying saucers but I suppose this kind of thing looks flying-saucerish to the Establishment."

BIOGRAPHICAL/CRITICAL SOURCES: Book World, May 7, 1972; *Detroit News,* May 28, 1972; *Best Sellers,* June 15, 1972; *Time,* June 19, 1972; *Life,* July 20, 1972; *America,* July 23, 1977.

* * *

MORGAN, Gerald 1925-

PERSONAL: Born May 8, 1925, in London, England; Canadian citizen; son of James M. and Catherine (Selwyn) Morgan; married, 1957; two children. *Education:* Attended Acadia University; Loyola College, Montreal, Que., B.A., 1951; University of Southampton, Master Mariner, 1953; University of Montreal, M.A. (philosophy), 1955, M.A. (English), 1959, Ph.D. (highest possible honours), 1962. *Home:* 12 Royal Roads, Victoria, British Columbia, Canada. *Office:* Department of English, Royal Roads Military College, Victoria, British Columbia, Canada.

CAREER: Navigation officer of steamship companies in England, Belgium, Canada, China, and Venezuela, 1940-53; *Ensign,* Montreal, Quebec, book-reviewer and translator, 1953-56; College Militaire Royal, St. Jean, Quebec, lecturer, 1955-60, assistant professor, 1960-63, professor of literature and philosophy and chairman of department, 1963-65; Royal Roads Military College, Victoria, British Columbia, professor of English and philosophy, 1965—. Has lectured at fourteen universities on Joseph Conrad. Trustee of Maritime Museum of British Columbia, 1971—. *Military service:* British Merchant Navy, 1940-46; became second officer. *Member:* International Association of University Professors of English, Canadian Association of Slavists (member of editorial committee, 1967), Humanities Association of Canada (member of national executive committee, 1965—; national president, 1969-71), Humanities Research Council of Canada (member of executive committee, 1970-72). *Awards, honors:* Canada Council senior fellowship, 1971.

WRITINGS: (Editor) *Big Chief of the Prairies,* Palm Publishers, 1956; (with Marshall McLuhan, Wilfrid Watson, and others) *Of Several Branches,* University of Toronto Press, 1968. Also editor with Wolfgang Luthe of *Autogenic Training: Correlationes Psychosomaticae.* Contributor to *Etudes Slaves, Humanities Association Bulletin, Canadian Literature, University of Toronto Quarterly,* and *Open Letter.* Assistant editor of *Etudes Slaves,* 1956-63.

WORK IN PROGRESS: Two books, *Critical Theorems* and *Joseph Conrad on the Sea;* editing a manuscript diary of the murder-voyage of Cutty Sark (1880); many stories and poems.

AVOCATIONAL INTERESTS: Music, history, painting.†

* * *

MORGAN, Raleigh, Jr. 1916-

PERSONAL: Born November 12, 1916, in Nashville, Tenn.; son of Raleigh and Adrien Louise (Beasley) Morgan; married Virginia Carol Moss (an elementary school teacher), December 12, 1941; children: Carol (Mrs. Donald Russell), Jill (Mrs. David Bragdon), Phyllis. *Education:* Fisk University, A.B., 1938; University of Michigan, A.M.,

1939, Ph.D., 1952. *Politics:* Democrat. *Religion:* Catholic. *Home:* 3157 Bluett Dr., Ann Arbor, Mich. 48105. *Office:* Department of Romance Languages, University of Michigan, Ann Arbor, Mich. 48109.

CAREER: High school teacher of French in St. Louis, Mo., 1940-42; North Carolina College at Durham (now North Carolina Central University), head of French department, 1946-49, 1951-56; U.S. Cultural Center, Cologne, Germany, director, 1956-57; U.S. Embassy, Bonn, Germany, deputy chief of cultural operations, 1957-59; Modern Language Association, Center for Applied Linguistics, Washington, D.C., associate director, 1959-61; Howard University, Washington, D.C., professor of Romance languages and head of department, 1961-65; University of Michigan, Ann Arbor, professor of Romance linguistics, 1965—. Lecturer in linguistics for U.S. Department of State in Nicaragua and Haiti, 1956, in Cameroun, Ivory Coast, Congo, Togo, Dahomey, Mali, Tchad, Algeria, 1964; lecturer in linguistics at the American University, 1959-62; lecturer for National Defense Education Act Summer Language Institute, Virginia State College, 1960, 1961; technical adviser of film series "Principles and Methods for Teaching Second Language," 1962; director of Summer Language Institute, Howard University, 1962, 1963, 1965; consulting linguist of Audio Lingual Materials French, Second Level, Modern Language Materials Development Center, N.Y., 1963; director of French language training, U.S. Peace Corps, Gabon, 1964; member of English training advisory panel, U.S. Information Agency, 1964-67; member of visiting committee for Board of Overseers, Harvard University, 1972—. Visiting professor of linguistics, Cornell University, 1973. Vice-chairman of the Ann Arbor Democratic Party, 1968-70; member of board of directors, Ann Arbor Community Center, 1969-71; member of budget committee, Michigan United Fund, 1969-72; member of Mayor's Ward Boundary Commission, Ann Arbor, 1971. *Military service:* U.S. Army, 1942-46; became second lieutenant.

MEMBER: International Linguistic Association, Societe de Linguistique Romane, Linguistic Society of America, College Language Association, Modern Language Association of America, Kappa Alpha Psi. *Awards, honors:* American Council of Learned Societies postdoctoral fellow, Indiana University, 1952; Carnegie faculty research grant, 1953; American Council of Learned Societies postdoctoral fellow, Georgetown University visiting scholar, 1967.

WRITINGS: Regional French of County Beauce: Quebec, Mouton, 1972. Contributor of articles and reviews to *Language Word, College Language Association Journal, International Journal of American Linguistics, Romance Philology,* and *Anthropological Linguistics.*

WORK IN PROGRESS: Research on Occitan dialects and Guadeloupean Creole.

* * *

MORGAN, Richard E(rnest) 1937-

PERSONAL: Born May 17, 1937, in Centre County, Pa.; son of James E. (an Army officer) and Helen (Hogge) Morgan; married Eva Corliss, June 19, 1959. *Education:* Bowdoin College, A.B., 1959; Columbia University, M.A., 1961, Ph.D., 1967. *Home address:* R.F.D.1, South Harpswell, Me. 04079. *Office:* Department of Government, Bowdoin College, Brunswick, Me. 04011.

CAREER: Columbia University, New York, N.Y., assistant professor of government, 1967-68; Bowdoin College, Brunswick, Me., associate professor of government, 1969—,

William Nelson Cromwell Professor of Constitutional and International Law and Government. *Military service:* U.S. Army, 1963-65; became first lieutenant. *Member:* American Political Science Association, Academy of Political Science, Law and Society Association.

WRITINGS: The Politics of Religious Conflict, Pegasus, 1968; (editor with James E. Connor) *The American Political System,* Harcourt, 1970; *The Supreme Court and Religion,* Free Press, 1972; (editor with Christian P. Potholm, and contributor) *Focus on Police,* Halsted, 1976. Editor, "Pegasus Studies in American Politics," Bobbs-Merrill, 1967—.

WORK IN PROGRESS: Information Gathering and the First Amendment: A Study in Constitutional Politics.

*   *   *

MORGAN, Roy A(mos) 1916-

PERSONAL: Born March 16, 1916, in Burke, S.D.; son of Albert Lawrence (a blacksmith) and Frances (Hare) Morgan; married Della Marie Johnson, March 14, 1944; children: Rhonda Lee (Mrs. Ronald Hutson), Roy Allan, Margaret Eleanor (Mrs. Steve Sandy), Jaynelle Irene (Mrs. Jose A. Martinez). *Education:* Colorado State University, B.S., 1943; South Dakota University, M.Ed., 1950; University of Wyoming, Ph.D., 1956. *Religion:* Lutheran. *Home address:* Route 1, Box 45, Portales, N.M. 88130. *Office:* Counseling and Testing, Eastern New Mexico University, Portales, N.M. 88130.

CAREER: High school teacher of science and mathematics, Redfield, S.D., 1948-51; superintendent of schools, Canistota, S.D., 1951-54; University Study Skills Center, Laramie, Wyo., assistant coordinator, 1954-55; coordinator of guidance service for public schools, Cody, Wyo., 1955-58; Western Illinois University, Macomb, assistant director of counseling, 1958-61; Eastern New Mexico University, Portales, associate professor of psychology and director of counseling and testing, 1961-78, associate professor emeritus, 1978—. Group counselor for non-university youth. *Military service:* U.S. Army, 1943-46. U.S. Army Reserve, 1946-72; retired as lieutenant colonel. *Member:* American Personnel and Guidance Association, American Psychological Association, Association for Counselor Education and Supervision, Association for Measurement and Evaluation in Guidance, Cardinal Key National Honor Sorority (national director, 1972—), American Biographical Institute, Rocky Mountain Association for Counselor Education and Guidance (past president), Scabbard and Blade (advisor, region XII), Community Services Center, Valle del Sol (secretary to board of directors), Phi Delta Kappa.

WRITINGS: (Contributor) Lyle L. Miller, *Increasing Reading Efficiency,* Holt, 1964; (with George L. Jones and Edgar L. Petty) *Effective Reading for College Students,* Appleton, 1968. Contributor to *Reading Today.* Member of editorial board, American Biological Institute, 1971-72.

WORK IN PROGRESS: A revision of *Effective Reading for College Students.*

*   *   *

MORIN, Relman George 1907-1973

September 11, 1907—July 16, 1973; American journalist and author. Obituaries: *New York Times,* July 17, 1973; *Washington Post,* July 17, 1973; *Newsweek,* July 30, 1973. (See index for *CA* sketch)

MORISSEAU, James J(oseph) 1929-

PERSONAL: Born April 29, 1929, in New York, N.Y.; son of Joseph Adolph (a photo-engraver) and Lavita (Clay) Morisseau. *Education:* New York University, B.A., 1950.

CAREER: Long Island Press, Jamaica, N.Y., reporter and deskman, 1954-58; *New York Herald Tribune,* New York City, education writer, 1959-62; Educational Facilities Laboratories, New York City, editorial associate, 1962-69; freelance writer, 1969—. Member of board of overseers, College of the Virgin Islands, 1961—. *Military service:* U.S. Air Force, Russian language technician, 1950-54; became staff sergeant. *Member:* Education Writers Association, Urban Writers Society, Overseas Press Club of America, Society for College and University Planning, Council of Educational Facility Planners.

WRITINGS: (With Mel Elfin, Bernard Asbell, Alvin Toffler, and Margaret Barker) *Bricks and Mortarboards,* Educational Facilities Laboratories, 1964; (contributor) Toffler, editor, *The Schoolhouse in the City,* Praeger, 1965; *The New Schools,* Van Nostrand, 1972. Contributor of articles to national magazines and newspapers, including *Saturday Review* and *Christian Science Monitor,* and to architecture, pharmaceutical, and education journals. Editor, *News from SCUP* and *Planning for Higher Education.*

WORK IN PROGRESS: A book on university planning for the 1970's, for Educational Facilities Laboratories and Academy for Educational Development.†

*   *   *

MORLAND, (John) Kenneth 1916-

PERSONAL: Born July 4, 1916, in Huntsville, Ala.; son of Howard C. and Ethel (Cowan) Morland; married Margaret Louise Ward, February 26, 1949; children: Margaret Carol, Katherine Louise, Evelyn Ward. *Education:* Birmingham-Southern College, B.S., 1938; Yale University, B.D., 1943; University of North Carolina at Chapel Hill, Ph.D., 1950. *Home:* 1619 Dogwood Lane, Lynchburg, Va. 24503. *Office:* Department of Sociology, Randolph-Macon Women's College, Lynchburg, Va. 24504.

CAREER: Yale University in China, Changsha, Hunan, instructor in English, 1943-46; Yale-in-China Program, New Haven, Conn., executive secretary, 1946-47; College of William and Mary, Williamsburg, Va., assistant professor of sociology, 1949-53; Randolph-Macon Women's College, Lynchburg, Va., professor of sociology, 1953—. Chairman of Board of National Ministries, American Baptist Churches, 1972-77; consultant to Civil Rights Commission, 1962, and U.S. Department of Commerce, 1964-65.

MEMBER: American Sociological Association (fellow), American Anthropological Association (fellow), American Association of University Professors (president of Virginia conference, 1964), Southern Sociological Society (member of executive committee, 1972-75), Southern Anthropological Society, Virginia Social Science Association (president, 1962-63). *Awards, honors:* Fulbright scholar, Chinese University of Hong Kong, 1966-67; U.S. Office of Education research grant, 1972; National Science Foundation research grants, 1975 and 1978; National Institute of Education research grant, 1975.

WRITINGS: Millways of Kent, University of North Carolina Press, 1958; *The Not So Solid South,* University of Georgia Press, 1971; (with J. O. Balswick, John Belcher, and Morton Rubin) *Social Problems,* Ronald, 1975; (with Harold Kaufman) *The South and the Search for Regional*

Identity, Mississippi State University, 1975; (with John Williams) *Race, Color, and the Young Child,* University of North Carolina Press, 1976. Contributor to professional journals, including *Social Forces, American Journal of Sociology, Journal of Social Psychology,* and *American Catholic Sociological Review.*

WORK IN PROGRESS: Research projects on racial attitudes and racial balance in public schools, on measuring race-awareness in young children, and on racial-ethnic identity in Chinese children in Hong Kong, Taiwan, and San Francisco.

* * *

MORONEY, John R. 1939-

PERSONAL: Born January 29, 1939, in Dallas, Tex.; son of John R. (a lawyer) and Irene (Lewis) Moroney; married Margaret Kearny, May 30, 1959; children: John, Stephen, Helen, Michael. *Education:* Southern Methodist University, B.A., 1960; Duke University, Ph.D., 1964. *Home:* 4735 Carondelet, New Orleans, La. 70115. *Office:* Department of Economics, Tulane University, New Orleans, La. 70118.

CAREER: Florida State University, Tallahassee, assistant professor of economics, 1964-66; Michigan State University, East Lansing, associate professor of economics, 1966-69; Tulane University, New Orleans, La., professor of economics, 1969—. Visiting professor of economics, Massachusetts Institute of Technology, 1975-76. *Member:* American Economic Association, Econometric Society, Southern Economic Association. *Awards, honors:* Relm Foundation fellow, 1966; Institute of Public Utilities fellowship, 1968; Social Science Research Council faculty research fellow, 1969; National Science Foundation, faculty research grant, 1975-76, grant for research applied to national needs, 1976-78.

WRITINGS: The Structure of Production in American Manufacturing, University of North Carolina Press, 1972. Contributor of articles to *Journal of Political Economy, Southern Economic Journal, Journal of Money, Credit, and Banking, Western Economic Journal, American Economic Review,* and other professional journals.

WORK IN PROGRESS: Study of production relations among capital, labor, and natural resources; study of the growth and cyclical stability of the American economy; study of income distribution and earnings of men and women in capitalistic and socialistic economies.

* * *

MORRIS, John O(sgood) 1918-

PERSONAL: Born July 11, 1918, in New York, N.Y.; son of Ray and Katharine (Grinnell) Morris; married Bernardine Day, June 28, 1947; children: Robert S., Bernardine S., Katharine C. *Education:* Yale University, B.A., 1941; University of Virginia, J.D., 1948.

CAREER: Affiliated with Kirlin Campbell & Keating, 1948-51, and Aetna Life Insurance Co., 1951-64; John O. Morris Associates, West Hartford, Conn., management consultant, beginning 1964. *Military service:* U.S. Naval Reserve, 1941-46; became lieutenant commander. *Member:* American Society for Training and Development, American Bar Association.

WRITINGS: Make Yourself Clear, McGraw, 1972; (with John Burgoyne) *Developing Resourceful Managers,* Institute of Personnel Management, 1973.†

MORRISON, Margaret Mackie 19(?)-1973 (March Cost, Peggy Morrison)

19(?)—February 7, 1973; Scottish-born novelist, biographer, and short story writer. Obituaries: *New York Times,* February 9, 1973; *Publishers Weekly,* February 26, 1973; *Current Biography,* April, 1973.

* * *

MORSS, Elisabeth W. 1918- (Elisabeth W. Mixter)

PERSONAL: Born March 1, 1918, in Brookline, Mass.; daughter of Samuel (a broker) and Anne D. (Williams) Mixter; married Henry A. Morss, Jr., January 21, 1950. *Education:* Studied at Winsor School and School of the Museum of Fine Arts, Boston. *Residence:* Marblehead, Mass.

CAREER: Before marriage worked with children's programs at Museum of Fine Arts, Boston, Mass.; artist specializing in cut-paper silhouettes and exhibiting under name, Elisabeth W. Mixter. *Member:* Herb Society of America, Boston Printmakers. *Awards, honors:* Prizes in national competitions for needlework.

WRITINGS—Self-illustrated verse: Herbs of a Rhyming Gardener, Branden, 1971; *A Christmas Medley,* Branden, 1971.

WORK IN PROGRESS: Illustrations in cut-paper silhouette for new edition of Beacon Hill Garden Club publication, *The Hidden Gardens of Beacon Hill.*

AVOCATIONAL INTERESTS: Gardening, especially with herbs; conservation.†

* * *

MOSESSON, Gloria R(ubin) (Kathryn French, Doris R. Miller)

PERSONAL: Surname is pronounced Moses-son; born in Brooklyn, N.Y.; daughter of Louis (a realtor) and Regina B. (Greenfield) Rubin; married Norman D. Mosesson (an executive), August 16, 1955; children: Eric, Neil, Roger, Carl, Carol. *Education:* Brooklyn College (now Brooklyn College of the City University of New York), B.A. (cum laude), 1943; Cornell University, M.S., 1945. *Religion:* Hebrew. *Home:* 290 West End Ave., New York, N.Y. 10023. *Office:* Thomas Nelson, Inc., 30 East 42nd St., New York, N.Y. 10017.

CAREER: Chemical Publishing Co., New York City, assistant editor, 1947-48; editor with Chartwell House, Inc., New York City, 1948-55, Educational Publishing Corp., New York City, 1956-61, Bobbs-Merrill Co., New York City, 1961-64, Meredith Press, New York City, 1964-70, and Thomas Nelson, Inc., New York City, 1970—. *Member:* American Literary Association, Women's National Book Association, National Hadassah, New York City Hadassah.

WRITINGS: Breeding Laboratory Animals, Sterling, 1968; *The Jewish War Veterans Story,* Jewish War Veterans of the U.S.A., 1971; (with Virginie Fowler Elbert) *Jewelry Craft for Beginners,* Bobbs-Merrill, 1975; *New Clothes from Old,* Bobbs-Merrill, 1977.

"Holly Story Book" series; adaptor under pseudonym Doris R. Miller, except as indicated; published by World Publishing: Charles Perrault, *Cinderella,* 1965; J.L.K. Grimm and W. K. Grimm, *Snow White,* 1965; Grimm and Grimm, *The Wolf and the Seven Little Goats,* 1965; Perrault, *Tom Thumb*, 1965; (under pseudonym Kathryn French) *Aladdin*, 1965; (under pseudonym Kathryn French) *Ali Baba*, 1965; *The Little Red Hen*, 1966; (editor) *Mother Goose* (selected rhymes), 1966; Perrault, *Puss in Boots*, 1966.

Contributor to *Standard Reference Encyclopedia*, *Xerox Children's Encyclopedia*, and *Hadassah*.

WORK IN PROGRESS: Several nonfiction books for children.

SIDELIGHTS: Gloria Mosesson told *CA:* "Although I had been writing for years, as part of being in the publishing industry, it had never occurred to me to write a book—that was something I directed others to do in my capacity as an editor. Then, a former company president for whom I had worked approached me to write the texts for the tales of the 'Holly' series being published by World, and I accepted as a challenge to try something new."

As for her more "unusual" books, she explains: "*Breeding Laboratory Animals* was the result of a business my husband was in at the time. Again, someone approached me to write because he felt that it was a subject of great interest. . . . The Jewish war veterans book came about in essentially the same way—someone asked me to do it, and I did, mostly to see if I could handle the research." The veterans' organization subsequently requested her to write a documentary script which resulted in a highly successful movie, prompting Mosesson to remark, "I had double satisfaction on that one."

Her two craft books—one on jewelry and one on sewing—were basically labors of love, for they required little research. "They both represent long-time hobbies," she says. "I had it all in my head because jewelry is my special weakness, and I spend a lot of time at the sewing machine."

A lack of time, however, is what prevents Mosesson from attempting additional writing projects. "I have never tried fiction, but perhaps I shall some day. If I do, it will definitely not be of the historical genre, for although I love reading it, what I'm anxious to avoid is the research. . . . I cannot write on speculation."

*   *   *

MOTLEY, Wilma E(lizabeth)   1912-

PERSONAL: Born October 10, 1912, in Des Moines, Iowa; daughter of Oscar Dayton (an insurance agent) and Evalina (Greene) Jenkins; married William George Motley (a dentist), July 15, 1934; children: William G. II, Carol E. Motley Martin. *Education:* University of Southern California, certificate in dental hygiene, 1933; also studied at Valley College. *Politics:* Republican. *Religion:* Religious Society of Friends (Quaker). *Home:* 18952 Blackhawk St., Northridge, Calif. 91324. *Office:* 4554 Sherman Oaks Ave., Sherman Oaks, Calif. 91403.

CAREER: Licensed dental hygienist in California, 1933, Alaska, 1959, and by National Board in Dental Hygiene, 1962; private practice in dental hygiene, 1929—. University of Southern California, part-time clinical instructor in dental hygiene, 1959-63, part-time assistant in prosthetics laboratory, 1960-62, lecturer in dental hygiene, 1963-70. Volunteer, Sister Kenny Polio Hospital, 1952-53; trustee, American Foundation for Dental Health.

MEMBER: American Dental Hygienists' Association (life member; president, 1966-68), American Association of Dental Editors (president, 1978-79), Southern California Dental Hygienist's Association (life member; president, 1961-62), San Fernando Valley Dental Hygienists' Society

(co-founder and life member), Los Angeles Dental Hygienists' Society, Los Angeles Speakers Club. *Awards, honors:* William J. Gies editorial award, 1974.

WRITINGS: Ethics, Jurisprudence, and History for the Dental Hygienist, Lea & Febiger, 1972, 2nd edition, 1976. Contributor to *Journal of the American Dental Hygienists' Association*, *Dental Economics*, and *San Fernando Valley Dental Society Bulletin*. Editor, *Journal of the American Dental Hygienists' Association*.

AVOCATIONAL INTERESTS: Travel, antiques, cooking, art.

*   *   *

MOTT, Vincent Valmon   1916-
(Lucien St. Andre)

PERSONAL: Born September 18, 1916, in Washington, La.; son of Lucius and Marie (Le Doux) Mott; married Margaret McDonald (a teacher), June 19, 1948; children: Vincent, Jr., Helene (Mrs. Robert Hinck), John Michael. *Education:* Xavier University, New Orleans, La., B.A. (cum laude), 1938; Fordham University, M.A., 1947, Ph.D., 1956. *Politics:* Liberal Democrat. *Religion:* Liberal Catholic. *Home:* 12 Leslie Ave., Florham Park, N.J. 07932. *Agent:* Harold Ober Associates, Inc., 40 East 49th St., New York, N.Y. 10017. *Office:* Department of Marketing, Seton Hall University, South Orange, N.J. 07079.

CAREER: University of Scranton, Scranton, Pa., instructor, 1947-49, assistant professor of social sciences, 1949-51; Seton Hall University, South Orange, N.J., lecturer, 1951-52, instructor in economics, 1952-53, assistant professor, 19t4-58, associate professor, 1958-66, professor of marketing, 1966—. Adjunct assistant professor of economics, St. Peter's College, 1955-60. President, Florham Park Press; member of board of advisors, Scranton Institute of Industrial Relations, 1949-50; member of board of trustees of LePlay Research, Inc., New York, N.Y., 1967—. *Military service:* U.S. Army, 1940-45. *Member:* American Association of University Professors, American Marketing Association.

WRITINGS: Principles of Economics, Florham, 1957; (under pseudonym Lucien St. Andre) *The American Matriarchy: A Study of Married Life in 1997 A.D.*, Florham, 1970; *The American Consumer: A Sociological Analysis*, Florham, 1972; (with Nicholas Chirovsky) *Philosophy in Economic Thought*, Florham, 1972. Contributing editor of *New Jersey Business*, 1956. Member of editorial board, *Journal of the American Academy of Marketing Science*.

WORK IN PROGRESS: Consumer Sociology.†

*   *   *

MOTTO, Anna Lydia

PERSONAL: Born in New York, N.Y.; daughter of Michael and Molly (Gross) Motto; married John R. Clark (a professor of English), November 7, 1959; children: Valerie Molly, Bradford Russell. *Education:* Queens College (now Queens College of the City University of New York), B.A. (cum laude), 1946; New York University, M.A., 1948; University of North Carolina, Ph.D., 1953. *Home:* 11712 Davis Rd., Tampa, Fla. 33617. *Office:* Department of Foreign Languages, University of South Florida, Tampa, Fla. 33620.

CAREER: Washington College, Chestertown, Md., assistant professor of classics, 1953-57; Alfred University, Alfred, N.Y., assistant professor of classics, 1958-65, chairman of department, 1958-65; Muhlenberg College, Allentown, Pa., associate professor of classics, 1965-66, chairman of department, 1965-66; St. John's University, Jamaica, N.Y., associate professor of classics, 1966-68; Drew University, Madison, N.J., professor of classics, 1968-73, chairman of department, 1968-73; University of South Florida, Tampa, professor of classics, 1973-74, professor of foreign languages and chairman of department, 1974—. Visiting professor of classics at University of Michigan, summer, 1969.

MEMBER: American Classical League, American Philological Association, Classical Society of the American Academy in Rome, Classical Association of the Atlantic States (vice president, 1972-73), Classical Association of the Middle West and South, Vergilian Society of Cumae, New Jersey Classical Association, New York Classical Club. *Awards, honors:* Fulbright grant, American Academy in Rome and Vergilian Society at Cumae, summer, 1956; grant from College Center of the Finger Lakes Research Council, for Senecan and Renaissance research, summer, 1964.

WRITINGS: Seneca Sourcebook: Guide to the Thought of Lucius Annaeus Seneca, Adolf Hakkert, 1970; *Seneca,* Twayne, 1973; (editor and contributor) *Satire: That Blasted Art,* Putnam, 1973. Contributor to transactions. Contributor of about forty articles, reviews, and poetic translations to journals in the classics, including *Classical World, Classical Journal, Classical Bulletin, Classical Outlook, Classical Philology, Mosaic, Renaissance Drama, L'Antiquite Classique,* and *American Journal of Philology.*

AVOCATIONAL INTERESTS: Travel, opera.

* * *

MOWATT, Ian 1948-

PERSONAL: Born November 15, 1948, in Oban, Scotland; son of Eric (a head postmaster) and Doreen (Galloway) Mowatt. *Education:* University of St. Andrews, M.A. (medieval history), 1971; University of Pennsylvania, M.A. (communications), 1973. *Politics:* Labour. *Home:* 11 Duntiblae Rd., Kirkintilloch, Glasgow, Scotland.

CAREER: Writer. *Awards, honors:* Thouron Award, 1971.

WRITINGS: Just Sheaffer; or, Storms in the Troubled Heir, Harcourt, 1973. Contributor to *Pennsylvania Review.*

WORK IN PROGRESS: A second humorous novel.

AVOCATIONAL INTERESTS: Golf, baseball, medieval dualist philosophy, hagiography.†

* * *

MUELLER, Kate Hevner 1898-

PERSONAL: Born November 1, 1898, in Derry, Pa.; daughter of Winnbert David and Joie (McNaughton) Hevner; married John Henry Mueller (a professor of sociology), September 3, 1935 (died, 1965). *Education:* Wilson College, B.A., 1920; Columbia University, M.A., 1923; University of Chicago, Ph.D., 1928. *Politics:* Republican. *Religion:* Presbyterian. *Home:* 1357 East Tenth, Bloomington, Ind. 47401. *Office:* School of Education, Indiana University, Bloomington, Ind. 47401.

CAREER: Wilson College, Chambersburg, Pa., instructor in psychology, 1923-26; University of Minnesota, Minneapolis, assistant professor of psychology, 1928-35; Indiana University at Bloomington, dean of women, 1937-47, educational adviser for women, 1948-49, associate professor, 1949-52, professor of higher education, 1952-70, professor emeritus, 1970—, director of Rockefeller orchestra project,

1967—. Specialist on women's education in Frankfort, Germany, U.S. State Department, High Commissioner for Germany, summer, 1951. Visiting summer professor at Pennsylvania State College (now University), 1949, University of Oregon, 1958, and University of North Carolina at Chapel Hill, 1959; visiting professor at Florida State University, 1970. Diplomate in counseling of American Psychological Association; associate in counseling, Hazen Foundation, 1945-48.

MEMBER: American Psychological Association (fellow; president of Esthetics Division, 1951-52; member of national council, 1950-52, 1954-56, 1960-62, 1966-69), National Association of Women Deans and Counselors (chairman of committee on research and publications, 1957-60), American College Personnel Association, Music Teachers' National Association, American Personnel and Guidance Association (member of advisory council, 1952-54), American Society for Aesthetics (charter member), National Education Association, Association for Higher Education (member of executive committee, 1961-64), American Association of University Women (chairman of national education committee, 1955-58), Indiana Association of Clinical and Applied Psychologists (vice-president, 1947-49), Phi Beta Kappa, Sigma Xi. *Awards, honors:* ScD., Wilson College, 1953; D.H.L., Mills College, 1963; Delta Kappa Gamma Biennial Award for best book on women, 1956, for *Educating Women for a Changing World.*

WRITINGS: An Outline of Psychology, Longmans, Green, 1934; *Appreciation of Music* and *Tests for Appreciation of Music,* University of Oregon Press, 1934; (with husband, John H. Mueller) *Trends in Musical Taste,* Indiana University Press, 1940; *Counseling for Mental Health,* American Council on Education, 1946; *Educating Women for a Changing World,* University of Minnesota Press, 1954; *Student Personnel Work in Higher Education,* Houghton, 1961; *A History and Analysis of the Repertoires of Twenty-Seven Major American Symphony Orchestras, 1842-1970,* Indiana University Press, 1973. Writer of "Oregon Music Discrimination Test," seven records produced by Stoelting Co., 1934.

Contributor: E. G. Williamson, editor, *Student Personnel Work,* University of Minnesota Press, 1949; *The Education of Women: Signs for the Future,* American Council on Education, 1959; Elizabeth Fitzgerald and Harold Grant, editors, *College Personnel Work in Higher Education,* Houghton, 1961; Seymour Farber and Roger Wilson, editors, *The Challenge to Women,* Basic Books, 1966; J. W. Greene and R. O. Oswald, editors, *Women: Equal but Different,* University of Kentucky Press, 1967; V. F. Calia and D. D. Wall, editors, *Pupil Personnel Administration: New Perspectives and Foundations,* C. C Thomas, 1968. Contributor of about seventy-five articles to psychology and education journals, and to general magazines including *Mademoiselle.*

* * *

MUIR, Jean 1906-1973

March 4, 1906—March 24, 1973; American mystery writer and journalist. Obituaries: *Washington Post,* March 27, 1973. (See index for *CA* sketch)

* * *

MULHOLLAND, John F(ield) 1903-

PERSONAL: Born October 26, 1903, in Ridgeway, Iowa; son of Roy Field and Clara (Smestead) Mulholland; married

Beulah Esther Westrum, June 30, 1947. *Education:* Carroll College, Waukesha, Wis., B.A., 1926; McCormick Theological Seminary, M.Div., 1930; University of Edinbourgh, graduate study, 1930-32. *Politics:* Independent. *Home:* 1350 Ala Moana, Apt. 2404, Honolulu, Hawaii 96814.

CAREER: High school teacher in Lake Mills, Wis., 1926-27; pastor of United Churches of Christ in Wisconsin and Minnesota, 1932-43; school chaplain in Honolulu, Hawaii, 1947-69; University of Hawaii, Honolulu, instructor in religion, 1971-72. Chairman of board of directors, Kalihi Palama Community Association. *Military service:* U.S. Army, chaplain, 1944-46. U.S. Army Reserve, 1946-53.

WRITINGS: Heroes of the Old Testament (booklet), Westminster, 1944; *Religion in Hawaii* (booklet), Kamehameha Schools Press, 1961; *Hawaii's Religions,* Tuttle, 1970. Contributor of articles to magazines.

WORK IN PROGRESS: Research on Hawaii's religions.

*   *   *

MULLALY, Edward (Joseph) 1941-

PERSONAL: Born February 16, 1941, in Saint John, New Brunswick, Canada; son of Edward Francis (a businessman) and Ethel (Kierstead) Mullaly; married Gertrude May Dallon (a teacher), May 16, 1970 (died January 1, 1978). *Education:* University of Windsor, B.A., 1963; University of New Brunswick, M.A., 1966, Ph.D., 1970. *Politics:* None. *Religion:* Roman Catholic. *Home:* 511 Mansfield St., Fredericton, New Brunswick, Canada. *Office:* Department of English, Carleton Hall, University of New Brunswick, Fredericton, New Brunswick, Canada.

CAREER: Saint Thomas University, Fredericton, New Brunswick, assistant professor of English, 1970-71; University of New Brunswick, Fredericton, assistant professor, 1971-76, associate professor of English, 1976—. *Member:* Canadian Association of American Studies, Association of College and University Teachers of English, Association for Canadian Theatre History. *Awards, honors:* Provincial and national awards for theater productions, including Dominion Drama Festival's Strand lighting award, 1966, for "Death of a Salesman," and "Wisdom" award, 1971, for best production of "Rosencrantz and Guildenstern Are Dead"; best director award from New Brunswick Drama League, 1971, for "Rosencrantz and Guildenstern Are Dead"; Canada Council research grant, 1974.

WRITINGS: Archibald MacLeish: A Checklist, Kent State University Press, 1973. Contributor of theater articles, reviews, and commentaries to CBC-Radio, *Atlantic Advocate, Performing Arts, Dalhousie Review,* and *Fiddlehead.*

WORK IN PROGRESS: Preparing an edition of Archibald MacLeish's early plays; research on New Brunswick nineteenth-century theatre history.

*   *   *

MULLER, Gilbert H(enry) 1941-

PERSONAL: Born November 8, 1941, in Brooklyn, N.Y.; son of Henry G. and Mildred (Tweed) Muller; married Laleh Mostafavi, June 25, 1964; children: Parisa, Darius. *Education:* University of Kentucky, B.A., 1963; Stanford University, M.A., 1966, Ph.D., 1967. *Home:* 23 Monfort Rd., Port Washington, N.Y. 11050. *Office:* LaGuardia Community College of the City University of New York, 31-10 Thomson Ave., Long Island City, N.Y. 11100.

CAREER: Pahlavi University, Shiraz, Iran, assistant professor of English and American literature, 1967-71; LaGuardia Community College of the City University of New York, Long Island City, N.Y., 1971—, began as assistant professor, currently associate professor of English and American literature. *Member:* Modern Language Association of America, American Studies Association, American Federation of Teachers, Professional Staff Congress, College English Association, New York State Teachers Association. *Awards, honors:* Woodrow Wilson fellowship, 1963; National Endowment for the Humanities fellowship, 1973.

WRITINGS: Nightmares and Visions: Flannery O'Connor and the Catholic Grotesque, University of Georgia Press, 1972; *Comparison and Contrast,* Harper, 1974; *The Basic English Handbook,* Harper, 1978; (with Harvey S. Wiener) *The Short Prose Reader,* McGraw, 1979. Contributor to literary journals and popular national magazines, including *Nation, New Republic, Georgia Review, Studies in Short Fiction,* and to *New York Times.*

WORK IN PROGRESS: A book on Faulkner's short fiction; editing an anthology of American literature in opposition, for Prentice-Hall.†

*   *   *

MUNRO, John (Henry Alexander) 1938-

PERSONAL: Born March 14, 1938, in Vancouver, British Columbia, Canada; son of Hector Gordon (a forest products executive) and Blanche (Almond) Munro; married Jeanette Roberta James (a pharmacist), May 25, 1968; children: Robert Ryder. *Education:* University of British Columbia, B.A. (honors), 1960; Yale University, M.A., 1961, Ph.D., 1965. *Home:* 39 South Kingslea Dr., Toronto, Ontario, Canada M8Y 2A5. *Office:* Department of Political Economy, University of Toronto, Toronto, Ontario, Canada M5S 1A1.

CAREER: University of British Columbia, Vancouver, instructor, 1964-65, assistant professor of history and economics, 1965-68; University of Toronto, Toronto, Ontario, associate professor, 1968-73, professor of economics, 1973—, associate director of Centre for Medieval Studies, 1976-79. Director, Friends of Chamber Music, 1967-68. *Member:* Economic History Society of Great Britain, American Economic History Association, Canadian Economics Association. *Awards, honors:* Canada Council fellowship, 1970-71, research grant, 1973.

WRITINGS: Wool, Cloth, and Gold: The Struggle for Bullion in Anglo-Burgundian Trade, circa 1340-1478, Editions de l'Universite de Bruxelles and University of Toronto Press, 1973; (contributor) Rogers Mynors, Douglas Thomson, and Wallace Ferguson, editors, "The Correspondence of Erasmus," University of Toronto Press, Volume I: *1484-1500,* 1974, Volume II: *1501-1514,* 1975; (contributor) Harry Miskimin, David Herlihy, and A. L. Udovitch, editors, *The Medieval City,* Yale University Press, 1977; (contributor) Fredi Chiapelli, editor, *The Dawn of Banking,* Yale University Press, 1978; (contributor) K. G. Ponting and N. B. Harte, editors, *Cloth and Clothing in Medieval Europe: Essays in Honour of Eleanora Carus-Wilson,* Pasold Research Fund, 1979. Consultant on the history of coinage, money, credit, and finance to "The Correspondence of Erasmus" series, University of Toronto Press, 1973—. Contributor to annals. Contributor of articles and reviews to professional journals, including *English Historical Review, Journal of Economic History, Canadian Historical Review, Journal of European Economic History, Textile History,* and other European journals.

WORK IN PROGRESS: A book tentatively entitled *Draperies Old and New: The Transformation of the Woollen Textile Industries in the Low Countries, 1250-1650.*

SIDELIGHTS: John Munro lived in Belgium for two years.

* * *

MUNSEY, Cecil (Richard, Jr.) 1935-
(C. Richardson)

PERSONAL: Born May 21, 1935, in Portsmouth, N.H.; son of Cecil Richard (a ship repairer) and Alma (Northup) Munsey; married Dolores Jean Murray (an elementary school teacher), February 18, 1956; children: Cecil Richard III. *Education:* Attended Sacramento City College, 1956-58; San Diego State College (now University), A.B., 1962, M.A., 1969; United States International University, Ph.D., 1973. *Home:* 13541 Willow Run Rd., Poway, Calif. 92064. *Office:* R. B. Spirits Shop, 12457 Rancho Bernardo Rd., San Diego, Calif. 92128.

CAREER: San Diego City Schools, San Diego, Calif., elementary school teacher, 1963-66, teacher of gifted elementary school children, 1966-69, teacher in model school program, 1970-71, curriculum resource teacher for gifted secondary school students, 1971-74; San Diego County Department of Education, San Diego, curriculum coordinator for community educational resources, 1974-78; R. B. Spirits Shop, San Diego, proprietor, 1978—. Adjunct professor of education, Alfred North Whitehead College, University of Redlands, 1976—. Historical glass consultant, Owens-Illinois Glass Co., 1973-74. Commentator for weekly radio program, ''Let's Talk about Antiques,'' KFSD-FM, 1975-76. *Military service:* U.S. Air Force, 1954-58.

MEMBER: National Education Association, National Association for Gifted Children, Association for the Gifted, U.S. International University Doctoral Society, Authors Guild, Authors League of America, American Cetacean Society, American Revenue Association, National Association of Newsletter Editors, American Institute of the History of the Pharmacy, Owens-Illinois Historical Bottle Collectors Guild, Federation of Historical Bottle Clubs, California Teachers Association, Association of California School Administrators, California Association for the Gifted (member at large), San Diego Teachers Association, Association of San Diego Educators for the Gifted, San Diego Association for the Gifted Children, San Diego Zoological Society, Green Valley Civic Association, Phi Delta Kappa. *Awards, honors:* Valley Forge Teachers Medal from Freedoms Foundation, 1965.

WRITINGS: Handbook for Elementary Principals and Teachers of Programs for the Gifted, San Diego City Schools, 1968; *Would You Believe: A Compilation of Unusual Facts Pertaining to Bottle Collecting,* Neyenesch, 1968; (with Millicent Holmberg) *Handbook and Price Guide to Avon Bottles,* Western World, 1969; (self-illustrated) *The Illustrated Guide to Collecting Bottles* (Book-of-the-Month Club and Better Homes and Gardens Book Club selection), Hawthorn, 1970; (self-illustrated) *The Illustrated Guide to the Collectibles of Coca-Cola,* Hawthorn, 1972; (co-author) *Resource Directory for Teachers of the Gifted,* San Diego City Schools, 1973; *Disneyana: Walt Disney Collectibles* (Better Homes and Gardens Book Club selection), Hawthorn, 1974; (co-author) *Mentally Gifted Minors Program Models,* California Association for the Gifted, 1976. Author of brochures and curriculum materials for San Diego City Schools. Contributor of several hundred articles to professional journals, occasionally under pseudonym, C. Richardson. Editor, *Bottleneck,* 1966-68, *National Bottle Gazette,* 1968-69, *Western Collector,* 1968-70, *USIU Doctoral Society Journal* (of U.S. International University Doctoral Society), 1970-71, *Human Behavior Research Journal,* 1971-72, *Programs for the Gifted Bulletin,* 1971-73, *Journal of the Federation of Historical Bottle Clubs,* 1972-77, and *CAG Communicator* (of California Association for the Gifted), 1973—. Book review editor, *Old Bottle Magazine;* antique bottles price guide editor, *Antique Trader;* Coca-Cola memorabilia editor, *Bottle News,* 1976-78.

WORK IN PROGRESS: That Disease Called Collecting; Corporate Collectibles.

AVOCATIONAL INTERESTS: Photography, swimming, running, hiking, bicycling, tennis, sailing, collecting antiques.

BIOGRAPHICAL/CRITICAL SOURCES: Owenita Sanderlin, *Creative Teaching,* A. S. Barnes, 1971; Sanderlin, *Teaching Gifted Children,* A. S. Barnes, 1973.

* * *

MUNSON, Byron Edwin 1921-

PERSONAL: Born June 6, 1921, in Elliot, Ill.; son of Elmer Martin (a farmer) and Pauline (Helgeland) Munson; married Eve Mae Fowler (secretary for a planning commission), July 23, 1945; children: Thomas, Allan, Dale, Cheryl (Mrs. Bill Cherikos). *Education:* University of Illinois, B.S. (with honors), 1949, M.A., 1950, Ph.D., 1954. *Home:* 1822 University Dr., Charleston, Ill. 61920. *Office:* Department of Sociology and Anthropology, Eastern Illinois University, Charleston, Ill. 61920.

CAREER: University of Illinois at Urbana-Champaign, research associate in sociology, 1950-53; North Texas State University, Denton, assistant professor, 1954-56, associate professor of sociology, 1956-58; Ohio State University, Columbus, associate professor and director of Office of Community Development, 1958-63, professor of sociology and director of Center for Community and Regional Analysis, 1963-67; Eastern Illinois University, Charleston, professor of sociology, 1968—, head of department of sociology and anthropology, 1968-71, director of graduate studies, 1971—. *Military service:* U.S. Navy, 1944-45.

MEMBER: American Sociological Association (fellow), Rural Sociological Society, American Association of University Professors, Midwest Sociological Society, Illinois Sociological Society, North Central Sociological Association, Psi Chi.

WRITINGS: (With R. A. Jones) *Housing Likes and Dislikes,* U.S. Housing and Home Finance Agency, 1952; *Changing Community Dimensions,* College of Commerce, Ohio State University, 1968. Writer of extension bulletins and other monographs on community development. Editor of and contributor to proceedings of community development conferences at Ohio State University.

WORK IN PROGRESS: The Urban Crisis.

* * *

MURPHY, Barbara Beasley 1933-

PERSONAL: Born February 4, 1933, in Springfield, Ohio; daughter of William De Ford (a physician) and Henryetta (Kurtz) Beasley; married Bill Murphy (a cartoonist and designer), 1961; children: Jennifer, Stephen. *Education:* Attended Drake University, 1951-53; University of North

Carolina, B.A., 1955. *Religion:* Lutheran. *Home:* 77 Valley Rd., New Rochelle, N.Y. 10804.

CAREER: Junior high school teacher of English in Euclid, Ohio, 1956-57; high school teacher of speech and drama in New York City, 1957-62. Actress at Wilmington Summer Theatre, Wilmington, Ohio, 1957. Member of design and building committees, New Saint Peter's Church, New York City. *Member:* Children's Writers and Artists Collaborative (founding member), Phi Beta Kappa. *Awards, honors:* Fellowship to Bread Loaf Writers' Conference, 1970.

WRITINGS: Home Free, illustrated by husband, Bill Murphy, Delacorte, 1970; (with Norman Baker) *Thor Heyerdahl and the Reed Boat Ra,* Lippincott, 1974; *Travels with Uncle Jack,* Scholastic Book Services, 1975; *No Place to Run,* Bradbury, 1977; (compiler with others and contributor) *New York Kids Catalogue,* Doubleday, 1979.

SIDELIGHTS: Barbara Murphy told *CA:* "I'm in love with the visual, with seeing. I'm not naturally good with words as many writers are. Words sometimes come slowly. But I can't draw or paint, so I write. Every time I see a beloved view I'm the kind of person who says, 'Look! Look! Isn't that terrific!' I feel grateful. The feeling comes often in New Mexico when my family and I are there. Same thing in New York City on an avenue at night with a thousand thousand lights. 'Look! Look! Isn't that terrific!' My kids often say, 'We know. We know.' But I have to say it.

"When I write, the story comes to me in pictures. I try to describe them well enough for a reader to see what I see. After the sentences are down, I mess around with the words, smoothing them like adobe, or plumping them up like pillows. It seems pretty egotistical writing down your images for a year or so and then waiting impatiently for other people to read them. My only excuse is that I'm grateful for the other writers who do it. Their words have added such richness to my life, I forgive the vanity and appreciate their impulse to share.

"At the same time I was writing *No Place to Run,* which takes place in New York City, I was helping build the new Saint Peter's Church in Manhattan at Citicorp Center. For eight years I served on the design and building committees and the church council. In that time we tore down the old structure, had the new one designed, comforted the congregation on the move, maintained a ministry to the city, and watched the new church rise from the excavation on tons of Bethlehem steel. . . . Now people come from all over to see the building. 'Look! Look! Isn't it terrific!' they sometimes say. I liked being a builder in a great city. Like writing it involved a vision and called forth an interpretation of what a city is. In the same way a book is an interpretation of what life is. Very passionate things . . . building and writing."

*   *   *

MURPHY, Raymond E(dward) 1898-

PERSONAL: Born July 24, 1898, in Apple River, Ill.; son of Edward and Ellen (Bermingham) Murphy; married Marion M. Fisher, May 23, 1926; children: Patrick Alan. *Education:* University of Missouri School of Mines and Metallurgy (now University of Missouri—Rolla), B.S., 1923; University of Wisconsin, M.S., 1926, Ph.D., 1930. *Politics:* Democrat. *Religion:* None. *Home:* 762 Juniper Ct., Sonoma, Calif. 95476. *Office:* Graduate School of Geography, Clark University, Worcester, Mass. 01610.

CAREER: Roxana Petroleum Corp., Tulsa, Okla., assistant engineer, 1923-24; University of Kentucky, Lexington, in-

structor in geology, 1926-27; Concord State Teachers College (now Concord College), Athens, W. Va., professor of geography, 1930-31; Pennsylvania State College (now University), College Park, assistant professor, 1931-37, associate professor, 1937-43, professor of geography, 1943-44; University of Hawaii, Honolulu, professor of geography, 1944-45; Clark University, Worcester, Mass., professor of economic geography, 1946-62, professor emeritus, 1968—, director of Graduate School of Geography, 1962-65. University of California, Berkeley, visiting professor, spring, 1958, research associate, 1976—. Conducted human geography field work in Caroline Islands (in cooperation with U.S. Navy), 1947. *Member:* Association of American Geographers, American Geographical Society (fellow), Royal Scottish Geographical Society (honorary member), Sigma Xi, Gamma Alpha. *Awards, honors:* U.S. Office of Naval Research grants, 1952, for geographic research, and 1953, for research on the central business districts of American cities.

WRITINGS: Geography of the Northwestern Pine Barrens of Wisconsin, Wisconsin Academy of Science, 1931; *The Mineral Industries of Pennsylvania: Trends of the Mineral Producing and Processing Industries,* Greater Pennsylvania Council, 1933; *The Geography of Johnstown, Pa.: An Industrial Center,* Mineral Industries Experiment Station, Pennsylvania State College, 1934; *The Economic Geography of York, Pa.: A City of Diversified Industries,* Mineral Industries Experiment Station, Pennsylvania State College, 1935; (with wife, Marion Murphy) *Pennsylvania: A Regional Geography,* Pennsylvania Book Service, 1937; (with Marion Murphy) *Pennsylvania Landscapes,* Pennsylvania Book Service, 1938, 3rd edition, Pennsylvania Valley Publishers, 1974; *World Survey* (to accompany *Goode's School Atlas),* two volumes, Rand McNally, 1947; (contributor) Preston E. James and Clarence F. Jones, editors, *American Geography: Inventory and Prospect,* Syracuse University Press, 1954; (contributor) Perry L. Norton, editor, *Urban Problems and Techniques,* [Lexington, Mass.], 1959; *The American City: An Urban Geography,* McGraw, 1966, 2nd edition, 1974; *Exercises in Urban Geography,* McGraw, 1968; *The Central Business District,* Aldine-Atherton, 1972. Contributor to annals, studies, reports, bulletins, proceedings, and yearbooks. Contributor to professional journals, including *Annals of the Association of American Geographers, Professional Geographer, Economic Geography, Journal of Geography, American City,* and *Geographical Review. Economic Geography,* assistant editor, 1946-49, editor, 1949-62, 1963-69, managing editor, 1962-63.

*   *   *

MURPHY, Robert Cushman 1887-1973

April 29, 1887—March 20, 1973; American ornithologist, museum curator, leader of scientific expeditions, writer, and conservationist. Obituaries: *New York Times,* March 21, 1973; *Washington Post,* March 21, 1973; *Time,* April 2, 1973. (See index for *CA* sketch)

*   *   *

MURPHY, Thomas P(atrick) 1931-

PERSONAL: Born November 26, 1931, in Flushing, N.Y.; son of Eugene P. (a truckdriver) and Delia (Coan) Murphy; married Marcella McAuley, February 4, 1956; children: Kevin, Michael, Thomas, Dolores, Daniel. *Education:* Queens College of the City of New York (now Queens College of the City University of New York), B.A., 1952; Georgetown University, M.A., 1960; St. John's University,

Jamaica, N.Y., Ph.D., 1963. *Home:* 12527 Heurich Rd., Silver Spring, Md. 20902. *Office:* Director, Federal Executive Institute, Charlottesville, Va. 22903.

CAREER: Federal Aviation Agency, Regional Office at Kennedy International Airport, New York, N.Y., executive officer in department of flight standards, 1958-61; National Aeronautics and Space Administration (NASA), Washington, D.C., assistant administrator for legislative affairs, 1961-66; University of Missouri—Kansas City, professor, 1966-71, director of Master's Program in Public Administration; University of Maryland, College Park, director of Institute for Urban Studies and professor of government and politics, 1971-78; Federal Executive Institute, Charlottesville, Va., director, 1978—. Member of board of trustees, Washington Center for Metropolitan Studies, 1974—. *Military service:* U.S. Air Force, Office of Special Investigations, special agent, 1952-57. *Member:* American Political Science Association (vice-president of Washington chapter, 1973-74; president, 1974-75), American Society for Public Administration (president of Kansas City chapter, 1968-69; member of national council, 1969-72), National Association of Schools of Public Affairs and Administration (member of council, 1970-73; vice-president, 1973-74; president, 1974-75), National Center for Public Service Internships (charter member; member of board of directors, 1971-73).

WRITINGS: (Contributor) Andrew M. Scott and Earle Wallace, editors, *Politics, U.S.A.,* 3rd edition, Macmillan, 1969; *Metropolitics and the Urban County,* National Association of Counties, 1970; (co-editor) *Emerging Patterns in Urban Administration,* Heath, 1970; *Science, Geopolitics, and Federal Spending,* Heath, 1971; (contributor) Joseph A. Uveges, Jr., editor, *The Dimensions of Public Administration: Introductory Readings,* Holbrook, 1971; *Pressures Upon Congress,* Barron's, 1972; *Government Management Internships and Executive Development,* Heath, 1973; (contributor) Walter Dean Burnham, editor, *Politics/America: The Cutting Edge of Change,* Van Nostrand, 1973; (contributor) Stanley Powers, F. Gerald Brown, and David S. Arnold, editors, *Developing Municipal Organization,* International City Management Association, 1974; (co-editor) *Organizing Public Services in Metropolitan America,* Heath, 1974; *The New Politics Congress,* Heath, 1974; (contributor) Thomas Reilly and Michael W. Sigoll, editors, *New Patterns in American Politics,* Praeger, 1975; (contributor) Robert A. Lineberry and Louis Masotti, editors, *Urban Problems and Public Policy,* Heath, 1975; *Universities in the Urban Crisis,* Dunellen, 1975; (co-author) *Urban Politics in the Suburban Era,* Dorsey, 1976; *The Politics of Congressional Committees,* Barron's, 1978; (editor) *Urban Politics,* Gale, 1978. Also author of monographs. Contributor of more than thirty-five articles and reviews to political science, public administration, and economics journals including *Economist, Systems and Procedures, Ethics, Public Administration Review, Polity, American Political Science Review, Policy Studies Journal, Administrative Science Quarterly,* and *American Journal of Economics and Sociology.* Member of editorial board of *Administration and Society.*

WORK IN PROGRESS: Books on urban law and public administration.

* * *

MURRAY, J(ohn) Alex

PERSONAL: Born in Hamilton, Ontario, Canada; married; children: three. *Education:* University of Windsor,

B.Comm., 1958; McMaster University, M.B.A., 1963; University of Illinois, Ph.D., 1967. *Home:* 4240 Mt. Carmel Crescent, Windsor, Ontario, Canada. *Office:* Faculty of Business Administration, University of Windsor, Windsor, Ontario, Canada.

CAREER: Servicemaster Associates International, Hamilton, Ontario, sales manager, 1958-60, general manager, 1960-63; University of Windsor, Windsor, Ontario, assistant professor, 1966-68, associate professor, 1968-72, professor of business administration, 1972—, director of Institute for Canadian American Studies, 1971—, acting dean, 1978-79. Visiting professor of international business, University of California, Los Angeles, 1977-78. Research associate at Bureau of Business Research, University of Michigan, 1968; member of staff of executive development programs, Banff School of Management, 1968—.

MEMBER: American Economic Association, American Marketing Association, Academy of International Business, Windsor Chamber of Commerce. *Awards, honors:* Canada Council senior research fellowships, 1970-71, 1971-72, 1972-73, 1974, 1976, 1977; senior research award from Samuel Bronfman Foundation, 1972-73.

WRITINGS: (With H. O. Helmers) *Explorations into Trade Liberalization: The Case of the U.S.-Canadian Automotive Aftermarket,* Gage, 1970; (with W. A. Preshing and E. G. Yaworsky) *Concepts and Canadian Cases in Marketing,* Longmans, 1973. Also editor, *Health Care Delivery Systems in North America,* 1976. Editor, *Canada: The Unknown Neighbor—Proceedings of the Twelfth Annual Canadian-American Seminar,* and *Alienation and Violence in the North American Community: Proceedings of the Thirteenth Annual Canadian-American Seminar,* both University of Windsor Press, 1972. Contributor to proceedings. Contributor to business journals, including *Marketing, Cost and Management, Journal of Production Management, Journal of Marketing Research, Commerceman,* and *Journal of Economic Literature.*

WORK IN PROGRESS: Research on international business intelligence systems of multinational enterprises; studying the accommodation process between the nation state and the multinational enterprise in Canada.

* * *

MURRAY, John Bernard 1915-

PERSONAL: Born August 6, 1915, in Wildwood, N.J.; son of John Bernard and Margaret (Magee) Murray. *Education:* St. Joseph's College, Princeton, N.J., B.A., 1937; Niagara University, B.S., 1944, M.A. (education), 1945; Fordham University, M.A. (psychology), 1949, Ph.D., 1957. *Office:* Department of Psychology, St. John's University, Grand Central and Utopia Pkwys., Jamaica, N.Y. 11439.

CAREER: Ordained Roman Catholic priest of Congregation of Missions (Vincentians), 1942; licensed psychologist and school psychologist in the state of New York; Niagara University, Niagara University, N.Y., assistant professor of philosophy and psychology, 1942-52; St. John's University, Jamaica, N.Y., associate professor, 1958-63, professor of psychology, 1963—, chairman of department, 1958-76, dean of School of Education, 1957-59. Visiting scientist, American Psychological Association, 1967-69.

MEMBER: American Psychological Association, American Association for the Advancement of Science, New York Academy of Science, Psi Chi, Sigma Chi.

WRITINGS—All published by St. John's University Press:

Statistics in Psychology and Education, 1964, revised edition, 1966; (editor) *Readings in Educational Psychology,* 1965, 2nd edition, 1968: *Educational Psychology,* 1965, 2nd edition, 1968; (editor) *Readings in Developmental Psychology,* 1965, revised edition, 1971; *Developmental Psychology,* 1967, revised edition, 1971. Contributor to *Catholic Encyclopedia for Youth.* Contributor of about sixty articles and reviews to theology, psychology, and education journals, including *Journal of Genetic Psychology, Psychological Reports, Perceptual and Motor Skills, Catholic Nurse, American Ecclesiastical Review,* and *Journal of General Psychology.*

* * *

MURRAY, Marian

PERSONAL: Born in Quincy, Mass.; daughter of Benjamin (a lumberman) and Sarah T. (Burke) Johnson; married John Lewis Murray (deceased); children: Janet Murray Ormond. *Education:* Wellesley College, B.A. and graduate study in history of art. *Politics:* Democrat. *Religion:* Unitarian Universalist. *Home:* 1618 Waldemere St., Sarasota, Fla. 33579. *Agent:* Paul R. Reynolds, Inc., 12 East 41st St., New York, N.Y. 10017.

CAREER: High school teacher in West Hartford, Conn., 1925-26; *Hartford Courant,* Hartford, Conn., feature writer, 1927-28; *Hartford Times,* Hartford, feature writer and art, book, and ballet critic, 1929-47, and, at one time, feature editor; Ringling Museums, Sarasota, Fla., member of public relations staff, 1948-55, assistant director, 1955-58; freelance writer, 1951—. Correspondent for *Palm Beach Life,* 1949-51; teacher of English and art history at private school. Publicity chairman, Sarasota Institute of Lifetime Learning. *Member:* Authors Guild, Florida Historical Association, Sarasota Art Association, Friends of the Arts and Sciences (Sarasota).

WRITINGS: Sarasota the Circus City (preschool coloring book), Dietz, 1951; *Here Comes the Circus* (preschool coloring book), Dietz, 1952; *Circus! From Rome to Ringling* (adult nonfiction), Appleton, 1956; *Children of the Big Top* (juvenile nonfiction), Little, Brown, 1958; *Hunting for Fossils* (adult nonfiction), Macmillan, 1967; *Plant Wizard: The Life of Lue Gim Gong* (juvenile nonfiction), Crowell-Collier, 1970; *Fossils in Florida* (adult nonfiction), Trend House, 1975.

WORK IN PROGRESS: A biography of Zora Neale Hurston, Negro writer and anthropologist.

SIDELIGHTS: Marian Murray writes, "For my books for children (always based on fact, though sometimes presented in fictionized form, as *Children of the Big Top*), I consult whatever sources are available, trying to be accurate, and to present in lively fashion dramatic material about human beings who have done something unusual or are otherwise important."

AVOCATIONAL INTERESTS: Sculpture (has exhibited her work in local shows).

* * *

MUSTAFA, Zaki   1934-

PERSONAL: Born November 17, 1934, in Dongola, Sudan; son of Abdel Mageed Yousuf (a businessman) and Amna M. I. (Shaltout) Mustafa; married Abdel Moneim Nasr Mahasin, May 10, 1957; children: Isam, Sawsan, Muna, Sohair. *Education:* University of Khartoum, LL.B. (with honors), 1959; London School of Economics and Political Science,

London, LL.M., 1961; School of Oriental and African Studies, London, Ph.D., 1969. *Religion:* Muslim. *Office:* Attorney-General's Chambers, Khartoum, Sudan.

CAREER: University of Khartoum, Khartoum, Sudan, tutor in Faculty of Law, 1959-61, lecturer, 1961-66, senior lecturer, 1966-69, dean of law, 1965-69; Ahmadu Bello University, Zaria, Nigeria, professor and dean of law, 1969-72; Haile Sellassie I University, Addis Ababa, Ethiopia, professor of law, 1972-73; Government of Sudan, attorney-general, 1973—. Legal advisor to Head of State, Sudan, 1965-69. National chairman, World Peace through Law Centre, 1965-69; chairman, Law of Obligations Reform Commission, 1967-69; member, Nigerian Law Revision Committee, 1971—. *Member:* Sudan Bar Association, Society of Public Teachers of Law (England), International African Law Association (England), International Association of Juridical Sciences (France), Association of African Law Schools (chairman, 1965—).

WRITINGS: (General editor) *Sudan Law Reports,* Faculty of Law, University of Khartoum, 1964, Oceana, 1969; *The Sudan Civil Law: Its Evolution and Main Characteristics* (in Arabic), Arab Institute for Higher Studies and Research (Cairo), 1968; *Sudan Criminal Cases,* Faculty of Law, University of Khartoum, 1971; *The Common Law in the Sudan: An Account of the "Justice, Equity and Good Conscience" Provision,* Oxford University Press, 1971. Also author of *The Legal System of the Sudan,* 1974.

WORK IN PROGRESS: A Constitutional History of the Sudan; a textbook of Muslim law.†

* * *

MUTHARIKA, B(rightson) W(ebster) T(hom)   1934-

PERSONAL: Born February 24, 1934, in Mikolongwe, Malawi; son of Ryson Thom (a teacher) and Ellen (Chingwalu) Mutharika; married Ethel Zwauya White Nyoni, April 4, 1966; children: Noma (daughter), Madaliso (son), Tapiwa (daughter). *Education:* University of Delhi, B.Com. (honors), 1961, M.A., 1963. *Religion:* Christian. *Office:* United Nations Economic Commission for Africa, P.O. Box 60008, Addis Ababa, Ethiopia.

CAREER: Government of Malawi, Zomba, Malawi, administrative officer, 1963-64; Government of Zambia, Lusaka, Zambia, administrative officer, 1965-66; United Nations Economic Commission for Africa, Addis Ababa, Ethiopia, 1966—, chief of Africa-European economic community section, 1972—. Member of Tariff Advisory Board in Malawi and Malawi Book Service, 1964; advisor to Zambian delegation, Conference on Economic Cooperation, Lusaka, 1965; member of United Nations Appointments and Promotions Panel, Addis Ababa, 1969-73. Part-time lecturer in accounting at Malawi Polytechnic, 1963, and College of Further Education in Zambia, 1965-66. *Member:* Royal Economic Society of London, Society for International Development (member of coordinating committee of Addis Ababa chapter), United Nations Association (vice-chairman of Addis Ababa chapter, 1972-73).

WRITINGS: Toward Multinational Economic Cooperation in Africa, Praeger, 1972. Contributor to *African Progress* and *African Development.* Author of studies for the United Nations Economic Commission for Africa.

WORK IN PROGRESS: Nations in Crisis and a novel, *Time to Say Good-bye.*

MYLER, Joseph L.   1905(?)-1973

1905(?)—July 5, 1973; American journalist and science writer. Obituaries: *Washington Post,* July 6, 1973.

* * *

MYRICK, Robert D(eWayne)   1935-

PERSONAL: Born May 13, 1935, in Wayne, Neb.; son of Wayne J. (a salesman) and Mary Ann (Roberts) Myrick; children: Mark, Susan, Karen. *Education:* Southern Oregon College, B.S., 1957, M.S., 1961; Arizona State University, Ph.D., 1967. *Home:* 4108 Alpine Dr., Gainesville, Fla. 32605. *Office:* Department of Counselor Education, University of Florida, 100 Norman Hall, Gainesville, Fla. 32601.

CAREER: Social studies teacher and dean of boys in high school in Phoenix, Ore., 1957-61; counselor in high school in Medford, Ore., 1963-65; Arizona State University, Tempe, assistant director of National Defense Education Act Elementary School Counseling Institute, 1965-67; University of Florida, Gainesville, assistant professor, 1967-70, associate professor, 1970-72, professor of education, 1972—. Visiting professor at Arizona State University, 1967, and University of Miami, Coral Gables, 1969. Counselor, Upward Bound Program, Phoenix, Ariz., 1967; co-director of Drive-in Elementary School Guidance Conference, Gainesville, 1974, and National Elementary School Guidance and Counseling Conference, Tampa, 1974-75. Consultant to Division of College Programs, U.S. Office of Education, 1970—; consultant to numerous school systems in several states, including Florida, Maryland, Kentucky, and Texas.

MEMBER: National Education Association, American Personnel and Guidance Association (chairman of media committee, 1976-77), American School Counselors Association, Association for Counselor Education and Supervision, Florida Personnel and Guidance Association (member of executive board, 1977-79; president, 1978-79), Florida Association for Counselor Education and Supervision (member of executive committee, 1968-69; treasurer, 1969-70; member of board of directors, 1971-73), Northern Florida Personnel and Guidance Association (president, 1969-70), Phi Delta Kappa. *Awards, honors:* Florida Educational Research and Development grant, 1972; U.S. Office of Education grant, 1973; outstanding member award, Florida Personnel and Guidance Association, 1974-75; U.S. Department of Health, Education, and Welfare grant, 1976-77; outstanding service award, Florida Association for Counselor Education and Supervision, 1977-78.

WRITINGS: (With Joe Wittmer) *School Counseling: Problems and Methods,* Goodyear Publishing, 1972; (contributor) *The Status of Guidance and Counseling in the Nation's Schools,* American Personnel and Guidance Association, 1973; (contributor with R. Johnson) D. Dinkmeyer, *Developing Understanding of Self and Others,* American Guidance Service, 1973; (with Wittmer) *Facilitative Teaching: Theory and Practice,* Goodyear Publishing, 1974; (with Johnson) *The Occupational Specialist in Florida* (monograph), Florida Department of Education, 1975; *Consultation as a Counselor Intervention* (monograph), American School Counselors Association, 1977; (with T. Errey) *Caring and Sharing: Becoming a Peer Facilitator,* Educational Media Corp., 1978; (with Errey) *Youth Helping Youth: A Handbook for Training Peer Facilitators,* Educational Media Corp., 1978.

Author, with Wittmer, of *The VEG: Does It Make a Difference?,* 1977. Also author, with D. Sorenson, of film scripts, "Peer Facilitators: Youth Helping Youth," 1976, "Developmental Counseling in the Elementary School," 1976, "The Middle School Years: Guidance for Transition," 1977, and "Leading Group Discussion," 1977. Contributor to *The Florida Elementary School Counselor's Handbook,* 1979. Author of column, "The Counselor's Workshop," in *Elementary School Guidance and Counseling Journal,* 1971-73. Contributor of over sixty articles to professional journals. Member of editorial board, *Elementary School Guidance and Counseling Journal,* 1970-72; editor, *Elementary School Guidance Journal,* 1972-78.

N

NACCI, Chris (Natale) 1909-

PERSONAL: Surname is pronounced Nay-cee; born December 24, 1909, in Abruzzi, Italy; son of Luigi (a miner) and Elisabetta (Iagnemma) Nacci; married Irene Fornella (a librarian), October 27, 1934; children: two daughters. Education: Ohio State University, B.Sc. (education) and B.Sc. (journalism), 1933, M.A., 1947; also studied at University of Wisconsin, summers, 1934, 1939; Universidad Nacional Autonoma de Mexico, D.Litt., 1951. Residence: Columbus, Ohio. Office: Department of Modern Languages, Capital University, East Main St., Columbus, Ohio 43209.

CAREER: High school teacher of French, Spanish, and journalism in Ohio, 1933-43; Standard Products Co., Detroit, Mich., head of public relations, 1943-45; Ohio State University, Columbus, member of faculty, teaching French and Spanish, 1945-47; Capital University, Columbus, member of faculty, teaching French, Spanish, and Italian, 1947-63; University of Akron, Akron, Ohio, member of faculty, teaching Spanish, 1963-68; Capital University, member of faculty, teaching Spanish and Italian, 1968—. Visiting professor and lecturer in Argentina, Uruguay, and Paraguay, under auspices of U.S. Department of State, 1955-57.

MEMBER: American Association of Teachers of Spanish and Portuguese (vice-president of Buckeye chapter, 1971-73; president, 1953-54), American Association of University Professors (president of local chapter, 1970-71), American Council of Teachers of Foreign Languages, Central States Modern Language Teachers Association. Awards, honors: Silver Award from U.S.-Argentine Cultural Institute, Buenos Aires, 1957.

WRITINGS: Concepcion del Mundo en el Teatro Mexicano del Siglo XX, Editora Economica, 1951; Veinticuatro Enfoques de la Actual Filosofia de la Educacion en los Estados Unidos, American Embassy (Buenos Aires), 1956, 2nd edition, 1957; Altamirano, Twayne, 1970. Wrote commentary for twenty-six half-hour Spanish language editions of Hollywood productions for WBNS-Television. Contributor to Hispania, Kentucky Foreign Language Quarterly, Anthology of American College Poetry Society, Educacion, Bond, and Icana.

WORK IN PROGRESS: Research on hispanic dramatic and narrative literature.

SIDELIGHTS: Chris Nacci has traveled extensively throughout the world, especially to the Spanish-speaking countries.

NAESS, Harald Sigurd 1925-

PERSONAL: Born December 27, 1925, in Kristiansand, Norway; son of Sigurd L. (a captain) and Sarah Elizabeth (Bonner) Naess; married Ann Mari Hofgaard, March 8, 1950; children: Morten, Petter, Sara Kristine. Education: Oslo University, Cand. Philol., 1952; University of Iceland, post-doctoral study, 1952. Home: 2586 Prairie Ridge Rd., Verona, Wis. 53593. Office: Department of Scandinavian Studies, University of Wisconsin, Madison, Wis. 53706.

CAREER: University of Durham, Newcastle-upon-Tyne, England, lecturer in Norwegian, 1953-59; University of Wisconsin—Madison, lecturer, 1959-61, associate professor, 1962-67, Torger Thompson Professor of Scandinavian Studies, 1968—. Member: Norwegian-American Historical Association, American Society for Eighteenth Century Studies, Society for the Advancement of Scandinavian Study (president, 1967-69). Awards, honors: Fulbright scholar, 1959-61.

WRITINGS: Knut Hamsun og Amerika, Gyldendal (Oslo), 1969; (editor with Sigmund Skard) Studies in Scandinavian-American Interrelations, Universitetsforlaget (Oslo), 1971; Norwegian Literary Bibliography, Department of Scandinavian Studies, University of Wisconsin, 1972; (editor) Norwegian Influence on the Upper Midwest, University of Minnesota—Duluth, 1976. Contributor of more than fifty articles on Scandinavian literature to journals in his field. Editor of Scandinavian Studies, 1974-78. Editor of Norwegian number of Fairleigh Dickinson University's Literary Review, 1969.

WORK IN PROGRESS: A book on Knut Hamsun for Twayne.

*   *   *

NAG, Moni 1925-

PERSONAL: Born April 1, 1925, in Silchar, India; son of Jogendra Chandra (a government employee) and Muktakeshi (Purkaystha) Nag; married Karabee Bose (a social worker), September 13, 1965; children: Rupak. Education: University of Calcutta, B.Sc. (honors in mathematics), 1944, M.Sc., 1946; Yale University, M.A., 1959, Ph.D., 1961. Home: 160 Highwood Ave., Leonia, N.J. 07605. Office: Population Council, 1 Dag Hammarskjold Plaza, New York, N.Y. 10017.

CAREER: Indian Statistical Institute, Calcutta, superintendent, 1947-48; Government of India, Anthropological Survey of India, Calcutta, statistician, 1948-57, 1961-62; Government of West Bengal, Calcutta Metropolitan Planning Organization, Calcutta, head of sociology section, 1962-64; Government of India, Anthropological Survey of India, superintending anthropologist, 1964-66; Columbia University, New York City, assistant professor, 1966-69, associate professor of anthropology, 1969-76, chief of social demography section at International Institute for the Study of Human Reproduction, 1968-76; Population Council, New York City, senior associate, 1976—. Has participated in and moderated international conferences and symposia. Member of board of directors, Sex Information and Education Council of the United States, 1969-72.

MEMBER: International Union of Anthropological and Ethnological Sciences (chairman of population commission, 1973—), International Union for the Scientific Study of Population, American Anthropological Association (fellow), Current Anthropology (associate), Society for Applied Anthropology (fellow), American Eugenic Society, Association for Asian Studies, Population Association of America, Indian Anthropological Society, Indian Science Congress Association, Tagore Society (New York, N.Y.; president, 1970). *Awards, honors:* Fulbright travel grant, 1957-61; Committee of Research on Sex of National Research Council fellowship, 1960-61.

WRITINGS: (Contributor) B. S. Guha, editor, *Studies in Social Tensions among the Refugees from Eastern Pakistan,* Department of Anthropology, Government of India, 1959; *Factors Affecting Human Fertility in Nonindustrial Societies: A Cross-Cultural Study,* Publications in Anthropology, Yale University, 1962; (contributor) Frank M. Lebar and others, editors, *Ethnic Groups of Mainland Southeast Asia,* Human Relations Area Files, 1964; (with Reuben Hill and Edwin D. Driver) *Needed Social Science Research in Population and Family Planning,* Ford Foundation, 1968; (editor with others) *Biological Components of Human Reproduction: Studies of Their Variations in Population Groups* (technical report), World Health Organization, 1969.

(Contributor) Steven Polgar, editor, *Culture and Population: A Collection of Current Studies,* Schenkman, 1971; (contributor) Lebar and others, editors, *Ethnic Groups of Insular Southeast Asia,* Human Relations Area Files, 1972; (contributor) Morton Fried, editor, *Explorations in Anthropology: Readings in Culture, Man and Nature,* Crowell, 1973; (contributor) *Population Debate,* United Nations, 1975; (editor and contributor) *Population and Social Organization,* Mouton, 1975; (contributor) Giri Raj Gupta, editor, *Contemporary India: Some Sociological Perspectives,* Vikas (Delhi), 1976; (contributor) John F. Marshall and Polgar, editors, *Culture, Natality, and Family Planning,* Carolina Population Center, 1976; (contributor) Sidney H. Newman and Zanvel E. Klein, editors, *Behavioral-Social Aspects of Contraceptive Sterilization,* Lexington Books, 1976; (contributor) *International Population Conference,* International Union for the Scientific Study of Population, 1977.

Contributor to proceedings and symposia, and to *Funk & Wagnalls New Encyclopedia.* Contributor of about forty articles and reviews to a variety of journals in the United States and abroad, including *Current Anthropology, Social and Economic Studies, Population Review, Social Welfare, Statesman, Indian Journal of Social Work, Journal of Family Welfare, Population Studies,* and *Demography India.*

NAGORSKI, Zygmunt 1885(?)-1973

1885(?)—January 20, 1973; Polish-born political leader and writer. Obituaries: *New York Times,* January 22, 1973.

* * *

NAKARAI, Toyozo W(ada) 1898-

PERSONAL: Born May 16, 1898, in Kyoto, Japan; came to United States in 1923, naturalized in 1953; son of Tsui and Wakae (Harada) Nakarai; married Frances A. Yorn, June 22, 1933; children: Charles Frederick Toyozo, Frederick Leroy. *Education:* Kokugakuin University, A.B., 1920; Butler University, A.B., 1924, A.M., 1925; University of Michigan, Ph.D., 1930; also studied at University of Chicago, New York University, Hebrew Union College, and Nippon University. *Home address:* Route 4, Box 240, Elizabethton, Tenn. 37643. *Office address:* Drawer Q, Emmanuel School of Religion, Milligan College, Tenn. 37682.

CAREER: Former Shinto priest, now ordained minister of Christian Churches; high school instructor in Tokyo, Japan, 1920-23; College of Missions, Indianapolis, Ind., instructor in Japanology, 1923-25; Butler University, Indianapolis, instructor, 1927-28, assistant professor, 1928-29, associate professor, 1929-31, professor of Semitics and head of department, 1931-58; Christian Theological Seminary, Indianapolis, professor of Semitics, 1958-65, professor emeritus, 1965—; Emmanuel School of Religion, Milligan College, Tenn., professor of Semitics, 1965-71, honored professor of Old Testament, 1971—. American School of Oriental Research, Jerusalem, visiting professor, 1947-48, honorary associate, 1962-63; visiting professor, Tainan Theological Seminary, Taiwan, 1963. *Member:* World Union of Jewish Studies, International Platform Association, International Institute for the Study of Religions, Society of Biblical Literature (president of Midwest branch, 1951-52), National Association of Professors of Hebrew (president, 1956-59), American Oriental Society, American Schools of Oriental Research, American Academy of Religion, American Association of University Professors, Society for the Scientific Study of Religion, Israel Society for Biblical Research, Israel Exploration Society, Phi Kappa Phi, Theta Phi, Eta Beta Rho. *Awards, honors:* J. I. Holcomb Award of Butler University, 1952; Baxter Foundation Award, 1953; other awards, mostly for teaching ability and Hebraic studies.

WRITINGS: A Study of the Kokin-shu, William Mitchell Printing Co., 1931; *Biblical Hebrew,* Bookman Associates, 1951, revised edition, Emmanuel School of Religion, 1976; (with others) *To Do and to Teach,* Lexington Theological Seminary, 1953; *An Elder's Public Prayers,* Carlton, 1968, revised edition, Exposition Press, 1978. Associate editor, *Hebrew Abstracts,* 1954-65, 1970-75; member of editorial committee, *Encounter,* 1957-65; member of editorial committee, *Hebrew Studies,* 1975-77; editor, *Iggeret,* 1975-77.

WORK IN PROGRESS: A textbook on the prophets of Israel.

SIDELIGHTS: Toyozo W. Nakarai told *CA:* "Much of my writing is motivated by my Judeo-Christian faith, and my desire to be a better teacher of Hebrew and related Semitic subjects. My early education in Shintoism, Buddhism, and other religions of the world has been a great help in my literary work. Fifty years ago, I was probably the only "Japanese" professor of Hebrew in a Christian institution of higher learning, teaching Hebrew, using a German textbook. In the course of my teaching, I discovered how so many textbooks on Hebrew borrowed the ideas of grammar from earlier textbooks on Arabic, ignoring the recent linguistic science. My lectures resulted in *Biblical Hebrew*, first published in 1951, and revised in 1976. More recently I have tried to take my students back to the Hebrew-Aramaic of two thousand years ago and bring them down to the Hebrew of modern Israel, as I teach the Bible (Old Testament) in Hebrew. It is hoped that a more intelligent appreciation of Judaism will be generated among Christian believers."

AVOCATIONAL INTERESTS: Fishing.

BIOGRAPHICAL/CRITICAL SOURCES: Encounter, Volume XXVI, number 2.

*   *   *

NAMEROFF, Rochelle 1943-

PERSONAL: Born May 21, 1943, in Milwaukee, Wis.; daughter of Philip and Esther (Pokrass) Nameroff; divorced. *Education:* University of California, Berkeley, A.B., 1970, M.A., 1972, Ph.D. candidate, 1972—. *Politics:* Democrat. *Religion:* Jewish. *Home:* 356 Ocean View, Kensington, Calif. 94707.

CAREER: Has worked as teacher, secretary, editor, and research assistant. *Member:* American Folklore Society, California Folklore Society, Phi Beta Kappa.

WRITINGS: Body Prints, Ithaca House, 1972. Work is anthologized in *Poems*, edited and compiled by Denise Levertov's workshop for Peoples' Park Benefit, Cloud Marauder, 1969, *Contemporaries: Twenty-Eight New American Poets*, edited by Jean Malley and Hale Tokay, Viking, 1972, and *This Is Women's Work*, Panjandrum Press, 1974.

WORK IN PROGRESS: A book of poems; a film screenplay; a detective novel; articles for academic journals.

AVOCATIONAL INTERESTS: Folklore, pop culture, films, comic and psychoanalytic theory, American humor, native American studies, American history.

*   *   *

NARDIN, Terry 1942-

PERSONAL: Born January 1, 1942, in New York, N.Y.; son of Warren (a designer) and Gloria (Vinci) Nardin; married Jane Baron, January 9, 1962; children: Rachel, Sophia. *Education:* Attended University of Chicago, 1959-61; New York University, B.A., 1963; Northwestern University, M.A., 1966, Ph.D., 1967. *Residence:* Milwaukee, Wis. *Office:* Department of Political Science, State University of New York at Buffalo, Amherst, N.Y. 14261.

CAREER: State University of New York at Buffalo, Amherst, assistant professor, 1967-73, associate professor of political science, 1973—. Has also taught at University of Hawaii, 1968, and University of Wisconsin—Madison, 1978. *Member:* International Studies Association, American Political Science Association, American Society for Political and Legal Philosophy. *Awards, honors:* National Science Foundation research grants, 1966-67, 1972-73; grant from Council for Intersocietal Studies, Northwestern University, 1968-71; State University of New York faculty research fellowships, 1971, 1972, 1978; Rockefeller Foundation humanities fellowship, 1978-79.

WRITINGS: Theories of Conflict Management, Canadian Peace Research Institute, 1971; *Violence and the State*, Sage Publications, 1971. Contributor to *Yale Review, American Political Science Review, British Journal of International Studies*, and other journals.

WORK IN PROGRESS: A book on international legal and moral theory.

NASATIR, David 1934-

PERSONAL: Born February 2, 1934, in Evanston, Ill.; son of Harry Aaron (a salesman) and Elsie (a teacher; maiden name, Markus) Nasatir; married Marilyn Jacobson, August 14, 1955; children: Gail, Robin. *Education:* Massachusetts Institute of Technology, B.S., 1955; Stanford University, M.A., 1956; University of California, Berkeley, Ph.D., 1966. *Office:* Behavioral Science Graduate Program, California State University, Dominguez Hills, 1000 East Victoria St., Carson, Calif. 90747.

CAREER: Taught in Argentina and Brazil, 1963-65; University of California, Berkeley, assistant professor, 1966-70, associate research sociologist, 1970-75; senior social scientist, San Francisco Bay Area Metropolitan Transportation Commission, 1975-76; American University, Washington, D.C., associate professor of sociology, 1976-77; California State University, Dominguez Hills, Carson, professor and chairman of Behavioral Science Graduate Program, 1977—. *Member:* American Sociological Association, American Association for Public Opinion Research, International Sociological Association.

WRITINGS: Social Science Data Archives in International Perspective, UNESCO, 1973. Contributor to *American Sociology Review, American Journal of Sociology, Public Opinion Quarterly, Drexel Library Quarterly*, and *Transaction*. Associate editor of *Sociology of Education*, 1969-72.

*   *   *

NASH, Allan N(ylin) 1932-

PERSONAL: Born December 3, 1932, in Tracy, Minn.; married; children: three. *Education:* Attended Macalester College, 1950-53; University of Minnesota, B.B.A., 1957, M.B.A., 1959, Ph.D., 1963. *Home:* 10003 Emack Rd., Beltsville, Md. 20705. *Office:* Department of Business Administration, University of Maryland, College Park, Md. 20742.

CAREER: University of Minnesota, Minneapolis, instructor in labor economics, 1959-60; University of Dayton, Dayton, Ohio, instructor, 1960-61, assistant professor of business administration, 1961-62; University of Minnesota, lecturer in business administration, 1962-63; University of Maryland, College Park, assistant professor, 1963-65, associate professor, 1966-73, professor of business administration, 1974—, chairman of Behavioral Science Division, 1967-69, director of graduate studies, 1978—. *Military service:* U.S. Army, 1953-55; served in Korea and Japan. *Member:* Academy of Management (member of board of directors and executive vice-president of Eastern academy; member of board of directors, organization of behavior division; chairperson, human resources committee, 1977-78). *Awards, honors:* Tozer Foundation scholar, 1962-63.

WRITINGS: (With T. A. Mahoney and T. H. Jerdee) *A Research Approach to Management Development: The Identification of Management Potential*, W. C. Brown, 1961; (with G. A. Brunner, F. T. Paine, and G. M. Smerck) *User Determined Attributes of Ideal Transportation Systems: An Empirical Study* (monograph), Bureau of Public Roads, 1966; (with Paine, Brunner, and S. J. Hille) *Consumer Conceived Attributes of Transportation Study: An Attitude Study* (monograph), Bureau of Public Roads, 1967; (with Hille, Brunner, and Paine) *Studying Transportation Systems from the Consumer Viewpoint: Some Recommendations* (monograph), Bureau of Public Roads, 1967; (with J. B. Miner) *Personnel and Labor Relations: An Evolutionary Approach*, Macmillan, 1975; (with S. J. Carroll) *The Man-*

agement of Compensation, Wadsworth, 1977. Contributor of about twenty-five articles to psychology and business administration journals.

WORK IN PROGRESS: The Evaluation of Performance, with Carroll.

* * *

NASH, Lee (Marten) 1927-

PERSONAL: Born September 10, 1927, in North Bend, Ore.; son of Ray (a businessman) and Grace (Miller) Nash; married Grayce Frey, July 27, 1951; children: Murray, LeAnn, Torrey. *Education:* Cascade College, A.B., 1950; University of Washington, Seattle, M.A., 1951; University of Oregon, Ph.D., 1961. *Politics:* Democrat. *Religion:* Society of Friends. *Home:* 191 Dogwood Dr., Dundee, Ore. 97115. *Office:* Division of Social Science, George Fox College, Newberg, Ore. 97132.

CAREER: Cascade College, Portland, Ore., assistant professor, 1951-56, associate professor, 1959-60, professor of history, 1960-67, dean of the college, 1962-67; Northern Arizona University, Flagstaff, professor of history, 1967-75; George Fox College, Newberg, Ore., chairman of Division of Social Science, 1975—. Research associate in history, University of Oregon, 1961-62. *Military service:* U.S. Army, 1946-47. *Member:* American Historical Association, Organization of American Historians, American Society of Church History, American Studies Association, Conference on Faith and History. *Awards, honors:* American Association for State and Local History grant-in-aid, 1969; Autzen Foundation research grant, 1970.

WRITINGS: (Contributor) Robert G. Clouse, Richard V. Pierard and Robert D. Linder, editors, *The Cross and the Flag: Evangelical Christianity and Contemporary Politics,* Creation House, 1972. Contributor to *Westminster Dictionary of Church History, American Quarterly, Christianity Today, Eternity, Oregon Historical Quarterly, Pacific Northwest Quarterly, Pacific Historical Review, Fides et Historia,* and *Christian Scholar's Review.* Member of editorial board of *Fides et Historia,* 1972—.

WORK IN PROGRESS: Scott of the Oregonian: Frontier Intellectual.

SIDELIGHTS: Lee Nash told *CA:* "History can and should be written to the standards of literature. Every historian, knowingly or not, makes multitudes of literary decisions in every chapter, as to form, arrangement, characterization, suspense, style, and diction. When those decisions are made consciously and sensitively, there is a much greater possibility of the finished historical work achieving status as literary art."

* * *

NAVARRA, John Gabriel 1927-

PERSONAL: Born July 3, 1927, in Bayonne, N.J.; son of Salvatore Anthony (a chemist) and Yolanda (Scala) Navarra; married Celeste Scala, September 12, 1947; children: John Gabriel, Jr., Elisa (Mrs. L. Michael Treadwell). *Education:* Columbia University, A.B., 1949, M.A., 1950, Ed.D., 1954. *Office address:* P.O. Box 647, Farmingdale, N.J. 07727.

CAREER: East Carolina College (now University), Greenville, N.C., associate professor of science, 1954-58; Jersey City State College, Jersey City, N.J., professor of science and chairman of Division of Science, 1958-68, professor of geoscience, 1968—. Visiting professor or lecturer at University of Washington, Seattle, University of Virginia, University of Hawaii, University of California, Los Angeles, Columbia University, Fordham University, and other institutions; visiting scientist to high schools under auspices of American Institute of Physics, 1960-63. Director of Learning Resources Laboratories, Farmingdale, N.J., 1967—; editorial director of Harper & Row-RCA Instructional Systems development program in computer-assisted instructional materials, 1967-69. Consultant in science education for Arabian American Oil Co., 1963; consultant to California Test Bureau, Coronet Films, Essex International Corp., Cascade Productions of California, and school systems; member of advisory committee, Scientific Products Corp. President, Council for Elementary Science International, 1958-60. *Military service:* U.S. Army Air Forces, 1944-45.

MEMBER: American Association for the Advancement of Science, National Association of Geology Teachers, American Geological Institute, American Educational Research Association, American Institute of Physics, National Association for Research in Science Teaching, U.S. Coast Guard Auxiliary (vice commander), Kappa Delta Pi, Iota Mu Pi. *Awards, honors:* Science Recognition Award of *Science Education,* 1961.

WRITINGS: The Development of Scientific Concepts in a Young Child, Teachers College Press, 1955; *Experimenting in Science,* with teacher's manual, Ginn, 1955, 3rd edition, 1961; (senior author) *Science Today for the Elementary School Teacher,* Harper, 1960; (with F. L. Fitzpatrick and others) *Policies for Science Education,* Teachers College Press, 1960; (contributor) Theodore Harris and Wilson Schwahn, editors, *Selected Readings on the Learning Process,* Oxford University Press, 1961; (member of editorial committee) *Research in the Teaching of Science,* U.S. Department of Health, Education, and Welfare, 1965; *Fundamentals of Optics,* Essex International, 1966; *Clocks, Calendars, and Carousels: A Book About Time,* Doubleday, 1967; *A Turtle in the House,* Doubleday, 1968; *Wide-World Weather,* Doubleday, 1968; *Our Noisy World,* Doubleday, 1969.

From Generation to Generation, Natural History Press, 1970; *The World You Inherit: A Story of Pollution,* National History Press, 1970; *Earth Science,* Wiley, 1971; *Nature Strikes Back,* Natural History Press, 1971; *Flying Today and Tomorrow,* Doubleday, 1973; *Wheels for Kids,* Doubleday, 1973; *Safe Motor Boating for Kids,* Doubleday, 1974; *Science in the Elementary School: Content and Methods,* C. E. Merrill, 1975; *Supercars,* Doubleday, 1975; *Supertrains,* Doubleday, 1976; *Superboats,* Doubleday, 1977; *Superplanes,* Doubleday, 1979; *Atmosphere, Weather, and Climate,* Saunders, 1979.

Series: (Senior author) "Today's Basic Science," nine books and nine manuals, Harper, 1963, revised edition, six books and six manuals, 1967; (senior author) "Junior High School Science Program," three books and three manuals, Harper, 1967; "InvestiGuide," seven books and three guides, Harper, 1967-68; "InvestiVision," twelve books, Harper, 1967-69; (senior author) "Young Scientist," six books and six manuals, Harper, 1971; (senior author) "Junior High Science Program," three books and three manuals, Harper, 1973.

Author of instructional manuals, *Elements of Electricity* and *Elements of Mechanics,* Essex International, 1962, and achievement tests. Contributor of more than fifty articles to professional journals; book reviewer, *Educational Forum.*

Editor and contributor, *Classroom Science Bulletin*, 1958-67; assistant editor and regional editor, *American Biology Teacher*, 1960—; contributing editor, *Instructor*, 1962-64; science editor, two newsletters of Croft Educational Services, 1964-67.

BIOGRAPHICAL/CRITICAL SOURCES: Science Education, February, 1961; Hillel Block, *The American Schoolbook*, Morrow, 1967; *Saturday Evening Post*, October 7, 1967.

*   *   *

NEARING, Scott 1883-

PERSONAL: Born August 6, 1883, in Morris Run, Pa.; son of Louis (a merchant) and Minnie (Zabriskie) Nearing; married Nellie Marguerite Seeds, June 10, 1908 (died, 1946); married Helen Knothe (secretary of Social Science Institute), 1947. *Education:* University of Pennsylvania, law student, 1901-02, B.S., 1905, Ph.D., 1909; Temple University, B.Oratory, 1905. *Politics:* Socialist-Communist. *Religion:* "To live superbly." *Home and office:* Harborside, Me. 04642.

CAREER: Pennsylvania Child Labor Commission, Philadelphia, secretary, 1905-07; University of Pennsylvania, Wharton School, Philadelphia, instructor, 1906-14, assistant professor of economics, 1914-15; Swarthmore College, Swarthmore, Pa., instructor in economics, 1908-13; University of Toledo, Toledo, Ohio, professor of social science and dean of College of Arts and Science, 1915-17. Author and pamphleteer, 1908—. Lecturer, Rand School of Social Science, 1916; chairman, Social Science Institute, 1953. Chairman, People's Council of America, 1917-18; Socialist candidate for U.S. Congress, 1919; defendant with American Socialist Society in civil liberties trial, charged with obstructing recruiting in armed forces, held in U.S. District Court, New York, 1919. *Awards, honors:* Honorary professor emeritus of economics from the Wharton School, University of Pennsylvania, 1973.

WRITINGS: (With F. D. Watson) *Economics*, Macmillan, 1908.

Wages in the United States, 1908-1910, Macmillan, 1911; *The Solution of the Child Labor Problem*, Moffat, Yard, 1911; *Social Adjustment* (doctoral thesis), Macmillan, 1911; *The Super Race: An American Problem*, Huebsch, 1912; (with wife, Nellie M. S. Nearing) *Woman and Social Progress: A Discussion of the Biologic, Domestic, Industrial and Social Possibilities of American Women*, Macmillan, 1912; *Social Religion: An Interpretation of Christianity in Terms of Modern Life*, Macmillan, 1913; *Social Sanity*, Moffat, Yard, 1913; *Financing the Wage-Earner's Family*, Huebsch, 1913; *Reducing the Cost of Living*, G. W. Jacobs, 1914; *Income: An Examination of the Returns for Services Rendered and from Property Owned in the United States*, Macmillan, 1915; *Anthracite: An Instance of Natural Resource Monopoly*, John C. Winston, 1915; *The New Education: A Review of Progressive Educational Movements of the Day* (collection of articles originally prepared for *Ladies' Home Journal*), Row, Peterson, 1915, reprinted, Arno, 1969; *Poverty and Riches: A Study of the Industrial Regime*, John C. Winston, 1916; (with Jessie Field) *Community Civics*, Macmillan, 1916; *Work and Pay*, Rand School of Social Science, 1917; *The Menace of Militarism*, Rand School of Social Science, 1917.

The American Empire, Rand School of Social Science, 1921; *The Next Step: A Plan for Economic World Federation*, privately printed, 1922; (with Bertrand A. Russell) *Debate*

between *Scott Nearing and Bertrand Russell*, League for Public Discussion, 1924; (with Joseph Freeman) *Dollar Diplomacy: A Study of American Imperialism*, Viking, 1925, reprinted, Arno, 1970; *Educational Frontiers: A Book about Simon Nelson Patten and Other Teachers*, Seltzer, 1925; *The British General Strike*, Vanguard, 1926; *Education in Soviet Russia*, International Publishers, 1926; (with Jack Hardy) *Economic Organization of the Soviet Union*, Vanguard, 1927; *Where Is Civilization Going?*, Vanguard, 1927; *Whither China? An Economic Interpretation of Recent Events in the Far East*, International Publishers, 1927; *Black America*, Vanguard, 1929, reprinted with new introduction by the author, Schocken, 1969.

The Twilight of Empire: An Economic Interpretation of Imperialist Cycles, Vanguard, 1930; *War: Organized Destruction and Mass Murder by Civilized Nations*, Vanguard, 1931; *Free Born* (novel), Urquhart Press, 1932; *Must We Starve?*, Vanguard, 1932; *Fascism*, privately printed, 1933; *Europe-West, East*, privately printed, 1935.

United World: The Road to International Peace, Open Road Press, 1944; *The Soviet Union as a World Power*, Island Workshop Press, 1945; *The Tragedy of Empire*, Island Workshop Press, 1945; *Democracy Is Not Enough*, Island Workshop Press, 1945; *War or Peace?*, Island Workshop Press, 1946.

Economics for the Power Age, John Day, 1952; *Man's Search for the Good Life*, Social Science Institute, 1954.

Freedom: Promise and Menace, Social Science Institute, 1961; *Socialism in Practice: The Transformation of Eastern Europe*, New Century Publishers, 1962; *The Conscience of a Radical*, Social Science Institute, 1965.

The Making of a Radical: A Political Autobiography, Harper, 1972; *Civilization and Beyond: Learning from History*, Social Science Institute, 1975.

With wife, Helen Nearing: *The Maple Sugar Book: Being a Plain Practical Account of the Art of Sugaring Designed to Promote an Acquaintance with the Ancient as Well as the Modern Practice, Together with Remarks on Pioneering as a Way of Living in the Twentieth Century*, John Day, 1950, reprinted, Schocken, 1971; *Living the Good Life: Being a Plain Practical Account of a Twenty Year Project on a Self-Subsistent Homestead in Vermont, Together with Remarks on How to Live Sanely and Simply in a Troubled World*, Social Science Institute, 1954, reprinted with an introduction by Paul Goodman, Schocken, 1970; *USA Today: Reporting Extensive Journeys and First-Hand Observations*, Social Science Institute, 1955; *The Brave New World* (on travels in Russia and China), Social Science Institute, 1958; *Socialists around the World*, Monthly Review Press, 1958; *Building and Using Our Sun-Heated Greenhouse*, Garden Way Press, 1977.

Booklets and pamphlets, published by Rand School of Social Science or Nearing affiliates, except as noted: *Women in American Industry*, American Baptist Publication Society, 1915; *The Germs of War*, National Rip-Saw Publishing, 1916; *The Great Madness: A Victory for the American Plutocracy*, 1917; *Work and Pay*, 1917; *The Coal Question*, 1918; *Labor and the League of Nations*, 1919; *Debs Decision*, 1919; *A Nation Divided*, Socialist Party, 1920; *Europe in Revolution*, 1920; *Europe and the Next War*, 1920; *The One Big Union of Business*, 1920; *The New Slavery*, Socialist Party, 1920; *Irrepressible America*, League for Industrial Democracy, 1922; *Oil and the Germs of War*, 1923; *Russia Turns East: The Triumph of Soviet Diplomacy in Asia*, 1926; *World Labor Unity*, 1926; *Glimpses of the Soviet*

Republic, 1926; *British Labor Bids for Power*, 1926; *Stopping a War: The Fight of the French Workers against the Moroccan Campaign of 1925*, 1926; *"To Promote the General Welfare,"* 1954; (with Helen Nearing) *Our Right to Travel*, 1959; *Soviet Education: What Does It Offer to America?*, 1959; *Cuba and Latin America: Eyewitness Report on the Continental Congress for Solidarity with Cuba*, 1963; *Economic Crisis in the United States*, 1961; and others.

Writer of newsletter, "World Events, Interpreted by Scott Nearing," 1944-54.

BIOGRAPHICAL/CRITICAL SOURCES: The Trial of Scott Nearing and the American Socialist Party, Rand School of Social Science, 1919, reprinted, Da Capo, 1970; *New Republic*, September 12, 1970; *Newsweek*, September 14, 1972.

* * *

NECHELES, Ruth F. 1936-

PERSONAL: First syllable of surname rhymes with "mesh"; born April 20, 1936, in Chicago, Ill.; daughter of John R. (a physician) and Henrietta (a physician; maiden name, Magnus) Necheles; married Leon Richard Jansyn, Jr. (an assistant professor), June 1, 1978. *Education:* University of Chicago, B.A., 1954, M.A., 1956, Ph.D., 1963; University of Heidelberg, graduate study, 1956-57. *Home:* 216 South Third Ave., Highland Park, N.J. 08904. *Office:* Department of History, Long Island University, Brooklyn Center, Brooklyn, N.Y. 11201.

CAREER: Worked as a high school teacher in Chicago, Ill., 1957-58; University of Virginia, Fredericksburg, assistant professor of history, 1962-64; Long Island University, Brooklyn Center, Brooklyn, N.Y., assistant professor, 1964-69, associate professor, 1969-73, professor of history, 1973—, chairman of department, 1976—. *Member:* American Historical Association, American Association of University Professors (president of chapter, 1972-74), American Society for Eighteenth Century Studies, Society for French Historical Studies, Societe d'Histoire Moderne, Conference on Jewish Social Studies. *Awards, honors:* West German Government fellowship, 1957; American Philosophical Society grant, 1966.

WRITINGS: The Abbe Gregoire, 1787-1831: The Odyssey of an Egalitarian, Greenwood Press, 1971. Contributor to *French Historical Studies, Jewish Social Studies, Studies in Eighteenth Century Culture, Journal of Modern History, Consortium on Revolutionary History*, and *Annales Historique de la Revolution Francaise*.

WORK IN PROGRESS: Editing Gregoire's diary of the Estates General; a monograph on Gregoire and the Constitutional Church, 1789-1802.

* * *

NEENAN, William B(raunger) 1929-

PERSONAL: Born January 9, 1929, in Sioux City, Iowa; son of Edward W. (a dentist) and Grace (Braunger) Neenan. *Education:* St. Louis University, A.B., 1954, M.A., 1956, S.T.L., 1961; St. Mary's College, graduate study, 1957; University of Michigan, Ph.D., 1966. *Politics:* Democrat. *Home:* 1000 East Ann, Apt. 3, Ann Arbor, Mich. 48104. *Office:* Department of Economics, University of Michigan, Ann Arbor, Mich. 48109.

CAREER: Roman Catholic priest of the Society of Jesus (Jesuits); St. Louis University, St. Louis, Mo., instructor in

economics, 1955-56; Creighton University, Omaha, Neb., instructor in economics, 1956-57; University of Michigan, Ann Arbor, assistant professor, 1967-71, associate professor, 1972-77, professor of economics, 1977—. *Member:* American Economic Association.

WRITINGS: Normative Evaluation of the Public Health Program, University of Michigan Press, 1967; *The Political Economy of Urban Areas*, Markham, 1972; (co-author) *Fiscal Interactions in a Metropolitan Area*, Lexington, 1974. Contributor to *Labor Law Journal of Finance, National Tax Journal, Canadian Journal of Economics*, and other periodicals.

* * *

NEFT, David S(amuel) 1937-

PERSONAL: Born January 9, 1937, in New York, N.Y.; son of Louis (an insurance broker) and Sue (Horowitz) Neft; married Naomi Silver, May 31, 1964; children: Michael, Deborah. *Education:* Columbia University, B.A., 1957, M.B.A., 1959, Ph.D., 1962. *Home:* 525 East 86th St., New York, N.Y. 10028. *Office:* Louis Harris & Associates, 630 Fifth Ave., New York, N.Y. 10020.

CAREER: Louis Harris & Associates, New York City, chief statistician, 1963-65; Information Concepts, Inc., New York City, treasurer and director, 1965-71; Sports Illustrated New Projects, Darien, Conn., general manager, 1971-73; president, Sports Productions Inc., beginning 1973; Louis Harris & Associates, New York City, executive vice-president, 1977—. Consultant to U.S. Department of Defense, 1963-64, and Center for Popular Research, Georgetown University, 1965-69. *Military service:* U.S. Army, 1961-63. *Member:* American Statistical Association, Society for American Baseball Research, American Geographical Society, Regional Science Association.

WRITINGS: Statistical Analysis for Areal Distributions, Regional Science Research Institute, 1966; (editor) *The Baseball Encyclopedia*, Macmillan, 1969; (with Richard M. Cohen and Jordan A. Deutsch) *Pro Football: The Early Years*, privately printed, 1978; (with Cohen and Deutsch) *The Great American Book of Lousy Baseball*, Dale Books, 1979; (with Cohen and Deutsch) *The Great American Book of Lousy Football*, Dale Books, 1979.

Compiler; all published by Grosset, except as indicated: (With Roland T. Johnson and Cohen) *The Sports Encyclopedia: Pro Football*, text by Deutsch, 1974, revised edition, 1979; (with Johnson and Cohen) *The Sports Encyclopedia: Baseball*, text by Deutsch, 1974, revised edition, 1979; (with Cohen and Deutsch) *Monday Morning Quarterback*, 1974, revised edition, 1979; (with others) *The Sports Encyclopedia: Pro Basketball*, 1975; (with others) *The Complete All-Time Pro Football Register*, abridged edition, 1975; (with others) *The Complete All-Time Baseball Register*, 1976; (with Johnson) *The All Sports World Record Book*, 1976; (with Cohen and Johnson) *The World Series*, text by Deutsch, Dial, 1976, revised edition, 1979; (with others) *The World Book of Odds*, 1978.

All published by Bobbs-Merrill: (With Deutsch, Cohen, and Johnson) *The Scrapbook History of Baseball*, 1975; (with Deutsch, Cohen, and Johnson) *The Scrapbook History of Pro Football*, 1976, revised edition, 1977; (with Cohen and Deutsch) *The Ohio State Football Scrapbook*, 1977; (with Cohen and Deutsch) *The Notre Dame Football Scrapbook*, 1977; (with Cohen and Deutsch) *The University of Michigan Football Scrapbook*, 1978. Contributor to *Geographical Review, Journal of Conflict Resolution, Professional Geographer*, and *Journal of Regional Science*.

SIDELIGHTS: David Neft developed the *Sports Illustrated* sports games: "Pro Football," "College Football," "Major League Baseball," "Handicap Golf," and "Decathlon." *Avocational interests:* Politics, contract bridge.

* * *

NEIGOFF, Anne

PERSONAL: Born in Chicago, Ill.; daughter of Joseph and Ester (Lichtenstein) Neigoff. *Education:* Attended Northwestern University. *Home:* 6547 North Kedzie Ave., Chicago, Ill. 60645. *Office:* Encyclopaedia Britannica Educational Corp., 425 North Michigan, Chicago, Ill. 60611.

CAREER: Children's Activities (magazine), Chicago, Ill., editor, 1956-57; Standard Educational Corp., Chicago, managing editor of *The Child's World,* 1957-70; currently project director, Encyclopaedia Britannica Educational Corp., Chicago. *Member:* Women's National Book Association (president of Chicago chapter, 1964-65), Children's Reading Round Table (president, 1960-61), Chicago Book Clinic, Chicago Press Club.

WRITINGS—All juveniles; published by Albert Whitman: *Dinner's Ready,* 1971; *A Cap for Jack, A Coat for Jill,* 1972; *New House, New Town,* 1973; *The Energy Workers,* 1975.

Published by Encyclopaedia Britannica Educational Corp.: *Where Plants Live,* 1972; *How Plants Grow,* 1972; *Plants and Their Seeds,* 1972; *Plants We Need,* 1972; *Who Works,* 1974; *Where People Work,* 1974; *When People Work,* 1974; *Why People Work,* 1974; *Work You Can Do,* 1974; *Why We Measure,* 1976; *How We Measure Distance,* 1976; *How We Measure Area,* 1976; *How We Measure Volume,* 1976; *How We Measure Mass and Weight,* 1976; *Dinosaurs,* 1977; *Animals of the Ice Age,* 1977; *Monsters and Myths,* 1977; *Sharks,* 1977; *Strange Animals of Today,* 1977.

* * *

NEIMARK, Edith D(eborah) 1928-

PERSONAL: Born May 24, 1928, in Long Branch, N.J.; daughter of Solomon J. and Regina (Stein) Neimark. *Education:* Skidmore College, B.A. (with honors), 1949; Indiana University, M.A., 1952, Ph.D., 1953. *Office:* Department of Psychology, Douglass College, Rutgers University, New Brunswick, N.J. 08903.

CAREER: Grafton State Hospital, Grafton, Mass., attendant, summer, 1949; Tulane University, New Orleans, La.; instructor in psychology, 1953-55; Goucher College, Towson, Md., assistant professor of psychology, 1955-56; Air Force Personnel and Training Research Center, Lackland Air Force Base, Tex., research psychologist, 1956-58; Rutgers University, Douglass College, New Brunswick, N.J., associate professor, 1964, professor of psychology, 1965—, chairman of department, 1966-71. *Member:* American Psychological Association, Psychonomic Society, Society for Research in Child Development, American Association for the Advancement of Science, American Association of University Professors, Midwestern Psychological Association, Eastern Psychological Association, Sigma Xi.

WRITINGS: (With W. K. Estes) *Stimulus Sampling Theory,* Holden-day, 1967; (contributor) F. D. Horowitz, editor, *Reviews of Child Development Research,* Volume IV, University of Chicago Press, 1975. Contributor of nearly fifty articles and reviews to psychology journals. Member of editorial board, *Child Development* and *Monographs of Society for Research in Child Development.*

NELKIN, Dorothy 1933-

PERSONAL: Born July 30, 1933, in Boston, Mass.; daughter of Henry and Helen (Fine) Wolfers; married Mark Nelkin (a physicist and professor at Cornell University), August 31, 1952; children: Lisa, Laurie. *Education:* Cornell University, B.A., 1954. *Office:* Science, Technology, and Society Program, Cornell University, Ithaca, N.Y. 14850.

CAREER: Cornell University, Ithaca, N.Y., director of migrant labor project, 1966-69, senior research associate in science, technology, and society program, 1969—, member of graduate faculty in public policy, 1971—.

WRITINGS: On the Season: Aspects of the Migrant Labor System, New York State School of Industrial and Labor Relations Press, 1970; (with William H. Friedland) *Migrant: Farm Workers in America's Northwest,* Holt, 1971; *Nuclear Power and Its Critics: The Cayuga Lake Controversy,* Cornell University Press, 1971; *The Politics of Housing Innovation: The Fate of the Civilian Industrial Technology Program,* Cornell University Press, 1971; *The University and Military Research: Moral Politics at M.I.T.,* Cornell University Press, 1972; *Methadone Maintenance: A Technological Fix,* Braziller, 1973; *Science Textbook Controversies,* M.I.T. Press, 1977; *Technological Decisions and Democracy,* Sage Publications, 1977.

AVOCATIONAL INTERESTS: Playing cello, tennis.

* * *

NELLI, Humbert S(teven) 1930-

PERSONAL: Born January 12, 1930, in Chicago, Ill.; son of Humbert Orazio (a professor of insurance) and Florence (Purcelli) Nelli; married Elizabeth Thomson, December 28, 1961; children: Steven, Christopher, William. *Education:* University of Georgia, B.C.S., 1951; Columbia University, M.A., 1956; University of Chicago, Ph.D., 1965. *Home:* 127 Westgate Dr., Lexington, Ky. 40504. *Office:* Department of History, University of Kentucky, Lexington, Ky. 40506.

CAREER: Karlsfeld Ordnance Depot, Munich, Germany, civilian chief of management branch, 1953-55; Fordham University, Bronx, N.Y., assistant professor of history, 1965-67; University of Kentucky, Lexington, 1967—, began as associate professor, currently professor of history. *Military service:* U.S. Army, 1951-53. *Member:* American Historical Association, Organization of American Historians, American Italian Historical Society (member of executive board), American Academy of Political and Social Sciences, Urban History Group, Immigration History Group, Phi Alpha Theta. *Awards, honors:* American Association for State and Local History award, 1966; University of Kentucky research award, 1972; National Endowment for the Humanities research grant, 1972-73.

WRITINGS: The Italians in Chicago, 1880-1930: A Study in Ethnic Mobility, Oxford University Press, 1970; (contributor) Raymond Mohl and Neil Betten, editors, *Urban America in Historical Perspective,* Weybright, 1970; (contributor) Kenneth Jackson and Stanley Schultz, editors, *Cities in American History,* Knopf, 1972; (contributor) Mohl and James Richardson, editors, *The Urban Experience: Themes in American History,* Wadsworth, 1972; (contributor) Francesco Cordasco, editor, *Studies in Italian-American Social History: Essays in Honor of Leonard Covello,* Rowman & Littlefield, 1975; *The Business of Crime: Italians and Syndicate Crime in the United States,* Oxford University Press, 1976; (editor) *The United States and Italy: The First Two Hundred Years,* American Italian Historical

Association, 1977. Contributor to history journals, *Mercurio, American Journal of Sociology,* and *Chicago Tribune.*

WORK IN PROGRESS: A book examining the Italian experience in the United States.

* * *

NELSON, Jan Alan 1935-

PERSONAL: Born March 25, 1935, in Pensacola, Fla.; son of Alan Clair (an engineer) and Janet (Lusk) Nelson; married Carol Burke, June 15, 1961; children: Erik Manly, Christian Peter. *Education:* Attended Pensacola Junior College, 1956-58; University of the South, B.A. (summa cum laude), 1960; University of North Carolina at Chapel Hill, M.A., 1962, Ph.D., 1964. *Politics:* Independent. *Religion:* Roman Catholic. *Office:* Department of Romance Languages, University of Alabama, University, Ala. 35486.

CAREER: University of Alabama, University, associate professor of Romance philology, 1967—. *Military service:* U.S. Army, 1953-56. *Member:* Societe Rencesvals, South Atlantic Modern Language Association.

WRITINGS: (Editor) Chretien de Troyes, *Yvain ou le Chevalier au Lion,* Appleton, 1968; (editor with Emmanuel J. Mickel) *Le Cycle de la Crosade,* Volume I: *La Naissance du Chevalier au Cygne,* University of Alabama Press, 1977.

WORK IN PROGRESS: Editing *Le Cycle de la Crosade,* Volume II: *Le Chevalier au Cygne.*

SIDELIGHTS: Jan Alan Nelson's major interests are in Old French, Old Provencal, Old Spanish, and Old Portuguese, particularly medieval literature and medieval techniques in the art of falconry.

* * *

NELSON, Ruth 1914-
(Ruth Nelson McHugh)

PERSONAL: Born July 24, 1914, in St. Louis, Mo.; daughter of Charles Oscar (a manufacturer) and Anne (Brough) Nelson; married Othon Quinche, June 12, 1946 (died, 1964); married Francis Dodd McHugh (an architect), April 16, 1966. *Education:* Northwestern University, B.M., 1935, M.M., 1940; New York University, graduate study, 1963; Columbia University, M.A., 1963, graduate study, 1964. *Home:* 7 Beverly Rd., Douglaston, N.Y. 11363. *Office:* Department of English, Five Towns College, 2350 Merrick Ave., Merrick, N.Y. 11566.

CAREER: Worked as a teacher in St. Louis, Mo. and Woodmere, N.Y., 1935-57; G. Hewlett High School, Hewlett, N.Y., humanities coordinator and teacher of English and creative writing, 1957-74; Five Towns College, Merrick, N.Y., teacher of English, 1974—.

WRITINGS: Enjoying English, Book 11, revised edition (Nelson not associated with previous editions), 1964; (editor with others) *New Dimensions in American Literature,* Books II and IV, McCormick-Mathers, 1966; (editor with B. P. Jaffe) *New Dimensions in English Literature,* Books III and IV, McCormick-Mathers, 1967. Also author of teachers' guides to *Enjoying English,* Book 12, Singer, 1966, *Life* Education Program, 1968-69 and Metropolitan Museum of Art programs, Macmillan, 1970. Contributor to professional journals.

SIDELIGHTS: Ruth Nelson told *CA:* "It's always worth it [to watch] a kid learn to pick up a pen [and] let go [his] thoughts—mining words into messages. [It is] genesis on constant rerun."

NESBIN, Esther W(inter) 1910-

PERSONAL: Born August 5, 1910, in Denver, Colo.; daughter of Oscar A. (an accountant) and Helen (Schmandt) Winter; married Anthony T. Nesbin, September 21, 1946 (died September, 1957). *Education:* University of Buffalo (now State University of New York at Buffalo), B.A., 1931, Library Science Certificate, 1932. *Politics:* Non-partisan. *Religion:* Christian. *Home address:* P.O. Box 102, San Marcos, Calif. 92069.

CAREER: Grosvenor Library, Buffalo, N.Y., reference assistant, 1931-42; University of Buffalo (now State University of New York at Buffalo), instructor in library science, 1939-42; Temple of the Jewelled Cross, Los Angeles, Calif., librarian, 1942-46; Palomar College, San Marcos, Calif., instructor in library techniques, 1947-77, librarian, 1947-65, director of library services, 1965-68, assistant dean of instruction for library services, 1969-77.

WRITINGS: Shaker Literature in the Grosvenor Library, Grosvenor Library, 1940, revised edition, edited by Jane VanArsdale, 1968; *Library Technology Study Manual,* privately printed, Volume I: *Library Service,* revised edition, 1972, Volume II: *Introduction to Library Resources and Careers,* revised edition, 1972, Volume III: *Support for Public Services,* revised edition, 1969, Volume IV: *Advanced Library Practice,* revised edition, 1973.

WORK IN PROGRESS: Editing *Symbolism through the Ages of Time* by Henrietta E. Schmandt.

AVOCATIONAL INTERESTS: Cactus and succulent garden, collecting wildflowers, collecting old children's books, flower arrangement.

* * *

NESBITT, George L(yman) 1903-

PERSONAL: Born August 31, 1903, in Davenport, Township, N.Y.; son of James Robert (a farmer) and Nella (Snyder) Nesbitt; married Helen Weld, June 17, 1939; children: Frances Elizabeth (Mrs. John W. Oppel), Margery Weld (Mrs. Peter D. Kingsley). *Education:* Hamilton College, A.B., 1924; Columbia University, A.M., 1927, Ph.D., 1934. *Politics:* Democrat. *Home:* Martin Rd., Clinton, N.Y. 13323. *Office:* Department of English, Hamilton College, Clinton, N.Y. 13323.

CAREER: Hamilton College, Clinton, N.Y., instructor in English, 1924-26; University of Delaware, Newark, instructor in English, 1927-28; Hamilton College, associate professor, 1930-41, professor of English, 1941-58, Hamilton B. Tompkins Professor of English Literature, 1958-73, professor emeritus, 1973—, head of department, 1952-68. *Member:* American Association of University Professors, Emerson Literary Society, Phi Beta Kappa.

WRITINGS: Benthamite Reviewing, Columbia University Press, 1934; *Wordsworth: The Biographical Background of His Poetry,* Pegasus, 1970.

SIDELIGHTS: Since 1961, George Nesbitt has spent two summers in England, and traveled in Italy, France, and Switzerland.

* * *

NEUBECK, Gerhard 1918-

PERSONAL: Born February 28, 1918, in Dortmund, Germany; naturalized U.S. citizen; married Ruth Hess, January 18, 1940; children: Ralph, Eva, Peter. *Education:* New York University, B.S., 1943; Northwestern University, M.A.,

1946; Columbia University, Ed.D., 1953. *Office:* Department of Family Social Science, 290 McNeal Hall, University of Minnesota, St. Paul, Minn. 55108.

CAREER: University of Minnesota, Minneapolis-St. Paul, senior personnel worker, Student Counseling Bureau, 1948-59, associate professor of family studies, 1959-66, professor, 1966-72, professor of family social science, 1972—, director, post-doctoral program for National Institute of Mental Health, 1964-69. Fulbright lecturer, Royal Graduate Teachers College (Copenhagen), 1960-61; maintains private practice in marriage counseling. *Member:* American Psychological Association, American Association of Marriage and Family Counselors (fellow; president, 1968-69), National Council on Family Relations (past chairman; president, 1977-78), American Association of Sex Educators and Counselors, Society for the Scientific Study of Sex, Minnesota Psychological Association, Minnesota Council on Family Relations.

WRITINGS: (Contributor) Hirsch L. Silverman, editor, *Marital Counseling: Psychology, Ideology, Science,* C. C Thomas, 1967; (contributor) Herbert Otto and John Mann, editors, *Ways of Growth,* Grossman, 1968; (editor) *Extra-Marital Relations,* Prentice-Hall, 1969; (contributor) James P. Semmens and Kermit E. Krantz, editors, *The Adolescent Experience,* Macmillan, 1970; (contributor) Otto, editor, *The Family in Search of a Future,* Appleton, 1970. Contributor of about fifteen articles and reviews to sociology and psychology journals.

* * *

NEUFFER, Claude Henry 1911-

PERSONAL: Surname pronounced "Knifer"; born November 2, 1911, in Abbeville, S.C.; son of Gottlob Augustus (a physician) and Florence (Henry) Neuffer; married Irene La Borde (a teacher and writer), March 1, 1953; children: Rene La Borde, Francis Henry, Pierre La Borde. *Education:* Clemson College (now University), B.S., 1933; University of South Carolina, M.A., 1937. *Religion:* Episcopalian. *Home:* 4532 Meadowood Rd., Columbia, S.C. 29206. *Office:* Department of English, University of South Carolina, Columbia, S.C. 29208.

CAREER: Georgia Military College, Milledgeville, professor of English, 1939-42; Presbyterian Junior College, Clinton, S.C., professor of English, 1946-47; University of South Carolina, Columbia, assistant professor, 1947-58, associate professor, 1958-73, professor of English, 1973—. *Military service:* U.S. Army Air Forces, 1942-46; served in China, Burma, and India; became sergeant. *Member:* American Dialect Society, American Name Society, South Caroliniana Society (president, 1969-72).

WRITINGS: The Christopher Happoldt Journal, Charleston Museum, 1960; (with wife, Irene La Borde Neuffer) *The Name Game: From Oyster Point to Keowee,* Sandlapper Press, 1972; (author of biographical sketch with Rene La Borde) J. Gordon Coogler, *Purely Original Verse,* Vogue Press, 1974. Editor, *Names in South Carolina* (annual place-name journal), 1954—, Volumes I-XII published as *Names in South Carolina, 1955-65,* C. H. Neuffer, 1967, Volumes XII-XXIV published as *Names in South Carolina, 1966-77,* C. H. Neuffer, 1976. Contributor of articles on place names and folklore to *Georgia Review, Names, Southern Folklore Journal, Sandlapper, American Speech,* and other periodicals.

SIDELIGHTS: Claude Neuffer told *CA,* "My interest in legends and origins of place names in South Carolina is a rare combination of vocation and avocation—pursued by correspondence and by travel throughout the state, in meetings with scholars or people on the land, from Stump House Mountain to Whooping Island." Neuffer co-founded *Names in South Carolina,* the first state place-name journal in the United States.

* * *

NEULINGER, John 1924-

PERSONAL: Born April 26, 1924, in Germany; son of Rudolf (a businessman) and Julie (Konirsch) Neulinger; children: Ronald. *Education:* Hunter College (now Hunter College of the City University of New York), B.A. (summa cum laude), 1960; New York University, Ph.D., 1965. *Home:* 68 West 68th St., New York, N.Y. 10023. *Office:* Department of Psychology, City College of the City University of New York, New York, N.Y. 10031.

CAREER: Russell Sage Foundation, New York City, research associate, 1964-65; New York University, New York City, research assistant professor of psychology, 1965-67; City College of the City University of New York, New York City, associate professor, 1967-78, professor of psychology, 1978—. *Member:* American Psychological Association, Gerontological Society, Phi Beta Kappa.

WRITINGS: (With O. G. Brim, Jr. and D. C. Glass) *Experiences and Attitudes of American Adults Concerning Standardized Intelligence Tests,* Russell Sage, 1965; (contributor) M. M. Katz, J. O. Cole, and W. E. Barton, editors, *The Role and Methodology of Classification in Psychiatry and Psychopathology,* U.S. Government Printing Office, 1967; (with Brim, Glass, and Ira J. Firestone) *American Attitudes Toward Intelligence,* Russell Sage, 1969; *The Psychology of Leisure,* C. C Thomas, 1974. Contributor to *Personnel and Guidance Journal, Journal of Leisure Research, Perceptual and Motor Skills, Pacific Sociological Review,* and other journals.

WORK IN PROGRESS: Research on social and psychological problems of leisure; *To Leisure: An Introduction,* for Allen & Bacon, completion expected in 1980.

* * *

NEUMEYER, Alfred 1900(?)-1973

1900(?)—January 21, 1973; American art historian and scholar. Obituaries: *New York Times,* January 25, 1973.

* * *

NEVINS, Francis M(ichael), Jr. 1943-

PERSONAL: Born January 6, 1943, in Bayonne, N.J.; son of Francis Michael and Rosemary (Konzelmann) Nevins; married Muriel Walter, June 6, 1966 (divorced, 1978). *Education:* St. Peter's College, A.B. (magna cum laude), 1964; New York University, J.D. (cum laude), 1967. *Home:* 4466 West Pine Blvd., Apt. 23-C, St. Louis, Mo. 63108. *Agent:* Oliver G. Swan, 280 Madison Ave., New York, N.Y. 10016. *Office:* School of Law, St. Louis University, 3642 Lindell Blvd., St. Louis, Mo. 63108.

CAREER: Admitted to the Bar of New Jersey, 1967; Clark Boardman, Ltd., New York, N.Y., assistant to editor in chief, 1967; St. Peter's College, Jersey City, N.J., adjunct instructor in government, 1967; Middlesex County Legal Services Corp., New Brunswick, N.J., staff attorney, 1970-71; St. Louis University, School of Law, St. Louis, Mo., assistant professor, 1971-75, associate professor, 1975-78, professor of law, 1978—. Advisor to the estate of mystery author, Cornell Woolrich. *Military service:* U.S. Army Reserve, 1968-70; became captain. *Member:* Association of American Law Schools (vice-chairperson of Law and the Arts section and Legal Research and Writing section, 1977), American Civil Liberties Union, Mystery Writers of America, Missouri Bar Commission on Citizenship Education. *Awards, honors:* Edgar Allen Poe Award, Mystery Writers of America, 1975, for *Royal Bloodlines: Ellery Queen, Author and Detective.*

WRITINGS: (Editor) *The Mystery Writer's Art,* Bowling Green University Popular Press, 1970; (editor) Cornell Woolrich, *Nightwebs,* Harper, 1971, revised edition, Avon, 1974; (with Chris Steinbrunner, Charles Shibuk, Marvin Lachman, and Otto Penzler) *Detectionary,* Hammermill Paper Co., 1971, revised edition, Overlook Press, 1977; (co-editor) *Multiplying Villianies: Selected Mystery Criticism of Anthony Boucher,* privately printed, 1973; *Royal Bloodlines: Ellery Queen, Author and Detective,* Bowling Green University Popular Press, 1974; *Publish and Perish* (novel), Putnam, 1975; *Corrupt and Ensnare* (novel), Putnam, 1978. Contributor to *New Republic, Journal of Popular Culture, Armchair Detective, Ellery Queen's Mystery Magazine, Alfred Hitchcock's Mystery Magazine, St. Louis Globe-Democrat,* and other periodicals. Member of editorial board, University of California, San Diego, "Mystery Library" series.

SIDELIGHTS: Francis Nevins told *CA:* "I was hooked on mystery fiction at the age of thirteen, after discovering Sherlock Holmes, Charlie Chan and Perry Mason. Before the end of my first year of high school I was reading and collecting mysteries at a fiendish pace: Ellery Queen, Cornell Woolrich and countless others whom I devoured furiously. It was only after about fifteen years of reading and three or four years of writing occasional reviews and articles about the genre and its practitioners that I took the plunge and tried to write a mystery myself. The eventual discovery that I could sell almost any story I wrote is a shock from which I still haven't recovered.

"I had become a law professor in those fifteen years, so it was natural to bestow the same vocation on my first series character, Loren Mensing. After putting him into several short stories I gave Loren a book-length case, *Publish and Perish,* which I hoped would be a good old-fashioned detective novel, full of legal gimmicks and counterplots and subtly planted clues and deductions, and with a detective who had rather progressive social and political ideas and an explicit sexual relationship with a woman and who had to take another person's life in a crisis. More recently I've been doing a series about Milo Turner, who is a more suitable hero for the cool and uncommitted Seventies: a con man. But my new novel, *Corrupt and Ensnare,* brings Loren back to center stage and into another labyrinth of legal gimmicks, counterplots, clues and deductions."

BIOGRAPHICAL/CRITICAL SOURCES: Chris Steinbrunner and Otto Penzler, *Encyclopedia of Mystery and Detection,* McGraw, 1976.

*   *   *

NEWCOMER, James (William) 1912-

PERSONAL: Born March 14, 1912, in Gibsonburg, Ohio; son of Rolland Truben (a pharmacist) and Mabel (Ervin) Newcomer; married Ruth Salisbury (a college science teacher), 1946; children: Jane Elisabeth, Robert Ervin, Mary Rolland. *Education:* Kenyon College, B.Phil. (magna cum laude), 1933; University of Michigan, M.A., 1938; Univer-

sity of Iowa, Ph.D., 1952. *Religion:* Episcopal. *Home:* 1100 Elizabeth Blvd., Fort Worth, Tex. 76110. *Office:* Texas Christian University Press, Fort Worth, Tex. 76129.

CAREER: Teacher in public schools, 1934-37; Elgin Academy and Junior College, Elgin, Ill., chairman of English department, 1937-42, assistant headmaster, 1938-42; Hockaday Junior College, Dallas, Tex., chairman of English department, 1946-51, dean of college, 1947-51; Olivet College, Olivet, Mich., professor of English, 1952-60, dean of college, 1952-60; Texas Woman's University, Denton, dean of faculty and dean of graduate studies, 1960-65; Texas Christian University, Fort Worth, vice-chancellor for academic affairs, 1965-72, vice-chancellor emeritus, 1972—, Trustees' Professor of English, 1972—, director of Texas Christian University Press, 1972—. Member of Scott Theatre Board; member of board of directors, Fort Worth Arts Council. *Military service:* U.S. Army, 1942-46; served in European theater; became second lieutenant.

MEMBER: Modern Language Association of America, College English Association (past president of Michigan chapter), National Council of Teachers of English, American Conference of Academic Deans, Council of Graduate Schools in the United States, American Committee for Irish Studies, Phi Beta Kappa.

WRITINGS: (Contributor) D. Louise Sharp, editor, *Why Teach?,* Holt, 1957; (with Earl J. McGarth and Kevin Bonnell) *Liberal Education and Pharmacy,* Teachers College, Columbia University, 1960; *Maria Edgeworth the Novelist,* Texas Christian University Press, 1967; *Maria Edgeworth,* Bucknell University Press, 1973. Anthologized in *A Part of Space: Ten Texas Writers,* edited by Betsy Feagan Colquitt, Texas Christian University Press, 1969. Contributor to *Eire-Ireland, Cimarron Review, Descant, Re: Arts and Letters, Criticism, College English, Studies in Short Fiction,* and to education journals. Member of editorial board, *College English,* 1963-65.

WORK IN PROGRESS: Two books, *Lady Morgan the Novelist* and a history of Luxembourg.

AVOCATIONAL INTERESTS: Chamber music.

*   *   *

NEWELL, Kenneth B(ernard) 1930-

PERSONAL: Born April 18, 1930, in Cohoes, N.Y.; son of John Kermit (a dealer in waste material) and Helen (Feinglas) Newell; married Rosalie Skolnik, July 8, 1968. *Education:* Lowell Technological Institute (now University of Lowell), B.S., 1951; Columbia University, A.M., 1953; University of Pennsylvania, Ph.D., 1964. *Office:* Department of English, Christopher Newport College, Newport News, Va. 23606.

CAREER: U.S. Navy Clothing Supply Office, Brooklyn, N.Y., textile technologist, 1952-53; Drexel Institute of Technology (now Drexel University), Evening College, Philadelphia, Pa., adjunct instructor in English, 1961-62; University of Kansas, Lawrence, assistant professor of English, 1962-66; University of California, Los Angeles, assistant professor of English, 1966-71; Virginia Commonwealth University, Richmond, associate professor of English, 1971-76; Christopher Newport College, Newport News, Va., associate professor of English, 1977—. *Military service:* U.S. Navy, 1953-56; became lieutenant. *Member:* Modern Language Association of America, American Association of University Professors.

WRITINGS: Structure in Four Novels by H. G. Wells,

Mouton, 1968; *Pattern Poetry: A Historical Critique from the Alexandrian Greeks to Dylan Thomas*, Marlborough, 1976. Contributor to literature journals, including *English Literature in Transition, PMLA, Studies in the Novel, Keats-Shelley Journal, Explicator, Journal of Modern Literature, Eire-Ireland, Extrapolation*, and *Improving College and University Teaching*.

WORK IN PROGRESS: A book on the fiction of George Moore, 1901-1906; a book on *Lord Jim* and its manuscript texts.

* * *

NEWHALL, Richard A.   1888-1973

June 12, 1888—June 18, 1973; American emeritus professor, writer, and authority on medieval English military history. Obituaries: *New York Times*, June 20, 1973.

* * *

NEWTON, Earle Williams   1917-

PERSONAL: Born April 10, 1917, in Cortland, N.Y.; son of Earle Williams (a manufacturer) and Anna (Moore) Newton; married Josephine Lyon, June 20, 1938; children: Earle W. III, Antoinette Lyon. *Education:* Amherst College, A.B. (magna cum laude), 1938; Columbia University, A.M., 1939, Ph.D., 1974. *Residence:* Brookfield, Vt. 05036.

CAREER: Vermont Historical Society, Montpelier, director, 1941-50; Old Sturbridge Village, Sturbridge, Mass., director, 1950-54; Bureau of Museums and Historic Sites of the State of Pennsylvania, Harrisburg, director, 1956-59; St. Augustine Historic Preservation Board, St. Augustine, Fla., director, 1960-68; Pensacola Historic Preservation Board, Pensacola, Fla., director, 1968-72; president, College of the Americas, 1972—; Richmondtown Restoration, Staten Island, N.Y., director, 1976-78. President, Pensacola Symphony Orchestra, 1970-71. *Member:* American Association for State and Local History (secretary-treasurer, 1947-53). *Awards, honors:* Awards of merit from American Institute of Graphic Arts, 1950, 1951, 1952; awards from American Association for State and Local History, 1950; Fulbright fellow at University of London, 1955-56; decorated commander of Order of Isabela la Catolica by Spanish government, 1965; decorated commander of Order of Merit by Spanish government, 1968; Mellon Foundation fellow, American Council on Education-Institute of College Presidents, 1972—.

WRITINGS: Before Pearl Harbor, Webster Publishing, 1942; (editor) *History of Vermont*, five volumes, Vermont Historical Society, 1947-50; *The Vermont Story: 1749-1949*, Vermont Historical Society, 1949; (editor with Ernest Dibble) *In Search of Gulf Coast History*, Pensacola Historic Preservation Board, 1970; (editor with Dibble) *Spain and Her Rivals on the Gulf Coast*, Pensacola Historic Preservation Board, 1971. Editor, *Vermont Quarterly*, 1944-50, and *Vermont Life*, 1946-50; editor and founder, *American Heritage*, 1949-54; member of editorial board, *Art in America*, 1953-55.

WORK IN PROGRESS: 1492: Watershed of History; a manual of historical administration; research on higher education.

* * *

NEWTON, Suzanne   1936-

PERSONAL: Born October 8, 1936, in Bunnlevel, N.C.; daughter of Hannis T. and Billie (O'Quinn) Latham; married Carl R. Newton (a civil servant), June 9, 1957; children: Michele, Erin, Heather, Craig. *Education:* Duke University, A.B., 1957. *Home:* 1211 Ashburton Rd., Raleigh, N.C. 27606.

MEMBER: North Carolina Writer's Conference, Authors Guild. *Awards, honors:* American Association of University Women (North Carolina chapter) Award for juvenile literature, 1971, for *Purro and the Prattleberries*, 1974, for *Care of Arnold's Corners*.

WRITINGS—All juveniles; all published by Westminster: *Purro and the Prattleberries*, 1971; *Care of Arnold's Corners* (Junior Literary Guild selection), 1974; *What Are You Up To, William Thomas?* (Junior Literary Guild selection), 1977; *Reubella and the Old Focus Home*, 1978. Contributor of short stories, poems, and articles to *Home Life, Parents' Magazine, Human Voice Quarterly, Southern Poetry Review*, and *Long View Journal*.

WORK IN PROGRESS: Short stories and a book.

SIDELIGHTS: Suzanne Newton told *CA:* "Writing is a part of me, but so is the business of enabling people to 'become.' I am involved in the Poetry-in-the-Schools project in North Carolina, in which poets and writers go into public school classrooms for a week at a time to help young people find the poetry that is inside them. It has been an exciting experience to see children find freedom in word creations of their own.

"As for my own writing, . . . I have a tendency to create 'heroic' characters—that is, people who risk, who dare against great odds, who are more visionary than anyone in their circumstances has a right to be, who stand up against the opposition and say all the smart things—although their knees knock—that I used to lie in bed at night and wish I had said. . . . An interesting thing has happened, though. The characters have become my models. As a result of creating them, I have come out of my shy, fearful self and have begun to risk and dare along with them! What I hope is that perhaps they may have that same effect upon some of my young readers."

* * *

NEY, James W(alter)   1932-

PERSONAL: Born July 28, 1932, in Nakuru, Kenya; son of Reginald Osborne (a realtor) and Elizabeth Grace (Aikens) Ney; married Joan Marie Allen, June 12, 1954; children: Cheryl Lynn, James Allan-Colby, Peter Cameron. *Education:* Wheaton College, Wheaton, Ill., A.B., 1955, A.M., 1957; University of Michigan, Ed.D., 1963. *Office:* Department of English, Arizona State University, Tempe, Ariz. 85281.

CAREER: Michigan State University, East Lansing, assistant professor of English, 1964-69; Arizona State University, Tempe, associate professor of English, 1969—. Visiting professor at University of Montreal, summer, 1962, University of Ryukyus, 1962-64, George Peabody College for Teachers, 1965, and University of Hawaii, 1967. Dialect geographer, Detroit Dialect Survey, 1966. *Member:* Modern Language Association of America, American Linguistic Society, National Council of Teachers of English, College English Association, Teachers of English to Speakers of Other Languages, Canadian Linguistic Society.

WRITINGS: (Editor with Shigeo Imamura) *Readings on American Society*, Blaisdell, 1969; (editor) *Readings on the Philosophy of Science*, Blaisdell, 1969; (editor) *Readings from Samuel Clemens*, Blaisdell, 1969; (contributor) Gary

Tate and Edward P. J. Corbett, editors, *Teaching High School Composition*, Oxford University Press, 1970; (with John Hand, Wayne Harsh, and Harold Shane) *Adventures in English: Experiences in Language*, Laidlaw Brothers, 1972; (with Hand, Harsh, and Shane) *Progress in English: Experience in Language*, Laidlaw Brothers, 1972; (with Hand, Harsh, and Shane) *Discovery in English: Experiences in Language*, Laidlaw Brothers, 1972; (with Hand, Harsh, and Shane) *Exploring in English: Experiences in Language*, Laidlaw Brothers, 1972; (with Hand, Harsh, and Bernarr Folta) *Growth in English: Experiences in Language*, Laidlaw Brothers, 1972; (with Hand, Harsh, and Folta) *Power in English: Experiences in Language*, Laidlaw Brothers, 1972; (contributor) James E. Alatis, editor, *Studies in Honor of Albert H. Marckwardt*, Teachers of English for Speakers of Other Languages, 1972; (with Masayuki Akiyama and Motohiro Fukushima) *American English for Japanese Students*, Nan'Undo, 1973; *Linguistics, Language Speaking and Composition in the Grades*, Mouton, 1975; *American Life in English Conversation*, Nan'Undo, 1975; (with Harsh and others) *English for Internal Communication*, American Book Co., 1978. Also author of "Good English" series, seven volumes, Laidlaw Brothers, 1979. Contributor of about sixty articles and reviews to language journals.

WORK IN PROGRESS: Papers on linguistic analysis; sentence combining for young students.

AVOCATIONAL INTERESTS: Travel (has lived or traveled in Japan, Taiwan, Philippines, Great Britain, Canada, Tahiti, Fiji, and Australia), Christian theology, and music appreciation.

* * *

NIATUM, Duane 1938-
(Duane McGinnis)

PERSONAL: Born February 13, 1938, in Seattle, Wash. *Education:* University of Washington, Seattle, B.A., 1970; Johns Hopkins University, M.A., 1972. *Home:* 2919 First Ave., Seattle, Wash. 98121.

CAREER: Poet. Johns Hopkins University, Baltimore, Md., instructor in American and European literature writing seminars, 1971-72; editor, Native American Authors Program, Harper & Row Publishers, Inc., 1973-74; free-lance editor, 1974—; Immaculate High School, Seattle, Wash., English and literature teacher, 1974-75; Seattle Arts Commission, Seattle, worked with elderly in artist-in-the-city program, 1977-78. Has worked as an assistant librarian for over three years in libraries at University of Washington, Seattle and New York Historical Society. Since 1969 has given more than 45 poetry readings at poetry and art festivals and educational institutions, including Portland Poetry Festival, Anacortes Arts Festival, Portland State University, Phoenix Indian High School, University of California, Berkeley, Library of Congress, and University of South Dakota; member of poet-in-schools programs in Arizona, New Mexico, and Oregon. Judged poetry contest for Washington Poets Association, 1975. *Military service:* U.S. Navy, 1955-59. *Awards, honors:* Pacific Northwest Writers Conference, first prize in poetry, 1966, 1970, third prize in poetry, 1968; honorable mention in poetry from *Story: The Yearbook of Discovery*, Scholastic Magazines, Inc., 1968; Mary K. Dearborn Literature Award, Seattle Music and Art Foundation, 1968; Washington Governor's Award, 1971; Carnegie Fund for Authors grant, 1975; P.E.N. Fund for Writers grant, 1976; invited to stay at Millay Colony for the Arts, 1976, and Yaddo, Saratoga Springs, N.Y., 1977.

WRITINGS—Poems, except as indicated: (Under name Duane McGinnis) *After the Death of an Elder Klallam*, Baleen Press, 1970; *A Cycle for the Woman in the Field*, Laughing Man Press, 1973; *Taos Pueblo and Other Poems*, Greenfield Review Press, 1973; *Ascending Red Cedar Moon*, Harper, 1974; (editor) *Carriers of the Dream Wheel: Contemporary Native American Poetry*, Harper, 1975; *Digging Out the Roots*, Harper, 1977; *Turning to the Rhythms of Her Song*, Jawbone Press, 1977; *To Bridge the Dream* (short story chapbook), A Press, 1978.

Poems represented in anthologies, including: *American Indian II*, University of South Dakota Press, 1971; *From the Belly of the Shark*, edited by Walter Lowenfels, Random House, 1973; *Voices from Wah'Kon-Tah: Contemporary Poetry of Native Americans*, International Publishers, 1974; *American Indian Prose and Poetry: We Wait in the Darkness*, edited by Gloria Levitas, Frank Robert, and Jacqueline Vivelo, Putnam, 1974; *The Uses of Poetry*, edited by Agnes Stein, Holt, 1975; *Giant Talk: An Anthology of Third World Writings*, edited by Quincy Troupe and Rainer Schulte, Vintage Books, 1975; *The First Skin around Me: Contemporary American Tribal Poetry*, Territorial Press, 1976; *Good Company: Poets at Michigan*, edited by Jeanne Rockwell, Noon Rock Press, 1977; *The Remembered Earth: Anthology of Contemporary Native American Literature*, edited by Geary Hobson, Red Earth Press, 1978; *Arrangement in Literature*, Scott, Foresman, 1979.

Also author of an experimental verse drama, "Breathless," first produced at University of Washington, Seattle, 1968. Contributor of poetry, short stories, essays, and reviews to periodicals. Guest editor of *Pacific Search*, 1975, *Niagra*, 1976, and *Western Edge*, 1978.

WORK IN PROGRESS: Song for the Harvester of Dreams.

SIDELIGHTS: Duane Niatum mentions painters of the impressionist and post-impressionist schools and music among early influences on his writing. "I studied the painters long before I studied the poets," he writes, "and have found paintings helpful to my poetry. . . .

"I spent two years in Japan, and its culture, especially its arts and philosophies, have had a major influence on the way I approach my work. It seems to me that there are a number of parallels that can be discovered between American Indian philosophies and those of the Orient. . . . I hope that by feeling close to the world of the Orient as well as the world of my Indian and European ancestors, I can deal with the chaos of everyday. That is why people are always in the foreground of my work. And this is related to something that my Indian grandfather and great-uncle taught me as a child, that is, to always humble my soul before the spiritual reality of things as well as man."

Niatum intends to teach for a few years "to see if I can do more than an adequate job." He adds: "I enjoy living with diversity. . . . Men and women, children and old folks, who mirror contrasting values, arts, faces, ways of being and doing, are what make me happy and sad, love and hate, appear and vanish."

* * *

NICHOLS, Irby C(oghill), Jr. 1926-

PERSONAL: Born April 10, 1926, in Baton Rogue, La.; son of Irby C. (a professor of mathematics) and Pauline (an artist; maiden name, Wright) Nichols; married Margaret Irby (an assistant professor of library science), April 18,

1953; children: Nina K., Irby III. *Education:* Louisiana State University, B.A., 1947; University of North Carolina, M.A., 1949; University of Michigan, Ph.D., 1955. *Politics:* Democrat. *Religion:* Episcopalian. *Home:* 2514 Royal Lane, Denton, Tex. 76201. *Office:* Department of History, North Texas State University, Box 6212, North Texas Station, Denton, Tex. 76203.

CAREER: Catawba College, Salisbury, N.C., instructor in modern European history, 1949; New Mexico Military Institute, Roswell, instructor, 1952-54, assistant professor of history, 1954-55; North Texas State University, Denton, assistant professor, 1955-57, associate professor, 1957-67, professor of history, 1967—. Visiting associate professor, Louisiana State University, 1962. Conducted research in British and French national archives, 1950, 1970; conducted radio news commentaries and interviews in Roswell, N.M., 1953-55. Trustee of Selwyn School, 1961-69; Canterbury House, trustee, 1967—, chairman of board of trustees, 1969-72. *Military service:* U.S. Marine Corps, 1944-46.

MEMBER: American Historical Association, American Academy of Arts and Sciences, Center for the Study of Democratic Institutions, Society for French Historical Studies, Southern Historical Association, Southwestern Social Science Association (chairman of history section, 1969-70), Phi Eta Sigma, Kappa Mu Epsilon, Phi Kappa Phi. *Awards, honors:* Louis Knott Koontz Award from Pacific Historical Association, 1968, for article, "Russian Ukase and the Monroe Doctrine"; Houston Shelton Award from North Texas State University, 1976, for excellence in teaching.

WRITINGS: (With Paul Smith, Dwane Kingery, and others) *North Texas State University: A Self-Study,* North Texas State University, 1962; *The European Pentarchy and the Congress of Verona, 1822,* Nijhoff, 1971. Also author of thirty abstracts for *Historical Abstracts,* 1955-56. Contributor to *Encyclopedia of World Biography;* contributor to history and social science journals. Associate editor of *Southwestern Social Science Quarterly,* 1961-64.

WORK IN PROGRESS: The Hanover Conference, 1821.

SIDELIGHTS: Irby C. Nichols comments: "It is difficult for me to understand why so many people question the relevance of history to contemporary problems. Truly, the essence of history is problems, not chronicles, but no system of social dialectics is definitive, because such factors as human courage, faith, and ambition are indefinable and unpredictable. Notwithstanding the influence of materialistic forces, accidents and men's free choice also have produced dynamic results through the continuum of history."

*   *   *

NICHOLS, Jack 1938-

PERSONAL: Born March 16, 1938, in Washington, D.C.; son of John and Mary (Finlayson) Nichols. *Education:* Attended school in Chevy Chase, Md. *Politics and religion:* "Fanatical devotion to the First Amendment." *Office:* Gay, 116 West 14th St., New York, N.Y. 10011.

CAREER: New York Post, Washington, D.C., assistant to bureau chief, 1961; Countrywide Publications, New York City, editor of six magazines: *Companion, Strange Unknown, Duke, Buccaneer, Jaguar,* and *Stud,* 1968-69; Milky Way Productions, New York City, managing editor of *Screw,* 1969-70; Four Swords, Inc., New York City, editor of *Gay,* 1970—. Has conducted campaigns to eradicate venereal disease among homosexuals, and other issues affecting homosexuals.

WRITINGS: (With Lige Clarke) *I Have More Fun with You than Anybody,* St. Martin's, 1972; (compiler with Clarke) *Roommates Can't Always Be Lovers,* St. Martin's, 1974; *Men's Liberation: A New Definition of Masculinity,* Penguin, 1975; *Welcome to Fire Island,* St. Martin's, 1976. Co-author with Clarke of regular column in *Screw.* Contributor of articles to *The Homosexual Citizen.*

WORK IN PROGRESS: Studying writings of Walt Whitman, with a book expected to result.

SIDELIGHTS: Jack Nichols was one of the early gay liberation activists. He was a founding member of the Mattachine Society of Washington in 1961 and received a homosexual deferment from military service. *Avocational interests:* Zen, Vedanta, yoga, "amalgamation of the planet's inhabitants."

BIOGRAPHICAL/CRITICAL SOURCES: Derek Miles, *The Dirtiest Dozen,* Midwood Books, 1971; Angelo D'Arcangelo, *Inside the Sexual Revolution,* Lancer, 1971; Donn Teal, *The Gay Militants,* Stein & Day, 1971; Kay Tobin and Randy Wicker, *The Gay Crusaders,* Paperback Library, 1972; John Francis Hunter, *The Gay Insider U.S.A.,* Stonehill, 1972; George Weinberg, *Society and the Healthy Homosexual,* St. Martin's, 1972.†

*   *   *

NICHOLS, William Thomas 1927-

PERSONAL: Born October 30, 1927, in Lakeland, Fla.; son of Fred Raymond and Burgess Bucknor (Baird) Nichols; married Evelyn Lee Carter, July 5, 1950; children: Victoria, Adele, Thomas, Don, Melody, Michelle. *Education:* University of Virginia, B.A. (with honors), 1951, Ph.D., 1962. *Politics:* Republican. *Religion:* Society of Friends (Quaker). *Home:* Route 2, Pulaski, Pa. 16143. *Office:* Department of Political Science, Westminster College, New Wilmington, Pa. 16142.

CAREER: University of Georgia, Athens, assistant professor of political science, 1962-63; Appalachian State University, Boone, N.C., assistant professor of political science, 1963-67, chairman of department, 1966-67; Converse College, Spartanburg, S.C., 1967-72, began as associate professor, became professor of political science and chairman of department; Westminster College, New Wilmington, Pa., professor of political science and chairman of department, 1972—, director of International Studies Institute, 1972—. Director, Institute on Constitutional Democracy and Totalitarianism, 1965-72. Member of Spartanburg Long Range Planning Committee, 1970-72, and Spartanburg Human Relations Committee, 1972. *Military service:* U.S. Army Air Forces, cryptographer, 1946-47; served in Japan.

MEMBER: International Studies Association, American Society of International Law, American Political Science Association, North American Simulation and Games Association (secretary-treasurer), Southern Political Science Association, South Carolina Political Science Association (secretary-treasurer), Phi Beta Kappa. *Awards, honors:* George Washington Honor Medal award from Freedoms Foundation, 1968, 1969, 1970, 1972; top national award for social studies training institute, 1971.

WRITINGS: Manual of American National Government, Kendall/Hunt, 1964, 6th edition (with H. P. Davis, Jr.), 1975. Contributor to *South Carolina Journal of Politics* and *South Carolina Education Journal.* Editor, *Social Studies Journal,* 1979.

NICHOLSON, C(harles) A. III 1922-

PERSONAL: Born July 2, 1922, in Binghamton, N.Y.; son of Charles A. (a naval officer) and Ruth (Johnson) Nicholson. *Education:* Princeton University, B.A. (magna cum laude), 1948. *Home and office:* 6222 Rex Dr., Dallas, Tex. 75230.

CAREER: McCann-Erickson (advertising agency), Dallas, Tex., account executive, 1956-57; Chance Vought Aircraft, Dallas, Tex., advertising manager, 1957-60; currently freelance writer in audiovisuals, film, and print.

WRITINGS: I Was a Stranger, Sheed, 1972. Author of documentary, public relations, training, and educational films.

*   *   *

NIEBUHR, Reinhold 1892-1971

PERSONAL: Born June 21, 1892, in Wright City, Mo.; son of Gustav (a minister) and Lydia (Hosto) Niebuhr; married Ursula Mary Keppel-Compton (a scholar-theologian), 1931; children: Christopher Robert, Barbara Elisabeth Niebuhr Sifton. *Education:* Attended Elmhurst College, 1910, and Eden Theological Seminary, 1910-13; Yale University, B.D., 1914, M.A., 1915. *Home:* Yale Hill, Stockbridge, Mass. 01262.

CAREER: Ordained to ministry of Evangelical Synod of North America (now part of the United Church of Christ), 1915; Bethel Evangelical Church, Detroit, Mich., pastor, 1915-28; Union Theological Seminary, New York, N.Y., associate professor of the philosophy of religion, 1928-30, William E. Dodge, Jr. Professor of Applied Christianity, 1930-55, Charles A. Briggs Graduate Professor of Ethics and Theology, 1955-60, professor emeritus, 1960-71, vice-president of the seminary, 1955-60. Gifford Lecturer, University of Edinburgh, 1939, also guest lecturer at Oxford, Yale, Harvard, Princeton, and other American and British universities. A founder of Americans for Democratic Action, and co-founder of Fellowship of Socialist Christians. Was a research associate, Institute of War and Peace Studies, Columbia University. *Member:* American Academy of Arts and Letters, Institute of Arts and Letters, and Alpha Sigma Phi. *Awards, honors:* D.D., Eden Theological Seminary, 1930, Grinnell College, 1936, Wesleyan College, 1937, University of Pennsylvania, 1938, Amherst College, 1941, Yale University, 1942, Oxford University, 1943, Harvard University, 1944, Princeton University, 1946, University of Glasgow, 1947, New York University, 1947, Hobart College, 1948, Dartmouth College, 1951, University of Manchester, 1954; LL.D., Occidental College, 1945; Litt.D., New School for Social Research, 1951, Hebrew University, Jerusalem, 1967; S.T.D., Columbia University, 1954; Presidential Medal of Freedom, 1964.

WRITINGS: Does Civilization Need Religion? A Study in the Social Resources and Limitations of Religion in Modern Life, Macmillan, 1927; *Leaves from the Notebook of a Tamed Cynic,* Willet, Clark & Colby, 1929, reprinted, Da Capo Press, 1976; *The Contribution of Religion to Social Work* (Forbes lectures), Columbia University Press, 1932, reprinted, AMS Press, 1971; *Moral Man and Immoral Society: A Study in Ethics and Politics,* Scribner, 1932, reprinted, 1960; *Reflections on the End of an Era,* Scribner, 1934; *An Interpretation of Christian Ethics* (Rauschenbusch Memorial lectures), Harper, 1935, reprinted, with a new preface by the author, Meridian, 1956; (with Sherwood Eddy) *Doom and Dawn,* Eddy & Page, 1936; *Beyond Tragedy: Essays on the Christian Interpretation of History,* Scribner, 1937, reprinted, Arno, 1976; *Do the State and Nation Belong to God or the Devil?* (Burge Memorial lecture), Student Christian Movement Press (London), 1937; *The Protestant Opposition Church Movement in Germany, 1934-1937* (pamphlet), Friends of Europe Publications (London), 1937.

Christianity and Power Politics, Scribner, 1940, reprinted, Archon Books, 1969; *Christian Realism in Contemporary American Theology,* G. E. Stechert, 1940; *Europe's Catastrophe and the Christian Faith,* Nisbet, 1940; *Why the Christian Church Is Not Pacifist,* Student Christian Movement Press (London), 1940; *The Nature and Destiny of Man: A Christian Interpretation* (Gifford lectures), Scribner, Volume I: *Human Nature,* 1941, Volume II: *Human Destiny,* 1943; *Jews after the War* (pamphlet), Inter-University Jewish Federation of Great Britain and Ireland, 1943; *The Children of Light and the Children of Darkness: A Vindication of Democracy and a Critique of Its Traditional Defence,* Scribner, 1944, reprinted, 1972; (editor) *This Ministry: The Contributions of Henry Sloane Coffin,* Scribner, 1945; *Discerning the Signs of the Times: Sermons for Today and Tomorrow,* Scribner, 1946; *Faith and History: A Comparison of Christian and Modern Views of History,* Scribner, 1949; *The Illusion of World Government,* illustrations by Kelly Oechsli, Graphics Group, 1949.

The Irony of American History, Scribner, 1952, reprinted, 1962; *Christian Realism and Political Problems,* Scribner, 1953, reprinted, A. M. Kelley, 1977; (author of commentary) Kenneth E. Boulding, *The Organizational Revolution,* Harper, 1953; *The Self and the Dramas of History,* Scribner, 1955; *Our Moral and Spiritual Resources for International Cooperation: A Work Paper by Reinhold Niebuhr,* with a discussion outline by F. Ernest Johnson, U.S. Government Printing Office, 1956; *Love and Justice: Selections from the Shorter Writings of Reinhold Niebuhr,* edited by D. B. Robertson, Westminster Press, 1957; *Pious and Secular America,* Scribner, 1958 (published in England as *The Godly and the Ungodly: Essays on the Religious and Secular Dimensions of Modern Life,* Faber, 1959), reprinted, A. M. Kelley, 1977; *The World Crisis and American Responsibility: Nine Essays,* edited by Ernest W. Lefever, Association Press, 1958, reprinted, Greenwood Press, 1974; *Essays in Applied Christianity,* edited by Robertson, Meridian, 1959; *The Structure of Nations and Empires: A Study of the Recurring Patterns and Problems of the Political Order in Relation to the Unique Problems of the Nuclear Age,* Scribner, 1959 (published in England as *Nations and Empires: Recurring Patterns in the Political Order,* Faber, 1960), reprinted, A. M. Kelley, 1977.

Reinhold Niebuhr on Politics: His Political Philosophy and Its Application to Our Age as Expressed in His Writings, edited by Harry R. Davis and Robert C. Good, Scribner, 1960; (with Alan Heimert) *A Nation so Conceived: Reflections on the History of America from Its Early Visions to Its Present Power,* Scribner, 1963; (with Bertrand Russell and Richard Stafford Cripps) *Que es, hoy, la democracia?,* Centro de Estudios y Documentacion Sociales, A. C., 1964; *Man's Nature and His Communities: Essays on the Dynamics and Enigmas of Man's Personal and Social Existence,* Scribner, 1965; (author of foreword) *Mississippi Black Paper,* Random House, 1965; *Faith and Politics: A Commentary on Religious, Social, and Political Thought in a Technological Age,* edited by Ronald H. Stone, Braziller, 1968; (with Paul E. Sigmund) *The Democratic Experience: Past and Prospects,* Praeger, 1969; *Reminiscences* (oral history), Microfilming Corp., 1972; *Reinhold Niebuhr, 1892-*

1971 (collection of works), edited by E. J. Tinsley, Epworth Press, 1973; *Justice and Mercy* (sermons and prayers), edited by Ursula M. Niebuhr, Harper, 1974.

Contributor: Henry Pitney Van Dusen, editor, *Ventures in Belief: Christian Convictions for a Day of Uncertainty,* Scribner, 1930; Arthur Lessner Swift, editor, *Religion Today: A Challenging Enigma,* McGraw, 1933; Arno L. Bader, T. Hornberger, S. K. Proctor, and C. Wells, editors, *Prose Patterns,* Harcourt, 1933; John Abbot Clark, editor, *College Book of Essays,* Holt, 1937; Julius Seelye Bixler, editor with others, *The Nature of Religious Experience: Essays in Honor of Douglas Clyde Macintosh,* Harper, 1937; Henry Recay Warfel, Ralph Henry Gabriel, and Stanley Thomas Williams, editors, *The American Mind,* revised edition, American Book Co., 1947; Charles Neider, editor, *Stature of Thomas Mann,* New Directions, 1947; *Modern Education and Human Values* (lectures), Volume II, University of Pittsburgh Press, 1948; Albert Craig Baird, editor, *Representative American Speeches: 1947-1948,* H. W. Wilson, 1949.

Elmer J. F. Arndt, editor, *Heritage of the Reformation,* R. R. Smith, 1950; Asher Norman Christenson and Euron Maurice Kirkpatrick, editors, *People, Politics, and the Politician: An Anthology of American Politics in Action,* revised edition, Holt, 1950; Hans J. Morgenthau, editor, *Germany and the Future of Europe,* University of Chicago Press, 1951; Daniel J. Bronstein and H. M. Schulweis, editors, *Approaches to the Philosophy of Religion,* Prentice-Hall, 1954; William Ebenstein, editor, *Modern Political Thought: The Great Issues,* Rinehart, 1954; *Religion and Freedom of Thought* (lectures), foreword by Henry Pitney Van Dusen, Doubleday, 1954; Whit Burnett, editor, *This Is My Philosophy,* Prentice-Hall, 1954; *Man in Contemporary Society: A Source Book,* Volume II, Columbia University Press, 1956; Edmund Fuller, editor, *Christian Idea of Education,* Yale University Press, 1957; Thomas Edwin Utley and John Stuart Maclure, editors, *Documents of Modern Political Thought,* Cambridge University Press, 1957; Albert Craig Baird, editor, *Representative American Speeches: 1956-1957,* H. W. Wilson, 1957; Joseph Henry Satin, editor, *Ideas in Context,* Houghton, 1958; Harold Peter Simonson, editor, *Cross Currents: A Collection of Essays from Contemporary Magazines,* Harper, 1959; Brand Blanshard, editor, *Education in the Age of Science,* Basic Books, 1959; Adrienne Koch, editor, *Philosophy for a Time of Crisis,* Dutton, 1959; Walter Leibrecht, editor, *Religion and Culture: Essays in Honor of Paul Tillich,* Harper, 1959; Huston Smith, editor, *Search for America,* Prentice-Hall, 1959; Marquis W. Childs and James B. Reston, editors, *Walter Lippmann and His Times,* Harcourt, 1959.

Hiram Haydn and Betsy Saunders, editors, *The American Scholar Reader,* Atheneum, 1960; Harold Karan Jacobson, editor, *American Foreign Policy,* Random House, 1960; Ivo Duchacek, editor, *Conflict and Cooperation among Nations,* Holt, 1960; George Bernard de Huszar, editor, *The Intellectuals: A Controversial Portrait,* Free Press, 1960; Harold E. Fey and Margaret Frakes, editors, *The Christian Century Reader,* Association Press, 1962; David Cooperman and Eugene Victor Walter, editors, *Power and Civilization: Political Thought in the Twentieth Century,* Crowell, 1962; Harry K. Girvetz, editor, *Contemporary Moral Issues,* Wadsworth, 1963; Henry M. Christman, editor, *One Hundred Years of the Nation,* Macmillan, 1965; Staughton Lynd, editor, *Nonviolence in America: A Documentary History,* Bobbs-Merrill, 1966; David L. Larson, editor, *The Puritan Ethic in United States Foreign Policy,* Van Nos-

trand, 1967; Edward Le Roy Long, Jr. and Robert T. Handy, editors, *Theology and Church in Times of Change,* Westminster Press, 1970; L. Finkelstein, editor, *Social Responsibility in an Age of Revolution,* Jewish Theological Seminary, 1971.

Other writings: (Consulting editor) "Christian Faith" series, Gollancz, 1956-71. Contributor of more than 1000 articles to *Atlantic, Harper's, Yale Review, American Scholar, Sewanee Review, Nation, Partisan Review, New Republic, Virginia Quarterly Review, New Leader,* and *Reporter.* Editor of *World Tomorrow, Christianity and Crisis,* and *Christianity and Society* (formerly *Radical Religion*); contributing editor of *Christian Century, Nation* (until 1952), and *New Leader.*

SIDELIGHTS: With a keen intellect, an understanding of opposing viewpoints, and an encyclopedic knowledge, Reinhold Niebuhr became what *Time* magazine called "the greatest Protestant theologian born in America since Jonathan Edwards." His influence in the theological world was extensive, but his life-long attempt at integrating Christian ethics with a practical political philosophy won him an impressive audience among secularists, including George F. Kennan (who described him as "the father of us all"), Arthur Schlesinger, Jr., Dean Acheson, McGeorge Bundy, Hans J. Morgenthau, and James Reston. His philosophy, which at various times of his life had been described as socialist, liberal, and pragmatist in politics, and conservative, neo-orthodox, and realist in theology, reflected his belief in the necessity for a complex explanation of reality.

In attempting to summarize Niebuhr's intellectual approach, Nathan Scott provides a method for understanding Niebuhr's multifaceted personality: "When full human truth is collapsed into some simplistic formula that overstresses either man's uniqueness and dignity or his affinity with the world of nature and his misery, then the consequence, inevitably, is a fatuous irrelevance to the real complexity of things."

In theology, Niebuhr combined the perspectives of Augustine, Luther, and Calvin, and arrived at the traditional Christian view of man as a creature flawed by the effects of original sin. This view brought Niebuhr into conflict with prevailing liberal Protestantism, which he regarded as "utopian." He rejected what he believed to be the two extremes of Protestantism, one that sought total withdrawal from the secular order, and the other which sought total immersion into the affairs of the world through the "social gospel." With his philosophy of "Christian realism" Niebuhr attempted to strike a middle course between the two by constructing a workable political philosophy built on the foundation of a vigorous and consistent Christianity.

His efforts, however, were not confined to theory. For most of his life he was deeply involved in political and moral concerns on a practical level. "His political biography reads like a history of the left in his time," said *Time.* In 1930, he ran unsuccessfully on the Socialist ticket for Congress in New York, and was involved in various pacifist causes until the Nazi occupation of the Rhineland in 1936, when he urged U.S. intervention on behalf of the Allies. Niebuhr viewed the expansionist policies of Hitler as profoundly anti-Christian and a threat to the Western democracies.

In 1902, at the age of ten, Niebuhr decided that he wanted to become a minister, in emulation of his father whom he regarded as "the most interesting man in town." After ordination, in 1915, Niebuhr was sent to a small church in Detroit. It was here that Niebuhr became familiar with modern industrialism which he thought dehumanizing. His Detroit experience (1915-28), Niebuhr considered, was crucial in the formulation of his basic political outlook. Thereafter, he began to identify with various liberal causes, always remaining anti-communist, however, and sharply critical of totalitarianism.

Niebuhr once wrote: "Among the many weaknesses of the Protestant movement, surely its indifference to the social substance of human existence is the most grievous one. In an industrial civilization and in an age of nuclear terror, the renewal of the church must certainly include full awareness of the fact that we are all involved in the virtues and the vices, the guilt and the promises of our generation. In a sense it is true that we cannot be saved unless we are all saved." But he warned against "a too-simple social radicalism [that] does not recognize how quickly the poor, the weak, the despised of yesterday may, on gaining a social victory over their detractors, exhibit the same arrogance."

Will Herberg, a Jewish theologian, once said: "No Protestant theologian has spoken so relevantly to our concerns in the Western world as has Reinhold Niebuhr. . . . [He is] one of the most creative and influential minds of our generation."

Niebuhr lectured widely throughout his academic career, which spanned nearly forty years. It was a rare Sunday when he was not invited to give a sermon somewhere. He was just as often critical of what he regarded as a misunderstanding of Christianity by Christians as he was of those of a purely secular character. He wrote, "If faith produces fanatic fury rather than charity, it becomes as sounding brass and a tinkling cymbal." His realistic view of man once lead him to remark, "Man's capacity for justice makes democracy possible; but man's inclination to injustice makes democracy necessary."

In eulogizing him, the *Christian Century* observed: "Reinhold Niebuhr was as conscious as any modern man that he faces the eternal in every moment and in every action of his life. No man brooded more than he over the limitations of all historical achievements nor was more persuaded of the power of faith to transcend those limitations. No man has been better prepared in mind to confront the end of history that is death's own promise."

In 1960, a professorship was established and funded in his honor at Union Theological Seminary by a cross-denominational group including Jacques Maritain, T. S. Eliot, Arnold Toynbee, and Eleanor Roosevelt. In 1973, the University of Notre Dame established an annual award in his honor, to be given to a member of the Notre Dame community.

BIOGRAPHICAL/CRITICAL SOURCES—Books: George Hammar, *Christian Realism in Contemporary American Theology: A Study of Reinhold Niebuhr, W. M. Horton, and H. P. Van Dusen,* Lundequistska Bokhandeln (Uppsala), 1940; David R. Davies, *Reinhold Niebuhr: Prophet from America,* J. Clarke, 1945, Macmillan, 1948; Mary Frances Thelen, *Man as Sinner in Contemporary American Realistic Theology,* King's Crown Press, 1946; Edward J. Carnell, *The Theology of Reinhold Niebuhr,* Eerdmans, 1951, revised edition, 1960; D. B. Robertson, *Reinhold Niebuhr's Works: A Bibliography,* Berea College Press, 1954; Charles W. Kegley and Robert W. Bretall, editors, *Reinhold Niebuhr: His Religious, Social, and Political Thought,* Macmillan, 1956; Holtan P. Odegard, *Sin and Science,* Antioch Press, 1956; Hans Hofmann, *The Theology of Reinhold Niebuhr,* Scribner, 1956; Donald B. Meyer, *The Protestant Search for Political Realism, 1919-1941,* Univer-

sity of California Press, 1960; Gordon Harland, *The Thought of Reinhold Niebuhr,* Oxford University Press, 1960; June R. Bingham, *Courage to Change: An Introduction to the Life and Thought of Reinhold Niebuhr,* Scribner, 1961; Harold R. Landon, *Reinhold Niebuhr: A Prophetic Voice in Our Time,* Seabury, 1962; Nathan A. Scott, Jr., *Reinhold Niebuhr,* University of Minnesota Press, 1963; Rachel H. King, *The Omission of the Holy Spirit,* Philosophical Library, 1964; Theodore Minnema, *The Social Ethics of Reinhold Niebuhr,* Eerdmans, 1968; Gabriel J. Fackre, *The Promise of Reinhold Niebuhr,* Lippincott, 1970; Ronald H. Stone, *Reinhold Niebuhr: Prophet to Politician,* Abingdon, 1972.

Periodicals: *New York Times,* June 2, 1971; *Time,* June 14, 1971; *America,* August 7, 1971; *Commentary,* September, 1972.†

(Died June 1, 1971)

* * *

NIEMI, Richard G(ene) 1941-

PERSONAL: Born January 10, 1941, in Green Bay, Wis.; son of Eugene (an accountant) and Dorothy (Stevens) Niemi; married Shirley Gill, August 4, 1962; children: Nancy, Patricia, Jennifer, Julie. *Education:* Lawrence University, B.A. (magna cum laude), 1962; University of Michigan, Ph.D., 1967. *Office:* Department of Political Science, University of Rochester, Rochester, N.Y. 14627.

CAREER: University of Rochester, Rochester, N.Y., assistant professor, 1967-71, associate professor, 1971-75, professor of political science, 1975—. Instructor, National Science Foundation College Science Improvement Program faculty seminar, summer, 1970; Thord-Gray Visiting Professor, University of Lund, Sweden, 1974. *Member:* Phi Beta Kappa, Pi Sigma Alpha. *Awards, honors:* Woodrow Wilson fellow, 1962-63; National Institute of Mental Health research grant, 1969-70; National Science Foundation research grants, 1970-71, 1973, 1975-77; Ford Foundation faculty research fellowship.

WRITINGS: (Editor with Herbert F. Weisberg, and contributor) *Probability Models of Collective Decision-Making,* C. E. Merrill, 1972; *How Family Members Perceive Each Other,* Yale University Press, 1974; (with M. Kent Jennings) *The Political Character of Adolescence,* Princeton University Press, 1974; (editor) *Politics of Future Citizens,* Jossey-Bass, 1975; (editor with Weisberg) *Controversies in American Voting Behavior,* W. H. Freeman, 1976.

WORK IN PROGRESS: With M. Kent Jennings, a follow-up to earlier study of high school seniors' views on politics; mathematical studies of voting.

* * *

NILES, John Jacob 1892-

PERSONAL: Born April 28, 1892, in Louisville, Ky.; son of John Thomas (a sheriff, farmer, singer, and square dance caller) and Lula Sarah (Reisch) Niles; married Rena Lipetz (a free-lance writer), March 21, 1936; children: Thomas Michael Tolliver, John Edward. *Education:* Attended University of Lyon, 1918-19, Schola Cantorum, 1919, University of London, 1919, and Cincinnati Conservatory of Music, 1920-23. *Religion:* Episcopalian. *Home and office:* Boot Hill Farm, R.F.D., 10, Lexington, Ky., 40511.

CAREER: Composer and concert singer; collector and arranger of American folk music. Has performed his own music in concerts throughout the United States, Europe, and

Canada, 1927—; has recorded music under RCA Victor, Tradition, Camden, and Folkways labels, and under his own label, Boone-Tolliver. Teacher of short courses at Harvard University, Juilliard School of Music, Curtis Institute, Eastman School of Music, and University of Missouri—Kansas City. Participant in the radio series, "John Jacob Niles' Salute to the Hills," broadcast by the University of Kentucky, 1937-40. *Military service:* U.S. Aviation Service, 1917-1919; served with Italian, French, Belgian, and English units; became first lieutenant; received War Cross from Italy and Belgium, and service citation from U.S. *Member:* American Society of Composers, Authors, and Publishers, American Folklore Society, Kentucky Folklore Society, American Dialect Society, Iroquois Hunt Club, American Federation of Television and Radio Artists. *Awards, honors:* Mus. D., Cincinnati Conservatory of Music, 1949; national citation, National Federation of Music Clubs, 1967; D.Litt., Transylvania University, 1969; M.F.A., Episcopal Theological Seminary (Lexington), 1970; D.Hum., University of Louisville, 1971; D.Litt., University of Kentucky, 1973.

WRITINGS—Collections of folk songs: *Impressions of a Negro Camp Meeting: Eight Traditional Tunes,* Carl Fischer, 1925; *Singing Soldiers* (song from World War I), Scribner, 1927, reprinted with an introduction by Leslie Shepard, Singing Tree Press, 1968; *Seven Kentucky Mountain Songs,* G. Schirmer, 1928; (with Douglas S. Moore and A. A. Wallgren) *Songs My Mother Never Taught Me* (songs from World War I), Macaulay, 1929; *Seven Negro Exaltations,* G. Schirmer, 1929; *Songs of the Hill-Folk,* G. Schirmer, 1934; *Ten Christmas Carols from the Southern Appalachian Mountains,* G. Schirmer, 1935; *More Songs of the Hill-Folk,* G. Schirmer, 1936; *Ballads, Carols, and Tragic Legends from the Southern Appalachian Mountains,* G. Schirmer, 1937, new edition, 1938; *The Singing Campus,* G. Schirmer, 1941; *The Anglo-American Ballad Study Book,* G. Schirmer, 1945; *The Anglo-American Carol Study Book,* G. Schirmer, 1948; *The Shape-Note Study Book,* G. Schirmer, 1950; *John Jacob Niles Suite,* compiled by Weldon Hart, G. Schirmer, 1952; *The Ballad Book of John Jacob Niles,* Houghton, 1961; (with Helen Louise Smith) *Folk Carols for Young Actors* (record included), Holt, 1962; (with Smith) *Folk Ballads for Young Actors* (record included), Holt, 1962; *John Jacob Niles' Song Book for Guitar,* arranged by Leon Block, G. Schirmer, 1963; *The John Jacob Niles Bicentennial Song-Book,* G. Schirmer, 1976.

Other books: *One Man's War* (narrative), Henry Holt, 1929; *One Woman's War* (narrative), Macaulay, 1930; (with wife, Rena Niles) *Mr. Poof's Discovery* (juvenile), Bur Press, 1947; *Rhymes for A. Wince* (nursery rhymes), Department of Special Collections, Margaret I. King Library (Lexington), 1971; (author of introduction) Jonathan Williams, *Appalachian Photographs of Doris Ulmann,* Jargon Society, 1971; *Brick Dust and Buttermilk,* Gnomon Distributors, 1977.

Other musical compositions; published by G. Schirmer: *Lamentation* (oratorio; first performed in Terre Haute, Ind., March 14, 1951), 1950; *Mary the Rose* (Christmas cantata), 1955; *Rhapsody for the Merry Month of May* (cantata), 1955; *The Little Family* (Easter carol), 1962; *Moses and Pharoah's Daughter,* 1962; *Reward* (for solo voice and piano; first performed by Richard Tucker), 1963.

Unpublished music: "Concerto for Piano and Orchestra in F-Minor," completed in 1957, first performed in Louisville, Ky. by Dupont Manual High School Orchestra, 1957; "Symphony No. 1," first performed in California by the

Sacramento Symphony Orchestra, 1963; "Melodies from an October Song Book," Opus 150; "Courting Time," Opus 152, no. 2; "Unused I Am to Lovers," Opus 153, no. 1; "Winter Lullaby," Opus 154, no. 1; "Niles-Merton Cycles," Opus 171, no. 1-11, and Opus 172, no. 12-22 (two compositions in the cycle, "Evening" and "The Nativity," have been published by G. Schirmer).

Collector or composer and arranger of over one thousand folk songs published individually by G. Schirmer, Mark Foster Music Co., Hirshaw Music Co., and Carl Fischer. Author of over 250 sonnets. Contributor to periodicals, including *Atlantic* and *Scribner's Magazine.*

WORK IN PROGRESS: Writing *The Autobiography of John Jacob Niles,* under a grant from the National Endowment for the Humanities.

SIDELIGHTS: John Jacob Niles told *CA* that "my concern has been the grassroots of America, especially as revealed in its balladry and folk music." Once called the "dean of American balladeers." Niles was one of the earliest collectors of Anglo-American folk music. In 1907 he began filling notebooks with tunes he heard in his native Kentucky; eventually, his gathering extended to the Southern Appalachian regions of North Carolina, Tennessee, Georgia, Alabama, Virginia, and West Virginia. By mid-1930 he is said to have had the largest private collection of folk songs in the world. Leslie Shepard writes that "these were not the impeccable scholarly collections of professors on university grants. Interspersed with the songs and a primitive musical shorthand were riddles, proverbs, and fragments of folk dialect and superstition. It was a very personal affair of hastily scrawled, tentatively noted pieces under difficult and even hazardous circumstances, garnered from farmers, preachers, handymen, old grannies, moonshiners, traveling people, and even jailbirds." "Black is the Color of My True Love's Hair," one of the most famous of these songs, was written in 1916 and has since been translated into thirty-two languages and adapted for full orchestra. Other well-known songs include "I Wonder As I Wander," "Venezuela," and "Go 'Way from My Window."

Niles' father encouraged him as a boy to make his own instruments, and except when using a piano, Niles always accompanies himself on a handmade eight-string dulcimer. He received $1.50 for his first paid performance in 1907; by 1930 he had appeared throughout America and much of Europe, and by 1950 had performed in every state of the United States, sometimes giving more than fifty concerts a year. Niles' father once told him, "Old-timely family music came from the people and it should go back to the people"; it was through the efforts of pioneers like Niles that the folk-singing concert became a vehicle for achieving this. In concert, as well as in writing his music, Niles introduces his songs with "chatty, humorous, casual, informative" descriptions, often including the historical or political background of the music. He is one of the few folk singers to use only material he has collected or composed. Niles' style, writes Shepard, "is nearer to the ancient minstrels than the country singers from whom he got these songs." Claude A. Lipscombe notes that Niles' ability to sing in the dialects of districts where he found the songs creates a vivid atmosphere: "With more simple rural audiences, he has often caused a furor of excitement and pathos. People have been very moved, to a point of extreme happiness and uncontrollable melancholy, by recollections his songs have brought forth."

AVOCATIONAL INTERESTS: Painting, wood carving, instrument making (dulcimers), farming, stone and brick masonry, and fox hunting.

BIOGRAPHICAL/CRITICAL SOURCES: Roderick Peattie, editor, *The Great Smokies and the Blue Ridge,* Vanguard, 1943; John T. Howard, *Our American Music,* 3rd edition, Crowell, 1946; Ray M. Lawless, *Folksingers and Folksongs in America,* Duell, Sloan & Pearce, 1960, 2nd edition, Meredith, 1965; Leslie Shepard, "John Jacob Niles," (booklet accompanying Folkways record album #FA 2373), Folkways Records, c.1964; Milton Okun, compiler, *Something to Sing About,* Macmillan, 1968.

* * *

NILSEN, Don L(ee) F(red) 1934-

PERSONAL: Born October 19, 1934, in Spanish Fork, Utah; son of Delles Fred (a farmer) and Jessie (Parmalee) Nilsen; married Alleen Pace (an associate professor at Arizona State University), March 21, 1958; children: Kelvin Don, Sean David, Nicolette Ann. *Education:* Brigham Young University, B.A., 1958; American University, M.A. in Ed., 1961; University of Michigan, Ph.D., 1971. *Politics:* Democrat. *Religion:* Church of Jesus Christ of Latter-day Saints (Mormon). *Home:* 1884 East Alameda, Tempe, Ariz. 85281. *Office:* Department of English, Arizona State University, Tempe, Ariz. 85281.

CAREER: Highland Park Junior College, Highland Park, Mich., instructor in English and French, 1961-62; Eastern Michigan University, Ypsilanti, instructor in French, 1963; State University of New York College at Oswego, assistant professor of English linguistics, 1964-66; University of Michigan, Ann Arbor, coordinator of teacher education program, 1966-67; Columbia University, Teachers College, New York, N.Y., composition specialist in Kabul, Afghanistan, 1967-69; University of Michigan, coordinator of teacher education program, 1969-71; University of Northern Iowa, Cedar Falls, assistant professor and director of linguistics, 1971-73; Arizona State University, Tempe, professor of English, 1973—. Associate director for languages, University of Pittsburgh, summer, 1964-65; visiting professor, University of Redlands, summer, 1966. *Military service:* U.S. Army, 1954-56. *Member:* Linguistic Society of America, National Association of Foreign Student Advisers, Teachers of English to Speakers of Other Languages, American Dialect Society, Modern Language Association of America, National Council of Teachers of English, Rocky Mountain Modern Language Association (program chairman and English linguistics chairman, 1978).

WRITINGS: (Contributor) Mario A. Pei, editor, *Language Today,* Funk, 1967; (with Maxine G. Phinney and others) *English Conversation Practices,* University of Michigan Press, 1968; (editor with Fazel Nur and Sajida Kamal) *A Linguisitic Reader for Afghan Composition Students,* Kabul University, 1969; (with wife, Alleen P. Nilsen) *Pronunciation Contrasts in English,* Regents Publishing, 1971, revised edition, 1972; *English Adverbials,* Mouton, 1972; *Toward a Semantic Specification of Deep Case,* Mouton, 1972; *The Instrumental Case in English: Syntatic and Semantic Considerations,* Mouton, 1973; *Semantic Theory,* Newbury House, 1975; *Language Play,* Newbury House, 1978. Contributor of articles and reviews to linguistic journals. Co-editor, *Public Doublespeak Newsletter;* editor, *Rocky Mountain Review.*

WORK IN PROGRESS: Reeling, Writhing, and Rhetoric: An Innovative Approach to Composition.

NILSSON, Usha Saksena 1930-
(Usha Priyamvada)

PERSONAL: Born December 24, 1930, in Kanpur, India; daughter of Damodar Prasad (a lawyer) and Priyamvada (Hajela) Saxena; married Kim Nilsson (an associate professor), September 1, 1962. *Education:* Allahabad University, India, B.A., 1951, M.A., 1953, Ph.D., 1956; Indiana University, post-doctoral study, 1961-63. *Religion:* Hindu. *Home:* 1219 Shorewood Blvd., Madison, Wis. 53705. *Office:* Department of South Asian Studies, University of Wisconsin, Madison, Wis. 53705.

CAREER: University of Delhi, Delhi, India, lecturer in English, 1956-59; Allahabad University, Allahabad, India, assistant professor of English studies, 1959-61; Indiana University at Bloomington, lecturer in comparative literature, 1962-63; University of Wisconsin—Madison, assistant professor, 1963-68, associate professor, 1968-77, professor of Indian language and literature, 1977—. Consultant to and language director of the Peace Corps, 1964. *Member:* Association of Asian Studies, Modern Language Association of America, American Association of University Professors. *Awards, honors:* Fulbright fellowship for post-doctoral study at Indiana University, 1961-62; best story award from *Arizona Quarterly,* 1965.

WRITINGS—All under name Usha Priyamvada: *Pachipan Khambe, Lal Divaren* (novel), Rajkamal, 1961; *Rukogi Nahin, Radhika?* (novel), Akshar Prakashan (New Delhi), 1966; *Ek Koi Dusra* (collection of short stories), Akshar Prakashan, 1966; *Intermediate Hindi,* Indian Language and Area Center, University of Wisconsin, 1967; *Readings in Hindi Literature,* Indian Language and Area Center, University of Wisconsin, 1967; *Mira Bai* (monograph with fifty poems translated into English), Ashitya Akademi (New Delhi), 1968; *Kitana Baraa Jhooth* (short stories), Rajamad, 1972; *Meri Priya Kahaniyam,* [India], 1974; *Hindi Stories,* South Asian Center (Madison, Wis.), 1976.

WORK IN PROGRESS: A novel, *Yatra Yen.*

* * *

NIMOCKS, Walter 1930-

PERSONAL: Born December 22, 1930, in Forrest City, Ark.; son of Alfred Byron (a merchant) and Eloise (Buford) Nimocks; married Susan Lee, January 24, 1959; children: Alfred, Jane, William. *Education:* University of Arkansas, B.S., 1952, M.A., 1956; Vanderbilt University, Ph.D,, 1965. *Politics:* Democrat. *Religion:* Episcopal. *Home:* 154 St. Mildred's Court, Danville, Ky. 40422. *Office:* Department of History, Centre College, Danville, Ky. 40422.

CAREER: Western Kentucky University, Bowling Green, instructor, 1960-62, assistant professor of history, 1962-66; Centre College, Danville, Kentucky, assistant professor, 1966-68, associate professor, 1968-72, professor of history, 1972—. *Military service:* U.S. Army Signal Corps, 1952-54; became first lieutenant. *Member:* American Historical Association, Southern Conference on British Studies. *Awards, honors:* Southern Fellowship Fund fellow, 1960; American Philosophical Society award, 1974.

WRITINGS: Milner's Young Men: The "Kindergarten" in Edwardian Imperial Affairs, Duke University Press, 1969. Contributor to *South Atlantic Quarterly.*

WORK IN PROGRESS: Research on Edwardian imperial politics.

BIOGRAPHICAL/CRITICAL SOURCES: Times Literary Supplement, June 4, 1970.

NISBET, Ada Blanche 1907-

PERSONAL: Born May 7, 1907, in Chicago, Ill.; daughter of James Robert (a pharmacist) and Bessie (Kelley) Nisbet. *Education:* Dominican College, San Rafael, Calif., A.B., 1929; University of California, Los Angeles, A.M., 1939, Ph.D., 1946. *Politics:* Democrat. *Religion:* Roman Catholic. *Home:* 605 San Lorenzo St., Santa Monica, Calif. 90402. *Office:* Department of English, University of California, Los Angeles, Calif. 90024.

CAREER: Mount St. Mary's College, Los Angeles, Calif., instructor in English, 1937-39; University of California, Los Angeles, instructor, 1946-48, assistant professor, 1948-54, associate professor, 1954-61, professor of English, 1961-70, professor emeritus, 1970—. Honorary adviser, Joint Programme of British University Summer Schools; appointed by governor of California Committee for State Fulbright Scholarships. *Member:* Modern Language Association of America, International Association of University Professors of English, American Association of University Professors, American Association of University Women, Phi Beta Kappa. *Awards, honors:* American Association of University Women fellowship, 1944-45; American Council of Learned Societies, grants, 1945, 1965, 1970, fellowship, 1963-64; Guggenheim fellowship, 1948-49, 1954-55; Institute for the Humanities grants, 1957, 1972; Theta Sigma Phi award for distinguished writing, 1959; Huntington Library grant, 1960; Ford Foundation grant, 1967-68; National Endowment for the Humanities fellowship, 1976-77.

WRITINGS: (Contributor) *Essays Critical and Historical, Dedicated to Lily B. Campbell,* University of California Press, 1950; *Dickens and Ellen Ternan,* University of California Press, 1952; *Newman the Man,* Plantin, 1960; (contributor) Lionel Stevenson, editor, *Victorian Fiction: A Guide to Research,* Harvard University Press, 1964; (editor with Blake Nevius) *Dickens Centennial Essays,* University of California Press, 1972. Contributor of articles to literature journals.

WORK IN PROGRESS: Charles Dickens: International Guide to Study and Research; British Comment on the United States: A Chronological Bibliography, 1832-1900; Dickens and America: A Study in Mutual Disillusion; British Champions of the American Negro: An Anthology.

SIDELIGHTS: Ada Blanche Nisbet's interest in Charles Dickens led to invitations from institutions in seventeen European countries to speak at programs honoring the centennial of Dickens' death (1970).

* * *

NISKANEN, William Arthur, Jr. 1933-

PERSONAL: Born March 13, 1933, in Bend, Ore.; son of William Arthur (a businessman) and Nina (McCord) Niskanen; married Helen Barr, August 3, 1957 (divorced, 1978); children: Lia Anne, Pamela Cay. *Education:* Harvard University, B.A., 1954; University of Chicago, M.A., 1955, Ph.D., 1962. *Home:* 9163 Lilley Rd., Plymouth, Mich. 48170. *Office:* Ford Motor Company World Headquarters, The American Road, Dearborn, Mich. 48121.

CAREER: Rand Corp., Santa Monica, Calif., economist, 1957-62; Office of Secretary of Defense, Arlington, Va., director of special studies, 1962-64; Institute for Defense Analyses, Arlington, division director, 1964-70; Office of Management and Budget, Washington, D.C., assistant director, 1970-72; University of California, Berkeley, professor of economics, 1972-75; Ford Motor Co., Dearborn,

Mich., director of economics, 1975—. *Member:* American Economic Association, Public Choice Society.

WRITINGS: Bureaucracy and Representative Government, Aldine-Atherton, 1971; *Structural Reform of the Federal Budget Process,* American Enterprise Institute, 1973. Co-editor of *Benefit-Cost Annual,* 1971-72.

WORK IN PROGRESS: Research on behavior of government organizations.

* * *

NOJIRI, Kiyohiko 1897-1973
(Jiro Osaragi)

1897—April 30, 1973; Japanese novelist and historian. Obituaries: *New York Times,* May 1, 1973.

* * *

NOLAND, Ronald G(ene) 1936-

PERSONAL: Born June 2, 1936, in Baton Rouge, La.; son of Ellis J. (an electrician) and Lillian (Dodge) Noland; married Juanie LeBlanc (a college professor), August 12, 1962; children: Timothy Scott. *Education:* Louisiana State University, B.S., 1958, M.Ed., 1962; University of Southern Mississippi, Ed.D., 1968. *Politics:* Democrat. *Religion:* Episcopalian. *Home:* 141 Thomas St., Auburn, Ala. 36830. *Office:* Department of Reading Education, Auburn University, 1118 Haley Center, Auburn, Ala. 36830.

CAREER: Louisiana State University, Baton Rouge, counselor, 1963-66; Northeast Louisiana State University (now Northeast Louisiana University), Monroe, assistant professor, 1960-68, associate professor of reading education, 1968-69; Auburn University, Auburn, Ala., assistant professor of reading education, 1969—, director of reading services, 1969—. *Military service:* U.S. Air Force, 1959-61. U.S. Air Force Reserve, 1961—; current rank, lieutenant colonel. *Member:* International Reading Association, National Education Association, College Reading Association, National Reading Conference, Alabama Reading Association, Alabama Education Association, Kappa Delta Pi, Phi Delta Kappa.

WRITINGS: An Introduction to Elementary Reading: Selected Materials, MSS Educational Publishing, 1971.

* * *

NOMAD, Max 1880(?)-1973

1880(?)—April 18, 1973; Expatriate Austrian political writer. Obituaries: *New York Times,* April 19, 1973.

* * *

NORQUEST, Carrol 1901-

PERSONAL: Born August 13, 1901, in York County, Neb.; son of Peter Magnus (a farmer) and Mary (Johnson) Norquest; married Lydia Nordmeyer (a church organist), February 28, 1934; children: Carrol, Jr., Erik, Marie (Mrs. Sterlen Sleeth), Ingrid (Mrs. Conrad Gardner), Dixie, Mark, Neil. *Education:* Attended Kansas State Agricultural College (now Kansas State University), 1920, and studied Spanish one year at Edinburg Junior College (now Pan American University). *Politics:* Republican. *Religion:* Lutheran. *Home address:* Route 4, Box 199, Edinburg, Tex. 78539.

CAREER: Farmer until a stroke forced his retirement in 1963.

WRITINGS: Rio Grande Wetbacks, University of New Mexico Press, 1972; (contributor) *Gift of the Rio*, Border Kingdom Press, 1975.

WORK IN PROGRESS: Count Off, a book about his family.

SIDELIGHTS: "Rather than let me vegetate [after a stroke], my wife kept harping at me to use my little talent to write up stories about our kids," Carrol Norquest told *CA.* "I didn't get started until I broke my leg a couple of years later. This really did stretch me out for a while.... After a couple years of this, my boy told me I should write down my wetback stories. That he wanted them if nothing else. A journalist professor at the college urged me to try to have them published. I did...."

The University of New Mexico Press used only half of Norquest's wetback tales in his first book, published when he was seventy-one. He still is adding to the stories, but would rather dwell on his seven children. Three of the Norquest daughters have university degrees in music (all seven are college graduates), each of the seven plays at least three instruments (some play five), and they sing. The last two years that all seven were home for Christmas, they gave full-length community concerts, one at Pan American University. But lawyer or businessman, according to Norquest, "the boys can all set a fence post which won't wiggle in line. They can patch flats, change machinery. Most of the kids can milk the cows, dehorn cattle, brand them, and fill up the back end of a shovel."

*   *   *

NORTON, Mary E(lizabeth)   1913-

PERSONAL: Born September 14, 1913, in Ann Arbor, Mich.; daughter of Richard and Jennie (Stephenson) Lunny; married Clark F. Norton (employed by Congressional Research Service, Library of Congress), August 24, 1940; children: Mary Beth, Clark R. *Education:* University of Michigan, A.B., 1935, M.A., 1938; American Academy of Rome, summer graduate study, 1966. *Politics:* Democrat. *Religion:* Methodist. *Home:* 3614 Melfa Lane, Bowie, Md. 20715. *Office:* Department of Classics, George Washington University, Washington, D.C. 20052.

CAREER: High school teacher in Farmington, Mich., 1935-40; DePauw University, Greencastle, Ind., instructor in classics, 1957-64; George Washington University, Washington, D.C., assistant professor, 1964-73, associate professorial lecturer in classics, 1973—. *Member:* American Classical League, American Philological Association, League of Women Voters (president of local chapter, 1954), Classical Association of Middle Atlantic States, Phi Beta Kappa, Phi Kappa Phi, Eta Sigma Phi, Pi Lambda Theta, Kappa Phi. *Awards, honors:* Fulbright fellowship, 1966.

WRITINGS: (Compiler) *A Selective Bibliography of the Teaching of Greek and Latin, 1920-1969*, Modern Language Association of America, 1971. Contributor to *Classical Outlook* and *Classical World*.

WORK IN PROGRESS: Classical Traditions in Colonial America.

*   *   *

NORTON, Paul Foote   1917-

PERSONAL: Born January 23, 1917, in Newton, Mass.; son of John Foote (a bacteriologist) and Margaret (Goodrich) Norton; married Alison Stuart (a writer), May 7, 1942; children: John Douglas, Mary Reed, Hilary Stuart. *Educa-*

tion: Oberlin College, B.A., 1938; Princeton University, M.F.A., 1947, Ph.D., 1952. *Politics:* Independent. *Home:* 57 Woodside Ave., Amherst, Mass. 01002. *Office:* Department of Art, University of Massachusetts, Amherst, Mass. 01002.

CAREER: Pennsylvania State University, University Park, assistant professor, 1947-53, associate professor of art history, 1953-58; University of Massachusetts—Amherst, associate professor, 1958-59, professor of art history, 1959—, head of department, 1958-71. Visiting associate professor at Amherst College, 1959-60. Chairman, Amherst Historical Commission, 1973-77. *Military service:* U.S. Navy, 1942-46; became lieutenant commander. *Member:* Society of Architectural Historians (member of board of directors, 1952, 1957-64, 1966-68), College Art Association, Archaeological Institute of America, National Trust (England), National Trust (United States), Royal Society of Arts (fellow), Societe francaise d'archeologie, Society of Architectural Bibliographers, Society of Architectural Historians (Great Britain), Pioneer America Society, Norsk Arkeologisk Selskap, Society for Preservation of New England Antiquities, Massachusetts Council on Art and Humanities (member of advisory committee). *Awards, honors:* American Council of Learned Societies fellowship, 1951-52; Fulbright senior research fellow in England, 1953-54; Ford Foundation grant for Asian-African studies, 1965; National Historical Publications commission grant, 1967-68; National Endowment for the Humanities senior research fellowship, 1971-72.

WRITINGS: (Contributor) Henry L. Savage, editor, *Nassau Hall*, Princeton University Press, 1956; (contributor) Terry B. Morton, editor, *Decatur House*, National Trust for Historic Preservation, 1967; (with Alan Gowans, J. T. Butler, and W. D. Garrett) *Arts in America: The Nineteenth Century*, Scribner, 1969; *B. H. Latrobe, Papers IX* (a bibliography), University of Virginia Press, 1972; *Amherst: A Guide to Its Architecture*, Amherst College Press, 1975; (contributor) W. H. Adams, editor, *Jefferson and the Arts: An Extended View*, National Gallery of Art, 1976; *Latrobe, Jefferson and the National Capitol*, Garland Publishing, 1977. Contributor to *Journal of the Society of Architectural Historians, Art Bulletin, Encyclopaedia Britannica, Encyclopedia of World Art, American Heritage*, and *Catholic Encyclopedia*. Editor of *Journal of the Society of Architectural Historians*, 1959-64.

WORK IN PROGRESS: Editing *Papers of Samuel McIntire of Salem*, a book containing all of McIntire's architectural drawings, trade papers, and correspondence, completion expected in 1981.

AVOCATIONAL INTERESTS: Tennis, golf, squash, flute.

BIOGRAPHICAL/CRITICAL SOURCES: Western Humanities Review, autumn, 1970.

*   *   *

NOSSITER, Bernard D(aniel)   1926-

PERSONAL: Born April 10, 1926; son of Murry (a businessman) and Rose (Weingarten) Nossiter; married Jacqueline Robinson, December 6, 1950; children: Daniel, Joshua, Adam, Jonathan. *Education:* Dartmouth College, B.A., 1947; Harvard University, M.A., 1949. *Home:* 52 South Eaton Place, London S.W.1, England. *Office: Washington Post*, 25 Upper Brook St., London W.1., England.

CAREER: Washington Post, Washington, D.C., London correspondent, 1971—. *Military service:* U.S. Army, Infantry, 1944-46, 1951-52; became second lieutenant. *Member:* Phi Beta Kappa. *Awards, honors:* Award from Hillman Foundation, 1965, for *The Mythmakers;* Overseas Press Club Award, 1966; Polk Award for national reporting, 1969.

WRITINGS: The Mythmakers, Houghton, 1964; *Soft State: A Newspaperman's Chronicle of India,* Harper, 1970; *Britain: A Future That Works,* Houghton, 1978.

BIOGRAPHICAL/CRITICAL SOURCES: Washington Post, October 24, 1970; *New York Times,* November 22, 1970.

*   *   *

NOVER, Barnet   1899-1973

February 11, 1899—April 15, 1973; American editor and columnist. Obituaries: *New York Times,* April 17, 1973.

*   *   *

NUGENT, Vincent Joseph   1913-

PERSONAL: Born July 30, 1913, in Philadelphia, Pa.; son of Frank J. (a chauffeur) and Mary (McCullaugh) Nugent. *Education:* St. Joseph's College, Princeton, N.J., B.A., 1937; graduate study at St. Vincent's Seminary, 1937-39, and Mary Immaculate Seminary, 1939-42; Catholic University of America, S.T.D., 1942. *Home:* 109 East 38th St., New York, N.Y. 10016. *Office:* 366 Fifth Ave., New York, N.Y. 10001.

CAREER: Ordained Roman Catholic priest, 1942; Mary Immaculate Seminary, Northampton, Pa., faculty member, 1944-45, professor of dogmatic theology, 1945-53; St. John's University, Jamaica, N.Y., professor of theology, 1953-65, established department of sacred science, 1953, chairman of graduate and undergraduate departments of theology, 1957-65, lecturer, and director of Mariological Institute, 1958-65; Society for Propagation of the Faith, New York, N.Y., assistant to Most Reverend Fulton J. Sheen, 1965-68. *Member:* Catholic Theological Society of America (charter member; director, 1955-66; vice-president, 1958-59; secretary, 1959-66), Mariological Society of America (director, 1960-62), Society of Catholic College Teachers of Sacred Doctrine (regional director of New York, 1958-60).

WRITINGS: Concept of Charity in Writings of St. Gregory the Great, Catholic University of America Press, 1944; *Christian Marriage,* St. John's University Press, 1958; (compiler) *Directory of American Catholic Theologians,*

CTSA Press, 1963, 2nd edition, 1965; *Greatest and Holiest Work of the Church,* SPOF Press, 1968. Contributor to theological journals. Member of board of editors, *World Mission.*

WORK IN PROGRESS: Missiology and lectures and symposia for clergy and laity.

*   *   *

NYQUIST, Thomas E.   1931-

PERSONAL: Born June 20, 1931, in Froid, Mont.; son of Richard Theodore (a farmer and rancher) and Lydia (Baker) Nyquist; married Corinne Johnson (director of World Study Center, State University of New York College at New Paltz), December 23, 1956; children: Jonathan Eugene, Lynn Marie. *Education:* Macalester College, B.A., 1956; Montana State University, M.A., 1958; Northwestern University, Ph.D., 1966. *Politics:* Democrat. *Home:* 62 South Chestnut, New Paltz, N.Y. 12561. *Office:* 3 Hohmann House, State University of New York College, New Paltz, N.Y. 12561.

CAREER: Institute of Social and Economic Research, Grahamstown, South Africa, research fellow, 1966-67; State University of New York College at New Paltz, assistant professor, 1968-70, associate professor of African studies, 1970-76, statewide coordinator of faculty retraining, 1976—. Ulster County legislator, 1976—. *Military service:* U.S. Army, 1952-54. *Member:* American Political Science Association, African Studies Association, New York African Studies Association (member of executive committee). *Awards, honors:* State University of New York Faculty research fellowships, 1969, 1975; Human Sciences Research Council (South Africa) grant, 1969-71.

WRITINGS: Toward a Theory of the African Upper Stratum in South Africa, Ohio State University Center for International Studies, 1972. Also author of *Black Dilemma: The African Upper Stratum in South Africa.* Contributor to *Middle East Journal, Toward Freedom, Northside Pilot, Bustan,* and *Viewpoints in Teaching and Learning.*

SIDELIGHTS: Thomas E. Nyquist told *CA:* "I like to think of myself as a scholar, researcher, writer, politician and administrator. But really I'm a misplaced farm boy who has long had the wandering spirit. Were there the time and had I the energy (and money!), I would like to see everything, taste everything, smell everything and touch everything—but particularly see everything."

O

OBICHERE, Boniface Ihewunwa 1932-

PERSONAL: Born November 4, 1932, in Awaka, Owerri, Nigeria; son of Eke and Ibari (Ikeri) Obichere; married Armer Gean Brown (a teacher), August 22, 1964; children: Chikere. *Education:* University of Minnesota, B.A. (with honors), 1961; University of California, Berkeley, M.A., 1963; Oxford University, D.Phil., 1967. *Religion:* Roman Catholic. *Home:* 973 Keniston Ave., Los Angeles, Calif. 90019. *Office:* Department of History, University of California, Los Angeles, Calif. 90024.

CAREER: Mount Saint Mary's Teachers' College, Azaraegbelu Owerri, Nigeria, senior prefect, 1956-57, tutor and lecturer in history, 1957-59, procurator, 1958-59; Oxford University, Institute of Commonwealth Studies, Oxford, England, tutor in history, 1966-67; University of California, Los Angeles, assistant professor, 1967-68, associate professor, 1969-73, professor of history, 1973—, director, African Studies Center, 1972-78. University of California, Extensions in Los Angeles and Irvine, associate professor of history, 1968-70; California State College (now University), Los Angeles, professor of history, 1969-70; University of Southern California, co-director of Ethnic Studies Program, 1969-70. Visiting professor, University of Hawaii, summers, 1969-70, University of Ghana, 1970-71, and University of Ibdan, Nigeria, 1976-77. Lecturer in African Affairs, Nations, Inc., 1963; lecturer, London Services Education Committee, 1966-67. Member of Urban League of Los Angeles and Town Hall of Los Angeles.

MEMBER: American Historical Association, African Studies Association of America, American Academy of Political and Social Sciences, American Political Science Association, American Academy of Arts and Sciences, International Studies Association of America, American Association of University Professors, Royal Africa Society (London), Societe Francaise D'Histoire D'Outre-Mer, International African Institute (London), Historical Association (London), Royal Historical Society (London), New York Academy of Political Science. *Awards, honors:* Nigerian federal government scholarship, 1959-63; Beit scholarships, Oxford University, 1964-67, 1965-66; Cyril Foster Fund research grant, Oxford University, 1966; Commonwealth Scholarship, England, 1966-67; American Council of Learned Societies and Social Science Research Council faculty research grant and fellowship in African studies, 1970-

71; Humanities Institute fellowship, University of California, 1972-73.

WRITINGS: (Contributor) Armstead Robinson and others, editors, *Black Studies in the University,* Yale University Press, 1969; (contributor) William Roger Louis and Prosser Gifford, editors, *Britain and France in Africa,* Yale University Press, 1971; *West African States and European Expansion: The Dahomy-Niger Hinterland: 1885-1898,* Yale University Press, 1971; *Studies in Southern Nigerian History,* Cass & Co., 1978; (editor) *Crisis in Zimbabwe,* Westview Press, in press; (editor) *Formation and Development of States in West Africa: The Nineteenth Century Experience,* Nok Publishers, in press. Contributor to *Encyclopaedia Britannica;* contributor to *Ivory Tower, Journal of Black Studies, Legon Observer,* and *Black Academy Review.* Editor and founder, *Journal of African Studies,* 1974—; editorial adviser, *Journal of Black Studies;* member of editorial board, *Black Academy Review, Transactions of the Historical Society of Ghana, African Affairs, Black Academy Press, Pan African Journal,* and *Studia Africana.*

WORK IN PROGRESS: Slavery in Ashanti and Dahomey; King Ghezo of Dahomey, 1818-1858, a biography.

AVOCATIONAL INTERESTS: Travel to Africa, West and Central Europe, North America, and the Pacific; photography, swimming, reading poetry.

* * *

OBIECHINA, Emmanuel Nwanonye 1933-

PERSONAL: Born September 20, 1933, in Nkpor, Nigeria; son of Enyibaku Osakwe (a farmer) and Udenweze (Obierika) Obiechina; married Maria Obiageli (a college teacher), April 25, 1964; children: Nnonye, Nneka, Ikenna, Nnenna. *Education:* Attended College of Mary Immaculate, Kafanchan, Nigeria, 1947-52, and College of Technology, Zaria, Nigeria, 1956-58; University of Ibadan, B.A. (honors), 1961; Cambridge University, Ph.D., 1966. *Religion:* Roman Catholic. *Home:* 801 Imoke St., Nsukka, Nigeria. *Office:* Department of English, University of Nigeria, Nsukka, Nigeria.

CAREER: St. Malachy's Teachers' College, Minna, Nigeria, tutor in English language and literature, 1953-56; Foreign Service, Lagos, Nigeria, foreign service officer, 1961-62; University of Nigeria, Nsukka, 1967—, began as lecturer, professor of English, 1974—, chairman of department,

1975-78, member of provisional governing council. Visiting fellow, Centre for African Studies, University of Cambridge, 1972-73; visiting associate professor of comparative literature, University of Washington, Seattle, summer, 1973. Member of governing councils of Benue Institute for Higher Education and Nigerian Institute for International Affairs. *Member:* Nigerian English Studies Association, Nigerian Academy of Arts, Science, and Technology, Modern Language Association of Nigeria, Frantz Fanon Research Centre, West African Modern Language Association. *Awards, honors:* Commonwealth academic fellowship, 1972-73; International Biographical Association fellowship, 1978.

WRITINGS: (Author of commentary, notes, and exercises) James Baldwin, *Go Tell It on the Mountain,* Longmans, Green, 1966; *Literature for the Masses,* Nwamife, 1971, revised edition published as *An African Popular Literature,* Cambridge University Press, 1973; (editor) *Onitsha Market Literature,* Heinemann, 1972; *Culture, Tradition, and Society in the West African Novel,* Cambridge University Press, 1975; *Locusts* (collection of poems), Greenfield Review Press, 1976; *Functional Ideology for African States* (essays), Afro-Press, 1978.

Contributor: Bernth Lindfors, editor, *Critical Perspectives on Amos Tutuola,* Three Continental Press, 1975; Lindfors and Ulla Schild, editors, *Neo-African Literature: Essays in Memory of Jahnheinz Jahn,* [Mainz, Germany], 1977; C.O.D. Ekwensi, editor, *FESTAC Anthology,* Lagos, 1977; D. I. Nwoga, editor, *Literature and Modern West African Culture,* Ethiope, 1978; G.E.K. Ofomata, editor, *Nsukka Environment,* Fourth Dimension Publishers. 1978; O. Kalu, editor, *Humanities Handbook,* Fourth Dimension Publishers, 1978; Lindfors, editor, *Critical Perspectives on Chinua Achebe,* Three Continental Press, 1978. Contributor to professional journals, including *Presence Africaine, Conch, African Literature Today, Literary Studies, African Forum, Okike, Muse, Ufahamu,* and *Research in African Literature.* Editor of *Dimension* (publication of Frantz Fanon Research Centre), *Conch, Okike, Nsukkascope,* and *Nsukka Studies in African Literature.*

WORK IN PROGRESS: Language and Theme in African Literature: Eight Essays (manuscript completed and awaiting publication); *A Literary History of West Africa; The Art of the Folktale: The Igbo Example.*

SIDELIGHTS: Emmanuel Nwanonye Obiechina told *CA:* "I have come increasingly to hold the view that in the peculiar circumstances of Africa's underdevelopment and multiple infirmities, it is the duty of the writer, whatever else his other considerations and driving force, to put his art and craft at the service of his people, to give a voice to the voiceless millions and inspiration to the downtrodden. He must be optimistic and humane, and should take his place on the opposite side of those who attempt to overwhelm the masses with cynicism and a feeling of hopelessness.

"African intellectuals of my generation are privileged in having one foot in the old, rural-based culture and the other foot in the modern stage. They are well-situated to build a bridge between a past that risks vanishing altogether and a future that might become nothing better than adventitious. I have striven in most of what I write, whether these be of the nature of intellectual discourse or of literary expression, to provide some kind of bridge between the past and the future.

"There is, therefore, in our kind of place and time a certain inevitability of a paradox, conflicting forces propel the writer towards revolutionary and conservative stances, revolutionary in the fight against those forces that oppress the human spirit and inhibit creative mobility in the masses, and conservative in projecting such values of the past that strengthen African humanism and harmonize individual with social interests. Most difficult of all is to write with love and hope in one's heart, in the face of so many paralyzing weaknesses and pervasive purposelessness. But the writer cannot make any impact in our kind of context without love for the people and hope for their redemption. This is the greatest test of all."

BIOGRAPHICAL/CRITICAL SOURCES: Harold R. Collins, *Amos Tutuola,* Twayne, 1969; Ruth Finnegan, *Oral Literature in Africa,* Oxford University Press, 1970; Hane Zell and Helen Silver, editors, *A Reader's Guide to African Literature,* Holmes & Meier, 1971; Eustace Palmer, *An Introduction to the African Novel,* Holmes & Meier, 1972; Bernth Lindfors, *Folklore in Nigerian Literature,* Holmes & Meier, 1974.

*   *   *

O'BRIAN, John Lord   1874-1973

October 14, 1874—April 10, 1973; American lawyer. Obituaries: *New York Times,* April 11, 1973; *Washington Post,* April 11, 1973; *Time,* April 23, 1973.

*   *   *

O'CONNELL, Richard L(eo), Jr.   1912-1975

PERSONAL: Born April 19, 1912, in Syracuse, N.Y.; son of Richard Leo (a telephone engineer) and Mary K. (Jones) O'Connell; married Carolla Brune Farris (a high school English teacher), March 17, 1948; children: Teresa, Richard III, Siobhan. *Education:* Attended Shakespeare Institute; Syracuse University, B.A., 1935; Yale University, M.F.A., 1938; University of Birmingham, Ph.D., 1958. *Religion:* Roman Catholic. *Home:* 1007 Eighth St., Las Vegas, N.M. 87701. *Office:* Division of Drama, Highlands University, Las Vegas, N.M. 87701.

CAREER: Worked as an actor, assistant director, and lighting technician in New York theaters, summers, 1936-37; University of Texas, Main University (now University of Texas at Austin), instructor in drama and director of experimental theater, 1938-40; Syracuse University, Syracuse, N.Y., instructor in drama in Extension School, 1940-41; Letterman General Hospital, San Francisco, Calif., civilian entertainment director, 1946; Pasadena Playhouse and School of Drama, Pasadena, Calif., associate director, 1946-48; Highlands University, Las Vegas, N.M., assistant professor, 1950-54, associate professor of drama, 1954-58, professor of speech and drama, 1958-75, director of drama, 1958-68, director of speech and drama, 1968-75. Served as adviser to John Houseman for Hollywood production of "The House of Bernarda Alba." Community Concerts Association, director, 1958-62, president, 1962-67, chairman of publicity and artists' reception, beginning 1967; chairman, New Mexico Council of American College Theatre Festival, 1968-69; president, New Mexico Theatre Guild, 1968-70. *Military service:* U.S. Army, 1941-46; served in France and Germany; became captain. *Member:* Phi Beta Kappa, Phi Kappa Phi.

WRITINGS—Translator with James Graham-Lujan: Federico Garcia-Lorca, *From Lorca's Theatre: Five Plays of Garcia-Lorca,* Scribner, 1941; Enrique Amorim, *The Horse and His Shadow,* Scribner, 1942; Garcia-Lorca, *Three Tragedies: "Blood Wedding," "Yerma,"* [and] *"Bernarda Alba,"* New Directions, 1947, reprinted, Greenwood, 1977; Garcia-Lorca, *Five Plays by Garcia-Lorca: Comedies and Tragicomedies,* New Directions, 1963.

Contributor of translations: Dudley Fitts, editor, *Latin American Poetry*, New Directions, 1942; German Arciniegas, *The Knight of Eldorado*, Viking, 1942; James Laughlin, editor, *New Directions #8*, New Directions, 1944. Contributor to *New Republic* and *Journal of Modern Language and Literature*.

WORK IN PROGRESS: Translating *Dramatic Fragments and Essays of Garcia-Lorca*, with James Graham-Lujan.†

(Died February 9, 1975)

* * *

O'CONNELL, Walter E(dward)   1925-

PERSONAL: Born August 2, 1925, in Reading, Mass.; son of Walter Edward (a nurse) and Margaret (Turner) O'-Connell; married Gloria Kane, August 5, 1960; children: Sherry (Mrs. Ray Housley), Beverly Early, Vicki (Mrs. Randy Duncan). *Education:* University of Massachusetts, B.A., 1950; University of Texas, M.A., 1952, Ph.D., 1958. *Home:* 3406 Yoakum Blvd., Houston, Tex. 77006. *Office:* V.A. Glass Ark Drug Dependent Treatment Center, 1320 McGowen St., Houston, Tex. 77004.

CAREER: Worked since age of thirteen as construction and factory laborer, secretary and psychiatric aide, among other jobs. Diplomate in clinical psychology, American Board of Examiners in Professional Psychology, 1964; certified and licensed psychologist in Texas. Veterans Administration hospital in Texas, psychology trainee, 1955-58; Veterans Administration Hospital, Waco, Tex., clinical and research psychologist, 1958-66; Veterans Administration Hospital, Houston, Tex., research associate, 1966-68, research psychologist, 1968-72; Veterans Administration, Glass Ark Drug Dependent Treatment Center, Houston, director, 1975—. Adjunct professor, Baylor University, 1959-66, clinical associate professor of psychology at College of Medicine, 1969—; extension professor, University of Texas, 1965-66; lecturer, University of St. Thomas (Houston), 1966—; member of faculty, Houston Cooperative Crime Prevention Program, 1967-68; clinical assistant professor of psychology, University of Houston, 1969—; visiting clinical professor, Alfred Adler Institute, Chicago, Minneapolis, and Toronto, 1969—, non-resident professor, 1971—. Has attended, organized and directed more than fifty action therapy workshops, death and transformation workshops, and human relations laboratories. Has appeared as guest on numerous television, radio, and film programs, and directed "Action Therapy" for Columbia Broadcasting System-Television in 1968. Consultant to numerous hospitals, schools, and government agencies. *Military service:* U.S. Army Air Forces, aerial gunner, 1943-45.

MEMBER: International Congress of Social Psychiatry (member of advisory committee, 1964, 1969), Interamerican Society of Psychology, American Psychological Association (fellow), American Academy of Psychotherapists, Psychologists Interested in Religious Issues, Academy of Religion and Mental Health (vice-president of Waco branch, 1965-67), American Psychology-Law Society, American Society of Adlerian Psychology (member of board of directors, 1966-69, 1969-72; vice-president, 1970-71; president, 1971-72), American Teilhard de Chardin Association, Amici Thomae Mori, Civil War Round Table (president, 1964-65), Foundation of Thanatology (associate), Biofeedback Research Society, Texas Society of Adlerian Psychology (president, 1970-71), Sigma Xi. *Awards, honors:* Veterans Administration awards, 1964, for superior performance, 1965, for outstanding performance, 1968, for special services; A.P.A.

Cattell competition award, 1969; Roth Foundation awards, 1969, 1970.

WRITINGS: (Contributor) W. L. Pew, editor, *The War between the Generations*, Alfred Adler Institute, 1968; *An Odyssey of a Psychologist*, MSS Educational Publishing, 1971; *Action Therapy and Adlerian Theory: Selected Papers*, Alfred Adler Institute, 1975; (editor) *Psychotherapy: Theoretical and Technical Readings*, MSS Information Corp., 1976; *Super-Natural Highs*, Alfred Adler Institute, 1979. Contributor to proceedings and to *New Catholic Encyclopedia*. Contributor of over two hundred articles and reviews to psychology journals, including *Journal of Individual Psychology, Existential Psychiatry, Individual Psychologist, Sexual Behavior, Professional Psychology, Journal of Religion and Health, Journal of Social Psychology,* and *Rational Living*. Member of editorial board, *Voices: The Art and Science of Psychotherapy*, 1965-70, and *Catholic Psychological Record*, 1968-69; associate editor of *Individual Psychologist*, 1968—; chairman of editorial committee, American Society of Adlerian Psychology, 1969—.

WORK IN PROGRESS: Research on humor and on action therapy, natural high therapy and psychotheology.

BIOGRAPHICAL/CRITICAL SOURCES: Journal of Humanistic Psychology, number 4, 1964; *Voices: The Art and Science of Psychotherapy*, Volume 2, number 2, 1966, Volume 5, number 3, 1970; *Houston Post*, August 13, 1967, October 15, 1967; *Texas Catholic Herald*, June 26, 1970; *S.J.: The Jesuit*, Volume 45, number 4, 1970; *National Enquirer*, December 5, 1971; *Journal of Individual Psychology*, number 28, 1972; *Moreana*, June, 1973.

* * *

O'CONNOR, Edward Dennis   1922-

PERSONAL: Born in 1922, in Denver, Colo. *Education:* University of Notre Dame, A.B., 1944; Angelicum (Rome), S.T.D., 1952. *Office:* Department of Theology, University of Notre Dame, Notre Dame, Ind. 46556.

CAREER: Ordained Roman Catholic priest of Congregation of the Holy Cross (C.S.C.), 1948; University of Notre Dame, Notre Dame, Ind., assistant professor, 1952-64, associate professor of theology, 1964—. Director of studies, Moreau Seminary, 1959-65; visiting lecturer, University of Toronto, 1961; visiting associate professor, Valparaiso University, summer, 1967. *Member:* International Mariological Academy, International Pontifical Theological Academy of the Lateran, International Scotist Society, Catholic Theological Society of America, American Catholic Mariological Society (president, 1962-64), Catholic Charismatic Renewal Service Committee. *Awards, honors:* Marian Library Award, University of Dayton, 1958; Hazen Foundation post-doctoral research grant, Germany, 1962-63; Bishop Wright Mariological Award, 1963; National Catholic Book Award, 1971, for *The Pentecostal Movement in the Catholic Church*.

WRITINGS: The Mystery of the Woman, University of Notre Dame Press, 1956; *The Dogma of the Immaculate Conception: History and Significance*, University of Notre Dame Press, 1958; *Faith in Synoptic Gospels*, University of Notre Dame Press, 1961; *The Pentecostal Movement in the Catholic Church*, Ave Maria Press, 1971; *The Gifts and Fruits of the Spirit*, Blackfriars, 1973; *Perspectives on Charismatic Renewal*, University of Notre Dame Press, 1975; *Pope Paul and the Spirit*, Ave Maria Press, 1978. Contributor to theology journals.

WORK IN PROGRESS: The Hidden Life of the Virgin Mary; The Catholic Vision.

*   *   *

O'DONNELL, Bernard 1929-

PERSONAL: Born July 26, 1929, in Teaneck, N.J.; son of James E. and Mabel (Kelly) O'Donnell; married Holly Fiebelkorn, June, 1973; children: Kelley, Colleen, Erin, Padraic, Erich. *Education:* St. Peter's College, B.S., 1956; Columbia University, M.A., 1957; Harvard University, Ed.D., 1963. *Office:* National Council of Teachers of English, 1111 Kenyon Rd., Urbana, Ill. 61801.

CAREER: West Virginia University, Morgantown, instructor in English, 1957-59; Ball State University, Muncie, Ind., assistant professor of English, 1963-65; University of Iowa, Iowa City, assistant professor of English, 1965-67; National Council of Teachers of English, Urbana, Ill., director of ERIC Clearinghouse on the Teaching of English, 1967-72, director of ERIC Clearinghouse on Reading and Communications Skills, 1972—. Visiting professor, University of Illinois, 1970-72. Member of board of directors, Champaign County Opportunities Industrialization Center. *Military service:* U.S. Army, 1951-53. *Member:* Conference of College Composition and Communication, National Council of Teachers of English, Conference on English Education, Modern Language Association of America, National Conference on Research in English, American Educational Research Association, American Dialect Society, Regional Conferences on English in the Two-Year College, Phi Delta Kappa.

WRITINGS: (Contributor) Jacob Leed, editor, *The Computer and Literary Style,* Kent State University Press, 1966; (editor with Donna Butler) *A Guide to Available Project English Materials,* National Council of Teachers of English, 1969; *An Analysis of Prose Style to Determine Authorship,* Mouton, 1970; *Aids to Curriculum Planning in English,* National Council of Teachers of English, 1972. Contributor to academic journals.

*   *   *

OFARI, Earl 1945-

PERSONAL: Born October 8, 1945, in Chicago, Ill.; son of Earl (a realty agent) and Nina (Brown) Hutchinson; married Yvonne Divans, June 2, 1968; children: Sikivu Hutchinson. *Education:* California State College (now University), Los Angeles, B.A., 1968; Cornell University, special graduate research project, 1970-71.

CAREER: Mafundi Institute, Los Angeles, Calif., instructor in journalism, beginning 1972; currently public affairs director for radio station KPFK. Editorial consultant for Monthly Review Publishers, 1970-71. *Member:* American Newspaper Guild, Sigma Delta Chi.

WRITINGS: The Myth of Black Capitalism, Monthly Review Press, 1970; *Let Your Motto Be Resistance,* Beacon Press, 1972. Contributor of articles to *Black Scholar, Black World, Presence Africaine, Harper's, American Dialogue, Monthly Review,* and *Los Angeles Times.*

WORK IN PROGRESS: Research on the history and politics of the class structures in the black community.

*   *   *

OFFUTT, Andrew J(efferson)
(John Cleve)

PERSONAL: Born in Louisville, Ky.; son of Andrew J. (a state supervisor of sanitarians) and Helen (Spaninger) Offutt; married Mary Josephine McCabe, October 19, 1957; children: Christopher John, Andrew Jefferson VI, Mary Scotty, Melissa Jo. *Education:* University of Louisville, B.A., Ph.D. "Once I left the educational system, I began educating myself. Tacitus, Gibbon, Freud, Havelock Ellis, Stendahl, Vardis Fisher, and Ayn Rand: all helped, with writing lessons from Twain, Ruark, Heinlein. School served its purpose: it prepared me for employment. My self-education continues." *Religion:* "Hominist (from ad majorem hominis gloriam)." *Residence:* Haldeman, Ky. *Agent:* Blassingame, McCauley & Wood, 60 East 42nd St., New York, N.Y. 10017.

CAREER: Section salesman for food sales, Procter & Gamble, 1955-62; National Executive Life Insurance Co., salesman in Lexington, Ky., 1962-63; Coastal States Life Insurance Co., manager of three agencies, with headquarters in Morehead, Ky., 1963-70; full-time writer, 1971—. Had weekly FM radio program, "Offutt Raps." Former president, Lexington Big Brothers. *Member:* Science Fiction Writers of America (former president, treasurer, and membership chairman). *Awards, honors:* First prize in *IF* short story contest, 1954; *The Castle Keeps* was nominated for both Nebula and Hugo awards, 1972-73.

WRITINGS: Evil Is Live Spelled Backwards, Paperback Library, 1970; *The Great 24-Hour Thing,* Orpheus Books, 1971; *The Castle Keeps,* Berkley Publishing, 1972; *Messenger of Zhuvastou,* Berkley Publishing, 1972; *Holly Would,* Berkley Publishing, 1973; *The Galactic Rejects,* Lothrop, 1973; *Ardor on Aros,* Dell, 1973; *Operation: Super Ms.,* Berkley Publishing, 1974; (with D. Bruce Berry) *The Genetic Bomb,* Warner Paperback, 1975; *Chieftain of Andor,* Dell, 1976; (contributor) Judy-Lynn Del Rey, editor, *Stellar Short Novels,* Ballantine, 1976; *My Lord Barbarian,* Ballantine, 1977.

"Cormac mac Art" series; published by Zebra Books except as indicated: *Sword of the Gael,* 1975; *The Undying Wizard,* 1976; *Sign of the Moonbow,* 1977; *The Mists of Doom,* 1977; (with Keith J. Taylor) *The Tower of Death,* Ace Books, 1979.

"War among the Gods" series; published by Jove Books: *The Iron Lords,* 1979; *The Lady of the Snowmist,* in press; *The Cerulean Hawk,* in press.

"Tiana" series; with Richard K. Lyon; published by Pocket Books: *Demon in the Mirror,* 1978; *The Eyes of Sarsis,* 1979; *Oath by the World Fires,* in press.

"Conan" series: *Conan and the Sorcerer,* Sunridge Press, 1978; *Conan the Mercenary,* Sunridge Press, 1979; *The Sword of Skelos,* Bantam, 1979.

Under pseudonym John Cleve: *Mongol!,* Brandon House, 1969; *Call Me Calamity,* Tower/Midwood, 1970. Some stories reprinted in anthologies including *World's Best Science Fiction: 1968,* Ace Books, 1969, and *World's Best Science Fiction: 1972-73,* edited by Donald A. Wolheim and Arthur W. Saha, DAW Books, 1973. Author of more than thirty other books under undisclosed pseudonyms. Contributor of over 30 short stories, novelettes, and articles to various magazines including *Writer's Digest.* Editor, *Swords Against Darkness* (paperback magazine), 1977-78.

WORK IN PROGRESS: "Always."

SIDELIGHTS: Andrew J. Offutt told *CA:* "[I] grew up on a farm with 35 Holstein cattle, two coonhounds, and six acres of tobacco—and hay fever. Later, being an insurance executive—having my 3-piece suits made, driving the

Mercedes up and down the highways from motel to motel, getting my hair cut at 11:15 every Friday, fighting the agents' crisis-of-the-day syndrome—had me drinking Alka Seltzer twice a day. In 1971 I got out of it and began writing full time." During his first two years of full-time writing, he wore out a Selectric typing element, "something the IBM people assured me was impossible. I was writing seven days a week. That isn't impossible, it's just not credible." He writes in long hand now and types his work soon after it is written "while I can still read it; my penmanship started off plain Bad and has tapered off since." Offutt claims he began writing at the age of eight because of "the usual writer's background of unhappy childhood. Teachers made fun of my drawing; for turning my spelling words-into-sentences exercises into *stories*. . . . [I] sought refuge in reading and ariting fantasy and then, once I'd read all the Tarzan books and discovered that [Edgar Rice] Burroughs had written a Mars series, I discovered science fiction. My constant longtime love affairs are with this language, with fantasy and science fiction, and with [my wife] Jodie. She is the sort of sane, unselfish, loving person all writers—cracked, egoistic, selfish, that's us—should link with. Mainly because of her, I no longer *have* to write; the compulsion's gone."

Offutt reads over twenty magazines a month "ranging from *Science News* and *Human Nature* and *National Geographic* through *Book Digest* and *Heavy Metal* through *Savage Sword of Conan*—and I read 15 or 20 'comic' books a month—all uncomical. We take lots of vitamins and no newspapers; the latter is obviously unnecessary to human life, while the former is totally necessary, and carefully removed from most of our store-boughten foods."

Offutt has chaired or been a member of over 100 panels at science fiction conventions including the World Science Fiction Convention and the World Fantasy Convention. He has spoken at universities and writer's workshops and is affiliated with the *Writer's Digest* Criticism Service.

Offutt considers himself "the luckiest guy on the planet; I don't work; I do my hobby full time and am well, well paid for it. It's almost enough to give a person religion."

AVOCATIONAL INTERESTS: Collecting illustrated books, watercolor drawing, ancient arms and armor, and graphic and comic art.

BIOGRAPHICAL/CRITICAL SOURCES: Tomorrow and . . ., Numbers 5-7, 1970-71; *Kirkus Reviews*, November 1, 1973; *Worlds of It*, November/December, 1973; *Publisher's Weekly*, October 7, 1974.

*   *   *

OGAWA, Tetsuro   1912-1978

PERSONAL: Born September 14, 1912, in Wakayama-ken, Japan; son of Arajiro and Hatsu (Shiba) Ogawa; married Sadako Uchida, April 3, 1938; children: Yukiko Watanabe, Hiroko, Mitsuko, Sei, Ken. *Education:* Kyoto University, B.A., 1935. *Religion:* Buddhism. *Home:* 3-4 Kamimaro, Tanabe, Wakayama-ken, Japan.

CAREER: High school teacher in Wakayama-ken, Japan, 1940-43, 1947-63; Technical High School, Tanabe, Wakayama-ken, principal, 1963-67; High School of Commerce, Tanabe, Wakayama-ken, principal, 1967-71. *Military service:* Japanese Army, 1943-45.

WRITINGS: Terraced Hell, Tuttle, 1972. Also author of a history of the battles in Northern Luzon, Philippines, written in Japanese.

WORK IN PROGRESS: Books on war history, especially World War II in the Philippines.

SIDELIGHTS: Tetsuro Ogawa told *CA:* "In *Terraced Hell* I tried to give details of the sufferings of the Japanese soldiers and civilians and the human sides of these Japanese who were then regarded as 'fiend-like' and merciless."

(Died October 4, 1978)

*   *   *

O'GRADY, Joseph P(atrick)   1934-

PERSONAL: Born June 13, 1934, in Philadelphia, Pa.; son of Michael Joseph and Nora (Gallagher) O'Grady; children: Joseph Patrick, Karen Marie, Noreen, Michelle, Michael. *Education:* La Salle College, B.A., 1956; University of Notre Dame, M.A., 1958; University of Pennsylvania, Ph.D., 1965. *Religion:* Roman Catholic. *Home:* 307 French Rd., Newtown Square, Pa. 19073. *Office:* Department of History, La Salle College, 20th and Olney Aves., Philadelphia, Pa. 19141.

CAREER: La Salle College, Philadelphia, Pa., instructor, 1956-62, assistant professor, 1962-67, associate professor, 1967-72, professor of history, 1972—, chairman of department, 1970-74. Lecturer, Immaculata College, 1960-61; visiting professor, Villanova University, 1972; member of consulting faculty, U.S. Army Command and General Staff College, 1969-72. *Military service:* U.S. Army Reserve, 1956—, active duty, 1957; present rank, lieutenant colonel.

MEMBER: American Historical Association, Organization of American Historians, Society for Historians of American Foreign Relations (executive secretary, 1967—), American Catholic Historical Association, Southern Historical Association, Immigrant History Group, Ethnic Studies Association (executive secretary, 1972—), Historical Society of Pennsylvania, Catholic Historical Association of Philadelphia, Library Company of Philadelphia, Phi Alpha Theta. *Awards, honors:* American Jewish Committee grant, 1968; Harry S Truman Institute grant, 1970.

WRITINGS: (Editor) *The Immigrants' Influence on Wilson's Peace Policies,* University Press of Kentucky, 1967; *How the Irish Became American,* Twayne, 1972; *Irish-Americans and Anglo-American Relations, 1880-1888* (reprint of thesis), Arno, 1977. Contributor to *Virginia Magazine, Journal of Church and State, Catholic Historical Review, Journal of Higher Education, American Jewish Quarterly, South Atlantic Quarterly,* and other professional journals.

WORK IN PROGRESS: America's Last Volunteer Army; Richmond and Her Immigrants; 1961: Kennedy's Critical Year; Anglo-American Relations in Period of Change; Viet Nam: National Interest or National Folly.

*   *   *

OLDERMAN, Raymond M.   1937-

PERSONAL: Born June 29, 1937, in New York, N.Y.; son of Cass (an industrial consultant) and Hilda (Klein) Olderman; married Star Schechter, January 27, 1963. *Education:* University of Connecticut, B.A., 1962, M.A., 1964; Indiana University, Ph.D., 1969. *Home:* 716 Dunning St., Madison, Wis. 53704. *Office:* Department of Contemporary Literature, University of Wisconsin, Madison, Wis. 53706.

CAREER: Miami University, Oxford, Ohio, assistant professor of contemporary literature, 1969-72; University of Wisconsin—Madison, associate professor of contemporary literature, 1972—. *Military service:* U.S. Army, 1955-57. *Member:* Modern Language Association of America, Phi Beta Kappa. *Awards, honors:* Explicator Award, 1972, from

The Explicator, for *Beyond the Waste Land* as the best book of explication.

WRITINGS: Beyond the Waste Land: A Study of the American Novel in the Nineteen-Sixties, Yale University Press, 1972. Contributor of articles to *Contemporary Literature*.

WORK IN PROGRESS: A book, *Waiting for Revelation: Fiction and the Birth of the Seventies*.

*　　　*　　　*

O'LEARY, K. Daniel 1940-

PERSONAL: Born October 3, 1940, in West Chester, Pa.; married Susan Gilbert (a psychologist); children: Michael, Kathryn. *Education:* Pennsylvania State University, B.A. (with high distinction), 1962; University of Illinois, M.A., 1965, Ph.D., 1967. *Office:* Department of Psychology, State University of New York, Stony Brook, N.Y. 11790.

CAREER: University of Illinois at Urbana-Champaign, instructor, 1966-67, assistant professor of psychology, 1967, research associate, 1966-67; State University of New York at Stony Brook, assistant professor, 1967-70, associate professor, 1970-73, professor of psychology, 1973—, chairman of department, 1978—, director of University Laboratory School, 1969—. Certified psychologist in private practice, Stony Brook, N.Y., 1969—. *Member:* American Psychological Association, Society for Research in Child Development, Day Care and Child Development Council of America. *Awards, honors:* Grants from U.S. Office of Education and National Institute of Mental Health.

WRITINGS: (Editor with wife, Susan G. O'Leary) *Classroom Management: The Successful Use of Behavior Modification*, Pergamon, 1972; (contributor) H. C. Quay and J. S. Werry, editors, *Behavior Disorders of Children*, Wiley, 1972; (contributor) Emilio Ribes and S. W. Bijou, editors, *Behavior Modification: Issues and Extensions*, Academic Press, 1973; (with G. T. Wilson) *Behavior Therapy: Application and Outcome*, Prentice-Hall, 1975; (with Wilson) *Principles of Behavior Therapy*, Prentice-Hall, 1979. Contributor to *Critical Issues in Research and Practice*, Research Press, 1973, and to more than twenty other books which carry reprints of his articles from *Exceptional Children*, *Journal of School Psychology*, and other journals. *Journal of Applied Behavior Analysis*, member of editorial board, 1970-72, associate editor, 1971-73; consulting editor, *Journal of Abnormal Child Psychology*.

WORK IN PROGRESS: Research in classroom management involving the use of token reinforcement programs, and in methodological problems of observation in field-experimental settings; clinical outcome research.

*　　　*　　　*

OLIVER, Mary Hempstone 1885(?)-1973

1885(?)—March 27, 1973. American poet and author of religious articles. Obituaries: *Washington Post*, April 2, 1973.

*　　　*　　　*

OLMSTED, Robert W(alsh) 1936-

PERSONAL: Born March 15, 1936, in Washington, D.C.; son of Victor H. (a musician) and Frances (an accountant; maiden name, Walsh) Olmsted; married Elaine Bennett, May 6, 1958; children: Lori Lane, Suzanne Marie, Julie Elizabeth, James Robert Mason. *Education:* Attended Yale University, 1955; Mansfield State College, B.A., 1969; Uni-

versity of Maine, M.A., 1971. *Politics:* "Opposed to whatever party is in power." *Religion:* "Radical." *Address:* R. D. 1, Meadows of Dan, Va. 24120.

CAREER: Life insurance salesman in Virginia and Pennsylvania, 1958-65; *Sunbury Daily Item*, Sunbury, Pa., reporter and photographer, 1965-67; teacher in Franklin, N.H., 1970-72, and Bigfork, Minn., 1972-76; Patrick County High School, Stuart, Va., teacher, 1978—. President of Northwoods Press, Inc. *Military service:* U.S. Air Force, Security Service, 1955-58.

WRITINGS—Published by Northwoods Press, except as indicated: *Northern Lights* (poems), privately printed, 1969; (editor) *New England Voices*, 1972; (editor and contributor) *Summertime*, 1972; (editor) *Man: When Born of Fire*, 1973; *The First Christmas Ever*, 1973, revised edition, Anthelion Press, 1976; (editor) *Rendezvous with the Sea*, 1976; (editor) *Poems for Coffee Breaking*, 1976; (editor) *Two Hundred Years to Here*, 1976; *Shadows on Cassiopeia*, 1976; (editor) *The Poetry Book*, 1976; (editor) *Showcase '76*, 1977.

Work is anthologized in *Living Lyrics*, edited by Lawrence Young, Young Publications, 1966; *College Poetry: 1968-1969*, edited by Denis Hartman, National Poetry Press, 1968; *Best Poems Published in the 1960's*, National Poetry Press, 1970. Contributor to magazines and newspapers, including *Sports Afield*, *Pennsylvania Angler*, *Virginia Wildlife*, and *New Review*. Editor, *Western Virginia Sportsman*, 1964.

WORK IN PROGRESS: Thoreau: Man or Myth.

AVOCATIONAL INTERESTS: Photography, fishing and outdoor sports.

*　　　*　　　*

OLSCHEWSKI, Alfred 1920-

PERSONAL: Surname is pronounced Ol-*chef*-ski; born March 8, 1920, in Gumbinnen, Germany; son of Otto (a building superintendent) and Lydia (Fabricius) Olschewski; married Evelyn Druyer Dunn (a communications administrator), August 25, 1968. *Education:* Academy of Art, Duesseldorf, Germany, graduate (with honors), 1954; attended Handwerk und Kunst, Kassel, Germany. *Home:* 77 Nagog Hill Rd., Acton, Mass. 01720.

CAREER: Colibris Editora Ltd., Rio de Janeiro, Brazil, illustrator and designer, 1954-59; Bolta Products, Lawrence, Mass., textile designer, 1961-69; free-lance illustrator and designer, 1969—; also works as a substitute art teacher in public schools. Member of De Cordova Museum and Acton Arts League.

WRITINGS—Self-illustrated children's books: *The Wheel Rolls Over*, Little, Brown, 1962; *We Fly*, Little, Brown, 1967; *Winterbird*, Houghton, 1969.

Illustrator: Freya Littledale, *The Magic Tablecloth*, Scholastic Book Services, 1972.

SIDELIGHTS: Alfred Olschewski told *CA*, "It can't be said often enough: a writer, an artist, anyone who does creative work must be honest with himself or herself in order to produce anything worthwhile." *Avocational interests:* Flying, gardening.

*　　　*　　　*

OLSON, Clair C(olby) 1901-1972

PERSONAL: Born April 30, 1901, in Milwaukee, Wis.; son of William Donald (an accountant) and Minnie (Hastings) Olson; married Grace Anderson, February 4, 1928; children: Catherine C. *Education:* Oberlin College, A.B. (cum laude), 1923; University of Chicago, A.M., 1926, Ph.D., 1938; also studied at Harvard University, summer, 1937. *Politics:* Republican. *Religion:* Presbyterian. *Home:* 807 West Alpine Ave., Stockton, Calif. 95204.

CAREER: Iowa State College of Agriculture and Mechanic Arts (now Iowa State University of Science and Technology), Ames, instructor in English, 1923-25; University of Rochester, Rochester, N.Y., instructor in English, 1926-32; Armour Institute of Technology (now Illinois Institute of Technology), Chicago, instructor in English, 1933-35; North Park College, Chicago, instructor in English, 1934-38; Milwaukee State College (now University of Wisconsin—Milwaukee), instructor in English, 1938-39; University of the Pacific, Stockton, Calif., associate professor, 1939-43, professor of English, 1943-71, chairman of department, 1939-71. Visiting professor, University of California, Berkeley, summer, 1947, University of Texas, summer, 1959, Morehouse College, 1972, and University of British Columbia, summer, 1972.

MEMBER: Modern Language Association of America, College English Association, American Musicological Society, Mediaeval Academy of America, American Association of University Professors, Philological Association of the Pacific Coast, Medieval Association of the Pacific (vice-president), Commonwealth Club of California, Philological Association of Central California (past president), College English Association of the San Francisco Bay Area (past president), San Francisco Browning Society, Phi Kappa Phi. *Awards, honors:* American Council of Learned Societies grants, summers, 1950-51, also 1958, 1963, 1967; Modern Language Association of America grants, summers, 1952, 1957; Danforth Foundation grant, 1957; American Philosophical Society grant, 1960, 1961.

WRITINGS: (Editor with Martin M. Crow) Edith Rickert, compiler, *Chaucer's World,* Columbia University Press, 1948; *The Emerging Biography of a Poet,* University of the Pacific, 1954; (editor with Crow) Rickert and John M. Manly, compilers, *Chaucer Life-Records,* Clarendon Press, 1966; (contributor) Beryl Rowland, editor, *Companion to Chaucer Studies,* Oxford University Press, 1968. Also author with Virginia E. Leland of *Geoffrey Chaucer: Poet as Man of Affairs.* Contributor of articles and reviews to *Speculum, School and Society, Newsletter of the College English Association, Modern Philology,* and other periodicals.†

(Died, 1972)

*   *   *

ORLEANS, Leo A(nton)   1924-

PERSONAL: Born June 13, 1924, in Sverdlovsk, Russia; came to United States in 1939; naturalized in 1944; son of Anton J. (a furrier) and Susan (Agranovich) Orleans; married Helen Willis, August 20, 1949; children: Nina, David. *Education:* University of Southern California, B.A., 1950; graduate study at George Washington University and American University, 1951-56. *Home:* 5301 Brinkley Rd., Camp Springs, Md. 20031.

CAREER: Library of Congress, Washington, D.C., senior research analyst, 1951-65; National Science Foundation, Washington, D.C., associate studies director of Office of Economic and Manpower Studies, 1965-66; Library of Congress, China research specialist, 1966-75. Consultant to National Science Foundation. *Military service:* U.S. Army Air Forces, 1943-46; served in Pacific Theater. *Member:* So-

ciety for International Development, Association for Asian Studies, Population Association of America, International Union for the Scientific Study of Population.

WRITINGS: Professional Manpower and Education in Communist China, National Science Foundation, 1961; *Every Fifth Child: The Population of China,* Stanford University Press, 1972; *A Bibliography of Chinese Sources on Medicine and Public Health in the People's Republic of China: 1960-1970,* John E. Fogarty International Center for Advanced Study in the Health Sciences, 1973.

Contributor: *Population Trends in Eastern Europe, the USSR, and Mainland China,* Milbank Memorial Fund, 1960; *Sciences in Communist China,* American Academy for the Advancement of Science, 1961; Ronald Freedman, editor, *Population: The Vital Revolution,* Anchor Books, 1964; Ruth Adams, editor, *Contemporary China,* Pantheon, 1966; William T. Liu, editor, *Chinese Society under Communism: A Reader,* Wiley, 1967; C. T. Hu, editor, *Aspects of Chinese Education,* Teachers College Press, 1969; Stewart E. Fraser, editor, *Education and Communism in China,* International Studies Group, 1969; William Petersen, editor, *Readings in Population,* Macmillan, 1972; Joseph R. Quinn, editor, *Medicine and Public Health in the People's Republic of China,* National Institute of Health, 1972; Charles K. Wilber, editor, *Development and Underdevelopment,* Random House, 1973; *Studies in Family Planning,* Population Council, 1973; *Science and Technology in the People's Republic of China,* Organization for Economic Co-Operation and Development, 1977; Thomas C. Emmel, editor, *Global Perspectives on Environment,* Mayfield, 1977; Neville Maxwell, editor, *China's Road to Development,* Pergamon, 1979.

Contributor to *Collier's Encyclopedia.* Contributor of articles and reviews to over twenty journals including *China Quarterly, Journal of Asian Studies, Bulletin of Atomic Scientists, Science, World Affairs, Political Science Quarterly, Comparative Education Review,* and *Current Scene.* Editor, *Chinese Education,* 1968-69.

WORK IN PROGRESS: Editing *A Selective Review of China's Science and Technology,* for Stanford University Press.

SIDELIGHTS: Leo A. Orleans was taken to China as a six-month-old child, and he lived there until 1939.

*   *   *

ORMOND, Richard (Louis)   1939-

PERSONAL: Born January 16, 1939, in Bath, England; son of Conrad Eric and Dorothea (Gibbons) Ormond; married Leonee Jasper (a university lecturer), 1963; children: Augustus, Marcus. *Education:* Christ Church, Oxford, M.A., 1962. *Home:* 8 Holly Ter., London N.6, England. *Office:* National Portrait Gallery, London W.C.2, England.

CAREER: National Portrait Gallery, London, England, assistant keeper, 1965-75, deputy keeper, 1975—. *Member:* Victorian Society, William Morris Society.

WRITINGS: Sargent: Paintings, Drawings, Watercolors, Phaidon, 1970; *Catalogue of Early Victorian Portraits in the National Portrait Gallery,* two volumes, H.M.S.O., 1973; (with wife, Leonee Ormond) *Lord Leighton,* Yale University Press, 1975; *Fate of Monarchy,* Phaidon, 1977. Contributor to *Apollo, Connoisseur, Burlington Magazine,* and *Country Life.*

WORK IN PROGRESS: A critical study and catalogue of the work of Sir Edwin Landseer.

O'ROURKE, Terrence James 1932-

PERSONAL: Born April 17, 1932, in Bellingham, Washington; son of Wilfred Hugh and Rose (McEvoy) O'Rourke; married Betty Holtzclaw, June 6, 1953 (divorced); married Sally W. Wagner, April 7, 1977; children: (first marriage) Kathleen Sue, Michael Kevin, Terrence Patrick. Education: Columbia Institute for the Deaf and Dumb (now Gallaudet College), A.B., 1953; further courses at Catholic University of America, 1963—, and University of Maryland, 1965—. Home: 8805 Arliss St., Silver Spring, Md. 20901. Office: T. J. Publishers, Inc., 817 Silver Spring Ave., Suite 305-D, Silver Spring, Md. 20910.

CAREER: Teacher at North Dakota School for the Deaf, Devils Lake, 1953-65, and North Carolina School for the Deaf, Morganton, 1956-60; Gallaudet College, Washington, D.C., instructor at Kendall School (laboratory school), 1960-62, instructor at college, 1962-68; National Association of the Deaf, Silver Spring, Md., director of communicative skills program, 1968-78; T. J. Publishers, Inc., Silver Spring, president, 1978—. Director of special institutes on psycholinguistics and total communication at Western Maryland College, 1971, and Lewis and Clark College, 1972; Gallaudet College, member of board of directors of Rehabilitation Counselor Training Program, member of advisory committee for Office of Demographic Studies. Member of executive committee, President's Committee on Employment of the Handicapped; chairperson, National Symposium on Sign Language Research and Teaching, 1977, 1978; member of board of commissioners, Commission on Rehabilitation Counselor Certification. Member: American Deafness and Rehabilitation Association, National Association of the Deaf, Sign Instructors Guidance Network (SIGN; member of evaluation team), American Coalition of Citizens with Disabilities (president).

WRITINGS: A Basic Course in Manual Communication, National Association of the Deaf, 1970, revised edition, 1973; (editor) Psycholinguistics and Total Communication: The State of the Art, American Annals of the Deaf, 1972; A Basic Vocabulary: American Sign Language for Parents and Children, T. J. Publishers, 1978.

WORK IN PROGRESS: A Basic Course in American Sign Language; research on sign language and reducing the time lag between research and its application in training programs; additional texts on sign language.

BIOGRAPHICAL/CRITICAL SOURCES: Deaf American, July-August, 1971; Disabled-USA, Volume I, number 9, 1978.

* * *

ORUM, Anthony M(endl) 1939-

PERSONAL: Born November 20, 1939, in Milwaukee, Wis.; son of Maurice Donald and Alma (Osterman) Orum; married Amy Wexler (a sociologist), June 21, 1964; children: Nicholas Andrew. Education: Antioch College, B.A., 1962; University of Chicago, M.A., 1965, Ph.D., 1967. Home: 1504 Ridgecrest, Austin, Tex. 78746. Office: Department of Sociology, University of Texas, Austin, Tex. 78712.

CAREER: Emory University, Atlanta, Ga., instructor, 1966-67, assistant professor of sociology, 1967-69; University of Illinois at Urbana-Champaign, assistant professor of sociology, 1969-72; University of Texas at Austin, associate professor of sociology, 1972—. Fellow, Center for Social Organization Studies, 1963-64; visiting associate professor, University of North Carolina at Chapel Hill, summer, 1978.

Member: American Sociological Association. Awards, honors: A.C.T. summer postdoctoral fellow, 1972.

WRITINGS: (Contributor) Norval Glenn and Charles M. Bonjean, editors, Blacks in America, Chandler Publishing, 1969; (contributor) Russell Endo and William Strawbridge, editors, Black America: Introductory Readings, Prentice-Hall, 1970; (contributor) Dan Nimmo and Bonjean, editors, Political Attitudes and Public Opinion, McKay, 1972; Black Students in Protest: A Study of the Origins of the Black Student Movement (monograph), American Sociological Association, 1972; (editor) The Seeds of Politics: Youth and Politics in America, Prentice-Hall, 1972; Introduction to Political Sociology: The Social Anatomy of the Body Politic, Prentice-Hall, 1978. Contributor to social science journals.

WORK IN PROGRESS: A symbolic theory of ethnicity; social constraints and the political arena.

* * *

ORVELL, Miles 1944-

PERSONAL: Born January 9, 1944, in New York, N.Y.; son of Samuel (a commercial artist) and Mary (Bass) Orvell; married Tamar Chipkin, January 21, 1965 (divorced, 1968). Education: Columbia University, A.B., 1964; Harvard University, M.A., 1965, Ph.D., 1970. Office: Department of English, Temple University, Philadelphia, Pa. 19122.

CAREER: Temple University, Philadelphia, Pa., assistant professor, 1969-74, associate professor of English, 1974—, director of American studies, 1975—. Member: Modern Language Association of America, American Studies Association, American Association of University Professors, Phi Beta Kappa. Awards, honors: Woodrow Wilson fellowship, 1964; National Endowment for the Humanities summer stipend, 1972.

WRITINGS: Invisible Parade: The Fiction of Flannery O'Connor, Temple University Press, 1973. Associate, Journal of Modern Literature.

WORK IN PROGRESS: Contributing an essay to Technology and the Literary Mind, edited by Michel Benamou; The Real Thing, a study of American realism.

* * *

ORY, Edward 1886-1973
(Kid Ory)

December 25, 1886—January 23, 1973; American Dixieland jazz trombonist, composer, and bandleader. Obituaries: New York Times, January 24, 1973; Newsweek, February 5, 1973.

* * *

OSTERWEIS, Rollin G(ustav) 1907-

PERSONAL: Born August 15, 1907, in West Haven, Conn.; son of Gustav (a cigar manufacturer and dealer in leaf tobacco) and Rose (Osterweis) Osterweis; married Ruth Mildred Loewenstein, September 27, 1932; children: Sally Jo (Mrs. Charles Kopman), Nancy (Mrs. Myles Alderman), Ruth Mildred (Mrs. Joel Selig), Rollyn Gay (Mrs. Daniel Krichbaum). Education: Yale University, B.A., 1930, M.A., 1943, Ph.D., 1946; also studied at Oxford University, summer, 1931, and Georgetown Foreign Service School, 1931-32. Politics: Independent. Religion: Reformed Jewish. Home: 396 St. Ronan St., New Haven, Conn. 06511. Office: Department of History, 771 Yale Station, Yale University, New Haven, Conn. 06520.

CAREER: Lewis Osterweis & Sons, New Haven, Conn., salesman, sales manager, and partner in charge of sales, 1932-42; Yale University, New Haven, Conn., instructor, 1943-45, 1946-48, assistant professor, 1949-54, associate professor, 1954-68, professor of history, 1968—, director of debating and public speaking, 1948—. Commissioner in charge of publications, Connecticut State Civil War Centennial Commission, 1961-65; president, New Haven Preservation Trust, 1971—.

MEMBER: American Historical Association, Organization of American Historians, American Forensic Association, Authors Club (London), Connecticut Academy of Arts and Sciences, Elizabethan Club (Yale University), Yale Faculty Club (president, 1970-72), New Haven Colony Historical Society (president, 1962-67).

WRITINGS: J. P. Benjamin, Putnam, 1933; *Rebecca Gratz,* Putnam, 1935; *Sesquicentennial History of Connecticut Academy of Arts and Sciences,* Yale University Press, 1949; *Romanticism and Nationalism in the Old South,* Yale University Press, 1949; *Three Centuries of New Haven: 1638-1938,* Yale University Press, 1963; (with Jacques Guicharnaud) *Santarem* (historical novel), Librairie Plon, 1959; *Charter No. 2: The Centennial History of the First New Haven National Bank,* Printing Office, Yale University Press, 1963; *The Myth of the Lost Cause: 1865-1900,* Shoestring, 1973; *The New Haven Green and the American Bicentennial,* Shoestring, 1976.

* * *

OSTHEIMER, John 1938-

PERSONAL: Born November 22, 1938, in Westchester, Pa.; son of Alfred J. (an insurance agent) and Ruth (McGargle) Ostheimer; married Nancy Cushing, June 17, 1963; children: Ellen, Gibson, William. *Education:* Yale University, B.A., 1960, M.A., 1964, Ph.D., 1967. *Home:* 1968 North Crescent Dr., Flagstaff, Ariz. 86001. *Office address:* Box 6023, Northern Arizona University, Flagstaff, Ariz. 86001.

CAREER: University College, Dar es Salaam, Tanzania, lecturer in political science, 1964-66; Southern Connecticut State College, New Haven, assistant professor of political science, 1966-67; Northern Arizona University, Flagstaff, assistant professor, 1967-71, associate professor of political science, 1971—. Member of Coconino County Welfare Advisory Council, 1971-73. *Member:* American Political Science Association, African Studies Association, American Academy of Political and Social Science, American Association of University Professors, Western Africanists Association (member of board of directors, 1969-72), Rocky Mountain Social Science Association (vice-president, 1971-72), Western Political Science Association. *Awards, honors:* Fulbright research scholar, 1973.

WRITINGS: Nigerian Politics, Harper, 1972; *Politics of the Western Indian Ocean Islands,* Praeger, 1975; *Life or Death—Who Controls?,* Springer Publishing, 1976. Contributor to *Rocky Mountain Social Science Journal, Journal of Social Psychology, Social Science Quarterly, Africa Today, African Review, Environmental Affairs, Journal of Commonwealth and Comparative Politics, Eisenhower Consortium Bulletin,* and *Policy Studies Journal.* Associate editor of *Social Science Journal,* 1972-78, and *Western Political Quarterly,* 1978—.

WORK IN PROGRESS: Research on American and international environmental politics.

SIDELIGHTS: John Ostheimer has traveled extensively in Europe, Africa, Southeast Asia, India, and the Indian Ocean islands.

* * *

OSTRY, Sylvia 1927-

PERSONAL: Born June 3, 1927, in Winnipeg, Manitoba, Canada; daughter of Morris J. and Betsy D. (Stoller) Knelman; married Bernard Ostry (assistant under-secretary of state of Canada), September 21, 1956; children: Adam, Jonathan. *Education:* University of Manitoba, pre-medical and medical student, 1943-46; McGill University, B.A. (honors), 1948, M.A., 1950, Ph.D. (in conjunction with Cambridge University), 1954. *Home:* Aylmer Rd., R.R.2, Aylmer East, Quebec, Canada. *Office:* Department of Consumer Corporate Affairs, Place du Portage, Ottawa, Ontario, Canada K1A 0C9.

CAREER: Sir George Williams University, Montreal, Quebec, lecturer in economics, 1948-50, 1951-54; McGill University, Montreal, lecturer in economics, 1952-55; Oxford University, Oxford, England, assistant research officer, Institute of Statistics, 1955-57; McGill University, assistant professor of economics, 1958-62; University of Montreal, Montreal, associate professor of economics, 1962-64; Dominion Bureau of Statistics, Ottawa, Ontario, assistant director of research, Labour Division, 1965, director of special manpower studies and consultation, 1965-69; Economic Council of Canada, Ottawa, director, 1969-72; Statistics Canada, Ottawa, chief statistician, 1972; Department of Consumer Corporate Affairs, Ottawa, deputy minister of consumer corporate affairs, 1975—. Member of management advisory council, Faculty Management Studies, University of Toronto; member of advisory council, Faculty Administrative Studies, York University; member of visiting committee of board overseers, Harvard University; member of board of governors, Carleton University; member of committee on university affairs, Province of Ontario, 1971-72; member of Ontario Selection Committee, Rhodes Scholarship Trust, 1976; member of board of directors, Data Clearing House for Social Sciences. Consultant to Senate of Canada, 1959-60, Government of Manitoba, 1961-62, Economic Council of Canada, 1964-65, and Department of Manpower and Immigration, 1966—.

MEMBER: American Economic Association, Canadian Economic Association, Canadian Political Science Association, Industrial Relations Research Association, Royal Economic Society. *Awards, honors:* Moyse traveling fellowship in England, 1950-51; grants from Canadian Social Science Research Council, 1959-60, 1960-61, and Canada Council, 1960, 1961; LL.D. from University of New Brunswick and York University, both 1971.

WRITINGS: (Contributor) John J. Deutsch and others, editors, *The Canadian Economy: Selected Readings,* Macmillan, 1961, revised edition, 1965; (with Harry D. Woods) *Labour Policy and Labour Economics in Canada,* Macmillan, 1962, St. Martin's, 1963, 2nd edition (with Mahmood A. Zaidi as additional co-author), St. Martin's, 1972; (contributor) *The Measurement and Interpretation of Job Vacancies,* Columbia University Press, 1966; (editor with T. K. Rymes) *Regional Statistical Studies,* University of Toronto Press, 1967; (contributor) R. W. Miller and Fraser Isbester, editors, *Canadian Labour in Transition,* Prentice-Hall, 1971.

Research monographs, published by Queen's Printer: (With F. T. Denton and Y. Kasahara) *Population and Labour*

Force Projections to 1970, 1964; (with Denton) *An Analysis of Post-War Unemployment,* 1964; (with Jenny Podoluk) *Economic Status of the Aging,* 1966; (with Noah Meltz) *The Female Worker: Labour Force and Occupational Trends,* 1966; (with Denton) *Historical Estimates of the Canadian Labour Force,* 1967; *Provincial Differences in Labour Force Participation,* 1968; *The Occupational Composition of the Canadian Labour Force,* 1968; *Unemployment in Canada,* 1968; *The Female Worker in Canada,* 1968; *Geographic Composition of the Canadian Labour Force,* 1968; (with Denton) *Working Life Tables for Canadian Males,* 1968.

*   *   *

OUTKA, Gene 1937-

PERSONAL: Born February 24, 1937, in Sioux Falls, S.D.; son of Harold Irvin and Gertrude Anne (Elliott) Outka; married Carole Lee DeVore, June 26, 1960; children: Paul Harold, Elizabeth Noelle. *Education:* University of Redlands, B.A., 1959; Yale University, B.D., 1962, Ph.D., 1967. *Religion:* Lutheran. *Home:* 280 Bayard Ave., North Haven, Conn. 06518. *Office:* Department of Religious Studies, Yale University, New Haven, Conn. 06520.

CAREER: Princeton University, Princeton, N.J., assistant professor, 1967-73, associate professor of ethics, 1973-75; Yale University, New Haven, Conn., associate professor of religious studies, 1975—. Visiting scholar at Georgetown University, 1972-73. *Member:* Society for Values in Higher Education, American Academy of Religion, American Society of Christian Ethics, American Theological Society. *Awards, honors:* Study fellow of American Council of Learned Societies, 1968-69; service fellow of U.S. Department of Health, Education and Welfare, 1972-73; D.H.L., University of Redlands, 1978.

WRITINGS: (Editor with Paul Ramsey, and contributor) *Norm and Context in Christian Ethics,* Scribner, 1968; *Agape: An Ethical Analysis,* Yale University Press, 1972; (editor with John P. Reeder, Jr., and contributor) *Religion and Morality,* Doubleday-Anchor, 1973; (contributor) Tom L. Beauchamp and LeRoy Walters, editors, *Contemporary Issues in Bioethics,* Dickenson, 1978.

BIOGRAPHICAL/CRITICAL SOURCES: Christian Century, December 25, 1968.

P

PALEN, J(oseph) John 1939-

PERSONAL: Born February 24, 1939, in Dubuque, Iowa; son of Joseph John and Mary (Toner) Palen; married Karen Doody, June 9, 1962; children: Joseph, Elizabeth, Ellen. *Education:* University of Notre Dame, B.A., 1961; University of Wisconsin, M.A., 1963, Ph.D., 1966. *Home:* 4189 North Bartlett, Shorewood, Wis. 53211. *Office:* Department of Sociology, University of Wisconsin, Milwaukee, Wis. 53211.

CAREER: University of Wisconsin—Milwaukee, instructor, 1966-67, associate professor, 1969-77, professor of sociology, 1977—. *Military service:* U.S. Army, taught at Industrial College of the Armed Forces and Army General Staff, 1967-69; became captain. *Member:* American Sociological Association, Population Association of America, Midwest Sociological Association.

WRITINGS: (With Karl Flaming) *Urban America: Conflict and Change,* Holt, 1972; *Metropolitan Milwaukee Fact Book, 1970,* Milwaukee Urban Observatory, 1972; *City Scenes: Problems and Prospects,* Little, Brown, 1977; *The Urban World,* McGraw, 1978; *Social Problems,* McGraw, 1979.

WORK IN PROGRESS: Revised edition of *The Urban World.*

* * *

PALEY, Nicholas M(iroslav) 1911-

PERSONAL: Born December 7, 1911, in Ukraine; son of John (an Orthodox priest) and Anna (Szkilniak) Paley; married Mary Temoshok, September 12, 1943; children: Nicholas B., Lydia A-M. *Education:* Ohio State University, B.A., 1943, M.A., 1947; Interamerican University, Monterrey, Mexico, Ph.D., 1968. *Home:* 2436 Shopiere Rd., Beloit, Wis. 53511. *Office:* Department of Modern Languages, Beloit College, Beloit, Wis. 53511.

CAREER: Beloit College, Beloit, Wis., instructor, 1950-54, assistant professor, 1954-58, associate professor, 1958-68, professor of modern languages, 1969—. Member of advisory board, Interamerican University.

WRITINGS: Nadiyni Dni (short stories; title means "Hopeful Days"), Academia, 1949; (translator from Spanish into Ukrainian) Pedro de Alarcon, *El sombrero de tres picos,* National Word (Pittsburgh), 1956; *Tesis profe-*

sionales, Ediciones Universitarias, 1969; (translator from Spanish into Ukrainian) *Lazarillo de Tormes,* J. Serediak, 1970; *Etcetera* (poetry), Arcadia, 1970; (translator from Spanish into Ukrainian) Manuel Tamayo y Baus, *Un drama nuevo* (title means "A New Drama"), J. Serediak, 1972; *Dos novelas de la tierra,* Editorial Universidad Inter-American de Monterrey, 1972; *Sentymentalna Ukraina* (sketches, humor, and satire; title means "Sentimental Ukraine"), J. Serediak, 1974; (translator from Spanish into Ukraine) *Palkoyu krov'yu* (short stories; title means "With Ardent Blood"), J. Serediak, 1978. Contributor of articles to literature journals.

WORK IN PROGRESS: Romantychna Ukrainia, a book of sketches, humor, and satire.

* * *

PALLISTER, Janis L(ouise) 1926-

PERSONAL: Born January 12, 1926, in Rochester, Minn.; daughter of George L. (an engineer) and Edith (Reed) Pallister. *Education:* University of Minnesota, B.A. (cum laude), 1946, M.A., 1948, Ph.D., 1964; also attended University of Wisconsin, 1950-52; Sorbonne, University of Paris, Certificat, 1959. *Politics:* Independent. *Religion:* Roman Catholic. *Home:* 211 State St., Bowling Green, Ohio 43402. *Office:* Department of Romance Languages, Bowling Green State University, Bowling Green, Ohio 43402.

CAREER: Black Hills Teachers College (now Black Hills State College), Spearfish, S.D., instructor in French, Spanish, and English, 1948-50; translator, Minnesota Mining and Manufacturing, 1953-54; Colby College, Waterville, Me., instructor in French, 1959-61; Bowling Green State University, Bowling Green, Ohio, instructor, 1961-65, assistant professor, 1965-68, associate professor, 1968-71, professor of French, 1971—. *Member:* American Association of Teachers of French, Modern Language Association of America, American Literary Translators Association, African Studies Association, African Literature Association, American Council on the Teaching of Foreign Languages, Modern Humanities Research Association, American Association of University Professors, Renaissance Society of America, Paul Claudel Society of America, Mediaeval Academy of America, Lambda Alpha Psi, Pi Delta Phi, Phi Sigma Iota, Sigma Delta Pi. *Awards, honors:* Tozer Foundation fellow, 1969; Greater University fellowship, 1959; Columbia University Translation Center Award, 1978.

WRITINGS: *The World View of Beroalde de Verville,* Vrin, 1971; *Mon Autre Lyre,* J. & C. Transcripts, 1971; *The Planting,* New Voices, 1972; *The Green Balloon* (poems), Northwoods Press, 1976; *Confrontations,* Westburg Associates, 1977; *Esanzo,* Naaman, 1977; *The Bruised Reed,* Naaman, 1978. Also author, with Ramona Cormier, of *Waiting for Death: The Philosophical Significance of "En attendant Godot",* University of Alabama Press. Contributor of more than eighty poems in English, Spanish, and French, and about thirty articles and reviews to professional and literary journals, including *Poetry Review, Poet and Critic, Encore, Haiku Highlights, Beyond Baroque, L'Esprit Createur, French Review, Claudel Studies,* and *Romance Notes.*

WORK IN PROGRESS: A critical edition of *Le Moyen de Parvenir,* by Beroalde de Verville.

SIDELIGHTS: Janis L. Pallister speaks French and Spanish, and reads German, Italian, Old French, Old Provencal, Portuguese, and Latin.

* * *

PALMER, C(yril) Everard 1930-

PERSONAL: Born October 15, 1930, in Kendal, Jamaica; son of Cyril (a farmer) and Vida Palmer. *Education:* Mico Training College, teaching diploma, 1955; Lakehead University, B.A. *Address:* P.O. Box 381, Red Rock, Ontario, Canada.

CAREER: Teacher in Ontario, 1965—.

WRITINGS—Juvenile: *A Broken Vessel,* Pioneer Press, 1960; *The Cloud with the Silver Lining,* Deutsch, 1966; *Big Doc Bitterdot,* Deutsch, 1968; *The Sun Salutes You,* Deutsch, 1970; *The Hummingbird People,* Deutsch, 1971; *A Cow Called Boy,* Bobbs-Merrill, 1971; *The Wooing of Beppo Tate,* Deutsch, 1972; *Baba and Mr. Big,* Bobbs-Merrill, 1972; *My Father Sun Sun Johnson,* Deutsch, 1974; *The Adventures of Jimmy Maxwell,* Ministry of Education, 1976; *A Taste of Danger,* Ministry of Education, 1976; *A Dog Called Houdini,* Deutsch, 1978.

BIOGRAPHICAL/CRITICAL SOURCES: *Times Literary Supplement,* April 16, 1970; *Books and Bookmen,* May, 1970.

* * *

PANIAGUA BERMUDEZ, Domingo 1880(?)-1973

1880(?)—March 25, 1973. Mexican-born American journalist and author. Obituaries: *Washington Post,* March 28, 1973.

* * *

PAPP, Charles Steven 1917-

PERSONAL: Born February 16, 1917; son of Alexander Joseph and Maria (Szoke) Papp; married Magda R. Matai (an agricultural inspector); children: Charles E., Magda. *Education:* Reformatus Collegium, Debrecen, Hungary, B.S., 1938; Franz Joseph University, M.A., 1942, Ph.D., 1944. *Home:* 7541 Albezzia Lane, Sacramento, Calif. 95828. *Office:* California State Department of Food and Agriculture, 1220 N St., Sacramento, Calif. 95828.

CAREER: Member of faculty, University of California, 1958-71; California State Department of Food and Agriculture, Sacramento, entomologist, 1971—.

WRITINGS: *A Manual of Seed Preparation,* Department of Agriculture (Hungary), 1942; *The Beetles of Hungary,*

Ruszkabanyai, 1943; *The Malaria,* Hungaria, 1948; *Sleeping Sickness, Kala Azar and the South American Espundia,* Hungaria, 1948; *The Hispinae of America,* Portuguese Academy of Sciences, 1952; *An Introduction to Scientific Illustration,* privately printed, 1963; *Scientific Illustration: Theory and Practice,* W. C. Brown, 1968; *A Spring I'll Never Forget,* Munsinger, 1970; *The Magic of Color Printing,* American Visual Aid Books, 1970; *Proofprints of Insect Illustrations,* Author's Studio, 1971; (with L. A. Swan) *The Common Insects of North America,* Harper, 1972. Contributor of about five hundred articles on agriculture and insects to scientific journals in the United States and abroad.

WORK IN PROGRESS: *North American Beetle Book;* with L. A. Swan, *Popular Medical Entomology; I Followed the Sunset,* an autobiography; with T. D. Eichlin, *Butterflies and Moths of North America.*

* * *

PARENTE, Sarah Eleanor 1913-

PERSONAL: Born January 15, 1913, in Ybbs, Austria; came to United States in 1930; U.S. citizen; daughter of Talis (a sea captain) and Madeleine (Benet) Andersen; married Charles Parente (an estate gardener), July 14, 1931 (died April 1, 1973); married Jerome Thyme, December 21, 1973; children: (first marriage) Eric, Philip, Louise. *Education:* "Self-taught." *Religion:* "Early Christian." *Politics:* "Late Democrat." *Home:* 31316 St. Margaret Dr., St. Clair Shores, Mich. 48082.

CAREER: Has worked as a cook, laundress, day-worker, switchboard operator, secretary, public relations writer, advertising copywriter, television actress, law clerk, and editor, among other occupations; Odd Fellow Products, Morossville, Mich., owner and general manager, 1965-69; The Herb Doctor (health food store), Ferndale, Mich., manager, 1969-74; free-lance writer, 1974—. Has organized and conducted numerous seminars on nutrition. *Member:* Autodidact Society, Progressive Gardening Club (president, 1967-72), Learn'n Gro Association (founder), NBTSAM. *Awards, honors:* Heckuva Nice Gal Award, Minnehaha County Chamber of Commerce, 1954.

WRITINGS: *Act I, Scene I* (autobiography), Gamboge Press, 1958; *Trial and Error* (gardening manual), Sunflower Press, 1959; *Screenings* (poetry), Hite Books, 1963; *Simply This* (autobiographical novel), Sedulous Press, 1965; *Wedell French: Revolutionary Hero* (juvenile), Laney, 1968; *Fur Girl: The Story of Tutu* (biography of a cat), Animal Books, 1970; *Striations* (poems), Countdown Press, 1972; *To Herb, or Not to Herb* (cookbook), Nutmeg Press, 1973; *Herbs Will Set You Free* (cookbook), Hemp Books, 1974; *Living Natural,* True-to-Life Books, 1978.

WORK IN PROGRESS: Research on the eating habits "of the average middle-class junk food addict"; *Spice Is Nice; Grow with Me.*

SIDELIGHTS: Sarah Parente discovered the world of herbs while nursing her husband through an illness. She told *CA:* "The doctor placed my husband on a severely restricted diet. He soon became bored with the prescribed menu, so after doing some research and experimenting I learned how to make his food more desirable through the use of herbs. This eventually led to my opening a natural food store and writing the two herb cookbooks.

Parente continues: "I wish more people would realize the importance of nutrition. After all, we are what we eat." *Avocational interests:* "Almost anything that is real," organic gardening, watching sailboats, walking, running, cross-country skiing, and ice-skating.

BIOGRAPHICAL/CRITICAL SOURCES: Gallery Journal, Volume IV, number 3, 1959; *Osage Review,* November, 1965; *Home and Farm News,* May, 1969; *Oregano Journal,* November 15, 1974.

* * *

PARKER, Clyde A.   1927-

PERSONAL: Born March 17, 1927, in Ogden, Utah; son of Thomas and Reka (van Braak) Parker; married Ilene Kendell, December 27, 1950; children: Thomas, Gregory, Camille, Lisa. *Education:* Brigham Young University, B.S. and M.S., 1952; University of Minnesota, Ph.D., 1957. *Politics:* Independent. *Religion:* Church of Jesus Christ of Latter-day Saints (Mormon). *Office:* 202 Burton Hall, University of Minnesota, Minneapolis, Minn. 55455.

CAREER: Teacher in schools of Ogden, Utah, 1952-53; Brigham Young University, Provo, Utah, counselor, 1953-55, associate professor of personnel and guidance, 1957-64; University of Minnesota, Minneapolis, associate professor, 1964-65, professor of educational psychology, 1965—, chairman of department of counseling and student personnel psychology, 1966-71, chairman of department of educational foundations, 1974—. Visiting professor at University of Missouri, summer, 1959, spring, 1963, Boston University, summer, 1960, and Utah State University, summer, 1962; Fulbright lecturer, U.S. Educational Foundation in India, 1971-72. *Member:* American Psychological Association, American Personnel and Guidance Association.

WRITINGS: (Editor) *Counseling Theories and Counselor Education,* Houghton, 1968; (editor) *Readings in Student Services,* U.S. Educational Foundation in India (New Delhi), 1972; (editor) *Psychological Consultation: Helping Teachers Meet Special Needs,* Council for Exceptional Children, 1975; (editor) *Encouraging Development in College Students,* University of Minnesota Press, 1978. Contributor to *Research on Religious Development,* Religious Education Association, 1971, and *Encyclopedia of Educational Research.* Contributor of articles and reviews to journals in his field.

* * *

PARKER, W(ilford) Oren   1911-

PERSONAL: Born December 1, 1911, in Lansing, Mich.; son of E. Wilford (superintendent of schools) and Alice (Oren) Parker; married Thelma F. Teschendorf, April 10, 1937; children: Margaret (Mrs. Clifton V. Rice), Wilford Oren, Jr. *Education:* University of Michigan, B.DD., 1934; Yale University, M.F.A., 1940. *Home:* 1732 Wightman St., Pittsburgh, Pa. 15217. *Office:* Department of Scene Design, Carnegie-Mellon University, Schenely Park, Pittsburgh, Pa. 15213.

CAREER: University of Michigan, Ann Arbor, assistant professor of scene design, 1934-38; Williams College, Williamstown, Mass., assistant professor of scene design, 1942-45; University of Texas, Main University (now University of Texas at Austin), assistant professor of scene design, 1944-45; Yale University, New Haven, Conn., assistant professor of scene design, 1945-63; Carnegie-Mellon University, Pittsburgh, Pa., professor of scene design, 1963-78, professor emeritus, 1978—. Scene designer for Columbia Broadcast System, 1951, Pittsburgh Civic Light Opera, 1963, and for Coca-Cola, American Motors and General Motors industrial shows. *Member:* United Scenic Artists, American Educational Theatre Association, Connecticut Academy of Arts and Sciences, Silvermine Guild of Artists, Michigan M Club, Michigan Union, Trigon, Yale University Alumni Association, Yale Dramatic Association, Yale Drama Alumni Association.

WRITINGS: Scene Design and Stage Lighting, Holt, 1963, 4th edition, 1978; *Scene-Graphic Techniques,* Carnegie-Mellon University Press, 1963.

WORK IN PROGRESS: Co-authoring a book, *Scenography of Light,* for Holt, completion expected in 1980.

* * *

PARKHURST, Helen   1887-1973

March 7, 1887—June 1, 1973; American educator. Obituaries: *New York Times,* June 3, 1973; *Washington Post,* June 4, 1973.

* * *

PARKS, Gordon (Alexander Buchanan)   1912-

PERSONAL: Born November 30, 1912, in Fort Scott, Kan.; son of Andrew Jackson and Sarah (Ross) Parks; married Sally Alvis, 1933 (divorced, 1961); married Elizabeth Campbell, December, 1962 (divorced, 1973); married Genevieve Young (a book editor), August 26, 1973; children: (first marriage) Gordon, Jr., Toni (Mrs. Jean-Luc Brouillaud), David; (second marriage) Leslie. *Education:* Attended high school in St. Paul, Minn. *Politics:* Democrat. *Religion:* Methodist. *Home:* 860 United Nations Plaza, New York, N.Y. 10017. *Agent:* (Film) Ben Benjamin, Creative Management Associates, 9255 Sunset Blvd., Los Angeles, Calif. 90069.

CAREER: Photographer, writer, film director, and composer. Worked at various jobs prior to 1937, when he focused on photography; photographer with Farm Security Administration, 1942-43, with Office of War Information, 1944, and with Standard Oil Co. of New Jersey, 1945-48; *Life,* New York City, photo-journalist, 1948-72; *Essence* (magazine), New York City, editorial director, 1970-73. Film director, 1968—, directing motion pictures for Warner Brothers-Seven Arts, Metro-Goldwyn-Mayer, and Paramount Pictures, including "The Learning Tree" (adapted by Parks from his novel of the same title; also see below), Warner Brothers, 1968, "Shaft," M.G.M., 1972, "Shaft's Big Score," M.G.M., 1972, "The Super Cops," M.G.M., 1974, and "Leadbelly," Paramount, 1975, as well as several documentaries. Composer of concertos and sonatas performed by symphony orchestras in the United States and Europe.

MEMBER: Authors Guild (member of council, 1973-74), Black Academy of Arts and Letters (fellow), Directors Guild of America (member of national council, 1973-76), Newspaper Guild, American Society of Magazine Photographers, American Society of Composers, Authors and Publishers, American Federation of Television and Radio Artists, National Association for the Advancement of Colored People, Directors Guild of New York (member of council), Players Club (New York), Kappa Alpha Mu.

AWARDS, HONORS: Rosenwald Foundation fellow, 1942; once chosen Photographer of the Year, Association of Magazine Photographers; Mass Media Award, National Conference of Christians and Jews, for outstanding contributions to better human relations, 1964; named photographer-writer who had done the most to promote understanding among nations of the world in an international vote conducted by the makers of Nikon photographic equipment, 1967; Carr Van Adna Award, 1970; Litt. D., Kansas State University, 1970; Spingarn Medal from National Association for the Advancement of Colored People, 1972; H.H.D., St. Olaf College, 1973; additional awards include honorary degrees from Fairfield University, 1969, Boston University, 1969, Macalaster College, 1974, Colby College, 1974, Lincoln University, 1975, and awards from Syracuse University School of Journalism, 1963, Philadelphia Museum of Art, 1964, and Art Directors Club, 1964.

WRITINGS: Flash Photography, [New York], 1947; *Camera Portraits: The Techniques and Principles of Documentary Portraiture,* F. Watts, 1948; *The Learning Tree* (autobiographical novel), Harper, 1963; *A Choice of Weapons* (autobiography), Harper, 1966; *A Poet and His Camera,* self-illustrated with photographs, Viking, 1968; *Gordon Parks: Whispers of Intimate Things* (poems), self-illustrated with photographs, Viking, 1971; *Born Black* (essays), self-illustrated with photographs, Lippincott, 1971; *In Love* (poems), self-illustrated with photographs, Lippincott, 1971; *Moments without Proper Names* (poems), self-illustrated with photographs, Viking, 1975; *Flavio,* Norton, 1978.

Also author of screenplay, "The Learning Tree" (adapted from his novel of the same title), and of several television documentaries. Contributor to *Show, Vogue, Venture,* and other periodicals.

WORK IN PROGRESS: Silence, a novel and screenplay.

SIDELIGHTS: Gordon Parks was the first black person to be signed as a director by a major Hollywood studio. His first film, "The Learning Tree," is an example of his numerous and varied talents; the motion picture was based on his autobiographical novel, it was adapted for the screen by the author, directed by him, and he composed the musical score. When asked why he is involved in so many different fields, Parks replies: "For a long time I passed it off as a sort of professional restlessness. But, in retrospect, I know that it was a desperate search for security within a society that held me inferior simply because I was black. It was a constant inner rebellion against failure. I was a poor black boy who wanted to be somebody. So I created desires until I was drowning neck deep in them before I would attempt to swim my way out. . . . Perhaps if I had been fortunate enough to have gone on to college, to study medicine, engineering or whatever, I would not have become involved in so many other things. More than likely I would have given all my time to one chosen avocation. As it happened I tried several fields. In case one failed me I could turn to another one. . . . I was forced to rid myself of the insecurities that the lack of education brought me. But, in retrospect, I honestly say that I enjoyed the uncertainty of the broader and more precarious adventure." Parks once told an interviewer that "people often ask, given the choice of growing up a well-bred white boy bound for Yale and groomed to be a physician, wouldn't you rather have that? I say, in spite of the bruises, the scars, the brutality, I wouldn't have it any other way."

A reviewer for *Variety* calls "The Learning Tree" a "sentimental, moving, superbly-made story of a teenage Negro in Kansas during the 1920's." In another review of the film, William Wolf writes: "Parks's strongest attribute is his wonderful humanism, and ability to follow the path of an artist rather than pound out a message. . . . Parks is obviously on the side of morality, regardless of color, and artists who follow a humanitarian path don't often fit into the

see-saw patterns of their time. Hopefully, Parks will continue making films, and will always retain his ability to see life in its entirety."

BIOGRAPHICAL/CRITICAL SOURCES: Newsweek, April 29, 1968; *Publisher's Weekly,* April 29, 1968; *Vogue,* October 1, 1968; *Variety,* November 6, 1968, June 25, 1969; *Show Business,* August 2, 1969; *Cue,* August 9, 1969; John D. Rolansky, editor, *Creativity,* North-Holland Publishing, 1970; *Horn Book,* April, 1971, August, 1971; Midge Turk, *Gordon Parks,* Crowell, 1971; Terry Harnan, *Gordon Parks: Black Photographer and Film Maker,* Garrard, 1972; *Contemporary Literary Criticism,* Volume I, Gale, 1973; *Washington Post,* October 20, 1978.†

* * *

PARNES, Herbert S(aul) 1919-

PERSONAL: Born April 4, 1919, in Pittsburgh, Pa.; son of Joseph and Bess (Treelisky) Parnes; married Atha R. Brackemyre, September 20, 1944; children: Jane (Mrs. Robert A. Baird), Marc, Gail. *Education:* University of Pittsburgh, A.B., 1939, M.A., 1941; Ohio State University, Ph.D., 1950. *Home:* 302 East Beaumont Rd., Columbus, Ohio 43214. *Office:* Department of Economics, Ohio State University, Columbus, Ohio 43210.

CAREER: University of Pittsburgh, Pittsburgh, Pa., instructor in economics, 1946-47; Ohio State University, Columbus, instructor, 1947-50, research associate, 1950-51, assistant professor, 1951-53, associate professor, 1953-58, professor of economics, 1958—, professor and chairperson of labor and human resources, 1975—. Visiting associate professor, Princeton University, 1954-55; visiting professor, University of Minnesota, summer, 1959. Consultant, Organization for Economic Cooperation and Development, Paris, 1961-62. *Military service:* U.S. Army, 1942-46; became second lieutenant. *Member:* American Economic Association, Industrial Relations Research Association, American Association of University Professors.

WRITINGS: Research on Labor Mobility, Social Science Research Council, 1954; *Union Strike Votes,* Industrial Relations Section, Princeton University, 1956; *Forecasting Educational Needs for Economic and Social Development,* Organization for Economic Cooperation and Development, 1962; (with G. L. Palmer and others) *The Reluctant Job Changer,* University of Pennsylvania Press, 1962; (editor and contributor) *Planning Education for Economic and Social Development,* Organization for Economic Cooperation and Development, 1963; (with others) *The Pre-Retirement Years,* U.S. Government Printing Office, Volume I-II, 1970, Volume III, 1972, Volume IV, 1975; (with others) *Career Thresholds,* U.S. Government Printing Office, Volume I, 1970, Volume III, 1972; (with others) *Dual Careers,* U.S. Department of Labor, Volume I, 1970, Volume IV, 1975.

Contributor: *The Measurement and Behavior of Unemployment,* Princeton University Press, for National Bureau of Economic Research, 1957; Herbert Henman, editor, *Employment Relations Research,* Harper, 1960; Don Adams, editor, *Educational Planning,* Syracuse University Press, 1964; *The Transition from School to Work,* Industrial Relations Section, Princeton University, 1968; *A Review of Industrial Relations Research,* Industrial Relations Research Association, 1970; Gloria Shatto, editor, *Employment of the Middle-Aged: Papers from Industrial Gerontology Seminars,* C. C Thomas, 1972; John Niland, editor, *Manpower for the Manpower Industry,* Cornell University Press, 1972;

Michael E. Borus, editor, *Evaluating the Impact of Manpower Programs,* Heath, 1972; *Labor Market Information for Youths,* Temple University School of Business Administration, 1975; James D. Smith, editor, *The Personal Distribution of Income and Wealth,* National Bureau of Economic Research, 1975. Contributor to *Educational Planning, World Yearbook of Education,* 1967, and *International Encyclopedia of the Social Sciences,* 1968. Contributor of articles and reviews to journals.

WORK IN PROGRESS: Longitudinal surveys of the labor force experience of men, 45-49, women, 30-44, and male and female youth, 14-24.

* * *

PARROTT, Fred J(ames) 1913-

PERSONAL: Born August 22, 1913, in Poughkeepsie, N.Y.; son of Fred Jay (a dentist) and Mary (De Forest) Parrott. *Education:* St. Lawrence University, B.A., 1935, M.A., 1941; Balliol College, Oxford, graduate study, 1944; Cornell University, Ph.D., 1948; Columbia University, postdoctoral study, 1950. *Home:* 121 West Montecito Way, San Diego, Calif. 92103.

CAREER: St. Lawrence University, Canton, N.Y., instructor in English and speech, director of radio workshop, 1936-48; Berea College, Berea, Ky., professor of English, director of dramatics laboratory, 1948-62; University of Maryland, Far East Division, Tokyo, Japan, lecturer in speech and theatre, 1962-66; Florida Agricultural and Mechanical University, Tallahassee, associate professor of humanities, 1966-75; also affiliated with University of Maryland, Far East Division, Tokyo, 1975-77. Consultant to Tokyo American Cultural Center. *Military service:* U.S. Army, 1942-45; became technical sergeant.

WRITINGS: The Mid-Nineteenth Century American Theatre, Cornell University, 1948; *The Wind in a Sieve,* W. C. Brown, 1969; *Introduction to African Arts of Kenya, Zaire, and Nigeria,* Arco, 1972; *The Great Registration Rebellion,* St. Andrews College Press, 1974. Also author of *Intercultural Humanities: Toward a Reappraisal.* Contributor of poems and reviews to journals in the United States and Japan.

WORK IN PROGRESS: Encountered in Tokyo; Bugs and Bonzai, poems; writings on inter-cultural humanities (African, Oriental, and Western).

* * *

PARRY, Marian 1924-

PERSONAL: Born January 28, 1924, in San Francisco, Calif.; daughter of Milman (a classicist) and Marian (Thanhouser) Parry; married Maury D. Feld (a librarian), April, 1952; children: Laura, Andrew. *Education:* University of California, Los Angeles, B.A., 1946; studied etching and lithography with Michael Ponce de Leon and stone engraving with Ben Shahn, and has taken other art courses. *Home:* 60 Martin St., Cambridge, Mass. 02138. *Office:* Radcliffe College, Cambridge, Mass. 02138.

CAREER: Former teacher of art in junior high school and nursery school, among other jobs; teacher of illustration and graphic design at Cambridge Center for Adult Education and Cambridge Art Association, both Cambridge, Mass., 1971—; Massachusetts College of Art, Boston, assistant professor in School of Graduate and Continuing Education, 1973-75; Radcliffe College, Cambridge, lecturer in seminar program, 1974—; Emmanuel College, Boston, lecturer in

English department, 1975-78. Visiting specialist in book arts, Wellesley College, 1972. Publisher of small limited editions of original prints under sign of Runcible Books; these editions are in the Wellesley College rare book collection, Metropolitan Museum of Art print collection, Harvard University's Houghton Library, and other collections; has had one-man shows at Hinckley & Brohel Galleries, New York and Washington, D.C., Smith College, Radcliffe Institute, and others; work also has been included in group shows in New York and Boston galleries and at Smith College Museum.

AWARDS, HONORS: Scholar at Radcliffe Institute, 1965-68; *The Birds of Basel* was chosen by *New York Times* as one of the ten best illustrated books of the year, 1969, and by American Institute of Graphic Arts as one of the fifty best illustrated books of that year.

WRITINGS—Self-illustrated: *Die Vogel* (children's book) Pharos Verlag (Basel), 1967, translation by the author published as *The Birds of Basel,* Knopf, 1969; *Roger and the Devil,* Knopf, 1972; *King of the Fish,* Macmillan, 1977.

Illustrator: Frederick Winsor, *Space Child's Mother Goose,* Simon & Schuster, 1958; Aristophanes, *Birds,* Limited Editions and Heritage Press, 1959; *Exercises in Perspective* (illustrations without text), Hinckley & Brohel, 1965; *City Mouse-Country Mouse and Two More Mouse Tales from Aesop,* Scholastic Book Services, 1970; Betty Levin, *The Zoo Conspiracy,* Hastings House, 1973; Mirra Ginsberg, *The Lazies,* Macmillan, 1973; Charlotte Pomerantz, *The Ballad of the Long-Tailed Rat,* Macmillan, 1975; Jagna Zahl, *More Bad Luck,* Branden Press, 1975. Illustrations have been published in *Atlantic, Scientific American, Gourmet, Charm, Audience,* and other magazines, and poems in *Atlantic, Antioch Review, Carleton Miscellany, Voices,* and *Approach.*

WORK IN PROGRESS: Illustrating a children's book for Prentice-Hall.

SIDELIGHTS: Marian Parry told *CA:* "Illustrated children's books continue the tradition of illustrated manuscripts before the invention of printing: They create worlds where the concrete and the fantastic are interrelated. The imagination of the young is a 'flexible flyer'—free for any flight into any new land or new vision.

"Writing and illustration for children is a concrete exploring of the imagination. On lucky days I make discoveries: a mouse winks, a fish speaks. When I'm really lucky, a child sees and hears."

* * *

PATRICK, Hugh 1930-

PERSONAL: Born February 22, 1930, in Goldsboro, N.C.; married Matsuno Kuhara, December 27, 1953; children: three. *Education:* Yale University, B.A., 1951; University of Michigan, M.A. (Far Eastern studies), 1955, M.A. (economics), 1957, Ph.D., 1960. *Home:* Christmas Tree Lane, Woodbridge, Conn. 06525. *Office:* Department of Economics, Yale University, 1987 Yale Station, New Haven, Conn. 06520.

CAREER: Economic analyst for U.S. Government, 1951-53; University of Michigan, Ann Arbor, lecturer in economics, 1958-60; Yale University, New Haven, Conn., assistant professor, 1960-64, associate professor, 1964-68, professor of Far Eastern economics, 1968—, member of Yale Economic Growth Center, 1961—, assistant director of center, 1964-65, acting associate director, 1966-67, director, 1976—, chairman of Council of East Asian Studies, 1967-75, director of Center for East Asian Studies, 1969-75. Visiting professor at University of Bombay, 1961-62; Fulbright research professor at Hitotsubashi University, Tokyo, Japan, 1964-65. Director of Brookings Institution project on contemporary Japanese economy, 1973-75; member of Joint Committee on Japanese Studies, Social Science Research Council, 1974—. Consultant to Committee for Economic Development and Hudson Institute.

MEMBER: Japan Society (director, 1972—; member of executive committee, 1973-77; member of nominating committee, 1975, 1976-78), Phi Beta Kappa, Phi Beta Phi. *Awards, honors:* Foreign area training fellowship from Ford Foundation, 1957-58, for research in Japan; grant from American Council of Learned Societies, Japan, 1962; Guggenheim fellowship, Japan, 1964-65; M.A., Yale University, 1968; faculty fellowship from Fulbright-Hays National Defense Education Act Center, Japan, 1968-69; Twentieth Century Fund research grant, 1972-73; distinguished lecturer, Association for Asian Studies, 1977.

WRITINGS: Monetary Policy and Central Banking in Contemporary Japan, University of Bombay Press, 1962; (editor and contributor with Henry Rosovsky) *Asia's New Giant: How the Japanese Economy Works,* Brookings Institution, 1976; (editor and author of introduction) *Japanese Industrialization and Its Social Consequences,* University of California Press, 1976.

Contributor: W. W. Lockwood, editor, *The State and Economic Enterprise in Modern Japan,* Princeton University Press, 1965; Rondo Cameron and others, editors, *Banking in the Early Stages of Industrialization,* Oxford University Press, 1967; Lawrence Klein and Kazushi Ohkawa, editors, *Economic Growth: The Japanese Experience Since the Meiji Era,* Irwin, 1968.

James B. Crowley, editor, *Modern East Asia: Essays in Interpretation,* Harcourt, 1970; James W. Morley, editor, *Dilemmas of Growth in Prewar Japan,* Princeton University Press, 1971; Teruo Shimano and Koichi Hamada, editors, *Nihon no Kinyu* (title means "Money in Japan"), Iwanami Shoten, 1971; Gustav Ranis, editor, *Government and Economic Development,* Yale University Press, 1971; Arnold W. Sametz, editor, *Financial Development and Economic Growth,* New York University Press, 1972; Kiyoshi Kojima, editor, *Structural Adjustments in Asian-Pacific Trade,* two volumes, Japan Economic Research Center, 1973.

Ezra F. Vogel, editor, *Modern Japanese Organization and Decision-making,* University of California Press, 1975; Harold F. Williamson, editor, *Evolution of International Managerial Structures,* University of Delaware Press, 1975; Lewis Austin, editor, *Japan: The Paradox of Progress,* Yale University Press, 1976; Ronald I. McKinnon, editor, *Money and Finance in Economic Growth and Development: Essays in Honor of Edward S. Shaw,* Dekker, 1976; (with Juro Teranishi) Adolpho Ferriera de Oliveira and others, editors, *Mercado de Capitais e Desenvolvimento Economico,* Instituto Brasileiro de Mercado de Capitais (Rio de Janeiro), 1977; *The Future of Productivity,* U.S. Government Printing Office, 1978; J. G. Crawford, Saburo Okita, and others, editors, *Raw Materials and Pacific Economic Integration,* Croom Helm, 1978. Also contributor, with Gary Saxonhouse, *China and Japan: A New Balance of Power,* edited by Donald C. Hellman, 1976.

Contributor to yearbooks and proceedings and to *Encyclopedia Americana* and *Encyclopaedia Britannica.* Contributor of more than thirty-five articles and reviews to professional journals in the United States and abroad, including

Fortune, Oriental Economist, Trade and Industry, Economic Development and Cultural Change, Review of Income and Wealth, and *Asian Survey.* Member of editorial advisory board, *Journal of Asian Studies,* 1963-66, *Journal of Economic History,* and *Journal of Japanese Studies;* member of advisory committee, *Japanese Economic Studies.*

*   *   *

PATTERSON, Charles E(dwin), Jr.   1934-

PERSONAL: Born December 10, 1934, in Washington, D.C.; son of Charles E. (a pharmacist) and Margaret Ellen (Gormley) Patterson; married Pennie Davis, August 22, 1958; children: Sharon Frances, Joyce Marie. *Education:* Attended Auburn University, 1953-54; Emory University, A.B., 1957, M.A., 1958; University of Birmingham, graduate study, 1958-59; University of Illinois, Ph.D., 1963. *Office:* U.S. Department of Housing and Urban Development, 451 Seventh St. S.W., Washington, D.C. 20410.

CAREER: U.S. Public Health Service, Communicable Disease Center, Atlanta, Ga., management trainee, summer, 1957; Lehigh University, Bethlehem, Pa., instructor, 1962-63, assistant professor of government, 1963-67; Joint Planning Commission of Lehigh and Northampton Counties, Lehigh Valley, Pa., research associate, 1967-68; University of Tennessee, Knoxville, associate professor of political science and assistant director of Bureau of Public Administration, 1968-72; U.S. Department of Housing and Urban Development, Washington, D.C., analyst, 1972—. Consultant to Oak Ridge National Laboratory Urban Decentralization Project, summer, 1969. *Member:* American Political Science Association, American Society for Public Administration, Phi Beta Kappa, Phi Eta Sigma, Pi Sigma Alpha. *Awards, honors:* Fulbright scholar, 1958-59; National Association of Schools of Public Affairs and Administration, and Department of Housing and Urban Development fellow, 1972-73; U.S. Department of Housing and Urban Development achievement awards, 1976, 1978.

WRITINGS: Selected Annotated Bibliography on Planning, Politics and Political Science, Council of Planning Librarians, 1963; (editor) *Economic Blight: A Regional Report on Community Improvement,* Joint Planning Commission of Lehigh and Northampton Counties, 1967; (editor) *A Comprehensive Plan, Borough of Wind Gap,* Joint Planning Commission of Lehigh and Northampton Counties, 1968; (with Harry F. Kelley, Jr.) *The Tennessee Bureaucrat,* Bureau of Public Administration, University of Tennessee, 1970; *The New Towns Movement,* Oak Ridge National Laboratory, 1971; (with Hyrum Plaas) *Local Government Modernization in the Southeast: A Survey of Recent Developments,* National Society for Public Administration, 1972. Contributor of articles to professional journals.

*   *   *

PATTERSON, Gerald R.   1926-

PERSONAL: Born July 24, 1926, in Lisbon, N.D.; son of Lloyd J. (an iron miner) and Alice J. Patterson; married Joan E. Hodecker, 1951 (divorced, 1972); children: Craig, Scot, Dana, Jane. *Education:* Attended Northland College, 1946-47, and Gustavus Adolphus College, 1947-48; University of Oregon, B.S., 1949, M.A., 1951; University of Minnesota, Ph.D., 1956. *Office:* Oregon Social Learning Center, 220 East 11th Ave., Eugene, Ore. 97401.

CAREER: Wilder Clinic, St. Paul, Minn., fellow in psychology, 1953-55; University of Nebraska, School of Medicine, Lincoln, instructor in medical psychology at Psychiatric Institute, 1955-57; University of Oregon, Eugene, assistant professor, 1957-60, associate professor, 1961-65, professor of psychology, 1965-66, research professor of education, 1967—, director of clinical training, 1965-66; Oregon Research Institute, Eugene, research associate, 1967-77; Oregon Social Learning Center, Eugene, research scientist, 1977—. Member of State Board of Psychologist Examiners, 1965-67. *Military service:* U.S. Army, Infantry, 1944; served in Okinawa.

MEMBER: Association for the Advancement of Behavior Therapy (president, 1971-72), American Psychological Association, Oregon Child Guidance Association (president, 1959-60). *Awards, honors:* U.S. Public Health Service grants, 1956-57, 1960-61, 1966-68, 1968-69; grant from Office of Scientific and Scholarly Research, 1960; National Institute of Mental Health grants, 1961-66, 1969-71, 1971-73; research scientist development award, 1968-73; grant from Center for Research and Demonstration in Early Education of Handicapped Children, 1969—.

WRITINGS: (With M. E. Gullion) *Living with Children: New Methods for Parents and Teachers,* Research Press, 1968, revised edition, 1976; (with R. S. Ray, D. A. Shaw, and J. A. Cobb) *Manual for Coding of Family Interactions,* ASIS National Auxiliary Publications, 1969; *Families: Applications of Social Learning to Family Life,* Research Press, 1971; (editor with others) *Behavior Change Annual,* Aldine, 1974; (with others) *A Social Learning Approach to Family Intervention,* Volume I: *Families with Aggressive Children,* Castalia, 1975. Also editor, with J. B. Reid, of *A Therapist's Manual: Problem Solving with Families of Aggressive Children,* 1978.

Contributor: Lester D. Crow, editor, *Readings in Abnormal Psychology,* Littlefield, 1958; L. P. Ullmann and Leonard Krasner, editors, *Case Studies in Behavior Modification,* Holt, 1965; Ullmann and Krasner, editors, *Research in Behavior Modification,* Holt, 1965; D. M. Gelfand, editor, *Social Learning in Childhood: Readings in Theory and Application,* Brooks/Cole, 1969; I. G. Sarason, editor, *Contemporary Research in Personality,* 2nd edition (Patterson was not associated with the first edition), Van Nostrand, 1969; C. M. Franks, editor, *Behavior Therapy: Appraisal and Status,* McGraw, 1969; L. A. Hamerlynck, P. O. Davidson, and L. E. Acker, editors, *Behavior Modification and Ideal Mental Health Services,* University of Calgary, 1969; F.A.M. Benson, editor, *Modifying Deviant Social Behaviors in Various Classroom Settings,* University of Oregon Press, 1969; J. D. Krumboltz and C. E. Thoresen, editors, *Behavioral Counseling: Cases and Techniques,* Holt, 1969.

Roger E. Ulrich, T. Stachnik, and J. Mabry, editors, *Control of Human Behavior,* Scott, Foresman, 1970; Charles Neuringer and J. L. Michael, editors, *Behavior Modification in Clinical Psychology,* Appleton, 1970; A. M. Graziano, editor, *Behavior Therapy with Children,* Aldine-Atherton, 1971; B. Ashem and E. G. Poser, editors, *Behavior Modification with Children,* Pergamon, 1971; E. A. Ramp and B. I. Hopkins, editors, *A New Direction for Education: Behavior Analysis,* Volume II, Department of Human Development, University of Kansas, 1971; A. E. Bergin and S. L. Garfield, editors, *Handbook of Psychotherapy and Behavior Change: An Empirical Analysis,* Wiley, 1971; F. W. Clark, D. R. Evans, and Hamerlynck, editors, *Implementing Behavioral Programs for Schools and Clinics,* Research Press, 1972; Roger E. Ulrich and P. T. Mountjoy, editors, *The Experimental Analysis of Social Behavior,*

Appleton, 1972; E. McGinnies and C. B. Ferster, editors, *The Reinforcement of Social Behavior: Selected Readings,* Houghton, 1973; D. Rubadeau and J. Heitzman, editors, *Behavior Modification Techniques for the Classroom,* Ginn, 1973; I. G. Sarason, editor, *Maladaptive Behavior,* Appleton, 1973; T. A. Chandler, editor, *Modifying Children's Behavior: A Book of Readings,* Research Press, 1973; Bergin, J. D. Frank, P. J. Lang, I. M. Marks, J. D. Matarazzo, and H. Strupp, editors, *Annual Review of Psychotherapy,* Aldine-Atherton, 1973; Hamerlynck, L. C. Handy, and E. J. Mash, editors, *Behavior Change: Methodology Concepts and Practice,* Research Press, 1973; R. B. Cattell and R. M. Dreger, editors, *Handbook of Modern Personality Theory,* Teachers College Press, 1973; H. E. Adams and I. P. Unikel, editors, *Issues and Trends in Behavior Therapy,* C. C Thomas, 1973; R. Stuart, R. Liberman, and S. Wilder, editors, *Advances in Behavior Therapy,* Academic Press, 1973; P. McReynolds, editor, *Advances in Psychological Assessment,* Volume III, Science & Behavior Books, 1973; J. F. Knutson, editor, *The Control of Aggression: Implications from Basic Research,* Aldine, 1973.

J. DeWit and W. Hartup, editors, *Determinants and Origins of Aggressive Behaviors,* Mouton, 1974; P. McReynolds, editor, *Advances in Psychological Assessment,* Jossey-Bass, 1975; T. Thompson and W. S. Dockens III, editors, *Applications of Behavior Modification,* Academic Press, 1975; P. C. Lee and R. S. Stewart, editors, *Sex Differences: Cultural and Psychodynamic Dimensions,* Dutton, 1976; R. B. Cattell and R. M. Dreger, editors, *Handbook of Modern Personality Theory,* Hemisphere, 1976; A. M. Graziano and M. A. O'Mara, editors, *Behavior Therapy with Children,* Aldine, 1976; D. Olson, editor, *Treating Relationships,* Graphic Publishing, 1976; H. Leitenberg, editor, *Handbook of Operant Techniques,* Prentice-Hall, 1976; E. Ribes-Inesta and A. Bandura, editors, *Analysis of Delinquency and Aggression,* Erlbaum, 1976; D. Baer, B. C. Etzel, and J. M. LeBlanc, editors, *New Development in Behavioral Research: Theory, Methods, and Applications,* Erlbaum, 1977; J. B. Reid, editor, *A Social Learning Approach to Family Intervention,* Volume II: *Observation in Home Settings,* Castalia, 1978; P. O. Sjoden, editor, *Trends in Behavior Therapy,* Academic Press, 1978.

Contributor to symposia, proceedings, and yearbooks. Contributor of articles to psychology and education journals, including *Journal of Consulting Psychology, Behavior Research and Therapy, Research in Education, Developmental Psychology, Journal of Personality and Social Psychology,* and *Journal of Child Psychology and Psychiatry.* Consulting editor, *Journal of Applied Behavior Analysis,* 1968-71, *Child Development,* 1971—, and *Journal of Consulting and Clinical Psychology,* 1978-79.

* * *

PATTERSON, L(loyd) G(eorge), Jr. 1929-

PERSONAL: Born February 15, 1929, in Niagara Falls, N.Y.; son of Lloyd George (a scientist) and Helen Elizabeth (Young) Patterson. *Education:* Hobart College, B.A., 1950; General Theological Seminary, New York, N.Y., S.T.B., 1953; Columbia University, Ph.D., 1958. *Politics:* "Democratic liberal." *Home:* 101 Brattle St., Cambridge, Mass. 02138. *Office:* Episcopal Theological School, Cambridge, Mass. 02138.

CAREER: Priest of Episcopal Church; General Theological Seminary, New York, N.Y., fellow and tutor, 1953-56; Christ Church, Bronxville, N.Y., curate, 1956-58; Episcopal

Theological School, Cambridge, Mass., instructor, 1958-61, assistant professor, 1961-64, associate professor, 1967-70, William Reed Huntington Professor of Historical Theology, 1970—. *Member:* Society of Biblical Literature and Exegesis, American Society of Church History, North Atlantic Patristic Seminar, Phi Beta Kappa.

WRITINGS: (Contributor) R. A. Norris, Jr., editor, *Lux in Lumine,* Seabury, 1966; *God and History in Early Christian Thought: A Study of Themes from Justin Martyr to Gregory the Great,* Seabury, 1967; *History and Guide to St. John's Chapel, Cambridge, Mass.,* Episcopal Theological School, 1973. Contributor to *Studia Patristica.*

WORK IN PROGRESS: The Image of the Image of God (tentative title), a study of Methodius of Olympus and his place in the history of Greek Christian Platonism.†

* * *

PATTERSON, William L(orenzo) 1890-

PERSONAL: Born August 27, 1890, in San Francisco, Calif.; son of James Edward (a cook and steward) and Mary (Gault) Patterson; married Louise Thompson, September 3, 1940; children: Lola, Anna, Mary-Lou. *Education:* University of California, B.A., 1919. *Politics:* Communist. *Religion:* None. *Home:* 101 West 147th St., New York, N.Y. 10039.

CAREER: Lawyer; Dyett-Hall & Patterson, New York, N.Y., partner, 1923-27. *Member:* International Labor Defense, Civil Rights Congress, International Organization to Help Workers (Moscow), International Negro Worker Committee (Hamburg). *Awards, honors:* Lenin Anniversary Medal, 1971; Paul Robeson Memorial Medal, Academy of Arts of the German Democratic Republic, 1978.

WRITINGS: We Charge Genocide: The Crime of Government against the Negro People, Civil Rights Congress, 1951, 3rd edition, 1952; *The Man Who Cried Genocide* (autobiography), International Publishers, 1971. Contributor to *New Time, African Communist, New World Review, Negro Worker,* and *Marxist Review.*

WORK IN PROGRESS: Black Liberation Struggles U.S.A.; a book on black American citizens as a new people and their political, economic and ideological responsibilities as human beings.

SIDELIGHTS: William L. Patterson has traveled in China, Europe, Cuba, West Indies, Panama, and Southeast Asia.

* * *

PAUL, Aileen 1917-

PERSONAL: Born June 2, 1917, in Waycross, Ga.; daughter of John Preston (a railroad dispatcher) and Edna (Samuelson) Phillips; married Sol Paul (a television magazine owner and publisher), June, 1943; married second husband, Fred Bartholomew (a television producer and former child movie star), December 12, 1953; children: (first marriage) Celia; (second marriage) K. T., Frederick. *Education:* Attended schools in the southwestern United States. *Religion:* Unitarian-Universalist. *Residence:* Leonia, N.J.

CAREER: Has worked for various radio stations as a promotion writer, researcher and writer of news material, production assistant, and salesperson of commerical time; WPIX-Television, New York City, producer and host of "New York Cooks" (thirty-minute daily cooking program), 1952-53; WNYC-Radio, New York City, host of "Children's Center," a weekly calendar, 1972-73. She has worked

as a public relations representative and publicist for firms including Proctor & Gamble, Bristol-Myers, and the Dow Chemical Co. She prepares food for photographs, and for television commercials and teaches weekly cooking and gardening classes to children in Leonia, N.J. She was education director of Northern Valley Consumers Cooperative (supermarkets in Leonia and Ridgefield) for eight years and continues as consultant to cooperatives.

MEMBER: Authors Guild, Academy of Television Arts and Sciences, American Women in Radio and Television, International Radio and Television Society, Cooperative Institute Association (president), American Civil Liberties Union, National Organization for Women (NOW), Another Mother for Peace. *Awards, honors:* "AM Broadcaster of the Year" awards from American Women in Radio and Television and from Society of European Stage Authors and Composers (SESAC).

WRITINGS—Published by Doubleday, except as indicated: (With Arthur Hawkins) *Kids Cooking: A First Cookbook for Children,* 1970; *Kids Gardening: A First Indoor Gardening Book for Children,* 1972; *Kids Camping,* 1973; (with Hawkins) *Candies, Cookies, Cakes,* 1974; *Kids Cooking Complete Meals,* 1975; *Kids Cooking without a Stove,* 1975; *Kids Indoor Gardening,* Archway, 1975; *Kids 50-State Cookbook,* 1976; *Kids Outdoor Gardening,* 1978. Contributor to numerous publications. Children's editor, *TV New York.*

SIDELIGHTS: Aileen Paul feels children are often excluded from adult activities and finds her work with young people helps to strengthen the bridge between their lives and the adult world. She is unusually active, but has said, "I'm a Gemini, and Geminis are known to be happiest when we're kept busy doing many things."

AVOCATIONAL INTERESTS: Travel, crewel embroidery, and bridge.

BIOGRAPHICAL/CRITICAL SOURCES: New York Times, February 10, 1968; *American Home,* June, 1972.†

* * *

PAUL, Roland A(rthur) 1937-

PERSONAL: Born January 19, 1937, in Memphis, Tenn.; son of Roland (an auto parts manager) and Hattye (Mincer) Paul; married Barbara Schlesinger, June 10, 1962; children: Deborah, Arthur. *Education:* Yale University, A.B. (summa cum laude), 1958; Harvard University, LL.B. (magna cum laude), 1961. *Religion:* Jewish. *Office:* Gilbert, Segall and Young, 405 Park Ave., New York, N.Y. 10022.

CAREER: Admitted to the Bar of State of New York, 1962; law clerk to Honorable Sterry R. Waterman, U.S. Court of Appeals, 2nd Circuit, N.Y., Conn., and Vt., 1961-62; U.S. Department of Defense, International Security Affairs, Washington, D.C., special assistant to general counsel and foreign affairs officer, 1962-64; Cravath, Swaine & Moore, New York City, attorney, 1964-69; U.S. Senate, Foreign Relations Committee, Washington, D.C., counsel to Subcommittee on U.S. Security Agreements and Commitments Abroad, 1969-71; Simpson Thacher & Bartlett, New York City, attorney, 1971-73; Gilbert, Segall and Young, New York City, attorney, 1973—. *Member:* Council on Foreign Relations, New York County Lawyers, Association of the Bar of the City of New York.

WRITINGS: American Military Commitments Abroad, Rutgers University Press, 1973. Contributor of articles to *Orbis, Foreign Affairs, New York Times, Business Lawyer,* and *University of Pennsylvania Law Review.*

WORK IN PROGRESS: Research on U.S. military commitments, on the basis for military intervention, and on U.S. security requirements.††

*   *   *

PAULEY, Bruce F. 1937-

PERSONAL: Born November 4, 1937, in Lincoln, Neb.; son of Carroll Righter (a retail lumberman) and Blanche M. (Hulsebus) Pauley; married Marianne B. Utz, December 21, 1963; children: Mark Allan, Glenn Hamilton. *Education:* Grinnell College, B.A., 1959; University of Nebraska, M.A., 1961; University of Rochester, Ph.D., 1966; also attended University of Vienna, 1957-58, and University of Graz, 1963-64. *Home:* 527 Whippoorwill Lane, Oviedo, Fla. 32765. *Office:* Department of History, Florida Technological University, Orlando, Fla. 32816.

CAREER: College of Wooster, Wooster, Ohio, instructor in history, 1964-65; University of Nebraska, Lincoln, instructor in history, 1965-66; University of Wyoming, Laramie, assistant professor of history, 1966-71; Florida Technological University, Orlando, 1971—, began as associate professor, currently professor of history. *Member:* American Historical Association, Conference Group for Central European History. *Awards, honors:* Fulbright fellowship, Graz, Austria, 1963-64; National Endowment for the Humanities summer stipend, 1972; American Philosophical Society research grant, 1972.

WRITINGS: The Habsburg Legacy: 1867-1939, Holt, 1972; *Hahnenschwanz und Hakenkreuz: Steirischer Heimatschutz und oesterreichischer Nationalsozialismus: 1918-1934,* Europa Verlag, 1972; *Hitler and the Forgotten Nazis,* University of North Carolina Press, in press. Contributor of articles and reviews to *Rocky Mountain Social Science Journal* and *Austrian History Yearbook.*

WORK IN PROGRESS: Research on the social history of Vienna, 1900-1955.

*   *   *

PAULI, Hartha (Ernestine) 1909-1973

September 4, 1909—February 9, 1973; Viennese-born biographer, playwright, and author of historical works, children's books, and short stories. Obituaries: *New York Times,* February 11, 1973; *Publishers Weekly,* February 19, 1973. (See index for *CA* sketch)

*   *   *

PAYNE, Joan Balfour   (?)-1973

(?)—January 6, 1973; American author and illustrator of children's books. Obituaries: *Library Journal,* April 15, 1973.

*   *   *

PAYNE, Mildred Y(ounger) 1906-

PERSONAL: Born February 3, 1906, in Adamsville, Tenn.; daughter of John Robert (a government employee) and Winifred (Carothers) Younger; married Spafford O. Payne, November 27, 1928 (died July 21, 1961); children: James Franklin. *Education:* Athens College, B.A., 1939; Murray State University, M.A., 1952; University of Arkansas, M.L.S., 1954. *Religion:* Presbyterian. *Home:* 6214 Shady Grove Lane, Memphis, Tenn. 38138.

CAREER: Athens College, Athens, Ala., instructor in Latin and religion, 1937-40; teacher of Latin, French, English, history, and sociology in public schools in Tennessee,

1942-54; University of Tennessee at Martin, assistant professor, 1954-64, associate professor, 1964-72, professor of English and chairman of department, 1973-74, professor emerita, 1974—. Member of board of directors, National Folk Festival, 1969-71.

MEMBER: National Education Association, National Council of Teachers of English (director of Tennessee area, 1967-69; judge for scholarship awards, 1972), American Association of University Professors, South Atlantic Modern Language Association, South Central Modern Language Association, Tennessee Education Association, Tennessee Council of Teachers of English (vice-president, 1973), Tennessee College English Association, Tennessee Philological Association (president, 1970), Tennessee Folklore Society (president, 1967-69), Kentucky Folklore Society, University of Tennessee at Martin Education Association, Phi Kappa Phi, Sigma Tau Delta, Kappa Delta Pi, Alpha Psi Omega. *Awards, honors:* Awards from Pi Sigma Phi, 1968, Phi Sigma Kappa, 1969, and Pi Kappa Alpha, 1970; named "outstanding teacher," 1971, by University of Tennessee Alumni.

WRITINGS: History of Presbyterians in West Tennessee, Davis Publications (Memphis), 1935; *Venite Adoremus: A Christmas Drama,* Davis Publications, 1936; *He Lives: An Easter Drama,* Davis Publications, 1937; (with Harry Harrison Kroll) *Mounds in the Mist,* A. S. Barnes, 1970; *Payne's Notes on Milton,* Continuing Education Division, University of Tennessee at Knoxville, 1971; *In the Eighteenth Century: Addison, Swift, and Steele,* Continuing Education Division, University of Tennessee at Knoxville, 1972; *Western Culture: Renaissance-Romantic,* University of Tennessee Press, 1972. Contributor of short stories to *Youth's Companion, Nashville Tennessean, Birmingham Age Herald,* and *Scholastic Magazine;* contributor of professional articles to *College English, Tennessee Poetry Journal, Tennessee Folklore Bulletin,* and other publications.

WORK IN PROGRESS: Opie Read: Tennessee's Pioneer Novelist; a bibliography of writings of Harry Harrison Kroll, for Memphis State University Press; *Ghost Gold,* a novel.

*   *   *

PEACOCKE, A(rthur) R(obert) 1924-

PERSONAL: Born November 29, 1924, in Watford, England; son of Arthur Charles (a butcher) and Rose (Lilly) Peacocke; married Rosemary W. Mann (H.M. Inspector of Schools), August 7, 1948; children: Christopher, Jane. *Education:* Exeter College, Oxford, B.A., and B.Sc., 1946, M.A. and D. Phil., 1948, D.Sc., 1961; University of Birmingham, Dip. Theol., 1960, B.D., 1971. *Office:* Clare College, Cambridge University, Cambridge, England.

CAREER: Ordained priest of Church of England, 1971; University of Birmingham, Birmingham, England, 1948-59, began as lecturer, became senior lecturer; St. Peter's College, Oxford University, Oxford, England, fellow, tutor, and lecturer in biochemistry, 1959-73; Clare College, Cambridge University, Cambridge, England, dean and fellow, 1973—. Member of Archbishop's Commission on Christian Doctrine, 1969-76; Hulsean Preacher, Cambridge University, 1976; Bampton Lecturer, Oxford University, 1978. *Member:* British Biophysical Society (chairman, 1969), Science and Religion Forum, Society for the Study of Theology. *Awards, honors:* Lecomte du Nouy prize, 1973.

WRITINGS: The Molecular Basis of Heredity, Butterworth, 1965, revised edition, 1967; *Science and the Christian*

Experiment, Oxford University Press, 1971; *The Osmotic Pressure of Biological Macromolecules,* Oxford University Press, 1974; *From Cosmos to Love,* Darton, Longman, & Todd, 1977; (contributor) W. Yourgrau and A. D. Breck, editors, *Cosmology, History, and Theology,* Plenum; 1977. Has written and delivered over 125 papers on physical biochemistry. Editor of monographs on physical biochemistry for Clarendon Press, 1967—, and for Oxford University Press. Member of editorial board, *Biophysics* and *Zygon.*

WORK IN PROGRESS: Research in the relation of science and theology, and certain theoretical aspects of physical biochemistry; *Creation and the World of Science,* for Oxford University Press.

*   *   *

PEARCE, Richard 1932-

PERSONAL: Born April 14, 1932, in New York, N.Y.; son of Samuel (a businessman) and Ethel (Braunstein) Pearce; married Jean Kudo, December 26, 1954; children: Karin, Emily. *Education:* Hobart College, B.A., 1953; Columbia University, M.A., 1957, Ph.D., 1963. *Home:* 13 Mansfield Ave., Norton, Mass. 02766. *Office:* Department of English, Wheaton College, Norton, Mass.

CAREER: Rutgers University, Newark Campus, Newark, N.J., instructor in English, 1958-59; Alfred University, Alfred, N.Y., instructor, 1959-63, assistant professor of English, 1963-64; Wheaton College, Norton, Mass., assistant professor, 1964-68, associate professor, 1968-72, professor of English, 1972—, A. Howard Meneely Professor, 1978—, chairman of department, 1971-72. *Military service:* U.S. Army, 1954-56. *Member:* Modern Language Association of America, American Association of University Professors, New England College English Association, Phi Beta Kappa. *Awards, honors:* American Council of Learned Societies grant, 1967; National Endowment for the Humanities grant, 1969; Ford Foundation grant, 1971.

WRITINGS: Stages of the Clown: Perspectives on Modern Fiction from Dostoyevsky to Beckett, Southern Illinois University Press, 1970; *William Styron,* University of Minnesota Press, 1971; (contributor) Earl Rovit, editor, *Twentieth-Century Views of Saul Bellow,* Prentice-Hall, 1974; (contributor) Raymond Federman, editor, *Surfiction: Fiction Now and Tomorrow,* Swallow Press, 1975; (contributor) Sarah Blacher Cohen, editor, *Comic Relief: Modes of Humor in Contemporary American Humor,* University of Illinois Press, 1978. Contributor of articles and reviews to literature journals and newspapers.

WORK IN PROGRESS: Critical Essays on Thomas Pynchon, for G. K. Hall; *The Novel in Motion: An Approach to Modern Fiction.*

*   *   *

PEDERSEN, Paul B(odholdt) 1936-

PERSONAL: Born May 19, 1936, in Ringsted, Iowa; married Joanne Marie Olmanson (a registered nurse), December 25, 1958; children: Karen Britt, Kai Berndt, Jon Olaf. *Education:* Grand View Junior College, A.A., 1956; University of Minnesota, B.A., 1958, M.A. (American studies), 1959, M.A. (educational psychology), 1966; Augustana Hospital, Chicago, Ill., certificate in pastoral care, 1961; Lutheran School of Theology, Maywood, Ill., M.Div., 1962; Cornell University, graduate study, 1962; Claremont Graduate School, Ph.D., 1968. *Politics:* Democrat. *Office:* International Student Adviser's Office, University of Minnesota, Minneapolis, Minn. 55455.

CAREER: Lutheran minister; Normensen University, Medan, Sumatra, Indonesia, chaplain, counselor, and lecturer in ethics, philosophy, and religion, 1962-65; University of Minnesota, Minneapolis, part-time counselor and adviser, 1965-66; Lutheran missionary in Kuala Lumpur, Malaysia, 1967-71; University of Minnesota, associate professor of counseling student personnel psychology and counselor and researcher at International Student Adviser's Office, 1971—. Field worker in North Sumatra, Lutheran World Federation (Geneva), 1962-65. Visiting lecturer in education, University of Malaysia, 1969-71. East-West Center, Honolulu, Hawaii, senior fellow of Culture Learning Institute, 1974-75, coordinator of program in cross-cultural counseling, 1975, coordinator of cross-cultural counseling workshop, 1976; higher education coordinator, Project Born Free, 1976-77. Asian consultant, Youth Research Center, Inc., Minneapolis, 1967-71.

MEMBER: International Education Association, International Association of Cross-Cultural Psychology, International Council of Psychologists, American Psychological Association. Society for the Psychological Study of Social Issues, Society for Intercultural Training and Research (member of executive committee), American College Health Association, Association of Asian Studies, Comparative Education Society, National Association for Foreign Student Affairs, Society for Cross-Cultural Research, Minnesota Psychological Association.

WRITINGS: Batak Blood and Protestant Soul: The Growth and Development of National Batak Churches in North Sumatra, Eerdmans, 1970; *Youth in Asia: A Report on Research among 451 Chinese- and English-speaking Youth Responding to a 400-Item Survey in English and Chinese* (monograph), Lutheran Church in Malaysia, 1970; *Youth in Southeast Asia: A Bibliography,* Institute of Southeast Asian Studies, 1971; (editor) *Readings in Intercultural Communication: Cross-Cultural Counseling,* Regional Center for International Education (Pittsburgh), 1974; (with S. Douglas) *Blood, Believer, and Brother: Voluntary Associations and National Development in West Malaysia* (monograph), Ohio University Press, 1974; (editor with J. Draguns) *Counseling across Cultures,* East-West Center, 1976; (editor with R. Brislin) *A Manual of Structured Experiences for Cross-Cultural Learning,* Intercultural Communication Network, 1976; (with Brislin) *Cross-Cultural Orientation Programs,* Wiley, 1976; (editor with D. Hoopes) *The State of the Art,* three volumes, Society for Intercultural Education, in press.

Contributor: J. Westermeyer and B. Maday, editor, *Culture and Mental Health,* Mouton, 1976; T. Kang, editor, *Ethnic Relations in the Asian Countries,* State University of New York at Buffalo, 1976; J. Berry and W. Lonner, editor, *Applied Cross-Cultural Psychology,* Swets and Zietlinger (Amsterdam), 1976; D. Hoopes, editor, *Readings in Intercultural Communication,* Volume V: *Intercultural Programming,* Intercultural Communications Network, 1976; R. Corsini, editor, *Contemporary Theories of Personality,* F. T. Peacock, 1977; M. Asante and E. Newmark, editors, *Handbook of Intercultural Communication,* State University of New York at Buffalo, in press; G. Coelho, editor, *Uprooting,* Pergamon, in press.

Author of numerous research reports. Contributor to *Collier's Encyclopedia;* contributor to *World Encounter, Journal of Pastoral Care, Journal of Christian Education, Current History, Educational Studies, New Nation,* and foreign publications.

SIDELIGHTS: Paul B. Pedersen speaks Malay, Danish, and Mandarin Chinese.

* 　 * 　 *

PEIRCE, J(ames) F(ranklin)　1918-

PERSONAL: Born July 27, 1918, in Edwardsville, Ill.; son of George Franklin (an electrical contractor) and Katherine Sara (Webb) Peirce; married Billie Jo Lochridge (a librarian), September 3, 1947; children: Janet Katherine. *Education:* University of Illinois, A.B., 1940; State University of Iowa, M.A., 1942; Agricultural and Mechanical College of Texas (now Texas A & M University), graduate study, 1949, 1950. *Politics:* Independent. *Religion:* Presbyterian. *Home:* 906 North Ave., Bryan, Tex. 77801. *Office:* Department of English, Texas A & M University, College Station, Tex. 77843.

CAREER: Speech and drama teacher in high school in Edwardsville, Ill., 1942; Texas A & M University, College Station, instructor, 1946-51, assistant professor, 1951-72, associate professor, 1972-77, professor of English, 1977—. Member of staff of Southwest Writers' Conference and Pineywoods Writers' Conference. *Military service:* U.S. Army, 1942-46. *Member:* College English Association, Conference of College Teachers of English, Mystery Writers of America, South-Central College English Association, South Central Modern Language Association, Texas Speech Association.

WRITINGS: (Contributor) Katharine Evans and J. Meredith Tatton, editors, *This Friendly Shore*, Naylor, 1955; *The Devil to Pay and Other Stories*, South & West, 1967; *Organization and Outlining*, Arco, 1971. Work represented in anthologies, including *The Best Detective Stories of 1972*, edited by Allen J. Hubin, Dutton, 1972. Contributor of over seventy-five articles, stories, and poems to *Playboy, Writer, Writer's Digest, Ellery Queen's Mystery Magazine,* and other popular and literary journals.

WORK IN PROGRESS: Two novels.

AVOCATIONAL INTERESTS: Travel (Mexico, Canada, England, and Europe).

* 　 * 　 *

PEPPER, Adeline

PERSONAL: Born in Madison, Wis.; daughter of John William (a technical engineer) and Emmeline (Able) Pepper. *Education:* University of Wisconsin, B.A. (with honors). *Home and office:* Roselle Park, N.J.

CAREER: Worked prior to 1956 as medical advertising writer for American Medical Association, Chicago, Ill., medical writer for American College of Surgeons, Chicago, advertising director of Mead Johnson & Co., Evansville, Ind., radio advertising writer for Knox Reeves, Inc., Minneapolis, Minn., and advertising writer for L. W. Frohlich Agency, New York, N.Y.; owner of Pep, Inc. (advertising service), formerly in Summit, N.J., and now in Plainfield, N.J., 1956—. Public relations writer for 1946 centennial of Pennsylvania Railroad; writer of advertising campaigns for E. R. Squibb & Sons and Ciba Pharmaceutical Co. Lecturer on the decorative arts of early New Jersey.

MEMBER: American Medical Writers Association, Authors League of America, Phi Kappa Phi, Theta Sigma Phi. *Awards, honors:* New Jersey Tercentenary Medal, 1964, for *Tours of Historic New Jersey;* New Jersey Association of Teachers of English Art History Award, 1972, and American Association for State and Local History Award of

Merit, 1972, both for *The Glass Gaffers of New Jersey;* New Jersey Tercentenary Medal for *Tours of Historic New Jersey.*

WRITINGS: Tours of Historic New Jersey, Van Nostrand, 1965, revised edition, Rutgers University Press, 1973; (contributor of New Jersey section) Eugene Fodor, editor, *New York-New Jersey* (Fodor's Guides to the United States series), McKay, 1966; (self-illustrated with photographs) *The Glass Gaffers of New Jersey, and Their Creations from 1939 to the Present,* Scribner, 1971. Contributor of travel, history, and antique articles and photographs to magazines and newspapers, including *Chicago Tribune, Ford Times, Frontiers, New York Times* and *New York News.*

WORK IN PROGRESS: "I'm doing detective work and photography for an art book."

SIDELIGHTS: Adeline Pepper is an authority on New Jersey landmarks and early decorative arts. Her book *Tours of Historic New Jersey* was chosen by the New Jersey Tercentenary Commission as its official state guide. For her book *The Glass Gaffers of New Jersey,* Pepper visited every glass house in New Jersey and talked to the master glassblowers ("gaffers") or to their descendants. She dug through the ruins of abandoned glass houses to recover examples of the glass they once made. The book has received high praise from glass collectors for its thorough and accurate research.

AVOCATIONAL INTERESTS: History of the Revolutionary War era, marine history, pre-Columbian archaeology, shell collecting, decorative arts and antiques.

BIOGRAPHICAL/CRITICAL SOURCES: Cleveland Plain Dealer, November 13, 1971; *Library Journal,* December 1, 1971; *New York Times,* February 27, 1972; *Glass,* January, 1973; Newark *Star-Ledger,* February 10, 1974.

* 　 * 　 *

PERADOTTO, John Joseph　1933-

PERSONAL: Born May 11, 1933, in Ottawa, Ill.; married Noreen Doran, 1959; children: four. *Education:* St. Louis University, A.B. (magna cum laude), 1957, M.A., 1958; Northwestern University, Ph.D., 1963. *Home:* 153 Meadowview Lane, Williamsville, N.Y. 14221. *Office:* Department of Classics, State University of New York, Buffalo, N.Y. 14260.

CAREER: Western Washington State College, Bellingham, instructor in classical studies and English, 1960-61; Georgetown University, Washington, D.C., instructor, 1961-63, assistant professor of classical studies, 1963-66; State University of New York at Buffalo, assistant professor, 1966-69, associate professor of classical studies, 1969-73; University of Texas at Austin, professor of classical studies and chairperson of department, 1973-74; State University of New York at Buffalo, professor of classical studies, 1974—, chairperson of department, 1974-77, dean of undergraduate education and associate vice-president for academic affairs, 1978—. Fellow at Center for Hellenic Studies of Harvard University, Washington, D.C, 1972-73.

WRITINGS: Classical Mythology: An Annotated Bibliographical Survey, American Philological Association, 1973. Contributor of articles and reviews to academic journals, including *Modern Language Notes, American Journal of Philology, Phoenix, Texas Studies in Literature and Language, Classical World,* and *Classical Journal. Arethusa,* founding associate editor, 1968-78, editor-in-chief, 1974—.

WORK IN PROGRESS: An anthology of literary excerpts,

critical essays, bibliography, and references to visual arts, for a course in Greek myth; "Myth versus Marchen in the Odyssey," a monograph; a study of an unnoticed aspect of the imagery of fire in Dante's *Inferno,* Canto 26; research on theory and experience in Aeschylus.

*   *   *

PERNICIARO, Tony   1917-

PERSONAL: Surname is pronounced Perr-knee-see-*ar*-row; born November 17, 1917, in Brooklyn, N.Y.; son of Luigi (a bricklayer) and Vitina (Leone) Perniciaro; married Frances Luppino (a teacher), March 6, 1946 (separated); children: Pia, Lisa. *Education:* Attended public schools. *Politics and religion:* "Don't know." *Home:* 409 Stockholm St., Brooklyn, N.Y. 11237.

CAREER: Tradesman (bricklayer, 1952—). *Military service:* U.S. Army, 1943-44.

WRITINGS: (Self-illustrated) *Tony the Bricklayer: Poem-Paintings,* Delacorte, 1972.

SIDELIGHTS: Tony Perniciaro writes that, in 1947, he was accused of disloyalty to the United States. He has worked with the "Poets in the Schools" program, reading his poetry in both Florida and New York. In 1973, he was banned from reading poetry in public schools in Tallahassee, Fla.

His book, *Tony the Bricklayer: Poem-Paintings,* contains short poems interspersed with his own drawings. The *Washington Post Book World* called it "direct, fresh, and striking."

BIOGRAPHICAL/CRITICAL SOURCES: Washington Post Book World, December 17, 1972.

*   *   *

PERRIN, Blanche Chenery   1894(?)-1973

April 5, 1894—June 27, 1973; American novelist and author of children's books. Obituaries: *Publishers Weekly,* July 30, 1973. (See index for *CA* sketch)

*   *   *

PERRY, Richard

PERSONAL: Born in Newport, Monmouthshire, England. *Education:* Cambridge University, B.A. *Residence:* Belford, Northumberland, England. *Agent:* Maurice Michael, Partridge Green, Horsham, Sussex, England.

CAREER: Author and naturalist.

WRITINGS: At the Turn of the Tide: A Book of Wild Birds, Lindsay Drummond, 1938, reprinted, Taplinger, 1972; *Lundy: Isle of Puffins,* Lindsay Drummond, 1940; *A Naturalist on Lindisfarne,* Lindsay Drummond, 1948; *Shetland Sanctuary,* Faber, 1949; *In the High Grampians,* Lindsay Drummond, 1949; *The Watcher and the Red Deer,* Hodge, 1952, reprinted, David & Charles, 1971; *The World of the Tiger,* Cassell, 1964, Atheneum, 1965; *The World of the Polar Bear,* Cassell, 1964, Washington University Press, 1966; *The World of the Giant Panda,* Cassell, 1964, Taplinger, 1969; *The World of the Walrus,* Cassell, 1967, Taplinger, 1968; *Bears,* Golden Cockerel, 1969; *The World of the Jaguar,* Taplinger, 1970; *Bears,* Arco, 1970; *The Unknown Ocean,* Taplinger, 1972; *The Polar Worlds,* Taplinger, 1973; *Changes,* Bobbs-Merrill, 1974; *Life at the Sea's Frontiers,* Taplinger, 1974; *Life in Forest and Jungle,* Taplinger, 1975; *Watching Sea Birds,* Taplinger, 1975; *Life in Desert and Plain,* Taplinger, 1976; *Wildlife in Britain and Ireland,* Croom Helm, 1978; *Highland Wildlife,* Croom Helm, 1979.

WORK IN PROGRESS: Mountain Wildlife, for Croom Helm.

*   *   *

PETERS, Eugene H(erbert)   1929-

PERSONAL: Born January 30, 1929, in San Francisco, Calif.; son of Emil W. and Louise (Snider) Peters; married Damaris Porter (a music professor), July 17, 1954; children: David Alan, Janet Elizabeth, Carol Jean. *Education:* Attended University of Texas, 1946-47; Texas Christian University, B.A., 1950; University of Chicago, B.D., 1953, Ph.D., 1960. *Religion:* Protestant (Disciples). *Office:* Department of Philosophy, Hiram College, Hiram, Ohio 44234.

CAREER: Phillips University, Enid, Okla., associate professor, 1957-61, professor of philosophical theology, 1961-62; Hiram College, Hiram, Ohio, professor of philosophy, 1962—. *Member:* American Philosophical Association, Phi Beta Kappa.

WRITINGS: The Creative Advance, Bethany Press, 1966; *Hartshorne and Neoclassical Metaphysics,* University of Nebraska Press, 1970.

SIDELIGHTS: In his first book, *The Creative Advance,* Eugene Peters attempts to clarify the concept of process philosophy, a complex method of interpreting reality in accordance with Christian ideology. Although Merle F. Allshouse of the *Christian Century* reacts enthusiastically to Peters' efforts to make this philosophy "approachable to the uninitiated," he feels that it is not technical enough for the specialist, nor theologically explicit enough for the layman. "All in all," he says, "it is clear that the ideal introduction to process theology remains to be written." On the other hand, Clark M. Williamson of the Christian Theological Seminary states: "Christian people who think seriously about their faith and who desire to integrate it within the whole of their understanding of the world will find this book quite helpful. . . . [It] suggests possibilities for relating the Christian faith to [reality] intelligibly."

BIOGRAPHICAL/CRITICAL SOURCES: Christian Century, March 29, 1967; *Encounter,* spring, 1967.

*   *   *

PETERSEN, David M(uir)   1939-

PERSONAL: Born December 13, 1939, in Petaluma, Calif.; son of Walter B. (a salesman) and Betty (Muir) Petersen; married Elizabeth Beer (a researcher), June 24, 1978. *Education:* University of Tennessee, B.S., 1962; University of Georgia, M.A., 1964; University of Kentucky, Ph.D., 1968. *Office:* Department of Sociology, Georgia State University, 33 Gilmer S.E., Atlanta, Ga. 30303.

CAREER: University of Kentucky, Lexington, lecturer, 1966-67; University of South Florida, Tampa, instructor, 1967-68; U.S. Bureau of Prisons, Washington, D.C., research sociologist, 1968-70; Ohio State University, Columbus, associate professor of sociology, 1970-72; University of Miami, Miami, Fla., associate professor of addiction science, beginning 1972; Resource Planning Corp., associate, beginning 1972; currently member of faculty, Georgia State University, Atlanta. Metropolitan Dade County Drug Program, research associate, beginning 1972. Instructor, Transylvania University, 1966; associate lecturer, George Washington University, 1968-70; lecturer, University of Maryland, 1970; professorial lecturer, American University, 1970. Consultant, New York State Narcotic Addiction Control Commission, 1972. *Military service:* U.S. Public Health

Service, 1968-70; became lieutenant commander. *Member:* American Sociological Association, Society for the Study of Social Problems, American Correctional Association, American Society of Criminology, American Social Health Association (member of Eastern Task Force on Drug Abuse, 1972-73), Southern Sociological Society.

WRITINGS: The Police, Discretion, and Law Enforcement Decisions: A Selected Bibliography, U.S. Bureau of Prisons, 1969; (editor with Nils Bateman) *Targets for Change: Perspectives on an Active Sociology,* Xerox Corp., 1971; (editor with Harwin Voss) *Ecology, Crime, and Delinquency,* Appleton, 1971; (editor with Marcello Truzzi) *Criminal Life: Views from the Inside,* Prentice-Hall, 1972; (editor with Charles Wellington Thomas) *Corrections: Problems and Prospects,* Prentice-Hall, 1975; (with Thomas) *Prison Organization and Inmate Subcultures,* Bobbs-Merrill, 1977. Contributor to *Sociology and Social Research* and *International Journal of Addictions.*

WORK IN PROGRESS: The Female Addict.

* * *

PETERSON, Douglas L(ee)   1924-

PERSONAL: Born April 12, 1924, in San Jose, Calif.; son of Brad and Lucille (Zanker) Peterson; married Margaret Lee Wilson, June 11, 1950; children: Kristin, Erin, Douglas. *Education:* Stanford University, A.B., 1949, M.A., 1950, Ph.D., 1956. *Office:* Department of English, Michigan State University, East Lansing, Mich. 48824.

CAREER: University of Texas at Austin, instructor in English, 1955-56; University of Washington, Seattle, assistant professor of English, 1956-60; California State University, Hayward, assistant professor, 1960-62, associate professor, 1962-64, professor of English, 1965-76, chairman of department, 1971-76, acting head of Division of Humanities, summer, 1970; University of Mississippi, University, chairman of English department, 1977-78; Michigan State University, East Lansing, professor of English, 1978—. Fulbright professor, University of Helsinki, 1964-65. *Military service:* U.S. Army Air Forces, 1943-46; became staff sergeant. *Member:* Modern Language Association of America, Renaissance Society of America. *Awards, honors:* Huntington Library grants, 1963, summer, 1967; Folger Shakespeare Library grant, summer, 1964.

WRITINGS: (Contributor) Edward Vasta, editor, *Middle English Survey,* University of Notre Dame Press, 1965; (contributor) Waldo F. McNeir and Thelma Greenfelt, editors, *Pacific Coast Studies in Shakespeare,* University of Oregon Press, 1966; *The English Lyric from Wyatt to Donne: A History of the Plain and Eloquent Styles,* Princeton University Press, 1967; *Time, Tide, and Tempest: A Study of Shakespeare's Romances,* Huntington Library Press, 1973. Contributor to literature journals.

WORK IN PROGRESS: Shakespeare and Ideal Comedy; Ideal Comedy: Its Origins and Development in the English Renaissance.

* * *

PETERSON, R(odney) D(elos)   1932-

PERSONAL: Born November 10, 1932, in Sioux Falls, S.D.; son of Severin I. (a farmer) and Vera (Blow) Peterson; married Evelyn F. Koubsky, December 26, 1965; children: Douglas, Russell, Stuart. *Education:* Attended Augustana College, Sioux Falls, S.D., 1950-52; Huron College, B.A., 1958; South Dakota State University, M.S., 1959; University of Nebraska, Ph.D., 1964. *Politics:* Democrat. *Religion:* None. *Home:* 1201 Steeple Chase Ct., Fort Collins, Colo. 80524. *Office:* Department of Economics, B-323 Social Sciences Bldg., Colorado State University, Fort Collins, Colo. 80523.

CAREER: University of Nebraska, Lincoln, instructor in business, 1963-64; Central Washington State College (now Central Washington University), Ellensburg, assistant professor of economics, 1964-65; University of Idaho, Moscow, assistant professor, 1965-67, associate professor of economics, 1967-68; Colorado State University, Fort Collins, associate professor, 1968-71, professor of economics, 1971—. Part-time instructor in adult education, University of Omaha, 1963-64; visiting assistant professor of agricultural economics, University of Nebraska, summer, 1956, 1964, 1966; visiting professor, Simon Fraser University, 1974-75. Member of Colorado Comprehensive Health Planning Council, 1970—. Research consultant to J. Walter Thompson Advertising Agency, Ayres & Associates, U.S. Department of Labor, and Antitrust Division of U.S. Department of Justice. *Military service:* U.S. Air Force, 1952-56; became staff sergeant; Nebraska Air National Guard, 1961-64; became captain.

MEMBER: American Economic Association, Midwest Economic Association, Western Economic Association, Delta Sigma Pi, Beta Gamma Sigma, Omicron Delta Epsilon. *Awards, honors:* U.S. Public Health Service grant to study economics of the medical equipment industry, 1967-69.

WRITINGS: Idaho's Minerals Industry: A Flow of Product Analysis (bulletin), Idaho Bureau of Mines and Geology, 1968; *Economic Structure of Idaho: A Provisional Input-Output Study* (bulletin), Idaho Bureau of Business & Economic Research, 1968; *The Content and Conduct of Technical Course Number Six: The Economics of Agricultural Production and Resource Use* (bulletin), Department of Economics, University of Nebraska, 1969; (contributor) E. M. Mazze, editor, *Readings in Marketing,* Chandler Publishing, 1970; (with Dale C. Dahl) *Purchased Farm Input Markets in the United States-1950-1971: A Bibliography of Economic Studies* (bulletin), University of Minnesota, 1971; *Purchased Farm Inputs in the North Central Region: A Descriptive Analysis of Selected Markets* (bulletin), Agricultural Experiment Station, University of Minnesota, 1971; *Economic Organization of the Medical Equipment Industry,* Lexington Books, 1973; *Study Guide to Accompany Goldberg's Economics,* Little, Brown, 1976.

Author of technical reports. Contributor of more than twenty-five articles to professional journals, including *Journal of the National Medical Association, Antitrust Law and Economic Review, Journal of Advertising Research, Journal of Developing Areas, Business and Society,* and *Colorado Agricultural Roundup.* Member of "articles in review" board, *Journal of Marketing,* 1966-70; member of board of editors, *Journal of Economic Issues.*

WORK IN PROGRESS: Research on the changes in capitalism and the direction it is taking and on comparative medical-care delivery systems.

SIDELIGHTS: R. D. Peterson writes: "I am a critic of modern American capitalism from the standpoint of its industrial organization and structure. As an economist, I lean toward the classical liberal ideology, ever stressing the right and responsibility of the individual to act morally on his own behalf. I feel that contemporary big business is responsible for corrupting some of our basic capitalist institutions. In essence, our economy is not far-removed from feudalism and mercantilism, and may be heading for fascism."

* * *

PETRINOVICH, Lewis 1930-

PERSONAL: Born June 12, 1930, in Wallace, Idaho; son of John (a miner) and Ollie Kate (Steward) Petrinovich; married Mary Mohr, November 27, 1948 (divorced, 1973); children: Katherine, Dawne, Denice, Mark, Karl. Education: University of Idaho, B.S., 1952; University of California, Berkeley, Ph.D., 1962. Office: Department of Psychology, University of California, Riverside, Calif. 92507.

CAREER: San Francisco State College (now University), San Francisco, Calif., instructor, 1957-59, assistant professor of psychology, 1959-63; State Univeristy of New York at Stony Brook, associate professor of psychology, 1963-68; University of California, Riverside, professor of psychology, 1968—, head of department, 1968-71. Visiting scientist, Center for Interdisciplinary Research, University of Bielefeld, 1977-78. Member: American Association for the Advancement of Science, Animal Behavior Society, Psychonomic Society, Cooper Ornithological Union, Western Psychological Association, Sigma Xi.

WRITINGS: (With H. C. Lindgren and Donn Byrne) Psychology: Introduction to the Study of Human Behavior, Wiley, 2nd edition, 1966; (with C. D. Hardyck) Introduction to Statistics for the Behavioral Sciences, Saunders, 1969, 2nd edition, 1976; (with Hardyck) Understanding Research in the Social Sciences, Saunders, 1975; (with J. L. McGaugh) Knowing, Thinking, and Believing, Plenum, 1976. Contributor to Journal of Comparative and Physiological Psychology, International Review of Neurobiology, Advances in Psychobiology, American Journal of Psychology, Psychoparmacologia, Journal of Consulting Psychology, Psychological Reports, Psychological Review, Psychological Bulletin, Behavioral Biology, Psychonomic Science, Journal of Chronic Diseases, Contemporary Psychology, Science, Journal of Verbal Learning and Verbal Behavior, Journal of Reading, and Animal Behavior.

WORK IN PROGRESS: Interdisciplinary Study of Development; Probabilistic Functionalism: A View of the History and Philosophy of Science; field research on the song development and habituation in white-crowned sparrows; field research on social behavior and reproductive success in northern and southern elephant seals.

SIDELIGHTS: Lewis Petrinovich is a professional jazz musician.

* * *

PETROV, Fyodor 1877(?)-1973

1877(?)—May 28, 1973; Russian revolutionary, science administrator, encyclopedia publisher and editor. Obituaries: New York Times, May 31, 1973.

* * *

PFOUTS, Ralph W(illiam) 1920-

PERSONAL: Born September 9, 1920, in Atchison, Kan.; son of Ralph Ulysses (a lawyer) and Alice (Oldham) Pfouts; married Jane Hoyer (a sociologist), January 31, 1945; children: James, Susan, Thomas, Elizabeth. Education: University of Kansas, B.A., 1942, M.A., 1947; University of North Carolina, Ph.D., 1952. Home: 502 Ransom St., Chapel Hill, N.C. 27514. Office: Department of Economics, University of North Carolina, Chapel Hill, N.C. 27514.

CAREER: University of North Carolina, Chapel Hill, instructor, 1947-50, lecturer, 1950-52, associate professor, 1952-58, professor of economics, 1958—, chairperson of department, 1962-68. Member of economics advisory committee of National Science Foundation, 1961-62. Military service: U.S. Naval Reserve, deck officer on anti-submarine duty, 1942-45; became lieutenant.

MEMBER: American Economic Association, Econometric Society, Population Association of America, American Statistical Association (president of North Carolina chapter, 1952-53), Southern Economic Association (vice-president, 1961-62; president, 1965-66), Atlantic Economic Society (vice-president, 1973-76; president, 1977—). Awards, honors: Social Science Research Council fellowship, Cambridge University, 1953-54; Ford Foundation faculty research fellowship, Massachusetts Institute of Technology, 1962-63.

WRITINGS: The Feasibility of the Shoe and Leather Industries in Kansas, University of Kansas Publications, 1947; (contributor) Paul Douglass, editor, Metropolitan Regionalism in Florida, Rollins College Publications, 1958; (editor and contributor) Techniques of Urban Economic Analysis, Chandler-Davis, 1960; (editor and contributor) Essays in Economics and Econometrics: A Volume in Honor of Harold Hotelling, University of North Carolina Press, 1960; (contributor) F. S. Chapin and S. F. Weiss, editors, Urban Growth Dynamics in a Regional Cluster of Cities, Wiley, 1962; Elementary Economics: A Mathematical Approach, Wiley, 1972. Author of research reports. Contributor to proceedings and to Dictionary of the Social Sciences. Contributor of more than eighty articles and reviews to professional journals, including Econometrica, History of Political Economy, International Economical Review, Financial Analysts Record, Naval Research Logistics Quarterly, and National Banking Review.

WORK IN PROGRESS: Research on methodology in economics and on the theory of the firm.

SIDELIGHTS: Ralph W. Pfouts writes: "Should a writer on scholarly and scientific subjects be included in the same category with authors of literature? At first one may be inclined to view them as essentially different. Yet the chemist is attempting to recreate some aspect of the world in symbolic terms so that his readers may understand and appreciate the world better than they did before; the novelist, in one of his functions at least, is doing the same thing. The economist is trying to explain human interactions so that his readers may grasp them more firmly and see their implications more fully. The dramatist or poet is doing basically the same thing. Creativity is the hallmark of enduring work in scientific fields just as it is in literary fields."

* * *

PHILIPS, G(eorge) Edward 1926-

PERSONAL: Born May 29, 1926, in Hamilton, Mont.; son of John Arthur (a government employee) and Mildred (Courtney) Philips; married Janet Olson, 1951 (divorced, 1973); married Linnea Hendrickson, 1977; children: (first marriage) John, Julia, Michael, Catherine, Joseph, Joan. Education: University of Montana, B.A., 1947; St. Louis University, A.M., 1951; Michigan State University, Ph.D., 1960. Politics: Democrat. Religion: Roman Catholic. Home: 1129 Dorum Ave., State College, Pa. 16801. Office: Department of Accounting, Pennsylvania State University, Business Administration Bldg., University Park, Pa. 16802.

CAREER: General Mills, Inc., San Francisco, Calif., accountant, 1947-49; Aquinas College, Grand Rapids, Mich., instructor in accounting, 1951-53, 1955-57; Seidman & Seidman, Grand Rapids, Mich., accountant, 1953-55; University of California, Los Angeles, assistant professor of accounting, 1960-64; Pennsylvania State University, University Park, associate professor, 1965-67, professor of accounting, 1967—. Fulbright lecturer in Helsinki, Finland, 1971. *Member:* American Institute of Certified Public Accountants, American Accounting Association, American Economic Association. *Awards, honors:* Ford Foundation fellow, 1959-60.

WRITINGS: Financial Statements: Problems from Current Practice, Prentice-Hall, 1969. Contributor of articles to *Accounting Review, Journal of Accounting Research, Accounting and Business Research,* and *Abacus.*

WORK IN PROGRESS: Research on international financial reporting and on financial accounting theory.

*   *   *

PHILLIPS, Elizabeth C(row) 1906-

PERSONAL: Born November 11, 1906, in Athens, Tenn.; daughter of George Porter (a merchant) and Blanche (McKeldin) Crow; married Jesse Clifton Sessions, December 11, 1934 (died August, 1937); married Joseph Waller Phillips, August 6, 1938 (divorced January, 1956). *Education:* Maryville College, B.A., 1928; University of North Carolina, graduate study, 1944; University of Tennessee, M.A., 1949, Ph.D., 1953. *Politics:* Democrat. *Religion:* Presbyterian. *Home:* 1010 South Prescott, Memphis, Tenn. 38111.

CAREER: Worked as a high school teacher in Tennessee and Georgia, 1928-47; Memphis State University, Memphis, Tenn., instructor, 1953-55, assistant professor, 1955-61, associate professor, 1961-67, professor of English, 1967-77, professor emeritus, 1977—. *Member:* American Studies Association, College English Association, American Association of University Women (president of Tennessee State Division, 1948-49), American Association of University Professors (president of Memphis State chapter, 1963-64), Modern Language Association of America, American Civil Liberties Union (member of board of directors of Tennessee affiliate, 1968-69), National Association for the Advancement of Colored People, Southern Christian Leadership Conference, Tennessee Philological Association (president, 1966-67), Tennessee Education Association, Phi Kappa Phi, Tennessee Council on Human Relations (member of board of directors, 1973—). *Awards, honors:* Dr. Martin Luther King, Jr. Human Rights Award from Memphis State University, 1976; Citizen of the Year award from Memphis Newspaper Guild, 1976.

WRITINGS—All published by Monarch: *Study Guide to Faulkner's "Absalom, Absalom,"* 1965; (with David Rogers) *Study Guide to "Modern American Drama,"* 1966; *Study Guide to Ellison's "Invisible Man,"* 1971; *Study Guide to Wright's "Native Son,"* 1972; *Study Guide to "The Works of Lorraine Hansberry,"* 1973; *Study Guide to "The Autobiography of Malcolm X,"* 1975. Contributor to *Tennessee Studies in Literature* and *Interpretations: Studies in Language and Literature.*

*   *   *

PICASSO, Pablo Ruiz 1881-1973

October 25, 1881—April 8, 1973; Spanish artist. Obituaries: *New York Times,* April 9, 1973, April 12, 1973, April 17, 1973; *Washington Post,* April 9, 1973, April 11, 1973; *Time,* April 23, 1973.

PIEPKORN, Arthur Carl 1907-1973

PERSONAL: Surname is pronounced *Peep*-corn; born June 21, 1907, in Milwaukee, Wis.; son of John Albert (a realtor) and Bertha Katherine (Taenzer) Piepkorn; married Miriam Agatha Sodergren, December 26, 1936; children: Mary Catherine (Mrs. Edward E. Eckart), Faith Elisabeth (Mrs. Richard E. Hoffman), Felicity Ann (Mrs. James C. Steere), Angela Dorothea. *Education:* Attended Concordia College, Milwaukee, Wis., 1923-25; Concordia Seminary, St. Louis, Mo., B.A., 1926, B.D., 1928; University of Chicago, Ph.D., 1930; postdoctoral study at Case Western Reserve University, 1939-40, Washington University, St. Louis, 1953-58, and University of Geneva, 1958-59. *Politics:* Independent. *Home:* 1 Dartford Ave., Clayton, Mo. 63105. *Office:* Concordia Seminary, 801 De Mun Ave., St. Louis, Mo. 63105.

CAREER: Lutheran pastor of churches in Missouri, Minnesota, and Ohio, 1930-40; Concordia Seminary, St. Louis, Mo., professor, 1951-63, graduate professor of systematic theology, 1963-73, chairman of department, 1962-66. Hein Lecturer, American Lutheran Church, 1959. Member of board of directors of Foundation for Reformation Research, 1969-73. *Military service:* U.S. Army Reserve, 1936-67, chaplain, active duty, 1940-51 (instructor in chaplains' school, 1942-44, 1946-48, commandant, 1948-50); became colonel; received Bronze Star Medal, Legion of Merit, Silver Medal of St. Martin of Tours, Order of St. John of Jerusalem.

MEMBER: American Academy of Political and Social Research, American Society for Reformation Research, American Society of Church History, Fellowship of St. Augustine, Laurentius Petri Sallskapet (Sweden), Lutheran Society for Worship, Music, and the Arts, Mariological Society of America, North American Academy of Ecumenists, Hymn Society of America. *Awards, honors:* Annual fellow, American School of Oriental Research, Bagdad, Iraq, 1932-33; Guggenheim fellow, 1958-59.

WRITINGS: The Historical Prism Inscriptions of Ashurbanipal, University of Chicago Press, 1933; *What the Symbolical Books of the Lutheran Church Have to Say about Worship and the Sacraments,* Concordia, 1952; (editor) Frederick Emanuel Mayer, *The Religious Bodies of America,* Concordia, 2nd edition (Piepkorn was not associated with 1st edition), 1954, 4th edition, 1961; *The Survival of the Historic Vestments in the Lutheran Church after 1555,* School for Graduate Studies, Concordia Seminary, 1955, 2nd edition, 1958; (contributor) Theodore G. Tappert, editor, *The Book of Concord: The Confessions of the Evangelical Lutheran Church,* Muhlenberg Press, 1959; *Reproductions of Sixteenth-Century Handwriting: Graded Samples of Sixteenth-Century Manuscripts Designed for Use in an Introductory Course in Sixteenth-Century Paleography,* Foundation for Reformation Research, 1969; *Armed Forces Chaplains, All Civilians?: A Feasibility Study,* General Commission on Chaplains and Armed Forces Personnel, 1972; *Profiles in Belief: The Religious Bodies of the United States and Canada,* Harper, Volume I: *Roman Catholic, Old Catholic, Eastern Orthodox,* 1977, Volume II: *Protestantism,* 1978, Volume III: *Pentecostalism and Fundamentalism,* in press. Also author of *Altar Decorum,* Department of Liturgics, Concordia Theological Seminary.

Contributor to *Encyclopaedia Britannica, Die Religion in Geschichte und Geganwart,* 3rd edition, *Evangelisches Kirchenlexicon, Lutheran Cyclopedia, New Catholic Encyclopedia,* and *Encyclopedia of the Lutheran Church;* contributor to theology journals, including *Marian Studies,*

Lutheran Witness, Lamp, Theological Studies, Jurist, Church History, Response, Sursum Corda, Una Sancta, and to *Journal of the Library of the Foundation for Reformation Research.* Editorial associate, *American Lutheran,* 1946-66; contributing editor, *Una Sancta,* 1945-51, 1963-71; member of editorial staff, *Concordia Theological Monthly,* 1953-73.†

(Died December, 1973)

* * *

PINARD, (J. L.-M.) Maurice   1929-

PERSONAL: Born April 25, 1929, in Drummondville, Quebec, Canada; son of Ernest (a businessman) and Aline (Masson) Pinard; married Minola Saragea, June 10, 1967. *Education:* University of Montreal, B.A. (magna cum laude), 1951, LL.L. (magna cum laude), 1954, M.A., 1955; University of Paris, Certificate in Sociology, 1956, in Social Psychology, 1957; Johns Hopkins University, Ph.D., 1967. *Religion:* Roman Catholic. *Home:* 3467 Vendome Ave., Montreal, Quebec Canada H4A 3M6. *Office:* Department of Sociology, McGill University, 855 Sherbrooke St. W., Montreal, Quebec, Canada H3A 2T7.

CAREER: Social Research Group, Montreal, Quebec, senior study director, 1957-59, part-time member, 1959—; University of Montreal, Montreal, assistant professor of sociology, 1959-60; McGill University, Montreal, assistant professor, 1963-67, associate professor, 1967-71, professor of sociology, 1971—. *Member:* American Sociological Association, Canadian Sociology and Anthropology Association, Canadian Political Science Association.

WRITINGS: The Rise of a Third Party, Prentice-Hall, 1972, enlarged edition, McGill-Queen's University Press, 1975. Contributor to sociology journals.

WORK IN PROGRESS: The Politics of Ethnic Conflict.

* * *

PIPER, Anson C(onant)   1918-

PERSONAL: Born August 24, 1918, in Newton, Mass.; son of Luther Warren and Elizabeth (Smith) Piper; married Miriam Simms, November 12, 1945; children: Jonathan, Victoria, Gregory. *Education:* Williams College, B.A., 1940; University of Wisconsin, M.A., 1947, Ph.D., 1953. *Politics:* Democrat. *Religion:* United Church of Christ. *Home:* 25 Baxter Rd., Williamstown, Mass. 01267. *Office:* Department of Romance Languages, Williams College, Williamstown, Mass. 01267.

CAREER: Williams College, Williamstown, Mass., instructor, 1949-52, assistant professor, 1952-58, associate professor, 1958-61, professor of Spanish and Portuguese, 1961—, head of department, 1961-71. Co-director of Study of Radiophonic Teaching in Latin America, International Research Associates, 1961-63. *Military service:* U.S. Navy, 1942-46; became lieutenant. *Member:* Modern Language Association of America, American Association of Teachers of Spanish and Portuguese (president of Western Massachusetts Chapter, 1966-68), Phi Beta Kappa. *Awards, honors:* Fulbright lectureship to Brazil, 1963-64; Gulbenkian fellowship, Portugal, 1967.

WRITINGS: Asi es la vida, Norton, 1958; (with Fernando Moura) *Basic Portuguese Vocabulary,* University of Louvain Press, 1968. Contributor of articles to *Hispania, Luso-Brazilian Review, Kentucky Romance Quarterly, Western Humanities Review, Berkshire Review, Anales Galdosianos, Revista Hispanica Moderna,* and *Revista de Estudios Hispanicos.*

WORK IN PROGRESS: Research in Romance linguistics.

* * *

PIPER, Don Courtney   1932-

PERSONAL: Born July 29, 1932, in Washington, D.C.; son of Don Carlos (a mathematician) and Alice (Courtney) Piper; married Rowena Inez Wise (an instructor), July 6, 1956; children: Sharon Leigh, Valarie Ann. *Education:* University of Maryland, B.A., 1954, M.A., 1958; Duke University, Ph.D., 1961; Hague Academy of International Law, postdoctoral study, 1962. *Home:* 4323 Woodberry St., University Park, Md. *Office:* Department of Government and Politics, University of Maryland, College Park, Md. 20742.

CAREER: Duke University, Durham, N.C., executive secretary of Commonwealth-Studies Center, 1962-64; University of Maryland, College Park, assistant professor, 1964-67, associate professor, 1967-69, professor of government and politics, 1969—, chairman of department, 1968-74, chairman of College Park Campus Senate, 1975-77. Research assistant, American Council on Education, 1966-67. Member of faculty advisory council and planning advisory council, Maryland State Board for Higher Education, 1977—. *Military service:* U.S. Air Force, 1955-58; became first lieutenant. *Member:* American Political Science Association, American Society of International Law, International Studies Association, International Law Association, American Association of University Professors, Southern Political Science Association, Phi Beta Kappa, Phi Kappa Phi, Pi Sigma Alpha. *Awards, honors:* Regents award for excellence in teaching, University of Maryland, 1966.

WRITINGS: (Editor with R. Taylor Cole) *Post-Primary Education and Political and Economic Development,* Duke University Press, 1964; (contributor) R. R. Wilson and others, editors, *The International Law Standard in Commonwealth Developments,* Duke University Press, 1966; (contributor) Stanley Metzger, editor, *The Law of International Trade,* Lerner Law Book Co., 1966; *The International Law of the Great Lakes: A Study of Canadian-United States Cooperation,* Duke University Press, 1967; (contributor) Richard Leach, editor, *Compacts of Antiquity: State Constitutions,* SPNA, 1969; (contributor) David Deener, editor, *De Lege Pactorum,* Duke University Press, 1970. Contributor of about twenty articles and reviews to journals of political science and law. Member of board of editors, *World Affairs;* member of editorial advisory committee, *International Legal Materials,* 1977-78.

* * *

PLANTE, Julian G(erard)

PERSONAL: Born in St. Paul Minn.; son of Roland Joseph (a carpenter and boatbuilder) and Mary Magdalen (Herold) Plante. *Education:* St. John's University, Collegeville, Minn., B.A.; Fordham University, M.A., 1963, Ph.D., 1972. *Home:* 111 Park Ave. S., St. Cloud, Minn. 56301. *Office:* Hill Monastic Manuscript Library, St. John's University, Collegeville, Minn. 56321.

CAREER: City College of the City University of New York, New York, N.Y., instructor in classical languages and Hebrew, 1964-66; St. John's University, Collegeville, Minn., assistant professor, 1966-72, research professor of classics, 1972—, curator and director, Hill Monastic Manuscript Library, 1966—. Assistant to president, Elmer R. Davis & Associates, Inc. (management consultants), 1964-66. Consultant to Augustinian Historical Institute, 1969-71. *Member:* International Council on Archives, International

Association of Papyrologists, American Philological Association, Mediaeval Academy of America, American Society of Papyrologists, American Association of University Professors, Vergilian Society, Midwest Mediaeval Conference.

WRITINGS: Checklist of Manuscripts Microfilmed for the Monastic Manuscript Library, Saint John's University, Collegeville, Minnesota, Volume I: Austrian Monasteries, St. John's University Press, Part I: *Goettweig, Heiligenkruez, Herzogenburg, Klosterneuburg, Kremsmuenster, Lambach, Lilienfield, Melk, Neukloster, Reichersberg, St. Florian, St. Poelten, Schlaegl, Schottenstift, Seitenstetten, and Wilhering,* 1967, Part II: *Admont, Altenburg, Bregenz, ... Wilten, Zwettl,* 1974; *Monastic Manuscript Microfilm Project, Progress Report VI,* St. John's University Press, 1970; (contributor) *Festschrift Marcel Richard,* [Leipzig], 1973; *Catalogue of the Manuscripts of Stift Reichersberg,* [Paris], 1973; (editor and contributor) *Translatio Studii: Manuscript and Library Studies Honoring Oliver L. Kapsner, O.S.B.,* [St. Paul, Minn.], 1973; *Monastic Manuscript Microfilm Project, Progress Report VII,* St. John's University Press, 1974; (contributor) *Studia Codicologica,* Akademie Verlag (Berlin), 1977. Contributor of articles and reviews to various learned journals.

WORK IN PROGRESS: The Medieval Library of Stift Reichersberg, Austria; transcription from German of *Regula S. Benedicti,* from an early sixteenth-century manuscript; commentaries on *Regula S. Benedicti* written before 1600; a newly-found Beneventan fragment of Hildemar's commentary on the *Regula S. Benedicti.*

SIDELIGHTS: Julian G. Plante has traveled to Ethiopia four times to assist in establishing the Ethiopian Manuscript Microfilm Library there. *Avocational interests:* Campanology, genealogy, travel, and music.

*   *   *

PLATT, Harrison Gray   1902-

PERSONAL: Born April 27, 1902, in Portland, Ore.; son of Harrison Gray (an attorney) and Nelly (Durham) Platt; married Rhoda Failing Burpee, August 19, 1925 (divorced, 1943); married Mary Alice Kaye, December 30, 1943; children: (first marriage) Harrison Gray III, William Brewster. *Education:* Reed College, B.A., 1925; Yale University, graduate study, 1925-26; Harvard University, M.A., 1927, additional graduate study, 1928-30. *Politics:* Democrat. *Religion:* "(Mildly) Episcopalian." *Home:* 160 East 48th St., New York, N.Y. 10017.

CAREER: Brown University, Providence, R.I., instructor in English, 1930-38; Reilly & Lee Co., Chicago, Ill., editor, 1941-43; Bobbs-Merrill Co., Inc., Indianapolis, Ind., associate editor, 1944-54, editor in general publications department, 1954-60; C. L. Barnhart, Bronxville, N.Y., technical editor of reference books, 1960-61, managing editor, 1961-63; Harcourt Brace Jovanovich, New York, N.Y., chief dictionary editor, 1963-78. *Wartime service:* U.S. Army, civilian managing editor of dictionary, 1944.

WRITINGS: (With Porter G. Perrin) *Current Expressions of Fact and Opinion,* Scott, Foresman, 1941; *How to Write Letters and Reports,* Scott, Foresman, 1943; (with Perrin, Robert Warnock, and Earl Ward) *Using Good English,* Scott, Foresman, 1944; (editor-in-chief) *Harcourt Brace Intermediate Dictionary,* Harcourt, 1968. Managing editor, *Dictionary of U.S. Army Terms,* U.S. Government Printing Office, 1944, and *World Book Encyclopedia Dictionary,* two volumes, Field Enterprises Educational Corp., 1963; editor-in-chief, *Harcourt Brace Jovanovich School Dictionary,*

Harcourt, 1968, 1972, 1977. Contributor to *American College Dictionary,* Random House, 1947. Contributor of short stories, poems, articles, and reviews to magazines and newspapers, including *Esquire, Saturday Evening Post, Chicago Daily News,* and *Chicago Tribune.*

WORK IN PROGRESS: Short papers; personal memoirs.

*   *   *

PLOG, Stanley C.   1930-

PERSONAL: Surname is pronounced with long "o"; born April 12, 1930, in Los Angeles, Calif.; son of Clifton G. and Edith C. (Swanson) Plog; married Georgia Perrin, September 5, 1953; children: Stephen, Gregory. *Education:* Occidental College, B.A. (magna cum laude), 1957; Harvard University, M.A., 1960, Ph.D., 1961. *Politics:* Republican. *Religion:* Protestant. *Home:* 12561 Middlecoff Pl., Granada Hills, Calif. 91344. *Office:* Plog Research, Inc., 18631 Sherman Way, Reseda, Calif. 91335.

CAREER: University of California, Los Angeles, assistant professor in Division of Medical Psychology at Medical Center Neuropsychiatric Institute, 1961-62, associate director of training program in social and community psychiatry, 1962-65, director of urban observatory in Institute of Government and Public Affairs, 1965-67; Behavior Science Corp., Los Angeles, Calif., president, 1963-73; Plog Research, Inc., Reseda, Calif., president, 1973—. Licensed psychologist in State of California. Research consultant in department of psychiatry, Harbor General Hospital, 1961-62. *Military service:* U.S. Air Force, 1950-53; became staff sergeant. *Member:* American Psychological Association, Travel Research Association, Western Psychological Association, Phi Beta Kappa.

WRITINGS: (Contributor) Darmine D. Clemente and Donald B. Lindsley, editors, *Brain Function, Agression, and Defense,* University of California Press, 1967; (with Robert B. Edgerton) *Perspectives in Mental Illness,* Holt, 1969; (with Paul I. Ahmed) *State Mental Hospitals: What Happens When They Close,* Plenum, 1976; (with Ahmed) *Principles and Techniques of Mental Health Consultation,* Plenum, 1977. Editor of Plenum's "Current Topics in Mental Health" series. Contributor to professional journals.

WORK IN PROGRESS: The Year 2000 and Mental Retardation, with Miles Santamour, for Plenum; *War Birds and the Men Who Fly Them,* with son, Gregory Plog.

SIDELIGHTS: Stanley Plog told *CA:* "I write a lot. Professional reports, speeches, journal articles, and books. I write because my profession requires it and, more important, because I want to write. It is not an easy task. It requires self-motivation and considerable self-discipline, but personal goals dictate that I must write. I have no choice but to communicate through written words placed appropriately on paper.

"My goal is to influence, persuade, educate, inform, or entertain. Whatever the specific result, I am impacting on the lives of others. I know of no other way that I can personally lead or influence so many people. The prospects are enormous. The great figures of history achieved their ultimate positions only because they, or someone else, wrote down and distributed their ideas as a permanent record.

"Writing is mystical—a combination of the human creative process with modern technology of the printing press. How is it that the human brain can combine words in new and unique patterns to express ideas that make sense to others; and, how can you escape the sense of magic and wonderment when you see your own books sitting on shelves of distant book stores.

"Writing is excitement—and self-effacing discipline—and personal power. It is a wonderful combination of many things that demands the most you can give in order to have maximum impact on others."

AVOCATIONAL INTERESTS: Tennis, photography.

* * *

POMORSKA, Krystyna 1928-

PERSONAL: Born April 5, 1928, in Lwow, Poland; daughter of Juliusz (a lawyer) and Maria (Ziemba) Pomorski; married Roman Jakobson (a professor), September 28, 1962. *Education:* Slowacki College, Warsaw, Poland, B.A., 1951; Warsaw University, M.A., 1955; University of Chicago, Ph.D., 1962. *Residence:* Cambridge, Mass. 02138. *Office:* Department of Humanities, Massachusetts Insitute of Technology, Cambridge, Mass. 02139.

CAREER: State Publishing House, Warsaw, Poland, editor, translator and consultant, 1952-59; Warsaw University, Warsaw, assistant of the chair of literary theory, 1956-59; Massachusetts Institute of Technology, Center for Communication Sciences, Cambridge, visiting scholar, 1960-61; University of Chicago, Chicago, Ill, assistant professor in Slavic department, 1961-62; Massachusetts Institute of Technology, assistant professor of modern languages, 1963-64, associate professor, 1964-70, professor of foreign literatures and linguistics, 1970—. *Member:* American Association for the Advancement of Slavic Studies.

WRITINGS: Russian Formalist Theory and Its Poetic Ambiance, Mouton, 1968; (editor) *Fifty Years of Russian Prose: From Pasternak to Solzhenitsyn,* M.I.T. Press, 1971; (editor with Ladislav Matejka) *Readings in Russian Poetics: Formalist and Structuralist Views,* M.I.T. Press, 1971; *Themes and Variations in Pasternak's Poetics,* Peter De Ridder Press (Lisse), 1975; *Dialogues with Roman Jakobson,* Flammarion, 1979.

WORK IN PROGRESS: On Future in Futurism, for Peter De Ridder Press.

* * *

POPE, Harrison (Graham), Jr. 1947-

PERSONAL: Born December 26, 1947, in Lynn, Mass.; son of Harrison Graham (a surgeon) and Alice (Rider) Pope. *Education:* Harvard University, B.A. (summa cum laude), 1969, graduate study, beginning 1969.

CAREER: Medical student. *Member:* Phi Beta Kappa.

WRITINGS: Voices from the Drug Culture, Beacon Press, 1971; *The Road East: America's New Discovery of Eastern Wisdom,* Beacon Press, 1974. Contributor of articles to botany and psychiatry journals.

AVOCATIONAL INTERESTS: French wine, scuba diving, high fidelity sound equipment, and butterfly collecting.

* * *

PORTER, Jack Nusan 1944-

PERSONAL: Original name, Yakov Nusan Puchtik, name legally changed in 1947; born December 2, 1944, in Rovno, Ukraine, Soviet Union; son of Irving Israel (a commander in the Russian partisans) and Faye (Merin) Porter; married Miriam Almuly, September 18, 1977. *Education:* Attended Jerusalem Teachers Institute, 1962-63; University of Wisconsin—Milwaukee, B.A. (cum laude), 1967; Northwestern

University, M.A., 1969, Ph.D., 1971. *Politics:* Democratic socialist. *Religion:* Jewish. *Home and office:* 28 Stanton Rd., Apt. 6, Brookline, Mass. 02146.

CAREER: Lecturer in sociology at Northwestern University, Evanston, Ill., 1968-69, and De Paul University, Chicago, Ill., 1969-70; Passavant-Wesley School of Nursing, Chicago, instructor in sociology, 1970-71; State University of New York College at Cortland, assistant professor of sociology, 1971-72; Boston College, Boston, Mass., lecturer in theology, 1973-74; Pine Manor College, Boston, instructor in social sciences, 1974-76; Emerson College, Boston, lecturer in Jewish history, 1976-77; Bunker Hill Community College, Boston, lecturer in cultural anthropology, 1977-78; instructor in Jewish history, sociology, and the history of the holocaust, Cambridge and Boston Centers of Adult Education, 1977-78; Contract Research Corp.-Social Science Research Institute, Boston, senior social science analyst, 1978—. Visiting lecturer in sociology, University of Lowell, 1978-79; has also lectured at other universities, including Harvard University, Boston University, Massachusetts Institute of Technology, and Northwestern University. Editorial consultant, Dushkin Publishing Group, 1971-74. American Film Festival juror, 1972.

MEMBER: American Sociological Association, Association for Jewish Studies, Association for the Sociological Study of Jewry, Union of Radical Sociologists, Association for Humanist Sociology, Society for the Study of Social Problems, American Professors for Peace in the Middle East, American Association of University Professors, American Civil Liberties Union, Midwest Sociological Society, Eastern Sociological Society, Massachusetts Sociological Society.

WRITINGS: Student Protest and the Technocratic Society, Zalonka Publications, 1973; (editor with Peter Dreier) *Jewish Radicalism,* Grove, 1973; (with Irvin Doress) *Kids in Cults,* Zalonka Publications, 1977; *The Sociology of American Jews: A Critical Anthology,* University Press of America, 1978. Contributing editor, *Encyclopedia of Sociology* and a college textbook, *Sociology.* Editor, "Annual Editions in Sociology," Dushkin Publishing Group, 1972-73. Contributor of over one hundred articles and reviews to journals, including *Society, Commonweal, American Journal of Sociology, Writers Digest, Change, American Jewish History,* and *Christianity and Crisis.* Associate editor, *International Review of Modern Sociology,* 1972-74; founder and editor, *Journal of the History of Sociology,* 1977—; member of editorial boards, *Genesis 2,* 1973-76, *Davka: UCLA Hillel Journal,* 1973-77, *Dialogue,* 1976-78, *Qualitative Sociology,* 1977—, and *Humanity and Society,* 1977—.

WORK IN PROGRESS: The Jewish Rebel; The Sociological Imagination of Film; Modern Maccabees: Jewish Resistance in Nazi Europe; a short history of anti-Semitism for students; a collection of essays on the question of socialism, Zionism, and Judaism; *Genocide: An International Approach,* an anthology.

SIDELIGHTS: Jack Nusan Porter writes: "I've decided to devote my life to the study of the two philosophies that are the foundation of all culture: religion and politics. Through this, I hope to better understand my past, my present, my future, and myself. My personal drive to write and to succeed probably comes from a sense of guilt—guilt arising from my parents' surviving the Nazi Holocaust. I feel that I owe them something. I need to tell the story of oppression, prejudice, and injustice. I must be a witness for them. Thus, writing becomes a passion, as all good writing must. But one must also write objectively. Such a balance is difficult; it takes a great deal of self-discipline.

"A new writer must listen to his own voice, must unlearn much of what he was taught in school. No one can write for a committee of teachers. One must find one's own voice. Finally, one must write as if to argue with the best minds in history—Freud, Marx, Spinoza—or others in one's speciality. But first one must *read* them; one must read the classics in philosophy, history, sociology, and psychology, and then argue with them. These 'quarrels' will result in writing that has great expanse and beauty. Otherwise, provincialism and superficiality will be the result. Don't lower your standards. Go for the highest. Then, if you don't make it, you will at least have failed at a higher level, and that is what the greatest writers were—magnificent failures."

BIOGRAPHICAL/CRITICAL SOURCES: Wisconsin Jewish Chronicle, December 15, 1972.

* * *

POSNER, Ernst (Maximilian) 1892-

PERSONAL: Born August 9, 1892, in Berlin, Germany; son of Carl (a professor) and Sophie (Rosenberg) Posner; married Katharina Melchior. *Education:* Attended University of Berlin, 1910-12, 1913-14, 1919-20, University of Bonn, summer, 1911, and University of Strasbourg, 1912-13; University of Berlin, Ph.D., 1920. *Religion:* Protestant. *Home:* Hotel Rose, D62 Wiesbaden, West Germany.

CAREER: Prussian Privy State Archives, Berlin, Germany, state archivist, 1921-35; American University, Washington, D.C., lecturer, 1939-40, adjunct professor, 1940-45, professor of history and archives administration, 1945-61, dean of Graduate School, 1955-57. Consultant, Rockefeller Foundation, 1966. *Military service:* German Army, 1914-18; became lieutenant; received Iron Cross I and II Class. *Member:* American Historical Association, American Association for State and Local History, Society of American Archivists (honorary member), International Archives Council (honorary member). *Awards, honors:* Great Cross of Merit of Federal Republic of Germany, 1967; Guggenheim fellow, 1957-58; Fulbright research grant, 1957-58.

WRITINGS: (Editor) *Acta Borussica: Denkmaeler der Preussischen Staatsverwaltung im 18. Jahrhundert* (documentary series dealing with internal history of Prussia during the eighteenth century), Preussische Akademie der Wissenschaften, Volume XI, 1922, Volume XII, 1926, Volume XIII, 1932, Volume XIV, 1933, Volume XV, 1936; (contributor) *Mitteldeutsche Lebensbilder* (biography of Ludwig P. F. vom Hagen), Historical Commission of Saxony, Volume II, 1927; (with Ernst Mueller) *Eubersicht ueber die Bestaende des Geheimen Staatsarchivs zu Berlin-Dahlem* (guide to holdings of Privy State Archives in Berlin-Dahlem), Preussische Archivverwaltung, Volume I, 1934; *Drei Vortraege zum Archivwesen der Gegenwart* (lectures at Royal Swedish State Archives), Bonniers, 1940; (contributor) Martino Giusti, editor, *Miscellanea archivistica Angelo Mercati*, Biblioteca Apostolica Vaticana, 1952; *American State Archives*, University of Chicago Press, 1964; *Archives and the Public Interest* (selected essays), edited by Kenneth Munden, Public Affairs Press, 1967; *Archives in the Ancient World*, Harvard University Press, 1972. U.S. Government publications include: *Military Government Information Guide: Information on German Records*, U.S. Department of War, 1945, and national archives guides to archival repositories in enemy and enemy-occupied coun-

tries, designed to assist allied forces in the protection and preservation of archives, 1943-45.

Contributor to *Jahresberichte fuer Deutsche Geschichte*, Volumes I-VI, 1926-32, *Encyclopedia Americana*, and *Collier's Encyclopedia*. Contributor of about thirty articles to *American Archivist*, and contributor to *American Historical Review, Archivalische Zeitschrift, Indian Archives, Virginia Magazine of History and Biography, Neues Archiv der Gesellschaft fuer aeltere Deutsche Geschichtskunde*, and other journals.

WORK IN PROGRESS: Archives in the Western World, Medieval and Modern Period.

SIDELIGHTS: Ernst Posner considers it his "good fortune to have been able to bring to the U.S. some of the European experience in preserving and making available the archives of the past."

BIOGRAPHICAL/CRITICAL SOURCES: Paul Lewinson, introduction to *Archives and the Public Interest*, Public Affairs Press, 1967; *Der Archivar*, Volume XX, 1967; *Jahrbuch fuer Amerikastudien*, Volume XV, 1970.

* * *

POTICHNYJ, Peter J(oseph) 1930-

PERSONAL: Born June 2, 1930, in Ukraine, U.S.S.R.; son of Peter and Aleksandra (Fedak) Potichnyj; married Tamara L. Sydoryk, November, 1957; children: Eugene Peter, Adriana Oksana. *Education:* Temple University, B.A., 1958; Columbia University, certificate of Russian Institute, 1961, M.A., 1961, Ph.D., 1966. *Home:* 49 Sunrise Crescent, Dundas, Ontario, Canada. *Office:* Department of Political Science, McMaster University, Hamilton, Ontario, Canada.

CAREER: Upsal College, East Orange, N.J., instructor in political science, 1961; McMaster University, Hamilton, Ontario, lecturer, 1964-66, assistant professor, 1966-70, associate professor, 1970-75, professor of political science, 1975—. Visiting professor, department of political science, Wilfred Laurier University, Waterloo, Ontario, 1972-75; professor of politology, Ukranian Free University, Munich, Germany, 1977—. Director of summer school in Ljubljana, Yugoslavia, 1970-72. Co-manager of International Conference of Slavists, 1974; member of International Committee on Soviet and East European Studies, 1977-81; member of board of directors, Canadian Federation for the Humanities, 1978-81. *Military service:* U.S. Marine Corps, 1952-54; became sergeant; received Purple Heart.

MEMBER: American Association for the Advancement of Slavic Studies, American Political Science Association, Academy of Political Science, American Academy of Political and Social Science, Canadian Association of University Teachers, Canadian Association of Slavists (secretary-treasurer, 1973-76; vice-president, 1976-77; president, 1977-78). *Awards, honors:* Research fellow, Russian Institute, Columbia University, 1971.

WRITINGS: (With G. Hodnett) *The Ukraine and the Czechoslovak Crisis*, Australian National University, 1970; (editor) *On the Current Situation in the Ukraine*, University of Michigan Press, 1970; *Soviet Agricultural Trade Unions, 1917-1970*, University of Toronto Press, 1972; (editor) *Dissent in the Soviet Union*, McMaster University Press, 1972; *The Sources and Development of Yugoslav Federal Idea*, Ukranian Technical-Economic Institute (Munich), 1974; (editor) *Ukraine in the Seventies*, Mosaic Press, 1975; (editor with J. P. Shapiro) *From the Cold War to Detente*, Praeger, 1976; (editor with Shapiro) *Change and Adaptation in Soviet and East European Politics,* Praeger, 1976; (editor with S. McInnes and W. McGrath) *The Soviet Union and East Europe into the 1980's: Multidisciplinary Perspectives,* Mosaic Press, 1978.

Also editor, with E. Shteudera, of monographs, *Litopys UPA,* Volume I, 1976, Volume II, 1977, Volume III, 1978; editor of *Poland and Ukraine: Past and Present,* 1978. Managing editor, *Canadian Association of Slavists Newsletter,* 1973-76; editor-in-chief, *Current Soviet Leaders/Les Leaders Sovietiques Contemporains,* 1974—.

WORK IN PROGRESS: Several monographs and articles; additional volumes of *Litopys UPA.*

SIDELIGHTS: Peter J. Potichnyj has competence in all Slavic languages, some of the Romance languages, and German.

*   *   *

POTTER, Jack M(ichael)   1936-

PERSONAL: Born October 13, 1936, in Oakdale, Tenn.; son of Gordon B. and Frances (Phillips) Potter; married Sulamith Heins (an anthropologist), September, 1970; children: Elizabeth Rachel. *Education:* University of California, Berkeley, A.B., 1958, Ph.D., 1964; University of Chicago, graduate study, 1958-59. *Office:* Department of Anthropology, University of California, Berkeley, Calif. 94720.

CAREER: University of California, Berkeley, assistant professor, 1964-68, associate professor, 1968-72, professor of anthropology, 1972—. *Member:* American Anthropological Association, Royal Anthropological Society.

WRITINGS: Peasant Society: A Reader, Little, Brown, 1967; *Capitalism and the Chinese Peasant,* University of California Press, 1968; *Thai Peasant Social Structure,* University of Chicago Press, 1976.

WORK IN PROGRESS: A book on Chinese peasants; a general introduction to anthropology, for Oxford University Press.

SIDELIGHTS: Jack Potter did fieldwork in Hong Kong, 1961-63, and in Thailand, 1971-72.

*   *   *

POTTER, Lois   1941-

PERSONAL: Born February 20, 1941, in Oakland, Calif.; daughter of George Vernon (a physician) and Lois (Dorais) Potter. *Education:* Sorbonne, University of Paris, Diplome, 1957; Bryn Mawr College, B.A., 1961; Girton College, Cambridge, Ph.D., 1965. *Politics:* "Vague." *Religion:* None. *Home:* 5 Lorne Rd., Leicester LE2 1YF, England. *Office:* Department of English, University of Leicester, Leicester LE1 7RH, England.

CAREER: University of Aberdeen, Aberdeen, Scotland, assistant lecturer in English, 1964-66; University of Leicester, Leicester, England, lecturer in English, 1966—. Has broadcast drama reviews and other material on local radio station. *Member:* Association of University Teachers (England). *Awards, honors:* Woodrow Wilson fellowship, 1961; Marshall scholarship, Cambridge University, 1961-64.

WRITINGS: A Preface to Milton, Scribner, 1971; (editor) John Milton, *Paradise Lost,* Book III, Cambridge University Press, 1976. Contributor to *English Studies* and *Times Educational Supplement.*

WORK IN PROGRESS: Editing volumes I and IV of *The*

Revels History of Drama in English; writing chapters on drama in the years 1500-1575 and 1642-1660.

AVOCATIONAL INTERESTS: Attending theater and opera, cooking, cats.

*   *   *

POWER, Paul F(rederick)   1925-

PERSONAL: Born January 1, 1925, in Wilmington, Del.; married, 1949; children: four. *Education:* Yale University, B.A., 1948; New York University, Ph.D., 1960. *Office:* Department of Political Science, University of Cincinnati, Cincinnati, Ohio 45221.

CAREER: University of Cincinnati, Cincinnati, Ohio, assistant professor, 1961-64, associate professor, 1964-69, professor of political science, 1969—. *Military service:* U.S. Army Air Forces, 1943-46; became sergeant. *Member:* International Studies Association, Association for Asian Studies, American Political Science Association, International Political Science Association.

WRITINGS: Gandhi on World Affairs, Allen & Unwin, 1961; (editor) *The Meanings of Gandhi,* University Press of Hawaii, 1971. Contributor to *Journal of Peace Research* and *American Political Science Review.*†

*   *   *

PRADA OROPEZA, Renato   1937-

PERSONAL: Born October 17, 1937, in Potosi, Bolivia; son of Augusto (an advocate) and Bertha (Oropeza) Prada; married Elda Rojas, December 17, 1956; children: Ingmar, Fabrizio. *Education:* Calatayud High School, bachelor of humanities, 1961; Normal Superior Catolica, high school teacher certification, 1964; Universita degli Studi di Roma, Ph.D., 1972. *Religion:* Roman Catholic. *Home:* Fochplein 19, Louvain, Belgium 3000. *Agent:* Carmen Ballcels, Urgel 241, Barcelona 11, Spain.

CAREER: High school teacher of Spanish and philosophy in Cochabamba, Bolivia, 1965-67; Normal Superior Catolica, Cochabamba, Bolivia, professor of philosophy, 1967-70. Maryknoll Institute, subdirector and professor of philosophy, 1963-67; Universidad Catolica, professor of philosophy, 1969-70. *Military service:* Bolivian Army, 1956. *Awards, honors:* Premio Municipal de Cuento, for *Argal,* 1967; Premio Nacional de Cuento, for "El combate," 1968; Premio Nacional de Novela, for *Los Fundadores del Alba,* 1969; Premio de Novela, Casa de las Americas (Cuba), for *Los Fundadores del Alba,* 1969.

WRITINGS: Argal (short stories), Los Amigos del Libro, 1967; *Ya nadie espera al hombre* (short stories), Don Bosco, 1969; *Al borde del silencio* (short stories), ALFA, 1969; *Los Fundadores del Alba,* Los Amigos del Libro, 1969, translation by Walter Redmond published as *The Breach,* Doubleday, 1971; *El ultimo filo,* Planeta, 1975.

WORK IN PROGRESS: El buen samaritano, a novel; research on theories of criticism.

AVOCATIONAL INTERESTS: Travel†

*   *   *

PRAWER, Joshua   1917-

PERSONAL: Born November 10, 1917, in Bedzin, Poland; son of Shlomo (a merchant) and Gittel (Schoenker) Prawer; married Hadassa Eiges (a teacher of art history), February 9, 1941; children: Ehud. *Education:* Hebrew University of Jerusalem, M.A., 1941, Ph.D., 1945. *Home:* 6 Alkalai St.,

Jerusalem, Israel. *Office address:* Israel Academy of Sciences and Humanities, P.O. Box 4040, Jerusalem, Israel.

CAREER: Hebrew University of Jerusalem, Jerusalem, Israel, senior lecturer, 1952-56, associate professor, 1956-58, professor of mediaeval history, 1958—, chairman of faculty of humanities, 1962-65; Israel Academy of Sciences and Humanities, Jerusalem, chairman of humanities, 1969—. Chairman of Pedagogical Secretariat, Israel Ministry of Education, 1957-59; academic head, Haifa University College, 1966-68. *Member:* Israel Academy of Sciences and Humanities, Mediaeval Academy of America, Academie des Inscriptions et Belles-Lettres (corresponding member).

Awards, honors: Prix Schlumberger of the Academie des Inscriptions et Belles-Lettres, France, 1967; Israel National Prize for Humanities, 1969; Doctor (honoris causa), University of Montpellier, France, 1969; Rotschilde Prize, 1972; Chevalier de l'Ordre National du Merite, 1973.

WRITINGS: Histoire du Royaume Latin de Jerusalem, two volumes, Centre National de la Recherche Scientifique, 1969-70; *The Crusaders' Kingdom: European Colonialism in the Middle Ages,* Praeger, 1972 (published in England as *The Latin Kingdom of Jerusalem: European Colonialism in the Middle Ages,* Weidenfeld & Nicolson, 1972); *The World of the Crusaders,* Weidenfeld & Nicolson, 1973; *Heiliges Land,* Hallwag, 1976; *Crusader Institutions,* Oxford University Press, 1979.

WORK IN PROGRESS: The Jews in the Latin Kingdom of Jerusalem, for Oxford University Press.

* * *

PRESCOTT, Orville 1906-

PERSONAL: Born September 8, 1906, in Cleveland, Ohio; son of Orville W. (a lumber merchant) and Eda (Sherwin) Prescott; married Lilias Dallas Ward-Smith, November 1, 1933; children: Peter S., Jennifer (Mrs. Edward C. McLean). *Education:* Williams College, B.A., 1930, D.Lit., 1959. *Home:* Stone House, 13 Hatfield Mews, New Canaan, Conn. 06840.

CAREER: Cleveland Town Tidings, Cleveland, Ohio, managing editor and columnist, 1931-32; *Newsweek,* New York City, member of editorial staff, 1933-36; *Cue,* New York City, member of editorial staff and book reviewer, 1936-47; *New York Times,* New York City, daily literary critic, 1942-66. Fiction reviewer, *Yale Review,* 1943-49; lecturer in literature, 1940-54. *Member:* International P.E.N., Authors League, Royal Society of Arts, Society of American Historians, Century Association (New York), Country Club (New Canaan).

WRITINGS: In My Opinion: An Inquiry into the Contemporary Novel, Bobbs-Merrill, 1952; *The Five-Dollar Gold Piece: The Development of a Point of View,* Random House, 1956; (editor) *Mid-Century: An Anthology of Distinguished Contemporary Short Stories,* Pocket Books, 1958; (editor) *The Undying Past* (anthology), Doubleday, 1961; (editor) *A Father Reads to His Children: An Anthology of Prose and Poetry,* Dutton, 1965; *Princes of the Renaissance,* Random House, 1969; (editor) *History as Literature* (anthology), Harper, 1970; *Lords of Italy,* Harper, 1972. Editor, "Crossroads of World History" series published by Doubleday.

AVOCATIONAL INTERESTS: Travel.

* * *

PRIBAM, Karl 1878(?)-1973

1878(?)—July 14, 1973; European-born economist, educator,

and author of books on unemployment, cartel problems, and other topics. Obituaries: *New York Times,* July 20, 1973.

* * *

PRICE, Olive 1903-
(Anne Cherryholmes, Barbara West)

PERSONAL: Born September 21, 1903, in Pittsburgh, Pa.; daughter of Harry Wilson (a police sergeant) and Lydia (Barchfeld) Price; married R. M. Cherryholmes, June 30, 1927. *Education:* Attended University of Pittsburgh, 1922-23. *Religion:* Baptist. *Residence:* Asbury, N.J. *Agent:* McIntosh & Otis, Inc., 475 Fifth Ave., New York, N.Y. 10017.

CAREER: Writer of books and plays for children and young people. Copywriter for department stores in Pittsburgh, Pa., 1923-28. *Member:* Kappa Delta (Xi chapter).

WRITINGS—For children and young people, except as indicated: *A Donkey for the King,* McGraw, 1945; *Miracle by the Sea,* McGraw, 1947; *Three Golden Rivers* (Catholic Book Club selection), Bobbs-Merrill, 1948; *The Valley of the Dragon,* Bobbs-Merrill, 1951; *The Story of Marco Polo* (selection of *Parents' Magazine* Book Club, People's Book Club, Boy's Club of America Book Club, and Sear's Book Club), Grosset, 1953; *The Story of Clara Barton* (Boy's Club of America Book Club selection), Grosset, 1954; *The Glass Mountain,* Washburn, 1954; *The Blue Harbor,* Washburn, 1956; *Snifty,* Westminster, 1957; *The Golden Wheel,* Westminster, 1958; *River Boy,* Westminster, 1959.

Reindeer Island, Westminster, 1960; *The Phantom Reindeer,* Coward, 1961; *Mystery of the Sunken City,* Westminster, 1962; *The Donkey with Diamond Ears,* Coward, 1962; *The Boy with One Shoe,* Coward, 1963; (under pseudonym Anne Cherryholmes) *The Island of the Silver Spoon,* Coward, 1963; (under pseudonym Anne Cherryholmes) *The Island of the Voyageurs,* Coward, 1964; *The Dog That Watched the Mountain,* Coward, 1967; *Kim Walk-In-My-Shoes* (Books for Brotherhood Book Club selection), Coward, 1968; *Rosa Bonheur: Painter of Animals,* Garrard, 1972.

Picture books adapted for children from literary classics; all published by Grosset: Alfred Ollivant, *Bob, Son of Battle,* 1960; Jack London, *Call of the Wild,* 1961; Margaret Sydney, *Five Little Peppers and How They Grew,* 1963.

Books of plays: *Short Plays from American History and Literature for Classroom Use: Grade Schools,* Samuel French, Volume I, 1925, Volume II, 1928, Volume III, 1929, Volume IV, 1935; *Plays for Schools,* Baker's Plays, 1927; *American History in Masque and Wig for Classroom Use,* Baker's Plays, 1931; *Plays for Young Children,* U.S. Bicentennial Commission to Celebrate the Bicentennial of George Washington's Birthday, 1932; *Plays of Far Places,* Baker's Plays, 1936; *Debutante Plays for Girls Twelve to Twenty,* Samuel French, 1936; *Plays of Belles and Beaux: Seven Short Plays for High School and Junior High,* Samuel French, 1937.

Plays published singly: *Lantern Light,* Samuel French, 1925; *The Gateway of Tomorrow* (an Americanization play), Scott Mitchell, 1929; *Washington Marches On,* U.S. Bicentennial Celebration, 1931; *Angelica, Inc.,* Samuel French, 1937; *The Young May Moon,* Samuel French, 1939; *Star Eternal,* Dramatists Play Service, 1939; *Holiday Hill,* Row, Peterson, 1940; *When the Bough Breaks,* Eldridge Entertainment House, 1940; *Freshman Bill,* Eldridge Entertainment House, 1941; *Announcing Antonia,* Samuel French, 1941; *Ask for the Moon,* Row, Peterson, 1942; *Sub-Deb Sue,*

Dramatists Play Service, 1942; *Family Tree*, Row, Peterson, 1943; (under pseudonym Barbara West) *Belles in Waiting*, Row, Peterson, 1943; *Out of the Mist*, Eldridge Entertainment House, 1943; *Magic on Main Street* (for women), Row, Peterson, 1945; *Stage Struck*, Row, Peterson, 1946; *Rummage Sale* (for women), Row, Peterson, 1946; *Sparkling Sixteen*, Northwestern Press, 1947. Also author of plays published in anthologies compiled by Robert Haven Schauffler, for Dodd, Mead.

Radio scripts: "Twelve Municipal Plays," "Sixteen and Six Fashion Programs," "Story Hour Books," all produced.

WORK IN PROGRESS: A novel for young people; research on Greece, Lebanon, and Israel, with a historical novel expected to result.

SIDELIGHTS: Debutante Plays for Girls Twelve to Twenty have been produced on television; *Snifty* has been broadcast on radio. Olive Price's books have been translated into Italian, Danish, Portuguese, Norwegian, and Hebrew. *American History in Masque and Wig for Classroom Use* has been published in Braille.

AVOCATIONAL INTERESTS: Travel (Europe, Canada, and the Caribbean).

*   *   *

PRIDE, Cletis 1925-

PERSONAL: Born May 31, 1925; son of Dawson Ellery and Pearl (Van Gilder) Pride; married Virginia Cross, July 8, 1949; children: Alan, David, John. *Education:* West Virginia University, B.S., 1953, M.A., 1963; University of North Carolina, Ph.D., 1970. *Politics:* Republican. *Religion:* Lutheran. *Home:* 712 Burnt Mills Court, Silver Spring, Md. 20901. *Office:* National Geographic Society, Washington, D.C. 20036.

CAREER: West Virginia University, Morgantown, news writer and editor, 1953-57, acting director of information services, 1958-63; United Fuel Gas Co., Charleston, W.Va., public relations writer, 1957-58; Duke University, Durham, N.C., news director, 1963-70; American College Public Relations Association (now Council for the Advancement and Support of Education), Washington, D.C., research director, 1970-74; National Geographic Society, Washington, D.C., assistant secretary, 1975—. *Military service:* U.S. Navy, 1943-46. *Member:* Association for Education in Journalism, American Society of Information Science, National Association of Science Writers, Kappa Tau Alpha.

WRITINGS: ACPRA Casebook of Institutional Advancement Programs, American College Public Relations Association, 1970; *Securing Support for Higher Education: A Bibliographical Handbook*, Praeger, 1972. Manuscript editor for National Geographic Society books. Contributor to *College & University Journal, Techniques*, and *Journalism Quarterly*.

AVOCATIONAL INTERESTS: Pastel drawing, gardening, chess, golf.

*   *   *

PRIMEAUX, Walter J(oseph) Jr. 1928-

PERSONAL: Surname is pronounced "premo"; born March 3, 1928, in Port Arthur, Tex.; son of Walter Joseph (a businessman) and Nola (Ledet) Primeaux; married Natalie Ardoin, December 26, 1948; children: Lawrence, David, Claire, Marlene, Marie, Joan, Catherine, Michelle. *Educa-*

tion: University of Southwestern Louisiana, B.S., 1951; University of Houston, M.A., 1966, Ph.D., 1967. *Religion:* Roman Catholic. *Office:* Department of Business Administration, University of Illinois, Urbana, Ill.

CAREER: Primeaux & Mouledous, Inc. (retail home appliance store), Abbeville, La., co-owner and vice-president, 1955-62; Southwest Louisiana Vocational-Technical School, Crowley, La., instructor in accounting, 1962-63; Nicholls State University, Thibodaux, La., associate professor of economics, 1966-68; McNeese State University, Lake Charles, La., professor of economics and chairman of department, 1968-69; University of Mississippi, University, associate professor, 1969-72, professor of economics, beginning 1972; currently a member of the faculty, University of Illinois at Urbana-Champaign. Instructor of accounting, Gulf Area Vocational-Technical School, 1957-60; economist, U.S. Corps of Engineers, 1964. Member of Abbeville Chamber of Commerce, 1958-62. *Military service:* U.S. Navy, 1946-47. *Member:* Royal Economic Society (England), American Economic Association, Southern Economic Society, Southwestern Social Science Association, Western Economic Association, Omicron Delta Epsilon. *Awards, honors:* Brookings Institution grant, 1971.

WRITINGS: (With others) *Personal Income Estimates for Mississippi Counties*, Bureau of Business and Economic Research, University of Mississippi, 1970; (contributor) *Fortran Applications in Business Administration*, Volume II, Graduate School of Business Administration, University of Michigan, 1971; (editor and contributor) *Essays in Business and Economics*, Bureau of Business and Economic Research, University of Mississippi, 1972; *An Analytical Predictive Model to Facilitate Managerial Effectiveness in Municipal Water Systems*, Water Resources Research Institute, Mississippi State University, 1972; (with Kenneth W. Hollman) *The Effect of Price and other Selected Variables on Water Consumption*, Water Resources Research Institute, Mississippi State University, 1973. Contributor of articles to *Antitrust Bulletin, Louisiana Studies, Journal of Business* (Chicago), *Marquette Business Review, Mississippi Business Review, Journal of Political Economy, Economic Inquiry*, and *Review of Economics and Statistics*.

WORK IN PROGRESS: Writing on competition between electric utility firms.

*   *   *

PROFFER, Carl R(ay) 1938-

PERSONAL: Born September 3, 1938, in New York, N.Y.; son of Carl W. (an engineer) and Evelyn (Dixon) Proffer; married Ellendea C. McInnes (an editor and publisher), October 28, 1967; children: Andrew, Christopher, Ian. *Education:* Attended University of Edinburgh, 1958-59, and Moscow State University, 1962; University of Michigan, B.A., 1960, M.A., 1961, Ph.D., 1963. *Home:* 2901 Heatherway, Ann Arbor, Mich. 48104. *Office:* Department of Slavic Languages, University of Michigan, Ann Arbor, Mich. 48104.

CAREER: Reed College, Portland, Ore., assistant professor of Russian, 1963-66; Indiana University at Bloomington, associate professor of Slavic, 1966-69; University of Michigan, Ann Arbor, professor of Slavic languages, 1969—. Co-partner and co-editor, Ardis Publishers, 1971—. *Member:* American Association of Teachers of Slavic and East European Languages, P.E.N. *Awards, honors:* Fulbright fellowship, 1969.

WRITINGS: The Simile and Gogol's "Dead Souls," Mouton, 1967; (editor) *Letters of Nikolai Gogol*, University of Michigan Press, 1967; *Keys to Lolita*, Indiana University Press, 1968; *The Critical Prose of Alexander Pushkin*, Indiana University Press, 1970; *From Karamzin to Bunin*, Indiana University Press, 1970; (translator with wife, Ellendea C. Proffer) *The Early Plays of M. Bulgakov*, Indiana University Press, 1972; (translator and editor with Ellendea C. Proffer) Mikhail Bulgakov, *Diaboliad and Other Stories*, Indiana University Press, 1972; *Soviet Criticism of American Literature*, Ardis, 1972; (editor) *A Book of Things about Vladimir Nabokov*, Ardis, 1974; (editor) *The Ardis Anthology of Recent Russian Liteature*, Ardis, 1975; (editor) *The Silver Age of Russian Culture*, Ardis, 1975; (translator) Sasha Sokolov, *A School for Fools*, Ardis, 1976. General editor, *The Unpublished Dostoevsky*, Ardis, 1973-77. Editor, *Russian Literature Triquarterly*, 1971—, and *Glagol*, 1977—.

WORK IN PROGRESS: A bibliography of English language translations and criticism of Russian literature from the earliest times to the present.

* * *

PROTHERO, R(alph) Mansell 1924-

PERSONAL: Born August 20, 1924, in Merthyr Tydfil, Wales; son of Ralph (a schoolmaster) and Charlotte (Mansell) Prothero; married Margaret Mary Cope (a lecturer and antique dealer), September 1, 1951; children: David, Jeremy, Ian, Sian, Jonathan, Simon. *Education:* University of Wales, B.A., 1945, M.A., 1947; University of Liverpool, Ph.D., 1962. *Home:* Vine House, Neston, Cheshire L64 9XE, England. *Office:* Department of Geography, University of Liverpool, Liverpool L69 3BX, England.

CAREER: University of Edinburgh, Edinburgh, Scotland, assistant in geography, 1947-50; Ibadan University, Ibadan, Nigeria, lecturer in geography and research fellow, 1950-55; University of Liverpool, Liverpool, England, lecturer, 1955-64, senior lecturer, 1964-68, reader, 1968-77, professor of geography, 1977—. Visiting professor at Hebrew University of Jerusalem, 1965, University of Minnesota, 1966, and National University of Mexico, 1977. Melville J. Herskovits Memorial Lecturer, Northwestern University, 1967. Consultant to World Health Organization (WHO). *Member:* Institute of British Geographers, International African Institute, International Union for the Scientific Study of Population, International Geographical Union (chairman of commission on population geography, 1964-68), American Geological Society. *Awards, honors:* Gill Memorial, Royal Geographical Society, 1969.

WRITINGS: (Editor with K. M. Barbour) *Essays on African Population*, Routledge & Kegan Paul, 1961; (editor with R. W. Steel) *Geographers and the Tropics*, Longmans, Green, 1964; *Migrants and Malaria*, Longmans, Green, 1965, University of Pittsburgh Press, 1968; (editor) *A Geography of Africa*, Routledge & Kegan Paul, 1969; (with Wilbur Zelinsky and L. A. Kosinski) *Geography and a Crowding World*, Oxford University Press, 1970; (editor) *People and Land in Africa South of the Sahara*, Oxford University Press, 1972; (with L. A. Kosinski) *People on the Move*, Methuen, 1975.

WORK IN PROGRESS: Studies of population mobility in tropical Africa and Mexico; cross-cultural studies of circulation, with Murray Chapman; geomedical monograph of Nigeria.

PROUSSIS, Costas M(ichael) 1911-

PERSONAL: Born June 26, 1911, in Cyprus; naturalized U.S. citizen in 1954; son of Michael and Despina (Savva) Proussis. *Education:* University of Athens, Lic.Phil., 1934; University of Chicago, Ph.D., 1951. *Religion:* Greek Orthodox. *Home:* 11 Lehigh Rd., Wellesley, Mass. 02181.

CAREER: Gymnasium Kyrenia, Kyrenia, Cyprus, vice-principal and teacher, 1935-36; Pancyprian Gymnasium, Nicosia, Cyprus, teacher of classics, 1936-48; Koraes School, Chicago, Ill., teacher of Greek, 1948-49; Plato School, Chicago, teacher and head of Greek department, 1952-57; Hellenic College, Brookline, Mass., assistant professor, 1957-59, associate professor, 1959-62, professor of classics, 1962-78, professor emeritus, 1978—, chairman of department of Greek, 1959-78, dean of studies, 1961-70.

MEMBER: Society of Cyprus Studies (treasurer, 1936-48), Greek Philological Association, Stasinos of Cyprus, Cyprus Folkloric Association, Cyprus Intellectual Association (secretary, 1947-48), Hellenic Philological and Scientific Association of Famagusta, American Philological Association, Modern Greek Studies Association, Center for Neo-Hellenic Studies, American Association of University Professors, Modern Language Association of America, Classical Association of New England, University of Chicago Alumni Association, Hellenic Cultural Circle of Chicago, Consular Corps College, International Consular Academy. *Awards, honors:* Academy of Athens Award, 1946; honorary consul of Cyprus at Boston, 1964—; Ecumenical Patriarchate Award, 1973.

WRITINGS: *Modern Greek Grammar*, New World, 1934; *Latin Grammar*, Pancyprian Gymnasium, 1943; *The Poet Kostis Palamas*, Pancyprian Gymnasium, 1943; *Historic Folk Songs of Cyprus*, Nicosia, 1945; *Aesthetic Culture*, Pancyprian Gymansium, 1946; *The Folklore of Dodecanese*, Nicosia, 1948; *Cyprus Prose Writing*, Nicosia, 1949; *The Athenian Iliad of Pisistratus*, Nicosia, 1951; (contributor) Paul Nash, Andreas Kazamias, and Henry Perkinson, editors, *The Educated Man*, Wiley, 1965; (contributor) Henri M. Peyre, editor, *Fiction in Several Languages*, Houghton, 1968; *Poems of Cyprus*, Council of Europe, 1970; *Alexandros Papadiamantis*, Philologike Kypros, 1970; *The Poet J. N. Gryparis*, Kypriaka Chronika, 1971; *Gianis Vlahogianis*, Nicosia, 1971; *Folklore and Cyprus*, Laographike Kypros, 1972; *Digenis Akritas in Cyprus*, Parnassus, 1972; *Poreia Zois*, Zavallis, 1975.

Contributor to journals, including *Cyprus Review*, *Our Century*, *Hellenic Creation*, *Athene*, *Classical Philology*, *Slavic and East European Journal*, *Speculum*, *Neo-Hellenica*, *Parnassos*, *Philologike Kypros*, *Pneumatike Kypros*, *Kypriaka Chronika*, *Laographike Kypros*, *Review of Literature and Arts*, *MLA International Bibliography*, and *Books Abroad*. Editor, *Meleti-Kritiki*, 1932, *Cyprus Letters*, 1934-57, *Cyprus Studies*, 1941-48, *Greek Orthodox Theological Review*, 1959—, and *Neo-Hellenika*.

WORK IN PROGRESS: Preparing a history of modern Greek literature, a collection of folktales and folk poems of Cyprus, and a book of critical essays on modern Greek poets; writing on aspects of ancient Greek tragedy, and on Kostis Palamas.

* * *

PRUGH, Jeff(ery Douglas) 1939-

PERSONAL: Surname sounds like "through"; born September 15, 1939, in Pittsburgh, Pa.; son of Harold Homer and Janice (Fryer) Prugh. *Education:* Attended Glendale College, 1958-60; University of Missouri, B. Journalism, 1962. *Home:* 25 Basswood Cir., Atlanta, Ga. 30328. *Agent:* Mike Hamilburg, 292 South La Cienega Blvd., Beverly Hills, Calif. *Office: Los Angeles Times,* Atlanta Bureau, 229 Peachtree St., Atlanta, Ga. 30303.

CAREER: Glendale News-Press, Glendale, Calif., reporter and copy editor, 1958-61; *Los Angeles Times,* Los Angeles, Calif., sports writer, 1962-75, bureau chief, Atlanta, Ga., 1976—. Moderator and host of weekly sports luncheon, Playboy Club of Los Angeles, 1969-70. *Military service:* U.S. Army Reserve, Armed Forces Radio Service, active duty, 1957.

MEMBER: U.S. Basketball Writers Association (president, 1971-72), Southern California Football Writers Association (president, 1969), Atlanta Press Club (secretary, 1978). *Awards, honors:* First prize for sports story from San Fernando Valley Press Club, 1970, for profile of basketball star Pete Maravich; best sports story award from Greater Los Angeles Press Club, 1972, for "The Coaches' Curse," a series of articles on college athletic recruiting; first prize in 1972-73 California-Nevada Associated Press writing contest.

WRITINGS: (Editor) *Sports Illustrated Guide to Volleyball,* Lippincott, 1972; (with Dwight Chapin) *The Wizard of Westwood* (biography of John Wooden, former basketball coach at University of California, Los Angeles), Houghton, 1973. Work is represented in *Best Sports Stories,* edited by Edward Ehre and Irving Marsh, Doubleday, 1967, 1971, and 1975. Contributor to *Sports Illustrated, Time,* and *Sporting News.*

SIDELIGHTS: Jeff Prugh was among the first American sports writers to visit Castro's Cuba for Olympic volleyball trials in Havana, August, 1971.

*   *   *

PUCKETT, Robert Hugh   1935-

PERSONAL: Born July 16, 1935, in Kansas City, Mo.; son of John William (a manager in a corporation) and Marjorie (Shirlaw) Puckett; married Barbara Chandley, December 23, 1964; children: Sarah Anne. *Education:* De Pauw University, B.A., 1957; University of Chicago, M.A., 1958, Ph.D., 1961. *Religion:* Congregationalist. *Home:* 122 Marigold Dr., Terre Haute, Ind. 47803. *Office:* Department of Political Science, Indiana State University, Terre Haute, Ind. 47809.

CAREER: Mary Washington College, Fredericksburg, Va., assistant professor of political science, 1961-63; University of Virginia, Charlottesville, assistant professor of political science, 1964-66; Michigan State University, East Lansing, assistant professor of social science, 1966-68; Indiana State University, Terre Haute, associate professor, 1968-72, professor of political science, 1972—. Consultant to Rand Corp., 1962-63. Visiting scholar, Massachusetts Institute of Technology, 1963-64. *Member:* American Political Science Association, International Studies Association, Midwest Political Science Association, Indiana Academy of Social Sciences, Indiana Political Science Association, Indianapolis Committee on Foreign Relations, Phi Beta Kappa, Phi Eta Sigma. *Awards, honors:* Social Science Research Council postdoctoral fellow, 1963-64; Outstanding Educators of America award, 1972.

WRITINGS: (Contributor) Oscar H. Rochtschaffen, editor, *Reflections on Space,* U.S. Air Force Academy, 1964;

America Faces the World: Isolationist Ideology in American Foreign Policy, MSS Information Corp., 1972. Contributor of articles and reviews to social science and military journals.

WORK IN PROGRESS: Research on American foreign policy options.

*   *   *

PURCELL, Theodore V(incent)   1911-

PERSONAL: Born June 6, 1911, in Evanston, Ill.; son of Theodore Vincent (a business executive) and Anna (Wallace) Purcell. *Education:* Dartmouth College, A.B., 1933; Loyola University, Chicago, A.M., 1945, S.T.L., 1946; Harvard University, A.M., 1949, Ph.D., 1952; also attended University of Paris. *Home:* 1320 36th St. N.W., Washington, D.C. 20007. *Office:* Jesuit Center for Social Studies, Georgetown University, Washington, D.C. 20007.

CAREER: Commonwealth Edison Co., Chicago, Ill., sales and merchandising work, 1933-36; entered Society of Jesus (Jesuits), 1936, and ordained Roman Catholic priest, 1945; Loyola University, Chicago, assistant professor, 1952-58, associate professor, 1958-61, professor of psychology and industrial relations, 1961-62; Institute of Social Order, St. Louis, Mo., director, 1962-65; Cambridge Center for Social Studies, Cambridge, Mass., director, 1965-68, research associate and member of board, 1965-71; Georgetown University, Washington, D.C., research professor, Jesuit Center for Social Studies, 1971—. William Jewett Tucker Lecturer, Dartmouth College, 1960-61; Harvard University, lecturer in social psychology, 1966-67, visiting lecturer at Episcopal Theological School, 1967-68; visiting professor at Sloan School of Management, Massachusetts Institute of Technology, 1970-71; visiting professor, Graduate School of Business, University of California, Berkeley, 1972, 1974. Member of Illinois Governor's Committee on Unemployment, 1961-62; commissioner, Illinois Commission on Human Relations, 1962-63; member of Illinois advisory committee, U.S. Commission on Civil Rights, 1962-65. Member of National Committee on Ethics, 1976—. Trustee, Creighton University, 1968—. Chairman of National Jesuit Advisory Committee on Investor Responsibility, 1974—.

MEMBER: International Association of Applied Psychology, American Psychological Association (fellow), Industrial Relations Research Association, Psychologists Interested in Religious Issues, Association for Social Economics, Academy of Management. *Awards, honors:* McKinsey Foundation award, 1968.

WRITINGS: The Worker Speaks His Mind on Company and Union, Harvard University Press, 1953; *Blue Collar Man: Patterns of Dual Allegiance in Industry,* Harvard University Press, 1960; (with Daniel P. Mulvey) *The Negro in the Electrical Industry,* University of Pennsylvania Press, 1971; (with Gerald Cavanagh) *Blacks in the Industrial World: Issues for the Manager,* Free Press, 1972.

Contributor: Edward C. Bursk, editor, *Human Relations for Management,* Harper, 1956; Robert F. Harvanek, editor, *Contemporary Thought and the Spiritual Exercises of St. Ignatius Loyola,* Loyola University (Chicago), 1963; Eli Ginzberg and Hyman Berman, editors, *The American Worker in the Twentieth Century,* Free Press of Glencoe, 1963; Arthur B. Shostak and William Gomberg, editors, *Blue Collar World,* Prentice-Hall, 1964; Daniel N. De-Lucca, editor, *Business in a Changing Social Order,* Council on Business Ethics, St. Joseph's College, 1965; Thomas M. Garrett, editor, *Cases in Business Ethics,* Appleton, 1968; Peter B. Doeringer, editor, *Programs to Employ the Disadvantaged,* Prentice-Hall, 1969; (with Frank J. Toner) S. Prakash Sethi, editor, *The Unstable Ground: Corporate Social Policy in a Dynamic Society,* Melville Publishing, 1974; Leonard J. Hausman and others, editors, *Equal Rights and Industrial Relations,* Industrial Relations Institute, 1977. Also author of several pamphlets published by American Management Association. Contributor to *New Catholic Encyclopedia* and to journals, including *Harvard Business Review* and *Personnel Psychology.*

WORK IN PROGRESS: Further studies on minority manpower and organizational psychology.

SIDELIGHTS: At the age of sixteen Purcell went to the Arctic as a crew member of the Borden-Field Museum expedition. In the 1950s he lived for a year and a half in the "Back-of-the-Yards" area of Chicago, interviewing workers in stockyards plants, union stewards, and foremen for his book, *The Worker Speaks His Mind.* He spent further time living among the subjects of his study for *Blacks in the Industrial World.*

*   *   *

PUTZAR, Edward (David) 1930-

PERSONAL: Born August 10, 1930, in San Francisco, Calif.; married, 1962. *Education:* University of California, Berkeley, A.B., 1952, M.A., 1960. *Residence:* Tucson, Ariz. *Office:* Department of Oriental Studies, University of Arizona, Tucson, Ariz. 85721.

CAREER: University of Arizona, Tucson, lecturer in oriental studies, 1962—. *Military service:* U.S. Army, 1952-55.

WRITINGS: Japanese Literature: A Historical Outline, University of Arizona Press, 1972. Contributor of scholarly articles on Japanese literature to journals; contributor of photographs to journals and portfolios.

Q

QUERY, William T(heodore), Jr. 1929-

PERSONAL: Born January 12, 1929, in Paducah, Ky.; son of William Theodore and Viola (Michael) Query; married Joy Neale (a professor of sociology), June 1, 1957; children: Jonathan, Evan, Mildred. *Education:* Illinois College, A.B., 1951; Drake University, M.A., 1956; University of Kentucky, Ph.D., 1961. *Home:* 3102 3rd St. N., Fargo, N.D. 58102. *Office:* Veterans Administration Hospital, Fargo, N.D.

CAREER: Veterans Administration Hospital, Lexington, Ky., ward psychologist, 1961-66; St. Wulstans Hospital, Malvern, England, psychologist, 1964-65; Veterans Administration Hospital, Fargo, N.D., chief of psychology service, 1966—. *Military service:* U.S. Army, 1951-53. *Member:* American Psychological Association, British Psychological Society, Society for Clinical and Experimental Hypnosis, Midwest Psychological Association.

WRITINGS: *Illness, Work and Poverty: Rehabilitation Hospital,* Jossey-Bass, 1968.

WORK IN PROGRESS: A text in clinical psychology; journal articles.

*   *   *

QUICK, Thomas L(ee) 1929-

PERSONAL: Born December 3, 1929, in Anderson, Ind.; son of Gail (a restaurateur) and Laura (Berry) Quick; married Janet L. Staggenburg, October 21, 1952; children: Pamela, Edward, Anthony, Timothy, Stephen, Gerald, Louisa. *Education:* Attended Columbia University, 1947-48; Fordham University, A.B., 1951, graduate study, 1951-52. *Residence:* Livingston, N.J. *Office:* Research Institute of America, 589 Fifth Ave., New York, N.Y. 10017.

CAREER: Lincoln National Life Insurance Co., Fort Wayne, Ind., specialist on employee benefit plans, 1954-61; Research Institute of America, New York, N.Y., district manager, 1961-66, managing editor, 1966—. *Military service:* U.S. Army, 1952-54; became sergeant. *Member:* American Society for Training and Development, National Organization Development Network.

WRITINGS: *Your Role in Task Force Management: The Dynamics of Corporate Change,* Doubleday, 1972; (co-author) *The Ambitious Woman's Guide to a Successful Career,* American Management Association, 1975; *Understanding People at Work: A Manager's Guide to the Behavioral Sciences,* Executive Enterprises, 1976; *Person to Person Managing: An Executive's Guide to Working Effectively with People,* St. Martin's Press, 1977. Managing editor of *Personal Report for the Executive.*

WORK IN PROGRESS: *Dynamics of Goals and Behavior Change* (tentative title), for Doubleday.

R

RAACK, R(ichard) C(harles) 1928-

PERSONAL: Surname is pronounced Rock; born July 10, 1928, in Los Angeles, Calif.; son of Charles Francis (an electrician) and Virginia (Names) Raack; married Marilyn Frances Loeffler (a teacher and writer), February 3, 1952 (divorced, 1978); children: Elizabeth Hope. *Education:* Attended Santa Barbara College (now University of California, Santa Barbara), 1946-47; University of California, Los Angeles, B.A., 1950, M.A., 1953; Harvard University, Ph.D., 1957. *Home:* 520 Connecticut St., San Francisco, Calif. 94107. *Office:* Department of History, California State University, Hayward, Calif. 94542.

CAREER: Rhode Island School of Design, Providence, instructor in history, 1956-57; Massachusetts Institute of Technology, Cambridge, instructor in history, 1957-59; Long Beach State College (now California State University, Long Beach), assistant professor of history, 1961-65; California State University, Hayward, assistant professor, 1965-66, associate professor, 1966-70, professor of history, 1970—. *Military service:* U.S. Air Force, 1951-52; became staff sergeant.

MEMBER: American Historical Association, American Association for the Advancement of Slavic Studies, Conference Group on Central European History, Group for Use of Psychology in History. *Awards, honors:* Film "Goodbye, Billy" has received honorable mention at San Francisco Film Festival, Chris certificate of merit at Columbus Film Festival, and was chosen as tour selection at Ann Arbor Film Festival, all in 1972; first prize, Oklahoma State University Filmathon, 1975, for "The Frozen War"; CINE Golden Eagle Award, 1976, for "Will Rogers' 1920's."

WRITINGS: The Fall of Stein, Harvard University Press, 1965.

Author and producer of films: (With William F. Malloch and Patrick H. Griffin) "Goodbye, Billy: America Goes to War, 1917-1918," Churchill Films, 1972; (with Malloch and Griffin) "The Frozen War: America Intervenes in Russia, 1918-1920," Cadre Films, 1973; (with Peter C. Rollins, Malloch, and Griffin) "Will Rogers' 1920's: A Cowboy's Guide to the Times," Churchill Films, 1976; (and editor) "Storm of Fire: World War II and the Destruction of Dresden," Churchill Films, 1978.

WORK IN PROGRESS: A monograph on the province of Poznania (Poland) before the Revolution of 1848; a film on Hitler's ailments.

RABINOWITCH, Eugene 1901-1973

April 27, 1901—May 15, 1973; Russian-born American atomic scientist, editor, and educator. Obituaries: *New York Times,* May 16, 1973; *Washington Post,* May 16, 1973; *Time,* May 28, 1973; *Newsweek,* May 28, 1973.

* * *

RADEST, Howard B(ernard) 1928-

PERSONAL: Born June 29, 1928, in New York, N.Y.; son of Louis and Gussie (Permison) Radest; married Rita Stollman (a teacher), December 22, 1951; children: Robert, Michael. *Education:* Columbia University, A.B., 1949, Ph.D., 1970; New School for Social Research, M.A., 1951. *Politics:* Independent Democrat. *Religion:* "Ethical culture." *Home:* 2-10 32nd St., Fair Lawn, N.J. 07410. *Office:* Department of Philosophy, Ramapo College, Mahwah, N.J. 07430.

CAREER: American Ethical Union, New York, N.Y., executive director, 1964-70; Ramapo College, Mahwah, N.J., associate professor, 1971-73, professor of philosophy, 1973—. Adjunct professor, Union Graduate School. *Military service:* U.S. Army, 1953-55. *Member:* American Philosophical Association, American Studies Association, Society for the Advancement of American Philosophy, Fraternity of Ethical Leaders, International Humanist and Ethical Union (secretary general, 1970—; co-chairman, 1975—), Phi Beta Kappa.

WRITINGS: Understanding Ethical Religion, American Ethical Union, 1959; *Perspectives in Religious Education,* American Ethical Union, 1960; *On Life and Meaning: Ethical Forum,* American Ethical Union, 1964; *Toward Common Ground,* Ungar, 1969; (editor) *To Seek a Humane World,* Pemberton Publishing, 1972; *Ethics and the Workplace,* Center for the Study of Values, University of Delaware, 1977; *The Work Ethic and Its Meaning: A White Paper,* American Ethical Union, 1978. Contributor to *Encyclopedia Americana* and *Encyclopedia Judaica.* Contributor of articles to *Ethics* and *Ramapo Papers.* Editor of *International Humanism* and *Ramapo Papers;* member of editorial board, *Humanist* and *Religious Humanism.*

WORK IN PROGRESS: A book on a philosophy of work; a book on liberal arts education in industrial society; research on Marxist humanism and on Catholic-humanist philosophy.

AVOCATIONAL INTERESTS: Baroque music for organ.

* * *

RADVANYI, Janos 1922-

PERSONAL: Born August 24, 1922, in Budapest, Hungary; son of Geza (a newspaperman) and Elizabeth (Lanyi) Radvanyi; married Julianna Magyeri, March 15, 1950; children: Julianna, Janos. *Education:* Academy of Foreign Affairs, Budapest, Hungary, Diploma, 1948; Graduate School of Diplomacy, Budapest, Diploma, 1954; Stanford University, M.A., 1969, Ph.D., 1971. *Office:* Department of History, Mississippi State University, State College, Miss. 39762.

CAREER: Hungarian Diplomatic Service, 1948-67, service includes country director in Russia and Yugoslavia, department head in Asia, Africa, Western Europe, and the United States, service abroad in Turkey, France, Switzerland, and Syria; San Francisco State College (now University), San Francisco, Calif., lecturer in history, 1970-71; Stanford University, Center for International Studies, Stanford, Calif., scholar-in-residence, 1970-71; Mississippi State University, State College, associate professor, 1971-73, professor of history, 1973—. *Awards, honors:* Ford Foundation fellow, 1968-70; Center for International Studies, Princeton University, fellow, 1975; Rockefeller Foundation research grant, 1975-77.

WRITINGS: Hungary and the Super Powers, Hoover Press, 1972; *Delusion and Reality: Gambits, Hoaxes and Diplomatic One-Upmanship in Vietnam,* Gateway Edition, 1978. Contributor to *Yearbook on International Communist Affairs.* Contributor of articles to *China Quarterly, Art International, Lugano Review, Life, Los Angeles Times,* and *Washington Post.*

* * *

RAIZIS, M(arios) Byron 1931-

PERSONAL: Born December 8, 1931, in Athens, Greece; son of George S. (a physician) and Marianthe (Polytarides) Raizis; married Catherine Sempepos, March 26, 1963 (divorced, 1972); children: Lydia Marianne, George Leander. *Education:* University of Athens, B.Phil. (cum laude), 1956; Purdue University, M.S., 1961; New York University, Ph.D., 1966. *Politics:* Liberal humanitarian. *Religion:* Orthodox Christian. *Home:* 512 South Forest St., Carbondale, Ill. 62901. *Office:* Department of English, Southern Illinois University, Carbondale, Ill. 62901.

CAREER: Spetsai College, Spetsai, Greece, instructor in English and drama, 1956-57; St. Demetrios School of Astoria, New York, N.Y., teacher and librarian, 1962-65; Wichita State University, Wichita, Kan., assistant professor of English, 1965-66; Southern Illinois University at Carbondale, associate professor, 1966-78, professor of English, 1978—. *Military service:* Hellenic army, 1957-58; became non-commissioned officer. *Member:* International Comparative Literature Association, Modern Language Association of America, American Comparative Literature Association, Modern Greek Studies Association, Byron Society, Rydal Mount Association, Center for Neo-Hellenic Studies. *Awards, honors:* National Endowment for the Humanities fellow, 1972-73.

WRITINGS: (Contributor) A. M. Decavalles, editor, *The Voice of Cyprus: An Anthology,* October House, 1967; (with Alexander Papas) *American Poets and the Greek Revolution,* Institute for Balkan Studies, 1972; *Dionysios Solomos,* Twayne, 1972; (editor) *Greek Revolution and the American*

Muse, Institute for Balkan Studies, 1972. Contributor of articles and translations to *Southern Review, Comparative Literature Studies, Philological Quarterly, Yearbook of General and Comparative Literature.* Editor of Greek issue of *Literary Review,* 1973.

WORK IN PROGRESS: A translation of the poetry of Dionysios Solomos.

* * *

RALEY, Harold (Cecil) 1934-

PERSONAL: Born November 23, 1934, in Hartselle, Ala.; son of William Bathel (a farmer) and Vernie (Hooper) Raley; married Victoria Gonzalez, August 26, 1962; children: Laura Maria, Ana Maria, David Julian. *Education:* Athens College, B.A., 1958; University of Alabama, M.A., 1961, Ph.D., 1966. *Religion:* Episcopalian. *Home:* 125 St. Cloud Dr., Friendswood, Tex. 77546. *Office:* Department of Spanish, University of Houston, Houston, Tex. 77004.

CAREER: North Texas State University, Denton, instructor in French and Spanish, 1962-64; Oklahoma State University, Stillwater, assistant professor, 1964-67, associate professor, 1967-71, professor of foreign languages, 1971-77, head of department of foreign languages, 1967-71; University of Houston, Houston, Tex., professor of foreign languages and chairman of department, 1977—. Visiting professor, Stephen F. Austin State College, summer, 1962, and University of Alabama, summer, 1966. *Military service:* U.S. Army Reserve, 1952-59. *Member:* Modern Language Association of America, American Association of Teachers of Spanish and Portuguese, South Central Modern Language Association.

WRITINGS: (Translator) Marias Aguilera, *Generations: A Historical Method,* University of Alabama Press, 1970; *Jose Ortega y Gasset: Philosopher of European Unity,* University of Alabama Press, 1971; (translator with Ida Blanche De Puy and Michael Rockland) Julian Marias, *America in the Fifties and Sixties,* Pennsylvania State University Press, 1972; *La vision responsable: La filosofia de Julian Marias,* Espasa Calpe, 1977; *Jose Ortega y Gasset: Filosofo de la unificacion europea,* Revista de Occidente, 1978. Contributor of articles and reviews to professional journals.

* * *

RAMSAUR, Ernest Edmondson, Jr. 1915-

PERSONAL: Born July 28, 1915, in Venice, Calif.; son of Ernest Edmondson (a dentist) and Lucy (Mitchell) Ramsaur; married second wife, Joan Connelly, September 13, 1965; children: (first marriage) Lucy, Anne, Lee, John B.; (second marriage) Susan. *Education:* University of California, Berkeley, A.B., 1935, F.A., 1938, Ph.D., 1947; University of Freiburg, graduate study, 1936-37. *Home:* 553 Valley View Way, Ventura, Calif. 93003. *Office:* Century 21, 2800 East Main St., Ventura, Calif. 93003.

CAREER: Robert College, Istanbul, Turkey, tutor, 1938-39; State University of Iowa, Iowa City, instructor in history, 1946-47; American Consulate, Istanbul, consular office, beginning 1948, cultural affairs officer, 1948-50; American Consulate, Bremen, Germany, vice-consul, 1950-52, consul, 1952-55; American Consulate, Toronto, Ontario, chief of consular section, 1955; U.S. Department of State, Washington, D.C., intelligence research officer, 1955-56, public affairs adviser, Office of German Affairs, 1956-58; American Embassy, Beirut, Lebanon, chief of political section, 1959-62; U.S. Department of State, adviser to Armed

Forces Staff College (Norfolk, Va.), 1962-64; U.S. Mission, Berlin, Germany, public affairs officer, 1964-67; Pennsylvania State University, University Park, diplomat in residence, 1967-68; American Embassy, Lagos, Nigeria, counselor for political affairs, 1968-70; U.S. Department of State, special assistant in public affairs to director of Bureau of International Scientific and Technological Affairs, 1970-71, officer in charge of scientific and technological relations with Western Europe, Australia, Japan, and Mainland China, 1971-73; Century 21, Ventura, Calif., part-time real estate agent, 1978—. *Military service:* U.S. Navy, 1942-46; became lieutenant senior grade; received Silver Star. U.S. Naval Reserve, 1946-59; became commander. *Member:* American Historical Association, American Association for the Advancement of Science, Psi Upsilon.

WRITINGS: The Young Turks, Princeton University Press, 1957, new edition, Russell, 1970.

* * *

RAMSEY, Paul 1924-

PERSONAL: Born November 26, 1924, in Atlanta, Ga.; son of Paul (in electrical business) and Lillian (Johnson) Ramsey; married Betty Miller (an artist), June 23, 1952; children: Starr, Lee, James, Sarah. *Education:* Attended University of Chattanooga (now University of Tennessee at Chattanooga), 1941-43; University of North Carolina, B.A., 1947, M.A., 1949; University of Minnesota, Ph.D., 1956. *Politics:* Independent. *Religion:* Episcopal. *Home:* 322 Pine Ridge Rd., Chattanooga, Tenn. 37405. *Office:* Department of English, University of Tennessee, Chattanooga, Tenn. 37403.

CAREER: University of Alabama, Tuscaloosa, instructor, 1948-50, assistant professor of English, 1953-56; Elmira College, Elmira, N.Y., assistant professor of English, 1956-62; University of the Pacific, Raymond College, Stockton, Calif., associate professor of English, 1962-64; University of the South, Sewanee, Tenn., associate professor of English, 1964-66; University of Tennessee at Chattanooga, poet-in-residence, 1966-68, 1969—, professor of English, 1966-68, alumni distinguished service professor, 1971—. Director, Tennessee Poetry Circuit, 1967—. *Military service:* U.S. Naval Reserve, 1944-46; became lieutenant. *Member:* National Council of Teachers of English, Academy of American Poets, Poetry Society of America, Bibliographical Society, Milton Society, South Atlantic Modern Language Association, Tennessee Philological Association. *Awards, honors:* Rochester Festival of Religious Arts First Prize, 1966, for "The Creatures"; South Atlantic Modern Language Association award, 1968, for *The Art of John Dryden;* Beaudoin Gem Stone Award, 1969, for "The Naming of Adam"; *Lyric* magazine Roberts Memorial Prize, 1972, for "In the Ice Forest"; English-Speaking Union Bicentennial Poetry Prize, 1976.

WRITINGS: The Lively and the Just, University of Alabama Press, 1962; (with Sy Kahn and Jane Taylor) *Triptych,* Raymond College Press, 1964; *In an Ordinary Place* (poems), North Carolina State University Press, 1965; *A Window for New York* (poems), Twowindows, 1968; *The Doors* (poems), Tennessee Poetry Press, 1968; *The Art of John Dryden,* University Press of Kentucky, 1969; *No Running on the Boardwalk* (poems), University of Georgia Press, 1975; *Eve, Singing,* Pennyroyal Press, 1977; *The Fickle Glass: A Study of Shakespeare's Sonnets,* AMS Press, 1978. Contributor of poems, short stories, essays, and book reviews to magazines and anthologies in the United States, Canada, England, Wales, Italy, India, and New Zealand. Also author of an annual chronicle of poetry for the *Sewanee Review.* Editor of *Factotum,* 1948-49.

WORK IN PROGRESS: A second novel; an edition of Shakespeare's sonnets; *Stars and Houses,* a book of poems; a collection of short fiction; a book on justice.

AVOCATIONAL INTERESTS: Bicycling, jogging.

BIOGRAPHICAL/CRITICAL SOURCES: Minnesota Review, fall, 1963; *Lillabulero,* summer, 1967; *Virginia Quarterly Review,* autumn, 1968; *Poetry,* June, 1969; *Journal of English and Germanic Philology,* April, 1971; *Chattanooga Times,* July 13, 1975; *Sandlapper,* October, 1975; *Appalachian Journal,* spring, 1976; *Choice,* July, 1976; *Commonweal,* October 22, 1976; *Cahiers Elisabethains,* April, 1977.

* * *

RANDALL, Charles Edgar 1897-

PERSONAL: Born December 4, 1897, in Selma, Calif.; son of Charles E. (a real estate salesman) and Mary Ellen (Ramsey) Randall; married Iva Gilman, August 29, 1929. *Education:* Stanford University, A.B., 1920; Oregon State College (now University), graduate study, 1921-22; George Washington University, M.A., 1930. *Politics:* Independent. *Home:* 1717 Besley Rd. N.E., Vienna, Va. 22180.

CAREER: San Jose Mercury-Herald, San Jose, Calif., correspondent, 1919, 1923-26; Bureau of Plant Industry, Washington, D.C., forest pathologist, 1921-23; *Alexandria Daily Gazette,* Alexandria, Va., managing editor, 1923-24; General Press Association, Washington, D.C., reporter, 1924-26; *United States News,* Washington, D.C., copy editor, 1926-27; U.S. Forest Service, Washington, D.C., chief of press information, 1927-59; *Journal of Forestry,* Washington, D.C., staff assistant, 1960—. *Military service:* U.S. Navy, 1918. *Member:* National Press Club, Society of American Foresters, American Forestry Association, Outdoor Writers Association.

WRITINGS: Famous Trees, U.S. Department of Agriculture, 1936; (with Wilbur H. Youngman) *Growing Your Trees,* American Forestry Association, 1968; *Enjoying Our Trees,* American Forestry Association, 1969; *Famous and Historic Trees of the United States,* American Forestry Association, 1975.

WORK IN PROGRESS: Some Important National Forests.

* * *

RANDALL, Florence Engel 1917-

PERSONAL: Born October 18, 1917, in Brooklyn, N.Y.; daughter of Stewart (an attorney) and Rachel (Seligman) Engel; married Murray Charles Randall (a sales executive), November 5, 1939; children: Susan (Mrs. Stephen Lipsig), Laurel, Stewart. *Education:* Attended New York University, 1937. *Residence:* Great Neck, N.Y. *Agent:* Raines & Raines, 475 Fifth Ave., New York, N.Y. 10017.

CAREER: Fiction writer. *Member:* Authors League of America, Science Fiction Writers of America. *Awards, honors: The Almost Year* was an American Library Association Notable Book in 1971.

WRITINGS: Hedgerow (adult novel), Harcourt, 1967; *The Place of Sapphires* (adult novel), Harcourt, 1969; *The Almost Year* (young adult novel), Atheneum, 1971; *Haldane Station,* Harcourt, 1973; *A Watcher in the Woods* (young adult novel), Atheneum, 1976. Short stories have been published in *Good Housekeeping, Harper's, Cosmopolitan, Redbook, Seventeen, Ladies' Home Journal, Ingenue, Woman's Day, Virginia Quarterly, Chatelaine,* and other magazines; one of her stories, "The Watchers," has been included in six anthologies.

SIDELIGHTS: Florence Engel Randall writes: "I have never been a short order cook, worked in a logging camp, hitchhiked around the country or done any of the marvelous things so dear to the copywriter of book jackets. I can't remember a time when I didn't want to be a writer, and yet for years I did everything I could to avoid it. I studied art, played the piano for hours, and even though I had sold my first short story when I was eighteen, it wasn't until many years later that I began to write again."

The film rights for *A Watcher in the Woods* were purchased by Walt Disney Productions for use as a television movie.

BIOGRAPHICAL/CRITICAL SOURCES: Writer, March, 1968, January, 1972; *Horn Book,* August, 1971.

* * *

RANDALL, Margaret 1936-

PERSONAL: Born December 6, 1936, in New York, N.Y.; daughter of John Philip (a teacher) and Elinor (Davidson) Randall; married Sam Jacobs, 1955 (divorced, 1958); married Sergio Mondragon, February 22, 1962 (divorced, 1968); children: Gregory, Sarah, Ximena, Anna. *Education:* Attended University of New Mexico, 1954-55. *Politics:* "I am a revolutionary aspiring to communist ideals and practice." *Religion:* None. *Residence:* Havana, Cuba. *Office:* Linea 53, Apt. 9, e/M y N, Vedado, La Habana 4, Cuba.

CAREER: Has worked as a teacher, model, waitress, and factory worker. Affiliated with Spanish Refugee Aid, Inc., New York, N.Y., 1960-61; *El Corno Emplumado,* Mexico City, Mexico, editor, 1962-69; Instituto Cubano del Libro, Editorial de Ciencias Sociales, Havana, Cuba, investigator and writer, 1969—. *Awards, honors:* Casa de Las Americas literary contest (Havana), judge, 1970.

WRITINGS—Books of poems, except as indicated: *Giant of Tears,* Tejon, 1959; *Ecstasy Is a Number,* Gutman Foundation, 1960; *Small Sounds from the Bass Fiddle,* Duende, 1964; *October,* El Corno Emplumado, 1965; *Twenty Five Stages of My Spine,* Elizabeth Press, 1968; *Water I Slip into at Night,* El Corno Emplumado, 1968; *Los Hippies: Expresion de una crises,* Siglo XXI, 1968; *Las Mujeres,* Siglo XXI, 1969; *La Mujer Cubana Ahora,* Cuban Book Institute, 1972; *Mujeres en la Revolucion,* Siglo XXI, 1972; *La Gloria de Caballo Loco,* Quimantu, 1973; *Part of the Solution* (poems and stories), New Directions, 1973; *This Great People Has Said Enough, and Has Begun to Move,* People's Press, 1973; *Carlota: Poems and Prose from Havana,* New Star, 1978; *Doris Tijerino: Inside the Nicaraguan Revolution,* New Star, 1978; *We,* Smyrna Press, 1978; (compiler, translator, and author of introduction) *Inside These Living Songs,* Colorado State University Review, 1978. Contributor of poems, articles, stories, and essays to magazines in the United States and abroad, including *Poetry Chicago, Evergreen Review, Nation, Monthly Review, Trobar,* and *Caterpillar.*

WORK IN PROGRESS: Research on women in the "third world"; research on cultural penetration in the "third world."

BIOGRAPHICAL/CRITICAL SOURCES: Poetry, June, 1967, July, 1969.

RANIS, Peter 1935-

PERSONAL: Born August 13, 1935, in Darmstadt, West Germany; son of Max (a lawyer) and Bettina (Goldschmidt) Ranis; married Gloria Tarshis, November 1, 1964 (divorced, February, 1976); children: Maria Kim, Paul Bernard. *Education:* Brandeis University, B.A., 1958; University of Washington, Seattle, M.A., 1960; New York University, Ph.D., 1965. *Politics:* Democrat. *Religion:* Jewish. *Office:* Department of Political Science, York College of the City University of New York, 150-14 Jamaica Ave., Jamaica, N.Y. 11432.

CAREER: Brookings Institution, Washington, D.C., research assistant, 1962-64; University of New Mexico, Albuquerque, assistant professor of political science, 1965-66; State University of New York at Stony Brook, assistant professor of political science, 1966-68; York College of the City University of New York, Jamaica, N.Y., associate professor of political science, 1968—, coordinator of department, 1970-72, chairman of department, 1975-77. Fulbright professor, National University of Cuyo, spring, 1970; visiting professor, Inter-American University, 1977-78. *Member:* American Political Science Association, Latin American Studies Association, American Association of University Professors, Center for Cuban Studies, Caucus for New Political Science, Sigma Delta Pi. *Awards, honors:* Organization of American States fellowship, Mexico, 1961, Argentina, 1974-75; Fulbright fellowship, Argentina, 1964-65; Social Science Research Council grant, summer, 1966.

WRITINGS: Modernity and Political Development in Five Latin American Countries, Studies in Comparative International Development, Rutgers University, 1968; (contributor) Frederick B. Pike, editor, *Latin American History: Selected Problems, Identity, Integration and Nationhood,* Harcourt, 1969; (contributor) Robert D. Tomasek, editor, *Latin American Politics: Studies in the Contemporary Scene,* Doubleday, 1970; (contributor) Weston H. Agor, editor, *Latin American Legislatures: Their Role and Influence,* Praeger, 1971; *Five Latin American Nations: A Comparative Political Study,* Macmillan, 1971. Contributor of articles and reviews to political science and history journals.

* * *

RANKIN, Jeannette 1880-1973

June 11, 1880—May 18, 1973; American politician, feminist, pacifist, and first woman to serve in U.S. Congress. Obituaries: *New York Times,* May 20, 1973; *Newsweek,* May 28, 1973; *Time,* May 28, 1973.

* * *

RAPOPORT, Anatol 1911-

PERSONAL: Born May 22, 1911, in Lozovaya, Russia; came to United States in 1922, naturalized in 1928; son of Boris and Adel (Rapoport) Rapoport; married Gwen Goodrich, January 29, 1949; children: Anya, Alexander, Charles Anthony. *Education:* University of Chicago, S.B., 1938, S.M., 1940, Ph.D., 1941. *Home:* 38 Wychwood Park, Toronto, Ontario, Canada M6G 2V5. *Office:* Department of Psychology, University of Toronto, Toronto, Ontario, Canada.

CAREER: Illinois Institute of Technology, Chicago, instructor in mathematics, 1946-47; University of Chicago, Chicago, Ill., member of faculty, 1947-51; Center for Advanced Study of Behavioral Sciences, Stanford, Calif., fellow, 1954-55; University of Michigan, Mental Health Research Institute, Ann Arbor, associate professor, 1955-60, professor of mathematical biology, 1960-70; University of Toronto, Toronto, Ontario, professor of psychology and mathematics, 1970—. *Military service:* U.S. Army Air Forces, 1942-46; became captain. *Member:* International Society for General Semantics (president, 1953-55), American Mathematical Society, American Academy of Arts and Sciences (fellow), American Association for the Advancement of Science, Sigma Xi. *Awards, honors:* D.H.L., Western Michigan University, 1971.

WRITINGS: Science and the Goals of Man, Harper, 1950; *Operational Philosophy,* Harper, 1953; *Fights, Games, and Debates,* University of Michigan Press, 1960; *Strategy and Conscience,* Harper, 1964; *Prisoner's Dilemma,* University of Michigan Press, 1965; *Two-Person Game Theory,* University of Michigan Press, 1966; *N-Person Game Theory,* University of Michigan Press, 1970; *The Big Two,* Pegasus, 1971; *Conflict in Man-Made Environment,* Penguin, 1974; (editor) *Game Theory as a Theory of Conflict Resolution,* D. Reidel, 1974; *Semantics,* Crowell, 1975; *The 2x2 Game,* University of Michigan Press, 1976. Editor of *General Systems,* 1956-77.

WORK IN PROGRESS: Research on applications of mathematics to biophysical and social sciences, and on the role of ideology and struggle for power in international relations.

* * *

RAPPAPORT, Roy A(braham) 1926-

PERSONAL: Born March 25, 1926, in New York, N.Y.; son of Murray (an accountant) and Judith (Israelson) Rappaport; married Ann Allison Hart, August 15, 1959; children: Amelia, Georgiana. *Education:* Attended Syracuse University, 1943-44; Cornell University, B.A., 1949, Ph.D., 1966. *Politics:* "New Left." *Religion:* Jewish. *Home:* 1316 Culver, Ann Arbor, Mich. *Office:* Department of Anthropology, University of Michigan, Ann Arbor, Mich. 48104.

CAREER: Avaloch Inn, Lenox, Mass., owner and manager, 1951-59; University of Michigan, Ann Arbor, assistant professor, 1965-68, associate professor, 1968-72, professor of anthropology, 1972—. *Military service:* U.S. Army, Infantry, 1943-46; received Purple Heart. *Member:* American Anthropological Association, American Ethnological Society. *Awards, honors:* Guggenheim fellowship, 1968-69; American Council of Learned Societies fellowship, 1972-73.

WRITINGS: (With Roger Green, Kay Green, wife, Ann Rappaport, and Janet Davidson) *The Archaeology of Mo'orea, French Polynesia,* American Museum of Natural History, 1967; *Pigs for the Ancestors: Ritual in the Ecology of a New Guinea People,* Yale University Press, 1968; *Ecology, Meaning and Religion,* North Atlantic Books, 1979. Contributor to *American Anthropologist, Ethnology, Scientific American, Journal of the Polynesian Society,* and other professional journals.

WORK IN PROGRESS: A book, tentatively entitled *On the Structure of Ritual,* for Cambridge University Press.

SIDELIGHTS: Roy A. Rappaport's travels include six months in the Society Islands and twenty months in New Guinea, mostly among the Maring speakers.

BIOGRAPHICAL/CRITICAL SOURCES: Journal of Asian Studies, May, 1969; *American Anthropologist,* June, 1969.

* * *

RAPPOPORT, Leon 1932-

PERSONAL: Born March 11, 1932, in New York, N.Y.:

son of Jack and Minnie (Himmel) Rappoport; married Karen Simon, August 15, 1955; children: Paul, Alex. *Education:* New York University, B.A., 1953; University of Colorado, M.A., 1962, Ph.D., 1963. *Politics:* Independent. *Religion:* Atheist. *Home:* 320 South Delaware, Manhattan, Kan. 66502. *Office:* Department of Psychology, Kansas State University, Manhattan, Kan. 66502.

CAREER: Youth House, New York City, assistant floor supervisor, 1954; Elmo Roper & Associates, New York City, assistant supervisor, 1956-58; Kansas State University, Manhattan, assistant professor, 1964-68, associate professor of psychology, 1968—. Visiting professor, Manhattanville College, 1972-73. *Military service:* U.S. Army, 1954-56. *Member:* American Psychological Association, Society for the Psychological Study of Social Issues, Southwestern Psychological Association. *Awards, honors:* National Institute of Mental Health fellowships, 1962-63, at Oslo University, 1963-64.

WRITINGS: (Contributor) Michael Wertheimer, editor, *Confrontation: Psychology and the Problems of Today,* Scott, Foresman, 1970; *Personality Development: The Chronology of Experience,* Scott, Foresman, 1972; (contributor) R. B. Leachman and Philip Althoff, editors, *Preventing Nuclear Theft: Guidelines for Industry and Government,* Praeger, 1972; (editor with David Summers) *Human Judgment and Social Interaction,* Holt, 1973; (contributor) T. Alden Williams and David Tarr, editors, *Modular Syllabus in National Security, Armed Forces and Society,* University Press of Kansas, 1973; (editor with George Kren) *Varieties of Psychohistory,* Springer Publishing, 1976.

Contributor to proceedings: contributor of about twenty-five articles to *Journal of Abnormal and Social Psychology, Psychological Reports, Contemporary Psychology, Human Relations, Journal of Conflict Resolutions, Child Development,* and other professional publications.

WORK IN PROGRESS: The Holocaust and the Human Condition, with George Kren.

* * *

RATH, Frederick L(ouis), Jr. 1913-

PERSONAL: Born May 19, 1913, in Brooklyn, N.Y.; son of Frederick Louis (a businessman) and Adeline (Kolkebeck) Rath; married Ann Richardson, July 14, 1946; children: William Richardson, David Frederick. *Education:* Dartmouth College, B.A., 1934; Harvard University, M.A., 1937. *Office:* Eastern National Park and Monument Association, 314 Market St., Philadelphia, Pa. 19106.

CAREER: U.S. Department of the Interior, National Park Service, Washington, D.C., historian, 1937-41, 1946-48; National Council for Historic Sites and Buildings, Washington, D.C., executive secretary, 1948-50; National Trust for Historic Preservation in the United States, Washington, D.C., co-founder director, 1950-56; New York State Historical Association, Cooperstown, vice-director, 1956-72; State of New York, Office of Parks and Recreation, Albany, deputy commissioner for historic preservation, 1972-78; Eastern National Park and Monument Association, Philadelphia, Pa., executive secretary, 1979—. Appointed to governor's Advisory Committee on Historic Preservation in New York State, 1968-73, chairman of committee, 1971-73. Member of board of directors, American Heritage Publishing Co., 1960-64; trustee, Hancock Shaker Village; member of advisory committee, South Street Seaport (New York, N.Y.); secretary, Cultural Resources Development International, Inc. Chairman of Cooperstown Planning

Commission and Cooperstown Architectural Control Board, 1959-73. *Military service:* U.S. Army, military intelligence, 1943-45; became master sergeant.

MEMBER: American Association for State and Local History (founding member; president, 1960-62), Eastern National Park and Monument Association (founding member; board chairman, 1976-78; executive secretary, 1979—), Rochester Museum and Science Center (fellow). *Awards, honors:* Award of merit from American Scenic and Historic Preservation Society, 1963; American Association for State and Local History award, 1971, for *Guide to Historic Preservation, Historical Agencies, and Museum Practices.*

WRITINGS: (With Lilli Rethi) *Franklin D. Roosevelt's Hyde Park,* Holt, 1948; (editor) *The New York State Historical Association and Its Museums: An Informal Guide,* New York State Historical Association, 1968; (editor with Merrilyn O'Connell) *A Bibliography of Historical Organization Practice,* American Association for State and Local History, Volume I: *Historic Preservation,* 1975, Volume II: *Care and Conservation of Collections,* 1977, Volume III: *Interpretation,* 1978. Also author of *Guide to Historic Preservation, Historical Agencies, and Museum Practices.*

WORK IN PROGRESS: Editing three additional volumes of *A Bibliography of Historical Organization Practice.*

SIDELIGHTS: As executive secretary of the Eastern National Park and Monument Association, Frederick L. Rath plans to expand the organization's publication program. The Eastern National Park and Monument Association is a nonprofit organization that works in coordination with the National Park Service.

* * *

RATHJEN, Frederick W(illiam) 1929-

PERSONAL: Born January 25, 1929, in Clarendon, Tex.; son of Frederick W. (a shoemaker) and Mary Beall (McGee) Rathjen; married Elizabeth Schweikert, June 28, 1953; children: Eric Jonathan, Kurt Norman. *Education:* University of Texas at Austin, B.A., 1950, M.A., 1956, Ph.D., 1970. *Politics:* Democrat. *Religion:* Lutheran. *Residence:* Canyon, Tex. *Office address:* Box 702, West Texas Station, Canyon, Tex. 79015.

CAREER: West Texas State University, Canyon, instructor, 1956-60, assistant professor, 1960-70, associate professor, 1970-76, professor of history, 1976—. *Military service:* U.S. Navy, 1950-54; became yeoman second class. *Member:* Organization of American Historians, Western History Association, Texas State Historical Association, Texas Association of College Teachers, Panhandle-Plains Historical Society.

WRITINGS: The Texas Panhandle Frontier, University of Texas Press, 1973. Contributor to *Southwestern Historical Quarterly.*

WORK IN PROGRESS: Research on southwestern United States, conservation history, and native American history.

AVOCATIONAL INTERESTS: Hunting, fishing, backpacking, canoeing, studying nature.

* * *

RATTI, Oscar

PERSONAL: Born in San Terenzo, La Spezia, Italy; son of Mario Randolfo and Anna Maria (Procida) Ratti; married Adele Westbrook (a writer and editor), September 22, 1969. *Education:* Studied jurisprudence at University of Genoa

and University of Naples; postgraduate study in classical languages and literature at Columbia University. *Home:* 270 West 11th St., New York, N.Y. 10014.

CAREER: Artist. Catholic Relief Services, Capua, Caserta, Italy, director of immigration office, 1952-59; Institutional Commodities Services, New York, N.Y., illustrator, 1960—. Free-lance artist and designer of book jackets and covers.

WRITINGS—With wife, Adele Westbrook: *Aikido and the Dynamic Sphere,* Tuttle, 1970; *Secrets of the Samurai,* Tuttle, 1973; (translators) Luisa C. Arano, *Medieval Health Handbook: Tacuinum Sanitatis,* Braziller, 1976.

WORK IN PROGRESS: Two books, *Budo: The Ethics of the Samurai* and *The Mystic Warrior;* illustrations for *Organic Gourmet, Max,* and *Who Lives by the Sword,* all by Adele Westbrook; writing or translating four other books with A. Westbrook.

AVOCATIONAL INTERESTS: Study of history and the classics, sports, Greek-Roman wrestling, Judo, and Aikido (black belt rank).

* * *

RAY, Joseph M(alchus) 1907-

PERSONAL: Born October 14, 1907, in Bowling Green, Ky.; son of Joseph Edward (a lumberman) and Vivia (Scott) Ray; married Jettie Hollingsworth, December 26, 1933; children: Scott Joseph, David Peter, Sally Ray Thomas. *Education:* University of Texas at Austin, B.A., 1932, M.A., 1933, Ph.D., 1937. *Politics:* Democrat. *Religion:* Protestant. *Home:* 817 University Ave., El Paso, Tex. 79902. *Office:* Department of Political Science, University of Texas at El Paso, El Paso, Tex. 79968.

CAREER: University of Texas, Main University (now University of Texas at Austin), instructor in government, 1934-37; North Texas State College (now University), Denton, associate professor of government, 1937-42; University of Alabama, University, associate professor of political science, 1942-46; University of Maryland, College Park, professor of government and politics, 1946-52, head of department, 1946-50, dean of College of Special and Continuation Studies, 1950-52; chief of Education and Libraries Branch, U.S. Air Force Headquarters, 1952-57; Amarillo College, Amarillo, Tex., president, 1957-60; University of Texas at El Paso, president, 1960-68, president emeritus, 1968—, H. Y. Benedict Professor of Political Science, 1968-75, professor emeritus, 1975—. Director of El Paso Branch, Federal Reserve Bank of Dallas, 1966-72. *Member:* American Political Science Association (member of executive council, 1947-50), American Society for Public Administration (member of council, 1964—), Southern Political Science Association (member of executive council, 1947-49), Phi Beta Kappa, Pi Sigma Alpha.

WRITINGS: Alabama's Heritage, Bureau of Public Administration, University of Alabama, 1947; *Maryland Fiscal Scene,* Bureau of Public Administration, University of Maryland, 1948; *On Becoming a University;* Texas Western Press, 1968; (editor) *The President: Rex, Princeps, Imperator?* Texas Western Press, 1969; (editor) *Thomason: The Autobiography of a Federal Judge,* Texas Western Press, 1971; (editor) Marvin Jones, *Memoirs: 1917-1973,* Texas Western Press, 1973; *The Coattailless Landslide,* Texas Western Press, 1974; *Fifty-Two Years a Newsman,* Texas Western Press, 1974; *Here Comes the Judge,* Texian Press, 1977. Writer of monographs and survey reports; contributor to professional journals.

RAYCRAFT, Donald R(obert) 1942-

PERSONAL: Born July 18, 1942; son of Donald J. and Emma Louise (Bartlett) Raycraft; married Carol Faulkner (a writer), June 8, 1965; children: Craig, Michael, Scott. *Education:* Illinois State University, B.S., 1964, M.S., 1966, Ph.D., 1972. *Home address:* R.R. 8, Normal, Ill. 61761.

CAREER: Eureka College, Eureka, Ill., assistant professor of education and psychology, 1969-77; currently a full-time writer.

WRITINGS—Published by Wallace-Homestead, except as indicated: *Early American Folk and Country Antiques,* Tuttle, 1971; (with wife, Carol Raycraft) *Early American Furniture* (manufacturer's booklet), 1972; (with C. Raycraft) *Early American Kitchen Antiques* (manufacturer's booklet), Volume I, 1974, Volume II, 1977; (with C. Raycraft) *Early American Lighting* (manufacturer's booklet), 1974; (with C. Raycraft) *American Country Pottery,* 1975; (with C. Raycraft) *American Country Baskets,* 1975; (with C. Raycraft) *Price Guide to American Country Pottery,* 1976; *American Victorian Furniture,* 1976; (with C. Raycraft) *Price Guide to American Country Antiques,* 1978; *Shaker: A Collector's Source Book,* 1979.

*   *   *

RAZAF, Andy 1895-1973

1895—February 4, 1973; American songwriter, lyricist, and poet. Obituaries: *New York Times,* February 5, 1973; *Washington Post,* February 5, 1973; *L'Express,* February 12-18, 1973.

*   *   *

RAZRAN, Gregory 1901-1973

PERSONAL: Born June 4, 1901, near Slutsk, Russia; came to United States in 1920, naturalized in 1927; son of Solomon H. (a merchant) and Riva (Ongeyber) Razran; married Elna Bernholz (a supervisor of guidance), September 15, 1939; children: Lydia Hooke. *Education:* Columbia University, B.S., 1927, M.A., 1928, Ph.D., 1933. *Home and office:* 555 Gulf Way, St. Petersburg Beach, Fla. 33706.

CAREER: Columbia University, New York City, instructor in psychology, 1930-38, research assistant, 1938-40; Queens College of the City University of New York, New York City, 1940-73, began as instructor, became professor of psychology, professor emeritus, 1971-73, chairman of department, 1945-66; Eckerd College, St. Petersburg, Fla., distinguished professor of psychology, 1972-73. Visiting professor, Hebrew University of Jerusalem, 1952. Co-chairman of International Pavlovian Conference on Higher Nervous Activity, New York City, 1961. *Wartime service:* Office of Strategic Service, statistical consultant, 1941-44. *Member:* American Association for the Advancement of Science (fellow), American Psychological Association, Eastern Psychological Association, New York Academy of Science, Florida Psychological Association (honorary member). *Awards, honors:* Guggenheim fellow, 1948-49.

WRITINGS: Mind in Evolution: An East-West Synthesis of Learned Behavior and Cognition, Houghton, 1971. Contributor of over one hundred and ten articles and monographs to journals in his field.

WORK IN PROGRESS: Research in genetics and classical conditioning.

SIDELIGHTS: Gregory Razran took leave of Queens College of the City University of New York in 1952 and went to Israel to assist in establishing a psychology department at the Hebrew University of Jerusalem. He was an authority on Soviet research in psychology and on five occasions visited the Soviet Union. Razran was able to read twelve European languages and was conversant in six.†

(Died August 31, 1973)

*   *   *

REAGAN, Sydney C(handler) 1916-

PERSONAL: Born January 7, 1916, in Fort Smith, Ark.; son of Sydney Chandler (an attorney) and Ollie (Wood) Reagan; married Barbara Ruth Benton (a professor of economics), June 8, 1940; children: Patricia Benton, Sydney Chandler III. *Education:* University of Texas, B.B.A. (with honors), 1937, J.D., 1941; Harvard University, M.Public Administration, 1949, Ph.D., 1954. *Religion:* Methodist. *Home:* 6815 Prestonshire, Dallas, Tex. 75225. *Office:* School of Business Administration, Southern Methodist University, Dallas, Tex. 75275.

CAREER: U.S. Department of Agriculture, Washington, D.C., economist and statistician, 1941-55; Southern Methodist University, Dallas, Tex., professor of real estate and regional science and chairman of the department, 1955—, director of Institute of Urban and Environmental Studies, 1968-73. Business consultant. General counsel, Southwestern Peanut Shellers Association, 1955—; member of board of directors and executive committee, Urban League of Greater Dallas, 1969—. *Member:* American Economic Association, American Real Estate and Urban Economics Association (director, 1969-72), American Farm Economists Association, National Association of Business Economists, Regional Science Association, Southwestern Social Science Association, Southern Case Writers Association, Texas Bar Association. *Awards, honors:* Piper Foundation award as an outstanding Texan professor, 1969.

WRITINGS: (Contributor) Paul Zook, editor, *Economic Development and International Trade: A Perspective,* Southern Methodist University Press, 1959; *The Future Role of the Central Business District of Dallas, Texas,* Business Executives Research Committee, Southern Methodist University, 1959; (senior author, with members of Business Executives Research Committee) *Report of the Campus Study Committee on Southern Methodist University-Church Relations,* Southern Methodist University, 1961; (senior author, with members of Campus Study Committee) *The Economy of the Central Business District of Dallas,* Southern Methodist University, 1961; *Report of the Task Force on the School of Business Administration,* Southern Methodist University, 1963; (senior author, with Walter E. Boles, Jr., and Theodore R. Eck) *Capitalism, Socialism and Central Planning,* edited by Wayne A. Leeman, Houghton, 1963; (with Barbara B. Reagan) *Economic Feasibility of Proposed Lake Shore Road in Malawi,* Surveys and Research Corp., 1965; (with Howard Lapin) *Regional Economic Development,* Texas Agricultural and Mechanical University, 1969; (with Svetozer Pejovich) *Crossroads Community Medical Study,* Institute of Urban and Environmental Studies, Southern Methodist University, 1970; (with Larry D. Reavis) *Crossroads Community Study for Dallas, Texas,* Institute of Urban and Environmental Studies, Southern Methodist University, 1970; (senior author, with Reavis) *The Economy and Trade of Texas,* Institute of Urban and Environmental Studies, Southern Methodist University, 1971. Also author of *Plan to Stabilize Economy and to Manage Resources in Texas in Event of an Enemy Nuclear Attack,* 1965.

Author of confidential reports and numerous cases and teaching notes in real estate, urban problems, and minority business enterprises; contributor to proceedings. Contributor to *Southwestern Social Science Quarterly* and *Health Reports*.

WORK IN PROGRESS: Continued research on urban and environmental problems.†

*   *   *

REAGIN, Ewell Kerr 1900-

PERSONAL: Born November 27, 1900, in Wales Station, Tenn.; son of Bushrod Johnson (a minister) and Madora (Kerr) Reagin; married Julian Rebecca Simpson, January 7, 1925; children: Ewell Julian, Rebekah (Mrs. Bruce E. Pherson). *Education:* Attended Maryville College, 1918; Bethel College, McKenzie, Tenn., B.A., 1922; University of Chicago, graduate study, 1924-25; Cumberland Presbyterian Theological Seminary, B.D., 1925; Birmingham-Southern College, M.A., 1925; Southern Methodist University, graduate study, 1933-35. *Politics:* Democrat. *Home and office:* 5526 Woodburn Dr., Knoxville, Tenn. 37919.

CAREER: Ordained minister of Cumberland Presbyterian Church, 1922; pastor in Sturgis, Ky., Birmingham, Ala., and McKenzie, Tenn., 1922-31; Bethel College, McKenzie, professor of Hebrew and religious education, 1931-44, president of college, 1939-44; Cumberland Presbyterian Theological Seminary (now Memphis Theological Seminary), Memphis, Tenn., dean, 1931-44; pastor in Knoxville, Tenn., 1944-69; University of Tennessee, Knoxville, professor of religion, 1970—, director of School of Religion, 1965—. Member of executive committee of Greater Knoxville Council on Aging. *Member:* Kappa Phi Kappa. *Awards, honors:* D.D., Bethel College, 1936.

WRITINGS: Essence of Our Faith, Cumberland Presbyterian Publishing House, 1931; *Principles of Personal Worship,* Cumberland Presbyterian Publishing House, 1938; *Now Faith Is,* Board of Foreign Missions, Cumberland Presbyterian Publishing House, 1955; *We Believe and So We Speak,* Department of Publishing, Cumberland Presbyterian Church, 1960; *What Cumberland Presbyterians Believe,* Frontier Press, 1968; *The Holy Spirit–Who?,* Frontier Press, 1971; *Truth Stories of the Bible,* University of Tennessee Press, 1977.

WORK IN PROGRESS: Encounter, a quarterly publication; Sunday school lessons for thirty-four county newspapers in Tennessee.

*   *   *

REANEY, James 1926-

PERSONAL: Born September 1, 1926, in South Easthope, Ontario, Canada; son of James Nesbitt and Elizabeth (Crerar) Reaney; married Colleen Thibaudeau, December 29, 1951; children: James Stewart, Susan Alice. *Education:* University of Toronto, B.A., 1948, M.A., 1949, Ph.D., 1958. *Agent:* Sybil Hutchinson, Apt. 409, Ramsden Pl., 50 Hillsboro Ave., Toronto, Ontario, Canada M5R 1S8. *Office:* Department of English, University of Western Ontario, London, Ontario, Canada N6A 2J9.

CAREER: University of Manitoba, Winnipeg, faculty member, 1949-57, assistant professor of English, 1957-60; University of Western Ontario, London, associate professor, 1960-63, professor of English, 1964—. *Member:* Association of Canadian University Teachers of English, Canadian Association of University Teachers, Canadian Theatre

Co-op, League of Canadian Poets, Royal Society of Canada.

WRITINGS—Poetry: The Red Heart, McClellan & Stewart, 1949; *A Suit of Nettles,* Macmillan, 1958, 2nd edition, 1975; *Twelve Letters to a Small Town,* Ryerson, 1962; *The Dance of Death at London, Ontario,* Alphabet Press, 1963; *Poems,* edited by Germaine Warkentin, New Press, 1972; *Selected Shorter Poems,* edited by Warkentin, Porcepic, 1976; *Selected Longer Poems,* edited by Warkentin, Porcepic, 1976.

Plays: *The Killdeer and Other Plays* (contains "Night-Blooming Cereus," broadcast as radio play, 1959, first produced in Toronto, 1960; "The Killdeer," [also see below], first produced in Toronto, 1960; "One-Man Masque," produced in Toronto, 1960; "Sun and Moon," first produced in Winnipeg, 1972), Macmillan, 1962; (with Alfred Kunz) *Let's Make a Carol: A Play with Music for Children,* Waterloo Music Co., 1965; *Colours in the Dark* (first produced in Stratford, Ontario, 1967), Talonbooks-Macmillan, 1970; *Masks of Childhood* (contains "The Killdeer," revised version, first produced in Vancouver, 1970; "The Easter Egg," first produced in Hamilton, Ontario, 1962; "Three Desks," first produced in Calgary, Alberta, 1967), edited by Brian Parker, New Press, 1972; *Listen to the Wind* (first produced in London, Ontario, 1965), Talonbooks, 1972; *Apple Butter and Other Plays for Children* (contains "Names and Nicknames," first produced in Winnipeg, 1963; " Apple Butter," first produced in London, Ontario, 1965; "Ignoramus"; "Geography Match"), Talonbooks, 1973; *The Donnellys: A Trilogy,* Part I: *Sticks and Stones* (first produced in Toronto, 1973), Porcepic, 1975, Part II: *The Saint Nicholas Hotel* (first produced in Toronto, 1974), Porcepic, 1976, Part III: *Handcuffs* (first produced in Toronto, 1975), Porcepic, 1976; (with John Beckwith) *All the Bees and All the Keys,* Porcepic, 1976; (with C. H. Gervais) *Baldoon* (two-act), Porcupine's Quill, 1977; *The Dismissal,* Porcepic, 1978.

Other: *The Boy with the "R" in His Hand* (juvenile novel), Macmillan, 1965; *Fourteen Barrels from Sea to Sea* (travel diary), Porcepic, 1977. Editor and founder of *Alphabet,* 1960-71.

WORK IN PROGRESS: A dramatisation of John Richardson's *Wacousta* and its sequel; plays on Emily Bronte and Chatterton.

SIDELIGHTS: James Reaney's book, *Fourteen Barrels from Sea to Sea,* is as unique as its title. Dubbing it a "travel book" for lack of a better term, he told *CA* that it is actually a commentary on the state of drama in Canada today. In the fall of 1976, Reaney took a sabbatical from the University of Western Ontario and accompanied a professional Canadian drama group as they toured Canada with "The Donnellys: A Trilogy." *Fourteen Barrels from Sea to Sea* is the subsequent record of his impressions and of the experiences of the NDWT Co. players while on this tour.

Reaney's play, "One-Man Masque," was adapted by Ron Cameron and published as *Masque* by Simon & Pierre in 1975.

BIOGRAPHICAL/CRITICAL SOURCES: Alvin Lee, *James Reaney,* Twayne, 1969; Ross Woodman, *James Reaney,* McClellan & Stewart (Toronto), 1972; James Stewart Reaney, *James Reaney,* Gage, 1976.

*   *   *

REBELSKY, Freda Gould 1931-

PERSONAL: Born March 11, 1931, in New York, N.Y.;

daughter of William (an engineer) and Sarah (Kaplan) Gould; married William Rebelsky (a manager), January 1, 1956; children: Samuel. *Educaion:* University of Chicago, B.A., 1950, M.A., 1954; Radcliffe College, Ph.D., 1961. *Home:* 1 Billings Park, Newton, Mass. 02158. *Office:* Department of Psychology, Boston University, 64 Cummington St., Boston, Mass. 02215.

CAREER: University of Chicago, Orthogenic School, Chicago, Ill., counselor, 1952-55; Kenyon & Eckhart, Inc., New York, N.Y., research assistant, 1956-58; Children's Hospital, Boston, Mass., research associate in Speech Research Laboratory, 1960-61; Massachusetts Institute of Technology, Cambridge, research associate on aphasia study, 1961-62; Boston University, Boston, Mass., assistant professor, 1961-68, associate professor, 1968-71, professor of psychology, 1971—. Visiting lecturer in child development, University of Utrecht, 1965-67.

MEMBER: American Psychological Association, American Association for the Advancement of Science, Society for Research in Child Development, Animal Behavior Society, American Association of University Professors, Association for Women in Psychology, Eastern Psychological Association, New England Psychological Association, Massachusetts Psychology Association, Sigma Xi, Psi Chi. *Awards, honors:* U.S. Office of Education grant to study relationship between perceptual and cognitive development, 1964-65; Boston University grants, 1967-70; U.S. Office of Economic Opportunity grants, 1967—; American Psychological Foundation award, 1970, for distinguished teaching; E. Harris Harbison Award from Danforth Foundation, 1971, for gifted teaching; Metcalf Award, 1978, for excellence in teaching.

WRITINGS: (Contributor) Edward Landy, editor, *Guidance in American Education: Backgrounds and Prospects,* Harvard University Press, 1964; (contributor) Yvonne Brackbill, editor, *Infancy and Early Childhood,* Free Press, 1967; *Child Development,* Simon & Schuster, 1968; (contributor) P. R. Dolecki, R. C. Johnson, and O. H. Mowrer, editors, *Conscience and Social Reality,* Holt, 1969; (contributor) Brackbill and H. E. Fitzgerald, editors, *Design and Method in Infant Research,* University of Chicago Press, 1969; (editor with Lynn Dorman, and contributor) *Child Behavior and Development: A Reader,* Knopf, 1970, 2nd edition, 1974; (with Dorman) *Growing Children,* Wadsworth, 1976. Contributor to *American Psychologist, Psychological Reports, Child Development,* and other psychology journals. Book reviewer, *Child Development Abstracts and Bibliography,* 1963-66, and *Boston Globe,* 1969.

WORK IN PROGRESS: Child Development for Teachers, for Brooks-Cole: *Laboratory Manual in Child Development,* with Deborah Manning and David Gallant.

*   *   *

REDDEN, James Erskine   1928-

PERSONAL: Born December 28, 1928, in Louisville, Ky.; son of James Clyde (a bodyman) and Leora Mae (Kerr) Redden; married Patricia Jane Stone (a piano teacher), April 7, 1950; children: Deborah Ann, Virginia Fay, Barry Howard, David Edward, Nathan Albert, Alexander Clyde. *Education:* University of Louisville, B.A., 1950; Indiana University, Ph.D., 1965. *Politics:* Independent. *Religion:* Church of Christ. *Home:* 702 West Elm, Carbondale, Ill. 62901. *Office:* Department of Linguistics, Southern Illinois University, Carbondale, Ill. 62901.

CAREER: Indiana University at Bloomington, teaching assistant in English as a foreign language, 1958-60; U.S. Department of State, Foreign Service Institute, Washington, D.C., linguist in African languages, 1961-65; American University of Beirut, Beirut, Lebanon, associate professor of linguistics and English as a foreign language, 1965-67; Southern Illinois University at Carbondale, professor of linguistics and English as a foreign language and chairman of the department, 1967—. Consultant to Ford Foundation, U.S. Agency for International Development, and ministries of education in the Middle East.

MEMBER: International Linguistic Association, Linguistic Society of America, American Anthropological Association, Teachers of English to Speakers of Other Languages, Canadian Linguistic Association, Linguistic Society of Australia, West Africa Linguistic Society, Eastern Africa Linguistic Association. *Awards, honors:* National Defense Education Act fellowship, 1960-61, to study Twi language and African area studies; American Council of Learned Societies grant, summer, 1963, to study Walapai Indian language; grant from U.S. Office of Education and Department of Health, Education and Welfare, 1971, to study Bantu languages in Africa; Fulbright senior research grant, University of Hamburg, 1973-74; grant from U.S. Office of Education, 1975-76, to write a grammar of Ewondo.

WRITINGS: Twi Basic Course, U.S. Government Printing Office, 1963; *Lingala Basic Course,* U.S. Government Printing Office, 1963; (with M. A. Lehr) *More Basic Course,* U.S. Government Printing Office, 1966; (editor) *English in Mali,* Volumes I and II, Southern Illinois University Press, 1970; (editor) *Advanced Studies in English,* Volumes I through XIII, Government of Nigeria, in press. Editor, *Proceedings* of the first and second International Conferences on Frontiers in Language Proficiency and Dominance Testing, 1977, 1978. Contributor to *Proceedings of the First Hokan Languages Conference, International Journal of American Linguistics, Language Learning,* and *Annals of the University of Abidjan.*

WORK IN PROGRESS: Several monographs, including *Historical Northwest Bantu Phonology, Walapai Syntax and Dictionary,* and an Ewondo grammar; more research on Walapai syntax.

SIDELIGHTS: James Redden has traveled extensively in Africa and the Middle East, and in Europe.

*   *   *

REECE, Benny R(amon)   1930-

PERSONAL: Born December 7, 1930, in Asheville, N.C.; son of Judson Jones (a farmer) and Ina (Blalock) Reece; married Ethel Van Dyke (a pharmacist), June 4, 1960; children: Judson Benjamin. *Education:* Duke University, A.B., 1953; University of North Carolina, M.A., 1954, Ph.D., 1957. *Politics:* Conservative. *Religion:* Presbyterian. *Home:* Roe Ford Rd., Greenville, S.C. 29609. *Office:* Department of Classical Languages, Furman University, Greenville, S.C. 29613.

CAREER: Mercer University, Macon, Ga., assistant professor of classics, 1957-61; Furman University, Greenville, S.C., associate professor of classical languages, 1961—, head of department, 1961-73. Visiting professor of classics, University of North Carolina, 1967. *Member:* American Philogical Association, Classical Association of the Middle West and South. *Awards, honors:* Fulbright scholar at University of Munich, 1957-58.

WRITINGS: (Editor) *Documents Illustrating Cicero's*

Consular Campaign, Furman University Press, 1967; *Plautus: Epidicus*, Furman University Press, 1967; *Sermones Ratherii Episcopi Veronensis*, Holy Cross Press, 1969; *Learning in the Tenth Century*, Furman University Press, 1968; *The Role of the Centurion in Ancient Society*, Cottonfield Press, 1975; *A Bibliography of First Appearances of the Writings by A. Conan Doyle*, Furman University Press, 1976. Contributor of articles to *Furman Studies*, *Classical Folia*, *Cluster*, *Latomus*, and *American Journal of Philology*.

* * *

REED, S(amuel) Kyle 1922-

PERSONAL: Born April 17, 1922, in Knoxville, Tenn.; son of William Bell and Mary (Cockrum) Reed; married Ann Ogle, March 29, 1952; children: Philip Ogle, Gregory Kyle. *Education:* Attended North Carolina State College of Agriculture and Engineering of University of North Carolina (now North Carolina State University at Raleigh), 1943-44; University of Tennessee, B.S., 1948; University of Edinburgh, Ph.D., 1950. *Religion:* Roman Catholic. *Home:* 12 Boxwood Sq., Knoxville, Tenn. 37919. *Office:* Department of Industrial Management, University of Tennessee, Knoxville, Tenn. 37916.

CAREER: Union Carbide Nuclear Co., Oak Ridge, Tenn., industrial engineer, 1951-58; Robertshaw-Fulton Co., Knoxville, Tenn., methods engineer, 1950-51; American Bridge Co., Ambridge, Pa., time study engineer, 1948-49; University of Tennessee, Knoxville, lecturer in industrial engineering, 1953-57, associate professor, 1958-67, professor of industrial management, 1967—; Doulet, Reed & Associates (consultants in industrial management and engineering), Knoxville, principal, 1959—. *Military service:* U.S. Army, 1943-46; became second lieutenant; received Bronze Star. *Member:* American Institute of Industrial Engineers (president of East Tennessee chapter, 1951-52; regional vice-president, 1953-54; national board member, 1954-57; director of East Tennessee chapter, 1971-72; vice-president, 1973-74), National Association of Purchasing Managers, Southern Management Association, Delta Sigma Pi, Sigma Nu. *Awards, honors:* Ford Foundation fellowship, 1962; Foundation for Economic Education fellowship, 1963; Alcoa Foundation fellowship, 1964.

WRITINGS: (With Gray J. Arnold and Robert S. Hoeke) *Production Scheduling Simulation*, Center for Business and Economic Research, University of Tennessee, 1971. Contributor to *Advanced Management*, *Factory*, *Tennessee Survey of Business*, *Southern Journal of Business*, *Tennessee Town and City*, and *APICS Quarterly Bulletin*.

* * *

REICHE, Reimut 1941-

PERSONAL: Born June 20, 1941, in Esslingen, Germany. *Education:* Attended Free University of West Berlin, 1963; University of Frankfurt, diplom soziologe, 1969. *Office:* Klinikum der J. W. Goethe-Universitaet, Zentrum der Psychos., Grundlagen der Medizin Poliklinik, Theodor-Stern-Kai 7, 6 Frankfort-am-Main 70, Germany.

CAREER: Psychoanalyst.

WRITINGS: (With Peter Gaeng) *Modelle der kolonialen Revolution: Beschreibung und Dokumente*, Suhrkamp, 1967; *Sexualitat und Klassenkampf*, Neue Kritik, 1968, translation by Susan Bennett published as *Sexuality and Class Struggle*, New Left Books, 1970; *Sexualitaet: Moral*

und Gesellschaft, Hessische Landeszentrale fuer Politische Bildung, 1971; (with Martin Dannecker) *Der gewoehnliche Homosexuelle: Eine Soziolog*, S. Fischer, 1974.

* * *

REIF, Rita 1929-

PERSONAL: Surname rhymes with "strife"; born June 12, 1929, in New York, N.Y.; daughter of Henry Vincent (an efficiency engineer) and Louise (Becker) Murphy; married Paul Reif (a composer), July 2, 1953 (died July, 1978); children: L. Leslie (son), Timothy. *Education:* Fordham University, B.S., 1950; Columbia University, M.A., 1951. *Home:* 57 West 58th St., New York, N.Y. 10019. *Agent:* Ann Elmo, 52 Vanderbilt Ave., New York, N.Y. 10017. *Office: New York Times*, 229 West 43rd St., New York, N.Y. 10036.

CAREER: New York Times, New York, N.Y., clerk and news assistant, 1947-56, reporter, 1956—, antiques columnist, 1972—, auction columnist, 1977—. Instructor in art history at New York University. *Awards, honors:* Dorothy Dawe Awards from American Furniture Mart, Chicago, Ill., 1969, 1970, and 1971; Press Award from National Society of Interior Designers, 1971.

WRITINGS: Living with Books, New York Times Co., 1968, revised edition, Quadrangle, 1973; *The Antique Collector's Guide to Styles and Prices*, Hawthorn, 1970; *Treasure Rooms of America's Mansions, Manors, and Houses*, Coward, 1970; *Home: It Takes More Than Money*, Quadrangle, 1975.

WORK IN PROGRESS: A book on art and antiques focusing on dealers, for Putnam.

* * *

REILLY, Michael (Francis) 1910(?)-1973

1910(?)—June 16, 1973; American Secret Service agent, personal bodyguard to Franklin Delano Roosevelt, and author of books on his White House experiences. Obituaries: *New York Times*, June 19, 1973.

* * *

REINHARDT, Jon M(c Ewen) 1936-

PERSONAL: Born February 8, 1936, in Thorsby, Ala.; son of Hubert Ephram (a wholesaler) and Doris (Freeman) Reinhardt; married Dorothy Becton, June 21, 1958; children: Brett Alyne (daughter), Christopher Brooke. *Education:* Birmingham-Southern College, B.A., 1959; Tulane University, M.A., 1964, Ph.D., 1967. *Home:* 3708 Woosley Rd., Pfafftown, N.C. 27040. *Office:* Wake Forest University, Reynolda Station, Box 7568, Winston-Salem, N.C. 27109.

CAREER: Hayes Aircraft Corp., Birmingham, Ala., illustrator, 1959-60; Birmingham Public Library, Birmingham, librarian, 1960-61; U.S. Air Force, Mobile, Ala., purchasing agent, 1961-64; Wake Forest University, Winston-Salem, N.C., assistant professor, 1967-71, associate professor of political science, 1971—. *Member:* American Association of Asian Studies, American Association of University Professors, Southern Political Science Association.

WRITINGS: Foreign Policy and National Integration: The Case of Indonesia, Yale University Press, 1971. Contributor to *Journal of Asian Studies*.

* * *

REIS, Richard H(erbert) 1930-

PERSONAL: Born September 21, 1930, in Arlington,

Mass.; son of Waldo F. and Ursula (Tetreau) Reis; married Kathleen Patnaude, October 13, 1956; children: Elizabeth, Matthew. *Education:* St. Lawrence University, A.B., 1952; Brown University, A.M., 1957, Ph.D., 1962. *Politics:* Democrat. *Religion:* Unitarian Universalist. *Home:* 429 Front St., Marion, Mass. 02738. *Office:* Department of English, Southeastern Massachusetts University, North Dartmouth, Mass. 02747.

CAREER: Brown University, Providence, R.I., instructor in English, 1959-61; Washington College, Chestertown, Md., instructor, 1961-62, assistant professor of English, 1962-65; Southeastern Massachusetts University, North Dartmouth, assistant professor, 1965-68, associate professor, 1968-73, professor of English, 1973—. *Member:* Modern Language Association of America, American Association of University Professors.

WRITINGS: George MacDonald, Twayne, 1972. Contributor of poetry to magazines.

WORK IN PROGRESS: Writing on rhyme in western tradition, and on Keats' "The Eve of St. Agnes"; a book of criticism to be entitled *Rex Stout,* for Twayne.

SIDELIGHTS: Richard H. Reis told *CA:* "I dislike being professionally cast as a professor of English, as though I were interested and competent in nothing else. I write about things that I'm interested in and know about, in whatever subject." *Avocational interests:* Politics, combinatorial mathematics, paleoanthropology, chess, molecular biology, colonial architecture.

* * *

REISS, Barbara Eve 1941-
(Barbara Eve)

PERSONAL: Surname rhymes with "peace"; born July 26, 1941, in Chicago, Ill.; daughter of William (a lawyer) and Nina (Spertus) Klevs; married James Alan Reiss (a poet and professor), June 21, 1964; children: Heather Eve, Crystal Jo. *Education:* University of Chicago, A.B., 1964; University of California, Davis, graduate study, 1964-65; Sarah Lawrence College, M.F.A., 1976. *Home:* 1290 Madison Ave., New York, N.Y. 10028.

CAREER: Miami University, Oxford, Ohio, instructor in English, 1967-68; Workman Publishing Co., New York City, editor, 1977-78; Bobbs-Merrill Co., Inc., New York City, editor, 1978—.

WRITINGS: (With James Dickey and husband, James Reiss) *Self-Interview: James Dickey,* Doubleday, 1970. Contributor of poems to anthologies; under name Barbara Eve: *Eating the Menu: A Contemporary American Poetry, 1970-74,* edited by Bruce E. Taylor, Kendall/Hunt, 1974; *Tangled Vines: A Collection of Mother and Daughter Poems,* edited by Lyn Lifshin, Beacon Press, 1978; *Woman: An Affirmation,* Heath, 1979. Contributor of book reviews to *Chicago Sun-Times, Cleveland Plain Dealer,* and *Cincinnati Enquirer;* contributor, under name Barbara Eve, of poems to *Antaeus, Agni Review, Esquire, Nation, New River Review, Poetry Now,* and *Prairie Schooner.*

WORK IN PROGRESS: The Skier, a book of poems.

SIDELIGHTS: Barbara Eve Reiss writes to *CA:* "I am deeply engaged in writing poetry. After working closely with James Dickey on *Self-Interview,* and being married to a man obsessed by poetry, it would have been remarkable if I had escaped the poetry bug."

REMMLING, Gunter W(erner) 1929-

PERSONAL: Born December 10, 1929, in Berlin, Germany; son of Gustav (an architect) and Charlotte (Werner) Remmling; married Elba Valdivia Reyes (a linguist), November 7, 1958; children: Anita Fay, Marc Erik. *Education:* Friedrich-Ebert-Gymnasium, A.B., 1948; graduate study at Worksop College, Nottingham, England, 1948, and Bard College, 1950-51; Free University of Berlin, Ph.D., 1956. *Residence:* Syracuse, N.Y. *Office:* Department of Sociology, Syracuse University, 500 University Pl., Syracuse, N.Y. 13210.

CAREER: Institute of Political Science, Berlin, Germany, research associate, 1956-57; Southern Illinois University at Edwardsville, lecturer, 1958-59, assistant professor, 1959-62, associate professor of sociology, 1962-68; Syracuse University, Syracuse, N.Y., professor of sociology, 1968—. Lecturer, KETC-Television, 1960-61. Consultant to Radio Free Berlin. *Member:* American Sociological Association. *Awards, honors:* Grant from U.S. State Department and Institute for International Education, 1950; American Philosophical Society grant, 1963.

WRITINGS: (Editor) *South American Sociologists: A Directory,* University of Texas Press, 1966; *Road to Suspicion: A Study of Modern Mentality and the Sociology of Knowledge,* Appleton, 1967; *Wissenssoziologie und Gesellschaftsplanung,* Ruhfus, 1968; (with Robert B. Campbell) *Basic Sociology,* Littlefield, 1970; (editor) *Towards the Sociology of Knowledge,* Routledge & Kegan Paul, 1973; *The Sociology of Karl Mannheim,* Routledge & Kegan Paul, 1975; (contributor) Clinton Joyce Jesser, editor, *Social Theory Revisited,* Dryden, 1975; *Der Weg in den Zweifel: Studien zur Krise des modernen Denkens,* F. Enke, 1975. Contributor to *Social Forces, Sociological Quarterly,* and foreign professional journals.

WORK IN PROGRESS: Co-authoring *Einfuhrung in die Soziologie,* for F. Enke.

SIDELIGHTS: Gunter Remmling has studied and conducted research in Germany, England, France, Austria, Italy, Canada, Mexico, Peru, Chile, Argentina, Uruguay, Brazil, and Venezuela.

* * *

RENDER, Sylvia Lyons 1913-

PERSONAL: Born June 8, 1913, in Atlanta, Ga.; daughter of Lewis Rudolph and Mamie Beatrice (Foster) Lyons; married Frank Wyatt Render, July 14, 1935 (divorced, November, 1941); children: Frank Wyatt II. *Education:* Tennessee Agricultural and Industrial State College (now Tennessee State University), B.S., 1934; University of Chicago, graduate study, 1934-35; Ohio State University, M.A., 1952; University of Wisconsin, further graduate study, summers, 1954, 1956; George Peabody College for Teachers, Ph.D., 1962. *Home:* 6429 Princeton Dr., Alexandria, Va. 22307. *Office:* Manuscript Division, Library of Congress, Washington, D.C. 20540.

CAREER: Ohio Bureau of Unemployment Compensation, Columbus, clerk, 1939-43; U.S. Employment Service, Columbus, Ohio, interviewer, 1943-44, assistant to statistician, 1944-46; Veterans Administration, Columbus, correspondence analyst, 1946-50; Florida Agricultural and Mechanical University, Tallahassee, instructor, 1952-56, assistant professor, 1956-60, associate professor, 1960-62, professor of English, 1962-64; North Carolina Central University, Durham, professor of English, 1964-75; Library of Congress,

Washington, D.C., manuscript historian and specialist in Afro-American history and culture, 1973—. Guest professor at George Peabody College for Teachers, summer, 1970. Consultant to Macmillan Co., National Endowment for the Humanities, Ford Foundation, North Carolina State Board of Education, and Durham County Board of Education.

MEMBER: Modern Language Association of America, College Language Association, National Council of Teachers of English (member of national committee, 1970-72), Association for the Study of Afro-American Life and History, South Atlantic Modern Language Association, Society for the Study of Southern Literature, Alpha Kappa Mu, Kappa Delta Pi. Awards, honors: American Philosophical Society research and writing grant, 1964; North Carolina Central University faculty research grants, 1965 and 1971; Duke University fellow in cooperative program in humanities, 1967-68; Ford Foundation research and writing grant, 1971; Outstanding Educator of America, 1972 and 1973; National Endowment for the Humanities fellowship for independent study and research.

WRITINGS: (Author of introduction) Charles W. Chesnutt, The Marrow of Tradition, Arno, 1969; (editor) Short Fiction of Charles W. Chesnutt, Howard University Press, 1974. Author of "Sylvia's Slant," a column in Ohio State News, 1949-50. Contributor to Encyclopaedia Britannica. Contributor to journals, including CLA Journal, North Carolina Folklore, Tennessee Folklore Society Bulletin, Quarterly Journal of the Library of Congress, and Library Lectures (journal of Louisiana State University Library).

WORK IN PROGRESS: A bio-critical study of Charles W. Chesnutt.

SIDELIGHTS: Sylvia Lyons Render told CA: "I believe in the essential worth of every individual. I consider love—in its broadest sense—and respect to be the most powerful of the forces determining human relations. I believe also that the survival and further development of our world civilization are dependent upon policies and practices which reflect much more widespread adherence to these concepts. Further, I hold that mutual love and respect may be more nearly realized through the interaction of individuals rather than through edicts propounded by government officials and/or representatives of private interests who ostensibly control large numbers of people. In my opinion, each person has more power and responsibility than he/she usually perceives.

"For many years the college classroom was my main forum for presenting such ideas; literature and history, particularly of Afro-Americans, were the disciplines through which I promoted the prerequisite development of healthy self-concepts as well as acceptance of and empathy for others, especially those viewed as markedly different. Now at our national library, I pursue the same goals, though more indirectly, while gathering, dispensing, and interpreting, here and abroad, largely factual information about Afro-American history and culture. My writing is directed to the same ends.

"From time to time I have observed adoption of the principles I have sought to inculcate by some of the individuals whose lives I have touched. A few have acknowledged my influence. That I have been able to contribute to the intellectual, aesthetic, and/or ethical growth of one or more human beings has been my most significant and satisfying accomplishment."

AVOCATIONAL INTERESTS: Music, books, travel, the outdoors, the past, the occult.

RENNER, John Wilson 1924-

PERSONAL: Born July 25, 1924, in DeSmet, S.D.; son of Harry Milton (a farmer) and Maud (Callahan) Renner; married Carol Jean Fennel, June 25, 1948; children: Mary Jo, Michael, David. Education: University of South Dakota, B.A., 1946, M.A., 1948; State University of Iowa, Ph.D., 1955. Politics: Democrat. Religion: Roman Catholic. Home: 409 North Mercedes Dr., Norman, Okla. 73069. Office: Department of Science Education, University of Oklahoma, Norman, Okla. 73069.

CAREER: High school science teacher, 1946-47; instructor in physics at University of South Dakota, Elk Point, 1947-48, 1949-52, and Moorhead State Teachers College (now Moorhead State University), Moorhead, Minn., 1948-49; State University of Iowa, Iowa City, physical science supervisor at university high school, 1952-55; University of Illinois at Urbana-Champaign, assistant professor of science education, 1955-56; director of National Radiological Defense School, U.S. Government, Civil Defense Administration, 1956-58; Creighton University, Omaha, Neb., assistant professor of physics and education and chairman of department of physics, 1958-59; associate executive secretary, National Science Teachers Association, 1959-62; University of Oklahoma, Norman, associate professor, 1962-65, professor of science education, 1965—. Consultant to World Book Encyclopedia and Science Curriculum Improvement Study. Military service: U.S. Navy, 1943-44. U.S. Army Reserve, 1948-56. Member: National Education Association, National Science Teachers Association, National Association for Research in Science Teaching (president, 1979-80), Central Association of Science and Mathematics Teachers, Oklahoma Science Teachers Association, Sigma Xi.

WRITINGS: Experiments and Exercises in Physics, Lippincott, 1961; (with others) Teaching Science in the Elementary School, Harper, 1968, revised edition, 1979; (with others) Guiding Learning in the Secondary School, Harper, 1972; (with Donald G. Stafford) Teaching Science in the Secondary School, Harper, 1972; Guiding Learning in the Elementary School, Harper, 1973; (with H. Packard, Peter W. Insley, and Roberta Huffmaster) Investigations in Physics, Lyons & Carnahan, 1974; (with Stafford) Research, Teaching and Learning with the Piaget Model, University of Oklahoma Press, 1976; (editor with Mary H. Saterstrom) Educators Guide to Free Science Materials, revised edition, Educators Progress Services, 1977; Physical Science: Inquiry and Investigation, Glencoe Press, 1977; The Learning Science Program (kindergarten through high school), seven books, Glencoe Press, 1977. Author of filmstrips and audiotape series. Contributor of about one hundred articles to journals in his field.

WORK IN PROGRESS: Laboratory programs for secondary school physics and chemistry.

SIDELIGHTS: John Renner has an interest in western art and jazz music. He played in a jazz band in the 1940's and has a fair-sized record collection.

*　　*　　*

RENO, Ottie W(ayne) 1929-

PERSONAL: Born April 7, 1929, in Pike County, Ohio; son of Eli Enos (a farmer) and Arbannah (Jones) Reno; married Janet Gay McCann, May 22, 1947; children: Ottie Wayne II, Jennifer Lynn, Lorna Victoria. Education: Franklin University, Associate in Business Administration, 1949, LL.B., 1953; Capital University, J.D., 1966. Politics: Democrat. Religion: Protestant. Home address: Route 5, Box

305, Lucasville, Ohio 45648. *Office:* Court House, Market and Second, Waverly, Ohio 45690.

CAREER: Attorney, 1953—. Pike County recorder, 1957-73; common pleas judge in probate and juvenile divisions in Waverly, Ohio, 1973—.

WRITINGS: The Story of Horseshoes, Vantage, 1963; *Pitching Championship Horseshoes,* A. S. Barnes, 1971, revised edition, 1973.

WORK IN PROGRESS: Political endeavors.

* * *

RENVOIZE, Jean

PERSONAL: Surname is pronounced Ren-voys; born in London, England; daughter of Walter (an artist) and Emily (Roffey) Renvoize; married Maurice Temple Smith (a publisher), September, 1956; children: Andrew, Alison. *Education:* Educated in England. *Home:* 13 Christchurch Hill, Hampstead, London N.W. 3, England. *Agent:* Harold Ober Associates, Inc., 40 East 49th St., New York, N.Y. 10017.

CAREER: A director of Maurice Temple Smith Ltd. and Book Representation Ltd. *Awards, honors: A Wild Thing* was an American Library Association Notable Book, 1970.

WRITINGS—Novels, except as indicated: *The Masker,* Secker & Warburg, 1960, World Publishing, 1961; *A Wild Thing,* Macmillan, 1970, Little, Brown, 1971; *The Net,* Stein & Day, 1973; *Children in Danger: The Causes and Prevention of Baby Battering* (nonfiction), Routledge & Kegan Paul, 1974; *Web of Violence: A Study of Family Violence* (nonfiction), Routledge & Kegan Paul, 1978.

SIDELIGHTS: Jean Renvoize told *CA:* "*A Wild Thing* was written as an adult novel and published as such in England, but the American publisher considered that the book would do best if presented as a young adult book in the States. It was inspired by a news item of an actual boy whose bones were found on a Scottish hillside and whose identity was discovered primarily from his dental condition. He was about twelve and an orphan. From that I developed the story of a girl of nearly sixteen whose eventual fate was similar."

* * *

RESTLE, Frank 1927-

PERSONAL: Born March 2, 1927, in Weehauken, N.J.; son of Frank Joseph (a businessman) and Isabel (Alexander) Restle; married Barbara Blackledge (a writer), September 3, 1950; children: Kathleen, Phillip, Andrea. *Education:* Lafayette College, A.B., 1950; Stanford University, M.A., 1952, Ph.D., 1954. *Home address:* P.O. Box 1022, Bloomington, Ind. 47401. *Office:* Department of Psychology, Indiana University, Bloomington, Ind. 47401.

CAREER: Human Resources Research Office (HumRRO), Washington, D.C., research associate, 1953-55; Center for the Advanced Study of the Behavioral Sciences, Stanford, Calif., fellow, 1955-56; Michigan State University of Agriculture and Applied Science (now Michigan State University), East Lansing, instructor, 1956-57, assistant professor, 1957-59, associate professor of psychology, 1959-61; Indiana University at Bloomington, associate professor, 1961-62, professor of psychology, 1962—. *Military service:* U.S. Army, 1945-48. *Member:* American Psychological Association, Society of Experimental Psychologists, American Association for the Advancement of Science, Midwestern Psychological Association (president, 1971-72), Sigma Xi. *Awards, honors:* Social Science Research Council fellowship, 1957; Guggenheim fellowship, 1977.

WRITINGS: Psychology of Judgment and Choice, Wiley, 1961; (with J. W. Ost, J. A. Allison, and William Vance) *A Laboratory Introduction to Psychology,* Academic Press, 1969; (with J. G. Greeno) *Introduction to Mathematical Psychology,* Addison-Wesley, 1970; *Mathematical Models in Psychology,* Penguin, 1971; *Learning: Animal Behavior and Human Cognition,* McGraw, 1975; (contributor) E. Leeuwenberg and H. Buffant, editors, *Formal Models of Perception,* Wiley, 1978; (editor with John N. Castellan, Jr., and contributor) *Cognitive Theory,* Volume III, Halsted Press, 1978. Contributor to *Journal of Experimental Psychology, Psychological Review, Perception and Psychophysics,* and *Psychological Bulletin.*

WORK IN PROGRESS: Research on visual perception, perception of music, comprehension of prose and poetry.

AVOCATIONAL INTERESTS: Studying interaction between science, art, and society.

* * *

REUBEN, David 1933-

PERSONAL: Born November 29, 1933, in Chicago, Ill.; son of Clifford Kalman and Francis (Harris) Reuben; married Barbara Hatounian, July 1, 1961; children: David Robert, Catherine, Amy. *Education:* University of Illinois, B.S., 1955, M.D., 1957. *Religion:* Apostolic. *Agent:* Don Congdon, Harold Matson Co., Inc., 22 East 40th St., New York, N.Y. 10016.

CAREER: Harvard University, School of Medicine, Cambridge, Mass., clinical research associate in psychiatry, 1959-61; private practice in psychiatry in San Diego, Calif., 1961-72, and presently in Arizona and Illinois. Frequent guest on television talk shows. *Military service:* U.S. Air Force, neuro-psychiatrist, 1959-61; became captain. *Member:* American Medical Association.

WRITINGS: Everything You Always Wanted to Know about Sex (But Were Afraid to Ask), McKay, 1969; *Any Woman Can!,* McKay, 1971; *How to Get More Out of Sex,* McKay, 1973; *The Save-Your-Life Diet,* Random House, 1975; (with wife, Barbara Reuben) *The Save-Your-Life-Diet High-Fiber Cook Book,* Random House, 1976; *Everything You Always Wanted to Know about Nutrition,* Simon & Schuster, 1978. Former author of newspaper column syndicated by *New York News* and *Chicago Tribune.* Contributor to *Reader's Digest.*

SIDELIGHTS: While critics have on the whole been unimpressed, the public has made David Reuben's books best sellers. *Everything You Always Wanted to Know about Sex,* "his schmaltzy, myth-defying sex manual," sold eight million copies in its first two years, says *Newsweek's* S. K. Oberbeck. Gore Vidal describes David Reuben as "a relentlessly cheery, often genuinely funny writer.... Essentially he is a moralist, expressing the hang-ups of today's middle-aged, middle-class urban American Jews." A *Time* reviewer refers to Reuben's "familiar casual coyness, strained informality, unconvincing case histories and weak jokes." *Everything You Always Wanted to Know about Sex* was made into a motion picture starring Woody Allen.

Reuben's latest book uses the same question-and-answer format as his first book, but the tone is entirely different. In *Everything You Always Wanted to Know about Nutrition,* says one reviewer, "Reuben provides frightening evidence that we are the worst fed people in the world, nutritionally, and that most of our ideas of what constitutes 'good' food have come from specious advertising and misled physicians.

Reuben is an angry, articulate man, and his book will raise goosebumps on the average consumer and, presumably, the hackles of the food industry.''

AVOCATIONAL INTERESTS: Marksmanship, judo.

BIOGRAPHICAL/CRITICAL SOURCES: Life, December 5, 1969, June 18, 1971, December 31, 1971; *New York Times Book Review,* February 1, 1970, September 12, 1971, December 19, 1971; *New York Times,* May 24, 1970; *Variety,* May 27, 1970; *Show Business,* May 30, 1970; *New York Review of Books,* June 4, 1970; *Observer,* November 22, 1970; *Book World,* February 21, 1971; *Saturday Review,* April 24, 1971; *Newsweek,* September 13, 1971; *Best Sellers,* September 15, 1971; *Time,* September 27, 1971; *L'Express,* October, 1971; *Critic,* November, 1971; *Journal of Marriage and the Family,* February, 1972; *Commentary,* May, 1972; *Books and Bookmen,* June, 1972, March, 1973; *Publishers Weekly,* July 3, 1978; *Kirkus Reviews,* July 15, 1978.

* * *

REUSS, Carl F(rederick) 1915-

PERSONAL: Surname pronounced Royce; born June 7, 1915, in Philadelphia, Pa.; son of Charles F. (a teacher and accountant) and Marie (Kick) Reuss; married Thelma Steinmann (a secretary), June 24, 1938; children: Paula L., Ellen (Mrs. Robert Schanz), Betty (Mrs. Wayne F. Shovelin). *Education:* University of Virginia, B.S., 1934, M.S., 1935, Ph.D., 1937. *Religion:* Lutheran. *Home:* 5311 Vincent Ave. S., Minneapolis, Minn. 55410. *Office:* American Lutheran Church, 422 South 5th St., Minneapolis, Minn. 55415.

CAREER: Washington State University, Pullman, assistant rural sociologist, 1937-44; Capital University, Columbus, Ohio, professor of sociology, 1944-48; Wartburg College, Waverly, Iowa, dean of the faculty, 1948-51; American Lutheran Church, Minneapolis, Minn., executive secretary of Board for Christian Social Action, 1951-60, director of research and analysis, 1961—. *Member:* American Sociological Association, Rural Sociological Society, National Council on Family Relations, World Future Society, Society for the Scientific Study of Religion, Alpha Kappa Delta, Phi Kappa Phi.

WRITINGS—Editor: *The Christian in His Social Living,* Board for Christian Social Action, 1960; *Conscience and Action,* Augsburg, 1971. Contributor to *Encyclopedia of the Lutheran Church, Lutheran World, Lutheran Standard, Rural Sociology,* and *American Sociological Review.*

WORK IN PROGRESS: Research on human sexuality, social responsibility of the Church, and indicators of religious vitality.

SIDELIGHTS: Carl F. Reuss writes *CA:* "My conviction is that the church corporately, and its members individually, must be well-informed on how trends, problems, and issues impact people, the church, and society as a whole. Such a solid fact base needs to undergird our efforts to seek peace, justice, equity, and opportunity for all persons.''

* * *

REYNOLDS, Louis B. 1917-

PERSONAL: Born February 23, 1917, in Verdery, S.C.; son of Albert (a farmer) and Josephine (Harris) Reynolds; married Bernice Johnson (an elementary teacher), May 28, 1938; children: Dawn (Mrs. Robert L. Jones), Joan (Mrs. Alvan R. Cruz). *Education:* Attended Oakwood College, 1934-36; Fisk University, B.A., 1958; Howard University, M.A., 1968. *Home:* 4125 Eaton's Creek Rd., Nashville,

Tenn. 37218. *Office:* Southern Publishing Association, 1900 Elm Hill Pike, Nashville, Tenn. 37210.

CAREER: Seventh-day Adventist pastor in St. Louis, St. Joseph, Sedalia, and Kansas City, Mo., 1936-44; Southern Publishing Association, Nashville, Tenn., editor, 1944-59; pastor in New Rochelle, N.Y., 1959-62; General Conference of Seventh-day Adventists, Washington, D.C., editor, 1962-75, field secretary, 1975-77; Southern Publishing Association, editor, 1977—. Member of board of directors, Oakwood College, Riverside Sanitarium and Hospital, and Southern Publishing Association. *Member:* Associated Church Press (member of board of directors), American Temperance Society, National Association for the Advancement of Colored People, Oakwood College Alumni Association (president, 1966-68). *Awards, honors:* Alumnus of the year, Oakwood College, 1960; LL.D. from Union Baptist Seminary.

WRITINGS—All published by Southern Publishing: *Dawn of a Brighter Day: Light through the Darkness Ahead,* 1945; (with C. L. Paddock) *Little Journeys into Storyland,* 1947; *Look to the Hills,* 1960; *Great Texts from Romans,* 1972; (with Robert H. Pierson) *Bible Answers to Today's Questions,* 1974. Columnist, *Kansas City Call,* 1939-44; editor, *Message,* 1944-59, 1977—.

WORK IN PROGRESS: We Have Tomorrow.

SIDELIGHTS: Louis B. Reynolds has traveled in seventy-eight foreign countries.

* * *

RICCIUTI, Edward R(aphael) 1938-

PERSONAL: Born May 27, 1938, in New York, N.Y.; son of Edward Albert (a psychologist) and Inez (a teacher; maiden name Gatti) Ricciuti; married Mercedes Margarita Hogan, October 26, 1962; children: Anna Maria Cristina Teresa, James Edward. *Education:* University of Notre Dame, B.A., 1959; Columbia University, University Certificate, 1965. *Politics:* Democrat. *Religion:* Roman Catholic. *Home address:* RFD 3, Box 39, Roast Meat Hill Rd., Killingworth, Conn., 06417. *Agent:* Curtis Brown Ltd., 575 Madison Ave., New York, N.Y. 10022.

CAREER: Copy boy for *New York Mirror,* New York City, and reporter on *Independent,* Rockland, N.Y., and *Herald-News,* Ridgewood, N.J., 1959-60; *Record,* Hackensack, N.J., reporter and science writer, 1960-64; associate editor of *Science World* and *Senior Science,* and contributing editor of *Junior Scholastic,* New York City, 1965-67; New York Zoological Society, Bronx, associate curator, 1967-68, editor and curator of publications and public relations, 1968-71. Consultant on nature and science to Connecticut Audubon Society, American Littoral Society, New York Zoological Society, New England Aquarium, and Mystic Marinelife Aquarium; consultant to American Museum of Natural History, 1964-65; president of Connecticut Zoological Society, 1969, and American Alligator Council; conservation commissioner in Fairfield, Conn., 1969-70; consultant on exhibit theme development, Baltimore Aquarium, 1977; producer of television announcements for Wildlife Management Institute; affiliated with Communications Specialists; member of the cast of ''Patchwork Family,'' WCBS-TV, New York City; member of board, Holy Land Conservation Fund, 1978. *Military service:* U.S. Marine Corps Reserve, 1957-63. *Member:* Society of Magazine Writers, Explorers Club (fellow). *Awards, honors:* Public education citation by the Animal Care Panel, 1964, for ''Monkeys, Mice and Medicine.''

WRITINGS: Animals and Atomic Research, U.S. Atomic Energy Commission, 1967; Catch a Whale by the Tail, Harper, 1969; (contributor) Laurance Pringle, editor, Discovering the Outdoors, Natural History Press, 1969; An Animal for Alan, Harper, 1970; Shelf Pets, Harper, 1971; The American Alligator: Its Life in the Wild, Harper, 1972; Dancers on the Beach, Crowell, 1973; Killers of the Seas, Walker & Co., 1973; To the Brink of Extinction, Harper, 1973; Donald and the Fish that Walked, Harper, 1974; Do Toads Give You Warts?, Walker & Co., 1975; Killer Animals, Walker & Co., 1976; (with Les Line) The Audubon Society Book of Wild Animals, Abrams, 1977; Sounds of Animals at Night, Harper, 1977; The Devil's Garden: Facts and Folklore of Perilous Plants, Walker & Co., 1978. Contributor to World Almanac, Parade, Family Health, On the Sound, Steelways, Computing Report, Science World, Scholastic Teacher, Audubon, Signature, Nature and Science, and Engineer. Contributing editor, Science World, Scholastic Magazines, Inc.

WORK IN PROGRESS: Four books on natural science.

SIDELIGHTS: Edward Ricciuti has studied wild animals in Europe, Africa, and Southeast Asia as well as in the Everglades, the Okefenokee Swamp, the Caroni and Nariva Swamps of Trinidad, and the Luquillo Forest of Puerto Rico. He has participated in expeditions to collect whales in Hudson Bay and sharks off the Atlantic and Pacific coasts. He is interested in the life of the sea, and has spent considerable time on the water and under the surface, especially in the Caribbean and the Long Island Sound area, as well as off both the East and West coasts.

*   *   *

RICE, Edward E(arl) 1909-

PERSONAL: Born February 6, 1909, in Saginaw, Mich.; son of William Edward (a salesman) and Katherine (Meyer) Rice; married Mary Kellogg (a weaver-designer), October 26, 1942. Education: Attended University of Wisconsin, 1926-28; University of Illinois, B.A., 1930; further study at Universidad Nacional de Mexico, 1931, California College of Chinese Studies (Peking), 1935-36, and National War College, 1951-52. Home and office: 1819 Lagoon View Dr., Tiburon, Calif. 94920.

CAREER: U.S. Department of State, Washington, D.C., foreign service officer (among other positions, served in China, 1935-45, and as Consul General in Hong Kong, 1964-67), 1935-69. Eliot Fitch Visiting Professor, Marquette University, Milwaukee, Wis., 1973—. Member: Commonwealth Club (San Francisco).

WRITINGS: Mao's Way, University of California Press, 1972.

WORK IN PROGRESS: A history of the Chinese Communist Party for the Hoover Institution; a book relating to People's Wars and U.S. policy, completion expected in 1979.

*   *   *

RICE, Julius 1923-

PERSONAL: Born May 22, 1923, in Johannesburg, South Africa; son of Meyer (a salesman) and Katie (Levy) Rice; married Valerie Goodman, July 7, 1946; children: Beverley, Leonie. Education: University of Witwatersrand, M.B.B.Ch., 1947. Home and office: 75 South Middle Neck Rd., Great Neck, Long Island, N.Y. 11021. Agent: Bernard Eiber, 123-60 83rd Ave., Kew Gardens, New York, N.Y. 11415.

CAREER: Kings Park State Hospital, Kings Park, Long Island, N.Y., director of rehabilitation services, 1969-73; State University of New York at Stony Brook, assistant professor of clinical psychiatry, 1972—; Long Island Jewish-Hillside Medical Center, New Hyde Park, N.Y., staff psychiatrist, 1973—. Consultant psychiatrist, South Oaks Hospital, 1970—. Member: American Psychiatric Association, British Medical Association, New York Academy of Sciences.

WRITINGS: Ups and Downs, Drugging and Duping, Macmillan, 1972.

*   *   *

RICHARDS, I(vor) A(rmstrong) 1893-

PERSONAL: Born February 26, 1893, in Sandbach, Cheshire, England; son of William Armstrong and Mary Anne (Haig) Richards; married Dorothea Eleanor Pilley, December 31, 1926. Education: Magdalene College, Cambridge, B.A., 1914, M.A., 1918, Litt. D., 1932. Home: Wentworth House, 2 Chesterton Rd., Cambridge, England. Office: Magdalene College, Cambridge, England.

CAREER: Harvard University, Cambridge, Mass., visiting lecturer, 1931, lecturer in literary criticism and director of Commission on English Language Studies, 1939-44, professor of English, 1944-63, professor emeritus, 1963—. Lecturer in English and moral sciences, Cambridge University, 1922, fellow of Magdalene College, 1925; visiting professor, Tsing Hua University, Peking, 1929-30. Director, The Orthological Institute of China, 1936-38. Member: Alpine Club. Awards, honors: King's Medal, 1933, for poetry; Litt. D., Harvard University, 1944; corresponding fellow of British Academy, 1959; Russell Loines Award for poetry from National Institute of Arts and Letters, 1962; honorary fellow of Magdalene College, 1964; Companion of Honour, 1964; American Academy of Arts and Sciences, member, 1970—; Emerson-Thoreau Medal of American Academy of Arts and Sciences, 1970; Creative Activity Medal of Brandeis University, 1972; LL. D., Cambridge University, 1977; Benjamin Franklin Medal of Royal Society of Arts, 1978.

WRITINGS: (With Charles K. Ogden and James Wood) The Foundations of Aesthetics, Allen & Unwin, 1922, 2nd edition, Lear, 1925, reprinted, Haskell House, 1974; (with Ogden) The Meaning of Meaning: A Study of the Influence of Language upon Thought and of the Science of Symbolism, with supplementary essays by B. Malinowski and F. G. Crookshank, Harcourt, 1923, 8th edition, 1956; Principles of Literary Criticism, Harcourt, 1925, 3rd edition, 1928, reprinted, Routledge & Kegan Paul, 1970; Science and Poetry, K. Paul, Trench, Trubner & Co., 1926, reprinted, Haskell House, 1974, revised edition, K. Paul, Trench, Trubner & Co., 1935, published as Poetries and Sciences, Norton, 1970; Practical Criticism: A Study of Literary Judgment, Harcourt, 1929, reprinted, 1964; Mencius on the Mind: Experiments in Multiple Definition, Harcourt, 1932; Basic Rules of Reason, K. Paul, Trench, Trubner & Co., 1933; Coleridge on Imagination, K. Paul, Trench, Trubner & Co., 1934, 2nd edition, Norton, 1950, 3rd edition, Routledge & Kegan Paul, 1962; Basic in Teaching: East and West, K. Paul, Trench, Trubner & Co., 1935; The Philosophy of Rhetoric (Mary Flexner lectures), Oxford University Press (New York), 1936, reprinted, 1965; Interpretation in Teaching, Harcourt, 1938, 2nd edition, Humanities, 1973; (with Ogden) Times of India Guide to Basic English, Times of India Press (Bombay), 1938; (contributor) James D. McCallum, editor, College Book of Essays, Harcourt, 1939.

How to Read a Page: A Course in Effective Reading, with an Introduction to a Hundred Great Words, Norton, 1942; (contributor) Allen Tate, editor, *The Language of Poetry*, Princeton University Press, 1942; (editor and translator) *The Republic of Plato*, Norton, 1942; (with Christine Gibson) *Words on Paper: First Steps in Reading*, Commission on English Language Studies, Harvard University, 1943; *Basic English and Its Uses*, Norton, 1943; *A World Language* (speech), New York Herald Tribune, 1944; (with Gibson) *Learning Basic English: A Practical Handbook for English-Speaking People*, Norton, 1945; *The Pocket Book of Basic English: A Self-Teaching Way into English with Directions in Spanish, French, Italian, Portuguese* [and] *German*, Pocket Books, 1945, revised edition, 1946, new edition (with Gibson) published as *English through Pictures*, Washington Square Press, Book I, 1958, Books II & III, 1973; *Nations and Peace*, pictures by Ramon Gordon, Simon & Schuster, 1947; (contributor) Mark Schorer, J. Miles, and G. McKenzie, editors, *Criticism: The Foundation of Modern Literary Judgment*, Harcourt, 1948; (contributor) Leonard Unger, editor, *T. S. Eliot: A Selected Critique*, Rinehart, 1948.

(With M. H. Illsley and Gibson) *French Self-Taught with Pictures*, Pocket Books, 1950, reissued as *French through Pictures*, 1953; (editor and author of introduction) Samuel Taylor Coleridge, *The Portable Coleridge*, Viking, 1950, reprinted, 1977; (with Ruth C. Metcalf and Gibson) *Spanish Self-Taught through Pictures*, Pocket Books, 1950, reissued as *Spanish through Pictures*, Books I & II, 1972; (editor and translator) Homer, *The Wrath of Achilles: The Iliad of Homer, Shortened*, Norton, 1950; (with others) *German through Pictures*, Pocket Books, 1953; (with David Weinstein and Gibson) *'Ivrit bi-te-munot* (title means "Hebrew through Pictures"), Pocket Books, 1954, new edition, Washington Square Press, 1961; (with Weinstein and Gibson) *Hebrew Reader*, Pocket Books, 1955 (also published as *Hakore ha-'ivri*, including an adapted version of *Words on Paper*, Pocket Books, 1955); (with Italo Evangelista and Gibson) *Italian through Pictures*, Pocket Books, 1955; *Speculative Instruments*, University of Chicago Press, 1955; (contributor) Stanley E. Hyman, editor, *The Critical Performance*, Vintage Books, 1956; (with Gibson) *First Steps in Reading English: A First Book for Readers to Be*, Washington Square Press, 1957; *Goodbye Earth and Other Poems*, Harcourt, 1958; (contributor) Irving Howe, editor, *Modern Literary Criticism*, Beacon Press, 1958; (contributor) Morris Weitz, editor, *Problems in Aesthetics*, Macmillan (New York), 1959; (contributor) Harold L. Beaver, editor, *American Critical Essays: Twentieth Century*, Oxford University Press, 1959.

Coleridge's Minor Poems (lecture), Folcroft, 1960; (with M. H. Illsley and Gibson) *A First Workbook of French for Use with "French through Pictures,"* Book I, Washington Square Press, 1960; (with Ruth C. Metcalf and Gibson) *A First Workbook of "Spanish through Pictures,"* Book I, Washington Square Press, 1960; (contributor) Maurice R. Stein, A. J. Vidich, and D. M. White, editors, *Identity with Anxiety*, Free Press, 1960; *The Screens and Other Poems*, Harcourt, 1960; (with Gibson) *A First Workbook of English for Use with "English through Pictures,"* Book I, Washington Square Press, 1960; (contributor) Rollo May, editor, *Symbolism in Religion and Literature*, Braziller, 1960; (contributor) Melvin M. Rader, editor, *A Modern Book of Esthetics*, Holt, 1960; (with Evelyn Jasiulko and Gibson) *Russian through Pictures*, Washington Square Press, 1961; *Tomorrow Morning, Faustus! An Infernal Comedy* (play),

Harcourt, 1962; (contributor) William Wasserstrom, editor, *The Dial: A Dial Miscellany*, Syracuse University Press, 1963; *Why So, Socrates? A Dramatic Version of Plato's Dialogues: Euthyphro, Apology, Crito, Phaedo*, Cambridge University Press, 1964; (with Gibson) *Development of Experimental Audio-Visual Devices and Materials for Beginning Readers*, Harvard University Press, 1965; (contributor) Allen Tate, editor, *T. S. Eliot*, Dial, 1966; (contributor) Harvey S. Gross, editor, *The Structure of Verse*, Fawcett, 1966; (contributor) Kathleen Coburn, editor, *Coleridge*, Prentice-Hall, 1967; *Design for Escape: World Education through Modern Media*, Harcourt, 1968; *So Much Nearer: Essays toward a World English*, Harcourt, 1968; (contributor) Paul J. Alpers, editor, *Elizabethan Poetry*, Oxford University Press, 1968; (contributor) Whitney F. Bolton and David Crystal, editors, *The English Language*, Volume II, Cambridge University Press, 1969.

(With Sheridan Baker and Jacques Barzun) *The Written Word*, Newbury House Publishers, 1971; *Internal Colloquies: Poems and Plays*, Harcourt, 1971; (with others) *Essays on Wyndom Lewis*, Norwood, 1974; (with Gibson) *Techniques in Language Control*, Newbury House, 1974; *Poetries: Their Media and Ends*, edited by Trevor Eaton, Mouton, 1974; *Beyond*, Harcourt, 1974; *Complementarities: Uncollected Essays and Reviews*, edited by John Paul Russo, Harvard University Press, 1976. Also author of *New and Selected Poems* and *How So, Socrates?*.

Represented in anthologies, including, *Poets and the Past*, edited by D. Ashton, Andre Emmerich Gallery (New York), 1959; *Poetry for Pleasure*, edited by I. M. Parsons, Doubleday, 1960; *Garlands for Christmas*, edited by C. Walsh, Macmillan, 1965. A verse play, *A Leak in the Universe*, was published in *Playbook: Five Plays for a New Theatre*, New Directions, 1956. Frequent contributor of articles to *Times Literary Supplement*.

SIDELIGHTS: I. A. Richards is credited with founding the modern school of literary criticism. He has had enormous influence, especially on William Empson and Kenneth Burke, and, according to Stanley Hyman, "almost no contemporary critic has written without being touched by Richards at some point." Although he considers himself to be primarily a poet, most of his work has been done in linguistics and criticism. His theory of criticism has been characterized by Gerald Graff as "at once romantic *and* positivistic . . . , the view that reason and rational discourse are at home in the realm . . . of 'facts'—and not of values." In *So Much Nearer*, Richards has suggested the usefulness of English as a world language, not merely to improve communication, but to "prevent world catastrophe" caused by problems heightened by language differences. Seymour Chatman has written: "For all we may criticize Richard's thought, his style of thinking, his Messianic urgings, he remains one of the wonders of the age. . . ."

AVOCATIONAL INTERESTS: Travel and mountaineering.

BIOGRAPHICAL/CRITICAL SOURCES—Books: F. R. Leavis, editor, *Determinations: Critical Essays*, Chatto & Windus, 1934; T. S. Eliot, *Use of Poetry and the Use of Criticism*, Faber, 1937; John Crowe Ransom, *World's Body*, Scribner, 1938; Max F. Eastman, *Enjoyment of Poetry: With Other Essays in Aesthetics*, Scribner, 1939; Stanley E. Hyman, *Armed Vision: A Study of the Methods of Modern Literary Criticism*, Knopf, 1948; Max Black, *Language and Philosophy: Studies in Method*, Cornell University Press, 1949; Robert W. Stallman, editor, *Critiques and Essays in*

Criticism, 1920-1948, Ronald, 1949; Eliseo Vivas, *Creation and Discovery: Essays in Criticism and Aesthetics,* Noonday, 1955; Murray Krieger, *The New Apologists for Poetry,* University of Minnesota Press, 1956; Raymond Williams, *Culture and Society, 1780-1950,* Columbia University Press, 1958; Allen Tate, *Collected Essays,* A. Swallow, 1959; John M. Murry, *Selected Criticism, 1916-1957,* Oxford University Press, 1960; George Watson, *The Literary Critics: A Study of English Descriptive Criticism,* Penguin, 1962; Morton D. Zabel, editor, *Literary Opinion in America,* Volume II, Peter Smith, 1963.

* * *

RICHARDSON, Howard (Dixon) 1917-

PERSONAL: Born December 2, 1917, in Spartanburg, S.C.; son of Frank Howard (a physician) and Clara (Dixon) Richardson. *Education:* Attended Mars Hill Junior College (now Mars Hill College), 1934-36; University of North Carolina, A.B., 1938, M.A., 1940; Alliance Francaise, Paris, degre avance, 1939; Sorbonne, University of Paris, graduate study, 1948-49; University of Iowa, Ph.D., 1960. *Home and office:* 207 Columbus Ave., New York, N.Y. 10023.

CAREER: Visiting lecturer for American National Theatre Academy before clubs, civic groups, college and university dramatic organizations, 1947—; Abbe Theatre School, New York City, instructor in playwriting, 1947-48; NBC-TV, New York City, staff writer for producer Warren Wade, 1947, author of series plays produced by Albert McCleery, 1948-50, story editor and associate producer for "American Inventory," 1955-56; Clark Center for Performing Arts, New York City, instructor in playwriting, 1960-61; Queens College of the City University of New York, New York City, visiting lecturer on playwriting, 1961-62; University of Oregon, Eugene, visiting associate professor of playwriting, 1963-64; University of North Dakota, Grand Forks, associate professor of drama, 1964-65; Sonoma County Theatre Guild, Sebastiana Theatre, Sonoma, Calif., creative director, 1964-65; San Fernando Valley State College (now California State University, Northridge), visiting lecturer in drama, 1965-66; College of the Virgin Islands, St. Thomas, chairman of speech department, 1968; North Dakota State University, Fargo, artist-in-residence, 1971. Served as travel tour guide in Europe and the Orient for Travcoa, Gateway Holidays, Arista, and Smithsonian Institution; lecturer on Greek drama for Mediterranean Black Sea cruise, Royal Viking Line, 1978. *Military service:* U.S. Army Air Forces, pilot, 1941-42. *Member:* Dramatists Guild, Actors Equity, American Theatre Association, American National Theatre Academy, Screen Writers Guild, American Speech Association, American College Theatre Association. *Awards, honors:* Maxwell Anderson Award from Stanford University, 1942, for best play in verse, "Barbara Allen" (later revised with William Berney as *Dark of the Moon*); Off-Broadway awards, 1951, for *Dark of the Moon.*

*WRITINGS—*All plays: (With William Berney) *Dark of the Moon* (two-act; first produced on Broadway at 46th St. Theatre, March 14, 1945; first produced in London at Lyric Hammersmith Theatre, May 3, 1950), Theatre Arts, 1949; *Design for a Stained Glass Window* (three-act; first produced on Broadway at Mansfield Theatre, January 23, 1950), Baker's Plays, 1950; *The Laundry* (three-act; adaptation of David Guerdon's "La Bunderie"; first produced Off-Broadway at Gate Theatre, February 13, 1963; first produced in London at Malvern Festival, July 26, 1966), Samuel French, 1970; (with Frances Goforth) *Ark of Safety* (two-act; first produced in Mars Hill, N.C. by Southern Appalachian Repertory Theatre, July 25, 1975), Samuel French, 1977.

Unpublished plays: (With Goforth) "Catch on the Wing," first produced at Theatre in the Dale, New Milford, Conn., July 2, 1947; (with Berney) "Sodom, Tennessee," first produced at Hayloft Theatre, Allentown, Pa., August 20, 1950; (with Goforth) "Le Chat dans le cage," first produced at Theatre Noctambule, Paris, February 11, 1951, produced as "The Cat in the Cage," at Hayloft Theatre, July 18, 1951; (with Goforth) "Widow's Walk," first produced at Barter Theatre, Abington, Va., July 24, 1952; (with Berney) "Mountain Fire," first produced at Royal Court Theatre, Liverpool, May 18, 1954; "Protective Custody," first produced on Broadway at Ambassador Theatre, December 28, 1956; "Giselle," first produced in London at Mount View Theatre, August 12, 1956; "Madame Thirteen," first produced at Santa Fe Theatre, August 1, 1959; "Birds of Prey," first produced at Hayloft Theatre, August 28, 1961. Author of plays for television programs, including "Cameo Theatre," "Alcoa Hour," "Goodyear Playhouse," "Alfred Hitchcock," and "Matinee Theatre." Translator of plays, including "The Laundry," included in *New Theatre of Europe,* edited by R. W. Corrigan, Dell, 1967. Contributor of articles to *Dramatists Guild Quarterly* and *Tulane Drama Review.*

AVOCATIONAL INTERESTS: Magic, experimental hypnosis in speech therapy.

* * *

RICHASON, Benjamin F(ranklin, Jr.) 1922-

PERSONAL: Born July 24, 1922, in Logansport, Ind.; son of Benjamin F. and Ruth (Tremps) Richason; married Beverly Elder, July 21, 1946; children: Benjamin F. III. *Education:* Indiana University, B.A., 1948, M.A., 1949; University of Nebraska, Ph.D., 1960. *Religion:* Presbyterian. *Home:* 308 East Roberta Ave., Waukesha, Wis. 53186. *Office:* Department of Geography, Carroll College, Waukesha, Wis. 53186.

CAREER: Morton Junior College, Cicero, Ill., instructor in geography, 1949-51; Carroll College, Waukesha, Wis., assistant professor, 1952-56, associate professor, 1956-59, professor of geography, 1959—, chairman of department, 1952—. Chairman of technical advisory committee on natural resources and environmental design, Southeastern Wisconsin Regional Planning Commission, 1961-68; president, Wisconsin Council for Conservation Education, 1962-63; member of panel of consultants, Bureau of Libraries and Education Technology, U.S. Office of Education, 1969—; director of Media Institute in Geographic Field Studies for Education Professions Development Act, Mexico, 1969. *Military service:* U.S. Army Air Forces, 1943-46. *Member:* National Council for Geographic Education (president, 1969; chairman of remote sensing committee), American Association for the Advancement of Science (fellow; member of council, 1968), Wisconsin Council for Geographic Education (president, 1977-78), Rotary Club (president of local chapter, 1966), Gamma Theta Upsilon, Sigma Xi. *Awards, honors:* Danforth teacher study grant, 1955-56; science faculty fellowship from National Science Foundation, 1958-59; Waukesha County Conservation Alliance Annual Award, 1961; Uhrig Award for excellence in teaching, 1970; George J. Miller distinguished service award from National Council for Geographic Education, 1976.

WRITINGS: Geography via Aerial Field Trips, National Council for Geographic Education, 1965; *Geography via the*

Audio-Visual-Tutorial Method, National Council for Geographic Education, 1969; *Atlas of Cultural Features*, Hubbard Press, 1972; *Complete College-Level Audio-Visual-Tutorial Series in Physical Geography*, Hubbard Press, 1972; (editor) *Introduction to Remote Sensing of the Environment*, with laboratory manual, Kendall/Hunt, 1978. Editor of *Bulletin of Wisconsin Council for Geographic Education*, 1961-68, and of Printed Materials Center of National Council for Geographic Education, 1970-72, and *Remote Sensing of the Electromagnetic Spectrum*, 1978—; associate editor of *Journal of Geography*, 1970-71.

WORK IN PROGRESS: Aerial photo interpretation of seasonal agricultural cultivation patterns; land cover analysis and enhancement of LANDSAT imagery.

SIDELIGHTS: Benjamin Richason has organized and conducted field trips in the Rocky Mountains and Great Plains, 1955, Ghost Ranch, New Mexico, 1964, Europe, 1965, 1970, 1977, and Jamaica and Puerto Rico, 1967-70, 1973-78. He also developed and implemented the first Audio-Visual Tutorial Laboratory in Geography in 1967.

* * *

RICHMOND, Al 1913-
(Joseph Morton)

PERSONAL: Original surname, Richman, legally changed in 1947; born November 17, 1913, in London, England; son of Samuel (a garment cutter) and Genya (Gorelick) Richman; married Merle Nance, June 30, 1947; children: David, Joseph. *Education:* Attended high school in New York, N.Y. *Politics:* Communist. *Religion:* None. *Home:* 2039 Broderick St., San Francisco, Calif. 94115. *Agent:* Tom Van Dycke, 90 Avenue Jean Jaures, Montfermeil, France.

CAREER: Organizer for Young Communist League in Philadelphia, Pa. and Baltimore, Md., 1931-32, and for Marine Workers Industrial Union in New York City and Philadelphia, 1932-34; *Daily* and *Sunday Worker*, New York City, copy reader and reporter, 1934-37; *Western Worker*, San Francisco, Calif., editor, 1937; *Daily People's World* (now *People's World*), San Francisco, managing editor, 1938-43, executive editor, 1946-69; Institute for Scientific Analysis, San Francisco, editor, 1975—. *Military service:* U.S. Army, Medical Corps, 1943-46; became technical sergeant.

WRITINGS: Native Daughter: The Story of Anita Whitney, privately printed, 1942; *A Long View from the Left: Memoirs of an American Revolutionary*, Houghton, 1973. Author of two pamphlets published under pseudonym Joseph Morton, *McCarthy—The Man and the Ism*, 1953, and *Depression: Hard Facts vs. Soft Soap*, 1954. Contributor to *Nation, Ramparts, New Masses, In These Times*, and *Political Affairs*.

WORK IN PROGRESS: A study of American radicalism at its peak in 1912, and its influence on the Progressive Era.

SIDELIGHTS: Al Richmond was indicted and arrested for conspiracy in 1951. He was convicted and sentenced to serve five years in prison, but secured a directed verdict of acquittal in the U.S. Supreme Court in 1957.

* * *

RICHMOND, Samuel B(ernard) 1919-

PERSONAL: Born October 14, 1919, in Boston, Mass. *Education:* Harvard University, A.B. (cum laude), 1940; Columbia University, M.B.A., 1948, Ph.D., 1951. *Office:* Owen Graduate School of Management, Vanderbilt University, Nashville, Tenn. 37203.

CAREER: U.S. Treasury Department and U.S. War Department, Boston, Mass., chemist, 1941-42; American Conditioning House, Boston, chemist, 1946; Columbia University, New York, N.Y., lecturer, 1947-48, instructor, 1948-51, assistant professor of statistics, 1951-55, assistant professor of economics and statistics, 1955-57, associate professor, 1957-60, professor of economics and statistics, 1960-76, Graduate School of Business, associate dean, 1971-72, acting dean, 1972; Vanderbilt University, Owen Graduate School of Management, Nashville, Tenn., dean, 1976—. Visiting assistant professor of statistics, Fordham University, 1952-53; visiting associate professor of economics and statistics, Case Institute of Technology (now Case Western Reserve University), 1958-59; lecturer in operations research, decision theory, and research techniques, University of Buenos Aires, 1964, 1965; visiting professor of operations research, University of Sherbrooke, 1967. Member of board of directors of Science Resources, Inc., 1961-63, Brandon Applied Systems, Inc., 1965-69, Corbin Ltd., 1969—, The P.S.T. Group, Inc., 1969—, and IMS International, Inc., 1976—. Consultant to corporations and government agencies, including U.S. Department of Agriculture, U.S. Department of Commerce, American Society of Composers, Authors and Publishers, Teleprompter Corp., Federal Aviation Authority, El-Al Israel Airlines, United Fruit Co., Pillsbury Co., Peavey Co., and Coca-Cola Co. *Military service:* U.S. Army Air Forces, weather officer and instructor at U.S. Army Weather School, 1943-45; became first lieutenant.

MEMBER: American Economic Association, American Statistical Association (member of board of directors, 1965-67; chairman of advisory committee to Civil Aeronautics Board, 1966—), Operations Research Society of America, Institute of Management Sciences. *Awards, honors:* Honorary award from Civil Aeronautics Board, 1971.

WRITINGS: Statistical Analysis, Ronald, 1957, 2nd edition, 1964; *Regulation and Competition in Air Transportation*, Columbia University Press, 1961; (contributor) T. J. Sielaff, editor, *Statistics in Action*, Lansford, 1963; (with Eli Ginzberg and Dale Hiestand) *Manpower for Aviation*, New York Conservation of Human Resources Project, Columbia University, 1964; (contributor) Stanley C. Hallander, editor, *Passenger Transportation*, Michigan State Business Studies, Michigan State University, 1968; *Operations Research for Management Decision*, Ronald, 1968. Contributor to economics, aeronautics, marketing, and management journals.

* * *

RICKENBACKER, Edward Vernon 1890-1973

October 8, 1890—July 23, 1973; American aviator, war hero, and industrialist. Obituaries: *New York Times*, July 24, 1973; *Washington Post*, July 24, 1973; *Time*, August 6, 1973.

* * *

RIEMER, George 1920-1973
(Seth Poole, Clint Schirmerhorn)

October 29, 1920—March 31, 1973; American author and magazine writer. Obituaries: *New York Times*, April 2, 1973. (See index for *CA* sketch)

* * *

RIESSEN, Martin Clare 1941-

PERSONAL: Born December 4, 1941, in Hinsdale, Ill.; son

of Clare William (an educator) and Mildred (Ludlow) Riessen; married Sally E. Lybek (an interior designer), December 19, 1964 (divorced, 1976); married April M. Satow, January 26, 1977; children: (second marriage) Jennifer Michele. *Education:* Northwestern University, B.S., 1964, M.A., 1966. *Religion:* Protestant. *Residence:* Boca West, Fla.

CAREER: Professional tennis player.

WRITINGS: (With Richard Evans) *Match Point,* Prentice-Hall, 1973.

* * *

RIESTERER, Berthold P(hillip) 1935-

PERSONAL: Born June 9, 1935, in Detroit, Mich.; married; children: two. *Education:* Wayne State University, A.B. (with high distinction), 1958, M.A., 1961, Ph.D., 1966. *Home:* 7227 Creekside Lane, Indianapolis, Ind. 46250. *Office:* Department of History, Indiana University-Purdue University, Indianapolis, Ind. 46202.

CAREER: Wayne State University, Detroit, Mich., instructor in history, 1964-65; Albion College, Albion, Mich., instructor, 1965-66, assistant professor of history, 1966-67; Indiana University-Purdue University at Indianapolis, assistant professor, 1967-70, associate professor of history, 1970—. *Member:* Phi Beta Kappa, Phi Alpha Theta, Delta Phi Alpha.

WRITINGS: (Contributor) H. V. White, editor, *The Uses of History: Festschrift for William J. Bossenbrook,* Wayne State University Press, 1968; *Karl Loewith's View of History: A Critical Appraisal of Historicism,* Nijhoff, 1969.

* * *

RITTENHOUSE, Mignon 1904-

PERSONAL: Born February 19, 1904, in New York, N.Y.; daughter of George (a Baptist minister) and Catherine (Meisser) Rittenhouse; married Horace Albro Woodmansee (a writer and editor), January 24, 1931 (died March 18, 1978); children: George Horace, Lois Kathleen Kellerman. *Education:* Attended Wheaton College, 1922-24. *Politics:* Independent Republican. *Religion:* Protestant. *Home and office:* 39-25 202nd St., Bayside, N.Y. 11361.

CAREER: Free-lance writer; *Brooklyn Eagle,* Brooklyn, N.Y., reporter and feature writer, 1924-36; *Morning Telegraph,* weekly movie columnist, 1926; editor for Dell Publishing Co., 1935, and Fawcett Publications, Inc., 1935-48; has worked in various capacities for Metro-Goldwyn-Mayer and Mack Sennett. *Member:* Authors League of America, Marquis Biographical Library Society.

WRITINGS: The Amazing Nellie Bly, Dutton, 1956, reprinted, Arno, 1977; *Seven Women Explorers,* Lippincott, 1964; *The Magic Keys of Christopher Columbus* (operetta), Schmitt, Hall & McCreary, 1971. Contributor to motion picture magazines; contributor of articles to *New York World* and poems to *Good Housekeeping, Today's Woman,* and poetry magazines.

WORK IN PROGRESS: Anne Bradstreet: The Flesh and the Spirit.

AVOCATIONAL INTERESTS: Travel, people.

* * *

RIVERO, Eliana Suarez 1942-

PERSONAL: Born November 7, 1942, in Artemisa, Cuba; daughter of Mario J. (an accountant) and Maria (Rivero) Suarez; married Angel Rivero (a Sears, Roebuck Co. manager), July 28, 1967; children: Elisabet. *Education:* Attended Virginia Intermont College, 1958-59, and University of Havana, 1959-60; University of Miami, Coral Gables, Fla., B.A., 1964, Ph.D., 1967. *Politics:* Independent. *Home:* 5818 East Third St., Tucson, Ariz. 85721. *Office:* Department of Romance Languages, University of Arizona, Tucson, Ariz. 85721.

CAREER: University of Arizona, Tucson, assistant professor, 1967—. *Member:* Modern Language Association of America, American Association of Teachers of Spanish and Portuguese, American Association of University Professors, Pacific Coast Council for Latin American Studies, Rocky Mountain Council of Latin American Studies (member of executive board). *Awards, honors:* American Council of Learned Societies travel grant, 1975.

WRITINGS: (Editor with Jose A. Balseiro) *Alejandro Casona, El Caballero de las Espuelas de Oro,* Oxford University Press, 1968; *El Gran Amor de Pablo Neruda,* Plaza Mayor, 1971; *De cal y arena,* Aldebaran, 1975; *Cuerpos breves,* Scorpion Press, 1976; *Siete Poetas,* Scorpion Press, 1978. Contributor to *Hispania, Alaluz, Explicacion de Textos Literarios, Revista,* and *Iberoamericana.*

WORK IN PROGRESS: Research on Latin American women in literature.

SIDELIGHTS: Eliana Rivero told *CA,* "I have gone more and more into creative writing, but I find that critical commentary adds to my knowledge of the phenomena of poetry in particular and language in general." *Avocational interests:* Travel in Latin America, Europe, England, and the West Indies; piano music.

* * *

ROBATHAN, Dorothy M(ae) 1898-

PERSONAL: Surname is pronounced *Rob-*a-than; born May 11, 1898, in Scranton, Pa.; daughter of Edward E. and Emilie (Evans) Robathan. *Education:* Wellesley College, B.A., 1919; Columbia University, A.M., 1921; University of Chicago, Ph.D., 1929. *Politics:* Republican. *Religion:* Protestant. *Home:* 285 Deyo Hill Rd., Johnson City, N.Y. 13790.

CAREER: Walnut Hill School in Natick, Mass., teacher of Latin, 1921-25; Northampton School for Girls, Northampton, Mass., head of Latin department, 1926-27; Wells College, Aurora, N.Y., instructor in Latin, 1930-31; Wellesley College, Wellesley, Mass., instructor, 1931-32, assistant professor, 1933-39, associate professor, 1939-47, professor of Latin, 1947-63, professor emeritus, 1963—, chairman of department, 1939-48. *Member:* American Philological Association (president, 1965), Mediaeval Academy of America, Renaissance Society of America, Archaeological Institute of America. *Awards, honors:* Research fellow, American Academy in Rome, 1948-49; American Council of Learned Societies grant, 1963-64.

WRITINGS: (Contributor) J. W. Thompson, editor, *Libraries of the Italian Renaissance,* University of Chicago Press, 1939; *The Monuments of Ancient Rome,* Bretschneider, 1950; (editor) *Studies in Honor of Ullman,* St. Louis University Press, 1960; *The Pseudo Ovidian 'De Vetula',* Hakkert, 1968. Contributor of articles to *American Journal of Philology, Classical Philology, Transactions of American Philology Association, Speculum,* and *Mediaevalia et Humanistica.*

WORK IN PROGRESS: Critical edition of Flavio Biondo's *Roma Instaurata.*

ROBB, James Willis 1918-

PERSONAL: Born June 27, 1918, in Jamaica, N.Y.; son of Stewart Everts and Clara (Mohrmann) Robb. *Education:* Attended Sorbonne, University of Paris, 1937-38; Colgate University, A.B. (cum laude), 1939; also attended Universidad Nacional de Mexico, summer, 1948; Middlebury College, A.M., 1950; Catholic University of America, Ph.D., 1958. *Office:* Department of Romance Languages, George Washington University, Washington, D.C. 20052.

CAREER: Norwich University, Northfield, Vt., instructor in Romance languages, 1946-50; George Washington University, Washington, D.C., assistant professor, 1950-58, associate professor, 1958-66, professor of Romance languages, 1966—. Member of board of advisors, Brazilian-American Cultural Institute, 1964—. *Military service:* U.S. Naval Reserve, naval observer in Brazil, active duty, 1942-46. *Member:* Modern Language Association of America, American Association of Teachers of Spanish and Portuguese (past chapter vice-president and president), Instituto Internacional de Literatura Iberoamericana, Phi Beta Kappa (member of board of electors), Sigma Delta Pi. *Awards, honors:* John F. Kennedy fellowship, Organization of American States, 1964, for research at Alfonso Reyes Library (Mexico City) and at other Mexican and Colombian institutions.

WRITINGS: El Estilo de Alfonso Reyes, Fondo de Cultura Economica, 1965, 2nd edition, 1978; *Repertorio Bibliografico de Alfonso Reyes,* Universidad Nacional Autonoma de Mexico, 1974; (editor) *Prosa y Poesia de Alfonso Reyes,* Catedra, 1975. Contributor to *New Catholic Encyclopedia, Funk and Wagnalls New Encyclopedia,* and *Funk and Wagnalls Yearbook;* contributor of about forty articles and reviews to literary journals.

*   *   *

ROBBERT, Louise Buenger 1925-

PERSONAL: Born August 18, 1925, in St. Paul, Minn.; daughter of Albert (an engineer) and Myrtle (Rubbert) Buenger; married George S. Robbert (an associate professor of historical theology), September 17, 1960; children: George Harold. *Education:* Carleton College, B.A., 1947; University of Cincinnati, M.A., 1948, B.Ed., 1949; University of Wisconsin, Ph.D., 1955. *Home:* 15 South Seminary Ter., St. Louis, Mo. 63105. *Office:* Department of History, University of Missouri, St. Louis, Mo. 63121.

CAREER: Smith College, Northampton, Mass., instructor in history, 1954-55; Hunter College (now Hunter College of the City University of New York), New York, N.Y., instructor in history, 1957-60; St. Louis College of Pharmacy, St. Louis, Mo., instructor in humanities, 1960-62; Texas Tech University, Lubbock, assistant professor, 1962-73, associate professor of history, 1973-75; University of Missouri—St. Louis, visiting associate professor of history, 1978—. *Member:* Mediaeval Academy of America, Mediaeval Club of New York (secretary-treasurer, 1958-60), Quarterly Club (president, 1972-74). *Awards, honors:* Fulbright scholarship, Italy, 1955-56, 1956-57; American Council of Learned Societies grant, 1960.

WRITINGS: (Contributor) D. Herlihy, R. S. Lopez, and V. Slessarev, editors, *Economy, Society, and Government in Medieval Italy: Essays in Memory of Robert L. Reynolds,* Kent State University Press, 1969; *The Venetian Money Market, 1150-1229,* Fondazione Giorgio Cini (Venice, Italy), 1972. Contributor to *Speculum.*

WORK IN PROGRESS: A contribution to *The History of the Crusades,* edited by Kenneth M. Setton, for the University of Pennsylvania Press.

*   *   *

ROBERTS, Chalmers M(cGeagh) 1910-

PERSONAL: Born November 18, 1910, in Pittsburgh, Pa.; son of Franklin B. (a dentist) and Lillian (McGeagh) Roberts; married Lois Hall, September 11, 1941; children: David H., Patricia E., Christopher C. *Education:* Amherst College, B.A., 1933. *Home:* 6699 Mac Arthur Blvd., Washington, D.C. 20016.

CAREER: Reporter for *Washington Post,* Washington, D.C., 1933-34, Associated Press, Pittsburgh, Pa., 1934-35, and *Toledo News-Bee,* Toledo, Ohio, 1936-38; *Japan Times,* Tokyo, copy editor, 1938-39; *Washington Daily News,* Washington, D.C., assistant managing editor, 1939-41; *Washington Times-Herald,* Washington, D.C., Sunday editor, 1941; *Life,* New York, N.Y., Washington picture editor, 1946-47; *Washington Post,* reporter of local and national news, 1949-53, chief diplomatic correspondent, 1953-71, columnist, 1971—. *Military service:* U.S. Army Air Forces, Intelligence, 1943-46; became captain. *Member:* American Newspaper Guild. *Awards, honors:* Sigma Delta Chi award, 1953; Washington Newspaper Guild national news award, 1954, 1960; Overseas Press Club citation, 1955; Washington Newspaper Guild Front Page grand prize, 1957, 1960; Raymond Clapper Memorial Award, 1957; L.H.D., Amherst College, 1963; Order of Merit, West Germany; Weintal Prize, 1975, for diplomatic reporting.

WRITINGS: Washington Past and Present, Public Affairs Press, 1950; (editor and contributor) *Can We Meet the Russians Half Way?,* Doubleday, 1958; *The Nuclear Years: The Arms Race and Arms Control, 1945-1970,* Praeger, 1970; *First Rough Draft,* Praeger, 1973; *The Washington Post: The First One Hundred Years,* Houghton, 1977. Contributor of articles to *Foreign Affairs, Foreign Policy, Atlantic Monthly,* and other periodicals.

BIOGRAPHICAL/CRITICAL SOURCES: New York Times, March 11, 1978.

*   *   *

ROBERTS, Jane 1929-
(Jane Roberts Butts)

PERSONAL: Born May 8, 1929, in Albany, N.Y.; daughter of Delmar Hubbell and Marie (Burdo) Roberts; married Robert F. Butts (an artist), December 27, 1954. *Education:* Attended Skidmore College for three years.

CAREER: Writer and psychic. Former teacher.

WRITINGS—Published by Prentice-Hall, except as indicated: *The Rebellers,* Ace, 1963; *How to Develop your E.S.P. Power,* Fell, 1966; *The Seth Material,* 1970; *Seth Speaks: The Eternal Validity of the Soul,* 1972; *The Education of Oversoul Seven,* 1973; *The Nature of Personal Reality: A Seth Book,* 1974; *Adventures in Consciousness: An Introduction to Aspect Psychology,* 1975; *Dialogues of the Soul and Mortal Self in Time* (poetry), 1975; *Psychic Politics,* 1976; *The Unknown Reality: A Seth Book,* Volume I, 1977, Volume II, 1979; *The World View: Paul Cezanne,* 1977; *The Afterdeath Journal of an American Philosopher,* 1978; *The Further Education of Oversoul Seven* (novel), 1979; *The Nature of the Psyche: A Seth Book,* 1979; *Emir's Education in the Proper Use of Magical Powers* (novel), Delacourt, 1979. Contributor of poetry to little literary magazines, and short stories to *Fantasy & Science Fiction.*

WORK IN PROGRESS: The Individual and the Nature of Mass Events: A Seth Book; From This Rich Bed, an autobiography; *Sumari Songs,* poems written while in trance.

SIDELIGHTS: Jane Roberts writes: "I think that the private creative psyche, mine and everyone else's, contains its own unique picture of the universe, and provides an original vantage point from which each of us views reality. With each new creative inspiration or act, I feel once more in touch with my origin, for I regard my writing and my life as springing from the same (mysterious) spontaneous source."

* * *

ROBERTS, Joseph B(oxley), Jr. 1918-

PERSONAL: Born February 13, 1918, in Yazoo City, Miss.; son of Joseph Boxley and Sheila (Hill) Roberts; married Nell Rose Dixon, 1939 (divorced, 1944); married Enyd Turner, November 19, 1945; children: (first marriage) Joseph Boxley III; (second marriage) Sheila Anne Tweed. *Education:* University of Alabama, B.A., 1950; University of North Carolina, M.A., 1954; University of Denver, Ph.D., 1959. *Politics:* Independent. *Religion:* Episcopalian. *Home:* 107 Richmond Ave., Troy, Ala. 36081. *Office:* Department of English, Troy State University, Troy, Ala. 36081.

CAREER: U.S. Army, enlisted man, 1942-43, officer with Air Transport Command, Army Air Forces, 1943-46, serving as information and education officer in British West Africa, Burma, and India; recalled to active duty with U.S. Air Force, 1951, and assigned to Headquarters, Military Air Transport Services, Washington, D.C., 1951-53; U.S. Military Academy, West Point, N.Y., instructor, 1953-54, assistant professor of English, 1954-56; U.S. Air Force Academy, Colorado Springs, Colo., assistant professor, 1956-60, associate professor of English, 1960-63; subsequently assigned to Office of Aerospace Research, 1963-66, Army Special Warfare School, Fort Bragg, Calif., 1966, Headquarters, Military Assistance Command, Vietnam, 1966-67, and to Air Force Special Warfare School; retired in rank of lieutenant colonel, 1968; Troy State University, Troy, Ala., professor of English, 1968—, chairman of department, 1968-71, dean of College of Arts and Sciences, 1971-72.

MEMBER: Modern Language Association of America, National Council of Teachers of English, Conference on College Composition and Communication, South Atlantic Modern Language Association, Phi Beta Kappa (president of local chapter, 1969-70), Phi Eta Sigma, Phi Kappa Phi (president of local chapter, 1972-73), Sigma Tau Delta. *Awards, honors—*Military: Bronze Star Medal and Air Force Commendation Medal.

WRITINGS: Airway to India (travel book), Army Services Forces, 1945; *Faint Voice Calling* (poems), Hippogryph Press, 1945; *Beginner's Handbook of Gold and Tropical Fish,* Denlinger's, 1947, revised edition, All-Pets Books, 1952; *Pet Shop Manual,* All-Pets Books, 1953; *Web of Our Life* (short stories), Humphries, 1957; (editor with Paul Briand) *The Sound of Wings: Readings for the Air Age,* Holt, 1957; *On Poetry and the Poetic Process* (critical essays), Troy State University Press, 1971. Author of a weekly newspaper column, "It Seems to Me," nationally syndicated by Contemporary Features Syndicate. Short story included in *Alabama Prize Stories—1970,* and three poems in *Perma Treasury of Love Poems.* Contributor of articles to scholarly journals, poems to *Empire, Beat of Wings, Alabama Sunday Magazine, Washington Post,* and other magazines and newspapers, and reviews to *Personalist, Airpower Historian,* and *Denver Post.*

WORK IN PROGRESS: A collection of poems, working title, "This above All"; gathering some columns for possible inclusion in a book; a short novel.

SIDELIGHTS: Joseph Roberts decided to become a teacher after discovering "the fun of scholarship" while studying creative writing at the University of Alabama. He says that he enjoys writing poetry most and short stories next, but "a good, brisk critical essay can be quite satisfying." As for his career as a newspaper columnist, Roberts adds, "I have found meeting the deadlines for my columns every week for the past five years has been a real challenge. I am surprised and delighted that I have not run out of something to write about and have managed to retain many of the readers who started with me. It has been a most gratifying experience."

* * *

ROBERTS, Oral 1918-

PERSONAL: Born January 24, 1918, in Pontotoc County, Okla.; son of Ellis M. (a minister) and Claudius (Irwin) Roberts; married Evelyn Lutman, December 25, 1938; children: Rebecca (Mrs. Marshall Nash), Ronald David, Richard Lee, Roberta (Mrs. Ron Potts). *Education:* Attended Oklahoma Baptist University, 1942-44, and Phillips University, 1947. *Religion:* Methodist. *Residence:* Tulsa, Oklahoma. *Office:* Office of the President, Oral Roberts University, 7777 South Lewis Ave., Tulsa, Okla. 74171.

CAREER: Faith-healer and preacher. Founder of Oral Roberts Evangelistic Association, 1947; founder and president, Oral Roberts University, Tulsa, Okla., 1963—. Director of Tulsa Chamber of Commerce. *Awards, honors:* Named Indian of the Year by the American Indian Exposition, 1963; member of Oklahoma Hall of Fame, 1972; named Oklahoman of the Year, 1974.

WRITINGS: Oral Roberts' Life Story: As Told By Himself, Oral Roberts Evangelistic Association, 1952; *God Is a Good God: Believe It and Come Alive,* Bobbs-Merrill, 1960; *My Story,* Summit Books, 1961; *God's Formula for Success and Prosperity,* Oklahoma Abundant Life Publication, 1966; *The Call: An Autobiography,* Doubleday, 1972; *The Miracle of Seed Faith,* Revell, 1977; *The Daily Guide to Miracles,* Revell, 1977; *How to Get Through Your Struggles,* Revell, 1978. Also author of numerous religious publications, many published by Oral Roberts Evangelistic Association, including: *Deliverance from Fear and from Sickness,* 1954, *Faith against Life's Storms,* 1957, *If You Need Healing Do These Things,* 1957, *Seven Divine Aids for Your Health,* 1960, *God Wants to Heal You,* 1969, and *The Miracle Book,* 1972. Contributor of articles to periodicals including *Redbook* and *Christian Today.*

SIDELIGHTS: J. J. Fitzpatrick writes that "to a vast number of people the name Oral Roberts is synonomous with a psalm-singing shyster who has made it big off religion, but to a multitude of others he is a genuine instrument of God's healing power." In answer to this Oral Roberts simply replies that he is "just the instrument of God who healed [me] and made [me] whole and then called [me] to share this witness with [my] generation."

Many people feel that it was television that brought Roberts the fame and fortune he enjoys today. James Morris in his book, *The Preachers,* writes that "since the early 1950's, the name of Oral Roberts has been synonymous with faith-healing for millions of people in the United States and countries all around the world. Many became his supporters because of Roberts' far-flung network of radio and television faith-healing programs. In more recent years he has reached out to other millions with his more modern television specials, hour-long programs which skillfully blend religion with musical entertainment provided by many of America's leading motion picture and television performers.... After more than twenty years in the religious spotlight, it is safe to say that except for Dr. Billy Graham, Oral Roberts is better known to the general public than any other preacher in America.''

In recent years Roberts has involved himself in areas other than preaching. As Morris points out, "more than faith healer and television star, Roberts is known also as educator, banker, college president...." In 1963, he founded Oral Roberts University "to institutionalize and extend his preaching and healing ministry." Within seven years after its establishment Oral Roberts University's enrollment grew from 300 to 1,800 students and its capital to $48 million.

Of his life, his accomplishments, and his success, Roberts writes: "When a man moves in God's will, the events and incidents of his life have a way of falling into place. A pattern develops, according to the divine plan. From my birth in 1918 when Mamma gave me to God, through 1946, [the year of his first miracle healing] the plan of God had been shaping me to reach the place where God could fully use me to bring the message of His healing power to my generation."

BIOGRAPHICAL/CRITICAL SOURCES—Books: Oral Roberts, Oral Roberts' Life Story: As Told By Himself, Oral Roberts Evangelistic Association, 1952; Roberts, My Story, Summit Books, 1961; Roberts, The Call: An Autobiography, Doubleday, 1972; James Morris, The Preachers, St. Martin's, 1973; Evelyn Roberts, His Darling Wife, Evelyn, Dial, 1976.

Periodicals: Esquire, June, 1971; McCalls, February, 1972; Newsweek, February 7, 1972; Redbook, January, 1974; Christian Century, March 1, 1978; Christian Today, May, 1978.

* * *

ROBERTS, Percival R(udolph) III 1935-

PERSONAL: Born November 2, 1935, in Wilmington, Del.; son of Percival R., Jr. and Mary Elizabeth (Eubanks) Roberts; married Mary Jane McVaugh, December 31, 1960; children: Julia Winona, Mary Christina. Education: University of Delaware, B.A., 1957, M.A., 1962; Illinois State University, Ed.D., 1967. Politics: Independent. Religion: Society of Friends (Quaker). Home: Raven Hill Farm, R.D.2, Bloomsburg, Pa. 17815. Office: Department of Art, Bloomsburg State College, Bloomsburg, Pa. 17815.

CAREER: Delaware Art Center, Wilmington, instructor in art, 1962-65; Illinois State University, Normal, lecturer in art, 1966-68; Bloomsburg State College, Bloomsburg, Pa., professor of art and chairman of department, 1968—. Director of art program, Lora Little School, 1960-65; instructor in art, University of Delaware, Extension Division, 1963; poet laureate, State of Delaware, 1965-67; visiting faculty member at University of Scranton, College Misericordia, and Goddard College; director, Broadway Gallery of Art; has had one-man shows at University of Delaware, 1962, National Design Center, 1968, Susquehanna University, 1971, Mansfield State College, 1970, Lycoming State College, 1972, and Clarion State College, 1974; has exhibited works at American Painters in Paris Exhibit, 1976, and Haas Gallery of Art, 1978. Military service: U.S. Naval Reserve, 1958-60. Member: National Art Education Association, United Poets Laureate International, American

Academy of Poets (founding member), American Poetry League, Eastern Arts Association, Midstate Artists Association, Delaware Association of Art Education (past president), Omicron Delta Kappa, Kappa Delta Pi. Awards, honors: Five Hundred SHIP Award from National Education Association, 1965; gold medal and Karta Award from Philippine President Marcos, 1966; American Poets Gold Cup Award, 1967; professional educator's award, state of Delaware; distinguished teaching award, 1975, distinguished academic service award, 1976, both from Commonwealth of Pennsylvania; first artist-in-residence at William Penn Memorial Museum.

WRITINGS: Arches, Delaware Poetry Center, 1962; Word Echoes, Accademia Leonardo da Vinci, 1966; Out, Out, Brief Candle, Prairie Press, 1967; Centaurian Flight, Mitre Press, 1968; Red Sky in the Morning, Mitre Press, 1974. Author of "Palimpsest" and "Focus on Poetry" columns. Contributor of articles, essays, and reviews to periodicals. Poetry editor, Normal News, 1965-68, Newark Weekly, 1963-67, and Newcastle Weekly, 1965-67.

WORK IN PROGRESS: Passages: The Botticelli Poems.

AVOCATIONAL INTERESTS: Operating his fifty-acre horse farm.

* * *

ROBERTS, Phyllis Barzillay 1932-

PERSONAL: Born October 27, 1932, in Baltimore, Md.; daughter of Harry (a clerk) and Eva (Monoker) Gilden; married Earl S. Roberts (a lawyer), June 18, 1967; children: Jonathan. Education: Goucher College, B.A., 1953; Hunter College (now Hunter College of the City University of New York), M.A., 1959; Columbia University, Ph.D., 1966. Politics: Democrat. Religion: Jewish. Home: 670 West End Ave., New York, N.Y. 10025. Office: Department of History, College of Staten Island of the City University of New York, Staten Island, N.Y. 10301.

CAREER: Skidmore College, Saratoga Springs, N.Y., instructor in history, 1963-64; Columbia University, New York City, instructor, 1964-66, assistant professor of history, 1966-67; College of Staten Island of the City University of New York, Staten Island, N.Y., assistant professor, 1967-70, associate professor, 1971-75, professor of history, 1976—; Graduate School and University Center of the City University of New York, New York City, professor of history, 1975—. Member: Conference on British Studies, Historical Association (England), Mediaeval Academy of America, American Historical Association, American Association of University Professors, American Association of University Women, Medieval Club of New York. Awards, honors: Fulbright scholar, University of London, 1961; American Association of University Women scholar, University of London, 1962; City University of New York faculty research award, 1977.

WRITINGS: Stephanus de Lingua-Tonante: Studies in the Sermons of Stephen Langton, Pontifical Institute of Mediaeval Studies, 1968. Contributor of articles to Medievalia et Humanistica, Mediaeval Studies, and Manuscripta.

WORK IN PROGRESS: Edition of a selection of sermons by Stephen Langton for the "Mediaeval Latin Texts" series, for the University of Toronto Press; a study of the cult of Thomas Becket in the medieval Latin preaching tradition.

SIDELIGHTS: Phyllis Roberts is competent in Latin, French, Hebrew, German, Greek, and Italian.

ROBERTS, Thomas J(ohn) 1925-

PERSONAL: Born June 10, 1925, in Omaha, Neb.; son of John Arthur (a lawyer) and Theresia (Solheid) Roberts; married Betty Nelson, December 1, 1951; children: Thomas Michael, Mark Brian, Daniel Alexander. Education: Attended St. Mary's College, Winona, Minn., 1943-44; University of Minnesota, B.A., 1948, M.A., 1952, Ph.D., 1958; University of Kansas, graduate study, 1952-55. Politics: Independent. Home: 164 South Eagleville Rd., Storrs, Conn. 06268. Office: Department of English, University of Connecticut, Storrs, Conn. 06268.

CAREER: University of Kansas, Lawrence, instructor in English, 1952-55; University of Minnesota, Minneapolis, instructor in English, 1955-58; American University in Cairo, Cairo, Egypt, assistant professor, 1958-60, associate professor of English, 1961-63; University of Alaska, Fairbanks, associate professor of English, 1960-61; University of Connecticut, Storrs, 1963—, began as assistant professor, currently professor of English. Military service: U.S. Navy, 1943-46. Member: Modern Language Association of America, National Council of Teachers of English.

WRITINGS: When Is Something Fiction?, Southern Illinois University Press, 1972. Contributor of articles to College English, Language and Style, New Literary History, and Trace. Co-editor of Graduate Student of English, 1957-60; editor of Exercise Exchange, 1968-71.

WORK IN PROGRESS: What Is Literature?; A Model of the Literary Interpreter; The Reading of Vernacular Genres.

*   *   *

ROBERTSON, Howard Stephen 1931-

PERSONAL: Born May 11, 1931, in Hamilton, Ontario, Canada; son of Norman Archibald and Amy (Judges) Robertson; married Barbara Mae Newton, September 14, 1953; children: Susanne, Edward. Education: McMaster University, B.A. (honors), 1953; Indiana University, A.M., 1956, Ph.D., 1960. Politics: Socialist (New Democratic Party of Canada). Home: 701 Don Mills Rd., Apt. 2102, Don Mills, Ontario, Canada. Office: Department of French, Glendon College, York University, 2275 Bayview Ave., Toronto, Ontario, Canada.

CAREER: University of Richmond, Richmond, Va., instructor in French and German, 1957-58; University of Akron, Akron, Ohio, assistant professor of French, 1959-61; University of Waterloo, Waterloo, Ontario, assistant professor of Romance languages, 1961-63; University of Alberta, Edmonton, associate professor of Romance languages, 1963-66; Case Western Reserve University, Cleveland, Ohio, associate professor of Romance languages, 1966-69; York University, Glendon College, Toronto, Ontario, professor of French, 1969—, chairman of Senate, 1972-73, member of board of governors, 1974-76. Member: Modern Language Association of America, Mediaeval Academy of America, Societe Rencesvals, Canadian Association of University Teachers. Awards, honors: Canada Council leave fellowship, 1977-78.

WRITINGS: La Chanson de Willame: A Critical Study, University of North Carolina Press, 1967; (translator) The Song of Roland, Dent, 1972. Contributor to Studies in Philology, Romance Notes, and Modern Language Journal.

WORK IN PROGRESS: A Critical Interpretation of the "Lais" of Marie de France.

ROBERTSON, Leon S(purgeon) 1936-

PERSONAL: Born October 28, 1936, in Christiansburg, Va.; son of Spurgeon (an electrician) and Ersell (Nolley) Robertson; married Nancy Anderson, September 3, 1958. Education: Carson-Newman College, B.A., 1958; University of Tennessee, Ph.D., 1963; Johns Hopkins University, postdoctoral study, 1965-66. Home: 2 Montgomery Pkwy., Branford, Conn. 06405. Office: 89 Trumbull St., Yale University, New Haven, Conn. 06520.

CAREER: Wake Forest University, Winston-Salem, N.C., assistant professor of sociology, 1962-65; Harvard University, Medical School, Boston, Mass., assistant professor of sociology, 1966-70; Insurance Institute for Highway Safety, Washington, D.C., senior behavioral scientist, 1970-78; Yale University, New Haven, Conn., senior research associate, 1978—. Member: American Sociological Association, American Public Health Association.

WRITINGS: (With Allan Mazur) Biology and Social Behavior, Free Press, 1972; Changing the Medical Care System, Praeger, 1974; (with Margaret C. Heagarty) Medical Sociology: A General Systems Approach, Nelson-Hall, 1975. Contributor of about sixty articles and reviews to professional journals, including Phylon, Science, Journal of Pediatrics, Journal of Educational Research, Social Science and Medicine, Journal of Forensic Sciences, and Law and Society Review.

*   *   *

ROBINETT, Betty Wallace 1919-

PERSONAL: Born June 23, 1919, in Detroit, Mich.; daughter of Henry Guy (an accountant) and Beulah (Reid) Wallace; married Ralph F. Robinett, April 10, 1952 (divorced, 1960); children: Richard. Education: Wayne University (now Wayne State University), B.A., 1940; University of Michigan, M.A., 1941, Ph.D., 1951. Religion: Christian Scientist. Home: 1909 East River Ter., Minneapolis, Minn. 55414. Office: 152 Klaeber Court, University of Minnesota, Minneapolis, Minn. 55455.

CAREER: University of Michigan, Ann Arbor, research associate and administrative secretary at English Language Institute, 1945-50, lecturer, 1950-51, instructor in English, 1951-52; University of Puerto Rico, Rio Piedras, assistant professor of English, 1952-53; University of Michigan, instructor in English, 1955-56; Inter-American University of Puerto Rico, San German, associate professor of English, 1957-59; Ball State Teachers College (now Ball State University), Muncie, Ind., assistant professor, 1959-63, associate professor, 1963-66, professor of English, 1966-68; University of Minnesota, Minneapolis, professor of linguistics, 1968—. Visiting professor at University of Hawaii and University of California, Los Angeles. Member of English teaching advisory panel, U.S. Information Agency, 1960-63; member of Fulbright awards screening committee for linguistics, 1973-76.

MEMBER: Linguistic Society of America, National Council of Teachers of English (director, 1965-71), Teachers of English to Speakers of Other Languages (president, 1973-74), National Association for Foreign Student Affairs, American Association of University Professors (trustee of Minnesota chapter, 1976-78), American Association for Applied Linguistics (member of executive committee, 1977-78). Awards, honors: U.S. State Department grant, 1962; University of Minnesota international programs grants, 1972 and 1977; Morse-Amoco award for excellence in teaching, 1977.

WRITINGS: (Author of pronunciation materials) Pauline M. Rojas and others, editors, *Fries American English Series,* Books I, II, and VI, Heath, 1952-55; (with Charles C. Fries and English Language Institute of University of Michigan) *English Pronunciation: Exercises in Sound Segments, Intonation, and Rhythm,* English Language Institute, University of Michigan, 1954; (with Clara Risso Costa) *La Familia Vazquez en los Estados Unidos,* Editorial del Departmento de Instruccion Publica (San Juan, Puerto Rico), 1954; *The Pronunciation of American English for Teachers of English as a Second Language,* Wahr, 1957; (with Theodore B. Karp and Patricia O'Connor) *Principles and Methods of Teaching a Second Language,* with motion picture series and instructor's manual, Center for Applied Linguistics, 1963; (editor) *On Teaching English to Speakers of Other Languages,* Series III, Teachers of English to Speakers of Other Languages, 1967; (with Clifford H. Prator) *Manual of American English Pronunciation,* 3rd edition (Robinett was not associated with earlier editions), Holt, 1972; *Teaching English to Speakers of Other Languages: Substance and Technique,* University of Minnesota Press, 1978. Author of monographs and contributor to newsletters. Contributor of articles and reviews to language journals, including *Language Learning* and *Classical Weekly.* Editor, *TESOL Quarterly,* 1967-72.

WORK IN PROGRESS: Studying the relationship between speech and writing; further research on methodology of teaching English to speakers of other languages; research on syntax of American sign language for the deaf.

*   *   *

ROBINSON, Donald L(eonard) 1936-

PERSONAL: Born December 28, 1936, in Buffalo, N.Y.; son of Sidney Smith (a steelworker) and Marion (a teacher and librarian; maiden name, Hershiser) Robinson; married Polly Allen (a writer and ethicist), June 11, 1960; children: John Samuel, David Wynn. *Education:* Yale University, B.A. (cum laude), 1958; Union Theological Seminary, New York, N.Y., B.D. (cum laude), 1962; Cornell University, Ph.D., 1966. *Politics:* Democrat. *Religion:* Episcopal. *Home:* 187 Elm St., Northampton, Mass. 01060. *Office:* Department of Government, Smith College, Northampton, Mass. 01060.

CAREER: Cornell University, Ithaca, N.Y., instructor in government, 1965-66; Smith College, Northampton, Mass., assistant professor, 1966-71, associate professor, 1971-78, professor of government, 1978—. Visiting assistant professor, Mount Holyoke College, 1968; visiting professor, University of Massachusetts, 1977. Director, Project '87 (a ten-year study of the U.S. Constitution), 1977-78. *Member:* American Political Science Association, Society for Values in Higher Education, Phi Beta Kappa.

WRITINGS: Slavery in the Structure of American Politics, 1765-1820, Harcourt, 1971. Contributor to *Nation, Yale Review, Signs,* and other journals. Member of editorial board of *Soundings.*

WORK IN PROGRESS: A book on the intentions of the Constitution's framers in the creation of the Presidency.

*   *   *

ROBINSON, Edward L(ouis) 1921-

PERSONAL: Born December 11, 1921, in Chicago, Ill.; son of Howard E. (a manufacturer) and Mildred (Walls) Robinson; married Joanne Peterson, March 5, 1955 (divorced);

married Mary Blair Smith, September 4, 1965; children: (first marriage) Randall, Shawn; (second marriage) Edward, Michael, Neil, Benjamin. *Education:* University of Iowa, B.A., 1944; University of Colorado, M.S., 1948; University of Minnesota, M.A., 1952. *Home:* 7104 Orkney Pky., Bethesda, Md. 20034. *Office:* United States Information Agency, 1776 Pennsylvania Ave. N.W., Washington, D.C. 20006.

CAREER: Worked as an advertising copywriter in San Francisco, Calif., 1948-50, and as a writer for educational television in Ames, Iowa, 1952-54; United States Information Agency, Washington, D.C., foreign service officer, 1954-66; free-lance writer, 1966-72; United States Information Agency, editor of *America Illustrated,* 1972—. *Military service:* U.S. Navy, 1943-46; became lieutenant junior grade.

WRITINGS: Sloth and Heathen Folly, Macmillan, 1972.

*   *   *

ROBINSON, Forrest G(len) 1940-

PERSONAL: Born December 2, 1940, in Milwaukee, Wis.; married Margaret Nell Gordon, December 22, 1968; children: Grace Gordon. *Education:* Northwestern University, A.B., 1963; Harvard University, M.A., 1964, Ph.D., 1968. *Residence:* Santa Cruz, Calif. *Office:* Department of English, University of California, Santa Cruz, Calif. 95060.

CAREER: Harvard University, Cambridge, Mass., instructor, 1967-69, assistant professor of literature, 1969-70; University of California, Santa Cruz, assistant professor of literature, 1970—. *Awards, honors:* Guggenheim fellow, 1972-73.

WRITINGS: (Editor) Philip Sidney, *An Apology for Poetry,* Bobbs-Merrill, 1970; *The Shape of Things Known,* Harvard University Press, 1972; (with wife, Margaret G. Robinson) *Wallace Stegner,* Twayne, 1976.

WORK IN PROGRESS: A biography of Henry A. Murray, Jr.; biographical and literary articles on Mark Twain.

*   *   *

ROBINSON, Jay (Luke) 1932-

PERSONAL: Born March 7, 1932, in Salt Lake City, Utah; son of Luke M. (a manager) and Hattie L. (Mumford) Robinson; married Machree Richardson (a researcher), April 23, 1954; children: Caitlin, Hilary, Matthew, Samuel. *Education:* University of California, Berkeley, B.A., 1954, M.A., 1958, Ph.D., 1962. *Home:* 2670 Page Ave., Ann Arbor, Mich. 48104. *Office:* Department of English, University of Michigan, Ann Arbor, Mich. 48104.

CAREER: Northwestern University, Evanston, Ill., instructor, 1961-63, assistant professor of English, 1963-65; University of Michigan, Ann Arbor, assistant professor, 1965-68, associate professor, 1968-74, professor of English and chairman of department, 1974—, executive director of Middle English dictionary project, 1974—. *Military service:* U.S. Marine Corps, 1954-56; became first lieutenant. *Member:* Linguistic Society of America, National Council of Teachers of English, Modern Language Association of America. *Awards, honors:* Fellow at Institute for Advanced Study in the Humanities, University of Edinburgh, 1972.

WRITINGS: (With H. R. Hungerford and James Sledd) *English Linguistics: An Introductory Reader,* Scott, Foresman, 1971; (with R. W. Bailey) *Varieties of Present-Day English,* Macmillan, 1973; (with Bailey and James Downer)

Michigan Early Modern English Materials, two volumes, University Microfilms, 1975; (with Bernard Van't Hul) *Language,* Scholastic Book Services, Volume I: *Words,* 1978, Volume II: *Sentences,* 1978, Volume III: *Variety,* 1978. Contributor of articles to professional journals.

WORK IN PROGRESS: An edition of James Melville's *Autobiography.*

*　　*　　*

ROBINSON, Raymond Henry 1927-

PERSONAL: Born July 23, 1927, in Clearfield, Pa.; son of Isaac Hartley and Helen M. (Bailey) Robinson. *Education:* Pennsylvania State University, B.A., 1949, M.A., 1950; Harvard University, Ph.D., 1958. *Home:* 61 Sheridan Rd., Wellesley, Mass. 02181. *Office:* Department of History, Northeastern University, Boston, Mass. 02115.

CAREER: Pennsylvania State University, Pottsville Center, instructor in history, 1950-51; Northeastern University, Boston, Mass., instructor, 1952-56, assistant professor of history, 1956-57; Northwestern University, Evanston, Ill., assistant professor of business history, 1957-61; Northeastern University, associate professor, 1961-62, professor of history, 1962—, chairman of department, 1961—. *Member:* American Historical Association, Organization of American Historians, American Guild of Organists, Bostonian Society, Wellesley Historical Society (past president; member of board of directors), Clearfield County Historical Society (Pennsylvania), Phi Beta Kappa, Phi Kappa Phi, Pi Gamma Mu, Phi Mu Alpha, Phi Eta Sigma, Phi Alpha Theta.

WRITINGS: The Growing of America: 1789-1848, Allyn & Bacon, 1973; (with Donald M. Jacobs) *America's Testing Time: 1848-1877,* Allyn & Bacon, 1973. Author of instructor's manuals and test booklets. Contributor to *Encyclopedia Americana* and *Notable American Woman, 1607-1950: A Biographical Dictionary.*

WORK IN PROGRESS: Biography of J.L.G. Ferris: American Historical Painter; Boston's Commonwealth Avenue: A Study in Land Use and Social Origins.

AVOCATIONAL INTERESTS: Collecting books, paintings, and prints about the life of George Washington; church organist.

*　　*　　*

ROBINSON, Robert (Reginald) 1922-

PERSONAL: Born March 10, 1922, in Orillia, Ontario, Canada; son of William Reginald (an insurance agent) and Alberta May (Ball) Robinson; married Marian Cecile Sabine (a free-lance writer), April 9, 1949; children: Paul, Derek, Trevor, Andrea. *Education:* Attended University of Toronto, 1942-45, and Yale University, summer, 1954. *Religion:* Christian. *Home:* 5 Shouldice Ct., Willowdale, Ontario, Canada M2L 2S3. *Office:* RRR Communications, Inc., 4 Lawton Blvd., Toronto, Ontario, Canada M4V 1Z4.

CAREER: Maclean-Hunter Publishing Co. Ltd., Toronto, Ontario, writer and editor, 1946-51; Health League of Canada, Toronto, public relations director and magazine editor, 1951-53; Addiction Research Foundation, Toronto, director of education, 1953-57; A. V. Roe Canada Ltd., Toronto, coordinator of public relations for a group of companies, 1957-59; director of education, Addiction Research Foundation, 1959-70 (producer of films "Margin for Safety," 1960, "Hospitality," 1960, "It's Best to Know," 1961, "Understanding Alcohol," 1964, "The Curious Habits of Man,"

1968, "The Argument," 1969, "US," 1970, "Hotel Dieu," 1970, "Two Festivals," 1971); RRR Communications, Inc., Toronto, president, 1972—. Technical adviser and consultant for about a dozen films on social problems.

WRITINGS: How about a Drink, illustrated by son, Derek Robinson, Westminster, 1973; *Scrap Arrow* (novel), General Publishing, 1975; *Under Wraps* (juvenile), Scholastic Publications, 1979. Editor, *SIDS, 1974.* Managing editor, *Journal of Otolaryngology* and *Journal of Rheumatology.*

WORK IN PROGRESS: Hume, a novel depicting the character of Galt, a southern Ontario town, in 1938.

*　　*　　*

ROBINSON, Rollo S(mith) 1915-

PERSONAL: Born June 16, 1915, in American Fork, Utah; son of O. W. and Electra (Smith) Robinson; married, 1942; children: Mike, Roy, Ruth, and Karen. *Education:* University of Utah, B.A., 1938; Oregon State University, M.S., 1950. *Home:* 1364 Cross, Ogden, Utah 84404.

CAREER: Teacher. *Military service:* U.S. Army Air Forces, 1941-45; became lieutenant colonel.

WRITINGS: Shots at Mule Deer, Winchester Western Press, 1972. Contributor of articles to magazines.

WORK IN PROGRESS: Shots at Elk; The Long Goodbye, a novel with a hunting background; *Rob McCloud,* a book for boys.†

*　　*　　*

ROCHE, Owen I. A. 1911(?)-1973

1911(?)—March 24, 1973; American author and consultant on international affairs. Obituaries: *New York Times,* March 31, 1973.

*　　*　　*

ROCK, William R(ay) 1930-

PERSONAL: Born April 8, 1930, in Mercersburg, Pa.; son of David R. and Mildred (Glee) Rock; married Suzanne J. Beck, June 18, 1955; children: Stephen, Anne, Brian. *Education:* Gettysburg College, B.A., 1951; Duke University, M.A., 1953, Ph.D., 1956. *Home:* 14543 Sand Ridge Rd., Bowling Green, Ohio 43402. *Office:* Department of History, Bowling Green State University, Bowling Green, Ohio 43402.

CAREER: Duke University, Durham, N.C., instructor in history, 1957-58; Bowling Green State University, Bowling Green, Ohio, instructor, 1958-61, assistant professor, 1961-65, associate professor, 1965-67, professor of history, 1967—. *Military service:* U.S. Army, 1955-57. *Member:* American Historical Association.

WRITINGS: Appeasement on Trial: British Foreign Policy and Its Critics, 1938-39, Archon Books, 1966; *Neville Chamberlain,* Twayne, 1969; *British Appeasement in the 1930's,* Norton, 1978.

WORK IN PROGRESS: Research in British foreign policy in the years immediately preceding World War II.

*　　*　　*

RODDICK, Ellen 1936-
(Ellen Meade)

PERSONAL: Born February 13, 1936, in Bronxville, N.Y.; daughter of Harrison A. (a management consultant) and Elizabeth (a teacher; maiden name, Henrici) Roddick; married Karl Haffenreffer, March, 1961 (divorced August, 1965); married Walter W. Meade (an editor-in-chief), November 2, 1967; children: (second marriage) Luke Harrison. *Education:* Wellesley College, B.A., 1958. *Politics:* Democrat. *Religion:* None. *Residence:* New York, N.Y. *Agent:* Claire Smith, Harold Ober Associates, Inc., 40 East 49th St., New York, N.Y. 10017.

CAREER: Office employee of United Recording Laboratories, New York City, 1958-59, and receptionist for Robert Saudek Associates, New York City, 1959-61; *Cosmopolitan,* New York City, secretary and assistant to the managing editor, 1965-67; *West Side News,* New York City, reporter, 1967. *Awards, honors: Young Filmmakers* was chosen by the New York Public Library as one of the fifteen best books for young adults published in 1969.

WRITINGS: (Under name Ellen Meade; with Rodger Larson) *Young Filmmakers,* Dutton, 1969; *Together* (novel), St. Martin's, 1979. Author of column "Dieter's Notebook" for *Cosmopolitan,* 1975—. Contributor of articles to *McCall's* and *Cosmopolitan.*

WORK IN PROGRESS: A novel.

AVOCATIONAL INTERESTS: The arts, travel, scuba diving, needlework.

*   *   *

RODNITZKY, Jerome Leon   1936-

PERSONAL: Born August 1, 1936, in Chicago, Ill.; son of Nathan (a salesman) and Ann (a credit reporter; maiden name, Orenstein) Rodnitzky; married Shirley Reiger, June 16, 1966; children: Mark Kennedy, Joan Baez. *Education:* University of Chicago, B.A., 1959, M.A., 1962; University of Illinois, Ph.D., 1967. *Politics:* Independent. *Religion:* Jewish. *Home:* 2505 Basswood Ct., Arlington, Tex. 76016. *Office:* Department of History, University of Texas, Arlington, Tex. 76010.

CAREER: University of Texas at Arlington, instructor, 1966-67, assistant professor, 1967-70, associate professor, 1971-76, professor of history, 1977—. *Member:* American Studies Association, American Association of University Professors, Popular Culture Association.

WRITINGS: (Contributor) John M. Nance, editor, *Some Reflections upon Modern America,* Texas A & M University Press, 1969; (contributor) Leon B. Blair, editor, *Essays on Radicalism in Contemporary America,* University of Texas Press, 1972; (contributor) Roy Browne and Marshall Fishwick, editors, *Heroes of Popular Culture,* Bowling Green University Press, 1972; (contributor) Gary L. Tate, editor, *From Discovery to Style,* Winthrop Publishing, 1973; (contributor) Robert E. Grinder, editor, *Studies in Adolescence,* 3rd edition, Macmillan, 1975; (contributor) Leonard Dinnerstein and Kenneth Jackson, editors, *American Vistas,* Volume II, 2nd edition, Oxford University Press, 1975; *Minstrels of the Dawn: The Folk-Protest Singer as a Cultural Hero,* Nelson-Hall, 1976. Contributor to proceedings of the Popular Culture Association. Contributor of articles and reviews to *Journal of Popular Culture, Popular Music and Society, South Atlantic Quarterly, Liberation, American Quarterly, Illinois Quarterly, Journal of the Illinois State Historical Society,* and other journals. Advisory editor, *Popular Music and Society.*

WORK IN PROGRESS: New Left Feminism: Women's Liberation as a Counter Culture.

SIDELIGHTS: Jerome L. Rodnitzky told *CA,* "I am interested in social, intellectual, and cultural approaches to change." An authority on the songs, writers, and performers of protest music, Rodnitzky's *Minstrels of the Dawn* has been called "an important interpretation of the American counterculture of the 1960s" by a reviewer for *Choice.*

BIOGRAPHICAL/CRITICAL SOURCES: Contemporary Sociology, March, 1977; *Choice,* May, 1977; *American Historical Review,* June, 1977.

*   *   *

ROGERS, Paul (Patrick)   1900-
(Homer Hardwick)

PERSONAL: Born January 5, 1900, in Snohomish, Wash.; son of Patrick S. (a minister) and Aberine (Davis) Rogers; married Lillian Douglass, June 15, 1922 (died, 1936); married Gerhild Brueggemann, December 22, 1961; children: (first marriage) Paul (died, 1976), Douglass. *Education:* University of Mississippi, B.Sc., 1921; Acadia University, M.A., 1925; Cornell University, Ph.D., 1928. *Politics:* Independent. *Religion:* Nonsectarian. *Home:* 8100 Hillrise Dr., Austin, Tex. 78759.

CAREER: University of Colorado, Boulder, teaching fellow in Romance languages, 1921-22; University of Nebraska, Lincoln, assistant instructor in Spanish, 1922-23; University of Cincinnati, Cincinnati, Ohio, instructor in Spanish, 1923-24; Acadia University, Wolfville, Nova Scotia, professor of Romance languages and head of department, 1924-25; Cornell University, Ithaca, N.Y., instructor in Spanish, 1925-28; University of Missouri—Columbia, assistant professor of Spanish, 1928-29; Oberlin College, Oberlin, Ohio, assistant professor, 1929-31, associate professor, 1931-46, professor of Romance languages, 1946-56, professor of Spanish and chairman of department of Spanish, 1956-62. Visiting professor of modern languages, University of New Mexico, 1963-64, and University of Missouri, 1967-70; visiting professor of Spanish, Pennsylvania State University, 1949, Appalachian State University, 1966-67, Southwestern University, 1974-75. Consultant to National Association on Standard Medical Vocabulary. Member of International Commission to Spain, 1937, and chancellor's council, University of Texas system.

MEMBER: Modern Language Association of America, American Association of Teachers of Spanish and Portuguese, American Association of University Professors, Phi Beta Kappa, Phi Kappa Phi, Alpha Phi Epsilon, Alpha Zeta Pi, Zeta Delta Pi. *Awards, honors:* Created Knight of Order of Isabella the Catholic (Spain), 1927.

WRITINGS: (Editor) Garcia Gutierrez, *El trovador,* Ginn, 1926; (editor) Ramon del Valle-Inclan, *Jardin umbrio,* Holt, 1928; (editor) Perez Galdos, *Juan Martin el Empecinado,* Stanford University Press, 1929; (editor) Fernan Caballero, *Cuentos de encantamiento,* Harper, 1932; (translator) Pablo Picasso, *Sueno y mentira de France,* [Paris], 1937.

Catalog of the Oberlin College Spanish Drama Collection, Oberlin College and American Council of Learned Societies, 1940; *Goldoni in Spain,* Academy Press, 1941; *Invitation to Spanish,* Stackpole, 1943; *The Spanish Drama Collection in the Oberlin College Library: Title and Reference Lists,* Oberlin College, 1946; (author of foreword) R. B. Gaither, *Handbook on Mexican Mercantile Law,* Academy Press, 1948; *Escritores contemporaneos de Mexico,* Houghton, 1949; (editor) Perez Galdos, *Dona Perfecta,* Ginn, 1950; (with Augusto Centeno) *Patterns of Spanish Conversation,* Houghton, 1951; (with Centeno) *Libro de repaso,* Dryden Press, 1952; (with William Holbrook) *Patterns of French Conversation,* Houghton, 1954; (under pseudonym

Homer Hardwick) *Winemaking at Home,* Funk, 1954, 2nd edition, 1970; *Spanish for the First Year,* Macmillan, 1957, 2nd edition (with workbook with Charles W. Butler), 1964; *Surtidores: Algunas poesias ineditas de Garcia Lorca,* Editorial Patria, 1957.

(Contributor) Stanley Burnshaw and others, editors, *The Poem Itself,* Holt, 1960; (with Butler) *Florilegio de cuentos espanoles,* Macmillan, 1961; *Florilegio de cuentos hispanoamericanos,* Macmillan, 1968; (contributor of translation) D. M. Rogers, editor, *Benito Perez Galdos,* Taurus, 1973; (with F. A. Lapuente) *Diccionario de seudonimos literarios espanoles,* Editorial Gredos, 1977; *The Spanish Civil War: An Exhibition,* Humanities Research Center, University of Texas at Austin, 1978. Also author of foreword, *Texas Collection of Comedias Sueltas.*

Contributor to bulletins. Contributor to *Encyclopedia International* and *New Catholic Encyclopedia.* Contributor of short stories in Spanish to *El Nacional,* and of articles and reviews to *Hispanic Review, Library Chronicle of the University of Texas at Austin, Hispania, Romanic Review, Philological Quarterly, Modern Language Notes,* and other language journals. Director honorario, *Anales Galdosianos.*

AVOCATIONAL INTERESTS: Fly fishing for trout, travel (Europe, Mexico).

* * *

ROGERS, William D(ill) 1927-

PERSONAL: Born May 12, 1927, in Wilmington, Del.; son of Louis Frederick and Margaret (Dill) Rogers; married Suzanne Rochford, June 25, 1951; children: William Dill, Jr., Daniel Rochford. *Education:* Princeton University, A.B. (with honors), 1948; Yale University, LL.B., 1951. *Home:* 2 Jefferson Run Rd., Great Falls, Va. 22066. *Office:* Arnold & Porter, 1229 19th St. N.W., Washington, D.C. 20036.

CAREER: Admitted to Bar, Washington, D.C., 1953; law clerk to U.S. Court of Appeals Judge Charles E. Clark, 1951-52, and U.S. Supreme Court Justice Stanley F. Reed, 1952-53; Arnold, Fortas & Porter, Washington, D.C., attorney, 1953-59, partner, 1959-62; U.S. Department of State, Washington, D.C., special counsel to U.S. coordinator for the Alliance for Progress (of Agency for International Development), 1962-63, deputy U.S. coordinator for the Alliance for Progress, 1963-65, deputy assistant administrator for Agency for International Development, 1963-65, chief of delegations to meetings of Inter-American Economic and Social Council, 1963, 1964, permanent alternate representative, 1964-65, U.S. representative to meetings of development assistance committee (Paris), 1964; Arnold & Porter, Washington, D.C., partner, 1965-74; U.S. Department of State, assistant secretary of state for inter-American affairs, 1974-76, under secretary of state for economic affairs, 1976; Arnold & Porter, partner, 1977—. Expert witness before Senate Foreign Relations Committee, 1964, and House of Representatives Appropriations Committee, 1964. Fellow, Hudson Institute. Director, Overseas Development Council, Fund for Multinational Management Education, Procedural Aspects of International Law Institute, and Institute for International and Foreign Trade Law; former director, Overseas Private Investment Corp. Center for Inter-American Relations, president, 1965-70, member of board of trustees; member of international affairs advisory group, Woodrow Wilson International Center for Scholars; chairman of board of advisors for international project, Center for Law and Social Policy; member of advisory board, Center for Strategic and International Studies. Member of New York Council on Foreign Relations. Former alternate governor of World Bank, Inter-American Development Bank, Asian Development Bank, and African Development Bank. Member of board of visitors, Foreign Service School, Georgetown University; past associate trustee, Council of the Americas.

MEMBER: American Society of International Law (president, 1972-74; member of board of review and development), American Bar Association, International Law Association, Inter-American Bar Association, Federal Bar Association, Inter-American Association for Democracy and Freedom. *Awards, honors:* Distinguished service award from U.S. Agency for International Development, 1965.

WRITINGS: The Twilight Struggle: The Alliance for Progress and the Politics of Development in Latin America, Random House, 1967; (contributor) Claudio Veliz, editor, *The United States and Latin America, Latin America and the Caribbean: A Handbook,* Anthony Blond, 1968. Contributor to magazines, law journals, and newspapers. Member of editorial board, *Foreign Policy Quarterly.*

BIOGRAPHICAL/CRITICAL SOURCES: New York Times Book Review, November 19, 1967; *New Republic,* February 10, 1968.

* * *

ROLAND, Charles P(ierce) 1918-

PERSONAL: Born April 8, 1918, in Maury City, Tenn.; son of Clifford Paul (a teacher and minister) and Grace (Paysinger) Roland; married Allie Lee Aycock, January 23, 1948; children: John Clifford, Karen Jean, Charles Franklin. *Education:* Attended Freed-Hardeman Junior College, 1934-36; Vanderbilt University, B.A., 1938; George Washington University, graduate study, 1946-47; Louisiana State University, M.A., 1948, Ph.D., 1951. *Home:* 814 Sherwood Dr., Lexington, Ky. 40502. *Office:* Department of History, University of Kentucky, Lexington, Ky. 40506.

CAREER: Worked as a history teacher in Tennessee, 1938-40; National Park Service, Washington, D.C., historical technician, 1940-42, 1946-47; Louisiana State University, Baton Rouge, instructor in history, 1950-51; Department of the Army, Office of Military History, Washington, D.C., assistant to chief historian, 1951-52; Tulane University, New Orleans, La., instructor, 1952-53, assistant professor, 1953-57, associate professor, 1957-60, professor of history, 1960-70, chairman of department, 1967-70; University of Kentucky, Lexington, alumni professor of history, 1970—. *Military service:* U.S. Army, 1942-46, 1951-52; became captain; received Bronze Star Medal and Purple Heart. *Member:* American Historical Association, Organization of American Historians, Southern Historical Association (member of executive council, 1965-69), Louisiana Historical Association (president, 1970). *Awards, honors:* Louisiana Literary Award from Louisiana Library Association, 1957; Guggenheim Foundation fellow, 1960-61; Distinguished Achievement in Research Award, University of Kentucky Research Foundation, 1977.

WRITINGS: Louisiana Sugar Plantations during the American Civil War, Brill, 1957; *The Confederacy,* University of Chicago Press, 1960; *Albert Sidney Johnston: Soldier of Three Republics,* University of Texas Press, 1964; (editor) Richard Taylor, *Destruction and Reconstruction: Personal Experiences of the Late War,* Blaisdell, 1968; (with Francis Butler Simkins) *A History of the South,* Knopf, 1972; *The Improbable Era: The South since World War II,* University of Kentucky Press, 1975.

WORK IN PROGRESS: A biography of Albert Benjamin "Happy" Chandler.

*   *   *

ROLLINS, C(alvin) D(wight) 1918-

PERSONAL: Born September 14, 1918, in Clay Center, Neb.; son of Calvin (a merchant) and Mary Merle (Eller) Rollins; married Helen Draper Abernathy (a civil servant), October 28, 1961; children: Mark Edward. *Education:* University of Nebraska, A.B., 1941; Cambridge University, graduate study, 1947-48; Oxford University, D.Phil., 1954. *Home:* 202 Separatist Rd., Storrs, Conn. 06268. *Office address:* Box U-54, University of Connecticut, Storrs, Conn. 06268.

CAREER: University of New Hampshire, Durham, instructor in English, 1946; Suffolk University, Boston, Mass., assistant professor of philosophy, 1947; Wesleyan University, Middletown, Conn., assistant professor of philosophy, 1951-52; University of Melbourne, Melbourne, Victoria, Australia, lecturer in philosophy, 1952-54; Brooklyn College (now Brooklyn College of City University of New York), Brooklyn, N.Y., substitute, 1954-55, assistant professor of philosophy, 1955-56; Oberlin College, Oberlin, Ohio, associate professor, 1956-61, professor of philosophy, 1961-65, chairman of department, 1957-65; University of Western Ontario, London, professor of philosophy, 1967-68; University of Connecticut, Storrs, professor of philosophy, 1968—, head of department, 1971-76. Fulbright visiting professor, Australian National University, 1965-67. *Military service:* U.S. Army Air Forces, 1942-46; became technical sergeant. *Member:* Mind Association, Aristotelian Society, American Philosophical Association. *Awards, honors:* Rockefeller postwar fellow, Cambridge University, 1947-48; Rhodes scholar, Oxford University, 1948-51; Mellon postdoctoral fellow, University of Pittsburgh, 1962-63.

WRITINGS: (Editor) *Knowledge and Experience,* University of Pittsburgh Press, 1963; (editor with Robert Brown) *Contemporary Philosophy in Australia,* Allen & Unwin, 1969. Contributor of articles to academic and philosophy journals.

WORK IN PROGRESS: Studies in Wittgenstein and Hume; a textbook of philosophical problems.

*   *   *

ROMAN, Daniel (David) 1921-

PERSONAL: Original surname, Romanow; name legally changed in 1951; born November 9, 1921, in Chicago, Ill.; son of Harry (a salesman) and Augusta (Levit) Romanow; married Rosalyn Goldman (with U.S. Government), July 4, 1958; children: Harlon Scott, Jody Coleen. *Education:* University of Southern California, B.S., 1949, M.A., 1953, Ph.D., 1956. *Home:* 864 New Mark Esplanade, Rockville, Md. 20850. *Office:* George Washington University, 21st and G Sts. N.W., Washington, D.C. 20006.

CAREER: University of Southern California, Los Angeles, instructor in economics, 1951-54; San Fernando Valley State College (now California State University), Northridge, professor of management, 1957-61; Florida State University, Tallahassee, professor of research and development administration at Eglin Air Force Base Graduate Center, 1961-62; American University, Washington, D.C., professor of production management and director of research and development and production management programs, 1962-67;

George Washington University, Washington, D.C., 1967—, currently professor of management science and director of programs on science, technology, and innovation. Adjunct professor, Polytechnic Institute of Brooklyn, 1963-64; visiting professor, Industrial College of the Armed Forces, 1967-73. Former public accountant; international consultant to government and industry. *Military service:* U.S. Naval Reserve, 1942-46; served in Pacific. *Member:* American Academy of Management (vice-president of eastern region, 1967-69), American Association for the Advancement of Science, National Association of Purchasing Management (chairman, academic advisory committee, 1972-74; director, certification program, 1973-75), National Institute of Government Purchasing.

WRITINGS: R & D Management: The Economics and Administration of Technology, Prentice-Hall, 1968.

Contributor: Huxley Madheim, Edward M. Mazze, and Louis L. Stern, editors, *Readings on Organization and Management,* Holt, 1963; William E. Schlender, William G. Scott, and Alan C. Filley, editors, *Management in Perspective,* Houghton, 1965; Dalton McFarland, editor, *Current Issues and Emerging Concepts in Management,* Houghton, 1966; Ralph I. Cole, editor, *Improving Effectiveness in R & D,* Thompson Book Co., 1967; H. C. Schulberg, A. Sheldon, and F. Baker, editors, *Program Evaluation in the Health Fields,* Behavioral Publications, 1969; D. R. Hampton, editor, *Modern Management,* Dickenson, 1970; Marvin Cetron and Joel Goldhar, editors, *The Science of Managing Organized Technology,* Volume IV, Gordon & Breach, 1970; John W. Bonge and Bruce P. Coleman, editors, *Readings in Business Policy,* Macmillan, 1971; David S. Brown, editor, *Federal Contributions to Management,* Praeger, 1971; Howard Koontz and Cyril O'Donnell, editors, *Management: A Book of Readings,* McGraw, 1972. Contributor of about twenty-five articles to business journals.

WORK IN PROGRESS: Science, Technology and Innovation: A Systems Approach, for Grid Publishing.

AVOCATIONAL INTERESTS: Fishing, golf, travel.

*   *   *

ROMANO, Clare

PERSONAL: Born in Palisade, N.J.; married John Ross (an artist, painter, and professor), November 23, 1943; children: Christopher, Timothy. *Education:* Attended Cooper Union School of Art, 1939-43, Ecole des Beaux Arts, Fontainebleau, France, 1949, and Instituto Statale d'Arte, Florence, Italy, 1959. *Home:* 110 Davison Pl., Englewood, N.J. 07631. *Office:* Pratt Graphic Art Center, New York, N.Y.

CAREER: Artist. Art Center of Northern New Jersey, Tenafly, instructor in painting and design, 1961-65; New School for Social Research, New York City, instructor in printmaking, 1960—; Pratt Graphic Art Center, New York City, instructor in printmaking, 1963—; Manhattanville College, Purchase, N.Y., instructor in printmaking, 1964-65; Pratt Institute, Brooklyn, N.Y., 1964—, began as assistant professor, currently associate professor in printmaking. U.S. Information Agency artist-in-residence at "Graphic Arts U.S.A.," an exhibition. Art has been exhibited in about forty one-person shows (including Associated American Artists Gallery, 1967, and Boston Museum of Fine Arts, 1968), many permanent collections (including Metropolitan Museum of Art, Library of Congress, Smithsonian Institution, National Collection of Fine Arts, and more than a dozen U.S. embassies abroad), private galleries, and American and foreign group exhibitions; art work has been commissioned by Jewish Museum, Hilton Hotel, International Graphic Arts Society, Philadelphia Print Club, and Manufacturers Hanover Trust; lecturer for television, colleges, and universities.

MEMBER: Society of American Graphic Artists (president, 1970-72), American Color Print Society, National Academy (associate member), Federation of Modern Painters and Sculptors, Print Club of Philadelphia, Boston Printmakers. *Awards, honors:* Purchase awards from Brooklyn Museum, 1951, Library of Congress, 1951, 1966, New Jersey State Museum, 1967, 1970, Boston Printmakers, 1967, eighth national print exhibit of Silvermine Guild, 1970; Louis Comfort Tiffany grant for printmaking, 1952; awards from Society of American Graphic Artists, 1953, 1962, 1967, 1968, 1971; Fulbright grant for printmaking in Florence, Italy, 1958-59; awards from Philadelphia Print Club, 1960, 1971, Montclair Museum, 1962; citation for professional achievement from Cooper Union School of Art, 1966; John Taylor Arms Memorial Prize from National Academy, 1967; presentation artist award from Boston Printmakers, 1967.

WRITINGS: (Contributor of woodcuts) May Garelick, *Manhattan Island,* Crowell, 1957; (contributor of woodcuts) Edgar Lee Masters, *Spoon River Anthology,* Macmillan, 1963; (contributor of woodcuts) Walt Whitman, *Leaves of Grass,* Crowell, 1964; (contributor of collagraphs) William Wadsworth Longfellow, *Poems of Longfellow,* Crowell, 1967; (author of introduction) Burton Wasserman, *Bridges of Vision,* New Jersey State Museum, 1969; (contributor of article and collagraph) Pat Gilmour, *Modern Prints,* Dutton, 1970; (with husband, John Ross) *The Complete Printmaker,* Free Press, 1972; (with J. Ross) *The Complete Intaglio Print,* Free Press, 1974; (with J. Ross) *The Complete New Techniques in Printmaking,* Free Press, 1974; (with J. Ross) *The Complete Relief Print,* Free Press, 1974; (with J. Ross) *The Complete Screen Print and the Lithograph,* Free Press, 1974. Contributor to *Artist's Proof,* 1966, and to *Encyclopedia Americana,* 1971.

BIOGRAPHICAL/CRITICAL SOURCES: Artist's Proof, Volume V, Pratt Graphic Art Center, 1964; *New York Times,* October 24, 1965; *Christian Science Monitor,* November 24, 1967; *Art News,* May, 1967; *Pratt Alumnus,* spring, 1967; Ray Faulkner and Edwin Ziegfeld, *Art Today,* Holt, 1969; Jules Heller, *Printmaking Today,* Holt, 1972.

*   *   *

ROMOSER, George K(enneth) 1929-

PERSONAL: Born September 14, 1929, in Kingston, N.Y.; son of Carl August (a clergyman) and Alva (Becker) Romoser; married Nancy Cushwa, June 16, 1954 (divorced, 1962); married Mechthild von Tresckow, April 30, 1967; children: (second marriage) Alexandra Ada, Valerie Anna. *Education:* Rutgers University, A.B., 1951; University of Chicago, A.M., 1954, Ph.D., 1958. *Home:* Shipmast Farm, Worster Rd., Eliot, Me. 03903. *Office:* Department of Political Science, University of New Hampshire, Durham, N.H. 03824.

CAREER: National Opinion Research Center, Chicago, Ill., research assistant, 1953; Freiburg University, Freiburg, Germany, Political Science Institute assistant, 1955-56; Ohio State University, Columbus, instructor in political science, 1957-61; Connecticut College, New London, associate professor of political science, 1963-67; University of New Hampshire, Durham, assistant professor, 1961-62, associate professor, 1967-69, professor of political science, 1969—, chairman of department, 1968-71. Fulbright professor, fac-

ulty of law, Mainz University, 1962-63; visiting summer professor at Free University, Berlin, 1964, Mannheim University, 1968, Johns Hopkins University, Bologna Center, 1969; visiting professor, Munich University, 1973-74. Consultant to committee on International Exchange of Persons, 1965-66. Co-founder, and chairman of Conference Group on German Politics, 1968—; chairman of committee on governmental reorganization of the Democratic Party, New Hampshire, 1962; Eliot (Me.) Planning Board, member, 1970-72, chairman, 1972; member of executive committee, Southern Maine Regional Planning Commission, 1971-72; Eliot (Me.) Board of Zoning Appeals, vice-chairman, 1978—; Eliot (Me.) Democratic Party, chairman, 1978—.

MEMBER: International Political Science Association, American Political Science Association, American Society for Legal and Political Philosophy, Conference Group on Central European History, Phi Delta Theta, Pi Sigma Alpha, Delta Phi Alpha, Phi Alpha Theta. *Awards, honors:* Social Science Research Council fellow, 1956-57; American Council of Learned Societies fellow, 1964; Order of Merit, First Class, Federal Republic of Germany, 1972; Fulbright research scholarship to Germany, 1973-74; Rockefeller fellow, Aspen Institute for Humanistic Studies, 1978—.

WRITINGS: (With W. G. Andrews, Roy Macridis, and John Armstrong) *European Politics,* Van Nostrand, 1969. Contributor to *Social Research, Review of Politics, American Political Science Review, Nation,* and *Dictionary of Historical Concepts.*

WORK IN PROGRESS: The Politics of Commitment: Left and Right Extremism in the Contemporary West; Terrorism and the Problem of Political Moderation.

*   *   *

RONNIE, Art(hur William) 1931-

PERSONAL: Born August 12, 1931, in Los Angeles, Calif.; son of Christian George (an engineer) and Ethel Mary (Moore) Ronnie; married Sharon Anne Vote, May 21, 1960; children: Christopher Patrick, Matthew Brian. *Education:* Los Angeles City College, A.A., 1952. *Politics:* Republican. *Religion:* Roman Catholic. *Home:* 950 Alta Pine Dr., Altadena, Calif. 91001. *Agent:* Ziegler, Diskant, Roth Agency, 9255 Sunset Blvd., Los Angeles, Calif. 90069. *Office:* Columbia Pictures Television, 4000 Warner Blvd., Burbank, Calif. 91505.

CAREER: Export manager and flower deliverer in Los Angeles, Calif., 1956; *Los Angeles Evening Herald & Express* (now *Los Angeles Herald-Examiner*), Los Angeles, Calif., reporter, radio editor, TV writer, and book reviewer, 1956-66; publicist for 20th Century-Fox Television, Paramount Television, MGM Television, and Columbia Pictures Television, 1966—. *Military service:* U.S. Naval Air Reserve, 1949-53. U.S. Army, 1954-56. *Member:* Catholic Press Council, Sherlock Holmes Society of Los Angeles, P.E.N.

WRITINGS: Locklear: The Man Who Walked on Wings, A. S. Barnes, 1973. Contributor of articles and photo layouts to *Air Classics, Aloft, American Heritage, American-Scandinavian Review, Architecture/West, Cross & Cockade Journal, Journal of Broadcasting, Life, Long Beach Independent Press-Telegram, Los Angeles Magazine, Opera News, Page One, Relics, San Francisco Magazine, Sea Classics, Sound Stage, Southwest Builder, Timer, TV Guide, TWA Ambassador, West, Westways,* and *Wisconsin American Automobile Association Motor News.*

WORK IN PROGRESS: Cat's Paw, a biography of Fritz Duquesne, a soldier of fortune and international spy for Germany in the Boer and two world wars; a history travel book based on a classic horror novel; a book on Sherlock Holmes.

AVOCATIONAL INTERESTS: Travel, book collecting (Ronnie has a fifteen-thousand-volume library, and a complete set of National Geographic from 1888 to the present).

*   *   *

ROPER, Ronnalie J. 1936-
(Ronnalie Roper Howard)

PERSONAL: Born September 25, 1936, in Havre, Mont.; daughter of Bill Clyde (a Federal Aviation Administration communicator) and Letha (Teeple) Roper. Education: University of Montana, B.A., 1958, M.A., 1960; Pennsylvania State University, Ph.D., 1968; Dickinson School of Law, J.D., 1976. Office: Pennsylvania Department of Education, Box 911, Harrisburg, Pa. 17126.

CAREER: University of Northern Colorado, Greeley, assistant professor of English, 1966-69; Slippery Rock State College, Slippery Rock, Pa., associate professor of English, 1969-71; Wilson College, Chambersburg, Pa., associate professor of English and academic dean, 1971-72; Pennsylvania Department of Education, Harrisburg, consultant on innovative programs in higher education, 1972—. Member: Women's Caucus for the Modern Languages (chairperson of Northeast region, 1971-72), American Civil Liberties Union, Pennsylvanians for Women's Rights.

WRITINGS: (Under name Ronnalie Roper Howard) The Dark Glass: Vision and Technique in the Poetry of Dante Gabriel Rossetti, Ohio University Press, 1972.

WORK IN PROGRESS: Research on women and minorities in higher education; research on sexism in higher education.

*   *   *

RORTY, James 1891(?)-1973

1891(?)—February 25, 1973; American editor, poet, journalist, and author. Obituaries: New York Times, February 26, 1973.

*   *   *

ROSA, Alfred F(elix) 1942-

PERSONAL: Born February 7, 1942, in Waterbury, Conn.; son of Gerard and Lucy (Pilla) Rosa; married Margaret Shafran (a teacher), August 19, 1967; children: Elizabeth Ann. Education: University of Connecticut, B.A., 1964; University of Massachusetts, M.A., 1966, Ph.D., 1971. Home: Juniper Ridge, Shelburne, Vt. 05482. Office: Department of English, University of Vermont, Burlington, Vt. 05405.

CAREER: University of Massachusetts—Amherst, visiting lecturer in English, 1969; University of Vermont, Burlington, instructor, 1969-71, assistant professor, 1971-78, professor of English, 1978—. Visiting lecturer, University of Massachusetts, 1969; Fulbright lecturer in American literature, Italy, 1973-74. Member: Modern Language Association of America.

WRITINGS: (Editor with Paul A. Eschholz and Virginia P. Clark) Language: Introductory Readings, St. Martin's, 1972, 2nd edition, 1977; Language Awareness, St. Martin's, 1974, 2nd edition, 1978; (with P.A. Eschholz) Contemporary

Fiction in America and England, 1950-1970, Gale, 1978; Subject and Strategy: A Rhetoric Reader, St. Martin's, 1978; (editor) The Old Century and the New: Essays in Honor of Charles Angoff, Fairleigh Dickinson University Press, 1978. Contributor to New England Quarterly, American Speech, Connecticut Review, Modern Fiction Studies, Explicator, Journal of Popular Culture, and many other journals. Founding editor of Massachusetts Studies in English; co-editor of Exercise Exchange.

WORK IN PROGRESS: St. Martin's College Handbook; Salem, Transcendentalism and Hawthorne; writing on contemporary literature, especially the short story, and on language; also short stories, plays, and poetry.

*   *   *

ROSE, Albert H(enry) 1903-

PERSONAL: Born March 9, 1903, in Coldwater, Ohio; son of Henry (a farmer) and Elisabeth (Severt) Rose. Education: University of Dayton, B.S., 1927; Western Reserve University (now Case Western Reserve University), A.M., 1941. Home: 310 Alumni Residence Apartments, University of Dayton, Dayton, Ohio 45469. Office: J-115, University of Dayton, Dayton, Ohio 45469.

CAREER: Member of Marianist religious order; University of Dayton, Dayton, Ohio, instructor, 1946-49, assistant professor, 1949-53, associate professor, 1953-60, professor of political science, 1960-66, chairman of department, 1951-66. Has lectured for Ford Foundation, Air Force War College, University of Chicago, Fels Foundation, and other institutions. Member of Human Resources Committee and Special Committee on Urban Resources (both of Montgomery County, Ohio); consultant to municipal governments. Member: American Political Science Association, National Municipal League, American Security Council, Writers Guild.

WRITINGS: Ohio Government: State and Local, Educational Press, 1953, new edition, Kendall/Hunt, 1975; Geography of International Relations, University of Dayton Press, 1966.

AVOCATIONAL INTERESTS: Public lecturing, civic and institutional activities.

*   *   *

ROSEMONT, Henry, Jr. 1934-

PERSONAL: Born December 20, 1934, in Chicago, Ill.; son of Henry Putney (a printer) and Sally (Janiak) Rosemont; married Mary McGuiness, March 5, 1955 (divorced, 1960); married JoAnn M. Barr (a teacher), December 11, 1961; children: (first marriage) Kathleen; (second marriage) Constance, Genevieve, Samantha. Education: University of Illinois, A.B., 1961; University of Washington, Seattle, Ph.D., 1967. Office: Department of Philosophy, St. Mary's College of Maryland, St. Mary's City, Md. 20686.

CAREER: Chicago & North Western Railway Co., Proviso Yards, Ill., yard clerk, 1952-60; Oakland University, Rochester, Mich., assistant professor of philosophy, 1965-69; Massachusetts Institute of Technology, Cambridge, research fellow in linguistics, 1969-72; Brooklyn College of the City University of New York, Brooklyn, N.Y., assistant professor, 1972-74, associate professor of philosophy, 1974-77; St. Mary's College of Maryland, St. Mary's City, professor of philosophy, 1977—. Visiting assistant professor at University of Illinois at Urbana-Champaign, 1970-71. Military service: U.S. Marine Corps, 1952-55; received letter of commendation and United Nations Medal. *Member:* Society for Asian and Comparative Philosophy (member board of directors, 1973—), American Academy of Religion, American Philosophical Association. *Awards, honors:* U.S. Steel fellowship, 1963-65; National Defense Foreign Language fellowship, 1965; National Science Foundation faculty fellowship, 1970; Center for Advanced Study fellowship, University of Illinois, 1971.

WRITINGS: State and Society in the Hsun Tzu, Monumenta Serica, 1971; (editor with Walter Feinberg) *Work, Technology, and Education,* University of Illinois Press, 1975; (translator with Daniel J. Cook) Gottfried Leibniz, *Discourse on the Natural Theology of the Chinese,* University Press of Hawaii, 1977. Book review editor, *Philosophy East & West,* 1972—.

WORK IN PROGRESS: Research on Chinese and formal language linguistic analysis, on Confucianism of the Chou Dynasty, and on foundations of anarchism.

* * *

ROSENBAUM, H. Jon 1941-

PERSONAL: Born March 18, 1941, in Plainfield, N.J.; son of Harvey (in real estate) and Pearl (Lando) Rosenbaum; married Betsey Joan Rubin (a social planner), June 11, 1967. *Education:* Attended University of Madrid, 1961, and London School of Economics and Political Science, 1961-62; University of Pennsylvania, B.A. (with honors), 1963; Fletcher School of Law and Diplomacy, Tufts University, M.A., 1964, M.A.L.D., 1965, Ph.D., 1967. *Home:* 424 North St. Asaph St., Alexandria, Va. 22214. *Office:* Office of the Special Representative for Trade Negotiations, 1800 G. St. N.W., Room 711, Washington, D.C.

CAREER: Wellesley College, Wellesley, Mass., instructor, 1967-68, assistant professor of political science, 1968-72; City College of the City University of New York, New York, N.Y., associate professor of political science, 1972-76; special assistant to Senator Jacob K. Javits, 1977; Executive Office of the President, Office of the Special Representative for Trade Negotiations, Washington, D.C., trade negotiator, 1978—. Visiting summer professor at Brazilian School of Public Administration, 1968, and Center for Intercultural Documentation, Cuernavaca, Mexico, 1969; summer guest scholar, Brazilian Institute of International Relations, 1970; fellow of Smithsonian Institution, Woodrow Wilson International Center for Scholars, 1970-71; research associate, Harvard University, Center for International Affairs, 1971; Brazilian coordinator for Roper Public Opinion Research Center, Williams College, 1968; member of national selection committee, Latin American Teaching Fellowship Program, 1969; trustee, Projecto Amistad, 1969—; consultant, Foreign Policy Research Institute, 1972-73.

MEMBER: American Political Science Association, Latin American Studies Association (chairman of regional liaison committee, 1972-73), New England Political Science Association, Pan American Society of New England, New England Council of Latin American Studies Association (founder and president, 1969-70; member of executive committee, 1970-71), Harvard Latin American Seminar, Pi Sigma Alpha. *Awards, honors:* Grants from American Council on Education and American Philosophical Society, 1968.

WRITINGS—Editor: (With William G. Tyler) *Contemporary Brazil: Issues in Economic and Political Development,* Praeger, 1972; (with R. G. Hellman) *Latin America: The*

Search for a New International Role, Halsted, 1975; (with Peter C. Sederberg) *Vigilante Politics,* University of Pennsylvania Press, 1976. Contributor of about forty articles to journals.

* * *

ROSENBAUM, Max 1923-

PERSONAL: Born April 23, 1923, in New York, N.Y.; son of Abraham and Rose (Wigderhaus) Rosenbaum; married Belle Wolkoff (a reading specialist), April 10, 1949; children: Rebecca, Joshua, Adam, Judith. *Education:* College of the City of New York (now City College of the City University of New York), B.S., 1943, M.S., 1945; New York University, Ph.D., 1948; psychoanalytic training at William Alanson White Institute, Postgraduate Center for Psychotherapy, Institute of National Psychological Association for Psychoanalysis. *Politics:* Democrat. *Religion:* Jewish. *Home:* West Shore Road, Sagamore Lake, Carmel, N.Y. 10512. *Office:* 150 East 56th St., New York, N.Y. 10022.

CAREER: Private practice of psychoanalysis in New York City, 1949—; Human Resources Development and Conservation Corp., Inc., New York City, president, 1972-76; Adelphi University, Garden City, N.Y., clinical professor of psychiatry, 1973—; New York University, New York City, clinical professor of psychiatry, 1976—. Radio lecturer on WMGM, New York City, 1948-53. Visiting lecturer at New York University, 1948-49, City College of the City University of New York, 1970-71, Brooklyn College of the City University of New York, 1970-72; visiting professor at Hunter College of the City University of New York, 1972. *Military service:* U.S. Army, 1945-46. *Member:* American Psychological Association (fellow), American Association for the Advancement of Science (fellow), American Sociological Association (fellow), American Group Psychotherapy Association (fellow), National Psychological Association of Psychoanalysis (fellow), Association for Group Psychoanalysis and Process, Eastern Psychological Association, Eastern Group Psychotherapy Society, New York State Psychological Association, New York Academy of Sciences (fellow).

WRITINGS: (With Hugh Mullan) *Group Psychotherapy,* Macmillan, 1962, 2nd edition, Free Press, 1978; (editor with Milton M. Berger) *Group Psychotherapy and Group Function,* Basic Books, 1962, 2nd edition, 1975; (editor) *Drug Abuse and Drug Addiction,* Gordon & Breach, 1973; (editor) *Group Psychotherapy from the Southwest,* Gordon & Breach, 1974; (with Alvin Snadowsky) *Intensive Group Experience,* Free Press, 1976; (editor with H. M. Rabin) *How to Begin a Psychotherapy Group: Six Approaches,* Gordon & Breach, 1976. Contributor to eleven books. Editor of *Group Process,* 1968—.

WORK IN PROGRESS: Three books.

* * *

ROSENBERGER, Francis Coleman 1915-

PERSONAL: Born March 22, 1915, in Manassas, Va.; son of George L. and Olive (Robertson) Rosenberger; married Lucinda Tavenner, April 30, 1941 (died, 1960); married Paulette Dionne, February 18, 1961 (divorced, 1962); married Astra Brennan, December 16, 1966. *Education:* Attended University of Virginia, 1932-36, 1937-40; George Washington University, LL.B. (since converted to J.D.), 1942. *Politics:* Democrat. *Religion:* Presbyterian. *Home:* 6809 Melrose Dr., McLean, Va. 22101. *Office:* 1775 Massachusetts Ave. N.W., Washington, D.C. 20036.

CAREER: Admitted to Virginia Bar, 1939, and Bar of U.S. Supreme Court, 1949; U.S. Senate, Washington, D.C., member of legal and legislative staff, 1942-78, Committee on the Judiciary, attorney, 1955-78, chief counsel and staff director, 1976-78; director, Project '87, 1979—. Writer and editor. Member: Federal Bar Association (president, Capitol Hill chapter, 1965-66), Columbia Historical Society of Washington, D.C., Cosmos Club. Awards, honors: Award of Merit, National Genealogical Society, 1958; Congressional fellow, American Political Science Association, 1963; Certificate of Commendation for scholarly editing of Records of the Columbia Historical Society of Washington, D.C., American Association for State and Local History, 1971.

WRITINGS: The Virginia Poems, hand-set edition, Gotham Book Mart, 1943; XII Poems, hand-set edition, Gotham Book Mart, 1946; (editor) Virginia Reader: A Treasury of Writings from the First Voyages to the Present, Dutton, 1948, reprinted, Octagon, 1972; Some Notes on the Rosenberger Family in Pennsylvania and Virginia, 1729-1950, privately printed, 1950; (editor) American Sampler: A Selection of New Poetry, hand-set edition, Prairie Press, 1951; (editor) Jefferson Reader: A Treasury of Writings about Thomas Jefferson, Dutton, 1953; (editor) The Robinson-Rosenberger Journey to the Gold Fields of California, 1849-1850: The Diary of Zirkle D. Robinson, hand-set edition, Prairie Press, 1966; One Season Here: Poems, University Press of Virginia, 1976; (editor) Washington and the Poet (anthology), University Press of Virginia, 1977; An Alphabet (poems), University Press of Virginia, 1978. Also author of a novel published under a pseudonym.

Poetry included in The Best Poems of 1942, Best Poems of 1943, American Writing 1944, Cross Section 1945, Cross Section 1947, and other collections. Poems have been published in about forty periodicals, including Poetry (Chicago), Poetry Quarterly (London), Queen's Quarterly (Canada), Quarterly Review of Literature, Southern Poetry Review, and Southwest Review. Book reviewer for Richmond Times-Dispatch, 1938-40, Washington Post, 1940-43, New York Herald Tribune Book Review, 1945-62, and Washington Star, 1967-71; occasional reviewer for New York Times Book Review, Virginia Quarterly Review, New Republic, and other publications.

Editor, Columbia Historical Society of Washington, D.C., 1960—, editing biennial volumes of Records of the Columbia Historical Society of Washington, D.C. Editor, Virginia Spectator (magazine), University of Virginia, 1938-39; member of editorial board, Federal Bar Journal, 1957-63.

SIDELIGHTS: "A sense of history, of place and of continuity, came easily in my childhood in Virginia," Francis Coleman Rosenberger says. "A great-uncle still lived in the house where my father was born and where my grandfather and great-grandfather had lived. Old papers and letters and books were not difficult to find. When I attended the University of Virginia, Mr. Jefferson was still spoken of, as William Howard Taft had observed, as if he were in the next room. When I edited the student magazine at the university it was the 100th anniversary volume. My literary tastes were influenced by two poets who were then at the university, Ben Belitt and Lawrence Lee."

BIOGRAPHICAL/CRITICAL SOURCES: Richmond Times-Dispatch, June 12, 1949.

ROSENBLATT, Fred 1914-
(Fred Dreyfus)

PERSONAL: Born November 29, 1914, in New York, N.Y.; son of Alexander Eugene (president of a chain of drug stores) and Beatrice (Geller) Rosenblatt; married Judith Ann Ginsburg (a horticulturist), October 15, 1945; children: Roger A., Leon M., Eric L. Education: New York University, B.A., 1935; Washington University, St. Louis, Mo., M.A., 1937. Politics: Democrat. Religion: Jewish. Office: National Features Syndicate, Inc., 1052A National Press Building, Washington, D.C. 20004.

CAREER: Has moderated numerous radio and television programs, including "Considered Opinion"; press secretary to U.S. Senator Estes Kefauver, 1952-56; National Features Syndicate, Inc., Washington, D.C., editor and publisher, 1965—. Trustee, New York College of Medicine; member of Committee for the Nation's Health. Military service: U.S. Army Air Forces, 1941-46; became sergeant. Member: National Press Club, National Press Photographers Association, New Hampshire State Society (president).

WRITINGS: Out of My Mind, Gallagher, 1962; Tararum, Foster Publishing, 1964; Barnabas, Paperback Library, 1968; Hughes, McKay, 1972. Also author of two suspense novels written under the pseudonym Fred Dreyfus. Daily columnist, Gallagher Syndicate, 1955-65; contributing editor, Nana.

WORK IN PROGRESS: Today's Physicians.††

*   *   *

ROSENBLUM, Gershen 1924-

PERSONAL: Born January 23, 1924, in Boston, Mass.; son of Benjamin and Rose (Naiman) Rosenblum; married Eleanor Slimp (a school committeewoman), August 30, 1951; children: Bruce, Steven, Kathryn. Education: Harvard University, A.B., 1947; Boston University, M.A., 1949, Ph.D., 1955. Home: 15 Bemis St., Newton, Mass. 02160. Office: Greater Laurence Mental Health Center, 581 Andover St., Laurence, Mass. 01843.

CAREER: South Shore Mental Health Center, Quincy, Mass., chief psychologist, 1960-67; Massachusetts Department of Mental Health, Dedham, Mass., mental health administrator, 1967-78; Boston University, Boston, Mass., lecturer in psychology, 1968-73; Greater Laurence Mental Health Center, Laurence, Mass., director, 1978—. Member of the professional advisory committee, Newton Mental Health Association, 1962-67. Military service: U.S. Army, 1943-46; became staff sergeant. Member: American Psychological Association, American Orthopsychiatric Association, Massachusetts Psychological Association, Massachusetts Public Health Association. Awards, honors: Distinguished Psychologist award from Massachusetts Psychological Association.

WRITINGS: (With Luleen Anderson, Chester Bennett, Saul Cooper, Leonard Hussol, and Donald Klein) Community Psychology, Boston University Press, 1966; (editor) Issues in Community Psychology and Preventive Mental Health, Behavioral Publications, 1971. Contributor to Community Mental Health Journal, Mental Hygiene, Massachusetts Journal of Mental Health, Journal of Child Psychology and Psychiatry and Allied Disciplines, and Journal of Education. Book review editor, Community Mental Health Journal, 1965—; member of editorial board of Massachusetts Journal of Mental Health, 1970-77.

WORK IN PROGRESS: Research on prevention of illness and positive aspects of mental health.

ROSENFELD, Edward J(ulius) 1943-

PERSONAL: Born August 26, 1943, in New York, N.Y.; son of Edward and Carolyn (Kaufman) Rosenfeld; married Delia Dela Rosa, July 20, 1971 (divorced, 1973). *Education:* Attended Centre College, 1961-62, and Columbia University, 1963, 1966-67. *Agent:* Peter Matson, Harold Matson Co., 22 East 40th St., New York, N.Y. 10016.

CAREER: Worked at a variety of jobs including messenger, clerk, office worker, furniture mover, teletype operator, switchboard operator, and researcher, 1959-69; writer.

WRITINGS: (Editor with John Brockman) *Real Time I,* Doubleday, 1973; (editor with Brockman) *Real Time 2,* Doubleday, 1973; *The Book of Highs,* Quadrangle, 1973. Contributor to *Boston after Dark* and to *Whole Earth Catalog.*

WORK IN PROGRESS: A collection of mystical wisdom sources, *The Mystical Way;* a novel set in the late eighteenth and early nineteenth centuries; a monthly magazine, *Consciousness.*

SIDELIGHTS: Edward J. Rosenfeld told *CA:* "I am particularly interested in the methods of encoding wisdom exemplified by the stories of the Zen, Hasidic, and Sufi masters."††

* * *

ROSENFIELD, Leonora Cohen 1909-

PERSONAL: Born February 14, 1909, in New York, N.Y.; daughter of Morris Raphael (a philosopher) and Mary (Ryshpan) Cohen; married Harry N. Rosenfield (an attorney), June 25, 1936; children: Marianne J. (Mrs. David J. Smigelskis). *Education:* Universite de Grenoble, Certificate, 1928; Sorbonne, University of Paris, Diploma, 1929; Smith College, B.A. (cum laude), 1930; Columbia University, M.A., 1931, Ph.D., 1940. *Religion:* Jewish. *Home:* 3749 Chesapeake St. N.W., Washington, D.C. 20016. *Office:* Department of French and Italian, University of Maryland, College Park, Md. 20742.

CAREER: Smith College, Northampton, Mass., instructor in French, 1934-35; Brooklyn College (now Brooklyn College of the City University of New York), New York, N.Y., instructor in French, 1936-46; U.S. Department of Agriculture, Graduate School, Washington, D.C., assistant professor of French, 1948-49; University of Maryland, College Park, instructor, 1947, assistant professor, 1947-59, associate professor, 1959-66, professor of French, 1966—. *Member:* Modern Language Association of America, American Association of Teachers of French, American Philosophical Association, History of Science Society, American Society for Eighteenth Century Studies, American Association of University Professors, Societe francaise d'Etudes du Dix-huitieme Siecle, Phi Beta Kappa, Sigma Delta Tau. *Awards, honors:* Modern Language Association grant, 1938; American Council of Learned Societies faculty study fellowship, 1951-52; University of Maryland graduate school grant, 1957.

WRITINGS: From Beast-Machine to Man-Machine: Animal Soul in French Letters from Descartes to La Mettrie, Oxford University Press, 1941, new edition, Octagon Books, 1968; (translator from the French) Alexandre Koyre, *Discovering Plato,* Columbia University Press, 1945; (contributor) David C. Cabeen, editor, *A Critical Bibliography of French Literature,* Volume III, Syracuse University Press, 1961; (author of preface) Morris R. Cohen, *The Meaning of Human History* (Carus lectures), 2nd edition,

Open Court, 1961; *Portrait of a Philosopher: Morris R. Cohen in Life and Letters,* Harcourt, 1962; (editor) Gaston Ignace Pardies, *Discours de la Connoissance des Bestes,* Johnson Reprint, 1972; (contributor) *Renaissance Studies in Honor of Isidore Silver,* Kentucky Romance Quarterly, 1974; (contributor) Roseann Runte, editor, *Studies in Eighteenth-Century Culture,* Volume VII, University of Wisconsin Press, 1978. Contributor of articles to *International Encyclopedia of the Social Sciences* and *Proceedings of the Tenth International Congress of Philosophy,* 1948-49. Contributor to numerous learned journals. Member, board of editorial consultants, *Journal of History of Philosophy.*

WORK IN PROGRESS: A source book on women's rights; contributing to *Enlightenment Studies in Honor of Lester G. Crocker,* for the Voltaire Foundation; compiling unpublished correspondence of Condorcet.

* * *

ROSENMAN, Samuel I(rving) 1896-1973

February 13, 1896—June 24, 1973; American lawyer, New York Supreme Court judge, and presidential counselor. Obituaries: *Washington Post,* June 25, 1973.

* * *

ROSENSTOCK-HUESSY, Eugen 1888-1973

July 6, 1888—February 24, 1973; German-born American educator, social philosopher and historian. Obituaries: *New York Times,* February 25, 1973; *Washington Post,* February 28, 1973. (See index for *CA* sketch)

* * *

ROSENTHAL, David 1916-

PERSONAL: Born July 19, 1916, in New York, N.Y.; son of Isaac and Sally (Greenberg) Rosenthal; married, September 6, 1950; children: Laura, Scott, Amy. *Education:* University of Akron, A.B., 1941; George Washington University, M.A., 1947; University of Chicago, Ph.D., 1952. *Home:* 9612 Alta Vista Ter., Bethesda, Md. 20014. *Office:* Laboratory of Psychology, National Institute of Mental Health, Bethesda, Md. 20014.

CAREER: William Alanson White Psychiatric Foundation, New York, N.Y., research associate, 1947-49; Johns Hopkins University, Baltimore, Md., instructor, 1951-53, assistant professor of medical psychology, 1953-55, psychologist, Johns Hopkins Hospital, 1951-55; National Institute of Mental Health, Bethesda, Md., research psychologist, Laboratory of Psychology, 1955-66, chief, Laboratory of Psychology, 1966—. Lecturer and consultant, Patuxent Institution, 1955—. *Military service:* U.S. Army, 1942-45. U.S. Public Health Service, commissioned scientist, Inactive Reserve, 1956—.

MEMBER: American Psychological Association, American Psychopathological Association, Maryland Psychological Association, Sigma Xi. *Awards, honors:* Superior Service Award, National Institute of Mental Health, 1969; Dean Research Award, 1971, for contribution to basic research in the behavioral sciences relevant to schizophrenia; Maryland Psychological Association Award, 1971, for outstanding contribution to psychology.

WRITINGS: (Editor and contributor) *The Genain Quadruplets,* Basic Books, 1963; (editor with S. S. Kety and contributor) *The Transmission of Schizophrenia,* Pergamon, 1968; *Genetic Theory and Abnormal Behavior,* McGraw, 1970; (author of foreword) James Shields and Irving I.

Gottesman, editors, *Man, Mind and Heredity: Selected Papers of Eliot Slater on Psychiatry and Genetics,* Johns Hopkins Press, 1971; *Genetics of Psychopathology,* Mc-Graw, 1971; (editor with Ronald R. Fieve and H. Brill) *Genetic Research in Psychiatry: Proceedings,* Johns Hopkins Press, 1975.

Contributor: F. B. Powdermaker and J. D. Frank, editors, *Group Psychotherapy: Studies in Methodology of Research and Therapy,* Harvard University Press, 1953; C. F. Reed, I. E. Alexander, and S. S. Tomkins, editors, *Psychopathology: A Source Book,* Harvard University Press, 1958; J. O. Cole and R. W. Gerard, editors, *Psychopharmacology: Problems in Evaluation,* National Academy of Sciences-National Research Council, 1959; John Romano, editor, *The Origins of Schizophrenia,* Excerpta Medica Foundation, 1967; D. C. Glass, editor, *Genetics: Biology and Behavior,* Rockefeller University Press and Russell Sage Foundation, 1968; Martin Manosevitz and others, editors, *Behavioral Genetics: Method and Research,* Appleton, 1969; D. N. Robinson, editor, *Heredity and Achievement,* Oxford University Press, 1970; Robert Cancro, editor, *The Schizophrenic Reactions: A Critique of the Concept, Hospital Treatment, and Current Research,* Brunner, 1970; Manfred Bleuler and Jules Angst, editors, *The Origin of Schizophrenia,* Verlag Hans Huber, 1971.

Contributor to *Encyclopedia of Mental Health* and more than eighty articles to psychology and medical journals. Member of editorial board, *Journal of Psychiatric Research,* 1964—; consulting editor, *Journal of Abnormal Psychology,* 1964—, *Personality: An International Journal,* 1969—, and *Journal of the American Association of Correctional Psychologists,* 1972—.

WORK IN PROGRESS: Continuing research in the nature and etiology of schizophrenia, in the development of personality and aberrant behavior, and in the processes and outcome of psychotherapy.

*   *   *

ROSENTHAL, Earl E(dgar)   1921-

PERSONAL: Born August 26, 1921, in Milwaukee, Wis.; son of Edgar Ernst and Renee (Wyler) Rosenthal. *Education:* University of Wisconsin—Milwaukee, B.S., 1943; New York University, Ph.D., 1953. *Home:* 5529 South University Ave., Chicago, Ill. 60637. *Office:* Cochrane-Woods Art Center, 5540 South University Ave., University of Chicago, Chicago, Ill. 60637.

CAREER: Milwaukee Art Institute, Milwaukee, Wis., assistant director, 1952-53; University of Chicago, Chicago, Ill., instructor, 1953-54, assistant professor, 1954-60, associate professor, 1960-68, professor of art history, 1968—. *Military service:* U.S. Naval Reserve, active duty, 1943-46; became lieutenant junior grade. *Member:* College Art Association of America, Society of Architectural Historians.

WRITINGS: The Cathedral of Granada: A Study in the Spanish Renaissance, Princeton University Press, 1961; (contributor) Tinsley Helton, editor, *The Renaissance: A Reconsideration of Theories and Interpretations of an Age,* University of Wisconsin Press, 1961; *Diego Siloe Arquitecto de la Catedral de Granada,* Universidad de Granada, 1966; (contributor) Louis Gottschalk, editor, *History of Mankind: The Foundations of the Modern World,* [New York], 1969. Also contributor to *Essays in Honor of Harold Wethey.* Contributor to *Jahrbuch der Kunsthistorischen Sammlungen in Wien,* and to professional journals including, *Journal of the Society of Architectural Historians, Gazette*

des Beaux-Arts, Art Bulletin, Art Quarterly, and *Journal of the Warburg and Courtauld Institutes.*

WORK IN PROGRESS: The Imperial Palace of Charles V on the Alhambra in Granada.

*   *   *

ROSENTHAL, Robert   1933-

PERSONAL: Born March 2, 1933, in Giessen, Germany; came to United States in 1940, naturalized citizen in 1946; son of Julius (a merchant) and Hermine (Kahn) Rosenthal; married Mary Lu Clayton, April 20, 1951; children: Roberta, David C., Virginia. *Education:* University of California, Los Angeles, A.B., 1953, Ph.D., 1956; postdoctoral clinical training in psychology at Wadsworth Veterans Administration Hospital, 1956-57, and Los Angeles Veterans Administration Mental Hygiene Clinic, 1957. *Politics:* Liberal. *Religion:* Jewish. *Home:* 12 Phinney Rd., Lexington, Mass. 02173. *Office:* Harvard University, 33 Kirkland St., Cambridge, Mass. 02138.

CAREER: Certified clinical psychologist in North Dakota; American Board of Examiners in Professional Psychology, diplomate; Los Angeles Area Veterans Administration, Los Angeles, Calif., clinical psychology trainee, 1954-57; University of California, Los Angeles, acting instructor in psychology, 1957; University of North Dakota, Grand Forks, assistant professor, 1957-58, associate professor of psychology, 1958-62, coordinator of clinical training, 1958-62; Harvard University, Cambridge, Mass., lecturer in clinical psychology, 1962-67, professor of social psychology, 1967—. Lecturer at University of Southern California, 1956-57, and Boston University, 1965-66; visiting associate professor, Ohio State University, 1960-61.

MEMBER: American Psychological Association (fellow), Society for Projective Techniques, Society of Experimental Social Psychology, American Association for the Advancement of Science (fellow), Eastern Psychological Association, Midwestern Psychological Association, North Dakota Psychological Association (past president), Massachusetts Psychological Association (fellow), Phi Beta Kappa, Sigma Xi. *Awards, honors:* American Association for the Advancement of Science socio-psychological prize, 1960; Cattell Fund Award from American Psychological Association, 1967; senior Fulbright scholar, Australian-American Educational Foundation, 1972; Guggenheim fellow, 1973-74.

WRITINGS: (Author of introduction) Oskar Pfungst, *Clever Hans,* Holt, 1965; *Experimenter Effects in Behavioral Research,* Appleton, 1966, enlarged edition, Halsted, 1976; (with Lenore Jacobson) *Pygmalion in the Classroom: Teacher Expectation and Pupil's Intellectual Development,* Holt, 1968; (with Ralph L. Rosnow, J. A. Cheyne, K. H. Craik, Benjamin Kleinmuntz, and R. H. Walters) *New Directions in Psychology,* Holt, 1970; (with Rosnow) *The Volunteer Subject,* Wiley-Interscience, 1975; (with Rosnow) *A Primer of Methods for the Behavioral Sciences,* Wiley, 1975; (author of foreword) P. M. Insel and L. F. Jacobson, editors, *What Do You Expect?,* Cummings, 1975; (with J. A. Hall, M. R. DiMatteo, P. L. Rogers, and D. Archer) *Sensitivity to Nonverbal Communication: The PONS Test,* Johns Hopkins Press, in press.

Contributor: D. P. Ray, editor, *Series Research in Social Psychology,* National Institute of Social and Behavioral Science, 1961; Brendan Maher, editor, *Progress in Experimental Personality Research,* Volume I, Academic Press, 1964; F. L. Ruch, editor, *Psychology and Life,* 7th edition, Scott, Foresman, 1967; Martin Deutsch, Irwin Katz, and

A. R. Jensen, editors, *Social Class, Race, and Psychological Development*, Holt, 1968; G. B. Gottsegen and M. G. Gottsegen, editors, *Professional School Psychology*, Volume III, Grune, 1969; R. C. Sprinthall and N. A. Sprinthall, editors, *Educational Psychology: Selected Readings*, Van Nostrand, 1969; (and editor with Rosnow) *Artifact in Behavioral Research*, Academic Press, 1969.

E. R. Tufte, editor, *The Quantitative Analysis of Social Problems*, Addison-Wesley, 1970; N. V. Overly, editor, *The Unstudied Curriculum: Its Impact on Children*, Association for Supervision and Curriculum Development, 1970; G. S. Lesser, editor, *Psychology and Educational Practice*, Scott, Foresman, 1971; J. D. Elashoff and R. E. Snow, editors, *Pygmalion Reconsidered*, Charles A. Jones Publishing, 1971; R. D. Strom, editor, *Teachers and the Learning Process*, Prentice-Hall, 1971; D. O'Sullivan and R. Traill, editors, *The Relation of Theory to Practice in Teacher Education*, National Association of Teacher Education, 1972; P. McReynolds, editor, *Advances in Psychological Assessment*, Volume IV, Jossey-Bass, 1978; A. Wolfgang, editor, *Nonverbal Behavior: Applications and Cross-Cultural Implications*, Academic Press, in press; S. Weitz, editor, *Nonverbal Communication*, revised edition, Oxford University Press, in press.

Author of psychological reports and monographs; contributor to bulletins, proceedings, annals, and yearbooks. Contributor of about a hundred articles to American, Canadian, Australian, and European psychology journals. Advisory editor, *Journal of Consulting and Clinical Psychology*, *Journal of Experimental Social Psychology*, and *Journal of Educational Psychology*.

WORK IN PROGRESS: Further research on nonverbal communication; comparing within and between-subject studies; *The Self-Fulfilling Prophecy;* co-authoring *Environmental Psychology and Nonverbal Behavior, The Behavioral and Brain Sciences,* and *An Introduction to Measuring Sensitivity to Nonverbal Cues: The PONS Test Manual;* editing *Skill in Nonverbal Communication.*

*   *   *

ROSKO, Milt 1930-

PERSONAL: Born July 19, 1930, in Newark, N.J.; son of Milton (a grocer) and Anna (Curlik) Rosko; married June Helen Whitmeyer, November 1, 1953; children: Linda June, Robert Milton. *Education:* Attended high school in Newark, N.J. *Politics:* Republican. *Religion:* Lutheran. *Home:* 268 High Tor Dr., Watchung, N.J. 07060.

CAREER: Anheuser-Busch, Inc., Newark, N.J., office manager, 1948—. *Military service:* U.S. Marine Corps, 1951-53; became sergeant. *Member:* Outdoor Writers Association of America (past member of board of directors), New Jersey Outdoor Writers Association, Rod and Gun Editors Association of Metropolitan New York (past president). *Awards, honors:* Wheels Afield Award from Outdoor Writers Association of America, 1965; Old Salt Award from New Jersey Travel and Resort Association, 1966.

WRITINGS: Secrets of Striped Bass Fishing, Macmillan, 1966; *Fishing from Boats,* Macmillan, 1968; *Spinfishing: The System That Does It All,* Macmillan, 1973. Outdoor columnist for *Angler's News and Soundings.* Contributor to *Salt Water Sportsman, Fishing World,* and other outdoor magazines.

WORK IN PROGRESS: A book tentatively entitled, *A Guide to Fresh Water Fishing in America.*

ROSNER, Stanley 1928-

PERSONAL: Born July 6, 1928, in Yonkers, N.Y.; son of David Jacob (a merchant) and Rose (Meyers) Rosner; married Blanche Altman (a social worker), February 20, 1955; children: David Joshua, Elisa Beth, Adam Jonathan, Jennifer Amy. *Education:* New York University, B.A., 1950; Boston University, M.A., 1951; New School for Social Research, Ph.D., 1956; Postgraduate Center for Mental Health, Certified in Psychotherapy and Psychoanalysis, 1967; Columbia University, postdoctoral study, 1971-72. *Home:* 18 Old Rock Rd., Weston, Conn. 06880. *Office:* Counseling and Psychotherapy Group, 1305 Post Rd., Fairfield, Conn. 06430; and 112 Main St., New Canaan, Conn. 06840.

CAREER: Grasslands Hospital, Valhalla, N.Y., junior psychologist, 1951-55; clinical psychologist, Manhattan State Hospital, 1955-56; Child Guidance Clinic of Greater Bridgeport, Bridgeport, Conn., chief clinical psychologist, 1956-60; Consultation Center, New Canaan, Conn., director of psychological services, 1960-70. In private practice, 1958—. Diplomate in clinical psychology of American Board of Examiners in Professional Psychology, 1961. Member of adjunct medical staff, Hall-Brooke Hospital; regional chairman, Association for Mental Health Affiliation with Israel.

MEMBER: American Psychological Association (fellow), American Orthopsychiatric Association (fellow), American Group Psychotherapy Association, Society for Personality Assessment (fellow), Council of Psychoanalytic Psychotherapists, American Association for the Advancement of Science, Connecticut Psychological Association (former president).

WRITINGS: (Editor with Lawrence Edwin Abt) *The Creative Experience,* Grossman, 1970; (with Laura Hobe) *The Marriage Gap,* McKay, 1974; (editor with Abt) *Essays in Creativity,* North River Press, 1974; (editor with Abt) *The Creative Expression,* North River Press, 1976. Contributor to psychology and psychoanalytic journals.

*   *   *

ROSS, Alan O(tto) 1921-

PERSONAL: Original name, Alan Otto Rosenmeyer; name legally changed in 1944; born December 7, 1921, in Frankfurt am Main, Germany; son of Walter M. (a physician) and Elizabeth (Keller) Rosenmeyer; married Ilse Wallis (a social worker), September 2, 1950; children: Judith L., Pamela W. *Education:* College of the City of New York (now City College of the City University of New York), B.S., 1949; Yale University, M.S., 1950, Ph.D., 1953. *Politics:* Independent. *Religion:* Unitarian. *Office:* Department of Psychology, State University of New York, Stony Brook, N.Y. 11794.

CAREER: Pittsburgh Child Guidance Center, Pittsburgh, Pa., chief psychologist, 1959-67; State University of New York at Stony Brook, professor of psychology, 1967—. Trustee of National Academy of Professional Psychology, 1972-76. *Military service:* U.S. Army, 1943-46, 1951-56; became first lieutenant. *Member:* American Psychological Association (fellow; president of Division of Clinical Psychology, 1965-66), American Board of Professional Psychology (vice-president, 1968-75).

WRITINGS: The Practice of Clinical Child Psychology, Grune, 1959; *The Exceptional Child in the Family,* Grune, 1964; (editor with E. L. Hoch and C. E. Winder) *The Professional Preparation of Clinical Psychologists,* American Psychological Association, 1966; *Psychological Disorders of Children,* McGraw, 1974; *Psychological Aspects of Learning Disabilities and Reading Disorders,* McGraw, 1976; *Learning Disability: The Unrealized Potential,* McGraw, 1977; (contributor) S. Garfield and A. Bergin, editors, *Handbook of Psychotherapy and Behavior Change,* Wiley, 1978; *Child Behavior Therapy,* Wiley, in press. Consulting editor of *Journal of Consulting and Clinical Psychology,* 1965-68, *Behavior Therapy,* 1974-77, and *Journal of Abnormal Child Psychology,* 1976—.

WORK IN PROGRESS: Research on reading disabilities and attention.

* * *

ROSS, Emory 1887-1973

July 28, 1887—March 16, 1973; American missionary and author. Obituaries: *New York Times,* March 18, 1973.

* * *

ROSS, Stephen David 1935-

PERSONAL: Born May 4, 1935, in New York, N.Y.; son of Allan (a printer) and Bessie (Schlosberg) Ross; married Marilyn Gaddis Rose (a professor of comparative literature), November 16, 1968; children: David Gaddis. *Education:* Columbia University, A.B., 1956, M.A., 1957, Ph.D., 1961. *Home:* 4 Johnson Ave., Binghamton, N.Y. 13905. *Office:* Department of Philosophy, State University of New York, Binghamton, N.Y. 13901.

CAREER: Queens College of the City University of New York, Flushing, N.Y., instructor in mathematics, 1961-63; University of Wisconsin—Milwaukee, assistant professor of philosophy, 1963-65; University of Colorado, Boulder, assistant professor of philosophy, 1965-67; State University of New York at Binghamton, assistant professor, 1967-69, associate professor, 1969-73, professor of philosophy, 1973—, director of accelerated programs, 1971—, chairman of department, 1979—. *Member:* American Philosophical Association, Phi Beta Kappa. *Awards, honors:* University of Wisconsin summer research grant, 1964; State University of New York summer research fellowships, 1968, 1969; Rockefeller Foundation humanities fellowship, 1975-76.

WRITINGS: The Meaning of Education, Nijhoff, 1966; *Literature and Philosophy: An Analysis of the Philosophical Novel,* Appleton, 1969; *The Scientific Process,* Nijhoff, 1971; *Moral Decision,* Freeman, Cooper, 1972; *The Nature of Moral Responsibility,* Wayne State University Press, 1973; *In Pursuit of Moral Value,* Freeman, Cooper, 1973. Contributor to scholarly journals.

WORK IN PROGRESS: Three books, *The Ultimate Cosmology: A Critique of Process and Reality, Learning and Discovery: An Essay in the University,* and *Intensity and Contrast: A Theory of the Arts.*

* * *

ROSS, Steven Thomas 1937-

PERSONAL: Born April 7, 1937, in New York, N.Y.; son of Michael and Ruth Ross; married, 1969. *Education:* Williams College, B.A., 1959; Princeton University, M.A., 1962, Ph.D., 1963. *Office:* Department of Strategy, Naval War College, Newport, R.I. 02840.

CAREER: University of Nebraska, Lincoln, instructor, 1963-64, assistant professor of history, 1964-67; University of Texas at Austin, assistant professor, 1967-68, associate professor of history, 1969-73; Naval War College, Newport,

R.I., professor of history, 1973—. *Member:* American Historical Association, Phi Beta Kappa. *Awards, honors:* Woodrow Wilson fellowship, 1959; Fels fellowship, 1962-63.

WRITINGS: European Diplomatic History, 1789-1815: France against Europe, Doubleday, 1969; *The French Revolution: Conflict or Continuity,* Holt, 1971; *Quest for Victory: French Republican Strategy, 1792-1799,* A. S. Barnes, 1973; *From Flintlock to Rifle: Infantry Tactics, 1740-1866,* Fairleigh Dickinson University, 1979.

* * *

ROSS, Thomas W(ynne) 1923-

PERSONAL: Born April 16, 1923, in Colorado Springs, Colo.; son of Thomas W. (an editor) and Marguerite (Stewart) Ross; married Mary E. McCarty (a realtor and banker), July 10, 1943; children: Thomas W. III, Margaret Ross Couper. *Education:* Colorado College, A.B., 1946, A.M., 1947; University of Michigan, Ph.D., 1951. *Politics:* Democrat. *Religion:* None. *Home:* 1709 North Tejon St., Colorado Springs, Colo. 80907.

CAREER: Colorado College, Colorado Springs, instructor, 1951-53, assistant professor, 1953-56, associate professor, 1958-63, professor of English, 1963—, assistant dean, 1954-56, director of admissions, 1958-61. Assistant professor at Massachusetts Institute of Technology, 1955; assistant director of Salzburg Seminar in American Studies, Salzburg, Austria, 1956-58; research fellow at University of Edinburgh, summer, 1962; NATO professor at University of Regensburg, 1969. *Military service:* U.S. Army, 1943-46; became sergeant. *Member:* Modern Language Association of America, Mediaeval Academy of America, American Association of University Professors, Phi Beta Kappa. *Awards, honors:* Research grant from American Philosophical Society, 1967.

WRITINGS: (Editor) Thomas Kyd, *The Spanish Tragedy,* University of California Press, 1968; *Chaucer's Bawdy,* Dutton, 1972; *A Book of Elizabethan Magic: Thomas Hill's Naturall and Artificial Conclusions,* Adler's Foreign Books, 1974.

WORK IN PROGRESS: An edition of Chaucer for the *Variorum Chaucer,* University of Oklahoma Press.

SIDELIGHTS: Thomas Ross is a jazz musician.

* * *

ROSSKOPF, Myron Frederick 1907-1973

October 2, 1907—January 31, 1973; American educator, researcher in cognitive development, and author of books on the theory and teaching of mathematics. Obituaries: *New York Times,* February 1, 1973. (See index for *CA* sketch)

* * *

ROTH, David F(rancisco) 1939-

PERSONAL: Born March 22, 1939; son of Louis E. (a merchant) and Sally (Breen) Roth. *Education:* Claremont Men's College, B.A., 1960; San Francisco State College (now University), M.A., 1964; Claremont Graduate School, Ph.D., 1968. *Religion:* Jewish. *Home:* 1035 North Rd., Coquitlam, British Columbia, Canada V3J 1R2.

CAREER: University of Wisconsin—Madison, assistant professor, 1968-69; Ohio State University, Columbus, research associate, 1969-70; Purdue University, Lafayette, Ind., associate professor of political science, 1970-77. Visiting professor, University of the Philippines, 1967, Simon

Fraser University, beginning 1977, and University of British Columbia, 1978-79. Consultant to various government officials in Malaysia, Colombia, and the Philippines, and United Nations ECAFE; consultant to Foster Parents (Haiti), 1976. Referee, General Learning Press, 1976. *Member:* American Political Science Association, World Futurist Society. *Awards, honors:* Good Neighbors Abroad grant, 1965; Fulbright fellowship, 1967; Purdue Research Foundation summer travel grant, 1971; World Order project grant, 1971; Malaysian government research grant, 1972; administration award from United Nations Asian Center for Development, 1975; International Development Research Center award.

WRITINGS: (Contributor) W. Spragens and R. Russell, editors, *Conflict and Crisis in American Politics,* Kendall/Hunt, 1970; (with Lee Wilson) *The Comparative Study of Politics: China, Soviet Union, Britain, France, Mexico and Nigeria,* Houghton, 1976. Also contributor to *Approaches to Rural Development in Asia.* Contributor of articles and book reviews to professional journals, including *International Behavioral Scientist, Journal of Southeast Asian Studies, Asian Survey, International Interaction, Journal of Politics,* and *American Political Science Review.* Referee, *Growth and Change,* 1975, 1976, and *Journal of Developing Areas,* 1975-76.

WORK IN PROGRESS: The Irony of the Technocratic Promise; The Would Be Warrior: Idi Amin, the Deviant-Traditional Political Leader.

* * *

ROTH, Robert Howard 1933-

PERSONAL: Born January 15, 1933, in Newark, N.J.; son of Max and Marion (Gurkewitz) Roth; married Estelle Goldstein, June 16, 1957; children: Lisa, Neil. *Education:* Juilliard School of Music, B.S., 1953; Columbia University, M.A., 1956, Ed.D., 1960. *Home:* 111 Gallinson Dr., Murray Hill, N.J. 07974. *Office:* Madison Medical Center, 28 Walnut St., Madison, N.J. 07940.

CAREER: Kean College of New Jersey, Union, instructor, 1960-63, assistant professor, 1963-65, associate professor, 1965-68, professor of psychology, 1968—; Madison Medical Center, Madison, N.J., private practice in clinical psychology, 1969—. *Member:* American Psychological Association, American Orthopsychiatric Association (fellow), American Group Psychotherapy Association, American Personnel and Guidance Association, American Association for the Advancement of Science, National Council on Family Relations, National Institute for the Psychotherapies, Sigmund Freud Society of America, Eastern Psychological Association, New Jersey Psychological Association, New Jersey Academy of Science, New York Academy of Sciences.

WRITINGS: (Editor) *Abnormal Psychology: Disorders of Behavior and Experience,* Selected Academic Readings, 1968; (editor) *Psychology of Personality,* Selected Academic Readings, 1968; (editor) *The Parameters of Personality,* MSS Educational Publishing, 1970; (editor) *Studies in Psychopathology,* MSS Educational Publishing, 1970; (editor) *Studies in Abnormal Psychology,* Xerox College Publishing, 1972; (editor) *Theoretical and Applied Studies in Personality,* Xerox College Publishing, 1972; (editor) *Psychological Studies in Personality,* Xerox College Publishing, 1978; (editor) *Abnormal Psychology in Perspective,* Xerox College Publishing, 1978.

ROTH, Wolfgang M(ax) W(ilhelm) 1930-

PERSONAL: Born October 1, 1930, in Darmstadt, Germany; Canadian citizen; son of L. Wilhelm and Katharina (Fiebig) Roth; married S(ylvia) Janet Pearson, July 7, 1956; children: Katherine, Paul, Christopher. *Education:* Attended University of Marburg, 1949-51, University of Tuebingen, 1952, and University of Heidelberg, 1953-55; Victoria University, Th.M., 1958, Th.D., 1959. *Home:* 1326 Davis St., Evanston, Ill. 60201. *Office:* Garrett-Evangelical Theological Seminary, 2121 Sheridan Rd., Evanston, Ill. 60201.

CAREER: Ordained minister, United Church of Canada, 1958; Leonard Theological College, Jabalpur, Madhya Pradesh, India, professor of Old and New Testament, 1960-65; Trinity Evangelical United Brethren Church, Chesley, Ontario, minister, 1965-67; Garrett-Evangelical Theological Seminary, Evanston, Ill., associate professor, 1967-71, professor of Old Testament, 1971—. *Member:* Society of Biblical Literature, American Oriental Society (secretary-treasurer of Middle West branch, 1968-71), American Catholic Biblical Association (associate member), American Academy of Religion.

WRITINGS: Numerical Sayings in the Old Testament, E. J. Brill, 1965; (editor with George Johnson) *The Church in the Modern World,* Ryerson, 1967; *Old Testament Theology,* Christian Literature Society (Madras), 1968; (editor with Horst Buerkle), *Indian Voices in Today's Theological Debate,* Lucknow Publishing House (Lucknow), 1972; (with George W. Hoyer) *Pentecost 2,* Fortress, 1974.†

* * *

ROTHCHILD, Donald (Sylvester) 1928-

PERSONAL: Born August 11, 1928, in New York, N.Y.; son of Sylvester E. (a businessman) and Alice (Levy) Rothchild; married Edith Lee White (a social worker), 1953; children: Derek, Maynard. *Education:* Kenyon College, B.A. (with high honors), 1949; University of California, Berkeley, M.A., 1954; Johns Hopkins University, Ph.D., 1958. *Politics:* Democrat. *Office:* Department of Political Science, University of California, Davis, Calif. 95616.

CAREER: Colby College, Waterville, Me., instructor, 1957-59, assistant professor, 1959-62, associate professor of political science, 1962-65; University of California, Davis, associate professor, 1965-69, professor of political science, 1969—. Fulbright lecturer, Makerere University, 1962-64; senior lecturer, University of Nairobi, 1966-67; Ford Foundation visiting professor, University of Zambia, 1970-71; director, Ghana Study Center, University of Ghana, 1975-77. *Military service:* U.S. Army, 1960-62. *Member:* African Studies Association, American Political Science Association, International Studies Association, Phi Beta Kappa.

WRITINGS: Toward Unity in Africa, Public Affairs Press, 1960; (contributor) Gwendolen M. Carter, editor, *Politics in Africa: Seven Cases,* Harcourt, 1966; (contributor) Carter, editor, *National Unity and Regionalism in Eight African States,* Cornell University Press, 1966; (editor) *Politics of Integration: An East African Documentary,* East African Publishing House, 1968; (editor with C. J. Gertzel and Maure Goldschmidt) *Government and Politics in Kenya,* East African Publishing House, 1969, International Publications Service, 1972; *Racial Bargaining in Independent Kenya: A Study of Minorities and Decolonization,* Oxford University Press, for Institute of Race Relations, 1973; (coauthor) *Scarcity, Choice, and Public Policy in Middle Africa,* University of California Press, 1978. Contributor to

Harper's and to political science and African studies journals.

WORK IN PROGRESS: Co-editing a book, *Eagle Entangled: U.S. Foreign Policy in a Complex World,* for Longman.

*   *   *

ROTHMAN, Milton A.   1919-

PERSONAL: Born November 30, 1919, in Philadelphia, Pa.; son of Isadore (a tailor) and Goldie (Glazer) Rothman; married Doris Weiss (a psychologist), April 22, 1950 (divorced, 1975); children: Anthony, Lynne. *Education:* Oregon State College (now University), B.S., 1944; University of Pennsylvania, M.S., 1948, Ph.D., 1952. *Home:* 553 North Judson St., Philadelphia, Pa. 19130. *Office:* Department of Physics, Trenton State College, Trenton, N.J. 08625.

CAREER: Bartol Research Foundation, Swarthmore, Pa., research physicist, 1952-59; Princeton Plasma Physics Laboratory, Princeton, N.J., research physicist, 1959-68; Trenton State College, Trenton, N.J., professor of physics, 1968—. *Military service:* U.S. Army, 1942-46; became sergeant. *Member:* American Physical Society, American Association of Physics Teachers, American Association for the Advancement of Science, Science Fiction Writers of America, Sigma Xi.

WRITINGS: The Laws of Physics, Basic Books, 1963; *Men and Discovery,* Norton, 1964; *Discovering the Natural Laws,* Doubleday, 1972; *The Cybernetic Revolution,* F. Watts, 1972; *Energy and the Future,* F. Watts, 1975. Represented in anthologies, including *Where Do We Go from Here* and *Best Science Fiction for 1973.* Contributor to *Physical Review, Physics of Fluids, Nuclear Fusion, Scientific American, Boys' Life, Astounding Science Fiction,* and *Galaxy.*

WORK IN PROGRESS: Miscellaneous articles.

*   *   *

ROY, David Tod   1933-

PERSONAL: Born April 5, 1933, in Nanking, China; son of Andrew Tod (a missionary) and Margaret (Crutchfield) Roy; married Barbara Chew (an assistant dean of students), February 4, 1967. *Education:* Harvard University, A.B., 1958, A.M., 1960, Ph.D., 1965. *Politics:* Independent. *Home:* 5453 South Woodlawn Ave., Chicago, Ill. 60615. *Office:* Department of Far Eastern Languages and Civilizations, University of Chicago, 5736 South Woodlawn Ave., Chicago, Ill. 60637.

CAREER: Princeton University, Princeton, N.J., assistant professor of Chinese literature, 1963-67; University of Chicago, Chicago, Ill., associate professor, 1967-73, professor of Chinese literature, 1973—, chairman of committee on Far Eastern studies, 1968-70, chairman of department, 1972—. Inter-University Program for Chinese Language Studies, Taipei, Taiwan, member of board of directors, 1968—, chairman of board, 1973-74. *Military service:* U.S. Army, 1954-56. *Member:* Association for Asian Studies, Chinese Language Teachers Association, American Association of University Professors, American Academy of Political and Social Science. *Awards, honors:* Fulbright-Hays advanced research grant for study in Japan, 1967.

WRITINGS: Kuo Mo-Jo: The Early Years, Harvard University Press, 1971. Contributor to *Encyclopaedia Britannica, Biographical Dictionary of Republican China,* and *Journal of the Association for Asian Studies.*

WORK IN PROGRESS: Kuo Mo-Jo's later career; traditional Chinese fiction and drama.†

*   *   *

RUBEL, Arthur J.   1924-

PERSONAL: Born August 29, 1924, in Shanghai, China; son of Arthur John (a salesman) and Marcella (Crohn) Rubel; married Phyllis L. Howard, 1954 (died, 1975); children: Laura. *Education:* Mexico City College, B.A., 1949; University of Chicago, M.A., 1957; University of North Carolina, Ph.D., 1962. *Home:* 1707 Mt. Vernon, East Lansing, Mich. 48823. *Office:* Department of Anthropology, Michigan State University, East Lansing, Mich. 48824.

CAREER: Warehouseman and longshoreman during his early career; ethnologist among Chinantec and Mixe Indians, 1951; research associate, University of Vermont; taught at University of North Carolina, Greensboro, 1963, and University of Texas, Main University (now University of Texas at Austin), 1964-66; University of Notre Dame, Notre Dame, Ind., associate professor, 1966-69, professor of anthropology, 1969-74; Michigan State University, East Lansing, professor of anthropology, 1974—. Researcher among Chicanos in Texas, 1956-59, in Province of Cebu, Philippines, 1969, among Chinantec Indians, 1970, among Chicanos in Chicago, Ill., 1972. Member of advisory group on educational anthropology and socio-linguistics for UNESCO; program adviser in population for Ford Foundation; consultant to Hogg Foundation for Mental Health; member of technical advisory group on maternal nutrition and family planning and consultant to Border Health Advisory Group, Pan-American Health Organization; consultant to Ford Foundation; member of advisory board of Mexico-United States Border Research Program. *Military service:* U.S. Navy, 1942-46. *Member:* American Anthropological Association (fellow), Society for Applied Anthropology (fellow; member of nominating committee for Margaret Mead Medal), American Ethnological Society, Group for Medical Anthropology, Council on Anthropology and Education, Ad Hoc Group on Middle American Studies, Central States Anthropological Society, Southern Anthropological Society.

WRITINGS: Across the Tracks: Mexican-Americans in a Texas City, University of Texas Press, 1966.

Contributor: S. N. Eisenstadt, editor, *Comparative Social Problems,* Free Press, 1964; Arthur J. Field, editor, *Urbanization and Work in Modernizing Societies,* Glengary Press, 1967; Manning Nash, editor, *Social Anthropology,* Volume VI: *Handbook of Middle American Indians,* University of Texas Press, 1967; Andreas M. Kazamias and E. H. Epstein, editors, *Schools in Transition,* Allyn & Bacon, 1968; John J. Burma, editor, *Mexican-Americans in the United States: A Reader,* Schenkman, 1970; Steven Polgar, editor, *Culture and Population: A Collection of Current Studies,* Population Center, University of North Carolina, 1971; Thomas Weaver, general editor, *As We See Ourselves,* Scott, Foresman, 1973. Also contributor to *Scientific Publications,* edited by George Foster. Contributor of about forty articles to anthropology journals. Consulting editor, *Culture, Medicine and Psychiatry;* member of advisory board, *Medical Anthropology.*

WORK IN PROGRESS: An epidemiological study of the etiology of a folk illness known as "susto," tentatively entitled *The Meaning of Magical Fright,* for University of California Press.

RUBEN, Brent David 1944-

PERSONAL: Born October 17, 1944, in Cedar Rapids, Iowa; son of Nate (Nebraska-Iowa area manager of Federal Housing Administration) and Ruth Ethel (Subotnik) Ruben; married Jann F. Mayberry (a teacher), October 2, 1967; children: Robbi Lynn. *Education:* State University of Iowa, B.A., 1966, M.A., 1968, Ph.D., 1970. *Home:* 2 Regina Dr., Belle Mead, N.J. 08502. *Office:* Institute for Communication Studies, Van Dyck Hall, Rutgers University, New Brunswick, N.J. 08903.

CAREER: State University of Iowa, Iowa City, instructor, 1969-70, assistant professor of communication, 1970-71, also associate of Institute for Communication Studies; Rutgers University, New Bruswick, N.J., assistant professor, 1971-74, associate professor of communication, 1975—, director of Institute for Communication Studies, 1971—, chairman of human communication studies, 1972—. Franklin Township human relations commissioner, 1972—; consultant to *New York Times,* United States Agency for International Development, National Association of Television and Radio Announcers, Canadian International Development Agency, Bell Canada, International Business Machines, and other organizations.

MEMBER: American Association for the Advancement of Science, Society for General Systems Research, International Institute of General Semantics, International Communication Association, Kappa Tau Alpha. *Awards, honors:* Research grant from National Association of Broadcasters, 1969, for study of family television viewing behavior; C. J. Nelson award for outstanding communication research at University of Iowa.

WRITINGS: (With Albert D. Talbott) *Communication Systems Simulation: Participant's Manual,* University of Iowa, 1970; (with Talbott, Lee M. Brown, and Henry G. LaBrie) *Intermedia: An Experienced-Based Journalism and Communication Training Program,* University Associates Press, 1970; (contributor) J. William Pfeiffer and John E. Jones, editors, *The 1972 Annual Handbook for Group Facilitators,* University Associates Press, 1972; (contributor) Robert S. Lee, editor, *Experience Learning,* Basic Books, 1972; (contributor and editor with Richard W. Budd) *Approaches to Human Communication,* Spartan Books, 1972, 2nd edition, Hayden Books, 1978; (with Budd) *Basic Human Communication: A Course of Study,* Hayden Books, 1973; (contributor and editor with John Y. Kim) *General Systems Theory and Human Communication,* Hayden Books, 1973; *Interact: A Communication-Behavior Simulation,* Mercer House Press, 1973; (with Budd) *Human Communications Handbook: Simulations and Games,* Hayden Books, Volume I, 1975, Volume II, 1978; *Interact II,* Avery Publishing, 1977; (with Budd) *Beyond Media: New Approaches to Mass Communication,* Hayden Books, 1979; (editor) *Interdisciplinary Approaches to Human Communication,* Hayden, 1979. Editor of *Communication Yearbook,* Transaction Books, Volume I, 1977, Volume II, 1978. Contributor to *Quarterly Journal of Speech, Communication Education,* and other periodicals in his field. Member of editorial board, Iowa Program for Human Development, 1969-70; contributing editor, *Communication,* 1971—; associate editor, *Newstatements, Communication Yearbook,* 1978-80, and *Communications Quarterly;* game and simulation reviewer, *Simulation and Games,* 1971—.

WORK IN PROGRESS: Communication and Human Behavior, completion expected in 1980.

RUBIN, David Lee 1939-

PERSONAL: Born September 30, 1939, in Indianapolis, Ind.; son of Ira Bertram (an analytical chemist) and Jeanne (Gamso) Rubin; married Carolyn Dettman, June 12, 1965; children: Timothy. *Education:* Attended University of Chicago, 1957-58; University of Tennessee, B.A., 1962; University of Paris, Certificats, 1963; University of Illinois at Urbana-Champaign, M.A., 1964, Ph.D., 1967. *Home:* 32 Lake Forest Dr., Charlottesville, Va. 22901. *Office:* Department of French, University of Virginia, Charlottesville, Va. 22903.

CAREER: University of Illinois at Urbana-Champaign, 1963-67, became instructor in French; University of Chicago, Chicago, Ill., assistant professor of French, 1967-69; University of Virginia, Charlottesville, assistant professor, 1969-74, associate professor of French, 1974—. *Member:* Modern Language Association of America, American Association of Teachers of French, North American Society for Seventeenth-Century French Studies. *Awards, honors:* Fulbright fellowship, 1962-63; Woodrow Wilson fellowship, 1963-64; University of Virginia, summer research grants, 1970, 1972, and 1976; associateship in the Center for Advanced Study, 1974.

WRITINGS: (Contributor) Robert Scholes, editor, *Poetic Theory/Poetic Practice,* Midwest Modern Language Association, 1969; *Higher, Hidden Order: Design and Meaning in the Odes of Malherbe,* University of North Carolina Press, 1972; (editor) *The Selected Poetry and Prose of John T. Napier,* Pikeville College Press, 1972; *Papers on French Seventeenth-Century Literature,* Editions Jean-Michel Place, Volume I (contributor), 1973, Volume VII (co-editor and contributor), 1977, Volume IX (co-editor), 1978; (contributor) G. B. Daniel, editor, *Moliere Studies,* University of North Carolina Press, 1974; (co-editor and contributor) *La coherence interieure,* Editions Jean-Michel Place, 1977. Also author of *The Knot of Artifice: French Poetics in the Age of Malherbe.* Contributor of articles and reviews to *Yale French Studies, L'Esprit Createur, French Review, Australian Journal of French Studies, Romance Notes, Oeuvres et Critiques, Revue de l'Universite d'Ottawa, Cahiers Maynard,* and other journals. Member of editorial boards, *Cahiers Maynard,* 1973—, *Oeuvres et Critiques,* 1974—, and Purdue University Monographs, 1977—.

WORK IN PROGRESS: Contributing to *Critical Bibliography of French Literature,* for Syracuse University Press; editing *Textes et Contextes: La poesie francaise du premier dix-septieme siecle; Unheard Music: La Fontaine's Fables and the Art of the Longer Poetic Cycle.*

SIDELIGHTS: David Lee Rubin told *CA:* "Because I believe that the best hope for the humanities is co-operative study of its objects for their own sake and in their own nature, I have invested my efforts in learning the arts of criticism and working closely with others similarly inclined—students, peers, and senior scholars." *Avocational interests:* Travel, art history, music.

* * *

RUBIN, Morton 1923-

PERSONAL: Born April 1, 1923, in Boston, Mass.; son of Benjamin M. and Bertha (Small) Rubin; married Mary Elizabeth Schlom (a librarian), April 25, 1954; children: Joel S., David E. *Education:* Boston University, B.A., 1946; University of North Carolina, M.A., 1947, Ph.D., 1950. *Religion:* Jewish. *Home:* 154 Allerton Rd., Newton, Mass.

02161. *Office:* Department of Sociology, Northeastern University, Boston, Mass. 02115.

CAREER: Affiliated with Research Division, Israel Ministry of Social Welfare, 1951-52; University of Wisconsin—Madison, instructor, 1952-54, assistant professor of sociology, 1954-57; Northeastern University, Boston, Mass., assistant professor, 1957-62, associate professor, 1962-74, professor of sociology, 1974—, acting chairman of department, 1969. Visiting fellow of Center for International Studies, Princeton University, 1954-55. President, Boston Intergroup Relations Council, 1963-64. *Military service:* U.S. Army, 1943-46; served in Europe. *Member:* American Sociological Association, Society for the Study of Social Problems, Massachusetts Sociological Association (vice-president, 1971-72). *Awards, honors:* Social Science Research Council grants, 1956, 1965; National Institute of Mental Health grant, 1962-63.

WRITINGS: Plantation County, University of North Carolina Press, 1951, revised edition, College & University Press, 1963; (contributor) M. B. Sussman, editor, *Community Structure and Analysis,* Crowell, 1959; (contributor) Arthur B. Shostack and William Gomberg, editors, *Blue Collar World,* Prentice-Hall, 1964; *Organized Citizen Participation in Boston,* Boston Urban Observatory and National League of Cities, 1971; *The Walls of Acre: Intergroup Relations and Urban Development in Israel,* Holt, 1974; (with J.K. Morland) *Social Problems in the U.S.,* Ronald, 1975. Contributor to sociology journals.

WORK IN PROGRESS: Boston and Its People: An Urban Sociology.

* * *

RUBINSTEIN, E(lliott) 1936-

PERSONAL: Born January 20, 1936, in New York, N.Y.; son of George (a businessman) and Sara (Berustein) Rubinstein. *Education:* Rutgers University, B.A., 1956; Columbia University, M.A., 1957, Ph.D., 1964. *Home:* 215 West 92nd, Apt. 8G, New York, N.Y. 10025. *Office:* Department of Performing and Creative Arts, College of Staten Island of the City University of New York, Staten Island, N.Y. 10301.

CAREER: Rutgers University, New Brunswick, N.J., instructor, 1961-64, assistant professor of English, 1964-67; College of Staten Island of the City University of New York, Staten Island, N.Y., assistant professor, 1968-71, associate professor of English, 1972—. *Awards, honors:* City University of New York grant, 1970.

WRITINGS: Literary Monographs II, Jane Austen's Novels: The Metaphor of Rank, University of Wisconsin Press, 1969; (editor) *Twentieth-Century Interpretations of "Pride and Prejudice,"* Prentice-Hall, 1969; *Filmguide to the General,* Indiana University, 1973. Contributor to *Nineteenth-Century Fiction, Minnesota Review, Studies in English Literature, Papers on English Language and Literature,* and *Sight and Sound.*

* * *

RUCKER, (Egbert) Darnell 1921-

PERSONAL: Born August 7, 1921, in Dyersburg, Tenn.; son of Egbert Algernon (a businessman) and Luella (Chamblin) Rucker; married Joy Barnett (director of public relations at Skidmore College), November 1, 1947; children: Mark Darnell, Scott Chamblin, Casey Barnett. *Education:* Georgia Institute of Technology, B.E.E., 1947; University

of Chicago, A.M., 1950, Ph.D., 1957. *Home:* 57 Bryan St., Saratoga Springs, N.Y. 12866. *Office:* Department of Philosophy, Skidmore College, Saratoga Springs, N.Y. 12866.

CAREER: Standard Oil Co. of New Jersey, Baton Rouge, La., engineer, 1947-49; University of Chicago, Chicago, Ill., lecturer in liberal arts, 1952-54; Colorado College, Colorado Springs, assistant professor, 1954-58, associate professor, 1958-64, professor of philosophy, 1964-68, chairman of department, 1966-68; Skidmore College, Saratoga Springs, N.Y., professor of philosophy, 1968—, chairman of department, 1977—. Has taught at John Hay Institutes in the Humanities, summers, 1962-65, and other summer institutes, 1966-71. Mountain-Plains Philosophical Conference, member of executive committee, 1956, 1957, 1963, 1964, chairman, 1963. *Military service:* U.S. Army, 1942-46; became lieutenant. *Member:* American Philosophical Association, American Association of University Professors (president of Skidmore chapter, 1969-70), National Association for Humanities Education. *Awards, honors:* American Council of Learned Societies fellowship, 1960-61.

WRITINGS: The Chicago Pragmatists, University of Minnesota Press, 1969; (contributor) Jo Ann Boydston, editor, *Guide to the Works of John Dewey,* Southern Illinois University Press, 1970; (contributor) Joan V. Bondurant, editor, *Conflict: Violence and Nonviolence,* Aldine-Atherton, 1971; (contributor) Walter Robert Corti, editor, *The Philosophy of George Herbert Mead,* Archiv fuer genetische Philosophie, 1973; (contributor) John P. Anton, editor, *Philosophy and the Civilizing Arts,* Ohio University Press, 1975; (author of introduction) *John Dewey: The Middle Works,* Volume III, Southern Illinois University Press, 1977; (contributor) Michael Jones, editor, *The Individual and Society,* University of Oklahoma Press, 1978. Contributor of about twenty-five articles and reviews to professional journals, including *Journal of Aesthetics and Art Criticism, Western Humanities Review, Dialogos, Journal of the History of Philosophy, Ethics, Humanities Journal, School and Society,* and *American Bar Association Journal.*

WORK IN PROGRESS: Research on the nature of the self, the nature of institutions, and contemporary social disruption.

* * *

RUDNICK, Hans H(einrich) 1935-

PERSONAL: Born November 1, 1935, in Belgard, Germany; son of Hans E. (a teacher) and Edit (Raettig) Rudnick; married Helene M. Weisberg (an academic advisor), September 8, 1963; children: Karen E., Martin H., Michael J. *Education:* University of Freiburg, Ph.D., 1966. *Home:* 112 Dogwood Lane, Carterville, Ill. 62918. *Office:* Department of English, Southern Illinois University, Carbondale, Ill. 62901.

CAREER: University of Pennsylvania, Philadelphia, lecturer in German, 1962-63; Southern Methodist University, Dallas, Tex., instructor in German, 1963-64; Southern Illinois University at Carbondale, associate professor of English and comparative literature, 1966—. *Member:* Modern Language Association of America, American Comparative Literature Association.

WRITINGS: (Translator) Kurd Lasswitz, *Two Planets,* Southern Illinois University Press, 1971; (editor and translator into German) Shakespeare, *Hamlet,* Reclam, 1972; (editor) Immanuel Kant, *Anthropology from a Pragmatic Point of View,* translation by Victor L. Dowdell, Southern Illinois University Press, 1978. Contributor to *Human Contest, Colloquia Germanica,* and *Deutsche Zeitung.*

WORK IN PROGRESS: Literature as a System, an edition of nineteenth-century British criticism, for Reclam.

*   *   *

RUDOLPH, Robert S. 1937-

PERSONAL: Born October 5, 1937; son of Robert H. (a carpenter) and Ida (Sigmund) Rudolph; married Gladys Barnett (a musician), August 6, 1960; children: Paul, Mary. *Education:* Temple University, B.A., 1959; University of Wisconsin, M.B., 1961, Ph.D., 1966. *Home:* 2802 Sagamore Rd., Toledo, Ohio 43606. *Office:* University of Toledo, 2801 Bancroft St., Toledo, Ohio 43606.

CAREER: Associated Hospital Service of Philadelphia, Philadelphia, Pa., sales writer, 1959; University of Toledo, Toledo, Ohio, assistant professor, 1965-68, associate professor of English, 1968—. Consultant to Houghton Mifflin Co., Holt, Rinehart & Winston, and Norton Co. *Member:* National Council of Teachers of English, College English Association of Ohio (secretary-treasurer, 1973-74, 1976-78).

WRITINGS: Wood County Place Names, University of Wisconsin Press, 1970.

*   *   *

RUECHELLE, Randall C(ummings) 1920-

PERSONAL: Born December 28, 1920, in Kalispell, Mont.; son of A. J. (an engineer) and Josephine (Cummings) Ruechelle; married Dorothy Marie Kunka, August 26, 1954; children: Lynn Marie, David Alan. *Education:* University of Chicago, A.B., 1942, M.A., 1944; graduate study at Northwestern University, 1949, and Washington State University, 1951; University of Southern California, Ph.D., 1953. *Politics:* Democrat. *Home:* 1212 Payne Ave., Modesto, Calif. 95351. *Office:* Department of Speech Communication, California State College, Stanislaus, Turlock, Calif. 95380.

CAREER: Michigan State University of Agriculture and Applied Science (now Michigan State University), East Lansing, instructor in speech, 1947-49; Northern Idaho College of Education (now Lewis-Clark State College), Lewiston, instructor in speech, 1949-51; Colorado State University, Fort Collins, associate professor, 1953-64, professor of speech, 1953-64, chairman of department, 1953-64; California State College, Stanislaus, Turlock, Calif., professor of speech and chairman of department, 1964—. Instructor in Peace Corps Training Program, summer, 1961. *Member:* International Communication Association, Speech Communication Association, Speech Association of America, American Association of University Professors, Western Speech Association.

WRITINGS: (With T. H. Napiecinski) *Speaking and Listening,* W. C. Brown, 1962; (with Napiecinski) *Beginning Speech,* Allyn & Bacon, 1964; (with Napiecinski) *Workbook for Speech,* Allyn & Bacon, 1964. Also author with M.C. Norton, of *Communication Theory: A Systems Approach.* Contributor to *Speech Monographs, Journal of Communication,* and other journals.

*   *   *

RUGG, Dean S(prague) 1923-

PERSONAL: Born January 17, 1923, in New York, N.Y.; son of Earle U. (a professor) and Cena (Sprague) Rugg; married June Kintzel, December 29, 1951; children: Brian E., Lawrence M., Andrea E. *Education:* Northwestern University, B.S., 1947, M.A., 1949; University of Maryland, Ph.D., 1962. *Home:* 3468 Woods Ave., Lincoln, Neb. 68510. *Office:* Department of Geography, University of Nebraska, Lincoln, Neb. 68588.

CAREER: Central Intelligence Agency, Washington, D.C., geographic analyst, 1950-56; U.S. State Department, Germany, foreign service, 1957-63; University of Nebraska, Lincoln, associate professor, 1964-69, professor of geography, 1969—. *Military service:* U.S. Marine Corps Reserve, 1943-46. *Member:* Association of American Geographers. *Awards, honors:* Fulbright research grant to Vienna, Austria, 1967-68.

WRITINGS: Spatial Foundations of Urbanism, W. C. Brown, 1972, 2nd edition, 1978; *Geography of Eastern Europe,* American Association for the Advancement of Slavic Studies, 1978.

WORK IN PROGRESS: Research on urban development and on East Europe.

*   *   *

RUIZ, Roberto 1925-

PERSONAL: Born December 20, 1925, in Madrid, Spain; son of Roberto (an accountant) and Antonia (Fernandez) Ruiz; married Beatrice Koffman, August 15, 1956; children: Antonia Isabel. *Education:* Universidad Nacional de Mexico, Maestro en Filosofia, 1952; Princeton University, M.A., 1956. *Home:* 4 Library Sq., Norton, Mass. 02766. *Office:* Department of Spanish, Wheaton College, Norton, Mass. 02766.

CAREER: Mt. Holyoke College, South Hadley, Mass., instructor in Spanish, 1953-56; Hunter College (now Hunter College of the City University of New York), New York, N.Y., lecturer in Spanish, 1956-58; Middlebury College, Middlebury, Vt., lecturer in Spanish, 1959-61; Dickinson College, Carlisle, Pa., assistant professor of Spanish, 1961-63; Wheaton College, Norton, Mass., associate professor, 1963-73, professor of Spanish, 1973—. *Member:* Modern Language Association of America, American Association of Teachers of Spanish and Portuguese.

WRITINGS: Esquemas (short stories), Bajel, 1954; *Plazas sin muros* (novel), De Andrea, 1960; *El ultimo oasis* (novel), J. Mortiz, 1964; *Los jueces implacables* (novel), J. Mortiz, 1970; *Paraiso cerrado, cielo abierto* (novel), J. Mortiz, 1977. Contributor of short stories to Spanish and Mexican literary journals.

WORK IN PROGRESS: Contra la luz que muere, a novel; *Cromos de galeria,* short stories.

SIDELIGHTS: "As a young man I used to feel sorry for people who did not write," Roberto Ruiz told *CA.* "Now I feel sorry for people who do. Then as now, however, I look upon creative writing as the only free activity left to us. Language is our first acquisition, and written language our ultimate treasure, a treasure that can only be increased by being expended and that only mental avarice can exhaust or devalue. The struggle of the creative writer against the demeaning of words requires a deeper love of freedom than any revolution, and unlike revolutions, it does not have to consolidate itself in bureaucracy and dogma. I believe that the future will consume and discard many a trade, but the creative writer, unless he persists in squashing his material into a meaningless pulp, will manage to survive. As long, that is, as mankind survives the threat of far more potent weapons than the N-bomb: ignorance, injustice, laziness and idiocy."

RUJA, Harry 1912-

PERSONAL: Born February 26, 1912, in Paterson, N.J.; son of Abram Joseph and Sarah (Skroopka) Ruja; married Rose Leah Rosenberg, December 22, 1940; children: Michele B. (Mrs. Ali Hebshi), Ellen Gay Ruja Tamarelle, Nancy Joanna (Mrs. John Terhorst). Education: University of California, Los Angeles, A.B., 1933; University of Chicago, M.A., 1934; Princeton University, Ph.D., 1936; San Diego State College (now University), M.A., 1953. Politics: Democrat. Religion: Judaism. Office: Department of Philosophy, San Diego State University, San Diego, Calif. 92182.

CAREER: Compton College, Compton, Calif., instructor in psychology and philosophy, 1939-47; San Diego State University, San Diego, Calif., assistant professor, 1947-53, associate professor, 1953-57, professor of psychology and philosophy, 1957-58, professor of philosophy, 1958—, chairman of department of philosophy, 1959-62, associate dean for curriculum, 1970-71, coordinator of Jewish studies, 1971-77. Visiting professor at University of Minnesota, summer, 1959, Pennsylvania State University, 1964-65, and C. W. Post Campus, Long Island University, summer, 1965. Vice-president, Jewish Social Service Agency, San Diego, 1956; vice-president, San Diego Jewish Community Center, 1961-63.

MEMBER: American Philosophical Association, American Civil Liberties Union (president, San Diego branch, 1957-58), Zionist Organization of America (president, San Diego district, 1973-75, southern California region, 1975-77), Labor Zionist Alliance (president of local chapter, 1976-77), United Professors of California (vice-president, college local, 1962; secretary, 1963, 1978—), California Employees Association, B'nai B'rith (president of San Diego lodge, 1958-59, 1973-74), Yiddish Literary and Musical Circle (president, 1962-64, 1967-71, 1972-74).

WRITINGS: Psychology for Life, McGraw, 1955; (editorial assistant) D. C. Williams, Principles of Empirical Realism, C. C Thomas, 1966; (contributor) David F. Pears, editor, Bertrand Russell: A Collection of Critical Essays, Doubleday, 1972; (compiler and editor) Bertrand Russell, Mortals and Others, Volume I, Allen & Unwin, 1975. Contributor to Jewish Spectator and other journals of Jewish interest, and to philosophy, psychology, and education journals. Member of board of editors, Philosophy and Phenomenological Research.

WORK IN PROGRESS: A comprehensive bibliography of Bertrand Russell; a discography of biblical music.

*   *   *

RUOFF, James E. 1925-

PERSONAL: Born April 12, 1925, in Seattle, Wash.; son of David Paul (a salesman) and Lorrayne (Cannon) Ruoff; married Jacquelyn Nadine Bollman (a psychologist), December 21, 1949; children: Mary Nadine, Thomas Matthew, Amy Jane. Education: University of Washington, B.A., 1949; University of Pennsylvania, M.A., 1951, Ph.D., 1954. Politics: Democrat. Religion: None. Home: 77 East 12th St., New York, N.Y. 10003. Office: Department of English, City College of the City University of New York, 133rd St. at Convent Ave., New York, N.Y. 10031.

CAREER: Alfred University, Alfred, N.Y., assistant professor of English, 1953-56; Washington State University, Pullman, assistant professor of English, 1956-60; Wichita State University, Wichita, Kan., assistant professor, 1960-

61, associate professor, 1961-62, professor of English, 1962-63; City College of the City University of New York, New York, N.Y., associate professor, 1964-73, professor of English, 1973—. Fulbright lecturer in Turkey, 1977-78. Military service: U.S. Army, 1943-46. Member: National Council of Teachers of English, Modern Language Association of America.

WRITINGS: (Editor) Major Elizabethan Poetry and Prose, Crowell, 1972; Crowell Handbook of Elizabethan and Stuart Literature, Crowell, 1973 (published in England as Macmillan's Handbook of Elizabethan and Stuart Literature, Macmillan, 1975); (with Edward G. Quinn and Joseph Grennen) Major Shakespearean Tragedies, Free Press, 1973. Contributor to scholarly journals.

*   *   *

RUOTOLO, Lucio P(eter) 1927-

PERSONAL: Surname is accented on first syllable; born March 14, 1927, in New York, N.Y.; son of Onorio (a sculptor) and Lucy (Sperling) Ruotolo; married Marcia Mauney, June 11, 1960; children: Cristina, Vanessa, Peter. Education: Colgate University, B.A., 1951; Columbia University, M.A., 1954, Ph.D., 1960. Politics: Democrat. Religion: Presbyterian. Home: 951 Mears Court, Stanford, Calif. 94305. Office: Department of English, Stanford University, Stanford, Calif. 94305.

CAREER: Stanford University, Stanford, Calif., instructor, 1957-61, assistant professor, 1961-66, associate professor, 1966-73, professor of English, 1973—, director of undergraduate studies, 1973—, chairman of modern thought and literature department, 1974-75. Member of board of directors, Peninsula Drama Guild, 1965-67; co-chairman, Stanford-Palo Alto Democratic Club, 1968; trustee, Virginia Woolf Society, 1975—. Military service: U.S. Army Air Forces, 1945-47. Awards, honors: Harvard University Press Thomas J. Wilson Memorial Prize, Board of Syndics, 1972, for Six Existential Heroes: The Politics of Faith.

WRITINGS: Six Existential Heroes: The Politics of Faith, Harvard University Press, 1972; (editor) Virginia Woolf, Freshwater, Harcourt, 1976. Contributor to Journal of the History of Ideas, Modern Language Quarterly, College English, Renascence, Christianity and Crisis, Motive, Virginia Woolf Miscellany, Women's Studies, and University of Toronto Quarterly. Film critic, Christianity and Crisis. Founding editor, Virginia Woolf Miscellany, 1974—.

WORK IN PROGRESS: Contributing to a volume of Virginia Woolf criticism, edited by Rolph Freedman; editing remaining unpublished Virginia Woolf manuscripts; a critical book on Virginia Woolf's novels.

BIOGRAPHICAL/CRITICAL SOURCES: Journal of the History of Ideas, June, 1969.

*   *   *

RUSALEM, Herbert 1918-

PERSONAL: Born December 4, 1918; son of Frank (a realtor) and Eva (Einwohner) Rusalem; married Helen Winter (a researcher), April 30, 1970. Education: Long Island University, B.A., 1948; Columbia University, M.A., 1949, Ed.D., 1951. Home: 16610 Meadow Park Dr., Sun City, Ariz. 85351.

CAREER: Federation of the Handicapped, New York City, associate executive director, 1950-53; Long Island University, Brooklyn, N.Y., assistant professor, 1951-53, associate professor of psychology, 1953-56; City University of New

York, New York City, associate professor of psychology, 1956-58; Columbia University, Teachers College, New York City, professor of psychology, 1968-77. Co-director, Learning Capacities Research Project. Consultant to national, state, and local societies and institutions, including City of New York, 1966—, New York University, 1966—, National Industries for the Blind, 1967—, State of New York, 1970—, and National Easter Seal Society, 1972—. *Member:* American Psychological Association (fellow), Academy of Certified Social Workers, National Association of Social Workers, American Personnel and Guidance Association, National Rehabilitation Association, Council for Exceptional Children.

WRITINGS: Vocational Development of the Deaf-Blind, Industrial Home for the Blind, 1960; *Guiding the Physically Handicapped College Student,* Teachers College Press, 1962; *Vocational Rehabilitation of the Older Disabled Worker,* Federation Employment & Guidance Service, 1968; (editor with David Maukin) *Vocational Rehabilitation of the Disabled: An Overview,* New York University Press, 1970; *Coping with the Unseen Environment,* Teachers College Press, 1972; (editor with David Malikin) *Contemporary Vocational Rehabilitation,* New York University Press, 1976. Author of several other reports on rehabilitation and adjustment; editor of proceedings. Research editor, *Journal of Rehabilitation Literature.*

WORK IN PROGRESS: A book on survival strategies.

* * *

RUSSELL, Daniel 1937-

PERSONAL: Born December 7, 1937, in Ilion, N.Y.; son of Shirley Laveck (a farmer) and Olive (Stearns) Russell; married Suzanne Plancon, March 26, 1966; children: Allison, Nicolas. *Education:* Hamilton College, B.A., 1959; New York University, M.A., 1961, Ph.D., 1968; graduate study at Universite de Lille, 1963-64, and Universite de Paris, 1964-65. *Office:* 1328 C.L., University of Pittsburgh, Pittsburgh, Pa. 15260.

CAREER: Hamilton College, Clinton, N.Y., instructor in Romance languages, 1965-68; University of Pittsburgh, Pittsburgh, Pa., assistant professor, 1968-74, associate professor of French, 1974—, director of University of Pittsburgh Program in France, 1971-72, and Medieval and Renaissance Studies Program, 1977—. *Member:* Modern Language Association of America, American Association of University Professors, Renaissance Society of America, American Association of Teachers of French.

WRITINGS: (Translator) Walter Weideli, *The Art of Berthold Brecht,* New York University Press, 1963; (translator) Gaston Bachebard, *The Poetics of Reverie,* Orion Press, 1969.

WORK IN PROGRESS: Emblems and Emblem Books in Renaissance France.

* * *

RUSSELL, Douglas A(ndrew) 1927-

PERSONAL: Born February 9, 1927, in Berkeley, Calif.; son of Foster Douglas (a salesman) and May Inez (Donnell) Russell; married Marilyn Carol Nelson (a teacher), December 26, 1953; children: Malcolm, Andrea. *Education:* Stanford University, B.A., 1949, M.A., 1950; Yale University, M.F.A., 1961. *Politics:* Independent. *Religion:* Unitarian Universalist. *Home:* 765 Mayfield Ave., Stanford, Calif. 94305. *Office:* Drama Department, Stanford University, Stanford, Calif. 94305.

CAREER: Carnegie-Mellon University, Pittsburgh, Pa., instructor in drama, 1950-51; Florida State University, Tallahassee, instructor in speech and drama, 1951-54; University of Kansas City (now University of Missouri—Kansas City), Kansas City, Mo., assistant professor of drama, 1955-59; Stanford University, Stanford, Calif., associate professor, 1961-77, professor of drama, 1977—, lecturer at Stanford in Austria, 1966-67, 1971, and Stanford in France, 1975. Director of costume for the Oregon Shakespeare Festival, summers, 1948-61; lecturer at Southern Oregon College, summers, 1949-52, American School in Lugano, 1967, University of Amsterdam, 1971, University of Exeter, 1971 and 1975, East Anglia University, 1971, and University of Bristol, 1971. Costume designer for American Conservatory Theatre, and Actor's Workshop, San Francisco, Old Globe, San Diego, Summer Repertory Theatre, Santa Rosa, Missouri Repertory Theatre, and Renaissance Festival, Victoria, British Columbia. *Military service:* U.S. Army, Signal Corps, 1945-46. *Member:* United Nations Association, American Association of University Professors, American Theatre Association, United Scenic Artists of America, United States Institute of Theatre Technology, California Theatre Association, Smithsonian Preservation Trust, Common Cause. *Awards, honors:* Fulbright fellowship, Stratford, England, 1954-55; Danforth teacher study grant, Yale University, 1959-60; Humanities and Science Research Award, Stanford University, 1973.

WRITINGS: Stage Costume Design, Prentice-Hall, 1973; *Theatrical Style: A Visual Approach to the Theatre,* Mayfield, 1976; *Anthology of Austrian Drama,* Associated University Presses, 1979. Contributor of articles to *Players Magazine, Educational Theatre Journal, Theatre Crafts,* and *Theatre Arts.*

WORK IN PROGRESS: Period Style for the Theatre, for Allyn & Bacon; *Foundations of Costume History; Shakespearean Costume Design.*

* * *

RUSSELL, Josiah Cox 1900-

PERSONAL: Born September 3, 1900, in Richmond, Ind.; son of Elbert (a university dean) and Lieuetta (Cox) Russell; married Ruth Winslow (a librarian), September 15, 1924; children: Elbert Winslow, Walter Howard, Joan. *Education:* Studied at University of Rome, 1921-22; Earlham College, A.B., 1922; Harvard University, A.M., 1923, Ph.D., 1926. *Politics:* Republican. *Religion:* Society of Friends (Quaker). *Home:* 16 South Wind Circle, St. Augustine, Fla. 32084.

CAREER: Colorado College, Colorado Springs, assistant professor of history, 1927-29; New Mexico Normal University (now New Mexico Highlands University), Las Vegas, professor of history and head of department, 1929-31; University of North Carolina at Chapel Hill, instructor, 1931-35, assistant professor, 1935-39, associate professor of history, 1939-46; University of New Mexico, Albuquerque, professor of history, 1946-65, professor emeritus, 1965—, head of department, 1946-53; Texas A & I University, Kingsville, professor of history, 1965-71. Fulbright professor, University College of Wales, 1952-53. District chairman Boy Scouts of America, Orange County, N.C., 1945-46; president, Albuquerque Retarded Children's Association, 1961-62.

MEMBER: American Historical Association, Mediaeval Academy of America, Population Association of America, American Association of University Professors (member of council, 1953-56). *Awards, honors:* Guggenheim fellow,

1930-31; grants from American Council of Learned Societies, 1933, 1934, American Philosophical Society, 1938-39, 1961, and Social Science Research Council, 1938, 1949, 1951; Piper Foundation Award (given annually to ten Texas professors in recognition of teaching), 1971.

WRITINGS: (Editor with J. P. Heironimua) *The Shorter Latin Poems of Master Henry of Avranches Relating to England,* Mediaeval Academy of America, 1935; *Dictionary of Writers of Thirteenth Century England,* Institute of Historical Research (London), 1936, reprinted, B. Franklin, 1971; *British Medieval Population,* University of New Mexico Press, 1948; (editor with William M. Dabney) *Dargan Historical Essays,* University of New Mexico Press, 1952; *Late Ancient and Medieval Population,* American Philosophical Society, 1958; *Jesus of Nazareth,* Pageant, 1967; *Medieval Regions and Their Cities,* Indiana University Press, 1972. Contributor of about eighty articles to learned journals.

WORK IN PROGRESS: Studies in medieval population, principally cemetery evidence; research in extrasensory perception.

* * *

RUSSO, John Paul 1944-

PERSONAL: Born May 31, 1944, in Boston, Mass.; son of Joseph E. T. and Theresa V. (Minichiello) Russo. *Education:* Harvard University, A.B., 1965, M.A., 1966, Ph.D., 1969. *Home:* 1420 Locust St., Philadelphia, Penn. *Office:* Department of English, Camden College, Rutgers University, Camden, N.J. 08102.

CAREER: Harvard University, Cambridge, Mass., assistant professor of English, 1969-73; University of Chicago, Chicago, Ill., assistant professor of English, 1973-77; Rutgers University, Camden College, Camden, N.J., associate professor of English, 1977—. *Member:* New England Modern Language Association.

WRITINGS: Alexander Pope: Tradition and Identity, Harvard University Press, 1972; (contributor) Reuben Brower, Helen Vendler, and John Holloway, editors, *I. A. Richards: Essays in His Honor,* Oxford University Press, 1973; (editor) *Complementaries: I. A. Richards' Uncollected Essays,* Harvard University Press, 1976.

WORK IN PROGRESS: A critical biography of I. A. Richards.

* * *

RUTTAN, Vernon W(esley) 1924-

PERSONAL: Born August 16, 1924, in Alden, Mich.; son of Ward W. (a farmer) and Marjorie Ann (Chaney) Ruttan; married Mabel Mayne Barone, July 30 1946; children: Lia Marie, Christopher II, Alison Elane, Lore Megan. *Education:* Attended Michigan State University, 1942-43; Yale University, B.A., 1948; University of Chicago, M.A., 1950, Ph.D., 1952. *Home address:* Box 92, Ely, Minn. 55731. *Office:* Department of Agricultural and Applied Economics, University of Minnesota, St. Paul, Minn. 55108.

CAREER: Tennessee Valley Authority, Knoxville, Tenn., economist in Division of Regional Studies, 1951-53, economist in office of general manager, 1953-54; Purdue University, Lafayette, Ind., assistant professor, 1955-57, associate professor, 1957-60, professor of agricultural economics, 1960-63; International Rice Research Institute, Los Banos, Laguna, Philippines, agricultural economist for Rockefeller Foundation, 1963-65; University of Minnesota, St. Paul,

professor of agricultural economics, 1965-73, head of department, 1965-70, director of Economic Development Center, 1970-73; Agricultural Development Council, Inc., New York, N.Y., president, 1973-77; University of Minnesota, professor of agricultural economics, 1977—. Associate agricultural economist, Giannini Foundation of Agricultural Economics, University of California, Berkeley 1958-59; staff economist, U.S. President's Council of Economic Advisers, 1963-65; member of research advisory committee, U.S. Agency for International Development, 1967—. Trustee, Agricultural Development Council, 1967-73. *Military service:* U.S. Army, 1943-46. *Member:* American Agricultural Economics Association (president, 1971-72).

WRITINGS: The Economic Demand for Irrigated Acreage: New Methodology and Some Preliminary Projections, 1954-1980, Johns Hopkins Press, for Resources for the Future, Inc., 1965; (with Jules Janick, R. W. Schery, and F. W. Woods) *Plant Science: An Introduction to World Crops,* W. H. Freeman, 1969; (with Yujiro Hayami) *Agricultural Development: An International Perspective,* Johns Hopkins Press, 1971; (with Hans Binswonger) *Induced Innovation: Technology, Institutions and Development,* Johns Hopkins Press, 1978. Contributor of over 100 articles to economics journals, including *American Journal of Agricultural Economics, American Economic Review, Food Research Institute Studies, Indian Journal of Agricultural Economics, Quarterly Journal of Economics, Journal of Political Economy, Journal of Farm Economics, Philippine Economic Review,* and *Review of Economics and Statistics.*

* * *

RUTTKOWSKI, Wolfgang Victor 1935-

PERSONAL: Born February 5, 1935, in Hirschberg, Germany; son of Victor Leopold (a banker) and Ursula (Drobnig) Ruttkowski. *Education:* University of Goettingen, M.A., 1961; McGill University, Ph.D., 1965; Kultusministerium, Hannover, Dr. Phil., 1967; also studied at University of Vienna and University of Berlin. *Office:* German Department, Temple University, Philadelphia, Pa. 19122.

CAREER: Schiller Gymnasium, Hannover, Germany, Studienreferender, 1961-63; University of Southern California, Los Angeles, assistant professor of German, 1965-68; New York University, New York, N.Y., associate professor of German and comparative literature, 1969-73; Temple University, Philadelphia, Pa., associate professor of German and comparative literature, 1974—. Visiting professor, University of California, Riverside, 1968-69; visiting professor of German literature, Tokyo University, Japan, 1972-74. *Member:* Modern Language Association of America, American Association of Teachers of German, Philological Association of the Pacific Coast, Japanische Gesellschaft fuer Germanistik.

WRITINGS: Das literarische Chanson in Deutschland, Francke Verlag, 1966; *Die literarischen Gattungen: Reflexionen ueber eine modifizierte Fundamentalpoetik,* Francke Verlag, 1968; (with R. E. Blake) *Glossaire de termes litteraires; Glossary of Literary Terms; Literaturwoerterbuch; for the Student of General and Comparative Literature in English, German, and French,* Francke Verlag, 1969; *Bibliographie der Gattungspoetik fuer den Studenten der Literaturwissenschaft. Ein abgekuerztes Verzeichnis von ueber 3000 Buechern, Dissertationen und Zeitschriftenartikeln in Deutsch, Englisch und Franzoesisch,* Max Hueber Verlag, 1973; *Typologien und Schichtenlehren. Bibliographieder internationalen Schrifttums bis 1970,* Rodopi Verlag, 1973; (editor and contributor) *Einfuehrung in die deutsche Literaturwissenschaft fuer Studenten,* Nashville Press, 1973; *Typen und Schichten: Zur Einteilung des Menschen und seiner Produkte,* Francke Verlag, 1978.

WORK IN PROGRESS: A Literary Nomenclator: A Glossary of Literary Terms in Dutch, English, French, German, Italian, Russian, and Spanish, for Francke Verlag.

* * *

RYAN, Herbert J(oseph) 1931-

PERSONAL: Born February 19, 1931, in Scarsdale, N.Y.; son of Herbert Joseph (a lawyer) and Elizabeth (Gallagher) Ryan. *Education:* Loyola University of Chicago, A.B., 1954, Ph.L., 1956, M.A., 1960; Woodstock College, S.T.L., 1963; Gregorian University, S.T.D., 1967. *Politics:* Independent. *Home:* 7101 West 80th St., Los Angeles, Calif. 90045. *Agent:* Thomas P. Coffey, P.O. Box 811, Denville, N.J. 07834. *Office:* Department of Religious Studies, Loyola Marymount University, Los Angeles, Calif. 90045.

CAREER: Entered Society of Jesus, 1949, ordained Roman Catholic priest, 1962; Woodstock College, New York, N.Y., assistant professor, 1967-70, associate professor of historical theology, 1970-74; Loyola Marymount University, Los Angeles, Calif., professor of historical theology, 1974—. Member of Anglican Roman Catholic International Commission and Anglican-Roman Catholic Consultation of the United States of America. *Member:* American Academy of Religion, Catholic Historical Society, Catholic Theological Society of America, Church Historical Society, Mediaeval Academy of America, American Academy of Ecumenists.

WRITINGS: The "De Praedestinatione" of John Scottus Eriugena, Gregorian University Press, 1967; (editor) *Episcopalians and Roman Catholics: Can They Ever Get Together?,* Dimension Books, 1972; (editor) *Documents on Anglican-Roman Catholic Relations,* United States Catholic Conference Press, 1973; (contributor) R. Terwilliger and U. Holmes, editors, *To Be a Priest,* Seabury, 1975; (contributor) L. Swidler, editor, *The Eucharist in Ecumenical Dialogue,* Paulist/Newman, 1976.

WORK IN PROGRESS: Ecumenical Spirituality; English translation of Eriugena's *De Praedestinatione; Exploring Christian Mysticism.*

* * *

RYAN, T. Antoinette 1924-

PERSONAL: Born May 1, 1924, in Montana; daughter of Benjamin W. and Mary B. (McHale) Ryan. *Education:* Sacramento State College (now California State University, Sacramento), B.A., 1949, M.A., 1952; graduate study at University of Geneva, 1953, and University of Oslo, 1956; Stanford University, Ph.D., 1963. *Residence:* Lexington, S.C. *Office:* College of Criminal Justice, University of South Carolina, Columbia, S.C. 29208.

CAREER: Sacramento City College, Sacramento, Calif., head counselor of extension division, 1957-60, director of testing, 1961-62, counselor, 1962-63; Oregon State University, Corvallis, associate professor of educational psychology, 1963-65, director of research coordinating unit, 1965-68; University of Hawaii, Honolulu, researcher and professor of educational psychology, 1968-76; University of South Carolina, Columbia, professor of criminal justice, 1976-77, associate dean of College of Criminal Justice, 1977—. Member of

President's Commission on Children and Youth, 1970. *Member:* American Correctional Association, American Educational Research Association (Division E vice-president, 1970-72), American Personnel and Guidance Association, American Psychological Association, Western Psychological Association, Pi Lambda Theta. *Awards, honors:* National award for outstanding research in guidance from American Personnel and Guidance Association, 1966; citation for research, American Psychological Association, 1976.

WRITINGS: (With Philip Perrone and others) *Guidance and the Emerging Adolescent,* Intext, 1970; *Organization and Administration of Guidance,* Interstate, 1972; *Generalized Planning Model for Corrections,* University of South Carolina, 1977; *Organization and Administration of Guidance: A Systems Approach,* Interstate, 1978; *Systems Models for Supervision,* American Personnel and Guidance Association, 1978. Contributor of over one hundred articles to *Educational Technology, Personnel and Guidance Journal,* and other journals. Consulting editor of *Journal of Counseling Psychology*

* * *

RYAN, Thomas Arthur 1911-

PERSONAL: Born September 15, 1911, in Batavia, N.Y.; son of Thomas Francis (a bookkeeper) and Ruby (Barber) Ryan; married Mary McElheny Shaw (a professor), September 12, 1935; children: Thomas A., Jr., Adelaide. *Education:* Cornell University, A.B., 1933, Ph.D., 1937. *Home:* 210 Mitchell St., Ithaca, N.Y. 14850. *Office:* Department of Psychology, 286 Social Science Bldg., Cornell University, Ithaca, N.Y. 14850.

CAREER: Cornell University, Ithaca, N.Y., instructor 1937-42, assistant professor, 1942-46, associate professor, 1946-49, professor of psychology, 1949-77, professor emeritus, 1977—, chairman of department, 1953-61. *Member:* American Psychological Association, American Statistical Association, Phi Beta Kappa, Sigma Xi.

WRITINGS: Work and Effort: The Psychology of Production, Ronald, 1947; (with P. C. Smith) *Principles of Industrial Psychology,* Ronald, 1954; *Intentional Behavior: An Approach to Human Motivation,* Ronald, 1970. Member of editorial board and book review editor, *American Journal of Psychology,* 1957-67, *Journal of Applied Psychology,* 1956-70, and *Journal for the Theory of Social Behavior,* 1971-77.

WORK IN PROGRESS: Research on statistical methodology, and on motivation in learning.

* * *

RYBALKA, Michel 1933-

PERSONAL: Born December 7, 1933, in Sens, France; son of Archyp and Antonina (Grzybowski) Rybalka; married Maya Coudroy (a professor), May 30, 1964; children: Paul-Stephane, Catherine, Pascaline. *Education:* University of Nancy, Licence es Lettres, 1956, 1962; University of California, Los Angeles, M.A., 1959, Ph.D., 1966. *Office:* Department of Romance Languages, Washington University, St. Louis, Mo. 63130.

CAREER: University of California, Santa Barbara, instructor in French, 1962-64; Reed College, Portland, Ore., assistant professor of French, 1964-66; University of Rochester, Rochester, N.Y., 1966-72, began as assistant professor, became associate professor of French; Washington University, St. Louis, Mo., professor of French, 1972—.

Military service: French Army, 1959-61; became sergeant. *Member:* Societe des Professeurs Francais en Amerique, College de Pataphysique, Modern Language Association of America, American Association of Teachers of French, Midwest Modern Language Association (vice-president, 1979). *Awards, honors:* Fulbright grant, 1957-58; Guggenheim fellowship, 1970-71.

WRITINGS: Boris Vian, Lettres Modernes, 1969; (with Michel Contat) *Les Ecrits de Sartre,* Gallimard, 1970, revised edition, translated by Richard McLeary, Northwestern University Press, 1973; (editor with Contat) Jean Paul Sartre, *Un Theatre de situations,* Gallimard, 1973, translation by Frank Jellinek published as *Sartre on Theater,* Pantheon, 1976. Also co-editor of *Les Romans de Jean Paul Sartre.* Contributor to *Le Monde, Le Nouvel Observateur, Magazine Litteraire, Les Temps Modernes, French Review, L'Esprit Createur, West Coast Review, Obliques, Telos, Contemporary French Civilization,* and *Subsidia Pataphysica.*

WORK IN PROGRESS: Dossier Sartre, for Belfond; *Les Ecrits et les films d'Alain Robbe-Grillet.*

*   *   *

RZHEVSKY, Leonid   1905-

PERSONAL: Born August 21, 1905, in Moscow, Russia; naturalized U.S. citizen, 1970; son of Denis and Elisabeth (de Roberty la Cerda) Surazhevsky; married Agnes Shishkov (a teacher at Fordham University), August 18, 1943. *Education:* Attended Moscow Second University, 1927-30; Lenin Pedagogical Institute, Ph.D.,1941. *Religion:* Russian Orthodox. *Home:* 1 Washington Square Village, Apt. 15-S, New York, N.Y. 10012.

CAREER: Pedagogical Institute, Moscow, Soviet Union (also Tula and Orechovo), associate professor of Russian language and literature, 1938-41; University of Lund, Lund, Sweden, university lektor, 1953-63; University of Oklahoma, Norman, professor of Russian literature, 1963-64; New York University, New York City, professor of Slavic literature, 1964-74, professor emeritus, 1974—. *Military service:* Russian Army, 1941; became lieutenant. *Member:* Modern Language Association of America, International P.E.N.

WRITINGS: Between Two Stars (novel), Chekhov Publishing, 1953; *To This Who Showed Us Light* (novel), Possev Verlag, 1960; *Two on the Stone* (short stories), [Munich], 1960; *Through the Straits* (short stories), [Munich], 1966; *The Language of Creative Writing,* New York University Press, 1970; *Three Themes on Dostoevsky,* [Frankfort on the Main], 1972; *Creator and Heroic Deed: Essays on the Art of Alexander Solzhenitsyn,* [Frankfort on the Main], 1972, translation by Sonja Miller published as *Solzhenitsyn: Creator and Heroic Deed,* University of Alabama Press, 1978; *Two Strokes of Time* (novel), Possev Verlag, 1976.

S

SACHS, Alexander 1893-1973

August 8, 1893—June 23, 1973; American economist, presidential adviser, corporation executive, consultant to government and private groups, and writer on his speciality. Obituaries: *Washington Post*, June 28, 1973.

* * *

SADECKY, Petr Milos 1943-

PERSONAL: Surname is pronounced Sad-etsky; born January 4, 1943, in Prague, Czechoslovakia; son of Frantisek (a teacher) and Zdenka (a teacher; maiden name Mikova) Sadecky; married Alenka Solar, 1969 (divorced, 1972); married Ursula Aufderhaar (a language teacher), 1972. *Education:* Enrolled at Faculty of Film and Television, Prague Academy of Arts, as youngest student, 1960, and studied there for total of five years, receiving diploma (with honors), 1967; also studied painting as external student at art academies in Prague and Kiev. *Religion:* Protestant.

CAREER: Made lecture tour in Czechoslovakia and Russia at invitation of Soviet Ministry of Culture, 1961; prior to 1966 was sent or invited to make educational and reporting trips totaling eighteen months in Russia, Central Asia, Siberia, Mongolia, North Korea, China, and Tibet; during this period also did free-lance reporting for newspapers in Prague and Tiflis and research for Committee for the Friendship of the Soviet and Czechoslovakian Peoples in Moscow; film historian and critic, Film Institute, Prague, Czechoslovakia, 1966; his "pro-communist involvement cooled down" when two of his books were banned, and he defected to West Germany as a political refugee, 1967; free-lance researcher for Institute for the Study of the U.S.S.R., Munich, Germany, 1967-71. *Military service:* Czechoslovakian Army, special corps, 1964-66. *Member:* International P.E.N., P.E.N. in Exile (London), Society of German Writers (Frankfort), Society of Authors (London), Authors League of America. *Awards, honors:* Decorated by Turkmenian Soviet Republic, 1965, for increasing the knowledge of Soviet culture.

WRITINGS: Istern, originalnoje javlenije mirovij kultury (title means "Eastern, Original Phenomenon in World Culture"), published by Institute of Folklore and Ethnography (Kiev), 1966, but confiscated before distribution; (with T. I. Rjepin) *Dostischenija i krizisy nacionalnyh kinematografij Sovetskogo Sojuza* (title means "Achievements and Crises of the National Cinematographies of the Soviet Union"), published by Film-Studio Tadschikfilm (Duschanbe), 1966, but confiscated before distribution; *Octobriana and the Russian Underground* (documentary report with commentary), Harper, 1971.

Co-compiler: Otakar Batlicka, *Na vlne 57 metro* (short stories; title means "On Wave 57 Meters"), [Ostrava], 1965; *Bibliografie fondu vychodnich kinematografii v Cs.Filmoven Archivu* (bibliography of Eastern films in the Czechoslovak Film Archives), Film Institute (Prague), 1967.

Author of scripts and co-director of television films produced in Prague, Bratislava, Warsaw, and Budapest: "Od Lincolna ke Kennedymu: Zrozeni a konec americkeho snu (title means "From Lincoln to Kennedy: Birth and Death of an American Dream"), 1962; (with Jan Moravec) "Soumrak indianu" (title means "Dusk of Indians"), 1963; "Sir Henry Rider Haggard," 1963; "Globetrotter Alfred Aloysius Horn," 1963; "Neni cesty do Tucumanu" (title means "There Is No Way to Tucuman"), 1963; "Cesta Rude Armady" (title means "Way of the Red Army"), 1964; "Mongolska rebelie" (title means "Mongolian Revolt"), 1965.

Unpublished books: "Eastern Reports" (on travels through Communist countries, 1960-66); (editor and author of introduction) "Diogenes on the Sputnik: Or, the Revolt of Modern Soviet Science Fiction"; "How a Dream is Killed" (pseudo-poetry on travels, 1967-71); "The Beauty of a Lie" (analysis of Soviet film art).

Author of booklets published by Czechoslovakian Army and Ministry of Culture. Also author of radio adaptations of the short stories published in *Na vlne 57 Metro,* 1965-68. Among about three hundred articles published in magazines and daily newspapers, 1960-66, were twenty analyses of Soviet cinematography and culture, and a series of polemics analyzing and acknowledging western culture. Some of his writing has been published under a withheld pseudonym.

WORK IN PROGRESS: Two books, *Anticommunist Manifesto* and *The Anatomy of Adventure;* film and television scripts based on *Octobriana and the Russian Underground.*

SIDELIGHTS: While growing up, Petr Sadecky was encouraged by his father "to become an enthusiastic admirer of Soviet revolutionary culture and of the communist system in general." After his defection to West Germany, he began traveling throughout the world, visiting Norway, Greenland,

Mexico, Brazil, United States, Canada, Australasia, and Africa, and other countries—"looking for adventure and the exotic." On these travels he did illustrations for classical adventure books for a west European publishing house.

Sadecky is fluent in Russian, English, and German, in addition to his native tongue, and speaks some Georgian and Armenian.

AVOCATIONAL INTERESTS: Paleontology, anthropology, ethnography, entomology, fencing, woodcraft, riding.

BIOGRAPHICAL/CRITICAL SOURCES: Sunday Telegraph Magazine (London), October 29, 1971; *Economist,* November 6, 1971; *Washington Post,* November 10, 1971; *Newsweek,* November 22, 1971; *Tattler,* December, 1971.††

* * *

SAFER, Elaine Berkman 1937-

PERSONAL: Born September 18, 1937, in Brooklyn, N.Y.; daughter of Israel (a social worker) and Sally (Bernstein) Berkman; married Daniel Safer (a physician), June 5, 1960; children: Debra, Alan, Judith. *Education:* Brooklyn College (now Brooklyn College of the City University of New York), B.A., 1958; University of Wisconsin, M.S., 1959; Case Western Reserve University, M.A., 1961, Ph.D., 1967. *Office:* Department of English, University of Delaware, Newark, Del. 19711.

CAREER: Northwestern University, Evanston, Ill., instructor in English, 1963-66; University of Delaware, Newark, assistant professor, 1967-73, associate professor of English, 1973—. *Member:* Milton Society of America, Renaissance Society of America, Modern Language Association of America, American Association of University Professors.

WRITINGS: (Editor with Thomas Erskine) *John Milton: L'Allegro and Il Penseroso,* C. E. Merrill, 1970. Contributor to *Milton Quarterly, Milton Encyclopedia, Improving College and University Teaching, Milton Studies,* and *Literature Film Quarterly.*

WORK IN PROGRESS: Several articles; a book on Milton's *Paradise Lost,* completion expected in 1979.

* * *

SAINE, Thomas P(rice) 1941-

PERSONAL: Born March 8, 1941, in Brooklyn, N.Y.; son of Clarence Price (an insurance underwriter) and Evelyn (Meadows) Saine; married Ute Mueller (a college teacher), July 27, 1963; children: Peter Kaspar, Jeremy Felix. *Education:* Yale University, B.A., 1962, M.Phil., 1967, Ph.D., 1968. *Office:* Department of German, University of California, Irvine, Calif. 92717.

CAREER: Yale University, New Haven, Conn., assistant professor, 1969-72, associate professor of German, 1972-75; University of California, Irvine, associate professor, 1975-76, professor of German, 1976—, chairman of department, 1976—. Visiting professor of German, University of Cincinnati, winter and spring, 1973-74. *Member:* Modern Language Association of America, American Lessing Society, American Society for Eighteenth Century Studies, American Association of Teachers of German, Goethe-Gesellschaft, Wiemar.

WRITINGS: Die aesthetische Theodizee. Karl Philipp Moritz und die Philosophie des 18. Jahrhunderts, Wilhelm Fink Verlag, 1971; *Georg Forster,* Twayne, 1972. Associate editor, *German Quarterly.*

WORK IN PROGRESS: A book on science, literature, philosophy, and theology in eighteenth-century Germany tentatively entitled *Von der Kopernikanischen bis zur Franzoesischen Revolution: Die Auseinandersetzung der deutshen Aufklaerung mit der Moderne,* for Erich Schmidt Verlag.

* * *

ST. ANTOINE, Theodore J(oseph) 1929-

PERSONAL: Born May 29, 1929, in St. Albans, Vt.; son of Arthur J. (a businessman) and M. Beatrice (Callery) St. Antoine; married Elizabeth Lloyd Frier, January 2, 1960; children: Arthur, Claire, Paul, Sara. *Education:* Fordham College, A.B. (summa cum laude), 1951; University of Michigan, J.D., 1954; University of London, graduate study, 1957-58. *Politics:* Democrat. *Religion:* Roman Catholic. *Home:* 1421 Roxbury Rd., Ann Arbor, Mich. 48104. *Office:* University of Michigan Law School, Ann Arbor, Mich. 48109.

CAREER: Admitted to the Bar of Michigan and the Bar of Ohio, 1954, the Bar of Washington, D.C., and the Bar of the U.S. Supreme Court, 1959; Squire, Sanders & Dempsey (law firm), Cleveland, Ohio, associate, 1954; Woll, Mayer & St. Antoine (law firm), Washington, D.C., partner, 1958-65; University of Michigan, Ann Arbor, 1965—, began as associate professor, currently professor of law, dean of Law School, 1971-78. Visiting professor of law, Duke University, 1978-79. Chairman of Michigan Governor's Workmen's Compensation Advisory Commission, 1974-75; president of National Resource Center for Consumers of Legal Services, 1974—; committee chairman, National Labor Relations Board Task Force, 1975-77. Member of panel of labor arbitrators, American Arbitration Association; member of panel of arbitrators, Federal Mediation and Conciliation Service. *Military service:* U.S. Army, 1955-57; became first lieutenant. *Member:* American Bar Association (secretary of labor relations law section, 1969-70, 1971-72), American Law Institute, Industrial Relations Research Association, Michigan Bar Association, Order of Coif, Phi Alpha Delta.

WRITINGS: (Editor with Russell A. Smith and Leroy S. Merrifield) *Labor Relations Law: Cases and Materials,* 4th edition (St. Antoine was not associated with previous editions), Bobbs-Merrill, 1968, 5th edition, 1974. Contributor to legal periodicals. Editor-in-chief of *Michigan Law Review,* 1953-54.

* * *

SAINT-JACQUES, Bernard 1928-

PERSONAL: Born April 26, 1928, in Montreal, Quebec, Canada; son of Albert and Germaine (Lefebvre) Saint-Jacques; married Marguerite Fauquenoy (a professor), April 3, 1967. *Education:* Montreal University, B.A., 1949, Licence, 1954; Sophia University, M.A., 1962; Georgetown University, M.A., 1964; University of Paris, Doctorate, 1966. *Office:* Department of Linguistics, University of British Columbia, Vancouver, British Columbia, Canada.

CAREER: University of British Columbia, Vancouver, assistant professor, 1967-69, associate professor, 1969-78, professor of linguistics and Asian studies, 1978—. *Member:* Linguistic Society of America, Linguistic Society of Japan.

WRITINGS: Analyse structurale de la syntaxe du japonais moderne, Librairie C. Klincksieck, 1966, translation by author published as *Structural Analysis of Modern Japanese,* University of British Columbia Press, 1971; *Aspects sociolinguistiques du bilinguisme Canadien,* International Center for Research on Bilingualism, 1976. Contributor to *Pacific Affairs, La linguistique, General Linguistics, Foundations of Language,* and *Word.*

WORK IN PROGRESS: Research in sociolinguistics.

* * *

SALGADO, Maria Antonia 1933-

PERSONAL: Born January 15, 1933, in Canary Islands, Spain; naturalized U.S. citizen, 1959; daughter of Felipe Antonio and Juliana (Garcia) Lopez; married Daniel E. Salgado (a meteorologist), June 12, 1954; children: Liane, Daniel, Jr. *Education:* Florida State University, B.A., 1958; University of North Carolina, M.A., 1960; University of Maryland, Ph.D., 1966. *Religion:* Roman Catholic. *Office:* Department of Romance Languages, University of North Carolina, Chapel Hill, N.C. 27514.

CAREER: University of Maryland, College Park, instructor in Spanish, 1964-67; University of North Carolina at Chapel Hill, assistant professor, 1967-72, associate professor, 1972-77, professor of Spanish and Spanish American literature, 1977—. *Member:* Asociacion Internacional de Hispanistas, Instituto Internacional de Literature Iberoamericana, Modern Language Association of America, American Association of Teachers of Spanish and Portuguese, South Atlantic Modern Language Association, Phi Beta Kappa, Sigma Delta Pi, Phi Kappa Phi. *Awards, honors:* Juan Ramon Jimenez prize, 1967, for *El arte polifacetico de las 'caricaturas liricas' juanramonianas.*

WRITINGS: El arte polifacetico de las 'caricaturas liricas' juanramonianas, Insula, 1968; *Hablemos! Textos contemporaneos para conversar o escriber,* Harper, 1976; *Rafael Arevalo Martinez,* Twayne, in press.

WORK IN PROGRESS: Artes poeticas del Modernismo.

* * *

SALISBURY, Ralph 1926-

PERSONAL: Born January 24, 1926, in Arlington, Iowa; son of Charles (a farmer) and Olive (McAllister) Salisbury; married Joyce Hurlbert, April 9, 1954 (divorced, 1963); married Ingrid Wendt (a poet), April 23, 1969; children: (first marriage) Jeffrey, Brian; (second marriage) Erin. *Education:* University of Iowa, M.F.A., 1951. *Politics:* "Yes." *Religion:* "Probably." *Residence:* Eugene, Ore. *Office:* Department of English, University of Oregon, Eugene, Ore. 97403.

CAREER: Agricultural and Mechanical College of Texas (now Texas A&M University), College Station, member of faculty, 1951-54; Drake University, Des Moines, Iowa, member of faculty, 1954-60; University of Oregon, Eugene, assistant professor, 1960-65, associate professor of English, 1965—. Lecturer, Fresno State College (now California State University, Fresno), 1970-71. *Military service:* U.S. Army Air Forces, 1944-46. *Awards, honors:* Chapelbrook Foundation Award, 1966, for work in poetry and fiction.

WRITINGS: Ghost Grapefruit, Ithaca House, 1972. Contributor of poems and short stories to *New Yorker, Poetry, Massachusetts Review, West Coast Review, Southwest Review, Perspective, Epoch,* and other journals. Editor, *Northwest Review,* 1965-70.

WORK IN PROGRESS: Poetry and short stories.

* * *

SALLIS, John C(leveland) 1938-

PERSONAL: Born June 8, 1938, in Poplar Grove, Ark.; son

of Chappelle H., Jr. and Mildred (Liming) Sallis; married Lois G. Price, December 27, 1959; children: Lauren, Kathryn. *Education:* University of Arkansas, B.A., 1959; Columbia University, graduate study, 1959-60; Tulane University, M.A., 1962, Ph.D., 1964. *Home:* 1944 Spring Valley Rd., Pittsburgh, Pa. 15243. *Office:* Department of Philosophy, Duquesne University, Pittsburgh, Pa. 15219.

CAREER: University of the South, Sewanee, Tenn., instructor in philosophy, 1964-66; Duquesne University, Pittsburgh, Pa., associate professor, 1960-70, professor of philosophy, 1970—. *Member:* American Philosophical Association, American Heidegger Conference, Hegel Society of America, Husserl Circle, Society for Phenomenology and Existential Philosophy. *Awards, honors:* Danforth fellowship, 1959-64; Alexander von Humboldt-Stiftung senior fellowship, 1974-75.

WRITINGS: Introduction to the Techniques of Symbolic Logic, Philosophical Press, 1966; *Heidegger and the Path of Thinking,* Duquesne University Press, 1970; *Phenomenology and the Return to Beginnings,* Humanities Press, 1973; *Being and Logos: The Way of Platonic Dialogue,* Humanities Press, 1975; *The Gathering of Reason,* Ohio University Press, 1978. Editor of philosophical series, Duquesne University Press. Contributor of over twenty articles to journals in his field. Founder and editor of *Research in Phenomenology,* 1971—.

WORK IN PROGRESS: A systematic study of imagination.

* * *

SALM, Peter 1919-

PERSONAL: Born August 23, 1919, in Hameln, Germany; son of Uri (a business executive) and Helen (Hahlo) Salm; married June Macy (an editorial writer), August 15, 1958; children: Anthony. *Education:* University of California, Los Angeles, B.A., 1951; Yale University, Ph.D., 1958. *Office:* Department of Comparative Literature, Case Western Reserve University, Cleveland, Ohio 44106.

CAREER: Wesleyan University, Middletown, Conn., instructor, 1957-59, assistant professor of German, 1959-62; Case Western Reserve University, Cleveland, Ohio, associate professor, 1963-65, professor of German and comparative literature, 1965—, chairman of department of German, 1965-68, chairman of comparative literature, 1968—, chairman of Division of Modern Languages and Literature, 1971—. *Military service:* U.S. Army Air Forces, 1942-46; became technical sergeant. *Member:* Modern Language Association of America, American Society for Eighteenth Century Studies, Phi Beta Kappa.

WRITINGS: (Translator) Goethe, *Faust,* Bantam, 1962; *Three Modes of Criticism: The Literary Theories of Scherer, Walzel and Staiger,* Press of Case Western Reserve University, 1968; *The Poem as Plant: A Biological View of Goethe's "Faust,"* Press of Case Western Reserve University, 1971. Contributor to *Germanic Review* and *German Quarterly.*

WORK IN PROGRESS: A book, tentatively entitled *Pinpoint of Eternity,* on the quest for simultaneity in literature.

* * *

SALOMON, Herman Prins 1930-

PERSONAL: Born March 1, 1930, in Amsterdam, Netherlands; U.S. citizen; son of Yvan (a tobacco planter) and Sophia Wilhelmina (Prins) Salomon. *Education:* New York

University, A.M., 1952, Ph.D., 1961; University of Amsterdam, graduate study, 1957. *Home:* 16 West 77th St., New York, N.Y. 10024. *Office:* Department of French, State University of New York, Albany, N.Y. 12203.

CAREER: Teacher of French at Dalton School for Girls, New York City, 1950-51, Maimonides Lyceum, Amsterdam, Netherlands, 1954-56, and New Lincoln School, New York City, 1957-61; Rutgers University, New Brunswick, N.J., instructor, 1961-62, assistant professor of French, 1962-65; Queens College of the City University of New York, Flushing, N.Y., associate professor of French, 1965-68; State University of New York at Albany, associate professor of Romance languages and literature, 1968—. *Member:* Modern Language Association of America, American Association of Teachers of French, Alliance Francaise, French Institute. *Awards, honors:* Chevalier des Palmes Academiques, France, 1966.

WRITINGS: Tartuffe devant l' Opinion Francaise, Presses Universitaires de France, 1962; (editor) Moliere, *Tartuffe,* Didier, 1964; (editor) Jean Racine, *Phedre,* Didier, 1966; (editor) Racine, *Athalie,* Didier, 1969; *"De Pinto Manuscript": A Seventeenth-Century Marrano Family History,* Van Gorcum, 1975; *Novas pontas de vista sobre a Inquiscao em Portugal,* Athena (Portugal), 1976. Contributor of forty-five articles and reviews on Spanish, Portuguese, and French topics to literary periodicals. Editor, *The American Sephardi,* Yeshiva University, 1967—.

SIDELIGHTS: Herman Salomon told *CA:* "I am principally interested in the role played by the Spanish and Portuguese New Christians in the 'Crisis of Conscience' which occurred in 17th century Europe. I speak and write Dutch, English, French, Portuguese, Italian, Spanish and German."

*　　*　　*

SAMPLEY, Arthur M(cCullough) 1903-1975

PERSONAL: Born January 9, 1903, in Leander, Tex.; son of John Lee (a ginner and grocer) and Annie (McCullough) Sampley; married Vera Almon, September 9, 1930 (died April 4, 1954); married Eva Joy McGuffin, July 5, 1961 (died April 22, 1968); stepchildren: Horace T. McGuffin, Ann McGuffin (Mrs. Woodrow Barton). *Education:* University of Texas, Main University (now University of Texas at Austin), B.A., 1923, M.A., 1925, Ph.D., 1930; Columbia University, B.S. in L.S., 1947. *Politics:* Democrat. *Religion:* Disciples of Christ. *Home:* 2011 West Oak, Denton, Tex. 76201. *Office address:* Box 5263, North Texas Station, Denton, Tex. 76203.

CAREER: University of Texas, Main University (now University of Texas at Austin), instructor in English, 1925-28; Louisiana State Normal College (now Northwestern State University of Louisiana), Natchitoches, associate professor of English, 1930-31; Sul Ross State Teachers College (now Sul Ross College), Alpine, Tex., professor of English, 1931-35, head of department, 1931-35; North Texas State University, Denton, professor of English, 1935-53, distinguished professor, 1953-75, director of libraries, 1944-53, vice-president for academic affairs, 1953-59. Visiting professor, University of Texas, 1940-41. *Military service:* U.S. Army Air Forces, 1943-44; became first lieutenant. *Member:* Modern Language Association of America, Poetry Society of America (vice-president of Southern division, 1954-75), Texas Institute of Letters (president, 1942, 1951-53), Poetry Society of Texas (president, 1951), Texas Library Association (president, 1949-50). *Awards, honors:*

Maxwell Anderson Award from Stanford University, 1939, for verse drama; Texas Institute of Letters awards, 1947, 1951, 1971, for best book of poetry by a Texan; state poet laureate of Texas, 1951-53; Edwin Markham Award from Poetry Society of America, 1964, 1965; James Joyce Award from Poetry Society of America, 1969.

WRITINGS: The Marriage of Francis Arden and Other One-Act Plays (contains "The Marriage of Francis Arden," "Bright Honor from Moon," "A Test for Lovers," and "The Last of All the Fairies"), Southwest Press, 1933; *This Is Our Time* (poems), Kaleidograph Press, 1943; *Of the Strong and the Fleet* (poems), Kaleidograph Press, 1947; *Furrow with Blackbirds* (poems), Kaleidograph Press, 1951; *Selected Poems, 1937-71,* North Texas State University Press, 1971. Contributor to literary journals.

WORK IN PROGRESS: Poems; research in twentieth-century American poetry.

BIOGRAPHICAL/CRITICAL SOURCES: Poets Laureate of Texas, Margaret Royalty Edwards, Naylor, 1966.†

(Died December 4, 1975)

*　　*　　*

SAMUELS, Charles Thomas 1936-1974

PERSONAL: Born February 20, 1936, in Brooklyn, N.Y.; son of Harry (a salesman) and Henrietta (Poll) Samuels; married Nada Sternberger (a journalist), December 29, 1957; children: Erika, Melissa. *Education:* Syracuse University, A.B., 1957; Ohio State University, M.A., 1958; University of California, Ph.D., 1961. *Home:* 88 Forest Rd., Williamstown, Mass. 01267. *Office:* Department of English, Williams College, Williamstown, Mass. 01267.

CAREER: Williams College, Williamstown, Mass., instructor, 1961-64, assistant professor, 1964-69, associate professor, 1969-74, professor of English, 1974. Fulbright lectureship, 1964-65; film specialist, Phi Beta Kappa visiting scholars program, 1974-75. *Awards, honors:* American Council of Learned Societies fellow, 1968; grant from American Philosophical Society, 1969; National Endowment for the Humanities senior fellow, 1971.

WRITINGS: John Updike, University of Minnesota Press, 1969; (editor) *A Casebook on Film,* Van Nostrand, 1970; *The Ambiguity of Henry James,* University of Illinois Press, 1971; *Encountering Directors,* Putnam, 1972; (with James Ridgeway, Fred Ferreti, Len Fulton, and others) *Print, Image, Sound,* American Library Association, 1972; *Mastering the Film and Other Essays,* edited by Lawrence Graver, University of Tennessee Press, 1977. Film critic for *American Scholar.* Contributor of book reciews to *Nation, Bookworld, New Republic,* and *New York Times.* Contributor to *Atlantic, Hudson Review* and *Modern Occasions.*†

(Died March 13, 1974)

*　　*　　*

SAMUELS, M(ichael) L(ouis) 1920-

PERSONAL: Born September 14, 1920, in London, England; son of Harry (a barrister-at-law) and Celine (Aronowitz) Samuels; married Hilary Samuel, December 21, 1950; children: Vivien Ruth. *Education:* Balliol College, Oxford, M.A., 1947. *Home:* 121 Dowanhill St., Glasgow G12 9DN, Scotland. *Office:* Department of English Language, University of Glasgow, Glasgow G12 8QQ, Scotland.

CAREER: University of Edinburgh, Edinburgh, Scotland, lecturer in English language, 1948-59; University of Glasgow, Glasgow, Scotland, professor of English language, 1959—. *Member:* Philological Society.

WRITINGS: Linguistic Evolution: With Special Reference to English, Cambridge University Press, 1972. Contributor to professional journals.

WORK IN PROGRESS: Research for two books tentatively entitled *Atlas of the Dialects of Later Middle English* and *Historical Thesaurus of English; Semantic Classification of the Whole English Vocabulary, Past and Present.*

* * *

SANDER, (Jane) Ellen 1944-

PERSONAL: Born January 7, 1944, in New York, N.Y.; daughter of Eitel Sander and Faye (Schnee) Sander; married; children: Marin Paul Sander-Holzman. *Religion:* Jewish. *Home:* 1549 Elevado St., Los Angeles, Calif. 90026.

CAREER: Has worked as a critic for television station KQED.

WRITINGS: Trips: Rock Life in the Sixties, Scribner, 1973. Rock critic for *Saturday Review,* 1968-72. Contributor to *Vogue, Sunday New York Times, Rolling Stone, Village Voice, Cavalier, World,* and *Realist.*

WORK IN PROGRESS: Children's short stories; a novel; a science fiction screenplay; an illustrated songbook.

AVOCATIONAL INTERESTS: Composing songs, juggling, the growth movement, films.

* * *

SANDERS, (Franklin) David 1934-

PERSONAL: Born October 25, 1934, in Baltimore, Md.; son of George H. and Lillian (Johnson) Sanders. *Education:* Bob Jones University, B.A. (magna cum laude), 1956; University of North Carolina, M.A., 1958, Ph.D., 1963. *Politics:* Democrat. *Religion:* Protestant. *Home:* 1709 South Elm St., Greenville, N.C. 27834. *Office:* Department of English, East Carolina University, Greenville, N.C. 27834.

CAREER: University of Richmond, Richmond, Va., instructor, 1961-63, assistant professor, 1963-66, associate professor of English, 1966-68; East Carolina University, Greenville, N.C., associate professor, 1968-76, professor of English, 1976—, coordinator of honors seminars program, director of undergraduate studies in English. Visiting associate professor at College of William and Mary, 1964; assistant director of Bread Loaf School of English, summers, 1965-71. *Member:* Modern Language Association of America, College English Association, American Association of University Professors, American Civil Liberties Union, Common Cause, South Atlantic Modern Language Association, North Carolina-Virginia College English Association (president, 1967-68). *Awards, honors:* National Defense Education Act fellowship, 1968.

WRITINGS: (With William Hoffman) *The Loser* (novel), Funk, 1968; (contributor) *Cultural Changes in Eastern North Carolina,* East Carolina University Press, 1973. Contributor of book reviews to *Richmond Times-Dispatch* and *Greenville Daily Reflector.*

WORK IN PROGRESS: Research on Shakespeare's plays and sonnets, and on Donne; a series of transparencies on poetry; *Poetry: Sight and Insight,* with James W. Kirkland, completion expected in 1980.

* * *

SANDERS, James Bernard 1924-

PERSONAL: Born May 28, 1924, in Winnipeg, Manitoba,

Canada; son of Bernard Eli (a railway employee) and Margaret (Russell) Sanders; married Simone Lucienne Lafond (a professor of French), July 29, 1948; children: Marie-France Anne (Mrs. Roy Penman), Eric James. *Education:* University of Manitoba, B.A. (honors), 1946, M.A., 1949; University of Paris, D.U., 1952. *Home:* 1595 Hillside Dr., London, Ontario, Canada N6G 2P7. *Office:* University College, University of Western Ontario, London, Ontario, Canada.

CAREER: University of Manitoba, Winnipeg, lecturer in French, 1948-51; University of Western Ontario, London, assistant professor (Waterloo College), 1954-56, associate professor of Romance languages, 1956-61, assistant professor (University College), 1961-63, associate professor, 1963-66, professor of French, 1966—.

MEMBER: Canadian Association of Teachers of French, Humanities Association of Canada (member of executive committee, 1964-68; vice-president, 1969-71), American Association of Teachers of French, International Association of Teachers of French. *Awards, honors:* Grants from Humanities Research Council of Canada, 1955-59; grants from Canada Council, 1955, 1959, 1968, 1971, 1976, and 1978.

WRITINGS: (With R. W. Torrens) *Contes de nos jours,* Copp, 1956, Heath, 1958; (with Torrens) *Le Double Mort de Frederic Belot,* Longmans, Green, 1958; (with Torrens) *La Communale,* Appleton, 1959; (with Torrens) *Contes d'aujourd'hui,* Holt, 1963; (with D. G. Creighton) *A Travers les siecles,* Macmillan, 1967; *George Ancey: Theatre,* Nizet, 1968; *Aux Sources de la verite du theatre moderne,* Minard, 1974; *Antoine a l'Odeon,* Minard, 1978. General editor, *Correspondance generale,* Volume VI, University of Montreal Press. Contributor to *Commentator, French Review, Waterloo Review, La Revue de l'Universite d'Ottawa, Cahiers naturalistes, Nineteenth-Century French Studies,* and *French Studies.* Member of editorial board, *Journal of Humanities Association of Canada.*

WORK IN PROGRESS: Annotating correspondence of Emile Zola relating to the theater, for inclusion in *Correspondance generale,* published by University of Montreal Press; *Antoine: lettres de jeunesse; correspondance du Theatre Libre.*

* * *

SANDERSON, Ivan T(erence) 1911-1973
(Terence Roberts)

January 30, 1911—February 19, 1973; Scottish-born naturalist, collector and exhibitor of rare animals, radio and television broadcaster, and author of adult and juvenile nature books. *Obituaries: New York Times,* February 21, 1973; *Publishers Weekly,* April 23, 1973. (See index for *CA* sketch)

* * *

SANTOSTEFANO, Sebastiano 1929-

PERSONAL: Born June 14, 1929, in Middletown, Conn.; son of Sebastiano and Josephine Santostefano; married Joan Callahan (an educator), July 11, 1953; children: Sebastian (deceased), Damon. *Education:* University of Connecticut, B.S. (with honors), 1953; Pennsylvania State University, M.S., 1954, Ph.D., 1957; Boston Psychoanalytic Society and Institute, Inc., graduate in adult psychoanalysis, 1972, and in child psychoanalysis, 1973. *Home:* 201 Lowell Rd., Wellesley Hills, Mass. 02181. *Office:* McLean Hospital, Belmont, Mass. 02178.

CAREER: Pennsylvania State University, University Park,

part-time personal adjustment counselor, 1954-55; Veterans Administration Neuropsychiatric Hospital, Pittsburgh, Pa., intern in clinical psychology, 1955-56; University of Colorado, School of Medicine, Denver, instructor, 1958-60, assistant professor of child psychology, 1960-64, director of child psychology, 1960-64; Clark University, Worcester, Mass., associate professor of psychology and director of research at Worcester Youth Guidance Center, 1964-67; Boston University, School of Medicine, Boston, Mass., associate professor, 1967-70, professor of child psychiatry, 1970-73, director of clinical child psychology, 1967-73; Harvard University Medical School, Cambridge, Mass., associate professor of psychiatry, 1973—; Hall-Mercer Children's Center of McLean Hospital, Belmont, Mass., director of department of child psychology and psycho-education, 1973—. Chief psychologist, Denver General Hospital, 1968-69. University of Massachusetts—Boston, visiting professor of psychology, 1969-73. Diplomate in clinical psychology, American Board of Examiners in Professional Psychology. *Awards, honors:* U.S. Public Health Service, postdoctoral fellow, 1957-58, career teacher fellow, 1958-60; Helena and Felix Deutsch Scientific Award, Boston Psychoanalytic Society, 1978. *Military service:* U.S. Army, medical technician, 1947-48.

MEMBER: American Psychological Association (fellow), American Psychoanalytic Association, American Association of Child Psychoanalysis, Society for Research in Child Development, Massachusetts Psychological Association (fellow), Boston Psychoanalytic Society.

WRITINGS: Training in Attention and Concentration: A Program of Cognitive Development for Children (monograph), Educational Research Associates, Inc., 1967; (contributor) David Moriarty, editor, *The Loss of Loved Ones,* C. C Thomas, 1967; (contributor) Stella Chess and Alexander Thomas, editors, *Annual Progress in Child Psychiatry and Child Development,* Brunner-Mazel, 1970; (contributor) B. B. Wolman, editor, *Manual of Child Psychotherapy,* McGraw, 1970; (contributor) H. E. Rie, editor, *Perspectives in Child Psychopathology,* Aldine-Atherton, 1971; *A Biodevelopmental Approach to Clinical Child Psychology: Cognitive Controls and Cognitive Control Therapy,* Wiley, 1978. Author of research reports. Contributor of about thirty-five articles to professional journals, including *American Psychologist, Journal of Pediatrics, Child Development,* and *Psychology in the Schools.* Consulting editor, *Developmental Psychology,* 1968-73; editor and member of editorial board, *McLean Then and Now,* McLean Hospital Journal, 1973—.

SIDELIGHTS: In the postscript of his most recent book, *A Biodevelopmental Approach to Clinical Child Psychology: Cognitive Controls and Cognitive Control Therapy,* Sebastiano Santostefano writes: "I am still very interested in any information that bears upon the issue [of whether and how psychotherapy could be modified for children with major ego dysfunctions and cognitive disabilities]. Whenever I have the opportunity, I evaluate the cognitive control functioning of children before and after therapy . . . and before and after a course in cognitive control therapy. I am especially interested in clinical situations in which intensive psychotherapy did not result in cognitive reorganization . . . and in which the child's need permitted us to make available cognitive control therapy. . . . I hope to learn more about when and whether a cognitive emphasis in therapy . . . is and is not the treatment of choice for children whose problems include major cognitive disabilities."

BIOGRAPHICAL/CRITICAL SOURCES: Sebastiano

Santostefano, *A Biodevelopmental Approach to Clinical Child Psychology: Cognitive Controls and Cognitive Control Therapy,* Wiley, 1978.

*   *   *

SARGENT, Frederic O(berlin) 1919-

PERSONAL: Born September 30, 1919, in Thetford, Vt.; son of Arthur Hayes (a minister) and Joanna (Kinsley) Sargent; married Shirley Fork, August 28, 1947; children: Blaine Pierre, Wendell Derek, Bettina Louise. *Education:* Colby College, B.A., 1942; also studied at University of Mexico, summer, 1947, and Sorbonne, University of Paris, 1949-50; University of Wisconsin—Madison, Ph.D., 1952. *Home:* 330 Spear, South Burlington, Vt. 05401. *Office:* University of Vermont, Burlington, Vt. 05401.

CAREER: Marshall Plan, Paris, France and Bonn, Germany, technical assistance officer, 1950-54; Colorado Agricultural and Mechanical College (now Colorado State University), Fort Collins, assistant professor of marketing, 1954-56; Agricultural and Mechanical College of Texas (now Texas A&M University), College Station, assistant professor of land economics, 1956-59; University of Guelph, Guelph, Ontario, associate professor of land economics, 1960-62; University of Vermont, Burlington, professor of resource economics, 1962—. President, Green Mountain Meadows, Inc., 1969-71; chairman, South Burlington Planning Commission, 1968-70. *Military service:* U.S. Army Air Forces, night fighter, 1942-45.

MEMBER: Northeast Agricultural Economic Association (member of board of directors, 1962—), Vermont Natural Resources Council (member of board of directors, 1966-69), Audubon Society (member of board of directors, 1966-69). *Awards, honors:* Citation of merit from American Scenic and Historic Preservation Society, 1969, for *Scenery Classification.*

WRITINGS: Four Fifteenth Night Fighter Squadrons, privately printed, 1946; (contributor) Alvin Bertrand and Richard Corty, editors, *Rural Land Tenure in the United States,* Louisiana State University Press, 1962; (editor with Ralph Krueger, Anton de Vos, and Norman Pearson, and contributor) *Regional and Resource Planning in Canada,* Holt, 1963, revised edition, 1970; (contributor) Krueger, editor, *A Preview of Resource Economic Problems in the Northeast,* Institute for Research on Land and Water Resource, Pennsylvania State University and Farm Foundation, 1965; *Principles of Regional Planning,* Conservation Foundation, 1967; *Scenery Classification,* Vermont Resources Research Center, 1967; *Open Space Plan for Chittenden County,* University of Vermont, 1972; *Guidelines for Environmental Planning,* University of Vermont, 1973; *Rural Environmental Planning,* privately printed, 1976.

Author of thirty research reports for state agricultural agencies in Colorado, Texas, and Vermont, and for other organizations. Author of "Our Natural Resources," a weekly column in five Vermont newspapers, 1966-68. Contributor of about twenty-five articles to professional journals, including *Land Economics, Agricultural History, Game and Fish, Progressive Farmer, New Englander, Vermont Real Estate,* and *Appraisal Journal.*

AVOCATIONAL INTERESTS: Biking, white-water canoeing, cross-country skiing, sailing, spelunking, snowshoeing.

SARIOLA, Sakari 1919-

PERSONAL: Given name is pronounced Zachary; born April 3, 1919, in Kalajoki, Finland; naturalized U.S. citizen, December 4, 1968; son of Aale Johannes (a Lutheran minister) and Olga (Huurre) Sariola; married Ana Teresa Blanco, April 2, 1949; children: Karin Theresa, Taina Marjatta. *Education:* University of Helsinki, M.A., 1946, Ph.D., 1954; University of Chicago, graduate study, 1948-49. *Home:* 2038 Alabama St., Lawrence, Kan. 66044. *Office:* 723 Fraser Hall, University of Kansas, Lawrence, Kan. 66044.

CAREER: Helsingin Sanomat, Helsinki, Finland, reporter and feature writer, 1945-46; Finnish War Relief Agency, Helsinki, chief of information, 1946-48; Inter-American Institute of Agricultural Sciences, Turrialba, Costa Rica, assistant sociologist in department of economics and rural life, 1949-51; Finnish State Liquor Monopoly, Helsinki, head of department of social research, 1951-54; United Nations Regional and Specialized Agencies, Latin America, conducted study on resettlement of Indian populations in Santa Cruz, Bolivia, 1954-55, conducted study of urbanization problems in San Jose, Costa Rica, 1955-57, UNESCO specialist in sociology and researcher at Interamerican Center for Rural Education, Rubio, Venezuela, 1957-59; University of Puerto Rico, Mayaguez, professor of sociology, 1960-63, chairman of department of social sciences, 1961-63; Louisiana State University, Baton Rouge, professor of sociology, 1963-65; University of Kansas, Lawrence, 1965—, began as associate professor, currently professor of sociology. Lecturer at School of Social Science, Helsinki, 1954; consultant and lecturer for Organization of American States training courses for Latin American sociologists, 1955-63. *Military service:* Finnish Army, 1940-44. *Member:* American Sociological Association. *Awards, honors:* International House fellowship, 1948-49.

WRITINGS: Power and Resistance: Colonial Heritage in Latin America, Cornell University Press, 1972; *The Puerto Rican Dilemma*, Kennikat, 1978. Also author of books in Finnish, monographs and research reports; contributor to transactions. Contributor to *Kansas Journal of Sociology, Rural Sociology*, and to Finnish professional journals.

WORK IN PROGRESS: Latin America: Thought and Reality; The Finnish Detente; research on power in history.

* * *

SATIN, Mark 1946-

PERSONAL: Born November 16, 1946, in New York, N.Y.; son of Joseph (a teacher) and Selma (Rosen) Satin. *Education:* University of British Columbia, B.A., 1972; attended University of Toronto, 1972. *Politics:* "Libertarian communist." *Religion:* Jewish.

CAREER: Red River Scene (newspaper), Moorhead, Minn., columnist, 1961-63; Toronto Anti-Draft Programme, Toronto, Ontario, director and counsellor, 1967-68; Ontario Department of Justice, Toronto, researcher, 1968; The Last Resort (a hostel for draft dodgers and military deserters), Vancouver, British Columbia, manager, 1968-69; *The Grape-Vancouver's Opposition Newspaper*, Vancouver, columnist and member of staff collective, beginning 1973.

WRITINGS: Manual for Draft-Age Immigrants to Canada, Toronto Anti-Draft Programme, 1968, 5th edition (with Toronto Anti-Draft Programme Collective), House of Ansi Press, 1971; *Confessions of a Young Exile*, Gage Educational Publishing (Agincourt, Ontario), 1976; *New Age*

Politics: The Emerging New Alternative to Marxism and Liberalism, Fairweather Press (Vancouver), 1976.

WORK IN PROGRESS: A novel.

SIDELIGHTS: Mark Satin was indicted for failure to report for a pre-induction physical examination in 1967, for failure to report for induction, 1967 and 1970, and for international flight to avoid prosecution in 1970.

BIOGRAPHICAL/CRITICAL SOURCES: Saturday Night Magazine, August, 1967; *Toronto Globe and Mail*, October 11, 1967.†

* * *

SAUSE, George G(abriel) 1919-

PERSONAL: Surname is pronounced "sauce"; born September 28, 1919, in Souderton, Pa.; son of George Gabriel and Maud (Nicholson) Sause; married Evelyn Gorman, June 23, 1948. *Education:* Moravian Theological Seminary (now Moravian College), B.S., 1941; Columbia University, Ph.D., 1952. *Politics:* Democrat. *Religion:* Presbyterian. *Home:* 622 West Lafayette St., Easton, Pa. 18042. *Office:* Office of the Provost, Markle Hall, Lafayette College, Easton, Pa. 18042.

CAREER: Moravian Theological Seminary (now Moravian College), Bethleham, Pa., assistant professor of economics, 1947-48; Lafayette College, Easton, Pa., instructor, 1950-52, assistant professor, 1952-57, associate professor, 1957-62, professor of economics, 1962—, Charles A. Dana Professor of Economics, 1972, head of department, 1970-72, provost and dean of faculty, 1972—. Instructor, American Institute of Banking, 1954-69; member of academic advisory council, Henry George School of Social Science, 1968—; member of board of trustees, Moravian College, 1968-70. Member of board of directors, Graded Tax League of Pennsylvania, 1968—; Lehigh-Delaware Development Council, Inc.; treasurer, 1960-77, member of board of directors, 1960—; member of local planning commission, 1962—, chairman, 1964-66, 1972-73, 1977—; member of Easton Democratic City Committee, 1954-72, chairman, 1970-72. *Military service:* U.S. Army Air Forces, 1942-45. U.S. Air Force Reserve, instructor, 1957-61.

MEMBER: American Economic Association, National Tax Association, Tax Institute of America (member of advisory council, 1965-68), American Finance Association, American Association of University Professors (vice-president of Lafayette College chapter, 1956-58; president, 1959-60, 1968-69), Reserve Officers Association (vice-president of Lehigh Valley chapter, 1958-59), Alumni Association of Moravian College (president, 1968-70; member of board of directors, 1965-71). *Awards, honors:* Moravian College Comenius Award for outstanding achievement, 1975.

WRITINGS: (With A. P. Becker, S. H. Evans, E. K. Moore, P. I. Prentice, and E. H. Spengler) *Tax Policies and Urban Renewal in New York City*, Citizens' Housing and Planning Council of New York, Inc., 1960; *Municipal Authorities: The Pennsylvania Experience*, Department of Internal Affairs, Commonwealth of Pennsylvania, 1962; *Money, Banking, and Economic Activity*, Heath, 1966; *Financial Analysis: Allentown, Pa.*, City of Allentown, Pa., 1966; *Capital Budget*, City of Easton, Pa., 1971. Author of reports. Contributor to finance, tax, economics, and sociology journals. Co-editor, *Mid-Eastern Counties Borough's Reporter*, 1955-65; member of editorial board, *American Journal of Economics and Sociology*, 1963—, and *Local Taxation: Quarterly Journal of Abstracts*, 1970—.

WORK IN PROGRESS: Economics of Higher Education.

SAVAGE, Brian 1933-

PERSONAL: Born February 5, 1933, in Cambridge, Mass.; son of John J. (a university professor) and Frances (O'Brien) Savage. *Education:* Fordham University, B.A., 1953; School of Visual Arts, further study, 1956-57. *Religion:* Roman Catholic. *Home:* 119 East 89th St., New York, N.Y. 10028.

CAREER: Free-lance magazine cartoonist. *Military service:* U.S. Army, 1953-55. *Member:* Cartoonists Guild (founding member; member of executive committee, 1968-72).

WRITINGS: So This Is Love, Playboy Press, 1971; *The Savage Eye,* Dell, 1971; *Play Me or Trade Me,* Dell, 1972; *Sex 'n' Violence,* Dell, 1973. Contributor of cartoons to *Esquire* and *Playboy.*

*   *   *

SAVAIN, Petion (?)-1973

(?)—July 26, 1973; Haitian artist and author. Obituaries: *New York Times,* July 29, 1973.

*   *   *

SAVELAND, Robert N(elson) 1921-

PERSONAL: Born February 9, 1921, in East Cleveland, Ohio; son of Lester R. (a sales representative) and Mabel (Nelson) Saveland; married Gladys Rae McDonald, August 13, 1945; children: Mary Sharron (Mrs. Kent Hannon), Robert N., Jr., James Middleton. *Education:* Washington University, St. Louis, Mo., A.B., 1943; Columbia University, M.A., 1946, Ed.D., 1952. *Home:* 5 South Stratford Dr., Athens, Ga. 30605. *Office:* 205 Dudley Hall, University of Georgia, Athens, Ga. 30602.

CAREER: Public schools of St. Louis, Mo., consultant in social studies, 1949-54; Ginn and Co., Boston, Mass., director of elementary social science publications, 1954-68; University of Georgia, Athens, professor of social science education, 1968—. *Military service:* U.S. Naval Reserve, 1941-45; became lieutenant. *Member:* Association of American Geographers, National Council for Geographic Education, National Association for Environmental Education, Conservation Education Association, Sierra Club, Georgia Conservancy, Phi Delta Kappa.

WRITINGS: A Geography of Missouri, Burton, 1952; (editor of textbook series) *Lands and Peoples of the World,* Ginn, 1956-65; *A Program on Earth-Sun Relations,* Ginn, 1961; *World Resources,* Ginn, 1968; *Handbook of Environmental Education,* Wiley, 1976. Also contributor to *Guide to Reading for Social Studies Teachers,* published by National Council for Social Studies, and *Geography in the Curriculum,* published by National Council for Geographic Education. Contributor to *Social Studies, Journal of Geography, Saturday Review, Boating, Southern Boating, September Days, Environmental Education,* and *Publisher's Weekly.* Ecology editor, *U.S.A. Today.*

*   *   *

SAVESON, John E(dward) 1923-

PERSONAL: Born August 20, 1923, in Chicago, Ill.; son of Irwin Leroy (an engineer) and Blanche (Clouse) Saveson; married Marilyn Buehrer, August 24, 1951; children: Skye, John, Catherine. *Education:* Denison University, B.A. (with honors), 1947; University of Chicago, M.A., 1948; Cambridge University, Ph.D., 1956. *Politics:* Independent.

Religion: "Quaker preference." *Home address:* P.O. Box 22, Mainesburg, Pa. 16932. *Office:* Department of English, Mansfield State College, Mansfield, Pa. 16933.

CAREER: Valparaiso University, Valparaiso, Ind., instructor in English, 1948-49; University of Maryland, College Park, instructor in Overseas Extension, 1954-55, instructor in English, 1955-56; Valparaiso University, assistant professor, 1956-59, associate professor, 1959-64, professor of English, 1964-66; Mansfield State College, Mansfield, Pa., professor of English and chairman of department, 1966—. Scholar in residence, Newberry Research Library, summers, 1970, 1973. *Military service:* U.S. Naval Reserve, active duty, 1943-46; became lieutenant junior grade. *Member:* Modern Language Association of America, Renaissance Society of America, American Association of University Professors, Phi Beta Kappa.

WRITINGS: Joseph Conrad: The Making of a Moralist, Editions Rodopi, 1972; *Conrad, the Later Moralist,* Editions Rodopi, 1974. Contributor of about twenty articles to literature journals.

WORK IN PROGRESS: A study of moral and philosophical assumptions among members of the Joseph Conrad circle, and a novel about World War II.

*   *   *

SAVILLE, Eugenia (Curtis) 1913-

PERSONAL: Born July 7, 1913, in Wayne County, Pa.; daughter of Henry Percy (an insurance businessman) and Eileen (Turk) Curtis; married Lloyd Blackstone Saville (a professor of economics), July 13, 1932; children: Curtis Lloyd, Lynn Adele. *Education:* New Jersey State Teachers College (now Trenton State College), B.S., 1934; Columbia University, M.A., 1942; University of North Carolina, graduate study, 1956-60; private piano study, 1931-45. *Home:* 1103 Anderson St., Durham, N.C. 27705. *Office:* Duke University, Box 6695, College Station, Durham, N.C. 27708.

CAREER: Music supervisor in public schools of Metuchen, N.J., 1937-42; Cornell University, Ithaca, N.Y., research assistant, 1942; American National Red Cross, Washington, D.C., home service correspondent, 1942-45; Duke University, Durham, N.C., instructor, 1947-50, assistant professor, 1950-60, associate professor of music history and literature, 1960—, director of Madrigal Singers, piano and harpsichord accompanist. *Member:* American Musicological Society, College Music Association, Music Library Association, Music Educators National Conference, American Association of University Professors, International Musicological Society, North Carolina Music Educators Conference. *Awards, honors:* Duke University research grants for study in Rome, 1954-55, Turin, 1959-60, and Tuscany, 1970, 1972-73, for research and writing, springs, 1976, 1977, 1978-79; Chapelbrook Foundation of Boston grant for study in Florence, 1965-66.

WRITINGS: Italian Vocal Duets from the Early Eighteenth Century, G. Schirmer, 1969. Contributor to the encyclopedia *Die Musik in Geschichte und Gegenwart,* edited by Friedrich Blume. Contributor to music journals, including *Journal of the American Musicological Society, Musical Quarterly,* and *Foutes Artes Musical.*

WORK IN PROGRESS: Clari and His Contemporaries in Tuscany.

AVOCATIONAL INTERESTS: Travel.

SAVITZ, Harriet May 1933-

PERSONAL: Born May 19, 1933, in Newark, N.J.; daughter of Samuel and Susan (Trulick) Blatstein; married Ephraim Savitz (a pharmacist); children: Beth, Steven. *Education:* Attended evening classes at Upsala College, one year, and Rutgers University, one year. *Religion:* Jewish. *Home address:* P.O. Box 181, Plymouth Meeting, Pa. 19462. *Agent:* Curtis Brown Ltd., 575 Madison Ave., New York, N.Y. 10022.

MEMBER: National League of American Pen Women, Children's Reading Roundtable (Philadelphia; co-founder; member of steering committee, 1966—), Philadelphia Book Sellers Association. *Awards, honors:* Nomination for the Dorothy Canfield Fisher Memorial Children's Book Award, 1971, for *Fly, Wheels, Fly!*.

WRITINGS—All published by John Day: (With M. Caporale Shecktor) *The Moon Is Mine* (short stories for children), 1968; (with Shector) *Peter and Other Stories* (juvenile), 1969; *Fly, Wheels, Fly!* (juvenile novel), 1970; *On the Move* (juvenile novel), 1973; *The Lionhearted*, 1975; *Wheelchair Champions—A History of Wheelchair Sports*, 1978. Stories have been included in collections, among them *Short Story Scene*, and published in *Boys' Life, Pet Fair, Children's Friend, Ranger Rick*, and other magazines and newspapers. Writer for Science Research Associates reading program, Lyons & Carnahan readers, and *Encyclopaedia Britannica*.

WORK IN PROGRESS: Wheelchair Champions—Part II: Across the U.S.A.

SIDELIGHTS: Harriet Savitz told *CA:* "My books are about the physically disabled [and] about the change in attitude among the disabled population. My writings deal with people of courage who want the rights long kept out of their reach, rights we so easily take for granted . . . the right of transportation, accessibility, education, social acceptance and perhaps the slight bonus of understanding. The books are about people who do not want to be looked on as different. The characters in my novels . . . love and fear and hate. Their difference shows only in the fact that they sit, not stand, through life. The people who travel through my books are fighters. They do not accept life as it is, but see a dream of how it might be were the Abs (Able-bodied) to get over their hang-ups."

Savitz based her book, *Fly, Wheels, Fly* on factual material drawn from her association with a group of paraplegics in the Norristown, Pa. area. They have formed an organization known as the Central Penn Wheelers. The group plays basketball and competes in other sports—all from their wheelchairs.

* * *

SAXBERG, Borje O(svald) 1928-

PERSONAL: Born January 25, 1928, in Helsingfors, Finland; son of Oskar V. (a mechanic) and Martha (Granberg) Saxberg; married Aase Haug, September 7, 1955; children: Bo, Bror. *Education:* Swedish Institute of Economics, Finland, B.A., 1950; Oregon State University, B.S., 1952; University of Illinois at Urbana-Champaign, M.S., 1953, Ph.D., 1958. *Home:* 4323 Northeast 44th St., Seattle, Wash. 98105. *Office:* Graduate School of Business, DJ-10, University of Washington, Seattle, Wash. 98195.

CAREER: University of Illinois at Urbana-Champaign, instructor in management, 1955-57; University of Washington, Seattle, assistant professor, 1957-60, associate professor, 1960-67, professor of management, 1967—, head of department, 1972-76, associate dean for graduate programs in the Graduate School of Business Administration, 1967-70. Visiting summer professor, University of Syracuse, 1961. *Member:* Academy of Management, American Sociological Association, Society for Applied Anthropology. *Awards, honors:* Ford Foundation post-doctoral faculty study fellowship at Cornell University, 1960-61.

WRITINGS: (Editor with Preston LeBreton, Sumner Marcus, and others) *Comparative Administrative Theory*, University of Washington Press, 1968; (with Henry P. Knowles) *Personality and Leadership Behavior*, Addison-Wesley, 1971; (with R. Joseph Monsen) *The World of Business*, Houghton, 2nd edition, 1971; (with Richard Johnson, Monsen, and Knowles) *Management, Systems, and Society*, Goodyear Publishing, 1976. Contributor of articles to *Management Science, Harvard Business Review, Business Horizons, Trusts and Estates, Economie Appliquee*, and *European Business*.

WORK IN PROGRESS: The Bureaucracy as an Organization.

AVOCATIONAL INTERESTS: France and French culture.

* * *

SCARBOROUGH, John 1940-

PERSONAL: Born September 3, 1940, in St. Louis, Mo.; son of William John (a college president and university administrator) and Irene (Parish) Scarborough; married Ruth Shimek, June 8, 1962 (divorced, April, 1971); married Lysa Gunlefinger, May 27, 1972; children: (first marriage) Deborah Ruth, John Andrew; (second marriage) Anne Elise. *Education:* Baker University, A.B., 1961; University of Kansas, medical student, 1961-62; University of Denver, M.A., 1963; University of Pennsylvania, graduate study, 1963; University of Illinois, Ph.D., 1967. *Politics:* "Slightly left of center." *Religion:* Unitarian Universalist. *Office:* Department of History, University of Kentucky, Lexington, Ky. 40506.

CAREER: West Virginia Wesleyan College, Buckhannon, instructor in European history, 1964; Northeast Missouri State College (now University), Kirksville, instructor in ancient history, 1966; University of Kentucky, Lexington, instructor, 1966-67, assistant professor, 1967-70, associate professor, 1970-77, professor of ancient and European history, 1977—, Hallam Professor of History, 1977-78. *Member:* American Society of Papyrologists, Association of Ancient Historians, Coleopterists Society, Society for Ancient Medicine (president, 1977-78), Society for the Promotion of Hellenic Studies, Science Fiction Writers of America, American Historical Associaion, American Association for the History of Medicine, American Philological Association, American Institute for the History of Pharmacy, Society for the Promotion of Roman Studies (England), Royal Numismatic Society (England), Classical Association (England), Classical Association of the Middle West and South. *Awards, honors:* University of Kentucky Research Foundation awards for study in England, Jordan, Italy, and Greece, 1968, 1969, 1971; Carnegie Foundation fellow, Institute of Greek Philosophy and Science, 1970; Phi Alpha Theta awards for best book in history, 1970, and best article in history, 1971; Great Teacher Award from University of Kentucky Alumni Association, 1971; American Council of Learned Societies fellow, Institute of Roman Law, 1972, 1973.

WRITINGS: Roman Medicine, Cornell University Press, 1969; Facts of Hellenic Life, Houghton, 1976. Contributor to Universal Encyclopedia (Italy) and Encyclopedia of Science Fiction (England); contributor to Medical History, Episteme, Pharmacy in History, Classical Journal, The Ancient World, Coleopterists Bulletin, Bulletin of the Science Fiction Writers of America, and other professional journals. Member of board of editors, Episteme; consulting editor, Classical Journal, Clio Medica, Pharmacy in History, and Journal of the History of Biology.

WORK IN PROGRESS: A series of articles on Nicander's toxicology for Pharmacy in History; a long-range project for a multi-volume history of Greek and Roman medicine; studies of Byzantine medicine, eastern European science fiction, Greek and Roman pharmacy, the history of entomology before Linnaeus, manuscript illumination, and the perception of animals and plants in ancient and medieval art.

SIDELIGHTS: John Scarborough told CA: "Quite often, I am called an 'odd bird' in academics, because I find the mix of medicine, zoology, art, science fiction, and ancient history so completely fascinating. Too much of the time ... university professors have forgotten their primary purpose in their own profession: education of students. That education proceeds ... from the solid command of a particular specialty by a teacher, but it also results from an internal honesty and enthusiasm on the part of the teacher, which is partially the recognition of the constantly changing nature of Knowledge itself. ... If there is any motivating factor that keeps me in teaching and writing, it is the simple curiosity about 'what makes us tick.' "

Scarborough feels that through the knowledge of such languages as Greek, Latin, French, German, Italian, Russian, Arabic, and Swedish, "there is revealed multiple universes of perceptions somewhat similar to our own, but not quite the same." He hopes that he can bring those similarities and differences to the attention of his readers in a way that "might stimulate them to think about how men and women seek security ... through self-imposed religious, intellectual, and philosophic constructs which are subject to change as men and women change."

AVOCATIONAL INTERESTS: Woodcarving, insect collecting.

*   *   *

SCARPITTI, Frank R(oland)   1936-

PERSONAL: Born November 12, 1936, in Butler, Pa.; married Ellen Canfield, September 5, 1959; children: Susan, Jeffrey. Education: Fenn College (now Cleveland State University), B.A., 1958; Ohio State University, M.A., 1959, Ph.D., 1962. Home: 104 Radcliffe Dr., Newark, Del. 19711. Office: Department of Sociology, University of Delaware, Newark, Del. 19711.

CAREER: University of Louisville, Louisville, Ky., instructor in sociology, 1961-62; University of Kentucky, Lexington, instructor in sociology, 1962-63; Rutgers University, New Brunswick, N.J., assistant professor of sociology, 1963-67; University of Delaware, Newark, associate professor, 1967-69, professor of sociology and chairman of department, 1969—. Member of juvenile delinquency task force, Governor's Commission on Crime and Administration of Justice; member of study committee, Delaware Law Enforcement Planning Agency; member of board of directors, Delaware Citizens' Crime Commission, 1968-75, and Commission of Criminology and Criminal Justice Education and Standards, 1977—.

MEMBER: American Sociological Association, Society for the Study of Social Problems, American Society of Criminology (vice-president, 1977-79), American Association of University Professors (vice-president of University of Delaware chapter, 1971-72), Eastern Sociological Society, Alpha Kappa Delta, Phi Kappa Phi, Omicron Delta Kappa. Awards, honors: Research fellowship from U.S. Public Health Service, 1960-61; Hofheimer Prize for Research from American Psychiatric Association, 1967; Danforth Foundation associate, 1968.

WRITINGS: (Contributor) Marvin Wolfgang, Leonard Savitz, and Norman Johnston, editors, The Sociology of Crime and Delinquency, Wiley, 1962; (contributor) Ruth Cavan, editor, A Reader in Juvenile Delinquency, Lippincott, 1964; (contributor) Walter C. Reckless and C. L. Newman, editors, Interdisciplinary Problems in Criminology, College of Commerce Publication Service, Ohio State University, 1965; (contributor) D. A. Mereness, editor, Readings in Psychiatric Nursing, W. C. Brown, 1966; (contributor) Joseph Zubin and Paul Hoch, editors, The Psychopathology of Schizophrenia, Grune, 1966; (with Simon Dinitz and Benjamin Pasamanick) Schizophrenics in the Community: An Experimental Study in the Prevention of Hospitalization, Appleton, 1967; (with Harry Gold) Combatting Social Problems: Techniques of Intervention, Holt, 1967; (contributor) Paul S. Gruabard, editor, Children against Schools, Follett, 1969; (contributor) Simon Dinitz, Alfred Clarke, and Russell Dynes, editors, Deviance: Studies in the Process in Stigmatization and Societal Reaction, Oxford University Press, 1969.

(With John H. McGrath) Youth and Drugs, Scott, Foresman, 1970; (contributor) S. H. Frey, editor, Adolescent Behavior in School, Rand McNally, 1970; (contributor) Norman Johnston, Leonard Savitz, and Marvin Wolfgang, editors, Sociology of Punishment and Correction, 2nd edition (Scarpitti was not associated with earlier edition), Wiley, 1970; (contributor) Peter Garabedian and D. C. Gibbons, editors, Becoming Delinquent, Aldine, 1970; (with Richard M. Stephenson) Group Interaction as Therapy, Greenwood Press, 1973; Social Problems, Holt, 1974, 2nd edition, 1977; (with Paul T. McFarlane) Deviance: Action, Reaction, Interaction, Addison-Wesley, 1975. Contributor of about twenty-five articles to professional journals, including Journal of the American Medical Association, Elementary School Journal, Archives of General Psychiatry, Social Forces, Federal Probation, Crime and Delinquency, and Journal of Rehabilitation.

WORK IN PROGRESS: Drugs and the Youthful User, for Sage Publications.

*   *   *

SCHAECHTER, Mordkhe   1927-

PERSONAL: Born December 1, 1927, in Cernauti, Rumania; son of Khayem Benyumen and Lifshe (Gottesman) Shekhter; married Charlotte Saffian; children: Rukhl, Gitl, Eydl, Binyumen. Education: Attended University of Bucharest, 1945-47; University of Vienna, Ph.D., 1951. Home: 3328 Bainbridge Ave., Bronx, N.Y. 10467. Office: Linguistics Dept., Columbia University, New York, N.Y. 10027.

CAREER: Jewish Theological Seminary, New York City, instructor in Yiddish, 1960-62; Jewish Teachers' Seminary, New York City, assistant professor of Yiddish language and literature, 1962—. Visiting assistant professor, Yeshiva University, 1968-73; Columbia University, research associate for Language and Culture Atlas of Ashkenazic Jewry,

1962-72, lecturer in Yiddish, 1972—. Teacher in Uriel Weinreich Language Program, summers, 1968—. Member of subcommittee for Romanization of Hebrew and Yiddish, National Standards Institute, 1969—. Chairman of subcommittee on publications and of committee on Yiddish terminology, YIVO Institute for Jewish Research, 1970-74. Chairman of board of directors, Benyumen Shekhter Foundation for the Advancement of Standard Yiddish.

WRITINGS: (Editor with Max Weinreich) *Yidisher ortografisher vegvayzer* (title means "Guide to Standardized Yiddish Othography"), Committee for the Implementation of Standardized Yiddish Orthography, 1961; (editor with M. Ravitch and Leo Steinberg) *Shteynberg-bukh* (title means "Festschrift in Honor of J. N. Steinberg"), [New York], 1961; *Elyokem tsuntzers verk: Kritishe oysgabe* (title means "Critical Edition of Eliakum Zunser's Works"), two volumes, YIVO Institute for Jewish Research, 1964; (contributor) Uriel Weinreich, editor, *English-Yiddish Yiddish-English Dictionary,* Macmillan, 1968; (contributor) Maurice Samuel, editor, *In Praise of Yiddish,* Cowles, 1971; (contributor) Weinreich, editor, *College Yiddish,* 5th edition, YIVO Institute for Jewish Research, 1972; *Food: A Yiddish Terminology,* Judah Zelitch Foundation, 1976; *Yiddish Two: A Textbook for Intermediate Courses,* Judah Zelitch Foundation, 1977. Also author of *Yiddish Botanical Terminology* and *Zumerleb in zumer-lager* (title means "Sports, Games, and Camp Terminology in Yiddish"). Contributor of articles and reviews to *Goldene keyt, Tsukunft, Almanakh yidish* and other publications. Co-editor, *Oyfn shvel,* 1957—; editor, *Yidishe shprakh,* 1971—.

* * *

SCHAIE, K(laus) Warner 1928-

PERSONAL: Born February 1, 1928, in Stettin, Germany (area now in Poland); became U.S. citizen in 1953; son of Sally (a merchant) and Lottie Louise (Gabriel) Schaie; married Coloma John Harrison, August 9, 1953 (divorced); married Joyce Kathleen Parr, July 4, 1974; children: (first marriage) Stephan Harrison Schaie; (second marriage) Christopher Parr Schaie. *Education:* City College of San Francisco, A.A., 1951; University of California, Berkeley, B.A., 1952; University of Washington, Seattle, M.S., 1953, Ph.D., 1956. *Office:* Ethel Percy Andrus Gerontology Center, University of Southern California, Los Angeles, Calif. 90007.

CAREER: Washington University Medical School, St. Louis, Mo., postdoctoral fellow in medical psychology, 1956-57; University of Nebraska—Lincoln, assistant professor, 1957-61, associate professor of psychology, 1961-64; West Virginia University, Morgantown, associate professor, 1964-67, professor of psychology and chairman of department, 1968-73, director of Human Resources Research Institute, 1965-68; University of Southern California, Ethel Percy Andrus Gerontology Center, Los Angeles, professor of psychology and director for research, 1973—, acting executive director and dean, 1978-79. Visiting professor at University of Missouri, summer, 1960, University of the Saar, summers, 1961, 1962, University of Washington, Seattle, summers, 1963, 1964, University of Bern, 1970-71, and Macquarrie University (Australia), 1976. Diplomate in clinical psychology, American Board of Examiners in Professional Psychology; licensed psychologist in state of California. Consultant to Veterans Administration, 1961-73, West Virginia Department of Mental Health, 1966-73, and National Center for Health Statistics, 1969-72; member of Developmental Behavioral Sciences Study Section, National Institutes of Health, 1970-72, chairman of section, 1972-74.

MEMBER: American Psychological Association (fellow), Gerontological Society, Society of Multivariate Experimental Psychology, Society for Research in Child Development, American Association of University Professors, Western Psychological Association.

WRITINGS: (With Robert Heiss) *Color and Personality: A Manual for the Color Pyramid Test,* Grune, 1964; *Theories and Methods of Research in Aging,* West Virginia University Library, 1968; (editor with P. B. Baltes) *Life-Span Developmental Psychology: Personality and Socialization,* Academic Press, 1973; (editor with V. E. Anderson, G. E. McClearn, and J. Money) *Developmental Human Behavior Genetics,* Heath-Lexington, 1975; (editor with J. E. Birren) *Handbook of the Psychology of Aging,* Van Nostrand, 1977; (with D. W. Woodruff, D. Kinney, and Birren) *Life-Span Developmental Psychology,* Houghton, in press.

Contributor: G. A. Talland, editor, *Human Behavior and Aging: Recent Advances in Research and Theory,* Academic Press, 1968; S. M. Chown and K. F. Riegel, editors, *Interdisciplinary Topics in Gerontology,* S. Karger, 1968; L. R. Goulet and Baltes, editors, *Life-Span Developmental Psychology: Research and Theory,* Academic Press, 1970; R. M. Dreger, editor, *Multivariate Personality: Contributions to the Understanding of Personality in Honor of Raymond B. Cattell,* Claitor's Book Store, 1971; J. R. Nesselroade and H. W. Reese, editors, *Life-Span Developmental Psychology: Methodological Issues,* Academic Press, 1973; Woodruff and Birren, editors, *Aging: Scientific Issues and Social Perspectives,* Van Nostrand, 1975; R. B. Cattell and Dreger, editors, *Handbook of Modern Personality Theory,* Hemisphere/Halsted, 1977; C. Eisdurfer and R. O. Friedel, editors, *Cognitive and Emotional Disturbances in the Elderly: Clinical Issues,* Year Book Medical Publishers, 1977; M. M. Seltzer, H. L. Stems, and T. Hickey, editors, *Gerontology in Higher Education: Prospects and Issues,* Wadsworth, 1978. Contributor to *International Encyclopedia of Neurobiology, Psychiatry, Psychoanalysis, and Psychology,* edited by B. B. Wolman, Aesculapius, 1977; contributor of over a hundred articles and monographs to professional journals.

WORK IN PROGRESS: Psychology of Adult Development, with J. Geiwitz for Little, Brown, completion expected in 1981.

SIDELIGHTS: K. Warner Schaie told *CA* that he became interested in gerontology while still an undergraduate at Berkeley, when he first studied old patients in his family physician's waiting room. "Ever since," Schaie explained, "I have tried to understand the complex pattern of age changes and generation differences in intellectual ability over the adult life span. My work has seriously questioned the myth of universal decline in ability with advancing age and I have been one of the major proponents of a life-span approach to developmental psychology. As a gerontologist, I have been active in stimulating inter-disciplinary research on aging, spanning the full range from single-cell biology to urban planning."

* * *

SCHANZER, George O(swald) 1914-

PERSONAL: Born October 26, 1914, in Vienna, Austria; son of Rudolf and Jenny (Thewett) Schanzer; married Maria Montanari, August 6, 1944; children: Jenny Schanzer Kracklauer, Louis, Monica, Robert. *Education:* University of Vienna, Jur. Dr., 1938; University of Missouri, M.A., 1946; State University of Iowa, Ph.D., 1950. *Home:* 230 Huxley Dr., Snyder, N.Y. 14226. *Office:* Department of Modern Languages and Literature, State University of New York, Buffalo, N.Y. 14260.

CAREER: University of Missouri—Columbia, instructor in Spanish, 1945-46; University of Kansas, Lawrence, assistant professor of Spanish, 1948-52; St. John's University, Jamaica, N.Y., associate professor, 1952-57, professor of Spanish, 1957-64; State University of New York at Buffalo, professor of Spanish, 1964—. Visiting professor at Hofstra College (now University), Queens College (now Queens College of the City University of New York), University of Wisconsin, and others. *Military service:* U.S. Army Air Forces, 1942-46; became master sergeant. *Member:* American Association of University Professors, Modern Language Association of America, American Association of Teachers of Spanish and Portuguese, International Institute of Ibero-American Literature. *Awards, honors:* Buenos Aires Convention grant, Montevideo, 1947-48; Fulbright research grant, Madrid, Spain, 1962-63; State University of New York research grant, 1966; Organization of American States grant, 1976.

WRITINGS: Russian Literature in the Hispanic World/La Literatura Rusa en el Mundo Hispanico, University of Toronto Press, 1972. Contributor of articles to *Revista Ibero-Americana, Symposium, Latin American Theatre Review,* and other periodicals. Associate editor of *Hispania,* 1965-68.

WORK IN PROGRESS: Writing on Spanish American theater and narrative.

*   *   *

SCHATZ, Sayre P(erry) 1922-

PERSONAL: Born June 9, 1922, in Philadelphia, Pa.; son of Harry F. (a mechanic) and Dora (Lewis) Schatz; married Letta Saroff (a writer), February 15, 1948; children: Judy, Benjamin. *Education:* University of Pennsylvania, B.S., 1946; New School for Social Research, M.A., 1949, Ph.D., 1955. *Home:* 7701 Woodlawn Ave., Melrose Park, Pa. 19126. *Office:* Department of Economics, Temple University, Philadelphia, Pa. 19122.

CAREER: Wayne University (now Wayne State University), Detroit, Mich., instructor in economics, 1949-50; Lincoln University, Jefferson City, Mo., lecturer, 1950-51, assistant professor of economics, 1951-56; Hofstra College (now University), Hempstead, N.Y., assistant professor, 1956-59, associate professor of economics, 1959-62; University of Ibadan, Nigerian Institute of Social and Economic Research, Ibadan, Nigeria, senior research fellow, 1962-65; Brooklyn College of the City University of New York, Brooklyn, N.Y., professor of economics, 1965-67; Temple University, Philadelphia, Pa., professor of economics, 1967—. Visiting professor at New School for Social Research, 1959-62, and Columbia University, 1965-67. Lecturer at Yale University, Ibadan University, University of Nigeria, Makerere University, Dar es Salaam University College, Nairobi University, and other universities, and for Liberia Department of Planning and Economic Affairs. *Military service:* U.S. Army, 1942-45; became sergeant.

MEMBER: American Economic Association, African Studies Association, American Association of University Professors, Nigerian Economic Society (treasurer and member of council, 1962-65). *Awards, honors:* Ford Foundation research fellowship, 1958-59, research fellow in Nigeria, 1961-62; Social Science Research Council African research grant, 1966.

WRITINGS: Development Bank Lending in Nigeria: The Federal Loans Board, Oxford University Press, 1964; *Economics, Politics, and Administration in Government Lending: The Regional Loans Boards of Nigeria,* Oxford University Press, 1970; (editor and contributor) *South of the Sahara: Development in African Economics,* Temple University Press, 1973; *Nigerian Capitalism* University of California Press, 1977.

Contributor: Joseph S. Roucek, Philip L. Harriman, and George de Huszar, editors, *Contemporary Social Science,* Volume I, Stackpole, 1953; Ignacy Sachs, editor, *Problemy Wzrostu Ekonomioznego Kraiow Slabo Roswinietych,* Polgos, 1958; John H. Hallowell, editor, *Development: For What,* Duke University Press, 1964; E. H. Whetham and J. I. Currie, editors *Readings in the Applied Economics of Africa,* Volume I: *Micro-Economics,* Cambridge University Press, 1967; David R. Kamerschen and Walter L. Johnson, editors, *Readings in Economic Development,* Southwestern Publishing, 1972. Contributor of about thirty-five articles, essays, and reviews to journals in the United States, Europe, South America, and Africa.

WORK IN PROGRESS: Writing on economic development policy in Africa and multinational corporations.

*   *   *

SCHAUF, George Edward 1925-

PERSONAL: Born March 1, 1925, in Los Angeles, Calif.; son of Henry George (a fireman) and Viola Lucille (Creason) Schauf; married Joanne Jenkins, December 28, 1948; children: Theresa (Mrs. Robert Mogadam), William Frederick, Caroline (deceased), Henry George II, Ralph Edward, Theodore Ignatius (deceased), Martha, George Joseph, Joan, George Edward, Jr. (deceased), John Anthony. *Education:* Attended University of Santa Clara, 1946-49; San Jose State College (now University), A.B., 1951, M.A., 1954; St. Louis University, M.D., 1957. *Politics:* Democrat. *Religion:* Roman Catholic. *Home:* 2748 Topeka St., Riverbank, Calif. 95367. *Office:* 3443 Atchison St., Riverbank, Calif. 95367.

CAREER: Diplomate, American Board of Family Practice, 1970. Physician and surgeon in private practice in Riverbank, Calif., 1958—. *Military service:* U.S. Army Air Forces, radio operator and mechanic instructor, 1943-46. *Member:* Pan American Medical Association, American Medical Association, American Society of Clinical Hypnosis, Royal Society of Health, California Medical Association, Stanislaus County Medical Society, Kiwanis. *Awards, honors:* Physicians recognition award from American Medical Association, 1969.

WRITINGS: Think, Eat and Lose Fat, Information, Inc., 1970; *Think Thin,* Fawcett, 1977. Contributor to *Nutrition Today, Consultant, Journal of the American Geriatrics Society,* and other journals.

WORK IN PROGRESS: Fat Wars: The GGF Strategy, for Fawcett.

SIDELIGHTS: George Schauf co-authored a record album, "The Power of Thinking Thin," with Jack Lalanne, 1969.

BIOGRAPHICAL/CRITICAL SOURCES: Science Digest, July, 1972; *Catholic Digest,* December, 1972.

*   *   *

SCHEIBLA, Shirley 1919-

PERSONAL: Surname sounds like "*shy*-blah"; born September 29, 1919, in Newport News, Va.; daughter of Wade Hampton (a business executive) and Maude (Bean) Hobbs; married Louis Collins Scheibla, Jr. (a consulting electrical engineer), September 12, 1941; children: Louis Collins III. *Education:* Attended College of William and Mary, 1938-39, and University of North Carolina, 1940-41. *Politics:* Independent. *Religion:* Baptist. *Home:* 6630 Tansey Dr., Falls Church, Va. 22042. *Office:* Barron's, Dow Jones & Co., Publishers, 22 Cortlandt St., New York, N.Y. 10007.

CAREER: Wall Street Journal, New York City, Washington staff correspondent, 1943-48; *Richmond News Leader,* Richmond, Va., Washington correspondent, 1948-51; *Daily Press,* Newport News, Va., Washington correspondent, 1948-51; *Barron's* (national business and financial weekly), New York City, Washington editor, 1958—. *Member:* Washington Press Club, Chi Delta Phi, Sigma Delta Chi.

WRITINGS: Poverty Is Where the Money Is, Arlington House, 1968. Contributor to *Business Week, Financial Times of London, King Features, Washington Sunday Star, Magazine Digest, Everybody's Digest, Woman,* North American Newspaper Alliance, *Steel Magazine, National Petroleum News, Platt's Oilgram, Telecommunications Reports, Paris Herald-Tribune,* and *Bankers' Magazine.*

SIDELIGHTS: Paul Mar said in his review of *Poverty Is Where the Money Is:* "[Shirley] Scheibla . . . seems not to have let a single instance of malfeasance in the community action programs or in the Job Corps elude her, and her dossier is probably accurate. She is always ready with her FBI file on everyone of left-wing orientation in community action. She is sensible enough to avoid charging conspiracy, but will she never ask herself where all the people who think as she does are? Why is it that they do not get involved in community work? She regards the whole poverty program as an exercise in futility. . . . [Her book] is a disconcerting reminder that compassion is a quality as unequally distributed as income."

* * *

SCHERER, William F(rederick) 1939-

PERSONAL: Born August 5, 1939, in Eureka, Ill.; son of Alfred Charles (a professor) and Louise A. (Foerter) Scherer; married Joanna L. Goble (a teacher and potter), May 11, 1968. *Education:* Attended University of Maryland (Munich), 1957-59, Ludwig-Maximilians Universitaet, Munich, 1959-60; University of Colorado, B.A. (cum laude), 1961; University of Southern California, M.A., 1962, Ph.D., 1967; University of Vienna, graduate study, 1964-65. *Home:* 340 Halemaumau Pl., Honolulu, Hawaii 96821. *Office:* Department of European Languages and Literature, University of Hawaii, Honolulu, Hawaii 96822.

CAREER: University of California, Berkeley, assistant professor of German, 1965-68; University of Hawaii, Honolulu, assistant professor, 1968-72, associate professor of German and European literature, 1972—, chairman of German Division, 1975-77, Graduate Program in German, 1975-78, and Study Abroad Committee, 1974—. Consultant to Modern Language Materials Development Center, Boulder, Colo., summer, 1962, and American Council on Education, 1969; regional director of Northern California American Association of Teachers of German Foreign Language Contest, Berkeley, 1965-68; visiting lecturer at Michigan State University, 1972; instructor and co-director of University of Hawaii Cultural Study Abroad in Europe, summers, 1973, 1974; keynote speaker, Hawaiian Association of Language

Teachers, 1973. *Member:* American Association of Teachers of German, International Working Circle of Scholars of Baroque Literature, American Society for German Literature of the Sixteenth and Seventeenth Centuries, American Council for the Study of Austrian Literature. American Council for the Teaching of Foreign Languages, Pacific Northwest Conference on the Teaching of Foreign Languages, Philological Association of the Pacific Coast, Hawaiian Association of Language Teachers, Honolulu Academy of Arts, Alpha Mu Gamma, Delta Phi Alpha. *Awards, honors:* Fulbright-Hays fellowship, University of Vienna, 1964-65; University of Hawaii Special Research Council Travel grants, 1969-73, for work in Germany, Austria, Switzerland, and at Yale University; American Philosophical Society fellow, 1974-75.

WRITINGS: (Contributor) *Europaeische Tradition und Deutscher Literaturbarock: Zum Problem von Ueberlieferung und Umgestaltung,* Francke Verlag, 1973. Contributor to *Proceedings* of the Pacific Northwest Conference on Foreign Languages, *Modern Language Quarterly, University of Dayton Review, Modern Language Notes, Modern Language Journal, Monatshefte, Bulletin* of the Rocky Mountain Modern Language Association, and *Proceedings* of the Australasian Language and Literature Association Congress of 1973.

WORK IN PROGRESS: "An Aesthetic Response to Medieval Lyric Poetry," and "Goethe's *Faust* and Its Significance for Modern Life," both articles; research on Albrecht Durer's diaries.

SIDELIGHTS: William Scherer has travelled extensively in the United States, Mexico, Canada, Central and Southern Europe, Scandinavia, Crete, Egypt, Morocco, and the Near East. He resided in Munich, Germany, 1951-54, 1956-60, in Vienna, Austria, 1964-65, and in Stuttgart, Germany, 1974-75. *Avocational interests:* Classical music, opera, puppetry, theories of education, folklore, lyric poetry, Egyptology, chess, cooking, swimming.

* * *

SCHICK, George B(aldwin Powell) 1903-

PERSONAL: Born July 20, 1903, in Aurora, Ill.; son of Guy A. (a real estate broker) and Laura (Powell) Schick; married Beth McDonald (a librarian), June 10, 1936; children: James B. M. *Education:* University of Chicago, Ph.B., 1926, M.A., 1928, Ph.D., 1953. *Politics:* Democrat. *Religion:* Episcopalian. *Home:* 5042 McKenzie Dr., Placentia, Calif. 92670. *Office:* Institute for Reading, California State University, 800 North State College Blvd., Fullerton, Calif. 92634.

CAREER: University of Arkansas, Fayetteville, instructor in English, 1928-30; Beloit College, Beloit, Wis., instructor in English, 1930-33; Gary Junior College, Gary, Ind., instructor in English, 1933-35, 1937-39 (part-time); Purdue University, Lafayette, Ind., instructor, 1935-39, assistant professor, 1939-40, associate professor, 1940-50, professor of English, 1950-70, professor emeritus, 1970—; California State University, Fullerton, professor of reading, 1970-76, professor emeritus, 1976—; currently consultant for writing and reading improvement and editor for professional and beginning writers. Instructor, University of Chicago, summer, 1930. Member of board of directors, National Reading Conference, 1965-69. *Military service:* U.S. Naval Reserve, 1943-63, active duty, 1943-46; became commander.

MEMBER: Modern Language Association of America, National Council of Teachers of English, College Reading

Association (member of board of directors, 1966-68), National Reading Association (past member of board of directors), American Association of University Professors, North Central Reading Association (member of executive board, 1959-70. *Awards, honors:* Awards from International Reading Association, 1967, 1969; Oscar S. Causey Award from National Reading Conference, 1970.

WRITINGS: (With Helen Frick) *Handbook for Instructors in Developmental Reading in Secondary School and College,* Psychotechnics, 1958; (contributor) *New Frontiers in Reading,* International Reading Association, 1960; (contributor) *Sequential Development of Reading Abilities,* University of Chicago, 1960; (with Bernard Schmidt and Melba Schumacher) *Design for Good Reading,* two volumes, Harcourt, 1962, 2nd edition, four volumes, 1969; (with Schmidt) *A Guidebook for the Teaching of Reading,* Psychotechnics, 1966; (with Alton Raygor) *Reading at Efficient Rates,* McGraw, 1971; (with Schmidt and Robert Cosgrove) *Developing Reading Efficiency,* C. E. Merrill, 1972.

Co-editor of yearbooks of National Reading Conference, 1967-71. Contributor to proceedings; contributor to professional journals. Editor, *Journal of Developmental Reading,* 1957-66; member of board of publications, International Reading Association, 1964; editor, *Journal of Reading,* 1964-66; member of editorial advisory board, *Journal of Reading Behavior,* 1968-72, *Journal of Reading,* 1974—.

WORK IN PROGRESS: A college text, tentatively entitled *Improving Comprehension through Vocabulary Growth.*

SIDELIGHTS: George Schick told *CA* that his motivations for writing fall into the categories of professional advancement, improvement of current educational practices and thinking, and personal satisfaction. "I now work as much with would-be new writers of professional material as I do with my own," he explained. "As for [the category of] personal satisfaction, I produce mostly brief essays of reminiscence of [an] historical-personal nature."

*   *   *

SCHILLER, Andrew   1919-

PERSONAL: Born February 1, 1919, in Hlohovec, Czechoslovakia; naturalized U.S. citizen; son of Kalman (an accountant) and Theresa (Prezlmayr) Schiller; married Evelyn Kovacs (an art instructor), February 24, 1944; children: Stephanie Maria, Geoffrey Coleman. *Education:* City College of New York (now City College of the City University of New York), B.S.S., 1942; University of Iowa, M.A., 1946, Ph.D., 1952. *Politics:* Liberal. *Religion:* Jewish. *Home:* 1030 North Kenilworth, Oak Park, Ill. 60302. *Office:* Department of Linguistics, University of Illinois at Chicago Circle, Chicago, Ill. 60680.

CAREER: Has worked as free-lance writer and staff writer for various radio stations in New York, N.Y.; University of Rochester, Rochester, N.Y., instructor in English, 1946-47; Ohio State University, Columbus, instructor in English, 1947-48; Wayne University (now Wayne State University), Detroit, Mich., instructor in English and linguistics, 1952-55; University of Illinois at Chicago Circle, Chicago, assistant professor, 1955-61, associate professor, 1961-65, professor of English and linguistics, 1965-73, head of department of linguistics, 1973—. *Military service:* U.S. Army, Signal Corps and Military Intelligence, 1942-46.

MEMBER: Linguistic Society of America, Modern Language Association of America, National Council of Teachers of English, American Association of University Professors, U.S. Chess Federation, Chicago Linguistic Society. *Awards, honors:* Award from Standard Oil Corp., 1966, for contribution to teaching undergraduates.

WRITINGS: (With W. Cabell Greet and William A. Jenkins) *In Other Words,* Scott, Foresman, Volume I: *A Beginning Thesaurus,* 1968, Volume II: *A Junior Thesaurus,* 1969; *Language and How to Use It,* Scott, Foresman, Books 1 and 2 (with Marion Monroe, Ralph Nichols, Jenkins, and Charlotte Huck), 1970, Books 3, 4, 5 and 6 (with Monroe, Nichols, Jenkins, and Huck), 1969, Books 7 and 8 (with Nichols, Jenkins, and Doris Welch), 1972; (with Monroe and Greet) *My Pictionary,* Scott, Foresman, 1970; (with Jenkins and Greet) *My First Picture Dictionary,* Scott, Foresman, 1970; (with Jenkins and Greet) *My Second Picture Dictionary,* Scott, Foresman, 1971. Co-author of Scott, Foresman series "Reading Systems," "Open Highways," and "Spelling Our Language." Contributor to anthologies; contributor to a variety of magazines, including *Harper's, Panorama, Kentucky Law Journal, Carleton Miscellany, Papers of the Michigan Academy of Science, Arts and Letters,* and English journals.

WORK IN PROGRESS: A book on relationships between structure of language and prose style; a book on relationships between linguistics and poetics.

*   *   *

SCHINDELER, Fred(erick) Fernand   1934-

PERSONAL: Born October 11, 1934, in Stettler, Alberta, Canada; son of Clement Gerrard (a mechanic) and Signe (Danielson) Schindeler; married Mildred Smith (a nurse), June 30, 1956; children: Trevor, Michele, Julia, Heidi. *Education:* Bethel College, St. Paul, Minn., B.A. (magna cum laude), 1957; Southern Baptist Theological Seminary, B.D., 1959; University of Toronto, M.A., 1961, Ph.D., 1965; also studied at Survey Research Center, Ann Arbor, Mich., 1966. *Home:* McDonald's Corners, Ontario, Canada K0G 1M0. *Office:* Institute of Development Management, P.O. Box 1357, Gaborone, Botswana.

CAREER: Baptist minister in Salem, Ind., 1958-59, and Fenelon Falls, Ontario, 1960-61; University of Toronto, Toronto, Ontario, instructor in political science, 1961-63; York University, Downsview, Ontario, lecturer, 1963-65, assistant professor, 1965-67, associate professor, 1967-72, professor of political science, 1972-73, Glendon College, administrative assistant to principal, 1965-66, acting dean, 1966-67, Institute for Behavioral Research, acting director, 1967-68, director, 1968-72; Government of Canada, Ministry of State for Urban Affairs, director of external research, 1973-74, director of urban institutions and services, 1974-77, Treasury Board, senior policy advisor, 1977-78; University of Botswana, Lesotho and Swaziland, Gaborone, Botswana, director, 1978—. Member of public affairs committee, Baptist Federation of Canada, 1965-68. Member of research committee, Institute of Public Administration of Canada, 1968-70; member of steering committee, Research Information Centre for the Social Sciences, 1969-70; member of standing committee on social science data archives, International Social Science Research Council, 1970-74; member of board of directors, Quantitative Data Clearing House for Social Science, 1972-77; president, Institute of Environmental Research, Inc., 1972-74. Presented radio and television programs for Canadian Broadcasting Corp. (CBC), WBEN-Television, and OCEA-Television. Borough of North York, alderman, 1970-72, chairman of development committee and member of planning board, 1972-73; member of board of directors, York Finch General Hospital, 1971-72.

MEMBER: International Political Science Association, American Political Science Association, Canadian Political Science Association, Canadian Institute on Public Affairs, Canadian Historical Association, Institute of Public Administration of Canada, American Association for Public Opinion Research, Canadian Association of University Teachers, World Association for Public Opinion Research, International Survey Library Association (member of executive committee of Roper Center, 1970-72), Social Planning Council of Metropolitan Toronto, Board of Trade of Metropolitan Toronto, Toronto Area Research Conference, York University Faculty Association (chairman, 1969-70). *Awards, honors:* York University research grants, 1964, 1966, 1967; Government of Ontario research grants, 1965, 1967, 1968; Inter-University Consortium for Political Research grant, University of Michigan, 1966; Social Science Research Council of Canada publication grant, 1967.

WRITINGS: Responsible Government in Ontario, University of Toronto Press, 1969; (with Raymond N. Morris, Ruth Morris, David Hoffman, and C. Michael Lanphier) *Attitudes Toward Federal Government Information,* Toronto Institute for Behavioural Research, York University, 1969; *Attitudes Towards Federal Government: A Summary Report to the Task Force on Government Information,* Institute on Behavioral Research, (Toronto), 1969; *Social and Cultural Change in Canada,* Volume two, Copp, 1970; (contributor) A. M. Willms and W. D. Kernaghan, editors, *Public Administration in Canada: Selected Readings,* revised edition, Methuen, 1970; (contributor) Robert F. Nixon, editor, *The Guelph Papers,* Peter Martin Associates, 1970; (contributor) T. A. Hockin, editor, *The Apex of Power: The Prime Minister and Political Leadership in Canada,* Prentice-Hall, 1971. Contributor to professional journals, including *Canadian Forum, Canadian Public Administration,* and *Journal of Canadian Studies.*

WORK IN PROGRESS: A book tentatively entitled *The Political Culture of Ontario,* with David Hoffman; *Political Attitudes in Ontario; The Social and Psychological Effects of Physical Changes in the Urban Environment.*

BIOGRAPHICAL/CRITICAL SOURCES: Canadian Forum, July, 1969, December, 1969.

*   *   *

SCHIRMER, Daniel B(oone) 1915-

PERSONAL: Born February 22, 1915, in Greenwich, Conn.; son of Joseph Matthew (a businessman) and Abigail (Boone) Schirmer; married Margaret Fellows (a teacher), March 15, 1941; children: Audrey, Abigail, Joseph. *Education:* Harvard University, A.B., 1937; Boston University, M.A., 1961, Ph.D., 1971. *Home:* 17 Gerry St., Cambridge, Mass. 02138.

CAREER: American Student Union, Boston, Mass., organizer, 1937-39; Communist Party, organizer in Vermont and Massachusetts, 1939-44, 1946-53; employed in industry in Boston, and elsewhere, 1953-67; Boston University, Boston, lecturer in European history, 1967-69; Goddard College, Cambridge-Goddard Graduate School, Cambridge, Mass., faculty member of Program in Social Change, 1974-77. *Military service:* U.S. Army, 1944-46; became sergeant.

WRITINGS: Republic or Empire, Schenkman, 1972. Contributor to *New Republic, Science and Society, American Report, Nation, Commonweal,* and *Progressive.*

WORK IN PROGRESS: A collection of anti-imperialist writings.

*   *   *

SCHLENTHER, Boyd (Stanley) 1936-

PERSONAL: Born July 25, 1936, in Seattle, Wash.; son of Stanley (an advertising executive) and Bernice (Shafsky) Schlenther; married Elizabeth Hurley, August 30, 1959; children: Deborah, Jessica. *Education:* Texas Christian University, B.A., 1957; San Francisco Theological Seminary, M.Div., 1960; University of Edinburgh, Ph.D., 1965. *Residence:* Aberystwyth, Wales. *Office:* Department of History, University of Aberystwyth, Aberystwyth, Wales.

CAREER: First Presbyterian Church, Denton, Tex., minister, 1966-70; University of Aberystwyth, Aberystwyth, Wales, lecturer, 1970-76, senior lecturer in history, 1976—. Occasional lecturer in history at North Texas State University; visiting professor of church history at United Theological College, Aberystwyth, 1973—. *Member:* British Association for American Studies, British Historical Association.

WRITINGS: The Life and Writings of Francis Makemie, Presbyterian Historical Society, 1971; (contributor) Ian Dunlop, editor, *Scottish Church History Society Records,* W. & W. Lindsay, 1976; (contributor) Colin MacLean, editor, *A Nation's Faith,* W. & R. Chambers, 1978.

WORK IN PROGRESS: The Diary of James Horne Morrison.

*   *   *

SCHLESINGER, Lawrence E(rwin) 1921-

PERSONAL: Born September 10, 1921, in Boston, Mass.; son of Fred Joseph (a postal clerk) and Celia (Golden) Schlesinger; married Muriel Davies, 1946; married Lorraine Liller, 1961; married June Stanley (manager of an answering service), April 28, 1966; children: (first marriare) Eric, Sybil. *Education:* Boston University, B.S., 1943, M.A., 1948, Ph.D., 1955. *Politics:* Democrat. *Religion:* Jewish. *Address:* P.O. Box 560, South Orleans, Mass. 02662.

CAREER: Clearwater Sun, Clearwater, Fla., reporter, 1946; Facts and Figures, Inc., Boston, Mass., field representative, 1947-48; Boston University, Boston, chief of interviewing staff, 1949-50; Massachusetts Institute of Technology, Cambridge, research associate, Center for International Studies, 1951-52; George Washington University, Washington, D.C., research scientist, Human Resources Research Office, 1952-55; University of Michigan, Ann Arbor, research associate, Research Center for Group Dynamics, 1955-59, lecturer for extension service, 1956-58; Wayne State University, Monteith College, Detroit, Mich., assistant professor of psychology, 1959-60; Boston University, instructor in School of Public Relations, 1959-61; George Washington University, associate research professor of psychology, 1961-67, director of Driver Behavior Research Project, 1961-67; U.S. Naval Academy, Annapolis, Md., professor of psychology, 1966-67; National Children's Rehabilitation Center, Leesburg, Va., director of research, 1970-74; currently consulting research social psychologist. Member of Adjunct Staff, National Training Laboratories Institute; consultant to International Safety Academy of Insurance Co. of North America, Epilepsy Foundation of America, and to government agencies, including Federal Aviation Agency. *Military service:* U.S. Army, writer and editor, 1943-46. *Member:* American Psychological Association, Society for the Psychological Study of Social Issues, International Association of Applied Social Scientists (charter member). *Awards, honors:* Sigmund Livingston Foundation fellowship for graduate study, 1950-51.

WRITINGS: Depth Driver Education Programmed Training Book, edited by Jac D. Meacham, J. Ravin Publications, 1963; *Is There a Teenage Driver in Your House?,* New American Library, 1967; (with Robert D. Campbell and Betty Jane Schuchman) *Planning the Man/Environmental Interaction,* Matrix Research, 1970; (contributor) T. W. Forbes, editor, *Human Factors in Highway Traffic Safety Research,* Wiley, 1972; (with Walter Sikes and Charles N. Seashore) *Reforming Higher Education from Within,* Jossey-Bass, 1974; (with Nguyen Nahn) *An Epidemiological Survey of Developmental Disabilities in the Commonwealth of Virginia,* National Rehabilitation Center, 1974; (with Donald S. Frank) *A Guide to Epilepsy for the Rehabilitation Counselor* (with cassette recordings), Epilepsy Foundation of America, 1976; *Safety Communication in Industry,* Garland Publishing, 1979. Also author of numerous technical reports on organizational behavior, communications, driver behavior, industrial safety, and rehabilitation. Contributor of research articles to more than fifteen journals.

WORK IN PROGRESS: Peer Self Help Groups; with Robert Campbell and R. L. Roark, *Man-Environment Systems.*

SIDELIGHTS: From a zenith of research activity, Lawrence Schlesinger says that he has been decompressing and spreading out his interests to include a wider variety of topics and a more relaxed way of looking at them. "In sum, I have shifted from the monastic research specialist in the laboratory to the consultant and communicator providing a pipeline between the research specialist and the world outside. My current interests are in human behavior in the world at large. . . ."

* * *

SCHLESINGER, Thomas O(tto)   1925-

PERSONAL: Born June 11, 1925, in Berlin, Germany; U.S. citizen; son of Fritz Werner (a certified public accountant) and Charlotte (Kornfeld) Schlesinger; married Patricia Powers, October 30, 1956; children: Ann, Peter. *Education:* University of Maryland, B.S., 1958; American University, M.A., 1966, Ph.D., 1967. *Residence:* New Hampton, N.H. *Office:* Department of Political Science, Plymouth State College, Plymouth, N.H. 03264.

CAREER: U.S. Army, began as private, 1943, commissioned lieutenant, member of Intelligence Corps, 1943-48, served in European Theater in World War II; served in Korean War, 1950-52; interpreter to U.S. commanders in Austria and Italy, 1954-57; instructor at U.S. Army Intelligence school, 1957-60; qualified as Special Forces officer (Green Beret), 1963; instructor at Special Warfare School, 1963-64; retired as major; State University of New York College at Fredonia, assistant professor of political science, 1967-70; Plymouth State College, Plymouth, N.H., 1970—, began as assistant professor, currently associate professor of political science. *Member:* International Studies Association, American Political Science Association, American Civil Liberties Union, Common Cause, American Association of University Professors (president of Plymouth, N.H. chapter, 1972—), Academy of Political Science, New England Political Science Association, Pi Sigma Alpha.

WRITINGS: Austrian Neutrality in Postwar Europe: Domestic Roots of a Foreign Policy, Wilhelm Braumuller,

1972. Contributor to *Polity* and *Military Review.* Political science consultant and reviewer for *Reprint Bulletin,* 1971—.†

* * *

SCHMELTZ, William Frederick   1924-

PERSONAL: Born November 30, 1924, in Toledo, Ohio; son of William Herman (a certified public accountant) and Augusta Sophie (Dicke) Schmeltz; married Peggy Lou Hurrelbrink, January 24, 1948; children: Randolph G., Catherine A., Christine D., Janet A. *Education:* Attended Ohio State University, 1942, and Bowling Green State University, 1943-44; University of Toledo, B.B.A. (magna cum laude), 1945; Harvard University, M.B.A., 1947; Case Western Reserve University, Ph.D., 1966. *Home:* 845 Scott Blvd., Bowling Green, Ohio 43402. *Office:* Department of Quantitative Analysis Control, Bowling Green State University, Bowling Green, Ohio 43403; and School of Business, Southern Illinois University, Edwardsville, Ill. 62901.

CAREER: Bowling Green State University, Bowling Green, Ohio, instructor, 1946-47, assistant professor, 1947-50, associate professor, 1950-54, professor of accounting, 1954-73, trustee professor, 1973-76, professor emeritus, 1976—, dean of College of Business Administration, 1960-67; Southern Illinois University at Edwardsville, professor of finance and accounting, 1976—. Certified Public Accountant, 1950; Certified Management Accountant, 1973. Director, Bank of Wood County, Bowling Green, Ohio, 1954—, Seeger Brass Co., Toledo, Ohio, 1957—, Computer Efficiency Corp., Miami, Fla., 1967—, and United Appraisal, Hartford, Conn., 1972—. *Military service:* U.S. Naval Reserve, 1943-46; became lieutenant junior grade. *Member:* American Institute of Certified Public Accountants, Financial Executives Institute, Financial Analysts Society, National Association of Accountants, American Accounting Association, Ohio Society of Certified Public Accountants.

WRITINGS: Accounting and Management Control Practices in Petroleum Refining, Press of Case Western Reserve University, 1966; *The Development of Financial Managers,* Financial Executives Institute, 1971.

WORK IN PROGRESS: Revision of *Accounting and Management Control Practices in Petroleum Refining.*

* * *

SCHMIDT, Dolores Barracano   1931-

PERSONAL: Born May 16, 1931, in New York, N.Y.; daughter of Ralph Henry and Josephine (Chianese) Barracano; married Earl Robert Schmidt (a history professor), June 27, 1959; children: Josephine, Robert, Francis. *Education:* Hunter College (now Hunter College of the City University of New York), A.B., 1953; University of Pennsylvania, M.A., 1956. *Politics:* Democrat. *Home:* 70 Fuller Rd., Albany, N.Y. 12203. *Office:* Affirmative Action, State University Plaza, State University of New York, Albany, N.Y. 12246.

CAREER: University of Nevada, Reno, instructor in English, 1957-59; Rutgers University, Camden, N.J., instructor in English, 1959-60; Eastern Illinois University, Charleston, assistant professor of English, 1960-61; Mayville State College, Mayville, N.D., assistant professor of English, 1961-62; Slippery Rock State College, Slippery Rock, Pa., assistant professor of English, 1968-73; State University of New York at Albany, assistant vice-chancellor for affirmative action, 1973—. Panelist at College

Conference of Composition and Communication, 1959. *Member:* Modern Language Association of America (member of program committee, 1971-76), National Council of Teachers of English, Conference on College Composition and Communication; American Studies Association (member of committee on status of women, 1972—), Coordinating Committee of Women Professional Historians, National Organization for Women, American Association of University Professors, Northeast Modern Language Association. *Awards, honors:* Second place award, 1962, in American Association of University Women creative writing competition.

WRITINGS: (With husband, Earl Robert Schmidt) *The 'Deputy' Reader: Studies in Moral Responsibility*, Scott, Foresman, 1965; (contributor) *Female Studies V: Women and Education, a Feminist Perspective*, Know, Inc., 1970; (with E. R. Schmidt) *Pittsburgh Regional Ecology*, Vulcan Press, 1972; *Images of Women: Guidelines to Selection of Textbooks* (pamphlet), Department of Public Instruction, Commonwealth of Pennsylvania, 1972. Editor of *Women and Literature: Research in Progress*, 1971-73; also contributor to *Women and American Studies*. Contributor to *College English, Prairie Schooner, McCall's, Redbook, Sexual Behavior, AAUP Bulletin*, and *AAUW Bulletin*. Research editor for *Whitman Variorum*, 1956-57; member of bibliography committee, *American Quarterly*, 1972—.

WORK IN PROGRESS: A book, *The Turning Point: The American Writer and Sexual Equality.*†

* * *

SCHMIDT, Royal Jae (Jr.) 1915-

PERSONAL: Born June 10, 1915, in Maywood, Ill.; son of Royal Jae (a lawyer) and Anna Mae (Smith) Schmidt; married Beverley Jean Smith, June 25, 1961; children: Royal Jae III, Harvey, Gary. *Education:* Lewis Institute of Technology, B.S., 1939; University of Chicago, M.A., 1947, Ph.D., 1957. *Religion:* Congregationalist. *Home:* 500 North Third Ave., Maywood, Ill. 60153. *Office:* Elmhurst College, South Prospect, Elmhurst, Ill. 60126.

CAREER: Elmhurst College, Elmhurst, Ill., assistant professor, 1948-55, associate professor, 1955-57, professor of history and political science, 1957—. Maywood Public Library, member of board of trustees, vice-president of board, 1971-72; vice-president, North Maywood Civic Association. *Member:* American Historical Association, American Political Science Association, International Studies Association, Illinois Historical Society, MacDowell Artists Association (past president).

WRITINGS: Bugles in a Dream: DuPage County in the Civil War, DuPage County Historical Society, 1962; *Versailles and the Ruhr: Seedbed of World War II*, Nijhoff, 1968. Contributor of articles and reviews to *Journal of the History of Ideas, Journal of the Illinois Historical Society, Choice, American Historical Review*, and *Midwest Political Science Review*.

WORK IN PROGRESS: Herbert Hoover and the Uncertain Peace.

AVOCATIONAL INTERESTS: Music, library administration, collecting books and ancient coins, travel.

BIOGRAPHICAL/CRITICAL SOURCES: Chicago Tribune, May 31, 1972.

* * *

SCHMITT, Karl Michael 1922-

PERSONAL: Born July 22, 1922, in Louisville, Ky.; son of Edward Peter (a railroadman) and Mary Ann (Iula) Schmitt; married Grace Leary (a librarian), June 18, 1949; children: Karl, Edward, Barbara, William, Michael. *Education:* Catholic University of America, B.A., 1947, M.A., 1949; University of Pennsylvania, Ph.D., 1954. *Politics:* Democrat. *Religion:* Roman Catholic. *Office:* Department of Government, University of Texas, Austin, Tex. 78712.

CAREER: Niagara University, Niagara University, N.Y., instructor, 1950-54, assistant professor of history, 1954-55; U.S. Department of State, Washington, D.C., intelligence research analyst, 1955-58; University of Texas at Austin, assistant professor, 1958-63, associate professor, 1963-66, professor of government, 1966—, chairperson of department 1975-79. Visiting assistant professor, University of California, Los Angeles, summer, 1959; visiting professor, National War College, 1970-71. Research contractor, U.S. Department of State, 1963, 1965-66. *Military service:* U.S. Army, Infantry, 1943-45. *Member:* American Catholic Historical Association (member of executive council, 1967-69), Conference on Latin American History, Southern Political Science Association, Southwest Council of Latin American Studies, Texas Catholic Historical Society (president, 1976-77).

WRITINGS: (With David D. Burks) *Evolution or Chaos: Dynamics of Latin American Politics and Government*, Praeger, 1964; *Linkages in Central American Education and Regional Integration* (monograph), U.S. Department of State, 1964; *Communism in Mexico: A Study in Political Frustration*, University of Texas Press, 1965; (with Carl Leiden) *The Politics of Violence: Revolution in the Modern World*, Prentice-Hall, 1968; (with Leiden and Murray Havens) *The Politics of Assassination*, Prentice-Hall, 1970; (editor and author of introduction and of bibliographical essay) *The Roman Catholic Church in Modern Latin America*, Knopf, 1972; *Mexico and the United States, 1821-1973: Conflict and Coexistence*, Wiley, 1974.

Contributor: A. Curtis Wilgus, editor, *The Caribbean: Mexico Today*, University of Florida Press, 1964; Jack Gabbert, editor, *American Foreign Policy and Revolutionary Change*, Washington State University Press, 1968; James F. Kirkham, Sheldon Levy, and William J. Crotty, editors, *Assassination and Political Violence*, U.S. Government Printing Office, 1969; Andrew Gyorgy and Hubert S. Gibbs, editors, *Problems in International Relations*, Prentice-Hall, 1970. Contributor to *Encyclopaedia Britannica, New Catholic Encyclopedia, Encyclopedia Americana, Americana Annual*, and to journals, including *Americas, Catholic Historical Review, Western Political Quarterly*, and *Hispanic American Historical Review*. Advisory editor, *Catholic Historical Review*, 1966-69.

* * *

SCHMITTER, Dean Morgan 1917-

PERSONAL: Born June 14, 1917, in Richland, Iowa; son of Otto W. and Amy Jane (Morgan) Schmitter; married Barbara Lewis, November 14, 1943 (died, 1958); married Barbara Stahl (dean of Barnard College), June 28, 1962; children: (second marriage) Amy Morgan. *Education:* Louisiana State University, B.A., 1938; Columbia University, M.A., 1947, Ph.D., 1955. *Residence:* Closter, N.J. *Office:* Columbia University, 116th St. and Broadway, New York, N.Y. 10027.

CAREER: Announcer and production manager for radio stations KWKH and KTBS, Shreveport, La., 1938-41; Columbia University, New York, N.Y., lecturer, 1947-50, instructor, 1950-55, assistant professor, 1955-60, associate professor, 1960-74, professor of English, 1974—. Moderator of "Dateline Columbia," for WNYC-Radio, 1953-58, and "Lamp Unto My Feet," for CBS-Television, about 1956; appeared as guest on "Invitation to Learning" for CBS-Radio, 1957-60; participant in "Charge Account," NBC-TV, 1960-62. *Military service:* U.S. Navy, 1941-45; became lieutenant; received Distinguished Flying Cross, Air Medal. *Member:* Modern Language Association of America, Renaissance Society of America, Milton Society, American Association of University Professors.

WRITINGS: (With J. W. Krutch, Alfred Kazin, R. P. Warren, and W. H. Auden) *English One Hundred,* with syllabus, Institute for University Studies, 1963, revised edition (with M. H. Nicolson and John H. Middendorf), 1970; (editor) *William Faulkner,* McGraw, 1972; *Mark Twain,* McGraw, 1974. Contributor to *Notes and Queries, Renaissance News, Journal of the History of Ideas, Review of English Studies,* and *Focus.*

* * *

SCHNEIDER, Benjamin 1938-

PERSONAL: Born August 11, 1938, in New York, N.Y.; son of Leo (an insurance man) and Rose (Cohen) Schneider; married H. Brenda Jacobson, January 29, 1961; children: Lee Andrew, Rhody Yve. *Education:* Alfred University, B.A., 1960; Bernard M. Baruch School of Business and Public Administration of the City College (now Bernard M. Baruch College of the City University of New York), M.B.A., 1962; University of Maryland, Ph.D., 1967. *Home:* 8612 Irvington Ave., Bethesda, Md. 20034. *Office:* Department of Psychology, University of Maryland, College Park, Md. 20742.

CAREER: Department of Labor, New York, N.Y., employment counselor, 1960-62; Yale University, New Haven, Conn., assistant professor of administrative sciences and psychology, 1967-71; University of Maryland, College Park, 1971—, currently professor of psychology and head of program in industrial organizational psychology. Consultant, Chase Manhattan Bank, Citibank, J. C. Penney Co., and American Telephone and Telegraph. *Military service:* U.S. Army, 1962-64; became first lieutenant. *Member:* American Psychological Association, Academy of Management, Eastern Psychological Association, Sigma Xi. *Awards, honors:* James McKeen Cattel Award from American Psychological Association, 1966 and 1971; Fulbright-Hays award, Bar-Ilan University, Israel, 1973-74.

WRITINGS: (With D. T. Hall) *Organizational Climates and Careers: The Work Lives of Priests,* Seminar Press, 1973; *Staffing Organizations,* Goodyear Publishing, 1976. Contributor to *Personnel Psychology, Journal of Applied Psychology,* and *Administrative Science Quarterly.* Member of editorial review boards, *Academy of Management Review* and *Administrative Science Quarterly.*

WORK IN PROGRESS: Perception and Organizational Behavior, with R. A. Snyder.

* * *

SCHNEIDER, Clement J(oseph) 1927-1972

PERSONAL: Born November 21, 1927, in New Franken, Wis.; son of Clem A. and Florence (Danine) Schneider. *Education:* St. Louis University, B.A., 1951, Ph.L., 1952, S.T.L., 1960; Cornell University, Ph.D., 1964. *Office:* Department of Sociology, Creighton University, Omaha, Neb.

CAREER: Joined Society of Jesus (Jesuits; S.J.), 1945, ordained Roman Catholic priest, 1958. Social science teacher in Roman Catholic high school and prefect of boarding school in Prairie du Chien, Wis., 1952-55; Creighton University, Omaha, Neb., assistant professor of sociology, 1965-72, acting chairman of department, 1965-67, vice-president for academic affairs, 1968-72, acting president of university, 1969-70. *Member:* American Sociological Association, American Association for Higher Education, American Association for the Advancement of Science, Association for the Sociology of Religion, Society for the Scientific Study of Religion, Gerontological Society, Midwest Sociological Society, Phi Kappa Phi.

WRITINGS: (With Gordon Streib) *Retirement in American Society: Impact and Process,* Cornell University Press, 1971.††

(Died October 20, 1972)

* * *

SCHOFIELD, Michael 1919-

PERSONAL: Born June 24, 1919, in Leeds, England; son of Snowden and Ella (Dawson) Schofield. *Education:* Cambridge University, M.A., 1940. *Home and office:* 28 Lyndhurst Gardens, London NW3 5NW, England.

CAREER: British Social Biology Council, London, England, research director, 1959-62; Central Council for Health Education, London, research director, 1963-65; self-employed, 1973—. *Military service:* Royal Air Force, 1940-45.

WRITINGS: Sexual Behavior of Young People, Longmans, Green, 1965; *Sociological Aspects of Homosexuality,* Longmans, Green, 1965; *Social Research,* Heinemann, 1969; (author of introduction) *The Release Report,* Sphere, 1969; *The Strange Case of Pot,* Penguin, 1971; (author of introduction) *Boy, Girl, Man, Woman,* Calder & Boyars, 1972; *The Sexual Behavior of Young Adults,* Allen Lane, 1973; *Promiscuity,* Gollancz, 1976; *Report of the Committee on the Operation of the Sexual Containment Act,* Davis-Poynter, 1978; (contributor) *Human Sexuality,* Cambridge University Press, 1979.

SIDELIGHTS: John Gray writes in his review of *Sexual Behavior of Young People:* "[Michael] Schofield presents, in what is sociologically and statistically an almost blameless manner, the results of interviews with 1,870 teenagers in seven different areas of England. . . . Those who have hopes of finding yet another scarifying expose of teenage immorality will be disappointed by this book. The facts are presented dispassionately, and are far less 'shocking' than the exposes would have us believe."

BIOGRAPHICAL/CRITICAL SOURCES: Books and Bookmen, February, 1969.

* * *

SCHOLL, Sharon L. 1932-

PERSONAL: Born May 13, 1932, in San Antonio, Tex.; daughter of George C. and Wanda (Dreeke) Schofield; married Harvey H. Scholl (a professor of music), June 13, 1953; children: Laura Ann, Lynn Carol. *Education:* Trinity University, B.M., 1953; Indiana University, M.M.Ed., 1959; Florida State University, Ph.D., 1966. *Home:* 6854 Howalt Dr., Jacksonville, Fla. 32211. *Office:* Department of Humanities, Jacksonville University, Jacksonville, Fla. 32211.

CAREER: Jacksonville University, Jacksonville, Fla., assistant professor of humanities, 1966—. Member of Historical and Cultural Commission, 1974-76, and Florida Endowment for the Humanities, 1977-81. *Member:* National Society for Humanities Education, American Association of University Professors, American Association for the Advancement of Humanities. *Awards, honors:* Humanist of the Year, National Association for Humanities Education, 1977.

WRITINGS: (With Sylvia White) *Music and the Culture of Man,* Holt, 1970. Contributor to *Best Friends, Response,* and *Humanities Journal.*

WORK IN PROGRESS: Research in basic introductory materials for undergraduate understanding of African culture, technology and modern culture, and religion and contemporary arts; research in utopian literature and cultural philosophy in comic strips.

* * *

SCHONBERG, Rosalyn Krokover 1913(?)-1973

1913(?)—June 14, 1973; American dance critic, columnist and author. Obituaries: *New York Times,* June 15, 1973.

* * *

SCHOONOVER, Thelma I(rene) 1907-

PERSONAL: Born January 8, 1907, in Columbus, Ohio; daughter of Harry O. (an auditor) and Nellie Maude (Patrick) Schoonover. *Education:* Ohio State University, B.S. in Ed., 1927, M.A., 1948, Ph.D., 1955. *Politics:* Republican. *Religion:* Episcopalian. *Home:* 355 Clinton Heights Ave., Columbus, Ohio 43202. *Office:* 236 East Town St., Suite 306, Columbus, Ohio 43215.

CAREER: Supervisor of county schools in Ohio, 1926-33; psychologist in categorical aid programs in Ohio, 1933-44; Franklin University, Columbus, Ohio, director of counseling and guidance, 1944-47; psychologist for Upper Arlington Schools, Arlington, Ohio, 1947-50; Board of Education, Akron, Ohio, chief psychologist, 1950-54; Capital University, Columbus, professor of psychology and head of department, 1954-72, professor emeritus, 1972—; psychologist in private practice, 1972—. Member of board of trustees, Franklin County Mental Health Association, 1960-68; Columbus Civil Service Commission, member, 1972—, president, 1974—. *Member:* American Psychological Association, American Association of University Women, Ohio Psychological Association, Ohio State University Alumni Association, Ohio State Alumnae Club, Phi Delta Gamma, Psi Chi, Pi Lambda Theta, Delta Kappa Gamma, Clintonville Women's Club.

WRITINGS: Measurement for Teachers, C. E. Merrill, 1968.

* * *

SCHRAMM, Richard (Howard) 1934-

PERSONAL: Born February 10, 1934, in Renigunta, India; son of Milton Howard (a minister) and Mary (Clossman) Schramm; married Janice Stewart, 1958 (divorced, 1976); children: Eric Stewart. *Education:* Capital University, B.Sc., 1955; Ohio University, M.A., 1961; Duke University, Ph.D., 1964. *Office:* Department of English, University of Utah, Salt Lake City, Utah 84112.

CAREER: Ohio University, Athens, instructor in English, 1960-61; University of North Carolina at Chapel Hill, instructor in English, 1963-64; California State University,

Northridge, assistant professor, 1964-68, associate professor, 1968-71, professor of English, 1971-73; University of Utah, Salt Lake City, visiting professor, 1971-73, professor of English, 1973—. Fulbright lecturer, University of Kerala (India), 1968-69. *Military service:* U.S. Army, 1957-59.

WRITINGS: Rooted in Silence (poems), Bobbs-Merrill, 1972. Contributor of poems to *New Yorker, Poetry, Quarterly Review of Literature, Shenandoah, Massachusetts Review, Southern Review, Antaeus, Poetry Northwest, Southern Poetry Review, Iowa Review, Midwest Quarterly,* and other journals.

WORK IN PROGRESS: A second volume of poems.

* * *

SCHREIBER, Ron 1934-

PERSONAL: Born January 25, 1934, in Chicago, Ill.; son of Paul R. and Adeline (Wencl) Schreiber. *Education:* Wesleyan University, B.A., 1955; Columbia University, M.A., 1959, Ph.D., 1967. *Politics:* Socialist. *Home:* 15 Westwood Rd., Somerville, Mass. 02143. *Office:* Department of English, University of Massachusetts, Boston, Mass.

CAREER: Hanging Loose (poetry magazine), New York, N.Y., editor, 1966—; University of Massachusetts—Boston, 1967—, began as assistant professor, currently associate professor of English. Editor, Alice James Books (a cooperative publishing firm), 1973-75, 1978. *Military service:* U.S. Army, 1955-57.

WRITINGS: (Editor) *Thirty-one New American Poets,* Hill & Wang, 1968; *Living Space* (poems), Hanging Loose, 1972; *Moving to a New Place* (poems), Alice James, 1975; *False Clues* (poems), Calamus Books, 1978; *Against that Time* (poems), Alice James, 1978.

* * *

SCHRIER, William 1900-1973

PERSONAL: Born December 7, 1900, in Kruiningen, Netherlands; naturalized U.S. citizen, 1913; son of Marinus and Neeltjy (Lemmers) Schrier; married Ada Ann Meyers (a beauty counselor), June 2, 1928; children: Sally Ann (Mrs. Robert M. Japinga). *Education:* Attended Kalamazoo College, 1920-22; University of Michigan, A.B., 1924, M.A., 1930, Ph.D., 1945; University of Colorado, law studies, 1926-27. *Religion:* Reformed Church in America. *Home and office:* 22 West 25th St., Holland, Mich. 49423.

CAREER: Instructor in speech at St. Louis University, St. Louis, Mo., 1924-26, and University of Colorado, Boulder, 1926-27; University of North Dakota, Grand Forks, instructor, 1927-29, assistant professor, 1929-34, professor of speech, 1934-39; Hope College, Holland, Mich., professor of speech and chairman of department, 1939-69. On leave from Hope College as teacher in University of California Far East Program at military posts in Japan and Korea, 1954-56. Speaker at more than two hundred high school commencements throughout Michigan; director of oratory, Michigan Intercollegiate Speech League, 1944-52. *Member:* Speech Association of America, Central States Speech Association, Michigan Speech Association, Pi Kappa Delta, Delta Sigma Rho, Rotary Club.

WRITINGS: Gerrit J. Diekema: Orator, privately printed, 1950; (editor) *Winning Hope College Orations—1914-1966,* privately printed in connection with Hope College Centennial, 1966; *Contest Oratory: A Handbook for High School and College Contestants and Coaches,* Scarecrow, 1971. Contributor of more than thirty articles to speech journals.

BIOGRAPHICAL/CRITICAL SOURCES: Vital Speeches, July 15, 1963.††

(Died March 20, 1973)

*   *   *

SCHROEDER, Albert H(enry) 1914-

PERSONAL: Born March 23, 1914, in Brooklyn, N.Y.; son of Henry W. (an importer) and Ida (LeHovey) Schroeder; married Ella Krienke, January 27, 1945; children: Stephen H., Christine A. (Mrs. Thomas Hueston), Scott G. Education: University of Arizona, B.A., 1938, M.A., 1941. Politics: Independent. Religion: Lutheran. Home: 1108 Barcelona Lane, Santa Fe, N.M. 87501.

CAREER: Foreman at archaeological site in Arizona, 1938-39; U.S. National Museum, assistant archaeologist in Mexico, 1940-41; U.S. National Park Service, ranger-naturalist, 1941, 1946, archaeologist in Santa Fe, N.M., 1951-54, Globe, Ariz., 1954-57, and Santa Fe, 1957-67, interpretive specialist, Santa Fe, 1967-73, chief of Division of Interpretation, 1973-76. Expert witness in Indian Land Claims Hearings, 1953-65, 1967-77; chairman of New Mexico Cultural Properties Review Committee, 1969—. Member of board of managers, School of American Research, 1965-71. Military service: U.S. Army, 1942-46; became technical sergeant. Member: Archaeological Society of New Mexico (president, 1965-71), Historical Society of New Mexico (1st vice-president, 1975—), Westerners Corral of Santa Fe (sheriff, 1968). Awards, honors: Meritorious Service Award, U.S. Department of Interior, 1956; Distinguished Service Award, U.S. Department of Interior, 1976.

WRITINGS: Archaeology of Zion National Park (monograph), Department of Anthropology, University of Utah, 1956; The Archaeological Excavations at Willow Beach, Arizona, 1950 (monograph), Department of Anthropology, University of Utah, 1961; (editor and translator with Daniel S. Matson) Gaspar Castano de Sosa, A Colony on the Move Journal: 1590-1591, School of American Research, 1965; (editor) Collected Papers in Honor of Lyndon Lane Hargrave, Archaeological Society of New Mexico, 1968; The Hoholcam, Sinagua, and the Hakataya (monograph), Imperial Valley College Museum Society, 1975. Also author of Collected Papers in Honor of Marjorie Ferguson Lambert, 1976. Contributor of more than one hundred forty archaeological and historical articles and reviews to journals. Editor, La Gaceta and Brand Book, Westerners Corral of Santa Fe, 1970—; member of editorial advisory committee for Southwest section, Handbook of the North American Indian, 1971—.

WORK IN PROGRESS: Collected Papers in Honor of Bertha Pauline Dutton.

*   *   *

SCHROEDER, Fred E(rich) H(arald) 1932-

PERSONAL: Surname is pronounced Shray-der; born June 3, 1932, in Manitowoc, Wis.; son of Alfred William (a cabinetmaker) and Sissel (Lovell) Schroeder; married Janet Knope (a library administrator), August 21, 1954; children: Erich Karl. Education: University of Wisconsin, B.S., 1960; University of Minnesota, M.A., 1963, Ph.D., 1968. Home: 10700 North Shore Dr., Duluth, Minn. 55804. Office: Humanities Program, University of Minnesota, Duluth, Minn. 55812.

CAREER: Elementary school teacher in Wisconsin, 1952-60; University of Minnesota—Duluth, instructor, 1963-68,

assistant professor, 1968-71, associate professor of English and humanities, 1971-74, professor of English, 1974-77, professor of English, humanities, and behavioral science, 1977—, director of humanities program, 1975—. Team leader and consultant, National Humanities Series, Princeton, N.J., 1969-71. Consultant, National American Studies Faculty, 1972-73, National Humanities Faculty, 1973—. Member: American Studies Association, National Association for Humanities Education, National Council of Teachers of English, Popular Culture Association, Midwest Popular Culture Association, American Association of University Professors. Awards, honors: Woodrow Wilson fellowship, 1960; National Endowment for the Humanities younger scholar fellowship, 1969; Institute of Human Values in Medicine fellow, 1976; Distinguished Achievement Award, Educational Press Association, 1978, for best feature article.

WRITINGS: Joining the Human Race: How to Teach the Humanities, Everett-Edwards, 1972; Outlaw Aesthetics: Arts and the Public Mind, Bowling Green University Press, 1977; (editor) Popular Culture before Printing, Bowling Green University Press, in press; (editor) Twentieth-Century Popular Culture in Museums, Libraries, and Archives, Bowling Green University Press, in press.

Contributor: Otis Winchester and Winston Weathers, editors, The Prevalent Forms of Prose, Houghton, 1968; Theodore L. Gross, editor, Representative Men: Cult Heroes of Our Time, Free Press, 1970; Ray B. Browne and Ronald J. Ambrosetti, editors, Popular Culture and Curricula, Bowling Green University Popular Press, 1970; Marshall Fishwick and Browne, editors, Icons of Popular Culture, Bowling Green University Popular Press, 1970; Hans P. Guth, editor, The Tools of English, teacher's guide, McGraw, 1971; Edward T. James and Janet W. James, editors, Notable American Women, 1607-1950, three volumes, Harvard University Press, 1971; James W. Corder, editor, Finding a Voice, Scott, Foresman, 1973; John Garraty and E. James, editors, Dictionary of American Biography, ten volumes, Scribner, 1974; Horace Newcomb, editor, Television: The Critical View, Oxford University Press, 1976, 2nd edition, 1979; Fishwick and Browne, editors, Icons of America, Bowling Green University Press, 1978. Also author of a leaflet entitled Designing Your Exhibit: Seven Ways to Look at an Artifact, for the American Association for State and Local History. Contributor to literary and interdisciplinary journals, including Dalhousie Review, Sewanee Review, English Journal, Soundings, American Quarterly, American Studies, Historic Preservation, and Western Humanities Review.

WORK IN PROGRESS: Research for a book on rural schools, completion expected in 1980; several detective novels to be co-authored by wife, Janet Schroeder; long-term research on interpretation of material culture in museums.

AVOCATIONAL INTERESTS: Collecting prints, drawings, and antiquities; woodworking, gardening, photography.

*   *   *

SCHULMAN, Rosalind 1914-

PERSONAL: Born June 9, 1914, in New York, N.Y.; daughter of Louis (a dentist) and Masha (Palley) Sadoff; married Sidney Schulman (an attorney), May 8, 1943. Education: Smith College, B.A., 1934; Columbia University, M.A., 1938; University of Pennsylvania, Ph.D., 1964. Poli-

tics: Democrat-Independent. *Religion:* Ethical. *Home:* 8B25 The Philadelphian, Philadelphia, Pa. 19130. *Office:* Department of Economics, Drexel University, Philadelphia, Pa. 19104.

CAREER: Industrial Union of Marine and Shipbuilding Workers of America (IUMSWA), AFL-CIO, Camden, N.J., director of research, 1943-64; Drexel University, Philadelphia, Pa., assistant professor, 1965-68, associate professor, 1968-72, professor of economics, 1972—. Member of board of directors of World Affairs Council of Philadelphia, 1962-65. Member of governor's energy council, state of Pennsylvania. *Member:* American Economic Association, American Statistical Association, American Association of University Professors, American Association of University Women, Industrial Relations Research Association, Regional Science Research Association, Phi Beta Kappa, Beta Gamma Sigma.

WRITINGS: The Nation That Invented the Steamship, IUMSWA (Camden, N.J.), 1947; *The Economics of Consumption for a Changing Society,* Drexel University Press, 1972.

* * *

SCHULTZ, John (Ludwig) 1932-

PERSONAL: Born July 28, 1932, in Columbia, Mo.; son of Gerard (an historian) and Jennie (Brumley) Schultz; married Anne G. Bray, December 12, 1962; children: Timmy, Susie. *Education:* Attended University of Chicago, University of Iowa, and University of Missouri—Columbia. *Office:* Department of Writing, Columbia College, Chicago, Ill. 60611.

CAREER: Columbia College, Chicago, Ill., chairman, department of writing, 1967—. *Military service:* U.S. Army, 1953-55.

WRITINGS: The Tongues of Men, Big Table Publishing, 1969; *No One Was Killed: Documentation and Meditation, Democratic Convention, Chicago, 1968,* Big Table Publishing, 1969; (editor) Richard R. Lingeman, *Don't You Know There's a War On?* Putnam, 1970; *Motion Will Be Denied: A New Report on the Chicago Conspiracy Trial,* Morrow, 1972; (editor) *Angels in My Oven,* Columbia College Press of Chicago, 1976; (editor) *The Story Workshop Reader,* Columbia College Press of Chicago, 1976. Editor, *Chicago, F Magazine,* beginning 1967; contributing editor, *Evergreen Review.*

WORK IN PROGRESS: A novel; a book on children.

SIDELIGHTS: John Schultz originated the Story Workshop method of teaching writing.

BIOGRAPHICAL/CRITICAL SOURCES: New York Times, November 22, 1969; *New York Review of Books,* May 21, 1970.†

* * *

SCHULZ, Juergen 1927-

PERSONAL: Born August 18, 1927, in Kiel, Germany; came to United States in 1938, naturalized in 1944; son of Johannes Martin Askan (an industrial engineer) and Ilse (Lebenbaum) Schulz; married Justine Hume, September 24, 1951; married second wife, Anne Markham (an art historian), June 17, 1968; children: (first marriage) Christoph (deceased), Ursula, Catherine; (second marriage) Jeremy. *Education:* University of California, Berkeley, B.A., 1950; Courtauld Institute of Art, London, Ph.D., 1958. *Home:* 192 Bowen St., Providence, R.I. 02906. *Office:* Department of Art, Brown University, Providence, R.I. 02912.

CAREER: San Francisco Chronicle, San Francisco, Calif., reporter, 1950-51; University of California, Berkeley, instructor, 1958-60, assistant professor, 1960-64, associate professor of history of art, 1964-68; Brown University, Providence, R.I., professor of history of art, 1968—, head of department, 1968-72. Member, Institute for Advanced Study, 1972-73; fellow, National Endowment for the Humanities, 1972-73, 1978-79. *Military service:* U.S. Army, 1945-48; became staff sergeant. *Member:* College Art Association of America, National Committee for the History of Art, Society of Architectural Historians, Renaissance Society of America, Verein zur Forderung des Kunsthistorischen Institutes in Florenz. *Awards, honors:* S. H. Kress Foundation fellow, 1965; Guggenheim Foundation fellow, 1966-67; Stella della Solidarieta Italiana (Grande Ufficiale), 1969, for assistance in the restoration of monuments and rehabilitation of institutions at Florence and Venice damaged during 1966-67 floods.

WRITINGS: Venetian Painted Ceilings of the Renaissance, University of California Press, 1968; *The Printed Plans and Panoramic Views of Venice, 1486-1797,* Fondazione Giorgio Cini, 1972. Contributor to *Burlington, Art Bulletin, Journal of the Warburg and Courtauld Institutes, Bollettino del Centro Internazionale di Studi d'Architettura 'A. Palladio'* and *Journal of Aesthetics and Art Criticism.*

WORK IN PROGRESS: A book on the history of Venetian secular building types from their origins to the Renaissance.

* * *

SCHULZE, Franz 1927-

PERSONAL: Born January 30, 1927, in Uniontown, Pa.; son of Franz (an engineer) and Anna Elizabeth (Krimmel) Schulze; married Marianne Gaw, June 24, 1961; children: Franz Clement Matthew, Lukas Andreas. *Education:* Attended Northwestern University, 1943; University of Chicago, Ph.B., 1945; Art Institute of Chicago, B.F.A., 1949, M.F.A., 1950; Akademie der bildenden Kunste, Munich, Germany, additional study, 1956-57. *Politics:* Independent. *Religion:* Agnostic. *Home:* 1296 St. Johns Ave., Highland Park, Ill. 60035. *Office:* Department of Fine Arts, Lake Forest College, Lake Forest, Ill. 60045.

CAREER: Purdue University, Lafayette, Ind., instructor in art, 1950-52; Lake Forest College, Lake Forest, Ill., assistant professor, 1952-55, associate professor, 1955-62, professor of art, 1962-74, Hollander Professor of Art, 1974—, chairman of department of fine arts, 1952-58, artist-in-residence, 1958-62. Lecturer in art, University of Chicago, 1952-53, 1974—; critic-in-residence and visiting professor of art, Colorado College, summers, 1966-71. Member of Louis Corinth Memorial Foundation and S. M. Toffler Foundation.

MEMBER: College Art Association, American Association of University Professors, Archives of American Art. *Awards, honors:* Adenauer fellowship in painting from Federal Republic of Germany, 1956-57; Ford Foundation traveling fellowship for art critics, 1964-65; Eli Lilly Foundation grant to study American art, 1968; Graham Foundation for Advanced Study in the Fine Arts grant to write about recent Chicago architecture, 1971; Harbison Award for excellence in teaching from Danforth Foundation, 1971; distinguished service award from Phi Beta Kappa (Chicago), 1972; merit award in arts from Cliff Dwellers Club (Chicago), 1973.

WRITINGS: Art, Architecture and Civilization, Scott, Foresman, 1968; *Fantastic Images: Chicago Art since 1945,* Follett, 1972; (with Lou Brock) *Stealing Is My Game,*

Prentice-Hall, 1976. Contributor to *Apollo, Art Journal, Art International, Art in America, Saturday Review, Modern Age, Perspective,* and *New York Times.* Chicago correspondent for *Christian Science Monitor,* 1958-62, *Art in America,* 1965-73, and *Art International,* 1966-67; art and architecture critic for *Chicagoan;* contributing editor, *Art News,* 1958-64, and *Inland Architect,* 1975—; art critic for *Chicago Daily News,* 1962—.

WORK IN PROGRESS: A book on Chicago architecture since 1945.†

*　　*　　*

SCHUR, Norman W(arren) 1907-

PERSONAL: Born October 7, 1907, in Boston, Mass.; son of Isaac H. (a banker) and Martha (Reinherz) Schur; married Marjorie Tas, December 31, 1941; children: Joanna (Mrs. Eric Weber), Christopher, Moira (Mrs. Kevin J. Craw), Geoffrey. *Education:* Harvard University, A.B. (summa cum laude), 1926; Columbia University, LL.B., 1930; also studied at University of Rome and Sorbonne, University of Paris. *Politics:* "Honesty." *Religion:* "No preference." *Home:* 37 Davis Hill Rd., Weston, Conn. 06883.

CAREER: Attorney. Proskauer, Rose & Paskus, New York City, associate, 1930-33; private practice of law, 1933-50; partner of law firms in New York City, Simons, Schur & Straus, 1950-53, Diamond, Schur, Perl & Sewel, 1953-56, Schur & Perl, 1956-58, and Schur, Rubin & Montgomery, 1960-65; counsel to Bernton, Hoeniger, Freitag & Abbey, New York City, 1965-74, and King & Plotkin, Stamford, Conn., 1965—. Was a consultant on American law and taxation, in England. *Member:* American Bar Association, New York State Bar Association, Bar Association of the City of New York, Phi Beta Kappa, Harvard Club (of New York), Coffee House Club, Wig and Pen Club (London), Mary Lebone Cricket Club (London), Kent County Cricket Club (Canterbury, England). *Awards, honors:* Franklin Medal and Derby Medal from Boston Latin School, 1923; Sheldon fellowship (Harvard), 1926.

WRITINGS: British Self-Taught: With Comments in American, Macmillan, 1972; *British English: A to Zed,* Verbatim Books, 1979.

WORK IN PROGRESS: American Self-Taught: With Comments in British.

*　　*　　*

SCHWAB, Peter 1940-

PERSONAL: Born November 15, 1940, in New York, N.Y.; son of Henry (a businessman) and Hilda (Hess) Schwab. *Education:* Fairleigh Dickinson University, B.A., 1962; New School for Social Research, M.A., 1966, Ph.D., 1969. *Residence:* New York, N.Y. *Office:* Department of Political Science, State University of New York College, Purchase, N.Y. 10577.

CAREER: Adelphi University, Garden City, N.Y., instructor, 1966-69, assistant professor of political science, 1969-71; State University of New York College at Purchase, assistant professor, 1971-73, associate professor of political science, 1973—. Lecturer, American Museum of Natural History. *Awards, honors:* Fulbright-Hays grant for research in Ethiopia, 1968; State University of New York research grant, 1972-73, 1974-75.

WRITINGS: (With George Frangos) *Greece under the Junta,* Facts on File, 1970; (editor) *Biafra,* Facts on File,

1971; (editor) *Ethiopia and Haile Selassie,* Facts on File, 1972; *Decision Making in Ethiopia,* Fairleigh Dickinson University Press, 1972; (with J. Lee Shneidman) *John F. Kennedy,* Twayne, 1973; *Is America Necessary,* West Publishing, 1976; *Human Rights: Cultural and Ideological Perspectives,* Praeger, 1979; *Haile Selassie: Ethiopia's Lion of Judah,* Nelson-Hall, 1979; (contributor) *Marxist Governments—A World Survey,* Macmillan, 1979. Contributor to *Encyclopedia Americana.* Contributor to *African Development, Journal Geneve Afrique, African Affairs, Plural Societies,* and *Journal of Modern African Studies.*

SIDELIGHTS: Peter Schwab has traveled in Asia, Europe, and most of Africa.

*　　*　　*

SCHWARTZ, Elias 1923-

PERSONAL: Born March 29, 1923, in New York, N.Y.; son of Charles Robert and Sadie (Brodsky) Schwartz; married Marjory Bagby, June 6, 1953; children: Martha, Peter, Paul, David, Daniel. *Education:* Attended College of the City of New York (now City College of the City University of New York), 1941-43; New York University, B.A., 1947; University of Chicago, M.A., 1949; Stanford University, Ph.D., 1954. *Politics:* McGovern Democrat. *Religion:* No formal religion. *Home:* 16 Beethoven St., Binghamton, N.Y. 13905. *Office:* Department of English, State University of New York, Binghamton, N.Y. 13901.

CAREER: University of Nebraska, Lincoln, instructor in English, 1949-50; University of Notre Dame, Notre Dame, Ind., instructor, 1954-57, assistant professor of English, 1957-62; State University of New York at Binghamton, professor of English, 1962—. *Military service:* U.S. Army Air Forces, 1943-46; became technical sergeant; received Air Medal and Purple Heart.

WRITINGS: The Forms of Feeling: Toward a Mimetic Theory of Literature, Kennikat, 1972; *The Mortal Worm: Shakespeare's Master Theme,* Kennikat, 1977. Contributor to *Modern Philology, Studies in Philology, Shakespeare Quarterly, College English,* and *Journal of English and Germanic Philology*

WORK IN PROGRESS: A book on Shakespeare's comedies.

AVOCATIONAL INTERESTS: Tennis and fishing.

*　　*　　*

SCHWARTZ, Emanual K. 1912-1973

June 11, 1912—January 22, 1973; American psychologist, educator, and author of essays and books on group psychotherapy. Obituaries: *New York Times,* January 25, 1973. (See index for *CA* sketch)

*　　*　　*

SCHWARTZMAN, David 1924-

PERSONAL: Born April 22, 1924, in Montreal, Quebec, Canada; son of Joseph and Jeannette (Zurick) Schwartzman; married Gertrude Schneiderman (a psychotherapist), June 17, 1951; children: Michael, Jason, Paul. *Education:* McGill University, B.A., 1945; University of Minnesota, graduate study, 1945-46; University of California, Berkeley, Ph.D., 1953. *Home:* 285 Central Park W., New York, N.Y. 10024. *Office:* New School for Social Research, 66 West 12th St., New York, N.Y. 10011.

CAREER: McGill University, Montreal, Quebec, lecturer

in economics, 1948-51; Dominion Bureau of Statistics, Ottawa, Ontario, economist, 1951-53; United 5¢ to $1.00 Stores, Montreal, economist, 1953-54; Columbia University, New York City, instructor in economics, 1954-58; New York University, New York City, assistant professor of economics, 1958-60; New School for Social Research, New York City, associate professor, 1960-64, professor of economics, 1964—, head of department, 1966-69. Member of the staff of National Bureau of Economic Research, 1963-69. Consultant, Royal Commission on Farm Machinery, 1968-70, President's Council on Wage and Price Stability, 1975-76. Adjunct member of Committee on Trade Regulation, New York County Lawyers Association; member of advisory board, Institute for Health, Economics, and Social Studies, 1976—. *Member:* American Economic Association, American Statistical Association, American Association of University Professors.

WRITINGS: The Decline of Service in Retail Trade: An Analysis of the Growth of Sales per Manhour, 1929-1963, Washington State University Press, 1970; *Oligopoly in the Farm Machinery Industry,* Information Canada, 1970; *The Expected Rate of Return from Pharmaceutical Research,* American Enterprise Institute, 1975; *Innovation in the Pharmaceutical Industry,* Johns Hopkins University Press, 1976. Contributor to *American Economic Review, Journal of Political Economics, Review of Economics and Statistics, Antitrust Bulletin, Economica,* and *Oxford Economics Papers.*

WORK IN PROGRESS: Research in economics of the drug industry, economics of energy, competition, and efficiency.

AVOCATIONAL INTERESTS: Bicycling, photography.

* * *

SCHWARTZMAN, Sylvan D(avid) 1913-

PERSONAL: Born December 8, 1913, in Baltimore, Md.; son of Jacob (a salesman) and Rose (Padve) Schwartzman; married Sylvia Cohen, September 22, 1940; children: Judith (Mrs. Howard Palay), Joel R. *Education:* University of Cincinnati, B.A., 1936, M.B.A., 1970; Hebrew Union College—Jewish Institute of Religion, Cincinnati, B.H.L., 1937, M.H.L. and Rabbi, 1941; Vanderbilt University, Ph.D., 1952. *Home:* 2561 Erie Ave., Cincinnati, Ohio 45208. *Office:* Hebrew Union College—Jewish Institute of Religion, 3101 Clifton Ave., Cincinnati, Ohio 45220.

CAREER: Director of religious education at temple in Boston, Mass., 1939-40; rabbi of congregation in Augusta, Ga., 1941-47; Union of American Hebrew Congregations, New York, N.Y., director of field activities, 1947-48; rabbi of congregation in Nashville, Tenn., 1948-50; Hebrew Union College—Jewish Institute of Religion, Cincinnati, Ohio, professor of Jewish religious education, 1950—, dean of Cincinnati campus, 1975-76. Vice-president, Bureau of Jewish Education, 1962-65. *Member:* Religious Education Association, National Association of Temple Educators (honorary board member), American Association of University Professors, Central Conference of American Rabbis (member of executive board, 1971-72). *Awards, honors:* National Association of Temple Educators Award for *Our Religion and Our Neighbors.*

WRITINGS: Rocket to Mars (Ashkenazic edition), Rocket Press, 1953; *The Story of Reform Judaism,* Union of American Hebrew Congregations, 1953; *Reform Judaism in the Making,* Union of American Hebrew Congregations, 1955; *Once upon a Lifetime,* Union of American Hebrew Congregations, 1958; (with David S. Hachen) *Meeting Your Life Problems,* Rocket Press, 1959; (with Milton G. Miller) *Our Religion and Our Neighbors,* Union of American Hebrew Congregations, 1959, 3rd edition, 1971; *Into the Underground Kingdom,* Rocket Press, 1960, Sephardic edition, 1975; *An Orientation to God, Prayer and Ethics,* Hebrew Union College—Jewish Institute of Religion, 1961; *An Orientation to the Religious School, the Temple and the Jewish Home,* Hebrew Union College—Jewish Institute of Religion, 1961; *The Commitments of Confirmation,* Rocket Press, 1961; (with Jack D. Spiro) *The Living Bible,* Union of American Hebrew Congregations, 1962; *Casebook: The Non-Text Sermon,* Hebrew Union College—Jewish Institute of Religion (Cincinnati), 1965; *Rocket to Mars* (Sephardic edition), Rocket Press, 1969; *Reform Judaism—Then and Now,* Union of American Hebrew Congregations, 1971; (with Richard Ball) *Elements of Financial Analysis,* Van Nostrand, 1977.

WORK IN PROGRESS: Working on experimental materials and curriculum in Jewish religious education; research in the psychology of adolescents and their religious needs.

AVOCATIONAL INTERESTS: Golf, stamp-collecting.

* * *

SCHWARZ, Hans 1939-

PERSONAL: Born January 5, 1939, in Schwabach, Bavaria, Germany; son of Johann Leonhard (a gardener) and Babette (Goetz) Schwarz; married May Louise Brown (a minister of music), March 3, 1967; children: Hans Fussell, Krista Barbara. *Education:* University of Erlangen, Dr.Theol. (summa cum laude), 1963; also studied at University of Goettingen, 1961, and Oberlin Graduate School of Theology, 1964-65. *Politics:* None. *Home:* 1459 Cottingham Court W., Columbus, Ohio 43209. *Office:* Lutheran Theological Seminary, Capital University, Columbus, Ohio 43209.

CAREER: Assistant minister in Lutheran church in Erlangen-Bruck, Germany, 1965-66; Capital University, Lutheran Theological Seminary, Columbus, Ohio, instructor, 1967-68, assistant professor, 1968-71, associate professor of systematic theology, 1971-78, Edward C. Fendt Professor of Systemic Theology, 1978—, interim campus pastor, 1969-70. Visiting professor, Pontifical Gregorian University, 1974. American Lutheran Church member of the National Commission of Faith and Order. *Member:* American Academy of Religion, American Association of University Professors, Ohio Theological Colloquium. *Awards, honors:* World Council of Churches fellowship, and Fulbright travel grant, both at Oberlin Graduate School of Theology, 1964-65; fellowship from German Research Society for Luther Studies, University of Erlangen, 1966-67; Fredrik A. Schiotz fellowship, 1973-74.

WRITINGS: Das Verstaendnis des Wunders bei Karl Heim und Rudolf Bultmann, Calwer Verlag, 1966; (with Hans Schulze) *Christliche Existenz in einer pluralistischen Gesellschaft,* Friedrich Wittig Verlag, 1971; *On the Way to the Future: A Christian View of Eschatology in the Light of Current Trends in Religion, Philosophy, and Science* (Religious Book Club selection), Augsburg, 1972; *The Search for God: Christianity-Atheism-Secularism-World Religions,* Augsburg, 1975; *Our Cosmic Journey: Christian Anthropology in the Light of Current Trends in the Sciences, Philosophy, and Theology* (Religious Book Club selection), Augsburg, 1977. Contributor to theology journals in Switzerland, Germany, Hungary, and the United States.

WORK IN PROGRESS: A textbook of ecclesiology written from a historical and systematic point of view.

AVOCATIONAL INTERESTS: Sports (skiing, soccer), chess, gardening art.

*   *   *

SCHWEITZER, Jerome William   1908-

PERSONAL: Born December 28, 1908, in Tuscaloosa, Ala.; son of Abraham (a merchant) and Mary (Spiro) Schweitzer; married Anne Rachel Stoler (a saleswoman), October 1, 1931. *Education:* University of Alabama, A.B., 1930, M.A., 1932; Johns Hopkins University, Ph.D., 1940; Universidad Nacional de Mexico, further study, summer, 1946. *Politics:* Independent. *Religion:* Jewish. *Home:* 14 Arcadia Dr., Tuscaloosa, Ala. 35401. *Office:* Box 3195, Eastside Station, Tuscaloosa, Ala. 35401.

CAREER: Tuscaloosa News, Tuscaloosa, Ala., reporter, 1928-31; University of Alabama, University, instructor, 1931-40, assistant professor, 1940-47, associate professor, 1947-51, professor of Romance languages, 1951-76, professor emeritus, 1976—, director of News Bureau, 1932-36; Schweitzer's Inc., Tuscaloosa, vice-president, 1978—. *Military service:* U.S. Army Reserve, 1931-68, active duty, 1942-45; became lieutenant colonel. *Member:* Modern Language Association of America, American Association of Teachers of Spanish and Portuguese, National Association of Retired Teachers, South Atlantic Modern Language Association, Alabama Association of Retired Teachers, Alabama Education Association, Comediantes, Phi Beta Kappa (president of Alabama chapter, 1960).

WRITINGS: Georges de Scudery's "Almahide," Johns Hopkins Press, 1939, reprinted, 1973; (with C. Beaumont Wicks) *The Parisian Stage: 1830-1850,* University of Alabama Press, 1961; (contributor) David Cabeen and Jules Brody, editors, *Critical Bibliography of French Literature: The Seventeenth Century,* Syracuse University Press, 1961; (contributor) George B. Daniel, Jr., editor, *Renaissance and Other Studies in Honor of William L. Wiley,* University of North Carolina Press, 1968; (author of preface) Harold Raley, *Jose Ortega y Gasset: Philosopher of European Unity,* University of Alabama Press, 1971; (editor with Claude K. Abraham and Jacqueline Van Baelen) *Le Theatre complet de Tristan l'Hermite,* University of Alabama Press, 1975. Member of editorial board, *Revista de Estudios Hispanicos;* editor, *Fort Benning Bayonet,* 1942-45. Contributor to learned journals.

*   *   *

SCHWITZGEBEL, Robert L.   1934-

PERSONAL: Born March 21, 1934, in Canton, Ohio; son of Harry C. and Mary (Blackburn) Schwitzgebel. *Education:* Heidelberg College, B.A., 1956; graduate study at Yale University, 1956-57, and University of Natal, 1957-58; Brandeis University, Ph.D., 1964; Harvard University, Ed.D., 1964; La Verne College Law Center, postdoctoral study, 1972. *Office:* Department of Psychology, Claremont Graduate School, Claremont, Calif. 91711.

CAREER: University of California, Los Angeles, assistant professor of psychology, 1964-68; Claremont Graduate School, Claremont, Calif., associate professor of psychology, 1969—. Consultant to Universal Pictures and California Youth Authority. *Member:* American Psychological Association, American Law-Psychology Society, Association for the Advancement of Behavior Therapy. *Awards, honors:* Danforth fellow, 1958-64; research grants from National Science Foundation, 1964-65, U.S. Office of Education, 1965-66, and National Institute of Mental Health, 1968-73.

WRITINGS: (Editor with brother, Ralph K. Schwitzgebel) *Psychotechnology: Electronic Control of Mind and Behavior,* Holt, 1973. Contributor to *Psychological Bulletin, American Psychologist,* and *Psychology Today.*

WORK IN PROGRESS: Research on behavior therapy, music, and law.

*   *   *

SCISM, Carol K.   1931-

PERSONAL: Surname is pronounced Siz-zum; born March 21, 1931, in Chicago, Ill.; daughter of Karl Franklin (a real estate appraiser) and Mary (McClure) Kaserman; married Frederick John Scism (a banker), September 26, 1953; children: John F., Jennifer J. *Education:* Cornell University, B.A., 1953. *Home:* 2807 Belgrave Rd., Pepper Pike, Ohio 44124. *Agent:* Dorothy Markinko, McIntosh & Otis, Inc., 475 Fifth Ave., New York, N.Y. 10017.

CAREER: Has worked as a secretary; now author of children's books.

WRITINGS—All published by Dial; all children's books: *Secret Emily,* 1972; *The Wizard of Walnut Street,* 1972. Contributor to children's magazines, including *Jack and Jill, News Time,* and *American Red Cross Junior News.*

WORK IN PROGRESS: Two other children's books; an adult book.

AVOCATIONAL INTERESTS: Reading (especially fiction), swimming, bicycling.†

*   *   *

SCOTT, Joseph Reid   1926-

PERSONAL: Born March 10, 1926, in Winslow, Ariz.; son of Joseph Shane (an engineer) and Edythe Mae (Phipps) Scott; married Carolyn Mae Gosnell (a secretary), December 20, 1950; children: Lynn Loreen, Marc Brian, Michelle Karen. *Education:* San Diego State College (now University), B.A. (with honors), 1950; University of California, Berkeley, M.A., 1952, Ph.D., 1962; also studied at Escuela Interamericana de Verano, summer, 1947, University of Madrid, summer, 1950, 1965-66, 1975-76, and University of Hawaii, 1963-64, 1967. *Home:* 2361 Walden Sq., San Jose, Calif. 95124. *Office:* San Jose State University, San Jose, Calif. 95192.

CAREER: San Jose State University, San Jose, Calif., instructor, 1955-57, assistant professor, 1957-62, associate professor, 1962-66, professor of Spanish, 1966—. Director of National Defense Education Act Summer Language Institutes, 1963-65; resident director of International Program in Spain, 1965-66, 1975-76; associate professor of Spanish, University of Hawaii, 1963-64, 1967; professor of Spanish, University of Veracruz, summer, 1971; head instructor and dean of Foreign Study League's six week study tour of Mexico, 1972. Consultant for bilingual education. Has taught Spanish to elementary school children, and led study groups to Mexico City. *Military service:* U.S. Army Air Forces, 1944-46. *Awards, honors:* Outstanding Teacher Award, California Foreign Language Teachers Association, 1977.

MEMBER: Modern Language Association of America, American Association of Teachers of Spanish and Portuguese, Foreign Language in the Elementary Schools (charter member), Foreign Language Association of Northern California, Foreign Language Association of Santa Clara County, Sigma Delta Pi (past president), Alpha Mu Gamma, Pi Delta Phi, Kappa Sigma.

WRITINGS: Un estudio comparativo de la pronunciacion espanola e inglesa, Hispanic Books, 1964, revised edition published as *La pronunciacion del espanol,* 1971; (author of preliminary note) Armando Jimenez, *Picardia mexicana,* 19th edition (Scott was not associated with earlier editions), Editorial E. Costa-Amic, 1966; *Cultural Understanding: Spanish—Level I,* Alameda County Schools, 1969, revised edition published as *Understanding Spanish-Speaking Cultures,* 1972; (contributor) William A. Manning, editor, *A Mosaic of Readings in Bilingual Education, English-Spanish,* Spartan Bookstore, 1975; (contributor) Holton and Gomez-Estrada, editors, *Espanol,* Norton, 1978. Author of final reports of National Defense Education Act (NDEA) Summer Language Institute, 1963-65. Contributor to *Hispania* and *Tower.*

WORK IN PROGRESS: Research on Spanish phonology; research on Hispanic civilization and culture and on teaching culture in the foreign language classroom; research on non-verbal communication.

SIDELIGHTS: Joseph Scott has traveled in Mexico, Spain and Portugal, and other countries in western Europe.

* * *

SCOTT, Ralph S(amuel) 1927-

PERSONAL: Born July 31, 1927, in Portage, Wis.; son of Ralph Martin (a grocer) and Mabel (Quamme) Scott; married Liesel Sattel, October 2, 1961; children: Kristina, Ingrid, Heidi. *Education:* Luther College, B.A., 1950; University of Wisconsin—Madison, M.S.W., 1953; University of Chicago, Ph.D., 1964. *Home:* 1515 Columbia Dr., Cedar Falls, Iowa 50613. *Office:* Department of Education, University of Northern Iowa, Cedar Falls, Iowa 50613.

CAREER: Worked as a social worker in Wisconsin, 1951-52, and Illinois, 1953-58; Frankfurt American Dependents School, Frankfurt, Germany, child guidance counselor, 1958-59; West Chicago Public Schools, Chicago, Ill., school social worker, 1959-62; Northwestern University Medical School, Evanston, Ill., instructor in pediatrics, 1963-65, clinical psychologist, 1963-65; University of Northern Iowa, Cedar Falls, associate professor, 1965-68, professor of education and psychology, 1968—, director of Education Clinic, 1965—. *Military service:* U.S. Army, 1945-47; became staff sergeant. *Member:* International Reading Association, American Psychological Association, American Educational Research Association, American Association for the Advancement of Science, Association for Childhood Education International, Iowa Psychological Association. *Awards, honors:* U.S. Department of Health, Education and Welfare grant, 1966-67; founder of Home Start, 1968, which was designated a national preschool model by the U.S. Office of Education.

WRITINGS: Fun at the Pond, Harper, 1966; (with Ned Rotekin and Kay Kramer), *Learning Readiness System,* Harper, 1968; (with Ann Dunbar and Jerry Nelson) *Learning Readiness System Seriatum Test,* Harper, 1968. Also co-author of *Beyond Busing: Some Constructive Alternatives.* Contributor to *Merrill-Palmer Quarterly, Journal of Genetic Psychology,* and *Reading Teacher.*

WORK IN PROGRESS: Two books, *Children of the Ghetto* and *Home Start.*

* * *

SEAMAN, William M(illard) 1907-

PERSONAL: Born December 26, 1907, in Wheeling, W.Va.; son of James Surratt (a grocer) and Lillie (Armstrong) Seaman; married Shirley Gardner, June 4, 1932; married second wife, Frances McDonald, July 16, 1964; children: (first marriage) Gregory, David, J. Arthur, Carolyn (Mrs. Steven Sokoloff). *Education:* College of Wooster, A.B., 1930; University of Illinois, M.A., 1931, Ph.D., 1939. *Politics:* Independent. *Religion:* Presbyterian. *Home:* 32 Forest Hills, Wheeling, W.Va. 26003.

CAREER: Knoxville College, Knoxville, Tenn., instructor in Latin and German, 1931-35; Alma College, Alma, Mich., assistant professor of Latin and Greek, 1936-42; Army Security Agency, Arlington, Va., research analyst, 1942-47; Michigan State University, East Lansing, associate professor, 1947-59, professor of Latin, Greek, and archaeology, 1959-74, professor emeritus, 1974—. Fulbright lecturer at Trinity College, Dublin, 1967-68. *Member:* American Philological Association, Archaeological Institute of America, American Classical League (former director of Service Bureau; president, 1969-72), Michigan Classical Conference (treasurer, 1959-62).

WRITINGS: (With Irene Strieby and Helen Vogt) *Seaman, Hunt, Wright Genealogy,* privately printed, 1957; (with Carolyn J. Matzke) *Forum Romanum,* American Classical League, 1972. Contributor of photographs on classical archaeology to numerous textbooks. Contributor of book reviews to *Classical Outlook;* contributor to *Upper Ohio Valley Historical Review* and *Wheeling Intelligencer.* Associate editor of *Classical Outlook,* 1960-69.

AVOCATIONAL INTERESTS: Photography, genealogy, local history.

* * *

SEARS, Sallie 1932-

PERSONAL: Born January 14, 1932, in Oklahoma City, Okla.; daughter of Paul B. (a professor and author) and Marjorie (McCutcheon) Sears. *Education:* Boston University, B.A., 1954; Brandeis University, M.A., 1956, Ph.D., 1963. *Residence:* New York, N.Y. *Office:* Department of English, State University of New York, Stony Brook, N.Y. 11790.

CAREER: Smith College, Northampton, Mass., instructor in English, 1957-60; Dominican College of Blauvelt, Blauvelt, N.Y., assistant professor of English, 1963-64; State University of New York at Stony Brook, assistant professor, 1964-69, associate professor of English, 1969—.

WRITINGS: The Negative Imagination: Form and Perspective in the Novels of Henry James, Cornell University Press, 1968; (editor with G. W. Lord) *The Discontinuous Universe: Selected Writings in Contemporary Consciousness,* Basic Books, 1972; (contributor) Jane Marcus, editor, *Back through Our Mothers,* Nebraska University Press, 1979.

WORK IN PROGRESS: A critical study of Virginia Woolf's late fiction; articles for various journals.

* * *

SEARY, E(dgar) R(onald) 1908-

PERSONAL: Born January 17, 1908, in Sheffield, England; naturalized Canadian citizen; son of Henry (an engineer) and Edith (Brunt) Seary; married Agnes Gwendolen Crookes (a professor), August 14, 1935; children: John Peter, Richard. *Education:* University of Sheffield, B.A. (honors), 1929, M.A., 1930, Ph.D., 1933. *Religion:* Anglican. *Home address:* P.O. Box 62, South River, Newfoundland, Canada

A0A 3W0. *Office:* Memorial University of Newfoundland, St. John's, Newfoundland, Canada.

CAREER: Dolmetscher-Institut, Mannheim, Germany, lecturer in English, 1933; Rhodes University, Grahamstown, South Africa, lecturer, 1935-45, senior lecturer in English language and literature, 1945-51; College of Arts and Sciences, Baghdad, Iraq, professor of English and head of department, 1951-53; Memorial University of Newfoundland, St. John's, professor of English language and literature, 1953-70, Henrietta Harvey Professor of English, 1970-78, professor emeritus, 1978—, head of department, 1954-70. *Military service:* South African Army, 1940-45; became captain. *Member:* Canadian Linguistic Association (president, 1960-62), Canadian Association of University Teachers of English (president, 1963-68), Canadian Institute of Onomastic Sciences (vice-president, 1966). *Awards, honors:* Centennial Medal from Government of Canada, 1967; Royal Historical Society (England; fellow, 1968); Society of Antiquaries (England; fellow, 1971); D.Litt. from Memorial University of Newfoundland, 1973, and University of Sheffield, 1971.

WRITINGS: A Biographical and Bibliographical Record of South African Literature in English, [Grahamstown], 1938; (editor) *South African Short Stories,* Oxford University Press, 1947; (with G. M. Story) *Reading English,* Macmillan (Toronto), 1958; (contributor) J. R. Smallwood, editor, *The Book of Newfoundland,* Volume III, Newfoundland Book Publishers, 1967; (with Story and William Kirwin) *The Avalon Peninsula of Newfoundland: An Ethno-Linguistic Study,* National Museum of Canada, 1968; *Place Names of the Avalon Peninsula of the Island of Newfoundland,* University of Toronto Press, 1971; *Family Names of the Island of Newfoundland,* Memorial University of Newfoundland Press, 1977. Contributor to *Chambers Encyclopaedia* and *Cassells Encyclopaedia of Literature.* Contributor to *Review of English Studies, Modern Language Review, Times Literary Supplement, Standpunte,* and other journals.

WORK IN PROGRESS: Studies in Newfoundland family and place names.

*   *   *

SEDLER, Robert Allen 1935-

PERSONAL: Born September 11, 1935, in Pittsburgh, Pa.; son of Jerome (a salesman) and Esther (Rosenberg) Sedler; married Rozanne Friedlander (a social worker), January 24, 1960; children: Eric Mark, Beth Ellen. *Education:* University of Pittsburgh, A.B., 1956, J.D., 1959. *Politics:* "Generally radical." *Religion:* Jewish. *Home:* 18851 Capitol, Southfield, Mich. 48075. *Office:* Law School, Wayne State University, Detroit, Mich. 48202.

CAREER: St. Louis University School of Law, St. Louis, Mo., assistant professor, 1961-64, associate professor of law, 1964-65; Haile Selassie I University, Addis Ababa, Ethiopia, associate professor of law, 1963-66, associate dean, 1963-66; University of Kentucky, Lexington, associate professor, 1966-68, professor of law, 1968-77; Wayne State University, Detroit, Mich., professor of law, 1977—. Kentucky Civil Liberties Union, member of board of directors, 1968—, general counsel, 1971-76. *Member:* Society of American Law Teachers (member of board of directors, 1974—), Phi Beta Kappa, Order of the Coif.

WRITINGS: The Conflict of Laws in Ethiopia, Haile Selassie I University and Oxford University Press (Nairobi), 1965; *Ethiopian Civil Procedure,* Haile Selassie I University

and Oxford University Press (Nairobi), 1968; (with Roger Cramton) *The Sum and Substance of the Conflict of Laws,* Creative Educational Services, 1977. Contributor to *Yale Law Journal, Columbia Law Review, New York University Law Review, Wisconsin Law Review, Vanderbilt Law Review, Iowa Law Review,* and others.

*   *   *

SEDURO, Vladimir 1910-
(Vladimir Hlybinny)

PERSONAL: Born December 24, 1910, in Minsk, Byelorussia; son of Illya Ivanovich (a worker) and Maria (Shaban) Seduro; married Irene Korkunov, November 12, 1946; children: Sofia (Mrs. Herb Starr). *Education:* State University (Minsk), B.A., 1933; Teachers College, State University of Leningrad, M.A., 1939; Academy of Sciences (Minsk), Ph.D., 1941; Columbia University, postdoctoral study, 1952-53. *Religion:* Greek Orthodox. *Home:* 29 Mellon Ave., Troy, N.Y. 12180.

CAREER: Columbia University, Research Program on the Union of Soviet Socialist Republics, New York, N.Y., senior fellow, 1951-57; Rensselaer Polytechnic Institute, Troy, N.Y., assistant professor, 1959-60, associate professor, 1960-62, professor of Russian, 1962-76, professor emeritus, 1976—, chairman of Russian program, 1959-76. Writer, Radio Liberation, 1951-59; professor of Russian literature, Middlebury College, summers, 1959-63; professor of Russian, Windham College, Institute of Critical Languages, 1967, and University of Illinois, summer, 1969.

MEMBER: American Association of Teachers of Slavic and East European Languages (vice-president of New York-New Jersey chapter, 1962-75), Association of Russian-American Scholars in the U.S.A., International Dostoevsky Society (American representative, 1970-77), North American Dostoevsky Society (vice-president, 1970-75; member of honorary advisory board, 1975—), Byelorussian-American Scientific and Literary Club (Troy; president, 1964—).

WRITINGS: Dostoevski Study in the U.S.S.R., Institute for the Study of the U.S.S.R. (Munich), 1955; *The Byelorussian Theater and Drama,* Research Program on the U.S.S.R., Columbia University, 1955; *Dostoevski in Russian Literary Criticism, 1846-1956,* Columbia University Press, 1957; (under pseudonym Vladimir Hlybinny) *Vierzig Jahre Weissruthenischer Kultur unter den Sowjets,* Institute for the Study of the U.S.S.R., (Munich), 1959; *Les Recents Developpements des Etudes sur Dostoievsky en Union Sovietique,* Institut d'etudes sur L'U.R.S.S. (Munich), 1960; (under pseudonym Valdimir Hlybinny) *On the Shores beneath the Sun: Byelorussian Stories,* Byelorussian-American Scientific and Literary Club, 1964; (under pseudonym Vladimir Hlybinny) *In the Holy Land,* On God's Highway Publishers (London), 1972; *Smolensk Land,* Byelorussian Publishing Society, 1973; *Dostoevski's Image in Russia Today,* Nordland, 1975; *Dostoevski in Russian Emigre Criticism,* Nordland, 1975; *Dostoevski in Russian and World Theatre,* Christopher, 1977.

WORK IN PROGRESS: Dostoevski and Solzhenitsyn.

SIDELIGHTS: William W. Pusey writes: "[Vladimir] Seduro's book [*Dostoevski in Russian Literary Criticism, 1846-1956*] is a masterpiece of scholarly research and presentation. While intended primarily for the specialist in Russian literature, it is also important for its sharply delineated picture of the vicissitudes to which both a great writer's reputation and the position of his critics are subject in a country with rigorous and shrewdly manipulated thought control."

Of its sequel, a reviewer for *Russian Literature Triquarterly* writes: "[*Dostoevski's Image in Russia Today*] is very useful. In summarizing the finding of dozens of scholars [Seduro] makes it possible for the student to direct his own future reading more intelligently and economically. He has the advantage of picking and choosing on the basis of one of the language's biggest and longest book reviews." Wladislaw G. Krasnow's review reinforces these critics' commendations. It states: "Seduro undoubtedly is one of a very few scholars outside Russia who would be so eminently qualified for the enormous task of surveying the ever-expanding flow of Soviet writings on Dostoevski. . . . Regardless of his great enthusiasm for the writer, [he] is not deaf to the anti-Dostoevski opinions. . . . Seduro's book should find its way onto the bookshelves of all students of both Dostoevski and Russia . . . for we owe to him our gratitude for his meticulous accumulation of valuable material on an important subject."

AVOCATIONAL INTERESTS: Collecting books, gardening, fishing, hunting.

BIOGRAPHICAL/CRITICAL SOURCES: Northwest Review, fall, 1957; Richmond *News-Leader,* January 3, 1958; *New Republic,* April 7, 1958; *Times Literary Supplement,* August 29, 1958; *Russian Literature Triquarterly,* Volume II, 1975; *Byelorussian Times,* December, 1975; *Russian Review,* July, 1976; *Queens Slavic Papers,* Volume II, 1978; *Cresset,* October, 1978.

* * *

SEELHAMMER, Ruth 1917-

PERSONAL: Born January 26, 1917, in Warden, Wash.; daughter of Edward J. and Elizabeth (Wahl) Beck; married Joseph J. Seelhammer, March 16, 1942. *Education:* Attended Sophia University, 1962; Gonzaga University, A.B., 1965. *Religion:* Roman Catholic. *Home:* 4325 North Rustle St., Spokane, Wash. 99205. *Office:* Crosby Library, Gonzaga University, Spokane, Wash. 99202.

CAREER: Gonzaga University, Crosby Library, Spokane, Wash., periodicals assistant, 1957-73, executive secretary to library director and curator of Hopkins Collection, 1973—. *Member:* Modern Language Association of America, Catholic Renaissance Society, Gamma Pi Epsilon. *Awards, honors: America* award, 1962, for essay, "How Should Western Man Approach the Orient."

WRITINGS: Hopkins Collected at Gonzaga, Loyola University Press (Chicago), 1970; (contributor) Peter Milward and Raymond Schoder, editors, *Readings of "The Wreck": Essays in Commemoration of the Centenary of G. M. Hopkins' "The Wreck of the Deutschland,"* Loyola University Press, 1976. Contributor to *Bulletin of Bibliography, Renascence, America, Stechert-Hafner Book News, Reflection, Charter,* and *Journal of Modern Literature.*

WORK IN PROGRESS: A Gerard Manley Hopkins volume for "Thesis Bibliography Series," for Pierian; a second volume of *Hopkins Collected at Gonzaga.*

* * *

SEGAL, Charles Paul 1936-

PERSONAL: Born March 19, 1936, in Boston, Mass.; son of Robert and Gladys (Barsky) Segal; married Esther Hawley Rogers, December 20, 1961; children: Joshua Hawley, Thaddeus Gabriel. *Education:* Harvard University, A.B., 1957, Ph.D., 1961; also attended American School of Classical Studies, Athens, Greece, 1957-58. *Home:* 245 Brook St., Providence, R.I. 02906. *Office:* Department of Classics, Brown University, Providence, R.I. 02912.

CAREER: Harvard University, Cambridge, Mass., instructor in classics, 1963-64; University of Pennsylvania, Philadelphia, assistant professor, 1964-65, associate professor of classics, 1965-67; Brown University, Providence, R.I., associate professor, 1968-70, professor of classics, 1970—, professor of comparative literature, 1978—, chairman of department of classics, 1978-81. Visiting professor and professor in charge, Intercollegiate Center for Classical Studies, Rome, 1970-72; visiting professor, Brandeis University, 1974, Ecole des Hautes Etudes, Paris, 1975-76, University of Melbourne, 1978, and Columbia University, 1979.

MEMBER: Ovidianum (International Ovidian Society; Bucharest; honorary member), American Philological Association, Virgilian Society, Classical Association of New England. *Awards, honors:* Fulbright fellowship, 1957-58; Prix de Rome, American Academy in Rome, 1961-63; fellowship from Center for Hellenic Studies (Washington, D.C.), 1967-68; American Council of Learned Studies travel grant, 1969, 1977; American Council of Learned Societies fellowship, 1974-75; National Endowment for the Humanities summer sipend, 1977; Fulbright senior scholar, Australia, 1978.

WRITINGS: (Contributor) Thomas Woodard, editor, *Sophocles: A Collection of Critical Essays,* Prentice-Hall, 1966; (contributor) Alex Page and Leon Barron, editors, *Masterpieces of Western Literature: Contemporary Essays in Interpretation,* Volume I, W. C. Brown, 1966; (contributor) D. J. Littlefield, editor, *Twentieth Century Interpretations of "The Frogs,"* Prentice-Hall, 1968; *Landscape in Ovid's "Metamorphoses": A Study in the Transformations of a Literary Symbol,* Franz Steiner Verlag, 1969; (contributor) *Proceedings of the First International Humanistic Symposium,* Hellenic Society for Humanistic Studies, Volume I, 1970; *The Theme of the Mutilation of the Corpse in "The Iliad,"* E. J. Brill, 1971; (contributor) *Collected Plays of Greek and Roman Ages,* Chukuma Shobo, 1972; (contributor) Hans-Joachim Newiger, editor, *Aristophanes und die alte Komoedie,* Wissenschafliche Buchgesellschaft, 1975; (contributor) Rolf Heine, editor, *Catull,* Wissenschafliche Buchgesellschaft, 1975. Contributor to *Cambridge History of Classical Literature,* Cambridge University Press; also contributor to *Encyclopedia Americana* and *Arete Encyclopedia.* Contributor, to classical journals in Europe, Australia, and the United States.

WORK IN PROGRESS: Tragedy and Civilization; a book on Euripedes' *Bacchae;* essays on classical myth and literature.

* * *

SEIDLIN, Oskar 1911-

PERSONAL: Born February 17, 1911, in Koenigshuette, Germany. *Education:* Attended University of Freiburg, University of Frankfurt, University of Berlin, and University of Lausanne, 1929-33; University of Basel, Ph.D., 1935. *Office:* Department of Germanic Languages, Indiana University, Bloomington, Ind. 47401.

CAREER: Smith College, Northampton, Mass., lecturer, 1939-41, assistant professor of German, 1941-46; Ohio State University, Columbus, assistant professor, 1946-48, associate professor, 1948-50, professor of German, 1950-72, regents' professor, 1966-72; Indiana University at Bloomington, professor, 1972-74, distinguished professor of German,

1974—. Guest professor, University of Washington, Seattle, 1949; summer professor, Middlebury College, 1939-41, 1946, 1948, 1951-52, 1957; Ford Foundation summer professor, University of Berlin, 1959. *Military service:* U.S. Army, 1942-46; became second lieutenant; received Bronze Star and special citations.

MEMBER: Modern Language Association of America (section chairman, 1949, 1958, 1969; first vice-president, 1965), American Association of Teachers of German, American Lessing Society (vice-president, 1968), Phi Beta Kappa (honorary member). *Awards, honors:* Eichendorff Medal, 1958; Guggenheim fellow, 1962-63 and 1976-77; Golden Goethe Medal, 1963; Alfred J. Wright Award, 1964; prize of German Academy of Language and Literature, 1968, for "Germanistik im Ausland"; D.H.L. from University of Michigan, 1969; member of Akademie der Wissenschaften (Goettingen), 1973; Kulturpreis of the Land Northrhine-Westphalia, 1975.

WRITINGS: Otto Brahm als Theaterkritiker, M. Niehans (Zurich), 1936, 2nd edition (Bonn), 1978; *Pedronis muss geholfen werden* (juvenile), Aarau, 1937, abridged edition published as *Waldwyl und die Theaterleute,* 1970, English translation by the author published as *Green Wagons,* Houghton, 1943; *Mein Bilderbuch* (verse), Oprecht (Zurich), 1938; (with Richard Plant) *S.O.S., Geneva* (juvenile), Viking, 1939; Elizabeth Mensel, editor, *Der goldene Apfel* (textbook), Crofts, 1942; (with W. P. Friederich) *An Outline History of German Literature,* Barnes & Noble, 1948; (editor) *Der Briefwechsel Schnitzler-Brahm,* Schriften der Gesellschaft fuer Theatergeschichte, (Berlin), 1953, 2nd enlarged edition (Tuebingen), 1975; *Essays in German and Comparative Literature,* University of North Carolina Press, 1961, 2nd edition, 1966; *Von Goethe zu Thomas Mann: 12 Versuche,* Vandenhoeck & Ruprecht, 1963, 2nd edition, 1969; *Versuche ueber Eichendorff,* Vandenhoeck & Ruprecht (Goettingen), 1965, 2nd edition, 1978; *Klassische und Moderne Klassiker,* Vandenhoeck & Ruprecht, 1972.

*   *   *

SELEGEN, Galina V(assily) 1899-

PERSONAL: Born February 28, 1899, in Russia; daughter of Vassily Michael and Anna Paul (Lariushkin) Selegen. *Education:* Indiana University, M.A., 1962, Ph.D., 1967. *Home:* 2480 16th St. N.W., Dorchester House, Apt. 435, Washington, D.C. 20009.

CAREER: U.S. Bureau of the Census, Washington, D.C., research associate, 1954-60; Florida State University, Tallahassee, assistant professor of Russian literature, 1964-71.

WRITINGS: The Most Intricate Design (literary criticism), Victor Kamkin, 1968. Also author of *The World as I See It* and *The People Is Silent.* Contributor of over sixty articles and short stories to Russian newspapers.

WORK IN PROGRESS: Soviet literature in the 1970's.

*   *   *

SEMPELL, Charlotte 1909-
(Charlotte Klenbort)

PERSONAL: Born February 8, 1909, in Germany; daughter of Oskar (a businessman) and Hedwig (Hasenclever) Sempell; married Chonel Klenbort (a writer), September 12, 1939; children: Daniel, Irene. *Education:* Studied at University of Berlin, 1928, and University of Goettingen, 1929; University of Munich, Ph.D, 1931. *Home:* 61 Goose Hill Rd., Chester, Conn. 06412.

CAREER: Brooklyn College of the City University of New York, Brooklyn, N.Y., adjunct associate professor of history, 1947-74. *Member:* American Historical Association, Modern European History, Group of Historians Using Psychology, Society of Applied Psychoanalysis.

WRITINGS: Otto von Bismarck, Twayne, 1973. Also author of articles on psychohistory.

WORK IN PROGRESS: Memoirs.

*   *   *

SENN, Fritz 1928-

PERSONAL: Born January 1, 1928, in Basle, Switzerland; son of Fritz and Caecilie (Edelmann) Senn; married Marguerite Helen Baldinger, 1953 (divorced, 1972); children: Mia, Mischa, Beda. *Education:* Attended University of Zurich, 1947-52. *Religion:* None. *Home:* Brunnmatt 1, 8103 Unterengstringen, Switzerland.

CAREER: University of Zurich, Zurich, Switzerland, lecturer, 1970, 1972-73. Has lectured at University of Geneva, University of Basle, University of Louvain, University of Berne, University of Erlangen, University of Bonn, University of Cologne, University of Regensburg, University of Copenhagen, College of Technology of Eindhoven, Mc-Master University, Villanova University, State University of New York at Binghamton, Southern Illinois University, and University of Tulsa. Visiting professor at State University of New York at Buffalo, 1968, Indiana University, 1970, 1971, Ohio State University, 1970, 1975, and University of Hawaii, 1974. Distinguished visiting professor, University of Delaware, 1977. James Joyce Foundation, Ltd., trustee, 1967—, president, 1977—; co-chairman and co-organizer of First International James Joyce Symposium in Dublin, June, 1967, Second International James Joyce Symposium in Dublin, June, 1969, and Third International James Joyce Symposium in Dublin, June, 1977, James Joyce Symposium, University of Hawaii, 1974, James Joyce Colloquium, State University of New York at Buffalo, 1976, and James Joyce Conference, Erie, Pa., 1978. Chairman and speaker of "Esslinger Gespraeche" (conference of German-speaking translators), 1976, 1977. Lecturer for the Goethe Institute in United States and Canada, fall, 1975. *Awards, honors:* Fellow of the School of Letters, Indiana University, 1970; Max Geilinger Foundation Award, Zurich, 1972; Dr.Phil., honoris causa, University of Cologne, 1972; Ehrengabe der Erziehungsdirektion des Kantons Zurich, 1975; Literatur-Ehengabe der Stadt Zurich, 1976.

WRITINGS—Editor: (With Clive Hart) *A Wake Digest,* Sidney University Press, 1968; (with Klaus Reichert and Dieter E. Zimmer) *Materialien zu James Joyce "Dubliners,"* Suhrkamp Verlag, 1969; *Briefe an Nora,* Suhrkamp Verlag, 1971; *New Light on Joyce from the Dublin Symposium,* Indiana University Press, 1972; (with Michael H. Begnal) *A Conceptual Guide to "Finnegan's Wake,"* Pennsylvania State University Press, 1974; (with Reichert) *Materialien zu James Joyce's "Ein Portraet des Kuenstlers als junger Mann,"* Suhrkamp Verlag, 1975; (with others) Arthur Schopenhauer, *Zurcher Ausgabe* (complete works), ten volumes, Diogenes Verlag, 1977.

Other: (Contributor) Richard Ellmann, editor, *James Joyce,* Rhein Verlag, 1961; (translator) James Joyce, *The Cat and the Devil,* Rhein Verlag, 1966; (contributor) John Vandenbergh, editor, *Stephen D.,* De Bezige Bij, 1968; (contributor) Thomas F. Staley and Bernard Benstock, editors, *Approaches to "Ulysses,"* University of Pittsburgh Press, 1970; *James Joyce, Aufsaetze,* Max Geilinger Stiftung,

1972; Hart and David Hayman, editors, *James Joyce's "Ulysses,"* University of California Press, 1974; L. Bonnerot, editor, *"Ulysses": Cinquante ans apres,* Etudes Anglaises, Didier, 1974. Contributor to *James Joyce Review, Die Tat, Analyst, A Wake Newslitter, Neue Zuercher Zeitung, James Joyce Quarterly, Zuercher Woche, Zolliker Bote, DU-atlantis, English Studies, Leuvense Bijdragen, Sprache im technischen Zeitalter, joycenotes, Utopia, Raam, Levende Talen, Die Weltwoche,* and *Der Landbote.* Co-editor and co-founder, *A Wake Newslitter,* 1962—; European editor, *James Joyce Quarterly.*

WORK IN PROGRESS: Studies in James Joyce; supervision of a translation of James Joyce.

*   *   *

SESSOMS, H(anson) Douglas 1931-

PERSONAL: Born July 18, 1931, in Wilmington, N.C.; son of Hanson and Sadie (Edens) Sessoms; married second wife, Anne Lassiter (a chemist), April 12, 1968; step-children: Benjamin, Robert. *Education:* Wilmington Junior College, A.A., 1951; University of North Carolina, A.B., 1953; University of Illinois, M.S., 1954; New York University, Ph.D., 1959. *Religion:* Methodist. *Home:* 805 Emory Dr., Chapel Hill, N.C. 27514. *Office:* Curriculum in Recreation Administration, University of North Carolina, Chapel Hill, N.C. 27514.

CAREER: University of North Carolina at Chapel Hill, assistant professor, 1959-63, associate professor, 1963-69, professor of recreation, 1969—. Visiting professor of recreation, Texas A & M University, 1972-73. *Member:* Society of Park and Recreation Educators (president, 1968-69; distinguished fellow, 1973), American Recreation and Park Society (member of board of directors, 1965-66), Southern Sociological Society, North Carolina Recreation and Park Society (fellow, 1971).

WRITINGS: (With Harold Meyer) *Community Recreation,* 4th edition (Sessoms was not associated with previous editions), Prentice-Hall, 1969, 5th edition published as *Introduction to Leisure Services,* 1975; (editor with Herbert Brantley) *Recreation: Issues and Perspectives,* Wing, 1969; (with Peter Verhoven) *Recreation Program Leadership and the Community College,* American Association of Junior Colleges, 1970; (with Thomas A. Stein) *Recreation and Special Population,* Holbrook Press, 1973, 2nd edition, 1977. Contributor to *Encyclopedia of Education, Encyclopedia of Social Work, Vital Speeches, Recreation Magazine, The Gerontologist, Journal of Leisure Research, Social Forces,* and *Journal of Leisure Sciences.*

WORK IN PROGRESS: Recreation Services and the Group Process, with John Stevenson; a chapter for inclusion in *Handbook of the Social Services,* to be published by Prentice-Hall.

*   *   *

SETHI, S. Prakash 1934-

PERSONAL: Born May 3, 1934, in Karachi, Pakistan; married Donna Emrich, 1969; children: Amit, Ravi (both sons). *Education:* Delhi School of Economics, University of Delhi, Graduate Diploma in Business Management, 1959; Columbia University, M.B.A., 1962, Ph.D., 1968. *Home:* 6920 Cliffbrook, Dallas, Tex. 75240. *Office:* School of Management and Administration, University of Texas at Dallas, Richardson, Tex. 75080.

CAREER: U.S. Agency for International Development,

New Delhi, India, program analyst for Industry Division, 1957-60; Esso International, New York, N.Y., part-time economic analyst, 1961-62; Remington Rand of India Ltd., Calcutta, marketing assistant and later regional manager, 1962-63; University of California, School of Business Administration, Berkeley, assistant professor, 1967-69, associate professor of business, 1971-77; University of Texas at Dallas, School of Management and Administration, Richardson, professor of international business and business and social policy, 1977—. Director, National Affiliation of Concerned Business Students and Center for Research in Business and Social Policy. Adviser, Council on Economic Priorities. *Member:* Academy of International Business, American Marketing Association, Institute of Management Sciences. *Awards, honors:* McKinsey Foundation prize for best article appearing in *California Management Review* during 1969-70.

WRITINGS: Business Corporations and the Black Man: An Analysis of Social Conflict, Chandler Publishing, 1970; *Up against the Corporate Wall: Modern Corporations and Social Issues of the Seventies,* with teacher's manual, Prentice-Hall, 1971; *Advanced Cases in Multinational Business Operations,* with teacher's manual, Goodyear Publishing, 1972; (editor with Jagdish N. Sheth) *Multinational Business Operations,* Goodyear Publishing, 1972; (co-author) *The Corporate Dilemma: Traditional Values and Contemporary Problems,* Prentice-Hall, 1973; *Japanese Business and Social Conflict: A Comparative Analysis of Response Patterns with American Business,* Ballinger, 1975; *Advocacy Advertising and Large Corporations: Social Conflict, Big Business Image, the News Media, and Public Policy,* Heath, 1977; *Promises of the Good Life: Social Consequences of Private Marketing Decisions,* Irwin, in press. Also editor, with Richard H. Holton, of *Management of the Multinationals: Policies, Research, Operations,* Free Press, and editor of *The Unstable Ground: Corporate Social Policy in a Dynamic Society,* Melville Publishers. Consulting editor, "Economic Institutions and Social Systems" series, Prentice-Hall. Contributor to marketing and other journals. Contributing editor, *Business and Society Review.*

WORK IN PROGRESS: Research for a book on the top management group in nine hundred U.S. major manufacturing, banking, and utility corporations; with Charles Ramand, *Understanding World Markets: A Handbook of Multinational Analysis; Corporate Executives as the Unwitting Criminal; Application of the U.S. Civil Rights Act of 1964 to the U.S. Subsidiaries of Foreign Multinational Corporations.*

*   *   *

SEVERINO, Alexandrino E(usebio) 1931-

PERSONAL: Born July 17, 1931, in Olhao, Portugal; son of Eusebio Joaquim (a fisherman) and Alexandrina (Rato) Severino; married Dorothea Bresslau, January 7, 1961; children: Alexandre Bresslau, Cornelia B., Roger B., Katherine B. *Education:* University of Rhode Island, B.A., 1958; University of Sao Paulo, Ph.D., 1966. *Religion:* Roman Catholic. *Home:* 6708 Rodney Court, Nashville, Tenn. 37205. *Office:* Furman Hall, No. 305, Vanderbilt University, Nashville, Tenn. 37235.

CAREER: University of Sao Paulo, Sao Paulo, Brazil, professor (Catedratico) of American literature, 1960-66; University of Texas at Austin, assistant professor, 1966-68, associate professor of Portuguese and Brazilian literature, 1968-69; Vanderbilt University, Nashville, Tenn., associate professor, 1969-74, professor of Portuguese and Brazilian literature, 1975—, chairman of department of Spanish and Portuguese, 1976—. *Military service:* U.S. Army, 1952-54. *Member:* Modern Language Association of America, American Association of Teachers of Spanish and Portuguese, Latin American Studies Association, American Association of University Professors, Mid-Atlantic Modern Language Association, South Central Modern Language Association, Northeastern Modern Language Association.

WRITINGS: (Translator) Phillip Young, Leon Edel, Hugh Holman, and William Van O'Connor, *Hemingway, Henry James, Wolfe, Faulkner,* Editora Martins, 1963; *Fernando Pessoa na Africa do Sul,* University of Marilia, 1969; (contributor) Riordan Roett, editor, *Brazil in the Sixties,* Vanderbilt University Press, 1972. Contributing editor, *Handbook of Latin American Studies,* Library of Congress, 1976—. Guest editor with Enrique Pupo-Walker, *Studies in Short Fiction,* winter, 1971.

WORK IN PROGRESS: The Contemporary Brazilian Novel; a study of the poetry of Fernando Pessoa.

* * *

SHADE, William G(erald) 1939-

PERSONAL: Born April 5, 1939, in Detroit, Mich.; son of William Stephen (an engineer) and Elaine (McMahon) Shade; married Mary Louisa Langford, August 11, 1962; children: Alexandra, Christopher. *Education:* Brown University, A.B., 1961, M.A., 1962; Wayne State University, Ph.D., 1966. *Politics:* Democrat. *Home:* 29 East Church St., Bethlehem, Pa. 18017. *Office:* Department of History, Lehigh University, Bethlehem, Pa. 18015.

CAREER: Temple University, Philadelphia, Pa., instructor in history, 1965-66; Lehigh University, Bethlehem, Pa., assistant professor, 1966-69, associate professor, 1969-76, professor of history, 1976—. Visiting assistant professor of history, Lafayette College, 1967; visiting associate professor of history, University of Virginia, 1972-73; visiting professor of history, University College, Galway, Ireland, 1977-78. Member of advisory board on national parks historic sites, buildings and monuments, Department of Interior. *Member:* American Historical Association, Organization of American Historians, American Studies Association, Social Science History Association, Pennsylvania Historical Association.

WRITINGS: (Editor) *Lawrence Henry Gipson: Four Dimensions,* Pennsylvania Historical Association, 1969; (editor with Roy Herrenkohl) *Seven on Black: Reflections on Negro Experience in America,* Lippincott, 1969; *Banks or No Banks: The Money Issue in Western Politics, 1832-1865,* Wayne State University Press, 1972; (editor with Jean E. Friedman) *Our American Sisters,* Allyn & Bacon, 1976; (with William Gudelunas) *Before the Molly Maguires: The Emergence of the Ethno-Religious Factor in the Politics of the Anthracite Region,* Arno, 1976. Contributor to *Dictionary of American History, Michigan History, Pennsylvania History, Journal of American History, Mid-America, Journal of Interdisciplinary History, Historian,* and *Social Science Quarterly.* Editor, *Pennsylvania History.*

WORK IN PROGRESS: Political Cultures of American States in 1850; Political Development in Nineteenth-Century America.

BIOGRAPHICAL/CRITICAL SOURCES: Christian Century, December 17, 1970.

SHADICK, Harold (Ernest) 1902-

PERSONAL: Born September 30, 1902, in London, England; son of Ernest Thomas (a printer) and Jessie (Cheeseman) Shadick; married Helen Lamkert, August 26, 1927. *Education:* University of Toronto, B.A., 1925, M.A., 1951; University of London, graduate study, 1930-31; University of Paris, graduate study, 1937-38. *Home:* 133 Cascadilla Park, Ithaca, N.Y. 14850. *Office:* Department of Asian Studies, Cornell University, Ithaca, N.Y. 14850.

CAREER: Yenching University, Peking, China, professor of Western language and literature, 1925-46; Cornell University, Ithaca, N.Y., professor of Chinese literature, 1946-71, professor emeritus, 1971—. *Member:* Association for Asian Studies, Conference on Chinese Oral and Performing Literature (chairman of executive committee), Phi Beta Kappa.

WRITINGS: (Translator) *The Travels of Lao Ts'an,* Cornell University Press, 1952; *A First Course in Literary Chinese,* Cornell University Press, 1968. Contributor of several articles on Chinese literature to *Collier's Encyclopedia.*

WORK IN PROGRESS: Translations of classical Chinese plays and of twentieth-century Chinese fiction; a grammar of classical Chinese.

AVOCATIONAL INTERESTS: Gardening ("somewhat influenced by Chinese and Japanese garden ideals") and music.

* * *

SHANKMAN, Florence V(ogel) 1912-

PERSONAL: Born July 16, 1912, in Norwalk, Conn.; daughter of Morris (a realtor and businessman) and Betty (Jacobson) Vogel; married Louis Shankman, August 29, 1937 (died December 25, 1952); children: Martin A., Robert S., Susan E. *Education:* Columbia University, B.S., 1934, M.A., 1936; New York University, M.A., 1955, Ed.D., 1959. *Home:* 32 West Ave., South Norwalk, Conn. 06854. *Office:* College of Education, Temple University, Philadelphia, Pa. 19122.

CAREER: Elementary teacher in public schools of Norwalk, Conn., 1930-37, New Rochelle, N.Y., 1950-51, Wilton, Conn., 1952-53, and Norwalk, 1953-59; substitute teacher in Connecticut schools, 1937-50, 1951-52; teacher of foreign-born and of high school equivalency courses in Norwalk, Conn., 1938-45; New York University, New York, N.Y., supervisor of instruction in Reading Institute, 1959-62; University of Bridgeport, Bridgeport, Conn., assistant professor of education, 1962-65; Keene State College, Keene, N.H., associate professor of education, 1965-67; Temple University, College of Education, Philadelphia, Pa., associate professor, 1967-72, professor of curriculum and instruction, 1972—. Visiting summer professor at University of Southern California, 1962, New York University, 1965, Colorado State College, 1967, and College of the Holy Names, 1969. Member of Academy of Reading Experts advising New York City Board of Education, 1960-67, and of Educational Policies Commission, New Hampshire, 1966-69. Consultant to school systems in six states; member of executive committee, Western Connecticut State College.

MEMBER: American Educational Research Association, National Society for the Study of Education, International Reading Association, American Psychological Association, National Council of Teachers of English, Association for Childhood Education International, Association for Supervision and Curriculum Development, World Educational

Fellowship, American Association of University Professors, American Association of University Women, National Association for the Education of Young Children, National League of American Pen Women, Reading Round Table of Children's Book Council, Jean Piaget Society, International Platform Association, Keystone State Reading Association, Delaware Valley Reading Association, Temple University Women's Faculty Club (president, 1976—), Pi Lambda Theta (president, Philadelphia area chapter, 1978—), Phi Delta Kappa (recording secretary, Temple University chapter, 1977—), Kappa Delta Pi.

WRITINGS: Successful Practices in Remedial Reading, Atherton, 1963; (with Robert Kranyik) *How to Teach Study Skills,* Atherton, 1963; (with Kranyik) *How to Teach Reference and Research Skills,* Atherton, 1964; (editor with Robert Emans) *Readings about Reading Instruction,* Simon & Schuster, 1968; (editor) *Readings in the Language Arts,* three volumes, Simon & Schuster, 1969; (editor and contributor) *Research Studies in Reading,* two volumes, Simon & Schuster, 1969; *Study Skills and Reference Skills as an Aid to College Success,* Keating & Joyce, 1969; (editor and contributor) *Reading Success with Young Children,* Simon & Schuster, 1970; (editor) *Reading for Inner City Children,* Simon & Schuster, 1970; (editor and contributor) *Specialized Methods of Teaching Reading,* MSS Educational Publishing, 1970; (editor) *Methods of Teaching Reading,* MSS Educational Publishing, 1970; (editor and contributor) *Teaching Reading and Language to Inner-City Children,* Simon & Schuster, 1971; *Teaching Techniques with Phonics, Linguistics, and Games,* Simon & Schuster, 1971; *Games and Activities to Reinforce Reading Skills,* MSS Educational Publishing, 1972; *Activities and Games to Reinforce Phonics and Linguistics,* 2nd edition, Simon & Schuster, 1973.

Writer of film script, "We Discover the Encyclopedia," Coronet Films, 1971. Author of column, "Linguistics and Word Study," in *Instructor,* 1968-69; author of workbooks, pamphlets, and crossword puzzles. Contributor of articles and reviews to professional journals. Member of national publications board, Pi Lambda Theta, 1975—.

WORK IN PROGRESS: Critical Reading and Study Skills.

BIOGRAPHICAL/CRITICAL SOURCES: Reading Teacher, April, 1965.

* * *

SHAPIRO, Harvey 1924-

PERSONAL: Born January 27, 1924, in Chicago, Ill.; son of Jacob (a businessman) and Dorothy (Cohen) Shapiro; married Edna Lewis Kaufman (a psychologist), July 23, 1953; children: Saul, Dan. *Education:* Yale University, B.A., 1947; Columbia University, M.A., 1948. *Home:* 264 Hicks St., Brooklyn, N.Y. 11201. *Office: New York Times,* 229 West 43rd St., New York, N.Y. 10036.

CAREER: Cornell University, Ithaca, N.Y., instructor in English, 1949-50, 1951-52; Bard College, Annandale-on-Hudson, N.Y., creative writing fellow, 1950-51; *Commentary,* New York City, assistant editor, 1955-56; *New Yorker,* New York City, fiction editor, 1956-57; *New York Times Magazine,* New York City, member of editorial staff, 1957-64, assistant editor, 1964-75; *New York Times Book Review,* New York City, editor, 1975—. *Military service:* U.S. Army Air Forces, 1943-45; became technical sergeant; received Distinguished Flying Cross and Air Medal with three oak leaf clusters. *Member:* Elizabethan Club (New Haven). *Awards, honors:* Rockefeller Foundation fellowship in poetry, 1968.

WRITINGS—All poetry: *The Eye,* Swallow Press, 1953; *The Book and Other Poems,* Cummington, 1955; *Mountain, Fire, Thornbush,* Swallow Press, 1961; *Battle Report,* Wesleyan University Press, 1966; *This World,* Wesleyan University Press, 1971; *Lauds,* Sun Press, 1975; *Lauds and Nightsounds,* Sun Press, 1978. Work is represented in *The Voice That Is Great within Us,* edited by Hayden Carruth, Bantam, 1970. Contributor to *Atlantic, Harper's, Poetry, New Yorker, Nation, Chelsea, Quarterly Review of Literature, Midstream,* and other periodicals.

WORK IN PROGRESS: A book of poems.

SIDELIGHTS: Harvey Shapiro told *CA* that he would accept Hayden Carruth's description of his work as reflecting "the tension between his orthodox religious background and his experiences in war and in modern city living."

* * *

SHAPLEY, Fern Rusk 1890-

PERSONAL: Born September 20, 1890, in Mahomet, Ill.; daughter of William Humphrey (a college professor) and Anna Lucinda (Renner) Rusk; married John Shapley (a university professor), September 19, 1918; children: Dora (Mrs. Uco van Wijk), Ellen (Mrs. James M. Fish). *Education:* University of Missouri, A.B., 1913, A.M., 1914, Ph.D., 1916; also studied at Bryn Mawr College, 1914-15, and in Europe, 1915. *Residence:* Washington, D.C. *Office:* National Gallery of Art, Sixth and Constitution, Washington, D.C. 20565.

CAREER: University of Missouri—Columbia, assistant professor of art, summer, 1925; National Gallery of Art, Washington, D.C., research assistant, 1943-47, curator of paintings, 1947-56, assistant chief curator, 1956-60; Samuel H. Kress Foundation, New York, N.Y., curator of research, 1960-72. *Member:* Phi Beta Kappa. *Awards, honors:* Fellowship for European study, 1915; A.E.D., University of Missouri, 1959.

WRITINGS: George Caleb Bingham: The Missouri Artist, Hugh Stephens, 1917; *European Paintings from the Gulbenkian Collection,* Smithsonian Institution, 1950; (with husband, John Shapley) *Comparisons in Art,* Phaidon, 1957; *Paintings from the Samuel H. Kress Collection: Italian Schools,* Phaidon, Volume I: *Thirteenth to Fifteenth Century,* 1966, Volume II: *Fifteenth to Sixteenth Century,* 1968, Volume III: *Sixteenth to Eighteenth Century,* 1973; *A Catalogue of Italian Paintings in the National Gallery of Art,* National Gallery of Art, 1978. Contributor to professional journals.

* * *

SHAPO, Marshall S(chambelan) 1936-

PERSONAL: Born October 1, 1936, in Philadelphia, Pa.; son of Mitchell (a government expediter and real estate broker) and Norma (Schambelan) Shapo; married Helene S. Seidner, June 21, 1959; children: Benjamin, Nathaniel. *Education:* University of Miami, Coral Gables, Fla., A.B., 1958, J.D., 1964; Harvard University, A.M., 1961, S.J.D., 1974. *Politics:* Democrat. *Religion:* Jewish. *Home:* 1910 Orrington Ave., Evanston, Ill. 60201. *Office:* School of Law, Northwestern University, 357 East Chicago Ave., Chicago, Ill. 60611.

CAREER: Admitted to the Bar of Florida, 1964, to the Bar of Virginia, 1977; University of Miami, Coral Gables, Fla., instructor in history, 1960-61; University of Texas at Austin, assistant professor, 1965-67, associate professor, 1967-69, professor of law, 1969-70; University of Virginia, Charlottesville, visiting professor, 1969-70, professor of law, 1970-78, Joseph M. Hartfield Professor, 1976-78; Northwestern University, School of Law, Chicago, Ill., Frederic P. Vose Professor, 1978—. Visiting summer professor, University of Michigan, 1973, Juristiches Seminar, University of Goettingen, 1976. Visiting fellow, Center for Socio-Legal Studies, Wolfson College, Oxford, England, 1975. Member of Center for Advanced Studies, University of Virginia, 1976-77. *Member:* Florida Bar, Virginia Bar, American Law Institute. *Awards, honors:* National Endowment for the Humanities senior fellow, 1974-75.

WRITINGS: (With Page Keeton) *Products and the Consumer: Defective and Dangerous Products,* Foundation Press, 1970; (with Keeton) *Products and the Consumer: Deceptive Practices,* Foundation Press, 1972; *Tort and Compensation Law,* West Publishing, 1976; *The Duty to Act: Tort Law, Power, and Public Policy,* University of Texas Press, 1978; *A Nation of Guinea Pigs,* Free Press, 1979. Contributor of articles to *Stanford Law Review, Texas Law Review, Cornell Law Review, Northwestern Law Review, University of Miami Law Review, Virginia Law Review, American Bar Association Journal, Pharos,* and *In Vitro.*

WORK IN PROGRESS: A revision of *Products and the Consumer: Defective and Dangerous Products;* a treatise on product liability.

*　　　*　　　*

SHATTO, Gloria M.　1931-

PERSONAL: Born October 11, 1931, in Houston, Tex.; daughter of Kenneth E. and Gertrude (Osborne) McDermith; married Robert J. Shatto (an electrical engineer), March 19, 1953; children: David Paul, Donald Patrick. *Education:* Rice University, B.A. (with honors), 1954, Ph.D., 1966. *Religion:* Methodist. *Home:* 9523 Burwick Dr., San Antonio, Tex. 78230. *Office:* Department of Business and Management Studies, Trinity University, 715 Stadium Dr., San Antonio, Tex. 78284.

CAREER: Humble Oil & Refining Co., Houston, Tex., market researcher, 1954-55; science and mathematics teacher in Cristobal, Canal Zone, 1955-56; mathematics teacher in Houston, 1956-60; University of Houston, Houston, assistant professor, 1965-69, associate professor of economics, 1969-72, graduate coordinator, economics department, 1970-71; Georgia Institute of Technology, College of Industrial Management, associate dean and professor of economics, 1973-77; Trinity University, San Antonio, Tex., George R. Brown Professor of Business, 1977—. Consultant to business and non-profit organizations. American Association of University Women Education Foundation, member, 1970—, chairman of committee on international fellowships and awards, 1974-76. Member of Texas governor's Commission on the Status of Women, 1970-72; member of Georgia governor's Commission on the Status of Women, 1974. Member of U.S. Treasury Small Business Advisory Commission, 1977—. Member of board of trustees, Georgia Tech Research Institute, 1975-77, Berry College and Berry Schools, 1976—. Financial Executives Institute, chairman of education committee, 1976-77, member of board of directors, 1977—. Presented several television interviews on "Kaleidoscope," 1968.

MEMBER: American Economic Association, American Finance Association, Royal Economic Society, Interstate Association of Commissions on the Status of Women,

American Association of University Women, Southern Economic Association (president, 1976-77), Southwestern Social Science Association, Phi Beta Kappa, Omicron Delta Epsilon, Phi Kappa Phi. *Awards, honors:* American Association of University Women fellowship, 1964-65; University of Houston faculty research grants, 1966, 1968; Organization of American States fellowship, summer, 1968.

WRITINGS: (Contributor) Philip B. Taylor, Jr., editor, *Contemporary Latin America,* Volume III, [Houston], 1970; (editor) *Employment of the Middle-aged: Papers from Industrial Gerontology Seminars,* C. C Thomas, 1972. Contributor to *Social Science Quarterly, Journal of Finance, Journal of Business* (Chicago), and other business and economics journals.

*　　　*　　　*

SHAW, William Harlan　1922-
(Harlan)

PERSONAL: Born April 3, 1922, near Tulia, Tex.; son of Willie Sample (a builder) and Delia Cates (Harlan) Shaw; married Marjorie Lee McQuade (a clerk), November 1, 1945; children: Delia Belle, Morgan Roe. *Education:* Hardin-Simmons University, B.A. (cum laude), 1943, M.A., 1949; Louisiana State University, Ph.D., 1955. *Politics:* Democrat. *Religion:* Presbyterian. *Home:* 7450 Fieldston Rd., New Orleans, La. 70126. *Office:* Department of Drama and Communications, University of New Orleans, Lakefront, New Orleans, La. 70122.

CAREER: Hardin-Simmons University, Abilene, Tex., instructor in drama, designer, and technical director, 1949-50; Illinois State University, Normal, assistant professor of drama, designer, and technical director, 1950-53; Hardin-Simmons University, assistant professor of drama and director of theater, 1955-56; Washington University, St. Louis, Mo., assistant professor of drama, designer, and technical director, 1956-61; Florida State University, Tallahassee, assistant professor, 1961-67, associate professor of drama, 1967-68, costume designer, 1961-68; University of New Orleans, New Orleans, La., associate professor, 1968-72, professor of drama and communications, 1972—, chairman of department, 1976—. Actor and designer, Penthouse Players (Abilene), 1948; designer and director, St. Louis Opera Guild, 1959-61; costumer for Eddie Dowling Foundation, 1961-68, and Asolo Theater Festival, 1962-68. Scene designer, U.S. Government Educational Laboratory Theater, 1969. Painter and sculptor, under pseudonym Harlan; art work exhibited in more than forty shows, including Ringling Museum, Abilene Museum, and St. Louis City Art Museum. *Military service:* U.S. Naval Reserve, active duty, 1943-45; became lieutenant junior grade.

MEMBER: American Theater Association, Speech Communication Association, Theaters of Louisiana, Alpha Psi Omega, Alpha Chi, Theta Alpha Phi. *Awards, honors:* Painting award, Texas Art Association, 1947; sculpture award, Abilene Art Association, 1956; opera setting award, National Opera Guild, 1957; painting awards, Kirkwood Art Association, 1958, 1959, 1960, 1961; painting award, Webster Groves Art Association, 1959; Sears-Roebuck painting award, 1965; award from Florida Development Commission, 1961-64, for generous contributions to promotion of Florida.

WRITINGS: (With August W. Staub and others) *Introduction to Theatrical Arts,* Kendall-Hunt, 1971, revised edition, 1975; *Basic Pattern Drafting for the Theatrical Costume Designer,* Drama Book Specialists, 1974.

Contributor of photographs: Charles Hoffer, *Understanding Music,* Wadsworth, 1967; Staub, *A Small Bare Space,* International Thespian Society, 1970; Staub, *Creating Theatre,* Harper, 1973.

Plays: (Adapter with Lawrence Skylstad) "The Killers," 1947; "The Nativity," 1950; "The Joseph Story" (adaptation), 1953; (adapter with Herbert Metz) "The Artificial Princess," 1953.

WORK IN PROGRESS: History of Men's Wear Since 1860.

* * *

SHEARD, Kevin 1916-

PERSONAL: Born January 30, 1916, in New York, N.Y.; son of Alec Michael (in finance) and Frances (Cox) Sheard; married Ruth L. Hyde, September 29, 1973; children: Wenda Jane, Sarah Anne, Elizabeth Margaret, Catherine Frances, Martha. *Education:* Williams College, B.A., 1947; University of Wisconsin, M.S., 1949; Xavier University, Cincinnati, Ohio, M.B.A., 1955; Loyola University of Chicago, J.D., 1959. *Office:* School of Law, Cleveland State University, Cleveland, Ohio 44115.

CAREER: Williams College, Williamstown, Mass., instructor in history, 1947-48; Baldwin-Wallace College, Berea, Ohio, assistant professor of business administration, 1955-58; University of Illinois at Urbana-Champaign, instructor in economics, 1958-59; Northern Michigan University, Marquette, associate professor of business administration, 1959-63; Cleveland State University, Cleveland, Ohio, assistant professor, 1963-64, professor of law, 1964—. *Military service:* U.S. Army, 1940-46; became major.

WRITINGS: Academic Heraldry in America, Northern Michigan University Press, 1962; (with Hugh Smith) *Academic Dress and Insignia of the World,* A. A. Balkema, 1970; *Law for Young People,* Newbury Press, 1978.

WORK IN PROGRESS: Law for Senior Citizens.

* * *

SHEEHAN, Bernard W(illiam) 1934-

PERSONAL: Born February 24, 1934, in New York, N.Y.; son of William J. and Margaret (Chidwick) Sheehan; married Janina Urich, September 14, 1957; children: Cornelius, Manya, Jessica. *Education:* Fordham University, B.S., 1957; University of Michigan, A.M., 1958; University of Virginia, Ph.D., 1965. *Religion:* Roman Catholic. *Home:* 914 Sowder Sq., Bloomington, Ind. 47401. *Office:* Department of History, Indiana University, Bloomington, Ind. 47401.

CAREER: Regis College, Denver, Colo., instructor in history, 1958-62; University of Alabama, University, assistant professor of history, 1965-66; College of William and Mary, Williamsburg, Va., assistant professor of history, 1966-69; Indiana University at Bloomington, associate professor of history, 1969—. Fellow, Institute of Early American History and Culture, Williamsburg, Va., 1966-69. *Member:* Organization of American Historians.

WRITINGS: Seeds of Extinction: Jeffersonian Philanthropy and the American Indian, University of North Carolina Press, 1973. Contributor to American historical journals. *Journal of American History,* associate editor, 1969-73, acting editor, 1973-74.

WORK IN PROGRESS: Studying early contacts between the white man and the Indian in the New World.

SHEWBRIDGE, Edythe A(nne) 1943-

PERSONAL: Born March 6, 1943, in New York, N.Y.; daughter of James Donald and Doris R. Shewbridge. *Education:* Long Island University, B.A. (cum laude), 1966; graduate study at New School for Social Research, 1968-70, and University of Virginia, Extension in Arlington, 1970-72. *Politics:* Independent liberal. *Religion:* Episcopalian. *Home:* 1200 South George Mason Dr., Arlington, Va. 22204.

CAREER: New York City Department of Social Services, New York, N.Y., caseworker, 1967-70. *Member:* Psi Chi, Sigma Tau Delta.

WRITINGS: Portraits of Poverty, Norton, 1972. Contributor to *Catholic Worker.*

WORK IN PROGRESS: A book about oppression and exploitation of mental patients.

* * *

SHIVERS, Alfred Samuel 1929-
(Samuel A. Shivers)

PERSONAL: Born January 16, 1929, in Lakeland, Fla.; son of Sam M. (a boilermaker) and Gracie (Cummings) Shivers; married Clare Ann Schneider, February 28, 1959; children: John Samuel, Ralph Allen, Paul Alfred. *Education:* University of Florida, B.A., 1955, M.A., 1959; Duke University, graduate study, 1959-60; Florida State University, Ph.D., 1962. *Politics:* Independent. *Religion:* Protestant. *Home:* 2400 Dogwood, Nacogdoches, Tex. 75961. *Office:* Department of English, Stephen F. Austin State University, Nacogdoches, Tex. 75961.

CAREER: Minerals Separation, Lakeland, Fla., assistant chemist, 1946-48; Wisconsin State College, Superior (now University of Wisconsin), assistant professor of English, 1962-63; Colorado State University, Fort Collins, assistant professor of English, 1963-64; Northern Illinois University, DeKalb, assistant professor of English, 1964-66; Stephen F. Austin State University, Nacogdoches, Tex., associate professor, 1966-67, professor of English, 1967—. *Military service:* U.S. Army, 1948-49. U.S. Air Force, 1949-52. U.S. Navy, 1957-59; became lieutenant junior grade. *Member:* National Council of Teachers of English. *Awards, honors:* Stephen F. Austin State University faculty research grants.

WRITINGS: Jessamyn West, Twayne, 1972; *Maxwell Anderson,* Twayne, 1976. Contributor of articles to *Alaska Review, Bulletin of Bibliography, Rocky Mountain News, Saturday Review, Milwaukee Journal,* and *Dalhousie Review;* contributor, under pseudonym Samuel A. Shivers, to *American Book Collector.*

WORK IN PROGRESS: A biography of Maxwell Anderson.

SIDELIGHTS: Alfred Samuel Shivers told *CA,* "I write scholarly books not only because I enjoy doing so, but because I think it disgraceful for a Ph.D. in academia—trained in the techniques of research and scholarly writing—not to fulfill himself in that way." *Avocational interests:* Raising rabbiteye blueberries, plums, and grapes.

* * *

SHLONSKY, Abraham 1898(?)-1973

1898(?)—May 18, 1973; Russian-born Israeli poet, writer, editor, translator, and journalist. Obituaries: *New York Times,* May 19, 1973.

SHOBLAD, Richard H(anson) 1937-

PERSONAL: Born January 20, 1937, in Seattle, Wash.; son of Ralph F. (a lumber broker) and Juanita (Swim) Shoblad; married Kathy K. Walker (divorced, 1961); married Linda Robinson (a faculty member of Portland State University), November, 1969. *Education:* Portland State University, B.S. (with honors), 1969, additional study, 1971-72.

CAREER: National Prisoners Alliance, Portland, Ore., national coordinator, 1970—. Guest lecturer, Pacific Lutheran University, Tacoma, Wash., beginning 1972. *Member:* National Prisoners Alliance, National Prisoners Coalition, Lifers Club, Ad-Hoc Police Commission Relations. *Awards, honors:* Ford Foundation fellow at State University of New York at Albany, 1970-71.

WRITINGS: (With Cliff Gradick) *The Extent and Cost of Drug Related Crimes,* Wiche, 1971; *Doing My Own Time,* Doubleday, 1972. Editor of *Jaico,* 1971—.

WORK IN PROGRESS: Research on prison labor and industries; editing National Prisoner Conference report, "Systematic Reduction of Prison and Jail Populations"; a book about the prisoner movement, *Some Call It Slavery;* a collection of articles for Syracuse University Research Corporation.††

*   *   *

SHOKEID, Moshe 1936-
(Moshe Minkovitz)

PERSONAL: Surname originally Minkovitz; born October 12, 1936, in Tel-Aviv, Palestine (now Israel); son of Yitzhak (member of an industrial cooperative) and Sara (Uzieli) Minkovitz. *Education:* Hebrew University of Jerusalem, B.A., 1960, M.A., 1964; University of Manchester, Ph.D., 1968. *Home:* 13 Nahum, Ramat-Chen, Ramat-Gan, Israel. *Office:* Department of Anthropology, Tel-Aviv University, Tel-Aviv, Israel.

CAREER: Jewish Agency, rural sociologist in land settlement department in Negev, Israel, 1961-64; University of Manchester, Manchester, England, research fellow in social anthropology, 1964-68; Tel-Aviv University, Tel-Aviv, Israel, lecturer, 1968-71, senior lecturer, 1971-75, associate professor of social anthropology, 1975—. *Military service:* Israeli Army, Artillery, 1954-56; became sergeant. *Member:* Association of Social Anthropologists (England; associate), Israeli Sociological Association.

WRITINGS: The Dual Heritage: Immigrants from the Atlas Mountains in an Israeli Village, Manchester University Press, 1971; (with Shlomo Deshen) *The Predicament of Homecoming: Cultural and Social Life of North African Immigrants in Israel,* Cornell University Press, 1974; (with Deshen) *The Generation of Transition: Continuity and Change among North African Immigrants,* Ben-Zvi Institute (Jerusalem), 1977. Contributor of chapters to books. Contributor to professional journals in Israel, United States, England, Canada, and France.

WORK IN PROGRESS: Distant Relations: Ethnicity, Politics, and Religion among Arabs and North African Immigrants, with Shlomo Deshen.

*   *   *

SHROUT, Thomas R(euben) 1919-

PERSONAL: Born September 24, 1919, in Independence, Mo.; son of Thomas Jefferson (a farmer) and Bernice (Jones) Shrout; married Anna Mildred Ray (a teacher), June 21,

1943; children: Martha Ann (Mrs. Jack P. Brown), Thomas R., Jr. *Education:* Transylvania University, A.B., 1940; College of the Bible, Lexington, Ky., B.D., 1943; Harvard University, S.T.M., 1949, Th.D., 1954. *Politics:* Democrat. *Home:* 109 North Ninth, Canton, Mo. 63435. *Office:* Department of Humanities, Culver-Stockton College, Canton, Mo. 63435.

CAREER: Ordained minister, Disciples of Christ (now joint standing with United Church of Christ), 1940; Missouri School of Religion, Columbia, assistant professor, 1954-55, associate professor, 1955-58, professor of religion, 1958-69, dean, 1958-69, president of School of Religion, 1968-69; Culver-Stockton College, Canton, Mo., professor of humanities, 1969—, chairman of department, 1969—. *Member:* Societas Novi Testimenti Studiorum, Society of Biblical Literature, American Academy of Religion, Kiwanis (Canton president, 1972-73), Pi Kappa Alpha.

WRITINGS: (Editor) *Preaching on New Testament Themes,* Bethany Press, 1964; *Lighting Up Life,* Bethany Press, 1972.

WORK IN PROGRESS: A book on the Apostle, Paul.

AVOCATIONAL INTERESTS: Antique autos, woodworking, gardening.

*   *   *

SHUB, David 1887-1973

September 13, 1887—May 27, 1973; Russian-born American writer, editor, and journalist. Obituaries: *New York Times,* May 29, 1973; *Washington Post,* May 31, 1973.

*   *   *

SHUB, Elizabeth

PERSONAL: Born in Vilno, Poland; daughter of Samuel (a writer) and Bessie (Lurie) Charney; married Boris Shub (deceased). *Education:* Attended Brooklyn College of the City University of New York. *Religion:* Jewish. *Home:* 185 West End Ave., New York, N.Y. 10023. *Office:* Macmillan Publishing Co., 866 Third Ave., New York, N.Y. 10022.

CAREER: Harper & Row Publishers, Inc., New York City, associate editor of children's books, 1965-66; Charles Scribner's Sons, New York City, associate editor of children's books, 1966-68; Macmillan Publishing Co., New York City, associate editor of children's books, 1968—. *Member:* P.E.N. *Awards, honors:* American Library Association Notable Book awards, 1969, for *Sir Ribbeck of Ribbeck of Havelland,* and 1971, for *About Wise Men and Simpletons;* Newbery Honor Book awards for *Zlateh the Goat, and Other Stories* and *When Shlemiel Went to Warsaw.*

WRITINGS: (Editor) Isaac Bashevis Singer, *The Estate,* translated by Joseph Singer and others, J. Cape, 1970, Dell, 1971; (adaptor) *Clever Kate,* Macmillan, 1973; *Seeing Is Believing,* Macmillan, 1979.

Translator: Brothers Grimm, *The Twelve Dancing Princesses,* Scribner, 1966; Brothers Grimm, *Jorinda and Joringel,* Scribner, 1968; Theodor Fontane, *Sir Ribbeck of Ribbeck of Havelland,* Macmillan, 1969; Janosch, *The Thieves and the Raven,* Macmillan, 1970; Brothers Grimm, *About Wise Men and Simpletons: Twelve Tales from Grimm,* Macmillan, 1971; Gerlinda Schneider, *Uncle Harry,* Macmillan, 1972; Antonella Bolliger-Savelli, *The Mouse and the Knitted Cat,* Macmillan, 1973; Bolliger-Savelli, *Miranda's Magic,* Macmillan, 1974; Wilhelm Hauff, *The Adventure of Little Monk,* Macmillan, 1974; Achim Brogek, *Good*

Morning Whale, Macmillan, 1975; Brothers Grimm, *The Fisherman and His Wife,* Macmillan, 1979.

Translator with the author, Isaac Bashevis Singer: *Zlateh the Goat, and Other Stories,* Harper, 1966; *The Fearsone Inn,* Scribner, 1967; *Mazel and Shlimazek, or the Milk of a Lioness,* Farrar, Straus, 1967; *When Shlemiel Went to Warsaw, and Other Stories,* Farrar, Straus, 1968; *Elijah the Slave,* Farrar, Straus, 1970; *Joseph and Koza, or the Sacrifice to the Vistula,* Farrar, Straus, 1970; *The Topsy-Turvy Emperor of China,* Harper, 1971; *Alone in the Wild Forest,* Farrar, Straus, 1971; *The Wicked City,* Farrar, Straus, 1972; *The Fools of Chelm,* Farrar, Straus, 1973.

BIOGRAPHICAL/CRITICAL SOURCES: New York Times Book Review, October 31, 1971.

* * *

SHURR, William H(oward) 1932-

PERSONAL: Born August 29, 1932, in Evanston, Ill.; son of L. Howard (an insurance company executive) and Mary (Hanagan) Shurr; married Georgia Grey Hooks (a professor of French), December 28, 1968; children: Emily. *Education:* Loyola University, Chicago, Ill., A.B., 1955, M.A., 1958, licentiates in philosophy, 1957, and theology, 1964; University of North Carolina at Chapel Hill, Ph.D., 1968. *Home:* 902 East B St., Moscow, Idaho 83843. *Office:* Department of English, Washington State University, Pullman, Wash. 99163.

CAREER: University of Tennessee, Chattanooga, assistant professor of English, 1968-72; Washington State University, Pullman, associate professor of English, 1972-74, professor of English and American studies, 1974—. *Member:* Modern Language Association of America, American Association of University Professors (president of local chapter, 1970-71), Society for the Study of Southern Literature, South Atlantic Modern Language Association, Melville Society, G. M. Hopkins Society. *Awards, honors:* Award from South Atlantic Modern Language Association, for book *The Mystery of Iniquity.*

WRITINGS: Prose and Poetry of England, Random House, 1965; *The Mystery of Iniquity: Melville as Poet, 1857-1891,* University Press of Kentucky, 1972. Contributor to professional journals.

WORK IN PROGRESS: A book about Calvinism in American literature; research on theological themes in literature, southern American literature, and theories of literature.

* * *

SHURTLEFF, Michael 1930-

PERSONAL: Born July 3, 1930; son of Charles J. and Ruth M. Shurtleff. *Education:* Lawrence University, B.A.; Yale University, M.F.A., 1952. *Home and office:* 22 West 24th St., New York, N.Y. 10010. *Agent:* Helen Merrill, 337 West 22nd St., New York, N.Y. 10011.

CAREER: Casting director for David Merrick, 1956-62; Talent Associates, New York City, director for David Susskind, 1963-64; Friday Theatre, New York City, founder and director, 1965—. Shurtleff Studio for How to Audition Classes, founder, and director, 1964—.

WRITINGS: Call Me By My Rightful Name, Dramatists Play Service, 1962; *Audition: Everything an Actor Needs to Know to Get the Part,* Walker & Co., 1978.

Plays: "I Hate to See a Party End," first produced Off-Broadway at Martinique Theatre, 1963; "The Moment of

Truth Is Near," first produced in New York at 48th Street Studio Theatre, November 17, 1967; "Life Among the Young People," first produced Off-Off-Broadway at Playbox Theatre, April 15, 1968; "Mor Power to You," first produced Off-Off-Broadway at Extension Theatre, 1969; "A Day in the Life of," first produced Off-Off-Broadway at Playbox Theatre, January 15, 1969; "The Four of Them," first produced in New York at 84th Street Theatre, December, 1971; "Take Very Good Care of Yourself," first produced in New York at Fifth Avenue Theatre, December 5, 1972. Also author of many one-act plays. Author of film script and director of "Call Me By My Rightful Name," (based on book of same name), released in 1973.

WORK IN PROGRESS: Happy New Year, Gregorio, a novel; "Love Is," a play, to be produced on Broadway; "Lock the Door Behind You"; a second novel, *Can't Get No Satisfaction.*

BIOGRAPHICAL/CRITICAL SOURCES: Village Voice, April 18, 1968.†

* * *

SICKELS, Robert J(udd) 1931-

PERSONAL: Born June 26, 1931, in Nyack, N.Y.; son of Robert and Dorothy (Judd) Sickels; married Alice Esterer, September 11, 1967; children: Stephen J., Wendy. *Education:* University of Chicago, B.A., 1950, M.A., 1954; Johns Hopkins University, Ph.D., 1960. *Office:* Department of Political Science, University of New Mexico, Albuquerque, N.M. 87106.

CAREER: President's Commission on Registration and Voting Participation, Washington, D.C., assistant staff director, 1963-64; U.S. Civil Service Commission, Washington, D.C., associate director of executive institutes, 1964-65; Purdue University, Lafayette, Ind., associate professor of political science, 1965-68; University of New Mexico, Albuquerque, associate professor, 1968-73, professor of political science, 1973—, chairman of department, 1976—.

WRITINGS: Race, Marriage, and the Law, University of New Mexico Press, 1972; *Presidential Transactions,* Prentice-Hall, 1974. Contributor to *Yale Law Journal, New Republic, American Political Science Review.*

WORK IN PROGRESS: A book, *The Presidency,* for Prentice-Hall, completion expected in 1980.

* * *

SIDDALL, William R(ichard) 1928-

PERSONAL: Born April 25, 1928, in Bronxville, N.Y.; son of Roger B. and Gertrude (FitzGerald) Siddall; married Abigail Tucker (a part-time editor), June 16, 1951; children: Nathaniel, Phoebe. *Education:* Harvard University, A.B., 1950; University of Washington, Seattle, M.A., 1955, Ph.D., 1959. *Politics:* Democratic. *Religion:* Unitarian Universalist. *Home:* 1616 Beechwood Terr., Manhattan, Kan. 66502. *Office:* Department of Geography, Kansas State University, Manhattan, Kan. 66506.

CAREER: General Electric Co., Boston, Mass., member of executive training program, 1951-53; Middlebury College, Middlebury, Vt., instructor, 1957-58, assistant professor of geography, 1958-60; Wisconsin State College, Superior (now University of Wisconsin—Superior), assistant professor of geography, 1960-62; Kansas State University, Manhattan, assistant professor, 1962-64, associate professor, 1964-70, professor of geography and chairman of department, 1970—. *Military service:* U.S. Air Force Reserve, 1951-53.

Member: Association of American Geographers, Transport Association of America, Nantucket Conservation Foundation.

WRITINGS: Transportation Geography: A Bibliography, Kansas State University Library, 1964, 3rd edition, 1969. Contributor to *Annals of the Association of American Geographers, Pacific Historical Review, Economic Geography, Geographical Review, Journal of Geography,* and *Comparative Studies in Society and History.*

WORK IN PROGRESS: Research in transportation geography, especially the relationship between transportation and environmental quality.

* * *

SIEGEL, Stanley E(lliot) 1928-

PERSONAL: Born May 7, 1928, in Long Branch, N.J.; son of Charles (a clothier) and Ida (Frankel) Siegel; married Norma Gene Stein, August 23, 1953; children: Charles, David, Martin. *Education:* Washington and Jefferson College, B.A., 1949; University of Maryland, M.A., 1950; Rice Institute (now University), Ph.D., 1953. *Religion:* Jewish. *Home:* 4107 Leeshire, Houston, Tex. 77025. *Office:* Department of History, University of Houston, Houston, Tex. 77004.

CAREER: University of Houston, Houston, Tex., instructor, 1953-54, assistant professor, 1954-57, associate professor, 1957-63, professor of American history, 1963—. *Member:* American Historical Association, Southern Historical Association, Texas State Historical Association.

WRITINGS: A Political History of the Texas Republic, 1836-1845, University of Texas Press, 1956; *Big Men Walked Here: A History of Washington-on-the-Brazos,* Pemberton, 1971; *The Poet President of Texas: A Life of Mirabeau B. Lamar,* Jenkins Publishing, 1977.

* * *

SIEMENS, Reynold Gerrard 1932-

PERSONAL: Born April 6, 1932, in Winnipeg, Manitoba, Canada; son of George G. (a teacher) and Tina (Heinrichs) Siemens; married Frances Klassen, June 24, 1963; children: Raymond, George. *Education:* University of Manitoba, B.A., 1963; Curtis Institute of Music, diploma, 1956; University of Wisconsin, M.A., 1964, Ph.D., 1966. *Office:* Department of English, University of Alberta, Edmonton, Alberta, Canada.

CAREER: American Society of Ancient Instruments, Philadelphia, Pa., gambist, 1953-56; Canadian Broadcasting Company and Boyd Neel Orchestra, Toronto, Ontario, cellist, 1949-62; University of Alberta, Edmonton, assistant professor, 1966-71, associate professor of English, 1971—. Visiting professor at University of British Columbia, 1967. *Member:* Modern Language Association of America, American Federation of Musicians of the United States and Canada, Canadian Association of University Teachers.

WRITINGS: The Wordsworth Collection: Dove Cottage Papers Facsimiles, University of Alberta Press, 1971. Contributor to *Renaissance Quarterly, PMLA, Wordsworth Circle,* and *Humanities Association Bulletin.*

WORK IN PROGRESS: Research in English Romanticism and in relations between literature and the other arts; records.

SILLEN, Samuel 1911(?)-1973

1911(?)—February 5, 1973; American author, editor, and literary critic. Obituaries: *New York Times,* February 6, 1973.

* * *

SILVERMAN, Robert E(ugene) 1924-

PERSONAL: Born March 1, 1924, in Providence, R.I.; son of Samuel and Natalie (Jess) Silverman; married Margaret Takacs (a professor), December 23, 1949; children: Jill Anne, Pamela Kaye. *Education:* Brown University, A.B., 1946; Indiana University, Ph.D., 1952. *Home:* 4 Avalon Rd., Great Neck, N.Y. 11021. *Office:* Department of Psychology, New York University, New York, N.Y. 10003.

CAREER: New York University, New York, N.Y., assistant professor, 1952-56, associate professor, 1956-60, professor of psychology, 1961—, chairman of department, 1961-69. Consultant to U.S. Veterans Administration, 1956, and Bolt, Beranek and Newman, Cambridge, Mass., 1964-71. *Military service:* U.S. Army, 1943-46; became technical sergeant. *Member:* American Psychological Association, American Association for the Advancement of Science, Psychonomic Society, Sigma Xi.

WRITINGS: How to Write a Program, Carlisle Publishers, 1970; *Psychology,* Prentice-Hall, 1971, 3rd edition, 1978; (compiler) *Readings for Psychology,* Appleton, 1971. Contributor to *Educational Technology.*

* * *

SILVING, Helen 1906-

PERSONAL: Born March 8, 1906, in Krakow, Poland; came to United States, 1939; naturalized citizen, 1944; daughter of Szaje (an industrialist) and Salomea (Bauminger) Silberpfennig; married Paul K. Ryu (a law professor), January 3, 1957. *Education:* University of Vienna, Dr.Pol.Sci., 1929, J.U.D., 1936; Columbia University, LL.B., 1944. *Religion:* Jewish. *Office:* Law School, University of Puerto Rico, Rio Piedras 00931, Puerto Rico.

CAREER: Admitted to the Bar of New York State, 1944, and to First Bar of Korea, 1964; Mudge, Stern, Williams & Tucker, New York, N.Y., associate attorney, 1944-45; U.S. Department of Justice, Washington, D.C., attorney, 1948-53; Harvard University, Law School, Cambridge, Mass., research associate, 1954-56; University of Puerto Rico, Rio Piedras, visiting professor, 1956-57, professor of law, 1957—. Advisor to the Legislative Penal Reform Commission and to the Justice Department of the Commonwealth of Puerto Rico, 1959-66. *Member:* International Association of Penal Law, World Peace Through Law, American Bar Association. *Awards, honors:* American Society of Criminology, special presidential citation, 1971.

WRITINGS: Essays on Criminal Procedure, Dennis, 1964; *Constituent Elements of Crime,* C. C Thomas, 1967; *Essays on Mental Incapacity and Criminal Conduct,* C. C Thomas, 1967; *Sources of Law,* W. S. Hein, 1968; *Criminal Justice,* two volumes, W. S. Hein, 1971. Contributor of articles to *Encyclopaedia Britannica, Catholic Encyclopedia,* to journals in her field, and in interdisciplinary areas, in various languages.

WORK IN PROGRESS: A book, *Sanctions,* with husband, Paul K. Ryu.

SIDELIGHTS: Helen Silving and her husband are competent in twelve languages.†

SIMKINS, Lawrence D(avid) 1933-

PERSONAL: Born January 18, 1933, in Philadelphia, Pa.; son of Samuel and Esther (Bolton) Simkins; married Paula Katz, June 17, 1956; children: Lee, Jeffrey, Troy. *Education:* Temple University, B.A., 1954; Lehigh University, B.A., 1956; University of Houston, Ph.D., 1959. *Office:* Department of Psychology, University of Missouri, Kansas City, Mo. 64110.

CAREER: University of Texas, Medical Branch, Galveston, resident in clinical psychology, 1958-59; Florida State University, Tallahassee, assistant professor of psychology, 1959-64; University of Missouri—Kansas City, associate professor, 1964-69, professor of psychology, 1969—, head of department, 1971-74. Fulbright professor at University of Istanbul, 1970-71. Member of board of directors, National Council on Alcoholism, Kansas City, Mo., 1967—. *Member:* American Psychological Association, American Association of University Professors, Association for the Advancement of Behavior Therapy, Association for Behavior Analysis, Biofeedback Society of America, Association of Applied Biofeedback Clinicians, Midwestern Psychological Association, Missouri Psychological Association, Missouri Biofeedback Society, Missouri Academy of Science, New York Academy of Sciences.

WRITINGS: The Basis of Psychology as a Behavioral Science, Blaisdell, 1969. Contributor to *Journal of Consulting Psychology, Journal of Personality, Journal of Verbal Learning and Verbal Behavior, Journal of Abnormal and Social Psychology, Journal of Educational Research, Psychological Reports, Journal of Psychology, Journal of Social Psychology, Psychological Record, Transactions, Missouri Academy of Science, Journal of Special Education, International Journal of Social Psychiatry,* and *Behavior Therapy.*

AVOCATIONAL INTERESTS: Drama.

* * *

SIMMONS, James E(dwin) 1923-

PERSONAL: Born July 13, 1923, in Toledo, Ohio; son of Guy B. (a businessman) and Ruth (Stitsworth) Simmons; married Katherine M. Blocker, June 21, 1947 (divorced, July 15, 1970); married Kathryn Witt, February 26, 1972; children: (first marriage) Christina, James M., Anne, Katherine L., Martha, Sarah, John. *Education:* University of Toledo, B.S., 1945; Ohio State University, M.D., 1947; University of Louisville, postdoctoral study, 1957-58. *Home:* 6461 Park Central Dr. W., Indianapolis, Ind. 46260. *Office:* School of Medicine, Indiana University, 1100 West Michigan, Indianapolis, Ind. 46202.

CAREER: St. Vincent's Hospital, Toledo, Ohio, intern, 1947-48; Menninger Foundation, Topeka, Kan., resident in psychiatry, 1948-51; Child Guidance Clinic of Marion County (Indiana), director, 1953-57; Indiana University, Indianapolis, instructor, 1955-56, assistant professor, 1956-58, associate professor, 1958-62, professor of child psychiatry, 1962—, coordinator, 1962-74, director of child psychiatry services, 1975, lecturer in School of Social Work, 1955-56, acting chairman of department of psychiatry, 1972, 1974-75. Lecturer, Kent School of Social Work, 1957-58; visiting professor, University of Melbourne, 1977. American Board of Psychiatry and Neurology, diplomate in psychiatry, 1954, diplomate in child psychiatry, 1960, examiner in psychiatry and child psychiatry, 1961-72, member of examination committee, 1974—. Member of board of directors, Child Guidance Clinic of Marion County, 1962-71; member

of governor's advisory committee, Indiana Soldiers' and Sailors' Children's Home, 1963-65; president of board of directors, Waycross, Inc. (Episcopal children's camp), 1965-67. Consultant to Marion County Juvenile Court, 1953-57, Kentucky Department of Mental Health, 1957-58, Jewish Social Services, 1960-66, Catholic Social Services, 1965-68, Indianapolis Family Service Association, 1969-72, and other agencies. *Military service:* U.S. Navy, psychiatrist, 1951-53; became lieutenant.

MEMBER: American Medical Association (member of Ad Hoc Committee on Mental Health of Children, 1975—), American Psychiatric Association (fellow), American Academy of Child Psychiatry (fellow), American Association of Psychiatric Services for Children (chairman of mid-Eastern region, 1965), Indiana Medical Association, Indiana Psychiatric Society, Indiana Association for Mental Health (member of board of directors, 1961-71; vice-president, 1963-66), Marion County Medical Association.

WRITINGS: (Contributor) Joseph Wortis, editor, *Recent Advances in Biological Psychiatry,* Volume V, Plenum, 1963; (contributor) D. Arn Van Krevelan, editor, *Child Psychiatry and Prevention,* Hans Huber, 1964; (contributor) Morris Green and Robert J. Haggerty, editors, *Ambulatory Pediatrics,* Saunders, 1968; *Psychiatric Examination of Children,* Lea & Febiger, 1969, 2nd edition, 1974; *Anleitung Zur Psychiatrischen Untersuchung Von Kindern,* F. K. Schattauer, 1972. Contributor of about fifteen articles to professional journals. Member of editorial board of *Journal of the American Academy of Child Psychiatry,* 1970-75. Editor, newsletter of American Association of Psychiatric Services for Children, 1969-74.

SIDELIGHTS: Psychiatric Examination of Children has been published in Spanish, Italian, and Portuguese.

* * *

SIMON, Alfred 1907-

PERSONAL: Born September 6, 1907, in Far Rockaway, N.Y.; son of Leo L. and Anna (Mayer) Simon. *Education:* Attended high school in New York, N.Y. *Home:* 400 East 59th St., New York, N.Y. 10022.

CAREER: Pianist. Rehearsal pianist for George Gershwin, 1931; World Broadcasting System, New York City, programmer and writer for transcription library service, 1935-42; WQXR-Radio, New York City, director of light music, 1942-67. Music consultant to Abe Burrows for play "Cactus Flower," 1965; music research consultant, Goodspeed Opera House, East Haddam, Conn., 1975—; member of board of directors, Light Opera of Manhattan, 1976—. *Member:* Veterans Hospital Radio and Television Guild (member of board of directors, 1963-69), Players (member of board of directors, 1972-77).

WRITINGS: (Editor with Richard Lewine) *Encyclopedia of Theatre Music,* Random House, 1961; (contributor) Howard Taubman, editor, *New York Times Guide to Listening Pleasure,* Macmillan, 1968; (with Lewine) *Songs of the American Theater: 1900-1971,* Dodd, 1973; (with Robert Kimball) *The Gershwins,* Atheneum, 1973. Has written liner notes and narration for record albums. Contributor to *Stereo Review.*

SIDELIGHTS: Alfred Simon has an extensive library of records, sheet music, and vocal scores of show music, much of it extremely rare.

SIMONS, John D(onald) 1935-

PERSONAL: Born October 5, 1935, in Lone Oak, Tex.; son of Howard (a teacher) and Mary (Graham) Simons; married Ursula Dreyhaupt (a college teacher), March 9, 1962. *Education:* University of Texas, B.A., 1959, M.A., 1961; Rice University, Ph.D., 1966. *Home:* 2106 Monticello Dr., Tallahassee, Fla. 32303. *Office:* Department of Modern Languages, Florida State University, Tallahassee, Fla. 32306.

CAREER: University of Iowa, Iowa City, assistant professor of German, 1966-70; Florida State University, Tallahassee, associate professor of German, 1970—. *Member:* Modern Language Association of America, South Atlantic Modern Language Association, American Association of University Professors, American Association of Teachers of German.

WRITINGS: Hermann Hesse's "Steppenwolf," Simon & Schuster, 1972; *Gunther Grass's "The Tin Drum,"* Simon & Schuster, 1973; *Thomas Mann,* Simon & Schuster, 1974. Also author of *The Novels of Hermann Hesse.* Contributor of articles and reviews to *Comparative Literature, Explicator,* and other professional journals.

WORK IN PROGRESS: Friedrich Schiller, for Twayne.

SIDELIGHTS: John D. Simons comments: "The advice which I would give to an aspiring writer is self discipline. Train yourself to resist the impulse to get up and take a break. . . . Why write? The *real* beneficiary is the writer, not the reader."

*   *   *

SIMPSON, Hassell A(lgernon) 1930-

PERSONAL: Born May 8, 1930, in Barksdale, S.C.; son of John Algernon (a farmer) and Jewel (Boroughs) Simpson; married Grace Pow, June 6, 1953; children: David Steadman, John Algernon II, William Gavin. *Education:* Clemson College (now University), B.A., 1952; Florida State University, M.A., 1957, Ph.D., 1962. *Home address:* Box 666, Hampden-Sydney, Va. 23943. *Office:* Department of English, Hampden-Sydney College in Virginia, Hampden-Sydney, Va. 23943.

CAREER: Greenville News, Greenville, S.C., copy desk man and reporter, 1954-55; Florida State University, Tallahassee, instructor in English, 1958-59; Auburn University, Auburn, Ala., instructor in English, 1959-62; Hampden-Sydney College in Virginia, Hampden-Sydney, associate professor, 1962-65, professor of English, 1965—, chairman of department, 1968-76, chairman of Division of Humanities, 1970-73. Member, Shakespeare Players, Inc. *Military service:* U.S. Army, 1952-54; became first lieutenant. *Member:* Modern Language Association of America, South Atlantic Modern Language Association, Society for the Study of Southern Literature.

WRITINGS: Rumer Godden, Twayne, 1973. Contributor of articles and reviews to *Saturday Review, English Journal, Explicator,* and *Georgia Review.*

WORK IN PROGRESS: A study of the black characters in the writings of William Faulkner; research for a critical work on John Steinbeck's fiction.

*   *   *

SIMPSON, William Hays 1903-

PERSONAL: Born November 24, 1903, in Madison Run, Va.; son of Charles Robert (a farmer) and Mable Noel (Minor) Simpson; married Mary Lucile McNab, December 27, 1930; children: John Noel. *Education:* Tusculum College, A.B., 1926; Duke University, M.A., 1928, Ph.D., 1935. *Religion:* Presbyterian. *Home:* 1406 Dollar Ave., Durham, N.C. 27706.

CAREER: Duke University, Durham, N.C., assistant professor, 1941-48, associate professor, 1949-60, professor of political science, 1961-73. *Member:* American Political Science Association, Southern Political Science Association.

WRITINGS: The Small Loan Problem of the Carolinas, Presbyterian College Press, 1941; *Life in Mill Communities,* Presbyterian College Press, 1943; *Southern Textile Communities,* Dowd Press, 1948; *Workmen's Compensation in South Carolina,* Dowd Press, 1949; (contributor) Paul David, Malcolm Moos, and Ralph Goldman, editors, *Presidential Nominating Politics,* Johns Hopkins Press, 1954; *America's Small Loan Problem,* Division of General Studies and Extension, University of South Carolina, 1963; *Some Aspects of America's Textile Industry with Special Reference to Cotton,* Division of General Studies, University of South Carolina, 1966; (contributor) David P. Deemer, editor, *De lege pactorum,* Duke University Press, 1970. Contributor to *Detroit Law Review, Iowa Law Review, Rocky Mountain Law Review, Law and Contemporary Problems, Tarheel Banker, McNeese Review, Textile Bulletin,* and *South Carolina Law Quarterly.* Author of pamphlets on consumer credit and loan problems.

WORK IN PROGRESS: Research on problems of the textile industry in the United States and England.

*   *   *

SIMS, Edward J(ames) 1927-

PERSONAL: Born March 13, 1927, in New Britain, Conn.; son of John F. and Rose (McKay) Sims. *Education:* Springfield College, B.S., 1951; State University of New York at Albany, M.A., 1952; Columbia University, Ed.D., 1964. *Politics:* Democratic Reform. *Home:* 179 Clarendon St., Springfield, Mass. 01109. *Office:* Department of English, Springfield College, 263 Alden St., Springfield, Mass. 01109.

CAREER: Springfield College, Springfield, Mass., assistant professor, 1952-59, associate professor, 1959-65, professor of English, 1965—. *Military service:* U.S. Maritime Service, 1945-47. *Member:* American Association of University Professors, College English Association, National Association of Teachers of English, American Civil Liberties Union.

WRITINGS: (Contributor) *Modern Journalism,* Pitman, 1962; (with James McGuire and Carrol Britch) *Public Speaking: Composition and Performance,* Kendall-Hunt Publishing, 1972; (with Reuben B. Frost) *Development of Human Values through Sports,* American Alliance for Health, Physical Education, and Recreation, 1974; (contributor) *Essays Honoring Thornton W. Merriam,* [Springfield, Mass.], 1974. Contributor to *Improving College and University Instruction* and *Exercise Exchange.*

WORK IN PROGRESS: A sports and literature anthology.

AVOCATIONAL INTERESTS: Gardening, politics, music, travel, sports.

*   *   *

SIMS, Harold D(ana) 1935-

PERSONAL: Born October 19, 1935, in Fort Myers, Fla.; son of Harvey Lee (a stationary engineer) and Mary F. (Dana) Sims; married Retsuko Hirasawa (a tutor in Japanese), April 15, 1965; children: Seijun (son), Emiliano (son).

Education: Stetson University, B.A., 1962; University of Florida, M.A., 1963, Ph.D., 1968; post-graduate study at University of California, Berkeley, 1964, and University of Texas at Austin, 1965. *Home:* 2348 Pittock St., Pittsburgh, Pa. 15217. *Office:* Department of History, University of Pittsburgh, Pittsburgh, Pa. 15260.

CAREER: University of Pittsburgh, Pittsburgh, Pa., instructor, 1966-68, assistant professor, 1968-72, associate professor of history, 1972—. *Military service:* U.S. Air Force, 1954-57. *Member:* Conference on Latin American History, Latin American Studies Association.

WRITINGS: La expulsion de los espanoles de Mexico (1821-1828), Fondo de Cultura Economica, 1974; *La reconquista de Mexico: La historia de las atentadas espanolas 1821-1830,* Editorial Tecnos (Madrid), 1979. Editor of "Occasional Papers Series," University of Pittsburgh, 1970-76.

WORK IN PROGRESS: Mexico y los espanoles 1821-1830, for Editorial Tecnos.

* * *

SINGER, Armand Edwards 1914-

PERSONAL: Born November 30, 1914, in Detroit, Mich.; son of Elvin Satori (a grand opera singer and teacher of voice) and Fredericka (Edwards) Singer; married Mary White (a teacher), August 8, 1940; children: Fredericka Ann Schmidt. *Education:* Amherst College, A.B., 1935; Duke University, M.A., 1939, Ph.D., 1944; Sorbonne, University of Paris, Diplome, 1939; Indiana University, postdoctoral study, 1964. *Politics:* Republican. *Religion:* Protestant. *Home:* 248 Grandview Ave., Morgantown, W.Va. 26505. *Office:* 205-C Chitwood Hall, West Virginia University, Morgantown, W.Va. 26506.

CAREER: Duke University, Durham, N.C., part-time instructor in Spanish and French, 1938-40; West Virginia University, Morgantown, instructor, 1940-47, assistant professor, 1947-55, associate professor, 1955-60, professor of Romance languages, 1960—, chairman of humanities program, 1963-72, and chairman of integrated studies, 1963, acting chairman, department of religion and program for the humanities, 1973. Member of board of directors, Community Concert, Morgantown, 1956-61. *Member:* Modern Language Association of America (member of National Delegate Assembly, 1975-77), American Association of Teachers of French, American Association of Teachers of Spanish and Portuguese, Modern Language Teachers Association, South Atlantic Modern Language Association (member of executive committee, 1972-74), Phi Beta Kappa.

WRITINGS: A Bibliography of the Don Juan Theme: Versions & Criticism, West Virginia University, 1954, revised edition, published as *The Don Juan Theme, A Bibliography: Versions and Criticisms,* 1965; (author and editor with wife, Mary W. Singer, Frank S. White, and R. Ryland White) *Four Score and Ten,* R. R. White, 1964; (editor and translator with John F. Stasny) *Humanities I: Anthology of Readings,* West Virginia University, 1966; (editor and translator with Stasny) *Humanities II: Anthology of Readings,* West Virginia University, 1967; *Paul Bourget,* Twayne, 1976; (contributor) Brigitte Wittmann, editor, *Don Juan: Darstellung und Deutung,* Wissenschaftliche Buchgesellschaft, 1976. Contributor of articles to *Columbia Dictionary of Modern European Literature.* Contributor of over one hundred articles and reviews to *Modern Language Journal, Modern Language Notes, West Virginia Philological Papers, Hispania, Nieman Reports, Comparative Literature Studies, Hispanic Review, Laurel Review, South Atlantic*

Bulletin, National Parks Magazine, Erasmus, American Philatelic Congress Yearbook and others. *West Virginia University Philological Papers,* editor, 1948-50, 1952-54, editor-in-chief, 1950-52, 1954—.

WORK IN PROGRESS: A book on Julien Benda, for Twayne; a book on postal stationery of Nepal, with Frank Vignola and Walter Hellrigl; a book of limericks.

SIDELIGHTS: Armand Singer told *CA:* "Writing is an excruciatingly difficult activity.... How often do most of us find the exact word, the fresh, definitive phrase to describe a point of view, an event, a person, a scene? Which is, of course, what keeps us in harness—that endless search—whether we are a Flaubert, composing masterpieces, or just hacks, explaining French past participles or the intricacies of Nepalese philately." *Avocational interests:* Photography, travel, philately, mountain climbing, carpentry.

* * *

SINGER, June K(urlander) 1918-

PERSONAL: Born October 23, 1918, in Cleveland, Ohio; daughter of Jonas E. (a dentist) and Regine (a journalist; maiden name, Jaulusz) Kurlander; married Richard E. Singer (died, 1965); children: Judith Singer Sharp (died, 1970). *Education:* Ohio State University, B.S.Ed., 1939; Northwestern University, M.A., 1959, Ph.D., 1968; C. G. Jung Institute, Zurich, Switzerland, diploma in analytical psychology, 1964. *Address:* 3200 Lake Shore Dr., Suite 807, Chicago, Ill. 60657.

CAREER: Science Research Associates, Chicago, Ill., writer and editor of vocational guidance and reading materials for young children, 1960; Sanatorium Bellevue, Kreuzlingen, Switzerland, clinical intern in psychology, 1962-64; private practice in analytical psychology and psychotherapy, 1964—. Psychologist at Virginia Frank Child Development Center, 1964-66; lecturer in psychology of C. G. Jung at University of Chicago, 1970.

MEMBER: International Association of Analytical Psychologists, American Psychological Association, Inter-Regional Society of Jungian Analysts (founding member), Authors Guild, Illinois Psychological Association, Analytical Psychology Club of Chicago (founding member), C. G. Jung Foundation (New York; member of board of trustees).

WRITINGS: The Unholy Bible: A Psychological Study of William Blake, Putnam, 1970; *Boundaries of the Soul: The Practice of Jung's Psychology,* Doubleday, 1972; *Androgyny: Toward a New Theory of Sexuality,* Doubleday, 1976. Contributor of articles and reviews to *Quadrant, Zygon, Spring, Psychology Today,* and *Chicago Daily News.*

SIDELIGHTS: Robert Stensrud calls *Androgyny* "an essential contribution to an understanding of the person. There are those who rehash the critical discoveries of others and those who make the discoveries. Dr. Singer belongs with the latter and more select group." But Carolyn Heilbrun, reviewing the same book for *Ms.,* describes it as "a muddled discussion of ancient beliefs, myths, and astrology."

BIOGRAPHICAL/CRITICAL SOURCES: Ms., November, 1976; *Best Sellers,* February, 1977; *Psychology Today,* March, 1977; *Science Books,* September, 1977; *Southwest Review,* autumn, 1977.

* * *

SINGER, Marshall R. 1932-

PERSONAL: Born May 24, 1932, in New York, N.Y.; son

of Samuel (a businessman) and Elizabeth (Feinberg) Singer; married Susan Mahler (a writer), 1960 (divorced, 1977); children: Shepard L., Paul B. *Education:* Brooklyn College (now Brooklyn College of the City University of New York), B.A., 1955; New School for Social Research, M.A., 1956; University of Ceylon, graduate study, 1956-57; Massachusetts Institute of Technology, Ph.D., 1962. *Office:* Graduate School of Public and International Affairs, University of Pittsburgh, Pittsburgh, Pa. 15213.

CAREER: Brooklyn College of the City University of New York, Brooklyn, N.Y., instructor, 1957-59, assistant professor of political science, 1960-64; University of Pittsburgh, Pittsburgh, Pa., professor of international and intercultural affairs, 1964—. Visiting adjunct professor at New York University, 1961-63, and Fordham University, 1964; visiting lecturer in political science, Escuela Superior de Administracion Publica of America Central, 1964; Ford Foundation Professor of Political Behavior, University of Malaya, 1969-71; research associate, Southern Asia Institute, Columbia University, 1971. Consultant to foreign universities, businesses, and other groups, including Peace Corps, Agency for International Development, Foreign Service Institute, and Malaysian Society for Public Administration. *Awards, honors:* Alvin Johnson scholarship, 1955; Fulbright scholarship, 1956; fellowship from Center for International Studies, Massachusetts Institute of Technology, 1958; Woodrow Wilson fellowship, 1959.

WRITINGS: The Emerging Elite: A Study of Political Leadership in Ceylon, M.I.T. Press, 1964; *Weak States in a World of Powers: The Dynamics of International Relationships,* Free Press, 1972; (contributor) James Rosenau, Fred Thompson, and Gavin Boyd, editors, *World Politics,* Free Press, 1976. Contributor to *Collier's Encyclopedia;* contributor to professional journals, including *International Journal of Comparative Sociology, Asian Survey, International Organization, Foreign Policy,* and *Christian Science Monitor.*

WORK IN PROGRESS: Intercultural Communications: A Study of Perceptions, Identities, and Behaviors.

*　　*　　*

SINGER, Norman 1925-

PERSONAL: Born August 10, 1925, in Chicago, Ill.; son of Robert (in advertising) and Rene (Duquesne) Singer; divorced. *Education:* Studied at Columbia University and University of California Extension in San Francisco. *Politics:* Democrat. *Religion:* None. *Home:* 1847 Hayes St., San Francisco, Calif. 94117. *Agent:* Ann Elmo Agency, Inc., 52 Vanderbilt Ave., New York, N.Y. 10017.

CAREER: Free-lance ghost-writer, gag-writer, editor, and novelist, 1967—.

WRITINGS—All novels: *Curtain of Flesh,* Traveller's Companion, 1968; *The Pornographer,* Ophelia Press, 1968; *The Babysitter,* Ophelia Press, 1968; *The Hungry Husband,* Olympia, 1969; *The Lay of the Land,* Ophelia Press, 1969; *The Man Who Raped San Francisco,* Olympia, 1969; *The Girl Explosion,* Olympia, 1971; *Coming on Strong,* Olympia, 1972; *The Girl Who Licked the World,* Olympia, 1972; *The Cannibals Next Door,* Olympia, 1972; *The Shakedown Kid,* Manor Books, 1975; *Diamond Stud,* Manor Books, 1976. Contributor to *Argosy.*

WORK IN PROGRESS: "Show biz memoirs of The Duncan Sisters;. . . a true-life crime novel, *He Who Kills My Daughter.*"

SIDELIGHTS: Norman Singer writes *CA,* "I am currently involved in free-lance ghostwriting, doing ten books a year, handling all categories of fiction and nonfiction." Film rights to *The Man Who Raped San Francisco* were sold in 1970. Singer has also sold translation rights to three of his novels.

BIOGRAPHICAL/CRITICAL SOURCES: Ramparts, August 10, 1968.

*　　*　　*

SINGH, Baljit 1929-

PERSONAL: Surname rhymes with "ring"; born October 1, 1929, in Budaum, India; son of Sardar Baboo (an architect and teacher) and Kartar (Kaur) Singh; married Barbara Leona Hassler, August 11, 1962; children: Balkrishna and Balram (sons). *Education:* Agra University, B.A., 1951; Aligarh Muslim University, M.A. and Diploma in Foreign Affairs, 1953; University of Pennsylvania, additional study, 1957-58; University of Maryland, Ph.D., 1961. *Politics:* Democrat. *Religion:* Buddhist. *Home:* 2400 Tulane Dr., Lansing, Mich. 48912. *Office:* College of Social Sciences, 205 Berkey Hall, Michigan State University, East Lansing, Mich. 48824.

CAREER: University of Baroda, Baroda, India, senior lecturer in political science, 1953-55; Indian School of International Studies, New Delhi, India, research fellow, 1955-57; Embassy of India, Washington, D.C., research assistant, 1958; Michigan State University, East Lansing, assistant professor of political science, 1961-62; Wayne State University, Detroit, Michigan, assistant professor of political science, 1962-63; Michigan State University, assistant professor, 1963-65, associate professor, 1965-71, professor of political science, 1971—, assistant dean, College of Social Sciences, 1967—. Instructor in government and politics, University of Maryland, summer, 1961; visiting professor, Oakland University, summer, 1963. *Military service:* Indian Army, National Cadet Corps, second lieutenant, 1953-55. Indian Army Reserves, 1955-57.

MEMBER: American Political Science Association, International Studies Association, Michigan Academy of Science, Arts, and Letters (program chairman, history and political science section, 1966), Pi Sigma Alpha, Delta Phi Epsilon. *Awards, honors:* Ford Foundation fellow at University of Pennsylvania, 1957-58, research grants, 1964, 1965-67, 1971; Asia Foundation travel and study fellow, 1961.

WRITINGS: (With Ko-Wang Mei) *The Theory and Practice of Modern Guerrilla Warfare,* Asia Publishing House, 1971; *Indian Foreign Policy: An Analysis,* Sindhu (Bombay), 1972, Asia Publishing House, 1976. Also author of numerous monographs on India's political and foreign policy. Contributor of numerous articles and bibliograhies to professional journals.

WORK IN PROGRESS: Two books, *Government and Politics in India: A Quarter Century of Independence* and *Introduction to International Organization.*†

*　　*　　*

SINNEMA, John R(alph) 1911-

PERSONAL: Born April 14, 1911, in Cleveland, Ohio; son of John (a contractor) and Johanna (Ten Hoopen) Sinnema; married Ruth Borneman, April 17, 1943. *Education:* Baldwin-Wallace College, A.B., 1933; Western Reserve University (now Case Western Reserve University), M.A., 1938; University of Michigan, graduate study, 1939-41; University of Cincinnati, Ph.D., 1949. *Politics:* Republican. *Religion:* United Methodist. *Home:* 204 Franklin Dr., Berea, Ohio 44017. *Office:* Ritter Library, Baldwin-Wallace College, Berea, Ohio 44017.

CAREER: Worked as a teacher in the Cleveland, Ohio, public schools, 1934-36; Baldwin-Wallace College, Berea, Ohio, instructor, 1936-41, assistant professor, 1941-50, associate professor, 1950-54, professor of German, 1954-75, director of American-German Institute, 1975—, dean of men, 1947-52. *Military service:* U.S. Army, 1943-45; became technical sergeant; received four battle stars. *Member:* Modern Language Association of America, Renaissance Society of America, Modern Humanities Research Association, American Association of Teachers of German, Society for German-American Studies, Midwest Modern Language Association, Central States Modern Language Teachers Association, Ohio College Association. *Awards, honors:* Officer's Cross of the Order of Merit from Federal Republic of Germany, 1968.

WRITINGS: (Contributor) Gottfried Merkel, editor, *On Romanticism and the Art of Translation*, Princeton University Press, 1956; *Hendrik van Veldeke*, Twayne, 1972. Contributor to *Modern Language Journal* and *German-American Studies*. Editorial consultant to *Britannica World Language Dictionary*, 1958.

WORK IN PROGRESS: Co-authoring *The German-Speaking Element in Greater Cleveland*.

* * *

SISCO, John I(sodore) 1931-

PERSONAL: Born June 27, 1931, in Jamestown, N.D.; son of Ralph N. and Evelyn (Garman) Sisco; married Glenaris Marx (a registered nurse), August 17, 1957; children: Jaclyn, Dale, Paul, Kim. *Education:* Valley City State Teacher's College (now Valley City State College), B.S., 1954; University of North Dakota, graduate study, 1955; Northwestern University, M.A., 1959; University of Minnesota, Ph.D., 1966. *Home:* 3113 McFarland Rd., Tampa, Fla. 33618. *Office:* Department of Communication, University of South Florida, Tampa, Fla. 33620.

CAREER: Worked as a high school speech teacher in Minnesota, 1954-62; Bemidji State College, Bemidji, Minn., instructor in speech, winter, 1962; University of Minnesota, Minneapolis, instructor in speech, 1962-65; University of Houston, Houston, Tex., assistant professor of speech, 1965-68; University of South Florida, Tampa, associate professor, 1968-77, professor of speech and chairman of department of communication, 1977—. State coordinator of the Florida Forensics Program, 1968—. *Member:* Speech Communication Association of America, Southern Speech Communication Association (vice-president, 1971-72; president, 1972-73), Minnesota Federation of Teachers (vice-president, 1961-65), Florida Speech Communication Association.

WRITINGS: A Guide to Fundamentals of Speech: Theory, Practice, Evaluation, McCutchan, 1968; (editor) *Florida Speech and Drama Curriculum Guide*, State Department of Education, 1972. Contributor of articles and book reviews to *Southern Speech Journal, Bulletin of the National Association of Secondary School Principals, Bulletin of the Minnesota Association of Secondary School Principals, Minnesota Teacher, Program Policy Manual of Florida Forensics Program*, and *Speech Teacher*.

SKAGGS, David Curtis (Jr.) 1937-

PERSONAL: Born March 23, 1937, in Topeka, Kan.; son of D(avid) Curtis (a merchant) and Eleanor-Beth (Baer) Skaggs; married Margo Clayton Tipton (a teacher), June 17, 1961; children: Jason Tipton, Philip Curtis. *Education:* Attended Trinity College, Hartford, Conn., 1955-56; University of Kansas, B.S., 1959, M.A., 1960; Georgetown University, Ph.D., 1966. *Religion:* Episcopalian. *Home:* 1314 Bourgogne Ave., Bowling Green, Ohio 43402. *Office:* Department of History, Bowling Green State University, Bowling Green, Ohio 43403.

CAREER: Bowling Green State University, Bowling Green, Ohio, instructor, 1965-66, assistant professor, 1966-69, associate professor, 1969-77, professor of history, 1977—. Visiting associate professor at University of Wisconsin, 1971-72. Member of consulting faculty of U.S. Army Command and Staff College, Ft. Leavenworth, 1970—. Member of Ohio American Revolution Bicentennial Commission, 1971—. *Military service:* U.S. Army, 1960-62; became lieutenant. U.S. Army Reserve, 1962—, current rank, major. *Member:* Organization of American Historians, American Historical Association, Maryland Historical Society, Kansas State Historical Society, Ohio Academy of History. Ohio Historical Society.

WRITINGS: (Editor with Virginia B. Platt) *Of Mother Country and Plantations: Proceedings of Twenty-Seventh Conference on Early American History*, Bowling Green State University Press, 1972; *Roots of Maryland Democracy, 1753-1776*, Greenwood Press, 1973; (editor) *The Old Northwest in the American Revolution*, Wisconsin State Historical Society, 1977. Contributor to *Journal of American History, William and Mary Quarterly, Maryland Historical Magazine*, and *Military Affairs*.

WORK IN PROGRESS: Poetic Writings of Thomas Cradock (1718-1770).

* * *

SKELLY, Madge 1903-

PERSONAL: Born May 9, 1903, in Pittsburgh, Pa.; daughter of Charles (an actor) and Juliet (an actress; maiden name, Purcell) Skelly; married Richard Foust, December 8, 1928 (died April 6, 1943). *Education:* Seton Hill College, B.A., 1924; Duquesne University, M.A., 1928; University of Arizona, speech pathology certificate, 1957; St. Louis University, Ph.D., 1961; postdoctoral study at University of Kansas, Columbia University, University of Miami, Jersig Clinic, Mayo Clinic, and Hines Research Institute. *Home and office:* Suite 24-D, 4466 West Pine Blvd., St. Louis, Mo. 63108.

CAREER: Professional actress, producer, and director, 1925-36; Duquesne University, Pittsburgh, Pa., professor of speech and dean of School of Drama, 1936-40; active in U.S.O. and professional theatre productions, 1940, 1942-44; Temple University, Philadelphia, Pa., instructor in speech and theatre, 1944-48; active in professional theatre, 1948-55; University of Arizona, Tucson, instructor in speech and theatre, 1955-57; Maryville College, St. Louis, Mo., associate professor of speech, 1958-63; Fontbonne College, St. Louis, professor of speech pathology, 1963-71; Southern Illinois University at Edwardsville, professor of audiology and speech pathology, 1973-75. St. Louis University, St. Louis, clinical supervisor, 1962-63, professor of communication disorders, 1970—, professor of community medicine, 1973—; director of speech and hearing service, Shriners Hospital for Crippled Children, St. Louis, 1964-71; chief of audiology and speech pathology service, Consolidated Veterans Administration Hospital, St. Louis, 1964-76. Consultant to Veterans Administration Hospitals and Missouri State Hospitals, 1976—. *Member:* International Association of Logopedics and Phoniatrics, Association of Military Surgeons of the United States, American Speech and Hearing Association (fellow), Council for Exceptional Children, Academy of Aphasia, Missouri Speech and Hearing Association (member of executive council, 1970-72; vice-president, 1972; president, 1973), Southern Illinois Speech and Hearing Association, Speech and Hearing Association of Greater St. Louis. *Awards, honors:* Newspaper Guild Award for Outstanding Women, 1949; Upjohn fellowship to England, 1951; Actors Fund Award, 1954; Federal Employee of the Year, 1969; St. Louis University Founders Day Award, 1970; Beta Sigma Phi International Woman of the Year Award, 1972; Rotary International Citizenship Award, 1973; Federal Woman's Award, 1974; Veterans of Foreign Wars Woman of the Year Award, 1975.

WRITINGS: Glossectomee Speech Rehabilitation, C. C Thomas, 1973; *Amerind Gestural Code,* Elsevier, 1979. Author of about twenty plays produced on stage or radio, including "The Other Kingdom." Contributor to *American Journal of Surgery, Journal of Plastic and Reconstructive Surgery, Journal of Missouri Speech and Hearing Association, Journal of Nursing, Archives of Rehabilitation Medicine,* and *Journal of Hearing and Speech Disorders.*

WORK IN PROGRESS: Language Laboratory as a Supplement in Aphasia Treatment; articles on communication disorders of the psychiatric patient; research on new techniques for the blind and deaf and the mentally retarded.

SIDELIGHTS: Madge Skelly made her stage debut as a child, touring with her mother in "East Lynne" and "Mrs. Wiggs of the Cabbage Patch." She made her Broadway debut in "Lady Behave" in 1943, and directed regional professional theater groups in Cambridge, Mass., 1945-50, and Manistee, Mich., 1951-62. Recently she has been travelling widely conducting professional workshops in glossectomee speech rehabilitation for the cancer patient, and use of the Amerind code for the speechless.

* * *

SKOGLUND, Elizabeth 1937-

PERSONAL: Born June 17, 1937, in Chicago, Ill.; daughter of Ragnar Emanuel (an engineer) and Elizabeth (Benson) Skoglund. *Education:* University of California, Los Angeles, B.A., 1959; Pasadena College, M.A., 1969. *Politics:* Republican. *Religion:* Protestant. *Home:* 1065 Harvard Rd., Burbank, Calif. 91501. *Office:* 303 South Glenoaks Blvd. Suite 14, Burbank, Calif. 91502.

CAREER: Marlborough School, Los Angeles, Calif., teacher, 1959-61; Glendale High School, Glendale, Calif., teacher, 1961-63; Glendale Family Service Association, Glendale, counselor, 1971—; marriage, family and child counselor in private practice, Burbank, Calif., 1972—. Consultant to Creative Life Foundation. *Member:* International Platform Association, Authors Guild, American Association of University Women, California Association of Family and Marriage Counselors, California Teacher's Association.

WRITINGS: Where Do I Go to Buy Happiness?, Inter-Varsity Press, 1972; *Your Troubled Children,* David Cook, 1975; *Woman Beyond Roleplay,* David Cook, 1975; *Loneliness,* Inter-Varsity Press, 1975; *The Whole Christian: How You Can Find Physical, Mental and Spiritual Health,* Harper, 1976; *To Anger with Love,* Harper, 1977; *Can I Talk to You?,* Regal Books, 1977; *Love Begins with Me,* Harper, 1978; *You Can Be Your Own Child's Counselor,* Regal Books, 1978. Contributor of articles to *Eternity, Decision,* and *Moody Monthly.*

WORK IN PROGRESS: A View From the Roof of Building B, a book on the humanization of school.

SIDELIGHTS: Elizabeth Skoglund told *CA:* "My writing of *Where Do I Go to Buy Happiness* was motivated by my work in the schools with high school young people, mainly those on drugs." Skoglund is interested in "combining the value of Christianity and psychology in my writing and counseling. The two have too long been separate while, in fact, they are mutually complementary."†

* * *

SKURNIK, W. A. E. 1926-

PERSONAL: Born February 13, 1926, in Binz, Germany; came to U.S. in 1950, naturalized U.S. citizen in 1954; son of Adolph (a journalist) and Ann S. (Selow) Skurnik; married Margaret Fulton, September 28, 1956; children: Ian Walter, Colin Alexander. *Education:* Attended New York University, 1953-54; University of Pennsylvania, A.A., 1958, B.A. (summa cum laude), 1960, M.A., 1961, Ph.D., 1964. *Home:* 4200 Eutaw Dr., Boulder, Colo. 80303. *Office:* Department of Political Science, University of Colorado, Boulder, Colo. 80302.

CAREER: U.S. Army, Frankfurt, Germany, chief personnel officer, 1946-49; U.S. High Command for Germany, Hanau, chief of civic activities section, 1949-50; American Express Co., Philadelphia, Pa., foreign travel consultant, 1953-58; University of Pennsylvania, Philadelphia, instructor in political science, 1960-61; Pennsylvania Military College, Chester, instructor, 1962-63, assistant professor of political science, 1963-65; University of Colorado, Boulder, assistant professor, 1965-68, associate professor, 1968-73, professor of political science, 1973—. *Military service:* U.S. Army, 1950-51. *Member:* International Studies Association, American Political Science Association, American Association of University Professors, African Studies Association, Rocky Mountain Africanist Association (chairman, 1966-71), Pi Sigma Alpha, Pi Gamma Mu, Phi Beta Kappa.

WRITINGS: (Editor) *African Political Thought,* University of Denver Press, 1968; (with Claude E. Welch, Jr., I. William Zartman, and others) *Soldier and State in Africa,* Northwestern University Press, 1970; *The Foreign Policy of Senegal,* Northwestern University Press, 1972. Contributor of articles and book reviews to *Current History, Africa Report, Journal of Modern African Studies, Journal of African History, African Forum, American Political Science Review,* and *Journal of Asian Studies.* Book review editor of *Africa Today,* 1966-71.

WORK IN PROGRESS: Book reviews on black African international relations literature; writing on American policy toward Africa, and on foreign news coverage.

SIDELIGHTS: W.A.E. Skurnik has traveled extensively in Europe and West Africa (Senegal, Guinea, Ivory Coast, Mali, Niger, Cameroun, Sierra Leone, Ghana, Dahomey, and Upper Volta).

* * *

SKVORECKA, Zdena Salivarova 1933-
(Zdena Salivarova)

PERSONAL: Born October 21, 1933, in Prague, Czechoslovakia; daughter of Jaroslav and Eugenie (Nosalova) Salivar;

married Josef Skvorecky (a professor of English), March 31, 1958. *Education:* Attended Prague Film Academy, 1965-68. *Politics:* None. *Religion:* Roman Catholic. *Home:* 487 Sackville St., Toronto, Ontario, Canada M4X IT6.

CAREER: State Ensemble of Songs and Dances, Prague, Czechoslovakia, singer, 1952-62; Magic Lantern Theatre, Prague, singer and dancer, 1958-62; Paravan Theatre, Prague, actress, 1962-65; Sixty-Eight Publishers Toronto, Toronto, Ontario, co-owner, 1971—. *Awards, honors:* Canada Council grant, 1974, senior grant, 1977-78; Egon Hostovsky Memorial Award for Best Czech Fiction in Exile, 1977, for *Nebe, peklo, raj.*

WRITINGS: Panska jizda (title means "Gentlemen's Ride"), Spisovatel, 1968; *Honzlova,* Sixty-Eight Publishers Toronto, 1972, published as *Summer in Prague,* Harper, 1973; *Nebe, peklo, raj* (title means "Ashes, Ashes, All Fell Down"), Sixty-Eight Publishers Toronto, 1977.

Translator into Czech: Georges Simenon, *Les freres Rico,* Ceskoslovensky Spisovatel, 1966; Leo Malet, *Le Soleil se leve derriere le Louvre,* Odeon Publishers (Prague), 1967; Pierre Souvestre and Marcel Allain, *Le Fiacre de Nuit,* Odeon Publishers (Prague), 1971.

WORK IN PROGRESS: Summer in Toronto, a novel.

SIDELIGHTS: The Soviet invasion of Czechoslovakia in 1968 forced Zdena Skvorecka and her husband to leave their home for political exile in Canada. She has traveled in China, North Korea, Mongolia, Russia, England, Norway, Sweden, Denmark, East and West Germany, France, Switzerland, Italy, Yugoslavia, and Austria. *Avocational interests:* Car driving.

* * *

SLAATTE, Howard A(lexander) 1919-

PERSONAL: Surname is pronounced *Slah*-te; born October 18, 1919, in Evanston, Ill.; son of Iver T. (a clergyman) and Ester Elina (Larsen) Slaatte; married Mildred Gegenheimer, June 20, 1952; children: Elaine (Mrs. Tu Van Tran), Mark Edwin, Paul Andrew. *Education:* Kendall College, A.A., 1940; University of North Dakota, B.A. (cum laude), 1942, graduate study, 1941-42; Drew University, B.D. (cum laude), 1945, Ph.D., 1956; Oxford University, graduate study, 1949-50. *Home:* 407 Grand Blvd., Huntington, W.Va. 25705. *Office:* Department of Philosophy, Marshall University, Huntington, W.Va. 25701.

CAREER: Co-pastor of Bethelship Methodist Church in Brooklyn, N.Y., 1942-45; minister of education at Methodist churches in New Jersey and Long Island, N.Y., 1945-49; pastor of Methodist churches, Detroit Conference, Detroit, Mich., 1950-56; Temple University, Philadelphia, Pa., associate professor of systematic theology, 1956-60; McMurry College, Abilene, Tex., visiting professor, 1960-63, professor of philosophy, 1963-65; Marshall University, Huntington, W.Va., professor of philosophy, 1965—, chairman of department, 1966—. Member of West Virginia Conference of United Methodist Church, 1966—. *Member:* American Philosophical Society, American Academy of Religion, American Ontoanalytical Society, West Virginia Philosophical Society (president, 1966-67). *Awards, honors:* Pilling traveling fellow from Drew University at Oxford University, 1949-50; Alumni Award, Kendall College, 1964; grants from National Science Foundation, 1965, 1971, and Marshall University, 1977, 1978.

WRITINGS: Time and Its End, Vantage, 1962; *Fire in the Brand,* Exposition, 1963; *The Pertinence of the Paradox,*

Humanities, 1968; *The Paradox of Existentialist Theology,* Humanities, 1971; *Modern Science and the Human Condition,* Intelman, 1974; *The Arminian Arm of Theology,* University Press of America, 1977. Contributor to philosophy and theology journals.

WORK IN PROGRESS: A critique of positivism, *The Dogma of Immaculate Perception.*

AVOCATIONAL INTERESTS: Singing (as baritone soloist and in operettas), collecting limestone fossils, drama, sports.

* * *

SLAKTER, Malcolm J(ulian) 1929-

PERSONAL: Born May 23, 1929, in Syracuse, N.Y.; son of Hyman S. (a salesman) and Rose (Elias) Slakter; married Fritzi Zinger, August 26, 1951 (divorced, 1977); children: Hedy Ann, Jeffrey David, Lawrence Jay. *Education:* Syracuse University, student, 1946-48, Ph.D., 1963; New York College for Teachers (now State University of New York at Albany), A.B., 1950, M.A., 1951. *Home:* 311 Countryside Lane, Williamsville, N.Y. 14221. *Office:* Department of Education, State University of New York, 309 Baldy Hall, Buffalo, N.Y. 14260.

CAREER: High school science and mathematics teacher in New York state, 1951-58; Syracuse University, Syracuse, N.Y., instructor in mathematics, 1958-62; University of California, Berkeley, assistant professor of educational statistics, 1963-65; State University of New York at Buffalo, associate professor, 1965-69, professor of education, 1969—. *Member:* American Educational Research Association, American Psychological Association, American Statistical Association, National Council of Measurement in Education, Phi Delta Kappa.

WRITINGS: Statistical Inference for Educational Researchers, Addison-Wesley, 1972. Contributor to *Journal of Educational Measurement, Journal of American Statistical Association, Educational and Psychological Measurement, Journal of Dental Research,* and other journals in his field.

* * *

SLEIGHT, Robert B(enton) 1922-

PERSONAL: Born September 16, 1922, in Hemlock, N.Y.; son of Edson F. and Marian (Hoppough) Sleight; married Dorothy M. Barden, May 7, 1944; children: Robert Barry. *Education:* Geneseo Teachers College (now State University of New York at Geneseo), B.Ed., 1946; Purdue University, M.S., 1947, Ph.D., 1949. *Home:* 3717 North 27th St., Arlington, Va. 22207. *Office:* Century Research Corp., 4113 Lee Highway, Arlington, Va. 22207.

CAREER: Johns Hopkins University, Baltimore, Md., assistant professor of psychology and research psychologist, 1948-51; Naval Research Laboratory, Washington, D.C., research scientist, 1951-52; Century Research Corp., Arlington, Va., president and chairman of board of directors, 1952—. Chairman of pedestrian committee, Highway Research Board; member of executive council, Arlington Committee of One Hundred, 1966, 1971, 1972; member of board of directors, Arlington Opera Theatre. *Military service:* U.S. Naval Reserve, aviator, active duty, 1943-45.

MEMBER: American Psychological Association (fellow), International Association of Applied Psychology, Human Factors Society (fellow), American Association for the Advancement of Science (fellow), American Ordnance Association, Riverwood Citizens Association (president, 1970), Sigma Xi.

WRITINGS: User Acceptance of the Air Car, U.S. Government Printing Office, 1962; *Practical Human Engineering Principles* (monograph), Century Research Corp., 1964; (contributor) Theodore Watson Forbes, editor, *Human Factors in Highway Traffic Safety Research,* Wiley, 1972. Contributor to *High Speed Ground Transportation Journal.*

WORK IN PROGRESS: Research on occupational interests, vandalism, walking behavior, accident-proneness, and desert environment.

*   *   *

SLJIVIC-SIMSIC, Biljana 1933-

PERSONAL: Name is pronounced Bilyana Shleevich-Shimshich; born January 20, 1933, in Belgrade, Yugoslavia; daughter of Branko (a professor and chairman of anatomy at University of Belgrade) and Radoyka (Pesic) Sljivic; divorced, 1962; children: Violet Ljubica. *Education:* University of Belgrade, diploma, 1955; Harvard University, A.M., 1963, Ph.D., 1966. *Religion:* Serbian Orthodox Church. *Home:* 110 Garfield Ave., Cherry Hill, N.J. 08034. *Office:* Department of Slavic Languages and Literature, University of Illinois at Chicago Circle, Chicago, Ill. 60607.

CAREER: University of Belgrade, Belgrade, Yugoslavia, assistant in Serbo-Croatian language, 1957-62; University of California, Los Angeles, acting instructor, 1964-65, acting assistant professor of Serbo-Croatian and Russian, 1965-66; University of Kentucky, Lexington, assistant professor of Russian, 1966-67; University of Pennsylvania, Philadelphia, assistant professor of Slavic linguistics, 1967-73; University of Illinois at Chicago Circle, Chicago, associate professor of Serbo-Croatian and Slavic linguistics, 1973—. Visiting lecturer, University of Clermont-Ferrand, 1959-61; visiting lecturer in Old Church Slavic, Princeton University, 1967-68. New Jersey real estate licensee, 1971—. *Member:* Modern Language Association of America, American Association of Teachers of Slavic and East European Languages (secretary of linguistics section, 1968; chairman of southwest Slavic linguistic section, 1973), American Association for South Slavic Studies (member of council, 1972), South Atlantic Modern Language Association.

WRITINGS: (Collaborator with Morton Benson, and compiler) *Serbo-Croatian-English Dictionary,* University of Pennsylvania Press, 1971; (collaborator with Samuel G. Armistead and Joseph H. Silverman, editors) *Judeo-Spanish Ballads from Bosnia,* University of Pennsylvania Press, 1971. Contributor to Slavic journals; translator from the Serbo-Croatian of poems and short story in *Literary Review.*

WORK IN PROGRESS: A monograph on Yugoslav folk mythology; *Andric's Reader,* for advanced students of Serbo-Croatian, with exercises and a grammatical survey.

SIDELIGHTS: In addition to her native language and English, Biljana Sljivic-Simsic speaks Russian and French; she reads Italian, Bulgarian, Polish, and Czech.†

*   *   *

SMALL, Norman M. 1944-

PERSONAL: Born September 11, 1944, in Philadelphia, Pa.; son of Harry and Rose Small; married Linda Hill, February 22, 1964; children: Denise, Kevin. *Education:* University of Florida, B.A., 1965, M.Ed., 1966, postgraduate studies, 1967. *Home:* 405 Lake Ned Rd., Winter Haven, Fla. 33880. *Office:* Theatre Program, Polk Community College, Winter Haven, Fla. 33880.

CAREER: Polk Community College, Winter Haven, Fla., professor of speech and drama, 1967—, director of theatre program, 1967—. President, Winter Haven Community Theatre.

WRITINGS: (With M. S. Sutton) *The Making of Drama: Idea and Performance,* Holbrook, 1972; *Introduction to Drama,* Lansford, 1972.

*   *   *

SMIGEL, Erwin O. 1917-1973

PERSONAL: Born November 3, 1917, in New York, N.Y.; son of Joseph O. and Ida (Sachs) Smigel. *Education:* University of North Carolina, A.B., 1939; New York University, M.A., 1942, Ph.D., 1949.

CAREER: New York University, New York, N.Y., instructor in sociology, 1946-48; Indiana University at Bloomington, instructor, 1948-50, assistant professor, 1950-57, associate professor of sociology, 1958-59; New York University, University College, associate professor, 1959-60, professor of sociology, 1960-62, chairman of department of sociology and anthropology, 1959-62, professor of sociology and chairman of department of sociology and anthropology at Washington Square College, 1962-66; Yale University, New Haven, Conn., professor of sociology, Graduate School of Arts and Sciences, beginning 1966, chairman of department, 1966-71. Visiting assistant professor, New York University, summer, 1956; U.S. Steel Union, lecturer, summers, 1950, 1951, 1958; visiting lecturer at School of Law, Yale University, 1965-67. Senior fellow in law and behavioral sciences, School of Law, University of Chicago, 1958-59; fellow in law and sociology, School of Law, Harvard University, 1971-72; senior research associate and member of executive committee, Center for Policy Research. Conducted "Sunrise Semester," on CBS-Television, 1970. *Military service:* U.S. Army Air Forces, 1942-46.

MEMBER: American Sociological Association, Society for the Study of Social Problems, American Association of University Professors (president of New York University chapter, beginning 1972), Eastern Sociological Association, Alpha Kappa Delta.

WRITINGS: (With father, Joseph O. Smigel and Wilma H. Reiter) *Nursing Home Administration,* C. C Thomas, 1962; (editor) *Work and Leisure,* College & University Press, 1963; *The Wall Street Lawyer: Professional Organization Man?,* Free Press, 1964, revised edition, Indiana University Press, 1969; (contributor) *Computer Technology: Concepts for Management* (monograph), Industrial Relations Counselors, Inc., 1965; (editor with H. Laurence Ross) *Crimes against Bureaucracy,* Van Nostrand, 1970; (editor) *Handbook on the Study of Social Problems,* Rand McNally, 1971. Contributor of articles and reviews to sociology and law journals. *Social Problems,* editor, 1958-61, associate editor, 1961-65; associate editor, *Estudios de Sociologia,* 1961-65; sociology editor, *Geriatric Institutions,* 1964-66; sociology editor, College & University Press, 1963-70.

WORK IN PROGRESS: The Corporate Counsel; a book on occupational sociology.†

(Died August 30, 1973)

*   *   *

SMITH, Alan M(cKinley) 1937-

PERSONAL: Born September 20, 1937, in Ann Arbor, Mich.; son of Ralph Grafton and Barbara (Paton) Smith;

married Frances Lewis (a secretary), September 9, 1961. *Education:* Dickinson College, A.B., 1959; University of Pittsburgh, M.A., 1960; Johns Hopkins University, Ph.D., 1967. *Politics:* Democrat. *Home:* 916 Grosvenor Pl., Oakland, Calif. 94610. *Office:* Department of History, California State University, Hayward, Calif. 94542.

CAREER: California State University, Hayward, assistant professor, 1964-70, associate professor of history, 1970—. *Member:* American Historical Association, Institute for Early American History and Culture, United Professors of California. *Awards, honors:* Colonial Williamsburg Foundation grant-in-aid, 1972.

WRITINGS: (With Bruce A. Glasrud) *Promises To Keep: A Portrayal of Non-Whites in America,* two volumes, Rand McNally, 1972. Contributor to *Pennsylvania History, Wisconsin Historical Magazine,* and *Maryland History Magazine.*

WORK IN PROGRESS: Research on the legal profession in eighteenth-century Virginia.†

*   *   *

SMITH, Bardwell L(eith)   1925-

PERSONAL: Born July 28, 1925, in Springfield, Mass.; son of Winthrop Hiram (an investment banker) and Gertrude (Ingram) Smith; married Charlotte McCorkindale, August 19, 1961; children: Peter M., Susan M., Laura Bardwell, Brooks Campbell, Samuel Bardwell. *Education:* Yale University, B.A. (magna cum laude), 1950, B.D. (magna cum laude), 1953, M.A., 1957, Ph.D., 1964; Harvard University, postdoctoral study, 1964-65; University of London, postdoctoral study, 1972-73. *Politics:* Democrat. *Home:* 104 Maple St., Northfield, Minn. 55057. *Office:* Department of Religion, Carleton College, Northfield, Minn. 55057.

CAREER: Episcopal clergyman, ordained, 1953; Yale University, New Haven, Conn., assistant in instruction in religion, 1958-60; Carleton College, Northfield, Minn., assistant professor, 1960-65, associate professor, 1965-69, professor of Asian religions, 1969—, John W. Nason Professor of Asian Studies, 1970—, dean of the college, 1967-72. *Military service:* U.S. Marine Corps, 1944-46; served in Pacific. *Member:* International Association of Buddhist Studies (member of executive committee, 1976—), American Academy of Religion (member of board of directors, 1969-72), American Society of Christian Ethics, American Oriental Society, Association for Asian Studies, Royal Asiatic Society, Society for Values in Higher Education, Society for the Scientific Study of Religion, American Association of University Professors, General Service Foundation (member of board of directors, 1971-76), Phi Beta Kappa. *Awards, honors:* Society for Values in Higher Education fellowship, 1953-54, 1956-58, 1964-65; Church Society for College Work fellowship, 1956-57; National Defense Education Act Post-Doctoral fellowship to Harvard University, 1964-65; American Council of Learned Societies grant for research on South Asia, 1972-73.

WRITINGS—Editor: (And contributor with Gananath Obeyesekere and Frank Reynolds) *The Two Wheels of Dhamma: Essays on the Theravada Tradition in India and Ceylon,* American Academy of Religion, 1972; (and contributor) *The Tenure Debate,* Jossey-Bass, 1973; *Tradition and Change in Theravada Buddhism: Essays on Ceylon and Thailand in the Nineteenth and Twentieth Centuries,* E. J. Brill, 1973; (with Giei Sato and Eshin Nishimura) *Unsui: A Diary of Zen Monastic Life,* University Press of Hawaii, 1973; (and contributor) *Religion and Social Conflict in South Asia,* E. J. Brill, 1976; (and contributor) *Hinduism: New Essays in the History of Religions,* E. J. Brill, 1976; (with John Curtis Perry, and contributor) *Essays on T'ang Society: The Interplay of Social, Political and Economic Forces,* E. J. Brill, 1976; (and contributor) *Religion and Legitimation of Power in Sri Lanka,* Anima Books, 1978; *Religion and Legitimation of Power in Thailand, Laos and Burma,* Anima Books, 1978; *Religion and the Legitimation of Power in South Asia,* E. J. Brill, 1978. Contributor to *Journal of American Academy of Religion, Anglican Theological Review, Commonweal, Japan Quarterly, Christian Century, Liberal Education,* and other journals and periodicals.

WORK IN PROGRESS: Editing with George Elison essays for a volume on aspects of sixteenth-century Japan; editing with Eleanor Zellior essays on aspects of the Gupta period in Indian history; research on religious, social, and cultural history of Sri Lanka.

*   *   *

SMITH, Benjamin Franklin   1902-

PERSONAL: Born July 23, 1902, in Copiah County, Miss.; son of Benjamin Franklin (a millwright) and Miranda (Ferguson) Smith; married Gertrude Bass, December 25, 1932; children: Mary Gayle (Mrs. H. D. Carleton), Riley Franklin. *Education:* Louisiana College, B.A., 1927; George Peabody College for Teachers, graduate study, 1931; Southern Baptist Theological Seminary, Th.M., 1937, Ph.D., 1942; University of Southern Mississippi, M.A., 1954. *Politics:* Independent. *Religion:* Baptist. *Home:* 3306 Arlington Loop, Hattiesburg, Miss. 39401.

CAREER: Ordained minister of Baptist Church, 1925; teacher and administrator for public high schools in St. Joseph, La., and Biloxi, Miss., 1927-34; pastor of churches in Lyon, Miss., 1939-42, Durant, Miss., 1942-43, and Magnolia, Miss., 1943-47; William Carey College, Hattiesburg, Miss., chairman of social studies department, 1947-56, chairman of Division of Religion and Philosophy, 1956-67, professor of religion and philosophy, 1967-72; family counselor in Hattiesburg, 1972—. *Member:* American Academy of Religion, Society for Philosophy of Religion, American Red Cross, Southern Baptist Historical Society, Mississippi Philosophy Association (president, 1966-67), Mississippi Baptist Convention (vice-president, 1945-46), Pi Kappa Delta, Phi Delta Kappa, Rotary (president of Durant chapter, 1943), Masons.

WRITINGS: Christian Baptism, Broadman, 1971. Contributor of curriculum materials to Baptist Sunday School Board, 1956-66.

WORK IN PROGRESS: Two books.

*   *   *

SMITH, Boyd M.   1888(?)-1973

1888(?)—May 31, 1973; American educator, architect, and dramatist. Obituaries: *New York Times,* June 2, 1973.

*   *   *

SMITH, C. U.   1901-
(Ophelia Mae Crowbate)

PERSONAL: Born July 29, 1901, in Seattle, Wash.; daughter of Ray Garfield (a logger) and Jennie Mae (Goodell) Oviatt; married second husband, Lee Ralph Smith (a seaman), December 24, 1945; children: (first marriage) five boys, three girls. *Education:* Educated in public schools. *Politics:* Democrat. *Religion:* "Free thinker." *Home and office address:* P.O. Box 10-636, Winslow, Bainbridge Island, Wash. 98110.

CAREER: Writer. *Member:* United Amateur Press Association, American Society of Composers, Authors and Publishers, Northwest Writers, Washington Pioneers Association, Sparkles of Happiness Club (Canada). *Awards, honors:* United Amateur Press Association awards of merit, 1967, 1970, 1971, 1972, 1973, all for *Ramrod,* outstanding achievement award, 1972, for poem "Eternity," certificate laureate, 1972, for short story "The Boy and the Crab," and reader's award, 1973, for poem "Do We Need It"; Eagle Feather Awards from *Lone Indian,* 1968, for poem "A Dollar Ninety Eight," 1970, for poem "Press Here," 1971, for poem "The Handshake," 1972, for poem "Yesterday's Front Porch," 1976, for short story, "Once Upon a Time" and for humorous subject, "The New Feather Tick," 1977, for short story, "The New Petticoat," 1978, for poem, "Take It or Leave It"; Lone Indian Fellowship certificate of honor, 1970; certificate of appreciation from Vilas Oneida Wilderness Society; certificate of merit from *North American Mentor,* 1976, for poem, "Hot Toast."

WRITINGS—Published by Carlton, except as indicated: *If the Shoe Fits Wear It,* 1962; *Through Hell in a Hand Basket,* 1963; *Hello! Hello! Party Line,* 1965; *The Morning and the Evening,* 1967; *Ramrod,* Prairie Press, 1970; *Smitty's Shorts,* Prairie Press, 1973; *Ramrod 2,* Prairie Press, 1976.

Work is represented in anthologies including *Year of the Poet,* edited by Jerry McCarty, Prairie Press, 1965; *First Poetry of 1966,* edited by Ronald Trimble, Prairie Press, 1966; *Mainstream American Poetry,* edited by Dick Scott, Prairie Press, 1966; *American Poets 1966,* edited by Stella Craft Trimble, Prairie Press, 1966; *Sixty-Seven Poets,* edited by McCarty, Prairie Press, 1967; *Poetry Parade No. 9,* edited by Marvin K. Barlow, Spinen Book Co., 1968; *Poetry Pageant,* Volume I, edited by Jean Wood, Magnetic Publishing Co., 1969; *70 Poets,* edited by McCarty, Prairie Press, 1970; *Echoes of Faith,* edited by Lincoln B. Young, Young Publications, 1970; *The 1971 Shore Poetry Anthology,* edited by Kenneth F. Kwint, Shore Publishing Co., 1971; *Grains of Sand,* edited by C. David Stephens, C. D. Stephens, 1971; *Yearbook of Modern Poetry,* edited by Jeanne Hollyfield, Young Publications, 1971; *New and Better World of Poetry,* edited by Frank Bensley, Lee Tour, and McCarty, Prairie Press, 1971; *Lyrics of Love,* edited by Hollyfield, Young Publications, 1972; *Golden Hours,* edited by W. C. Lowery, Edmunds Publishing Co., 1972; *From an Owl's Nest,* Prairie Poet Books, 1975; *Cravings of the Valiant Soul,* edited by Sal St. John Buttau and Susan Linda Gerstle, New Worlds Unlimited, 1978. Also author of numerous songs. Editor, *Ramrod,* 1965—.

WORK IN PROGRESS: Moving West.

SIDELIGHTS: All of C. U. Smith's books are included in the "Harris Collection of American Poetry" at John D. Rockefeller, Jr. Library of Brown University and also in the Washington State Library at Olympia.

*   *   *

SMITH, Clifford Neal 1923-

PERSONAL: Born May 30, 1923, in Wakita, Okla.; son of Jesse Newton (a businessman) and Inez L. (Jones) Smith; married Anna Piszczan-Czaja; children: Helen I. (Mrs. Dennis Barrette). *Education:* Oklahoma State University, B.Sci., 1943; University of Chicago, M.A., 1948; Columbia University, doctoral candidate, 1960. *Religion:* Society of

Friends (Quaker). *Home address:* P.O. Box 117, McNeal, Ariz. 85617.

CAREER: U.S. Department of State, Washington, D.C., selector of displaced persons for immigration to the United States for U.S. Displaced Persons Commission in Munich, Germany, 1948-51; Phillips Petroleum Co., Caracas, Venezuela, chief clerk and internal auditor, 1951-58; Mobil International Oil Co., New York, N.Y., market planner in Hamburg, Germany and Geneva, Switzerland, 1960-66; Northern Illinois University, DeKalb, assistant professor of management, 1966-70. Instructor in English at Centro Venezolano-Americano (of U.S. Information Service Cultural Center—Caracas), 1953-58, director, 1958; member of regional executive board of American Friends Service Committee and Friends Committee on National Legislation (Quaker lobby).

MEMBER: Society for the Advancement of Management, National Genealogical Society, Midwest Planning Association, Illinois State Genealogical Society (member of board of directors), Sigma Iota Epsilon, Sons of the Revolution, Sons of the American Revolution, Society of the Descendants of the Colonial Clergy, Phi Eta Sigma, and Beta Alpha Psi.

WRITINGS: (Contributor) H. Ned Seelye, editor, *A Handbook on Latin America for Teachers,* Office of the Superintendent of Public Instruction (Springfield, Ill.), 1968; (contributor) Elmer H. Burack and James W. Walker, editors, *Manpower Planning and Programming for Change,* Allyn & Bacon, 1971; *Federal Land Series: A Calendar of Archival Materials on the Land Patents Issued by the United States Government,* American Library Association, Volume I: *1788-1810,* 1972, Volume II: *Federal Bounty-Land Warrants of the American Revolution,* 1973, Volume III: *1810-1814,* 1979; (with Anna Piszczan-Czaja Smith) *Encyclopedia of German-American Genealogical Research,* Bowker, 1976; (with A. Smith) *American Genealogical Resources in German Archives,* Verlag Dokumentation Saur, 1977.

Monographs, all published by Westland Publications: *Brunswick Deserter-Immigrants of the American Revolution,* 1973; *Mercenaries from Ansbach and Bayreuth, Germany, Who Remained in America after the Revolution,* 1974; *Emigrants from Saxony (Grandduchy of Sachsen-Weimar-Eisenach) to America, 1854, 1859,* 1974; *British Deportees to America, Part I: 1760-1763,* 1974, *Part II: 1764-1765,* 1978; *Muster Rolls and Prisoner-of-War Lists in American Archival Collections Pertaining to the German Mercenary Troops Who Served with the British Forces during the American Revolution,* three parts, 1974-76; *Mercenaries from Hessen-Hanau Who Remained in Canada and the United States after the American Revolution,* 1976; *Emigrants from the Principality of Hessen-Hanau, Germany, 1741-1767,* 1978. Has designed and written computer-assisted simulations. Contributor to proceedings and conferences. Contributor of more than a hundred articles and reviews to professional publications, including *Journal of International Business, New Directions in Teaching, Long Range Planning Journal, Explorations in Economic History, Business History, American Perspective, Friends Journal, Chicago-Kent Law Journal, National Genealogical Society Quarterly,* and *Illinois State Genealogical Society Quarterly.* Editor, *Manager's Key* (of Sigma Iota Epsilon), May, 1970; contributing editor, *National Genealogical Society Quarterly,* 1973—, *Genealogical Journal* (Utah), 1977—.

WORK IN PROGRESS: Five volumes for the German-American Genealogical Research Monograph Series, to be published in 1979-80; other volumes of Federal Land Series, to be devoted to Virginia land grants, 1810-1830, for American Library Association; *British Deportees to America, Part III: 1766-1767,* for British-American Genealogical Research Monograph Series, Westland Publications.

SIDELIGHTS: "I am compiling this information not only for current use," Clifford Neal Smith told *CA,* "but particularly for the use of researchers five hundred years hence, when the original materials may have disintegrated or been destroyed." He added that he is considering a proposal to transcribe, translate, and annotate the vast files of the Hamburg police authorities regarding emigration from central European countries (Germany, Austria, Hungary, Czechoslovakia, Poland, and Russia).

*   *   *

SMITH, D(wight) Moody, Jr. 1931-

PERSONAL: Born November 20, 1931, in Murfreesboro, Tenn.; son of Dwight Moody and Nellie (Beckwith) Smith; married Jane Allen, November 26, 1954; children: Cynthia Beckwith, Catherine Mitchell, David Burton, John Allen. *Education:* Davidson College, A.B., 1954; Duke University, B.D., 1957; Yale University, M.A., 1958, Ph.D., 1961. *Home:* 2728 Spencer St., Durham, N.C. 27705. *Office address:* Box 35, Divinity School, Duke University, Durham, N.C. 27706.

CAREER: Ordained minister of United Methodist Church, 1959; Methodist Theological School in Ohio, Delaware, Ohio, instructor, 1960-61, assistant professor of New Testament, 1961-65; Duke University, Divinity School, Durham, N.C., associate professor, 1965-70, professor of New Testament, 1970—, director of graduate studies in religion, 1974—. Visiting instructor at Ohio Wesleyan University, 1960-61. *Member:* Society for Values in Higher Education, Society of Biblical Literature, Studiorum Novi Testamenti Societas, Phi Beta Kappa. *Awards, honors:* Lilly post-doctoral fellowship in religion, 1963-64; Guggenheim fellowship, 1970-71; Association of Theological Schools research grant, 1977-78.

WRITINGS: The Composition and Order of the Fourth Gospel, Yale University Press, 1965; (with Robert A. Spivey) *Anatomy of the New Testament,* Macmillan, 1969, revised edition, 1974; *John* (gospel commentary), Fortress, 1976. Contributor to *Journal of Biblical Literature, New Testament Studies, Journal of Religion, Interpretation, Catholic Biblical Quarterly,* and *Journal of American Academy of Religion.*

WORK IN PROGRESS: Research on the relation of fourth gospel to synoptics; New Testament exegesis and theology.

*   *   *

SMITH, Delos Owen 1905-1973

March 2, 1905—May 31, 1973; American editor and journalist. Obituaries: *New York Times,* June 2, 1973.

*   *   *

SMITH, Donal Ian Bryce 1934-

PERSONAL: Born February 4, 1934, in Auckland, New Zealand; son of Edward Bruce (a school headmaster) and Judy (Jaffrey) Smith; married Marjory Jill Evans, December 5, 1959; children: Matthew, Penelope, Caitlin. *Education:* Auckland University, B.A., 1954, M.A., 1955; Oxford University, D.Phil., 1963.

CAREER: University of Toronto, University College, Toronto, Ontario, lecturer, 1960-63, assistant professor, 1963-68, associate professor, 1968-72, professor of English, beginning 1972. *Member:* Vincent's Club. *Awards, honors:* Canada Council senior fellow, 1965-66; Nuffield Foundation travel award, 1971-72.

WRITINGS: (Editor) *Editing Eighteenth Century Texts,* University of Toronto Press, 1968; (editor) *Rehearsal Transprosed and Rehearsal Transpros'd: The Second Part,* Clarendon Press, 1971; (editor and contributor) *Editing Seventeenth Century Prose,* Hakkert, 1972. Contributor to scholarly journals.

WORK IN PROGRESS: A complete edition of Marvell's prose.††

*   *   *

SMITH, Goldwin (Albert) 1912-

PERSONAL: Born February 25, 1912, in Uxbridge, Ontario, Canada; son of Chester and Viola (Hollingshead) Smith; married Emily C. T. Bateman, May, 1939; children: Goldwin Ian, Douglas Bateman, Bruce David. *Education:* University of Western Ontario, B.A., 1933; University of Toronto, M.A., 1934; Cornell University, Ph.D., 1937. *Religion:* Episcopalian. *Home:* 63 Hall Pl., Grosse Pointe Farms, Mich. 48236. *Office:* Department of History, Wayne State University, Detroit, Mich. 48202.

CAREER: National Selective Service, Ottawa, Ontario, chief of Priorities Division, 1941-43; special assistant to Undersecretary of State for External Affairs, Ottawa, 1943-45; University of Missouri—Columbia, instructor in history, 1937-38; University of Iowa, Iowa City, instructor, 1938-41, assistant professor, 1941-43, associate professor of history, 1943-47; Wayne State University, Detroit, Mich., associate professor, 1947-50, professor of history, 1950—. Advisory editor, Charles Scribner's Sons.

MEMBER: American Historical Association, Renaissance Society of America, Council of British Studies, Organization of American Historians, Council on Basic Education, Royal Historical Society (fellow), Canadian Historical Association, Detroit Committee on Foreign Affairs, Phi Beta Kappa. *Awards, honors:* D.Litt., University of Western Ontario, 1966.

WRITINGS: The Treaty of Washington, Cornell University Press, 1941; (with Earl J. McGrath and others) *Towards General Education,* Macmillan, 1947; *A History of England,* Scribner, 1949, 4th edition, 1974; *A Legal and Constitutional History of England,* Scribner, 1955; *The Heritage of Man,* Scribner, 1960; *England: A Short History,* Scribner, 1972; (with A. L. Rowse and J. H. Hexter) *The Professor and the Public,* Wayne State University Press, 1972. Contributor of articles and reviews to professional journals.

WORK IN PROGRESS: A biography of Henry VII.

*   *   *

SMITH, Mary Elizabeth 1932-

PERSONAL: Born August 2, 1932, in Three Rivers, Mich.; daughter of Emery Crum (an insurance salesman) and Margaret (Anderson) Smith. *Education:* University of Michigan, B.A., 1954; Columbia University, M.A., 1960; Yale University, Ph.D., 1966. *Office:* Department of Art, University of New Mexico, Albuquerque, N.M. 87131.

CAREER: American Management Association, New York City, library assistant, 1954-56, editorial assistant, 1956-57, assistant editor, 1957; American Exporter Publications, New York City, assistant to research and service manager, 1958-59; *New York Times,* New York City, telephone classified ad-taker, 1959-61; University of New Mexico, Albuquerque, N.M., assistant professor, 1966-71, associate professor of art history, 1971—. *Member:* College Art Association, Latin American Studies Association, Society for American Archaeology. *Awards, honors:* Doherty Foundation fellowship, 1962-63, and Pan American Union fellowship, 1963-64, for research and field work in Mexico.

WRITINGS: Las glosas del Codice Colombino/The Glosses of Codex Colombino, published with Alfonso Caso's, *Interpretacion del Codice Colombino/Interpretation of the Codex Colombino,* Sociedad Mexicana de Antropologia, 1966; *Picture Writing from Ancient Southern Mexico: Mixtec Place Signs and Maps,* University of Oklahoma Press, 1973. Contributor of articles to *Tlalocan.*

WORK IN PROGRESS: Research on pictorial manuscripts from the Mixtec-speaking region of southern Mexico.††

*   *   *

SMITH, P(eter) J(ohn)   1931-

PERSONAL: Born September 18, 1931, in New Zealand; son of Sydney Charles (a railwayman) and Ethel May (Pettit) Smith; married Sheana Mary Lee, May 30, 1959; children: Katrina, Hugh. *Education:* University of New Zealand, B.A., 1953, M.A., 1954; University of Toronto, diploma of town and regional planning, 1959; University of Edinburgh, Ph.D., 1964. *Politics:* None. *Religion:* None. *Home:* 64 Marlboro Rd., Edmonton, Alberta, Canada. *Office:* Department of Geography, University of Alberta, Edmonton, Alberta, Canada.

CAREER: Worked as a teacher in New Zealand and England, 1952-55; City of Calgary, Calgary, Alberta, planner, 1956-59; University of Alberta, Edmonton, assistant professor, 1959-64, associate professor, 1964-69, professor of geography, 1969—, head of department, 1967-75. *Member:* Canadian Association of Geographers (councillor, 1966-70; vice-president, 1972-73; president, 1973-74), Canadian Institute of Manners, American Association of Geographers, New Zealand Geographical Society, Community Planning Association of Canada (Edmonton regional executive, 1961-62), Alberta Geographical Society (treasurer, 1965-67; vice-president, 1967-68; president, 1968-69). *Awards, honors:* Certificate of distinction from Town Planning Institute of Canada, 1959; Canada Council fellowship, 1970-71, 1977-78.

WRITINGS: Population and Production: An Introduction to Some Problems in Economic Geography, Dent, 1967, revised edition, 1971; (editor) *The Prairie Provinces,* University of Toronto Press, 1972. Also editor of *Edmonton: The Emerging Metropolitan Pattern,* 1978. Contributor to geographical journals, including *Plan Canada, Ekistics, Annals of the Association of American Geographers, Economic Geography, Geography, Scottish Geographical Magazine, Journal for Geography,* and *Western Geographical Series.* Editor, *Canadian Association of Geographers Newsletter,* 1969-76, *Canadian Geographer,* 1978—.

WORK IN PROGRESS: A monograph, *The Edmonton-Calgary Corridor,* for University of Alberta Department of Geography; *Towards the Respectable City: Urban Renewal in Mid-Victorian Edinburgh,* completion expected in 1979-80.

SMITH, Patrick J(ohn)   1932-

PERSONAL: Born December 11, 1932, in New York, N.Y.; son of H. Ben and Geraldine (Wilson) Smith; married Elisabeth Munro, November 7, 1964; children: Douglass, Matthew. *Education:* Princeton University, A.B., 1955. *Residence:* New York, N.Y.

CAREER: Musical Newsletter, New York City, editor-publisher, beginning 1970. *High Fidelity-Musical America,* New York City, critic and book editor, beginning 1964. *Military service:* U.S. Army Reserve, 1954-62. *Member:* Authors Guild, Music Critics Association, American Musicological Society, Royal Society for the Arts.

WRITINGS: The Tenth Muse: A Historical Study of the Opera Libretto, Knopf, 1970.††

*   *   *

SMITH, Peter H(opkinson)   1940-

PERSONAL: Born January 17, 1940, in Brooklyn, N.Y.; son of Joseph Hopkinson (in advertising) and Mary Edna (Sullivan) Smith; married Mary Grant, September 8, 1962 (divorced, April 17, 1976); married Frances Gouda, November 25, 1978; children: (first marriage) Jonathan Yeardley, Peter Hopkinson II. *Education:* Harvard University, B.A., 1961; Columbia University, M.A., 1963, Ph.D., 1966. *Residence:* Madison, Wis. *Office:* Department of History, University of Wisconsin, Madison, Wis. 53706.

CAREER: Dartmouth College, Hanover, N.H., assistant professor of history, 1966-68; University of Wisconsin—Madison, assistant professor, 1968-69, associate professor, 1969-72, professor of history, 1972—, chairperson of Ibero-American Studies program, 1971-72, chairperson of department of history, 1976-79, associate dean of graduate school, 1978—. Visiting researcher, Colegio de Mexico, 1968-69; visiting member, Institute for Advanced Study (Princeton, N.J.), 1972-73; visiting professor, University of Michigan, summer, 1975; staff member, Newberry Library summer institute on historical methodology, 1975-77. Member of history advisory committee of Mathematical Social Sciences Board, 1977—. *Member:* American Historical Association (member of committee on quantitative research, 1975—), Latin American Studies Association (member of executive council, 1977—), Conference on Latin American History (member of committee on quantitative research), American Political Science Association, Instituto de Desarrollo Economico y Social (Buenos Aires). *Awards, honors:* Woodrow Wilson fellow, 1961-62; Social Science Research Council/American Council of Learned Societies research grants, 1967, 1969-70; American Philosophical Society research grants, 1969, 1974; University of Wisconsin grants-in-aid, 1970-75; research grants from American Council of Learned Societies, Institute for Advanced Study, and National Endowment for the Humanities, 1972-73; John Simon Guggenheim Memorial Foundation fellowship, 1975-76; H. I. Romnes faculty fellowship, University of Wisconsin, 1975.

WRITINGS: Politics and Beef in Argentina: Patterns of Conflict and Change, Columbia University Press, 1969; *Argentina and the Failure of Democracy: Conflict among Social Elites, 1904-1955,* University of Wisconsin Press, 1974; (editor with Richard Graham) *New Approaches to Latin American History,* University of Texas Press, 1974; *Labyrinths of Power: Political Recruitment in Twentieth-Centruy Mexico,* Princeton University Press, 1978.

Contributor: David S. Smith, editor, *Prospects for Latin*

America, Columbia University Press, 1970; Robert S. Byars and Joseph L. Love, editors, *Quantitative Social Science Research in Latin America,* University of Illinois Press, 1973; James W. Wilkie, Michael C. Meyer, and Edna Monzon de Wilkie, editors, *Contemporary Mexico: Papers of the IV International Congress of Mexican History,* Latin American Center, University of California at Los Angeles, 1976; William O. Aydelotte, editor, *The Dimensions of Parliamentary History,* Princeton University Press, 1977; Jose Luis Reyna and Richard S. Weinart, editors, *Authoritarianism in Mexico,* Institute for the Study of Human Issues, 1977; Juan J. Linz and Alfred Stepan, editors, *The Breakdown of Democratic Regimes: Latin America,* Johns Hopkins University Press, 1978. Contributor to professional journals, including *William and Mary Quarterly, American Economist, Journal of Inter-American Studies, Hispanic American Historical Review, Desarrollo Economico, Political Science Quarterly, Latin American Research Review, Historia Mexicana, Historical Methods Newsletter, Foro Internacional,* and *Boletin de Estudios Latinoamericanos y del Caribe.* Member of advisory board, *Statistical Abstract on Latin America,* 1977—.

WORK IN PROGRESS: History, Measurement, and Time, completion expected in 1980.

BIOGRAPHICAL/CRITICAL SOURCES: Annals of the American Academy of Political and Social Science, July, 1969, March, 1975; *American Political Science Review,* September, 1969; *Journal of Economic History,* September, 1969; *Business History Review,* winter, 1969; *History: Reviews of New Books,* April, 1975; *Times Literary Supplement,* August 15, 1975.

*   *   *

SMITH, Richard Harris 1946-

PERSONAL: Born September 10, 1946, in Oakland, Calif.; son of Morris (a businessman) and Belle (Riskin) Smith. *Education:* University of California, Berkeley, B.A., 1967, M.A., 1970. *Politics:* Democratic. *Religion:* Jewish. *Address:* c/o University of California Press, Berkeley, Calif. *Agent:* Maxmilian Becker, 115 East 82nd St., New York, N.Y. 10028.

CAREER: California Democratic Party, San Francisco, member of campaign staff, 1964; Central Intelligence Agency, Washington, D.C., research analyst, 1967-68; McGovern for President Campaign, San Francisco, Calif., field representative, 1971-72; free-lance writer, 1972—.

WRITINGS: O.S.S.: The Secret History of America's First Central Intelligence Agency, University of California Press, 1972; *Spymaster's Odyssey,* Coward, in press.

WORK IN PROGRESS: A history of the Underground Railroad, completion expected in 1980.

SIDELIGHTS: Richard Harris Smith told *CA:* "My apparent obsession with 'secret history' can be explained (though not excused) by an adolescent literary diet of the French romantics—Dumas remains an idol—and a long line of Russian ancestors. I confess to being a knowledgeable bibliomaniac, a fanatical reader of Edwardian romances and pre-World War II whodunits, a moderately proficient pianist, and an occasional historian."

*   *   *

SMITH, Richard K(ent) 1936-

PERSONAL: Born June 30, 1936, in Billings, Mont.; son of Bennett Hamer (a lawyer and businessman) and Barbara Del

Sur Smith; married Juliana Martin Gallardo, December 29, 1960 (divorced, 1972); children: Kent Martin. *Education:* Attended Idaho State University, 1956-59, and University of Utah, 1954-55; University of Montana, B.A., 1960, M.A., 1962; Tulane University, Ph.D., 1965. *Home:* 4257 Arnold St. N.E., Salem, Ore., 97303. *Office:* Department of Psychology, Fairview Hospital and Training Center, Salem, Ore. 97310.

CAREER: Tulane University, New Orleans, La., instructor in psychology, 1964-65; Auburn University, Auburn, Ala., assistant professor of psychology, 1965-68; Louisiana State University in New Orleans, associate professor of psychology, 1968-71; Willamette University, Salem, Ore., visiting associate professor of psychology, 1971-73; Fairview Hospital and Training Center, Salem, psychologist and director of Child Development Unit, 1973—. Consultant to Veterans Administration Hospital, Tuskegee, Ala., 1967-68; member of Drug Abuse Research Team, Medical School, Tulane University, 1970-71. *Member:* American Psychological Association, Association for Advancement of Behavior Therapy, Oregon Psychological Association.

WRITINGS: (With R. D. Olson and G. A. Olson) *Learning in the Classroom: Theory and Application,* McCutchan, 1971. Contributor of articles to *Psychological Reports, Perceptual and Motor Skills,* and *Psychological Record.*

WORK IN PROGRESS: Research on principles and techniques of self-modification, habit breaking and creation, willpower, rehabilitation, and self-improvement programs.

*   *   *

SMITH, Robert Griffin, Jr. 1920-

PERSONAL: Born September 25, 1920, in Bainbridge, Ga.; son of Robert Griffin and Ethel (Haire) Smith; married Mary Chamberlain, October 26, 1944; children: Philip Wesley, Alicia Nancy. *Education:* University of Florida, B.A., 1942, M.A., 1947; University of Illinois, Ph.D., 1950. *Office:* Office of the Chief of Naval Operations, OP987H, Washington, D.C. 20350.

CAREER: Supervisory research psychologist with U.S. Air Force, 1950-57; Texas Technological College (now Texas Tech University), Lubbock, associate professor of psychology, 1957-58; Human Resources Research Organization, Alexandria, Va., research psychologist and executive, 1958-75; U.S. Navy, Washington, D.C., research and development planner. *Member:* National Society for Programmed Instruction (president, 1963-64), American Psychological Association.

WRITINGS: Innovations in Teaching and Training, American Data Processing, 1968; *The Engineering of Training Systems,* Heath, 1971. Contributor to *Macmillan Encyclopedia of Education.*

*   *   *

SMOLAR, Boris (Ber) 1897-

PERSONAL: Born May 27, 1897, in Rovno, Ukraine; came to United States in 1919; son of Leizer-Leivia (a teacher) and Miriam (Shearer) Smolar; married Genia Lewin, February 26, 1934. *Education:* Attended Haven School, 1919-20, Lewis Institute, 1920-21 (both Chicago, Ill.), and Northwestern University, 1923. *Religion:* Jewish. *Home:* 147 West 79th St., New York, N.Y. 10024.

CAREER: Jewish Daily Forward, Chicago, Ill., editorial staff, 1920-24; Jewish Telegraphic Agency, New York City, 1924—, began as associate editor, later chief European correspondent in London, Moscow, Berlin, and other capitals, became editor-in-chief, editor-in-chief emeritus, 1967—. Roving correspondent in Europe for *New York World*, 1928-30. Member of board of directors and national council, American Jewish Joint Distribution Committee, 1968—; member of board of directors, YIVO Institute for Jewish Research, 1967—. Participant in United Jewish Appeal study missions to Israel, Germany, and Poland. *Member:* American Academy of Political and Social Science, United Nations Correspondents Association, P.E.N. *Awards, honors:* Alumna Pax Medal, awarded by Pope Paul VI, 1965; National Council of Christians and Jews citation for promoting Christian-Jewish amity; Israel Silver Medal (Shekel), Bronze Peace Medal, and other Israeli government awards; honorary doctorate in Hebrew letters from Baltimore Hebrew College, 1973.

WRITINGS: Drei Prinzen (title means "Three Princes"), [Odessa], 1915; *Die Kishefmacherin* (title means "The Witch"), [Warsaw], 1922; *Die Lebedige Arithmetic* (title means "Lively Arithmetic"), [Warsaw], 1922; *Kinderland* (title means "The Land of Children"), [Berlin], 1923; *Kinderwelt* (title means "Kiddies' Corner"), [New York], 1924; *Soviet Jewry Today and Tomorrow*, Macmillan, 1971. Writer of a syndicated weekly column, "Between You and Me," in the English-Jewish press, and a Sunday column in the Jewish Daily Forward.

SIDELIGHTS: Boris Smolar was stationed in Berlin during the ascent of the Nazi regime, reporting news of Germany's treatment of Jews. His dispatches appeared in the American and British press, and led to his expulsion from Germany in 1937 for "endangering the interests of the Reich." He covered the Arab riots in Palestine in 1929 and 1936, has visited Israel every year since 1948, and traveled to the U.S.S.R. to study the problems of Soviet Jewry.

*   *   *

SMYTHE, Donald 1927-

PERSONAL: Born December 22, 1927, in Lorain, Ohio; son of John Joseph (a lawyer) and Dorothy (Bodmann) Smythe. *Education:* John Carroll University, B.A., 1948; Loyola University, Chicago, Ill., M.A., 1955; Georgetown University, Ph.D., 1961. *Politics:* Democrat. *Home and office:* Rodman Hall, John Carroll University, Cleveland, Ohio 44118.

CAREER: Ordained Roman Catholic priest of Society of Jesus (Jesuit), 1964; John Carroll University, Cleveland, Ohio, assistant professor, 1965-71, associate professor of history, 1971—. *Member:* American Military Institute, Organization of American Historians, Ohio Academy of History. *Awards, honors:* Martha Kinney Cooper Ohioana Library Association prize, 1974, for *Guerrilla Warrior*.

WRITINGS: Guerrilla Warrior: The Early Life of John J. Pershing, Scribner, 1973. Contributor to *Pacific Historical Review, Montana, Missouri Historical Review, Mid-America, Nebraska History, New Mexico Historical Review, Philippine Studies, New York History, Woodstock Letters, America, Military Affairs, Military Review, Prologue, Army, Soldiers,* and *Stars and Stripes.*

WORK IN PROGRESS: Researching volume II of a biography of General John J. Pershing, *General of the Armies,* completion expected in 1981.

*   *   *

SNOWDEN, Frank M(artin), Jr. 1911-

PERSONAL: Born July 17, 1911, in York County, Va.; son

of Frank Martin and Alice (Phillips) Snowden; married Elaine Hill (a high school teacher), June 8, 1935; children: Jane Alice, Frank M. III. *Education:* Harvard University, A.B., 1932, A.M., 1933, Ph.D., 1944; American Academy in Rome, graduate study, summer, 1938. *Home:* 4200 Massachusetts Ave. N.W., Washington, D.C. 20016. *Office:* Department of Classics, Howard University, Washington, D.C. 20001.

CAREER: Virginia State College, Petersburg, instructor in classics, 1933-36; Spelman College, Atlanta, Ga., instructor in classics, 1936-40; Howard University, Washington, D.C., instructor, 1942-44, associate professor, 1944-45, professor of classics 1945—, head of department, 1942—, director of summer school, 1942-54, director of evening school and adult education, 1942-48, chairman of humanities program, 1950-51, dean of College of Liberal Arts, 1956-68. U.S. Department of State lecturer in French West Africa, Gold Coast, Libya, Italy, Greece, and Austria, 1953; cultural attache at American Embassy, Rome, Italy, 1954-56; U.S. Foreign Service Institute lecturer, 1956-68, lecturing in India, 1957, in Brazil, summer, 1960; visiting scholar, University Center in Virginia, 1971-72; scholar-in-residence, Villa Bellagio, Rockefeller Foundation, Lake Como, Italy, 1977. Member of U.S. delegation in Paris, UNESCO, 1958, 1960; studied higher education in the Soviet Union, 1958. Member, U.S. National Commission for UNESCO, 1958-61; member of board, National Humanities Faculty, 1970-73.

MEMBER: American Philological Association (member of board of directors, 1976-79), American Archaeological Institute (Washington, D.C. Chapter; vice-president, 1968-70; president, 1970-71), American Conference of Academic Deans (chairman, 1963-64), American Council on Education, Classical Society, Vergilian Society of America (trustee, 1956-60), American Academy in Rome, Washington Classical Club (vice-president, 1949-50), Cosmos Club, Harvard Club. *Awards, honors:* Fulbright research scholar in Italy, 1949-50; LL.D., Bard College, 1957; Medaglia d'Oro from Italy, 1958, for outstanding work on Italian culture and education; American Council of Learned Societies fellowship, 1962-63; National Endowment for the Humanities grant, 1970, for research in North Africa; Charles J. Goodwin Award of Merit, American Philological Association, 1973, for *Blacks in Antiquity: Ethiopians in the Greco-Roman Experience;* Woodrow Wilson International Center for Scholars fellow, 1977; named Distinguished Member of Faculty, Howard University, 1977.

WRITINGS: Blacks in Antiquity: Ethiopians in the Greco-Roman Experience, Belknap Press, 1971; (contributor) R. I. Rotberg and M. L. Kilson, editors, *The African Diaspora: Interpretive Essays,* Harvard University Press, 1976; (with Jean Leclant, Jean Vercoutter, and Jehan Desanges) *The Image of the Black in Western Art I: From the Pharoahs to the Fall of the Roman Empire,* Morrow, 1976. Contributor to *The Interpreter's Dictionary of the Bible* and to scholarly journals, including *American Anthropologist, American Journal of Philology, L'Antiquite Classique,* and *Traditio.*

SIDELIGHTS: Reviewing *Blacks in Antiquity: Ethiopians in the Greco-Roman Experience,* L. Castiglione writes that the book "examines the meeting of the Greco-Roman world and the black peoples of Africa exhaustively.... It uses the literary sources from Homer to the Fathers of the Church, the utilizable inscriptions ... as well as the representations from all branches of the art of antiquity. It is characterized by an admirable fullness in the survey of modern literature.... The archaeologist can be especially grateful to [Frank] Snowden for giving a considerably richer and broader illustrated survey of the representations of Negro and Negroid figures in ancient art than any work dealing with the subject hitherto." Henri Metzger calls the book "the work of a gifted connoisseur of Greco-Roman antiquity who moves with ease among texts and representational monuments.... The richness of information, abundance and variety of illustrations make this work a well organized document, easy to consult, which will find its place in all libraries." Paul MacKendrick comments: "The novelty of this book, the fruit of a lifetime's labor of love ... lies in the exhaustive, impeccable scholarship with which it documents and illustrates its conclusion, that there is no evidence for racism or color prejudice in Greco-Roman antiquity.... In short, in 'the first major encounter in European records of blacks in a predominantly white society, the Greeks and Romans counted black peoples in.'"

John Russell believes that *The Image of the Black in Western Art I: From the Pharoahs to the Fall of the Roman Empire,* which has also been published in French, "has the kind of stately and illimitably generous presentation that is usually reserved for the white man's glorification of himself. Of course the subject deserves it. There is everything to be said for a book that ransacks the world for superlative works of art from ancient Egypt, ancient Greece, ancient Rome, and ancient Northern Africa.... This book ... is a gift to humanity."

BIOGRAPHICAL/CRITICAL SOURCES: African Historical Studies, Volume IV, 1971; *Revue des etudes anciennes,* Volume LXXIII, 1971; *Acta archaelogica academiae scientiarum hungaricae,* Volume XXLV, 1972; *American Journal of Philology,* Volume XCIV, 1973; *L'Antiquite Classique,* Volume XLIV, 1975; *New York Times Book Review,* December 5, 1976; *Washington Post,* October 21, 1978.

* * *

SNYDER, E(ugene) V(incent) 1943-

PERSONAL: Born January 1, 1943, in New York, N.Y.; son of Eugene Vincent and Mary (Farrell) Snyder; married Nancy Leonhardt (a writer), May 12, 1968; children: Laura Jean. *Education:* Hofstra University, B.A., 1964, M.A., 1967; New York University, studying for doctoral degree, 1971—. *Agent:* Scott Meredith Literary Agency, Inc., 845 Third Ave., New York, N.Y. 10022. *Office:* Brookdale Community College, 765 Newman Springs Rd., Lincroft, N.J. 07738.

CAREER: Brookdale Community College, Lincroft, N.J., assistant professor of English composition, 1970—. *Military service:* U.S. Army, 1967-69; served in Germany and Vietnam; became captain; received Bronze Star Medal. *Member:* Speech Association of America, National Education Association, American Association of Junior Colleges, American College Theater Association, Science Fiction Writers of America, Okinawan-American Karate Association, Alpha Psi Omega.

WRITINGS: (With William Jon Watkins) *Ecodeath,* Doubleday, 1972.

WORK IN PROGRESS: Twilight, a novel; *The Energy Brokers.*

AVOCATIONAL INTERESTS: The martial arts (including karate), tennis, golf.†

* * *

SNYDER, Henry Leonard 1929-

PERSONAL: Born November 3, 1929, in Hayward, Calif.; son of Henry Runyon (an engineer) and Mary (Rosenberg) Snyder; married Janette Marie Hannus (a psychiatric social worker), July 21, 1961; children: Michael Jesse, Christopher Henry, David Lyle. *Education:* University of California, Berkeley, B.A., 1951, M.A., 1960, Ph.D., 1963. *Politics:* Republican. *Religion:* Congregational. *Home:* 1324 Strong Ave., Lawrence, Kan. 66044. *Office:* Department of History, University of Kansas, Lawrence, Kan. 66044.

CAREER: Dohrmann Commercial Co., San Francisco, Calif., senior buyer of china and glass, 1951-59; University of Kansas, Lawrence, assistant professor, 1965-67, associate professor, 1967-71, professor of history, 1971—, assistant dean of faculties, 1967-70, associate dean of research administration, 1970-74, dean, 1974-78. Visiting lecturer at Bedford College, University of London, 1965-66. *Military service:* U.S. Army Reserve, 1951—; current rank, lieutenant colonel. *Member:* American Historical Association, American Association of University Professors, Conference on British Studies, Conference on Irish Studies, Royal Historical Society (fellow), Bibliographical Society (fellow), Historical Association (England). *Awards, honors:* American Council of Learned Societies senior fellow, 1969-70; National Endowment for the Humanities senior fellow, 1979-80.

WRITINGS: (Editor) *The Marlborough-Godolphin Correspondence, 1701-1711,* three volumes, Clarendon Press, 1973. Contributor to *Huntington Library Quarterly, Historical Journal, Bulletin of the Institute of Historical Research, Library, Philological Quarterly, Studies in Bibliography,* and *Journal of the Society for Army Historical Research.*

WORK IN PROGRESS: A book on the Godolphin Ministry, 1702-1710; the lives of John, Duke of Marlboro, and Sidney, Earl of Godolphin; the life and letters of Arthur Maynwaring.

* * *

SNYDER, Joan 1943-

PERSONAL: Born November 11, 1943, in San Francisco, Calif.; daughter of John A. (a general contractor) and Estelle (Lanch) Moran; married Jerome F. Snyder (an attorney), March 21, 1964; children: Jonathan Jerome. *Education:* Attended University of California, Los Angeles, 1961-63, and University of California, Berkeley, 1963-64; University of Nevada, Las Vegas, B.S., 1966, M.A., 1968, M.A. candidate in theatre arts, 1973—. *Home:* 3369 Nahatan Way, Las Vegas, Nev. 89109.

CAREER: University of Nevada, Las Vegas, instructor in drama, 1967-69, part-time instructor in drama, 1969-72; Edward W. Clark High School, Las Vegas, Nev., drama director, 1966-67, 1969-73. *Member:* Nevada State Council on the Arts, Phi Kappa Phi.

WRITINGS: The Dynamics of Acting, National Textbook Co., 1971; (with Jerry Crawford) *Acting: In Person and in Style,* W. C. Brown, 1976. Contributor to *Nevada Educational Journal.*

AVOCATIONAL INTERESTS: Travel.†

* * *

SNYDER, John P(arr) 1926-

PERSONAL: Born April 12, 1926, in Indianapolis, Ind.; son of Ralph W. (an accountant) and Freda (Parr) Snyder; married Jeanne Kallmeyer (a social worker), May 3, 1952; children: Barbara, Carolyn. *Education:* Purdue University, B.S.Ch.E., 1948; Massachusetts Institute of Technology,

S.M.Ch.E.P., 1949. *Politics:* Democratic. *Religion:* Quaker. *Home:* 32 Sherwood Ave., Madison, N.J. 07940. *Office:* CIBA-GEIGY Corp., 556 Morris Ave., Summit, N.J. 07901.

CAREER: CIBA-GEIGY Corp., Summit, N.J., 1956—, began as senior project engineer, currently part-time senior staff engineer. Part-time physical scientist for U.S. Geological Survey, 1978—. Registered as professional engineer in New Jersey and Ohio. Delegate to the Democratic National Convention, 1968. *Member:* American Institute of Chemical Engineers, American Congress on Surveying and Mapping. *Awards, honors:* Award of merit from American Association for State and Local History, 1970, for *The Story of New Jersey's Civil Boundaries, 1606-1968;* John Wesley Powell Award from U.S. Geological Survey, 1978.

WRITINGS: The Story of New Jersey's Civil Boundaries, 1606-1968, New Jersey Bureau of Geology and Topography, 1969; *The Mapping of New Jersey: The Men and the Art,* Rutgers University Press, 1973; *The Mapping of New Jersey in the American Revolution,* New Jersey Historical Commission, 1975. Contributor of articles on map projections to various journals.

*   *   *

SOCHEN, June   1937-

PERSONAL: Born November 26, 1937, in Chicago, Ill.; daughter of Sam (a grocer) and Ruth (Finkelstein) Sochen. *Education:* University of Chicago, B.A., 1958; Northwestern University, M.A., 1960, Ph.D., 1967. *Home:* 6238 North Harding Ave., Chicago, Ill. 60659. *Office:* Department of History, Northeastern Illinois University, Chicago, Ill. 60625.

CAREER: Northeastern Illinois University, Chicago, instructor, 1964-67, assistant professor, 1967-69, associate professor, 1969-72, professor of history, 1972—. *Member:* American Historical Association, American Studies Association. *Awards, honors:* National Endowment for the Humanities grant, 1971.

WRITINGS: (Editor) *The Black Man and the American Dream: 1900-1930,* Quadrangle, 1971; (editor) *The New Feminism in Twentieth Century America,* Heath, 1971; *The Unbridgeable Gap: Blacks and Their Quest for the American Dream,* Rand McNally, 1972; *The New Woman: Feminism in Greenwich Village, 1910-1920,* Quadrangle, 1972; (editor with Duke Frederick and William Howenstine) *Destroy to Create: Interaction with the Environment,* Dryden, 1972; *Movers and Shakers: American Women Thinkers and Activists, 1900-1970,* Quadrangle, 1973; *Herstory: A Woman's View of American History,* Alfred Publishing, 1974; (contributor) Martin Jackson and John O'Connor, editors, *American History/American Film,* Ungar, 1979.

WORK IN PROGRESS: The Eclectic American: A Study in Twentieth-Century U.S. Cultural History.

AVOCATIONAL INTERESTS: Reading, tennis, writing fiction.

*   *   *

SOLBERG, Winton U(dell)   1922-

PERSONAL: Born January 11, 1922, in Aberdeen, S.D.; son of Ole Alexander and Bertha G. (Tschappat) Solberg; married Ruth Constance Walton (a teacher), November 8, 1952; children: Gail Elizabeth, Andrew Walton, Kristin Ruth. *Education:* University of South Dakota, A.B. (magna cum laude), 1943; American University, Biarritz, France,

graduate study, 1946; Harvard University, A.M. 1947, Ph.D., 1954. *Religion:* Episcopal. *Home:* 508 West Delaware Ave., Urbana, Ill. 61801. *Office:* Department of History, 309 Gregory Hall, University of Illinois, Urbana, Ill. 61801.

CAREER: United States Military Academy, West Point, N.Y., instructor in history, 1951-54; Yale University, New Haven, Conn., instructor, 1954-56, assistant professor of history, 1956-58; Macalester College, St. Paul, Minn., James Wallace Professor of History, 1958-62; University of Illinois at Urbana-Champaign, associate professor, 1962-67, professor of history, 1967—, chairman of department, 1970-72. Fulbright lecturer, Johns Hopkins University, Bologna, Italy, 1967-68, and Moscow State University, 1978. *Military service:* U.S. Army, 1943-46, 1951-54; became lieutenant colonel. *Member:* American Historical Association, Organization of American Historians, American Studies Association, American Association of University Professors (member of national council, 1969-72; member of committee on academic freedom and tenure, 1968-77; first vice-president, 1974-76), Southern Historical Association, Phi Beta Kappa. *Awards, honors:* Morse Fellowship, Yale University, 1957-58; Huntington Library summer research fellow, 1959; National Endowment for the Humanities, senior fellowship, 1974-75.

WRITINGS: The Federal Convention and the Formation of the Union of American States, Bobbs-Merrill, 1958; *The University of Illinois, 1867-1894: An Intellectual and Cultural History,* University of Illinois Press, 1968; *Redeem the Time: The Puritan Sabbath in Early America,* Harvard University Press, 1977. Contributor to journals in his field.

WORK IN PROGRESS: A book on the coming of the American enlightenment.

*   *   *

SOLMON, Lewis C(alvin)   1942-

PERSONAL: Born July 17, 1942, in Toronto, Ontario, Canada; son of Eddie and Eva (Eisner) Solmon; married Vicki Reiken, July 15, 1965; children: Kira, Matthew. *Education:* University of Toronto, B.Com., 1964; University of Chicago, A.M., 1967, Ph.D., 1968. *Religion:* Jewish. *Office:* Higher Education Research Institute, 924 Westwood Blvd., Los Angeles, Calif. 90024.

CAREER: Purdue University, Krannert School of Industrial Administration, West Lafayette, Ind., assistant professor of economics, 1967-69; National Bureau of Economic Research, New York City, research fellow, 1969-70; City University of New York, New York City, assistant professor of economics at City College and Graduate School and University Center, 1970-72; National Research Council, Washington, D.C., staff director of Board on Human Resources, 1972-74; Higher Education Research Institute, Los Angeles, Calif., executive officer and secretary-treasurer. Research associate, National Bureau of Economic Research, 1970-74. Visiting associate professor, Virginia Polytechnic Institute, 1973-74; associate professor in residence, Graduate School of Education, University of California, Los Angeles. Member of Manpower Institute's Education-Manpower Council. *Member:* American Economic Association, American Economic History Association, American Association for Higher Education, American Educational Research Association. *Awards, honors:* National Academy of Education and National Academy of Sciences grant, 1971, to study quality of colleges; National Institute of Education grant, 1973, to study discrimination against women in graduate education; cited as one of one hundred top young leaders in American Academy by *Change,* 1978.

WRITINGS: Economics, Appleton, 1972, revised edition, Addison-Wesley, 1976; (co-author) *Does College Matter?: Some Evidence on the Impacts of Higher Education,* Academic Press, 1973; *Male and Female Graduate Students: The Question of Equal Opportunity,* Praeger, 1976; (with Ann S. Bisconti) *College Education on the Job—The Graduate's Viewpoint,* College Placement Council, 1976; (with Bisconti and Nancy L. Ochsner) *Job Satisfaction after College: The Graduate's Viewpoint,* College Placement Council, 1976; (with Bisconti) *College as Training Ground for Jobs,* Praeger, 1977; (with Ochsner and Margo-Lea Hurwicz) *The Labor Market for Humanities Ph.D.'s—An Empirical Analysis,* Praeger, in press. Also author of *Reassessing the Link between Work and Education,* Volume I: *New Directions for Education and Work,* 1978. Contributor to education and other journals, including *Change, Journal of Higher Education, National Review, Explorations in Economic Research, American Psychologist, Current Issues in Higher Education,* and *Journal of Educational Staffing.* Editor-in-chief, *New Directions for Education and Work,* Jossey-Bass, 1977—.

WORK IN PROGRESS: Research on the effects of quality of colleges on returns to education.†

*   *   *

SOLOMON, Janis Little   1938-
(Janis Little Gellinek)

PERSONAL: Born June 9, 1938, in Ranger, Tex.; daughter of Clarence L. (an engineer) and Lily May (Watkins) Little; married Christian Gellinek, June 5, 1962 (divorced, 1972); married Morton Solomon (a physician), 1978. *Education:* University of Texas, B.A., 1960; Albert-Ludwigs-Universitat, graduate study, 1960-61; Yale University, M.A., 1964, Ph.D., 1965. *Home:* 3 Northwood Rd., Quaker Hill, Conn. 06375. *Office:* Department of German, Box 1506, Connecticut College, New London, Conn. 06320.

CAREER: Connecticut College, New London, instructor, 1965-66, assistant professor, 1966-72, associate professor, 1972-78, professor of German, 1978—, head of department, 1971—. *Member:* Modern Language Association of America, American Association of University Professors, American Association of Teachers of German, Phi Beta Kappa. *Awards, honors:* Fulbright scholar, 1960-61; Woodrow Wilson fellow, 1961-62; Alexander-von-Humboldt fellow, 1972-73.

WRITINGS: (Under name Janis Little Gellinek) *Die Weltliche Lyrik von Martin Opitz,* Francke, 1972. Contributor of articles and reviews to journals in her field.

WORK IN PROGRESS: Articles on sixteenth- and seventeenth-century literature, also on Buechner and Nietzsche.

AVOCATIONAL INTERESTS: Music, painting, travel.

*   *   *

SOLOMON, Maynard (Elliott)   1930-

PERSONAL: Born January 5, 1930, in New York, N.Y.; son of Benjamin (an executive) and Dora (Levine) Solomon; married Eva Tevan, January 22, 1951; children: Mark, Nina, Maury. *Education:* Brooklyn College (now Brooklyn College of the City University of New York), B.A., 1950; Columbia University, graduate study, 1950-52. *Home:* 1 West 72nd St., New York, N.Y. 10023. *Office:* Vanguard Records, 71 West 23rd St., New York, N.Y. 10010.

CAREER: Vanguard Records, New York, N.Y., co-founder and co-owner, 1950—. *Member:* American Musicological Society, Record Industry Association of America (member of executive board, 1972-73), Phi Beta Kappa.

WRITINGS: Marxism and Art, Knopf, 1973; *Beethoven,* Schirmer, 1977; (contributor) Alan Tyson, editor, *Beethoven Studies,* Volume II, Oxford University Press, 1978; (editor) *Myth, Creativity, Psychoanalysis: Essays in Honor of Harry Slochower,* Wayne State University Press, 1978. Contributor of articles to *Musical Quarterly, Music and Letters, Music Review, American Imago,* and *Telos.* Associate editor, *American Imago.*

WORK IN PROGRESS: Two books, *The Origins of Music,* completion expected in 1980, and *Schubert,* completion expected in 1981; editing and translating *Aus dem Schwarzspanierhause,* by Gerhard von Breuning.

*   *   *

SOLOMON, Robert C(harles)   1942-

PERSONAL: Born September 14, 1942, in Detroit, Mich.; son of Charles M. (an attorney) and Vita (Petrosky) Solomon. *Education:* University of Pennsylvania, B.A., 1963; University of Michigan, M.A., 1965, Ph.D., 1967. *Office:* Department of Philosophy, University of Texas, Austin, Tex. 78712.

CAREER: Member of faculty of Princeton University, Princeton, N.J., 1966-68, of University of Southern California at Los Angeles, 1968-69, and University of Pittsburgh, Pittsburgh, Pa., 1969-71; University of Texas at Austin, 1972—, began as visiting associate professor, currently professor of philosophy. Has held visiting positions at University of Pennsylvania, University of Auckland, and La Trobe University. *Member:* American Philosophical Association.

WRITINGS: From Rationalism to Existentialism, Harper, 1972; *Phenomenology and Existentialism,* Harper, 1972; *Nietzsche,* Doubleday, 1973; *The Passions,* Doubleday, 1976; *Introducing Philosophy,* Harcourt, 1977; *Minerva's Bird: Philosophy in Europe 1750-1850,* Harcourt, 1979. Writer of several published and recorded songs.

WORK IN PROGRESS: In the Spirit of Hegel.

*   *   *

SOLOMON, Stanley J.   1937-

PERSONAL: Born January 3, 1937, in New York, N.Y.; son of David and Lee (Segal) Solomon; married Barbara Hochster (a professor of English), January 26, 1958; children: Nancy Jane, Jennifer Ann. *Education:* Brooklyn College (now Brooklyn College of the City University of New York), B.A., 1957; University of Kansas, M.A., 1960; Temple University, Ph.D., 1968. *Home:* 1 Edna Pl., New Rochelle, N.Y. *Office:* Department of English, Iona College, 715 North Ave., New Rochelle, N.Y. 10801.

CAREER: Doane College, Crete, Neb., instructor in English, 1960-62; Chatham College, Pittsburgh, Pa., instructor in English, 1962-64; Iona College, New Rochelle, N.Y., assistant professor, 1968-69, associate professor of English, 1969-72, professor of English, 1972—, chairman of department, 1971-74, administrator of communication arts department, 1973-76. Visiting assistant professor, Temple University, 1967-68. Elected chairman, New Rochelle Council of the Arts, 1976. *Member:* Modern Language Association of America (member of executive committee of Film Division, 1978-82), American Association of University Professors,

American Film Institute, Association for Multi-Image, Cinema Society, University Film Association.

WRITINGS: (Editor with Warren Kliewer) *Kansas Renaissance,* Coronado Press, 1961; *Armageddon; Stopover* (two one-act plays), Lutheran Church of America, 1969; *The Film Idea,* Harcourt, 1972; *The Classic Cinema: Essays in Criticism,* Harcourt, 1973; *Beyond Formula: American Film Genres,* Harcourt, 1976. Contributor of articles, poetry and fiction to periodicals, including *Modern Drama, Film Heritage, Western Humanities Review, Enlightenment Essays, Shaw Review, Victorian Poetry, Educational Theatre Journal, Journal of Narrative Technique, Erasmus Review, Carnegie Review, University Review, College English, Prairie Schooner,* and *Beloit Poetry Journal.*

WORK IN PROGRESS: A book on the theory of multi-image.

* * *

SORKIN, Alan Lowell 1941-

PERSONAL: Born November 2, 1941, in Baltimore, Md.; son of Martin and Sally (Sternberg) Sorkin; married Sylvia Jean Smardo, September 9, 1967; children: David Lowell, Suzanne Elizabeth. *Education:* Johns Hopkins University, B.A. (with honors), 1963, M.A., 1964, Ph.D., 1966. *Politics:* Republican. *Religion:* Roman Catholic. *Home:* 9110 Ramblebrook Rd., Baltimore, Md. 21236. *Office:* Department of Economics, University of Maryland Baltimore County, 5401 Wilkens Ave., Baltimore, Md. 21228.

CAREER: Bureau of Labor Statistics, Washington, D.C., economist, summers, 1963-64; Research Analysis Corp., McLean, Va., economic analyst, 1966-67; Brookings Institution, Washington, D.C., research associate in economics, 1967-69; Johns Hopkins University, Baltimore, Md., assistant professor, 1969-72, associate professor of international health and economics, 1972-74; University of Maryland Baltimore County, Baltimore, professor of economics and chairman of department, 1974—. Lecturer at Goucher College and George Washington University, 1966-67; part-time professor of health economics, University of Maryland Medical School, 1974—. *Member:* American Economic Association, Phi Beta Kappa.

WRITINGS: American Indians and Federal Aid, Brookings Institution, 1971; (with others) *Health and Economic Development: An Annotated, Indexed Bibliography,* Department of International Health, Johns Hopkins University, 1972; *Education, Unemployment and Economic Growth,* Heath Lexington, 1974; *Health Economics: An Introduction,* Heath Lexington, 1975; *Health Economics for Developing Nations,* Heath Lexington, 1976; *Health Manpower: An Economic Perspective,* Heath Lexington, 1977; *The Urban American Indian: An Interdisciplinary Focus,* Heath Lexington, 1978. Contributor of more than thirty articles and reviews to education and social science journals, including *Journal of Negro Education, Growth and Change: A Journal of Regional Development, Social Forces, College and University, Monthly Labor Review, American Journal of Economics and Sociology, Journal of Economic Studies,* and *Journal of Economic Literature.*

WORK IN PROGRESS: Research on correlates of declining birth rates in Punjab; a monograph on the economic aspects of health manpower; a study of the economic and social position of American Indians living in cities.

SOWELL, Thomas 1930-

PERSONAL: Born June 30, 1930, in Gastonia, N.C.; married Alma Jean Parr; children: two. *Education:* Harvard University, A.B. (magna cum laude), 1958; Columbia University, A.M., 1959; University of Chicago, Ph.D., 1968. *Office:* Urban Institute, 2100 M St. N.W., Washington, D.C. 20037.

CAREER: U.S. Department of Labor, Washington, D.C., economist, 1961-62; Rutgers University, Douglass College, New Brunswick, N.J., instructor in economics, 1962-63; Howard University, Washington, D.C., lecturer in economics, 1963-64; American Telephone & Telegraph Co., New York, N.Y., economic analyst, 1964-65; Cornell University, Ithaca, N.Y., assistant professor of economics, 1965-69, director of Summer Intensive Training Program in Economic Theory, 1968; Brandeis University, Waltham, Mass., associate professor of economics, 1969-70; University of California, Los Angeles, associate professor of economics, 1970-72; Urban Institute, Washington, D.C., project director, 1972—.

WRITINGS: (Contributor) I. H. Rima, editor, *Readings in the History of Economic Thought,* Holt, 1970; *Economics: Analysis and Issues,* Scott, Foresman, 1971; *Black Education: Myths and Tragedies,* McKay, 1972; *Say's Law: An Historical Analysis,* Princeton University Press, 1972; *Classical Economics Reconsidered,* Princeton University Press, 1974; *Affirmative Action Reconsidered: Was It Necessary in Academia?,* American Enterprise Publications, 1975; *Race and Economics,* Longman, 1975. Contributor to *History of Political Economy, Oxford Economic Papers, Canadian Journal of Economics and Political Science, Industrial and Labor Relations Review, Economica, American Economic Review, Social Research, Ethics, Bell Telephone Magazine, Quarterly Review of Economics and Business, AAUP Bulletin, Education Digest, Western Review, Journal of Economic Issues, University of Chicago Magazine, Congressional Record, New York Times Magazine, Review of Black Political Economy,* and *Administrative Science Quarterly.*†

* * *

SPALDING, Billups Phinizy 1930-

PERSONAL: Born September 29, 1930, in Atlanta, Ga.; son of D. Hughes and Bolling (Phinizy) Spalding; married Margaret Anne Roscoe, August 18, 1969; children: Billups Phinizy, Jr., David Bushrod, Margaret Hughes. *Education:* University of Georgia, A.B., 1953, M.A., 1957; University of North Carolina, Ph.D., 1963. *Politics:* Democratic. *Religion:* Roman Catholic. *Home:* 573 Hill St., Athens, Ga. 30606. *Office:* Department of History, University of Georgia, Athens, Ga. 30601.

CAREER: College of Charleston, Charleston, S.C., assistant professor of history, 1963-66; University of Georgia, Athens, assistant professor, 1966-70, associate professor of history, 1970—. Fulbright lecturer, University of Genoa, 1976. Member of state and regional history panel, National Endowment for the Humanities; chairman, Phinizy Lectureships; member of national Register Review Board, state of Georgia; curator of Georgia Historical Society, 1967—; director of University of Georgia Foundation, 1968—; trustee of Athens-Clarke Heritage Foundation. *Military service:* U.S. Navy, 1953-55. *Member:* Le Petite Club Francais (London), Johnson Society (England), Southern Historical Association, Georgia Conservancy, Georgia Historical Society, Athens Historical Society (president, 1969), Athens

Country Club, Piedmont Driving Club. *Awards, honors:* Southern Books Award, 1968, for *The Merit and Reward of a Good Intention.*

WRITINGS: The Merit and Reward of a Good Intention, Ashantilly Press, 1968; *Oglethorpe in America,* University of Chicago Press, 1977; *History of Georgia,* University of Georgia Press, 1977. Contributor to *Georgia Review, South Carolina Historical Magazine, Georgia Law Review, Georgia Historical Quarterly, Journal of Mississippi History,* and others. Editor, *Georgia Historical Quarterly,* 1974—.

WORK IN PROGRESS: History of the Medical College of Georgia; research on the Roman Catholic Irish of Savannah and Charleston.

* * *

SPEELMAN, Arlene 1916-

PERSONAL: Born July 17, 1916, in Dubuque, Iowa; daughter of John Robert (a car salesman) and Sada (McGarvey) Frentress; married Milton Sacks (a hospital administrator), December 31, 1963. *Education:* University of Iowa, B.S., 1938; University of Chicago, M.S., 1948. *Religion:* Protestant. *Residence:* Naples, Fla.

CAREER: University of Colorado at the Colorado State Hospital, Pueblo, instructor in psychiatric nursing, 1941-44; Methodist Hospital, Madison, Wis., director of nursing education, 1944-46; Idaho State Hospital, Blackfoot, Idaho, director of nursing service and education, 1950-52; Copley Memorial Hospital, Aurora, Ill., director of nursing service and education, 1952-55; Dixon State School for Mentally Retarded, Dixon, Ill., director of practical nursing school, 1955-61. Member of the board of Flint Visiting Nurse Association; member of budget committee of Genesee County United Way; treasurer of East Central District Hospital Auxiliaries. *Member:* American Association of University Women, American Association of Retired Persons, American Hibiscus Society, Canaan Club of America (vice-president, 1972-73, president, 1973-75).

WRITINGS: Examination Review for Practical Nurses, Putnam, 1962, 3rd edition, 1976. Also author of *Emotional Aspects of Growth and Development.*

SIDELIGHTS: Arlene Speelman says her principal hobby is "gourmet cooking for large groups." She has a collection of over 300 cookbooks. She is also active in the Canaan Club of America, as the owner of one of these rare dogs. This breed was mentioned in the Bible, and there are about 300 in the United States today. Speelman also grows fifty varieties of specimen hibiscus.

* * *

SPENCER, Edgar Winston 1931-

PERSONAL: Born May 27, 1931, in Monticello, Ark.; son of Terrel Ford Spencer; married Elizabeth Humphris, November 28, 1958; children: Elizabeth Shawn, Kristen Shannon. *Education:* Washington & Lee University, B.S., 1953; Columbia University, Ph.D., 1957. *Politics:* Independent. *Religion:* Unitarian Universalist. *Address:* P.O. Box 1055, Lexington, Va. 24450. *Office:* Department of Geology, Washington & Lee University, Lexington, Va. 24450.

CAREER: Hunter College of City University of New York, New York, N.Y., lecturer, 1954-56, instructor in geology, 1957; Washington & Lee University, Lexington, Va., assistant professor and acting chairman of department, 1957-59,

associate professor, 1959-63, professor of geology, 1963—, chairman of department, 1959—. *Member:* Geological Society of America (fellow), American Geophysical Union, American Association of Petroleum Geologists, National Association of Geology Teachers, Phi Beta Kappa, Sigma Xi. *Awards, honors:* National Science Foundation faculty fellow in tectonics in New Zealand and Australia, 1965-66.

WRITINGS: Basic Concepts of Physical Geology, Crowell, 1962; *Basic Concepts of Historical Geology,* Crowell, 1962; *Geology: A Survey of Earth Science,* Crowell, 1965; *Introduction to the Structure of the Earth,* McGraw, 1969, 2nd edition, 1977; *The Dynamics of the Earth,* Crowell, 1972.

WORK IN PROGRESS: Research on the structure of the Appalachian Mountains in Virginia.

* * *

SPIEGEL, Don(ald Elwin) 1926-

PERSONAL: Born May 6, 1926, in Randall, Kan.; son of Jacob A. (a farmer) and Laura (Levi) Spiegel; married Patricia Keith (a professor of psychology), June 17, 1966; children: Gary Brian. *Education:* University of Kansas, B.A., 1951, M.A., 1955, Ph.D., 1958. *Home and office:* 5143 Tyrone Ave., Sherman Oaks, Calif. 91403.

CAREER: Trainee in clinical psychology at Veterans Administration Hospitals in Topeka, Kan. and Kansas City, Mo., 1954-58; Brentwood Veterans Administration Neuropsychiatric Hospital, Los Angeles, Calif., clinical research psychologist, 1958-71; University of California, Los Angeles, adjunct associate professor of psychiatry, 1970-75; Veterans Administration Extended Care Hospital, Los Angeles, Calif., chief of restoration program, 1971-72. Vice-president, Psychological Center, Los Angeles, 1972-73. *Military service:* U.S. Army, 1951-53. *Member:* American Psychological Association, California State Psychological Association, Los Angeles County Psychological Association. *Awards, honors:* National Institute of Mental Health grant to compare community volunteer programs, 1969-72.

WRITINGS: (Editor with wife, Patricia Keith-Spiegel, and contributor) *Outsiders USA: Original Essays on Twenty-Four Outgroups in American Society,* Rinehart, 1973. Contributor of over forty articles to psychology and psychiatry journals.

WORK IN PROGRESS: Ex-Mental Patients for Social Action; The Spiegel Personality Inventory; The Spiegel Environmental Relations Inventory.

* * *

SPIER, Robert F(orest) G(ayton) 1922-

PERSONAL: Surname sounds like "spear"; born June 12, 1922, in Seattle, Wash.; son of Leslie and Erna (Gunther) Spier; married Veva Drake, March 15, 1951; children: Martha, Stephen. *Education:* Attended University of New Mexico, 1942; University of California, Berkeley, B.A., 1947; Harvard University, A.M., 1949, Ph.D., 1954. *Home:* 708 Morningside Dr., Columbia, Mo. 65201. *Office:* Department of Anthropology, University of Missouri, Columbia, Mo. 65211.

CAREER: University of Missouri—Columbia, instructor in anthropology, 1949-51; University of Minnesota, Minneapolis, instructor in anthropology, 1951-52; University of Missouri—Columbia, instructor, 1952-54, assistant professor, 1954-61, associate professor, 1961-66, professor of anthropology, 1966—. Visiting associate professor, University of

Oregon, 1962-63; visiting professor at Oregon State System of Higher Education, summer, 1957, University of Wisconsin, summer, 1958, University of California, Berkeley, summers, 1965, 1966, 1973, and Indiana University, summer, 1967. Commissioner of City of Columbia Board of Electrical Examiners, 1971-77. *Military service:* U.S. Army, 1942-46. *Member:* American Anthropological Association (fellow), Society for the History of Technology, Central States Anthropological Society. *Awards, honors:* Wenner-Gren Foundation grant-in-aid, 1956; North Atlantic Treaty Organization science fellowship, 1960-61; National Science Foundation grant, 1961-62, for the development of teaching aids in basic anthropometry; American Philosophical Society, Penrose Fund grant-in-aid, 1964.

WRITINGS: Field Handbook on the Human Skeleton, Missouri Archaeological Society, 1962; (with D. R. Henning and J. R. Vincent) *Graphic Teaching Aids in Basic Anthropometry,* University of Missouri Press, 1962; (contributor) J. A. Clifton, editor, *Introduction to Cultural Anthropology,* Houghton, 1968; *From the Hand of Man: Primitive and Preindustrial Technology,* Houghton, 1970; *Surveying and Mapping: A Manual of Simplified Techniques,* Holt, 1970; (contributor) *Handbook of North American Indians,* revised edition, Smithsonian Institution, 1978. Contributor to *Southwestern Journal of Anthropology, American Anthropologist, Missouri Archaeologist, Man, Ethnohistory, California Historical Society Quarterly, Actas, American Antiquity, Social Progress, Encyclopedia Americana,* and *American Historical Anthropology.* Advisory editor to *Technology and Culture,* 1963—.

WORK IN PROGRESS: Museum studies of Norwegian-American tools.

AVOCATIONAL INTERESTS: Handcrafts, bicycling, race-walking.

* * *

SPIER, William H. 1907(?)-1973

1907(?)—May 30, 1973; American radio and television scriptwriter, director, and producer. Obituaries: *New York Times,* June 1, 1973.

* * *

SPITZ, David 1916-

PERSONAL: Born December 13, 1916, in New York, N.Y.; son of Geza and Irma (Lampel) Spitz; married Ruth Sachere (a labor economist), October 25, 1942 (divorced January, 1975); married Elaine Wollan Mates (a political theorist), February 9, 1975; children: (first marriage) Deborah, Janet. *Education:* College of the City of New York (now City College of the City University of New York), B.S.S. (with honors), 1937; Columbia University, A.M., 1939, Ph.D., 1948. *Home:* 6 Beaver Dr., Locust Valley, N.Y. 11560. *Office:* Graduate School and University Center of the City University of New York, 33 West 42nd St., New York, N.Y. 10036.

CAREER: Ohio State University, Columbus, instructor, 1947-49, assistant professor, 1949-52, associate professor, 1952-57, professor of political science, 1957-70; City University of New York, Hunter College and Graduate School and University Center, New York, N.Y., professor of political science, 1970—. Visiting professor at Hunter College (now Hunter College of the City University of New York), summer, 1954, Cornell University, 1958-59, and Kenyon College, 1960-61; Fulbright visiting professor, Johns Hopkins

University, Bologna Center, 1962-63; visiting professor at American seminar in political science, Nice, France, summer, 1963, and University of California, Berkeley, summer, 1967. *Military service:* U.S. Army, 1941-45.

MEMBER: American Political Science Association, American Society for Political and Legal Philosophy, Conference for the Study of Political Thought, American Association of University Professors, American Civil Liberties Union, National Association for the Advancement of Colored People. *Awards, honors:* Professor of the Year, College of Arts and Sciences, Ohio State University, 1950; fellowships from Fund for the Advancement of Education, 1951-52, Fund for the Republic, 1955, Rockefeller Foundation, 1955-56, 1960, 1978-79, and National Endowment for the Humanities, 1976; LL.D., Dillard University, 1978.

WRITINGS: Patterns of Anti-Democratic Thought, Macmillan, 1949, revised edition, Free Press, 1965; *Democracy and the Challenge of Power,* Columbia University Press, 1958; *The Liberal Idea of Freedom,* University of Arizona Press, 1964; (editor) *Political Theory and Social Change,* Atherton, 1967; (editor) R. M. MacIver, *Politics and Society,* Atherton, 1969; (editor) John Stuart Mill, *On Liberty,* Norton, 1975. Member of editorial board of *Dissent.*

WORK IN PROGRESS: Research on liberty, equality, power, and liberalism.

* * *

SPITZER, Morton Edward

PERSONAL: Born in New York, N.Y.; son of Henry Lawrence (a salesman) and Martha (Miscel) Spitzer; married Nancy Dinetz, October 10, 1965; children: Matthew Cook, Douglas Sherman. *Education:* Brooklyn College (now Brooklyn College of the City University of New York), B.A., 1957; North Carolina State University, M.S., 1959; New York University, Ph.D., 1964. *Home:* 14726 Oak Bend, Houston, Tex. 77079. *Office:* Prudential Insurance Co., 6500 West Loop S., Bellaire, Tex. 77401.

CAREER: Standard Oil of New Jersey, New York City, research assistant, 1958-60; Brooklyn College of the City University of New York, New York City, instructor in psychology, 1960-62; International Business Machines Corp., New York City, research associate, 1962-63; Prudential Insurance Co., associate director in Newark, N.J., beginning 1964, currently vice-president of marketing in Bellaire, Tex. Adjunct associate professor at Graduate Business School, New York University, 1969-76. *Member:* American Psychological Association, American Association for the Advancement of Science, Eastern Psychological Association, Metropolitan New York Association for Applied Psychology (president, 1971-72), Sigma Xi.

WRITINGS: (With William C. Byham) *The Law and Personnel Testing,* American Management Association, 1971. Contributor to *Personnel Psychology* and *Journal of Experimental Psychology.*

AVOCATIONAL INTERESTS: Historical reading, poetry, tennis, travel.

* * *

SPRAGENS, William C(lark) 1925-

PERSONAL: Born October 1, 1925, in Lebanon, Ky.; son of T. Eugene (a banker) and Edna (Clark) Spragens; married Elaine Dunham, June 14, 1964. *Education:* University of Kentucky, A.B., 1947, M.A., 1952; Michigan State University, Ph.D., 1966. *Politics:* Democratic Party. *Religion:*

Presbyterian. *Home:* 607 Lafayette Ave., Bowling Green, Ohio 43402. *Office:* Department of Political Science, Bowling Green State University, Bowling Green, Ohio 43403.

CAREER: Lexington Herald, Lexington, Ky., assistant state editor, 1947-50; *Owensboro Messenger,* Owensboro, Ky., city editor, 1952-55; *Dayton Journal Herald,* Dayton, Ohio, political writer, 1955-58; *Fort Wayne Journal-Gazette,* Fort Wayne, Ind., editor and political writer, 1958-60; University of Tennessee, Knoxville, instructor in political science, 1962-64; Millikin University, Decatur, Ill., assistant professor of political science, 1965-67; Wisconsin State University (now University of Wisconsin), Oshkosh, assistant professor of political science, 1967-69; Bowling Green State University, Bowling Green, Ohio, associate professor of political science, 1969—. *Military service:* U.S. Army, 1943-45. *Member:* International Institute for Sociological Research (life fellow), American Political Science Association, American Academy of Political and Social Sciences, Academy of Political Science, Center for the Study of Democratic Institutions, Midwest Political Science Association, Southern Political Science Association, Center for the Study of the Presidency.

WRITINGS: (Contributor) Joseph S. Roucek, editor, *The Slow Learner,* Philosophical Library, 1969; (with Robert W. Russell) *Conflict and Crisis in American Politics,* Kendall/Hunt, 1970; (contributor) Roucek and Thomas Kiernan, editors, *The Negro Impact on Western Civilization,* Philosophical Library, 1970; *The Presidency and the Mass Media in the Age of Television,* University Press of America, 1978. Contributor of articles and book reviews to *Midwest Journal of Political Science, Political Science Quarterly, Western Political Quarterly, Journal of Negro History, International Behavioural Scientist, Il Politico,* and *Wisconsin Review.*

WORK IN PROGRESS: Public policy workbook; biography of White House press secretaries.

SIDELIGHTS: William Spragens is active in Wood County and Ohio politics. He ran for election as an alternate delegate for George McGovern from Ohio to the 1972 Democratic National Convention. Although defeated, he received more than 400,000 votes. During 1978 he served as a policy analyst on the Democratic National Committee staff in Washington, D.C.

* * *

SPRAGUE, Howard B(ennet) 1898-

PERSONAL: Born December 11, 1898, in Cortland, Neb.; son of Elmer Ellsworth (a minister) and Lucy Kent (Manville) Sprague; married J. Barbara Stetson, March 1, 1944; children: Kent Merriman. *Education:* University of Nebraska, B.S., 1921, M.S., 1923; Rutgers University, Ph.D., 1926. *Home:* 560 West Ridge, State College, Pa. 16801. *Office:* 1010 16th St. N.W., Washington, D.C. 20036.

CAREER: University of Minnesota, Minneapolis, assistant professor of agronomy, 1926-27; Rutgers University, New Brunswick, N.J., associate professor, 1927-28, professor of agronomy, 1928-42, department chairman, 1927-42; Texas Research Foundation, Renner, director of Agricultural Research Division, 1946-53; Pennsylvania State University, University Park, professor of agronomy, department chairman, and chairman of Plant Sciences Division, 1953-64; U.S. National Academy of Sciences, and National Research Council, Washington, D.C., executive secretary, 1964-68; U.S. Agency for International Development, Washington,

D.C., agricultural consultant, 1968—. *Military service:* U.S. Army, 1917-19. U.S. Army Air Forces, 1942-46. U.S. Air Force, 1951-53. U.S. Air Force Reserve, 1953-61; became colonel. *Member:* American Society of Agronomy (fellow; president, 1964; honorary member, 1977), American Association for the Advancement of Science (fellow; section vice-president, 1956; executive secretary, 1958-66), American Grassland Council (president, 1953-56), Crop Science Society of America (president, 1960), American Forage and Grassland Council (president, 1953-56), American Society of Range Management, Genetics Society of America, Plant Physiology Society, Society of American Military Engineers, Soil Conservation Society of America. *Awards, honors:* Medallion award from American Forage and Grassland Council, 1964.

WRITINGS: Better Lawns, McGraw, 1941; *Grasslands: Their Role in the Agriculture of the U.S.,* American Association for the Advancement of Science, 1958; *Hunger Signs in Crops,* McKay, 1964; *Turf Management Handbook,* Interstate, 1970; *Field Guide on the Production and Harvest of Staple Food Crops and Associated Cash Crops in the Tropics and Subtropics,* U.S. Agency for International Development, 1972. Contributor of more than twenty-five scientific and professional articles to science journals and agricultural bulletins.

* * *

SPRUNGER, Keith L(a Verne) 1935-

PERSONAL: Born March 16, 1935, in Berne, Ind.; son of Arley and Lillian (Mettler) Sprunger; married Aldine Mary Slagell, June 13, 1959; children: David, Mary, Philip. *Education:* Wheaton College, Wheaton, Ill., B.A., 1957; University of Illinois, M.A., 1958, Ph.D., 1963. *Politics:* Independent. *Religion:* Mennonite. *Home:* 2412 College Ave., North Newton, Kan. 67117. *Office:* Department of History, Bethel College, North Newton, Kan. 67117.

CAREER: High school history teacher in Berne, Ind., 1958-60; Bethel College, North Newton, Kan., assistant professor, 1963-66, associate professor, 1966-70, professor of history, 1970—, head of department, 1963—, head of Social Studies Division, 1970-73, 1977-79. *Member:* American Historical Association, American Society of Church History, Conference on Faith and History, Conference on British Studies, American Association of University Professors, Kansas History Teachers Association, Pi Gamma Mu, Phi Alpha Theta. *Awards, honors:* American Council of Learned Societies summer research grant, 1967; American Philosophical Society summer research grant, 1967; Social Science Research Council grant, 1969; American Philosophical Society grant, 1969; E. Harris Harbison Award, Danforth Foundation, 1972; American Council of Learned Societies fellowship, 1976-77.

WRITINGS: The Learned Doctor William Ames, University of Illinois Press, 1972; *Voices against War,* Bethel College, 1973; (contributor) *Handbook to the History of Christianity,* Eerdmans, 1977. Contributor of articles and book reviews to *Church History, Harvard Theological Review, New England Quarterly, Mennonite Quarterly Review, Journal of the History of Ideas, Historian, Mennonite Life,* and *Bethel College Bulletin.* Associate editor of *Fides et Historia,* 1973—.

WORK IN PROGRESS: A book tentatively entitled, *Puritanism in the Netherlands: A History of English and Scottish Churches, 1550-1700;* an oral history of conscientious objection.

SIDELIGHTS: Keith L. Sprunger told CA: "My long range interest in history is English-Dutch Puritanism. History for me is also a personal exploration of values and identity—Mennonite, Anabaptist history, the story of conscientious objection in World War I, World War II, the Vietnam War. Our Bethel history department is building an oral history collection of the experiences of Mennonite conscientious objectors, which is of more than academic concern to me."

* * *

STABLER, Arthur P(hillips) 1919-

PERSONAL: Born April 23, 1919, in Sandy Spring, Md.; son of Frederic and Mary (Phillips) Stabler; married Jane Gamble, April 26, 1944 (divorced, 1974); married Nancy Nadas, June 25, 1975; children: (first marriage) Frederic, Jennifer. Education: University of Pennsylvania, B.A., 1941, M.A., 1947; University of Virginia, Ph.D., 1958. Politics: Liberal. Office: Department of Foreign Languages and Literatures, Washington State University, Pullman, Wash. 99163.

CAREER: Bowdoin College, Brunswick, Me., instructor in French, 1947-49; University of Virginia, Charlottesville, instructor in French, 1949-51, 1956-58; Denison University, Granville, Ohio, instructor in French and German, 1952-56; North Texas State University, Denton, assistant professor of French and German, 1958-59; Lake Erie College, Painesville, Ohio, associate professor of foreign languages and director of language skills, 1959-61; University of Massachusetts—Amherst, associate professor of French, 1961-62; Washington State University, Pullman, associate professor, 1962-65, professor of foreign languages and literatures, 1966—. Military service: U.S. Army, Infantry, 1943-46. U.S. Army Reserve, 1951-66; military intelligence; became captain. Member: Modern Language Association of America, American Association of Teachers of French, Renaissance Society of America, Philological Association of the Pacific Coast, Western Shakespeare Seminar, Phi Beta Kappa. Awards, honors: Medal of Alliance Francaise, 1940; Fulbright scholar at University of Grenoble, 1951-52.

WRITINGS: The Legend of Marguerite de Roberval, Washington State University Press, 1972; Four French Renaissance Plays, Washington State University Press, 1978. Contributor to Modern Language Association publications, Studies in Philology, Shakespeare Studies, Etudes Anglaises, Etudes rabelaisiennes, Bibliotheque d'Humanisme et Renaissance, and other journals. Contributing editor, Shakespeare Newsletter, 1973—.

WORK IN PROGRESS: With Roger Schlesinger, Andre Thevet on North America; a "Great American novel."

SIDELIGHTS: Arthur Stabler wrote to CA: "Like many another who yearned to write, I spent the better part of my first half-century in frustration, paralyzed in front of the page blanche (you should have studied French). Then I got going on some academic writing . . . which served two functions: it broke the paralysis, and gave me much valuable practice in the art, the drudgery of writing. . . . Now, concurrently with my academic writing, I am several hundreds of pages along with my real work, my magnum opus, which intends to be a threat to Proust, Thomas Wolfe, and Nabokov (to whom it will owe much). The message, then, is go ahead and write: write anything, but write for publication; it is the best discipline. And don't give up!'' .

BIOGRAPHICAL/CRITICAL SOURCES: Shakespeare Newsletter, December, 1972; New England Quarterly, June, 1973.

STAHL, O(scar) Glenn 1910-

PERSONAL: Born April 30, 1910, in Evansville, Ind.; son of Oscar A. (a business executive) and Mayme (Wittmer) Stahl; married Marie Jane Rueter, June 26, 1934; children: Elaine Marie (Mrs. Gerhard W. Leo), Alan G. Education: Evansville College (now University of Evansville), B.A., 1931; University of Wisconsin, M.A., 1933; New York University, Ph.D., 1936. Politics: Independent. Religion: Presbyterian. Home and office: 3600 North Piedmont St., Arlington, Va. 22207.

CAREER: Tennessee Valley Authority, Washington, D.C., personnel worker, 1935-41; Federal Security Agency (now Department of Health, Education and Welfare), Washington, D.C., chief of classification and deputy director of personnel, 1941-48, director of personnel, 1948-51; Federal Personnel Council, Washington, D.C., executive vice-chairman, 1951-54; U.S. Civil Service Commission, Washington, D.C., director of bureau of policies and standards, 1955-69; International Personnel Management Association, Washington, D.C., Washington representative, 1971-73, special consultant, 1973-76; Public Administration Service-Governmental Affairs Institute, Washington, D.C., special consultant, 1973-75. Former faculty member at New York University, 1933-35, University of Tennessee, 1939, graduate school of U.S. Department of Agriculture, 1941-49; adjunct professor of public administration at American University, 1949-69. Visiting lecturer at Florida State University, University of Southern California, University of Chicago, Dartmouth College, University of Virginia, University of Wisconsin, Princeton University, Karachi University, New Delhi University, Tribhuvan University, Nova University, University of Denver, University of Pittsburgh, George Mason University, and Mississippi State University. A representative of the United States at international conferences in Ethiopia, Costa Rica, Ireland, Soviet Union, Austria, Germany; United Nations technical advisor to Venezuela, 1958 and 1972; Ford Foundation consultant to India and Nepal 1968, 1969, and 1971, and to Pakistan, 1974; Agency for International Development advisor to Pakistan, 1969, 1971. Member of Arlington County School Board, 1948-50; president of Arlington Committee to Preserve Public Schools, 1958-61. Member: International Personnel Management Association (member of executive council, 1951-54; president, 1965-66), American Political Science Association, American Society for Public Administration. Awards, honors: U.S. Civil Service Commission distinguished service award, 1960; Stockberger Award from Society for Personnel Administration, 1961; Career Service Award of National Civil Service League, 1967; honorary life membership in International Personnel Management Association, 1968.

WRITINGS: Training Career Public Servants for the City of New York, New York University Press, 1936; (with William E. Mosher and others) Public Personnel Administration, 4th edition (Stahl was not associated with earlier editions), Harper, 1956, 6th edition (sole author), 1971, 7th edition, 1976; The Personnel Job of Government Managers, International Personnel Management Association, 1971; (co-editor) Police Personnel Administration, Police Foundation, 1974. Contributor of over fifty articles to journals. Editor of Personnel Administration, 1945-55.

WORK IN PROGRESS: Short stories about his wife's colonial-era ancestors.

SIDELIGHTS: Some editions of O. Glenn Stahl's Public Personnel Administration have been published in Spanish and some in Japanese.

STALDER, Valerie

PERSONAL: Born in Reading, England; daughter of Lawrence Martin (a chemical export director) and Gladys (Vale) Whittington; married Moritz Stalder; married Terje Jacobsen (an architect). *Education:* Educated in private school in Reading, England. *Politics:* "Varies." *Religion:* "Still waiting for one to convince me." *Home and office:* Polarhiet, Holtveien, Tromsoe, Norway.

CAREER: Writer and professional photographer. *Member:* Professional Photographers of America, Royal Photographic Society (England), Society of Authors (England). *Awards, honors:* Has won prizes in Kodak International Color Competition, at World's Fair of New York, 1964; Asahi Pentax International Photography Contest, 1965; Time/Life "made in Japan" photography contest, 1967.

WRITINGS: (With photographs by author) *Lappland: Journey by Reindeer Sledge,* Kodansha, 1971; *Legends and Folktales of Lappland,* Mowbrays, 1972; *Even the Devil Is Afraid of a Shrew,* Addison-Wesley, 1972. Contributor to magazines throughout the world.

WORK IN PROGRESS: Three books on cancer: "the first from the point of view of the patient, the second an attack on doctors, and the third a novel about how two different women cope with the same problem."

SIDELIGHTS: Valerie Stalder's works in progress are inspired by her own struggle against cancer. "I think I am at last coming out on top," she added. She speaks French, German, Spanish, Swiss-German, Norwegian, and Italian. *Avocational interests:* Music, dancing, food and cooking (has won prizes for her cooking), embroidery, clothes, and winter sports.

* * *

STAMBOLIAN, George 1938-

PERSONAL: Born April 10, 1938, in Bridgeport, Conn.; son of John George (a tailor) and Rose (Alboyagian) Stambolian. *Education:* Dartmouth College, B.A., 1960; University of Wisconsin, M.A., 1961, Ph.D., 1969; also studied at Sorbonne, University of Paris, 1962-63. *Residence:* Wellesley, Mass. *Office:* Department of French, Wellesley College, Wellesley, Mass. 02181.

CAREER: Wellesley College, Wellesley, Mass., 1965—, began as assistant professor, currently professor of French and comparative literature, chairman of department of French, 1975-78. *Member:* Modern Language Association of America, American Association of University Professors, Societe des Amis de Marcel Proust, Proust Research Association, Beckett Society, Northeast Theatre Conference, Phi Beta Kappa.

WRITINGS: Marcel Proust and the Creative Encounter, University of Chicago Press, 1972; (editor) *Twentieth Century Fiction: Essays for Germaine Bree,* Rutgers University Press, 1975; (editor with Elaine Marks) *Homosexualities and French Literature,* Cornell University Press, 1979. Contributor to *Journal of Popular Culture* and *Christopher Street.*

WORK IN PROGRESS: A book on contemporary representation of the human body in literature and the visual arts.

AVOCATIONAL INTERESTS: Archaeology, diplomatic and military history, modern art.

* * *

STANDLEY, Fred L(loyd) 1932-

PERSONAL: Born December 3, 1932, in Huntington, W.Va.; son of Lloyd A. and Dorothy P. (Adkins) Standley; married Nancy V. Pav (a professor), September 8, 1956. *Education:* West Virginia Wesleyan College, B.A., 1954; Garrett Theological Seminary, M.Div., 1959; Northwestern University, M.A., 1959, Ph.D., 1963. *Politics:* Democrat. *Religion:* Methodist. *Home:* 2412 Perez Ave., Tallahassee, Fla. 32304. *Office:* Department of English, Florida State University, Tallahassee, Fla. 32306.

CAREER: MacMurray College, Jacksonville, Ill., instructor in English, 1959-60; Florida State University, Tallahassee, assistant professor, 1963-68, associate professor, 1968-72, professor of English, 1972—, chairman of department, 1973—. *Member:* Modern Language Association of America, National Council of Teachers of English, College English Association, American Association of University Professors, American Civil Liberties Union, Society for Values in Higher Education (fellow), South Atlantic Modern Language Association. *Awards, honors:* National Endowment for Humanities summer fellowship, 1969; Florida State University faculty development grant, 1971.

WRITINGS: Stopford Brooke, Twayne, 1972; (contributor) Richard Layman, editor, *American Novelists since World War II,* Gale, 1978; *James Baldwin: A Reference Guide,* G. K. Hall, 1979.

WORK IN PROGRESS: James Baldwin: Disturber of the Peace.

* * *

STANLEY, George F(rancis) G(ilman) 1907-

PERSONAL: Born July 6, 1907, in Calgary, Alberta, Canada; son of John Henry (a business executive) and Della Catherine (Lillywhite) Stanley; married Ruth Lynette Hill, August 26, 1946; children: Della Margaret Maude, Marietta Ruth Ellen, Laurie Catherine Christina. *Education:* University of Alberta, B.A., 1929; Keble College, Oxford, B.A., 1931, B.Litt., 1933, M.A. and D.Phil., 1936. *Religion:* Anglican. *Home address:* Frosty Hollow, Rural Route 1, Sackville, New Brunswick, Canada.

CAREER: Mount Allison University, Sackville, New Brunswick, professor of history, 1936-40; University of British Columbia, Vancouver, professor of Canadian history, 1947-49; Royal Military College of Canada, Kingston, Ontario, professor of history and head of department, 1949-69, dean of arts, 1963-69; Mount Allison University, director of Canadian studies, 1969-75. Former member, Archaeological and Historic Sites Board of Ontario. *Military service:* Canadian Army, deputy director of historical section, General Staff Overseas, 1940-47; became lieutenant colonel; received Chevalier de l'Ordre Militaire et Hospitalier de St. Lazare.

MEMBER: Royal Society of Canada (fellow), Company of Military Historians (governor, 1967-74), Royal Historical Society (fellow), Institut d'histoire de l'amerique francaise, Kingston Historical Society (past president), Canadian Historical Association (past president). *Awards, honors:* Rhodes scholar, 1929; Guggenheim fellow, 1948-49; Tyrrell medal from Royal Society of Canada, 1957; D.esL., Universite Laval, 1965; D.Litt., Mount Allison University, 1967, University of New Brunswick, 1975; LL.D., St. Dunstans University, 1969, University of Alberta, 1971, Royal Military College, 1972, Dalhousie University, 1977; D.C.L., St. Francis Xavier University, 1974; Government of Canada, Centennial Medal, 1967, Officer of Order of Canada, 1976, Jubilee Medal, 1978; Officer of the Venerable Order of St. John, 1978.

WRITINGS: Birth of Western Canada, Longmans, Green, 1936, 2nd edition, University of Toronto Press, 1960; *Canada's Soldiers,* Macmillan, 1954, 3rd revised edition, 1974; *In Search of the Magnetic North,* Macmillan, 1955; *In the Face of Danger,* Lake Superior Regiment, 1960; *For Want of a Horse,* Tribune, 1961; (editor) *Canadian Universities Today,* University of Toronto Press, 1961; *Louis Riel,* Ryerson, 1963, McGraw, 1972; *The Story of Canada's Flag,* Ryerson, 1965; (editor) *Pioneers of Canadian Science,* University of Toronto Press, 1966; *New France: The Last Phase, 1744-1763,* McClelland & Stewart, 1968; *A Short History of the Canadian Constitution,* Ryerson, 1969; *Mapping the Frontier,* University of Washington, Seattle, 1970; *Canada Invaded 1775-1776,* Hakkert, 1973; *The Military and Hospitaller Order of St. Lazarus: A Short History of the Canadian Grand Priory,* Tribune, 1977. Contributor to *Encyclopedia Americana, Encyclopaedia Britannica,* and *Canadian Encyclopedia;* contributor of articles to history journals.

WORK IN PROGRESS: A book on the Canadian War of 1812, for Canadian War Museum.

AVOCATIONAL INTERESTS: Canadian antiques, music, Canadian literature and art.

* * *

STAR, Shirley A(nn) 1918-1976

PERSONAL: Born February 18, 1918, in Chicago, Ill.; daughter of Harry I. (a druggist) and Esther F. (Eagle) Star; married Winston I. Breslin, 1961 (died March 12, 1962). *Education:* University of Chicago, A.B., 1939, Ph.D., 1950; Merritt Community College, A.A. (data processing-computers), 1972. *Politics:* Liberal independent. *Religion:* Jewish. *Home:* 2710 Macomb St. N.W., Washington, D.C. 20008. *Office:* Bureau of Social Science Research, Inc., 1990 M St. N.W., Washington, D.C. 20036.

CAREER: U.S. War Department, Washington, D.C., senior analyst, Research Branch, Information and Education Division, 1942-46, senior analyst, special committee for the re-analysis of research branch experience, Social Science Research Council, 1946; University of Chicago, Chicago, Ill., senior study director, National Opinion Research Center, and research associate in sociology, 1947-60; Johns Hopkins University, School of Hygiene and Public Health, Baltimore, Md., associate professor of mental hygiene, 1961-62; University of Chicago, project director, Center for Urban Studies, and research associate in sociology, 1964-66; University of California, Berkeley, visiting lecturer in sociology, 1966-68; independent consultant on research design, 1968-76. Senior research associate, Bureau of Social Science Research, 1973-76. Consultancies include U.S. Bureau of the Census, Department of Housing and Urban Development, National Science Foundation, and California Department of Public Health. *Member:* American Sociological Association (member of council, methodology section, 1959-61), International Sociological Association, Society for Social Research, World Association for Public Opinion Research, Society for the Study of Social Problems.

WRITINGS: (With Samuel A. Stouffer and others) *The American Soldier: Adjustment during Army Life,* Princeton University Press, 1949; (with Stouffer and others) *The American Soldier: Combat and Its Aftermath,* Princeton University Press, 1949; (with Stouffer and others) *Measurement and Prediction,* Princeton University Press, 1950, (with others) *Psychiatry, the Press and the Public,* American Psychiatric Association, 1956; (with Edward E. Schwartz

and William Sample) *The Midway Office: An Experiment in the Organization of Work Groups,* National Association of Social Workers, 1972.

Writer of a number of privately printed or unpublished research reports. Contributor to *Contributions to Urban Sociology,* 1964, and *Encyclopedia of Mental Health.* Associate editor, *Sociometry,* 1956-63, and *Social Problems* 1958-61; advisory editor, *Sociological Methodology* (annual), 1971-74.†

(Died April 27, 1976)

* * *

STARR, William Thomas 1910-

PERSONAL: Born March 11, 1910, in Kirksville, Mo.; son of Elmer Gordon (a pharmacist) and Bessie (Smith) Starr; married Omega Means (a writer), July 19, 1934; children: William Lawrence, Jeffrey Gordon. *Education:* Northeast Missouri State Teachers College (now Northeast Missouri State University), B.S. in Ed., 1931; University of Oregon, M.A., 1932, Ph.D., 1938. *Home:* 814 Ridge Terrace, Evanston, Ill. 60201. *Office:* Department of French and Italian, Northwestern University, Evanston, Ill. 60201.

CAREER: University of Arizona, Tucson, instructor in French, 1936-38; Phoenix Junior College, Phoenix, Ariz., instructor in modern languages, 1938-39; Gettysburg College, Gettysburg, Pa., assistant professor of Romance languages, 1940-45; Northwestern University, Evanston, Ill., instructor, 1945-58, assistant professor, 1948-57, associate professor, 1957-67, professor of Romance languages, 1967—. Consultant to John Crerar Library, 1956-59. *Member:* Modern Language Association of America, American Association of Teachers of French, American Association of Teachers of Italian, Societe des amis de Romain Rolland, American Association of University Professors.

WRITINGS: Romain Rolland's Internationalism, University of Oregon Press, 1939; *A Critical Bibliography of the Published Works of Romain Rolland,* Northwestern University Press, 1950; *Romain Rolland and a World at War,* Northwestern University Press, 1956; *Romain Rolland, One against Many: A Biography,* Mouton, 1971. Contributor to *French Review, Romanic Review, Symposium, Modern Language Quarterly, Shaw Bulletin, Annali dell'Instituto Universitario Orientale, Neophilologus, Philological Quarterly, English Language Notes,* and *Comparative Literature.* Editor of *French VI Bibliography for the Study of Nineteenth-Century French Literature,* 1954-69.

WORK IN PROGRESS: Research on myth and symbolism in the works of Romain Rolland; research on the place of Romain Rolland in the European novel, 1900 to 1950.

AVOCATIONAL INTERESTS: Travel, musical instruments (recorder and flute).

* * *

STASCH, Stanley F. 1931-

PERSONAL: Born August 20, 1931, in Chicago, Ill.; son of Emil and Martha (Lyczko) Stasch. *Education:* University of Notre Dame, B.S.E.E., 1953, M.S.E.E., 1957; Northwestern University, M.B.A., 1961, Ph.D., 1964. *Home:* 556 West Arlington Place, Chicago, Ill. 60614. *Office:* School of Business Administration, Loyola University of Chicago, 420 North Michigan Ave., Chicago, Ill. 60611.

CAREER: Sperry Gyroscope Co., Great Neck, N.Y., electrical engineer and systems engineer, 1953, 1956; Motorola,

Inc., Chicago, Ill., employed in Communications Division, 1957-61, became marketing manager, closed circuit television department; Northwestern University, Evanston, Ill., instructor, 1963-64, assistant professor, 1964-67, associate professor of marketing, 1967-77; Loyola University of Chicago, School of Business Administration, Chicago, Charles H. Kellstadt Professor of Marketing, 1977—. *Military service:* U.S. Army, 1954-55, electrical engineer. *Member:* Operations Research Society of America, Institute of Management Sciences, American Marketing Association.

WRITINGS: (With others) *Managerial Analysis in Marketing,* Scott, Foresman, 1970; (editor with others) *Perspectives in Marketing Management,* Scott, Foresman, 1971; *Systems Analysis for Marketing Planning and Control,* Scott, Foresman, 1972; (with others) *Market Research: Text and Cases,* 4th edition (Stasch was not associated with earlier editions), Irwin, 1977.

Contributor: R. M. Haas, editor, *Science, Technology and Marketing,* American Marketing Association, 1966; R. B. Cunningham, editor, *Dynamic Competition in Utility Marketing,* American Marketing Association, 1967; R. L. King, editor, *Marketing and the New Science of Planning,* American Marketing Association, 1968; Louis P. Bucklin, editor, *Vertical Marketing Systems,* Scott, Foresman, 1970; Davis A. Aaker, editor, *Multivariate Analysis in Marketing: Theory and Application,* Wadsworth, 1971; S. H. Britt, editor, *Marketing Managers Hand Book,* Dartnell, 1973. Contributor to business journals.

WORK IN PROGRESS: Further research in areas of marketing strategy and planning, product management, and marketing research.

*   *   *

STEAMER, Robert J(ulius) 1920-

PERSONAL: Born October 14, 1920, in Rochester, N.Y.; son of William August and Lotte (Becker) Steamer; married Jean Worden, April 12, 1947; children: Gregg Robert, James Worden. *Education:* Bucknell University, B.A., 1947; University of Virginia, M.A., 1952; Cornell University, Ph.D., 1954; Oxford University, postdoctoral study, 1968-69. *Politics:* Democrat. *Religion:* Episcopalian. *Home:* 28 Hartford St., Medfield, Mass. 02052. *Office:* University of Massachusetts, 100 Arlington St., Boston, Mass. 02116.

CAREER: Oglethorpe University, Atlanta, Ga., assistant professor of political science, 1952-55; University of Massachusetts—Amherst, assistant professor of political science, 1955-56; Louisiana State University, Baton Rouge, associate professor of political science, 1956-62; Lake Forest College, Lake Forest, Ill., professor of political science and chairman of department of government, 1962-72; University of Massachusetts—Boston, professor of political science, 1972—, dean of Liberal Arts College, 1974-76, vice chancellor and provost, 1976—. Visiting professor at Tulane University, 1958, Cornell University, 1960, University of California, Los Angeles, 1965, and University of Massachusetts, 1966. Staff consultant, U.S. Commission on Civil Rights, 1961; police and fire commissioner of Lake Forest, Ill., 1971-72. *Military service:* U.S. Army Air Forces, 1942-46. U.S. Air Force Reserve, 1946-66; became lieutenant colonel.

MEMBER: American Political Science Association, American Association of University Professors, Midwest Political Science Association (vice-president, 1971), New England Political Science Association (president-elect, 1978). *Awards, honors:* Lilly Foundation research grant, 1967.

WRITINGS: (With Fred V. Cahill, Jr.) *The Constitution: Cases and Comments,* Ronald, 1959; (contributor) Allen P. Sindler, editor, *Change in the Contemporary South,* Duke University Press, 1963; *The Supreme Court in Crisis: A History of Conflict,* University of Massachusetts Press, 1971; *The Supreme Court: Constitutional Revision and the New Constructionism,* Burgess, 1972. Contributor to *American Educator Encyclopedia;* contributor of about sixty-five articles and reviews to law and political science journals.

WORK IN PROGRESS: American Constitutional Law.

*   *   *

STECK, James S(perow) 1911-

PERSONAL: Born February 21, 1911, in Mercersburg, Pa.; son of Luther Roman (a teacher and merchant) and Mary Bess (Sperow) Steck; married Rachel V. Shuck, April 20, 1946; children: Philip R., Sarah Melissa. *Education:* Fairmont State College, B.A. (cum laude), 1941; University of Virginia, M.A., 1948; Pennsylvania State University, D.Ed., 1968. *Politics:* Republican. *Religion:* Presbyterian. *Home:* 4111 Ricklyn Dr., Chambersburg, Pa. 17201. *Office:* DHC-115, Department of English, Shippensburg State College, Shippensburg, Pa. 17257.

CAREER: Worked as a high school English teacher in Hagerstown, Md., 1941-42, 1954-56; Union College, Barbourville, Ky., assistant professor, 1950-51, associate professor of English, 1951-54, head of division of languages, 1950-54; Shippensburg State College, Shippensburg, Pa., associate professor, 1956-68, professor of English, 1968-76, professor emeritus, 1976—. *Military service:* U.S. Army, 1942-46; became first lieutenant. *Member:* Modern Language Association of America, Pennsylvania State Education Association, Sigma Pi, Hagerstown Lodge, A. F. & A. M., Tall Cedars of Lebanon.

WRITINGS: The Intellectual Pleasures of the Puritans, Shippensburg Collegiate Press, 1967; (editor with Mabel E. Lindner and Mark Lipper) *Thoughts of George W. Reisinger,* Shippensburg Collegiate Press, 1969. Contributor to *Papers of the Bibliographical Society of the University of Virginia, Studies in Bibliography,* and *Ohio Association of School Librarians Bulletin.*

WORK IN PROGRESS: The Fiction of W. H. Hudson.

*   *   *

STEED, Gitel P. 1914-1977

PERSONAL: Born May 3, 1914, in Cleveland, Ohio; daughter of Jakob and Sara (Aurbach) Poznanski; married Robert Steed (an artist), February 20, 1942; children: Andrew Hart. *Education:* New York University, B.A., 1938; Columbia University, Ph.D., 1969. *Home:* 455 West 21st St., New York, N.Y. 10011. *Office:* Department of Anthropology, Hofstra University, Hempstead, N.Y. 11550.

CAREER: Yale University, Institute of Human Relations, New Haven, Conn., senior editor, cross-cultural research, 1943; Hunter College (now Hunter College of the City University of New York), New York City, lecturer in anthropology, 1945-47; Columbia University, New York City, Research in Contemporary Culture Project, staff consultant, 1947-48, director of contemporary India field project, 1949-54, beginning 1955; Hofstra University, Hempstead, N.Y., assistant professor, 1963-72, associate professor of anthropology, 1972-77. Visiting professor, Fisk University, 1946. *Member:* American Anthropological Association, Association for Asian Studies, Society for Applied Anthropology, Phi Beta Kappa.

WRITINGS: (With McKim Mamott) *Village India,* University of Chicago Press, 1955; *Caste and Kinship in Rural Gujarat (India)* (monograph), University of Chicago Press, 1973. Editor-in-chief, *Monthly Summary Race Relations,* 1946.

WORK IN PROGRESS: Personalities in a Village Context (tentative title).

SIDELIGHTS: Gitel Steed was known for her anthropological field work with the Blackfoot Indians as well as for her work in India.

BIOGRAPHICAL/CRITICAL SOURCES: New York Times, September 9, 1977.†

(Died September 6, 1977)

*   *   *

STEEGER, Henry   1903-

PERSONAL: Born May 26, 1903, in New York, N.Y.; son of Henry (a manufacturer) and Adelaide (von Holsten) Steeger; married Shirley R. Meeker, July 1, 1928; children: Henry, Susan Shirley (Mrs. John Hall), Nancy Victoria (Mrs. Richard Jennings). *Education:* Princeton University, B.A., 1925; University of Berlin, graduate study, 1926. *Religion:* Presbyterian. *Home:* 1060 Fifth Ave., New York, N.Y. 10028. *Agent:* Paul R. Reynolds, Inc., 12 East 41st St., New York, N.Y. 10017. *Office:* 420 Lexington Ave., New York, N.Y. 10017.

CAREER: Dell Publishing Co., New York City, editor, 1927-29; Popular Publications, New York City, publisher and president, 1930—. President of New Publications, Recreational Reading, Post Periodicals, Inc., 1936-60, Fictioneers, Inc., 1939-58, All-Fiction Field, Inc., 1942-58, Long Island Printing Corp., 1955-60. Real estate operator, New York, 1926—. Advisor to department of sociology, Princeton University, 1963-70. President of Society for Rehabilitation of Facially Disfigured, Inc., and United Seamen's Service; vice-president of Madison Square Boys Club; co-founder of Court of Last Resort. Trustee of Wilberforce University, Manhatten Eye, Ear, and Throat Hospital; associate member of board of trustees of New York University Medical Center. *Military service:* U.S. Coast Guard, 1942-46; became lieutenant commander. *Member:* Authors League, Young Democrats of America (member of executive committee, 1930-34), National Urban League (president, 1960-64), Magazine Publishers Association (director, 1965; member of executive committee, 1968), U.S. Lawn Tennis Association, Quoque Field Club, River Club, Explorers Club, Princeton Club, Overseas Press Club, Dutch Treat Club.

WRITINGS: You Can Remake America, Doubleday, 1969. Contributor of editorials to *Argosy.*

WORK IN PROGRESS: The Rise and Fall of the Pulps.

BIOGRAPHICAL/CRITICAL SOURCES: Best Sellers, April 15, 1969.

*   *   *

STEELE, Henry   1931-
(W. Anson Pinkerton)

PERSONAL: Born May 12, 1931, in Houston, Tex.; son of Henry Benton (a school principal) and Doris (Binford) Steele; married Janet Moran, September 14, 1960; children: Richard Henry, Stuart Randolph, Nelson Adams. *Education:* University of Stockholm, certificate in economics, 1952; Rice University, B.A., 1953; Massachusetts Institute

of Technology, Ph.D., 1957. *Politics:* Independent. *Home:* 2176 Dryden Rd., Houston, Tex. 77025. *Office:* 3100 Cullen, University of Houston, Houston, Tex. 77004.

CAREER: Rice University, Houston, Tex., assistant professor, 1957-66, associate professor of economics, 1966-68; University of Houston, Houston, Tex., professor of economics, 1968—. Economic consultant to RAND Corp., Stanford Research Institute, and governments of Canada, Venezuela, and United States. *Member:* Phi Beta Kappa.

WRITINGS: An Analysis of the Problems of Cost Determination for the Discovery, Development, and Production of Liquid Hydrogen and Natural Gas Resources (monograph), Rice University Press, 1959; *Index Numbers and Cost Analysis: An Application to the Petroleum Industry* (monograph), Rice University Press, 1963; (with Sam Schurr and Paul Homan) *Middle Eastern Oil and the Western World: Problems and Prospects,* Elsevier Press, 1971; *The Economic Potentialities of Synthetic Liquid Fuels from Oil Shales,* Arno, 1979. Contributor, occasionally under pseudonym W. Anson Pinkerton, to *American Economic Review, Journal of Law and Economics, Southern Economic Journal, Western Economic Journal, Journal of Industrial Economics, American Journal of Economics and Sociology, Natural Resources Journal, Journal of the American Medical Association,* and *Drug News.*

WORK IN PROGRESS: With J. M. Griffin, a textbook on energy economics and policy, for Academic Press.

*   *   *

STEENSMA, Robert Charles   1930-

PERSONAL: Born November 24, 1930, in Sioux Falls, S.D.; son of Anton Charles and Martha (Johnson) Steensma; married Sharon Carol Hogge (a college teacher), September 5, 1964; children: Craig, Michael, Laura, Kathryn, Rebecca. *Education:* Augustana College, Sioux Falls, S.D., B.A., 1952; University of South Dakota, M.A., 1955; University of Kentucky, Ph.D., 1961. *Politics:* Republican. *Religion:* Lutheran. *Home:* 3127 South 2850 East, Salt Lake City, Utah 84109. *Office:* Department of English, University of Utah, Salt Lake City, Utah 84112.

CAREER: Augustana College, Sioux Falls, S.D., instructor in English, 1955-57; University of South Dakota, Vermillion, assistant professor of English, 1959-62; Utah State University, Logan, assistant professor of English, 1962-66; University of Utah, Salt Lake City, associate professor, 1966-71, professor of English, 1971—, director of advanced placement, 1968-76. Fulbright lecturer at University of Jyvaskyla, Finland, 1972-73. *Military service:* U.S. Naval Reserve, 1948—; current rank, captain. *Member:* American Society for Eighteenth-Century Studies, U.S. Naval Institute, Naval Historical Foundation, Oceanic Society, Rocky Mountain Modern Language Association, Western Literature Association.

WRITINGS: (Editor) *Sir William Temple: On the Origin and Nature of Government,* Augustan Reprint Society, 1964; *Sir William Temple,* Twayne, 1971. Contributor to *College English, Shakespeare Newsletter, Naval War College Review, North Dakota Quarterly, Western Humanities Review, U.S. Naval Institute Proceedings, Walt Whitman Review,* and *Utah Libraries.*

WORK IN PROGRESS: Dr. John Arbuthnot, for Twayne.

AVOCATIONAL INTERESTS: Photography.

STEGMAN, Michael A(llen) 1940-

PERSONAL: Born October 12, 1940, in Brooklyn, N.Y.; son of Robert and Natalie (Ohrbach) Stegman; married Nancy Weiss (a data processing coordinator), August 12, 1962; children: Laurie Michelle, Karen Jill. *Education:* Brooklyn College of the City University of New York, B.A., 1962; University of Pennsylvania, M.C.P., 1964, Ph.D., 1966. *Office:* Department of City and Regional Planning, University of North Carolina, Chapel Hill, N.C. 27514.

CAREER: Department of Welfare, New York, N.Y., social investigator, 1962; University of North Carolina, Chapel Hill, assistant professor, 1966-69, associate professor of city and regional planning, 1969—, research associate of Institute for Research in Social Science, 1966—. Commissioner, Chapel Hill Housing Authority, 1969-71; chairman, Chapel Hill Redevelopment Commission, 1971—. *Member:* National Association of Housing and Redevelopment Officials, American Urban Economic and Real Estate Association, American Institute of Planners, Planners for Equal Opportunity, Urban America.

WRITINGS: (With Paul Niebanck and John B. Pope) *The Elderly in Older Areas: Problems of Adaptation and the Effects of Relocation,* Institute of Environmental Studies, University of Pennsylvania, 1965; (with Julie Reich and Nancy W. Stegman) *Relocating the Dispossessed Elderly: A Study of Mexican Americans,* Institute of Environmental Studies, University of Pennsylvania, 1966; (with others) *Moving Behavior and Residential Choice: A National Survey,* National Cooperative Research Program, Highway Research Board, National Research Council, 1968.

(Contributor) J. K. Hadden, L. H. Masotte, and C. J. Larson, editors, *Metropolis in Crisis,* 2nd edition, F. E. Peacock, 1971; (editor) *Housing and Economics: The American Dilemma,* M.I.T. Press, 1971; (editor) *The Role of Housing in the State Development Plan: A Summary Report,* Department of Administration, State Planning Division, 1972; (with Philip Emmi and Michael Busko) *Housing Legislation in North Carolina,* Department of Administration, State Planning Division, 1972; (with Howard J. Sumka) *The Housing Outlook in North Carolina: Projections to 1980,* Department of Administration, State Planning Division, 1972; *A Review of Housing Activities in Selected States: Action Proposals for North Carolina,* Department of Administration, State Planning Division, 1972; *The Multiple Roles of State Housing Finance Agencies: The North Carolina Housing Corporation,* Department of Administration, State Planning Division, 1972; *Housing Investment in the Inner-City: The Dynamics of Decay,* M.I.T. Press, 1972; *Nonmetropolitan Urban Housing: An Economic Analysis of Problems and Policies,* Ballinger, 1976.

Contributor to *Encyclopedia of Social Work;* contributor to architecture and planning journals. Member of editorial advisory board, *Journal of the American Institute of Planners,* 1968—.

WORK IN PROGRESS: Housing and Poverty, with William G. Grigsby, Louis Rosenberg, and James Taylor.†

*   *   *

STEICHEN, Edward 1879-1973

March 27, 1879—March 25, 1973; American photographer and artist. Obituaries: *New York Times,* March 26, 1973; *Washington Post,* March 26, 1973; *Time,* April 9, 1973.

STEIN, R(ichard) Conrad 1937-

PERSONAL: Born April 22, 1937, in Chicago, Ill.; son of Konrad G. (a truckdriver) and Mary (Kariolich) Stein. *Education:* University of Illinois, B.A., 1964. *Politics:* "Varies, but mainly Democratic." *Religion:* Roman Catholic.

CAREER: Has worked at a variety of jobs, including social worker, truckdriver, merchant seaman, machinist, and salesman. *Military service:* U.S. Marine Corps, 1955-58; became sergeant.

WRITINGS—For children; published by Children's Press, except as noted: *Steel Driving Man: The Legend of John Henry,* 1969; *My Tribe,* 1970; *No Hablo Ingles,* 1970; *Hey, Texie!,* 1970; *Look to the Light Side,* 1970; *A World of Books,* 1970; *People Are My Profession,* 1970; *Benjamin Franklin,* Rand McNally, 1972.

"Cornerstones of Freedom" series, published by Children's Press: *The Story of D-Day,* 1977; *The Story of the Battle for Iwo Jima,* 1977; *The Story of the Battle of the Bulge,* 1977; *The Story of the U.S.S. Arizona,* 1977; *The Story of the Golden Spike,* 1978; *The Story of the Homestead Act,* 1978; *The Story of the Lewis and Clark Expedition,* 1978.†

*   *   *

STELTER, Gilbert Arthur 1933-

PERSONAL: Born June 13, 1933, in Lamont, Alberta, Canada; son of Arthur (a farmer) and Elsie (Driesner) Stelter; married Sally Shortliffe, May 27, 1961; children: David, James, Gordon. *Education:* Moravian College, B.A., 1956; University of Alberta, B.D., 1959, Ph.D., 1968. *Home:* 66 Park Ave., Guelph, Ontario, Canada. *Office:* Department of History, University of Guelph, Guelph, Ontario, Canada.

CAREER: University of Alberta, Edmonton, lecturer in history, 1963-64; Laurentian University, Sudbury, Ontario, assistant professor, 1964-69, associate professor of history, 1969-74, chairman of department, 1969-72; University of Guelph, Guelph, Ontario, associate professor of history, 1974—. *Member:* American Historical Association, Canadian Historical Association, Ontario Historical Society. *Awards, honors:* Canada Council research grants, 1971-72, 1973-74; Queen Elizabeth Silver Jubilee Medal, 1977.

WRITINGS: Community Development in Northeastern Ontario: A Selected Bibliography, Laurentian University Press, 1971; *Canadian Urban History: A Selected Bibliography,* Laurentian University Press, 1972; *The Northern Ontario Mining Frontier,* National Museum of Man, 1974; *The Canadian City: Essays in Urban History,* McClelland & Stewart, 1977; *A Usable Urban Past: Politics and Planning in Modern Canadian Cities,* Macmillan, 1978. Contributor to *Histoire sociale, Plan Canada, Urban History Yearbook, Journal of Interdisciplinary History, American Historical Review, Canadian Historical Review, Western Historical Quarterly,* and *Urban History Review.* Member of editorial board of *Laurentian University Review,* 1967—, *Urban History Review,* 1972—, and *Urban History Yearbook,* 1974—.

WORK IN PROGRESS: Shaping the Canadian Urban Landscape; New Towns in a New Land: A History of Canadian Urban Development to 1850.

*   *   *

STEPHAN, John J(ason) 1941-

PERSONAL: Born March 8, 1941, in Chicago, Ill.; son of

John W. (an artist) and Ruth (a poet and novelist; maiden name, Walgreen) Stephan; married Barbara Brooks (a craft designer), June 22, 1963. *Education:* Harvard University, B.A., 1963, M.A., 1964; School of Oriental and African Studies, London, Ph.D., 1969. *Home:* 4334 Round Top Dr., Honolulu, Hawaii 96822. *Agent:* W. Reiss, c/o Paul Reynolds, Inc., 12 East 41st St., New York, N.Y. 10017. *Office:* Department of History, University of Hawaii, 2530 Dole St., Honolulu, Hawaii 96822.

CAREER: Waseda University, Social Science Research Center, Tokyo, Japan, research associate, 1969-70; University of Hawaii, Honolulu, assistant professor, 1970-72, associate professor, 1972-77, professor of history, 1977—. *Member:* Association for Asian Studies (life member), International House of Japan (life member). *Awards, honors:* Fulbright fellow in Japan, 1967-68; Japan culture translation prize, 1973; Japan Foundation professional fellowship, 1977.

WRITINGS: Sakhalin: A History, Clarendon Press, 1971; *The Kurile Islands: Russo-Japanese Frontier in the Pacific,* Oxford University Press, 1974; *The Russian Fascists: Tragedy and Farce in Exile,* Harper, 1978. Contributor of articles on Japan and U.S.S.R. to *Asian Survey* and *Modern Asian Studies.* Far Eastern editor of *Harvard Review,* 1962-63.

WORK IN PROGRESS: Russia in the Pacific, 1648 to the Present; research into Russo-Japanese and Soviet-Japanese relations.

*   *   *

STERN, Guy 1922-

PERSONAL: Born January 14, 1922, in Hildesheim, Germany; came to United States in 1937, naturalized in 1943; son of Julius and Hedwig (Silberberg) Stern; married Margith Langweiler, 1948 (divorced, 1977); children: Mark. *Education:* Attended St. Louis University, 1940-42; Hofstra College (now Hofstra University), B.A., 1948; Columbia University, M.A. (with honors), 1950, Ph.D. (with honors), 1953. *Home:* 630 Merrick Ave., Detroit, Mich. 48202. *Office:* Office of the Vice-President, Wayne State University, Detroit, Mich. 48202.

CAREER: Columbia University, New York, N.Y., lecturer, 1948-49, instructor in German, 1950-55, summer instructor, 1955-61; Denison University, Granville, Ohio, assistant professor, 1955-58, associate professor of German, 1958-63; University of Cincinnati, Cincinnati, Ohio, professor of German literature and head of department of Germanic languages and literatures, 1963-73, dean of university, 1973-76; University of Maryland, College Park, professor of German and chairman of department, 1976-78; Wayne State University, Detroit, Mich., vice-president and provost, 1978—. Leo Baeck Institute, New York, fellow, 1964—, member of board of directors, 1967—; guest professor, Goethe Institute, Munich, summers, 1963-66. Advisory editor for languages and linguistics, Dover Publications, Inc., 1957—. *Military service:* U.S. Army, Military Intelligence, 1942-45; received Bronze Star.

MEMBER: American Association of Teachers of German (president, 1970-72), American Council for German Studies (national secretary), American Comparative Literature Association, Modern Language Association of America, American Association of University Professors, South Atlantic Modern Language Association, Midwest Modern Language Association. *Awards, honors:* Fulbright grant for research at University of Munich, 1961-63; Bollingen Foundation research fellow, 1962-63; U.S. Office of Education grants for work-study in Hamburg, 1967.

WRITINGS: Brierlich Erzaehlt, Norton, 1956; *Listen and Learn German,* Dover, 1957; *Say It in German,* Dover, 1958; *Uebung macht der Meister,* Norton, 1958; *An Invitation to German Poetry,* Dover, 1960; *Hints on Speaking German,* Dover, 1961; *Quick Change Pattern Drills,* Regents Publishing, Volume I, 1962, Volume II, 1963; (editor) *Konstellationen: Die grossen Novellen des "Neuen Merkur,"* Deutsche Verlags Anstalt, 1964; *Efraim Frisch: Zum Verstaendnis des Geistigen,* Lambert Schneider Verlag, 1964; *Hoer zu und Rat mit,* McGraw, 1964; (with Gustave Mathieu) *In Briefen erzaehlt,* Max Hueber Verlag, 1965; (editor) *Nelly Sachs Ausgewaehlte Gedichte,* Harcourt, 1968; *War, Weimar, and Literature: The Story of the Neue Merkur,* Pennsylvania State University Press, 1971; (compiler with Mathieu) *German Poetry: A Selection,* Dover, 1971; (with Everett F. Bleiler) *Essential German Grammar,* Teach Yourself Books, 1975. Also contributor to *Revolte und Experiment, Die Literatur der Sechziger Jahre in Ost und West,* edited by Wolfgang Paulsen, 1971, *Exil und inhere Emigration II,* edited by Peter Hohendahl and Egon Schwarz, 1972, *Der deutsche Roman und seine historischen und politischen Bedingungen,* edited by Paulsen, and (with Dorothy Wartenberg) *Gegenwartsliteratur und Drittes Reich: Deutsche Autoren in der Auseinandersetzung mit der Vergangenheit,* edited by Hans Wagener. Contributor of articles and reviews to language journals. Associate editor, *Lessing Yearbook.*

WORK IN PROGRESS: Further studies on eighteenth and nineteenth-century literature and on German literature in exile.

*   *   *

STERN, Milton R(alph) 1928-

PERSONAL: Born August 22, 1928, in Boston, Mass.; son of David and Elizabeth (Landfield) Stern; married Harriet Marks, December 3, 1949; children: Kathy Lee, Paul Frederick. *Education:* Northeastern University, A.B., 1949; University of Connecticut, M.A., 1951; Michigan State University, Ph.D., 1955. *Politics:* Democrat. *Home:* 49 Separatist Rd., Storrs, Conn. 06268. *Office:* Department of English, University of Connecticut, Storrs, Conn. 06268.

CAREER: University of Illinois at Urbana-Champaign, instructor, 1954-56, assistant professor of English, 1957-58; University of Connecticut, Storrs, assistant professor, 1958-60, associate professor, 1960-64, professor of English, 1964-76, Alumni Distinguished Professor, 1976—. Visiting professor, University of Wyoming, Coe Institute, 1964. Fulbright professor at University of Warsaw, 1964-65. Connecticut Humanities Council, secretary-treasurer, 1972, vice-president, 1973-74, president, 1975-77. *Member:* Modern Language Association of America, American Federation of Teachers, American Association of University Professors, American Studies Association. *Awards, honors:* American Council of Learned Societies award, 1960; Outstanding Teacher award, University of Connecticut, 1969; Guggenheim fellow, 1971-72; National Humanities Institute fellow, Yale University, 1977-78.

WRITINGS: The Fine Hammered Steel of Herman Melville, University of Illinois, 1957; (editor) Herman Melville, *Typee* [and] *Billy Budd,* Dutton, 1958; *Discussions of "Moby Dick,"* Heath, 1960; (with S. L. Gross) *American Literature Survey,* four volumes, Viking, 1962, revised edition, 1974; *The Golden Moment: Novels of F. Scott Fitzgerald,* University of Illinois, 1971; (editor) Melville, *Billy Budd,* Bobbs-Merrill, 1974.

WORK IN PROGRESS: The Politics of American Literature.

* * *

STETLER, Russell (Dearnley, Jr.) 1945-

PERSONAL: Born January 15, 1945, in Philadelphia, Pa.; son of Russell Dearnley (a sign painter) and Martha (Schultz) Stetler. *Education:* Haverford College, B.A. (with honors), 1966; New School for Social Research, graduate study, 1966-67. *Home:* Apartado 16, Adjuntas, Puerto Rico 00601.

CAREER: Bertrand Russell Peace Foundation, London, England, director, 1966-68; Hendon College, London, lecturer in sociology of the cinema, 1968-69; Atlantic Peace Foundation, London, research director, 1969-70; Archetype, Inc., Berkeley, Calif., president, 1971-78. Broadcast journalist, Internews (Berkeley), 1973-78; publisher, *Westworks* (Berkeley), 1977—; affiliated with Ramparts Press, 1971—.

WRITINGS: The Battle of Bogside, Sheed, 1970; (editor) *The Military Art of People's War,* Monthly Review Press, 1970; (editor) *Palestine: The Arab-Israeli Conflict,* Ramparts Press, 1972; (editor with Peter Dale Scott and Paul L. Hoch) *The Assassinations: Dallas and Beyond,* Random House, 1976. Contributor to *Temps Modernes, Ramparts, Scanlan's, Monthly Review, Inquiry, New Society,* and *Spokesman.*

WORK IN PROGRESS: A biography of Clark Foreman.

AVOCATIONAL INTERESTS: Travel (Europe, Asia, North Africa).

* * *

STEVEN, Hugh 1931-

PERSONAL: Born March 21, 1931, in Vancouver, British Columbia, Canada; son of David and Mable (Knowles) Steven; married Norma Van Boeyen (an editor, writer, and typist), May 5, 1951; children: Wendy, Dave, Lee, Karen. *Education:* Attended Summer Institute of Linguistics, 1956, University of Oklahoma, 1967, and Regent College, 1969. *Religion:* Protestant. *Home:* 1309 North Linwood Ave., Santa Ana, Calif. 92701. *Office:* Wycliffe Bible Translators, Inc., Huntington Beach, Calif. 92648.

CAREER: Woodward Stores Ltd., Vancouver, British Columbia, junior manager, 1949-56; Wycliffe Bible Translators, Inc., Huntington Beach, Calif., buyer and administrator in public relations in Mexico, 1956-67, regional secretary and writer in Chicago, Ill., 1968-69, author-at-large, 1970— (work has taken him to South Pacific, Latin America, Africa, Europe, and Vietnam).

WRITINGS: Manuel, Revell, 1970; *You Eat Bananas,* Regal Books (Glendale, Calif.), 1971; (with James C. Hefley) *Miracles in Mexico,* Moody, 1972; *Night of the Long Knives,* Regal Books, 1972; *The Reproducers,* Regal Books, 1972; (with Cornell Capa) *Language and Faith,* Wycliffe Bible Translators, Inc., 1972; *The Measure of Greatness,* Revell, 1973; *It Takes Time to Love,* Wycliffe, 1974; *Kim,* Harvest, 1975; *They Dared to Be Different,* Harvest, 1976; *To the Ends of the Earth,* Christian Herald Publishers, 1978; *The Man with the Noisy Heart,* Moody, 1979. Contributor of more than two hundred articles to Christian denominational magazines, including *World Vision* and *Christian Herald.* Contributing editor, *Translation;* editor, Regal Books (Glendale, Calif.) and Moody Press (Chicago, Ill.).

WORK IN PROGRESS: A book on Wycliffe's work in Ecuador; a book for junior high school students.

* * *

STEVENSON, Suzanne Silvercruys 1898(?)-1973

1898(?)—March 31, 1973; American sculptor, author, and lecturer. Obituaries: *Washington Post,* April 3, 1973.

* * *

STEVENSON, Victoria F. 1878(?)-1973

1878(?)—April 26, 1973; American writer of children's books and books for the blind. Obituaries: *Washington Post,* April 30, 1973.

* * *

STEVENSON, (Stanley) Warren 1933-

PERSONAL: Born September 20, 1933, in Hamilton, Ontario, Canada; son of Stanley and Winnifred (Lord) Stevenson; married Mary Berdey, July 3, 1954; children: Jonathan (died, 1969), Catherine, Susan, Maria, William. *Education:* Bishop's University, B.A. (honors), 1952; McGill University, M.A., 1954; Northwestern University, Ph.D., 1956. *Home:* 3076 Discovery St., Vancouver, British Columbia, Canada. *Office:* Department of English, University of British Columbia, Vancouver, British Columbia, Canada.

CAREER: Frontier College, Toronto, Ontario, instructor in English, 1954; University of Saskatchewan, Saskatoon, instructor in English, 1956-59; University of Manitoba, Winnipeg, instructor in English, 1959-60; University of British Columbia, Vancouver, instructor, 1961-63, assistant professor, 1963-67, associate professor of English, 1967—. *Member:* Association of Canadian University Teachers of English. *Awards, honors:* Borestone Mountain Poetry Award, 1966; Canada Council fellowships, 1967-68, 1973-74, 1978-79.

WRITINGS: Soundings, Anansi, 1970; *Divine Analogy: The Creation Motif in Blake and Coleridge,* Salzburg Studies in English, University of Salzburg, 1972; *Then and Now* (poetry), Fiddlehead Books, 1977. Contributor to *Studies in Romanticism, Alphabet, Personalist, Blake Studies,* and *Texas Studies in Literature and Language.*

* * *

STEWARD, F(rederick) C(ampion) 1904-

PERSONAL: Born June 16, 1904, in London, England; son of Frederick Walter (a clergyman) and Mary (Daglish) Steward; married Anne Temple Gordon, September 7, 1929; children: Frederick Gordon. *Education:* University of Leeds, B.Sc. (first class honors), 1924, Ph.D., 1926; University of London, D.Sc., 1937. *Home:* 1612 Inglewood Dr., Charlottesville, Va. 22901. *Office:* Department of Biology, State University of New York, Stony Brook, N.Y. 11794.

CAREER: University of Leeds, Leeds, England, lecturer in botany, 1929-33; University of London, London, England, reader in botany, 1934-47; University of Rochester, Rochester, N.Y., professor of botany, 1946-50, chairman of department, 1946-50; Cornell University, Ithaca, N.Y., professor of botany, 1950-65, Charles A. Alexander Professor of Biology, 1965-72, professor emeritus, 1972—, director, Laboratory of Cell Physiology and Growth, 1963-72; adjunct professor of biology, State University of New York at Stony Brook. *Wartime service:* Ministry of Aircraft Production (England), director of aircraft equipment, 1940-45.

MEMBER: Royal Society (fellow), American Academy of Arts and Sciences (fellow). Awards, honors: Rockefeller Foundation fellow, 1927-29, 1933-34; merit award from Botanical Society of America, 1961; Stephen Hales Prize from American Society of Plant Physiologists, 1964.

WRITINGS: (Editor) Plant Physiology: A Treatise, six volumes, Academic Press, 1959-72; Plants at Work, Addison-Wesley, 1964; About Plants, Addison-Wesley, 1966; Growth and Organization of Plants, Addison-Wesley, 1968; (with A. D. Krikorian) Plants, Chemicals, and Growth, Academic Press, 1971.

AVOCATIONAL INTERESTS: Travel, gardening, swimming.

*   *   *

STEWART, Charles J(oseph) 1936-

PERSONAL: Born July 3, 1936, in Terre Haute, Ind.; son of Charles H. and Freida (Harrison) Stewart; married Jane Blest, July 19, 1958; children: Gregory, David, Melissa. Education: Indiana State University, B.S., 1958; University of Illinois, M.A., 1960, Ph.D., 1963. Politics: Democrat. Religion: Roman Catholic. Home: 621 Wilshire Ave., West Lafayette, Ind. 47906. Office: Department of Communication, Purdue University, West Lafayette, Ind. 47907.

CAREER: Purdue University, West Lafayette, Ind., instructor, 1961-63, assistant professor, 1963-67, associate professor, 1967-72, professor of communication, 1972—. Military service: Indiana Air National Guard, 1954-61. U.S. Air Force, 1961-62; became staff sergeant. Member: Speech Communication Association, Religious Speech Communication Association, Central States Speech Association, Indiana Speech Association.

WRITINGS: (Editor with Bruce Kendall) A Man Named John F. Kennedy, Paulist-Newman, 1964; (editor with Kendall) On Speech and Speakers, Holt, 1968; (contributor) DeWitte T. Holland, editor, Preaching in American History, Abingdon, 1969; (contributor) Holland, editor, Sermons in American History, Abingdon, 1971; (editor) On Speech Communication, Holt, 1972; (editor with Gerald Mohrmann and Donovan Ochs) Explorations in Rhetorical Criticism, Pennsylvania State University Press, 1972; (with William Cash) Interviewing: Principles and Practices, W. C. Brown, 1974, 2nd edition, 1978; (contributor) Jane Blankenship and Hermann G. Stelzner, Rhetoric and Communication, University of Illinois Press, 1976. Contributor of articles to history and speech journals.

WORK IN PROGRESS: Social Movements: A Rhetorical Perspective; The Rhetoric of Protest Music; Andrew Johnson and the Press: Prelude to Impeachment.

SIDELIGHTS: Charles Stewart told CA: "I believe research and writing must be integral parts of a university professor's life. Through writing I feel I contribute to the field of communication, gain valuable materials for teaching, and continue to grow intellectually and professionally long after my graduate studies have ended. I firmly believe that the master teacher is one who writes to share findings, new ideas, and ways of handling materials."

*   *   *

STEWART, Rhea Talley 1915-

PERSONAL: Born July 29, 1915, in Richmond, Va.; daughter of Thomas Irving (a lawyer) and Laura (Lordley) Talley; married Arthur Stewart, June 21, 1958. Education: University of Richmond, B.A., 1935. Politics: Democrat.

Religion: Protestant. Home: 179 Boulder Rd., Manchester, Conn. 06040.

CAREER: Richmond Times-Dispatch, Richmond, Va., feature writer and editor, 1935-43; Louisville Courier-Journal, Louisville, Ky., feature writer, 1943-46; free-lance writer in New York, N.Y., with her own bureau for newspapers. Awards, honors: Virginia Press Association sweepstakes prizes for feature writing, 1941, for article on Italian seamen interned in Hampton Roads, Va., and 1942, for article on John D. Rockefeller's life in Williamsburg, Va.

WRITINGS: Fire in Afghanistan, Doubleday, 1973. Contributor to Woman's Home Companion, Venture, Cue, New York Times Sunday Magazine, and other periodicals.

WORK IN PROGRESS: Murder in Good Taste, a novel; Going to Afghanistan, a book for children; a history of Afghanistan after 1929.

SIDELIGHTS: Rhea Talley Stewart wrote CA: "I wrote my first book after a lifetime of writing newspaper and magazine articles. . . . Fire in Afghanistan is the factual story of a king who tried in the 1920's to make his country very progressive very fast and was thrown out. When I started, I expected to produce the equivalent of a long feature story between hard covers. Instead, I am told that I have influenced Afghan history, and the regime which seized power in Afghanistan in early 1978 is printing excerpts from Fire in Afghanistan in the Farsi language newspapers. I turned out to be writing an expose of certain events that had been hushed up." Stewart has traveled extensively in central Asia, especially in Afghanistan and the Yemen Arab Republic. Avocational interests: Photography.

*   *   *

STEWART, Zeph 1921-

PERSONAL: Born January 1, 1921, in Jackson, Mich.; son of James Garfield (a lawyer and judge) and Harriet (Potter) Stewart; married Diana Childers, December 29, 1959; children: Sarah Barton, Christopher Childers, Mary Alden. Education: Yale University, A.B., 1942. Politics: Independent. Religion: Protestant Episcopal. Home: 104 School St., Belmont, Mass. 02178. Office: Department of Classics, Harvard University, Cambridge, Mass. 02138.

CAREER: Harvard University, Cambridge, Mass., assistant professor, 1953-55, associate professor, 1955-62, professor of Greek and Latin, 1962—, chairman of department of classics, 1977—. Winslow Lecturer, Hamilton College, 1979. Master of Lowell House, 1963-75. Member of Yale University Council, 1976—. Trustee of Hotchkiss School, Bishop Rhinelander Foundation, Loeb Classical Library, and Radcliffe College. Member of advisory council, department of classics, Princeton University, 1970—. Military service: U.S. Army, 1943-47, 1951-53; became captain; received Legion of Merit. Member: Elizabethan Club, Century Association, American Academy of Arts and Sciences (fellow), American Philological Association, Archaeological Institute of America, Signet Society, Classical Association of New England, Teachers of Classics in New England (president), Phi Beta Kappa. Awards, honors: A.M., Harvard University, 1955; Guggenheim fellow, 1965-66.

WRITINGS: (Editor) The Ancient World: Justice, Heroism, and Responsibility, Prentice-Hall, 1966; (editor) Arthur Darby Nock: Essays on Religion and the Ancient World, Harvard University Press, 1972; (contributor) R. Bianchi, editor, Storia e civilta dei Greci, Volume IV, Bompiani

(Milan), 1977. Contributor of articles and reviews to *American Journal of Philology, Journal of Theological Studies, Journal of Roman Studies, Classical Philology, Classical World,* and *Harvard Studies in Classical Philology.*

WORK IN PROGRESS: The Graeco-Roman Background of the New Testament.

*   *   *

STICH, Stephen P(eter) 1943-

PERSONAL: Born May 9, 1943, in New York, N.Y.; son of Samuel J. (an attorney) and Sylvia (Siegel) Stich; married Judith Ann Gagnon, December 20, 1971. *Education:* University of Pennsylvania, B.A. (summa cum laude), 1964; Princeton University, Ph.D., 1968. *Home:* 4320 Clagett Rd., University Park, Md. 20782. *Office:* Department of Philosophy, University of Maryland, College Park, Md. 20742.

CAREER: University of Michigan, Ann Arbor, assistant professor, 1967-73, associate professor of philosophy, 1973-78; University of Maryland, College Park, associate professor of philosophy, 1978—, member of committee on history and philosophy of science, 1978—. *Member:* American Philosophical Association, American Association of University Professors, Phi Beta Kappa. *Awards, honors:* Danforth fellow, 1964-67; Woodrow Wilson fellowships, 1964-65, 1967; National Endowment for the Humanities, Younger Humanist fellowship, 1974; Fulbright senior research scholar at University of Bristol, 1978; American Council of Learned Societies fellow, 1978-79.

WRITINGS: (Editor and contributor) *Innate Ideas,* University of California Press, 1975; (editor with David A. Jackson and contributor) *The Recombinant DNA Debate,* Prentice-Hall, in press. Contributor to professional journals, including *Journal of Philosophy, Nous, Philosophical Review, Philosophia, Ratio* (English edition), *Philosophical Studies,* and *Canadian Journal of Philosophy.*

WORK IN PROGRESS: The Case against Belief: A Study in the Foundations of Cognitive Psychology.

*   *   *

STICKELLS, Austin T. 1914-

PERSONAL: Born June 26, 1914, in Boston, Mass.; son of Thomas G. and Mary C. Stickells; married Henrietta Tapper (an attorney), December 14, 1947; children: Susan P., Stephen C., Peter R. *Education:* Washington University, St. Louis, Mo., LL.B., 1938; Boston University, LL.M., 1947, M.B.A., 1956; Harvard University, graduate study, 1948. *Home:* 8 Nantucket Rd., Wellesley Hills, Mass. *Office:* 765 Commonwealth Ave., Boston, Mass. 02215.

CAREER: Admitted to the Bar of Missouri, 1938, and the Bar of Massachusetts, 1946; practiced law in Missouri, 1938-46, Massachusetts, 1946-50; Boston University, Boston, Mass., assistant professor, 1947-49, associate professor, 1949-50, professor of law, 1950—. *Military service:* U.S. Army, Infantry, and Judge Advocate Corps, 1941-45; became lieutenant colonel; received Purple Heart, Bronze Star, Silver Star, Combat Infantry Badge. *Member:* American Bar Association.

WRITINGS: (With Carl Everberg) *Manual on Uniform Commerical Code: Massachusetts,* Boston Law Book Co., 1963; *Legal Control of Business Practice,* Baker, Voorhis, 1965; *Federal Control of Business: Antitrust Laws,* Lawyers Cooperative Publishing Co., 1972.

WORK IN PROGRESS: Research on antitrust laws.

*   *   *

STIGLER, George Joseph 1911-

PERSONAL: Born January 17, 1911, in Renton, Wash.; son of Joseph and Elizabeth (Hungler) Stigler; married Margaret Mack, December 26, 1936 (died August, 1970); children: Stephen M., David M., Joseph M. *Education:* University of Washington, Seattle, B.B.A., 1931; Northwestern University, M.B.A., 1932; University of Chicago, Ph.D., 1938. *Home:* 2621 Brassie Ave., Flossmoor, Ill. 60422. *Office:* University of Chicago, 1101 East 58th St., Chicago, Ill. 60637.

CAREER: Iowa State College, Ames, assistant professor of economics, 1936-38; University of Minnesota, Minneapolis, assistant professor, 1938-41, associate professor, 1941-44, professor of economics, 1944-46; Brown University, Providence, R.I., professor of economics, 1946-47; Columbia University, New York, N.Y., professor of economics, 1947-58; University of Chicago, Chicago, Ill., Charles R. Walgreen Distinguished Service Professor of American Institutions, 1958—. Lecturer, London School of Economics, 1948; fellow, Center for Advanced Study in the Behavioral Sciences, 1957-58; fellow, Academy for Policy Study; director, Center for the Study of the Economy and the State, 1977—. Member of attorney general's committee for study of antitrust laws, 1954-55; member of Blue Ribbon Defense Panel, 1969-70; vice-chairman, Securities Investor Protection Commission, 1971-74. Trustee, Carleton College.

MEMBER: American Economic Association (member of executive committee; vice-president, 1958; president, 1964), Econometric Society (fellow), American Statistical Association (fellow), American Philosophical Society, Royal Economic Society, Mount Pelerin Society (president, 1977-78). *Awards, honors:* Guggenheim fellowship, 1955.

WRITINGS: Production and Distribution Theories, Macmillan, 1940; *The Theory of Competitive Price,* Macmillan, 1942; *The Theory of Price,* Macmillan, 1946, 3rd edition, 1966; (with Milton Friedman) *Roofs or Ceilings,* Foundation for Economic Education, 1946; *Trends in Output and Employment,* National Bureau of Economic Research, 1947; (with Kenneth Boulding) *Five Lectures on Economic Problems,* Macmillan, 1949; (editor with Boulding) *Readings in Price Theory,* Macmillan, 1952; *Trends in Employment in the Service Industries,* National Bureau of Economic Research, 1956; (with David Blank) *Supply and Demand for Scientific Personnel,* Agathon Press, 1957; *Capital and Rates of Return in Manufacturing,* National Bureau of Economic Research, 1963; *The Intellectual and the Market Place and Other Essays,* Free Press, 1963; *Essays in the History of Economics,* University of Chicago Press, 1964; *The Organization of Industry,* Irwin, 1968; (with James K. Kindahl) *The Behavior of Industrial Prices,* National Bureau of Economic Research, 1970; *The Citizen and the State,* University of Chicago Press, 1975. Contributor to economics journals. Editor, *Journal of Political Economy.*

*   *   *

STILLWELL, Margaret Bingham 1887-

PERSONAL: Born January 26, 1887, in Providence, R.I.; daughter of Edward Augustus (an organist) and Mary Elizabeth (Pindar-Bingham) Stillwell. *Education:* Special student, Rhode Island School of Design, 1899-1905, 1923-25; Brown University, A.B., 1909. *Politics:* Independent. *Religion:* Episcopalian. *Home:* Royal Manor, East Greenwich, R.I. 02818.

CAREER: John Carter Brown Library, Providence, R.I., assistant, 1907-14; New York Public Library, New York City, head cataloguer in Rare-Book Division, 1914-17; Annmary Brown Memorial Library of Incunabula, Providence, librarian and curator, 1917-53, librarian emerita, 1954—; Columbia University, School of Library Science, New York City, lecturer on incunabula and Americana, 1927-32; Brown University, Providence, research professor of bibliography, 1947-53, professor emerita, 1954—. American correspondant, Kommission fuer den *Gesamtkatalog der Wiegendrucke* (Berlin), 1924-38. American secretary, Wiegendruck Gesellschaft (Berlin), 1932-38. Providence Athenaeum, member of board of directors, 1944-51, vice-president of board, 1947-51; Greenville Public Library, secretary, 1955-62, chairman of building committee, 1955-56, 1965-66. *Member:* Bibliographical Society of America (vice-president, 1935-36), Institute d'Etudes Europeenes et Mondiales (corresponding member), National Society of Colonial Dames, Hroswitha Club (New York City), Providence Art Club, Phi Beta Kappa, Grolier Club (honorary member). *Awards, honors:* Brown University, A.M., 1925, Litt.D., 1942; President's Fellowship from Brown University, 1951; Litt.D., University of Rhode Island, 1952; honorary fellow, Pierpont Morgan Library.

WRITINGS: The Heritage of the Modern Printer, New York Public Library, 1916; *Washington Eulogies,* New York Public Library, 1916; *General Hawkins as He Revealed Himself to His Librarian,* Bibliographical Society of America, 1923; *The Fasciculus Temporum,* Harvard University Press, 1924; *The Annmary Brown Memorial Library* (descriptive essay), Akerman-Standard Press, 1925; *Incunabula and Americana, 1450-1800: A Key to Bibliographical Study,* Columbia University Press, 1931; *Gutenberg and the Catholicon of 1460,* Brickrow Bookshop, 1936; (contributor) L. C. Wroth, editor, *A History of the Printed Book,* Dolphin, 1938.

The Annmary Brown Memorial: A Booklover's Shrine, Akerman-Standard Press, 1940; (editor) *Incunabula in American Libraries: A Second Census,* Bibliographical Society of America, 1940; *Noah's Ark in Early Woodcuts and Modern Rhymes,* Brickrow Bookshops, 1942; (self-illustrated) *While Benefit Street Was Young,* Akerman-Standard Press, 1943; (self-illustrated) *The Pageant of Benefit Street Down Through the Years,* Akerman-Standard Press, 1945; *Printing in the Fifteenth and Sixteenth Centuries as Represented in the Hunt Botanical Library,* Hunt Botanical Library, 1958.

An Awakening Interest in Science, 1450-1550: Astronomy, Mathematics, Medicine, Natural Science, Physics, Technology, Bibliographical Society of America, 1970; *The Beginning of the World of Books: 1450-1550,* Bibliographical Society of America, 1972. Also author of *Librarians Are Human: Memories In and Out of the Rare-Book World,* 1973, and *Rhythm and Rhymes: The Songs of a Bookworm,* 1977.

WORK IN PROGRESS: Gutenberg, the Typographer: An Interpretation of the Gutenberg Documents; The Heritage and Early Background of the First Printed Books.

AVOCATIONAL INTERESTS: Equal status and opportunities for professional women.

*   *   *

STIMPSON, Catherine R(oslyn) 1936-

PERSONAL: Born June 4, 1936, in Bellingham, Wash. *Education:* Bryn Mawr College, A.B. (magna cum laude),

1958; Newnham College, Cambridge, B.A. (honors), 1960, M.A., 1965; Columbia University, Ph.D. (with distinction), 1967; Yale University, postdoctoral study, fall, 1969. *Agent:* Gloria Safier, 667 Madison Ave., New York, N.Y. 10021. *Office:* Department of English, Barnard College, New York, N.Y. 10027.

CAREER: Barnard College, New York, N.Y., lecturer, 1963-64, instructor, 1964-67, assistant professor of English, 1967—, first acting director of Women's Center and its executive committee. Lecturer for colleges and clubs. Consultant to Affirmative Action Institutes. *Awards, honors:* Woodrow Wilson fellow, 1958; Fulbright fellowship for study in England, 1958-60; National Humanities Institute fellow, 1975-76.

WRITINGS: (Editor) John Bunyan, *Pilgrim's Progress,* Signet, 1964; *J.R.R. Tolkien,* Columbia University Press, 1969; (contributor) Vivian Gornick and B. K. Moran, editors, *Women in Sexist Society,* Basic Books, 1971; (general editor) *Women and the Equal Rights Amendment,* Bowker, 1972; *Class Notes* (novel), Quadrangle, in press. Contributor to *Encyclopedia Americana;* contributor to *Change, Ms., Nation, New Republic, Transatlantic Review,* and *Aphra.* Editor, *Signs: Journal of Women in Culture and Society;* member of board of editors, *Women's Studies: An Interdisciplinary Journal.*

WORK IN PROGRESS: Critical essays; a novel.

*   *   *

STITELMAN, Leonard (Arnold) 1932-

PERSONAL: Born May 17, 1932, in Brooklyn, N.Y.; son of Hyman (a pharmacist) and Ruth (Kaplan) Stitelman; married second wife, Kay Masters (a social worker), April 7, 1971; children: (first marriage) Joel, Kenneth; (second marriage) Andrew. *Education:* Brooklyn College (now Brooklyn College of the City University of New York), B.A., 1953; Columbia University, M.A., 1959; University of Colorado, Ph.D., 1965. *Religion:* Jewish. *Home:* 3316 Wyoming N.E., Albuquerque, N.M. 87111. *Office:* Public Administration Division, University of New Mexico, Albuquerque, N.M. 87131.

CAREER: Wayne State University, Detroit, Mich., assistant professor, 1965-68, associate professor of political science, 1968-74; University of New Mexico, Albuquerque, professor of political science and professor of public administration, 1974—, director of Public Administration Division, 1974—. *Military service:* U.S. Army, 1954-56. *Member:* American Society for Public Administration.

WRITINGS: Automation in Government, Metropolitan Fund, 1967; *Decision Making by Congressional Committees,* Science Research Associates, 1969; *The Congressman at Work,* Science Research Associates, 1969; *Regional Cooperative Computer Plan: A Model for the Detroit Region,* Metropolitan Fund, 1970; *Local Government Programs for the Aged,* International City Management Association, 1973; (contributor) Nicholas Henry, editor, *Doing Public Administration,* Allyn & Bacon, 1978. Contributor of articles to *Urban Affairs Quarterly, Midwest Review of Public Administration, Michigan Academy,* and *Data Processing.*

*   *   *

STITES, Francis N(oel) 1938-

PERSONAL: Born December 25, 1938, in Indianapolis, Ind.; son of Francis Charles (a telephoneman) and Grace

(Cooper) Stites; married Joan C. Dionis, August 27, 1966; children: Madelaine Marie, Audrey Elizabeth. *Education:* Marian College, Indianapolis, Ind., B.A., 1960; Indiana University, M.A., 1965, Ph.D., 1968. *Home:* 6286 Anvil Lake Ave., San Diego, Calif. 92119. *Office:* Department of History, San Diego State University, San Diego, Calif. 92182.

CAREER: High school teacher of history and English, 1961-64; Earlham College, Richmond, Ind., instructor in American history, 1966-67; San Diego State University, San Diego, Calif., 1968—, began as associate professor, currently professor of history. *Member:* American Historical Association, Organization of American Historians, American Society for Legal History, Indiana Historical Society.

WRITINGS: Private Interest and Public Gain: The Dartmouth College Case, 1819, University of Massachusetts Press, 1972. Also author of a biography of John Marshall.

*   *   *

STOCK, Brian 1939-

PERSONAL: Born June 8, 1939, in Spokane, Wash.; son of Edward Sydney and Ada (Mintz) Stock; married Beatrice Blinder (a bookbinder), December 29, 1967; children: Maxime. *Education:* Attended University of Toronto, 1958-60; Harvard University, A.B., 1962; Cambridge University, Ph.D., 1965. *Politics:* Independent. *Religion:* None. *Home:* 3 Laurier Ave., Toronto, Ontario, Canada. *Office:* University of Toronto, 59 Queen's Park E., Toronto, Ontario, Canada.

CAREER: University of Toronto, Toronto, Ontario, assistant professor, 1966-71, associate professor, 1971-73, professor of history, 1973—.

WRITINGS: Medieval Latin Lyrics, Godine, 1971; *Myth and Science in the Twelfth Century,* Princeton University Press, 1972. Contributor to *Times Literary Supplement, Atlantic Monthly,* and journals of international opinion.

WORK IN PROGRESS: A study of twelfth-century life and thought.

SIDELIGHTS: Brian Stock has lived and studied in Paris and Rome.

*   *   *

STOCK, R(obert) D(ouglas) 1941-

PERSONAL: Born December 2, 1941, in Akron, Ohio; son of Robert P. (a chemical engineer) and Barbara (Broughton) Stock; married Barbara Jergovich, 1975. *Education:* Kent State University, B.A., 1963; Princeton University, M.A., 1965, Ph.D., 1967. *Politics:* Conservative. *Religion:* Episcopalian. *Home:* 1925 Van Dorn St., Lincoln, Neb. 68502. *Office:* Department of English, University of Nebraska, 304 Andrews Hall, Lincoln, Neb. 68502.

CAREER: University of Nebraska, Lincoln, assistant professor, 1967-72, associate professor, 1972-77, professor of English, 1977—. *Member:* Modern Language Association of America, American Society for Eighteenth-Century Studies.

WRITINGS: Samuel Johnson and Neoclassical Dramatic Theory, University of Nebraska Press, 1973; *Samuel Johnson's Literary Criticism,* University of Nebraska Press, 1974.

WORK IN PROGRESS: The Holy and the Demonic in 18th Century Literature.

SIDELIGHTS: R. D. Stock told *CA:* "I have been especially interested in studying the decline in modern society of the 'enchanted view,' or a sense of the numinous—a phenomenon remarked by such diverse thinkers as Carl Jung, Emile Durkheim, Robert Nisbet. As a writer, consequently, I have been much occupied with the eighteenth century, when the decay of those feelings first became evident in a forcible way, and with those writers since who have endeavored through their philosophical and imaginative works to revive a sense of the supernatural world, or at least to retard the secularizing and trivializing forces of modernism. 'Emancipation' is a word celebrated by many contemporary writers, but the emancipation I should like to observe is from the trite and dogmatic materialism to which many of them, it seems, subscribe.''

*   *   *

STOKES, William Lee 1915-

PERSONAL: Born March 27, 1915, in Hiawatha, Utah; son of William Peace (a rancher) and Grace Elizabeth (Cox) Stokes; married Betty Asenath Curtis (a teacher), September 7, 1939; children: Betty Lee (Mrs. Kent C. Huff), Mary Susan (Mrs. E. Brian Griffith), William Michael, Patricia Jane. *Education:* Brigham Young University, B.S., 1937, M.S., 1938; Princeton University, Ph.D., 1941. *Religion:* Church of Jesus Christ of Latter-day Saints (Mormon). *Home:* 1354 Second Ave., Salt Lake City, Utah 84103. *Office:* Department of Geological and Geophysical Sciences, University of Utah, Salt Lake City, Utah 84112.

CAREER: U.S. Geological Survey, junior geologist, 1942-43, geologist, 1943-47; University of Utah, Salt Lake City, assistant professor, 1947-49, associate professor, 1949-54, professor of geology, 1954—, head of department, 1954-68, director of Earth Science Museum, 1961-68, director of Cooperative Dinosaur Project, 1960-68. Geological consultant, Standard Oil Co., summers, 1950-52, and Atomic Energy Commission, summers, 1953-55. *Member:* Geological Society of America, American Association of Petroleum Geologists, Society of Vertebrate Paleontologists, Society of Economic Paleontologists and Mineralogists, American Geophysical Union, American Association for the Advancement of Science, Utah Geological Association (president, 1951), Sigma Xi, Phi Kappa Phi.

WRITINGS: (With D. J. Varnes) *Glossary of Selected Geologic Terms,* Colorado Scientific Society, 1955; *Essentials of Earth History: An Introduction to Historical Geology,* Prentice-Hall, 1960, 3rd edition, 1972; (with M. D. Picard and Sheldon Judson) *Introduction to Geology: Physical and Historical,* Prentice-Hall, 1968, 2nd edition, 1978; *Scenes of the Plateau Lands,* privately printed, 1968. Author and editor of guidebooks for geological excursions. Contributor of about 130 articles to scientific journals. Associate editor, *Bulletin of American Association of Petroleum Geologists,* 1954-66.

WORK IN PROGRESS: A book on dinosaurs; a book on controversy between science and religion; a book on the geology of Utah; descriptive semi-popular explanations of natural sciences.

BIOGRAPHICAL/CRITICAL SOURCES: Utah Natural History, Volume III, number 3, 1971.

*   *   *

STOKOE, William C(larence), Jr. 1919-

PERSONAL: Surname rhymes with "smoky"; born July 21, 1919, in Lancaster, N.H.; son of William C. (a farmer) and Marie (Stafford) Stokoe; married Ruth A. Palmeter, November 21, 1942; children: Helen (Mrs. David Phillips), James Stafford. *Education:* Cornell University, A.B., 1942, Ph.D., 1946. *Religion:* Presbyterian. *Home:* 9306 Mintwood St., Silver Spring, Md. 20901. *Office:* Linguistics Research Laboratory, Gallaudet College, Washington, D.C. 20002.

CAREER: Wells College, Aurora, N.Y., assistant professor, 1946-53, associate professor of English, 1953-55, chairman of department, 1950-52; Gallaudet College, Washington, D.C., professor of English, 1955-69, professor of linguistics and English, 1969—, chairman of department of English, 1955-71, director of Linguistics Research Laboratory, 1957—. President, Linstok Press, Inc., 1977—. Visiting fellow of Clare Hall, Cambridge University, 1977. *Member:* Modern Language Association of America, Linguistic Society of America, American Association for the Advancement of Science, American Anthropological Association, American Association of University Professors, Phi Beta Kappa, Phi Kappa Phi, St. Andrew's Society of Washington, D.C. (president, 1970). *Awards, honors:* Grants from American Council of Learned Societies, 1957, and National Science Foundation, 1960-62, 1962-63.

WRITINGS: Sign Language Structure, Department of Anthropology and Linguistics, University of Buffalo, 1960, revised edition, 1978; *A Calculus of Structure,* Gallaudet College Press, 1960, revised edition, Bobbs-Merrill, 1964; (with Dorothy Sueoka and Carl Croneberg) *A Dictionary of American Sign Language,* Gallaudet College Press, 1965, revised edition, Linstok Press, 1976; *Semiotics and Human Sign Language,* Mouton, 1972. Associate editor, *American Annals of the Deaf,* 1956-58; editor, *Sign Language Studies,* 1972—; editor, *Signs for Our Times,* 1971—.

WORK IN PROGRESS: Research on semantics and grammar of American sign language, and a contrastive study of sign language and English.

*   *   *

STOLZENBACH, Norma Frizzell 1904-

PERSONAL: Born February 6, 1904, in Goldthwaite, Tex.; daughter of Joseph H. and Ella Sophia (Phinney) Frizzell; married Conrad Stolzenbach (a consultant), June 2, 1929 (died December, 1976); children: Conrad, Jr. *Education:* University of Toledo, B.A., 1948; University of Michigan, M.A., 1949, Ph.D., 1954. *Religion:* Episcopalian. *Home:* 2119 Evergreen Rd., Toledo, Ohio 43606. *Office:* Department of Speech, University of Toledo, Bancroft, Toledo, Ohio 43606.

CAREER: University of Toledo, Toledo, Ohio, director of university theater, 1943-47, lecturer in English and radio, 1947-49, assistant professor of English, 1949-55, associate professor of theater, 1955-66, professor of speech communication, 1968-72, professor emerita, 1972—, director of theater activities, 1955-68. *Member:* National Collegiate Players, Phi Kappa Phi, Pi Lambda Theta (life member).

WRITINGS: The History of Theatre in Toledo, Ohio, Northwest Historical Society, 1950; *Fundamentals of Oral Interpretation,* University of Toledo Press, 1968. Author of opera libretto, "In the Name of Culture." Contributor to *Educational Horizons* and *Quarterly Journal of Historical Society of Northwest Ohio.* Author of 180 thirty-minute radio scripts for the University of Toledo weekly show, 1947-55.

WORK IN PROGRESS: Handbook of English and American Diction; short stories, essays, and articles.

AVOCATIONAL INTERESTS: Painting in oils, travel.

STONE, James H(erbert) 1918-

PERSONAL: Born September 10, 1918, in Little Rock, Ark.; son of Calvin Perry (a professor) and Minnie Ruth (Kemper) Stone; married Margaret M. Hale (a Girl Scout Council field officer), June 22, 1941; children: Judith (Mrs. Michael Meyers), Laura (Mrs. Michael Keplinger), Margaret R., Abigail. *Education:* Attended Pomona College, 1935-36; Stanford University, A.B., 1939; Yale University, Ph.D., 1947. *Religion:* Methodist. *Home:* 365 Lincoln Ave., Palo Alto, Calif. 94301. *Office:* Department of Humanities, San Francisco State University, San Francisco, Calif. 94132.

CAREER: Stanford University, Palo Alto, Calif., instructor, 1947-52, acting associate professor of history, 1960-61; San Francisco State University, San Francisco, Calif., assistant professor, 1952-56, associate professor, 1956-60, professor of humanities, 1961—, head of department, 1961-64, coordinator of American studies program, 1958-73. Acting instructor at the University of California, Berkeley, summer, 1952. *Military service:* U.S. Army, Medical Service Corps, 1942-46; served in China-Burma-India Theatre; became first lieutenant. *Member:* Organization of American Historians, American Studies Association (co-founder, Northern California chapter; chapter president, 1956-58; national convention program chairman, 1973), American Historical Association, California Humanities Association (co-founder, 1969; member of board of governors, 1969-72), Phi Beta Kappa. *Awards, honors:* American Philosophical Society grant, 1965; U.S. Office of Education grant, 1965.

WRITINGS: Crisis Fleeting, U.S. Government Printing Office, 1969. Contributor to *Encyclopaedia Britannica,* and to *Journal of Abnormal and Social Psychology, New England Quarterly, Harvard Business History Review, Improving College and University Teaching, Main Currents in Modern Thought, Infantry Journal, Military Surgeon,* and *Military Review.*

WORK IN PROGRESS: Research on theory and methods in interdisciplinary education and research.

*   *   *

STONE, William F(rank) 1931-

PERSONAL: Born December 29, 1931, in Camden, Me.; son of Frank H. and Marjorie (Curtis) Stone; married Elaine Spruce, 1950 (divorced, 1962); married Mary Perry (a nurse), March 22, 1962; children: (first marriage) William, Jr., Katherine, Suzanne; (second marriage) Curtis, Jeffrey. *Education:* University of Maine, B.A., 1956; University of Florida, M.A., 1961, Ph.D., 1963. *Politics:* Democrat. *Religion:* Episcopalian. *Home:* 431 Hancock St., Bangor, Me. 04401. *Office:* Department of Psychology, University of Maine, Orono, Me. 04473.

CAREER: Veterans Administration Hospital, Coral Gables, Fla., research trainee in comparative and social psychology and personality, 1960-63; Wilson College, Chambersburg, Pa., assistant professor of psychology, 1963-64; Lafayette College, Easton, Pa., assistant professor of psychology, 1964-66; University of Maine at Orono, assistant professor, 1966-68, associate professor, 1968-74, professor of psychology, 1974—, research associate in Manpower Research Project, 1966-70. Visiting associate professor of psychology, University of Florida, 1970-71; visiting scholar in political science, Duke University, 1977-78. *Member:* International Society of Political Psychology, American Psychological Association, Society for the Psychological

Study of Social Issues, Eastern Psychological Association, New England Social Psychological Association.

WRITINGS: (Contributor) Elliott McGinnis and C. B. Ferster, editors, *The Reinforcement of Social Behavior,* Houghton, 1971; *The Psychology of Politics,* Free Press, 1974; (contributor) Margaret G. Hermann, editor, *A Psychological Examination of Political Leaders,* Free Press, 1977. Author of psychological reports. Contributor of articles and reviews to psychology journals, including *Journal of Social Psychology, Contemporary Psychology, Journal of Personality and Social Psychology,* and *Journal of Personality.*

* * *

STONEBURNER, (Charles Joseph) Tony 1926-

PERSONAL: Born December 14, 1926, in Brooklyn, N.Y.; son of Charles William (a clergyman) and Margaret Lois (Timmons) Stoneburner; married Ruth Ann Harmon, December 23, 1956 (divorced, 1961); married Patricia Louise Pickett (an educator), July 21, 1962; children: (first marriage) David Victor; (second marriage) Carol Elizabeth. *Education:* DePauw University, A.B., 1946; Drew University, B.D., 1950; University of Michigan, M.A., 1962, Ph.D., 1966. *Politics:* "Christian Anarchist." *Home:* 203 North Plum St., Granville, Ohio 43023. *Office:* Department of English, Denison University, Granville, Ohio 43023.

CAREER: Methodist minister in Northeast Ohio Conference, 1950-56; Kansas Wesleyan University, Salina, director of religious life, 1956-59; Wesley Foundation, Ann Arbor, Mich., associate director, 1962-63; Denison University, Granville, Ohio, assistant professor, 1966-71, associate professor, 1971-77, professor of English, 1977—. Examiner for the North Central Association of Colleges and Secondary Schools; member of board of Catholic Art Association, and Church Society for College Work. *Member:* Society for the Arts, Religion, and Contemporary Culture (fellow). *Awards, honors:* Hopwood major poetry award (first prize), 1965, for *Axiom & Idiom.*

WRITINGS: A Recognition of Austin Warren, Ann Arbor Press, 1966; (editor) *A Meeting of Poets and Theologians to Discuss Parable Myth and Language,* Church Society for College Work, 1968; (editor) *A List of Letters by David Jones,* Limekiln Press, 1977.

Contributor: M. B. Bioy, Jr., editor, *Multi-Media Worship,* Seabury, 1969; Bioy, editor, *Community on Campus,* Seabury, 1972; H. Howard, editor, *Humanities, Religion, and the Arts Tomorrow,* Holt, 1972; G. A. White and C. Newman, editors, *Literature in Revolution,* Holt, 1972; M. Simon and H. Gross, editors, *Teacher and Critic: Essays By and About Austin Warren,* Plantin, 1976. Contributor of essays to *Agenda, Anglican Theological Review, Crux, East-West Review, Semeia, TriQuarterly,* and of poems to *Analect, Catholic Worker, Christian Century, Motive,* and other periodicals.

WORK IN PROGRESS: A long poem of many small sections in modernist mode; biographical essays on David Jones, Denise Levertov, and Gary Synder; research on the literary forms of religious writings.

SIDELIGHTS: Tony Stoneburner told *CA:* "My occupation is the teaching of reading and writing in English; my profession [is the] theology of literature; my vocation [is] poetry. My prose explores almost equally the preoccupations of my occupation, my profession, and my vocation. My poetry tries to delineate the worlds of the ancestral farm, Christian mythology, the contridictions of being 'a man of God,'

domestic existence, Penobscot Bay, and life on the midwestern frontier, in a fluctuation between ecstasy and irony or in a coincidence of the ordinary and the extraordinary."

* * *

STORER, Norman W(illiam) 1930-

PERSONAL: Born May 8, 1930, in Middletown, Conn.; son of Norman Wyman (an astronomer) and Mary Emily (House) Storer; married Ada Joan Van Valkenburg, 1951 (divorced, 1975); married Mary P. Hiatt, 1975; children: (first marriage) Martin Wilson, Thomas Wyman. *Education:* Attended Park College, 1948-50; University of Kansas, A.B., 1952, M.A., 1956; Cornell University, Ph.D., 1961. *Politics:* Democrat. *Religion:* None. *Home:* 311 East 23rd St., Apt. 8BB, New York, N.Y. 10010. *Office:* Department of Sociology, Bernard M. Baruch College of the City University of New York, 17 Lexington Ave., New York, N.Y. 10010.

CAREER: Harvard University, Cambridge, Mass., instructor, 1960-62, lecturer, 1962-63, assistant professor of sociology, 1963-66; Social Science Research Council, New York City, staff associate, 1966-70; Bernard M. Baruch College of the City University of New York, New York City, professor of sociology and chairman of department, 1970—; Graduate School and University Center of the City University of New York, New York City, member of faculty, Ph.D. Program in Sociology, 1971—. *Military service:* U.S. Army Reserve, active duty, 1953-55; became sergeant. *Member:* American Sociological Association, American Association for the Advancement of Science, Eastern Sociological Society, Phi Beta Kappa.

WRITINGS: The Social System of Science, Holt, 1966; *Focus on Society: An Introduction to Sociology,* Addison-Wesley, 1973, revised edition, 1979; (editor) Robert K. Merton, *The Sociology of Science: Theoretical and Empirical Investigations,* University of Chicago Press, 1973; (contributor) Donald Goldsmith, editor, *Scientists Confront Velikovsky,* Cornell University Press, 1977. Contributor to sociology journals.

* * *

STOUTAMIRE, Albert 1921-

PERSONAL: Born June 19, 1921, in Broadway, Va.; son of Frederick Ashton (a physician) and Elsie (Smith) Stoutamire; married Anne Jurgens, December 26, 1947; children: Robert Paschal. *Education:* Virginia Commonwealth University, B.S., 1947; Columbia University, M.A., 1953; Florida State University, Ed.D., 1960. *Religion:* Presbyterian. *Home:* Route 6, Box 185AG, Lake Charles, La. 70605. *Office:* Department of Music, McNeese State University, Lake Charles, La. 70609.

CAREER: Free-lance musician and full-time music teacher in Richmond, Va. public schools, 1947-57; LaGrange College, LaGrange, Ga., professor of music, 1958-61; McNeese State University, Lake Charles, La., professor of music, 1961—. *Military service:* U.S. Army, 1943-46. *Member:* American Federation of Musicians, National Association of College Wind and Percussion Instructors, American Society of Composers, Authors and Publishers, Music Educators National Conference, Phi Mu Alpha, Phi Delta Kappa.

WRITINGS: Music of the Old South: Colony to Confederacy, Fairleigh Dickinson University Press, 1972; (with Kenneth Henderson) *Bach-Rock Band Book* (musical compositions and arrangements), Pro Art, 1972; (with Henderson)

Duets for All (musical compositions and arrangements), Pro Art, 1973; *Right on Band Book,* Pro Art, 1974; *Bow Pick 'n' Rock,* Pro Art, 1975; *Stringing Along,* Pro Art, 1976; *Toot, Strum and Drum,* Pro Art, 1977; (with Norman Smith) *Band Music Notes,* privately printed, 1977. Author of other instrumental and choral works for young musicians. Contributor to *Instrumentalist, Music Educators Journal, Georgia Music News, Journal of Research in Music Education, NACWPI Bulletin, American Music Teacher,* and *Louisiana Musician.*

WORK IN PROGRESS: Aids for Band, a style and technique book; musical compositions and arrangements for school musicians.

BIOGRAPHICAL/CRITICAL SOURCES: Louisiana Musician, September, 1972, September, 1977.

* * *

STRASSMANN, W(olfgang) Paul   1926-

PERSONAL: Born July 26, 1926, in Berlin, Germany; naturalized U.S. citizen; married; children: three. *Education:* University of Texas, B.A. (magna cum laude), 1949; Columbia University, M.A., 1950; University of Maryland, Ph.D., 1956; also studied at Rice Institute, Universidad Nacional de Mexico, and Sorbonne, University of Paris. *Office:* Department of Economics, Michigan State University, East Lansing, Mich. 48823.

CAREER: U.S. Department of Commerce, Washington, D.C., international economist specializing in Central America, 1950-52; University of Maryland, College Park, instructor in economics, spring, 1955; Michigan State University, East Lansing, instructor, 1956-57, assistant professor, 1957-59, associate professor, 1959-63, professor of economics, 1963—. Visiting scholar, London School of Economics and Political Science, University of London, 1965-66; senior research director, International Labor Office (Geneva), 1969-70, 1973-74. Member of Inter-Agency Employment Mission to Colombia, 1970; chairman of Task Force on Appropriate Housing Technology, National Academy of Sciences, 1971-73, and Task Force on Housing and Urban Infrastructure, 1974-76. Consultant to Agency for International Development, Brookings Institution, National Academy of Science and Engineering, United Nations, and World Bank. *Military service:* U.S. Navy, 1944-46. *Member:* International Association for Housing Science (member of economic committee, 1971—), Organisation for Economic Co-operation and Development (member of housing employment research project steering committee, 1970-73), Association for Evolutionary Economics (member of executive board, 1976—), Phi Beta Kappa. *Awards, honors:* Social Science Research Council grant, 1960-61; Rockefeller Foundation grant for research in Mexico, 1960-61; Ford Foundation faculty fellowship, 1962-63, 1963-66; Midwest Universities Consortium for International Activities grant for research in Peru, 1968, 1973-75.

WRITINGS: Economic Growth in Northern Michigan, Institute for Community Development, Michigan State University, 1958; *The Urban Economies of Southern Michigan,* Institute for Community Development, Michigan State University, 1958; *Risk and Technological Innovation: American Manufacturing Methods in the Nineteenth Century,* Cornell University Press, 1959; *Technological Change and Economic Development: The Manufacturing Experience of Mexico and Puerto Rico,* Cornell University Press, 1968; (editor) *Automation in Developing Countries,* International Labor Office, 1972; (with C. Araud, G. Boon, and V.

Urquidi) *Studies on Employment in the Mexican Housing Industry,* Organisation for Economic Co-operation and Development, 1973; *Employment Generation through Residential Construction in Rio De Janeiro,* Agency for International Development, 1975; *Housing and Building Technology in Developing Countries,* International Business and Economic Studies, Michigan State University, 1978.

Contributor: John J. Johnson, editor, *Continuity and Change in Latin America,* Stanford University Press, 1964; Dudley Seers, editor, *Towards Full Employment: A Program for Colombia, Prepared by a U.N. Inter-Agency Team,* International Labor Office, 1970; Stanley M. Davis, editor, *Comparative Management: Organizational and Cultural Perspectives,* Prentice-Hall, 1971; Walter Galenson, editor, *Essays on Employment,* International Labor Office, 1971; Davis and Goodman, editors, *Workers and Managers in Latin America,* Heath, 1972; E. Rogers and R. Solo, editors, *Inducing Technological Change for Economic Growth,* Michigan State University Press, 1972; Vasily Kouskoulas, editor, *Urban Housing,* Wayne State University, 1973; Richard Jolly and others, editors, *Third World Employment,* Penguin, 1973; Kouskoulas and Robert Lytle, editors, *Urban Housing and Transportation,* Wayne State University, 1975; Warren Samuels, editor, *The Chicago School of Political Economy,* Michigan State University, 1976; *Low Income Housing—Technology and Policy,* Asian Institute of Technology (Bangkok), 1977; Patrick Kelly and Melvin Kranzberg, editors, *Technological Innovation: A Critical Review of Current Knowledge,* San Francisco Press, 1978.

Contributor of more than thirty articles and reviews to national and foreign economic journals, including *Quarterly Journal of Economics, Business History Review, Journal of Economic History, Review of Economic Studies, Business Topics, Inter-American Economic Affairs,* and *International Labor Review.* Member of editorial board, *Technology and Culture, Journal of Developing Areas,* and *Journal of Economic Issues.*

* * *

STRAUCH, Carl F(erdinand)   1908-

PERSONAL: Born September 25, 1908, in Bethlehem, Pa.; son of Henry (a merchant) and Anna (Foesch) Strauch; married Helen Dery, September 1, 1937; children: Helen. *Education:* Muhlenberg College, A.B., 1930; Lehigh University, M.A., 1934; Yale University, Ph.D., 1946. *Politics:* Democratic. *Religion:* Lutheran. *Home:* 1531 High St., Bethlehem, Pa. 18018. *Office:* Department of English, Lehigh University, Bethlehem, Pa. 18018.

CAREER: Lehigh University, Bethlehem, Pa., instructor, 1934-37, 1939-41, assistant professor, 1941-46, associate professor, 1946-52, professor of English, 1952—. *Member:* Modern Language Association of America, Bibliographical Society of America, American Studies Association, Emerson Society, Phi Beta Kappa, Omega Delta Kappa. *Awards, honors:* Lehigh Institute research grant-in-aid, 1949-50; American Philosophical Society grant-in-aid, 1950-55.

WRITINGS: (Editor) *Reed's Growth of the Mind,* Holt, 1965; (editor with others) *American Literary Masters,* Holt, 1970; (editor) *Style in the American Renaissance,* Transcendental, 1970. Contributor to *PMLA, Harvard Library Bulletin,* and *Wisconsin Studies in Contemporary Literature.*

WORK IN PROGRESS: Editing Emerson's poems as part of the Modern Language Association of America's "Collected Works'' for Harvard University Press; a book of scholarly essays on Emerson's poems.

* * *

STRAUSS, W(allace) Patrick 1923-

PERSONAL: Born March 17, 1923, in St. Louis, Mo.; son of Alvin William and Helen (Decker) Strauss; married Laura McPhee (a librarian), October 5, 1951; children: Jane McPhee. *Education:* Attended University of California, Berkeley, 1941-42; Occidental College, A.B., 1948; Stanford University, M.A., 1949; University of Paris, graduate study, 1949-50; Columbia University, Ph.D., 1958. *Home:* 3554 Second St., Hadley, Mich. 48440. *Office:* Department of History, Oakland University, Rochester, Mich.

CAREER: Menlo College, Menlo Park, Calif., instructor in algebra, 1948-49; marketing executive in New York, 1951-58; Columbia University, New York, N.Y., lecturer in American history, 1958; San Francisco State College (now University), San Francisco, Calif., instructor in history, assistant to the president, 1958-60; General Beadle State College (now Dakota State College), Madison, S.D., assistant professor of history, 1960-61; Michigan State University, East Lansing, assistant professor of American thought and language, 1961-66; Oakland University, Rochester, Mich., associate professor, 1966-70, professor of history, 1970—. Fulbright lecturer at University of Hong Kong, 1964-65, 1970-71, and Chinese University, Hong Kong, 1964-65. *Military service:* U.S. Army, 1942-46; became first lieutenant.

WRITINGS: Americans in Polynesia, 1783-1842, Michigan State University Press, 1964; (editor) *Stars and Spars: The American Navy in the Age of Sail,* Ginn/Blaisdell, 1969; *Isolation and Involvement: An Interpretive History of American Diplomacy,* Xerox College Publishing, 1972. Contributor of articles to *Pacific Historical Review, Historical Studies Australia and New Zealand,* and *United States Naval Institute Proceedings.*

WORK IN PROGRESS: A monograph on early American consuls.

* * *

STROBRIDGE, Truman R(ussell) 1927-

PERSONAL: Born October 15, 1927, in Sault Sainte Marie, Mich.; son of Roy Jamie and Ethel A. (Goodeman) Strobridge; married Mary Witeck (an accountant), August 25, 1959; children: Lance Jamie. *Education:* Michigan State University, B.A., 1951, M.A., 1957; American University, additional study, 1959-62. *Politics:* Republican. *Religion:* Baptist. *Home:* Ruffweg 1B, 7000 Stuttgart 75, Germany. *Mailing address:* Headquarters, U.S. European Command, Box 165, APO New York 09128.

CAREER: Sailor, construction worker, farm hand, dock worker, factory worker, milkman, light-truck driver, high school teacher, Internal Revenue officer; National Archives, Washington, D.C., archivist, 1959-61; U.S. Marine Corps, Washington, D.C., historian, 1961-63; Headquarters, Alaskan Command, Anchorage, Alaska, command historian, 1964-67; Office of Commander-in-Chief, Pacific, Honolulu, Hawaii, senior historian, 1967-70; U.S. Coast Guard, Washington, D.C., historian, 1970-76; U.S. Army, Armament Material Readiness Command, Rock Island, Ill., historian, 1977-78, command historian, U.S. European Command, Stuttgart, Germany, 1978—. Instructor in history at University of Alaska, 1964-67. *Military service:* U.S. Army Air Forces, 1946-47; became sergeant. *Member:* In-

ternational Platform Association, American Historical Association, Organization of American Historians, Company of Military Historians. *Awards, honors:* National Archives scholarship from American University, 1959.

WRITINGS: Operation 'Helping Hand': The Army and the Alaskan Earthquake, U.S. Army, Alaska, 1964; *Strength in the North,* Alaskan Command, 1966; (with George W. Garand) *Western Pacific Operations: History of U.S. Marine Corps Operations in World War II,* U.S. Government Printing Office, 1970; (editor) *U.S. Coast Guard Annotated Bibliography,* U.S. Government Printing Office, 1972; *History of Public Works in the United States, 1776-1976,* American Public Works Association, 1976. Contributor to *Pacific Northwest Quarterly, Art Journal, Inland Seas, Arizona and the West, International Defense Review, Polar Record, Arctic, American Neptune,* and other journals.

WORK IN PROGRESS: Strong to Save: The U.S. Coast Guard and Maritime Safety, for Scholarly Resources.

BIOGRAPHICAL/CRITICAL SOURCES: Knik Knak, February, 1965.

* * *

STRONG, Donald Stuart 1912-

PERSONAL: Born December 31, 1912, in New York, N.Y.; son of Harry Cannell (a railroad executive) and Marion (Stuart) Strong; married Emily Jo Trenckmann (executive director of local Planned Parenthood program), June 8, 1940 (died December 22, 1974); married Florrie Belle Pennington (a clinical psychologist), June 17, 1977; children: (first marriage) Elizabeth (Mrs. David M. Gitlitz), Stuart, Kathleen. *Education:* Oberlin College, A.B., 1934; University of Chicago, Ph.D., 1939. *Politics:* Democrat. *Religion:* Presbyterian. *Office:* Department of Political Science, University of Alabama, University, Ala. 35486.

CAREER: Western Reserve University (now Case Western Reserve University), Cleveland, Ohio, instructor in political science, 1937-39; University of Texas, Main University (now University of Texas at Austin), instructor in political science, 1939-46; University of Alabama, University, assistant professor, 1946-49, associate professor, 1949-52, professor of political science, 1952—. *Member:* Southern Political Science Association (vice-president, 1966; president, 1970).

WRITINGS: Organized Anti-Semitism in America, Public Affairs Press, 1941; (contributor) Malcolm Macdonald and others, editors, *Outside Readings in American Government,* Crowell, 1949; (with Alexander Heard) *Southern Primaries and Elections: 1920-1949,* University of Alabama Press, 1950; (contributor) Arnold Rose, editor, *Race Prejudice and Discrimination,* Knopf, 1951; *Election Officer's Handbook,* Bureau of Public Administration, University of Alabama, 1952, revised edition, 1960; (contributor) P. T. David, Malcolm Moos, and Ralph M. Goldman, editors, *Presidential Nominating Politics in 1952,* Johns Hopkins Press, 1954; *The Presidential Election in the South: 1952,* Bureau of Public Administration, University of Alabama, 1955; *Registration of Voters in Alabama,* Bureau of Public Administration, University of Alabama, 1956.

Urban Republicanism in the South, Bureau of Public Administration, University of Alabama, 1960; (contributor) Allan P. Sindler, editor, *Change in the Contemporary South,* Duke University Press, 1963; (contributor) Robert B. Highsaw, editor, *The Deep South in Transformation,*

University of Alabama Press, 1964; *Negroes, Ballots, and Judges: National Voting Rights Legislation in the Federal Courts,* University of Alabama Press, 1968; (contributor) William C. Harvard, editor, *The Changing Politics of the South,* Louisianna State University Press, 1972; *Issue Voting and Party Realignment,* University of Alabama Press, 1977. Contributor to *Encyclopaedia Britannica.* Contributor to *American Political Science Review, Journal of Politics,* and *Journal of Negro Education.* Editor, *Journal of Politics,* 1971-74.

AVOCATIONAL INTERESTS: Canoeing, photography, bird study.

*   *   *

STRUNG, Norman 1941-
(Bart Yaeger, Asouff Barkee)

PERSONAL: Born October 21, 1941, in New York, N.Y.; son of August (a banker) and Marion (Hoffmann) Strung; married Priscilla Hoerschgen, October, 1963. *Education:* Montana State University, B.S., 1963; University of Montana, additional study, 1963-64. *Politics:* "Three-quarters Democrat, one-quarter unpredictable." *Religion:* "Pantheist." *Home address:* Route 3, Box 189, Bozeman, Mont. 59715. *Agent:* McIntosh & Otis, Inc., 475 Fifth Ave., New York, N.Y. 10017.

CAREER: Free-lance writer. Has worked as a clamdigger, carpenter, and a licensed hunting and fishing guide. Instructor in English, Montana State University, Bozeman, 1964-67. *Member:* Outdoor Writers of America (member of board of directors, 1972-75, 1978-81), Society of Magazine Writers, Authors League, Treasure State Outfitters.

WRITINGS: (With Dan Morris) *The Fisherman's Almanac,* Macmillan, 1970; (with Morris) *Family Fun Around the Water,* Cowles, 1970; *The Hunter's Almanac,* Macmillan, 1971; *Camping in Comfort,* Lippincott, 1971; (contributor) Dan and Inez Morris, editors, *The Complete Outdoor Cookbook,* Hawthorn, 1971; *Deer Hunting,* Lippincott, 1974; *Misty Mornings and Moonless Nights: A Waterfowler's Guide,* Macmillan, 1974; (editor) *Communicating the Outdoor Experience,* Outdoor Writers Association of America, 1975; (with Sam Curtis and Earl Perry) *Whitewater!,* Macmillan, 1975; *An Encyclopedia of Knives,* Lippincott, 1976; *The Complete Hunter's Catalog,* Lippincott, 1977. Contributor, occasionally under pseudonyms Bart Yaeger and Asouff Barkee, to national magazines, including *Field & Stream, Boys' Life, Sports Afield, Outdoor Life, Fishing World,* and *Gray's Sporting Journal.*

WORK IN PROGRESS: To Catch a Trout, for Stein & Day.

SIDELIGHTS: Norman Strung told *CA:* "You can trace all these things to the tap root of independence. I am a writer because a writer is the most independent of beings; independent of thought, action, income and lifestyle, ultimately, with only himself to blame for success or failure. The word 'freelance' is one of the most accurate in our language. But that root feeds a tree with many branches. I must recognize a love of language and the printed word; its ability to communicate with uncommon grace victories and defeats and love and beauty. To influence, to converse, to shape thoughts, to put myself on paper and have the me that is in works worthy enough to be read by another human being. If for some reason I ceased to write professionally, I would write an awful lot of letters. Then, somewhere near the tip of the tree, greens my 'specialty,' outdoor writing. It is too easy to say that I am an outdoor writer because I love the outdoors be-

cause they are the only place where you really have a place in life. But that is the theme . . . or philosophy if you will . . . that nourishes my writing and my life."

*   *   *

STUART, Irving R. 1916-

PERSONAL: Born March 15, 1916, in New York, N.Y.; son of Simon and Lena Stuart; married Helen G. Sheffield (a teacher), June 28, 1941. *Education:* City College (now City College of the City University of New York), B.S.S., 1938, M.S., 1948; New York University, Ph.D., 1951. *Residence:* White Plains, N.Y. *Office:* Department of Psychology, Herbert H. Lehman College of the City University of New York, Bronx, N.Y. 10468.

CAREER: Clinical psychologist; Herbert H. Lehman College of the City University of New York, Bronx, N.Y., assistant professor, 1954-65, associate professor, 1965-71, professor of psychology, 1971—. *Military service:* U.S. Army, 1943-46. *Member:* International Council of Psychology, American Psychological Association, Interamerican Society of Psychology.

WRITINGS: (Editor with L. E. Abt) *Children of Separation and Divorce,* Grossman, 1972; (editor with Abt) *Interracial Marriage,* Grossman, 1973; (editor with Abt) *Social Psychology and Discretionary Law,* Van Nostrand, 1978. Contributor to *Journal of Social Psychology, Journal of Aesthetic Education,* and *International Journal of Social Psychiatry.*

*   *   *

STUART, Jane 1942-
(Jane Stuart Juergensmeyer)

PERSONAL: Born August 20, 1942, in Ashland, Ky.; daughter of Jesse Hilton (a writer) and Naomi Deane (Norris) Stuart; married Julian Conrad Juergensmeyer (a professor of law), August 20, 1963; children: Conrad Stuart, Erik Markstrom. *Education:* Attended American University at Cairo, 1961-62, and University of Kentucky, 1962; Western Reserve University (now Case Western Reserve University), A.B. (magna cum laude), 1964; Indiana University, M.A. (classics), 1967, M.A. (Italian), 1969, Ph.D., 1971; also attended Anglo-American Cultural Institute for Modern Greek (Athens), summer, 1966, and Universite d'Aix-Marseilles, spring, 1968; independent study in Italy, summer, 1969, and Kenya and Uganda, summer, 1972. *Home:* 3619 North West 38th St., Gainesville, Fla. 32611.

CAREER: Latin teacher in private school in Miami, Fla., fall, 1962; Haile Selassie I University, Addis Ababa, Ethiopia, lecturer in Italian, 1968-69; writer, lecturer, and translator, 1969—. Has also taught in the elementary schools of Greysbranch and Wurtland, Ky., at the British School in Addis Ababa, and at the University of Florida. *Member:* Phi Beta Kappa, Eta Sigma Phi.

WRITINGS: A Year's Harvest (poems), Landmark House, 1957; *Eyes of the Mole* (poems), Staunton & Lee, 1967; *White Barn* (poems), Whippoorwill, 1973; *Yellowhawk* (novel), McGraw, 1973. Also author of novels, *Passerman's Hollow,* 1974, *Land of the Fox,* 1975, and *Gideon's Children,* 1976.

Work represented in anthologies, including: *Kentucky Contemporary Poetry: I & II,* edited by Joy Bale, Bean Publishing, 1965-66; *Fire, Sleet and Candelight,* edited by August Derleth, Staunton & Lee, 1963; *Short Stories for Discussion,* edited by Albert K. Ridout and Jesse Stuart, Scribner,

1965; *Poems from the Hills: 1971*, edited by William Plumley, M. H. C. Publications, 1971; *Who Speaks for Appalachia*, edited by Cecille Haddix, 1975; *Voices from the Hills: Selected Readings from Southern Appalachia*, edited by R. J. Higgs and A. N. Manning, Ungar, 1976. Work also appears in *Stories from the Hills*, edited by Plumley.

Book reviewer, *Louisville Courier Journal*, 1967. Contributor of stories, poems, translations, and reviews to magazines and newspapers, including *Lyric, Educational Forum, Progressive Farmer, Activist, Ladies' Home Journal, Pegasus, National Wildlife, Literature East and West*, and *Discourse*. Contributing editor, *Playgirl*, 1973.

WORK IN PROGRESS: Recollections; translating *Poems of Alcaeus* and poetry of Eugenio Montale.

AVOCATIONAL INTERESTS: Travel (Eastern and Western Europe, Africa, Central America).

* * *

STUART, Richard Bernard 1933-

PERSONAL: Born October 8, 1933, in Newark, N.J.; son of Charles Lewis (a businessman) and Frances (Dimond) Stuart; married Freida Marsha Pritzker (a marriage counselor and sex therapist), April 23, 1965; children: Jesse, Reid, Toby Evan, Gregory Lyal. *Education:* New York University, B.A., 1955; Columbia University, M.S., 1960, D.S.W., 1965. *Residence:* Salt Lake City, Utah. *Office:* Bureau of Marriage and Family Counseling, University of Utah, Salt Lake City, Utah.

CAREER: University of Michigan, Ann Arbor, professor and fellow at Center for Human Growth and Development, 1965-73; University of British Columbia, Vancouver, professor in School of Medicine, 1973-75; State University of New York at Stony Brook, professor of psychology, 1975-77; University of Utah, Salt Lake City, professor of psychology and social work, and director of Bureau of Marriage and Family Counseling, 1977—. President of Behavior Change Systems, 1968—; president of Behavior Change Laboratories, 1969—; psychological director, Weight Watchers International, 1972—. *Member:* American Psychological Association (fellow), Child Welfare League of America (member of executive research board, 1972—), Association for the Advancement of Behavior Therapy (member of board of directors, 1972—), Behavior Therapy and Research Society, Canadian Psychological Association, Psi Chi.

WRITINGS: Trick or Treatment, Research Press, 1971; (with Barbara Davis) *Slim Chance in a Fat World*, Research Press, 1972, revised edition, 1978; (with Marjorie Schuman) *Tripping and Toking in Mid-America*, American Psychological Association, 1973; *Behavioral Self-Management*, Brunner, 1977; *Act Thin, Stay Thin*, Norton, 1978; (with Brenda Roper) *Marital Therapy: A Social Learning Approach*, Brunner, 1979. Contributor of over 100 articles to professional journals. Member of editorial board, *Behavior Therapy*, 1972—, *Journal of Applied Behavioral Analysis*, 1972—, and *Behaviour Therapy and Experimental Psychiatry*, 1972—.

WORK IN PROGRESS: Managing Depression, for Norton.

* * *

STUB, Holger R(ichard) 1922-

PERSONAL: Born December 2, 1922, in Elk Horn, Iowa; son of C. A. (a clergyman) and Anna M. Stub; married Elin Holst (a librarian), September 11, 1948; children: Lisa, Peter. *Education:* University of Minnesota, B.A., 1948, M.A., 1950, Ph.D., 1958. *Home:* 628 South Mt. Pleasant Rd., Philadelphia, Pa. 19119. *Office:* Urban Studies, College of Liberal Arts, Temple University, Philadelphia, Pa. 19122.

CAREER: State of Minnesota, Department of Civil Service, personnel officer, 1950-52; Wisconsin State University—La Crosse (now University of Wisconsin—La Crosse), instructor in sociology, 1956-58; University of Minnesota, Duluth, assistant professor, 1958-61, associate professor of sociology, 1961-62; Temple University, Philadelphia, Pa., assistant professor, 1962-67, associate professor of sociology, 1967—, chairman of urban studies, 1970-78, co-director of National Science Undergraduate Research Program, 1967-69. *Military service:* U.S. Army, 1943-45; became sergeant.

MEMBER: American Sociological Association (fellow), Society for the Psychological Study of Social Issues, Society for the Study of Social Problems, Eastern Sociological Society, Alpha Kappa Delta, Phi Alpha Theta. *Awards, honors:* Ford Foundation fellowship, 1955-56; Tozer Foundation scholarship, 1955.

WRITINGS: (Contributor) Arnold M. Rose, editor, *Mental Health and Disorder*, Norton, 1955; *Migration to Duluth: 1958, 1959*, Social Science Research Trust Fund, University of Minnesota, 1961; (contributor) Jeanette Folta and others, editors, *Sociological Concepts in Patient Care*, Wiley, 1967; (with Robert Bell) *Sociology of Education*, revised edition (Stub was not associated with earlier edition), Dorsey, 1969; *Status Communities in Modern Society: Alternatives to Class Analysis*, Dryden, 1972. Contributor to *American Sociological Review, British Journal of Sociology*, and *Criminology, Law and Police Science*.

WORK IN PROGRESS: A Quiet Revolution: The Social Consequences of Long Life; A Study of Celebrities: The Social Characteristics of the International Set, a monograph; research on attitudes, values, ideology, and self-esteem of black adolescent youths who are members of legitimized groups, with a book expected to result.

* * *

STUCKEY, William Joseph 1923-

PERSONAL: Born January 15, 1923, in St. Louis, Mo.; son of Julian Rube (an engineer) and Mary (Connor) Stuckey; married June Mathews, August 27, 1956; children: Elizabeth, Sarah, John. *Education:* Washington University, St. Louis, Mo., A.B., 1949, Ph.D., 1959; University of Iowa, M.F.A., 1952. *Politics:* Democrat. *Religion:* Episcopalian. *Home:* 400 Valley View Lane, Lafayette, Ind. 47905. *Office:* Department of English, Purdue University, West Lafayette, Ind. 47907.

CAREER: Iowa State College of Agriculture and Mechanical Arts (now Iowa State University of Science and Technology), Ames, instructor in English, 1951-53; Washington University, St. Louis, Mo., instructor in English, 1957-58; Hamline University, St. Paul, Minn., instructor, 1958-59, assistant professor of English, 1959-61; Purdue University, West Lafayette, Ind., assistant professor, 1961-66, associate professor, 1966-72, professor of English, 1972—. *Military service:* U.S. Army, 1941-43; served in European theater; became sergeant. *Member:* Modern Language Association of America, National Council of Teachers of English.

WRITINGS: The Pulitzer Prize Novels: A Critical Back-

ward Look, Oklahoma University Press, 1966; *Caroline Gordon,* Twayne, 1972. Contributor to *Critique, Arizona Quarterly Review, Western Humanities Review,* and other literature journals. Editor, *Minnesota Review;* fiction editor, *Quartet;* advisory editor, *Modern Fiction Studies.*

WORK IN PROGRESS: Revising *The Pulitzer Prize Novels;* a fictional book for children; short stories; poems.

* * *

STUMPF, Samuel Enoch 1918-

PERSONAL: Born February 3, 1918, in Cleveland, Ohio; son of Louis (a clergyman) and Elizabeth (Jergens) Stumpf; married Jean Goodman, July 3, 1943; children: Paul, Mark, Samuel, Jr. *Education:* University of California, B.S., 1940; Andover Newton Theological School, B.D., 1943; Columbia University, graduate study, 1946; University of Chicago, Ph.D., 1948. *Home:* 424 Page Rd., Nashville, Tenn. 37205. *Office:* School of Law, Vanderbilt University, Nashville, Tenn. 37203.

CAREER: Vanderbilt University, Nashville, Tenn., assistant professor, 1948-49, associate professor, 1949-52, professor of philosophy and chairman of department, 1952-67, lecturer in jurisprudence in School of Law, 1950-58, assistant to chancellor, 1966-67; Cornell College, Mount Vernon, Iowa, president, 1967-74; Vanderbilt University, research professor of jurisprudence, 1974-77, research professor of medical philosophy, 1974—, professor of law, 1977—. Gates lecturer at Grinnell College, 1951; Calkins lecturer, Stetson University, 1956; Keese lecturer, University of Chattanooga; Decell lecturer, Millsaps College; consultant to judicial council of American Medical Association. *Military service:* U.S. Naval Reserve, 1943-46; served as chaplain. *Member:* Associated Colleges of the Midwest (vice-president), Association of American Colleges, Iowa College Foundation (member of executive committee), Phi Beta Kappa. *Awards, honors:* Ford Foundation fellowship, Harvard University, 1955; Rockefeller Foundation fellowship, Oxford University, 1958-59.

WRITINGS: A Democratic Manifesto, Vanderbilt University Press, 1954; *Morality and the Law,* Vanderbilt University Press, 1966; *Socrates to Sartre: A History of Philosophy,* McGraw, 1966, 2nd edition, 1975; *Philosophical Problems,* McGraw, 1971; *Philosophy: History and Problems,* McGraw, 1971, 2nd edition, 1977; *Elements of Philosophy,* McGraw, 1979. Contributor to learned and professional journals, including *Harvard Law Review, Christian Scholar, Vanderbilt Law Review, Annals of Internal Medicine,* and *Archives de Philophie du Droit.*

* * *

STURDIVANT, Frederick D(avid) 1937-

PERSONAL: Born October 17, 1937, in Whitewright, Tex.; son of Wyatt A. (a machinist) and Juanita (Phillips) Sturdivant; married Patricia A. Robinson, December 22, 1959; children: Kaira, Lisha, Brian. *Education:* San Jose State College (now University), B.S. (with honors), 1959; University of Oregon, M.B.A., 1960; Stanford University, additional study, summer, 1961; Northwestern University, Ph.D., 1963. *Politics:* Democrat. *Home:* 2500 Stonehaven Ct. S., Columbus, Ohio 43220. *Office:* College of Administrative Science, Ohio State University, 1775 South College Rd., Columbus, Ohio 43210.

CAREER: University of Southern California, Los Angeles, assistant professor of marketing, 1964-67; University of

Texas at Austin, associate professor of marketing administration, 1967-70; Harvard University, Cambridge, Mass., associate professor, 1970-72, visiting professor of business administration, 1972-73; Ohio State University, Columbus, Meshulam Riklis Professor of Business and Its Environment, 1972—. Principal, Management Analysis Center, Inc. *Member:* American Marketing Association, Business History Society, Association for Consumer Research, Southwestern Social Science Association. *Awards, honors:* Ford Foundation fellowship, summer, 1963; teaching excellence awards from University of Texas, 1968, 1969, 1970.

WRITINGS: (With others) *Competition and Human Behavior,* Appleton, 1968; *The Ghetto Marketplace,* Free Press, 1969; (with Robert J. Holloway) *Bibliography on Marketing to Low-Income Consumers,* U.S. Department of Commerce, 1969, revised edition, 1971; *Growth through Service: A History of American Hospital Supply Corporation,* Northwestern University Press, 1970; (with others) *Managerial Analysis in Marketing,* Scott, Foresman, 1970; (contributor) Louis P. Bucklin, editor, *Vertical Marketing Systems,* Scott, Foresman, 1970; (compiler with others) *Perspectives in Marketing Management,* Scott, Foresman, 1971; *Marketing and the Low-Income Consumer,* U.S. Department of Commerce, 1971; (with Orange A. Smalley) *The Credit Merchants: A History of Speigel, Inc.,* Southern Illinois University Press, 1973; (contributor) Fred C. Allvine, editor, *Public Policy and Marketing Practices,* American Marketing Association, 1973; (contributor) Scott Ward and Thomas S. Robertson, *Consumer Behavior: Theoretical Foundations,* Prentice-Hall, 1973; (contributor) Robert N. Katz, editor, *Protecting Consumer Interests: Private Initiative and Public Response,* Ballinger, 1976; *Business and Society: A Managerial Approach,* Irwin, 1977; (with Larry M. Robinson) *The Corporate Social Challenge: Cases and Commentaries,* Irwin, 1977; (with Alan R. Andreasen) *Minorities and Marketing: Research Challenges,* American Marketing Association, 1977.

Contributor to proceedings. Contributor of over twenty articles and reviews to professional journals, including *Harvard Business Review, Social Science Quarterly, Journal of Marketing, Quarterly Review of Economics and Business, Law and Contemporary Problems, Mississippi Valley Journal of Business and Economics,* and *California Management Review.*

* * *

STYLES, Jimmie C(arter) 1931-

PERSONAL: Born October 17, 1931, in Bellville, Ga.; son of Roy Thelmer (a minister) and Hellon (Benton) Styles; married Jimmie Strickland (an artist), January 4, 1952; children: Dennis, Denise, Duaine. *Education:* Georgia Southern College, B.A., 1956; George Peabody College for Teachers, M.A., 1958, Ed.S., 1962. *Religion:* Baptist. *Home:* 1800 Calais Rd., Fort Worth, Tex. 76116. *Office:* Tarrant County Junior College, 1400 Electric Service Building, Fort Worth, Tex. 76102.

CAREER: Junior College of Broward County, Fort Lauderdale, Fla., director of educational data system, 1962-65; Tarrant County Junior College, Fort Worth, Tex., assistant to president, 1965-66, vice president for program development, 1966-67, vice president for research and development, 1967-69, vice chancellor for research and development, 1969—. Chairman of committee of examiners in mathematics for comparative guidance and placement program, Educational Testing Service, 1971-72; chairman of public relations and publicity committee, Consumer Credit Counseling Service (Fort Worth), 1971-72. Consultant to United Fund, International Business Machines, Law Enforcement Assistance Administration (of U.S. Department of Justice), University Research Corp. (of Institute for Justice and Law Enforcement), National Clinic on Technical Education, and other organizations and educational institutions.

MEMBER: American Technical Education Association (trustee, 1972-73), Association for Higher Education, National Association for Educational Data Systems, National Council of Local Administrators, Texas Association for Educational Data Systems (president, 1968-69; member of board of directors, 1966-70), Texas Junior College Teachers Association, Texas State Teachers Association, Phi Delta Kappa, Delta Pi Epsilon, Fort Worth Chamber of Commerce, Fort Worth Founders' Lions Club.

WRITINGS: Guidelines for Work Experience Programs in the Criminal Justice System, American Association of Junior Colleges, 1969; *Law Enforcement Training and the Community College: Alternatives for Affiliation,* American Association of Junior Colleges, 1970; *Law Enforcement (Police Science Technology): A Suggested Two-Year Post High School Curriculum,* U.S. Office of Education, 1971; *Positive Approaches to Business Management,* Institute of Higher Education, University of Florida, 1971; *Handbook of Narcotics Control,* Prentice-Hall, 1972; *Organized Crime: Concepts and Control,* Prentice-Hall, 1973. Author of reports. Contributor to proceedings and to *Criminal Justice Education and Training.*

WORK IN PROGRESS: Fiction dealing with man's reactions to society's pressures, bias, and prejudice.

* * *

SUBBIAH, B(ommireddi) V(enkata)   1917-1975

PERSONAL: Born January 13, 1917, in Dornipadu, India; son of B. V. and Venkatamma Kondiah; married Satya Achuta, August, 1947; children: Papa (daughter), Sangevi (son). *Education:* Ceded District College, B.A., 1936; New York University, M.P.A., 1960, Ph.D. (Distinguished Merit Certificate), 1965. *Home:* 417 Circle Dr., Hurricane, W.Va. 25526. *Office:* Department of Political Science, West Virginia State College, Institute, W.Va. 25112.

CAREER: Andhra State Government, India, assistant secretary, 1943-65; Elizabeth City State University, Elizabeth City, N.C., professor of political science and head of department, 1965-67; West Virginia State College, Institute, professor of political science, 1967-75, head of department, 1967-75, project director of managerial training program, 1971-75. *Member:* International Platform Association, International Biographical Association (fellow), Smithsonian Institution, Civitan Club. *Awards, honors:* Higher Education Act grant, West Virginia State College, 1971; Intergovernment Personnel Act grant, summer, 1972.

WRITINGS: The Tragedy of a Papal Decree, Vantage, 1971; *The World Population Crisis,* Kitab Mahal, 1972, text edition, Verry, 1973.

WORK IN PROGRESS: A New System of Criminal Justice for Modern America. †

(Died March, 1975)

* * *

SUDMAN, Seymour   1928-

PERSONAL: Born August 9, 1928, in Chicago, Ill.; son of Harry (a newsdealer) and Fannie (Shulman) Sudman; married Blanche Berland, June 24, 1951; children: Emily, Harold, Carol. *Education:* Roosevelt University, B.S., 1949; University of Chicago, Ph.D., 1962. *Office:* Department of Business Administration, University of Illinois, 427 David Kinley, Urbana, Ill. 61801.

CAREER: Roosevelt University, Chicago, Ill., statistician, 1949-51; Ordnance Ammunition Command, Joliet, Ill., analytical statistician, 1951-52; University of Chicago, Chicago, analyst for cosmic ray project, 1954-55; Market Research Corp. of America, Chicago, chief of statistics in Consumer Panel Division, 1955-62; University of Chicago, director of sampling and senior study director of National Opinion Research Center, and lecturer in business, 1962-68; University of Illinois at Urbana-Champaign, associate professor, 1968-71, professor of business administration and sociology, 1971—, director of sampling at Survey Research Laboratory, 1968—. *Military service:* U.S. Army, Signal Corps, 1952-54; became sergeant. *Member:* American Statistical Association, American Marketing Association, American Sociological Association, American Association for Public Opinion Research, American Association for the Advancement of Science.

WRITINGS: (Contributor) Wenzil Dolva, editor, *Marketing Keys to Profit in the 1960's,* American Marketing Association, 1960; (contributor) Frederick Webster, editor, *New Directions in Marketing,* American Marketing Association, 1965; *Reducing the Cost of Surveys,* Aldine, 1967; (contributor) Joseph Seibert and Gordon Wills, editors, *Readings in Marketing Research,* Penguin, 1970; (with Norman Bradburn and Galen Gockel) *Racially Integrated Housing in American Neighborhoods,* National Opinion Research Center, University of Chicago, 1970; (with Robert Ferber) *Experiments in Obtaining Consumer Expenditures of Durable Goods by Recall Procedures,* Survey Research Laboratory, University of Illinois, 1971; (with Bradburn and Gockel) *Side by Side: Integrated Neighborhoods in America,* Quadrangle, 1971; (contributor) Irving Spergel, editor, *Handbook of Community Organizations,* McGraw, 1973; (contributor) Ferber, editor, *Handbook of Marketing Research,* McGraw, 1973; (with Bradburn) *Response Effects in Surveys,* Aldine, 1974; (editor with Allan Andreasen) *Public Policy and Marketing Thought,* American Marketing Association, 1976; *Applied Sampling,* Academic Press, 1976; (contributor) *Annual Review of Sociology,* Annual Reviews, 1976; (editor with others) *Advances in Health Survey Research,* U.S. Government Printing Office, Volume I, 1976, Volume II, 1978; (with Bradburn) *Experiments on Response Effects to Threatening Questions,* Jossey-Bass, 1979; (with Ferber) *Consumer Panels,* American Marketing Association, 1979; (with Linda Lannom) *Comparison of Alternative Panel Procedures for Obtaining Health Data,* U.S. Government Printing Office, 1979.

Author of reports; contributor to proceedings. Contributor of about fifty articles and reviews to professional journals, including *Journal of the American Statistical Association, Journal of Marketing Research, Journal of Business, Public Opinion Quarterly, American Journal of Sociology,* and *Journal of Marketing.*

* * *

SUEDFELD, Peter   1935-

PERSONAL: Suedfeld is original family surname; born August 30, 1935, in Budapest, Hungary; came to United States, 1948, naturalized in 1952; son of Leslie John (a musician) and Jolan (Eichenbaum) Field; married Gabrielle Debra Guterman, June 11, 1961; children: Michael Thomas, Joanne Ruth, David Lee. *Education:* Queens College (now Queens College of the City University of New York), B.A., 1960; Princeton University, M.A., 1962, Ph.D., 1963. *Office:* Department of Psychology, University of British Columbia, Vancouver, British Columbia, Canada.

CAREER: Trenton State College, Trenton, N.J., lecturer in psychology, 1963-64; University of Illinois at Urbana-Champaign, visiting assistant professor of psychology, 1964-65; Rutgers University, University College, New Brunswick, N.J., assistant professor, 1965-67, associate professor, 1967-71, professor of psychology, 1971-72, head of department, 1967-72; University of British Columbia, Vancouver, professor of psychology and head of department, 1972—. Co-director, study on human responses to highway noise, 1972; chairman of symposia; consultant to Peace Corps, 1965-67, Canadian Penitentiary Service, and other organizations. *Military service:* U.S. Army, 1955-58. U.S. Air Force Reserve, 1958-70; became first lieutenant.

MEMBER: Canadian Psychological Association (fellow), American Psychological Association (fellow), Psychonomic Society, Society for Experimental Social Psychology, American Association for the Advancement of Science, Phi Beta Kappa, Sigma Xi, Psi Chi.

WRITINGS: Social Processes, W. C. Brown, 1966; (contributor) J. P. Zubek, editor, *Sensory Deprivation: Fifteen Years of Research,* Appleton, 1969; (contributor) Frank Cox, editor, *Psychology,* W. C. Brown, 1970; (editor with H. M. Schroder, and contributor) *Personality Theory and Information Processing,* Ronald, 1971; (editor and contributor) *Attitude Change: The Competing Views,* Aldine-Atherton, 1971; (contributor) J. V. McConnell and Marijan Schutjer, editors, *Science, Sex, and Sacred Cows,* Harcourt, 1971; (editor with J. Russell) *The Behavioral Basis of Design,* two volumes, Dowden, 1976-77; (contributor) R. B. Stuart, editor, *Behavioral Self-Management: Strategies, Techniques, and Outcomes,* Brunner, 1977; B. King, S. Strenfert, and F. E. Fiedler, editors, *Managerial Control and Organizational Democracy,* Winston, 1978; H. Mandl and G. L. Huber, editors, *Kognitive Komplexitat,* Hegrefe Verlag, 1978; (with P. B. Landon) R. D. Hare and D. Schalling, editors, *Psychopathic Behavior,* Wiley, 1978. Contributor of more than eighty articles and reviews to psychology journals, including *Perceptual and Motor Skills, International Journal of the Addictions, Journal of Personality, Animal Behaviour, Representative Research in Social Psychology,* and *Journal of Experimental Psychology.* Editor, *Journal of Applied Social Psychology.* Member of editorial board, *Canadian Journal of Psychology.*

WORK IN PROGRESS: Therapeutic Uses of Restricted Stimulation, for Wiley.

* * *

SUGGS, George G(raham), Jr. 1929-

PERSONAL: Born October 17, 1929, in Bladenboro, N.C.; son of George Graham and Carrie Melissa (Edwards) Suggs; married Helen Virginia Kindall (a teacher), May 15, 1954; children: George Owen, Ellen Suzanne, Regina Beth, Lorrie Melissa. *Education:* Attended Wake Forest College (now University), 1947-49; University of Colorado, B.A., 1955, M.A., 1957, Ph.D., 1964; Northwestern University, graduate study, 1959-60. *Politics:* Democrat. *Religion:* Methodist. *Home:* 2537 Tulip Lane, Cape Girardeau, Mo. 63701. *Office:* Department of History, Southeast Missouri State University, Cape Girardeau, Mo. 63701.

CAREER: Worked as a high school history teacher in Whiteville and Charlotte, N.C., 1949-61; Southeast Missouri State University, Cape Girardeau, assistant professor, 1964-67, associate professor, 1967-69, professor of history, 1969—. *Military service:* U.S. Air Force, 1951-53. *Member:* American Association of University Professors, Organization of American Historians, National Education Association, Missouri State Teachers Association.

WRITINGS: Colorado's War on Militant Unionism, Wayne State University Press, 1972; (editor) *Perspectives on the American Revolution: A Bicentennial Contribution,* Southern Illinois University Press, 1977. Contributor to *Labor History, Western Historical Quarterly, Journal of the West, Colorado Magazine,* and *Missouri Life.*

WORK IN PROGRESS: Research on the labor history of the Missouri Lead Belt.

* * *

SULLIVAN, Walter (Laurence) 1924-

PERSONAL: Born January 4, 1924, in Nashville, Tenn.; son of Walter Laurence and Aline (Armstrong) Sullivan; married Jane Harrison (a college teacher), August 30, 1947; children: Pamela Holmes (Mrs. James Gordon Chenery), Walter Laurence, Jr., John Harrison. *Education:* Vanderbilt University, B.A., 1947; University of Iowa, M.F.A., 1949. *Politics:* Independent. *Religion:* Roman Catholic. *Home:* 6104 Chickering Ct., Nashville, Tenn. 37215. *Agent:* Diarmuid Russell, Russell & Volkening, Inc., 551 Fifth Ave., New York, N.Y. 10017. *Office:* Department of English, Vanderbilt University, Nashville, Tenn. 37235.

CAREER: Vanderbilt University, Nashville, Tenn., instructor, 1949-52, assistant professor, 1952-57, associate professor, 1957-63, professor of fiction writing and of modern British and American literature, 1963—. *Military service:* U.S. Marine Corps, 1943-46; became first lieutenant. *Member:* Modern Language Association of America, South Atlantic Modern Language Association, University Club of Nashville.

WRITINGS: Sojourn of a Stranger (novel), Holt, 1957; *The Long, Long Love* (novel), Holt, 1959; *Death by Melancholy* (criticism), Louisiana State University Press, 1972; *A Requiem for the Renascence* (criticism), University of Georgia Press, 1976. Contributor of short stories and articles to literary journals.

WORK IN PROGRESS: A novel; writing on the Catholic novels of Evelyn Waugh; a book on the Southern literary renascence from a contemporary perspective.

SIDELIGHTS: Walter Sullivan told *CA* "that ours is a very bad age for art in general and for the creation of literature in particular." Because of this, Sullivan currently spends more time "trying to explain the age and the artist's relationship to it" than writing fiction. He is, however, "writing longish short stories which appear in literary quarterlies." Someday, he hopes to devote all of his time to writing fiction. Sullivan says, "I brood a lot, which may be, for me at least, the most essential step in the act of writing."

* * *

SUMMERS, Joseph H(olmes) 1920-

PERSONAL: Born February 9, 1920, in Louisville, Ky.; son of Hollis Spurgeon (a minister) and Hazel (Holmes) Summers; married U. T. Miller (a teacher), September 24, 1943; children: Mary Elliott, Hazel Lincoln, Joseph Holmes, Jr. *Education:* Harvard University, A.B. (magna cum laude), 1941, M.A., 1948, Ph.D., 1950. *Politics:* Democrat. *Religion:* Episcopalian. *Home:* 179 Crosman Ter., Rochester, N.Y. 14620. *Office:* Department of English, University of Rochester, Rochester, N.Y. 14627.

CAREER: Bard College, Annandale-on-Hudson, N.Y., instructor in literature, 1948-50; University of Connecticut, Storrs, assistant professor, 1950-55, associate professor of English, 1955-59; Washington University, St. Louis, Mo., professor of English, 1959-66, chairman of department, 1960-61, 1963-64; Michigan State University, East Lansing, professor of English, 1966-69; University of Rochester, Rochester, N.Y., professor of English, 1969—. Visiting professor at Amherst College, 1962-63, Oxford University, 1966-67, and University of Kent, 1972. *Member:* International Association of University Professors of English, Modern Language Association of America, Phi Beta Kappa. *Awards, honors:* Fund for Advancement of Learning fellow in Italy, 1952-53; Guggenheim fellow in England, 1957-58; Fulbright fellow at All Souls College, Oxford University, 1966-67.

WRITINGS: George Herbert: His Religion and Art, Harvard University Press, 1954; (editor) Andrew Marvell, *Andrew Marvell: Selected Poems,* Dell, 1961; *The Muse's Method: An Introduction to "Paradise Lost",* Harvard University Press, 1962; (editor) *The Lyric and Dramatic Milton: Selected Papers from the English Institute,* Columbia University Press, 1965; (editor) George Herbert, *George Herbert: Selected Poetry,* New American Library, 1967; *The Heirs of Donne and Jonson,* Oxford University Press, 1970. General editor, *Discussions of Literature,* twenty-five volumes, Heath, 1960-66. Contributor of articles to literature journals.

WORK IN PROGRESS: A series of essays on Shakespeare's plays.

*   *   *

SUNGOLOWSKY, Joseph 1931-

PERSONAL: Born December 21, 1931, in Charleroi, Belgium; naturalized U.S. citizen; son of Aaron Gerson (a rabbi) and Esther (Berger) Sungolowsky; married Honey Himelstein, August 20, 1967; children: Robert Yves, Elissa Jeanine. *Education:* Lycee de Nice, Baccalaureat-es-Lettres, 1950; Yeshiva University, B.A., 1955; New York University, M.A., 1958; Yale University, Ph.D., 1963. *Home:* 136-14 76th Rd., Flushing, N.Y. 11367. *Office:* Department of Romance Languages, Queens College of the City University of New York, Flushing, N.Y. 11367.

CAREER: Yale University, New Haven, Conn., instructor in French, 1959-62; Vassar College, Poughkeepsie, N.Y., instructor, 1962-63, assistant professor of French, 1963-65; Queens College of the City University of New York, Flushing, N.Y., assistant professor, 1965-71, associate professor of French, 1972—. *Member:* American Association of Teachers of French, Modern Language Association of America, Societe des Professeurs Francais en Amerique, Association Internationale des Etudes Francaises.

WRITINGS: Alfred de Vigny et le dix-huitieme siecle, Nizet, 1968; *Beaumarchais,* Twayne, 1974. Contributor of articles and reviews to language and literary journals.

WORK IN PROGRESS: Research on religious themes in eighteenth- and nineteenth-century French literature.

BIOGRAPHICAL/CRITICAL SOURCES: French Review, October, 1969.

SUNOO, Harold Hak-Won 1918-

PERSONAL: Born February 2, 1918, in Korea; son of Sung-ho (a farmer) and Chae-ho (Whang) Sunoo; married Sonia Shinn (a college dean of women), February 6, 1942; children: Jan Jungmin, Cooke Jungguk. *Education:* Pasadena College, B.A., 1942; University of Washington, Seattle, M.A., 1945; Charles University of Prague, Ph.D., 1950. *Politics:* Democrat. *Religion:* Methodist. *Home:* 312 South Main St., Fayette, Mo. 65248. *Office:* Department of Political Science, Central Methodist College, Fayette, Mo. 65248.

CAREER: University of California, Berkeley, instructor in Asian studies, 1942-43; University of Washington, Seattle, lecturer in Asian studies, 1943-49; *San Francisco Chronicle,* San Francisco, Calif., member of editorial staff, 1950-55; self-employed in San Francisco, 1955-60; *Korean Herald,* Seoul, editor-in-chief, 1960; Central Methodist College, Fayette, Mo., professor of political science, 1963-65, distinguished professor and chairman of department, 1965—. Visiting professor, City College of the City University of New York, 1973—. President, Korean American Cultural Foundation. *Military service:* U.S. Army Air Forces, 1945-46. *Member:* American Political Science Association, Association of Asian Studies, Missouri Political Science Association, Omicron Delta Kappa, Pi Gamma Mu.

WRITINGS: Korean Text Book, University of Washington Press, 1945; *Korean Grammar,* Oriental Institute (Prague), 1952; *Sino-Soviet Conflict,* Hungum-sa, 1965; *Modernization of Korean Democracy,* Taehan Munhwasa, 1967; *Korea: A Political History in Modern Times,* Kunkuk University Press, 1970; *Repressive State and Resisting Church: The Politics of CIA in South Korea,* Korean-American Cultural Association, 1975; *Japanese Militarism: Past and Present,* Nelson Hall, 1975; *America's Dilemma in Asia,* Nelson Hall, 1978. Also editor of *Koreans in America, Whither Korea?,* 1977, and *Korean Women,* 1978. Editor, *Korean Review,* 1948-49.

WORK IN PROGRESS: Confucianism: An Interpretation; History of Korean Immigrants in America; a short story collection, *Korean in America; Witnesses from Prison.*

*   *   *

SUPPE, Frederick (Roy) 1940-

PERSONAL: Surname rhymes with "guppy"; born February 22, 1940, in Los Angeles, Calif.; son of Jack Kingsley (a merchant) and Gertrude (Cross) Suppe. *Education:* University of California, Riverside, A.B., 1962; University of Michigan, A.M., 1964, Ph.D., 1967. *Politics:* Democrat. *Religion:* "Lapsed Catholic." *Office:* Committee on the History and Philosophy of Science, University of Maryland, College Park, Md. 20742.

CAREER: University of Michigan, Ann Arbor, instructor in philosophy and assistant in research, 1964-67; University of Illinois at Urbana-Champaign, assistant professor of philosophy, 1967-73; University of Maryland, College Park, associate professor of philosophy, 1973—, chairperson, program in History and Philosophy of Science. Visiting instructor, Indian Institute of Technology, Kanpur, India, 1965-67. *Member:* American Philosophical Association, Association for Symbolic Logic, American Association for the Advancement of Science, Philosophy of Science Association, History of Science Society, Sigma Xi. *Awards, honors:* National Science Foundation summer fellowship in linguistics, 1965, grant, 1973-75; American Council of Learned Societies travel grant, 1974; Amicus Poloniae Award, 1974.

WRITINGS: (Editor and author of introduction) *The Structure of Scientific Theories,* University of Illinois Press, 1973, 2nd edition, 1977; (contributor) W. Leinfellner and E. Kohler, editors, *Developments in the Methodology of Social Science,* Reidel, 1974; (contributor) Przecki, and others, editors, *Formal Methods of the Methodology of Social Science,* Ossolineum, 1976; (contributor) J. Meiland and M. Krause, editors, *Relativism,* Princeton University Press, 1978. Contributor to *Philosophy of Science, Journal of Philosophy, Synthese, Philosophical Studies, Proceedings of the First Ottawa Conference on Conceptual Basis of Classification, Ruch Filozoficzny, Teaching Philosophy, Poland,* and *International Journal of General Systems.*

WORK IN PROGRESS: Facts, Theories, and Scientific Observation; Recreational Sex: The Moral Dimensions; Discovery and Diagnosis; research and writing of various scientific articles for journals.

SIDELIGHTS: Frederick Suppe told *CA* that he bought an inter-city apartment building in an historic preservation district in Washington, D.C., which "I am restoring to its former grandeur—doing most of the labor, design, and reconstruction myself. The latter is at least as challenging and rewarding as being a writer, scholar, or academician. As I have become well-established professionally, I have felt it increasingly important to be an openly and professionally 'gay' academician and writer, and now devote a portion of my professional efforts to matters that are directly relevant to homosexual issues; these efforts include pioneering 'gay studies' courses, corresponding and writing on homosexual issues.... Especially important, whether in writing or in teaching, is being a 'successful role model' for newly-out homosexuals. This growing concern with homosexual issues in my more recent work does not constitute a break with my previous research and writing interests in the philosophy of science, for throughout the history of writings on sexual morality scientific findings on human sexuality have played a far more decisive role than in moral deliberations on other issues."

AVOCATIONAL INTERESTS: Skiing, golf, cooking, collecting antiques, and restoring old houses.

*   *   *

SURTZ, Edward 1910(?)-1973

1910(?)—January 18, 1973; American scholar of English Renaissance literature, teacher, and authority on Thomas More. Obituaries: *New York Times,* January 20, 1973.

*   *   *

SUTER, Ronald 1930-

PERSONAL: Born November 1, 1930, in Geneva, Switzerland; son of Eugene (an insurance agent) and Mary (Baenziger) Suter; married Carmen Mateu, April 9, 1958; children: Sonia, Monica. *Education:* University of Chicago, A.B., 1953; Oxford University, B.A., 1959, M.A., 1962; Stanford University, Ph.D., 1967. *Home:* 955 Lilac Ave., East Lansing, Mich. 48823. *Office:* Department of Philosophy, Morrill Hall, Michigan State University, East Lansing, Mich. 48824.

CAREER: Middlebury College, Middlebury, Vt., instructor in philosophy, 1962-63; Michigan State University, East Lansing, instructor, 1963-66, assistant professor, 1966-69, associate professor of philosophy, 1969—, director of Isenberg Memorial Series, fall, 1968. *Military service:* U.S. Army, 1953-55. *Member:* American Philosophical Associa-

tion. *Awards, honors:* Grant from Council for Philosophical Studies, 1966, to attend summer institute in ethics and philosophy of the mind; grant from National Endowment for the Humanities, summer, 1970.

WRITINGS: (Editor and author of introduction) *The Isenberg Memorial Lectures: 1965-66,* Michigan State University Press, 1969. Contributor to philosophy journals, including *Philosophy and Phenomenological Research, Personalist, Mind, Convivium, Philosophical Review of National Taiwan University, Philosophical Quarterly,* and *Revue internationale de philosophie.*

WORK IN PROGRESS: A critique of Descartes' theory of knowledge; examining the nature of emotions, moral reasoning, and the case against ethical definism.

SIDELIGHTS: Ronald Suter told *CA,* "Ludwig Wittgenstein's later philosophy has had a strong influence on my thinking. The fields of philosophy which interest me most are aesthetics, ethics, philosophy of language, and philosophy of mind." Several of Suter's articles have been translated into Spanish, German, and Chinese.

BIOGRAPHICAL/CRITICAL SOURCES: Review of Metaphysics, December, 1968; *Philosophy and Phenomenological Research,* March, 1969.

*   *   *

SUTHERLAND, Arthur Eugene, Jr. 1902-1973

February 9, 1902—March 8, 1973; American lawyer, educator, and author of books on constitutional law and other topics. Obituaries: *New York Times,* March 10, 1973. (See index for *CA* sketch)

*   *   *

SUTHERLAND, Jon Nicholas 1941-

PERSONAL: Born December 8, 1941, in San Diego, Calif.; son of Verne Nicholas (self-employed) and Margaret (Callard) Sutherland. *Education:* San Diego State College (now University), A.B., 1963; Harvard University, A.M., 1964; University of California, Los Angeles, Ph.D., 1967. *Home:* 3747 Amaryllis Dr., San Diego, Calif. 92106. *Office:* Department of History, San Diego State University, San Diego, Calif. 92182.

CAREER: San Diego State University, San Diego, California, associate professor of history, 1967-71, 1972—. Fellow in law and history, Harvard University, Cambridge, Mass., 1971-72. *Member:* American Historical Association, Medieval Academy of America, American Society for Legal History, American Numismatic Society, Classical Alliance of the Western States (vice-president, 1970-73).

WRITINGS: (With Michael Werthman) *Comparative Concepts of Law and Order,* Scott, Foresman, 1971; (with Robert Detweiler and Werthman) *Environmental Decay in Its Historical Context,* Scott, Foresman, 1973.

WORK IN PROGRESS: Biography of Lindprand of Cremona; research in medieval legal history, especially bloodfeud and revenge; urban institutions of Italy and their legal relationships with the medieval countryside.†

*   *   *

SVEJDA, George J. 1927-

PERSONAL: Born March 12, 1927, in Horni Vilimec, Czechoslovakia; U.S. citizen; son of Francis (a clerk) and Frances (Krejca) Svejda; married Hana de Slais (a native of Venezuela), May 6, 1967; children: Jana Marie, Andrea

Frances, George Patrick, Dana Catherine. *Education:* Attended Masaryk College, Ludwigsburg, Germany, 1949-50; St. Procopius College (now Illinois Benedictine College), B.A., 1952, graduate study, 1953-54; Georgetown University, Ph.D., 1959; University of Pennsylvania, postdoctoral study, 1961-63. *Politics:* No affiliation. *Religion:* Roman Catholic. *Home:* 1007 Cliftonbrook Lane, Silver Spring, Md. 20904. *Office:* National Park Service, U.S. Department of the Interior, Washington, D.C. 20240.

CAREER: Columbia University, New York, N.Y., research associate in political science, 1958-59; Library of Congress, Washington, D.C., European exchange specialist, 1959-61; Franklin Institute, Philadelphia, Pa., technical writer, 1962; U.S. Department of the Interior, National Park Service, Washington, D.C., historian, 1962—. *Member:* Organization of American Historians, American Academy of Political and Social Science, Phi Alpha Theta.

WRITINGS—Published by Office of Archaeology and Historic Preservation, National Park Service, except as indicated: (Contributor) Vladimir Kucera and Alfred Novacek, editors, *Czechs and Nebraska,* Quiz Graphic Arts (Ord, Neb.), 1967; *Castle Garden as an Immigrant Depot, 1855-1890,* 1968; *History of the Star Spangled Banner from 1814 to the Present,* 1969; *Irish Immigrant Participation in the Construction of the Erie Canal,* 1969; *Quartering, Disciplining, and Supplying the Army at Morristown, 1779-1780,* 1970; (contributor) *Panorama,* Czechoslovak National Council of American (Cicero, Illinois), 1970. Writer of several other studies and reports on national monuments and historic sites, including Fort McHenry and the Statue of Liberty. Contributor to proceedings and *Encyclopedia of Southern History.*

WORK IN PROGRESS: A history of immigration to the United States during the nineteenth century, an expansion of his book on Castle Garden as an immigrant depot, and a book on Revolutionary War encampments of the American Continental Army at Morristown, New Jersey.

SIDELIGHTS: Besides Czech and Slovak, George Svejda is fluent in German, competent in Russian, Polish, and Ukrainian, and "fair" in Latin and French.

*   *   *

SWANSON, Donald Roland 1927-

PERSONAL: Born November 20, 1927, in Pittsburgh, Pa.; son of Roland E. (an engineer) and Ruth Amelia (Uddstrom) Swanson; married Willa Gray (an editor and photographer), September 3, 1955. *Education:* Washington and Jefferson College, B.A., 1953; University of Connecticut, M.A., 1955; Rutgers University, Ph.D., 1965. *Home:* 1550 Benson Dr., Dayton, Ohio 45406. *Office:* Department of English, Wright State University, Dayton, Ohio 45435.

CAREER: University of Connecticut, Storrs, instructor in English, 1953-55; Upsala College, East Orange, N.J., instructor, 1955-58, assistant professor, 1958-66, associate professor of English, 1966-71; Wright State University, Dayton, Ohio, professor of English, 1971—. *Military service:* U.S. Navy, 1945-46. *Member:* English Institute, Modern Language Association of America, College English Association (treasurer, 1971-73; director, 1974-77), American Association of University Professors. *Awards, honors:* Upsala College research fellowships, 1960, 1963, 1966, 1969; Wright State University Liberal Arts grant, 1972.

WRITINGS: Three Conquerors, Mouton, 1969; *Richard Hughes,* Twayne, 1979. Contributor to *BSU Forum, Amer-*

ican Transcendental Quarterly, Lock Haven Review, ESQ, CEA Critic, Explicator, and *Antioch Review.*

*   *   *

SWARTHOUT, Kathryn 1919-

PERSONAL: Born January 8, 1919, in Columbus, Mont.; daughter of Lige Hood and Blair (Cox) Vaughn; married Glendon Fred Swarthout (a professor of English and writer), December 28, 1940; children: Miles Hood. *Education:* Ward-Belmont, A.A., 1938; University of Michigan, A.B., 1940; Michigan State University, M.A., 1956. *Religion:* Protestant. *Home:* 5045 Tamanar Way, Scottsdale, Ariz. 85253. *Agent:* Owen Laster, William Morris Agency, 1350 Ave. of the Americas, New York, N.Y. 10019.

CAREER: Teacher in elementary grades, 1954-59; writer for children. *Member:* League of Women Voters.

WRITINGS—Juvenile books with husband, Glendon Swarthout: *The Ghost and the Magic Saber,* Random House, 1963; *Whichaway,* Random House, 1966; *The Button Boat,* Doubleday, 1969; *TV Thompson,* Doubleday, 1972; *Whales to See The,* Doubleday, 1975. Author of column, "Lifesavors," in *Woman's Day.*

*   *   *

SWARTZ, Robert D(avid) 1937-

PERSONAL: Born May 17, 1937, in New York, N.Y.; son of Sam and Frances (Hocheiser) Swartz; married Elizabeth J. Lindsay, June 17, 1971. *Education:* Columbia University, A.B., 1959, B.S., 1960, M.A., 1962; Northwestern University, Ph.D., 1967. *Office:* Department of Geography, 225 State Hall, Wayne State University, Detroit, Mich. 48202.

CAREER: Sears, Roebuck & Co., Chicago, Ill., international research, 1963-67; Wayne State University, Detroit, Mich., assistant professor, 1967-72, associate professor of geography, 1972—, chairman of department, 1978—. *Member:* Association of American Geographers, Sigma Xi.

WRITINGS: (Editor) *Metropolitan America: Geographic Perspectives and Teaching Strategies,* National Council for Geographic Education, 1972.

*   *   *

SWEENEY, Thomas J(ohn) 1936-

PERSONAL: Born August 25, 1936; son of Thomas (a printer) and Sarah (Mitchell) Sweeney; married Elizabeth Jackson, August 22, 1959; children: Elizabeth R., Ann K., Thomas P., Kathryn S., Michael J. *Education:* University of Akron, B.A., 1959; University of Wisconsin, M.S., 1960; Ohio State University, Ph.D., 1964. *Religion:* Roman Catholic. *Home:* 40 Morris, Athens, Ohio 45701. *Office:* McCracken Hall, Ohio University, Athens, Ohio 45701.

CAREER: Social studies teacher in public schools in Akron, Ohio, 1958-60, 1961; Ohio State University, Columbus, instructor in education, 1961-63; counselor in public schools in Grove City, Ohio, 1963-64; University of South Carolina, Columbia, assistant professor, 1964-67, associate professor of counselor education and chairman of department, 1967-72; Ohio University, Athens, professor of applied behavioral sciences, 1972—, director of educational leadership, 1976-78. Chairman, South Carolina Governor's Task Force on Manpower Needs in Vocational Rehabilitation, 1968; delegate to White House Conference, South Carolina Commission on Children and Youth, 1970. *Military service:* U.S. Army Reserve, 1958-66, active duty, 1960-61; became captain.

MEMBER: American Psychological Association, American Personnel and Guidance Association (president-elect), American School Counseling Association, Association for Counseling Education and Supervision (president, 1976-77), National Vocational Guidance Association, Southern Association of Counseling Education and Supervision (president, 1972-73), South Carolina Personnel and Guidance Association (president, 1966-68). *Awards, honors:* Commendation from General Electric Foundation, 1973, for leadership and service; outstanding achievement award from Ohio Personnel and Guidance Association, 1977; Association for Counseling Education and Supervision leadership award, 1978; Ohio Public Network Broadcasters outstanding instructural services award, 1978, for "Coping with Kids."

WRITINGS: Rural Poor Students and Guidance (monograph), Houghton, 1971; *Adlerian Counseling*, Houghton, 1975. Also author of twelve half-hour programs, "Coping with Kids." Contributor of articles to counseling and guidance journals.

WORK IN PROGRESS: Family Counseling: A Historic Approach to Intervention; Career Changing: Not Just Kid Stuff.

*   *   *

SWEET, James Stouder 1918-

PERSONAL: Born February 18, 1918, in Fort Wayne, Ind.; son of Warren V. and Alice C. (Stouder) Sweet; married Vivian R. Roe (a concert violinist), June 5, 1948; children: Jeffrey, Stuart, Cynthia. *Education:* DePauw University, B.A., 1940; University of California, Los Angeles, M.A., 1949, Ph.D., 1955; Harvard University, M.A., 1951. *Politics:* Whig. *Religion:* Zoroastrian. *Home:* 1417 Rosalie, Evanston, Ill. 60201. *Office:* Office of Public Information, University of Chicago, 4801 South Ellis, Chicago, Ill. 60637.

CAREER: Franco-American Institute, Dijon, France, instructor in English, 1944; Library of Congress, Washington, D.C., intermission broadcast assistant, 1951-56, bibliographer, 1953-55, senior historian of Legislative Review Service, 1955-57; *Encyclopaedia Britannica,* Chicago, Ill., assistant editor, 1957-59; Illinois Crime Prevention Bureau, Chicago, information officer, 1960; Portland Cement Association, Chicago, senior writer, 1961-66; Northwestern University, Evanston, Ill., science writer and editor, 1966-71; University of Chicago, Office of Public Information, Chicago, assistant director for Science Information Services, 1971—. Free-lance writer and editor, 1951—. *Military service:* U.S. Army, 1941-45; became technical sergeant. *Member:* National Association of Science Writers, American Medical Writers Association (president of Chicago chapter, 1978-79), Chicago Headline Club.

WRITINGS: (Contributor) Roy P. Basler, Donald H. Mugridge, and Blanche P. McCrum, editors, *A Guide to the Study of the United States of America,* Library of Congress-Government Printing Office, 1960; (with Oscar Ornati) *Poverty amid Affluence,* Twentieth Century Fund, 1966; *Poverty in the United States of America,* Public Affairs Committee, 1967; *Civics,* LaSalle Extension University, 1967; (executive editor) *Illustrated Atlas of Today's World,* Rand McNally, 1967. Author of film scripts for *Encyclopaedia Britannica* and Coronet Films. Author of Congressional documents and reports, 1956-57.

WORK IN PROGRESS: Research on the history of American "mug" books; a history of American taxes; magazine articles and book reviews.

SWEETSER, Mary (Chisholm) 1894-
(Ted Sweetser)

PERSONAL: Born June 11, 1894, in Malden, Mass.; daughter of William Frank (a businessman) and Nellie (Hopkins) Chisholm; married Sidney M. Sweetser, June 11, 1921 (died, 1963); children: Donald Arthur, Jean Carol (Mrs. Walter E. Kelley). *Education:* Studied at School of Practical Art; studied creative writing at Boston Center for Adult Education. *Politics:* Republican. *Religion:* Methodist.

CAREER: W. P. B. Brooks & Co., Boston, Mass., stenographer, 1913-15; F. J. Fawcett, Boston, stenographer and bookkeeper, 1915-21; Star Island Writers' Conference, Portsmouth, N.H., founder and director, 1956-72. *Member:* Manuscript Club of Boston (president, 1956-58), Couples' Club. *Awards, honors:* Eleanor Widger prize from Manuscript Club of Boston, 1949, 1955, 1963.

WRITINGS: The Extra Gift (juvenile), Macrae, 1969. Contributor to *Rural New Yorker, Bengalese Magazine, Grade Teacher, Hearthstone, Trailer Topics, Northern Sportsman* (under pseudonym, Ted Sweetser), *Forest and Outdoors, American Forests, Southern Farm and Home, Highway Traveler, Galaxy,* and *Yankee,* and to major newspapers.†

*   *   *

SWEEZY, Alan Richardson 1907-

PERSONAL: Born June 29, 1907, in New York, N.Y.; son of Everett B. and Caroline (Wilson) Sweezy; married Susan Shepherd, August 4, 1937; children: Sara (Mrs. Boyd Berry), Caroline, Cornelia (Mrs. Steve Cope). *Education:* Harvard University, B.A., 1929, Ph.D., 1934; University of Vienna, graduate studies, 1932-33. *Residence:* Pasadena, Calif. *Office:* Department of Economics, California Institute of Technology, Pasadena, Calif. 91125.

CAREER: Harvard University, Cambridge, Mass., instructor in economics, 1934-38; Federal Reserve Board, Washington, D.C., Division of Research and Statistics, economist, 1938-39; Federal Works Agency, Washington, D.C., economist, 1939-40; Williams College, Williamstown, Mass., associate professor, 1940-46, professor of economics, 1946-47; California Institute of Technology, Pasadena, visiting professor, 1949-50, professor of economics, beginning 1950, associate director of Caltech Population Program, beginning 1970. Member of board of directors of Planned Parenthood-World Population, beginning 1967, chairman, beginning 1972. *Awards, honors:* Sheldon fellowship from Harvard University to study at University of Vienna, 1932-33.

WRITINGS: (Contributor) Harrison Brown and Ed Hutchings, Jr., editors, *Are Our Descendants Doomed?,* Viking, 1972; (editor with Brown, and contributor) *Population: Perspective 1971,* Freeman, Cooper, 1972.

Contributor to *Quarterly Journal of Economics, Population Studies, Science,* and *Proceedings of the American Economic Association.*††

*   *   *

SWENSON, Loyd S(ylvan), Jr. 1932-

PERSONAL: Born May 28, 1932, in Waco, Tex.; son of Loyd Sylvan and Swanell (Hoel) Swenson; married Jean Ellen Youngblood, July 29, 1955 (divorced June, 1977); children: Jan C., Karen A., Neil J. *Education:* Rice Institute (now University), A.B., 1954; Claremont University College (now Claremont Graduate School), Ph.D., 1962. *Religion:* Unitarian Universalist. *Home:* 6200 Marinette 215A,

Houston, Tex. 77036. *Office:* Department of History, University of Houston, Houston, Tex. 77004.

CAREER: University of California, Riverside, associate in history, 1961-63; University of Houston, Houston, Tex., instructor, 1962-63, assistant professor, 1963-67, associate professor, 1968-73, professor of history, 1973—. Contract historian, National Aeronautics and Space Administration, Manned Spacecraft Center, 1963-65, 1969—. *Military service:* U.S. Navy, 1954-57. U.S. Naval Reserve, 1957-70; became lieutenant. *Member:* American Historical Association, History of Science Society, American Studies Association, Society for the History of Technology (member of executive council, 1971-74), American Civil Liberties Union, Mensa, Common Cause, American Institute of Aeronautics and Astronautics.

WRITINGS: (With James M. Grimwood and Charles C. Alexander) *This New Ocean: A History of Project Mercury,* Government Printing Office, for National Aeronautics and Space Administration, 1966; *The Ethereal Aether: A History of the Michelson-Morley-Miller Aether-Drift Experiments, 1880-1930,* University of Texas Press, 1972.

WORK IN PROGRESS: Genesis of Relativity: Einstein in Context, for Burt Franklin; *Apollo Spacecraft Program History,* for U.S. Government Printing Office.

* * *

SWINGLE, Paul G(eorge)   1937-

PERSONAL: Born May 14, 1937, in New York, N.Y.; married, 1960; children: two. *Education:* Hofstra University, B.A., 1960, M.A., 1962; University of Massachusetts, Ph.D., 1964. *Office:* School of Psychology, University of Ottawa, Ottawa, Ontario, Canada.

CAREER: Dalhousie University, Halifax, Nova Scotia, assistant professor of psychology, 1964-66; McGill University, Montreal, Quebec, associate professor of psychology, 1966-69; McMaster University, Hamilton, Ontario, associate professor of psychology, 1969-72; University of Ottawa, Ottawa, Ontario, professor of psychology, 1972—. *Member:* American Association for the Advancement of Science, American Psychological Association, Psychonomic Society, Eastern Psychological Association, New York Academy of Science, Phi Kappa Phi, Psi Chi. *Awards, honors:* National Research Council of Canada fellowship, 1965; National Health and Welfare of Canada fellowship, 1966-69; Defense Research Board of Canada fellowship, 1969-73; Canada Council fellowship, 1978-79.

WRITINGS: Experiments in Social Psychology, Academic Press, 1968, revised edition, 1969; (editor and contributor) *The Structure of Conflict,* Academic Press, 1970; (editor) *Social Psychology in Natural Settings,* Aldine-Atherton, 1973; *The Management of Power,* Erlbaum, 1976. Contributor to psychology journals, and to *Engineers' Digest* and *Canadian Association of University Teachers Bulletin.*

WORK IN PROGRESS: Research on conflict resolution and therapeutic intervention.

* * *

SYMONS, R(obert) D(avid)   1898-1973

PERSONAL: Surname is pronounced *Sim*-mons; born April 7, 1898, in Mayfield, Sussex, England; emigrated to Canada in 1914; son of William Christian (an artist) and Constance Cecilia (a musician; maiden name, Davenport) Symons; married Maud Macmillan; married second wife, Hope Onslow, October 11, 1945; children: (first marriage) James,

Hugh, Peter; (second marriage) Marygold. *Education:* Received private education. *Politics:* Conservative. *Religion:* Anglican. *Home:* Silton, Saskatchewan, Canada.

CAREER: Painter with one-man and group shows throughout Canada and the United States; work is represented in private and public collections, including Glenbow Foundation, Edmonton Art Gallery Museum of Natural History in Regina, and Bank of Montreal. Worked as game guardian, rancher, cowboy, naturalist, and lecturer; made numerous radio and television appearances, beginning 1958. *Military service:* Canadian Army, Infantry, 1915-18. Imperial Army, Fusiliers, 1918-19; became lieutenant. *Member:* Canadian Authors Association (Saskatchewan regional director), Saskatchewan Writers' Guild (life member), Saskatchewan Natural History Society (honorary president, 1970-71), Upper Cache Creek Cattleman's Association (life member). *Awards, honors:* Conservation award from Saskatchewan Natural History Society, 1965; LL.D., University of Saskatchewan, 1970.

WRITINGS—Self-illustrated: *Many Trails,* Longmans, Green (Canada), 1963; *Hours and the Birds: A Saskatchewan Record,* University of Toronto Press, 1967; *The Broken Snare* (Book-of-the-Month Club selection), Doubleday, 1970; *Still the Wind Blows* (historical novel), Western Producer, 1971; *Where the Wagon Led: One Man's Memories of the Cowboy's Life in the Old West* (Book-of-the-Month Club selection), Doubleday, 1973; *North by West: Two Stories from the Frontier,* Doubleday, 1973; *Silton Seasons: From the Diary of a Countryman,* Doubleday, 1975.

Also author, with Lee R. Updike, of *The First People: An Artist's Reconstruction of Five Native Canadian Cultures;* author of unpublished works, *The Savour of Salt* (short stories), *Many Patrols* (excerpts from the diary of a game officer), *The Flame and the Thorn* (biographical anthology), and editor of *Companions of the Peace* (diaries of Anglican missionary, Monica Storrs).

Contributor of articles and stories to magazines and newspapers, including *Canadian Cattlemen, Field* (London), *Canadian Poetry, Family Herald, Alaska Highway News,* and *Leader-Post* (Regina).

SIDELIGHTS: All of R. D. Symons' writing, and much of his painting, was done after he was stricken with leukemia. His work reflects his love for nature and natural people, including Canadian Indians with whom he had lived from time to time, and his hatred for the damage now being done to the environment.†

(Died February 1, 1973)

* * *

SZANTO, George H.   1940-

PERSONAL: Born June 4, 1940, in Londonderry, Northern Ireland; son of Mike M. and Dora (Zollschan) Szanto; married Alison Andrew, February 26, 1963; children: Elisabeth, David. *Education:* Dartmouth College, B.A., 1962; graduate study at University of Frankfurt am Main, 1962-63, and University of Aix-Marseille, 1965-66; Harvard University, Ph.D., 1967. *Home:* 41 Dufferin Rd., Montreal, Quebec, Canada. *Office:* Department of Comparative Literature, McGill University, Montreal, Quebec, Canada.

CAREER: University of California at San Diego, La Jolla, assistant professor of dramatic and comparative literature, 1967-74 (on leave, 1973-74), head of comparative literature section, 1972-73; McGill University, Montreal, Quebec, associate professor of comparative literature, 1974—, chairman of committee on humanistic studies and committee for modern languages, 1975—. Executive director, New Heritage Theatre, 1970-74. *Member:* Modern Language Association of America, Canadian Comparative Literature Association (member of executive committee, 1977—), International Comparative Literature Association, Canadian Group for Studies in Paraliterature (chairman, 1976-77), Writers Union of Canada, Guild of Canadian Playwrights.

WRITINGS: Narrative Consciousness: Structure and Perception in the Fiction of Kafka, Beckett and Robbe-Grillet, University of Texas Press, 1972; *Sixteen Ways to Skin a Cat* (stories), Intermedia, 1977; *Theater and Propaganda,* University of Texas Press, 1978; *After the Ceremony* (play), Playwrights Co-op Press, 1978. Also author of plays, "The New Black Crook," 1971, and with Milton Savage, "Chinchilla!," 1972. Member of editorial board, *Europa* (journal of the Interuniversity Centre for European Studies), 1977—; co-founder and co-editor, *Culture and Context,* 1977—.

WORK IN PROGRESS: The Matter of Quality, completion expected in 1981.

* * *

SZYLIOWICZ, Joseph S. 1931-

PERSONAL: Born December 7, 1931, in Charleroi, Belgium; son of Jules and M. (Hecht) Szyliowicz; married Irene Lust, March 19, 1960; children: Michael, Dara. *Education:* University of Denver, A.B., 1953; Johns Hopkins University, M.A., 1955; Columbia University, Ph.D., 1961. *Home:* 5450 South Newport Circle, Englewood, Colo. 80110. *Office:* Graduate School of International Studies, University of Denver, Denver, Colo. 80210.

CAREER: Institute of Applied Linguistics and Overseas Training Service, Washington, D.C., electronic language specialist, 1959-60; *Columbia Encyclopedia,* New York, N.Y., associate staff member for third edition of encyclopedia, 1960-61; Brooklyn College of the City University of New York, Brooklyn, N.Y., lecturer, 1961-64, assistant professor, 1965-69, associate professor, 1969-74, professor of Middle East Studies, 1974—. Director, Program in Technology, Modernization, and International Studies, University of Denver, 1972—. Acting director, American Research Institute (Turkey), 1964-65. *Military service:* U.S. Army Reserve, 1953-59. *Member:* American Political Science Association, International Studies Association, Middle East Studies Association, Turkish Studies Association (president, 1974-76), American Association of University Professors, Colorado Association for International Education (chairman of executive board, 1970), Phi Beta Kappa, Pi Gamma Mu, Tau Kappa Alpha.

WRITINGS: (Editor with Benjamin Rivlin) *The Contemporary Middle East: Tradition and Innovation,* Random House, 1965; *Political Change in Rural Turkey: A Case Study,* Mouton, 1966; *A Political Analysis of Student Activism: The Turkish Case* (monograph), Professional Papers in Comparative Politics, 1972; *Education and Modernization in the Middle East,* Cornell University Press, 1973; (co-author) *The Energy Crisis and U.S. Foreign Policy,* Praeger, 1975; (co-author) *Petro-Politics and the Atlantic Alliance* (monograph), National Defense University, 1976. Contributor of articles to political science journals. "Monograph Series in World Affairs," acting editor, 1967-68, editor, 1971-75.

WORK IN PROGRESS: The Ottoman Administrative Elite.

AVOCATIONAL INTERESTS: Photography, expeditions, travel.

T

TAIRA, Koji 1926-

PERSONAL: Surname originally Kiyomura; name legally changed, 1933; born November 7, 1926, in Hirara, Japan; son of Konin (an author) and Kimiko (Taira) Kiyomura; married Setsuko Miyagi, May 1, 1957; children: Karl Shinya, Henry Tatsuya. *Education:* University of New Mexico, B.A., 1953; University of Wisconsin, M.A., 1954; Stanford University, Ph.D., 1961. *Office:* Institute of Labor and Industrial Relations, University of Illinois, 504 East Armory, Champaign, Ill. 61820.

CAREER: University of Washington, Seattle, assistant professor of economics, 1961-62; International Labor Office, Geneva, Switzerland, official, 1962-65; Stanford University, Stanford, Calif., associate professor of economics, 1966-69; University of Illinois at Urbana-Champaign, professor of economics, 1970—. *Member:* American Economic Association, Association for Asian Studies, Society for International Development, Industrial Relations Research Association, Association for Comparative Economics. *Awards, honors:* Eliot Jones Award from Western Economic Association, 1961; first prize, Newcomen Awards in Business History, 1970.

WRITINGS: Economic Development and the Labor Market in Japan, Columbia University Press, 1970; *Ningensei no Keizaigaku* (title means "Humanists' Economics"), Diamond, 1970; (translator into Japanese) Irving Kristol and Daniel Bell, editors, *Capitalism Today,* Diamond, 1973; *Nihonkoku kaizo shiron* (title means "Reforming the Constitution of Japan"), Kondansha, 1974; (with Mikio Sumiya) *An Outline of Japanese Economic History,* University of Tokyo Press, 1978. Contributor of about eighty articles to professional journals.

WORK IN PROGRESS: Industrial relations in Japan and Japan-United States economic relations.

*   *   *

TAKAHASHI, Yasundo 1912-

PERSONAL: Born June 12, 1912, in Nagoya-shi, Japan; son of Sakunosuke (an artist) and Teruko (Umemura) Takahashi; married Kuwaki Kusunoki, April 9, 1940; children: Yuri (Mrs. J. Canfield). *Education:* University of Tokyo, B.S., 1935, Ph.D., 1946. *Home:* 135 York Ave., Kensington, Calif. 94708. *Office:* Department of Mechanical Engineering, University of California, Berkeley, Calif. 94720.

CAREER: Japanese National Railways, Tokyo, Japan, design engineer, 1935-37; Yokohama Technical College, Yokohama, Japan, professor of mechanical engineering, 1937-40; Nagoya University, Nagoya, Japan, professor of mechanical engineering, 1940-44; University of Tokyo, Tokyo, professor of mechanical engineering, 1944-58; University of California, Berkeley, professor of mechanical engineering, 1958—. Visiting professor at University of Grenoble, 1965 and 1970, Tokyo Institute of Technology, 1965 and 1970, National Polytechnic Institute, Mexico, 1972, University of La Plata, Argentina, 1973, Keio-University, Japan, 1977. *Member:* Japan Society of Instrument and Control Engineering (honorary member), Instrument Society of America, American Society of Mechanical Engineers (fellow). *Awards, honors:* Fulbright scholarship at Massachusetts Institute of Technology, 1954-55; Doctor Honoris Causa, National Polytechnic Institute of Grenoble, 1978.

WRITINGS: Theory of Automatic Control, Iwanami, 1954, revised edition, 1959; *Automatic Control System Design Manual,* Kyoritsu, 1954, revised edition, 1970; *Systems and Control,* Iwanami, 1968, revised edition, 1978; (with D. Auslander and M. J. Rabins) *Control,* Addison-Wesley, 1970; *Theory of Dynamic Systems via Computer,* Kagakugijutsu-sha, 1971; (with Auslander and Rabins) *Introducing Systems and Control,* McGraw, 1974. Editor emeritus of *Journal of Dynamic Systems, Measurement, and Control* of American Society of Mechanical Engineers.

WORK IN PROGRESS: Research on dynamics and simulation of ecological and population systems.

*   *   *

TALBERT, Charles H(arold) 1934-

PERSONAL: Born March 19, 1934, in Jackson, Miss.; son of Carl E. (a minister) and Audrey (Hale) Talbert; married Betty Weaver, June 30, 1961; children: Caroline O'Neil, Charles Richard. *Education:* Howard College (now Samford University), B.A., 1956; Southern Baptist Theological Seminary, B.D., 1959; Vanderbilt University, Ph.D., 1963. *Politics:* Democrat. *Religion:* Baptist. *Home:* 3091 Prytania Rd., Winston-Salem, N.C. 27106. *Office:* Department of Religious Studies, Wake Forest University, Winston-Salem, N.C. 27109.

CAREER: Wake Forest University, Winston-Salem, N.C., assistant professor, 1963-68, associate professor, 1969-74, professor of religious studies, 1974—. *Member:* Society of Biblical Literature, Society for New Testament Studies, Catholic Biblical Association, Society for Values in Higher Education, American Association of University Professors, Association of Baptist Professors of Religion. *Awards, honors:* Cooperative Program in Humanities fellowship, 1968-69; Society for Religion in Higher Education fellowship, 1971-72; Reynolds research leave, 1979.

WRITINGS: Luke and the Gnostics, Abingdon, 1966; *Reimarus: Fragments,* Fortress, 1970; *Literary Patterns, Theological Themes and the Genre of Luke-Acts,* Scholars Press, 1974; *What Is a Gospel?,* Fortress, 1977; (editor) *Perspectives on Luke-Acts,* Association of Baptist Professors of Religion, 1978.

WORK IN PROGRESS: Commentary of the Gospel of Luke; The Historical Jesus and the Development of Early Christian Christology.

SIDELIGHTS: Charles Talbert is competent in Hebrew, Greek, Latin, French, German, and Italian.

*   *   *

TANNER, Clara L(ee) 1905-

PERSONAL: Born May 28, 1905, in Biscoe, N.C.; daughter of Joseph Conrad and Clara Dargon (Lee) Fraps; married John Frederick Tanner (a shop owner and operator), January 22, 1936; children: Sandra (Mrs. Karl E. Elers). *Education:* University of Arizona, A.B., 1927, M.A., 1928; graduate study at National University of Mexico, 1929, and University of Chicago, Oriental Institute, 1934. *Address:* P.O. Box 40904, Tucson, Ariz. 85717. *Office:* Department of Anthropology, University of Arizona, Tucson, Ariz. 85721.

CAREER: University of Arizona, Tucson, instructor, 1928-35, assistant professor, 1935-57, associate professor, 1957-68, professor of anthropology, 1968-75, professor emeritus, 1975—. Assistant professor, University of Denver, summer, 1949; archaeological field work in northern Arizona, summer, 1930. *Member:* American Anthropological Association, Society for American Archaeology, National Federation of Press Women, Arizona Archaeological and Historical Society, Arizona Academy of Science, Arizona Historical Society, Arizona Press Women, New Mexico Archaeological Society, Sigma Xi, Delta Kappa Gamma, Theta Sigma Phi, Phi Beta Kappa. *Awards, honors:* Fiftieth anniversary medal from Inter-Tribal Indian Ceremonial Association, 1970; named woman of the year by Arizona Press Women, 1971-72.

WRITINGS: Southwest Indian Painting, University of Arizona Press, 1957; *Southwest Indian Craft Arts,* University of Arizona Press, 1968; *The James T. Bialac Collection of Southwest Indian Paintings,* Arizona State Museum, 1968; *Southwest Indian Painting: A Changing Art,* University of Arizona Press, 1973; *Portraits and Turquoise of Southwest Indians,* Manley, 1975; *Prehistoric Southwestern Craft Arts,* University of Arizona Press, 1976; (editor) *Arizona Highways Indian Arts and Crafts,* Arizona Highways, 1976. Contributor of more than a hundred articles to magazines, scientific journals, and newspapers. Editor of *Kiva,* 1938-49.

WORK IN PROGRESS: A monograph on Apache Indian basketry.

*   *   *

TANNER, James T(homas) F(ontenot) 1937-

PERSONAL: Born October 27, 1937, in Woodsboro,

Texas; son of Leonard Jefferson (a farmer) and Mildred (Burney) Tanner. *Education:* Texas Wesleyan College, B.A., 1961; Texas Technological College (now Texas Tech University), M.A., 1963, Ph.D., 1965. *Politics:* Democrat. *Religion:* Unitarian Universalist. *Office:* Department of English, North Texas State University, Denton Tex. 76203.

CAREER: Wayne State University, Detroit, Mich., instructor in English, 1964-65; North Texas State University, Denton, assistant professor, 1965-69, associate professor of English, 1969—. *Military service:* U.S. Army, 1956-59. *Member:* Modern Language Association of America, National Council of Teachers of English, Modern Humanities Research Association.

WRITINGS: Walt Whitman: A Supplementary Bibliography, 1961-1967, Kent State University Press, 1968; (with J. Don Vann) *Samuel Beckett: A Checklist of Criticism,* Kent State University Press, 1969. Contributor to bulletins and to professional journals, including *Walt Whitman Review, Dickinson Review, Emerson Society Quarterly,* and *Rectangle.* Contributing editor of *Annual Bibliography of English Language and Literature,* 1968—.

WORK IN PROGRESS: A book on the critical historical position of New England transcendentalists; a book on Walt Whitman; research on existentialism and literature.†

*   *   *

TAPIA, Ralph J(ohn) 1925-

PERSONAL: Born June 24, 1925, in Fresno, Calif.; son of Raphael A. (a retired land owner) and Elvira V. (Gonzalez) Tapia. *Education:* Gregorian University, S.T.B., 1948, S.T.L., 1950, S.T.D., 1955; Pontifical Academy of St. Thomas, Ph.D., 1949; Catholic University of America, M.A., 1959. *Politics:* Republican. *Residence:* New York, N.Y. *Office:* Department of Theology, Fordham University, Bronx, N.Y. 10458.

CAREER: Ordained Roman Catholic priest in diocese of Fresno, Calif., 1955; named monsignor, 1963. Fordham University, Bronx, N.Y., instructor, 1959-61, assistant professor, 1961-70, associate professor, 1970-75, professor of Christian ethics, 1975—. Lecturer at Notre Dame College of Staten Island, 1962-65, Manhattan College, 1966, and St. John's University, 1967; also lectured at Fresno State College (now California State University, Fresno), and College of New Rochelle. *Member:* American Association of University Professors, Theological Society of America, Catholic Theological Society of America, College Theology Society of America, American Catholic Historical Association, Catholic College Teachers of Sacred Doctrine, New York Athletic Club. *Awards, honors:* Named honorary Papal Chamberlain by Pope Paul VI, 1964.

WRITINGS: El Texto 'I ad corintios, c. XV, vv. 21-22, Editorial Jus (Mexico), 1955; *The Theology of Christ: Commentary,* Bruce, 1970; *The Alumbrados of Toledo,* Weber & Sons, 1974. Contributor to *Thought, New Catholic Encyclopedia, Homiletic and Pastoral Review, Cord,* and other publications.

WORK IN PROGRESS: Three books, *Faith Today, Faith and Modern Man,* and *Drugs and the Religious Experience.*

*   *   *

TAPLINGER, Richard Jacques 1911-1973

April 14, 1911—February 13, 1973; American publisher and author. Obituaries: *New York Times,* February 15, 1973; *Publishers Weekly,* February 26, 1973.

TAPP, June Louin 1929-

PERSONAL: Born June 11, 1929, in New York, N.Y.; daughter of Robert B. (a commercial artist) and Hannah (Wacholder) Louin; married Robert B. Tapp (a professor), May 6, 1949; children: Mara Anne, Kami Debra. *Education:* University of Southern California, B.A. (magna cum laude), 1951, M.S., 1952; Syracuse University, Ph.D., 1963. *Politics:* Democrat. *Office:* Office of the Provost, University of California, San Diego, La Jolla, Calif. 92037.

CAREER: St. Lawrence University, Canton, N.Y., instructor in psychology and educational psychology, 1952-55; Syracuse University, Syracuse, N.Y., assistant instructor in citizenship at Maxwell Graduate School, 1955-56; Albert Schweitzer College, Churwaldern, Switzerland, tutor in psychology and sociology, 1957-58; Harvey Mudd College, Claremont, Calif., assistant professor of psychology, 1961-64; University of Chicago, Chicago, Ill., assistant professor, 1964-67, associate professorial lecturer in the social sciences, 1967-72, research associate with Committee on Human Development, 1964-67, staff associate on Committee for Asian Studies, 1968-72; University of Minnesota, Minneapolis, professor of child psychology and criminal justice studies, 1972-76; currently affiliated with Office of the Provost, University of California, San Diego, La Jolla. Administrative assistant, Moran Crime Institute, St. Lawrence University, summers, 1954-60. American Bar Foundation, project director and senior research social scientist, 1967-72, affiliated scholar, 1972—; member of White House Conference on Children, 1970, and Conference on Youth, 1971; member of planning committee for research in child development, U.S. National Commission to UNESCO, 1972—; member of Minnesota Task Force on Criminal Justice Standards and Goals, 1974-76. Consultant in psychology, University of Poona, India, 1963.

MEMBER: International Association for Cross-Cultural Psychology, International Association of Law and Social Philosophy, Interamerican Society of Psychology, American Psychological Association, Society for Research in Child Development, American Psychology-Law Society (member of board of directors; president, 1972-73), Law and Society Association (secretary, 1972-73), Society for Psychological Study of Social Issues (member of council, 1972-74), American Sociological Association, American Association for the Advancement of Science, Midwestern Psychological Association, Phi Beta Kappa, Phi Kappa Phi, Psi Chi, Alpha Kappa Delta.

AWARDS, HONORS: National Institute of Mental Health grant for Indian youth project at University of Poona, 1963-64; American Psychological Association travel grants, 1966, 1969, 1972, 1976; Early Education Research Committee grant, 1968; Social Science Research Committee grant, 1969-70; faculty fellow, University of Minnesota, 1972; liberal arts fellow, Harvard University, 1972; Distinguished Alumna Award, Syracuse University, 1974.

WRITINGS: (Contributor) *Educational Rehabilitation: An Evaluation of the Adult Basic Education Program of the State of Illinois,* Greenleigh Associates, Inc., 1965; (with Fred Krinsky) *Ambivalent America: A Psycho-Political Dialogue,* Glencoe Press, 1971; (contributor) S. E. Golann and Carl Eisdorfer, editors, *Handbook of Community Psychology and Mental Health,* Appleton, 1972; (contributor) Samuel Krislov and others, editors, *Compliance and the Law: A Multi-disciplinary Approach,* Sage Publications, 1972; (contributor) Krislov, editor, *American Government: The Clash of Issues,* Prentice-Hall, 1972; (contributor) J. R.

Pennock and J. W. Chapman, editors, *The Limits of Law: Nomos XV,* Atherton, 1973; (with Felice J. Levine) *The Psychology of Criminal Identification: The Gap from Wade to Kirby,* American Bar Foundation, 1973; (with Levine) *Law, Justice, and the Individual in Society,* Holt, 1977.

Author of psychology reports for U.S. Office of Education, U.S. Department of Labor, and American Bar Foundation. Contributor to proceedings and symposia. Contributor of about twenty-five articles and reviews to professional journals, including *Journal of Youth and Adolescence, Journal of Social Issues, Psychology Today, Trans-action, Law and Society Review, Journal of Engineering Education, Personalist, Opaque Projection Techniques, Educational Screen,* and *Social Education.* Member of editorial board, *Law and Society Review* and *Journal of Youth and Adolescence.*

WORK IN PROGRESS: Contributing to *Law and Social Deviance,* edited by S. A. Shah and George Weber; *The Jurisprudence of Youth,* a monograph, with F. J. Levine; a cross-cultural research project relating ethnicity and legality.

SIDELIGHTS: June Louin Tapp's research and teaching include travel and study in England, Scotland, France, Belgium, Netherlands, Lichtenstein, Germany, Austria, Hungary, Czechoslovakia, Italy, Spain, Yugoslavia, Soviet Union, Greece, Thailand, Japan, Denmark, Finland, Sweden, Canada, and Mexico.

*   *   *

TAPP, Robert B(erg) 1925-

PERSONAL: Born May 21, 1925, in Hollywood, Calif.; son of Charles (a market owner) and Ora (Berg) Tapp; married June Louin (a professor), May 6, 1949; children: Mara Anne, Kami Debra. *Education:* University of Southern California, B.S., 1945, Ph.D., 1952. *Politics:* Democrat. *Religion:* Unitarian Universalist. *Home:* 2631 East Lake of the Isles, Minneapolis, Minn. 55408. *Office:* Departments of Humanities and Religious Studies, University of Minnesota, Minneapolis, Minn. 55455.

CAREER: University of Southern California, Los Angeles, lecturer in general studies, 1950-52; St. Lawrence University, Canton, N.Y., Dockstader Professor of Theology, 1952-60; Scripps College, Claremont, Calif., associate professor of religion, 1960-64; Meadville Theological School of Lombard College, Chicago, Ill., professor of philosophy of religion, 1964-72; University of Chicago, Chicago, professorial lecturer in social science, 1968-72; University of Minnesota, Minneapolis, professor of humanities and religious studies, 1972—. American professor, Albert Schweitzer College, Switzerland, 1957-58; visiting professor of theology, Starr King School of the Ministry, summer, 1959. President of Values Research Foundation; chairman of committee on theology and frontiers of learning, Unitarian Universalist Association, 1960-63. *Military service:* U.S. Naval Reserve, 1943-46; became ensign. *Member:* American Society for Study of Religion, Association for Asian Study, Society for Scientific Study of Religion, American Philosophical Association, American Sociological Association. *Awards, honors:* American Institute of Indian Studies faculty fellow, 1963; Social Science Research Council faculty research grant.

WRITINGS: Religion among the Unitarian Universalists: Converts in the Stepfathers' House, Seminar Press, 1973. Contributor of articles and reviews to scholarly journals.

WORK IN PROGRESS: A book, *Comparative Savior-Heroes: A Study in Religions.*

TARN, John Nelson   1934-

PERSONAL: Born November 23, 1934, in Newcastle, England; son of Percival Nelson (a shipbroker) and Mary I. (Purvis) Tarn. *Education:* King's College, Durham, B.Arch. (first class honors), 1957; Gonville and Caius College, Cambridge, Ph.D., 1961. *Religion:* Anglican. *Home:* 2 Ashmore Close, Caldy, Wirral L48 2JX, England. *Office:* School of Architecture, University of Liverpool, Liverpool L69 3BX, England.

CAREER: Assistant architect in private practice, Newcastle-upon-Tyne, England, 1960-63; University of Sheffield, Sheffield, England, lecturer in architecture, 1963-70; University of Nottingham, Nottingham, England, professor of architecture, 1970-73; University of Liverpool, Liverpool, England, Roscoe Professor of Architecture, 1974—. *Member:* Royal Institute of British Architects (fellow), Royal Society of Arts (fellow), Royal Historical Society (fellow).

WRITINGS: Working Class Housing in Nineteenth Century Britain, Wittenborn, 1971; *Five Per Cent Philanthropy: An Account of Housing in Urban Areas,* Cambridge University Press, 1972; *The Peak District National Park: Its Architecture,* Peak Park Planning Board, 1973.

WORK IN PROGRESS: An architectural history of Sheffield.

*   *   *

TARPLEY, Fred   1932-

PERSONAL: Born January 27, 1932, in Leonard, Tex.; son of Fred Frost (a pharmacist) and Adelle (McCorstin) Tarpley; married Jolene Connatser, February 22, 1969. *Education:* East Texas State Teachers College (now East Texas State University), B.A., 1951, M.A., 1954; University of Minnesota, graduate study, 1956; Louisiana State University, Ph.D., 1960. *Politics:* Democrat. *Religion:* Methodist. *Home:* Route 1, Campbell, Tex. 75422. *Office:* Department of English, East Texas State University, Commerce, Tex. 75428.

CAREER: East Texas State University, Commerce, instructor, 1957-60, assistant professor, 1960-62, associate professor, 1962-65, professor of English, 1965—, head of department of literature and languages, 1973—. Director, South Central Names Institute, and Place Name Survey of the United States, 1973—. *Military service:* U.S. Air Force, 1952-56; served in Japan. *Member:* Modern Language Association of America, American Dialect Society, American Name Society, National Council of Teachers of English, Linguistic Society of America, International Society for General Semantics, International Platform Association, Texas Council of Teachers of English (executive secretary, 1973—), Sigma Phi Epsilon.

WRITINGS—Published by Names Institute Press, except as indicated: *Place Names of Texas,* East Texas State University Press, 1969; *From Blinky to Blue-John: A Word Atlas of Northeast Texas,* University Press (Wolfe City, Tex.), 1971; (editor with Ann Moseley) *Of Edsels and Marauders,* 1972; (editor) *Love and Wrestling, Butch and O.K.,* 1973; (editor) *They Had to Call It Something,* 1974; (editor) *Naughty Names,* 1975; (editor) *Labeled for Life,* 1977; (editor) *Ethnic Names,* 1978.

WORK IN PROGRESS: Further research on place names of Texas and dialects of minority groups.

SIDELIGHTS: Fred Tarpley told *CA:* "My work focuses on preserving regional dialect, explaining place name origins, and exploring fascinating topics in onomastics. The dialect interviews for *From Blinky to Blue-John* report Texas vocabulary which is quickly passing from the scene. *Place Names of Texas* reports the reasons behind the naming of 2,600 spots on the map, and I am now completing a dictionary of 65,000 Texas place names. The Names Institute publications include papers on a variety of names studies, from names of bars and apartment buildings, to names in literature, to names of commercial outhouse rentals."

*   *   *

TAYLOR, Karl K.   1938-

PERSONAL: Born December 2, 1938, in Peoria, Ill.; son of Harry K. and Edna Rose (Thurman) Taylor; married Nancy Coon, September 3, 1961; children: David, Andrea, Amy. *Education:* Knox College, B.A., 1960; University of Illinois at Urbana-Champaign, M.A., 1962, Ph.D., 1978. *Home:* 108 South Market, Washington, Ill. 61571. *Office:* Department of Adult Basic Education, Illinois Central College, East Peoria, Ill. 61635.

CAREER: Spoon River College, Canton, Ill., instructor in English, 1965-67; Illinois Central College, East Peoria, associate professor of English and chairman of department of adult basic education, 1967—. *Military service:* U.S. Army, 1963-65; became captain. *Member:* International Reading Association, National Council of Teachers of English, Midwest Regional Conference on English in the Two-Year College (treasurer, 1970-72), Phi Delta Kappa, Phi Gamma Delta.

WRITINGS: (Editor with Fred W. Soady, Jr.) *Violence: An Element of American Life,* Holbrook, 1972; (with Tom Zimanzl) *Writing from Example,* Prentice-Hall, 1972; *Stages in Writing,* McGraw, 1973.

*   *   *

TAYLOR, (M.) Lee   1930-

PERSONAL: Born February 13, 1930, in Missouri; married Jacquelin K. Taylor (a teacher), 1953; children: Michelle. *Education:* San Jose State College (now University), B.A., 1952; Louisiana State University, M.A., 1956, Ph.D., 1958. *Politics:* Republican. *Religion:* Presbyterian. *Office:* Department of Sociology, University of Texas, Arlington, Tex. 76010.

CAREER: University of Minnesota, Minneapolis, assistant professor of sociology, 1958-61; Louisiana State University, Baton Rouge, associate professor of sociology, 1961-65; Tulane University, New Orleans, La., professor of sociology, 1965-66; Cornell University, Ithaca, N.Y., professor of sociology and assistant director of research, 1966-69; Louisiana State University in New Orleans (now University of New Orleans), professor of sociology and director of urban studies, 1969-72; University of Texas at Arlington, professor of sociology, 1972—. *Awards, honors:* Rockefeller research grant.

WRITINGS: (With A. R. Jones) *Rural Life and Urbanized Society,* Oxford University Press, 1964; *Urban-Rural Problems,* Dickenson, 1968; *Occupational Sociology,* Oxford University Press, 1968; (editor with J. Paul Leadans) *Workers in Agribusiness: Profile, Images, Recruitment, Mobility, Occupations,* New York State College of Agriculture, Cornell University, 1970; (with William Reeder and J. J. Managalam) *Internationalizing Rural Sociology: Training, Practice, Recruitment,* New York State College of Agriculture, Cornell University, 1970; (editor with Earl Hedrick) *Handbook for Louisiana Municipal Officials*, Urban Studies Institute, Louisiana State University in New Orleans, 1971; (editor with William Burch and Neil Cheek) *Social Behavior, Natural Resources and the Environment*, Harper, 1972; *Idea People*, Nelson-Hall, 1975.

WORK IN PROGRESS: Sociology and Urban Planning, a book about urban life and planning on a world-wide scale.

* * *

TAYLOR, Lloyd A(ndrew)   1921-

PERSONAL: Born October 4, 1921, in Omaha, Neb.; son of William Anson (a laborer) and Kathryn (Sutton) Taylor; married Dorothy Johnson (an elementary school teacher), May 18, 1943; children: Tom, Kathryn, Jean, Jane. *Education:* Manhattan Bible College, A.B., 1943; Phillips University, B.A., 1947, M.Div., 1970; Kansas State University, M.S., 1957; Nebraska University, Ph.D., 1968. *Politics:* Democrat. *Home:* 2721 Shirley Dr., Enid, Okla. 73701. *Office:* Department of Sociology, Phillips University, Box 2244 University Station, Enid, Okla. 73701.

CAREER: Ordained minister of Disciples of Christ, 1940; Manhattan Bible College, Manhattan, Kan., professor of social studies, 1945-57; Phillips University, Enid, Okla., professor of sociology, 1957—. Lecturer in sociology, Oklahoma State University, 1967-70. Host of daily radio show, "Thought for Living," 1968—. *Member:* American Sociological Association, Midwest Sociological Association, Southwest Sociological Association, Oklahoma Sociological Association (president, 1972), Phi Kappa Phi, Delta Epsilon Chi.

WRITINGS: (With Gene Acuff and Donald Allen) *From Man to Society: Introduction to Sociology*, Dryden Press, 1973.

WORK IN PROGRESS: A monograph on overurbanization and developing countries.

* * *

TAYLOR, Ronald J(ack)   1926-

PERSONAL: Born May 19, 1926, in London, England; married Alma Hauck; children: one son, one daughter. *Education:* Royal Academy of Music, London, L.R.A.M., 1942; King's College, London, B.A., 1949, M.A., 1951, Ph.D., 1965. *Office:* Department of German, University of Sussex, Falmer, Brighton, Sussex, England.

CAREER: University of Mainz, Mainz, Germany, lektor, 1947-48; University College of Swansea, Swansea, Wales, lecturer, 1950-58, senior lecturer in German, 1959-64; University of Sussex, Falmer, Brighton, England, professor of German, 1965—. Visiting professor at University of Chicago, 1960, Northwestern University, 1963-64, and University of British Columbia, 1975, 1976. Former piano recitalist and music critic.

WRITINGS: (With A. T. Hatto) *The Songs of Neidhart von Reuental*, Manchester University Press, 1958; (editor) Ernst T. W. Hoffmann, *Das Fraulein von Scuderi*, Thomas Nelson, 1959; (with Walter Gottschalk) *A German-English Dictionary of Idioms*, Max Hueber, 1960, 3rd edition, 1970; *Hoffman*, Hillary House, 1963; *Die Melodien der weltlichen Lieder des Mittelalters*, two volumes, J. B. Metzler, 1964; (editor, transcriber, and author of textual and musical commentaries) *The Art of the Minnesinger: Songs of the Thirteenth Century*, two volumes, University of Wales Press, 1968; *The Romantic Tradition in Germany*, Methuen, 1970; *The Intellectual Tradition of Modern Germany*, two vol-

umes, G. Bell, 1972, Barnes & Noble, 1973; *Richard Wagner: His Life, Art and Thought*, Elek, 1978. Also author of *Literature and Society in Germany, 1918-1945*.

Translator: Ernst T. W. Hoffmann, *The Devil's Elixirs*, J. Calder, 1963; J. von Eichendorff, *Memoirs of a Good-for-Nothing*, Calder & Boyars, 1966; T. Storm, *Immensee*, Calder & Boyars, 1966; G. Keller, *A Village Romeo and Juliet*, Calder & Boyars, 1966; B. Boesch, editor, *German Literature: A Critical Survey*, Methuen, 1971; H. von Einem, *Michelangelo*, Methuen, 1973; K. Lorenz, *Behind the Mirror*, Methuen, 1977; (editor) *Politics and Aesthetics*, New Left Books, 1978. Contributor to *Encyclopaedia Britannica*, to language journals, and to *Times Literary Supplement*.

WORK IN PROGRESS: The Political and Philosophical Thought of Richard Wagner for Elek.

* * *

TEDESCHI, (Theodore) James, Jr.   1928-

PERSONAL: Surname is pronounced Ted-es-ski; born October 4, 1928, in Coatesville, Pa.; son of James Tedeschi (a barber) and Mable Bossert; married Leatha Peddicord, June 12, 1952; children: James Bradley, Jamie Susan, Nancy Kathryn, Linda Ann, James Anthony. *Education:* University of Miami, A.B. (cum laude), 1956, M.S., 1958; University of Michigan, Ph.D., 1960. *Home:* 13 Valencia Lane, Elnora, N.Y. *Office:* Department of Psychology, State University of New York, Albany, N.Y. 12222.

CAREER: Utah State University, Logan, assistant professor of psychology, 1959-61; University of Miami, Coral Gables, Fla., assistant professor, 1961-67, associate professor of psychology, 1967-69; U.S. International University, San Diego, Calif., professor of social psychology, 1969-70; State University of New York at Albany, professor of social psychology, 1970—. *Military service:* U.S. Army, 1951-52. *Member:* Society of Experimental Social Psychologists, American Psychological Association (fellow). *Awards, honors:* Outstanding Teacher Award, University of Miami, 1967; Society for the Psychological Study of Social Issues grant, 1968; National Science Foundation grant, 1970-73; U.S. Office of Education grant, 1971; State University of New York at Albany institutional grants, 1971, 1972-73.

WRITINGS: (Editor) *The Social Influence Processes*, Aldine, 1972; (with B. R. Schlenker and T. V. Bonoma) *Conflict, Power, and Games: The Experimental Study of Interpersonal Behavior*, Aldine, 1973; (editor) *Perspectives on Social Power*, Aldine, 1974; (with S. Lindskold) *Social Psychology: Interdependence, Interaction, and Influence*, Wiley, 1976.

Contributor: L. Wrightsman, editor, *Contemporary Viewpoints in Social Psychology*, Brooks/Cole, 1968; M. Levitt and B. Rubenstein, editors, *The Mental Health Field: A Critical Appraisal*, Wayne State University Press, 1970; P. Swingle, editor, *The Structure of Conflict*, Academic Press, 1970; S. Kriskly, K. O. Boyum, J. N. Clar, R. C. Schaefer, and S. C. White, editors, *Compliance and the Law*, Sage Publications, 1972; G. Zaltman, P. Kotler, and I. Kaufman, editors, *Creating Social Change*, Holt, 1972; H. C. Lindgren, editor, *Contemporary Research in Social Psychology: A Book of Readings*, 2nd edition, Wiley, 1973; T. Huston, editor, *Perspectives in Interpersonal Attraction*, Academic Press, 1974; W. E. Scott and L. L. Cummings, editors, *Readings in Organizational Behavior and Human Performance*, Irwin, 1975; L. Socyka and P. Bastos, editors, *Territoria, Conflito e agresseo*, Livraria Bertrand, 1976; G.

Marin, editor, *Lecturas de psicologia social contemporanea*, Trillas, 1976; A. J. Chapman and H. C. Foot, editors, *Humor and Laughter: Theory, Research, and Applications*, Wiley, 1976; D. Krebs, editor, *Readings in Social Psychology: Contemporary Perspective*, Harper, 1977; D. Druckman, editor, *Dimensions and Processes of Inter-Party Negotiations: A Social Psychological Perspective*, Halstead, 1977; T. Milburn and T. V. Bonoma, editors, *Conflict and Power*, Halstead, 1979.

Contributor of articles to numerous journals, including *Journal of Social Psychology, Journal of Personality and Social Psychology, Sociometry, Journal of Conflict Resolution, Behavioral Science, Human Relations, American Psychologist, Professional Psychology, Journal of Humanistic Psychology, British Journal of Clinical and Social Psychology, Canadian Journal of Behavioral Science, Contemporary Psychology, Journal of Experimental Social Psychology,* and *Journal of Research in Personality.*

AVOCATIONAL INTERESTS: Travel, theater, sports, foreign movies, ballet, and chamber music.

*   *   *

TELLER, James D(avid) 1906-

PERSONAL: Born December 26, 1906, in Nassau, Bahamas; son of David Millard (a seaman) and Ermyn (Sturrup) Teller; married Clara Hilberg, January 11, 1930; children: Kathryn (Mrs. Don C. Stearns), James David, Jr. *Education:* Ohio State University, B.S., 1930, M.A., 1935, Ph.D., 1943. *Politics:* Democrat. *Religion:* Episcopalian. *Home:* 1105 Hadrian Court, Irving, Tex. 75062. *Office:* University of Dallas, Irving, Tex. 75061.

CAREER: High school mathematics teacher in Ohio, 1930-34; high school physics teacher in Florida, 1934-38; Ohio State University, Columbus, instructor in education, 1938-43; U.S. War Department, New York, N.Y., psychologist, 1943-45; Office of U.S. Adjutant General, Washington, D.C., director of psychological testing, 1945-49; Office of U.S. Secretary of Defense, Washington, D.C., psychologist and chief of qualifications research, 1949-51; U.S. Air Force Headquarters, Washington, D.C., technical director of personnel classification, 1951-60, psychologist in personnel measurement, 1960-65; University of Dallas, Irving, Tex., professor of education, 1967-72, professor emeritus, 1972—, dean, 1967-71. Adjunct professor at American University, 1950-67, and University of Virginia, 1965-67. Has served as consultant to thirteen air forces of North Atlantic Treaty Organization (NATO) members, including those of Norway, 1952-60, and France, 1957-60, and to thirteen Latin American and Asian air forces, including that of Peru, 1958-60.

MEMBER: American Association for the Advancement of Science (fellow), American Educational Research Association, Phi Delta Kappa, Pi Sigma Alpha, Phi Alpha Theta, Kappa Delta Pi. *Awards, honors:* Charles B. Brickell Memorial Scholarship, 1926-30, at Ohio State University; civilian meritorious service award from U.S. War Department, 1947.

WRITINGS: The Educational Views and Influence of Thomas Henry Huxley, Ohio State University, 1935; *Louis Agassiz: Scientist and Teacher*, Ohio State University Press, 1947; (with H. G. Good) *A History of Western Education*, 3rd edition (Teller was not associated with earlier editions), Macmillan, 1969; (with Good) *A History of American Education*, 3rd edition (Teller was not associated with earlier editions), Macmillan, 1973. Contributor to education and science journals.

WORK IN PROGRESS: Series of monographs on "Great Teachers of Science," including Michael Farady, John Tyndall, and Joseph Henry.

*   *   *

TENNOV, Dorothy 1928-

PERSONAL: Surname originally Tennow; legally changed, March 30, 1973; born August 29, 1928, in Montgomery, Ala.; daughter of Daniel E. (a teacher) and Lois (Moore) Tennow; children: Randall, Russell, Daniel. *Education:* Brooklyn College (now Brooklyn College of the City University of New York), B.A., 1950; University of Connecticut, M.A., 1954, Ph.D., 1964. *Home and office:* 181 Boston Ave., Stratford, Conn. 06497.

CAREER: University of Connecticut, Storrs, instructor in psychology, 1962-64; University of Bridgeport, Bridgeport, Conn., assistant professor, 1964-70, associate professor, 1970-75, professor of psychology, 1975—. Lecturer in Norway, England, Scotland, and Germany. Has private consultation practice in personal and behavioral consultation; created C1C2 Project, self-help program for women, and "Neighbors," a woman's consumer medical project, 1972; has made television and radio broadcasts. Member of board of directors, Mental Health Association, Stamford, Conn., 1963-65. *Member:* American Psychological Association, Association for the Advancement of Behavior Therapy, American Association for the Advancement of Science, Association for Women in Psychology, National Organization of Women, Association for Behavior Analysis, British Psychological Society.

WRITINGS: The CIC Project: Self-Help for Women, privately printed, 1972; *Neighbors: Women's Consumer Medical Project*, privately printed, 1972; *Open Rapping*, Know, Inc., 1972; *Psychotherapy: The Hazardous Cure*, Abelard, 1975; *Super Self: A Woman's Guide to Self-Management*, Funk, 1977; *Love and Limerence: The Experience of Being in Love*, Stein & Day, in press. Contributor to popular and professional journals, including *American Psychologist, Educate, Women Speaking, Women's World, Educational Technology, Contemporary Psychology,* and *Family Circle.*

*   *   *

TERRELL, Robert L(ouis) 1943-

PERSONAL: Born July 19, 1943; son of Jack (a laborer) and Bessie (Naylor) Terrell; married Venita L. Sharpe, March, 1967; children: Iman Makeba. *Education:* Morehouse College, B.A., 1969; University of California, Berkeley, M.A. *Agent:* Lois Wallace, William Morris Agency, 1350 Avenue of the Americas, New York, N.Y.

CAREER: New York Post, New York, N.Y., reporter, 1967-68; Southern Regional Council, Atlanta, Ga., researcher and writer, 1968-69; Clark College, Atlanta, instructor at Negro College Newspaper Editor's Workshop, summer, 1969; *San Francisco Chronicle*, San Francisco, Calif., copy editor, 1970; Golden Gate College, San Francisco, instructor in writing and literature at School of Law, 1970-71; St. Mary's College, Moraga, Calif., assistant professor of social and psycholingual foundations of education, beginning 1971. Lecturer at Institute of Industrial Relations, University of California, Berkeley, spring, 1971. Member of board of directors, California Council on the Education of Teachers. *Member:* American Educational Research Association.

WRITINGS: (With Cleveland Sellers) *The River of No*

Return: The Autobiography of a Black Militant and the Life and Death of SNCC, Morrow, 1973. Contributor to *A Handbook on the War in Asia*. Contributor of articles and poems to magazines and newspapers, including *Evergreen Review, Eye, New South, Commonweal, Urban West, Negro Digest, Great Speckled Bird, Guardian, New York Post*, and *San Francisco Examiner*. Editor, *California Journal of Teachers Education*, 1972—.

WORK IN PROGRESS: Research for a book on the counter-culture in Berkeley, Calif.; collecting material for an anthology on Black colleges.†

* * *

TERRILL, Tom E(dward) 1935-

PERSONAL: Born September 15, 1935, in Oklahoma City, Okla.; son of D. Willard (a credit manager) and Velma D. (Mitchell) Terrill; married Sarah J. Northington, July 22, 1961; children: Andrea Bennett, Mitchell Northington. *Education:* Westminster College, Fulton, Mo., B.A., 1957; Princeton Theological Seminary, B.D., 1961; University of Wisconsin, M.A., 1963, certificate in African studies, 1965, Ph.D., 1966. *Religion:* Episcopalian. *Residence:* Columbia, S.C. *Office:* Department of History, University of South Carolina, Columbia, S.C. 29208.

CAREER: Hiram College, Hiram, Ohio, assistant professor of history, 1965-66; University of South Carolina, Columbia, assistant professor, 1966-70, associate professor of history, 1970—. Visiting lecturer, Allen University, 1967-70; visiting associate professor, Lutheran Seminary (Columbia, S.C), spring, 1971. *Member:* American Historical Association, Organization of American Historians, Economic History Association, Southern Historical Association, Southern Labor Studies Association. *Awards, honors:* Grants from American Philosophical Society, National Endowment for the Humanities, and South Carolina Committee for the Humanities.

WRITINGS: (Author of foreword) Asa H. Gordon, *Sketches of Negro Life and History in South Carolina*, 2nd edition (Terrill was not associated with earlier edition), University of South Carolina Press, 1971; *The Tariff, Politics, and American Foreign Policy: 1877-1901*, Greenwood Publishing, 1973; (editor with Jerrold Hirsch) *Such as Us: Southern Voices of the Thirties*, University of North Carolina Press, 1978. Contributor to *Journal of American History, Ohio History, Reviews in American History*, and *Journal of Economic History*.

WORK IN PROGRESS: A social history of southern textile workers; an oral history of the New South.

* * *

TERRY, Robert Meredith 1939-

PERSONAL: Born December 16, 1939, in Danville, Va.; son of Willard (a florist) and Martha (Willeford) Terry; married Anne Beggarly (a registered nurse), January 30, 1965; children: Michael Reynolds, Christopher Robert, Meredith Anne. *Education:* Attended Middlebury College, summers, 1961, 1962; Randolph-Macon College, B.A., 1962; attended Indiana University, summer, 1964; Duke University, Ph.D., 1966. *Religion:* Presbyterian. *Home:* 1504 Cloister Dr., Richmond, Va. 23233. *Office:* Department of Modern Foreign Languages, University of Richmond, Box 25, Richmond, Va. 23173.

CAREER: University of Florida, Gainesville, assistant professor of French, 1966-68; University of Richmond, Rich-

mond, Va., associate professor of French, 1968—. *Member:* American Association of Teachers of French, American Council on the Teaching of Foreign Languages, Mediaeval Academy of America, Phi Beta Kappa, Omicron Delta Kappa.

WRITINGS: Contemporary French Interrogative Structures, Editions Cosmos, 1970. Contributor to *French Review* and *Foreign Language Annals*.

WORK IN PROGRESS: En Bref . . . Enfin: A Modified Self-Pacing Approach to Intermediate French Grammar.

* * *

THALBERG, Irving 1930-

PERSONAL: Born August 24, 1930, in Los Angeles, Calif.; son of Irving Grant (a movie producer) and Norma (Shearer) Thalberg; married Suzanne McCormick, August 21, 1956 (divorced, 1969); children: Shoshana, Deborah, Elana. *Education:* Attended Sorbonne, University of Paris, 1951-52; Stanford University, B.A., 1953, Ph.D., 1960. *Politics:* "Radical . . ." *Religion:* "Jewish Atheist." *Office:* Department of Philosophy, University of Illinois at Chicago Circle, Chicago, Ill. 60680.

CAREER: Oberlin College, Oberlin, Ohio, assistant professor of philosophy, 1960-63; University of Illinois at Chicago Circle, Chicago, assistant professor, 1965-66, associate professor, 1966-69, professor of philosophy, 1969—. Visiting assistant professor of philosophy at Stanford University, summer, 1963, and University of Washington, 1963-64; visiting professor of philosophy, Sir George Williams University, summer, 1969. *Military service:* U.S. Army, 1953-56. *Member:* American Philosophical Association, American Civil Liberties Union, National Association for the Advancement of Colored People.

WRITINGS: (Contributor) Stuart Hampshire, editor, *Philosophy of Mind*, Harper, 1966; (contributor) Robert Bronaugh, Antonio Marras, and Robert Binkley, editors, *Agent, Action, and Reason*, University of Toronto Press, 1971; (contributor) G. W. Mortimore, editor, *Weakness of Will*, Macmillan, 1971; *Enigmas of Agency: Studies in the Philosophy of Human Action*, Allen & Unwin, 1972; (contributor) R. Wollheim, editor, *Freud*, Doubleday, 1974; (contributor) M. Brand and D. Walton, editors, *Action Theory*, D. Reidel, 1976; *Perception, Emotion and Action*, Blackwell, 1977; (contributor) S. Spicker and T. Englehardt, editors, *Mental Health: Philosophical Perspectives*, D. Reidel, 1978. Contributor to proceedings and symposia and to *Encyclopedia of Philosophy*; contributor of articles and reviews to philosophy journals in the United States and abroad, including *Analysis, Journal of Philosophy, Mind, Scientia, Philosophy and Phenomenological Research, Dialogue*, and *Theoria*.

WORK IN PROGRESS: Contributing to *In Search of Self*.

* * *

THALHEIMER, Ross 1905-1977

PERSONAL: Born November 21, 1905, in Baltimore, Md.; son of Samson (a businessman) and Merla (Friedenwald) Thalheimer; married Geraldine Woods, 1930 (divorced, 1936); married Helen Kehlman (a piano teacher), 1951. *Education:* Johns Hopkins University, A.B., 1925, Ph.D., 1929; Cambridge University, additional study, 1925-26, and 1932-33; further study at Columbia University, American Psychoanalytic Institute, and Postgraduate Center for Mental Health, 1946-48. *Politics:* Independent. *Religion:* Jewish ("non-practicing"). *Home:* 161 West 54th St., No. 301, New

York, N.Y. 10019. *Office:* American Institute for Psychotherapy and Psychoanalysis, 140 West 58th St., New York, N.Y. 10019.

CAREER: Johns Hopkins University, Baltimore, Md., instructor in philosophy, 1927-28, 1929-30, 1936-37; University of Washington, Seattle, instructor in philosophy and sociology, 1928-29; Johns Hopkins University, fellow, 1934-35; University of Baltimore, Baltimore, professor of psychology and sociology, 1935-37; American Federation of Teachers, Washington, D.C., legislative representative, 1938-40; private practice as psychotherapist, New York, N.Y., beginning 1946. Founder and director of Community Guidance Service, Inc., New York, N.Y., beginning 1953, American Institute for Psychotherapy and Psychoanalysis, beginning 1960, and International Council on the Psychological Dangers to World Peace, beginning 1960. Gave series of radio lectures on WBAL, 1935-36, and WOR, 1958-60. President of Thalheimer Foundation, Inc., 1957-77; donor of annual Thalheimer Awards to National Association for the Advancement of Colored People, 1944-77, and National Urban League, 1947-61. *Military service:* U.S. Army, 1941-46; became staff sergeant. *Member:* American Psychological Association (fellow), American Philosophical Association.

WRITINGS: A Critical Examination of the Epistemological and Psychophysical Doctrines of Bertrand Russell, Williams & Wilkins, 1931; *Reflections: Biopsychological, Psychoanalytic, Philosophical, Socio-Political, Aesthetic and Personal,* Philosophical Library, 1972. Contributor to philosophy, psychology, and education journals. Editor, *Washington Newsletter,* 1939-40.

WORK IN PROGRESS: A collection of poems.

SIDELIGHTS: Ross Thalheimer told *CA* that his interests "range from philosophy to animal behavior and from psychotherapy to trees." Thalheimer ran for a seat in the U.S. Congress as an independent candidate in 1936.†

(Died February 20, 1977)

* * *

THEEN, Rolf H(einz) W(ilhelm) 1937-

PERSONAL: Born February 20, 1937, in Stadthagen, Germany; naturalized U.S. citizen in 1962; son of Walter (a clerk) and Gertrud (Tysper) Theen; married Norma Plunkett, June 14, 1959; children: Tanya Sue, Terrell Rene. *Education:* Manchester College, B.A. (magna cum laude), 1959; Indiana University, M.A., 1962, Russian area certificate (with distinction), 1962, Ph.D., 1964; graduate study at University of Amsterdam, 1962-63, and University of Geneva, 1963; postdoctoral study at Moscow State University, 1967-68. *Home:* 717 Orchard Dr., Lafayette, Ind. 47905. *Office:* Department of Political Science, Purdue University, West Lafayette, Ind. 47907.

CAREER: Iowa State University, Ames, assistant professor, 1964-67, associate professor of political science, 1968-70; Purdue University, West Lafayette, Ind., associate professor, 1971-73, professor of political science, 1974—. *Member:* American Political Science Association, American Association for the Advancement of Slavic Studies, Tau Kappa Alpha. *Awards, honors:* American Philosophical Society research grants at Hoover Institution on War, Revolution and Peace, summer, 1965, 1970; Iowa State University travel grant, 1966; Inter-University Committee on Travel Grants grant, 1967-68, for study at Moscow State University; Sciences and Humanities Research Institute grant at Iowa State University, summer, 1969; Wilton Park

Award for International Service, 1970; American Council of Learned Societies and Social Research Council grant at International Institute for Social History, Amsterdam, spring and summer, 1971; Purdue Research Foundation, faculty research grant, summer, 1972, international travel grant, summer, 1973; National Endowment for the Humanities senior fellowship, 1975; Woodrow Wilson International Center for Scholars fellowship at Kennan Institute for Advanced Russian Studies, summer, 1976.

WRITINGS: (Editor, translator, and author of foreword) N. Valentinov, *The Early Years of Lenin,* University of Michigan Press, 1969; *Lenin: Genesis and Development of a Revolutionary,* Lippincott, 1973. Contributor to *Canadian Slavic Studies, World Politics, Canadian-American Slavic Studies, Problems of Communism, Problemas Internacionales, Russian Review, Jahrbuecher fuer Geschichte Osteuropas, American Political Science Review, Slavic Review, Annals of the American Academy of Political and Social Science,* and *Journal of Modern History.* Corresponding editor, *Canadian-American Slavic Studies,* 1972—; political science editor, *Soviet Union/L'Union Sovietique,* 1972—; contributing editor, *American Bibliography of Slavic and East European Studies,* 1972-73.

WORK IN PROGRESS: The Political Ideas of P. N. Tkachev; The Jacobin Tradition in Russian Social Thought: From the Decembrists to Lenin.

AVOCATIONAL INTERESTS: Gardening, music, stamp collecting.

* * *

THEIS, Paul A(nthony) 1923-

PERSONAL: Surname is pronounced "Tice"; born February 14, 1923, in Fort Wayne, Ind.; son of Albert Peter (a businessman) and Josephine Mary (Kinn) Theis; married Nancy Ann Wilbur, August 21, 1971; children: Mitchell Albert. *Education:* University of Notre Dame, B.A., 1948; Georgetown University, B.S., 1949; American University, further study, 1949-52. *Politics:* Republican. *Religion:* Roman Catholic. *Home:* 2903 Garfield St. N.W., Washington, D.C. 20008. *Office:* 1301 Longworth House Office Bldg., Washington, D.C. 20515.

CAREER: Army Times, Washington, D.C., reporter, 1949-50; Fairchild Publications, Washington, D.C., reporter, 1950-53; *Newsweek,* Washington, D.C., correspondent, 1953-54; executive assistant to a member of U.S. Congress, Washington, D.C., 1955-57; Republican Congressional Committee, Washington, D.C., director of public relations, 1957-74; executive editor to President Gerald R. Ford, 1974-76; U.S. Department of Agriculture, Washington, D.C., deputy undersecretary of agriculture for congressional and public affairs, 1976-77; U.S. House of Representatives, Washington, D.C., staff consultant, 1977—. *Military service:* U.S. Army Air Forces, 1943-46; became major; received Air Medal with two oak leaf clusters. *Member:* Public Relations Society of America, National Press Club, Capitol Hill Club, Congressional Flying Club, Notre Dame Alumni Association, Georgetown Alumni Association.

WRITINGS: (Editor with Edmund Henshaw) *Who's Who in American Politics,* Bowker, 1968-76; (with William Steponkus) *All about Politics,* Bowker, 1972.

SIDELIGHTS: Paul A. Theis invented, with Donald Zahn, "Hat in the Ring," a political game.

THEODORATUS, Robert J(ames) 1928-

PERSONAL: Born June 24, 1928, in Bellingham, Wash.; son of Harry James (a laborer) and Ethel Irene (House) Theodoratus; married M. Kathleen Uribe (a free-lance writer), August 9, 1962; children: Sarah Elena, Amelia Elizabeth, Demetri Hilario. *Education:* State College of Washington (now Washington State University), B.A., 1950; University of Washington, M.A., 1953, Ph.D., 1961. *Religion:* Greek Orthodox. *Home:* 726 Mathews, Fort Collins, Colo. 80521. *Office:* Department of Anthropology, Colorado State University, Fort Collins, Colo. 80521.

CAREER: Sacramento State College (now California State University, Sacramento), assistant professor of anthropology, 1962-66; Colorado State University, Fort Collins, associate professor of anthropology, 1966—. *Member:* Royal Anthropological Institute of Great Britain and Ireland, Folklore Society (London), Polynesian Society, American Anthropological Association, American Association for the Advancement of Science, American Ethnological Society, Society for Folk Life Studies.

WRITINGS: Europe: A Selected Ethnographic Bibliography, Human Relations Area Files Press, 1969; *A Greek Community in America: Tacoma, Washington,* Sacramento Anthropological Society, 1971; (editor) Ruth Benedict, *Rumanian Culture and Behavior,* Department of Anthropology, Colorado State University, 1972.

WORK IN PROGRESS: An edition of *W. Sieroszewskii: The Yakut* (translated from Russian), originally published in St. Petersburgh in 1896.

* * *

THEODORE, Athena 1919-

PERSONAL: Born January 24, 1919, in Nashua, N.H.; daughter of Michael (a tailor) and Mary (Karvelas) Rentoumis; married Chris A. Theodore (a professor), September 8, 1951; children: Arthur, Suzanne, Stuart. *Education:* State Teachers College at Salem (now Salem State College), B.S., 1941; Boston University, M.Ed., 1950, M.A., 1951, Ph.D., 1956. *Home and office:* 27 Turning Mill Rd., Lexington, Mass. 02173.

CAREER: Simmons College, Boston, Mass., instructor, 1956-61, assistant professor, 1961-67, associate professor, 1967-73, professor of sociology, 1973—. *Military service:* U.S. Naval Reserve, 1943-46; became lieutenant. *Member:* American Sociological Association, American Economic Association, American Association of University Professors, American Statistical Association, Society for the Study of Social Problems, Eastern Sociological Association, Massachusetts Sociological Association (president, 1975-76).

WRITINGS: (Editor) *The Professional Woman,* Schenkman, 1971. Contributor to professional journals.

WORK IN PROGRESS: Academic Women in Protest.

* * *

THIESSEN, John (Jack) 1931-

PERSONAL: Born April 14, 1931, in DeSalaberry, Manitoba, Canada; son of Peter and Helena (Sawatzky) Thiessen; married Irmgard Kramer (a professor of psychology), August 17, 1961 (divorced); children: John Wolfgang Amadeus, Anita Tamara. *Education:* Attended Mennonite Collegiate Institute, 1952-54, and United College, 1954-56; Marburg University, Ph.D., 1961. *Religion:* Mennonite.

Home address: Box 29, Tourond, Little Bo Peep Haven, Manitoba, Canada. *Office:* Department of German, University of Winnipeg, Winnipeg, Manitoba, Canada.

CAREER: University of Winnipeg, Winnipeg, Manitoba, assistant professor, 1961-67, associate professor, 1967-73, professor of German, 1973—, head of department, 1961-77. Member of board, Winnipeg Symphony, 1977—. *Awards, honors:* Canada Council leave fellowship, 1976-77.

WRITINGS: Studien zum niederdeutschen Wortschatz der kanadischen Mennoniten, Elwert, 1963; *Yiddish in Canada: The Death of a Language?,* Simon & Schuster, 1974; *Mennonite Low German Dictionary,* Elwert, 1977. Contributor of stories in Low German and English to *Mennonite Mirror;* contributor of articles to *Canadian Literature.*

WORK IN PROGRESS: The Origin and Etymology of Mennonite Family Names.

* * *

THIHER, Allen 1941-

PERSONAL: Surname rhymes with "fire"; born April 4, 1941, in Fort Worth, Tex.; son of Ottah A. (a salesman) and Helen (Massy) Thiher. *Education:* University of Texas, B.A., 1963; University of Wisconsin, M.A., 1964, Ph.D., 1968. *Home:* 105 Meadow Lane, Columbia, Mo. 65201. *Office:* Department of Romance Languages, University of Missouri, Columbia, Mo. 65211.

CAREER: Middlebury College, Middlebury, Vt., assistant professor of French, 1969-76; University of Missouri—Columbia, associate professor of French, 1976—. *Member:* Modern Language Association of America, American Association of Teachers of French, American Association of University Professors.

WRITINGS: Celine: The Novel as Delirium, Rutgers University Press, 1972. Contributor of essays to *Modern Fiction, Modern Drama, PMLA, Philological Quarterly, Romance Notes, Literature/Film Quarterly, Dada/Surrealism, Kentucky Quarterly of Romance Studies,* and *Boundary 2.*

WORK IN PROGRESS: A book on modern language theories and contemporary fiction.

* * *

THOMAS, Anna (Irena) 1948-

PERSONAL: Born July 12, 1948, in Stuttgart, Germany; daughter of Jan and Aniela (Kozerski) Thomas. *Education:* University of California, Los Angeles, B.A., 1972. *Residence:* Los Angeles, Calif. 90064. *Agent:* Roberta Pryor, International Creative Management, 40 West 57th St., New York, N.Y. 10019.

CAREER: "A variety of poorly-paid odd jobs which could hardly be called a career of any sort"; free-lance writer and film-maker; film work includes editing, producing, and directing.

WRITINGS: The Vegetarian Epicure, Knopf, Book I, 1972, Book II, 1978. Also author and co-author of several feature screenplays.

WORK IN PROGRESS: Writing another feature screenplay, for Twentieth Century-Fox.

SIDELIGHTS: Anna Thomas told *CA:* "I've been tremendously lucky to be able to make a living doing things that I really enjoy. My film work was a pure labor of love for some years, and is now paying dividends monetarily as well as aesthetically. But I was doubly fortunate: I was able to turn an avocation into a second career by writing cookbooks. My interest in food has provided me not only with many pleasant hours at the table with my friends, but through my books has also supported me during those rough early years of breaking into a film career. The success of these books has delighted me!'' The first book of *The Vegetarian Epicure* was a best seller in the United States and was also published in Great Britain and translated into Spanish and Dutch. Both volumes are also being translated into German.

* * *

THOMAS, Charles W. 1903-1973

September 3, 1903—March 3, 1973; retired Coast Guard rear admiral, polar explorer and ice-breaking expert, war hero, and writer on his experiences. Obituaries: *New York Times*, March 10, 1973.

* * *

THOMAS, Jack Ray 1931-

PERSONAL: Born December 23, 1931, in Youngstown, Ohio; son of Ira Crebs (a factory worker) and Hazel (Mc-Laughlin) Thomas; married Darlene Slaven, December 28, 1957; children: Jack Ray Jr., Kurt Eric, Bradley Ira. *Education:* Youngstown University, B.A., 1954; Kent State University, M.A., 1960; Ohio State University, Ph.D., 1962. *Home:* 1054 Bourgogne Ave., Bowling Green, Ohio 43402. *Office:* 202 Williams Hall, Department of History, Bowling Green State University, Bowling Green, Ohio 43403.

CAREER: Wisconsin State University (now University of Wisconsin—Eau Claire), Eau Claire, assistant professor of Latin American history, 1962-65; Bowling Green State University, Bowling Green, Ohio, associate professor of Latin American history, 1965—. *Military service:* U.S. Army, 1954-56. *Member:* American Historical Association, Conference on Latin American History, Latin American Studies Association, Midwest Council for Latin American Studies, Ohio Academy of History. *Awards, honors:* National Endowment for the Humanities fellowship, 1968.

WRITINGS: Latin America, Oxford Book Co., 1972; (with Louis Patsouras) *Varieties and Problems of Twentieth-Century Socialism,* Nelson Hall, 1979. Contributor to *Hispanic American Historical Review, Journal of Inter-American Studies, Historian, Social Science,* and *Americas*.

WORK IN PROGRESS: Nineteenth-Century Latin American Historiography; Abroad in Yankeeland: Latin American Travelers in Nineteenth-Century United States.

* * *

THOMAS, Norman L(ee) 1925-

PERSONAL: Born January 24, 1925, in San Fernando, Calif.; son of Ollie L. (a railroad engineer) and Lillian (Gillespie) Thomas; married Marjorie O'Brien (a teacher), November 28, 1953; children: Brian L., Lynn M., Cheryl A., Timothy N. *Education:* University of California, Berkeley, B.A., 1955, M.A., 1959; Claremont University Center (now Claremont Graduate School), Ph.D., 1970. *Politics:* Democrat. *Religion:* Unitarian Universalist. *Home:* 1209 North C St., Indianola, Iowa 50125. *Office:* Department of Philosophy, Simpson College, Indianola, Iowa 50125.

CAREER: Teacher of mathematics in Danville, Calif., 1956-60; California State College, Bakersfield, associate professor, 1960-65, professor of philosophy, 1965-69, head of department, 1967-69; Simpson College, Indianola, Iowa, professor of philosophy, 1969—, head of department, 1971—. Owner of Top Flying Service, 1972—. Chairman of

media committee, Iowa Humanities Board. Producer of three films. *Military service:* U.S. Navy, 1943-46, 1951-55; carrier pilot; became lieutenant. *Member:* American Philosophical Association, History of Science Society, American Association of University Professors (local president, 1965-67, 1971-73), American Association for the Advancement of Science.

WRITINGS: Modern Logic, Barnes & Noble, 1966, 3rd revised edition, Harper, 1968; *Voices of South Dakota* (poetry), South Dakota State Poetry Society, 1977. Also author of *Lyrical Iowa,* Iowa Poetry Association, 1973-78, and *Brochure of Poems,* Iowa Poetry Day Association, 1976-78.

WORK IN PROGRESS: Introduction to Ethics and Problems of Morality; Systematic Ethics and *Practical Morality; The Sound of His Own Grunt,* a collection of poetry.

SIDELIGHTS: Norman Thomas told *CA:* ''My writing interests are in ethics, poetry, and the history and philosophy of science. In the latter I express, essentially, the views of Thomas S. Kuhn under whom I studied at the University of California at Berkeley. I describe my ethical philosophy as existential pragmatism, which means for me a kind of consistent relativism that is founded upon the recognition of moral diversity coupled with the need for personal commitment and the honest acceptance of full responsibility for one's being and one's actions.

''I am not necessarily a traditionalist in the field of poetry, but I do appreciate structure and form and find it a challenge that is amply rewarded when I can compose a poem that expresses with integrity some of my deepest feelings within the rigorous requirements of a sonnet scheme or a rhyming couplet. I do not deprecate the contemporary move toward non-structure and licentious verse, but I approach it with caution and a fair degree of suspicion.''

* * *

THOMAS, William L(eRoy, Jr.) 1920-

PERSONAL: Born March 18, 1920, in Long Beach, Calif.; son of William LeRoy (an attorney) and Margaret Lucile (Young) Thomas; married Mildred Phyllis Smith, April 10, 1942 (divorced August 28, 1964); married Loida Ayson Aquino, August 29, 1964; children: (first marriage) Barbara Jean, Lawrence Charles, Virginia Jane, Margaret Joan, Pamela June; (second marriage) William John Aquino, Lloyd Aquino Thomas. *Education:* University of California, Los Angeles, A.B., 1941, M.A., 1948; Yale University, Ph.D., 1955. *Home:* 758 Muirfield Ct., Hayward, Calif. 94544. *Office:* Department of Geography, California State University, Hayward, Calif. 94542.

CAREER: Vega Aircraft Corp., Burbank, Calif., bill of materials clerk, 1941-42; Rutgers University, New Brunswick, N.J., instructor in geology and geography, 1947-50; Yale University, New Haven, Conn., research assistant, 1949-50; Wenner-Gren Foundation for Anthropological Research, New York, N.Y., assistant director of research, 1950-57; University of California, Riverside, assistant professor, 1957-63, associate professor of geography, 1963; California State University, Hayward, professor of anthropology and geography, 1963-71, professor of geography and Southeast Asian studies, 1971—, chairman of department, 1963-66, 1971-74. Lecturer in geography, Yale University, 1955-56; visiting professor at University of Nevada, summer, 1964, Louisiana State University, spring, 1966, University of Hawaii, summer, 1966, University of Wisconsin—Madison, fall, 1966, and University of Toronto, fall, 1968, 1969; guest lecturer, University of Minnesota, 1966;

visiting research associate, Institute of Philippine Culture (Ateneo de Manila University), 1969-70, 1976-77. Organizer of international symposium, "Man's Role in Changing the Face of the Earth," 1955. Field research in Philippines, 1961-62, 1976-77, and Philippines, Thailand, and Burma, 1970. Geographer and consultant, Pacific Missile Range, U.S. Navy, 1968, 1969. Consultant to Economic Cooperation Administration, 1950-51, and National Academy of Sciences-National Research Council, 1957, 1971-73. *Military service:* U.S. Army, Corps of Engineers, 1942-45; served in Australia, New Guinea, and Philippines; became first lieutenant.

MEMBER: Association of American Geographers (chairman of New York Metropolitan Division, 1954-55; Pacific coast regional councilor, 1971-74), Asia Society, Association for Asian Studies, Association of Pacific Coast Geographers (president, 1977-78), Pacific Science Association (member of scientific committee on geography, 1961-65, 1971-75), California Council for Geographic Education (president, 1967-68), Asian Studies Council of California State Colleges (chairman, 1971-72). *Awards, honors:* Citation for meritorious contribution to field of geography from Association of American Geographers, 1961, for *Man's Role in Changing the Face of the Earth* and *Man, Time, and Space in Southern California;* Fulbright senior scholar, University of Western Australia, 1974.

WRITINGS: (With John F. Embree) *Ethnic Groups of Northern Southeast Asia,* with maps, Southeast Asia Studies, Yale University, 1950; (with Anna M. Pikelis) *International Directory of Anthropological Institutions,* Wenner-Gren Foundation, 1953; (with J. E. Spencer) *Asia East by South: A Cultural Geography,* Wiley, 1954, 2nd edition, 1971; (editor) *Yearbook of Anthropology: 1955,* Wenner-Gren Foundation, 1955; (editor) *Current Anthropology,* University of Chicago Press, 1956; (editor) *Man's Role in Changing the Face of the Earth,* University of Chicago Press, for Wenner-Gren Foundation and National Science Foundation, 1956; *Land, Man, and Culture in Mainland Southeast Asia,* privately printed, 1957; *Academic Master Plan to 1970 for the Riverside Campus, University of California,* Chancellor's Advisory Committee on Academic Master Plan, University of California, 1959; (editor, author of introduction, and contributor of maps, diagrams, and photographs) *Man, Time, and Space in Southern California,* Association of American Geographers, 1959.

Pacific Air Transport (monograph), with maps, University of California, Riverside, 1960; (contributor) F. R. Fosberg, editor, *Man's Place in the Island Ecosystem,* Bishop Museum Press, 1963; (contributor) Glenn Cunningham, editor, *Day Tours: Geographical Journeys in the Los Angeles Area,* Pacific Books, 1964; *The Science of Geography,* National Academy of Sciences-National Research Council, 1965; (contributor) Herman R. Friis, editor, *The Pacific Basin: A History of Its Geographical Exploration,* American Geographical Society, 1967; (editor) *Improving the Education of Teachers of Geography* (brochure), California State Department of Education, for Geography Panel of Statewide Social Sciences Study Committee, 1967; (contributor) Andrew P. Vayda, editor, *Peoples and Cultures of the Pacific,* Natural History Press, 1968; *Academic Master Plan to 1978 for California State College, Hayward,* Committee on College Policy and Academic Development, California State College, Hayward, 1968; (with J. E. Spencer) *Cultural Geography: An Evolutionary Introduction to Our Humanized Earth,* with instructor's manual, Wiley, 1969; (editor) *Academic Master Plan to 1978: California State*

College, Hayward, Office of the President, California State College, Hayward, 1969.

Introducing Cultural Geography, Wiley, 1973, 2nd edition, 1978; *Paths to Asia: Asian Studies at Australian Universities,* Centre for Asian Studies, University of Western Australia, 1974. Also author of monograph, *The Ilocano Environment.*

Contributor of maps: Andrew H. Clark, *The Invasion of New Zealand by People, Plants, and Animals,* Rutgers University Press, 1949; John Lloyd Stephens, *Incidents of Travel in Central America, Chiapas, and Yucatan,* edited by Richard N. Predmore, two volumes, Rutgers University Press, 1950.

Editor of library brochures, all published by University of California, Riverside, in 1960: Robert E. Frenkel, *Adak, Alaska;* Frenkel, *Anchorage, Alaska;* Frenkel, *Attu, Alaska;* Thomas E. Thorp, *Biak Island, Netherlands New Guinea;* Elliot G. McIntire, *Canton Island, Phoenix Islands;* Alvin W. Urquhart, *Christmas Island, Indian Ocean;* Urquhart, *Cocos (Keeling) Islands, Indian Ocean;* Richard I. Gates, *Dutch Harbor, Alaska;* John M. Street, *Emirau Harbor, Bismarck Archipelago;* Street, *Eniwetok Island, Marshall Islands;* Frenkel, *Fairbanks, Alaska;* McIntire, *Hawaiian Islands;* Thorp, *Johnston Island;* McIntire, *Kapingamarangi Atoll, Caroline Islands;* Frenkel and Gates, *Ketchikan, Alaska;* Gates, *Kodiak, Alaska;* Urquhart, *Majuro Atoll, Marshall Islands;* Street, *Manus Island, Admiralty Islands;* Thorp, *Midway Islands;* Frenkel, *Nome, Alaska;* John H. Winslow, *San Nicolas Island, Ventura County;* Gates, *Sitka, Alaska;* McIntire, *Taongi Atoll, Marshall Islands;* McIntire, *Tutuila Island, American Samoa;* Thorp, *Waigeo Island, Netherlands New Guinea;* Thorp, *Wake Island.*

Editor, "Man and Environment," series in geography, Duxbury, 1969-75. Contributor to reports and to *Encyclopaedia Britannica.* Contributor of more than forty-six articles and reviews to professional journals, including *Geographical Review, California Geographer, Science, Manila Chronicle* (U.S. edition), *Landscape, Professional Geographer, Ethnohistory, American Sociological Review, American Anthropologist, Canadian Geographer, Economic Geography, Philippines Geographical Journal,* and *Yearbook* of the Association of Pacific Coast Geographers. Editor, *Bulletin* of American Anthropological Association, 1958-59.

AVOCATIONAL INTERESTS: Travel, hiking, gardening, family activities.

*   *   *

THOMLINSON, Ralph   1925-

PERSONAL: Born February 12, 1925, in St. Louis, Mo.; son of Ralph (a singer and actor) and Ora (Barr) Thomlinson; married Margaret Willits, December 21, 1946; children: Elizabeth B., William L. *Education:* Oberlin College, B.A., 1948; Yale University, M.A., 1949; Columbia University, Ph.D., 1960. *Office:* Department of Sociology, California State University, Los Angeles, Calif. 90032.

CAREER: Assistant city planner in Montclair, N.J., 1949-50, and Paterson, N.J., 1950; medical actuarial statistics assistant, Metropolitan Life Insurance Co., 1952-53; University of Wisconsin—Madison, instructor in statistics, 1953-56; Denison University, Granville, Ohio, instructor in sociology and anthropology, 1956-59; California State University, Los Angeles, assistant professor, 1959-62, associate professor, 1962-65, professor of sociology, 1965—, chairman of department, 1967-69. Academic visitor, London School of Economics and Political Science, University of London, 1973; visiting scholar, National Institute for Demographic Study, Paris, France, 1973-74. Demographic adviser, Institute of Population Studies, Chulalongkorn University, Bangkok, Thailand, 1969-71; resident adviser, Center for Demographic Research and Study, Rabat, Morocco, 1972-73. Short-term consultant to research centers in Kenya, Philippines, Korea, Taiwan, Singapore, Egypt, and Hong Kong, 1969-73. *Military service:* U.S. Army, 1943-45; served in France and Germany. *Member:* International Union for Scientific Study of Population, Population Association of America, American Sociological Association (fellow), International Association of Survey Statisticians, Association for Asian Studies.

WRITINGS: Population Dynamics: Causes and Consequences of World Demographic Change, Random House, 1965, 2nd edition, 1976; *Sociological Concepts and Research,* Random House, 1965; *Demographic Problems: Controversy over Population Control,* Dickenson, 1967, 2nd edition, 1975; *Urban Structure: The Social and Spatial Character of Cities,* Random House, 1969; *Thailand's Population: Facts, Trends, Problems, and Policies,* Thai Watana Panich Press Co., 1971; (editor with Visid Prachuabmoh) *The Potharam Study,* Chulalongkorn University, 1971; (with Prachuabmoh and Lincoln Polissar) *The Methodology of the Longitudinal Study of Social, Economic, and Demographic Change,* Chulalongkorn University, 1971. Contributor of articles to social science and statistics journals.

SIDELIGHTS: Ralph Thomlinson comments: "Most people think there is a special knack to being a writer—a quirk of emotional or mental ability that somehow enables an otherwise ordinary person to phrase sentences that others want to read. 'Oh, what a book I could write if only I could put it down on paper.' Or, 'I have a great idea for a book; all I need is somebody to write it down for me.' Like calling in a TV repairman.

"As a part-time writer of scholarly and college text books, I offer my own experience to aspiring writers who have to hold down a full-time job. A prerequisite is interest. The subject must be fascinating and I must learn something new while writing. If I try to write primarily for the income or for the lure of siring a thing that stands unaided on a shelf, I lose interest and never finish Chapter I. That said, how does one find the time?

"Start during a vacation. Work ten to twelve hours a day, never quitting before midnight and sometimes continuing to five A.M. Do this seven days a week. Back on the job, there are some free evenings and weekends. Keep at the early A.M. quitting time three or four days a week, and don't waste Saturday afternoons at golf. Stick to this schedule for a month or two, then knock off for a few months to renew the energy cells; repeat this cycle until you have a completed manuscript. (My longest book required three years of elapsed time to write, including 18 months of actual writing; my shortest, ten months elapsed and 6 weeks writing.) But don't try it unless you have the will power to work when tired and the stamina never to break down—or at least the drive to get back to the desk the following day. If possible, never get sick or sociable for more than a few hours at a time.

"So you see, the magic ingredients in my type of writing are not hard to define: knowledge and hard work. If you have the experience to know something worth saying, then place

yourself before a blank sheet of paper (and there is nothing more humbling than a blank page), take up some kind of writing implement, and proceed to fill the page with words. Since they won't look impressive the first time, you then cast that page into the wastebasket and try again until satisfied that the words convey a thought clearly and not too dully. Repeat, as the teacher says, five hundred times. Then you are a writer. A very tired person, but a writer."

*   *   *

THOMPSON, A(lbert) Gray 1928-

PERSONAL: Born December 5, 1928, in San Francisco, Calif.; son of Albert Gray (a welder) and Marie (Herrmann) Thompson; married F. Carolyn Hinton (a teacher), July 6, 1957; children: Albert III, Michael, Ann, Christopher, Mark. *Education:* University of Santa Clara, A.B., 1951; University of San Francisco, M.A., 1953; University of California, Berkeley, Ed.D., 1965. *Home address:* Box 154C, Route 2, Campbellsport, Wis. 53010. *Office:* Department of Education, Marquette University, Nicolas Hall, Milwaukee, Wis. 53233.

CAREER: Teacher in public schools of Redwood City, Calif., 1953-59, elementary school principal, 1959-66; Marquette University, Milwaukee, Wis., director of student teaching, 1967-71, director of teacher education, 1971—. Fulbright-Hays scholar, Ministry of Education and Anahuac University, Mexico, 1979. *Member:* National Education Association, American Association of University Professors, Phi Delta Kappa (president, 1970).

WRITINGS: Readings for Curriculum Workers, Associated Educational Services, 1969; (with Margaret Gillespie) *Social Studies for Living in a Multi-Ethnic Society,* C. E. Merrill, 1973; (with Richard Mevissen) *Teaching and Catechesis,* Redemptorist Fathers (Waterford, Wisc.), 1977. Also author, with Russell H. Ziemer, of *Impact of Collective Bargaining on Curriculum Instruction,* 1975. Contributor to *Catholic Education Review, Phi Delta Kappan,* and *American Journal of Medical Technology.* Editor of *Marquette University Education Review,* fall, 1971.

*   *   *

THOMPSON, Dennis L. 1935-

PERSONAL: Born February 20, 1935, in Preston, Idaho; son of Ivan Hall (a farmer) and Ella (Lundquist) Thompson; married Karen Chatterton, September 17, 1958; children: Catherine, Nan, Jennifer, Benjamin Alexander, Elizabeth Anne, Thomas Christian, Ian Hall. *Education:* University of Idaho, B.A., 1960; Arizona State University, M.A., 1961; University of California, Santa Barbara, Ph.D., 1968. *Politics:* Republican. *Religion:* Church of Jesus Christ of Latter-day Saints. *Home:* 215 East 140 N., Lindon, Utah 84062. *Office:* Department of Government, Brigham Young University, Provo, Utah 84602.

CAREER: Farmer in Weston, Idaho, 1952-53, 1958-59; Office of the Governor, Phoenix, Ariz., staff assistant, 1959-60; U.S. Department of State, Washington, D.C., foreign service officer, 1962-65; University of California, Santa Barbara, lecturer in political science, 1966-67; University of Arizona, Tucson, assistant professor of political science, 1967-70; University of Utah, Salt Lake City, assistant professor of political science, 1970-73; State University of New York at Binghamton, associate professor of political science, 1973-77; Brigham Young University, Provo, Utah, professor of public policy, 1977—. *Military service:* U.S. Army, 1960-62; became first lieutenant. *Member:* American

Society for Public Administration (president of local New York chapter, 1976), Policy Studies Organization, Western Political Science Association, Pacific Northwest Conference on International Relations (president, 1955).

WRITINGS: (With Vincent Marando) *The Metropolitan County in Arizona,* University of Arizona Press, 1971; (editor) *Politics, Policy, and Natural Resources,* Free Press, 1972; (with Benjamin Chinitz) *Local Planning and Special Revenue Sharing,* New York Institute, 1975; *Taxation of American Railroads,* National Science Foundation, 1978. Contributor to *Western Political Quarterly, Pacific Northwest Quarterly, Journal of Church and State,* and *Journal of Police Science and Administration.* Associate editor of *Western Political Quarterly,* 1972—.

WORK IN PROGRESS: Research on private performance of public functions.

* * *

THOMPSON, Jack Maynard 1924-

PERSONAL: Born May 3, 1924, in Santa Rosa, Calif.; son of Melvin Moore (a professional golfer) and Violet (Moore) Thompson; married Margaret R. Toleman (a probation officer), June 1, 1951; children: Terry, Laurie, Tammy. *Education:* San Jose State College (now University), A.B., 1949, M.A., 1950; University of California, Berkeley, Ed.D., 1967. *Politics:* Independent. *Home:* 5838 Monte Verde Dr., Santa Rosa, Calif. 95405. *Office:* Sonoma County Office of Education, 2555 Mendocino Ave., Room 111E, Santa Rosa, Calif. 95401.

CAREER: Psychologist and superintendent of special education in public schools in Nevada City, Calif., 1953-56; Sonoma County Office of Education, Santa Rosa, Calif., psychologist and director of curriculum services, 1956—. Diplomate in school psychology, American Board of Professional Psychology. Associate professor, San Jose State College (now University), 1967. Consultant, Sonoma County Probation Department, 1960—. *Military service:* U.S. Navy, 1942-46, 1951-53; became lieutenant commander; received Air Medals. *Member:* American Psychological Association, California Guidance and Personnel Association, California Association for Counselor Education and Supervision, California Teachers Association, Psi Chi, Phi Delta Kappa. *Awards, honors:* California Association of Measurement and Guidance research award, 1968.

WRITINGS: (With Carmen Finley) *California Abbreviated WISC,* West Psychological Service, 1966; (with Robert Sones) *Education Apperception Test,* West Psychological Service, 1972. Author of research reports; contributor to education and psychology journals.

* * *

THOMPSON, Josiah 1935-

PERSONAL: Born January 17, 1935, in East Liverpool, Ohio; son of Josiah D. (a salesman) and Marion (Postles) Thompson; married Nancy Willis, December 27, 1958; children: Lis, Everson. *Education:* Yale University, B.A., 1957, M.A., 1962, Ph.D., 1964. *Agent:* Gerard McCauley, P.O. Box 456, Cranbury, N.J. 08512. *Office:* Department of Philosophy, Haverford College, Haverford, Pa. 19041.

CAREER: Yale University, New Haven, Conn., instructor in philosophy, 1964-65; Haverford College, Haverford, Pa., assistant professor, 1965-70, associate professor, 1970-76, professor of philosophy, 1976—. Consultant to *Life* magazine on the assassination of President John F. Kennedy.

Military service: U.S. Naval Reserve, 1957-59; became lieutenant junior grade. *Member:* American Association of University Professors. *Awards, honors:* Guggenheim fellow, 1969-70.

WRITINGS: The Lonely Labyrinth, Southern Illinois University Press, 1967; *Six Seconds in Dallas,* Geis, 1967; (editor) *Kierkegaard: A Collection of Critical Essays,* Doubleday, 1972; *Kierkegaard,* Knopf, 1973.

WORK IN PROGRESS: An untitled novel; a critical biography of Friedrich Nietzsche.

SIDELIGHTS: Josiah Thompson's second book, *Six Seconds in Dallas,* is the result of his exhaustive research on the assassination of President John F. Kennedy. Calvin Trillin says that in the course of this research Thompson "learned to use an Abney level, a tool valuable in measuring angles, including the trajectories of bullets, and he has gone to Dallas, stood on Elm Street, early on Sunday morning when the traffic is light, and measured the angle from the sixth floor of the Texas School Book Depository.... Although his interest in firearms had never extended past what he was required to learn in the Navy, he now owns a display board of the various types of bullets that could have theoretically been used in the assassination, and a rifle of the type Oswald was said to have used, so that he can personally get some idea of how its bolt operates."

A. V. Krebs, Jr., writes that in *Six Seconds in Dallas* Thompson "chooses to concentrate solely on the six important seconds in Dealy Plaza. Using sketches of the important Abraham Zapruder film (*Life,* owner of the original print refused Thompson permission to reproduce the individual frames), 21 other known still and motion pictures taken in the plaza, and numerous drawings and charts (all conveniently appearing alongside the relevant text), Thompson carefully and systematically shows how the [Warren] Commission's 'single bullet theory' is implausible, i.e., the same bullet which first hit Kennedy could not have also wounded Texas Gov. John Connally. Once one admits that Kennedy and Connally were hit separately (because the alleged murder weapon could not possibly reload and fire again that fast), then the presence of two gunmen is inescapable and one therefore by definition has a conspiracy. Thompson, after pointing out the Commission's major errors in evaluating those six crucial seconds, shows how available evidence suggests that there were three riflemen firing at the Presidential motorcade."

Even though Thompson was prohibited by *Life* from reproducing frames of the famous Zapruder film, he did, as Fred J. Cook points out, have "one great advantage. He happened to be employed as an adviser by *Life,* and *Life* possessed the original of the Zapruder film, which few persons have seen. The film in the National Archives in Washington, the one used by the FBI and the Warren Commission, is a copy of a copy—and so not nearly so clear and sharp as the original [that] Thompson was privileged to study."

BIOGRAPHICAL/CRITICAL SOURCES: New Yorker, June 10, 1967; *New York Times,* December 9, 1967; *New York Times Book Review,* February 18, 1968; *Nation,* February 26, 1968; *Commonweal,* September 20, 1968.

* * *

THOMPSON, Lawrance (Roger) 1906-1973

April 3, 1906—April 15, 1973; American educator, curator of rare books and manuscripts, biographer, editor, and author. Obituaries: *Washington Post,* April 17, 1973; *Newsweek,*

April 30, 1973; *Publishers Weekly*, April 30, 1973. (See index for *CA* sketch)

* * *

THOMSON, Douglas Ferguson Scott 1919-

PERSONAL: Born October 13, 1919, in Bridge of Weir, Renfrewshire, Scotland; son of James Scott (a shipbroker) and Louise Ferguson (Pearson) Thomson; married Eleanor Mary Hodgkins, June 27, 1953; children: James, Sarah, Jessica. *Education:* Merton College, Oxford, B.A. (honors), 1946, M.A., 1946. *Home:* 116 Manor Rd. E., Toronto, Ontario, Canada M4S 1P8. *Office:* Department of Classics, University College, University of Toronto, Toronto, Ontario, Canada M5S 1A1.

CAREER: University of Toronto, University College, Toronto, Ontario, lecturer, 1948-54, assistant professor, 1954-62, associate professor, 1962-69, professor of Latin, 1969—. Visiting professor at University of North Carolina, 1967-68. *Military service:* British Army, 1939-45; became captain; Canadian Officers' Training Corps, 1954-60; became major. *Member:* Society for the Promotion of Roman Studies, Classical Association of Canada, American Philological Association.

WRITINGS: (Translator) *Erasmus and Cambridge*, introduction and commentary by H. C. Porter, University of Toronto Press, 1963, revised edition, 1970; (contributor) T. A. Dorey, editor, *Erasmus*, Routledge & Kegan Paul, 1970; (translator) *Collected Works of Erasmus*, University of Toronto Press, 1973—; *Catullus: A Critical Edition*, University of North Carolina Press, 1978.

WORK IN PROGRESS: Research on Catullus, Erasmus, and Renaissance Latin verse.

* * *

THOMSON, S(amuel) Harrison 1895-1975

PERSONAL: Born November 5, 1895, in Pasadena, Calif.; son of Williell (a clergyman) and Clara (Thompson) Thomson; married Rosamund Dargan, January 30, 1936; children: Williell Riddett, Clara Day. *Education:* Princeton University, A.B., 1923; Charles University, Dr.Phil., 1925; Oxford University, B.Litt., 1926. *Politics:* Republican. *Religion:* Presbyterian. *Home and office:* 3639 Broadway, Boulder, Colo. 80302.

CAREER: Princeton University, Princeton, N.J., instructor in Biblical literature, 1926-29; California Institute of Technology, Pasadena, assistant professor of history, 1929-31; American Council of Learned Societies, traveling fellow, 1931-33; University of Chicago, Chicago, Ill., assistant professor of modern history, 1934-35; Carleton College, Northfield, Minn., associate professor of European history, 1935-36, director of admissions, 1935-36; University of Colorado, Boulder, professor of history, 1936-65, professor emeritus, 1965-75, director of Center for Slavic and East European Studies, 1960-64. Visiting professor at University of Michigan, 1941, Indiana University, 1950-51, University of Washington, 1964-65, and University of California, Los Angeles, 1965-66. Fulbright professor at University of Vienna, 1959; Masaryk Lecturer at University of Toronto, 1949. Director of United States Information Service and cultural relations attache, United States Embassy in Warsaw, Poland, 1945-46; special assistant to U.S. Ambassador to Czechoslovakia, 1945. *Military service:* U.S. Army, 1917-19; served in France.

MEMBER: American Historical Association, Mediaeval

Academy of America (fellow; first vice-president, 1959-62), Polish Academy of Sciences (fellow), History of Science Society (member of council, 1947-53), American Council of Learned Societies and Social Science Research Council (member of combined Slavic committee, 1947-51, 1955-59; chairman of Western Slavic Conference, 1963), Polish Institute of Arts and Sciences (honorary fellow), Societe Philosophique de Louvain (associate member), Society of Medieval Languages and Literature, American Society of Church History, Phi Beta Kappa, Town and Gown Club (Boulder). *Awards, honors:* Huntington Library fellow, 1929-30; D.Litt. from Oxford University, 1942; Czechoslovak State Prize for literature, 1944; Haskins Medal from Mediaeval Academy of America, 1951; Institute for Advanced Study fellow, 1955-56.

WRITINGS: (Editor) Jan Hus, *Mistra Jana Husi Tractatus responsivus*, Praha, 1927; *Summa de Ente John Wyclif*, Clarendon Press, 1930; (editor) *Writings of Robert Grosseteste*, Cambridge University Press, 1940; *Czechoslovakia in European History*, Princeton University Press, 1943, revised edition, 1953; (editor with L. I. Strakhovsky) *Handbook of Slavic Studies*, Harvard University Press, 1949; *De Ecclesia Magistri Johannis Hus*, University of Colorado Press, 1956; *Guide to Historical Literature*, American Historical Association, 1961; *Europe in Renaissance and Reformation*, Harcourt, 1963; *Latin Bookhands of the Later Middle Ages*, Cambridge University Press, 1969; *Das Zeitalter der Renaissance von Petrarca bis Erasmus*, Kindler, 1969. Contributor to American and European journals. Editor of *Progress of Medieval Studies in the United States and Canada*, 1937-64, *Journal of Central European Affairs*, 1941-65, and *Medievalia et Humanistica*, 1943-67; member of editorial board, *Slavic and East European Review*, 1941-61.

BIOGRAPHICAL/CRITICAL SOURCES: Lubomyr R. Wynar, *S. Harrison Thomas: A Bio-Bibliography*, University Library, University of Colorado, 1963; Paul M. Clogan, editor, *In Honor of S. Harrison Thomson*, Press of Case Western Reserve University, 1970.†

(Died November 19, 1975)

* * *

THOMSON, Virgil (Garnett) 1896-

PERSONAL: Born November 25, 1896, in Kansas City, Mo.; son of Quincy Alfred (a postal clerk) and Clara May (Gaines) Thomson. *Education:* Junior College of Kansas City (now Metropolitan Junior College—Kansas City), A.A., 1919; Harvard University, A.B., 1922; studied music privately with Nadia Boulanger, 1921-22, and Rosario Scalero and Chalmers Clifton, 1923-24; studied piano under H. Gebhard and organ under W. Goodrich. *Home and office:* 222 West 23rd St., New York, N.Y. 10011.

CAREER: Composer, music critic, and conductor; Harvard University, Cambridge, Mass., assistant instructor in music, 1920-25; King's Chapel, Boston, Mass., organist, 1922-23; lived in Paris, France, 1925-40; *New York Herald Tribune*, New York, N.Y., music critic, 1940-54. Musical director, Friends and Enemies of Modern Music, 1934-37. Schlee Professor of Music, State University of New York at Buffalo, 1963; Regents Professor of Music, University of California, Los Angeles, 1965; Mellon Professor of Music, Carnegie Institute of Technology (now Carnegie-Mellon University), 1966-67; visiting professor of music, Trinity College, Hartford, Conn., 1968. *Military service:* U.S. Aviation Service, 1917-1918; became second lieutenant.

MEMBER: American Academy of Arts and Letters, American Academy of Arts and Sciences (fellow), American Guild of Authors and Composers (member of board, 1957-59), American Society of Composers, Authors and Publishers (member of board of review, 1959-68), American Federation of Musicians, American Guild of Musical Artists, Newspaper Guild. *Awards, honors:* David Bispham Medal for American Opera, 1934, for "Four Saints in Three Acts"; Officer of Legion d'Honneur (France), 1947; Pulitzer Prize in Music, 1949, for film score of "Louisiana Story"; Academic Medal from New York University, 1961; Gold Medal for Music from National Institute of Arts and Letters, 1966; Creative Arts Award from Brandeis University, 1968. D.F.A. from Syracuse University, 1949, Roosevelt University, 1968, and University of Missouri, 1971; Lit.D. from Rutgers University, 1956; L.H.D. from Park College, 1966, and Johns Hopkins University, 1978; Mus.D. from Fairfield University, 1968, New York University, 1971, and Columbia University, 1978.

WRITINGS: The State of Music, Morrow, 1939, reprinted, Greenwood Press, 1974, 2nd edition, Random House, 1961; *The Musical Scene,* Knopf, 1945, reprinted, Greenwood Press, 1968; *The Art of Judging Music,* Knopf, 1948, reprinted, Greenwood Press, 1969; *Music Right and Left,* Holt, 1951, reprinted, Greenwood Press, 1969; *Virgil Thomson* (autobiography), Knopf, 1966; *Music Reviewed, 1940-1954,* Random House, 1967; *American Music since 1910,* Holt, 1971.

Orchestral works: "Two Sentimental Tangos," completed 1923; *Symphony on the Hymn Tune,* completed 1928, Southern Music Publishing Co., 1954; *Symphony No. 2,* completed 1931, published by Belwin-Mills; *Suite from "The Plow That Broke the Plains"* (also see below), completed 1936, published by G. Schirmer; *Suite from "The River"* (also see below), completed 1937, Southern Music Publishing Co., 1958; *Suite from "Filling Station"* (also see below), completed 1937, published by Boosey & Hawkes; "Portraits for Orchestra" (includes *The John Mosher Waltzes,* published by Boosey & Hawkes; "The Mayor LaGuardia Waltzes"; "Canons for Dorothy Thompson"; *Fanfare for France* [arranger; original score by Max Kahn], published by Boosey & Hawkes; *Cantabile for Strings* [arranger; original score by Nicolas de Chatelain], published by G. Schirmer; *Barcarolle for Woodwinds* [arranger; original score by Georges Hugnet], published by G. Schirmer; *Fugue* [arranger; original score by Alexander Smallens], published by G. Schirmer; *Tango Lullaby* [arranger; original score by Flavie Alvarez de Toledo], published by G. Schirmer; "Meditation" [arranger; original score by Jere Abbott]; "Percussion Piece" [arranger; original score by Jessie K. Lasell]; *Bugles and Birds* [arranger; original score by Pablo Picasso], published by G. Schirmer; "Pastorale" [arranger; original score by Aaron Copeland]), completed 1937-44.

Fugue and Chorale on "Yankee Doodle," completed 1945, published by G. Schirmer; *The Seine at Night,* completed 1947, published by G. Schirmer; *Suite from "Louisiana Story"* (also see below), completed 1948, published by G. Schirmer; *Acadian Songs and Dances,* completed 1948, published by G. Schirmer; *Wheat Field at Noon,* completed 1948, published by G. Schirmer; *A Solemn Music for Band,* completed 1949, published by G. Schirmer; "Suite from 'The Mother of Us All'" (also see below), completed 1949; *Sea Piece with Birds,* completed 1952, published by G. Schirmer; (transcriber) Johannes Brahms, *Eleven Chorale-Preludes,* completed 1956, published by Boosey & Hawkes;

"The Lively Arts Fugue," completed 1957; *Fugues and Cantilenas,* completed 1959, published by Boosey & Hawkes; *A Solemn Music for Orchestra,* completed 1961, published by G. Schirmer; *A Joyful Fugue,* completed 1962, published by G. Schirmer; *Ode to the Wonders of Nature,* completed 1965, published by G. Schirmer; *Fantasy in Homage to an Earlier England,* completed 1966, published by G. Schirmer; *Pilgrims and Pioneers,* completed 1964, published by G. Schirmer; *Edges: A Portrait of Robert Indiana,* completed 1969, G. Schirmer, 1972; *Study Piece: Portrait of a Lady,* completed 1969, G. Schirmer, 1972; *Metropolitan Museum Fanfare,* completed 1970, G. Schirmer, 1972; *Third Symphony,* completed 1972, Boosey & Hawkes, 1974.

Choral music: *De Profundis,* completed 1920, published by Weintraub Music Co.; "Sanctus," completed 1921; *Tribulationes Civitatum,* completed 1922, published by Weintraub Music Co.; *Agnus Dei,* completed 1924, published by Theodore Presser; *Three Antiphonal Psalms,* completed 1924, published by MCA Music Corp.; "Fete Polonaise," completed 1924; "Benedictus," completed 1926; *Saints' Procession,* completed 1928, published by G. Schirmer; *Seven Choruses from the "Medea" of Euripides,* completed 1934, published by G. Schirmer; *Missa Brevis,* completed 1934, published by MCA Music Corp.; *My Shepherd Will Supply My Need,* completed 1937, published by H. W. Gray; *Scenes from the Holy Infancy According to Saint Matthew,* completed 1937, published by G. Schirmer; *Welcome to the New Year,* completed 1941, published by Holt; *Surrey Apple Howler's Song,* completed 1941, published by Holt; *The Bugle Song,* completed 1941, published by Holt; *Hymns from the Old South,* completed 1949, published by H. W. Gray.

Kyrie, completed 1953, published by H. W. Gray; *Tiger! Tiger!,* completed 1955, published by F. Colombo; "Song for the Stable," completed 1955; "Never Another," completed 1955; *Crossing Brooklyn Ferry,* completed 1958, published by Boosey & Hawkes; *Missa Pro Defunctis,* completed 1960, published by H. W. Gray; *Dance in Praise,* completed 1962, published by G. Schirmer; *My Master Hath a Garden,* completed 1963, G. Schirmer, 1964; *The Holly and the Ivy,* completed 1963, published by G. Schirmer; *Five Auvergnat Folk Songs from the Cantaloube,* completed 1964, published by Theodore Presser; *When I Survey the Bright Celestial Sphere,* completed 1964, H. W. Gray, 1965; *The Nativity, as Sung by the Shepherds,* completed 1967, published by G. Schirmer; "How Will Ye Have Your Partridge Today?," completed 1967; "A Hymn for Pratt Institute," completed 1968; *Cantata on Poems of Edward Lear,* completed 1974, published by G. Schirmer.

Works for voice; with piano accompaniment, except as indicated: "Vernal Equinox," completed 1920; "The Sunflower," completed 1920; "Three Sentences from the 'Song of Solomon,'" completed 1924; *Susie Asado,* completed 1926, published by Boosey & Hawkes; *The Tiger,* completed 1926, published by G. Schirmer; *Five Phrases from the 'Song of Solomon'"* (with percussion), completed 1926, published by Carl Fischer; *Capital Capitals,* completed 1927, published by Boosey & Hawkes; *Preciosilla,* completed 1927, published by G. Schirmer; *Une Melodie dite "La Valse Gregorienne,"* completed 1927, published by Southern Music Publishing Co.; "A son Altesse la Princesse," completed 1928; *Jour de chaleur aux bains de mer,* completed 1928, Boosey & Hawkes, 1963; *La Seine,* completed 1928, published by Parnassus; *Le Berceau de Gertrude Stein,* completed 1928, published by Southern Music

Publishing Co.; *Commentaire sur Saint Jerome*, completed 1928, published by Southern Music Publishing Co.; "Les Soirees Bagnolaises," completed 1928; *Portrait of F. B.*, completed 1929, published by G. Schirmer; *Le Singe et le Leopard*, completed 1930, Southern Music Publishing Co., 1973; "Oraison Funebre," completed 1930; *Air de Phedre*, completed 1930, Southern Music Publishing Co., 1974; *Film: Deux Soeurs qui ne sont pas soeurs*, completed 1930, published by Southern Music Publishing Co.; "Chamber Music," completed 1931; *La Belle en dormant*, completed 1931, published by Boosey & Hawkes; *Pigeons on the Grass Alas*, completed 1934, published by G. Schirmer; "Go to Sleep, Alexander Smallens, Jr." (unaccompanied), completed 1935; "Go to Sleep, Pare McTaggett Lorentz" (unaccompanied), completed 1937; *Dirge*, completed 1939, published by G. Schirmer; *The Bugle Song*, completed 1941, published by Holt.

Old English Songs, completed 1955, published by H. W. Gray; *Take, O Take Those Lips Away*, completed 1956, published by Southern Music Publishing Co.; *Tell Me Where Is Fancy Bred*, completed 1957, published by Southern Music Publishing Co.; *Was This Fair Face*, completed 1957, published by Southern Music Publishing Co.; *Pardon, Goddess of the Night*, completed 1957, published by Southern Music Publishing Co.; *Sigh No More Ladies*, completed 1957, published by Southern Music Publishing Co.; *Tres Estampas de Ninez*, completed 1957, published by Southern Music Publishing Co.; *If Thou Hast a Reason Dost Desire to Know*, completed 1958, published by Southern Music Publishing Co.; *Mostly about Love*, completed 1959, G. Schirmer, 1964; *Mass for Solo Voice and Piano*, completed 1960, published by G. Schirmer; *Praises and Prayers*, completed 1963, published by G. Schirmer; *Two by Marianne Moore*, completed 1963, published by G. Schirmer; "Love Scene: Juan and Haidee," completed 1967; *From "Sneden's Landing Variations,"* completed 1972, published by Lingua Press; *The Courtship of the Yongly Bongly Bo*, completed 1974, published by G. Schirmer.

Chamber music: *Sonata da Chiesa*, completed 1926, Boosey & Hawkes, 1974; "Portraits for Violin Alone," completed 1928-40; *Five Portraits for Four Clarinets*, completed 1929, published by G. Schirmer; *Le Bains-Bar*, completed 1929, published by Carl Fischer; "Portraits for Violin and Piano," completed 1930-40; *Sonata for Violin and Piano*, completed 1930, published by Boosey & Hawkes; *Stabat Mater*, completed 1931, published by Boosey & Hawkes; *String Quartet No. 1*, completed 1931, published by Boosey & Hawkes; *Serenade for Flute and Violin*, completed 1931, published by Southern Music Publishing Co.; *String Quartet No. 2*, completed 1932, published by Boosey & Hawkes; *Four Portraits for Violoncello and Piano*, completed 1942, published by G. Schirmer; *Sonata for Flute Alone*, completed 1943, published by Theodore Presser; *Three Portraits*, completed 1947, published by G. Schirmer; *At the Beach*, completed 1949, published by Carl Fischer; *Four Songs to Poems of Thomas Campion*, completed 1951, published by Southern Music Publishing Co.; *Concerto for Flute, Strings, Harp and Percussion*, completed 1954, published by F. Colombo; *Lamentations: Etude for Accordion*, completed 1959, published by Santee Music Press; "Variations for Koto," completed 1961; "Etude for Cello and Piano," completed 1966; *Family Portrait*, completed 1974, published by G. Schirmer.

Works for solo piano: "Prelude for Piano," completed 1921; *Synthetic Waltzes*, completed 1925, published by Theodore Presser; *Five Inventions for Piano*, completed 1926, pub-

lished by Theodore Presser; *Ten Easy Pieces and a Coda*, completed 1926, published by Southern Music Publishing Co.; "Piano Sonata No. 1," completed 1929; "Piano Sonata No. 2," completed 1929; *Portraits for Piano Solo*, completed 1929-45, published by G. Schirmer (some also published separately); *Nine Portraits for Piano*, completed 1930-48, Southern Music Publishing Co., 1974; *Piano Sonata No. 3*, completed 1930, published by Southern Music Publishing Co.; *Piano Sonata No. 4*, completed 1940, published by Southern Music Publishing Co.; *Nine Etudes for Piano*, completed 1940-51, published by Carl Fischer; *Ten Etudes for Piano*, completed 1943-44, published by Carl Fischer; *Walking Song* (from "Tuesday in November"; see below), completed 1945, published by G. Schirmer; *Happy Birthday for Mrs. Zimbalist*, completed 1951, published by C. F. Peters; "A Portrait of Willy Eisenhart for His Birthday," completed 1972.

Works for solo organ: *Fanfare*, completed 1922, published by H. W. Gray; *Pastorale on a Christmas Plainsong*, completed 1922, published by H. W. Gray; *Prelude*, completed 1922, published by G. Schirmer; *Passacaglia*, completed 1922, G. Schirmer, 1974; *Five Chorale-Preludes*, completed 1924, published by H. W. Gray; *Variations and Fugues on Sunday School Tunes*, completed 1927, published by H. W. Gray; *Church Organ Wedding Music*, completed 1940, published by Randall M. Egan; *Pange Lingua*, completed 1962, published by G. Schirmer.

Work for solo instrument(s); accompanied by orchestra: *Concerto for Violoncello and Orchestra*, completed 1950, published by F. Colombo; *Five Songs from William Blake*, completed 1951, published by Southern Music Publishing Co.; *Concerto for Flute, Harp, and Percussion*, completed 1954, published by F. Colombo; *Mass for Solo Voice and Orchestra*, completed 1962, published by G. Schirmer; *The Feast of Love*, completed 1964, G. Schirmer, 1977; *Autumn*, completed 1964, published by G. Schirmer; *Ship Wreck and Love Scene from Byron's "Don Juan,"* completed 1967, published by Southern Music Publishing Co.

Operas: *Four Saints in Three Acts* (first produced in Hartford, Conn. at Avery Memorial Theatre, February 8, 1934; produced on Broadway at 44th Street Theatre, February 20, 1934), libretto by Gertrude Stein, completed 1928, Music Press, 1948; *The Mother of Us All* (first produced in New York, N.Y. at Brander Matthews Theatre, May 7, 1947), libretto by Stein, completed 1947, published by G. Schirmer; *Lord Byron* (first produced in New York, N.Y. at Julliard Theatre, April 20, 1972), libretto by Jack Larson, completed 1968, Southern Music Publishing Co., 1976.

Ballets: *Filling Station* (first produced in Hartford, Conn. at Avery Memorial Theatre, January 6, 1937), completed 1937, published by Boosey & Hawkes; *Bayou* (first produced in New York, N.Y. at New York City Center, 1952), completed 1952, published by G. Schirmer; "The Harvest According" (first produced in New York, N.Y. at Metropolitan Opera House, October, 1954), completed 1954; *Hurrah!* (first produced in Peninsula, Ohio at the Blossom Music Center, July 5, 1975), completed 1975, published by Belwin-Mills; *Parson Weems and the Cherry Tree* (first produced in Amherst, Mass. at University of Massachusetts, November 1, 1975), completed 1975, published by G. Schirmer.

Film scores: "The Plow That Broke the Plains," produced by U.S. Government, 1936; "The River," produced by U.S. Government, 1937; "The Spanish Earth," produced by Contemporary Historians, 1937; "Tuesday in November," produced by Paramount, 1945; "Louisiana Story," produced by Lopert Films, 1948; "The Goddess," produced by Columbia, 1957; "Power among Men," produced by United Nations, 1958; "Journey to America," produced for U.S. Pavilion, New York World's Fair, 1964.

Incidental music for plays: "Le Droit de Varech," 1930; "A Bride for the Unicorn," 1934; "Macbeth," 1936; "Injunction Granted, a Living Newspaper," 1936; "Horse Eats Hat," 1936; "Hamlet," 1936; "Antony and Cleopatra," 1937; "Androcles and the Lion," 1938; "The Trojan Women," 1940; "Sound Track of the Life of a Careful Man," 1941; Oidipous Tyrannos," 1941; "King Lear," 1952; "The Grass Harp," 1953; "Ondine," 1954; "King John," 1956; "Measure fr Measure," 1956; "Othello," 1957; "The Merchant of Venice," 1957; "Much Ado about Nothing," 1957; "Bertha," 1959.

Contributor of articles on music to *Vanity Fair, New Republic, Boston Transcript, Modern Music, New York Review of Books,* and other publications. Music editor, "The Sounds of History: The Words and Music of America's Past," twelve LP records, Time/Life, 1963-64.

WORK IN PROGRESS: "I'm reluctant to talk about music in progress—it brings bad luck. After you get to the middle of something, it's all right, but up to that point you don't really believe in it."

SIDELIGHTS: A multi-talented individual, Virgil Thomson is known and respected for his work as composer, music critic, and conductor. In the last capacity he has introduced many new important American musical works to numerous cities in the United States and Europe. As a critic he is recognized as a sometimes ascerbic, sometimes humorous, sometimes iconoclastic writer who has a consummate command of the English language. And as a composer, Thomson is now acknowledged as one of the most important Americans in the musical world, one who has brought his own unique theories to successful fruition.

The key to Thomson's work lies in his feeling for two very different cities: Kansas City and Paris. Both have been immensely important to his development and both are reflected in his style. "I wrote in Paris," Thomson says, "music that was always, in one way or another, about Kansas City. I wanted Paris to know Kansas City, to understand the ways we like to think and feel on the banks of the Kaw and the Missouri." It was during his stay in Paris that he became involved with the literary circles of the 1920's that included Gide, Picasso, Cocteau, Hemingway, Fitzgerald, and Gertrude Stein. With Stein he wrote his first opera, "Four Saints in Three Acts." The work became a sensation in the music world and made him famous.

Leaving Paris after the Nazi invasion, Thomson began his long association as chief music critic with the *New York Herald Tribune.* Joseph Machlis writes: "He ... soon established himself as one of the most penetrating chroniclers of the music scene. He was outspoken in his judgments and, a great virtue in a critic, he was not afraid to be wrong.... He had his prejudices and his blind spots. But even those musicians who disagreed with his columns could not resist reading them." In his criticism Thomson not only makes thoughtful and incisive judgments, but he does so with artistry. Kenneth Connelly comments: "His prose, like his music may achieve grandeur and pomp, but he generally avoids that, feels no automatic awe before the idols of the tribe, detests the calculated swoon and panegyrical outpouring, and spends little energy on the ineffable.... His habit of speaking as directly as possible about what is concretely perceptible in terms of his vastly informed awareness and

honest intelligence eventuates in an unrhetorical style notable for its compression, and very sensitive and flexible in its diction and syntax. If he sometimes seems irreverent or tactless, he is saved by his loving involvement with life and by his unsleeping wit. His particular triumph is his ability to express a strong individuality, which may appear eccentric or petulant on occasion, and still convince the reader that he is reporting with an unusually high degree of pertinence and accuracy." Jay Harrison adds, "As [a] writer he has done more for contemporary music than any man of his time."

Criticism of his books has been equally favorable. Reviewing Thomson's autobiography, Harold Clurman comments: "His style is straightforward, colloquial speech set in a syntax of almost Georgian elegance.... One does get a lively sense of the growth of modern American music when Thomson and others were trying to 'establish' it." Robert Craft believes that "this autobiography by the ranking critic-composer is indispensable to anyone concerned with the contemporary musical scene. To others I recommend its skillful characterizations of the intellectual moods and its distinctions between the fashion symptoms and the main lines of development of Paris and New York between the wars. As a chronicle of that period it is one of the most readable in existence. Unlike many authors of indispensable books, Mr. Thomson is always perspicuous, always enviably fluent, and nearly always engaging."

On being an American composer, Thomson has commented: "The way to write American music is simple. All you have to do is to be an American and then write any kind of music you wish." Kathleen Hoover believes that "culturally, Virgil brought up himself. He absorbed pioneer values and Christian virtues in heaping measure from his family, but his artistic proclivities are not traceable to any forebears." Thomson's music, according to Machlis, "is rooted in the hymns and folk tunes, the Civil War melodies and popular waltzes amid which he grew up. His direct, forthright melodies, supported by plain harmonies, are altogether American in character. Thus, Thomson's work represents an unusual mixture of Parisian sophistication and good American homespun."

"The Mother of Us All," an opera written in collaboration with Gertrude Stein and considered by many critics to be Thomson's best musical work, is a tribute to feminist Susan B. Anthony. In keeping with the subject, the composer chose particularly American music—folk dances, marches, revival hymns, along with original tunes. Harold C. Schonberg called the opera Thomson's "finest work" which "may be recognized as one of the few examples of genuine Americana on the lyric stage." Another Thomson work, "Filling Station," was the first successful ballet on an American theme and the first ballet to be created and performed exclusively by Americans. It's hero is Mac, a gas station attendant, who stops an attempted holdup and helps to catch the would-be robber and represents a uniquely American protagonist in contrast to the heroes chosen for most European ballets.

Thomson's later work evolved into what Machlis calls "a new romanticism, ... music that was simple and elegant, that would entertain and please, and that would not be above spoofing itself occasionally. He had talent as a humorist to begin with. He developed a gift for parody and satire that endeared him to those listeners who enjoy a good music joke." Discussing Thomson's latest opera, "Lord Byron," which did not receive much favorable criticism, Andrew Porter finds that "Thomson has the gift to be simple; his notes come down where they ought to be, in the place just right. But his simplicity is that of a master, not a naif. The music is not artless but careful, refined and purified by a process that has not destroyed its zest. "Lord Byron,' while decorous and controlled, is also lively; Thomson's evident joy in setting down a witty musical idea as neatly as possible proves infectious. The opera may lack the fresh, free lyric inspiration of 'The Mother of Us All,' his masterpiece, and it is certainly a less moving work. . . . But it does not deserve neglect.''

Aaron Copeland believes that it is his lack of "weightiness" that caused many critics and musicians to initially ignore much of Thomson's work. But, as Copeland writes: "Thomson is a man with a thesis. Whether or not his own compositions really come off, his theory about music has validity for all of us. For a long time now, ever since the middle '20s, Thomson has maintained that so-called modern music is much too involved and pretentious in every way. While most composers of the musical left are busily engaged in inventing all sorts of new rhythmic and harmonic devices, intent upon being as original and different as possible, Thomson goes to the opposite extreme and deliberately writes music as ordinary as possible—so ordinary, in fact, that at first hearing it often strikes one as being merely foolish. But even if we agree that the music is sometimes foolish, the idea behind it is not so foolish. This idea is derived from the conviction that modern music has forgotten its audience almost completely, that the purpose of music is not to impress and overwhelm the listener but to entertain and charm him. Thomson seems determined to win adherents through music of an absolute simplicity and directness.'' In this simplicity and freedom Thomson is, Copeland believes, "a unique personality in the recent history of our music.''

AVOCATIONAL INTERESTS: Cooking and conversation.

BIOGRAPHICAL/CRITICAL SOURCES—Books: Claire R. Reis, *Composers in America*, revised and enlarged edition, Macmillan, 1947; Madeline Goss, *Modern Music Makers: Contemporary American Composers*, Dutton, 1952; Gilbert Chase, *America's Music*, McGraw, 1955, revised edition, 1966; Kathleen Hoover and John Cage, *Virgil Thomson: His Life and Music*, Yoseloff, 1959; Joseph Machlis, *American Composers of Our Time*, Crowell, 1963; Katherine B. Shippen and Anca Seidlove, *The Heritage of Music*, Viking, 1963; Wilfred Mellers, *Music in a New Found Land*, Knopf, 1965; Virgil Thomson, *Virgil Thomson*, Knopf, 1966; Aaron Copeland, *The New Music*, revised and enlarged edition, Norton, 1968.

Periodicals: *Musical Magazine*, February, 1962; *New York Times*, April 1, 1964, November 25, 1976; *New York Times Book Review*, October 9, 1966; *Nation*, October 24, 1966; *Harper*, December, 1966; *Times Literary Supplement*, March 23, 1967, December 3, 1971; *Commentary*, May, 1967; *Yale Review*, June, 1967; *Virginia Quarterly Review*, spring, 1967; *Saturday Review*, September 25, 1971, May 20, 1972; *Music Library Association Notes*, December, 1971; *New Yorker*, April 29, 1972, March 3, 1973, January 17, 1977; *New Republic*, May 6, 1972.

*   *   *

THORNDIKE, Susan   1944-

PERSONAL: Born July 7, 1944, in East Bridgewater, Mass.; daughter of John Beverly (an attorney) and Helen (Roach) Thorndike; married Louis B. Dotti, Jr. *Education:* Brandeis University, B.A., 1966. *Residence:* New York, N.Y.

CAREER: Doubleday & Co., New York City, editorial assistant in juvenile book department, 1966-72; Crown Publishers, New York City, assistant editor of juvenile books, 1972-73; Four Winds Press, New York City, associate editor of juvenile books, beginning 1973; Random House, Inc., New York City, senior editor, 1976-77. *Member:* Feminists on Children's Media (founding member).

WRITINGS—Juvenile: (Compiler with others) *Little Miss Muffet Fights Back* (bibliography of non-sexist literature), Feminists on Children's Media, 1971; *The Electric Radish*, Doubleday, 1973.

WORK IN PROGRESS: A children's magazine, *Young New York.*

*   *   *

THORNE, Florence Calvert   1878(?)-1973

1878(?)—March 12, 1973; American director of research for national labor organization and biographer of Samuel Gompers. Obituaries: *New York Times*, March 17, 1973.

*   *   *

THROWER, Norman J(oseph) W(illiam)   1919-

PERSONAL: Born October 23, 1919, in Crowthorne, England; naturalized U.S. citizen; son of Gordon William and Ethel (Bayley) Thrower; married Elizabeth Martin, August, 1947; children: Mildred Page, Anne Bayley, Mary Elizabeth. *Education:* University of Virginia, B.A., 1953; University of Wisconsin, M.A., 1955, Ph.D., 1958. *Religion:* Presbyterian. *Home:* 751 Swarthmore Ave., Pacific Palisades, Calif. 90272. *Office:* Department of Geography, University of California, Los Angeles, Calif. 90024.

CAREER: University of California, Los Angeles, assistant professor, 1957-61, associate professor, 1961-64, professor of geography, 1964—, William Andrews Clark Library Professor, 1972-73. Member of advisory board, John Simon Guggenheim Foundation, 1978—. Editorial advisor to McGraw-Hill Book Co., Hammond, and other publishing companies. *Member:* Association of American Geographers, Society for the History of Discoveries (vice-iresident, 1972-73; president, 1974-75), International Cartographic Association (corresponding member), American Congress on Surveying and Mapping, Sir Francis Drake Commission of the State of California (president, 1975—). *Awards, honors:* Guggenheim fellow, 1963-64; American Philosophical Society-Penrose Fund grant, 1971-72.

WRITINGS: (Contributor) H. Friis, editor, *The Pacific Basin*, American Geographical Society, 1964; *Original Survey and Land Subdivision*, Rand McNally, 1966; (editor) *Man's Domain: A Thematic Atlas of the World*, McGraw, 1968, 3rd edition, 1975; *Maps and Man: An Examination of Cartography in Relation to Culture and Civilization*, Prentice-Hall, 1972, 3rd edition, 1977; (contributor) H. Mooney and F. di Castri, editors, *Ecological Studies, Mediterranean Type Ecosystems*, Springer Verlag, 1973; (contributor) F. Chiappelli, editor, *First Images of America: The Impact of the New World on the Old*, University of California Press, 1976; (contributor) Mooney, editor, *Convergent Evolution in Chile and California*, Dowden, 1977; (coauthor and editor) *Chile-California Mediterranean Scrub Atlas: A Comparative Analysis*, Dowden, 1977; *The Compleat Plattmaker: Essays on Chart and Globe Making in England in the 17th and 18th Centuries*, University of California Press, 1978; *The Three Voyages of Edmond Halley in the 'Paramore,' 1698-1701*, Hakluyt Society, 1978. Contributor of articles to geography and cartography journals. Map supplement editor, Association of American Geographers, 1964-73. Member of editorial board, *Cartographica*, 1970—.

SIDELIGHTS: Norman J. W. Thrower told *CA*, "My writings reflect a personal concern with those areas where art and science meet, especially in the fields of geographical discovery and cartography."

* * *

THUM, Gladys 1920-

PERSONAL: Born November 9, 1920, in St. Louis, Mo.; daughter of Frank Charles and Louise (Holle) Thum. *Education:* Washington University, St. Louis, Mo., B.A., 1948, M.A., 1950; University of California, Berkeley, graduate study, 1952; St. Louis University, Ph.D., 1975. *Home:* 6507 Grammond, St. Louis, Mo. 63139. *Agent:* Lurton Blassingame, Blassingame, McCauley & Wood, 60 East 42nd St., New York, N.Y. 10017. *Office:* Department of English, Florissant Valley Community College, 3400 Pershall Rd., St. Louis, Mo. 63135.

CAREER: Administrative assistant, information specialist and officer, teacher, and chief of U.S. broadcast and visual news for the U.S. Department of State and Department of Defense in Washington, D.C., Vietnam, Cambodia, Laos, Okinawa, Japan, 1941-44, 1950-63; Florissant Valley Community College, St. Louis, Mo., assistant professor, 1965-67, associate professor, 1968-75, professor of English and communications, 1976—. *Military service:* U.S. Army Air Forces, Air Transport Command, 1944-46; public relations writer. *Member:* International Psywar Society, Midwest Modern Language Association, Missouri Writers Guild, Missouri Association of Junior Colleges, St. Louis Poetry Center (member of board of chancellors), St. Louis Writers Guild.

WRITINGS: (With sister, Marcella Thum) *The Persuaders*, Atheneum, 1972; *Persuasion and Propaganda*, McDougal, Littell, 1974. Contributor of articles to newspapers and journals.

WORK IN PROGRESS: Propaganda Analysis: Funny Fuzzy Images.

* * *

THURSBY, Vincent Victor 1918-

PERSONAL: Born February 20, 1918, in Akron, Ohio; son of Reynold Raymond (a corporation department manager) and Ella (Alexander) Thursby; married Mary Agnes Foust (a law librarian), September 18, 1943. *Education:* Vanderbilt University, B.A., 1942, M.A., 1947, Ph.D., 1950. *Home:* 1111 North Gulfstream Ave., Apt. 7-B, Sarasota, Fla. 33577.

CAREER: Bucknell University, Lewisburg, Pa., assistant professor of political science, 1949-50; Florida State University, Tallahassee, associate professor, 1950-53, professor of government, 1953-77, professor emeritus, 1977—, assistant graduate dean, 1965-68, associate graduate dean, 1968-77. *Military service:* U.S. Army Air Forces, 1942-45. *Member:* American Political Science Association, Southern Political Science Association (member of executive council, 1956-58; vice-president, 1962), Phi Alpha Theta, Pi Sigma Alpha, Lambda Chi Alpha, Raven Society.

WRITINGS: Interstate Cooperation, Public Affairs Press, 1953; (contributor) *A Survey Report on the Impact of Federal Grants-in-Aid on the Structure and Functions of State and Local Governments*, U.S. Government Printing Office,

1955; (with Raymond F. Bellamy, Harrison Chase, and Sadie Young) *A Preface to the Social Sciences*, McGraw, 1956; (with A. M. Hartsfield) *Federal Grant-in-Aid Programs in Florida*, Institute of Governmental Research, Florida State University, 1964; (with Hartsfield) *Index to the Journal of the Proceedings of the Constitutional Convention of the State of Florida, 1885*, Institute of Governmental Research, Florida State University, 1965; (with James A. Gould) *Contemporary Political Thought: Issues in Scope, Value, and Direction*, Holt, 1969.

* * *

TILSON, Everett 1923-

PERSONAL: Born February 17, 1923, in Marion, Va.; son of Arthur Lee (a farmer) and Margaret (Cullop) Tilson; married Mary Milburn (a teacher), August 28, 1944; children: Stephen, Lee, Hazel, Joseph. *Education:* King College, A.B., 1944; Vanderbilt University, B.D., 1946, Ph.D., 1952; Hebrew Union College, graduate study, 1949-50; Yale University, postdoctoral study, 1954-55; Heidelberg University, postdoctoral study, 1967-68. *Home:* 126 Pennsylvania Ave., Delaware, Ohio 43015. *Office:* Methodist Theological School, Delaware, Ohio 43015.

CAREER: Clergyman of Methodist Church; Vanderbilt University, Divinity School, Nashville, Tenn., instructor, 1952-55, assistant professor, 1955-58, associate professor of biblical theology, 1958-60; Methodist Theological School, Delaware, Ohio, professor of Old Testament, 1960—. *Member:* American Association of University Professors, Society of Biblical Literature and Exegesis, American Academy of Religion, American Schools of Oriental Research, National Association of Biblical Instructors (president of Southern section, 1960-61). *Awards, honors:* Human Relations Award from Delaware Council on Human Relations, 1964.

WRITINGS: The Conscience of Culture, Board of Education of the Methodist Church, 1953; *Should Christians . . . ?*, Abingdon, 1957; *Segregation and the Bible*, Abingdon, 1958; (contributor with Martin Luther King, Jr. and others) Alfred Davies, editor, *The Pulpit Speaks on Race*, Abingdon, 1965; *Fit to Live in God's World*, Graded Press, 1966; (contributor) Gerald A. Anderson, editor, *Christian Mission in Theological Perspective*, Abingdon, 1969; *Decision for Destiny*, Board of Global Ministries of the United Methodist Church, 1975. Contributor to *Christian Century, British Weekly, Journal of Religious Thought, Interpretation, World Christian Digest*, and *Pulpit*.

WORK IN PROGRESS: A book, *The Old Testament in Historical Context*.

* * *

TIMBERLAKE, Charles E(dward) 1935-

PERSONAL: Born September 9, 1935, in South Shore, Ky.; son of Howard Ellis (a mechanic) and Mabel (Collier) Timberlake; married Patricia Perkins (a librarian), December 23, 1957; children: Mark Brewster, Daniel Edward, Eric Collier. *Education:* Berea College, B.A., 1957; Claremont University College (now Claremont Graduate School), M.A., 1962; University of Washington, Seattle, Ph.D., 1968. *Home address:* Route 4, Box 173, Columbia, Mo. 65201. *Office:* Department of History, University of Missouri, Columbia, Mo. 65211.

CAREER: High school history teacher in Barstow, Calif., 1959-60, and Claremont, Calif., 1960-61; University of

Washington, Seattle, research bibliographer in Russian and Far East Institute, 1961-62, teaching assistant in American and Russian history, 1962-64; University of Missouri—Columbia, assistant professor, 1967-73, associate professor of Russian history, 1973—. *Member:* American Historical Association, American Association for the Advancement of Slavic Studies (member of bibliography and documentation committee, 1972-76, and national program committee, 1976), American Association of University Professors, Central Slavic Conference (secretary-treasurer, 1968; president, 1969, 1977; member of executive board), Missouri Historical Society, Phi Alpha Theta. *Awards, honors:* University of Missouri research grants, 1969, 1970, 1973, 1976, 1978; American Philosophical Society award, 1970; National Endowment for the Humanities summer stipend, 1970; senior exchange scholar in the Soviet Union, International Research and Exchanges Board, 1971; Earhart Foundation fellowship, 1972; American Council of Learned Societies fellowship, 1978-79.

WRITINGS: (Editor and contributor) *Essays on Russian Liberalism,* University of Missouri Press, 1972; (contributor) Bernard Eissenstat, editor, *The Soviet Union: The Seventies and Beyond,* Heath, 1975; (contributor) Paul A. Horecky and David Kraus, compilers and editors, *East Central and Southeastern Europe: A Handbook of Library Resources in North America,* American Bibliographic Center-Clio Press, 1976; *Detente: A Documentary Record,* Praeger, 1979. Contributor to *Modern Encyclopedia of Russian and Soviet History.* Contributor to professional journals, including *Slavic Review, New Mexico Historical Review, Yale University Library Gazette,* and *Pacific Northwest Quarterly.*

WORK IN PROGRESS: Three monographs, *Ivan Il'ich Petrunkevich and the Fate of Russian Liberalism, American Utopian Societies in the Soviet Union in the 1920's,* and *A History of Russian Liberalism.*

AVOCATIONAL INTERESTS: Travel, camping, hiking, fishing, photography.

*   *   *

TINKER, Spencer Wilkie 1909-

PERSONAL: Born January 29, 1909, in Anamoose, N.D.; son of Luke and Anna Virginia (Overholser) Tinker; married Gwendolyn Eder, September 17, 1938; children: George Allen. *Education:* University of Washington, Seattle, B.S., 1931; University of Hawaii, M.S., 1934. *Religion:* Congregationalist. *Home:* 1121 Hunakai St., Honolulu, Hawaii 96816.

CAREER: University of Hawaii, Honolulu, instructor in zoology, 1934-35, instructor, 1935-55, assistant professor, 1955-62, associate professor of education, 1962-70, researcher, 1970-72, director of Waikiki Aquarium, 1940-72. *Military service:* U.S. Army, Quartermaster Corps, 1941-46; became captain.

WRITINGS: Animals of Hawaii, privately printed, 1938; *Stories of Hawaiian Animals for Boys and Girls,* privately printed, 1940; *Hawaiian Fishes,* Tongg Publishing, 1944; *Pacific Sea Shells,* privately printed, 1952; *Pacific Crustacea,* Tuttle, 1965; *Sharks and Rays,* Tuttle, 1973; *Fishes of Hawaii,* Hawaiian Service, Inc., 1978.

*   *   *

TIPTON, Charles Leon 1932-

PERSONAL: Born September 20, 1932, in Erick, Okla.;

married, 1953; children: two. *Education:* El Camino College, A.A., 1956; University of Southern California, A.B., 1958, M.A., 1961, Ph.D., 1964. *Home:* 2527 Nottingham Rd., Bethlehem, Pa. 18017. *Office:* Department of History, Lehigh University, Bethlehem, Pa. 18015.

CAREER: Los Angeles State College of Applied Arts and Sciences (now California State University), Los Angeles, Calif., instructor in history, 1960; University of Southern California, Los Angeles, lecture in history, 1960-62; Ohio State University, Columbus, instructor in history, 1962-63; Lehigh University, Bethlehem, Pa., assistant professor, 1964-67, associate professor, 1967-71, professor of history, 1971—. *Military service:* U.S. Army, 1952-54; became sergeant.

MEMBER: American Historical Association, Medieval Academy of America, Conference on British Studies, American Catholic Historical Association, Malta Historical Society, British Records Association, Phi Beta Kappa, Phi Alpha Theta. *Awards, honors:* Fulbright grant, 1963-64, and National Foundation for the Humanities fellowship, 1967-68, both for research at Archives of the Knights of St. John of Jerusalem in Valletta, Malta; American Philosophical Society research grant, 1967, 1977.

WRITINGS: The Knights Hospitallers in Ireland: Documents from the Malta Archives, Irish Historical Manuscripts Commission, 1969; (contributor) R. Nevill Hadcock and Aubrey Gwynn, editors, *Medieval Religious Houses in Ireland,* Longmans, Green, 1970; (contributor) J. F. Lydon and F. X. Martin, editors, *Guide to the Sources for the History of Medieval Ireland,* University College, Dublin, 1971; (contributor) A. T. Gaydon, editor, *Victoria History of Shropshire,* Constable, 1971; (editor) *Nationalism in the Middle Ages,* Holt, 1971. Contributor to annals, proceedings, and yearbooks. Contributor of articles and reviews to professional journals, including *Speculum, Catholic Historical Review, American Historical Review,* and *Historian.*

*   *   *

TITTLE, Charles R(ay) 1939-

PERSONAL: Born March 26, 1939, in Hope, Ark.; son of Clovis G. (an automobile mechanic) and Nettie (McCorkle) Tittle; children: Mark, Shauna. *Education:* Ouachita Baptist College (now University), B.A. (summa cum laude), 1961; University of Texas, M.A., 1963, Ph.D., 1965. *Politics:* Democrat. *Home:* 671 Northwest 12th Ter., Boca Raton, Fla. 33432. *Office:* Department of Sociology and Social Psychology, Florida Atlantic University, Boca Raton, Fla. 33432.

CAREER: Indiana University at Bloomington, assistant professor, 1965-69, associate professor of sociology, 1969-70; Florida Atlantic University, Boca Raton, associate professor, 1970-73, professor of sociology, 1973—, acting chairman of department of sociology and social psychology, 1972-73, chairman of department, 1973-75. *Member:* American Sociological Association, Southern Sociological Association. *Awards, honors:* Woodrow Wilson fellowship, 1961-62; Danforth fellowship, 1961-65; National Institute of Mental Health biomedical sciences research grant, 1966; National Science Foundation grants, 1967-69, 1972-74.

WRITINGS: Society of Subordinates: Inmate Organization in a Narcotic Hospital, Indiana University Press, 1972.

Contributor: Norman K. Denzin, editor, *Sociological Methods,* Aldine, 1970; Gene F. Summers, editor, *Attitude Measurement,* Rand McNally, 1970; Stewart H. Britt, editor,

Consumer Behavior in Theory and Action, Wiley, 1971; C. David Mortenson and Kenneth K. Sereno, editors, *Advances in Communication Research,* Harper, 1972; Simon Rottenberg, editor, *The Economics of Crime and Punishment,* American Enterprise Institute for Public Research, 1973; Allen E. Liska, editor, *The Impact of Attitudes on Behavior: The Attitude-Behavior Consistency Controversy,* Schenkman, 1973; Sheldon Messinger and others, editors, *Crime and Justice Annual, 1973,* Aldine, 1974; Walter Gove, editor, *Societal Reaction and Deviant Behavior: The Evaluation of a Theory,* Halsted, 1975; William J. Chambliss, editor, *Criminal Law in Action,* Hamilton, 1975; Robert G. Leger and John R. Stratton, editors, *The Sociology of Corrections,* Wiley, 1977; Stewart McCaulay and Lawrence Friedman, editors, *Law and the Behavioral Sciences,* Bobbs-Merrill, 1977; Norman Johnston and Leonard D. Savitz, editors, *Justice and Corrections,* Wiley, 1978; Burt Galaway and Joe Hudson, editors, *Offender Restitution in Theory and Action,* Heath, 1978.

Contributor of articles and reviews to *Law and Society Review, Social Problems, Social Forces, American Sociological Review, Journal of Health and Social Behavior, Sociometry, Public Opinion Quarterly, American Journal of Sociology, Criminology, Sociological Quarterly,* and *Sociological Focus.*

WORK IN PROGRESS: Deviance and Consequences.

*   *   *

TOBACK, James 1944-

PERSONAL: Born November 23, 1944, in New York, N.Y.; son of Irwin Lionel (a stockbroker) and Selma (Levy) Toback; married Consuelo Sarah Churchill Rusell, April 26, 1968 (divorced). *Education:* Harvard University, A.B., 1966; Columbia University, M.A., 1967. *Politics:* Unaffiliated. *Religion:* Jewish. *Home:* 11 East 87th St., New York, N.Y. 10028. *Agent:* Lynn Nesbit, International Famous Agency, 1301 Avenue of the Americas, New York, N.Y. 10019.

CAREER: Screenwriter. Instructor in English, City College of the City University of New York, New York, N.Y., beginning 1968. *Member:* Harvard Club of New York.

WRITINGS: Jim: The Author's Self-Centered Memoir on the Great Jim Brown, Doubleday, 1971.

Screenplays: "The Gambler," Paramount, 1974; "Fingers," directed by Toback, Brut Productions, 1978. Author of a sports column appearing in *Lifestyle;* film critic for *Dissent.* Contributor of articles to numerous magazines including *Esquire, Sport, Village Voice, Harper's,* and *Commentary.* Former contributing editor, *Sport.*

SIDELIGHTS: James Toback's book, *Jim: The Author's Self-Centered Memoir on the Great Jim Brown* is a book describing Toback's friendship with the football superstar and actor, Jim Brown. The two men first meet when Toback flew to Los Angeles to interview Brown. During the interview, the men became good friends which eventually led to Toback becoming Brown's houseguest indefinitely.

C. C. Hernton writes that Toback's book "reads like an autobiographical-biographical sensitivity encounter between Toback and Brown." Allen Cohen feels that "this is a puzzling book which . . . becomes more of an ego trip in which Toback goes through a typical middle-class, white-liberal, ambiguous relationship with a black. . . . It all leads to a deep personal friendship. That's what it says; and this reviewer believes it, but he doesn't feel it. If the book was intended to

get below the surface of Jim Brown and James Toback—the individuals and their relationship—the effort has failed."

Writing about Toback's ability as a screenwriter, a reviewer for *Village Voice* writes: "Toback, like Paul Schrader, is a flashy wordsmith whose aggressive self-promotion has generated more attention than the quality of his work deserves. 'Fingers'—like his script for 'The Gambler'—attempts to suspend a contemporary hustler between an intellectual's heaven and a lowlife's hell."

Pauline Kael feels "Fingers" "is a howl of ambition, and you get the feeling that at least two-thirds of it is still locked up in the writer-director's head—that he simply did not have the experience, the cast, or the budget to get more of his exuberantly melodramatic fantasy onto the screen. Still, what's there has the wild self-dramatization that one associates with the young Tennessee Williams, or with Mailer when he gets high on excess. Insanity, violent bouts of sex, Jacobean revenge killings—nothing is too much for Toback in his exhilarated state. There's almost a swagger in the way he consciously goes beyond the rationally acceptable: He's looking for art in that beyond, wanting the unknown—the dangerous—to take over. It's a willed hysteria."

Kael continues: "'Fingers' tries to create the screen equivalent of a tropical region of the mind; it's an educated man's high-powered masochistic fairy tale, the story of a descent into madness. Toback is trying hard for purgative effects; he wants to show us man stripped down to a cowering, naked animal waiting in the jungle. Normality doesn't interest Toback; he's playing the literary-adolescent's game of wanting to go crazy so he can watch his own reactions. And because he doesn't censor his masculine racial fantasies, his foolishness and his terrible ideas pour out freely."

BIOGRAPHICAL/CRITICAL SOURCES: Time, April 5, 1971, April 3, 1978; *New York Times Book Review,* May 16, 1971; *New Yorker,* March 13, 1978; *Village Voice,* March 13, 1978; *Newsweek,* March 20, 1978.†

*   *   *

TOBIAS, Henry J(ack) 1925-

PERSONAL: Born March 11, 1925, in Paterson, N.J.; son of Isadore (a painter) and Dora (Medwied) Tobias; married Suzanne Simons, March 21, 1948 (divorced, 1961); married Haven Bonette, September 10, 1963; children: (first marriage) Ann, Heidi; (second marriage) Ruth. *Education:* Ohio State University, B.A., 1947; Yale University, M.A., 1950; Stanford University, Ph.D., 1958. *Religion:* Jewish. *Home:* 1602 Barwick, Norman, Okla. 73069. *Office:* Department of History, University of Oklahoma, Norman, Okla. 73069.

CAREER: Elmira College, Elmira, N.Y., instructor, 1957-58, assistant professor of history, 1958-59; University of New Mexico, Albuquerque, assistant professor, 1959-67, associate professor of history, 1967-69; Kansas State University, Manhattan, professor of history, 1970-71, head of department, 1970-71; University of Oklahoma, Norman, associate professor, 1969-70, professor of history, 1971—, chairman of department, 1972-76. *Military service:* U.S. Army, 1943-45. *Member:* American Association for the Advancement of Slavic Studies, American Historical Association, Southwest Association of Slavic Studies (vice-president, 1971-72; president, 1972-73).

WRITINGS: (Editor with Charles E. Woodhouse, and contributor) *Minorities and Politics,* University of New Mexico Press, 1969; *The Jewish Bund in Russia: From Its Origins to 1905,* Stanford University Press, 1972. Contributor to *Rus-*

sian Review, Comparative Studies in Society and History, Journal of Central European Affairs, American Slavic and East European Review, and *Mexican Quarterly Review.*
WORK IN PROGRESS: The Jewish Bund in Russia: From 1905 to 1921.

*   *   *

TODD, William Burton 1919-

PERSONAL: Born April 11, 1919, in Chester, Pa.; son of William Booth (an engineer) and Edith (Burton) Todd; married Mary Chestnut, December 6, 1942 (divorced, 1969); married Ann Bowden (a library administrator), November 23, 1969; children: (first marriage) Marilyn (Mrs. Edward Guinn), Susan (Mrs. Antonius M. Kramer), Deborah, Terence. *Education:* Lehigh University, B.A. (with high honors), 1940, M.A., 1947; University of Chicago, Ph.D. (with honors), 1949. *Religion:* Episcopalian. *Home:* 2424 Wooldridge Dr., Austin, Tex. 78703. *Office:* Department of English, University of Texas, Austin, Tex. 78712.

CAREER: Salem College, Winston-Salem, N.C., professor of English and chairman of department, 1949-55; Harvard University, Houghton Library, Cambridge, Mass., assistant librarian, 1955-58; University of Texas at Austin, professor of English, 1958—. Oxford University, J.P.R. Lyell Reader in Bibliography, 1969-70, visiting fellow of All Souls College, 1970; D. Nichol Smith Lecturer, Australian National University, 1973; Cecil Oldman Memorial Lecturer, Leeds University, 1975; Andrew Osborn Lecturer, University of Western Ontario, 1978. Consultant to National Library of Australia, 1973, and National Endowment for the Humanities Research Tools Program, 1977-78. *Military service:* U.S. Army, Infantry, 1941-45; became major; received Bronze Star Medal and Purple Heart.

MEMBER: Modern Language Association of America, Private Libraries Association, American Library Association, Bibliographical Society (London), Bibliographical Society of America, Printing Historical Society, Johnsonians, English Institute, Virginia Bibliographical Society, Grolier Club, Codrington Club, Phi Beta Kappa, Eta Sigma Phi. *Awards, honors:* Fulbright research fellow, 1952-53; American Council of Learned Societies fellow, 1961-62; Guggenheim fellow, 1965-66; Oldman Memorial Award, Leeds University, 1975; Mark Fitch Prize, Leeds University, 1975; L.H.D., LeHigh University, 1975.

WRITINGS: (Editor) Oliver Goldsmith, *Prospect of Society,* Water Lane Press, 1954; *New Adventures among Old Books,* University Press of Kansas, 1958; (editor) Edmund Burke, *Reflections on the Revolution in France,* Holt, 1959, revised edition, annotated by Conor Cruise O'Brien, Penguin, 1969; (editor) *Thomas J. Wise Centenary Studies,* University of Texas Press, 1959; (editor with E. Stenbock-Fermor) *The Kilgour Collection of Russian Literature: 1750-1920,* Harvard University Press, 1959; *Prize Books: Awards Granted to Scholars: 1671-1935,* University of Texas Press, 1961; *Bibliography of Edmund Burke,* Hart-Davis, 1964; (editor) *Guy of Warwick,* University of Texas Press, 1968; (editor) *Suppressed Commentaries on the Wiseian Forgeries,* University of Texas Press, 1969; *Directory of London Printers: 1800-1840,* Printing Historical Society, 1972; (editor) *Hume and the Enlightenment,* Humanities Research Center, University of Texas, 1974; (editor with R. H. Campbell and A. S. Skinner) Adam Smith, *The Wealth of Nations,* Oxford University Press, 1976. Author of fourteen monographs. Contributor of over 300 articles to periodicals. Editor, *Papers* of Bibliographical Society of America, 1967—.

SIDELIGHTS: William Burton Todd told *CA* that his works on printing history "frequently overturn long-cherished bibliographical traditions." He has shown a 'counterfeit edition' of Cicero to be genuine, a 'rare privately printed edition' of Goldsmith's *Deserted Village* to be a piracy, and many other books to be something more than scholars had assumed. He has analyzed the Nuremburg Chronicle, the second Shakespeare Folio, and works of Richard Nixon and Mao Tse-Tung. The London *Times Literary Supplement* has called him "Inspector-General for all bibliographical heresies." Todd explains: "I am always attracted by whatever is peculiar, textually or typographically. However great the author, however grand his literary performance, there usually lurks behind the printed word some unusual story, something distorted or concealed, and all this I am ever determined to expose."

*   *   *

TODRANK, Gustave H(erman) 1924-

PERSONAL: Born April 9, 1924, in Huntingburg, Ind.; son of Christian William (a contractor and farmer) and Lillian Catherine (Ahrens) Todrank; married Elizabeth Chalmers (a reading specialist), June 25, 1949; children: Stephen Knight, Josephine. *Education:* DePauw University, B.A., 1948; Boston University, S.T.B., 1951, Ph.D., 1956. *Home:* 38 Pleasant St., Waterville, Me. 04901. *Office:* Department of Philosophy, Colby College, Waterville, Me. 04901.

CAREER: Ordained minister of United Church of Christ, 1951; minister in Newton, Mass., 1951-56; Colby College, Waterville, Me., instructor, 1956-58, assistant professor, 1958-62, associate professor, 1962-70, professor of philosophy and religion, 1970—. *Member:* American Philosophical Association, American Academy of Religion, Phi Beta Kappa.

WRITINGS: The Secular Search for a New Christ, Westminster, 1969.

*   *   *

TOKA, Salchak Kalbakkhoreviich 1901-1973

1901—May 11, 1973; Soviet Asian political leader and author of novels, plays, and articles. Obituaries: *New York Times,* May 13, 1973.

*   *   *

TOMPKINS, C(linton) David 1937-

PERSONAL: Born January 9, 1937, in Battle Creek, Mich.; son of Clinton and Mary (Prill) Tompkins; divorced; children: Joan Marie, Robert David. *Education:* Northwestern University, B.S., 1959, M.A., 1959; University of Wisconsin, M.S., 1962; University of Michigan, Ph.D., 1966. *Home:* 319 Third St., Wilmette, Ill. 60091; and 12143 D. Avenue East, Richland, Mich. (summer). *Office:* Department of History, Northeastern Illinois University, Chicago, Ill. 60625.

CAREER: Western Michigan University, Kalamazoo, instructor in history, 1963-66; University of Illinois, Chicago, assistant professor of history, 1966-68; Northeastern Illinois University, Chicago, associate professor, 1968-71, professor of history, 1971—, chairman of department, 1971-77. *Member:* American Historical Association, Organization of American Historians, Society of Historians of American Foreign Relations.

WRITINGS: Senator Arthur H. Vandenberg: The Evolution of a Modern Republican, 1884-1945, Michigan State

University Press, 1970. Contributor of numerous articles and reviews to periodicals.

WORK IN PROGRESS: Republican Statesman: Arthur H. Vandenberg and Bipartisan Foreign Policy, 1945-51; Franklin D. Roosevelt and the Making of the United Nations.

* * *

TONKIN, Humphrey 1939-

PERSONAL: Born December 2, 1939, in Truro, England; son of George L. (a businessman) and Lorna (Sandry) Tonkin; married S. Julie Winberg, March 9, 1968. *Education:* St. John's College, Cambridge, B.A., 1962, M.A., 1966; Harvard University, A.M., 1966, Ph.D., 1966. *Home:* 35 Violet Lane, Lansdowne, Pa. 19050. *Office:* Department of English, University of Pennsylvania, Philadelphia, Pa. 19104.

CAREER: University of Pennsylvania, Philadelphia, assistant professor, 1966-71, associate professor of English, 1971—, vice-provost for undergraduate studies, 1972-75, coordinator of international programs, 1976—. Member of board of directors of Pennsylvania Council on International Education and World Affairs Council of Philadelphia. *Member:* International Studies Association, Universal Esperanto Association (president, 1974—), Esperanto League for North America, Modern Language Association of America, Milton Society of America, Renaissance Society of America, American Council on the Teaching of Foreign Languages, American Comparative Literature Association, Spenser Society (member of board of directors). *Awards, honors:* Guggenheim fellow, 1975.

WRITINGS: (Editor) *Sir Walter Raleigh 1900-1968: Elizabethan Bibliographies Supplements,* Nether Press, 1971; *Spenser's Courteous Pastoral,* Clarendon Press, 1972; (translator into Esperanto) A. A. Milne, *Winnie-La-Pu,* Dutton, 1972; (editor) *Esperanto and International Language Problems: A Research Bibliography,* Esperantic Studies Foundation, 1972, 4th edition, 1977. Contributor to *Seventeenth Century News, Comparative Literature Studies, Ohio Review, Centennial Review, Language and Style, PMLA, Modern Philology, Studies in English Literature,* and *World Literature Today.* Editor, *International Education Review* and *Esperanto Documents.*

WORK IN PROGRESS: Books on Spenser's *Faerie Queene* and on Renaissance poetry.

* * *

TOPPING, Audrey R(onning) 1928-

PERSONAL: Born May 21, 1928, in Camrose, Alberta, Canada; daughter of Chester Alvin (a Canadian diplomat) and Inga (Horte) Ronning; married Seymour Topping (managing editor of *New York Times*), November 11, 1949; children: Susan, Karen, Lesley, Rebecca, Joanna. *Education:* Attended Camrose Lutheran College, 1943-46, University of Nanking, 1946-48, University of British Columbia, 1948-49, and Berlin Art Academy, 1956-58. *Home and office:* 5 Heathcote Rd., Scarsdale, N.Y. 10583. *Agent:* Photo Research, 60 East 56th St., New York, N.Y.

CAREER: Free-lance writer, photographer, filmmaker, sculptor, and lecturer. China photographs have been exhibited at Hallmark Gallery and Overseas Press Club (both New York, N.Y.); work has also been shown in Berlin and London; has had one-woman shows at University of Delaware, Westchester Community College, Neikrug Gallery,

and Katonah Gallery. Advisor, In the Public Interest; director, United Nations—Scarsdale Chapter. Member of China Council. Trustee, Fund for Peace. *Member:* Foreign Policy Association (director), Asia Society.

WRITINGS: (With husband, Seymour Topping, Tillman Durdin, and James Reston) *Report from Red China,* Quadrangle, 1971; *A Day on a Chinese Commune* (juvenile), Grosset, 1972; *Holiday in Peking* (juvenile), Grosset, 1972; *Dawn Wakes in the East,* Harper, 1973. Author of "China Today," a series of six film scripts and photographs for Spoken Arts; assistant producer of "The Forbidden City," for National Broadcasting Co. Contributor of photographs and articles to *New York Times, Vogue, Harper's, National Geographic, Time, Newsweek, Horizon, Art in America, House and Garden,* and *Life.*

WORK IN PROGRESS: The Walled in Kingdom, for Random House; an historical novel about American missionaries in China.

SIDELIGHTS: Audrey R. Topping's associations with China began with her grandparents, the first Lutheran missionaries in China, and continued with her father, an old friend of Premier Chou En-Lai. Since her marriage, she and her family have lived in Saigon, London, Berlin, Moscow, India, and Hong Kong. She has visited China six times since the Communist revolution.

BIOGRAPHICAL/CRITICAL SOURCES: National Geographic, December, 1971, April, 1978; Seymour Topping, *Journey Between Two Chinas,* Harper, 1972; Chester Ronning, *Memoirs of China in Revolution,* Random House, 1974.

* * *

TOPPING, C(oral) W(esley) 1889-
(Wesley Topping)

PERSONAL: Born July 30, 1889, in Fitzroy, Canada; son of N. B. (a clergyman) and Catherine (Cooke) Topping; married Marjorie Ellis, August 25, 1925 (died January 8, 1972); children: William Ellis, Helen May (Mrs. Douglas Whiffin). *Education:* Queen's University at Kingston, B.A., 1912; Wesleyan Theological College, Montreal, B.D., 1921, S.T.D., 1925; Union Theological Seminary, New York, N.Y., S.T.M., 1921; Columbia University, M.A., 1921, Ph.D., 1929. *Politics:* Liberal. *Religion:* United Church. *Home:* 4665 West Tenth Ave., Apt. 904, Vancouver, British Columbia, Canada V6R 2J4.

CAREER: Ordained clergyman. Worked on farms, in a brick yard, on a railroad, and at Governor Kingston Gaol, 1917-19; University of Puget Sound, Tacoma, Wash., professor of history and sociology, 1923-29; University of British Columbia, Vancouver, associate professor of economics, political science, and sociology, 1929-42, professor of sociology, 1942-54, professor emeritus, 1954—. Visiting professor of criminology, University of Minnesota, 1946-47; professor of sociology at Wisconsin State College—Superior (now University of Wisconsin—Superior), 1959, and Willamette University, 1959-60; visiting professor at Queen's University at Kingston, Boston University, Claremont Colleges, and University of California, Los Angeles. *Military service:* Canadian Army, 1914-17; received Mons Star. Canadian Officers Training Corps, University of British Columbia Contingent, second in command, 1936-46. With Sixth Field Ambulance and 21st Battalion, Canadian Army, Infantry, 1939-45; became major.

MEMBER: American Sociological Association (fellow),

Canadian Sociological and Anthropological Association, National Society of Criminology, Canadian Association for the Prevention of Crime, National Society of Poets, Royal Canadian Legion (life member), Pacific Sociological Association, Social Science Research Council of the Pacific, John Howard Society of British Columbia (life member of board of directors), Faculty Club of University of British Columbia, West Point Grey Civic Association, Elizabeth Fry Society of British Columbia (patron and life member). *Awards, honors:* Canadian Social Science Research Council grant, 1942; Social Science Research Council (U.S.) grant, 1943.

WRITINGS: Canadian Penal Institutions, Ryerson, 1929, University of Chicago Press, 1930, revised edition, Humphries, 1943; (with Elmer Pendell) *Society under Analysis,* Cattell, 1942; (with Eric Pepler and E.G.B. Stevens) *Report of the British Columbia Crime Commission: 1950,* Queen's Printer, 1950; *The Family and Modern Marriage,* Bouregy & Curl, 1953; *Crime and You* (first appeared in *Winnipeg Tribune*), Ryerson, 1960; *Jewish Flower Child* (novel), McClelland & Stewart, 1970; *Hot Words with Music* (poems), Village Printwrights, 1971; *Jesus Christ Rabblerouser* (play), College Printers, 1975; *The Jesus Revolution,* College Printers, 1976. Contributor to annals and proceedings. Contributor to *Chatelaine, Saturday Night, Prison World,* sociology journals, and Canadian newspapers.

WORK IN PROGRESS: Asia: An Overview; Europe: An Overview; The Quest for Happiness; The Quest for Justice; The Quest for Truth; two plays, "Ici Vous Parlez Francais" and "Cry Strike, Cry Havoc."

SIDELIGHTS: C. W. Topping told *CA* that he began writing because he came to the conclusion that "the written word stood up much longer than the spoken word. My original aim was to save the fool from the foolkiller, but I found the task beyond my powers." Speaking of his novel, *Jewish Flower Child,* he states that it "was written to prove to the powerful men and women who dominate the Churches that Jesus of Nazareth repudiated the use of force in the achievement of his Kingdom of Heaven on Earth. Christianity, at its best, works like yeast in meal, like salt, like a seed thrust into soil."

*   *   *

TORBERT, William Rockwell 1944-

PERSONAL: Born February 8, 1944, in Washington, D.C.; son of Horace Gates, Jr. (a foreign service officer) and Anne (Holloway) Torbert. *Education:* Yale University, B.A. (magna cum laude), 1965, Ph.D., 1971. *Home and office:* 66 Palfrey Rd., Belmont, Mass. 02178.

CAREER: Legislative intern for Senator Claiborne Pell, summer, 1963; Rogers' Exploration Co., Mogadiscio, Somalia, surveyor, summer, 1963; consultant to Phillips Academy, Andover, Mass., 1968-69, and Danforth Foundation, St. Louis, Mo., 1969-70; Southern Methodist University, Dallas, Tex., assistant professor of business administration, 1970-72; Harvard University, Cambridge, Mass., associate professor of education, 1972-76; The Theatre of Inquiry, Inc., Belmont, Mass., president, 1977—. *Member:* Society for Values in Higher Education, Phi Beta Kappa. *Awards, honors:* Danforth Foundation fellowship, 1966-70.

WRITINGS: (Contributor) Philip Runkel, Roger Harrison, and Margaret Runkel, editors, *The Changing College Classroom,* Jossey-Bass, 1969; (with Malcolm P. Rogers) *Being for the Most Part Puppets: Interactions among Men's Labor, Leisure, and Politics,* Schenkman, 1973; *Learning from*

Experience: Toward Consciousness, Columbia University Press, 1973; *Creating a Community of Inquiry,* Wiley, 1976; (contributor) Arthur Chickering, editor, *The Future American College,* Jossey-Bass, 1979. Contributor to *Journal of Applied Behavioral Science, Humanitas,* and *Journal of Higher Education.* Vice-chairman, *Yale Daily News,* 1963-64.

*   *   *

TOWN, Harold (Barling) 1924-

PERSONAL: Born June 13, 1924, in Toronto, Ontario, Canada; son of William Harry and Ellen Noelice (Watson) Town; married Trudella Carol Tredwell (a librarian), September 7, 1957; children: Heather Allison, Shelley Katherine. *Education:* Ontario College of Art, O.C.A., 1945. *Home:* 9 Castle Frank Crescent, Toronto, Ontario, Canada M4W 3A2. *Office:* 25 Severn St., Toronto, Ontario, Canada.

CAREER: Artist (painter, sculptor, print-maker). Art represented in numerous permanent collections, including Museum of Modern Art (New York, N.Y.), Guggenheim Museum, Tate Gallery (London), National Gallery of Canada, Stedelijk Museum (Amsterdam), Museum of Modern Art (Sao Paulo), Museo de Arte Contemporaneo (Santiago), Galleria d'Art di Villa Ciani (Lugano, Switzerland), and Albertina Museum (Vienna). Commissioned work includes murals for St. Lawrence Seaway and Power Dam (Cornwall, Ontario), 1958, mural and sculpture for Malton International Airport (Ontario), 1962-63, mural for Telegram Building (Toronto), 1963, and painting for Queen's Park Project (Toronto), 1967. Exhibitions include: Venice Biennale, 1956, 1964, 1972; Sao Paulo Biennale, 1957, 1961; 2nd, 3rd, 4th, 5th, and 6th exposition gravure (Ljubljana, Yugoslavia); Documenta (Kassel, Germany), 1964; Carnegie International, 1964; Arte de America y Espana, 1964-65; British International Print Biennale, Bradford, 1968; Harold Town: The First Exhibition of New York, 1969-73, Robert McLaughlin Gallery (Oshawa, Ontario), 1973; Indications . . . Harold Town, 1944-75, Art Gallery of Windsor (Windsor, Ontario), 1975. Has designed sets and costumes for National Ballet Co. of Canada. Member of board of governors, Ontario Art College, 1970-71.

MEMBER: Royal Canadian Academy. *Awards, honors:* Medal from Toronto Art Directors, 1949, 1950, 1954; Arno Prize, Sao Paulo Biennale, 1957; international prize for exhibition of drawings and prints, Lugano, Switzerland, 1958; fellowship for Instituto de Cultura Hispanica, Arte de America y Espana, 1963; medal from Montreal Art Directors Club, 1963; A. H. Robinson Award from Montreal Museum of Fine Arts, 1963; women's committee award from Toronto Art Gallery, 1963; D.H.L., York University, 1966; centennial medal, Government of Canada, 1967; named Officer of the Order of Canada, 1969; honorary fellow, Founders College, York University.

WRITINGS—All published by McClelland and Stewart: *Enigmas* (self-illustrated), 1964; *Drawings [by] Harold Town,* with introduction and text by Robert Fulford, 1969; *Silent Stars, Sound Stars, Film Stars* (self-illustrated), 1971; *Albert Franck: Keeper of the Lanes,* 1974; (with David Silcox) *Tom Thomson: The Silence and the Storm,* 1977.

Illustrator: Irving Layton, editor, *Love Where the Nights Are Long,* 1962; Sylvia Fraser, *Pandora,* 1972. Has also illustrated book covers. Columnist, *Toronto Life,* 1966-71. Contributor to *Canadian Forum, Image, Canadian Art Today, Great Canadians, Imperial Oil Review, Chatelaine, Globe & Mail,* and other journals and newspapers.

WORK IN PROGRESS: An illustrated book, *The Toy Horse;* a biography of James Wilson Morrice, with David Silcox.

BIOGRAPHICAL/CRITICAL SOURCES: Herbert Read, *A Concise History of Modern Painting,* Praeger, 1959; Harriet Janis and Rudi Blesh, *Collage,* Chilton, 1962; Kurt Sternelk, compiler, *Graphic Arts in the Twentieth Century,* Praeger, 1963; *Artscanada,* April-May, 1971; *Playback,* McClelland and Stewart, 1978.

* * *

TOWNSEND, Charles E(dward) 1932-

PERSONAL: Born September 29, 1932, in New Rochelle, N.Y.; son of Charles Edward (in advertising) and Lois (Fukushima) Townsend; married Janet Linner, 1957; children: Erica, Sylvia, Louise. *Education:* Yale University, A.B., 1954; Harvard University, A.M., 1960, Ph.D., 1962. *Home:* 145 Hickory Ct., Princeton, N.J. 08540. *Office:* Department of Slavic Languages and Literature, Princeton University, 028 East Pyne, Princeton, N.J. 08540.

CAREER: Harvard University, Cambridge, Mass., instructor, 1962-65, assistant professor of Slavic languages and literature, 1965-66; Princeton University, Princeton, N.J., assistant professor, 1966-68, associate professor, 1968-71, professor of Slavic languages and literature, 1971—, chairman of department, 1970—, director of Critical Languages Program, 1968-70. Fulbright scholar at University of Bonn, 1954-55. *Military service:* U.S. Army, 1955-58. *Member:* American Association of Teachers of Slavic and East European Languages, Linguistic Society of America. *Awards, honors:* Recipient of numerous grants and fellowships.

WRITINGS: Russian Word-Formation, McGraw, 1968; *Continuing with Russian,* McGraw, 1970; *Memoirs of Natal'ja Borisovna Dolgorukaja,* Slavica, 1977.

* * *

TRACI, Philip (Joseph) 1934-

PERSONAL: Surname is pronounced *Tray*-see; born June 27, 1934, in East Cleveland, Ohio; son of Joseph Anthony and Mary Elizabeth (Gallitte) Traci. *Education:* Western Reserve University (now Case Western Reserve University), B.A. (magna cum laude), 1956; Duke University, M.A., 1958, Ph.D., 1965; also studied at Harvard University, 1959-60. *Residence:* Detroit, Mich. *Office:* Department of English, Wayne State University, Detroit, Mich. 48202.

CAREER: Tufts University, Medford, Mass., instructor in English, 1959-60, 1961-63; Sir George Williams University, Montreal, Quebec, assistant professor of English, 1965-66; Drew University, Madison N.J., assistant professor of English, 1966-69; Wayne State University, Detroit, Mich., associate professor of English, 1969—. *Member:* Modern Language Association of America, Renaissance Society of America, Shakespeare Association of America, Midwestern Modern Language Association, Southeastern Renaissance Conference, Michigan College English Association, Michigan Academy of Arts and Sciences, Phi Beta Kappa. *Awards, honors:* Danforth grant, 1963-64.

WRITINGS: The Love Play of "Antony and Cleopatra": A Critical Study of Shakespeare's Play, Mouton, 1970. Contributor to literature journals, including *South Atlantic Quarterly, English Journal, Renaissance Papers, Drama Critique,* and *Discourse: A Review of the Liberal Arts.*

TRAGER, George L(eonard) 1906-

PERSONAL: Born March 22, 1906, in Newark, N.J.; son of Leon (a mechanical engineer) and Anna (Emilfork) Trager; married Sadie Grabelle, June 24, 1929 (died February 20, 1950); married Edith E. Crowell Johnson, March 1, 1951 (divorced February 20, 1961); married Felicia E. Harben (a university professor), June 10, 1961 (died February 21, 1972); children: (first marriage) George W., Jane (Mrs. Thomas Welles), T. Snyder; (second marriage) James Crowell, Geoffrey Crossland, John Noyes; (third marriage) Edward Harben, Anne Valerie. *Education:* Rutgers University, B.Litt., 1926; Columbia University, A.M., 1929, Ph.D., 1932. *Politics:* Democrat. *Religion:* Episcopalian. *Address:* P.O. Box 85, Taos, N.M. 87571.

CAREER: Teacher in public schools in New Jersey, 1927-29; Midland College, Fremont, Neb., assistant professor of modern languages, 1929-30; Adams State College, Alamosa, Colo., professor of foreign languages, 1934-36; Yale University, New Haven, Conn., Sterling Research Fellow, 1936-41, assistant professor of Slavic, 1942-44; U.S. Department of the Interior, Geography Division, Washington, D.C., chief of linguistics branch, 1944-46; University of Oklahoma, Norman, professor of anthropology, 1946-48; U.S. Department of State, Foreign Service Institute, Washington, D.C., professor of linguistics and director of linguistic research, 1948-53; American University, Washington, D.C., assistant director, Human Relations Area Files, 1955-56; State University of New York at Buffalo, professor of anthropology and linguistics, 1956-67, chairman of department of modern languages, 1956-68; Southern Methodist University, Dallas, Tex., professor of anthropology, 1967-71, professor emeritus, 1971—; Northern Illinois University, DeKalb, professor of anthropology, 1971-74; Fort Burgwin Research Center, Taos, N.M., research associate, 1974—. Visiting professor, Georgetown University, Institute of Languages and Linguistics, 1954-55; psychiatric interview researcher, State University of New York, Upstate Medical Center, 1956-59; Ford Foundation lecturer in linguistics, University of Edinburgh, 1959.

MEMBER: Linguistic Society of America (president, 1960), American Anthropological Association (fellow), American Association for the Advancement of Science (fellow), American Folklore Society, Societe des Americanistes, Societe de Linguistique, International Phonetic Association (London), Current Anthropology Associates, Sigma Xi. *Awards, honors:* Yale University Institute of Human Relations summer grant, 1937; Guggenheim fellow at Yale University, 1942-43; American Philosophical Society grant, 1947; National Science Foundation research grants, 1960-62 (New Mexico), 1963-64, 1965-67; Center for Advanced Study in the Behavioral Sciences fellow, 1962-63.

WRITINGS: The Kiev Fragment, Linguistic Society of America, 1932; *The Use of Latin Demonstratives,* Institute of French Studies, 1934; (with Bernard Bloch) *Outline of Linguistic Analysis,* Linguistic Society of America, 1942; (with H. L. Smith) *An Outline of English Structure,* Studies in Linguistics, 1951; *Semology, Metalinguistics and Translation,* Mouton, 1968; *Language and Languages,* Intext, 1972. Contributor of about three hundred articles and reviews to professional journals. Editor and founder, *Studies in Linguistics.*

WORK IN PROGRESS: English and Its Relatives; The Non-Western Languages; further research on language and culture of Indians of Taos Pueblo, N.M., and related peoples of the American Southwest.†

TRASK, Roger R(eed) 1930-

PERSONAL: Born September 14, 1930, in Erie, Pa.; son of Hugh A. (a postman) and Ruth (Miller) Trask; married Dorothy Buettner, January 14, 1956; children: Julianne, Laurence, Carolyn. *Education:* Thiel College, A.B., 1952; Pennsylvania State University, M.A., 1954, Ph.D., 1959. *Home:* 8431 Del Rey Ct., No. 6, Tampa, Fla. 33617. *Office:* Department of Interdisciplinary Social Sciences, University of South Florida, Tampa, Fla. 33620.

CAREER: Upsala College, East Orange, N.J., instructor, 1959-60, assistant professor of history, 1960-62; Thiel College, Greenville, Pa., assistant professor of history, 1962-64; Macalester College, St. Paul, Minn., assistant professor, 1964-68, associate professor, 1968-72, professor of history, 1972-74; University of South Florida, Tampa, professor of history and international studies, 1974—. Visiting lecturer at University of Illinois, 1967-68. Chief historian, U.S. Nuclear Regulatory Commission, Washington, D.C., 1977-78. *Military service:* U.S. Army, 1954-55. *Member:* American Historical Association, Organization of American Historians, Society for Historians of American Foreign Relations.

WRITINGS: (Contributor) Sidney Devere Brown, editor, *Studies in Asia, 1967,* University of Nebraska Press, 1968; (editor with D. F. Trask and Michael C. Meyer) *A Bibliography of the United States-Latin American Relations since 1810,* University of Nebraska Press, 1968; (editor with J. A. DeNovo and others) *Selected Readings in American History,* two volumes, Scribner, 1969; *The United States Response to Turkish Nationalism and Reform, 1914-1939,* University of Minnesota Press, 1971; (contributor) Roberto Esquenazi-Mayo and Meyer, editors, *Latin American Scholarship since World War II,* University of Nebraska Press, 1971; (contributor) *The Gilded Age and After,* Scribner, 1972. Contributor to *Business History Review, Pennsylvania History, Diplomatic History, Historian, Muslim World,* and *Mid-America.*

WORK IN PROGRESS: A book on the relations of the United States and Mexico, 1876-1911; an interpretive history of United States-Latin American relations since the American Revolution.

*   *   *

TRAUGOTT, Elizabeth Closs 1939-
  (Elizabeth Closs)

PERSONAL: Born April 9, 1939; daughter of August (a professor) and Hannah (Priebsch) Closs; married John L. Traugott (a professor), September 25, 1967; children: Isabel M. *Education:* Oxford University, B.A., 1960, M.A., 1964; University of California, Berkeley, Ph.D., 1964. *Home:* 270 Alvarado Rd., Berkeley, Calif. 94705. *Office:* Department of English, Stanford University, Stanford, Calif. 94305.

CAREER: University of California, Berkeley, assistant professor of English, 1964-69; Stanford University, Stanford, Calif., lecturer, 1968-71, associate professor, 1971-76, professor of linguistics and English, 1976—. Lecturer in linguistics at University of East Africa, 1965-66, and University of York, 1966-67. *Member:* Linguistic Society of America, Linguistic Society of Great Britain, International Linguistic Association, Philological Association of the Pacific Coast, California Linguistic Association. *Awards, honors:* American Council of Learned Societies fellow, 1975-76.

WRITINGS: A History of English Syntax: A Transformational Approach to the History of English Sentence Structure, Holt, 1972; (contributor) D. Harrison and T. Trebasso,

editors, *Black English,* Erlbaum Associates, 1975; (contributor) A. Valdman, editor, *Pidgin and Creole Linguistics,* Indiana University Press, 1977. Contributor to language journals, sometimes under the name, Elizabeth Closs, including *Language, Lingua, Journal of African Languages, Journal of Linguistics,* and *Semiotica.*

WORK IN PROGRESS: Research on relation of language acquistion to historical change in language, on relation of time to space terms in language, and on linguistics and literature.

*   *   *

TRAUPMAN, John C. 1923-

PERSONAL: Born January 2, 1923, in Nazareth, Pa.; son of John and Marie (Bani) Traupman; married Polly Temmel, April 23, 1949; children: Diane. *Education:* Moravian College, B.A., 1948; Princeton University, M.A., 1950, Ph.D., 1956. *Politics:* Republican. *Religion:* Roman Catholic. *Home:* 201 Tower Lane, Penn Valley, Nazareth, Pa. 19072. *Office:* Department of Classical Languages, St. Joseph's University, 54th St. and City Ave., Philadelphia, Pa. 19131.

CAREER: St. Joseph's University, Philadelphia, Pa., member of classical languages faculty, 1951—. *Military service:* U.S. Army, 1943-46; became sergeant major. *Member:* American Philological Association, Classical Association of the Atlantic States, Classical and Modern Language League (president, 1968-73), Pennsylvania Classical Association (president, 1971-73), Philadelphia Classical Society.

WRITINGS: (Compiler) *New College Latin and English Dictionary,* Bantam, 1966; (compiler) *Bantam German and (American) English Dictionary,* Bantam, 1979.

*   *   *

TRELL, Max 1900-

PERSONAL: Born September 6, 1900, in New York, N.Y.; son of Salomon and Sophia (Levine) Trell; married Bluma L. Popkin (a professor of classics), September 6, 1926; children: Max, Jr. *Education:* Columbia University, B.A., 1923; Sorbonne, University of Paris, graduate study, 1929-30. *Politics:* Democrat. *Home:* 110 Bleecker St., New York, N.Y. 10012; and Park West Apts., London W.2, England.

CAREER: Zits Theatrical Weekly, New York City, reporter, 1924; *New York Daily News,* New York City, reporter, 1925-27; Warner Brothers, New York City, story editor, 1927-32; *Pictorial Review,* New York City, associate editor, 1934-39. Producer and director of films for Columbia Pictures, "Arrivederci Roma," 1960, and "The Making of Oliver Cromwell," 1970. *Military service:* U.S. Navy, officers' training, World War I. U.S. Army, Signal Corps, training films section, 1942-46; became captain. *Member:* Screen Writers Guild West. *Awards, honors:* Academy Award for story and narration, 1947, for "Climbing the Matterhorn," a short movie; Freedoms Foundation Award, 1948, for story and continuity of "Dick's Adventures," a syndicated cartoon feature based on American history.

WRITINGS: Tom and Mot (juvenile), Cosmopolitan Book Corp., 1930; *Lawyer Man* (novel), Macauley, 1934; *Shirley Temple: My Life and Times,* Saalfield, 1938; *Now I Am Eight: By Shirley Temple As Told to Max Trell,* Saalfield, 1938; *Just This Once* (novel), Cosmopolitan Book Corp., 1950; *Prince Valiant* (text adaptation of comic strip by the artist Hal Foster), five volumes, Hastings House, 1951-54; *The Small Gods and Mr. Barnum* (novel), Saturday Review Press, 1971.

Author of screenplays: "High Conquest," 1947; "Climbing the Matterhorn," 1947; "Sixteen Fathoms Deep," 1948; "New Mexico," 1950; "Hell Below Zero," 1954. Author of daily syndicated juvenile fiction for King Features, Inc., 1926-56, and author of syndicated cartoon feature, "Dick's Adventures."

WORK IN PROGRESS: Research for a biography of Peter the Great.

SIDELIGHTS: Max Trell told *CA:* "Around the turn of the century I emerged in a tenement in the lower east end of New York, kicking and screaming as customary. Years later my mother in a confidential mood let me in on a secret. I was not kicking. I was dancing. I was not screaming. I was singing 'I love New York.' Having established this, let me proceed with New York vis-a-vis me. For instance, my formal education began in the streets of New York, my formula education reached a climax in the potted ivy cloisters of Columbia University, Morningside Heights, New York, class (if this is the proper word) of 1923. Being now ready to take on the world, I found myself more than ever taken on by New York, viz., the *Bronx Home News, Zit's Theatrical Weekly* (mainly Broadway demi-scandal), the *New York Daily News, Pictorial Review* magazine . . . King Features Syndicate . . . Warner Brothers Pictures (east Coast story department, New York), Signal Corps, U.S. Army, training films section (Paramount Studios, Astoria, L.I., New York), post bellum stories, articles, books, all published in New York, some written near a window overlooking the United Nations, some written and re-written by a window thirty floors up looking over but never overlooking New York harbor; some titles turning up on the shelves and in the catalogue files at the New York Public Library; some titles turning rebel and chasing the dollar to Hollywood and the pound sterling to London. To top it all, I married in New York, had a son in New York, and my wife is a professor at New York University, Washington Square, Greenwich Village, the oldest and youngest heart beat of New York. One day from a cloud above or a brimstone pond below I will have the eternity to figure out what this all means and whether my mother gave me New York, or New York gave me my mother along with all else."

Max Trell's *Lawyer Man* was adapted for movie production by Warner Brothers in 1935 and his *Just This Once* by Metro-Goldwyn-Mayer in 1951. Trell has traveled widely in the United States and abroad, including the Near East. He reads French, German, and Spanish, a little Italian and Dutch.

* * *

TREMBLAY, Marc-Adelard 1922-

PERSONAL: Born April 24, 1922, in Les Eboulements, Quebec, Canada; son of Willie and Laurette (Tremblay) Tremblay; married Jacqueline Cyr, December 27, 1949; children: Genevieve, Lorraine, Marc, Colette, Dominique, Suzanne. *Education:* University of Montreal, B.A., 1944, L.S.A., 1948; Laval University, M.A., 1950; Cornell University, Ph.D., 1954. *Religion:* Roman Catholic. *Home:* 835 Nouvelle-Orleans, Sainte Foy, Quebec, Canada. *Office:* Dean, Graduate School, Laval University, Quebec, Quebec, Canada.

CAREER: Cornell University, Ithaca, N.Y., research associate, 1953-56; Laval University, Quebec, Quebec, assistant professor, 1956-58, associate professor, 1958-63, professor of anthropology, 1963-69, vice-dean of social sciences, 1969-71, dean of graduate school, 1971—. *Member:* American

Anthropological Association (fellow), Society for Applied Anthropology, Canadian Sociology and Anthropology Association (founding president, 1965), Canadian Association of University Teachers, Royal Society of Canada, Academie des Sciences Morales et Politiques (Canada).

WRITINGS: (With C. C. Hughes, R.N. Rapoport, and A. H. Leighton) *People of Cove and Woodlot,* Basic Books, 1960; (with G. Fortin) *Les Comportements economiques de la famille salariee,* Laval University, 1964; *Initiation a la recherche dans les sciences humaines,* McGraw, 1968; (with Marc Laplante) *Famille et parente en Acadie,* National Museum, 1971; (editor with G. Gold) *Communautes et culture,* Holt, 1972. Contributor of more than sixty articles to journals in his field.

WORK IN PROGRESS: Towards an Anthropology of Health; The Ethnology of the North Shore of the St. Lawrence River.

* * *

TRIANDIS, Harry C(haralambos) 1926-

PERSONAL: Born October 16, 1926, in Patras, Greece; son of Christos C. (an engineer) and Louise (Nicocavouras) Triandis; married Leigh Minturn, December 29, 1958 (divorced June, 1966); married Pola Fotitch (a translator), December 23, 1966; children: (second marriage) Louise Tatiana. *Education:* McGill University, B.Eng., 1951; University of Toronto, M.Com., 1954; Cornell University, Ph.D., 1958. *Politics:* Independent. *Religion:* Unaffiliated. *Home:* 1 Lake Park Rd., Champaign, Ill. 61820. *Office:* Department of Psychology, University of Illinois, Champaign, Ill. 61820.

CAREER: Proctor & Gamble of Canada, Hamilton, Ontario, methods engineer, 1951-54; McGill University, Montreal, Quebec, lecturer in industrial engineering, 1954; University of Illinois at Urbana-Champaign, assistant professor, 1958-61, associate professor, 1961-66, professor of psychology, 1966—. Lecturer, National Science Foundation Visiting Scientist Program, 1961-62. Consultant to U.S. Navy, U.S. Information Service, and National Science Foundation. *Member:* American Psychological Association (fellow), American Association for the Advancement of Science, International Association of Cross-Cultural Psychologists (president, 1974-76). *Awards, honors:* Ford Foundation faculty fellow, 1964-65; Guggenheim fellow, 1972-73.

WRITINGS: (With Leigh M. Triandis) *A Cross-Cultural Study of Social Distance* (monograph), American Psychological Association, 1962; (with Vasso Vassiliou and Maria Nassiakou) *Three Studies of Subjective Culture* (monograph), American Psychological Association, 1968; *Attitude and Attitude Change,* Wiley, 1971; *The Analysis of Subjective Culture,* Wiley, 1972; *Variations of Black and White Perceptions of the Social Environment,* University of Illinois Press, 1976; *Interpersonal Behavior,* Brooks/Cole, 1977. Member of editorial board of *Journal of Applied Psychology, Journal of Cross-Cultural Psychology, Journal of Applied Social Psychology,* and *Sociometry.*

WORK IN PROGRESS: Studying adjustment of blacks to white middle-class jobs; developing materials to provide cross-cultural training; research on black and white middle-class subjective cultures.

AVOCATIONAL INTERESTS: Chamber music.

* * *

TRINKLEIN, Frederick E(rnst) 1924-

PERSONAL: Born April 12, 1924, in Frankenmuth, Mich.;

son of Richard Jacob (a merchant) and Louise (Gugel) Trinklein; married Margaret Friedrich, June 8, 1946; children: Susan, Gretchen, Friedrich, Barbara, John. *Education:* Concordia Teachers College, River Forest, Ill., B.S., 1945; Northwestern University, M.A., 1952; University of Wisconsin—Milwaukee, graduate study, 1961. *Religion:* Lutheran (Missouri Synod). *Home and office:* 131 Brookville Rd., Brookville, N.Y. 11545. *Agent:* Gerald McCauley, 209 East 56th St., New York, N.Y. 10022.

CAREER: Parochial elementary school teacher-principal in Alva, Okla., 1946-47; parochial high school science-mathematics chairman in Racine, Wis., 1947-62; Long Island Lutheran High School, Brookville, N.Y., science chairman, 1962—. Adjunct assistant professor in astronomy at Nassau Community College and C. W. Post College, 1970—. Conducted solar eclipse expeditions to southern Mexico, 1970, East Africa, 1973, and Western Australia, 1974; consultant and designer, Trippensee Planetarium Co. *Member:* National Science Teachers Association, American Association for the Advancement of Science, American Association of Physics Teachers, National Aerospace Education Association, Association of Lutheran Secondary Schools (member of curriculum commission).

WRITINGS: (With Charles M. Huffer) *Modern Space Science,* Holt, 1961; (with Huffer and Mark Bunge) *An Introduction to Astronomy,* Holt, 1967, 2nd edition, 1973; (with John E. Williams, H. Clark Metcalf, and Ralph W. Lefler) *Modern Physics,* Holt, 1968, revised edition, 1976; *The God of Science,* Eerdmans, 1971. Writer of educational syllabi, religious tracts, and contributor to journals.

WORK IN PROGRESS: With John E. Williams and H. Clark Metcalfe, a revision of *Modern Physics;* with Enrico Cantore, a revision of *The God of Science,* for Institute for Scientific Humanism.

SIDELIGHTS: Frederick Trinklein lectures extensively in churches on the relationship between reason and faith. *The God of Science* relates his interviews with thirty-eight leading European and American scientists and technologists on this topic. Trinklein says: "I agree emphatically with the statement by the late Dr. Wernher von Braun that science and faith are the two predominant forces of the Twentieth Century. Furthermore, I am convinced that when the true harmony between these two forces is established, we will enter upon an era of unprecedented progress and integrity."

*   *   *

TRISCO, Robert Frederick   1929-

PERSONAL: Born November 11, 1929, in Chicago, Ill.; son of Richard E. and Harriet Rose (Hardt) Trisco. *Education:* St. Mary of the Lake Seminary, B.A., 1951; Pontifical Gregorian University, S.T.L., 1955, Hist.Eccl.D., 1962. *Home and office address:* Catholic University of America, Washington, D.C. 20064.

CAREER: Ordained priest, 1954; Catholic University of America, Washington, D.C., instructor, 1959-63, assistant professor, 1963-65, associate professor, 1965-75, professor of church history, 1975—, vice-rector for academic affairs, 1966-68. *Peritus* of Second Vatican Council, 1962-65; president of American Subcommission for Comparative Church History, 1978-80. *Member:* American Catholic Historical Association (executive secretary, 1961—), American Society of Church History. *Awards, honors:* Benemerenti gold medal of Pope Pius XII, 1957.

WRITINGS: The Holy See and the Nascent Church in the

Middle Western United States, 1826-1850, Gregorian University Press, 1962; (contributor) John Tracy Ellis, editor, *The Catholic Priest in the United States: Historical Investigations,* St. John's University Press, 1971; (editor) *Catholics in America, 1776-1976,* National Conference of Catholic Bishops, 1976; (contributor) Huber Jedin, editor, *Handbuch der Kirchengeschichte,* Volume VII: *1914-1970,* Herder, 1978. *Catholic Historical Review,* associate editor, 1959-63, editor, 1963—.

WORK IN PROGRESS: Chicago in the History of American Catholicism to 1915.

*   *   *

TROMANHAUSER, Edward (Downer)   1932-

PERSONAL: Born August 30, 1932, in Minneapolis, Minn.; son of Haver D. and Frances L. (Rowe) Tromanhauser. *Education:* Northern Illinois University, B.A., 1966; Chicago State University, M.S., 1973; University of Illinois at Urbana-Champaign, M.A., 1975. *Politics:* Liberal. *Religion:* Protestant. *Home:* 831 North Fair Oaks, Oak Park, Ill. 60302. *Agent:* Ellen Levine, Curtis Brown Ltd., 60 East 56th St., New York, N.Y. 10022. *Office:* Department of Psychology, Chicago State University, Chicago, Ill.

CAREER: Contact, Inc., Chicago, Ill., vice-president, 1971; Chicago State University, Chicago, Ill., assistant professor of psychology and director of Center for Corrections, 1970—. Member of executive committee of Chicago Alliance for a Safer City; member of executive committee and training director for Project Reconciliation; president of Illinois Academy of Criminology, 1975; member of board of trustees of Institute for Social Adjustment. *Member:* American Correctional Association, American Academy of Criminology, National Council on Crime and Delinquency.

WRITINGS: (Editor) *Study Guide for Educational Psychology,* Chicago City Colleges, 1968; (with H. Jack Griswold and others) *An Eye for an Eye,* Holt, 1970; (co-author) *An Introduction to Corrections Counseling,* Chicago State University, 1971; (contributor) *Justice, Punishment, Treatment,* Free Press, 1973; (contributor) *American Courts and Justice,* American Judicature Society, 1976. Author with Gus Wilhelmy, *Volunteer Training Manual,* for the Portland Cement Association in 1971. Contributor to *Journal of Clinical Psychology, American Correctional Association Journal, Journal of Correctional Education, Illinois Journal of Rehabilitation Counseling, New York Law Review, Chicago-Kent Law Review,* and *Crime and Delinquency.*

WORK IN PROGRESS: Co-authoring *The Addicts World,* a book about drug addiction, for Hawthorn; editing *Workbook in Educational Psychology* and *Corrections: A Policy Perspective.*

*   *   *

TRUE, Michael   1933-

PERSONAL: Born November 8, 1933, in Oklahoma City, Okla.; son of Guy Herbert and Agnes (Murphy) True; married Mary Patricia Delaney, April 20, 1958; children: Mary, Michael, John, Christopher, Elizabeth, Anne. *Education:* University of Oklahoma, B.A., 1955; University of Minnesota, M.A., 1957; Duke University, Ph.D., 1964; Harvard University, postdoctoral study, 1967-68. *Religion:* Roman Catholic. *Home:* 4 Westland St., Worcester, Mass. 01602. *Office:* Department of English, Assumption College, Worcester, Mass. 01609.

CAREER: Remington Rand Univac, St. Paul, Minn., technical writer, 1958-59; Duke University, Durham, N.C., lecturer in English, 1960-61; North Carolina College at Durham (now North Carolina Central University), lecturer in English, 1961; Indiana State University, Terre Haute, assistant professor of English, 1961-65; Assumption College, Worcester, Mass., associate professor of English, 1965—, chairman of department, 1974-76. Visiting professor of education and English, Clark University, 1967—; visiting scholar, Columbia University, 1976-77. Consultant in non-fiction writing, Upper Midwest Writer's Conference, 1973, 1975, 1977-78; consultant to University of Central Arkansas Writers Conference, 1976-77. Member, National Humanities Faculty, 1977—. *Military service:* U.S. Army, 1957-58. *Member:* American Studies Association, National Council of Teachers of English (director, 1973-78), Modern Language Association of America, New England College English Association (director, 1965-69, 1975—).

WRITINGS: Should the Catholic College Survive? and Other Impertinent Questions, Assumption Student Press, 1971; *Worcester Poets, with Notes Toward a Literary History,* Worcester County Poetry Association, 1972; (contributor of critical essays) James Vinson, editor, *Contemporary Poets,* St. Martin's, 1975; (contributor) *Three Mountains Press Poetry Anthology, 1975,* edited by Denis Carbonneau, Three Mountains Press, 1976; *Poets in the Schools: A Handbook,* National Council of Teachers of English, 1976; *Thomas Paine* (pamphlet), Scribner, 1978. Contributor to *Commonweal, Progressive, New Republic, National Catholic Reporter, Cross-Currents, Critic, Papers on Language and Literature, Catholic Worker, Bulletin of the New York Public Library, Win,* and other professional journals. Editor, *Worcester Review.*

WORK IN PROGRESS: A study of the American radical tradition in literature, from Thomas Paine to Paul Goodman and Dorothy Day; essays on the poetry of Wilfred Owen and the fiction of J. F. Powers; encouraging and building communities of nonviolence.

SIDELIGHTS: Michael True told *CA:* "Anything that I have written that I can reread without embarassment was usually written with a mind to recovering the sound and rhythm of language heard and still sounding in my ear. It is the language of my native locale, probably, or of a particular moment, place, or person. I am fascinated by the ordinary—the mundane, if you will, and by people who try to build community nonviolently, through their lives and their art. I began as a teacher, not knowing how to write. But I'm learning. As my writing improves, so does my teaching (I think). I hope I can keep that going. I want to write good clear prose, like Orwell's. I want to write a 'listening' prose that says to the reader: 'I am truly interested in your response, in what you have to say'; that says, 'I respect your life, the confusion and pain of it'; that says, 'I allow for your ignorance, so that you and I can acknowledge what we don't know, and so find out and move on.'"

*   *   *

TRUEBLOOD, D(avid) Elton 1900-

PERSONAL: Born December 12, 1900, in Pleasantville, Iowa; son of Samuel J. (a farmer) and Effie (Crew) Trueblood; married Pauline Goodenow, August 24, 1924 (died, 1955); married Virginia Hodgin, August 5, 1956; children: (first marriage) Martin, Arnold, Samuel J. II, Elizabeth (Mrs. Daniel Derr). *Education:* Penn College (now William Penn College), A.B., 1922; attended Brown University, 1922-23, and Hartford Theological Seminary, 1923-24; Har-

vard University, S.T.B., 1926; Johns Hopkins University, Ph.D., 1934. *Politics:* Republican. *Religion:* Quaker. *Home:* 230 College Ave., Richmond, Ind. 47374. *Office:* Earlham College, Richmond, Ind. 47374.

CAREER: Guilford College, Greensboro, N.C., dean of men and professor of philosophy, 1927-30; Haverford College, Haverford, Pa., assistant professor of philosophy, 1933-36; Stanford University, Stanford, Calif., professor of philosophy of religion, 1936-45, chaplain, 1936-45; Earlham College, Richmond, Ind., professor of philosophy, 1946-66, Doan Distinguished Professor, 1964, professor-at-large, 1966—. Acting chaplain at Harvard University, summer, 1935; fellow of Woodbrooke, 1939; Swarthmore Lecturer, London, England, 1939; acting professor at Harvard University, 1944, and Garrett Theological Seminary, 1944, 1945, 1946; Purington lecturer at Mount Holyoke College, 1970. Chief of religious information for U.S. Information Agency, 1954-55; member of board of directors at William Penn College; founder and president of Yokefellow International.

MEMBER: Council on Religion in International Affairs (honorary trustee). *Awards, honors:* Litt.D., Washington and Lee University, 1949, University of Vermont, 1951, William Penn College, 1959, Tarkio College, 1963; LL.D., Miami University, Oxford, Ohio, 1951; S.T.D., Ripon College, 1954, McKendree College, 1969; L.H.D., Simpson College, 1955, Otterbein College, 1960, Pepperdine University, 1971; D.D., Kenyon College, 1964; named churchman of the year by *American Heritage,* 1960.

WRITINGS: The Essence of Spiritual Religion, Harper, 1936, new edition, 1975; *The Trustworthiness of Religious Experience,* Allen & Unwin, 1939; *The Knowledge of God,* Harper, 1939; *The Logic of Belief,* Harper, 1942; *The Predicament of Modern Man,* Harper, 1944; *Foundations for Reconstruction,* Harper, 1946, new edition, Word Books, 1972; *Dr. Johnson's Prayers,* Harper, 1947; *Alternative to Futility,* Harper, 1948, new edition, Word Books, 1972; *The Common Ventures of Life: Marriage-Birth-Work-Death,* Harper, 1949, new edition, Word Books, 1975.

The Signs of Hope in a Century of Despair, Harper, 1950; *The Life We Prize,* Harper, 1951; *Your Other Vocation,* Harper, 1952, new edition, 1976; (with wife, Pauline Trueblood) *The Recovery of Family Life,* Harper, 1953; *Declaration of Freedom,* Harper, 1955; *Philosophy of Religion,* Harper, 1957; *The Yoke of Christ,* Harper, 1958; *The Idea of a College,* Harper, 1959; *Confronting Christ,* Harper, 1960; *The Company of the Committed,* Harper, 1961; *General Philosophy,* Harper, 1963; *The Humor of Christ,* Harper, 1964; *The Lord's Prayers,* Harper, 1965; *The People Called Quakers,* Harper, 1966; *The Incendiary Fellowship,* Harper, 1967; *Robert Barclay,* Harper, 1968; *A Place to Stand,* Harper, 1969.

The New Man for Our Time, Harper, 1970; *The Future of the Christian,* Harper, 1971; *The Validity of the Christian Mission,* Harper, 1972; *Abraham Lincoln: Theologian of American Anguish,* Harper, 1973; *While It Is Day* (autobiography), Harper, 1974. Contributor to magazines. Editor of *Friend,* 1935-45.

*   *   *

TRUZZI, Marcello 1935-

PERSONAL: Born September 6, 1935, in Copenhagen, Denmark; son of Massimiliano and Sofia (Zyrlin) Truzzi; married Patricia L. Eatherly (a commercial artist), November 20, 1958; children: Gianni Amile, Kristofer Stuart. *Education:* Florida State University, B.A., 1957; University of Florida, M.A., 1962; Cornell University, Ph.D., 1970. *Politics:* Liberal Democrat. *Religion:* Agnostic. *Home:* 1323 Culver Rd., Ann Arbor, Mich. 48103. *Office:* Department of Sociology, Eastern Michigan University, Ypsilanti, Mich. 48197.

CAREER: University of South Florida, Tampa, instructor in sociology, 1966-68; University of Michigan, Ann Arbor, assistant professor of sociology, 1968-71; New College, Sarasota, Fla., associate professor of sociology, 1971-74; Eastern Michigan University, Ypsilanti, professor of sociology, 1974—. Visiting instructor in sociology, Cornell University, summers, 1965, 1968, 1971. *Military service:* U.S. Army, 1958-60. *Member:* American Sociological Association, American Psychological Association, American Anthropological Association, American Association for the Advancement of Science.

WRITINGS: (Editor) *Sociology and Everyday Life,* Prentice-Hall, 1968; *Caldron Cookery: An Authentic Guide for Coven Connoisseurs,* Meredith, 1969; (editor) *Sociology: The Classic Statements,* Prentice-Hall, 1971; (editor with D. M. Petersen) *Criminal Life,* Prentice-Hall, 1972; (editor with P. K. Manning) *Youth and Sociology,* Prentice-Hall, 1972. Contributor of articles and reviews to psychology, sociology, and folklore journals, and to *Sing Out!, Journal of Popular Culture, World Topics,* and *Fate.* Editor of *Subterranean Sociology Newsletter,* 1967—, *Explorations,* 1972-74, *Zetetic,* 1976-77, and *Zetetic Scholar,* 1978—; associate editor of *American Sociologist,* 1968-70; editor of special issue, *Journal of Popular Culture,* Volume VI, number 3, 1972.

WORK IN PROGRESS: An introductory sociology textbook; a monograph on science and the paranormal.

AVOCATIONAL INTERESTS: Conjuring, hypnosis, ventriloquism, Forteana.

BIOGRAPHICAL/CRITICAL SOURCES: New York, October 27, 1969; *New York Times,* March 14, 1970, June 25, 1978; *Floridan* (of *St. Petersburg Times*), November 28, 1971; *Time,* May 28, 1973.

*   *   *

TUCKER, Harry, Jr. 1921-

PERSONAL: Born September 5, 1921, in Raleigh, N.C.; son of Harry St. George (a professor) and Mary (Briggs) Tucker; married Mathilda Bauer, November 7, 1955; children: Agatha Lucy, Mary Rita, Sara Mildred, Eugenia Marie, Robert Ludwig. *Education:* University of North Carolina, B.A., 1942, M.A., 1948; Ohio State University, Ph.D., 1950. *Religion:* Roman Catholic. *Home:* 510 Burton St., Raleigh, N.C. 27608. *Office:* Department of Modern Languages, North Carolina State University, Raleigh, N.C. 27607.

CAREER: West Virginia University, Morgantown, instructor in German, 1950-51; University of Virginia, Charlottesville, assistant professor of German, 1952-62; Parsons College, Fairfield, Iowa, 1962-67, began as associate professor, became professor of German; North Carolina State University at Raleigh, associate professor of German, 1967—. *Military service:* U.S. Army, 1942-45. *Member:* American Association of Teachers of German, Modern Language Association of America, South Atlantic Modern Language Association.

WRITINGS: (Translator, author of introduction, and editor) Otto Rank, *The Double,* University of North Carolina Press, 1971. Contributor to *Modern Language Quarterly* and *Montshefte.*

TULASIEWICZ, J(an) B(runo) 1913-

PERSONAL: Born May 16, 1913, in Stanislawow, Poland; son of Mieczyslaw and Paulina (Rzemieniecka) Tulasiewicz; married Siegrid Perkins, 1936; children: Kristyna. *Education:* University of Jana Kazimierza, Jur.D., 1933; University of Michigan, Ph.D., 1953. *Home:* 725 West 19th, Cedar Falls, Iowa 50613. *Office:* Department of Economics, University of Northern Iowa, Cedar Falls, Iowa 50613.

CAREER: University of Northern Iowa, Cedar Falls, associate professor, 1956-61, professor of economics, 1961—. *Member:* American Economic Association, American Econometric Association, American Association of University Professors.

WRITINGS: Man in Society, Brown Co., 1960; *Economic Growth and Development: A Case Study,* Morris, 1971; *Economic Growth Development, Planning, Theory, and Policy of East European Countries,* Morris, 1978.

*   *   *

TUOHY, William S. 1938-

PERSONAL: Born June 17, 1938, in Jamestown, N.Y.; son of Raymond J. and Jeanette (Skinner) Tuohy. *Education:* Cornell University, B.A., 1961; Stanford University, M.A., 1963, Ph.D., 1967. *Home:* 1012 Spruce St., Berkeley, Calif. 94707. *Office:* Department of Political Science, San Francisco State University, San Francisco, Calif. 94132.

CAREER: University of California, Davis, assistant professor of political science, 1967-75; San Francisco State University, San Francisco, Calif., lecturer, 1977—.

WRITINGS: (With Barry Ames) *Mexican University Students in Politics,* Monograph Series in World Affairs, University of Denver, 1970; (with Richard Fagen) *Politics and Privilege in a Mexican City,* Stanford University Press, 1972; (contributor) Clarence Thurber and Lawrence Graham, editors, *Development Administration in Latin America,* Duke University Press, 1973. Contributor of articles to political science journals and newspapers.

WORK IN PROGRESS: Research on mental health policies and programs in the United States.

SIDELIGHTS: William S. Tuohy has lived with Indians in the Andes of Peru, 1961, and in Mexico, 1966. He has traveled throughout Latin America.

*   *   *

TURKI, Fawaz 1940-

PERSONAL: Born June 10, 1940, in Haifa, Palestine (now Israel). *Education:* Attended Bournemouth College. *Politics:* "Identify with the left."

CAREER: Writer.

WRITINGS: The Disinherited: Journal of a Palestinian Exile, Monthly Review Press, 1972. Contributor to *Ramparts* and *International Herald Tribune.*

WORK IN PROGRESS: A book on revolt in Palestine, 1936-1939.

SIDELIGHTS: Fawaz Turki told *CA:* "In my writing I draw heavily on the tragic experience of the Palestinian condition which I lived right through my growing up years in a refugee camp." He has also lived in India, the Orient, and Australia.

BIOGRAPHICAL/CRITICAL SOURCES: Washington Post, September 25, 1972.††

TURNER, Herbert Snipes 1891-1976

PERSONAL: Born November 18, 1891, in Mebane, N.C.; son of Edgar Craig (a farmer) and Jennie (Thompson) Turner; married Elizabeth Phillips, September 28, 1918; children: Herbert Sidwell, David Phillips. *Education:* Davidson College, A.B., 1913, Union Theological Seminary, Virginia, B.D., 1917, D.D., 1922. *Home:* 315 North Coalter St., Staunton, Va. 24401.

CAREER: Ordained minister of Presbyterian Church, December 31, 1917; pastor of Bethel Presbyterian Church, Staunton, Va., 1919-47; Mary Baldwin College, Staunton, professor of religion and philosophy, 1939-62, professor emeritus, 1962-76. Trustee, Mary Baldwin College, 1939-47. *Member:* American Philosophical Association.

WRITINGS: Bethel and Her Ministers, William Byrd Press, 1946, 2nd edition, 1974; *Church in the Old Fields,* University of North Carolina Press, 1962; *The Dreamer: Archibald DeBow Murphey, 1777-1832,* McClure Press, 1971; *The Scott Family of Hawfields,* Seeman Press, 1971.

WORK IN PROGRESS: Essays on the Christian Faith.†

(Died November 9, 1976)

* * *

TURNER, Justin George 1898-1976

PERSONAL: Born November 5, 1898, in Chicago, Ill.; son of Oscar and Bessie (Taxey) Turner; married Gertrude Levin, July 27, 1932; children: Paul S., Linda Barbara (Mrs. Charles Sachs). *Education:* Attended University of Chicago, 1916-18; De Paul University, LL.B., 1920. *Politics:* Democrat. *Religion:* Jewish. *Home:* 1115 South Elm Dr., Los Angeles, Calif. *Agent:* Charles B. Bloch & Associates, 614 North LaPeer Dr., Los Angeles, Calif.

CAREER: Admitted to practice before the bar in Illinois; Turner & Turner, Chicago, Ill., partner, 1921-43; Town Investments, Chicago, and Los Angeles, Calif., partner, 1932-50; Turner Investments, Los Angeles, partner, beginning 1950. Consultant, manuscript department, University of California, Los Angeles, beginning 1956; former chairman of board of governors, University of Judaism; former trustee, National Foundation for Jewish Culture; former member of board of directors, Jewish Institute of Religion, California School of Hebrew Union College, and University of Southern California. President, American-Jewish Tercentenary Committee of California, 1954-55; vice-president, National Lincoln Civil War Council, beginning 1958; honorary member, National Civil War Centennial Commission, beginning 1960; president, California Civil War Centennial Commission, 1961-65; member of Civil War Centennial-Jewish Historical Commission. Fellow, Pierpont Morgan Library, 1959. *Military service:* U.S. Army, 1918.

MEMBER: American Association for State and Local History, American Historical Association, American Studies Association, Bibliographical Society of America, Society of American Archivists, Jewish Publication Society (former trustee), Keats-Shelley Society, Renaissance Society of America, America; History and Life, Lincoln Fellowship, Manuscript Society (president, 1951-53), American Jewish Historical Society (life member; vice-president), Organization of American Historians, Modern Language Association of America, Western History Association, Pacific Coast Historical Society, Mississippi Valley Historical Association, Illinois Historical Society, California Historical Commission, Lincoln Sesquicentennial Association of California (past chairman), Historical Society of Southern California (life member; president, 1962-63; chairman of board of directors), Southern California Jewish Historical Society (honorary president), Civil War Round Table of Southern California (president, 1955-56), Book Club of California, Chicago Historical Society (life member), Friends of the Library (University of Southern California; member of board of directors), Friends of Jewish Community Library of Los Angeles (president, beginning 1954), Friends of the Library (University of California, Los Angeles; president, 1957-60), Bibliophiles (Brandeis University), B'Nai B'rith (president of Austin branch, 1931-33; member of Chicago council, 1933-35), Masonic Lodge, Hillcrest Country Club (Los Angeles), Faculty Club (University of California, Los Angeles), Convenant Club (Chicago), Confederate Club (London), Alpha Epsilon Pi. *Awards, honors:* LL.D., Lincoln College, 1955; L.H.D., University of Judaism, 1960; diploma of honor, Lincoln Memorial University, 1962; national award for community service, 1964, from Jewish Theological Seminary of America.

WRITINGS: (Co-author) *Lincoln: A Contemporary Portrait,* Doubleday, 1962; (editor with Linda L. Turner) *Mary Lincoln: Her Life and Letters* (a History Book Club selection), Knopf, 1972. Contributor of articles and reviews to history journals. Member of editorial board or publication committee of *America, History and Literature, Pacific Historian,* Historical Society of Southern California, *America: History and Life,* and Lincoln Sesquicentennial Association.

WORK IN PROGRESS: Noah Brooks, a biography; *The Signers of Independence of the State of Israel.*

SIDELIGHTS: Mary Lincoln: Her Life and Letters was adapted into a play, "Look Away." *Avocational interests:* Collecting historical manuscripts, golf.†

(Died June 16, 1976)

* * *

TURNER, Ronald Cordell 1939-

PERSONAL: Born May 2, 1939, in Spokane, Wash.; son of Raymond Waldo and Hazel (Moore) Turner; married Audrey Jean Wendlandt (a librarian), January 28, 1961; children: Renn Joline. *Education:* Whitworth College, B.A., 1961; University of Madrid, graduate study, 1961-62; Harvard University, A.M., 1963, Ph.D., 1966. *Religion:* Presbyterian. *Home:* 6920 North Cochran St., Spokane, Wash. 99208. *Office:* American Sign & Indicator Corp., North 23-10 Fancher Way, Spokane, Wash. 99206.

CAREER: Dartmouth College, Hanover, N.H., assistant professor of romance languages, 1966-68; Washington State University, Pullman, research associate in computing science, 1968-69; Whitworth College, Spokane, Wash., assistant professor of modern languages, 1969-72, associate professor of linguistics, 1972-74; Washington State University, Pullman, instructor in computing science, 1974-75; American Sign & Indicator Corp., Spokane, software engineer, 1975—. *Member:* Association for Computing Machinery, Association of Computational Linguistics. *Awards, honors:* Fulbright study award, 1961-62; Danforth graduate fellowship, 1961-66; Younger Humanist research grant from National Endowment for the Humanities, 1972.

WRITINGS: Workbook for Elementary Spanish, Odyssey, 1969; (reviser) *Modern Spanish,* 3rd edition, Harcourt, 1972; *Real-Time Programming with Microcomputers,* Lexington Books, 1978. Contributor to *Lingua, Hispania, Computers in the Humanities, Linguistics,* and *Library Journal Book Review.*

WORK IN PROGRESS: Christians in Careers; computer-assisted research in Spanish stylistics; study in natural vs. artificial languages.

AVOCATIONAL INTERESTS: Flying (Turner is a private pilot), woodworking, photography.

*   *   *

TURNER, Thomas B(ourne)   1902-

PERSONAL: Born January 28, 1902, in Prince Frederick, Md.; son of George Dorsey and Virginia (Lyles) Turner; married Anne Somervell, October 22, 1927 (died, 1960); married Lorna Mary Caithness Levy, September 16, 1961; children: Anne Somervell (Mrs. John A. Pope, Jr.), Pattie Bourne (Mrs. Robert M. Hall). *Education:* St. John's College, Annapolis, Md., B.S., 1921; University of Maryland, M.D., 1925. *Politics:* Democrat. *Religion:* Episcopalian. *Home:* 1426 Park Ave., Baltimore, Md. 21217. *Office:* Johns Hopkins Medical School, 720 Rutland Ave., Baltimore, Md. 21205.

CAREER: Rockefeller Foundation, International Health Division, New York, N.Y., staff member, 1932-39; Johns Hopkins University, Baltimore, Md., professor of microbiology, School of Hygiene and Public Health, 1939-57, assistant professor, School of Medicine, 1929-32, professor of microbiology, 1957-71, professor emeritus, 1971—, dean of the medical faculty, 1957-68, dean emeritus, 1968—. Member, board of visitors and governors of St. John's College, 1950—. *Military service:* U.S. Army, 1942-46; became colonel, received Legion of Merit. *Member:* Association of American Physicians, Society for Clinical Investigation (member emeritus), Association of American Medical Colleges (president, 1965-66), Phi Beta Kappa, Kappa Alpha. *Awards, honors:* Sc.D., University of Maryland, 1966; William Freeman Snow Medal from American Social Health Association, 1969.

WRITINGS: Biology of the Treponematoses, World Health Organization, 1957; *Fundamentals of Medical Education,* C. C Thomas, 1963. Also author of *Heritage of Excellence: The Johns Hopkins Medical Institution, 1914-1947,* Johns Hopkins Press. Contributor of about one hundred articles to journals.

*   *   *

TUSHINGHAM, A(rlotte) Douglas   1914-

PERSONAL: Born January 19, 1914, in Toronto, Ontario, Canada; son of Arthur Douglas (a telephone company employee) and Lottie Elizabeth (Betts) Tushingham; married Margaret McAndrew Thomson, April 9, 1948; children: Margaret Elizabeth (Mrs. John Christopher Wylie), Ian Douglas David. *Education:* University of Toronto, B.A., 1936; University of Chicago, B.D., 1941, Ph.D., 1948. *Home:* 19 Eastbourne Ave., Toronto, Ontario, Canada M5P 2E8. *Office:* Royal Ontario Museum, 100 Queen's Park, Toronto, Ontario, Canada M5S 2C6.

CAREER: Ordained minister of United Church of Canada, 1953. University of Chicago, Chicago, Ill., instructor in Biblical subjects and archaeology, 1948-50; American School of Oriental Research, Jerusalem, Jordan (now Israel), special fellow, 1951, annual professor of American Schools, 1952, director, 1952-53; Queen's University, Kingston, Ontario, associate professor of archaeology, 1953-55; University of Toronto, Toronto, Ontario, professor of Near Eastern Studies, 1955—. Royal Ontario Museum, Toronto, head of Art and Archaeology Division, 1955-64, chief archaeologist,

1964—. Has participated in and directed excavations at Jericho, Dhiban, Jerusalem, and the Dead Sea caves; has been responsible for administration of field projects in Mexico, British Honduras, Peru, England, Iran, Canada, and Turkey. Trustee, American Schools of Oriental Research, 1953, 1954. *Military service:* Royal Canadian Navy, 1942-45. Royal Canadian Naval (Volunteer) Reserve, 1945—; currently lieutenant commander.

MEMBER: Canadian Museums Association (fellow; president, 1964, 1965), Archaeological Institute of America (president of Toronto society, 1955-70), American Oriental Society, Society of Antiquaries (London, England; fellow), Ontario Archaeological Society, Toronto Historical Board (chairman, 1966—). *Awards, honors:* Gold medal from Government of Iran, 1969, for crown jewels research; Medal of Service from City of Toronto, 1971.

WRITINGS: (With Allan Fleming) *The Art of Fine Printing: The Bible in Print,* Royal Ontario Museum, 1956; (author of foreword and introduction), *Masks: The Many Faces of Man* (photographs), Royal Ontario Museum, 1959; *The Beardmore Relics: Hoax or History?,* Royal Ontario Museum, 1966; (with V. B. Meen) *Crown Jewels of Iran,* University of Toronto Press, 1968; (with Denis Baly) *Atlas of the Biblical World,* World Publishing, 1971; *Excavations at Dibon (Dhiban) in Moab,* American Schools of Oriental Research, 1972. Editor, *Archaeological Newsletter* of Royal Ontario Museum, 1965—.

WORK IN PROGRESS: A book on excavations of Old City of Jerusalem carried out by British School of Archaeology and Royal Ontario Museum, 1961-67.

AVOCATIONAL INTERESTS: Travel, art history, music, reading, renovating houses.

*   *   *

TUTTLE, Howard Nelson   1935-

PERSONAL: Born December 15, 1935, in Salt Lake City, Utah; son of Howard Milton (a salesman) and Emily (Nelson) Tuttle; married Carolyn Padelford (a teacher), 1963; children: Carl Emerson, Laura. *Education:* University of Utah, B.A., 1958, M.A., 1959; Harvard University, M.A., 1962; Brandeis University, Ph.D., 1967. *Home:* 725 Loma Vista N.E., Albuquerque, N.M. 87106. *Office:* Department of Philosophy, University of New Mexico, Albuquerque, N.M. 87106.

CAREER: Boston University, Boston, Mass., instructor in English, 1962-64; Regis College for Women (now Regis College), Weston, Mass., instructor in history, 1964-67; University of New Mexico, Albuquerque, assistant professor, 1967-71, associate professor of philosophy, 1971—. *Member:* American Philosophical Association, American Association of University Professors.

WRITINGS: Wilhelm Dilthey's Philosophy of Historical Understanding, E. J. Brill, 1969; *Fire Night: A Story of Pompeii, August 24, 79 A.D.* (juvenile novel), Vantage Press, 1978.

WORK IN PROGRESS: Research on the history of contemporary German philosophy; an anthology of readings in twentieth-century political philosophy.

BIOGRAPHICAL/CRITICAL SOURCES: Review of Metaphysics, December, 1970; *Sophia Anno,* Volume XXXIX, number 3, December, 1971.

TUTTLETON, James Welsey 1934-

PERSONAL: Born August 19, 1934, in St. Louis, Mo.; son of Clarence M. (a minister) and Nora Tuttleton. *Education:* Harding College, B.A., 1955; University of North Carolina, M.A., 1957, Ph.D., 1963. *Home:* 2A Washington Mews, New York, N.Y. 10003. *Office:* Department of English, New York University, New York, N.Y. 10003.

CAREER: Clemson University, Clemson, S.C., instructor in English, 1956-59; University of North Carolina at Chapel Hill, instructor in English, 1962-63; University of Wisconsin—Madison, assistant professor of English, 1963-68; New York University, New York, N.Y., 1968—, began as associate professor, currently professor of English, chairman of department, 1974—. *Military service:* U.S. Air Force Reserve, 1957-63. *Member:* Modern Language Association of America, American Studies Association, American Association of University Professors. *Awards, honors:* National Endowment for the Humanities fellowship, 1967-68.

WRITINGS: (Contributor) Agnes McNeill Donohue, editor, *A Casebook on "The Grapes of Wrath,"* Crowell, 1968; (contributor) C.W.E. Bigsby, editor, *The Black American Writer,* two volumes, Everett-Edwards, 1969; *The Novel of Manners in America,* University of North Carolina Press, 1972; *Thomas Wentworth Higginson,* Twayne, 1978; *Henry James's "The American,"* Norton, 1978. Contributor to literature journals, including *Personalist, English Language Notes, Modern Fiction Studies, American Speech,* and *American Literature.*

WORK IN PROGRESS: Editing *Companions of Columbus,* by Washington Irving; a critical study of Edith Wharton's fiction.

* * *

TWOMBLY, Wells A. 1935-1977

PERSONAL: Born October 24, 1935, in St. Johnsbury, Vt.; son of Albert F. and Dale (Wells) Twombly; married Margaret Zera, December 9, 1955; children: Wells, Jr., Scott, Jason, Dale (daughter). *Education:* University of Connecticut, B.A., 1957; University of Houston, M.A., 1966. *Politics:* Democrat. *Religion:* Episcopalian.

CAREER: Willimantic Daily Chronicle, Willimantic, Conn., columnist-editor, 1956-58; *Pasadena Star-News,* Pasadena, Calif., columnist, 1958-59; *Hollywood Citizen-News,* Hollywood, Calif., columnist, 1959-62; *San Fernando Valley Times,* Hollywood, columnist, 1959-62; *Houston Chronicle,* Houston, Tex., columnist, 1962-68; *Detroit Free Press,* Detroit, Mich., columnist, 1968-69; *San Francisco Examiner,* San Francisco, Calif., columnist, 1969-72. Sports director for KXYZ, Houston, Tex., 1964-66. *Member:* Baseball Writers of America, Football Writers of America, Delta Chi. *Awards, honors:* Named Texas sports writer of the year, 1966-67; United Press International awards, 1966, 1967, 1968; best sports story of the year award from Newspaper Publishers Association, 1967; best sports story of the year award for E. P. Dutton series, 1970; best sports story of the year awards from San Francisco Press Club, 1970, 1971; named California sports writer of the year, 1971.

WRITINGS: Blanda: Alive and Kicking, Nash Publishing, 1972; *Oakland's Raiders: Fireworks, and Fury,* Prentice-Hall, 1973; *Shake Down the Thunder!* (a biography of Frank Leahy), Chilton, 1974; *200 Years of Sport in America: A Pageant of a Nation at Play,* McGraw, 1976. Contributor of over one hundred magazine articles to *Sport, New York Times Sunday Magazine, Esquire, Playboy, Saturday Evening Post, Golf, Pro, West,* and other periodicals. Weekly columnist for *St. Louis Sporting News;* columnist for *Clear Creek* and *Rolling Stone.*

SIDELIGHTS: Wells Twombly tried to explain the critical acclaim he'd received in this way: "Maybe it's because I write in essay-style, try to remember what I learned in English classes, don't consider athletes anything more godly than the man who delivers the mail. I also try to be a newsman and a writer first, a sloppy, hero-worshipping sports writer way, way down the track. My motivation for getting into this business was twofold: (1) It was all I ever wanted to do from age four onward and (2) It seemed like the most sensible way to live without working and see the world on somebody else's money."

BIOGRAPHICAL/CRITICAL SOURCES: Newsweek, July 1, 1968; *Editor and Publisher,* August 7, 1971; *New York Times,* May 31, 1977.†

(Died May 30, 1977)

* * *

TYLER, Richard W(illis) 1917-

PERSONAL: Born January 7, 1917, in Willington, Conn.; son of Frederic Spencer (a banker) and Jessie (Reed) Tyler; married Elizabeth McKenzie, September 4, 1946; children: Ann Elizabeth, Jane Margaret. *Education:* Connecticut State College (now University of Connecticut), B.A., 1938; Brown University, Ph.D., 1946. *Home:* 1901 B St., Lincoln, Neb. 68502. *Office:* Department of Modern Languages and Literatures, University of Nebraska, Lincoln, Neb. 68588.

CAREER: University of Iowa, Iowa City, visiting lecturer in Romance languages, 1944-46; University of Texas, Main University (now University of Texas at Austin), assistant professor, 1946-52, associate professor of Romance languages, 1952-65; University of Nebraska, Lincoln, professor of modern languages, 1965—. *Member:* Asociacion Internacional de Hispanistas, Modern Language Association of America, American Association of Teachers of Spanish and Portuguese, American Association of University Professors, Comediantes, Midwest Modern Language Association, Rocky Mountain Modern Language Association, American Civil Liberties Union, Sons of the American Revolution, National Wildlife Federation, Baker Street Irregulars (propaganda minister, 1967—).

WRITINGS: (With D. K. Barton and Pedro N. Trakas) *Beginning Spanish Course,* Heath, 1954, 3rd edition, 1972; (with S. G. Morley) *Los nombres de personajes en las comedias de Lope de Vega,* University of California Press, 1961; (editor) Lope de Vega, *La corona de Hungria,* University of North Carolina, 1972. Also editor of *Los comendadores de Cordoba,* by Lope de Vega.

WORK IN PROGRESS: Editing collected works of Antonio Mira de Amescua; research on settings of Lope de Vega's plays and on character names in work of Pedro Calderon de la Barca; compiling a book on great baseball players, with E. J. Mickel.

AVOCATIONAL INTERESTS: Travel (Europe, especially Spain), professional sports.

* * *

TYRRELL, Joseph M(orten) 1927-

PERSONAL: Born September 19, 1927, in Kirkland Lake,

Ontario, Canada; came to U.S., 1956; son of George C. (an apple grower) and Dora M. (Joslin) Tyrrell; married Margaret Smith, December 17, 1955; children: Anne K. M., Joseph D. G., Diana J. B. *Education:* University of Toronto, B.A., 1950, M.A., 1955; University of Rennes, Diplome de Langue Francaise, 1951; Emory University, Ph.D., 1961. *Home:* 1407 Westover Ave., Norfolk, Va. 23507. *Office:* Department of History, Old Dominion University, Norfolk, Va. 23508.

CAREER: College of Charleston, Charleston, S.C., acting assistant professor of history, 1958-59; Old Dominion University, Norfolk, Va., assistant professor, 1959-63, associate professor, 1963-67, professor of history, 1967—. *Member:* American Historical Association, Mediaeval Academy of America, Society for French Historical Studies, Societe des Antiquaires de l'Ouest (France), International Commission for the History of Representative and Parliamentary Institutions, American Association of University Professors, Champlain Society (Toronto), Southeast Medieval Association.

WRITINGS: A History of the Estates of Poitou, Mouton, 1968. Also author of *Louis XI of France.* Contributor to *Mediaeval Studies* and *Journal of Popular Culture.*

AVOCATIONAL INTERESTS: International travel and psychic phenomena.

* * *

TYRRELL, Robert 1929-

PERSONAL: Born April 7, 1929, in Horwich, Lancashire, England; son of James (a fitter) and Doris (Widdup) Tyrrell; married Barbara Denney, July 5, 1957; children: Katharine, Alison, Judith. *Education:* Attended secondary school in Lancashire, England, 1940-46. *Politics:* Liberal. *Religion:* None. *Home and office:* 51 Glenhouse Rd., Eltham, London SE9 1JH, England.

CAREER: Bolton Evening News, Bolton, Lancashire, England, reporter, 1947-50; sub-editor, *Leicester Evening Mail,* Leicester, England, 1950-51, *Bristol Evening Post,* Bristol, England, 1951-52, and British Broadcasting Corp., London, England, 1952-55; Independent Television News, London, newswriter, editor, producer, and director, 1955-63; freelance film and television producer-director specializing in industrial films, 1963—, produced "This Is Your Life" for Thames Television, 1969-71. *Member:* British Academy of Film and Television Arts. *Awards, honors:* Shell International award, 1965, for film "The Vital Few"; Emmy award, 1966, for "Big Deal at Gothenburg"; Silver Medal of Venice Festival of Art Films, 1970, for "Mister Lowry"; Certificate of Creative Excellence from Chicago Festival of Industrial Films, 1974, for "Passengers without Passports."

WRITINGS: The Work of the Television Journalist, Focal Press, 1972.

Films; all as writer/director: "Turn-up for Tony," 1964; "The Vital Few," 1965; "Big Deal at Gothenburg," 1966; "Mister Lowry," 1970; "See What the Boys in the Back Room Have Got," 1972; "The Happy Revolution," 1972; "Passengers without Passports," 1973; "The Future of Us All," 1974; "For the Record," 1974; "Leyland—Search for Safety," 1974; "Gateway to the Future," 1975; "Let's Talk in Pictures," 1975; "A World on Wheels," 1976; "Kingdom of Opportunity," 1977; "Al Intillakah," 1977; "Partners in Progress," 1977; "Leyland Vehicles," 1978; "Dubai Police," 1978; "The Innovators," 1978. Also writer and director of numerous small productions for Chrysler Corp., the Royal Navy, British Gas, Electricity Council, and others. Contributor to magazines.

WORK IN PROGRESS: Preparing a revised edition of *The Work of the Television Journalist.*

SIDELIGHTS: While working for Independent Television News in 1962, Robert Tyrrell produced the first transatlantic newscast from New York to the United Kingdom via the Telstar satellite. Done in collaboration with CBS-TV, the broadcast featured newscasters Brian Connell and Charles Collingwood reporting on the Adolf Eichmann trial in Jerusalem. *Avocational interests:* Music, energy industries, good food and wine, travel.

U

ULLIAN, Joseph S(ilbert) 1930-

PERSONAL: Surname is pronounced "Yoo-li-un"; born November 9, 1930, in Ann Arbor, Mich.; son of Hyman B. (an engineer) and Frieda (an educator; maiden name, Silbert) Ullian. Education: Harvard University, A.B., 1952, A.M., 1953, Ph.D., 1957. Home: 984 Tornoe Rd., Santa Barbara, Calif. 93105. Office: Department of Philosophy, Washington University, St. Louis, Mo. 63130.

CAREER: Stanford University, Stanford, Calif., instructor in philosophy, 1957-58; Johns Hopkins University, Baltimore, Md., assistant professor of philosophy, 1958-60; University of Pennsylvania, Philadelphia, research associate in linguistics, 1961-62; University of Chicago, Chicago, Ill., visiting assistant professor of philosophy, 1962-63; University of California, Santa Barbara, assistant professor of philosophy, 1964-66; Washington University, St. Louis, Mo., associate professor, 1965-70, professor of philosophy, 1970—. Visiting lecturer at University of California, Berkeley, 1961. Consultant to System Development Corp., Santa Monica, Calif., 1962-70. Member: American Philosophical Association, American Mathematical Society, Association for Symbolic Logic, Philosophy of Science Association, Association for Computing Machinery, American Association of University Professors, Phi Beta Kappa. Awards, honors: National Science Foundation grant, 1967-68.

WRITINGS: (With W. V. Quine) The Web of Belief, Random House, 1970, 2nd edition, 1978. Contributor to Journal of Philosophy, Journal of Symbolic Logic, Journal of the Association for Computing Machinery, and other professional journals.

WORK IN PROGRESS: Research in logic, the philosophy of mathematics and of science, and automata theory.

AVOCATIONAL INTERESTS: Acting, gardening, baseball, basketball, and music.

* * *

ULLMAN, Montague 1916-

PERSONAL: Born September 9, 1916, in New York, N.Y.; son of William and Nettie (Eisler) Ullman; married Janet Simon, January 26, 1941; children: Susan, William, Lucy. Education: College of the City of New York (now City College of the City University of New York), B.S., 1934; New York University, M.D., 1938. Home and office: 55 Orlando Ave., Ardsley, N.Y. 10502.

CAREER: Licensed to practice medicine in New York, 1941; certified by American Board of Psychiatry and Neurology, 1945; private psychoanalytic practice, 1946-66; State University of New York, Downstate Medical Center, Brooklyn, associate professor, 1961-63, professor of psychiatry, 1963-76; member of faculty, Westchester Center for the Study of Psychoanalysis and Psychotherapy, 1976—. Director of department of psychiatry, Maimonides Medical Center, Brooklyn, N.Y., 1961-74; director, Maimonides Comunity Mental Health Center, Brooklyn, 1967-73. Consultant in mental hygiene and psychiatry, Skidmore College, 1957-71; supervising consultant, Institute for Psychoanalytic Psychotherapy (Sweden), 1974—. Military service: U.S. Army, 1942-45; became captain. Member: Society of Medical Psychoanalysts (president, 1957-58), American Psychiatric Association (life fellow), American Association for the Advancement of Science (fellow), American Society for Psychical Research (president, 1971—), Parapsychological Association (president, 1966), Alpha Omega Alpha, Sigma Xi. Awards, honors: Parapsychological Award from Parapsychology Foundation, 1968.

WRITINGS: Behavioral Changes in Patients Following Strokes, C. C Thomas, 1962; (editor with Robert Cavanna) Proceedings of the International Conference on Hypnosis, Drugs, Dreams and Psi (held at Le Piol, France, 1967), Garrett Press, 1968; (with Gertrude Stokes) A Giant Step, Faculty Press, 1969; (with Alan Vaughn and Stanley Krippner) Dream Telepathy, Macmillan, 1973.

WORK IN PROGRESS: Working with Dreams, for Delacorte; Working with Dreams in Small Groups.

SIDELIGHTS: Montague Ullman told CA: "An early interest in psychical research developed during undergraduate days surfaced again during my early years of psychoanalytic practice. This came to fruition when, after leaving practice and joining the Maimonides Medical Center on a full time basis, the Dream Laboratory was established in 1962. This was the first Dream Laboratory in the country devoted to experimental studies on dream telepathy." His present concern is to help bring people back into an active and helpful relationship with their own dream life.

AVOCATIONAL INTERESTS: Jogging, tennis.

* * *

ULMER, S(hirley) Sidney 1923-

PERSONAL: Born April 15, 1923, in North, S.C.; son of

Shirley Shakespeare (a real estate broker) and Anna (Reed) Ulmer; married Margaret Anel Lipscomb, March 18, 1946; children: Margaret A., William E., Shirley S., John L., Mary E. *Education:* Furman University, B.A. (cum laude), 1952; Duke University, M.A., 1954, Ph.D., 1956. *Politics:* Democrat. *Religion:* Protestant. *Home:* 1701 Williamsburg Rd., Lexington, Ky. 40504. *Office:* Department of Political Science, University of Kentucky, Lexington, Ky. 40506.

CAREER: Duke University, Durham, N.C., instructor in political science, 1954-55; Michigan State University, East Lansing, instructor, 1956-58, assistant professor, 1958-61, associate professor of political science, 1961-63, chairman of department, 1961-62; University of Kentucky, Lexington, professor of political science, 1963-78, Alumni Professor, 1978—, chairman of department, 1963-69. Visiting summer professor, State University of New York at Buffalo, 1969, and University of Wisconsin, 1974; lecturer at University of Texas, University of Wisconsin, University of Georgia, and other universities. Member of behavioral sciences committee, National Academy of Sciences, 1964-66; member of political science panel, National Science Foundation, 1969-71. *Military service:* U.S. Army Air Forces, 1942-45; served in Pacific; received Air Medal with four oak-leaf clusters.

MEMBER: American Political Science Association, Law and Society Association, Midwest Political Science Association, Inter-University Consortium for Political Research (member of executive council, 1966-68; chairman of council, 1967-68), Southern Political Science Association (member of executive council, 1965-67; vice-president, 1966-67; president, 1971-72), Kentucky Conference of Political Scientists (vice-president, 1966-67), Phi Beta Kappa. *Awards, honors:* Research grants from National Science Foundation, Social Science Research Council, Institute of American Freedom, and other foundations, 1965—; Sang Award from University of Kentucky, 1973-74, for outstanding contributions to graduate education.

WRITINGS: (Editor and contributor) *Introductory Readings in Political Behavior,* Rand McNally, 1961; *Military Justice and the Right to Counsel,* University of Kentucky Press, 1970; (editor and author of introductory chapter) *Political Decision-Making,* Van Nostrand, 1970; *Courts as Small and Not So Small Groups,* General Learning Press, 1971.

Contributor: John Schmidhauser, editor, *Constitutional Law in the Political Process,* Rand McNally, 1962; Nelson W. Polsby, Robert A. Dentler, and Paul A. Smith, editors, *Politics and Social Life,* Houghton, 1963; Glendon Schubert, editor, *Judicial Decision-Making,* Free Press, 1963; Schubert, editor, *Judicial Behavior: A Reader in Theory and Research,* Rand McNally, 1964; Joseph Bernd, editor, *Mathematical Applications in Political Science,* Southern Methodist University Press, 1965; Hans Baade, editor, *Jurimetrics,* Basic Books, 1965; Frank Munger, editor, *American State Politics,* Crowell, 1966; Charles Press and Oliver P. Williams, editors, *Democracy in the Fifty States,* Rand McNally, 1966; Bernd, editor, *Mathematical Applications in Political Science III,* University Press of Virginia, 1967; T. Jahnige and S. Goldman, editors, *The Federal Judicial System,* Holt, 1968; Rita James Simon, editor, *The Sociology of Law,* Chandler Publishing, 1968; D. K. Downey and J. O. Graham, editors, *Quantitative History,* Dorsey, 1969; B. Sternsher, editor, *The Negro in Depression and War: Prelude to Revolution, 1930-1945,* Quadrangle, 1969; Joel Grossman and Joe Tanenhaus, editors, *The Frontiers of Judicial Research,* Wiley, 1969.

Carl Beck, editor, *Law and Justice,* Duke University Press, 1970; Fred W. Grupp and Marvin Maurer, editors, *Political Behavior in the United States,* Appleton, 1970; Robert P. Swierenga, editor, *Quantification in American History,* Atheneum, 1970; Michael Leiserson, E. W. Kelley, and Sven Groennings, editors, *The Study of Coalition Behavior,* Holt, 1970; H. Ball and T. P. Lauth, editors, *Changing Perspectives in Contemporary Political Analysis,* Prentice-Hall, 1971; S. Brenner, editor, *American Judicial Behavior,* MSS Information Corp., 1973; J. Herndon, editor, *Mathematical Applications in Political Science-VII,* University Press of Virginia, 1974; W. Murphy and C. H. Pritchett, editors, *Courts, Judges, and Politics,* Random House, 1974; Stuart Nagel, editor, *Modeling the Criminal Justice System,* Sage Publications, Inc., 1978.

Contributor of more than thirty articles and about thirty reviews to law and political science journals. Member of board of editors, *Midwest Journal of Political Science,* 1962-63, and *Journal of Politics,* 1965-71; editorial associate, *American Political Science Review,* 1963-66.

*   *   *

ULRICH, Roger E(lwood)   1931-

PERSONAL: Born August 30, 1931, in Peoria, Ill.; son of Ralph Crawford and Della (Smith) Ulrich; married Carole Lou McNish (an education coordinator), August 28, 1959; children: Thomas Alan, Traci Ellen, Kristan Sue. *Education:* North Central College, B.S., 1953; Bradley University, M.A., 1957; University of Illinois, graduate study, 1956-58; Southern Illinois University, Ph.D., 1961; Indiana University, postdoctoral study, 1962. *Office:* Behavioral Research Center, Western Michigan University, Kalamazoo, Mich. 49001.

CAREER: Bradley University, Peoria, Ill., counselor, 1955; Illinois Wesleyan University, Bloomington, administrative assistant, 1956-58, associate professor of psychology and chairman of department, 1961-65; Illinois Soldier's and Sailor's Children's School, Normal, instructor, 1958; Southern Illinois University at Carbondale, counselor, 1958; Anna State Hospital, Anna, Ill., clinical psychologist, 1959, research assistant in Behavior Research Laboratory, 1959-61; Illinois State University, Normal, associate professor of psychology, 1962-63; Western Michigan University, Kalamazoo, professor of psychology and head of department, 1965-67, research professor, 1967—. President, Behavior Development Corp., Kalamazoo, Mich., 1967—. Consulting psychologist to Kalamazoo Valley Intermediate School District, 1966-71. *Military service:* U.S. Navy, 1950-54. *Member:* American Psychological Association (fellow), Psychonomic Society, American Association for the Advancement of Science (fellow), Midwestern Psychological Association, New York Academy of Science, Michigan Academy of Science, Michigan Psychological Association.

WRITINGS: (Editor with Thomas Stachnik and John Mabry) *Control of Human Behavior,* Scott, Foresman, Volume I: *Expanding the Behavioral Laboratory,* 1966, Volume II: *From Cure to Prevention,* 1970, Volume III: *In Education,* 1974; (with Richard Malott and Donald Whaley) *Analysis of Behavior: Principles and Applications,* W. C. Brown, 1967; (with Paul Mountjoy) *The Experimental Analysis of Social Behavior,* Appleton, 1972. Author of scripts for educational films. Editor, *Behavior Modification Monographs;* advisory editor, *Journal of the Experimental Analysis of Behavior;* member of editorial board, *Journal of Applied Behavior Analysis.*

WORK IN PROGRESS: Research on aggression, on early education, and on experimental living.†

* * *

UNBEGAUN, Boris Ottokar   1898-1973

August 23, 1898—March 4, 1973; Russian-born American professor, authority on Slavic philology, author, and dictionary editor. Obituaries: *New York Times*, March 6, 1973.

* * *

UNGERER, Jean Thomas   1931-
(Tomi Ungerer)

PERSONAL: Born November 28, 1931, in Strasbourg, France; came to United States in 1957; son of Theodor and Alice (Essler) Ungerer; married former wife Miriam Lancaster, 1959; married Yvonne Deborah Wright, 1971; children: (previous marriage) Pamela, Michele, Phoebe Alexis. *Education:* Attended Art Decoratif, Strasbourg. *Residence:* Nova Scotia, Canada.

CAREER: Cartoonist, painter, writer, and illustrator. *Military service:* French Desert Police, Camel Caravan. *Member:* Society of Illustrators, American Institute of Graphic Arts, Authors Guild. *Awards, honors: Book World* Children's Spring Book Awards, 1958, for *Crichtor,* and 1967, for *Moon Man;* Society of Illustrators Gold Medal, 1960; *New York Times'* Choice of Best Illustrated Children's Books of the Year, 1962, for *Three Robbers,* and 1971, for *The Beast of Monsieur Racine;* American Institute of Graphic Arts award, 1969, for *The Hat;* Children's Book Showcase title, 1972, for *The Beast of Monsieur Racine.*

WRITINGS—All under name Tomi Ungerer; juvenile; all self-illustrated: *The Mellops Go Flying,* Harper, 1957; *The Mellops Go Diving for Treasure,* Harper, 1957; *The Mellops Strike Oil,* Harper, 1958; *Adelaide,* Harper, 1959; *Emile,* Harper, 1960; *Christmas Eve at the Mellops,* Harper, 1960; *Rufus,* Harper, 1961; *Snail, Where Are You?,* Harper, 1962; *Three Robbers,* Atheneum, 1962; (with Miriam Ungerer) *Come into My Parlor,* Atheneum, 1963; (with William Cole) *Frances Face-Maker,* World Publishing, 1963; *The Mellops Go Spelunking,* Harper, 1963; *One, Two, Where's My Shoe,* Harper, 1964; *Orlando The Brave Vulture,* Harper, 1966; *Moon Man,* Harper, 1967; *Zeralda's Ogre,* Harper, 1967; *Ask Me a Question,* Harper, 1968; *Crichtor,* Scholastic Book Services, 1969; *The Hat,* Parents' Magazine Press, 1970; *The Beast of Monsieur Racine,* Farrar, Straus, 1971; *I Am Papa Snap and These Are My Favorite No-Such Stories,* Harper, 1972; *No Kiss for Mother,* Harper, 1973; *Allumette,* Parents' Magazine Press, 1974; *The Great Song Book,* Doubleday, 1978.

Adult: *Inside Marriage,* Grove, 1958; *Horrible,* Atheneum, 1960; *Herz infrakt,* Keel (Zurich), 1962; *Underground Sketchbook of Tomi Ungerer,* Viking, 1964; *The Party,* Paragraphic Books, 1966; *Compromises,* Farrar, Straus, 1970; *Fornicon,* Grove, 1970; *America: Zeichnungen, 1956-1971,* Diogenes Verlag, 1974; *Adam and Eve,* J. Cape, 1976.

Other: (With W. Cole) *A Cat Hater's Handbook, or The Ailurophobe's Delight,* Dial, 1963. Also author of *Basil Ratski, Sex Maniac, Mirror Man,* and *Mr. Tall and Mr. Small* (with Barbara Brennen).

Illustrator: Millicent E. Selsam, *Seeds and More Seeds,* Harper, 1959; Mary Stolz, *Fredou,* Harper, 1962; John Hollander, *A Book of Various Owls,* Norton, 1963; Jeff Brown, *Flat Stanley,* Harper, 1964; Andre Hodeir, *Warwick's Three Bottles,* Grove, 1966; Cole, *Oh, What Nonsense,* Viking, 1966; M. Ungerer, *The Too Hot to Cook Book,* Walker, 1966; Cole, *What's Good for a Four-Year-Old,* Holt, 1967; Jean B. Showalter, *Donkey Ride,* Doubleday, 1967; Edward Lear, *Lear's Nonsense Verses,* Grosset, 1967; Cole, *A Case of the Giggles,* World Publishing, 1967 (published in England as *Limerick Giggles, Joke Giggles: Collected by William Cole,* Bodley Head, 1969); Andre Hodeir, *Cleopatra Goes Sledding,* Grove, 1968; Barbara Shook Hazen, *The Sorcerer's Apprentice,* Lancelot Press, 1969; Cole, *The Book of Giggles,* World Publishing, 1970; Cole, *That Pest, Jonathan,* Harper, 1970; Cole, *Oh, How Silly,* Viking, 1970; Cole, *Beastly Boys and Ghastly Girls,* World Publishing, 1971; Jack Rennert, editor, *The Poster Art of Tomi Ungerer,* Darien House, 1971; Cole, *Oh, That's Ridiculous,* Viking, 1972; (and compiler) *A Storybook from Tomi Ungerer,* F. Watts, 1974.

Ungerer has done work for the Canadian Broadcasting Corp., the State of New York and the *Village Voice;* his work has appeared in *Holiday* and *Playboy.*

SIDELIGHTS: Critics generally agree that Tomi Ungerer has an extraordinary talent, but reviews show that the talent is a controversial one. According to Eliot Freemont-Smith and Karla Kuskin, "The pen of Tomi Ungerer . . . has a built-in leer." A *Junior Bookshelf* reviewer agrees, commenting that "satire [is] never far below the surface in Ungerer, that master of the sick joke." According to John Gruen, Ungerer's "particular genius is for transforming human cruelty, violence, and sadism into blackest, sickest laughter. . . . [He] makes clear that the pen is not only mightier but far deadlier than the sword." Gruen concedes that Ungerer "sometimes does go too far. But by going too far he heightens the effectiveness and value of black humor, giving it the bite and sharpness that are required in a world turning in ever-increasing chaos."

In light of this, it may be somewhat distressing to realize that much of Ungerer's work is aimed at children. Yet John Flaherty points out that he has a gentler side. In *I Am Papa Snap and These Are My Favorite No-Such Stories,* "there is a patented Ungerer whimsy: a dragon that is used to light cigars, a steamroller in a kitchen that is used to press clothes and flatten pizza dough, a slingshot David sitting in a floating bathtub who sinks a Goliath of a battleship with a single twang of a rubber band. But Ungerer will be Ungerer, so he closes with a scare: a great illustration of 'a hungry sofa' that devours Papa Snap. . . . I hope the sofa suffers from indigestion."

A reviewer for *Junior Bookshelf* takes note of the less whimsical touches that are equally a part of Ungerer's style. "Some parents may be distressed by the sickness," he comments, "but probably their children will be moved only to delighted laughter." According to R. A. Siegel, "the text of the climactic episode [in *The Beast of Monsieur Racine*] reads, 'Unspeakable acts were performed.' And they are. But they are in keeping with a child's more innocent concept of what might be 'unspeakable acts.' . . . [These things are] all in good fun if not in good taste and very much in keeping with the carnival licentiousness of the comic grotesque. Children's humor is full of . . . innocent sexual allusions." John A. Cunliffe defends some elements of Ungerer's books, saying, "Most children, from about six to eight, will take the gruesome humor in their stride, and find this book hilarious, but it is not for the oversensitive."

Tomi Ungerer's juvenile literature has an advantage over more run-of-the-mill childrens' books in that it is extremely honest. "Among Ungerer's endearing qualities are a total candor and a lack of condescension," says one reviewer. The adults in his tales treat children with loving kindness and respect no oftener than they do in life.... On the other hand, [he] is no romantic concerning the sweet innocence of the young." Yet he seems to understand them. As one reviewer comments, "Part of Ungerer's charm in this forty-page tantrum [*No Kiss for Mother*] is his instinctive grasp of the anger of impotence that grips all small children during large chunks of their early lives. It is a rage directed at the limitations of childhood itself." The refreshing honesty and sharp satire attract the older audience of parents. It is frequently commented that his books are not just for children; that his side-jokes command the attention of the adults without confusing the children.

"Tomi Ungerer's books for adults are completely different and not intended for the innocent eyes of his younger audience," notes Joan Hess Michel. "They are sophisticated, sharply satiric criticisms of our social scene today. They are effective without words ..., [and are] not for the tender skinned nor the prudish. Ungerer's drawings vividly present his scathing contempt of those things in the world around him which he feels to be foolish or corrupt. We squirm to see our vanity and greed exposed. These illustrations are so different from the gentle charm and whimsey of Tomi's children's books that it is difficult to believe that they come from the same pen. Yet artistic talent is evident in both; in the books for young children the wonder, magical make-believe, and imaginative innocence is dominant."

Tomi Ungerer told *CA:* "I feel that the greater part of my education came from my travels through Europe, walking and hitchhiking, earning my way by odd jobs, and of course painting, drawing, and working in the graphic arts. My work bends itself upon my constantly changing interests. Right now I live on the land and enjoy cutting meat. Who knows, tomorrow I might fancy cutting up people; the artist is both surgeon and butcher."

AVOCATIONAL INTERESTS: Collecting antique toys, making kites, speleology, archaeology, mineralogy, and geology.

BIOGRAPHICAL/CRITICAL SOURCES: Graphis, Volume 15, Graphis Press, March/April, 1959, Volume 27, 1971/72; *Horizon Magazine,* January, 1960; Diana Klemin, *The Art of Art for Children's Books,* Clarkson Potter, 1966; *Times Literary Supplement,* May 25, 1967; *Book World,* September 10, 1967; *New Yorker,* December 16, 1967; John Gruen, *Close-Up,* Viking, 1968; *Junior Bookshelf,* Febru-

ary, 1968, December, 1972; *American Artist,* May, 1969; Lee Bennett Hopkins, *Books Are by People,* Citation, 1969; *New York Times Book Review,* September 19, 1970, November 7, 1971, February 20, 1972, May 7, 1972; Selma G. Lanes, *Down the Rabbit Hole,* Atheneum, 1971; *Christian Science Monitor,* November 11, 1971; Tomi Ungerer, Seibundo-Shinkosha Publishers (Tokyo), 1971; *Children's Book Review,* February, 1971; *Atlantic Monthly,* January, 1974; *New York,* December 16, 1974; *The Lion and the Unicorn,* Volume I, Number 1, 1977; (under name Tomi Ungerer) *Children's Literature Review,* Volume III, Gale, 1978.†

* * *

UVEGES, Joseph A(ndrew), Jr. 1938-

PERSONAL: Surname is pronounced U-*vee*-guess; born August 29, 1938, in Newark, N.J.; son of Joseph Andrew and E. Dorothy (Greenfield) Uveges; married Joyce Oldaker, August 12, 1961; children: Michael Andrew, Stephen Scott, Dana Jill, Kathryn Ann. *Education:* Attended Youngstown University, 1956-57; Ohio Northern University, A.B. (cum laude), 1961; University of Florida, M.A., 1962, Ph.D., 1964. *Religion:* Methodist. *Home:* 860 Nutwood Ave., Bowling Green, Ky. 42101. *Office:* Department of Government, Western Kentucky University, 316 Grise Hall, Bowling Green, Ky. 42101.

CAREER: Ohio Northern University, Ada, instructor, 1964-67, assistant professor of political science, 1967-68; Western Kentucky University, Bowling Green, assistant professor, 1968-70, associate professor of political science, 1970-73, professor of public affairs, 1973—. Chairman of undergraduate programs section, National Association of Schools of Public Affairs and Administration. *Member:* American Society for Public Administration, Southern Political Science Association, Midwest Conference of Political Science, Kentucky Conference of Political Science, Pi Sigma Alpha, Theta Alpha Phi, Phi Eta Sigma.

WRITINGS: Federal-State Relations in Interstate Highway Administration (monograph), Public Administration Clearing House, 1963; (editor) *The Dimensions of Public Administration: Introductory Readings,* Holbrook, 1971, 3rd edition, Allyn & Bacon, 1978; (editor) *Cases in Public Administration,* Holbrook, 1978. Contributor to *Western Alumnus* and *Choice.*

WORK IN PROGRESS: Research on financial administration and budgeting in government.

V

VACHON, Brian 1941-

PERSONAL: Born October 3, 1941, in Washington, D.C.; son of John F. (a photographer) and Millicent Emily (Leeper) Vachon; married Nancy Cargill (a copy editor), November 18, 1971. *Education:* Attended Villanova University, 1959-61, and University of Tennessee, 1962. *Home:* 4 Pinewood Rd., Montpelier, Vt. 05602. *Office: Vermont Life,* Montpelier, Vt. 05602.

CAREER: Newsweek, New York City, associate editor, 1968; *New York Daily News,* New York City, reporter, 1969-70; *Saturday Review,* New York City, senior editor, 1971-72; *Vermont Life,* Montpelier, Vt., editor, 1973—. *Military service:* U.S. Army Reserve, 1963-69.

WRITINGS: A Time to Be Born, Prentice-Hall, 1972. Contributor to *McCall's, Newsweek, Playboy, New York Times,* and other periodicals.

WORK IN PROGRESS: Research on adoption in America; magazine articles.

* * *

VALGARDSON, W(illiam) D(empsey) 1939-

PERSONAL: Born May 7, 1939, in Winnipeg, Manitoba, Canada; son of Dempsey Alfred Herbert (a fisherman) and Rachel (Smith) Valgardson; married Mary Anne Tooth, May 28, 1960; children: Nancy-Rae, Val. *Education:* University of Manitoba, B.A., 1961, B.Ed., 1966; University of Iowa, M.F.A., 1969. *Religion:* Lutheran. *Home:* 3221 Doncaster Dr., Victoria, British Columbia, Canada. *Office:* Department of Creative Writing, University of Victoria, Victoria, British Columbia, Canada.

CAREER: English teacher in Riverton, Manitoba, 1961-62; art teacher in Transcona, Manitoba, 1963-64; English teacher in Snow Lake, Manitoba, 1964-65, Pinawa, Manitoba, 1965-67, and Tuxedo, Manitoba, 1969-70; Cottey College, Nevada, Mo., instructor, 1970-72, assistant professor of English, 1972-73, chairman of department, 1971-74; currently associate professor, University of Victoria, Victoria, British Columbia. *Member:* Writer's Union of Canada, American Writer's Program. *Awards, honors:* First prize from religious arts festival, Rochester, N.Y., 1968, for poem "Paul Isefeld: Fisherman"; international scholarship to Writer's Workshop, University of Iowa, 1968; Canada Council grant, summer, 1968; honorable mention in Hallmark poetry competition, 1969, for "Realization in a Spin-

ning Wheel"; first prize for non-fiction from *Winnipeg Free Press,* 1970, for article "The Hitchhikers"; second prize from Manitoba branch of Canadian Author's Association, 1970, for poem "Raspberries"; President's Medal, University of Western Ontario, 1971, for short story "Bloodflowers"; Star award from *Kansas City Star*-Hallmark competitions, 1972, for poem "Val Playing"; Bread Loaf scholarship, 1972.

WRITINGS: Bloodflowers (short stories), Oberon, 1973; *God Is Not a Fish Inspector* (short stories), Oberon, 1975; *In the Gutting Shed* (poems), Turnstone Press, 1976. Also author of short story collection, *Red Dust,* Oberon.

Contributor to anthologies, including: *The Best American Short Stories 1971,* edited by Martha Foley and David Burnett, Houghton, 1971; *Stories from Western Canada,* edited by Rudy Wiebe, Macmillan, 1972; *Sunlight and Shadows,* New English Library, 1974; *New Canadian Stories,* Oberon, 1974; *New Canadian Fiction,* Bantam, 1975; *Moderne Erzahler der Welt-Kanada,* Erdman, 1976. Contributor of articles, stories, and poems to literary journals, including *Alphabet, Fiddlehead, Atlantic Advocate, Tamarack Review, Dalhousie Review, Queen's Quarterly, Antigonish Review, Windsor Review, Inscape, Canadian Forum, New Student Review, Jeopardy, Midwest Quarterly,* and *Reader's Quarterly of Icelandic Literature and Thought.*

WORK IN PROGRESS: A novel.

SIDELIGHTS: W. D. Valgardson's childhood in an Icelandic-Canadian fishing village has provided themes and settings for his stories. He is especially interested in the effects of isolation upon people. Reviewing *God Is Not a Fish Inspector,* Adrian Vale comments that Valgardson's "Manitoba countryside has close affinities with Egdon Heath. There is death and suicide and isolation. These elementals, however, are not dragged in to inflate a final paragraph; they come as hammer-blows, falling inevitably and with complete artistic rightness. Mr. Valgardson is an authoritative writer; he leaves the reader with no inclination to gainsay him or the truth of the events he describes."

BIOGRAPHICAL/CRITICAL SOURCES: Irish Times, July 10, 1976.

* * *

VALGEMAE, Mardi 1935-

PERSONAL: Born November 10, 1935, in Viljandi, Estonia; son of Parfeni (a builder) and Ella (Peterson) Valgemae; married Mare Kivijarv, December 28, 1957; children: Monika L., Sven M. *Education:* Rutgers University, B.A., 1957; University of California, Los Angeles, Ph.D., 1964. *Home:* 31-32 77th St., Jackson Heights, N.Y. 11370. *Office:* Department of English, Herbert H. Lehman College of the City University of New York, Bronx, N.Y. 10468.

CAREER: University of California, Los Angeles, assistant professor of English, 1964-68; Herbert H. Lehman College of the City University of New York, Bronx, N.Y., associate professor, 1968-74, professor of English, 1975—. *Military service:* U.S. Army, 1958-60; became first lieutenant. *Member:* Modern Language Association of America, American Comparative Literature Association, Association for the Advancement of Baltic Studies, Phi Beta Kappa. *Awards, honors:* Woodrow Wilson fellow, 1960-61.

WRITINGS: Accelerated Grimace: Expressionism in the American Drama of the 1920's, Southern Illinois University Press, 1972; (editor with Ziedonis, Puhrel, and Silbajoris) *Baltic Literature and Linguistics,* Association for the Advancement of Baltic Studies, 1973; (contributor) Ulrich Weisstein, editor, *Expressionism as an International Literary Phenomenon,* Didier, 1973; (contributor) Parming and Jarvesoo, editors, *A Case Study of a Soviet Republic: Estonian SSR,* Westview Press, 1978. Contributor of articles to *Modern Drama, Comparative Drama, Educational Theatre Journal, Modern International Drama, Yale University Library Gazette, Huntington Library Quarterly, Twentieth Century Literature, Books Abroad,* and other periodicals.

WORK IN PROGRESS: The Playwright as Wrighter, a book on the shift from verbal to visual dramaturgy.

*   *   *

Van CLEVE, Thomas Curtis   1888-1976

PERSONAL: Born May 1, 1888, in Malden, Mo.; son of George Thomas (a physician) and Vera E. (James) Van Cleve. *Education:* University of Missouri—Columbia, A.B., 1911, M.A., 1912; University of Wisconsin, Ph.D., 1923. *Address:* P.O. Box 157, Brunswick, Me. 04011. *Office:* Bowdoin College, Brunswick, Me. 04011.

CAREER: Bowdoin College, Brunswick, Me., instructor, 1915-19, assistant professor, 1919-22, Thomas Brackett Reed Professor of History and Poltical Science, 1922-54, professor of history emeritus, 1954-76. Visiting professor, University of South Carolina, 1955-56. *Military service:* U.S. Army, 1917-19, 1942-46; became colonel. *Member:* American Historical Association, Mediaeval Academy of America, Royal Historical Society (London; fellow). *Awards, honors:* Litt.D., Bowdoin College, 1954.

WRITINGS: Markward of Anweiler and the Sicilian Regency: A Study of Hohenstaufen Policy in Italy, Princeton University Press, 1937; (contributor) Kenneth M. Setton, principal editor, *A History of the Crusades,* Volume II, University of Pennsylvania Press, 1962; *The Emperor Frederick II of Hohenstaufen: Immutator Mundi,* Clarendon Press, 1972.

WORK IN PROGRESS: Observations and Experiences of an Intelligence Officer in Two World Wars.†

(Died February 10, 1976)

*   *   *

Van der HORST, Brian   1944-

PERSONAL: Born September 11, 1944, in New York,

N.Y.; son of Louis F. von Pritzelwitz (a surgeon) and Mimi (Jennewein) Van der Horst. *Education:* Attended Duke University and New School for Social Research. *Office:* c/o est Foundation, 765 California St, San Francisco, Calif.

CAREER: Publicist, Loew's Theatres, New York City, 1965-66, and Metro-Goldwyn-Mayer, Inc., New York City, 1966-67; Twentieth Century-Fox Film Corp., New York City, national publicity coordinator, 1967-70; Cannon Group, Inc., New York City, vice-president, advertising and public relations, 1970-71; Atlantic Recording Corp., New York City, director of advertising and public relations, 1971-72; free-lance writer, 1973-74; columnist for *Playboy, Village Voice,* and *Practical Psychology for Physicians,* 1974-77; est Foundation, San Francisco, Calif., manager of public information office, 1977—.

WRITINGS: Folk Music in America, F. Watts, 1972; *Rock Music,* F. Watts, 1973. Contributing editor, *Graduate Review,* 1977—; music editor, *In New York;* music critic, *New York Free Press* and *West Side News;* film critic, *Circus.*

WORK IN PROGRESS: Novels.

AVOCATIONAL INTERESTS: Playing musical instruments.

*   *   *

van der KROEF, Justus M(aria)   1925-

PERSONAL: Born October 30, 1925, in Djakarta, Indonesia; naturalized U.S. citizen; son of Hendrik L. (a naval officer) and Maria (van Lokven) van der Kroef; married Orell Joan Ellison (a librarian), 1955; children: Adrian Hendrik, Sri Orell. *Education:* Millsaps College, B.A., 1944; University of North Carolina, M.A., 1947; Columbia University, Ph.D., 1953. *Politics:* Conservative. *Religion:* Presbyterian. *Home:* 165 Linden Ave., Bridgeport, Conn. 06602. *Office:* Department of Political Science, University of Bridgeport, Bridgeport, Conn. 06602.

CAREER: Michigan State University, East Lansing, instructor in history, 1948-52, assistant professor of foreign studies, 1952-55; University of Bridgeport, Bridgeport, Conn., associate professor, 1959-65, professor of political science, 1965-68, C. A. Dana Professor of Political Science, 1968—, chairman of department, 1965—. Visiting professor, Nanyang University, 1963-64, University of the Philippines, 1966, and University of British Columbia, 1974. Editorial director, Communications Research Services. Member of national advisory board, Charles Edison Memorial Youth Fund, 1972—. *Military service:* Royal Netherlands Marine Corps, 1944-45. *Member:* American Political Science Association, University Professors for Academic Order (national president, 1971-72), American-Asian Educational Exchange (director, 1968—). *Awards, honors:* Senior fellow of Research Institute on Communist Affairs (Columbia University), 1965-66; post-doctoral fellow, University of Queensland (Australia) 1968-69.

WRITINGS: Indonesia in the Modern World, Masa Baru and William Heinman, Volume I, 1954, Volume II, 1956; *The West New Guinea Dispute,* Institute of Pacific Relations, 1958; *Indonesian Social Evolution: Some Psychological Considerations,* van der Peet, 1958; *The Communist Party of Indonesia: Its History, Program and Tactics,* University of British Columbia Press, 1965; *Communism in Malaysia and Singapore: A Contemporary Survey,* Nijhoff, 1967; *Indonesia after Sukarno,* University of British Columbia Press, 1971. Also author of *The Lives of SEATO.* Member of editorial advisory board, *Journal of Asian Af-*

fairs, 1975—, and *World Affairs*, 1976—; book review editor, *Asian Thought and Society*, 1976—.

WORK IN PROGRESS: Guerilla Insurgency in Southeast Asia; Communism in Southeast Asia: A Historical and Political Analysis.

* * *

van der MERWE, Nikolaas J(ohannes) 1940-

PERSONAL: Born August 11, 1940, in Riviersonderend, South Africa; son of Johannes Abraham (a school principal) and Rachel Maria (Burger) van der Merwe; married Julia A. Feeny, November 11, 1962 (divorced, 1969); married Karen Elaine Bardon, February 19, 1973; children: (first marriage) Kerstin. *Education:* Yale University, B.A., 1962, M.A., 1965, Ph.D., 1966. *Home:* 35 Duignam Rd., Kalk Bay 7975, Cape, South Africa. *Office:* Department of Archaeology, University of Cape Town, Rondebosch 7700, South Africa.

CAREER: Archaeologist. State University of New York at Binghamton, assistant professor, 1966-69, associate professor of anthropology, 1969-73; University of Cape Town, Rondebosch, South Africa, professor of archaeology, 1974—. Adjunct associate professor of anthropology, State University of New York at Binghamton, 1974—. *Member:* American Anthropological Association (fellow), Southern African Association of Archaeologists, Royal Society of South Africa (fellow), Pan African Association of Prehistory, West African Association of Archaeologists (founder member), South African Society for Quarternary Research, Aircraft Owners and Pilots Association, Sigma Xi.

WRITINGS: The Carbon-14 Dating of Iron, University of Chicago, 1969. Contributor of articles to *Current Anthropology, World Archaeology, American Antiquity, Private Pilot, South African Archaeological Bulletin,* and *Early Man.*

WORK IN PROGRESS: A study of pre-industrial metallurgy in Africa; the carbon-13 contents of human skeletons as a measure of prehistoric diets in North America.

SIDELIGHTS: Nikolaas van der Merwe "started training as a physicist and became interested in archaeological dating methods; finally switched to archaeology entirely.... Enthusiastic pilot of small aircraft, which comes in handy on expeditions for aerial survey and transportation."

* * *

VANDERSEE, Charles (Andrew) 1938-

PERSONAL: Born March 25, 1938, in Gary, Ind.; son of Harvey F. and Louise (Bauer) Vandersee. *Education:* Valparaiso University, B.A., 1960; University of California, Los Angeles, M.A., 1961, Ph.D., 1964. *Religion:* Lutheran. *Office:* 401 Cabell Hall, University of Virginia, Charlottesville, Va. 22903.

CAREER: University of Virginia, Charlottesville, assistant professor, 1964-70, associate professor of English, 1970—, assistant dean of College of Arts and Sciences, 1970—, director of Echols Scholars Program, 1973—. *Member:* Modern Language Association of America, Society for Values in Higher Education, American Studies Association, Lutheran Human Relations Association, Raven Society. *Awards, honors:* Danforth fellowship, 1960; Woodrow Wilson fellowship, 1960; Bruern fellow in American literature, University of Leeds, 1968-69; American Council of Learned Societies fellowship, 1972-73; National Endowment for the Humanities research grant, 1977-78.

WRITINGS: (Editor) John Hay, *The Bread-Winners,* Col-

lege & University Press, 1973. Contributor of articles to periodicals, including *South Atlantic Quarterly, American Quarterly, Shakespeare Survey, American Literary Realism, Journal of American Studies,* and *Cresset;* contributor of poetry to *West Coast Poetry Review, Texas Quarterly, Sou'wester, Southern Poetry Review, Sewanee Review, Poetry Now,* and other periodicals.

WORK IN PROGRESS: Editing with Ernest Samuels and J. C. Levinson a new six-volume edition of the letters of Henry Adams, for Harvard University Press and Massachusetts Historical Society.

* * *

VAN DUSEN, Robert LaBranche 1929-

PERSONAL: Born May 5, 1929, in New York, N.Y.; son of William Haigh (a manufacturer) and Virginia (LaBranche) Van Dusen. *Education:* Harvard University, B.A., 1951; University of Texas at Austin, M.A., 1959, Ph.D., 1964. *Politics:* Republican. *Religion:* Presbyterian. *Home:* 1001 Main St. W., Hamilton, Ontario, Canada. *Office:* Department of German, McMaster University, Hamilton, Ontario, Canada.

CAREER: McMaster University, Hamilton, Ontario, lecturer, 1960-63, assistant professor, 1963-68, associate professor of German, 1968—. *Military service:* U.S. Army, 1951-54; became sergeant. *Member:* Canadian Association of University Teachers of German, Association for Eighteenth-Century Studies at McMaster University, Harvard Clubs of New York City and Toronto. *Awards, honors:* Canada Council grant, 1967-68.

WRITINGS: Christian Garve and English Belles-Lettres, Berne H. Lang, 1970; *The Literary Ambitions and Achievements of Alexander von Humboldt,* Berne H. Lang, 1972; (contributor) P. Fritz and D. Williams, editors, *The Triumph of Culture: Eighteenth-Century Perspectives,* Hakkert, 1972. Contributor of reviews to periodicals, including *Seminar* and *Canadian Modern Language Review.*

WORK IN PROGRESS: An evaluation of the literary works of Friedrich Wilhelm Zachariae; an analysis of Goethe's autobiography, *Poetry and Truth;* a study of Christian Garve's concept of Shakespeare as a dramatist.

* * *

VAN NOSTRAND, A(lbert) D(ouglass) 1922-

PERSONAL: Born May 25, 1922, in Babylon, N.Y.; son of Leroy (a salesman) and Madalene (Haff) Van Nostrand; married Nancy Willard Connely (a registered nurse), September 3, 1943 (divorced); children: Christie (Mrs. Harlow Sarles), Douglas Willard, Amy, Jillian, Kipp Fletcher. *Education:* Amherst College, B.A., 1943; Harvard University, M.A., 1948, Ph.D., 1951. *Politics:* Independent. *Religion:* Protestant. *Home:* 48 Aberdeen Rd., Riverside, R.I. 02915. *Office:* Department of English, Brown University, Providence, R.I. 02912.

CAREER: Brown University, Providence, R.I., assistant professor, 1951-57, associate professor, 1957-68, professor of English, 1968—, chairman of department, 1973-78. Fulbright lecturer in Brazil, 1961-62. Academic director, Inter American University Foundation, 1969-71; director, Center for Research in Writing, 1975—. Member of National Humanities Faculty, 1972—, member of board of trustees, 1977—. Consultant to U.S. State Department, 1962, 1967, 1968, 1972, 1973. Barrington Public Library, trustee, 1957-70, chairman of board of trustees, 1964-70. *Military service:*

U.S. Naval Reserve, active duty, 1943-46; served in Atlantic and Mediterranean theaters. *Member:* American Studies Association (member of executive committee, 1956-61), Modern Language Association of America, Rhetoric Society of America, National Council of Teachers of English, American Association of University Professors. *Awards, honors:* Peabody Award in educational television, 1957; Guggenheim fellowship, 1957-58; senior humanist, National Humanities Series, 1971-72; L.H.D., Doane College, 1979.

WRITINGS: (Editor) *Literary Criticism in America: An Anthology,* Bobbs-Merrill, 1957; (editor with C. H. Watts) *The Conscious Voice: An Anthology of American Poetry From the Seventeenth Century to the Present,* Bobbs-Merrill, 1959; *The Denatured Novel,* Bobbs-Merrill, 1960; *Major Book Markets in South America,* U.S. Department of State, 1962; *Everyman His Own Poet,* McGraw, 1968; (with others) *Functional Writing,* Houghton, 1978.

Television scripts: (With J. B. Bessinger, Jr.) "A Prospect of Literature," an eight-part series, 1956; "The American Scene," a series of thirteen programs, 1957. Author of "Exiles in the House," a multi-media dramatization, 1971. Contributor to journals, including *ADE Bulletin, American Quarterly, CEA Critic, Educational Technology,* and *Social Education.*

WORK IN PROGRESS: The Inference Construct: A Model of the Writing Process.

BIOGRAPHICAL/CRITICAL SOURCES: Christian Science Monitor, September 8, 1960; *Saturday Review of Literature,* September 24, 1960; *New York Times Book Review,* October 9, 1960; *Christian Century,* August 7, 1968; *Virginia Quarterly Review,* February, 1969; *New York Times,* November 24, 1976; *Time,* April 18, 1977; *Boston Herald,* January 5, 1978.

*   *   *

Van SICKLE, Neil D(avid)   1915-

PERSONAL: Born July 8, 1915, in Minot, N.D.; son of Guy Robin (a farm real estate dealer) and Hilda (Rosenquist) Van Sickle; married Marjorie Sims, December 28, 1938; children: Anne (Mrs. John N. Kelley), Kathleen (Mrs. Ray Leatham), Peter S., Jane (Mrs. Grayden L. Wengert). *Education:* United States Military Academy, B.S., 1938; attended Armed Forces Staff College, Norfolk, 1946-47; attended War College, Maxwell Air Force Base, 1953. *Office and home address:* Route 1, Box 241, Rapid City, S.D. 57701.

CAREER: U.S. Air Force, career officer, 1938-68; retired as major general. Commissioned second lieutenant in U.S. Army cavalry, 1938; transferred to U.S. Army Air Forces, 1940; assigned to anti-submarine warfare, Atlantic, 1942-43; assigned to bomber offensive, Japan, 1944-45; member of U.S. military staff committee, United Nations, 1946-47; operations officer, Yukon Air Division, Fairbanks, Alaska, 1948-50; chief of aircraft programming, Headquarters, U.S. Air Force, 1950-53; deputy, then commander, 28th Bombardment Wing, Strategic Air Command, Rapid City, S.D., 1954-57; chief of staff, U.S. Taiwan Defense Command, 1957-59; assistant chief of staff operations, Pacific Air Forces, Hickam Air Force Base, Hawaii, 1959-61; commander of Navigator Training Wing, Mather Air Force Base, Calif., 1961-63; chief of flying training, Air Training Command, Randolph Air Force Base, Tex., 1963-65; commander of U.S. Air Force Recruiting Service, 1965-66; deputy inspector general of U.S. Air Force, 1966-68. Avia-

tion consultant for Lockheed Aircraft International in Geneva, 1970-72, and Saudi Arabia, 1971-72. Chairman of South Dakota Constitutional Revision Commission. *Member:* Aviation/Space Writers Association. *Awards, honors—Military:* Distinguished Service Medal; Legion of Merit; Bronze Star; Air Medal with two oak leaf clusters.

WRITINGS: Modern Airmanship, Van Nostrand, 1959, 4th edition, 1971.

WORK IN PROGRESS: Fifth edition of *Modern Airmanship.*

SIDELIGHTS: Neil D. Van Sickle raises Irish Connemara ponies on his ranch in the Black Hills.

*   *   *

Van TASSEL, Alfred J.   1910-

PERSONAL: Born August 9, 1910, in Twin Falls, Idaho; son of Joseph Henry (an attorney) and Sadie (Bunclark) Van Tassel; married Beatrice Halpern (a public relations executive), September 22, 1933; children: Carl J., Eric. R. *Education:* University of California, Berkeley, B.S., 1934; University of Pennsylvania, graduate study, 1939-41; Columbia University, Ph.D., 1964. *Politics:* Democrat. *Home:* 2 Hemlock Lane, Glen Cove, N.Y. 11542. *Office:* School of Business, Hofstra University, Hempstead, N.Y. 11542.

CAREER: U.S. Senate Small Business Committee, Washington, D.C., staff studies director, 1944-45; United Nations, New York City, economist, 1947-53; Columbia University, New York City, lecturer in economics, 1964-66; University of Illinois at Urbana-Champaign, visiting research professor, 1966-67; Hofstra University, Hempstead, N.Y., professor of business research, 1967-75, professor emeritus, 1975—. Executive secretary of United Nations Scientific Conference on Conservation and Utilization of Resources, 1949; research project review officer of U.S. Environmental Protection Agency, 1972—; member of Long Island Association Committee which conducted a successful campaign for separate statistical treatment of Long Island in federal statistics. *Member:* American Economic Association, Academy of Political Science, Hofstra University Club.

WRITINGS: (With David Bluestone) *Mechanization in the Brick Industry,* Works Progress Administration, 1939; *Mechanization in the Lumber Industry,* Works Progress Administration, 1940; (editor and contributor) *Environmental Side Effects of Rising Industrial Output,* Heath, 1971; (editor and contributor) *Our Environment: Outlook for 1980,* Heath, 1973; (editor and contributor) *The Environmental Price of Energy,* Heath, 1975. Editor of *Illinois Business Review,* 1966-67.

WORK IN PROGRESS: The Carter Administration and Energy and the Environment.

SIDELIGHTS: Alfred J. Van Tassel told *CA:* "My undergraduate training was in chemistry and physics at Berkeley which introduced me to the gloomy perspective of a universe running down in accordance with the second law of thermodynamics. This influence was strengthened by a reading of Henry Adams' *Tendency of History,* a neglected work, which considered the propensity of history to accelerate the exhaustion of resources, and, more generally, the accumulation of the contradictions in man's relation to the universe."

After becoming a professor of business research at Hofstra University, Van Tassel was able to pursue his interest in environmental change. With the help of graduate students, he set out to discover the impact of industrial growth on the environment and the relation of environmental developments to the energy crisis. The findings of this extensive research project were published in three separate works, *Environmental Side Effects of Rising Industrial Output, Our Environment: Outlook for 1980,* and *The Environmental Price of Energy.*

BIOGRAPHICAL/CRITICAL SOURCES: Newsday, October 24, 1972, October 28, 1972.

* * *

VAN TRUMP, James D(enholm)   1908-

PERSONAL: Born July 20, 1908, in Pittsburgh, Pa.; son of James C. and Jeanne (Denholm) Van Trump. *Education:* Attended Carnegie Institute of Technology (now Carnegie-Mellon University), 1926-27; University of Pittsburgh, B.A., 1931, M.A., 1932. *Politics:* Republican. *Religion:* Episcopalian. *Home:* 4614 Fifth Ave., Pittsburgh, Pa. 15213. *Office:* Pittsburgh History and Landmarks Foundation, 1 Landmarks Sq., Pittsburgh, Pa. 15212.

CAREER: Hunt Botanical Library, Pittsburgh, Pa., bibliographer, 1958-62; Pittsburgh History and Landmarks Foundation, Pittsburgh, Pa., vice-president and director of research, 1964—. Visiting critic, department of architecture, Carnegie Institute of Technology, 1960-68; visiting professor of fine arts, University of Pittsburgh, 1968-71. Vice-president, Van Trump, Ziegler & Shane, Inc. 1964-71; vice-president, Ober Park Associates, Inc., 1972—; chairman of board, Landmarks Planning, Inc., 1972—; vice-president, Landmarks Design Services, Inc., 1978—. Recording collaborator, Historic American Buildings Survey, 1956-61. *Member:* Society of Architectural Historians, Victorian Society, National Trust for Historic Preservation, American Institute of Architects (honorary member), Historical Society of Western Pennsylvania, Botanical Society of Western Pennsylvania, Pittsburgh Press Club, University Club (Pittsburgh). *Awards, honors:* Golden Quill award for journalistic achievement in western Pennsylvania, 1962, 1963.

*WRITINGS—*All published by Pittsburgh History and Landmarks Foundation, except as indicated: *An Architectural Tour of Pittsburgh,* 1959, revised edition, 1968; *The Philadelphia Story of the Pittsburgh Bibliophiles,* Pittsburgh Bibliophiles, 1964; *Bellefield's Tower: The Centenary of the Bellefield Presbyterian Church,* Bellefield Presbyterian Church, 1966; *Legend in Modern Gothic: The Union Trust Building,* 1966; (with Arthur P. Ziegler, Jr.) *The Landmark Architecture of Allegheny County, Pennsylvania,* 1967; *Evergreen Hamlet,* 1967; *September Solstice, 1966: The Virginia Journey of the Pittsburgh Bibliophiles,* Pittsburgh Bibliophiles, 1967; *Pittsburgh's Neglected Gateway: The Rotunda of the Pennsylvania Railroad Station,* 1968; *An American Palace of Culture: The Carnegie Institute and Library of Pittsburgh,* 1970; *The Gothic Revived: A Medieval Excursion in Pittsburgh,* 1977; *Our Eastern Domes,* 1974; *Station Square: A Golden Age Revived,* 1978. Also author of pamphlets and exhibition catalogues. Contributor of articles to architecture, history, engineering, and antique journals. Editor, *Charette: Pennsylvania Journal of Architecture,* 1961-71; contributing editor, *Pennsylvania Professional Engineer,* 1965-71; general editor, Allegheny Press, 1972-74.

WORK IN PROGRESS: Pittsburgh's Court Houses: Two Centuries of Legal Architecture in Allegheny County, Pennsylvania; a book on architectural history of East Street and Dutchtown areas of Pittsburgh.

BIOGRAPHICAL/CRITICAL SOURCES: Charette: Pennsylvania Journal of Architecture, September, 1961.

* * *

VAQAR, Nasrollah   1920-

PERSONAL: Born May 20, 1920, in Tehran, Iran; son of Hossein (a government employee) and Khadijeh Vaqar; married Joanne Twomey (a social worker), July 13, 1957; children: Ameneh M., Behzad S. *Education:* University of Tehran, LL.B., 1943; University of Kansas, M.A., 1951, Ph.D., 1956. *Politics:* "None in the modern sense of the word." *Religion:* Islam.

CAREER: Ministry of Finance, Tehran, Iran, administrator, 1941-49; Ripon College, Ripon, Wis., assistant professor of economics, 1956-57; Illinois Wesleyan University, Bloomington, assistant professor of economics, 1957-58; Portland State University, Portland, Ore., assistant professor, 1959-64, associate professor, 1965-72, professor of monetary theory, beginning 1973; director of economic research, Central Bank of Iran, Tehran. Senior economist, Plan Organization (Iran), 1958-59, and Iranian Economic Mission, 1964-65; economic advisor, Central Bank of Iran, 1970-72. *Awards, honors:* Science medal from Ministry of Education (Iran), 1941; economics-in-action fellow, Case Institute of Technology, 1957; central banking fellow, Federal Reserve Bank of Chicago, 1957, and Federal Reserve Bank of San Francisco, 1967.

WRITINGS: (Translator from the English into Persian and author of notes) Maurice Sheldon Amos, *British Justice,* Victory Press (Tehran), 1945; (translator from the English into Persian) Bertrand Russell, *Freedom of Thought and Official Propaganda,* Iran Party, 1947; (translator from the English into Persian, and author of notes) Harlan M. Smith, *The Essentials of Money and Banking,* 25th Shahrivar Press, 1971; (editor) *Dictionary of Money and Banking Terms* (in English and Persian), 25th Shahrivar Press, 1971. Contributor of articles to economics, business, and Middle East studies journals, including *Middle East Economic Papers.* Editor-in-chief, *Daneshjoo,* 1954-55.

WORK IN PROGRESS: Commercial Banking in the Economy.†

* * *

VARESE, Louise   1890-

PERSONAL: Born November 22, 1890, in Pittsburgh, Pa.; daughter of John Lindsay (a lawyer) and Louise (Taylor) McCutcheon; married Allen Norton, November, 1911 (deceased); married Edgard Varese, 1922 (deceased); children: (first marriage) Michael T. *Education:* Attended Smith College. *Politics:* Liberal. *Religion:* None. *Home and office:* 188 Sullivan St., New York, N.Y. 10012.

CAREER: Writer and translator. *Awards, honors:* Denyse Clairouin Award, 1948; named Chevalier de l'Ordre des Arts et des Lettres, 1958, and Officier de l'Ordre des Arts et des Lettres, October 21, 1968.

WRITINGS: Varese: A Looking Glass Diary, Norton, Volume I, 1972.

Translator: St. John Perse, *Eloges and Other Poems,* Norton, 1944; Arthur Rimbaud, *Season in Hell,* New Directions, 1945; Rimbaud, *Prose Poems from "The Illuminations,"* New Directions, 1946; Georges Bernanos, *Joy,* Pantheon, 1946; Charles Baudelaire, *Paris Spleen,* New Directions, 1947; Marcel Proust, *Pleasures and Regrets,* Crown, 1948; Jean-Paul Sartre, *The Chips Are Down,* Lear,

1948; (translator of prose poems and essays) Paul Valery, *Selected Writings*, New Directions, 1950; Stendahl, *Lucien Leuwen*, Volume I: *The Green Huntsman*, Volume II: *The Telegraph*, New Directions, 1950; Julien Gracq, *Castle of Argol*, New Directions, 1951; Adam Mickiewicz, *The Great Improvisation*, Voyages Press, 1956; Henry Michaux, *Miserable Miracle*, City Lights, 1963.

Translator; all by Georges Simenon; published by Prentice-Hall, except as indicated: *The Snow Was Black*, 1950; *The Heart of a Man*, 1951; *The Girl in His Past*, 1952; *Act of Passion*, 1952; *Satan's Children* (includes: *I Take This Woman* and *Four Days in a Lifetime*), 1953; *Inspector Maigret and the Killers*, Doubleday, 1954; (contributor of translation) *Tidal Wave*, Doubleday, 1954; *The Fugitive*, Doubleday, 1955.

WORK IN PROGRESS: Varese: A Looking Glass Diary, Volume II.

*   *   *

VARMA, Baidya Nath   1921-

PERSONAL: Born January 1, 1921, in Bargaon, India; son of Ananta Lal and Shakuntala (Devi) Das; married Savitri Devi, April 30, 1942; children: Ashoka, Rani, Ravi, Sarita. *Education:* University of Patna, B.A. (with distinction), 1941; University of Missouri, M.A., 1949; Columbia University, Ph.D., 1958. *Home:* 62 Belvedere Dr., Yonkers, N.Y. 10705. *Office:* Department of Sociology, City College of the City University of New York, New York, N.Y. 10031.

CAREER: United Nations, New York City, radio broadcaster, 1949-54; Cornell University, Ithaca, N.Y., associate editor and research associate, 1954-55; Columbia University, New York City, lecturer in Hindi, 1956-58; Hofstra University, Hempstead, N.Y., instructor, 1958-59, assistant professor of sociology, 1959-60; City College of the City University of New York, New York City, lecturer, 1960-61, assistant professor, 1961-66, associate professor, 1967-77, professor of sociology, 1978—. Lecturer for Cooperative for American Relief Everywhere (CARE) and International Study and Research Institute. Consultant to Indian Law Institute and U.S. Information Service. *Member:* American Sociological Association, American Anthropological Association, Society for Asian Studies, International Sociological Association, South Asian Sociologists (president), La Societe Toqueville. *Awards, honors:* International Certificate of Merit from Government of East Germany, 1965, for *Contemporary India*.

WRITINGS: (With Elizabeth Bacon) *India: A Sociological Background*, Human Relations Area Files, 1956; (editor and contributor) *A New Survey of the Social Sciences*, Asia Publishing House, 1962; *Contemporary India*, Asia Publishing House, 1965; *A Manifesto for India*, Hindustan Times, 1971; (editor) *The New Social Sciences*, Greenwood Press, 1976; *Modernization for What?*, Routledge & Kegan Paul, 1979. Also script writer and narrator for newsreels and documentary films for "News of the Day" and Hearst Metrotone News. Contributor of articles to learned journals.

WORK IN PROGRESS: The American Dream, a story of an individual and his adopted society; *The Elite of India*, a book based on several hundred interviews; *Power: A Macroanalysis;* a book on civilization.

SIDELIGHTS: Baidya Nath Varma told *CA:* "I have been a writer all my life. However, I have never thought of writing as my vocation. The idea bores me. One should express himself in whatever way one wishes. . . .

"Why do I write? Because at times there is no better way of expressing oneself and enjoying it in the process. My friends, the newspapers and journals for whom I occasionally dash off a piece at the last minute know that I would write only if there is a calling from the muse. Otherwise I would enjoy life, doing other creative things. What pleases me most is when younger people read my pieces and tell me that the glimpse of bygone days was such an eye-opener for them. So I keep writing on."

BIOGRAPHICAL/CRITICAL SOURCES: Indian Journal of Social Research, Volume VI, Number 3.

*   *   *

VAUGHN, Charles L(e Claire)   1911-

PERSONAL: Born October 5, 1911, in Emporia, Kan.; son of Charles (a builder) and Anna (Jones) Vaughn; married Kathleen Inez Thayer (a teacher), November 5, 1935; children: Michael T., Charles R., Kathleen V. (Mrs. Alan M. Wright), Richard J. *Education:* Kansas State Teachers College of Emporia (now Emporia State University), B.S., 1931; University of Chicago, Ph.D., 1936. *Home and office:* 41 Stratford Rd., Needham, Mass. 02192.

CAREER: Diplomate of American Board of Examiners in Professional Psychology; licensed psychologist in States of New York, Massachusetts, and Connecticut; Wayne County Training School, Northville, Mich., research associate, 1935-37; Detroit Recorders Court, Psychiatric Clinic, Detroit, Mich., clinical psychologist, 1937-40; University of Arizona, Tucson, head of student guidance, 1940-43; Psychological Corp. (independent marketing research agency), New York, N.Y., assistant director of marketing research and senior account executive, 1946-59; Dunlap Associates, Inc., Stamford, Conn., consultant and senior psychologist, 1959-61; Boston College, Chestnut Hill, Mass., associate professor, 1961-77, director of Bureau of Business Research, 1961-68, director of Franchise Industry Training Project, 1966-67, 1968, director of Office of Special Programs, 1968-77; president of Vaughn Co., 1977—. Lecturer at Western Washington College of Education (now Western Washington University), summer, 1941, and New York University, 1946-47. Has testified before U.S. Senate subcommittee on antitrust and monopoly, 1966, and Federal Trade Commission, 1972. *Military service:* U.S. Naval Reserve, aviation psychologist, active duty, 1943-46; became lieutenant.

MEMBER: American Association for Public Opinion Research, American Psychological Association (fellow), Eastern Psychological Association, Advertising Club of Greater Boston, Sigma Xi, Kappa Delta Pi. *Awards, honors:* Award from International Franchise Association, 1965.

WRITINGS: (Editor with Richard J. Thorman) *Maximizing Efficiency in Defense Marketing*, Bureau of Business Research, Boston College, 1962; (editor) *Government Industry Cooperation in Long Range Planning: Proceedings of the Second Conference on Marketing in the Defense Industries*, Boston College Press, 1963; (with Richard M. Doherty, G. Paul Draheim, and Donald J. White) *An Economic Study of Sea Scallop Production in the United States and Canada*, Bureau of Business Research, Boston College, 1963; (editor) *A Preview of Retailing in New England, 1963-1968: A Series of Award Lectures Given on the Occasion of the Twenty-Fifth Anniversary of the Founding of the College of Business Administration at Boston College*, Bureau of Business Research, Boston College, 1963; (with John L. Baldwin) *Communications Seminar of the Advertising Club of*

Greater Boston, Advertising Club of Greater Boston, 1963; (editor with Archibald S. Alexander, Harold Asher, Arthur W. Barber, and others) *The Next Five Years in the Defense Industries: Cost Reduction, Partial Disarmament,* Boston College Press, 1964; (with Mary Wilcox and Joseph Salvatore) *Manpower Skills Survey: Boston Standard Metropolitan Statistical Area,* Boston College Press, 1964.

(Editor with David B. Slater and contributor) *Franchising Today: Report of the Special Management Conference on Franchising,* Volume I, Matthew Bender, 1965, Volume II, Matthew Bender, 1967, Volume III, Farnsworth, 1968, Volume IV, Farnsworth, 1969, Volume V, Farnsworth, 1970; (with Harold A. Peterson, Joseph P. McKenna, William C. McInnes, and Raymond J. Aherne) *New York Coffee and Sugar Exchange, Inc.: Its Role in the Marketing of Sugar,* Hobbs, Dorman, 1965; (editor) *Adaptability for Survival in the Defense Industries,* Boston College Press, 1965; (editor) *The Changing Boundaries of the Defense Industries in the Next Five Years: Proceedings of the Fifth Annual Management Conference on Marketing in the Defense Industries,* Boston College Press, 1966; (with Joseph D. O'Brien) *Franchise Industry Training: Summer Youth Program–Final Report,* Bureau of Business Research, Boston College, 1966; (with O'Brien) *Franchise Industry Training (FIT),* Bureau of Business Research, Boston College, Volume I, 1966, Volume II, 1968; (editor) *Systems Approach to Social Problems: Proceedings of the Sixth Management Conference on Marketing in the Defense Industries,* Boston College Press, 1968; (with Leonard Casey and Alan Ross) *A Study of Profit Potentials in Extended Care Facilities,* Center for the Study of Franchise Distribution and Smaller Business, Boston College, 1968; (with Harold G. Wren) *A Study of Taxation of Life Insurance Companies in the Commonwealth of Massachusetts,* Bureau of Business Research, Boston College, 1969.

An Evaluation of the Westinghouse Security Systems Franchise, Center for the Study of Franchise Distribution and Smaller Business, Boston College, 1970; *The Vaughn Report on Franchising of Fast Food Restaurants: Six Categories of Franchises,* Farnsworth, 1970; *National Survey of the Oyster Industry's Problems,* Boston College Press, 1973; *Franchising: Its Nature, Scope, Advantages, and Development,* Heath, 1974, revised edition, 1979. Contributor to proceedings and conferences. Contributor of articles and book reviews to psychology, marketing, and advertising journals, and to *Scientific Monthly, American Journal of Syphilis, Gonorrhea, and Venereal Disease, Public Opinion Quarterly, Fishery Industrial Research, U.S. News and World Report, Popular Mechanics,* and *Cornell Hotel and Restaurant Administration Quarterly.*

WORK IN PROGRESS: Further research on franchising.

* * *

VAUGHN, Ruth 1935-

PERSONAL: Born August 31, 1935, in Wellington, Tex.; daughter of S. L. (a clergyman) and Nora (Knowles) Wood; married Bill Vaughn (a professor of speech and clergyman), February 14, 1955; children: Billy Edward, Ronald Charles. *Education:* University of Kansas, B.A., 1968, M.A., 1969; University of Oklahoma, Ph.D. *Politics:* Republican. *Religion:* Church of the Nazarene. *Home:* 6151 West Fremont Dr., Littleton, Colo. 80123.

CAREER: Bethany Nazarene College, Bethany, Okla., assistant professor of speech and creative writing, 1968-76. *Member:* International Platform Association, Pi Lambda

Theta, Theta Sigma Phi, Phi Delta Lambda. *Awards, honors: What I Will Tell My Children about God* was chosen "book of the year" by Church Schools Reading League, 1966.

WRITINGS: Fun for Christian Youth, Beacon Hill, 1960; *Lord, Keep the Ducks!,* Beacon Hill, 1961; *Choice Readings,* Broadman, 1962; *It's Fun to Be a Girl,* Beacon Hill, 1963; *Dreams Can Come True,* Beacon Hill, 1964; *God's Masterpiece,* Standard Publishing, 1965; *What I Will Tell My Children about God,* Beacon Hill, 1966; *Playlets and Skits,* Standard Publishing, 1967; *No Matter the Weather,* Beacon Hill, 1968; *Skits that Win,* Zondervan, 1968; *Silhouette of a Storm,* Latourette, 1969.

That First Year, Gatspel, 1970; *Fools Have No Miracles,* Beacon Hill, 1971; *Celebrate with Words,* Broadman, 1972; *Hey! Have You Heard?,* Zondervan, 1973; *Thank You for Caring,* World Wide Publications, 1974; *Even When I Cry,* Moody, 1975; *Proclaiming Christ in the Caribbean,* Beacon Hill, 1976; *More Skits that Win,* Zondervan, 1977; *Curtain Raisers,* Standard Publishing, 1978; *To Be a Mother,* Thomas Nelson, 1978; *To Be a Graduate,* Thomas Nelson, 1979. Also author of *Baby's Album,* Gospel Publishing.

Author of numerous stageplays based on works by other authors, and of several original plays, including "Lions Can't Eat Truth," "The Man on the Center Cross," and "God's Dream"; author of several filmstrip and movie scripts; author of "I Will Lift Up My Eyes," a syndicated newspaper column. Contributor of more than two thousand short stories and articles to religious publications.

WORK IN PROGRESS: A devotional book; two plays, "The Greatest Faith Ever Known" and "The Silver Chalice."

AVOCATIONAL INTERESTS: Bicycling, boating, skiing, reading, music, cake decorating, gourmet cooking.

* * *

VEANER, Allen B(arnet) 1929-

PERSONAL: Born March 17, 1929, in Harrisburg, Pa.; son of Israel Ivan and Molly (Samson) Veaner; married Rosalind Wilder, March 29, 1953 (divorced, 1971); children: Julie Ellen, Bonnie Ann. *Education:* Gettysburg College, B.A. (magna cum laude), 1949; Hebrew Union College—Jewish Institute of Religion, New York, B.H.L., 1952, M.A., 1969; Harvard University, further study, 1956-57; Simmons College, M.L.S., 1960. *Address:* P.O. Box 1297, Goleta, Calif. 93017. *Office:* Main Library, University of California, Santa Barbara, Calif. 93106.

CAREER: Rabbi; Harvard University, Cambridge, Mass., cataloger, 1957-59, head of photoreproduction department, 1959-64; Stanford University Libraries, Stanford, Calif., chief of acquistions, 1964-67, assistant director, 1967-77; University of California, Santa Barbara, university librarian, 1977—. Microreproduction consultant, Ecole Pratique des Etudes Hautes, Paris, 1963. Lecturer in library science, University of Denver, 1969, 1972. *Military service:* U.S. Army, chaplain with rank of first lieutenant, 1954-56. *Member:* American Library Association, National Microfilm Association, Society of Photographic Scientists and Engineers, American Society for Information Science, Phi Beta Kappa, Citroen Car Club. *Awards, honors:* Council on Library Resources fellowship, 1971.

WRITINGS: The Evaluation of Micropublications, American Library Association, 1971; (editor with Paul J. Fasana) *Collaborative Library Systems Development,* M.I.T. Press,

1971; *Studies in Micropublishing, 1853-1976*, Microform Review, 1976. Writer of *Final Report on Colorado Academic Libraries Book Processing Center*, University of Colorado Library, 1972. Contributor of about ninety-five articles to professional journals. Assistant editor, *Library Resources and Technical Services*, 1963-69; founding editor and editor-in-chief, *Microform Review*, 1971—.

WORK IN PROGRESS: A variety of articles for professional journals.

SIDELIGHTS: Allen Veaner told *CA*, "I have always been a hopeless logophile but didn't start writing until 1961 when a colleague asked me to prepare a literature survey on a technical subject." Since that time Veaner has produced about four or five items, chiefly technical papers on library science, each year. Veaner's latest work *Studies in Micropublishing, 1853-1976*, a historical survey of the technical development of publishing in microform, represents a departure from the strictly technical inclination of his earlier writings. He has recently become interested in creative writing. He says, "more and more I hunger for the time and resources to write fiction."

He is an admirer of Vladimir Nabokov whose work he regards as the "pinnacle of achievement in English prose." He also admires "Thor Heyerdahl for his compelling narrative power and persuasiveness, Jamaica Kincaid for her evocative imagery, and Kurt Vonnegut for his ability to combine social criticism with literary invention."

* * *

VENDLER, Helen Hennessy   1933-

PERSONAL: Born April 30, 1933, in Boston, Mass.; daughter of George (a teacher) and Helen (Conway) Hennessy. *Education:* Emmanuel College, A.B., 1954; Harvard University, Ph.D., 1960. *Residence:* Brookline, Mass. *Office:* Department of English, Boston University, Boston, Mass. 02215.

CAREER: Cornell University, Ithaca, N.Y., instructor in English, 1960-63; Haverford College, Haverford, Pa., lecturer in English, 1963-64; Swarthmore College, Swarthmore, Pa., lecturer in English, 1963-64; Smith College, Northampton, Mass., assistant professor of English, 1964-66; Boston University, Boston, Mass., associate professor, 1966-68, professor of English, 1968—. National Book Awards juror, 1973; Pulitzer Prize juror, 1974, 1976, and 1978. *Member:* Modern Language Association of America (member of executive council, 1972-75; 2nd vice-president, 1978; 1st vice-president, 1979; president, 1980), American Academy of Arts and Sciences (member of council, 1976-80), English Institute (member of supervisory committee, 1968-71; trustee, 1977—). *Awards, honors:* Lowell Prize of Modern Language Association of America and Explicator Prize of *Explicator Magazine*, 1969, both for *On Extended Wings;* award from National Institute of Arts and Letters, 1975; Guggenheim fellow; American Council of Learned Societies fellow.

WRITINGS: Yeats's *"Vision" and the Later Plays*, Harvard University Press, 1963; *On Extended Wings: Wallace Stevens' Longer Poems*, Harvard University Press, 1969; (editor with Reuben Brower and John Hollander) *I. A. Richards: Essays in His Honor*, Oxford University Press, 1973; *The Poetry of George Herbert*, Harvard University Press, 1975. Poetry reviewer, *New Yorker*, 1978—.

WORK IN PROGRESS: A book, *The Odes of Keats*.

BIOGRAPHICAL/CRITICAL SOURCES: New York Times Book Review, October 5, 1969.

VERENE, Donald Phillip   1937-

PERSONAL: Born October 24, 1937, in Galesburg, Ill.; son of Phillip Nelson and Eleanor (Grant) Verene; married Molly Black, October 13, 1960; children: Christopher Phillip. *Education:* Knox College, A.B. (cum laude), 1959; Washington University, St. Louis, A.M., 1962, Ph.D., 1964. *Home:* 326 Ridge Ave., State College, Pa. 16801. *Office:* Department of Philosophy, Pennsylvania State University, University Park, Pa. 16802.

CAREER: Northern Illinois University, DeKalb, assistant professor, 1964-69, associate professor of philosophy, 1969-71; Pennsylvania State University, University Park, visiting associate professor, 1970, associate professor of philosophy, 1971—. Visiting assistant professor, Washington University, St. Louis, Mo., summer, 1965. *Member:* American Philosophical Association, Society for Phenomenology and Existential Philosophy, Metaphysical Society of America, American Society for Aesthetics, Hegel Society of America (treasurer and member of executive council, 1969—), Society for Philosophy of Creativity (secretary of Eastern Division, 1971—), Southern Society for Philosophy and Psychology.

WRITINGS: (Editor) *Man and Culture: A Philosophical Anthology*, Dell, 1970; (contributor) Z. A. Pelczynski, editor, *Hegel's Political Philosophy*, Cambridge University Press, 1971; (editor) *Sexual Love and Western Morality*, Harper, 1972. Contributor to *Akten des XIV. International Kongresses fuer Philosophie* and to journals.

WORK IN PROGRESS: Research in philosophical theory of culture, theory of myth, theory of technological consciousness and in Ernst Cassirer's philosophy of symbolic forms.

* * *

VERMEULE, Cornelius Clarkson III   1925-
(Isao Tsukinabe)

PERSONAL: Last syllable of surname pronounced "mule"; born August 10, 1925, in Queenstown, Ireland; son of Cornelius Clarkson (an engineer) and Catherine (Comstock) Vermeule; married Emily Dickinson Townsend (a university professor), April 2, 1957; children: Emily Dickinson Blake, Cornelius Adrian Comstock. *Education:* Harvard University, A.B., 1947, M.A., 1950; University College, London, Ph.D., 1953. *Politics:* Liberal. *Religion:* Catholic. *Office:* Museum of Fine Arts, Boston, Mass. 02115.

CAREER: University of Michigan, Ann Arbor, assistant professor of fine arts, 1953-55; Bryn Mawr College, Bryn Mawr, Pa., assistant professor of archaeology, 1955-57; Museum of Fine Arts, Boston, Mass., curator of classical art, 1957—, director pro tem, 1972-73. Lecturer in fine arts at Smith College, 1960-64, and at Boston University, Harvard University, and Wellesley College; professor of classical archaeology, Yale University, 1973-74; visiting professor of fine arts, Boston College, 1978—. *Military service:* U.S. Army, 1943-52; became captain. *Member:* College Art Association (life member), Archaeological Institute of America (member of executive committee, 1962), Royal Numismatic Society (fellow), American Numismatic Society (member of council, 1960—; life fellow), Hellenic Society, Roman Society, Colonial Lords of Manors, Massachusetts Historical Society (curator of coins, 1965—), Holland Society of New York, Tavern Club. *Awards, honors:* Guggenheim fellow, 1969; Boston College Bicentennial Medal, 1976.

WRITINGS: (With Norman Jacobs) *Japanese Coinage,* Numismatic Review, 1953; *A Bibliography of Applied Numismatics in the Fields of Greek and Roman Archaeology and the Fine Arts,* Spink, 1956; *Cameo and Intaglio,* University of Pennsylvania Museum, 1956; *Roman Numismatic Art A.D. 200-400,* Spink, 1957; *Aspects of Victoria on Roman Coins, Gems, and in Monumental Art,* Spink, 1958; *The Goddess Roma in the Art of the Roman Empire,* Johnson, 1959; *Hellenistic and Roman Cuirassed Statues,* Munksgaard, 1959.

The Dal Pozzo-Albani Drawings of Classical Antiquities in the British Museum, American Philosophical Society, 1960; *Roman Medallions,* Museum of Fine Arts (Boston), 1962; (with Charles Mercer) *Alexander the Great* (juvenile), Harper, 1963; *European Art and the Classical Past,* Harvard University Press, 1964; (under pseudonym Isao Tsukinabe) *Old Bodrum,* Somerset Society, 1964; *Greek and Roman Portraits in North American Collections Open to the Public,* American Philosophical Society, 1964; *The Dal Pozzo-Albani Drawings of Classical Antiquities in the Royal Library at Windsor Castle,* American Philosophical Society, 1966; *Small Sculptures in the Museum of Fine Arts, Boston,* [Chicago], 1966; *Roman Imperial Art in Greece and Asia Minor,* Harvard University Press, 1968; *Polykleitos,* Museum of Fine Arts (Boston), 1969.

Numismatic Art in America: Aesthetics of U.S. Coinage, Harvard University Press, 1971; (with Mary Comstock) *Greek, Etruscan, and Roman Bronzes in the Museum of Fine Arts,* New York Graphic Society, 1971; *Greek, Etruscan and Roman Art: The Classical Collection of the Museum of Fine Arts, Boston,* New York Graphic Society, 1971; *Art of Cyprus,* New York Graphic Society, 1972; *Greek and Roman Cyprus,* Museum of Fine Arts (Boston), 1976; (with Comstock) *Sculpture in Stone,* Museum of Fine Arts (Boston), 1976; *Greek Sculpture and Roman Taste,* University of Michigan Press, 1977. Contributor to proceedings and to journals in his field.

WORK IN PROGRESS: Catalogues for the Museum of Fine Arts, Boston; monographs on classical art.

AVOCATIONAL INTERESTS: With wife, excavating Bronze Age city on Cyprus; raising dogs (dalmatians).

*　　*　　*

VERNADSKY, George   1887-1973

August 20, 1887—June 12, 1973; Russian-born American professor, author, and authority on early Russian history. Obituaries: *Publishers Weekly,* June 25, 1973.

*　　*　　*

VERNON, John   1943-

PERSONAL: Born June 3, 1943, in Cambridge, Mass.; son of Elijah James (a printer) and Ruth (Martin) Vernon; married Ann Frick (a painter), June 30, 1968; children: Charles. *Education:* Boston College, B.A., 1965; University of California, Davis, M.A., 1967, Ph.D., 1969. *Office:* Department of English, State University of New York, Binghamton, N.Y. 13901.

CAREER: Poet; University of Utah, Salt Lake City, assistant professor of English, 1969-71; State University of New York at Binghamton, assistant professor of English, 1971—. *Member:* Sierra Club, National Audubon Society.

WRITINGS: The Garden and the Map: Schizophrenia in Twentieth-Century Literature and Culture, University of Illinois Press, 1973; *Ann* (poems), Iris Press, 1976; *Poetry and*

the Body, University of Illinois Press, 1978. Contributor of poems to journals, including *Paris Review, Epoch, Chicago Review, New American Review,* and *Poetry Northwest,* and of essays to *American Review,* and *Iowa Review.*

WORK IN PROGRESS: A novel; more poetry.

*　　*　　*

VERNON, McCay   1928-

PERSONAL: Born October 14, 1928, in Washington, D.C.; son of Percy McCay (an army officer) and Terese (Hall) Vernon; married Edith Goldston (a microbiologist), June 8, 1951; children: Eve. *Education:* University of Florida, B.A., 1951; Gallaudet College, M.S., 1955; Florida State University, M.A., 1958; Claremont Graduate School and University Center (now Claremont Graduate School), Ph.D., 1966. *Politics:* Independent. *Religion:* Protestant. *Home:* 37 Ridge Rd., Westminster, Md. 21157. *Office:* Department of Psychology, Western Maryland College, Westminster, Md. 21157.

CAREER: Teacher, coach, and counselor at Florida School for Deaf and Blind, 1951-54, at Texas School for the Deaf, 1955-56, and Colorado School for Deaf and Blind, 1956-58; psychologist and teacher, California School for the Deaf, 1958-62; Riverside County General Hospital, Calif., clinical psychologist, 1962-63; California Baptist College, Riverside, associate professor and lecturer, summer and part-time, 1962-64; University of Illinois, Institute for Research on Exceptional Children, Urbana, research associate, 1964-65; DePaul University, Chicago, Ill., research associate professor, 1965-66; Vocational Rehabilitation Administration, Institute for Psychosomatic and Psychiatric Research, Michael Reese Hospital, Chicago, research psychologist and project director, 1966-69; Western Maryland College, Westminster, professor of psychology, 1969—. Psychologist in private practice, Westminster, Md., 1969—. Lecturer, California State College (now California State University), Los Angeles, summer and winter, 1963. Psychological consultant, St. Elizabeth's Hospital, Washington, D.C. *Military service:* U.S. Army, 1946-48. *Member:* National Association of the Deaf, American Psychological Association, Academy of Rehabilitation Audiology, Council for Exceptional Children (member of board). *Awards, honors:* Distinguished Service Award, National Association of the Deaf, 1972.

WRITINGS: Multiply Handicapped Deaf Children: Medical, Psychological, and Educational Considerations, Council for Exceptional Children, 1969; (with Eugene Mindel) *They Grow in Silence,* National Association of the Deaf, 1971.

Contributor: Stephen P. Quigley, editor, *Interpreting for Deaf People,* Division of Vocational Rehabilitation, U.S. Dept. of Health, Education, and Welfare, 1966; W. N. Craig and H. W. Barkuloo, editors, *Psychologists to Deaf Children: A Developing Perspective,* University of Pittsburgh, 1968; J. M. Wolf and R. M. Anderson, editors, *The Multiply Handicapped Child,* C. C Thomas, 1969; W. A. Daniels, editor, *The Adolescent Patient,* Mosby, 1970; S. G. Fletcher and F. S. Berg, editors, *The Hard-of-Hearing Child,* Grune, 1970; Hallowell Davis and S. R. Silverman, editors, *Hearing and Deafness,* 3rd edition (Vernon did not contribute to earlier editions), Holt, 1970; John C. Gowen and others, editors, *The Guidance of Exceptional Children,* McKay, 1970, 2nd edition, 1972; D. E. Rose, editor, *Audiological Assessment,* Prentice-Hall, 1971; E. P. Trapp and Philip Himelstein, editors, *Readings on the Exceptional*

Child: Research and Theory, 2nd edition (Vernon did not contribute to earlier edition), Appleton, 1972; Pearl B. Coulter and V. A. Christopherson, editors, *Rehabilitation Nursing,* McGraw, 1974. Contributor to other books and to *Exceptional Child Annual;* contributor of more than sixty articles to professional journals. Editor, *American Annals of the Deaf,* 1969—.

WORK IN PROGRESS: A textbook on the psychological aspects of deafness and profound hearing loss.

SIDELIGHTS: McCay Vernon, whose wife is deaf, is fluent in sign language. *Avocational interests:* Gardening, nature, sports, reading, art.

*   *   *

VICKERS, (Charles) Geoffrey 1894-

PERSONAL: Born October 13, 1894, in Nottingham, England; son of Charles Henry (a lace maker) and Jessie Anna (Lomas) Vickers; married Helen Tregoning Newton, March 21, 1918 (divorced, 1934); married Ethel Ellen Tweed, October 11, 1935 (died, 1972); children: (first marriage) Pamela Tregoning (Mrs. Robin Beatson Miller), Douglas Burnell Horsey; (second marriage) Hugh. *Education:* Merton College, Oxford, B.A., 1921. *Home:* The Grange, Manor Road, Coring, Reading RG8 9EA, England.

CAREER: Solicitor in London, England, admitted to practice, 1924; Slaughter & May (solicitors), London, partner, 1926-40; director of economic intelligence in Ministry of Economic Warfare, and member of Joint Intelligence Committee of British Chiefs of Staff, London, 1941-45; member of British National Coal Board, London, 1945-55; director of Parkinson Cowan, 1955-65. Member of London Passenger Transport Board, 1942-45, and Medical Research Council, 1952-60. Visiting fellow of Nuffield College, Oxford University, 1939-41. *Military service:* British Army, Infantry, 1915-19; became major; received Victoria Cross; recommissioned in World War II, 1940-44; retired as colonel. *Member:* Royal College of Psychiatrists (honorary fellow). *Awards, honors:* Knighted by H.M. King George VI for services rendered in World War II, 1946; M.A., Oxford University, 1951.

WRITINGS: The Undirected Society, Toronto University Press, 1959; *The Art of Judgement,* Basic Books, 1965; *Toward a Sociology of Management,* Basic Books, 1967; *Value Systems and Social Process,* Basic Books, 1968; *Freedom in a Rocking Boat,* Basic Books, 1972; *Making Institutions Work,* Wiley, 1973. Contributor to professional journals.

WORK IN PROGRESS: Research on the future course of social learning and social controls and the resultant changes in Western societies, especially in the pattern and ethics of distribution.

*   *   *

VICKREY, William (Spencer) 1914-

PERSONAL: Born June 21, 1914, in Victoria, British Columbia, Canada; brought to United States, 1914; son of Charles Vernon and Ada Eliza (Spencer) Vickrey; married Cecile Montez Thompson (a teacher of dyslexic children), July 21, 1951. *Education:* Yale University, B.S. (with high honors), 1935; Columbia University, M.A., 1937, Ph.D., 1947. *Politics:* "Liberal/Socialist/Social Democrat." *Religion:* Society of Friends. *Home:* 162 Warburton Ave., Hastings-on-Hudson, N.Y. 10706. *Office:* 1009 International Affairs Bldg., Columbia University, New York, N.Y. 10027.

CAREER: Research assistant, Twentieth Century Fund tax study, 1936-37, and power study, 1939-40; U.S. Government, Washington, D.C., National Resource Committee, junior economist, 1937-38, Office of Price Administration, economist, 1940-41, Tax Research Division, Treasury Department, senior economist, 1941-43; Columbia University, New York, N.Y., lecturer, 1946-48, assistant professor, 1948-50, associate professor, 1950-58, professor of economics, 1958—, McVickar Professor of Political Economy, 1971—, chairman of department, 1964-67. Visiting lecturer, Monash University, 1971. Member of tax missions to Puerto Rico, 1946, Japan, 1949-50, Venezuela, 1959, and Liberia, 1969; member of Ford Foundation consulting team, Calcutta Metropolitan Planning Organization, 1962-63. Director, National Bureau of Economic Research, 1973—. Interregional advisor, United Nations Center for Development Programs, Planning and Policy, 1974-75. *Wartime service:* Civilian public service as conscientious objector, 1943-46.

MEMBER: Econometric Society (fellow), American Economic Association (chairman of transportation and public utilities group, 1969), American Statistical Association, Royal Economic Society, Tax Institute, Transportation Research Forum, National Planning Association, Metropolitan Economic Association (chairman, 1964-65), Citizens' Union, New York City Club. *Awards, honors:* Guggenheim fellowship, 1955-56; Ford research professor, 1961; Center for Advanced Study in the Behavioral Sciences fellow, 1967-68; American Academy of Arts and Sciences fellow, 1974—.

WRITINGS: Agenda for Progressive Taxation, Ronald, 1949, reprinted with introductory note by the author, Augustus M. Kelley, 1971; (with Carl S. Shoup and C. Lowell Harriss) *The Fiscal System of the Federal District of Venezuela,* Garamond Press, 1960; *Microstatics,* Harcourt, 1964; *Metastatics and Macroeconomics,* Harcourt, 1964; (with Shoup, Douglas Dosser, and Rudolph Penner) *The Tax System of Liberia: Report of the Tax Mission,* Columbia University Press, 1970.

Contributor: *Studies in Current Tax Problems,* Twentieth Century Fund, 1938; *Electric Power and Government Policy,* Twentieth Century Fund, 1948; *Studies in Income and Wealth,* National Bureau of Economic Research, 1949; Arthur D. Ward, editor, *Goals of Economic Life,* National Council of Churches, 1950; Kenneth K. Kurihara, editor, *Post-Keynesian Economics,* Rutgers University Press, 1954; Joseph F. McCloskey and John M. Coppinger, editors, *Operations Research for Management,* Johns Hopkins Press, 1956; Carl S. Shoup and Richard A. Musgrave, editors, *Readings in the Economics of Taxation,* Irwin, 1959; A. W. Tucker and R. D. Luce, editors, *Contributions to the Theory of Games,* Volume IV, Princeton University Press, 1959.

R. W. Pfouts, editor, *Essays in Economics and Econometrics,* University of North Carolina Press, 1960; Selma J. Mushkin, editor, *Economics of Higher Education,* U.S. Office of Education, 1962; Howard G. Schaller, editor, *Public Expenditure Decisions in the Urban Community,* Resources for the Future, 1963; Robert Dorfman, editor, *Measuring Benefits of Government Investments,* Brookings Institution, 1965; Donald Grunewald and Henry L. Bass, editors, *Public Policy and the Modern Corporation,* Appleton, 1966; Mason Gaffney, editor, *Extractive Resources and Taxation,* University of Wisconsin Press, 1967; Joseph E. Haring, editor, *The New Economics of Regulated Industries: Rate-Making in a Dynamic Economy,* Occidental College, 1968; George M. Smerk, editor, *Readings in Urban Transportation,* Indiana University Press, 1968; Kenneth Arrow and Tibor Scitovsky, editors, *Readings in Welfare Economics,* Irwin, 1969, revised edition, 1973; Horst Claus Reektenwald, editor, *Finanztheorie,* Kiepenhauer & Witsch, 1969; Neil Chamberlain, editor, *Contemporary Economic Issues,* Irwin, 1969.

R. W. Houghton, editor, *Public Finance,* Penguin, 1970; Frank Emerson, editor, *The Economics of Environmental Problems,* University of Michigan Press, 1972; Richard M. Bird and John G. Head, editors, *Modern Fiscal Issues: Essays in Honor of Carl S. Shoup,* University of Toronto Press, 1972; Mushkin, editor, *Public Prices for Public Products,* Urban Institute, 1972; Haring, editor, *Utility Regulation under Inflation,* Occidental College Press, 1972; James R. Nelson, editor, *Criteria for Transport Pricing,* Cornell Maritime Press, 1973; E. S. Phelps, editor, *Altruism Morality and Economic Theory,* Russell Sage, 1973; Ronald E. Grieson, editor, *Urban Economics: Readings and Analysis,* Little, Brown, 1973; Phelps, editor, *Economic Justice,* Penguin, 1973; Martin S. Feldstein and Robert P. Inman, editors, *The Economics of Public Services,* Macmillan (London), 1977.

Writer of technical monographs on New York City transit. Contributor to *Encyclopedia Americana* and *Encyclopedia of the Social Sciences.* Contributor of more than fifty articles and reviews to journals in United States and abroad. Member of editorial boards, *Journal of Transport Economics and Policy,* 1967—, and *Public Finance Quarterly,* 1973—.

WORK IN PROGRESS: A treatise on the theory and practice of marginal cost pricing; research on responsive pricing for utilities; developing simulated future market systems for sale of airline reservations; generating exhaustive undominated itineraries for travel guides; research on low-loss traction for rapid transit; devising efficient and equitable transition provisions in tax reform, including cumulative averaging.

SIDELIGHTS: William Vickrey is convinced that "sophisticated pricing methods, if they can be freed from the shibboleths of financial solvency on the one hand and Thomist notions of justice on the other, can produce revolutionary improvements in life in our cities."

* * *

VIGNESS, Paul G.   1894-

PERSONAL: Born September 4, 1894, in Jewell, Iowa; son of Lauritz Andrew (a minister) and Margaret (Krogness) Vigness; married Olive Carolyn Havneros, August 18, 1920; children: Kathryn (Mrs. S. A. Brye), Evelyn Vigness Sharples, Pauleen (Mrs. F. J. Sharples). *Education:* St. Olaf College, A.B., 1918; Stanford University, M.A., 1924, Ph.D., 1931. *Politics:* Republican. *Religion:* Lutheran. *Home:* 400 South Wheeler St., Tacoma, Wash. 98444.

CAREER: Taught American history in high school at Alameda, Calif., 1924-56; Pacific Lutheran University, Tacoma, Wash., associate professor of American history and history of the Christian Church, 1956-65; Purdue University, West Lafayette, Ind., professor of American history, 1966-68; Faith Lutheran Seminary, Tacoma, Wash., teacher of history of the Christian Church, 1972—. Lecturer in political science, University of California, 1934-44. *Military service:* U.S. Army, 1918-19. *Member:* California Teachers Association (member of state council), Kiwanis International.

WRITINGS: The Neutrality of Norway in the First World War, Stanford University Press, 1932; *History of Alameda,* two volumes, privately printed, 1939; *The German Occupation of Norway,* Vantage, 1970. Contributor of articles to *National Education Association Journal* and *Christian Heritage.*

WORK IN PROGRESS: My Five Worlds, an autobiographical review of this century.

AVOCATIONAL INTERESTS: Sports fan, golf.

* * *

VINCENT, William S(hafer)   1907-

PERSONAL: Born December 12, 1907, in Tupelo, Miss.; son of William Shafer and Jessie (Clark) Vincent; married Janet Inglis Newton, August 31, 1937. *Education:* College of William and Mary, A.B., 1934; Columbia University, A.M., 1940, Ph.D., 1944. *Politics:* Republican. *Religion:* Episcopalian. *Residence:* Salisbury, Conn. 06068. *Office:* Teachers College, Columbia University, New York, N.Y. 10027.

CAREER: Columbia University, Teachers College, New York, N.Y., research associate, 1943-46; Pennsylvania State College (now University), University Park, 1946-49, began as assistant professor, became professor of education; Columbia University, Teachers College, professor of research in education, 1950-73, professor emeritus, 1973—, director of Citizens Education Project, 1950-60, director of Institute for Administrative Research, 1950-73; chairman, Vincent & Olson School Evaluation Services, 1973. Consultant to *Encyclopaedia Britannica* Films, Inc. 1945-46; executive secretary to Pennsylvania School Study Council, 1946-49, and consultant to Educational Policies Commission; associate, instructional film research project, Pennsylvania State College (now University), 1947-49; Metropolitan School Study Council, executive secretary, 1957-59, general secretary, 1959-72; general secretary, Associated Public School Systems, 1959-72; director, Central School Boards Commission on Educational Research, 1959-72. *Member:* National Education Association, Sigma Phi Epsilon.

WRITINGS: What Schools Can Do, Metropolitan School Study Council, 1944; *Emerging Patterns of Public School Practice,* Teachers College, Columbia University, 1945, reprinted, AMS Press, 1972; (with Paul R. Mort) *A Look at Our Schools,* William R. Hecht, 1946; (with others) *Tools for Teaching,* Metropolitan School Study Council, 1948; (with Mort) *Modern Educational Practice,* McGraw, 1950; (with James E. Russell) *You and the Draft,* Science Research Associates, 1952, revised edition, 1956; (with Mort) *Introduction to American Education,* McGraw, 1954; *Building Better Programs in Citizenship,* Teachers College, Columbia University, 1958; *Roles of the Citizen,* Harper, 1959; (with William H. Hartley) *American Civics,* Harcourt, 1967, 2nd revised edition, 1974; (with Marilyn Gittel and T. Edward Hollander) *Investigation of Fiscally Independent and Dependent City School Districts,* City University Research Foundation, 1967; *The Influence of Statutory Controls on the Fiscal Capability of School Boards,* Teachers College, Columbia University, 1969; (with Martin N. Olson) *Measurement of School Quality and Its Determiners,* [Walden, N.Y.], 1972; *Improbable Planet,* Vantage, 1976. Also author of *What Education Our Money Buys,* 1943, and *Interaction between Schools and Local Community Groups,* with John S. Kopp and Eugene E. McCleary, 1950.

Author of films: "The Teacher as Observer and Guide," 1946; (with F. T. Matthewson) "Integrated Art and Home Economics," 1946; (with J. D. Roberts and others) "Education for Citizenship," 1947; "Teachers at Work," 1948; "A Day in the Life of a Five-Year-Old." 1949.

WORK IN PROGRESS: Analysis of factors influencing school quality; development of instruments to measure school quality. †

* * *

VIVERS, Eileen Elliott 1905-
(Eileen Elliott Quigley)

PERSONAL: Born April 6, 1905, in Trimble, Mo.; daughter of Clifton Carpenter (a government employee) and Elizabeth Maria (Thomas) Elliott; married Floyd Walker Quigley, February 11, 1950 (died, 1966); married Paul A. Vivers, August 24, 1976. *Education:* Northwest Missouri State Teachers College (now Northwest Missouri State University), B.S., 1937; Columbia University, M.A., 1940; University of Missouri, Ed.D., 1947. *Religion:* Episcopalian. *Home:* Villa 207, 631 Southwest Sixth St., Pompano Beach, Fla. 33060.

CAREER: Stephens College, Columbia, Mo., chairman of department of foods and nutrition, 1942-44; Santa Barbara College (now University of California, Santa Barbara), assistant professor of home economics, 1944-47; Stout Institute, Menominee, Wis., professor of foods and nutrition and chairman of department, 1947-48; Southern Illinois University at Carbondale, professor of home economics, 1948-69, chairman of department, 1948-57, dean of School of Home Economics, 1957-69, dean and professor emerita, 1969—. Member of Illinois Governor's Commission on the Status of Women, 1966-69. *Member:* American Association for the Advancement of Science (fellow), American Home Economics Association, American Vocational Association, National Association of State Universities and Land Grant Colleges (secretary of council, 1967-68), National Education Association, American Association of University Professors, Illinois Home Economics Association (president, 1968-69), Illinois Vocational Association (president, 1953-54), Illinois Vocational Homemaking Teachers Association (president, 1953-54), Kappa Omicron Phi (member of national council, 1947-54), Pi Lambda Theta. *Awards, honors:* Received distinguished alumna award, 1977, from Northwest Missouri State University; home economics building renamed Eileen E. Quigley Hall, 1978, Southern Illinois University at Carbondale; proclaimed a leader in the field of home economics in the state and nation by governor of Illinois, 1978.

WRITINGS—Under name Eileen Elliott Quigley: *Introduction to Home Economics*, Macmillan, 1969, 2nd edition, 1974. Also a contributor to *Career and Job Opportunities as a Trained Teacher of Home Economics*. Contributor of articles to home economics, nutrition, vocational, and education journals, including *Journal of Home Economics, Illinois Vocational Progress, Canadian Nutrition Journal*, and *Educational Horizons*.

WORK IN PROGRESS: A third edition of *Introduction to Home Economics*.

* * *

VOEHRINGER, Erich F(rederick) 1905-1973

September 23, 1905—January 18, 1973; American missionary, pastor, and author. Obituaries: *New York Times*, January 20, 1973. (See index for *CA* sketch)

* * *

VOGENITZ, David George 1930-
(David George)

PERSONAL: Born January 4, 1930, in Milwaukee, Wis.; son of George H. and Cecile A. (Boutotte de Chaquette) Vogenitz; married former spouse, Gretchen van Clumpner, 1951. *Education:* University of Wisconsin, B.A., 1952; California State College (now University), Long Beach, M.A., 1961; Ball State University, M.A., 1972; also studied at Marquette University, and Universities of Frankfurt, London, Seville, and Madrid. *Residence:* Surfside, Calif. *Office:* Society of Spanish Studies, 1019 Shattuck Ave., Berkeley, Calif. 94707.

CAREER: Has been free-lance photo-journalist, research director of nonprofit organization, commercial artist, teacher, poet, and lecturer in Spanish folklore. Spencerian College, Milwaukee, Wis., lecturer in speech and drama, 1955-56; U.S. Dept. of Defense Schools, Frankfurt, Germany, teacher of social studies, 1961-62; Society of Spanish Studies, Seville, Spain, research director, 1963—. Lecturer in English for U.S. Information Service, University of Seville, 1963-64; lecturer in education, University of Maryland (Seville), 1965; lecturer in art, Marymount College (Seville), 1967. *Military service:* U.S. Army, Counter-Intelligence Corps, 1953-55; served in Germany. *Member:* Society of Authors (London), Gypsy Lore Society (Liverpool), Pomezia (Barcelona), Institute de Cultura Hispanica (Madrid).

WRITINGS—Under name David George: *The Gypsy with the Green Guitar*, Society of Spanish Studies (Madrid), 1967, revised edition, 1973; *The Flamenco Guitar: From Its Birth in the Hands of the Guitarrero to Its Ultimate Celebration in the Hands of the Flamenco Guitarist*, Society of Spanish Studies, 1969. Contributor of poems, short stories, and articles to journals.

WORK IN PROGRESS: The Flamenco Dancer and *The Flamenco Singer* to complete the trilogy of dance, song, and guitar; *The Andalucian Gypsy;* a book about the bullfight; a book on Federico Garcia Lorca; a novel, *The Dark Eclipse*.

AVOCATIONAL INTERESTS: Astronomy, painting, polo, judo.†

* * *

VOIGT, David Quentin 1926-

PERSONAL: Born August 9, 1926, in Reading, Pa.; son of Henry William (a professor of English) and Ethel Helena (Osmond) Voigt; married Virginia Louise Erb (an elementary teacher), December 27, 1951; children: David Jonathan, Mark William. *Education:* Albright College, B.S., 1948; Columbia University, M.A., 1949; Syracuse University, Ph.D., 1962. *Politics:* Democrat. *Religion:* Protestant. *Home:* 112 A Mifflin Blvd., Reading, Pa. 19607. *Office:* Department of Sociology, Albright College, Reading, Pa. 19603.

CAREER: Albright College, Reading, Pa., associate professor, 1964-72, professor of sociology and anthropology, 1972—. Adjunct professor of anthropology and sociology at Franklin and Marshall College, 1970-71. Coach of Brookline Colts (baseball team), Reading, 1972—. *Military service:* U.S. Army Air Forces, 1944-46; U.S. Air Force Reserve, beginning 1947; retired as major. *Member:* American Sociology Association (fellow), American Anthropological Association (fellow), Society for American Baseball Research (former president), North American Society for Sports History, Northeastern Anthropological Association, Eastern Sociological Association, Pennsylvania Sociology Society (secretary-treasurer, 1966-68; president, 1970-72). *Awards, honors:* Lindback Award for Distinguished Teaching, 1974; Albright College Distinguished Alumnus Award, 1977.

WRITINGS: American Baseball: From Gentleman's Sport to Commissioner System, University of Oklahoma Press, 1966; *American Baseball: From the Commissioners to Continental Expansion*, University of Oklahoma Press, 1970; *America's Leisure Revolution: Essays in the Sociology of Leisure and Sport*, Albright College Printing Office, 1970, new edition, 1974; *A Little League Journal*, Bowling Green University Press, 1974; *America through Baseball*, Nelson-Hall, 1976. Contributor to *Dictionary of American Biography*. Contributor of articles to *New England Quarterly*, *Abraham Lincoln Quarterly*, *Journal of Popular Culture*, *Journal of Leisure Research*, *Journal of Sports History*, *Journal of the Society for American Baseball Research*, and historical journals.

WORK IN PROGRESS: A book, *American Baseball: The Age of Expansion*.

SIDELIGHTS: David Quentin Voigt writes *CA*, "My research and writing [have] been geared to the idea that organized sport furnishes a mirror for viewing the processes of American societal development and change." *Avocational interests:* Manager of little league and junior league teams.

* * *

von KOERBER, Hans Nordewin 1886-
(Aristos Euphemides)

PERSONAL: Born July 23, 1886, in Germany; son of Theodor Max (in the Imperial Army) and Elise (von Otto) von Koerber; married Margaret Elizabeth von Boetticher, November 13, 1922 (died, 1949); married Hildegard Ellen von Boetticher (a secretary), June 14, 1955. *Education:* Attended University of Berlin, 1906-08, University of Bonn, 1911-12, and Cambridge University, 1909-11; University of Marburg, Ph.D., 1920. *Religion:* Christian. *Residence:* Warner Springs, Calif. 92086. *Office:* Divine Word Foundation, Inc., Warner Springs, Calif. 92086.

CAREER: University of Amoy, Fukien, China, professor of geography, 1924-25; University of the Philippines, Quezon City, professor of comparative religion and oriental linguistics, 1926-28; University of Southern California, Los Angeles, professor of Asian studies, 1928-52, professor emeritus, 1952—; Divine Word Foundation, Inc., Warner Springs, Calif., founder and translator, 1962—. Curator of Asian arts, Los Angeles Museum of Science, History, and Art, 1930-47. Counselor to Chinese Consulate, Los Angeles, 1933-41. Ordained minister of the Covenant Church of America. *Member:* University Club of Los Angeles, Phi Beta Kappa, Sovereign Order of Saint John of Jerusalem (bailif of the commanderies of San Diego and Colorado).

WRITINGS: Das Tibetische Verbalsystem, University of Marburg, 1919; *Morphology of the Tibetan Language*, Suttonhouse, 1935; *Tibetan Literature: Its Contribution Through Western Explorers*, University of Southern California, 1935; *A Word on Philology*, University of New Mexico, 1937; *Comparative Study of the Turkish, Mongol and Japanese Languages*, University of Southern California, 1937; *Kuan Yin: The Buddhist Madonna*, University of Southern California, 1941; (contributing editor, in charge of Chinese, Japanese, and German sections) John E. Lanz, editor, *Aviation Dictionary in Nine Languages*, Perkins, 1944; *About Basic Concepts and Words in Languages of Eurasia*, University of Southern California, 1946.

(Under pseudonym Aristos Euphemides) *The Cosmic Mystery*, Christopher, 1963; *The Significance of Matter*, Divine Word Foundation, 1968; *The Contamination of Divine Truth*, Divine Word Foundation, 1968; *A New Revelation?*, Divine Word Foundation, 1971; (with Fred S. Bunger) *A New Light Shines Out of Present Darkness*, Dorrance, 1971. Also author of articles and booklets on philology, philosophy, and metaphysics.

WORK IN PROGRESS: Translations from the German and Spanish original texts of the books of the New Revelation for Divine Word Foundation, Inc.

SIDELIGHTS: Hans von Koerber has competence in Latin, Greek, Hebrew, Sanskrit, Arabic, Tibetan, Chinese, Japanese, Malay, French and Spanish. He has reading ability in twenty-six languages.

* * *

Von WIREN-GARCZYNSKI, Vera 1931-

PERSONAL: Born July 6, 1931, in Novi Sad, Yugoslavia; daughter of Robert Ritter (an Imperial Russian Navy officer) and Elena (Dubarry) von Wiren; children: Robert Von Wiren-Garczynski. *Education:* Brooklyn College (now Brooklyn College of the City University of New York), B.A. (with honors), 1958; Columbia University, M.A., 1961; New York University, Ph.D., 1965. *Politics:* Republican. *Religion:* Russian Orthodox. *Home:* 3 Northfield Rd., Glen Cove, N.Y. 11542. *Office:* City College of the City University of New York, 138th St. and Convent Ave., New York, N.Y. 10031.

CAREER: City University of New York, Queens College, Flushing, N.Y., lecturer in Slavic literatures, 1962-64, City College, New York, N.Y., lecturer, 1964-65, instructor, 1965-67, assistant professor, 1967-72, associate professor of Slavic literatures, Russian studies, and psychology, 1972—. Visiting lecturer at Columbia University, summer, 1964, and Indiana University, summer, 1965. Has lectured in Strasbourg, Pakistan, Canada, and Ireland, and researched in Europe, including Russia.

MEMBER: Modern Language Association of America, American Association for the Advancement of Slavic Studies, American Association of Teachers of Slavic and East European Languages, International Federation of Modern Languages and Literatures, Polish Institute of Arts and Sciences. *Awards, honors:* Research grants from Humanities Fund, summer, 1966, American Council of Learned Societies, summer, 1966, summer, 1969, City University of New York, summer, 1967, summer, 1970, summer, 1971.

WRITINGS: (Editor and author of introduction with Leo Hamalian, and contributor of translations) *Seven Russian Short Novel Masterpieces*, Popular Library, 1967; (editor and author of introduction) Mikhail Mikhailovich Zoshchenko, *Pered Voskhodom Solntsa*, Inter-Language Literary Associates, 1967, revised edition published as *Before the Sunrise*, Chekhov Publishing, 1973; (contributor of translation) H. B. Segel, editor, *Literature of Eighteenth-Century Russia*, Dutton, 1967; (contributor of translation from the Polish) Leopold Tyrmand, editor, *Exploration in Freedom: Prose, Narrative and Poetry from "Kultura,"* Free Press, 1970; (contributor of translation from the Polish) Tyrmand, editor, *Kultura Critical Essays*, Free Press, 1970; *Mikhail Zoshchenko: His Life and Works*, Twayne, 1971.

Contributor to proceedings. Contributor of articles, translations, and reviews to *Russian Review, Slavic and East European Journal, Word, Odyssey Review*, and foreign publications.

WORK IN PROGRESS: The Freudian Episode in Soviet Russia.

SIDELIGHTS: Vera Von Wiren-Garczynski speaks Serbo-croatian, Ukrainian, German, French, Polish, Russian, and Hungarian.†

* * *

VORPAHL, Ben Merchant 1937-

PERSONAL: Born June 17, 1937, in Cedar City, Utah; son of Adolph Frank (a rancher) and Dorothy (Merchant) Vorpahl; married Julie Schwid, August 20, 1960; children: Cresseida Merchant. Education: University of Wyoming, B.A., 1959; University of Washington, Seattle, M.A., 1961; University of Wisconsin, Ph.D., 1964. Home: 1990 Cherokee Cir., Athens, Ga. Office: Department of English, University of Georgia, Athens, Ga. 30602.

CAREER: University of California, Los Angeles, assistant professor of American literature, 1965-73; University of Georgia, Athens, associate professor of American literature, 1973—. Member: Modern Language Association of America, Western Literature Association, Philological Association of the Pacific Coast. Awards, honors: National Endowment for the Humanities fellow, 1972-73.

WRITINGS: (Editor) My Dear Wister: The Frederic Remington-Owen Wister Letters, American West, 1972; Frederic Remington and the West: With the Eye of the Mind, University of Texas Press, 1978. Contributor of articles to history and literature journals.

WORK IN PROGRESS: A Gentleman's Lie: William Faulkner's Antic History; Process of Elimination: A Critical Biography of Frederic Remington; Philadelphia's Prodigal Son: A Critical Biography of Owen Wister.

* * *

VOSE, Clement E(llery) 1923-

PERSONAL: Born March 18, 1923, in Caribou, Me.; son of Arthur G. (a telephone company manager) and Florence (a journalist; maiden name, Murphy) Vose; married Doris Foran, December 27, 1947; children: John S., Celia L. Education: University of Maine, B.A., 1947; University of Wisconsin, M.A., 1949, Ph.D., 1952. Home: 20 Miles Ave., Middletown, Conn. 06457. Office: Department of Government, Wesleyan University, Middletown, Conn. 06457.

CAREER: Beloit College, Beloit, Wis., instructor in government, 1952-53; Western Reserve University (now Case Western Reserve University), Cleveland, Ohio, assistant professor of political science, 1953-55; Bowdoin College, Brunswick, Me., associate professor of government, 1955-58; Wesleyan University, Middletown, Conn., associate professor, 1958-61, professor, 1961—, John E. Andrus Professor of Government, 1965—, chairman of department, 1961-73, 1978—. Visiting professor, University of Wisconsin, 1960, Yale University, 1962, Columbia University, 1968. Member of Governor of Maine's Committee on State Government, 1956-58. Research director for study of constitutional change, Twentieth Century Fund, 1969-70; member, National Archives Advisory Council, 1971—. Military service: U.S. Army, Infantry, 1943-46; became staff sergeant; received Purple Heart. Member: American Political Science Association, American Association for the Advancement of Science, Society of American Archivists. Awards, honors: Social Science Research Council grant, 1956-58; Rockefeller Foundation Research grant, 1958-59; senior fellow, Law School, Yale University, 1958-59, 1963-64.

WRITINGS: Caucasians Only: The Supreme Court, the NAACP and the Restrictive Covenant Cases, University of

California Press, 1959; Constitutional Change: Amendment Politics and Supreme Court Litigation since 1900, Heath-Lexington, 1972; A Guide to Library Sources in Political Science: American Government (monograph), American Political Science Association, 1975. Contributor to political science and law journals.

WORK IN PROGRESS: Research on social, political, and legal background and history of United States-Canadian migratory bird regulations, 1900-1920.

* * *

VOSS, James F(rederick) 1930-

PERSONAL: Born December 5, 1930, in Chicago, Ill.; son of Leo Carl (a business executive) and Lydia (Israce) Voss; married Marilyn Lydie Timm, June 20, 1953; children: Barbara, Katherine, Mark, Carol, David. Education: Valparaiso University, B.A., 1952; University of Wisconsin, M.S., 1954, Ph.D., 1956. Religion: Lutheran. Home: 115 Glen David Dr., Pittsburgh, Pa. 15238. Office: Department of Psychology, University of Pittsburgh, Fifth Ave., Pittsburgh, Pa. 15213.

CAREER: Wisconsin State College (now University of Wisconsin—Eau Claire), Eau Claire, assistant professor of psychology, 1956-58; College of Wooster, Wooster, Ohio, assistant professor, 1958-61, associate professor of psychology, 1961-63; University of Pittsburgh, Pittsburgh, Pa., associate professor, 1963-65, professor of psychology, 1965—, head of department, 1968-70. Visiting professor, University of Wisconsin, summer, 1965. Member: American Psychological Association (fellow), American Association of University Professors, American Association for the Advancement of Science, American Educational Research Association, Midwestern Psychological Association, Eastern Psychological Association, Sigma Xi. Awards, honors: National Science Foundation fellow at Indiana University, 1960; National Institute of Mental Health fellow, 1970-71.

WRITINGS: (Editor and contributor) Approaches to Thought, C. E. Merrill, 1969; (contributor) R. Glaser, editor, The Nature of Reinforcement, C. E. Merrill, 1971. Contributor to Journal of Experimental Psychology, American Journal of Psychology, and Science.

WORK IN PROGRESS: Topics in Learning and Performance, with R. F. Thompson, for Academic Press; Introductory Psychology.

* * *

VUJICA, Stanko M(irko) 1909-1976

PERSONAL: Born November 27, 1909, in Busovaca, Yugoslavia; naturalized U.S. citizen; son of Nicholas (a railroad worker) and Maria (Frankovic) Vujica; married December 11, 1946; wife's name, Nada (died June 10, 1971). Education: University of Innsbruck, lic.phil., 1936; University of Zagreb, Ph.D., 1937. Home: 95 Miner St., Wilkes-Barre, Pa. 18702. Office: Department of Philosophy, Wilkes College, Wilkes-Barre, Pa. 18703.

CAREER: Institute of Philosophy, Sarajevo, Yugoslavia, professor of philosophy, 1937-43; Wilkes College, Wilkes-Barre, Pa., 1947-76, became professor of philosophy and chairman of department, professor emeritus, 1975-76. Member: American Philosophical Association, Croation Academy of America (past president), American Association of University Professors. Awards, honors: Fulbright research scholar in Pakistan, 1960-61.

WRITINGS: Croatia's Struggle for Independence, Croatian National Committee, 1966; *Razmatranja o sadasnjosti Hruata* (title means "Meditations on Croatia Today"), Croatia Press, 1968; *The Young Marx or the Old,* [Eastern Europe], 1968; *Kroz izbjeglicku prizmu; politicke polemike i pouke,* [Munich], 1972. Contributor of articles to *Observer, Pakistan Philosophy Journal,* and to Croatian journals in the United States. Member of editorial board, *Journal of Croatian Studies.*

WORK IN PROGRESS: Philosophic meditations.

SIDELIGHTS: Stanko Vujica traveled extensively. Besides English and Croatian (his mother-tongue) he knew Latin, German, French, and Italian.†

(Died September 6, 1976)

W

WAENGLER, Hans-Heinrich B. 1921-

PERSONAL: Born May 20, 1921, in Hamburg, Germany; son of Johannes G. F. (a merchant) and Agathe (Lohse) Waengler; married Ilse G. Vagt, April 29, 1944 (divorced, 1977); married Jacqueline Ann Bauman, July 21, 1978; children: (first marriage) Ute-Maria (Mrs. Craig A. Conly), Christiane. *Education:* University of Hamburg, Ph.D., 1949, Dr.phil.habil., 1957. *Home:* Benzen 13 (Sonnenhof) 3030 Walsrode 1, West Germany. *Office:* Universitaet Hannover, Bismarckstrasse 2, 3000 Hannover 1, West Germany.

CAREER: University of Hamburg, Hamburg, Germany, instructor, 1949-53, assistant professor, 1953-58, associate professor of phonetics, 1958-64; University of Colorado at Boulder, visiting professor, 1962-63, professor of linguistics and phonetics, 1964—, director of phonetics laboratory, 1966—, director of sound laboratories, 1968—, head of Phonetics Division, 1968—, director of clinical training and services in department of speech pathology and audiology, beginning 1970; University of Hannover, Hannover, West Germany, professor, 1978—. Instructor, Volkshochschule Hamburg, 1951-64; adjunct professor at Paedagogische Hochschule, Hannover, 1956-64, and Musikhochschule, Hamburg, 1959-64; visiting summer professor at Stanford University, 1958-61, and University of Scranton, 1968-69. *Military service:* German Navy, 1941-45.

MEMBER: International Society of Phonetic Sciences, International Association of Logopedics and Phoniatrics, Linguistic Society of America, American Council on the Teaching of Foreign Languages, Modern Language Association of America, American Association of Teachers of German, American Speech and Hearing Association, Societas Linguistica Europaea, Deutsche Gesellschaft fuer Sprechkunde und Sprecherziehung, Deutsche Gesellschaft fuer Sprach- und Stimmheilkunde, Linguistic Circle of Colorado (president, 1968-69).

WRITINGS: Ueber koordinierte Reaktionen der Atmung auf sprecherische Ansdrucksgestaltungen, Hamburger Phonetische Beitraege, 1953, 2nd edition, Buske, 1973; *Atlas deutscher Sprachlaute,* Akademie-Verlag, 1958, 6th edition, 1976, translation published as *Atlas of German Speech Sounds,* 1968; *Grundriss einer Phonetik des Deutschen,* N. G. Elwert-Verlag, 1960, 3rd edition, 1974, translation published as *An Outline of German Phonetics,* EMC Corp.,

1969; *Leitfaden der paedagogischen Stimmbehandlung,* Carl Marhold-Verlag, 1961, 3rd edition, 1974; *Kleine deutsche Aussprachelehre,* N. G. Elwert-Verlag, 1962, 2nd edition, 1968; *Instruction in German Pronunciation,* EMC Corp., 1963, 3rd edition, 1972; *Rangwoerterbuch hochdeutscher Umgangssprache,* N. G. Elwert-Verlag, 1964; *Zur Tonologie des Hausa,* Akademie-Verlag, 1964; *Patterns in German Stress and Intonation,* EMC Corp., 1966; (with George A. C. Scherer) *Contemporary German,* McGraw, 1966, 2nd edition (with R. L. Kyes), 1971; (with E. M. Birkmaier and K. O. Anderson) *Deutsch unserer Zeit,* Holt, 1969; *Physiologische Phonetik,* N. G. Elwert-Verlag, 1972; (with Jon G. Lyon) *Covert Articulation in Adult Listeners: Its Relationship to Listening Ability and Graded Verbal Stimuli,* Buske, 1976; (with Jacqueline A. Bauman) *Measurements of Sound Duration in the Speech of Apraxis Adults,* Buske, 1977. Contributor of about sixty articles and reviews to encyclopedias and journals in the United States and abroad.

WORK IN PROGRESS: Seventh edition of *Atlas deutscher Sprachlaute;* with wife, Jacqueline A. Bauman-Waengler, *The Treatment of Communication Disorders (Logo-pardics)* and *Physiological Phonetics.*

*   *   *

WAGENVOORD, James 1937-

PERSONAL: Born April 3, 1937, in Lansing, Mich.; son of Frederick William (a broadcaster) and Helen (Sammon) Wagenvoord; married Anita K. Laidman (an artist and designer), November 29, 1969. *Education:* Attended University of Connecticut, 1953-54; Duke University, B.A., 1957. *Home:* 340 East 66th St., New York, N.Y. 10021. *Agent:* Wendy Weil, Julian Bach Literary Agency, Inc., 3 East 48th St., New York, N.Y. 10017. *Office:* Plenary Publications International, Inc., 300 East 40th St., New York, N.Y. 10016.

CAREER: Time, Inc., New York City, chief of Time-Life Editorial Service, 1960-67; full-time writer, 1967-77; Plenary Publications International, Inc., New York City, editor-in-chief, 1977—. *Military service:* U.S. Army Reserve, Medical Corps, active duty, 1958-59. *Member:* Authors League of America, New York Historical Society, University Club.

WRITINGS: (With Lynn Bailey) *How to Surf,* Collier, 1968; *The Violent World of Touch Football,* Doubleday,

1968; *Flying Kites,* Macmillan, 1968; *Bikes and Riders,* Van Nostrand, 1972; *Hangin' Out: City Kids, City Games,* Lippincott, 1974; *City Lives,* Holt, 1976; (with Yukiko Irwin) *Shiatzu: Japanese Finger Pressure for Energy, Sexual Vitality and Relief from Tension and Pain,* Lippincott, 1976; *Men: A Book for Women,* Avon, 1978; *The Man's Book,* Avon, 1978; *Women: A Book for Men,* Avon, 1979.

General editor and contributor of photographs: Enzo Domini, *The Book of Soccer,* Van Nostrand, 1972; Peter Wood, *The Book of Squash,* Van Nostrand, 1972; George Adams, *How to Photograph a Woman,* Avon, 1979.

WORK IN PROGRESS: The Silver Book, with Douglas Colligan; *Ring the Bells of Heaven.*

BIOGRAPHICAL/CRITICAL SOURCES: Virginia Quarterly Review, winter, 1969.

* * *

WAGNER, Philip L(aurence) 1921-

PERSONAL: Born October 7, 1921, in San Jose, Calif.; son of Leo L. (a businessman) and Jeanette (Bookmyer) Wagner; married Alicja Iwanska, June 10, 1956 (divorced November 27, 1964); married Margret Kautz, June 22, 1965; children: (second marriage) Tomas Carl. *Education:* University of California, Berkeley, A.B., 1947, M.A., 1950, Ph.D., 1953. *Home:* 995 Aubeneau Crescent, West Vancouver, British Columbia, Canada V7T 1T4. *Office:* Department of Geography, Simon Fraser University, Burnaby, British Columbia, Canada V5A 1S6.

CAREER: Teacher of geography, University of California Extension—Far East Program, 1953-54; University of Chicago, Chicago, Ill., research associate, 1954-55, assistant professor, 1955-61; University of California, Davis, assistant professor, 1961-62, associate professor, 1962-67; Simon Fraser University, Burnaby, British Columbia, professor of geography, 1967—. *Military service:* U.S. Army, 1942-46; became captain. *Member:* Canadian Association of Geographers, Association of American Geographers, American Geographical Society, American Anthropological Association, Phi Beta Kappa.

WRITINGS: The Human Use of the Earth, Free Press, 1960; (editor with M. W. Mikesell) *Readings in Cultural Geography,* University of Chicago Press, 1962; *Environments and Peoples,* Prentice-Hall, 1972; (contributor) Charles A. Reed, editor, *Origins of Agriculture,* Mouton, 1977. Contributor to professional journals.

WORK IN PROGRESS: Research on cultural geography, notably language distributions.

SIDELIGHTS: Philip L. Wagner speaks Spanish, French, and German, and reads Russian, Polish, Italian, and Dutch.

* * *

WAGNER, Roy 1938-

PERSONAL: Born October 2, 1938, in Cleveland, Ohio; son of Richard Robert (a policeman) and Florence (Mueller) Wagner; married Brenda Sue Geilhausen, June 14, 1968; children: Erika Susan, Jonathan Richard. *Education:* Harvard University, A.B., 1961; University of Chicago, A.M., 1962, Ph.D., 1966. *Home address:* R.R. 1, Box 196-B, Ruckersville, Va. 22968. *Office:* Department of Anthropology, University of Virginia, Charlottesville, Va. 22904.

CAREER: Southern Illinois University at Carbondale, assistant professor of anthropology, 1966-68; Northwestern University, Evanston, Ill., associate professor of anthropol-

ogy, 1968-74; University of Virginia, Charlottesville, professor of anthropology, 1974—. *Member:* American Anthropological Association (fellow), Current Anthropology (associate member).

WRITINGS: The Curse of Souw: Principles of Daribi Clan Definition and Alliance, University of Chicago Press, 1967; *Habu: The Innovation of Meaning in Daribi Religion,* University of Chicago Press, 1972; *The Invention of Culture,* Prentice-Hall, 1975; *Lethal Speech: Daribi Myth as Symbolic Obviation,* Cornell University Press, 1978. Contributor of articles to professional journals.

WORK IN PROGRESS: A book on self-signifying symbols; research on coastal New Guinea peoples.

SIDELIGHTS: Roy Wagner conducted research among the Daribi of Karimui Patrol Post in Papua-New Guinea, 1963-65, 1968-69.

BIOGRAPHICAL/CRITICAL SOURCES: Journal of the Polynesian Society, December, 1971.

* * *

WAKELEY, John H(albert) 1932-

PERSONAL: Born November 2, 1932, in Bucyrus, Ohio; son of John Matthews (a truckdriver) and Winifred (Kanable) Wakeley; married Esther Sue Reed, 1956; children: Laina, Dan, Joe, Sara. *Education:* College of Wooster, A.B., 1954; North Carolina State College of Agriculture and Mechanical Arts (now North Carolina State University), M.S., 1958; Michigan State University of Agriculture and Applied Science (now Michigan State University), Ph.D., 1961. *Home:* 1602 Clifton, Lansing, Mich. 48910. *Office:* Department of Psychology, Michigan State University, East Lansing, Mich. 48823.

CAREER: Corning Glass Works, Corning, N.Y., personnel researcher, 1961-64; Michigan State University, East Lansing, 1964—, began as assistant professor, professor of psychology, 1972—, chairman of department, 1973—. *Military service:* U.S. Army, 1954-56. *Member:* American Psychological Association, American Association for the Advancement of Science, Sigma Xi.

WRITINGS: (With Henry Clay Smith) *Psychology of Industrial Behavior,* 3rd edition (Wakeley was not associated with earlier editions), McGraw, 1972; (with C. F. Frost and R. A. Ruh) *The Scanlon Plan for Organization Development,* Michigan State University Press, 1974. Contributor to psychology and business journals.

WORK IN PROGRESS: Research on interviewing.

* * *

WALDECK, Peter Bruce 1940-

PERSONAL: Born April 6, 1940, in Wyandotte, Mich.; son of William Francis (a chemist) and Helen (Penniman) Waldeck; married Lois Kalber, February 5, 1966 (divorced, 1970); married Rita Nonemaker (a teacher), October 30, 1971. *Education:* Oberlin College, B.A., 1962; University of Connecticut, M.A., 1966, Ph.D., 1967. *Home:* R.D. 2, Port Trevorton, Pa. 17864. *Office:* Department of German, Susquehanna University, Selinsgrove, Pa. 17870.

CAREER: University of Massachusetts—Amherst, assistant professor of German, 1967-70; Susquehanna University, Selinsgrove, Pa., associate professor of German, 1970—. *Member:* American Association of University Professors, Modern Language Association of America, Phi Beta Kappa, Phi Kappa Phi.

WRITINGS: Die Kindheitsproblematik bei Hermann Broch, Fink, 1968; *The Split Self from Goethe to Broch,* Bucknell University Press, in press. Contributor to *Orbis Litterarum, Colloquia Germanica, Monatshefte,* and *Susquehanna Studies.*

WORK IN PROGRESS: Studying comedy, tragedy, and anxiety.

* * *

WALEN, Harry L(eonard) 1915-

PERSONAL: Born June 26, 1915, in Winchester, Mass.; son of Harry L. and Alice (Garland) Walen; married Elizabeth Benson, June 26, 1939; children: Harry B., Kimball F., Robert L. *Education:* Harvard University, A.B. (cum laude), 1937, A.M., 1942. *Home:* 6 Floral St., Newton Highlands, Mass. 02161. *Office:* Needham High School, Needham, Mass. 02194.

CAREER: English teacher and department head at Los Alamos Ranch School, Los Alamos, N.M., 1937-42; Groton School, Groton, Mass., teacher of English, 1942-46; Newton High School, Newton, Mass., English teacher, 1946-51, assistant principal, 1951-54; Ginn & Co., Boston, Mass., directing editor of secondary school English textbooks, 1955-61; Needham High School, Needham, Mass., principal, 1961-71, graduate placement adviser, 1972—. Instructor in English, Newton Junior College, 1946-51. Alderman of Newton, Mass., 1960-71. *Member:* National Association of Secondary School Principals, National Council of Teachers of English, Headmasters Association, New England Association of Teachers of English (past president), New England Association of Schools and Colleges (past member of executive board), Massachusetts Secondary School Principals Association, Boston Authors Club, Society of Mayflower Descendants, Harvard Club of Boston, and numerous other historical and geneological societies. *Awards, honors:* John Hay fellow in humanities at Colorado College, 1965; citations from National Council of Teachers of English, and U.S. Commissioner of Education, 1970; annual Harry L. Walen book award for creative writing at Needham High School was named in his honor, 1972.

WRITINGS: The Family Travel Camper, Berkeley Enterprises, 1955, revised edition, 1959; (with Edward Gordon, Robert Bennett, and Verda Evans) *Types of Literature,* Ginn, 1964, revised edition, 1978; (with Gordon, Henry Terrie, and Andrew Porter) *American Literature,* Ginn, 1964, revised edition, 1978; (with Gordon, Armour Craig, and Frank Rice) *English Literature,* Ginn, 1964; (contributor) Grinder, editor, *Studies in Adolescence,* Ginn, 1975. Also author of monographs on English learning environments and career education. Contributor of articles and poetry to *English Journal, NASSP Bulletin* of the National Association of Secondary School Principals, *English Leaflet, Educational Leadership, Groton School Quarterly, College Verse, English Education,* and other language and education journals.

WORK IN PROGRESS: Poetry; research and writing in geneology; materials on education.

* * *

WALINSKY, Ossip J. 1887(?)-1973

1887(?)—March 4, 1973; Lithuanian-born American union president, Jewish community leader, author, and poet. Obituaries: *New York Times,* March 6, 1973.

WALKER, Albert L(yell) 1907-

PERSONAL: Born January 20, 1907, in Oklahoma City, Okla.; son of James Francis Docetti (a businessman) and Neva (Roberts) Walker; married Frances R. Zang, December, 1928 (divorced, 1947); married Jauvanta Maurine Young, September 1, 1948; children: (first marriage) Judith Lyell, Anthony Lyell. *Education:* Park College, B.A., 1929; University of Iowa, M.A., 1930, Ph.D., 1936. *Home:* 3620 Story St., Ames, Iowa 50010. *Office:* Department of English, Iowa State University, Ames, Iowa 50010.

CAREER: University of Arkansas, Fayetteville, instructor in English, 1930-32; Iowa State University, Ames, instructor, 1935-36, assistant professor, 1936-40, associate professor, 1940-42, professor of English, 1942-77, professor emeritus, 1977—, director of freshman English and chairman of curriculum committee of College of Sciences and Humanities, 1942-59, chairman of English and speech department, 1959-69, chairman of English department, 1969-72. General Education Board fellow at University of Chicago, summers, 1940, 1941, spring and summer, 1942. *Member:* Modern Language Association of America, American Association of University Professors, National Council of Teachers of English, Phi Kappa Phi, Lampos (honorary society).

WRITINGS: (With R. B. Orlovich, Keith Huntress, and Barriss Mills) *Minimum Essentials of Good Writing,* Heath, 1952; (with Orlovich, Huntress, and Mills) *Essentials of Good Writing,* Heath, 1959; (with Elisabeth Schneider and Herbert E. Childs) *The Range of Literature: An Introduction to Prose and Verse,* American Book Co., 1960, 3rd edition, Van Nostrand, 1973; (with Schneider and Childs) *The Range of Literature: Drama,* Van Nostrand, 1973; (with Schneider and Childs) *The Range of Literature: Poetry,* Van Nostrand, 1974. Also co-author with Schneider and Childs of *The Range of Literature: Fiction,* Van Nostrand. Contributor of articles to journals.

WORK IN PROGRESS: Convention in Shakespeare's Use of Metaphor: Dramatic versus Lyric Metaphor; short stories.

* * *

WALKER, Nicolette (Daisy) Milnes 1943-

PERSONAL: Born March 15, 1943, in Altrincham, Cheshire, England; daughter of John Henry Milnes (a surgeon) and Mary Joyce (Moon) Walker; married Bruce Gordon Coward (a publisher), February 26, 1972; children: twin daughters. *Education:* University of Bristol, B.Sc., 1964, M.Sc., 1969. *Agent:* Lloyd-George & Coward, 31 Theberton St., London N1 0QY, England.

CAREER: British Aircraft Corp., Bristol, England, technical psychologist, 1966-70; University of Wales, Institute of Science and Technology, Cardiff, research psychologist, 1970-71. *Member:* British Psychological Society, Ergonomics Research Society, Little Ship Club, Dale Yacht Club, Ocean Cruising Club. *Awards, honors:* Member of Order of the British Empire, 1972.

WRITINGS: When I Put Out to Sea, Stein & Day, 1972; (author of introduction) *Dinghy Sailing,* Seeley Service, 1978.

WORK IN PROGRESS: Editing a yachting manual.

SIDELIGHTS: Nicolette Walker was the first woman to sail alone, non-stop across the Atlantic Ocean, making the journey June 12-July 26, 1971.

WALL, Richard 1944-

PERSONAL: Born June 2, 1944, in Abergavenny, England; son of Percy (a clerk) and Winifred Elizabeth (Champion) Wall; married Diane Rachelle Lipson, March 30, 1969; children: Ingrid, David. *Education:* Kings College, London, B.A. (honors), 1965; University College, London, M.Phil., 1968. *Politics:* Socialist. *Home:* 6 Metcalfe Rd., Cambridge, England. *Office:* Cambridge Group for the History of Population and Social Structure, 27 Trumpington St., Cambridge, England.

CAREER: Cambridge Group for the History of Population and Social Structure, Cambridge, England, research officer, 1968—. *Member:* International Union for the Scientific Study of Population, Societe de Demographie Historique.

WRITINGS: (With others) *The Railway to Walthanstow and Chingford,* Walthanstow Antiquarian Society, 1970; (editor with Peter Laslett) *Household and Family in Past Time,* Cambridge University Press, 1972. Editor of "Pioneers in Demography," a series published by Gregg International.

WORK IN PROGRESS: Research on household structure and kinship network in England since the sixteenth century.

*   *   *

WALLACE, Samuel E(ugene) 1935-

PERSONAL: Born July 8, 1935, in Grandview, Mo.; son of John T. (a printer) and Mary E. (Talley) Wallace; married Sondra Barnes (divorced, 1962); married Susan Mervin (a speech therapist), October 8, 1966; children: (first marriage) Michele Re. *Education:* William Jewell College, B.A., 1956; University of Minnesota, M.A., 1958, Ph.D., 1960. *Politics:* Democrat. *Religion:* Presbyterian. *Home:* 1623 Cove Creek Lane, Knoxville, Tenn. 37919. *Office:* Department of Sociology, University of Tennessee, Knoxville, Tenn. 37916.

CAREER: University of Puerto Rico, Rio Piedras, associate project director of study of San Juan, for Social Science Research Center, 1959-60, assistant professor, 1960-62, associate professor of sociology, 1963-64; Columbia University, New York, N.Y., director of Bowery study for Bureau of Applied Research, 1964-65, principal investigator for Latin American violence study, 1965; Brandeis University, Waltham, Mass., assistant professor of sociology, 1965-73; University of Tennessee at Knoxville, 1973—, currently professor of sociology and chairman of urban studies department. Visiting professor at Queens College of the City University of New York, 1965, 1968, Sir George Williams University, 1967, and Massachusetts College of Optometry, 1970-71. Consultant, Puerto Rican Institute of Psychiatry, 1961-62, and Puerto Rican Urban Renewal and Housing Corp., 1961-64; supervisor, National Institute of Mental Health Field Training Program, 1965-69; designer, Media Systems for College Classrooms, 1969-70; principal investigator on study of eye and vision care professionals, New England Council of Optometrists, 1969-71; principal investigator for Practitioner Performance in Pathology Detection, American Optometric Association, 1970. Director of project on widows of suicidees, Laboratory of Community Psychiatry, School of Medicine, Harvard University, 1958—. *Member:* Society for the Study of Social Problems, American Sociological Association, Eastern Sociological Association, Southern Sociological Society, Mid-South Sociological Association (president).

WRITINGS: (With Theodore Caplow and Keith Lovald) *A General Report on the Problems of Relocating the Popula-*tion of the Lower Loop, Minneapolis Housing Authority, 1958; *Planning San Juan,* Social Science Research Center, University of Puerto Rico, 1961; *The Tenant's View of Experimental Housing,* Puerto Rico Urban Renewal and Housing Corp., 1963; (with Caplow and Sheldon Stryker) *The Urban Ambience,* Bedminster, 1964; (editor) *Urbanismo,* University of Puerto Rico, 1964; *Skid Row and Its Inhabitants,* Bureau of Applied Social Research, Columbia University, 1964; *Skid Row as a Way of Life,* Bedminster, 1964; (contributor) Simon Dinitz, Alfred C. Clarke, and Russell R. Dynes, editors, *Deviance: Studies in the Process of Stigmatization and Societal Reaction,* Oxford University Press, 1969; *Field Methods Training Program,* Brandeis University, 1969; (editor) *Total Institutions,* Aldine, 1971; *New Englanders, Their Eyes and the Men Who Profess to Care for Them,* New England Council of Optometrists, 1972; *After Suicide,* Wiley, 1973. Contributor to professional journals.

WORK IN PROGRESS: *The Urban Environment,* with six video cassettes, for Dorsey; *Suicide and Euthanasia: The Rights of Personhood,* for University of Tennessee Press.

AVOCATIONAL INTERESTS: Camping.

*   *   *

WALLACE, William A(ugustine) 1918-

PERSONAL: Born May 11, 1918, in New York, N.Y.; son of William A. (a businessman) and Louise C. (Teufel) Wallace. *Education:* Manhattan College, B.E.E., 1940; Catholic University of America, M.S., 1952; Dominican House of Studies, S.T.B., 1952, S.T.L. and S.T.Lr., 1954; University of Fribourg, Ph.D., 1959, Th.D., 1961; Dominican Order, Rome, Italy, S.T.Mag., 1967. *Home:* 487 Michigan Ave. N.E., Washington, D.C. 20017. *Office:* Catholic University of America, Washington, D.C. 20064.

CAREER: Entered Order of Preachers (Dominican), 1946, ordained Roman Catholic priest, 1953; St. Stephen's College, Dover, Mass., professor of philosophy, 1954-62; Catholic University of America, Washington, D.C., editor of *New Catholic Encyclopedia* and lecturer in philosophy, 1963-65; Harvard University, Cambridge, Mass., research associate in history of science, 1965-67; Dominican House of Studies, Washington, D.C., Regent of Studies and professor, 1968-70; Catholic University of America, Washington, D.C., professorial lecturer in philosophy of science, 1968-70, professor of history and philosophy of science, 1970—. Senior fellow at Folger Institute, 1975-76; member of Institute for Advanced Study, Princeton University, 1976-77; director general of Leonine Commission, 1976—. Member of corporation of Providence College, 1967—. *Military service:* U.S. Navy, ordnance and operations officer, 1941-46; served in Pacific theater; became lieutenant commander; received Legion of Merit.

MEMBER: American Catholic Philosophical Association (president, 1969-70), History of Science Society, Philosophy of Science Association, Phi Beta Kappa, Sigma Xi. *Awards, honors:* National Science Foundation grants, 1965-67, 1972-74, 1975-77, to study precursors of Galileo; D.Sc., Providence College, 1973; D. Litt., Molloy College, 1974; L.H.D., Manhattan College, 1975.

WRITINGS: Scientific Methodology of Theodoric of Freiberg, University of Fribourg Press, 1959; (contributor) J. A. Weisheipl, editor, *The Dignity of Science,* Thomist Press, 1961; *The Role of Demonstration in Moral Theology,* Thomist Press, 1962; *Einstein, Galileo, and Aquinas,* Thomist Press, 1963; *Cosmogony,* McGraw, 1967; (contributor)

R. S. Cohen and M. W. Wartofsky, editors, *Boston Studies in the Philosophy of Science*, Volume III, Humanities Press, 1968; *Causality and Scientific Explanation*, University of Michigan Press, Volume I, 1972, Volume II, 1974; (contributor) Edward Grant, editor, *A Source Book in Medieval Science*, Harvard University Press, 1974; *The Elements of Philosophy*, Alba, 1977; *Galileo's Early Notebooks*, University of Notre Dame Press, 1977; (contributor) D. C. Lindberg, editor, *Science in the Middle Ages*, University of Chicago Press, 1978.

Contributor to *Proceedings of the American Catholic Philosophical Association, New Catholic Encyclopedia, Dictionary of Scientific Biography,* and *Dictionary of the History of Ideas.* Contributor of more than sixty articles to journals in his field, including *Thomist, New Scholasticism, Journal of the Washington Academy of Sciences, Isis, British Journal for the History of Science,* and *Journal of the History of Ideas.* Staff editor, *New Catholic Encyclopedia,* fifteen volumes, McGraw, 1967. Associate editor, *Thomist,* 1962—.

WORK IN PROGRESS: Prelude to Galileo; editing critical editions of St. Thomas Aquinas' works; studying the transition from medieval to early modern science, with an emphasis on the early writings of Galileo.

* * *

WALLEY, David 1945-

PERSONAL: Born March 18, 1945, in Plainfield, N.J.; son of Miron Monroe (a lawyer) and Sylvia (Silot) Walley. *Education:* Rutgers University, B.A., 1967; Hofstra University, graduate study, 1967-68. *Politics:* "Pro life." *Religion:* Jewish. *Home:* 525 West End Ave., New York, N.Y. 10024. *Agent:* P. Seidel, 164 East 93rd St., New York, N.Y. 10028.

CAREER: Rock and roll music promoter, critic (has written for *Jazz and Pop, East Village Other,* and *New York Ace*), and journalist.

WRITINGS: (Contributor) Jonathan Eisen, editor, *The Age of Rock 2,* Random House, 1970; (contributor) T. Becker, editor, *Government Lawlessness in America,* Oxford University Press, 1971; *No Commercial Potential: The Saga of Frank Zappa and the Mothers of Invention,* Outerbridge & Lazard, 1972; *Nothing in Moderation: A Biography of Ernie Kovacs,* Drake, 1975, published as *The Ernie Kovacs Phile: The Zany Pioneer of Early Tv,* Bolder Books, 1978. Also author or co-author of *California Carmel Plum* (poems), *Its Been Real: An Agony in Five Fits* (play), and *Exhibit A* (film).

WORK IN PROGRESS: Decadent Memories, "a rock and roll mystery chronicling the crimes against consciousness which have been perpetrated by the music business over the last decade."

SIDELIGHTS: David Walley told *CA:* "I think of myself as a cultural historian as I have written on two essential cultural figures from two different ages, Zappa and Kovacs." Walley is quite concerned about current trends in rock and roll and the culture in general. "Rock and Roll," he says, "is an essential metaphor of the Sixties because it was more than just entertainment. It was a lifestyle, a culture, an intellectual viewpoint. It was the first wave of a new consciousness which is just now, ten years later, starting to be felt worldwide."

Walley says that "the Seventies have been a period of reflection and retrenchment." He speculates that "the Eighties will be in some ways like the Sixties, only the heads of the Sixties will be linking up with the heads of the late Seventies like the heads of the Sixties linked up at least spiritually with the Beats. . . . Things will pickup in the Eighties—They'll have to. The music scene is tentative like that-punk is bad theater, a merchandizing trick, but it could lead to some interesting ideas. American culture needs all the ideas it can get."

AVOCATIONAL INTERESTS: Electronic music.

* * *

WALLIS, W(ilson) Allen 1912-

PERSONAL: Born November 5, 1912, in Philadelphia, Pa.; son of Wilson Dallam (a physical anthropologist) and Grace (Allen) Wallis; married Anne Armstrong, October 5, 1935; children: Nancy (Mrs. Carl R. Ingling, Jr.), Virginia (Mrs. Jack S. Cates). *Education:* University of Minnesota, A.B. (magna cum laude), 1932; graduate study at University of Minnesota, 1932-33, University of Chicago, 1933-35, and Columbia University, 1935-36. *Home:* 255 Allens Creek Rd., Rochester, N.Y. 14618. *Office:* University of Rochester, Rochester, N.Y. 14627.

CAREER: National Resources Committee, Washington, D.C., 1935-37, began as assistant economist, became associate economist; Yale University, New Haven, Conn., instructor in political economy, 1937-38; Stanford University, Stanford, Calif., 1938-46, began as assistant professor, became associate professor of economics; University of Chicago, Chicago, Ill., professor of statistics and economics, 1946-62, chairman of department of statistics, 1949-57, dean of Graduate School of Business, 1961-62; University of Rochester, Rochester, N.Y., president, 1962-70, chancellor, 1970—. Carnegie research associate, National Bureau of Economic Research, 1939-40, 1941. Fellow, Center for Advanced Study in the Behavioral Sciences, 1956-57. Special assistant to President Dwight D. Eisenhower, 1959-61. Director of research in statistical research group, Office of Scientific Research and Development, Columbia University, 1942-46; director, Ford Foundation program of university surveys of behavioral sciences, 1953-54. Tax Foundation, Inc., trustee, 1961—, chairman of board of trustees, 1972-75. Director, Civic Music Association (Rochester), 1963-69; trustee, International Museum of Photography (George Eastman House, Inc.), 1963—; chairman, Rochester Bach Festival, 1964-67; member of executive committee, Memorial Art Gallery, 1966—.

MEMBER: International Statistical Institute, American Academy of Arts and Sciences, American Association for the Advancement of Science, American Economic Association (member of executive committee, 1962-64), American Society for Quality Control, American Statistical Association (president, 1965), Institute of Mathematical Statistics, Mont Pelerin Society, Rochester Society for Quality Control, Phi Beta Kappa, Alpha Phi Omega, Beta Gamma Sigma.

WRITINGS: (With others) *Consumer Expenditures in the United States,* National Resources Committee, 1939; (with Geoffrey H. Moore) *A Significance Test for Time Series and Other Ordered Observations,* National Bureau of Economic Research, 1941; (contributor) O. R. Lang and others, editors, *Studies in Mathematical Economics and Econometrics,* University of Chicago Press, 1942; (with Milton Friedman) *Sequential Analysis of Statistical Data: Applications,* Columbia University Press, 1945; (with others) *Techniques of Statistical Analysis,* McGraw, 1947; (with others) *Sampling Inspection,* McGraw, 1948; (with others) *Accep-*

tance Sampling: A Symposium, American Statistical Association, 1950; (with Harry V. Roberts) *Statistics: A New Approach,* Free Press, 1956; (contributor) *Increasing Understanding of Public Problems and Policies,* Farm Foundation, 1960; (contributor) H. Schoeck and J. W. Wiggins, editors, *The New Argument in Economics: The Public versus the Private Sector,* Van Nostrand, 1963; (with James Tobin) *Welfare Programs: An Economic Appraisal,* American Enterprise Institute for Public Policy Research, 1968; *An Overgoverned Society,* Free Press, 1976. Contributor of about forty articles to *Saturday Review, Atlantic Monthly,* and to economics and statistics journals.

* * *

WALLS, Dwayne E(stes) 1932-

PERSONAL: Born May 16, 1932, in Morganton, N.C.; son of William Roy (a clergyman) and Dora (Buchanan) Walls; married Judith Michaels (a teacher), September 20, 1958; children: Helen Elizabeth, Dwayne E., Jr. *Education:* Attended Lenoir Rhyne College, 1950, 1953-54, and University of North Carolina, 1953-57. *Politics:* Democrat. *Religion:* Protestant. *Home address:* Route 3, Box 105, Pittsboro, N.C. 27312. *Agent:* Sterling Lord Agency, 660 Madison Ave., New York, N.Y. 10021. *Office:* Department of Journalism, North Carolina State University, Raleigh, N.C. 27607.

CAREER: News bureau writer, University of North Carolina, 1954-55, alumni association editorial assistant, 1955-56; *Durham Sun,* Durham, N.C., staff writer, 1956-57; *Durham Morning Herald,* Durham, staff writer, 1957-59; *Chapel Hill Weekly,* Chapel Hill, N.C., news editor, 1959-61; *Charlotte Observer,* Charlotte, N.C., staff writer, 1961-71; free-lance writer, 1971—; Duke University, Durham, part-time research associate, 1972-73; Southern Regional Council, Atlanta, Ga., program officer, 1973-75; currently lecturer in journalism at North Carolina State University at Raleigh. Research associate and adjunct lecturer at University of North Carolina, 1969-71. *Military service:* U.S. Air Force, 1951-53. *Member:* American Political Science Association. *Awards, honors:* George Polk Memorial award; Sidney Hillman Foundation award; American Political Science Award for Excellence in Public Affairs Reporting; three awards from the National Conference of Christians and Jews; five awards from the North Carolina Press Association; two awards from Atlanta chapter of Sigma Delta Chi; fellowships from National Endowment for the Humanities, American Political Science Association, Ford Foundation, and Louis M. Rabinowitz Foundation.

WRITINGS: Fayette County, Tennessee: Tragedy and Confrontation, Southern Regional Council, 1969; *The Klan: Collapsed and Dormant,* Race Relations Information Center, 1970; *The Chickenbone Special,* Harcourt, 1971; (editor) *Amazing Disgrace,* South Carolina Council on Human Relations, 1972. Contributor to *Editor and Publisher* and *Saturday Review.*

WORK IN PROGRESS: Two books, *The culture of Poverty in an East Tennessee Coal Field* and *The Kidwells.*

* * *

WALLWORK, Ernest (Edward) 1937-

PERSONAL: Born October 6, 1937, in Orange, N.J.; son of Ernest E. (a wholesale merchant) and Irene Baldwin (Smith) Wallwork; married Nancy Walker Veeder, December 14, 1963 (divorced May, 1972); married Anne Elizabeth Shere, May 24, 1973. *Education:* Bucknell University, B.S., 1959;

Harvard University, M.B.A., 1961, Ph.D., 1970; Yale University, B.D., 1964. *Politics:* Democrat. *Home:* 57 Edgehill Rd., New Haven, Conn. 06511. *Office:* Department of Religious Studies, Yale University, 320 Temple St., New Haven, Conn. 06511.

CAREER: Massachusetts Institute of Technology, Cambridge, chaplain (licensed, but not ordained by Presbyterian Church), 1967-68; Wellesley College, Wellesley, Mass., assistant professor of religion, 1968-72; Harvard University, Cambridge, Mass., visiting scholar, 1972-74; Union Theological Seminary, New York, N.Y., visiting assistant professor, 1973-74; Yale University, New Haven, Conn., associate professor of religious ethics, 1974—. Director of Presbyterian Foundation. *Member:* American Academy of Religion (director of New England region, 1978-79), American Society of Christian Ethics, Society for the Scientific Study of Religion, Society for Religion in Higher Education, Institute for Society, Ethics, and the Life Sciences, American Civil Liberties Union, Conference Internationale de Sociologie Religieuse. *Awards, honors:* National Endowment for the Humanities fellowship, 1972-73; named "major figure" by Society for the Scientific Study of Religion, 1975.

WRITINGS: Durkheim: Morality and Milieu, Harvard University Press, 1972; (with Roger Johnson and others) *Critical Issues in Modern Religion,* Prentice-Hall, 1973; (contributor) Eugene Kennedy, editor, *Human Rights and Psychological Research,* Crowell, 1975; (contributor) William Rogers and David Barnard, editors, *Nourishing the Humanistic in Medicine: A Dialogue with the Social Sciences,* University of Pittsburgh Press, 1978; (contributor) John Broughton and D. J. Freeman-Moir, editors, *The Foundations of Cognitive-Developmental Psychology,* Johnson-Ablex Press, 1979; (contributor) Brenda Munsey, editor, *Kohlberg and Moral Education: Basic Issues in Philosophy, Psychology, Religion, and Education,* Religious Education Press, 1979.

* * *

WALMSLEY, Arnold Robert 1912-
(Nicholas Roland)

PERSONAL: Born August 29, 1912, in Cotta, Ceylon; son of A. M. (an Anglican priest) and A. J. (Murgatroyd) Walmsley; married Frances Councell de Moulpied, 1944. *Education:* Hertford College, Oxford, M.A. (first class honors), 1935. *Religion:* Roman Catholic. *Home:* Manor Farm, Dunmow Rd., Bishop's Stortford, Hertfordshire, England.

CAREER: Private secretary in Vienna, Austria, 1935-38; with British Foreign Office, 1939-45; British Diplomatic Service, foreign service, 1946-70; British consul in Jerusalem, 1950-54; head of Arabian Department, 1961; counsellor in Khartoum, 1963-65; director of Middle East Centre of Arab Studies, Lebanon, 1965-69. *Awards, honors:* Member of the Order of the British Empire, 1946; companion of the Order of St. Michael and St. George, 1963.

WRITINGS—Novels under pseudonym Nicholas Roland: *The Great One,* Houghton, 1968; *Natural Causes,* Aurora Publishers, 1970; *Who Came by Night,* Holt, 1972.

BIOGRAPHICAL/CRITICAL SOURCES: New Statesman, March 24, 1967; *Times Literary Supplement,* May 4, 1967; *New York Times Book Review,* January 14, 1968; *New York Times,* January 31, 1968; *Best Sellers,* February 1, 1968; *Punch,* April 16, 1969.

WALSH, Timothy J(ames) 1927-

PERSONAL: Born March 31, 1927, in New York, N.Y.; son of Timothy J. and Anne M. Walsh; married Dorothy Powers, November 24, 1951; children: Mary Cathleen. *Education:* Fordham University, A.B., 1949; St. John's University, Jamaica, N.Y., J.D., 1956; New York University, LL.M., 1962. *Home:* 74 Oak Lane, Pelham Manor, N.Y. 10803. *Office address:* Harris & Walsh, Management Consultants, Inc., P.O. Box 698, New Rochelle, N.Y. 10802.

CAREER: Admitted to the Bar of New York State, 1957, and the Bar of U.S. Supreme Court, 1968; private practice of law in New York, N.Y. and Westchester County, N.Y., 1957—; sales and managerial positions with Retail Credit Co., 1949-51; A.B. Dumont Laboratories, Clifton, N.J., security manager, 1956-59; Sperry Rand Corp., Sperry Gyroscope Division, Great Neck, N.Y., security manager, 1959-66; Harris & Walsh, Management Consultants, Inc., New Rochelle, N.Y., president, 1966—. Assistant professor at Fordham University, 1954-59, and New York University, 1964-68. Lecturer at Michigan State University of Agriculture and Applied Science (now Michigan State University), 1962, and Purdue University, 1963. *Military service:* U.S. Naval Reserve, 1945-46. U.S. Air Force, 1951-53; became captain. *Member:* International Association of Chiefs of Police, American Society for Industrial Security (president, 1964; chairman of the board, 1965), National Fire Protection Association, American Arbitration Association, Electronic Industries Association (former chairman of labor law and security committees), New York State Bar Association.

WRITINGS: (With R. J. Healy) *Industrial Security Management: A Cost Effective Approach,* American Management Association, 1971; *Protecting Your Business against Espionage,* American Management Association, 1973; (with Healy) *Protection of Assets Manual,* Insurors Press, 1973. Also contributor to *Maintenance Engineering Handbook,* 3rd edition, in press, *Personnel and Industrial Relations Manual,* and *Designers' Handbook of Building Security.* Contributor to *Fortune, Wall Street Journal, Security Management, Police,* and *Management Review.*

* * *

WALSTON, Marie 1925-
(Joseph Walston)

PERSONAL: Born March 19, 1925, in Clarksville, Ark.; daughter of George Albert (a farmer) and Elsie (Wood) Williams; married Joseph Robert Walston (an engineer), April 14, 1943; children: Marshall, Kenneth, Michael, Linda (Mrs. Michael Bennett). *Education:* Northwestern University, B.A., 1948. *Home:* 8314 Riverview, Kansas City, Kan. 66112.

CAREER: Worked as a teacher in Chicago, Ill., 1949-52; free-lance writer. *Member:* National League of American Pen Women (president of Kansas City branch, 1968-70), Kansas Authors, Missouri Archaelogical Society, Kansas Area Chamber of Commerce, Ozark Writers, Wyandotte County Christian Women's Club, Woman's City Club.

WRITINGS: Paul from Tarsus to Rome, Viking, 1964; *These Were My Hills,* Judson, 1972. Author of *To See the Wind,* Judson; also author of six adult Sunday School quarterlies for *Southern Baptist,* 1968-72. Contributor of articles and short stories, some under pseudonym Joseph Walston, to *Houseboating, Outdoors, Argosy, Kansas City Star, Wee Wisdom, Modern Romance, Homelife, Together, Presby-*

terian Survey, War Cry, Upper Room, Kiwanis, Negro Digest, and *Sunday Digest.*

WORK IN PROGRESS: A novel, *The Lonely Game;* an adult Sunday School quarterly.

* * *

WALTER, Gladys Mae 1901-1973

PERSONAL: Born May 20, 1901, in Aurora, Neb.; daughter of Paul John (a farmer) and Margaret Ann (Stuart) Burkhart; married Dale P. Smith, 1920 (deceased); married Clayton E. Walter, 1937 (deceased); children: (first marriage) Raymond E., Wayne F., Emily Anne Smith Claas, Jason L.; (second marriage) C. Burke. *Education:* Studied at Kearney State College. *Politics:* Republican. *Religion:* Protestant. *Home and office:* 804 J St., Aurora, Neb. 68818.

CAREER: Has worked as managing editor of weekly newspaper, clerk, bookkeeper, cannery worker, and elementary school teacher. *Member:* Nebraska Writers Guild.

WRITINGS: The Solid Rock, Herald House, 1942, reprinted, 1975; *Three Jumps Ahead of the Squirrels,* Herald House, 1971. Contributor of about sixty articles and short stories to magazines and newspapers.

WORK IN PROGRESS: Laughing Her Weigh Through College and *Invincible City,* both novels.†

(Died July 28, 1973)

* * *

WALTHER, R(ichard) E(rnest) 1921-

PERSONAL: Born November 12, 1921, in Des Moines, Iowa; son of Rudolph Herman and Ruth (Leekley) Walther; married Viola Eugenia Godwin, May 4, 1951; children: Mark Edward, Diane Elaine. *Education:* Texas Christian University, B.A., 1949, M.A., 1953; Yale University, Certificate of Institute for Alcohol Studies, 1949; North Texas State University, Ed.D., 1961. *Home and office:* 2260 East Orange Grove Blvd., Pasadena, Calif. 91104.

CAREER: Ambassador College, Pasadena, Calif., associate professor of education, beginning 1971, director of learning resources, 1972-77, director of institutional studies, 1977-78; Walther & Associates, Pasadena, director, 1978—. *Member:* American Psychological Association, National Society for Programmed Instruction.

WRITINGS: (Contributor) *Reappraising Crime Treatment,* National Probation and Parole Association, 1953; *Handling Behavior Problems,* Glenwood Press, 1962; *Writer's Guide for Preparing Programmed Instructional Materials,* U.S. Industries, Inc., 1965; *Evaluation Design for Project Writers,* Office of Education, U.S. Department of Health, Education and Welfare, 1967; *Autotutor Program Production,* Bell Telephone Laboratories, Inc., 1970; *Techniques of Instruction,* Bell Telephone Laboratories, Inc., 1971; *Systemic Grading,* Ambassador College, 1975; *A.C.E. Test Construction,* Ambassador College, 1976; *How to Teach Concepts,* Ambassador College, 1976. Also author of films, "The Perfect Commercial," 1975, "The Second Beginning," 1976, "Visual Antonyms," 1976, "Timing Background Music," 1976, "Community Action at Its Best," 1977, "Sound Tracks You Can Do," 1977, and "Job Fair '78," 1978.

WORK IN PROGRESS: The PIC Story.

SIDELIGHTS: R. E. Walther told *CA:* "Most of my writing is in the form of scripts and educational or instructional materials written to achieve specified objectives.

However, within this framework I find rich opportunities for creativity, humor, [and] personal compassion.''

* * *

WALTON, Craig 1934-

PERSONAL: Born December 6, 1934, in Los Angeles, Calif.; son of Delvy Thomas (an attorney) and Florence (Higgins) Walton; married Nancy Young, June 6, 1965; children: Richard Craig, Kerry Morrigan. *Education:* Pomona College, B.A. (cum laude), 1961; Claremont Graduate School, Ph.D., 1965. *Home:* 3420 Perliter Ave., North Las Vegas, Nev. 89030. *Office:* Department of Philosophy, University of Nevada, Las Vegas, Nev. 89154.

CAREER: University of Southern California, Los Angeles, instructor, 1964-65, assistant professor of philosophy, 1965-68; Northern Illinois University, DeKalb, assistant professor, 1968-70, associate professor of philosophy, 1971-72; University of Nevada, Las Vegas, associate professor, 1972-76, professor of philosophy, 1976—. Visiting assistant professor, Emory University, 1971. *Military service:* U.S. Air Force, 1955-59; became first lieutenant. *Member:* American Philosophical Association, Society for the Study of History of Philosophy (founder and executive secretary), Renaissance of Society of America, American Society for Eighteenth Century Studies, Metaphysical Society of America, American Association of University Professors, Phi Beta Kappa.

WRITINGS: *De la Recherche du Bien: A Study of Malebranche's Science of Ethics,* Nijhoff, 1972; (contributor) Ralph Ross and others, editors, *Thomas Hobbes in His Time,* University of Minnesota Press, 1975; (editor with John P. Anton) *Philosophy and the Civilizing Arts,* Ohio University Press, 1975. Contributor of articles and reviews to journals in his field. Book review editor and member of board of directors, *Journal of the History of Philosophy.*

WORK IN PROGRESS: *The Art of Judgment: Socrates and the Problem of Human Wisdom in Early Modern Philosophy; Love and Human Wisdom;* editing *Hobbes's Science of Natural Justice* and *Philosophers and Their Histories.*

* * *

WALTON, Hanes, Jr. 1942-

PERSONAL: Born September 25, 1942, in Augusta, Ga.; son of Thomas Hanes and Estelle (Brown) Walton; married Gloria Travis, November 1, 1964 (divorced). *Education:* Morehouse College, A.B., 1963; Atlanta University, M.A., 1964; Howard University, Ph.D., 1967. *Address:* P.O. Box 1364, Savannah, Ga. 31402. *Office:* Department of Political Science, Savannah State College, Savannah, Ga. 31404.

CAREER: Savannah State College, Savannah, Ga., associate professor, 1967-70, professor, 1970-72, Calloway Professor of Political Science, 1972—. Atlanta University, instructor, summer, 1971, professor of political science, 1971-73; visiting professor, Georgia Southern College, 1973—; free-lance writer. *Member:* American Political Science Association, American Academy of Social and Political Science, National Conference of Black Political Scientists, National Academy of Sciences (member of executive council, 1975-78), Association for the Study of Negro Life and History, Southern Political Science Association, Phi Beta Kappa. *Awards, honors:* Social Science Research Council fellow, 1969-71; Ford Foundation fellow, 1970-71; John Simon Guggenheim fellow, 1971-72; American Society of Public Administration fellow, 1975-76.

WRITINGS: *The Negro in Third Party Politics,* Dorrance, 1969; *The Political Philosophy of Martin Luther King, Jr.,* Greenwood Press, 1971; *Black Politics: A Theoretical and Structural Analysis,* Lippincott, 1972; *Black Political Parties: A Historical and Political Analysis,* Free Press, 1972; *The Poetry of Black Politics,* Regency Press, 1972; *The Study and Analysis of Black Politics: A Bibliography,* Scarecrow, 1973; *Black Republicans: The Politics of the Black and Tans,* Scarecrow, 1975. Contributor of sixty articles to *Black Politician, Quarterly Review of Higher Education, Ebony, Phylon, New South,* and *Negro Educational Review.*

WORK IN PROGRESS: A book, *Black Political Behavior.*

* * *

WALTZER, Herbert 1930-

PERSONAL: Born May 29, 1930, in Brooklyn, N.Y.; son of Samuel (a newspaper deliveryman) and Pearl (Bernstein) Waltzer; married Marilyn Lois Fischvogt, June 11, 1962; children: Adam Koehler and Sarah Lee (twins), Samuel John. *Education:* New York University, B.A., 1951, M.A., 1954, Ph.D., 1959. *Home:* 3 Bull Run Dr., Oxford, Ohio 45056. *Office:* Department of Political Science, Miami University, Oxford, Ohio 45056.

CAREER: Radio Free Europe, New York City, program production coordinator, 1951; New York University, New York City, instructor in political science, 1954-55; Miami University, Oxford, Ohio, assistant professor, 1957-62, associate professor, 1962-66, professor of political science, 1966—, chairman of department, 1970—. Vice-president of Oxford City Planning Commission, 1962-64; director of Southwest Ohio Center for Education in Politics, 1971-74. *Military service:* U.S. Air Force, 1955-57; became captain. *Member:* International Communication Association, American Political Science Association, Society for Italian Historical Studies, Conference Group on Italian Politics, Midwest Political Science Association (member of executive council, 1977-80), Midwest Association for Public Opinion Research, Southern Political Science Association, Ohio Association of Political Scientists and Economists (vice-president, 1971-72; president, 1972-73). *Awards, honors:* National Convention faculty fellowship, 1964; research grants from Rockefeller Foundation and Social Science Research Foundation.

WRITINGS: *American Government: Principles, Institutions and Processes,* Visual Education, 1962; (contributor) Malcolm Jewell, editor, *The Politics of Reapportionment,* Aldine-Atherton, 1963; *Revue of American Government,* Visual Education, 1965; (with R. Christenson, A. Engel, D. Jacobs, and M. Rejai) *Ideologies and Modern Politics,* Dodd, 1971, 2nd edition, Harper, 1976; *The Job of Academic Department Chairman,* American Council on Education, 1975; (contributor) John D. Millett, editor, *New Structures of Campus Power,* Jossey-Bass, 1978. Contributor of articles to *Public Opinion Quarterly, Western Political Quarterly,* and *Midwest Review of Public Administration.*

* * *

WANG, John Ching-yu 1934-

PERSONAL: Born November 20, 1934, in China; married Connie Pao, August 15, 1964; children: Amy, Michael. *Education:* National Taiwan University, B.A., 1957; University of Minnesota, M.A., 1962; Cornell University, Ph.D., 1968. *Home:* 1047 Vernier Pl., Stanford, Calif. 94305. *Office:* Department of Asian Languages, Stanford University, Stanford, Calif. 94305.

CAREER: University of Iowa, Iowa City, instructor in Chinese, 1962-63; University of Michigan, Ann Arbor, assistant professor of Chinese, 1966-69; Stanford University, Stanford, Calif., associate professor of Chinese, 1969—. *Military service:* Army of the Republic of China, 1957-59; became second lieutenant. *Member:* Chinese Language Teachers Association (member of executive committee, 1976-79), Association for Asian Studies (member of board of directors, 1978-81), Modern Language Association of America.

WRITINGS: Chin-sheng T'an, Twayne, 1972; (contributor) *Etudes D' Histoire et de Literature Chinoises*, Bibliotheque de L'Institut des Hautes Etudes Chinoises, 1976; (contributor) Adele Rickett, editor, *Chinese Approaches to Literature*, Princeton University Press, 1977; (contributor) Andrew H. Plaks, editor, *Chinese Narrative*, Princeton University Press, 1977. Member of editorial board, *Journal of the Chinese Language Teachers Association*, 1975—.

WORK IN PROGRESS: The Narrative Art in Chinese Literature.

*   *   *

WARD, Norman   1918-

PERSONAL: Born May 10, 1918, in Hamilton, Ontario, Canada; son of Arthur Bramwell (a salesman) and Rachel (McQueen) Ward; married Betty Davis (a writer), September 11, 1943; children: Nora (Mrs. James Russell), Nancy (Mrs. Tom Johnson), Rick, Don, Colin, Michael. *Education:* McMaster University, B.A. (honors), 1941; University of Toronto, M.A., 1943, Ph.D., 1949. *Politics:* None. *Religion:* Protestant. *Home:* 412 Albert Ave., Saskatoon, Saskatchewan, Canada S7N 1G3. *Office:* Department of Political Science, University of Saskatchewan, Saskatoon, Saskatchewan, Canada S7N 0W0.

CAREER: University of Saskatchewan, Saskatoon, instructor, 1945-47, assistant professor, 1948-52, associate professor, 1952-56, professor of political science, 1956—, Britnell Professor, 1967—. Vice-chairman of Saskatchewan Archives Board and Saskatchewan Electoral Boundaries Commission; member of advisory committee on election expenses, 1964-66. Labor conciliator. *Member:* Royal Society of Canada (fellow), Canadian Political Science Association, Writers Union of Canada, Saskatchewan Writers Guild (chairman, 1971-72). *Awards, honors:* Leacock medal for humor, 1961; Killam Senior Research Scholarship, 1974; LL.D., McMaster University, 1974, and Queen's College, 1977; certificate of commendation from American Association for State and Local History for *Politics in Saskatchewan;* Officer, Order of Canada.

WRITINGS: Government in Canada, Gage, 1960; *Mice in the Beer*, Longmans, Green, 1960; *The Canadian House of Commons: Representation*, University of Toronto Press, 1960; *The Public Purse: A Study in Canadian Democracy*, University of Toronto Press, 1962; *The Fully Processed Cheese*, Longmans, Green (Canada), 1964; (editor) *A Party Politician: The Memoirs of Chubby Power*, Macmillan (Canada), 1966; (editor with Duff Spafford) *Politics in Saskatchewan*, Longmans, Green (Canada), 1968; (with David Hoffman) *Bilingualism and Biculturalism in the Canadian House of Commons*, Queen's Printer (Ottawa), 1970; (revisor) R. Mac G. Dawson, *Democratic Government in Canada*, 4th edition, University of Toronto Press, 1971; (revisor) Dawson, *The Government of Canada*, 5th edition, University of Toronto Press, 1971; *Her Majesty's Mice*, McClelland & Stewart, 1977.

WORK IN PROGRESS: A biography of the Right Honorable J. G. Gardiner; a study of a Quaker community in Saskatchewan, with wife, Betty Davis Ward; a book of humorous writing.

*   *   *

WARD, Richard J(oseph)   1921-

PERSONAL: Born November 7, 1921, in Beverly, Mass.; son of Ralph W. (a landscape architect) and Margaret (Lyons) Ward; married Cecilia Butler (a banker), September 1, 1951; children: Timothy, Richard, Jr., Mary, Christopher. *Education:* Harvard University, B.S., 1946; University of Michigan, M.A., 1948, Ph.D., 1958; summer graduate study at Middlebury College, 1947, 1948, and at Seattle University, 1949. *Politics:* Democrat. *Religion:* Roman Catholic. *Home:* 20 Pleasant St., South Dartmouth, Mass. 02748. *Office:* Office of the Dean, College of Business and Industry, Southeastern Massachusetts University, North Dartmouth, Mass. 02747.

CAREER: Bates College, Lewiston, Me., instructor in economics, 1948-50; University of Michigan, Ann Arbor, research analyst, 1951-52; Fordham University, Bronx, N.Y., assistant professor of economics, 1953-58; California Texas Oil Corp., New York, N.Y., senior economist, 1958-60; Long Island University, Brookville, N.Y., associate professor of economics, 1960-65, head of department, 1960-61, 1963-65; U.S. Agency for International Development, director of planning in Jordan, 1961-63, chief of planning in Washington, D.C., 1965-69; Peat, Marwick, Mitchell & Co., Washington, D.C., manager, 1969-71; R. L. Hines Associates, Inc., Washington, D.C., vice-president, 1971-73; Peat, Marwick, Mitchell & Co., manager, 1973-75; Southeastern Massachusetts University, North Dartmouth, dean of College of Business and Industry, 1975—. Lecturer in economics, University of Maryland, College Park, 1967-71. *Military service:* U.S. Naval Reserve, 1943-46; became lieutenant. *Member:* American Economic Association, Association for Social Economics (executive council, 1969-70, vice-president, 1971, president, 1972). *Awards, honors:* Cited by U.S. government for distinguished service, U.S. A.I.D. mission to Jordan, 1963.

WRITINGS: (Co-editor with Lawrence Hoffman) *Readings in Economics from Fortune*, Holt, 1960; (contributor) *Production Management Analysis*, Harcourt, 1966; (editor) *The Challenge of Development*, Aldine, 1967; *Economics: Its Principles and Means*, Sadlier, 1967; (with D. Peretz and E. Wilson) *Palestine Entity?*, Middle East Institute, 1970; *Development Problems for the 1970's*, Dunellen, 1973; (contributor) *Readings in Economic Policy*, Houghton, 1976; (with others) *The Palestine State: A Rational Approach*, Kennikat, 1977; *Study of Middle East Economics*, Kennikat, 1978. Also contributor to *Non-Aligned Third World Annual*, Books International, 1970, and *The Economist Looks at Society*, edited by Edwin Dole, 1973. Contributor of numerous articles and books reviews to magazines and journals, including *Journal of Industrial Economics, Engineering Economist, America, Indian Journal of Economics, International Affairs, Review of Social Economists, American Economic Review, Kyklos,* and *Fortune.*

WORK IN PROGRESS: Elements of Peace in the Middle East; Paradoxes of Modern Life; The Hearing.

*   *   *

WARDEN, John   1936-

PERSONAL: Born March 2, 1936, in Bromley, Kent, England; son of George and Dorothy (Roberts) Warden; married Susan Lewis, January 2, 1960; children: Joanna, Rachel, Thomas, Daniel. *Education:* Gonville and Caius College, Cambridge, B.A., 1959. *Home:* 26 Conlins Rd., West Hill, Ontario, Canada M1C 1C3. *Office:* Scarborough College, University of Toronto, West Hill, Ontario, Canada.

CAREER: Marlborough College, Wiltshire, England, teacher of classics, 1959-63; University of Ghana, Legon, Accra, lecturer in classics, 1964-66; University of Toronto, Scarborough College, Toronto, Ontario, assistant professor, 1966-68, associate professor of classics, 1968—.

WRITINGS: The Poems of Propertius, Bobbs-Merrill, 1972.

WORK IN PROGRESS: Research on Propertius and Ficino.

*   *   *

WARMAN, Henry J(ohn) 1907-

PERSONAL: Born January 27, 1907, in Scranton, Pa.; son of Frederic William (a miner) and Alice (Foraker) Warman; married Retta Ann Montgomery, August 16, 1931; children: Montgomery, Frederic, Mary Esther (Mrs. Thomas L. Edgerton). *Education:* Bloomsburg State Teachers College (now Bloomsburg State College), B.S.Ed., 1932; Temple University, M.S. Ed., 1938; Clark University, Ph.D., 1945. *Religion:* Congregationalist. *Home:* 193 Lovell St., Worcester, Mass. 01603. *Office:* Graduate School of Geography, Clark University, Worcester, Mass. 01610.

CAREER: Lackawanna Railroad, Scranton, Pa., claim adjuster, 1924-28; teacher of mathematics and geography and athletic director in schools in Norristown, Pa., 1932-42; Clark University, Worcester, Mass., instructor, 1942-45, assistant professor, 1945-51, associate professor, 1951-60, professor of geography, 1960—. Has taught at University of British Columbia, University of Southern California, Northwestern University, University of Colorado, Michigan State University, and Fresno State College (now California State University, Fresno). U.S. Representative, Pan American Conference on Geography and History, Mexico, 1955. Director, National Defense Education Act (N.D.E.A.) institute in geography, 1966-67. Has conducted field research in Lesser and Greater Antilles, Latin America, Canada, India, and western Europe. *Military service:* U.S. Army, instructor in specialist training program, 1943-44.

MEMBER: International Geographic Union, Association of American Geographers, American Geographical Society, National Council for Geographic Education (president, 1954), American Meteorological Society, National Council for the Social Studies, American Association of University Professors, National Geographic Society, New England Geographical Conference, New England Association of Social Studies Teachers (president, 1954-55), Clark Alumni Association (president, 1956), Gamma Theta Upsilon (president, 1962-63). *Awards, honors:* Atwood research grants to Latin America, 1958-59, and spring, 1969; Ford Foundation grant for experimental project on high school geography, 1962-63.

WRITINGS: Geography: Backgrounds, Techniques and Prospects (a textbook for teachers), Clark University Press, 1954; *Carto-Craft Research Studies,* Denoyer-Geppert, 1963; (contributor) Wilhelmina Hill, editor, *Curriculum Guide for Geographic Education,* Publications Center, Illinois State University, 1964; (with Clyde F. Kohn) *Man's*

World: A Physical Geography, Scholastic Book Services, 1966; *The Changing Earth and Its People,* Allyn & Bacon, 1966; *Our Changing Nation and Its Neighbors,* Allyn & Bacon, 1967; *Man and His Changing Culture,* Allyn & Bacon, 1967; *Geography: Factors and Concepts,* with instructor's manual, Appleton, 1968. Author of overhead projector maps for Allyn & Bacon; author of fourteen geography film scripts for Coronet Films, Inc. Contributor to *Lands and People Encyclopedia,* and to yearbooks; contributor to education and geography journals, including *Economic Geography, Journal of Geography, Professional Geographer, Education,* and *Progressive Education,* and to newspapers.

WORK IN PROGRESS: Three books, *Human Resources of the United States,* for Rand McNally, *Geography in Education: Backgrounds, Techniques, and Prospects,* and *A Little Patch of Ground.*

*   *   *

WARNE, William E(lmo) 1905-

PERSONAL: Born September 2, 1905, in Seafield, Ind.; son of William R. (a farmer) and Nettie Jane (Williams) Warne; married Edith M. Peterson, July 9, 1919; children: Jane (Mrs. David C. Beeder), William Robert, Margaret (Mrs. John W. Monroe). *Education:* University of California, Berkeley, A.B., 1927. *Home and office:* 2090 Eighth Ave., Sacramento, Calif. 95818.

CAREER: Reporter for *San Francisco Bulletin,* San Francisco, Calif., and *Oakland Post-Enquirer,* Oakland, Calif., 1925-27; news editor for *Brawley News,* Brawley, Calif., and *Calexico Chronicle,* Calexico, Calif., 1927-28; Associated Press, editor and night manager in Los Angeles, Calif., 1928-31, correspondent in San Diego, Calif., 1931-33, and Washington, D.C., 1933-35; U.S. Department of Interior, Bureau of Reclamation, Washington, D.C., editor, 1935-37, chief of information, 1937-42, assistant commander, 1943-47; War Production Board, Washington, D.C., chief of staff of war production drive, 1942; U.S. Department of Interior, Washington, D.C., assistant director of Division of Power, 1942-43, director of information, 1943, assistant secretary, 1947-51, assistant secretary of Water and Power Development, 1950-51; U.S. Department of State, Agency for International Development, minister in charge of technological cooperation for Iran, 1951-55, and Brazil, 1955-56, minister and economic coordinator for Korea, 1956-59; State of California, Department of Fish and Game, director, 1959-60, Department of Agriculture, director, 1960-61, Department of Water Resources, director, 1961-67; Development & Resources Corp., Sacramento, Calif., vice-president of water resources, 1967-69; consultant in water resources, Sacramento, 1969—. Member of staff of Third World Powers Conference, 1936; president of Group Health Association, Inc., 1947-51; member of U.S. delegation to 2nd Inter-American Conference on Indian Life, Peru, 1949, and of U.S. delegation to 4th World Power Conference, London, 1950; member of board of Near East Foundation, 1956-58, 1959-64; member of governor of California's cabinet, 1961; Regents lecturer, University of California, Davis, 1967; member of U.S. committees of International Commission on Large Dams and International Commission on Irrigation and Drainage. *Military service:* U.S. Army Reserve, 1927-37; became second lieutenant.

MEMBER: National Academy of Public Administration, National Press Club, Sutter Club (Sacramento), Explorers Club, Sigma Delta Chi, Lambda Chi Alpha. *Awards, honors:* Distinguished service award from U.S. Department of Interior, 1951; distinguished public service honor from Foreign Operations Administration, 1955; Order of Crown from Shah of Iran, 1955; outstanding service citation from United Nations Command, 1959; LL.D., Seoul National University, 1959; award of achievement, Lambda Chi Alpha, 1963.

WRITINGS: Mission for Peace: Point 4 in Iran, Bobbs-Merrill, 1956; *Bureau of Reclamation,* Praeger, 1973. Also co-author of *Mass Transfer of Water over Long Distances for Regional Development: The California Experience,* Tenth Congress, International Commission on Irrigation and Drainage, 1978. Contributor of articles to technical journals and newspapers.

WORK IN PROGRESS: History of the Development of the Imperial Valley, completion expected in 1979.

SIDELIGHTS: William E. Warne's book, *Mission for Peace: Point 4 in Iran,* has been translated and published in Iran and Korea.

*   *   *

WARREN, Jefferson T(rowbridge) 1912-

PERSONAL: Born October 4, 1912, in Louisville, Ky.; son of Henry B. and Mary M. (Hartwell) Warren; married Dorothy Ann Edin, June 15, 1940; children: Robin M., Dean S. *Education:* University of Minnesota, B.A. (magna cum laude), 1947, M.A., 1957. *Religion:* Methodist. *Home:* 6609 Southwest 65th St., South Miami, Fla. 33143.

CAREER: Minneapolis Daily Times, Minneapolis, Minn., editorial artist, 1944-45; Minneapolis Public Museum, Minneapolis, curator, 1947-57; John Woodman Higgins Armory, Worcester, Mass., director, 1957-62; Vizcaya-Dade County Art Museum, Miami, Fla., director, 1962-75. Superintendent of Museum Division of Dade County Park and Recreation Department, 1962-75. Member of Folk Arts Foundation Committee of Minnesota Territorial Centennial, 1948, Minnesota Statehood Centennial Commission Exhibits Advisory Committee, 1956-57, and of Dade County Cultural Advisory Committee; trustee of Greater Miami Cultural Arts Center and of Northborough (Mass.) Historical Society; delegate to United Nations Educational Scientific and Cultural Organization for Museums.

WRITINGS: Exhibit Methods, Sterling, 1972. Contributor of articles to *Grolier Encyclopedia,* and to *Museum News, Coins and Medals, Archaeology, Midwest Museums Conference Quarterly,* and *Vizcaya Guide.*

WORK IN PROGRESS: Research in decorative arts and design.

*   *   *

WARRINER, Charles K(ing) 1920-

PERSONAL: Born August 26, 1920, in Coloma, Mich.; son of Harold Charles and Dorothy (Baker) Warriner; married Marian E. Ford, August 29, 1942; children: Douglas A., David P., Ruth E. *Education:* Hillsdale College, A.B., 1942; University of Chicago, M.A., 1948, Ph.D., 1953. *Home:* 701 Tennessee St., Lawrence, Kan. 66044. *Office:* Department of Sociology, University of Kansas, Lawrence, Kan. 66044.

CAREER: Social Research, Inc., Chicago, Ill., research associate, 1947-48; University of Kansas, Lawrence, instructor, 1948-53, assistant professor, 1953-57, associate professor, 1959-63, professor of sociology, 1963—, head of department, 1962-69. Visiting professor at Cornell Univer-

sity, 1967-68. *Member:* American Sociological Association, Society for the Study of Social Problems, American Association of University Professors, Midwest Sociological Association (president, 1977-78). *Awards, honors:* Fulbright research scholar in the Philippines, 1948-49.

WRITINGS: The Emergence of Society, Dorsey, 1970. Contributor of articles to *American Journal of Sociology, American Sociological Review, Sociology Quarterly, Social Forces.* Associate editor, *Social Problems,* 1962-65, *Sociological Quarterly,* 1964-65, *American Studies,* 1977—.

WORK IN PROGRESS: Research in American universities and their faculties.

*   *   *

WARTOFSKY, Marx W(illiam) 1928-

PERSONAL: Born August 5, 1928, in Brooklyn, N.Y.; son of Isaac Leon (a cutter) and Esther (Antosofsky) Wartofsky; married Alice Belzer, February 18, 1949 (divorced, 1975); children: Steven Andrew, David Jeremy. *Education:* Attended Brooklyn College (now Brooklyn College of the City University of New York), 1945; Columbia University, A.B., 1948, A.M., 1949, Ph.D., 1952. *Home:* 239 Commonwealth Ave., #62, Boston, Mass. *Office:* Department of Philosophy, Boston University, Boston, Mass. 02215.

CAREER: Boston University, Boston, Mass., instructor, 1957-59, assistant professor, 1959-63, associate professor, 1963-67, professor of philosophy, 1967—, chairman of department, 1967-73. Research associate in psychology, Harvard University, 1965-66; visiting professor of philosophy, Brandeis University, 1966-67. Director, Boston Colloquium for the Philosophy of Science, 1960—; member of executive committee, Boston Area Faculty Group on Public Issues, 1965-71; member of selection panel, National Science Foundation science faculty fellowships, 1966-67.

MEMBER: American Philosophical Association (secretary-treasurer), American Association for the Advancement of Science, Metaphysical Society, Philosophy of Science Association, American Society for Aesthetics, Study Group for the Philosophy of Knowledge, American Association of University Professors (president of Boston University chapter, 1964-65, member of National Council, 1970-73), American Civil Liberties Union, Massachusetts Civil Liberties Union (member of advisory board, 1968-71), Columbia College Alumni Association, Phi Beta Kappa. *Awards, honors:* American Council of Learned Societies grant-in-aid, 1960-61; Boston University summer research grants, 1963, 1968, 1970; National Science Foundation faculty fellowship, 1965-66; Faculty Publications award, 1970.

WRITINGS: (Contributor) Norman Torrey and Otis Fellows, editors, *Diderot Studies II,* Syracuse University Press, 1953; (contributor) Nicholas Lobkowicz, editor, *Marx and the Western World,* University of Notre Dame Press, 1967; *Conceptual Foundations of Scientific Thought,* Macmillan, 1968; (contributor) Stanford Anderson, editor, *Planning for Diversity and Choice,* M.I.T. Press, 1968; (contributor) Rubin Gotesky and Erwin Laszlo, editors, *Human Dignity: This Century and the Next,* Gordon & Breach, 1970; (contributor) Theodore Mischel, editor, *Cognitive Development and Epistemology,* Academic Press, 1971; (contributor) Israel Scheffler and Richard Rudner, editors, *Logic and Art: Essays in Honor of Nelson Goodman,* Bobbs-Merrill, 1972; (with Carol C. Gould) *Women and Philosophy: Toward a Theory of Liberation,* Putnam, 1976; *Feuerbach,* Cambridge University Press, 1977. Also editor or co-editor of *Boston Studies in the Philosophy of Science,*

1963—. Contributor to *Macmillan Encyclopedia of Education;* contributor to philosophy journals. Member of board of editors, *Synthese,* 1967—; member of consulting editorial board, *Journal of Value Inquiry,* 1967—; editor, *Philosophical Forum: A Quarterly,* 1967—.

WORK IN PROGRESS: Editing *Hegel and the Sciences,* with Robert S. Cohen.†

* * *

WASHBURN, Wilcomb Edward 1925-

PERSONAL: Born January 13, 1925, in Ottawa, Kan.; son of Harold Edward (a professor) and Sidsell Marie (Nelson) Washburn; married Lelia Elizabeth Kanavarioti (a professor), July 14, 1951; children: Harold Kitsos, Edward Alexandros. *Education:* Dartmouth College, A.B. (summa cum laude), 1948; Harvard University, Ph.D., 1955. *Office:* American Studies Program, Smithsonian Institution, Washington, D.C. 20560.

CAREER: Toyama Military Government, Toyama Prefecture, Japan, civil information officer and education officer, 1946-47; Institute of Early American History and Culture, Williamsburg, Va., fellow, 1955-58; Smithsonian Institution, Washington, D.C., curator of Division of Political History, 1958-65, director of American Studies Program, 1965—. American University, professorial lecturer, 1961-63, adjunct professor, 1963-66. *Military service:* U.S. Marine Corps, 1943-46, 1951-52. U.S. Marine Corps Reserve, 1952-77; retired as colonel.

MEMBER: American Anthropological Association (fellow), American Antiquarian Society, American Association for the Advancement of Science, American Historical Association, American Society for Ethnohistory (president, 1957-58), American Studies Association (president, 1978-80), Conference on British Studies, National Trust for Historic Preservation, Organization of American Historians, Society for the History of Discoveries (president, 1963-64, 1964-65), International Studies Association, Southern Historical Association, Western Historical Association, Virginia Historical Association, New Hampshire Historical Society, Colonial Society of Massachusetts, Columbia Historical Society (president, 1975—), Japan-America Society of Washington (member of board of trustees), Cosmos Club. *Awards, honors:* D.H.L., St. Mary's College of Maryland, 1971.

WRITINGS: The Governor and the Rebel: A History of Bacon's Rebellion in Virginia, University of North Carolina Press, 1957; (contributor of bibliography) William H. Fenton, *American Indian and White Relations to 1830: Needs and Opportunities for Study,* University of North Carolina Press, 1957; (contributor) James Morton Smith, editor, *Seventeenth-Century America: Essays in Colonial History,* University of North Carolina Press, 1959.

(Contributor) *Contributions from the Museum of History and Technology,* Smithsonian Institution, 1962; (editor) *The Indian and the White Man,* Doubleday, 1964; (author of introduction) John W. DeForest, *History of the Indians of Connecticut from the Earliest Known Period to 1850,* Archon, 1964; (contributor) George A. Billias, editor, *Law and Authority in Colonial America,* Barre, 1965; (contributor) Roscoe D. Hughes and Henry Leidheiser, Jr., editors, *Exploring Virginia's Human Resources,* University Press of Virginia, 1965; (editor) *The Great Design: Two Lectures on the Smithson Bequest by John Quincy Adams,* Smithsonian Institution, 1965; (contributor) Daniel J. Boorstin, editor, *An American Primer,* University of Chicago Press, 1966; (contributor) Herman R. Friis, editor, *The Pacific Basin: A*

History of Geographical Exploration, American Geographical Society, 1967; (contributor) W. M. Whitehill, editor, *A Cabinet of Curiosities: Five Episodes in the Evolution of American Museums,* University Press of Virginia, 1967.

(Contributor) Ray B. Browne, Larry N. Landrum, and William K. Bottoroff, editors, *Challenges in American Culture,* Bowling Green University Popular Press, 1970; *Red Man's Land, White Man's Law: A Study of the Past and Present Status of the American Indian,* Scribner, 1971; (editor) *Proceedings of the Vinland Map Conference,* University of Chicago Press, 1971; *The Indian in America,* Harper, 1975; *The Assault on Indian Tribalism: The General Allotment Law (Dawes Act) of 1887,* Lippincott, 1976; *The Cosmos Club of Washington: A Centennial History, 1878-1978,* [Washington, D.C.], 1978. Contributor to *American Historical Review, Museum News, Ethnohistory, American Archivist,* and other professional publications. Advisory editor, *Terrae Incognitae* (annals of the Society for the History of Discoveries).

SIDELIGHTS: Wilcomb Edward Washburn's book, *The Indian in America,* was translated into Japanese in 1977.

* * *

WATKINS, Arthur Rich 1916-

PERSONAL: Born July 31, 1916, in Salt Lake City, Utah; son of Arthur Vivian (a U.S. Senator and lawyer) and Andrea (Rich) Watkins; married Ruth Hansen, June 6, 1941; children: Annette (Mrs. Robert Howlett), Arthur Lynn, Laurel (Mrs. Mark B. Taylor), Bryan, Ida Marie, Denise, Paul, Ronald. *Education:* Attended University of Besancon, 1939; Brigham Young University, B.A., 1941, M.A., 1942; Stanford University, Ph.D., 1948; postdoctoral study at University of Oslo, 1961, and at George Washington University and Georgetown University, 1964. *Politics:* Republican. *Religion:* Church of Jesus Christ of Latter-day Saints. *Home:* 351 East 720 St. S., Orem, Utah 84057. *Office:* Brigham Young University, 270 Maeser Building, Provo, Utah 84601.

CAREER: Stanford University, Palo Alto, Calif., part-time instructor in German, 1946-48; Brigham Young University, Provo, Utah, assistant professor of modern languages, 1948-50; Weber State College, Ogden, Utah, instructor in modern languages, 1950-52; Brigham Young University, Provo, Utah, associate professor, 1952-56, professor of German languages, 1956—, acting chairman of department of languages, 1953-54, chairman of department of Germanic and Slavic languages, 1969-71. Church of Jesus Christ of Latter-day Saints, president of Austrian Mission, 1966-69, Italian Mission, 1978-80. *Military service:* U.S. Army, Signal Intelligence, 1942-45. *Member:* American Association of Teachers of German, American Council on the Teaching of Foreign Languages, Rocky Mountain Modern Language Association. *Awards, honors:* Guest of Federal Republic of Germany, summer, 1958.

WRITINGS: (With R. Max Rogers) *Interessantes Deutsch,* Brigham Young University Press, 1957; (with Rogers) *German through Conversational Patterns,* Dodd, 1965, revised edition, with teacher's manual and workbook, Harper, 1973; (with Rogers and Walter H. Speidel) *Reviewing German,* Dodd, 1969. Also author of *Scenes from German Drama,* with Rogers and Speidel, 1978.

WORK IN PROGRESS: Norwegian through Conversational Patterns.

SIDELIGHTS: Arthur Rich Watkins has taught German,

French, Italian, Gothic, Norwegian, Old High German, Middle High German, and Russian. He has studied Greek, Latin, Hebrew, and Old Norse.†

*   *   *

WATKINS, William Jon   1942-

PERSONAL: Born July 19, 1942, in Coaldale, Pa.; son of Charles W. J. (a steelworker and coal miner) and Edna (Pearson) Watkins; married Sandra L. Preno (a registered nurse), July 25, 1961; children: Tara Lee, Wade William, Chadom Charles. *Education:* Rutgers University, B.S., 1964, M.Ed., 1965. *Agent:* The Sand Agency, 1406 Garven Ave., Ocean, N.J. 07712.

CAREER: Delaware Valley College, Doylestown, Pa., instructor in English, 1965-68; high school teacher in Asbury Park, N.J., 1968-69; Brookdale Community College, Lincroft, N.J., instructor, 1969, assistant professor, 1970, associate professor of humanities, 1971-79. *Member:* Authors Guild. *Awards, honors:* Per Se Award for one-act plays, 1970, for "Judas Wheel."

WRITINGS—Science fiction novels, except as indicated: (With E. V. Snyder) *Ecodeath,* Doubleday, 1972; *The God Machine,* Doubleday, 1973; *Clickwhistle,* Doubleday, 1973; *A Fair Advantage,* Prentice-Hall, 1975; (with Snyder) *The Litany of Sh'reev,* Doubleday, 1976; *Tracker: The Story of Tom Brown, Jr.* (nonfiction), Prentice-Hall, 1978; *What Rough Beast,* Playboy Press, in press. Also author of "Judas Wheel," a one-act play, first produced in Warrensburg, Mo. at Central Missouri State College, February 12, 1970.

WORK IN PROGRESS: Psychic Experiment Book, Magical Sex, Soots and Seets, A Lander's Guide, nonfiction; *Holy and Unholy War,* a historical trilogy.

SIDELIGHTS: William Watkins told *CA:* "As a writer, I feel like a twenty-year journeyman shoemaker who learned his trade making everything from dancing pumps to work boots. I pay a lot of attention to my craft. Everywhere I go, I check the glue, the stitching, the eyelet work of people's lives seeing if I can learn something more about how to put shoes together. Most of my shoes fit feet that haven't been made yet or will never be made, so I wear them myself. They don't fit even me sometimes, but I wear them anyway rather than waste the leather. The shoes I sell are almost always piecework for big factories who all belong to the same conglomerate. There's a big demand for plastic slippers. Nobody wants to pay the price of glass. I make them out of glass anyway. The pay's the same, but the people who wear them sometimes notice the difference."

*   *   *

WATSON, James B(ennett)   1918-

PERSONAL: Born August 10, 1918, in Chicago, Ill.; son of James B. (a lawyer) and Elizabeth Kidder (Thaxter) Watson; married Virginia Drew (an anthropologist), March 18, 1943; children: Anne Thaxter, James Bennett. *Education:* Attended University of Maine, 1936-37, and New Jersey State College, 1937-39; University of Chicago, A.B., 1941, A.M., 1945, Ph.D., 1948. *Home:* 9010 North Mercer Way, Mercer Island, Wash. 98040. *Office:* Department of Anthropology, DH-05, University of Washington, Seattle, Wash. 98195.

CAREER: University of Sao Paulo, School of Sociology and Political Science, Sao Paulo, Brazil, assistant professor of ethnology, 1944-45; Beloit College, Beloit, Wis., assistant professor of anthropology, 1945-46; University of Okla-

homa, Norman, associate professor of anthropology, 1946-47; Washington University, St. Louis, Mo., associate professor of anthropology, 1947-54; University of Washington, Seattle, professor of anthropology, 1955—, chairman of department, 1955-60. Ad hoc consultant on economic development, United Nations Development Program, summer, 1967. *Member:* American Association for the Advancement of Science (fellow; chairman of anthropology section, 1979-80), American Anthropological Association (fellow), Royal Anthropological Institute of Great Britain and Ireland (fellow), Polynesian Society, American Ethnological Society, Society for Applied Anthropology. *Awards, honors:* Ford Foundation fellow in New Guinea, 1953-55; research grant from National Science Foundation, 1960—.

WRITINGS: (Editor) *New Guinea: The Central Highlands,* American Anthropological Association, 1964; (editor with Solon T. Kimball) *Crossing Cultural Boundaries,* Chandler Publishing, 1972; (with wife, Virginia Watson) *Batainabura of New Guinea,* Human Relations Area File Press, 1972. Also general editor of *Anthropological Studies in the Eastern Highlands of New Guinea,* University of Washington Press, 1972—. Contributor to *Journal of Polynesian Society, Southwestern Journal of Anthropology, Oceania,* and *Ethnology.*

WORK IN PROGRESS: Tairora: An Eastern Highlands People of New Guinea, for University of Washington Press.

AVOCATIONAL INTERESTS: Sailing.

*   *   *

WATSON, Julia   1943-
(Jane de Vere, Julia Fitzgerald, Julia Hamilton)

PERSONAL: Born September 18, 1943, in Bangor, North Wales; daughter of J. L. (chief engineer for British Broadcasting Corp.) and N.J.P. (Smith) Watson; divorced; children: Juliet, Cassian. *Education:* Attended school in Yorkshire, England. *Home:* 4 Lansdowne Grove, Hough Green, Chester, Cheshire, England.

CAREER: Has worked as artist, jewelry designer, fashion model and historical consultant. *Member:* Historical Association, Society of Authors, Romantic Novelists' Association, Medieval Academy of America.

WRITINGS: The Lovechild, Bantam, 1968; *Medici Mistress,* Corgi, 1968; *The Gentian Trilogy,* Corgi, Volume I: *A Mistress for the Valois,* 1970, Volume II: *The King's Mistress,* 1970, Volume III: *The Wolf and the Unicorn,* 1971; *Winter of the Witch,* Corgi, 1971, Bantam, 1972; *The Tudor Rose,* Corgi, 1972; *Saffron at the Court of Edward III,* Corgi, 1972.

Under pseudonym Julia Hamilton: *Last of the Tudors,* R. Hale, 1971; *Katherine of Aragon,* Beagle Books, 1972; *Anne of Cleves,* Beagle Books, 1972; *Son of York,* Sphere Books, 1973. Also author of "Habsburg" series, four books, R. Hale, 1977-78.

Under pseudonym Jane de Vere: *The Scarlet Women,* Corgi, 1969.

Under pseudonym Julia Fitzgerald: *Royal Slave,* Ballantine, 1978.

WORK IN PROGRESS: A Victorian novel about a half-Welsh slum girl's rise to fame.

SIDELIGHTS: Julia Watson told *CA:* "There is no doubt that I love writing. Although the technique of writing can be learned, true writers are born, not made. Setbacks and rejection slips cannot deter the writer who was born to write. I was 17 when I began *The Lovechild,* my first historical novel. As in all my other historicals, I aimed for authenticity and accuracy, attention to detail, as well as a good, compelling storyline. *The Lovechild* was published in Britain, America, France, and Sweden, and serialised in a French magazine and a Swiss newspaper. My 18th historical comes out this year.... These successes are the exciting things which sustain a writer during his or her solitary career. Nothing makes me happier than to know I have given my many readers enjoyment. If my books failed to do this, I would not stop writing (for that would be impossible), but I would certainly not expect to be published."

AVOCATIONAL INTERESTS: Antiques (especially jewelry), books, art, fashion and costume, cinema as art.

* * *

WATT, Donald 1938-

PERSONAL: Born October 21, 1938, in Malden, Mass. *Education:* Boston College, B.A., 1960, M.A., 1961; University of Connecticut, Ph.D., 1968. *Home:* 21 North View Dr., Geneseo, N.Y. *Office:* State University of New York College at Geneseo, Geneseo, N.Y. 14454.

CAREER: State University of New York College at Geneseo, 1967—, currently professor of English. *Military service:* U.S. Army, 1963-65; became captain. *Member:* Modern Language Association of America.

WRITINGS: (Editor) *The Collected Poetry of Aldous Huxley,* Harper, 1971, (editor) *Aldous Huxley: The Critical Heritage,* Routledge & Kegan Paul, 1975; (contributor) Robert Kuehn, editor, *Aldous Huxley: A Collection of Critical Essays,* Prentice-Hall, 1975; (contributor) Martin Greenberg and Joe Olander, editors, *Asimov,* Taplinger, 1977; (contributor) Greenberg and Olander, editors, *Ray Bradbury,* Taplinger, 1978. Contributor to literary journals.

SIDELIGHTS: Donald Watt told *CA:* "The song has love and marriage going together like a horse and carriage. I may be too old-fashioned, but I believe college teaching and professional criticism also should go hand in hand. A teacher with something to say to his students should be in written touch with his professional colleagues. Teaching and writing are mutually nourishing activities. If what I am writing isn't good enough for me to use in my classes, I don't publish it. And I must own to being new-fashioned enough to admit that some of the stimulation for my writing comes directly from the classroom."

* * *

WATTS, Alan Wilson 1915-1973

PERSONAL: Born Janaury 6, 1915, in Chislehurst, England; came to United States in 1938, naturalized in 1943; son of Laurence Wilson and Emily Mary (Buchan) Watts; married Eleanor Everett, April 2, 1938 (divorced, 1950); married Dorothy DeWitt, June 29, 1950 (divorced, 1963); married Mary Jane Yates King, December 4, 1963; children: (first marriage) Joan (Mrs. Timothy Tabernik), Ann (Mrs. Joel Andrews); (second marriage) Tia, Mark, Richard, Lila, Diane. *Education:* Seabury-Western Theological Seminary, S.T.M., 1948; University of Vermont, D.D., 1958. *Politics:* "Unclassifiable." *Home address:* P.O. Box 857, Sausalito, Calif. 94965. *Agent:* Henry Volkening, 551 Fifth Ave., New York, N.Y. 10017.

CAREER: Ordained Anglican priest, 1944; Northwestern University, Evanston, Ill., religious counselor, 1944-50; University of the Pacific, American Academy of Asian Studies, San Francisco, Calif., professor of comparative philosophy, 1951-57, dean, 1953-56; writer and lecturer, 1956-73. Visiting scholar, San Jose State College (now University), 1968; research consultant, Maryland Psychiatric Research Center, 1969. Guest lecturer at numerous universities, colleges, and medical schools in the U.S., Canada, Europe, and Asia, including Harvard University, Yale University, Cambridge University, Cornell University, University of Chicago, University of Hawaii, University of California, University of Michigan, University of Vermont, University of Montana, University of Wyoming, University of Indiana, University of Oregon, University of Utah, University of Wisconsin, C. G. Jung Institute (Zurich), New School for Social Research, and Washington School of Psychiatry. National Educational Television, director of "Eastern Wisdom and Modern Life" series, originating from station KQED in San Francisco, 1959-60, 1961, and author and presenter of radio lectures in syndication. Member of council of executive committee, World Congress of Faiths, 1937-39. *Member:* American Oriental Society, Society for Comparative Philosophy (president). *Awards, honors:* Bollingen Foundation research fellow, 1951-53, 1962-64; Harvard University research fellow, 1962-64.

WRITINGS: Outline of Zen Buddhism, Golden Vista Press (London), 1933, published as *Zen Buddhism: A New Outline and Introduction,* Buddhist Society (London), 1947, revised and enlarged edition published as *Zen,* James Ladd Delkin, 1948; *Seven Symbols of Life,* Buddhist Society, 1936; *The Spirit of Zen,* J. Murray, 1936, 3rd edition, 1958, Grove, 1960; *The Legacy of Asia and Western Man,* J. Murray, 1937, University of Chicago Press, 1938; *The Psychology of Acceptance,* Analytical Psychology Club of New York, 1939; *The Meaning of Happiness,* Harper, 1940, 2nd edition, James Ladd Delkin, 1953, reprinted, Harper, 1970; *The Theologica Mystica of St. Dionysus,* Holy Cross Press, 1944, revised edition, Society of Comparative Philosophy, 1971; *The Meaning of Priesthood,* Advent Papers, 1946; *Behold the Spirit,* Pantheon, 1947, new edition, 1971.

Easter: Its Story and Meaning, Schuman, 1950; *The Supreme Identity,* Pantheon, 1950, new edition, 1972; *The Wisdom of Insecurity,* Pantheon, 1951; *Myth and Ritual in Christianity,* Vaguard, 1953, new edition, Thames & Hudson, 1959; *The Way of Liberation in Zen Buddhism* (monograph), American Academy of Asian Studies, 1955, new edition, Society of Comparative Philosophy, 1973; *The Way of Zen* (also see below), Pantheon, 1957; *Nature, Man and Woman* (also see below), Pantheon, 1958; *Beat Zen, Square Zen and Zen,* (pamphlet; first published in *Chicago Review,* summer, 1958), City Lights, 1959, reprinted, Vintage, 1970; *This Is It* (essays), Pantheon, 1960; (contributor) C. C. Brinton, editor, *The Fate of Man,* Braziller, 1961; *Psychotherapy East and West* (also see below), Pantheon, 1961; *The Joyous Cosmology,* foreword by Timothy Leary and Richard Alpert, Pantheon, 1962; *The Two Hands of God: The Myths of Polarity,* Braziller, 1963; *Beyond Theology: The Art of Godmanship,* Pantheon, 1964; (editor) John W. Perry, *Lord of the Four Quarters: Myths of the Royal Father,* Braziller, 1965; *The Book: On the Taboo Against Knowing Who You Are,* Pantheon, 1966; *Nonsense,* Stolen Paper Editions, 1967, new edition, Dutton, 1977.

Does It Matter?: Essays on Man's Relation to Materiality, Pantheon, 1970; (with Eliot Elisofon, photographer) *Erotic Spirituality: Vision of Konarak,* Macmillan, 1971; *In My Own Way: An Autobiography, 1915-1945,* Pantheon, 1972; *The Art of Contemplation,* Pantheon, 1972; *Cloud Hidden, Whereabouts Unknown,* Pantheon, 1973; (editor with R. F.

Hull) Eugene Herrigel, *Method of Zen,* Random House, 1974; *The Essence of Alan Watts,* Celestial Arts, Book I: *God,* 1974, Book II: *Meditation,* 1974, Book III: *Nothingness,* 1974, Book IV: *Death,* 1975, Book V: *The Nature of Man,* 1975, Book VI: *Time,* 1975, Book VII: *Philosophical Fantasies,* 1975, Book VIII: *Ego,* 1975, Book IX: *The Cosmic Drama,* 1975, published in one volume as *The Essence of Alan Watts,* 1977; (with Al Chung-liang Huang) *Tao: The Watercourse Way,* Pantheon, 1975; *Three* (contains *The Way of Zen, Nature, Man, and Woman,* and *Psychotherapy East and West),* Pantheon, 1977. Contributor to *New Republic, New York Times, Playboy, Earth,* and other periodicals. Editor, *The Middle Way* (London), 1934-38; co-editor of series, "Wisdom of the East," published by Dutton and J. Murray, 1938-41.

SIDELIGHTS: Once called "the brain and Buddha of American Zen," Alan Watts was a leading figure in the popularization of Eastern religious philosophy, especially an ancient form of Mahayana Buddhism known as Zen, in the United States. He was a catalyst for the "Zen boom" in the nineteen-fifties and sixties. His influence on many of the writers and thinkers of the time as well as the counter-culture is well documented.

In spite of a staunch Anglican upbringing and education, Watts' fascination with Eastern ideas began in his early adolescence. His first encounter came at the age of twelve through the popular Sax Rohmer novels. While still in his teens, Watts broadened his knowledge considerably through frequent visits to the Buddhist Lodge in London and the "Magic Bookshop." He also encountered and fell under the influence of the Yugoslavic mystic Dimitri Mitrivinovic. Though none of these experiences were to take immediate effect in action, they proved to be a solid foundation for his later life.

In the meantime Watts was receiving a preparatory education for the priesthood. In 1944, after coming to the United States, he was ordained an Anglican priest. His initial task was to give religious instruction and counseling to the students at Northwestern University. While at Northwestern, Watts fell out of step with Christianity; he questioned its "linearity" of thought, "its one-way-street version of history and its obsessive verbosity as if the will of God could be expressed in the strung out form of statements and commands—so curiously unlike the patterns and forms of nature."

Watts returned to his adolescent fascination, Eastern philosophy, with great fervor. The Oriental perception of life with its stress on contemplation and union with nature better fit his own outlook. He became a spiritual questor. Although his name was closely associated with Zen Buddhism, he had no single religious affiliation. He said, "I do not label myself a Zen Buddhist, nor belong to any religious sect, on the ground that partisanship in religion closes the mind."

Watts characterized himself as a spiritual "entertainer." His many lucid and enjoyable books and radio presentations exemplified his ability to entertain. But his real aim was to somehow communicate the bounty of his spiritual quest to an audience that was largely unaware of the workings of Eastern religious philosophy. He said: "My own work, though it may seem at times to be a system of ideas, is basically an attempt to describe mystical experience—not of formal visions and supernatural beings, but reality as seen and felt directly in a silence of words and mindings. In this I set myself the same impossible task as the poet: to say what cannot be said. Indeed, much of my work is poetry disguised

as prose (with margins adjusted) so that people will read it. As poets value the sounds of words above their meanings, and images above arguments, I am trying to get thinking people to be aware of the actual vibrations of life as they would listen to music."

Watts' lecture "Divine Madness" was recorded by Super-scope Educational Products in 1972. He also contributed to the phonograph recording "The Occult Explosion" on United Artists Records in 1973.

BIOGRAPHICAL/CRITICAL SOURCES: Sewanee Review, summer, 1953; *Life,* April 21, 1961; *New Republic,* May 1, 1965; *The "Deep-In" View: A Conversation with Alan Watts, Dust Magazine* (dustbooks), 1965; *Redbook,* May 1966; Alan Watts, *In My Own Way: An Autobiography, 1915-1945,* Pantheon, 1972; *New York Times Book Review,* November 12, 1972; *New York Times,* December 16, 1972.†

(Died November 16, 1973)

*   *   *

WATTS, Lew   1922-

PERSONAL: Born March 7, 1922, in Orange, N.J.; son of Llewellyn, Jr. (chairman of New York Mercantile Exchange) and Irene (Hinrichs) Watts; married Barbara Gould (an artist), February 19, 1955; children: Jennifer, Juliette, Irene. *Education:* Attended Lafayette College, 1939-41; Drew University, A.B., 1943; also attended Montclair State College, 1964-65, and Fairleigh-Dickinson University, 1965-66. *Politics:* Conservative. *Religion:* Methodist. *Home and office:* Peddie School, Hightstown, N.J. 08520.

CAREER: Professional baseball player, 1947-50; New York Mercantile Exchange, New York, N.Y., broker and salesman, 1950-58; Manufacturers Life Insurance Co., Newark, N.J., member of staff in sales and management, 1958-63; mathematics teacher and athletic coach at several high schools, 1963-72; Peddie School, Hightstown, N.J., mathematics teacher, instructor in the study of jazz, and athletic coach, 1972—. Member, Babe Ruth Baseball advisory council, 1978—. *Military service:* U.S. Naval Reserve, active duty, 1943-46; became lieutenant junior grade; received Purple Heart. *Member:* Association of Professional Ballplayers, College Baseball Coaches Association, New Jersey Coaches Association, New Jersey Association of Teachers of Mathematics.

WRITINGS: You Can Play Better Baseball, Dell, 1956; *The Fine Art of Baseball,* Prentice-Hall, 1964, revised edition, 1973; (contributor) *The Best in Baseball,* Scholastic Press, 1970; *Babe Ruth Managers Manual,* Dees Communications, 1977, revised edition, 1978. Editorial consultant, *Babe Ruth Baseball Training Course,* 1978. Contributor of over fifty articles to *Scholastic Coach.*

WORK IN PROGRESS: A textbook, *A Survey of Jazz.*

AVOCATIONAL INTERESTS: Jazz.

*   *   *

WATTS, May Theilgaard   1893-1975

PERSONAL: Maiden name is pronounced *Tile*-guard; born May 1, 1893, in Chicago, Ill.; daughter of Hermann David (a gardener) and Claudia (Andersen) Theilgaard; married Raymond Watts, December 27, 1924 (died, 1966); children: Erica, Nancy, Tom, Peter. *Education:* University of Chicago, B.S., 1918. *Politics:* Democrat. *Office:* Morton Arboretum, Lisle, Ill. 60540.

CAREER: Elementary school teacher in Illinois, 1911-18; high school teacher of science in Illinois, 1918-24; Morton Arboretum, Lisle, Ill., staff naturalist, 1942-61, naturalist emeritus, 1961-75. Founder and chairman of Illinois Prairie Path, beginning 1965. Conductor of weekly, half-hour program on Channel 11, Chicago, 1956. *Member:* Writers Guild, Society of Interpretive Naturalists (honorary), Friends of Our Native Landscape (honorary), Naperville Garden Club (honorary), Ravinia Garden Club (honorary), Phi Beta Kappa. *Awards, honors:* Conservation award of Garden Club of America, 1954; president's award of DuPage Audubon Society, 1965; special citation from Illinois Parks and Recreation, 1966; teaching citation of National Horticultural Society, 1971; Scott Foundation of Swarthmore College horticultural award, 1972; book of the year award of Chicago Geographical Society, 1972; Hutchinson Medal of Chicago Horticultural Society, 1972; citation from Illinois House of Representatives, 1972. May Theilgaard Watts Reading Garden of Morton Arboretum was named for her in 1963.

WRITINGS: Reading the Landscape, Macmillan, 1957, revised and expanded edition, published as *Reading the Landscape of America,* 1975; *Trees for Young People,* Doubleday, 1964; *Reading the Landscape of Europe,* Harper, 1971 (published in England as *The Countryside around You,* Cassell, 1973). Also author of several nature handbooks, including *Flower Finder, Master Tree Finder, Desert Tree Finder,* and *Winter Tree Finder,* all for Nature Study Guild. Contributor of articles to *Landscape, Subversive Science,* and other publications; author of "Nature Afoot," a weekly column in *Chicago Tribune,* 1964.

BIOGRAPHICAL/CRITICAL SOURCES: Morton Arboretum Quarterly, spring, 1976.†

(Died August 20, 1975)

*   *   *

WAUGH, Coulton   1896(?)-1973

1896(?)—May 23, 1973; American artist, cartoonist, and author. Obituaries: *New York Times,* May 27, 1973.

*   *   *

WAYMAN, Norbury Lansing   1912-

PERSONAL: Born August 14, 1912, in Washington, D.C.; son of Edgar Hunt and Bertha (Lansing) Wayman; married Amy Penn, October 1, 1937. *Education:* Hadley Technical School, art student, 1930-33; also attended Washington University, St. Louis, Mo., 1934. *Home:* 8137 Park Ridge Dr., St. Louis, Mo. 63123. *Office:* Community Development Agency, 1015 Locust St., St. Louis, Mo. 63101.

CAREER: Commercial artist in St. Louis, Mo., 1934-41; Curtiss-Wright Corp., St. Louis, illustrator, 1942-45; Harland Bartholomew & Associates, St. Louis, plan technician, 1945-50; St. Louis Housing Authority, St. Louis, plan technician, 1950-55; City Plan Commission, St. Louis, city planner, 1955-75; Community Development Agency, St. Louis, historian, 1975—. About twenty of his drawings of steamboats are exhibited at Boatmen's National Bank (St. Louis) and are part of the bank's permanent collection. *Member:* National Trust for Historic Preservation, Missouri Historical Society, State Historical Society of Missouri, Landmarks Association (St. Louis), Sons and Daughters of Pioneer Rivermen (Marietta, Ohio).

WRITINGS: (Self-illustrated) *A Pictorial History of St. Louis,* privately printed, 1968; *History of Physical Growth*

of St. Louis, City Plan Commission, 1968; *Life on the River,* Crown, 1971; *Histories of St. Louis Neighborhoods,* Community Development Agency, 1978.

WORK IN PROGRESS: Historical research on transportation and urban history; a book, *Pictorial History of World's Fairs and Expositions.*

SIDELIGHTS: Norbury Lansing Wayman writes *CA,* "My desire [is] to combine my two major interests of history and drawing, which have given me a most pleasant outlook upon life."

BIOGRAPHICAL/CRITICAL SOURCES: St. Louis Dispatch, June 14, 1964.

*   *   *

WEAVER, Warren, Jr.   1923-

PERSONAL: Born February 7, 1923, in Madison, Wis.; son of Warren and Mary (Hemenway) Weaver; married Barbara Woodall, July 8, 1950 (divorced, February, 1975); married Marianne Means, February 10, 1977; children: (first marriage) Carolyn (Mrs. Mark Grazier), Sally, Melissa, Anne. *Education:* Amherst College, A.B., 1943; Columbia University, M.S., 1947; Albany Law School, LL.B., 1958. *Home:* 1521 31st St. N.W., Washington, D.C. 20002. *Agent:* David Obst, 1910 N St. N.W., Washington, D.C. 20036. *Office:* New York Times, 1920 L St. N.W., Washington, D.C. 20036.

CAREER: Admitted to the Bar of the State of New York, 1959; *Watertown Daily Times,* Watertown, N.Y., reporter and assistant state editor, 1947-48; *New York Times,* New York, N.Y., reporter, 1948-50, resident correspondent and chief of Albany, N.Y. bureau, 1950-62, staff member of Washington, D.C. bureau, 1962—, national political correspondent, 1966-68, Congressional correspondent, 1969-72, Supreme Court correspondent, 1972-75, 1977-78. *Military service:* U.S. Naval Reserve, 1942-46; became lieutenant junior grade *Member:* New York State Legislative Correspondents Association (president, 1957), Washington Press Club.

WRITINGS: Making Our Government Work, Coward, 1964; *Both Your Houses: The Truth about Congress,* Praeger, 1972.

Contributor: *The Kennedy Years,* Viking, 1964; *The New York Times Election Handbook,* Bantam, 1964, 2nd edition, 1968; *The Road to the White House,* McGraw, 1965; *Washington, D.C.: The New York Times Guide to the Nation's Capital,* Bantam, 1967. Contributor to *Saturday Review* and *Esquire.*

AVOCATIONAL INTERESTS: Cooking, contemporary music, carpentry, model ship building.

*   *   *

WEBER, Eugene   1939-

PERSONAL: Born July 21, 1939, in Vassar, Mich.; son of Elmer (a businessman) and Agnes (Haubenstricker) Weber. *Education:* Williams College, B.A., 1961; Harvard University, M.A., 1963, Ph.D., 1966. *Home:* 409 Strath Haven Ave., Swarthmore, Pa. 19081. *Office:* Department of Modern Languages, Swarthmore College, Swarthmore, Pa. 19081.

CAREER: Harvard University, Cambridge, Mass., instructor, 1966-68, assistant professor of German, 1968-73; Swarthmore College, Swarthmore, Pa., professor of German, 1973—. *Member:* Modern Language Association of

America, Hofmannsthal-Gesellschaft, American Association of Teachers of German, Phi Beta Kappa. *Awards, honors:* Woodward Wilson fellow, 1961, 1965; Sheldon traveling fellowship, 1966; American Council of Learned Societies fellow, 1972-73; National Endowment for the Humanities fellowship, 1976-77.

WRITINGS: (Editor with Robert Spaethling) *A Reader in German Literature,* Oxford University Press, 1969; (editor with Spaethling) *Literatur I,* Oxford University Press, 1972; (editor) *Hugo von Hofmannsthal / Richard Beer-Hofmann, Briefwechsel,* S. Fischer Verlag, 1972. Contributor to *Euphorion, Neue Zuercher Zeitung, Hofmannsthal-Blaetter, Journal of English and Germanic Philology,* and *Books Abroad.*

* * *

WEBSTER, Harvey (Curtis) 1906-

PERSONAL: Born November 6, 1906, in Chicago, Ill.; son of Gilbert Ira (a civil engineer) and Beatrice (Dunham) Webster; married Lucille Audine Jones (a college teacher), 1932. *Education:* Oberlin College, A.B., 1927, M.A., 1929; University of Michigan, Ph.D., 1935. *Politics:* Socialist. *Home:* 1201 South Congress, Austin, Tex. 78704. *Agent:* Timothy Seldes, 551 Fifth Ave., New York, N.Y.

CAREER: University of Michigan, Ann Arbor, instructor in English, 1929-33; Colorado State College of Agriculture and Mechanic Arts (now Colorado State University), Fort Collins, instructor in English, 1935-36; University of Louisville, Louisville, Ky., assistant professor, 1936-42, associate professor, 1942-50, professor of English, 1950-73, professor emeritus, 1976—. Fulbright professor at University of Durham, 1950-51, and University of Leeds, 1961-62. *Member:* Modern Language Association of America, American Association of University Professors (president of University of Louisville chapter, 1949-50).

WRITINGS: On a Darkling Plain: The Life and Thought of Thomas Hardy, University of Chicago Press, 1947, revised edition, Archon Press, 1964; (editor) *The Mayor of Casterbridge,* Holt, 1948; (author of introduction) Mark Twain, *Life on the Mississippi,* Harper, 1965; (author of introduction) Henry Thoreau, *Walden and Civil Disobedience,* Harper, 1965; *After the Trauma,* University Press of Kentucky, 1970; (editor) *Selected Poems of Hortence Flexner,* University of Louisville, 1975; (author of preface) *Graham Greene, a Checklist,* University Press of Kentucky, 1978. Contributor to *Poetry, New Republic, Saturday Review, Nation, New York Times,* and *Louisville Courier Journal.*

WORK IN PROGRESS: A book on James Hanley.

* * *

WEBSTER, Paul 1916-

PERSONAL: Born May 1, 1916, in San Francisco, Calif.; son of Norman P. (a scale adjuster for U.S. Mint) and Ellen Alice (Sullivan) Webster; married Margaret Jean Madsen, 1943; children; Wendy, James, Timothy, Susan, Betsy, Barbara, Richard. *Education:* Marin Junior College, A.A., 1940; attended San Jose State College (now University), 1942. *Home:* 415 Winter St., Nevada City, Calif. 95959. *Office:* 11671 Maltman Dr., Grass Valley, Calif. 95945; and P.O. Box 932, Nevada City, Calif. 95959.

CAREER: Sacramento Bee, Sacramento, Calif., staff writer and photographer, 1959-66; *Feather River Bulletin,* Feather River, Calif., editor, 1968; *Nevada County Independent,* Nevada City, Calif., editor and publisher, 1969-73; De-

Crepit Press, Nevada City, owner, 1968—. Former editor of *Snow Travel,* a magazine.

WRITINGS: The Mighty Sierra, American West, 1972, deluxe edition, Crown, 1972.

WORK IN PROGRESS: A book on the foothills of the Sierra Nevada; research on California gold country architecture; a photo book on the High Sierra.

* * *

WEDDING, Donald Keith 1934-

PERSONAL: Born October 28, 1934, in Louisville, Ky.; son of Joseph Hilmon (an executive) and Caroline Louise (Stamler) Wedding; married Mary Ellen Karwacki, June 12, 1962; children: Carol Ann Marie, Donald Keith, Mary Ellen Victoria, Daniel Keith. *Education:* University of Louisville, B.Ch.E., 1957; American University, J.D., 1963; University of Toledo, M.B.A., 1968. *Politics:* Independent. *Home:* 4533 Wedgewood, Toledo, Ohio 43615. *Office:* College of Business Administration, University of Toledo, Toledo, Ohio 43606.

CAREER: Admitted to Bars of Pennsylvania, Ohio, Washington, D.C., U.S. Patent Office, Canadian Patent Office, Canadian Trademarks Office, United Kingdom Charter Institute (chartered patent agent); also admitted to practice before U.S. Supreme Court, U.S. Federal District Courts, U.S. Tax Court, U.S. Court of Claims, U.S. Court of Military Appeals, and higher courts of Pennsylvania and Ohio. Patent examiner in Washington, D.C., 1960-63; private practice as patent attorney, 1963—; University of Toledo, Toledo, Ohio, assistant professor of business administration, 1968—.

MEMBER: American Bar Association, American Patent Law Association, Patent Office Society, American Chemical Society, American Association for the Advancement of Science, Institute of Electrical and Electronics Engineers, Society for Information Display, American Marketing Association, American Management Association, American Business Law Association, American Civil Liberties Union (treasurer and member of regional board of directors), Archaeological Institute of America, American Museum of Natural History, Pennsylvania Bar Association, Ohio Bar Association, Kentucky Historical Society, West Central Kentucky Historical Society, Allegheny County Bar Association, Toledo Bar Association, Pittsburgh Patent Law Association, Toledo Patent Law Association, Toledo Ballet Association, Sigma Nu Phi, Theta Tau, Alpha Kappa Psi, Alpha Tau Omega, Free and Accepted Masons, Order of Kentucky Colonels, Filson Club (Kentucky).

WRITINGS: Brief Case Incidents in Business and Government, University of Toledo, 1970; *Antitrust Cases,* University of Toledo, 1970. Contributor of over a dozen articles to professional journals. Staff editor, *American University Law Review,* 1962-63; staff referee, *American Business Law Journal,* 1972—.

WORK IN PROGRESS: Research on product liability, trade secrets, pyramid marketing, and macrotechnology.†

* * *

WEINBERG, Kenneth G. 1920-

PERSONAL: Born October 22, 1920, in Akron, Ohio; married Helen Arnstein (a teacher and author), September 11, 1949; children: Janet, Hugh, John. *Education:* Miami University, Oxford, Ohio, B.A., 1940; Harvard University, LL.B., 1948. *Agent:* Gunther Stuhlmann, Box 276, Becket,

Mass. 01223. *Office:* Guren, Merritt, Sogg & Cohen, 650 Terminal Tower, Cleveland, Ohio 42113.

CAREER: State of Ohio, Office of the Secretary of State, corporation counsel, 1949-51; U.S. Government, Office of Price Stabilization, regional counsel, 1951-52; attorney in Cleveland, Ohio, 1952—, currently with Guren, Merritt, Sogg & Cohen. *Military service:* U.S. Army, 1941-45; became captain; received Distinguished Flying Cross, Air Medal, and Purple Heart.

WRITINGS: Black Victory: Carl Stokes and the Winning of Cleveland, Quadrangle, 1968; *A Man's Home, A Man's Castle,* Saturday Review Press, 1971. Contributor to law and politics journals.

WORK IN PROGRESS: A satirical novel on legal practice in America.

* * *

WEINBERG, Kurt   1912-

PERSONAL: Born February 24, 1912, in Hannover, Germany; came to United States in 1941, naturalized U.S. citizen; son of Paul and Frieda (Wolff) Weinberg; married Florence M. Byham (a professor of French and Spanish literature), December 3, 1933. *Education:* Trinity College, Hartford, Conn., M.A., 1949; Yale University, Ph.D., 1953. *Home:* 290 Forest Hills Rd., Rochester, N.Y. 14625. *Office:* Department of Foreign Languages, University of Rochester, Rochester, N.Y. 14627.

CAREER: Hunter College (now Hunter College of the City University of New York), New York, N.Y., instructor in French, 1953-54; University of Iowa, Ames, visiting professor of French, 1954-55; University of British Columbia, Vancouver, visiting lecturer, 1955-57, assistant professor of French, 1957-62; University of Rochester, Rochester, N.Y., professor of French, German, and comparative literature, 1962-77, professor emeritus, 1977—. Visiting lecturer at universities in Berlin, Bonn, Cologne, Hamburg, Marburg, Heidelberg, Wuerzburg, and in the United States. *Military service:* French Army, Foreign Legion, 1939-40. U.S. Army, 1942-45; became staff sergeant. *Member:* Modern Language Association of America, American Comparative Literature Association, Elizabethan Club (Yale University; associate member). *Awards, honors:* Guggenheim fellow, 1960; National Endowment for the Humanities senior fellow, 1974-75.

WRITINGS: Henri Heine, "Romantique defroque," heraut du symbolisme francais, Yale University Press, 1954; (contributor) Curt von Faber du Faur, editor, *German Baroque Literature,* Yale University Press, 1959; *Kafkas Dichtungen: Die Travestien des Mythos,* Francke Verlag, 1963; (contributor) Walter Pabst, editor, *Der moderne franzoesische Roman: Interpretationen,* Erich Schmidt Verlag, 1968; *On Gide's "Promethee": Private Myth and Public Mystification,* Princeton University Press, 1972; (contributor) Eberhard Leube and Ludwig Schrader, editors, *Interpretation und Vergleich: Festschrift fuer Walter Pabst,* Erich Schmidt Verlag, 1972; *The Figure of Faust in Valery and Goethe: An Exegesis of "Mon Faust",* Princeton University Press, 1976; (contributor) Pabst, editor, *Die moderne franzoesische Lyrik,* Schmidt Verlag, 1976; (contributor) Barbara C. Bowen, editor, *The French Renaissance Mind: Studies Presented to W. G. Moore,* L'Esprit Createur, 1976. Contributor to *Encyclopedia of World Literature in the Twentieth Century, Yearbook of Comparative Criticism, Encyclopedia of Poetry and Poetics,* and *Encyclopedia of Philosophy;* contributor to literary and language journals.

WORK IN PROGRESS: A study of role-playing by literary characters from the barogue to the present; a monograph on Nietzsche and the rhetorical tradition; research on the topos of the hero in the cave, from Calderon to Stendhal; research on the verbal archetype.

SIDELIGHTS: Kurt Weinberg speaks French, German, Spanish, Italian, Portuguese, and reads Latin and some Greek.

* * *

WEINBERG, Martin S(tephen)   1939-

PERSONAL: Born January 23, 1939, in Albany, N.Y.; son of Fred C. and Edith (Lupatkin) Weinberg; married Barbara Appleman, December 22, 1963; children: Ellana Fayth, Marion Debra. *Education:* St. Lawrence University, B.A., 1960; University of Massachusetts, M.A., 1961; Northwestern University, Ph.D., 1965. *Office:* Institute for Sex Research, Indiana University, Bloomington, Ind. 47401.

CAREER: Rutgers University, New Brunswick, N.J., assistant professor of sociology, 1965-68; Indiana University at Bloomington, associate professor, 1968-74, professor of sociology, 1974—, senior research sociologist, Institute for Sex Research, 1968—. *Member:* Phi Beta Kappa.

WRITINGS: (With Earl Rubington) *Deviance: The Interactionist Perspective,* Macmillan, 1968, 3rd edition, 1978; (with Rubington) *The Study of Social Problems: Five Perspectives,* Oxford University Press, 1971, 2nd edition, 1977; (with Colin Williams) *Homosexuals and the Military: A Study of Less than Honorable Discharge,* Harper, 1971; (editor with Alan Bell) *Homosexuality: An Annotated Bibliography,* Harper, 1972; (with Rubington) *The Solution of Social Problems: Five Perspectives,* Oxford University Press, 1973; (with Williams) *Male Homosexuals: Their Problems and Adaptations,* Oxford University Press, 1974; *Sex Research: Studies from the Kinsey Institute,* Oxford University Press, 1976; (with Bell) *Homosexualities: A Study of Diversity among Men and Women,* Simon & Schuster, 1978. Contributor of articles to sociology and psychiatry journals.

WORK IN PROGRESS: A book, with Alan Bell and Sue Kiefer Hammersmith, entitled *Sexual Preference: Its Development among Men and Women.*

* * *

WEINBERG, Werner   1915-

PERSONAL: Born May 30, 1915, in Rheda, Germany; naturalized U.S. citizen; son of Eli and Paula (Gruenewald) Weinberg; married Lisl Halberstadt, December 21, 1938; children: Susie (Mrs. Barrie Konicov). *Education:* Hebrew Teachers Seminary, Wuerzburg, Germany, graduate, 1936; University of Louisville, M.A., 1953; Hebrew Union College—Jewish Institute of Religion, Cincinnati, Ph.D., 1961. *Home:* 735 Red Bud Ave., Cincinnati, Ohio 45229. *Office:* Hebrew Union College—Jewish Institute of Religion, 3101 Clifton Ave., Cincinnati, Ohio 45220.

CAREER: Held in German concentration camps, 1943-45; Hebrew Union College—Jewish Institute of Religion, Cincinnati, Ohio, instructor, 1961-62, assistant professor, 1962-65, associate professor, 1965-70, professor of Hebrew language and literature, 1970—. *Member:* World Union of Jewish Studies, National Association of Professors of Hebrew, Israel Association for Applied Linguistics, Society of Biblical Literature. *Awards, honors:* Hebrew Union College scholarship for research in Israel, 1963; research grant from the Federal Republic of Germany, 1965; Fulbright scholarship, 1969-70.

WRITINGS: Die Reste Des Juedischdeutschen, Kohlhammer (Stuttgart), 1969, 2nd edition, 1973; *Tikun haketiv ha'ivri* (title means "The Reform of Hebrew Orthography"), Magnes Press (Jerusalem), 1972; *How Do You Spell Chanukah?,* Hebrew Union College, 1976; *Tale of a Torah Scroll,* Hebrew Union College, 1976. Contributor to *Hebrew Union College Annual* and to *Encyclopedia Judaica.* Contributor of articles and reviews in the fields of Hebrew and Judeo-German linguistics and literatures to journals. Associate editor, *Hebrew Abstracts;* member of editorial board, *Hebrew Union College Annual.*

WORK IN PROGRESS: Der religioese Wortschatz der deutschen Juden; Hebrew Phonology: A College Textbook; The Decline of Judeo-German.

SIDELIGHTS: Werner Weinberg told *CA:* "After trying in vain to break into the *belles lettres* market with three novels and a dozen short stories, I gave up writing fiction. Since then, I have become quite successful in scholarly publishings: books, articles, reviews in the areas of Hebrew and Judeo-German (not quite Yiddish) linguistics and literatures. I write in English, German, or Hebrew, depending on the topic and the projected readership. I have also read many papers in learned societies. With all this, the failure to place my novels (all dealing with the Holocaust) still hurts."

*   *   *

WEINSTEIN, Allen 1937-

PERSONAL: Born September 1, 1937, in New York, N.Y.; son of Samuel (a storekeeper) and Sarah (Popkoff) Weinstein; married Diane Gilbert, June 14, 1969; children: Andrew Samuel, David Meyer. *Education:* College of the City of New York (now City College of the City University of New York), B.A., 1960; Yale University, M.A., 1962, Ph.D., 1967. *Politics:* Democrat. *Religion:* Jewish. *Home:* 36 Paradise Rd., Northampton, Mass. 01060. *Agent:* Julian Bach, 3 East 48th St., New York, N.Y. 10017. *Office:* Department of History, Smith College, Northampton, Mass. 01060.

CAREER: University of Maryland, College Park, lecturer in history, 1964-66; Smith College, Northampton, Mass., 1966—, began as associate professor, currently professor of history, director of American studies, 1972-77. Senior Fulbright lecturer at Australian universities, 1971. Director of project on access and privacy, Twentieth-Century Fund, 1977-78. Member of humanities advisory council, Massachusetts Council on the Arts, 1975-77. *Member:* American Historical Association, Organization of American Historians, Columbia University Seminar in American Civilization (associate). *Awards, honors:* National Endowment for the Humanities research grant, 1968; Binkley-Stephenson Prize for best article in *Journal of American History,* 1968; American Council of Learned Societies fellow, 1975; Harry S Truman Library Institute award, 1975; National Endowment for the Humanities fellow, Hoover Institution, 1977-78.

WRITINGS: (Editor with F. O. Gatell) *American Themes: Essays in Historiography,* Oxford University Press, 1968; (editor with Gatell) *American Negro Slavery: A Modern Reader,* Oxford University Press, 1968, 3rd revised edition, 1978; (editor with Gatell) *The Segregation Era: A Modern Reader,* Oxford University Press, 1969; *Prelude to Populism: Origins of the Silver Issue,* Yale University Press, 1970; (general editor) *Random House Readings in American History,* six volumes, Random House, 1970; *Origins of Modern America, 1865-1900,* Random House, 1970; (with R. J. Wilson) *Freedom and Crisis: An American History,* Random House, 1974, 2nd edition, 1978; *Perjury: The Hiss-Chambers Case,* Knopf, 1978. Contributor of articles to numerous publications, including *American Historical Review, American Scholar, Commentary, Journal of American History, Journal of American Studies, Nation, New York Times Book Review, TransAction, Business History Review, Esquire, New York Times,* and *New Republic.*

WORK IN PROGRESS: The Assault on Secrecy; The Haunted Wood: The Pursuit of Subversion in America, 1940-1960; Theft of the Bomb?: The Rosenberg Case and Soviet Atomic Espionage; Harry S Truman and the Founding of Israel, with Moshe Ma'Oz.

SIDELIGHTS: In 1950, Alger Hiss, former U.S. State Department aide, was convicted on two counts of perjury: one for denying that he met with *Time* editor Whittaker Chambers in February or March of 1938, and the second for testifying that he did not provide Chambers, an admitted Communist spy, with classified documents. For more than thirty years Hiss has maintained his innocence. He insists that Chambers was a pathological liar, that he was an early victim of Communist witch-hunt tactics, and that his case was used by certain ruthless politicians to further their own careers. Hiss's grand jury testimony and the outcome of the trial came to represent far more than the guilt or innocence of an individual. As Peter Steinfels puts it: "A lot of symbolism was pumped into the Hiss case. Hiss represented the New Deal. Hiss represented the 'best people,' the Ivy League crowd with pin-stripes and pinko sympathies. Hiss represented the victim of anti-Communist hysteria, of HUAC [House Unamerican Activities Committee] and McCarthyism."

Allen Weinstein began research on the Hiss-Chambers case in 1969, convinced, he said, that Alger Hiss was innocent. "My first article on the case," he told a *Publishers Weekly* interviewer, "indicates my sympathy for Hiss." In 1972, representatives of the American Civil Liberties Union convinced him to sue, under the Freedom of Information Act, for access to the FBI files on the case. In November, 1973, Weinstein was given the files which were to change his opinion of Hiss. He says, "I thought the suit would go on for years. But then came Watergate and then Elliot Richardson as Attorney General, and suddenly there were the Hiss files." Weinstein and several research assistants studied 40,000 pages of documents; he traveled 125,000 miles and interviewed hundreds of people who had been involved with the case, including forty who supposedly had never been questioned before; he interviewed Alger Hiss and his wife. The book which resulted from this extensive research, *Perjury: The Hiss-Chambers Case,* concluded that the jury "made no mistake in finding Alger Hiss guilty as charged."

Weinstein's work on the controversial case provoked immediate and intense controversy itself. The book was hailed by conservatives as the definitive treatise on the subject, and denounced by liberals as one more card in a deck stacked against Alger Hiss. George F. Will writes: "Occasionally a work of history is a historic event. This is one such. It is stunningly meticulous, and a monument to the intellectual ideal of truth stalked to its hiding place. It also is a substantial public service. It comes as Hiss is attempting to get his conviction expunged as a miscarriage of justice, and when anti-anti-Communism is in season. It is based on 40,000 pages of previously classified material, and meetings with forty people involved but never before interviewed, including retired Soviet agents who confirm Whittaker Chambers's testimony. The myth of Hiss's innocence suffers the death of a thousand cuts, delicate destruction by a scholar's scalpel. . . . Weinstein demonstrates that Hiss lied about the transfer of his car to Communists; lied when he said he received a gift rug from Chambers in 1935 rather than 1937; lied when he said he did not remember how he had disposed of the typewriter [on which secret documents had been copied]; lied by omitting from a list of former maids the name of the one to whose family he gave the typewriter. For as long as possible, Hiss hid even from his attorneys the fact that he had located the typewriter. A spare recitation of the documented lies would fill pages. For thirty years, Hiss's allies have swept evidence beneath the rug, no matter how lumpy the rug has become. But no rug is large enough to cover Weinstein's mountain of incriminating evidence."

One of Weinstein's earliest and most vocal critics was Victor Navasky, editor of the *Nation*. Navasky believes that a review of Weinstein's writings "reveals no commitment to the innocence of Alger Hiss. If he did believe Hiss to be innocent, he never said so in print—certainly not in his major writings on the case in *The American Scholar* (1971), *Esquire* (1975), *The New York Times* (1976), and *The New York Review of Books* (1976). . . . Whatever his original motives and aspirations, Professor Weinstein is now an embattled partisan, hopelessly mired in the perspective of one side, his narrative obfuscatory, his interpretations improbable, his omissions strategic, his vocabulary manipulative, his standards double, his 'corroborations' circular, and suspect, his reporting astonishingly erratic (brilliantly enterprising where it serves, nonexistent where it complicates, and frequently unreliable). His conversion from scholar to partisan, along with a rhetoric and methodology that confuse his beliefs with his data, make it impossible for the nonspecialist to render an honest verdict on the case. This condition, however, should not inhibit us from rendering a necessarily negative verdict on the scholarship itself." In regard to the FBI files, Navasky writes: "[Weinstein] makes the mistake of assuming the FBI memorandums provide answers rather than clues. Taking such documents at face value may be a sign of naivete rather than malevolence."

Victor Navasky checked with seven of Weinstein's key sources to confirm the accuracy of statements attributed to them. Six of them claimed that Weinstein had distorted some or all of their quotes. According to a *Newsweek* article, Weinstein replied by showing reporters "a mass of tape recordings and interview transcripts that he said confirmed his account. The reasons for the attack on his research, he asserted, was simply that liberals feel 'betrayed' by his affirmation of Hiss's guilt." Navasky's conclusion: "Whatever new data Weinstein may have gathered are fatally tainted by his unprofessionalism, his apparent intolerance for ambiguity, especially when it gets in the way of his thesis. It would be a tragedy if the immediate impact of this unfair book were to deprive Alger Hiss, now 73, of a fair hearing on his upcoming *coram nobis* petition to set aside the verdict of the trial (his first court challenge to his perjury conviction since 1952). One suspects, though, that the only permanent damage Weinstein has wrought may be to the reputations of himself and those who too eagerly endorse his findings. The target of *Perjury* is Alger Hiss and his claim of innocence, but its temporary victim is historical truth."

John Chabot Smith, author of *Alger Hiss: The True Story,* in which he asserted Hiss's innocence, and reporter at the trial in 1949-50, also questions the seriousness of Weinstein's scholarship in *Perjury*. He calls the book "a sadly disjointed work, in which research reports seem to have been pasted together without sufficient context or interpretation on the professor's part to make them useful. There is little or no critical analysis of the validity of the material quoted or the reliability of the sources; Weinstein's technique is to argue with every statement that seems to support Hiss, and accept every pro-Chambers statement without question. Where errors, inconsistencies, and perjuries on Chambers's part appear in the record, Weinstein readily forgives them, or ignores them altogether. . . . Weinstein makes no claim that the evidence he has assembled in support of his own position is conclusive; he describes it as 'occasionally contradictory, sometimes spotty.' He doesn't seem to have examined it very carefully, and he has left out some of the most significant new material." Smith believes that Weinstein relies too heavily on interviews with prejudicial parties rather than concentrating on the newly-released FBI files. He writes: "Weinstein pays less attention to these documents than to other material he got from former associates of Whittaker Chambers and alleged members of various Communist underground groups and Soviet spy organizations, though none of these people had anything useful to tell him about Hiss, and only one of them even claimed to have met him."

Smith's own study of the documents revealed that "it was not only Chambers the perjurer and Nixon the popularity-seeker who contrived the miscarriage of justice by which Hiss was convicted. Groundwork had been laid for them by the self-serving actions of J. Edgar Hoover and James F. Byrnes, not to mention the personal resentments of the respected 'adviser to Presidents,' Bernard Baruch. By condemning Hiss unheard, without revealing his accuser or the accusations against him, they sealed his fate before he or the public knew anything about it. This is not a 'conspiracy theory,' as Weinstein likes to say; it is an observation of the way this bit of history happened. It is based on documents Weinstein evidently overlooked, part of a huge volume of new documentation that deserves further study, from scholars less committed to their own theory of the Hiss-Chambers case, and better qualified to study it. . . . What other useful material in these documents Weinstein may have ignored or misrepresented we will not know until a more thorough and genuinely scholarly work of research has been done."

The battle over the guilt or innocence of Alger Hiss has raged for over thirty years; it is being fought as vigorously today as it was in 1950 when the verdict was handed down. And, if the reaction to *Perjury* is any indication, the battle will continue for at least another thirty years. The lines were drawn at the time of the trial and sides are still being chosen: liberals, New Dealers, anti-McCarthyites, anti-Nixonites, and "anti-anti-Communists" on the left; and conservatives, anti-Communists, anti-Liberal Press, "witch-hunters" on the right. As John Chabot Smith puts it, the controversy revolves around two men "one convicted of perjury and the other a confessed perjurer whose testimony helped convict the other. . . ." Weinstein, in a *Time* interview, states his case simply: "In the end, Chambers's version turned out to be truthful, and Hiss's version did not. Alger Hiss is a victim of the facts." In truth, the case may be so complicated and the arguments so involved and so far removed from what actually occurred, that nothing short of a monumental revelation could hope to resolve the debate.

BIOGRAPHICAL/CRITICAL SOURCES: Time, February 13, 1978; *Saturday Review,* April 1, 1978; *Newsweek,* April 3, 1978, April 17, 1978, March 20, 1978; *New York Times,* April 7, 1978; *Nation,* April 8, 1978, April 28, 1978;

New York Times Book Review, April 9, 1978; *Booklist*, April 15, 1978; *Book World*, April 16, 1978; *Village Voice*, April 17, 1978; *Christian Science Monitor*, April 19, 1978; *New York Review of Books*, April 20, 1978; *National Review*, April 28, 1978, May 12, 1978; *Wall Street Journal*, May 3, 1978; *New Yorker*, May 22, 1978; *Commonweal*, May 26, 1978, July 7, 1978; *Harper's*, June, 1978.

* * *

WEINTAL, Edward 1901-1973

March 21, 1901—January 24, 1973; Polish-born American diplomatic correspondent, magazine editor, author, and information agency official. Obituaries: *New York Times*, January 25, 1973; *Newsweek*, February 5, 1973.

* * *

WEIR, Thomas R(obert) 1912-

PERSONAL: Born July 13, 1912, in Winnipeg, Manitoba, Canada; son of Thomas Reid (a salesman) and Helen (Feir) Weir; married Marcella G. Deane-Freeman, December 18, 1943; children: Laurence, Catherine. *Education:* University of Manitoba, B.A., 1941; Syracuse University, M.A., 1944; University of Wisconsin, Ph.D., 1951. *Religion:* Protestant. *Home:* GR 6, Box 18, R.R.1, St. Norbert, Manitoba, Canada R3V 1L2. *Office:* Department of Geography, University of Manitoba, Winnipeg, Manitoba, Canada R3T 2N2.

CAREER: University of British Columbia, Vancouver, instructor, 1945-47; University of Manitoba, Winnipeg, assistant professor, 1949-51, associate professor, 1951-55, professor of geography, 1955-77, professor emeritus, 1977—, head of department, 1951-71. Member of Assiniboine South School Board, 1971-73. *Member:* International Geographical Union (member of Canadian committee, 1954-57), Canadian Association of Geographers (vice-president, 1965-66; president, 1966-67), Association of American Geographers (councillor, 1965-66).

WRITINGS: Ranching in the Southern Interior Plateau of British Columbia, Volume IV, Geographical Branch, Ottawa, 1955, revised edition, 1964; *An Economic Atlas of Manitoba*, Department of Industry and Commerce, Manitoba, 1960; *An Atlas of the Prairie Provinces*, Oxford University Press, 1971; (with George S. Tomkins and Theo. L. Hills) *Canada: A Regional Geography*, Gage, 1971; *Atlas of Winnipeg*, University of Toronto Press, 1978.

WORK IN PROGRESS: Queensland Cattle Industry; Atlas of Manitoba.

* * *

WEISBERG, Harold 1913-

PERSONAL: Born April 8, 1913, in Philadelphia, Pa.; son of Fred and Sarah (Spiegel) Weisberg; married Lillian Stone, August 3, 1942. *Education:* Attended University of Delaware, 1930-33. *Home:* Route 12, Frederick, Md. 21701.

CAREER: Free-lance journalist and author. Reporter on *Wilmington Morning News* and *Wilmington Sunday Star*, 1930-33; correspondent for *Phildelphia Ledger* and other newspapers, 1930-33; Senate editor and investigator, 1936-39; Washington correspondent for *Click*, 1940-42. *Military service:* Office of Strategic Services, 1943-47.

WRITINGS: Whitewash: The Report on the Warren Report, privately printed, 1965; *Whitewash II: The FBI-Secret Service Coverup*, privately printed, 1966; *Photographic*

Whitewash: Suppressed Kennedy Assassination Pictures, privately printed, 1967, revised edition, 1976; *Oswald in New Orleans*, Canyon Books, 1967; *Frame-up: The Martin Luther King-James Earl Ray Case*, Outerbridge & Dienstfrey, 1971; *Whitewash IV: Top Secret JFK Assassination Transcript*, privately printed, 1974; *Post Mortem: JFK Assassination Cover-up Smashed!*, privately printed, 1975.

SIDELIGHTS: Harold Weisberg told *CA:* "I have probably filed more law suits under the [Freedom of Information] Act than any other private person, certainly more than any one writer. I am confident I have published more formerly top secret records in facsimile than anyone else. Facsimile provides full and direct access to scholars and private citizens, with all annotations, comments and file designations on the formerly suppressed records.

"As of July, 1978, I had obtained more than 150,000 pages of these previously hidden official records. This is much more than anyone can publish. To assure perpetual and uninhibited access, I have established a public archive at the University of Wisconsin, Stevens Point branch because the history faculty there includes the outstanding bibliographer in the field, Dr. David Wrone. When all my relevant records are deposited, they may total a million pages.

"In my suit C.A. 77-2155 in federal district court for the District of Columbia, Judge Gerhard Gesell stated that were it not for my diligence and persistence the Freedom of Information Act as we know it today would not exist. In recognition of this and of my making all the records I receive available to others, he held that I fill a public role that under the Act requires the FBI to provide me with its records without cost. I make these records available to other writers prior to my use because I stay too busy freeing still other records by court and administrative proceedings to be able to find time for my own writing. Starvation in the midst of plenty!

"As a result of my decade-long struggles for freedom of information with the records of the intelligence agencies, particularly the FBI and the CIA, my work has grown from the first critical analysis of the Warren Commission's report into what my first book forecast, a vast, in-depth study of our basic institutions in time of great stress. Facts about these most subversive of crimes in a representative society, assassinations, are now really secondary in the great scope of the work and the records obtained.

"My files now include a large selection of the late J. Edgar Hoover's personal notations, often diatribes that were never expected to be seen by other than top-level FBI eyes. These range from calling FBI special agents 'blabbermouths' to describing Dr. Martin Luther King, Jr. as a 'tom cat' and Gerald Ford (who was Hoover's informant inside the Warren Commission . . .) as a 'toad.'"

* * *

WEISE, R. Eric 1933-

PERSONAL: Born January 30, 1933, in Charleston, W.Va.; son of Harry E. and Millie (Miller) Weise; married Betty Miller (an artist), December 19, 1959; children: Rebecca, Michelle, Michael. *Education:* University of Cincinnati, B.A., 1954, M.A., 1963; Indiana University, Ph.D., 1966. *Office:* Department of Political Science, McMicken College of Arts and Sciences, University of Cincinnati, Cincinnati, Ohio 45221.

CAREER: Cincinnati Milling Machine Co., Cincinnati, Ohio, market researcher, 1956-59; Insurance Association Agency, Cincinnati, proprietor, 1959-62; University of Cincinnati, Cincinnati, instructor, 1964-65, assistant professor, 1965-68, associate professor, 1968-75, professor of political science, 1975—. Campaign director for U.S. Senator Robert Taft, Jr., 1970. Chairman and founder, Robert A. Taft Institute of Government; member of Ohio Governor's Conference, 1971; consultant to U.S. Department of Justice and Institute of Governmental Research; member of President's Commission on White House Fellows, 1975-78.

MEMBER: American Political Science Association, American Foreign Service Association, American Association of University Professors, Midwest Political Science Association, Sigma Phi Epsilon, Omicron Delta Kappa. *Awards, honors:* Taft faculty research and travel grant, 1970.

WRITINGS: The Kenwood Study, Institute of Governmental Research, 1968; (editor with Alfred de Grazia) *Old Government, New People: Readings for the New Politics,* Scott, Foresman, 1971; *Eight Branches: American Government Today,* Collegiate Publishing, 1975. Author of syndicated column, "Ohio Poll," 1973-76. Author of numerous scholarly articles and government reports.

*　　*　　*

WEISGERBER, Charles A(ugust) 1912-1977

PERSONAL: Born September 11, 1912, in Cincinnati, Ohio; son of August and Mary (Krieg) Weisgerber. *Education:* Attended Xavier University, Cincinnati, 1930-34; Loyola University, West Baden Division, A.B., 1935, M.A., 1940, S.T.L., 1944; Loyola University, Chicago, Ill., Ph.D., 1949. *Home:* Lansing-Reilly Hall, University of Detroit, Detroit, Mich. 48221. *Office:* Department of Psychology, University of Detroit, Detroit, Mich. 48221.

CAREER: Entered Roman Catholic Society of Jesus (Jesuit), 1930, ordained priest, 1943; worked as a teacher in Chicago, Ill., 1937-38, and Detroit, Mich., 1938-40; Sarah Fisher Home for Children, Detroit, psychologist, 1950-53; University of Detroit, Detroit, instructor, 1949-51, assistant professor, 1951-53, associate professor, 1953-60, professor of psychology, 1960-77, head of department, 1953-64, assistant dean of Graduate School, 1955-56, acting dean, 1957-58. Trustee of University of Detroit, 1957-67. *Member:* American Psychological Association, American Association for the Advancement of Science, Institutes of Religion and Health, Psychologists Interested in Religious Issues, Michigan Psychological Association, Delta Epsilon Sigma, Alpha Sigma Nu.

WRITINGS: (With Vincent Herr, Magda Arnold, and Paul D'Arcy) *Screening Candidates for the Priesthood and the Religious Life,* Loyola University Press, 1962; *Psychological Assessment of Candidates for a Religious Order,* Loyola University Press, 1969; *Testing the Seminarian: A Review of Research,* Center for Applied Research in the Apostolate, 1977. Contributor to *Modern Schoolman, Journal of General Psychology, Child Development, Journal of Clinical Psychology, Journal of Social Psychology, Ministry Studies,* and *Counseling and Values.*

WORK IN PROGRESS: Research in psychological testing and in feelings and emotions.†

(Died January 9, 1977)

*　　*　　*

WEISHEIPL, James A(thanasius) 1923-

PERSONAL: Surname is pronounced Wys-hypl; born July 3, 1923, in Oshkosh, Wis.; son of John Joseph and Mary (Gralla) Weisheipl. *Education:* College of St. Thomas Aquinas, River Forest, Ill., Ph.Lic., 1946, S.T.Lr., 1950; Universita de San Tommaso de urbe, Ph.D., 1953; Oxford University, D.Phil., 1957. *Home and office:* Pontifical Institute of Mediaeval Studies, 59 Queen's Park Crescent, Toronto, Ontario, Canada M5S 2C4.

CAREER: Roman Catholic priest of Dominican Order; ordained June 7, 1949; Hawkesyard Priory, Staffordshire, England, exchange lecturer, 1950-52; College of St. Thomas Aquinas, River Forest, Ill., associate professor, 1957, professor of medieval philosophy, 1957-65; Pontifical Institute of Mediaeval Studies, Toronto, Ontario, associate professor, 1964-68, professor of history of medieval science, 1968—. Founder and director of Leonine Commission, Yale University, 1965-68. *Member:* Societe Internationale Pour l'Etude de la Philosophie Medievale, American Catholic Philosophical Association (president, 1963-64), Mediaeval Academy of America. *Awards, honors:* S.T.M., Dominican Order, Rome, 1978.

WRITINGS: Nature and Gravitation, Aquinas Library, 1955; *Development of Physical Theory in the Middle Ages,* Sheed (London), 1959, Sheed (New York), 1960; (editor) *The Dignity of Science,* Thomist Press, 1961; *Friar Thomas d'Aquino,* Doubleday, 1974.

Contributor: M. Regis, editor, *The Catholic Bookman's Guide,* Hawthorn, 1962; E. McMullin, editor, *The Concept of Matter,* University of Notre Dame, 1963; V. E. Smith, editor, *The Logic of Science,* St. John's University, 1964; *Oxford Studies Presented to Daniel Callus,* [Oxford], 1964; McMullin, editor, *Galileo: Man of Science,* Basic Books, 1967; R. M. McInerny, editor, *New Themes in Christian Philosophy,* University of Notre Dame, 1968; *Melanges Charles De Koninck,* Laval (Quebec), 1968; *St. Thomas Aquinas, 1274-1974: Commemorative Studies,* PIMS (Toronto), 1974; *Opera Omnia Alberti Magni,* [Cologne], 1975; D. Lindberg, editor, *Science in the Middle Ages,* University of Chicago Press, 1978. Also contributor to *New Catholic Encyclopedia, Encyclopedia of Philosophy, Encyclopaedia Britannica,* and *Encyclopedia Americana;* associate editor in philosophy, *New Catholic Encyclopedia.*

WORK IN PROGRESS: Aristotle's Physics in the Middle Ages; editing *Albertus Magnus and the Sciences: Commemorative Essays.*

SIDELIGHTS: James A. Weisheipl told *CA:* "Undoubtedly having deaf-mute parents makes me try to communicate with utmost simplicity in both writing and preaching. It is hard work, but I strive for only three qualities: accuracy, clarity, and brevity; or, as St. Thomas Aquinas would say: *veritas, claritas, brevitas.*"

*　　*　　*

WEISS, G(ustav) A(dolf) M(ichael) 1922-

PERSONAL: Born June 24, 1922, in Bratislava, Czechoslovakia; son of Gustav and Christa (Frodl) Weiss; married Christel Petersen, March 9, 1946 (died, 1975); children: Sabine Sobek, Christian, Katrin. *Education:* Attended Hochschule fuer Bodenkultur, 1941-43; Hochschule fuer angewandte Kunst, Bachelor of Art, 1950; graduate study at Bergakademie Freiberg, 1950-53. *Religion:* Evangelical. *Home:* Unter den Eichen 90, Berlin-West 45, Germany D1000. *Agent:* Kurt Bernheim, Bonnier Building, 605 Madison Ave., New York, N.Y. 10022. *Office:* Ullstein Publishers, Lindenstrasse 66, Berlin, Germany D1000.

CAREER: Silikattechnik (journal), Berlin, Germany, chief editor, 1950-61; Ullstein Publishers, Berlin, lecturer and reader, 1961—. Director of ceramics department, School for Industrial Design, Halle, 1958-61; free-lance artist and potter.

WRITINGS—Published by Ullstein, except as indicated: Ullstein Porzellanbuch, 1964, translation by Janet Seligman published as The Book of Porcelain, Praeger, 1971; Ullstein Glaeserbuch, 1966, translation by Seligman published with added appendix on American glass as The Book of Glass, Praeger, 1971; Ullstein Fayencenbuch, 1970; Freude an Keramik, 1972; Alte Keramik neu entdeckt, 1979.

WORK IN PROGRESS: A book on ceramics.

BIOGRAPHICAL/CRITICAL SOURCES: Silikattechnik, Number 8, 1961.

* * *

WEISS, Renee Karol 1923-

PERSONAL: Born September 11, 1923, in Allentown, Pa.; daughter of Abraham S. (a businessman) and Betty (Levitt) Karol; married Theodore Weiss (a professor, poet, publisher, and editor), July 6, 1941. Education: Bard College, B.A., 1951. Home: 26 Haslet Ave., Princeton, N.J. 08540.

CAREER: Quarterly Review of Literature, Princeton, N.J., editor with husband, Theodore Weiss, and business manager, 1944—. Kindergarten teacher, 1955-58; violinist at various times with Bard College Chamber Ensembles, Hudson Valley Philharmonic Orchestra and Quartet, Woodstock Quartet, Oxford University Symphony (Oxford, England), Miami Symphony Orchestra, and North Carolina State Symphony.

WRITINGS: To Win a Race (based on a theme from Chuang-tsu), Macmillan, 1966; (compiler) A Paper Zoo: A Collection of Animal Poems by Modern American Poets, Macmillan, 1968; A Bird from the Sea, Crowell, 1970; (editor with husband, Theodore Weiss) Contemporary Poetry: A Retrospective from the "Quarterly Review of Literature," Princeton University Press, 1976.

WORK IN PROGRESS: Stories and anthologies.

* * *

WEISS, Samuel A(bba) 1922-

PERSONAL: Born October 20, 1922, in Rochester, N.Y.; son of Morris (an engrosser) and Celia (Salzberg) Weiss; married Rana Schima (an editor), June 2, 1962. Education: Brooklyn College (now Brooklyn College of the City University of New York), B.A. (cum laude), 1945; Columbia University, M.A., 1946, Ph.D., 1953. Home: 677 Wrightwood, Chicago, Ill. 60614. Office: Department of English, University of Illinois at Chicago Circle, Chicago, Ill. 60680.

CAREER: Mohawk Valley Community College, Utica, N.Y., instructor in English, 1946-48; Long Island University, Brooklyn, N.Y., instructor in English, 1949; Knoxville College, Knoxville, Tenn., associate professor of English, 1955-57, chairman of department, 1955-57; University of Illinois at Chicago Circle, Chicago, assistant professor, 1957-62, associate professor, 1963-68, professor of English, 1968—. Summer research fellow, University of Illinois, 1962. Member: National Association of Teachers of English, American Association of University Professors.

WRITINGS: (Editor) Drama in the Modern World, Heath, 1964, alternate edition, 1974; (editor) Drama in the Western World, Heath, 1968. Contributor to Encyclopedia of Twentieth-Century Literature and to English and theater journals.

WORK IN PROGRESS: Editing unpublished letters of George Bernard Shaw to his German language translator, Siegfried Trebitsch.

* * *

WEITZ, Henry 1911-

PERSONAL: Born November 12, 1911, in New York, N.Y.; son of Abraham and Emma (Newman) Weitz; married Ellen Wilson, March 27, 1937. Education: Dartmouth College, A.B., 1933; Rutgers University, Ed.M., 1936, Ed.D., 1942. Home: 2716 Circle Dr., Durham, N.C. 27706.

CAREER: Worked as a high school teacher in New Jersey, 1933-42; University of Delaware, Newark, director of psychological services center, 1946-50; Duke University, Durham, N.C., associate professor, 1950-68, professor of education, 1968-78. Fulbright professor at University of Ceylon, 1963-64. Diplomate, American Board of Examiners in Professional Psychology, 1949. Consultant to U.S. Education Foundation in India, 1971-72. Military service: U.S. Army, 1942-46; became major; received Army Commendation Medal. Member: American Psychological Association, American Personnel and Guidance Association. Awards, honors: American Personnel and Guidance Association, research award, 1963, honorable mention, 1971.

WRITINGS: Behavior Change through Guidance, Wiley, 1963, revised edition, Krieger, 1976; Organization of Student Services in Indian Colleges and Universities, U.S. Education Foundation, 1972.

WORK IN PROGRESS: Energy discharge in human behavior.

* * *

WEITZMANN, Kurt 1904-

PERSONAL: Born March 7, 1904, in Almerode, Germany; came to United States, 1935, naturalized, 1940; son of Wilhelm and Antonie (Keiper) Weitzmann; married Josepha Fiedler, January 13, 1932. Education: Attended Universities of Muenster, Wuerzburg, Vienna, and Berlin, 1923-29; University of Berlin, Ph.D., 1929. Home: 30 Nassau St., Princeton, N.J. 08540. Office: Department of Art and Archaeology, Princeton University, Princeton, N.J. 08540.

CAREER: German Archaeological Institute, Berlin, Germany, scholar at branch in Athens, Greece, 1931, work in Berlin, 1932-34; Institute for Advanced Study, Princeton, N.J., permanent member, 1935-72; Princeton University, Princeton, N.J., associate professor, 1945-50, professor of art and archaeology, 1950-72, professor emeritus, 1972—. Visiting lecturer, Yale University, 1954-55; visiting professor, University of Alexandria, Alexandria, Egypt, 1960; guest professor, University of Bonn, 1962. Member of board of scholars, Dumbarton Oaks Research Library and Collection, 1949-72. Metropolitan Museum of Art, honorary trustee, consultative curator at the cloisters and department of medieval art, 1972—. Made expeditions to Mount Athos, 1932-54, and Mount Sinai, 1956-65.

MEMBER: American Academy of Arts and Sciences (fellow), Mediaeval Academy of America (fellow), German Archaeological Institute (fellow), Archaeological Institute of America, College Art Association, American Philosophical Society, Association Internationals des Etudes Byzantines (vice-president), British Academy (corresponding member), Academy of Sciences (Goettingen; corresponding member), Academy of Sciences, Pontificia Academia Romana di Archeologia (Rome; corresponding member).

AWARDS, HONORS: Doctor honoris causa, University of Heidelberg, 1967; L.H.D., University of Chicago, 1968; Prix Schlumberger of Academie des Inscriptions et Belles Lettres (Paris), 1969; Haskins Medal of Medieval Academy of America for studies in classical and Byzantine manuscript illumination; Charles Rufus Morey Book Award, College Art Association, for *Sinai Icons*, Volume I; honorary fellow, Pierpont Morgan Library.

WRITINGS: (With Adolph Goldschmidt) *Die Byzantinischen Elfenbeinskulpturen des X.-XIII. Jahrhunderts*, Cassirer, Volume I, 1930, Volume II, 1934, both volumes reprinted, 1978; *Die Armenische Buchmalerei des 10. und beginnenden 11. Jahrhunderts*, Bamberg, 1933; *Die Byzantinische Buchmalerei des 9. und 10. Jahrhunderts*, G. Mann, 1935; *Illustrations in Roll and Codex: A Study of the Origin and Method of Text Illustration*, Princeton University Press, 1947, 2nd edition, 1970; *The Joshua Roll: A Work of the Macedonian Renaissance*, Princeton University Press, 1948.

Greek Mythology in Byzantine Art, Princeton University Press, 1951; *The Fresco Cycle of S. Maria di Castelseprio*, Princeton University Press, 1951; *Ancient Book Illumination* (Martin Classical Lectures), Harvard University Press, 1959; *Geistige Grundlagen und Wesen der Makedonischen Renaissance*, Westdeutscher Verlag, 1963; (with Manolis Chatzidakis, Krsto Miatev, and Svetozar Radojcic) *Fruehe Ikonen*, Verlag Anton Schroll, 1965.

Studies in Classical and Byzantine Manuscript Illumination, edited by H. L. Kessler, University of Chicago Press, 1971; *Catalogue of the Dumbarton Oaks Collection of Ivories*, J. J. Augustin, 1972; *The Church and Fortress of Justinian (on Mount Sinai)*, University of Michigan Press, 1973; *Sinai Icons*, Volume I, Princeton University Press, 1976; *Late Antique and Early Christian Book Illumination*, Braziller, 1977; *The Icon*, Braziller, 1978; *The Miniatures of the Sacra Parallela Parisinus Graecus 923*, Princeton University Press, in press.

Editor: (With Ernest T. DeWald and A. M. Friend, Jr.) *The Illustrations in the Manuscripts of the Septuagint*, Volume III, Parts 1 and 2, Princeton University Press, 1941-42; *Studies in Honor of A. M. Friend, Jr.*, Princeton University Press, 1966; (with others) *Treasurs of Icons: Sixth to Seventeenth Centuries*, Abrams, 1967; *Age of Spirituality: Late Antique and Early Christian Art, Third to Seventh Century*, Metropolitan Museum of Art, in press. Editor, "Studies in Manuscript Illumination," Princeton University Press, 1956—. Contributor to more than thirty journals in United States and Europe.

* * *

WELCH, Claude E(merson), Jr. 1939-

PERSONAL: Born June 12, 1939, in Boston, Mass.; son of Claude Emerson (a surgeon) and Phyllis (Paton) Welch; married Nancy Edwards, June 19, 1961; children: Elisabeth, Sarah Jane, Martha, Christopher. *Education:* Harvard University, B.A., 1961; St. Antony's College, Oxford, D.Phil., 1964. *Politics:* Democratic. *Religion:* Protestant. *Home:* 120 Burroughs Dr., Buffalo, N.Y. 14226. *Office:* 562 Capen Hall, State University of New York, Buffalo, N.Y. 14260.

CAREER: State University of New York at Buffalo, assistant professor, 1964-68, associate professor, 1968-72, professor of political science, 1972—, dean of Division of Undergraduate Studies, 1967-70, associate vice-president for academic affairs, 1976—. *Member:* American Political Science Association, African Studies Association (fellow),

Inter-University Seminar on Armed Forces and Society (member of executive council), Phi Beta Kappa.

WRITINGS: Dream of Unity, Cornell University Press, 1966; (editor) *Political Modernization*, Duxbury, 1967, revised edition, 1971; (editor) *Soldier and State in Africa*, Northwestern University, 1970; (editor with Mavis Bunker Taintor) *Revolution and Political Change*, Duxbury, 1972; (with Arthur Smith) *Military Role and Rule*, Duxbury, 1974; (editor) *Civilian Control of the Military*, State University of New York Press, 1976.

WORK IN PROGRESS: A book on rural uprisings, *Anatomy of Rebellion*.

* * *

WELCH, June Rayfield 1927-

PERSONAL: Born November 24, 1927, in Brownwood, Tex.; son of Frank A. (an engineer) and Elzina (Prigmore) Welch; married June Curtis, January 31, 1948 (divorced); children: Ransom Frank, Susan Curtis. *Education:* Texas Christian University, B.A., 1949; George Washington University, J.D., 1951; Texas Technological College (now Texas Tech University), M.A., 1953; Arlington State College (now University of Texas at Arlington), B.A., 1966. *Religion:* Christian. *Home:* 3827 Farmville, Dallas, Tex. *Office:* Department of History, University of Dallas, Irving, Tex. 75061.

CAREER: Secretary to Sen. Lyndon B. Johnson, 1950; admitted to Texas Bar, 1952; attorney in private practice in Lubbock, Tex., 1952-53; Cober, Welch & Wright, Grand Prairie, Tex., partner, 1957-59; Ashley & Welch, Dallas, Tex., partner, 1959-67; University of Dallas, Irving, Tex., lecturer in business law and history, 1965-67, assistant professor of history, 1967—, academic dean, 1967-69, chairman of department, 1969—. Instructor in government, Texas Technological College (now Texas Tech University), 1952-53; instructor in history and government, Texas Christian University, 1954-58. Assistant city attorney, Fort Worth, 1953-55; city attorney, Grand Prairie, 1955-59; attorney for Hurst-Enless and Grand Prairie Independent School District, 1956-60; city attorney, Grapevine, 1957-60. *Military service:* U.S. Merchant Marine, 1945. U.S. Army, 1946-48; became sergeant. U.S. Air Force Reserve, 1950—; present rank, lieutenant colonel. *Member:* American Bar Association, American Historical Society, Texas Bar Association, Texas Historical Society, Phi Alpha Theta, Alpha Tau Omega.

WRITINGS—Published by G.L.A. Press, except as indicated: *A Family History*, Taylor Publishing, 1965; *Texas: New Perspectives*, Steck, 1971; *The Texas Courthouse*, 1971; *Historic Sites of Texas*, 1972; *Dave's Tune*, 1973; *People and Places in the Texas Past*, 1974; *And Here's to Charley Boyd*, 1975; *The Glory that Was Texas*, 1975; *Going Great in the Lone Star State*, 1976; *The Texas Governor*, 1977; *The Texas Senator*, 1978. Contributor of articles and short stories to magazines.

WORK IN PROGRESS: A comprehensive history of Texas; a novel.

* * *

WELLS, C(olin) M(ichael) 1933-

PERSONAL: Born November 15, 1933, in West Bridgford, England; Canadian citizen; son of Alfred Henry (a lace manufacturer) and Ada (Nicholls) Wells; married Catherine Hughes (a teacher), July 23, 1960; children: Christopher,

Dominic. *Education:* Oxford University, M.A., 1959, D.Phil., 1965. *Home:* 39 Charles St., Ottawa, Ontario, Canada K1M 1R3. *Office:* Department of Classical Studies, University of Ottawa, Ottawa, Ontario, Canada K1N 6N5.

CAREER: University of Ottawa, Ottawa, Ontario, lecturer, 1960-62, assistant professor, 1962-66, associate professor, 1966-71, professor of classical studies, 1971—, chairman of department, 1967-72. Visiting fellow, Brasenose College, Oxford University, 1973-74. President of Montessori Schools of Ottawa, 1966-72. *Military service:* British Army, 1954-56; became second lieutenant. *Member:* Classical Association of Canada, American Philological Association, Archaeological Institute of America. *Awards, honors:* Canada Council, fellow, 1962-64, research fellow, 1973-74.

WRITINGS: The German Policy of Augustus: An Examination of the Archaeological Evidence, Clarendon Press, 1972. Contributor to *Journal of Roman Studies, American Journal of Philology,* and *Phoenix.* Editor of *Classical News and Views,* 1966—.

WORK IN PROGRESS: Research on Roman frontiers and Roman cities.†

* * *

WELLS, Jerome C(ovell)   1936-

PERSONAL: Born May 8, 1936, in Detroit, Mich.; son of Ray Isaac (an attorney) and Mary Elizabeth (Covell) Wells; married Nancy Ellen Prime, August 16, 1963; children: David Jerome. *Education:* University of Michigan, B.A., 1958, Ph.D., 1964; Johns Hopkins University, M.A., 1961. *Politics:* Democrat. *Religion:* Presbyterian. *Home:* 6633 Aylesboro, Pittsburgh, Pa. 15217. *Office:* Department of Economics, University of Pittsburgh, Pittsburgh, Pa. 15213.

CAREER: University of Michigan, Ann Arbor, instructor in economics, 1959-61, 1962-63; University of Pittsburgh, Pittsburgh, Pa., assistant professor, 1964-69, associate professor of economics, 1969—. Visiting lecturer, University of Ibadan, Nigeria, 1961-62; visiting professor of economics, Almadu Bello University, Zaria, Nigeria, 1975-76. *Member:* African Studies Association, American Economic Association, American Agricultural Economic Association, Nigerian Economic Society. *Awards, honors:* Nigerian Institute for Social and Economic Research and University of Michigan Center for Research for Economic Development research fellow, 1965-67.

WRITINGS: (Contributor) Carl K. Eicher and Carl Liedholm, editors, *Growth and Development of the Nigerian Economy,* Michigan State University Press, 1970; *Agricultural Policy and Economic Growth in Nigeria: 1962-67,* Oxford University Press, 1972. Contributor to *Nigerian Opinion, Nigerian Journal of Economics and Social Studies,* and *Conference Proceedings of Nigerian Institute of Social and Economic Research.*

WORK IN PROGRESS: Research on development economics; review of development theories; study of sources of income convergence in Appalachian region.

* * *

WENG, Byron S. J.   1934-

PERSONAL: Born September 3, 1934, in Formosa (Taiwan); married Carolyn Hope Gasaway, November, 1963; children: Keith, Kevin. *Education:* National Taiwan University, LL.B., 1957; University of Wisconsin, M.S., 1961, Ph.D., 1971. *Home:* Flat 8A, University Residence No. 5, Chinese University of Hong Kong, Shatin, New Ter-

ritories, Hong Kong. *Office:* Department of Government and Public Administration, Chinese University of Hong Kong, Shatin, New Territories, Hong Kong.

CAREER: Miami University, Oxford, Ohio, instructor in political science, 1964-65; Wright State University, Dayton, Ohio, instructor, 1965-70, assistant professor, 1971-73, associate professor, 1973-77, professor of political science, 1977—; Chinese University of Hong Kong, Hong Kong, lecturer, 1972-74, senior lecturer, 1974—. Lecturer, University of Dayton, 1971-72; visiting associate professor, Antioch College, 1975-76. Member of board of directors, Dayton Council on World Affairs, 1971-73; member of executive committee, Dayton regional office, American Friends Service Committee, 1974-78. *Military service:* Chinese Air Force (Republic of China), judge advocate, 1958-59. *Member:* American Political Science Association, Association for Asian Studies, Peace Research Society, American Society of International Law, Delta Tau Kappa. *Awards, honors:* Faculty seminar awards, Regional Council for International Education, 1965, 1967.

WRITINGS: Peking's United Nations Policy: Continuity and Change, Praeger, 1972; (contributor) Shao-Chuan Leng and Hungdah Chiu, editors, *Law in Chinese Foreign Policy,* Oceana, 1972; (contributor) Jerome A. Cohen, editor, *China's Practice in International Law,* Harvard University Press, 1972; (contributor) Samuel Kim and James Hsiung, editors, *China in the Global Community,* Princeton University Press, in press; (contributor) Gilbert Chan, editor, *China under Communism,* Westview Press, in press. Contributor to international affairs journals.

WORK IN PROGRESS: Research for two book-length studies, *Peking's Foreign Policy System* and *Foreign Policy and Relations of the Republic of China (Taiwan).*

* * *

WERNER, John R(oland)   1930-

PERSONAL: Born September 28, 1930, in Philadelphia, Pa.; son of John Herman (an editor) and Bess (Turner) Werner; married Helen Booras (a teacher), May 26, 1958; children: John Calvin, Elisabeth Helen. *Education:* Shelton College, B.A., 1951; Faith Theological Seminary, B.D., 1954; University of Pennsylvania, M.A., 1956, Ph.D., 1962; American School of Classical Studies, Athens, graduate study, 1957-58. *Home:* 2127 Northmoor Dr., Carrollton, Tex. 75006.

CAREER: Clergyman of Reformed Presbyterian Church; American Academy, Athens, Greece, Latin teacher, 1958-59; University of Pittsburgh, Pittsburgh, Pa., instructor in Greek, 1960-61; Trinity Christian College, Palos Heights, Ill., 1962-72, became professor of Latin, Greek, and ancient history; currently research consultant in translation to Wycliffe Bible Translators. *Member:* Evangelical Theological Society, Near East Archaeological Society.

WRITINGS: Greek: A Programmed Primer, Trinity Christian College, 1969, 3rd edition, Craig Press, 1972.

SIDELIGHTS: John R. Werner told *CA: "Greek: A Programmed Primer* was prepared over a ten year period, with yearly revision based on student feedback. Despite lack of publicity, it has had considerable use by both individual students and classes, both in America and abroad."

* * *

WERTHEIM, Stanley   1930-

PERSONAL: Born November 11, 1930, in Westphalia,

Germany; son of Max and Lotte (Nassau) Wertheim; married Mary D. Conroy, March 9, 1963. *Education:* Attended University of Oklahoma, 1949-50; New York University, B.A., 1953, M.A., 1954, Ph.D., 1963; Columbia University, graduate study, 1954-55. *Home:* 180 Cabrini Blvd., New York, N.Y. 10033. *Office:* Department of English, William Paterson College of New Jersey, Wayne, N.J. 07473.

CAREER: New York University, University College, New York, N.Y., instructor in English, 1955-62; Fairleigh Dickinson University, Teaneck, N.J., instructor, 1962-63, assistant professor of English, 1963-69; Jersey City State College, Jersey City, N.J., associate professor of English, 1969-70; William Paterson College of New Jersey, Wayne, associate professor, 1970-78, professor of English, 1978—, chairman of department, 1970-72. *Member:* English Graduate Association of New York University (president, 1968-70).

WRITINGS: (Contributor) William G. Gibson, editor, "The Red Badge of Courage" and Selected Prose and Poetry, Holt, 1968; (editor and author of introduction) *Studies in "Maggie" and "George's Mother,"* C. E. Merrill, 1970; (with Theodore L. Gross) *Hawthorne, Melville, Stephen Crane: A Critical Bibliography,* Free Press, 1971. Writer of study guides, *Thomas Wolfe,* Study Masters, 1964, and *Sinclair Lewis' "Main Street,"* Monarch, 1967. Contributor of articles, notes, and reviews to literature journals. Associate editor, *Literature and Psychology,* 1968-75.

*   *   *

WESCHLER, Louis F(redrick)   1933-

PERSONAL: Born March 17, 1933, in San Pedro, Calif.; son of Louis Francis (a longshoreman) and Eva Otela (Miller) Weschler; married S. Joan Barnes (a teacher), December 5, 1954; children: Suzanne Karoline, Sally Katherine. *Education:* Long Beach State College (now California State University, Long Beach), B.A., 1958; University of California, Los Angeles, M.A., 1960, Ph.D., 1966. *Residence:* Davis, Calif. *Office:* Department of Public Administration, University of Southern California, Los Angeles, Calif. 90024.

CAREER: University of California, Davis, assistant professor of political science, 1963-70, research associate, Institute of Governmental Affairs, 1963-68; University of Washington, Seattle, assistant professor of political science, 1970-71; University of Southern California, Los Angeles, associate professor of public administration, 1971—. *Military service:* U.S. Army, Infantry, 1954-56. *Member:* American Political Science Association, American Association for the Advancement of Science, American Society for Public Administration, Western Political Science Association.

WRITINGS: (With John R. Owens and Edmond G. Costantini) *California Politics and Parties,* Macmillan, 1970; (with Larry Peterman) *American Political Thought,* Appleton, 1971; (co-author) *Study of Environmental Management in Puget Sound,* University of Washington Press, 1973.

*   *   *

WESLEY, George R(andolph)   1931-

PERSONAL: Born July 31, 1931, in Houston, Tex.; son of George (a salesman) and Flora (Black) Wesley; married Ingrid Kremer, November 25, 1963 (divorced, 1968); children: Lynda Jacqueline, Charles Edward, Phyllis Michelle, Carla Cassandra. *Education:* Jones County Junior College, A.A., 1950; attended University of Mississippi, 1950-52; University of Houston, B.A., 1957; University of Denver, M.A.,

1959, Ph.D., 1965. *Politics:* Democrat. *Home:* Route 3, Box 308, Boone, N.C. 28607. *Office:* Department of Psychology, Appalachian State University, S-W 214, Boone, N.C. 28607.

CAREER: Northeastern Junior College, Sterling, Colo., instructor in psychology, 1961-63; Memorial University of Newfoundland, St. John's, assistant professor of psychology, 1966-67; Appalachian State University, Boone, N.C., professor of psychology, 1963-66, 1967—. Assistant director, Appalachian Regional Bureau of Government, 1977—. *Military service:* U.S. Army, 1950-52; became sergeant. *Member:* American Association of University Professors (vice-president of local chapter, 1968-69), National Education Association, North Carolina Psychological Association, North Carolina Education Association, Phi Delta Kappa, Kappa Delta Pi.

WRITINGS: (Editor) *Educational Psychology Revisited,* Simon & Schuster, 1970; *The U.S. of A. and Other Writings,* Vantage, 1971; *A Primer of Misbehavior,* Nelson-Hall, 1972; (with Don Clark) *Interpret Your Dreams,* Kendall/Hunt, 1975; (with Tom Joyner) *Pigmy in the Mist,* Ashley Books, 1975; *Spare the Rod,* University Press of America, 1978. Also author, with B. E. Sweatt, Jr., of *Letters to My Shrink,* 1973. Contributor to journals.

WORK IN PROGRESS: A History of Hysteria.

*   *   *

WEST, Henry Woolliscroft   1925-

PERSONAL: Born March 18, 1925, in Staffordshire, England; son of Henry and Lilian (Bayley) West; married Eileen Yardley (a teacher), June 14, 1952; children: Catharine Ann, Hilary Clare. *Education:* St. Catharine's College, Cambridge, B.A., 1949, M.A., 1954, Ph.D., 1969. *Religion:* Church of England. *Home:* Lowfield, 12 Almoners Ave., Cambridge, England. *Office:* Department of Land Economy, Cambridge University, Cambridge, England.

CAREER: Government of Uganda, staff surveyor, 1951-54, divisional and provincial lands and surveys officer, 1954-60, superintendent of surveys, 1961-62, assistant commissioner of lands and surveys, 1962-64; Cambridge University, Cambridge, England, assistant director of research in land economy, 1967-72, assistant director of development studies, 1973—, fellow of Wolfson College. *Military service:* British Army, 1943-45. Indian Army, 1945-47. *Member:* Royal Geographical Society (fellow), Royal Institution of Chartered Surveyors (fellow).

WRITINGS: *The Mailo System in Buganda,* Government of Uganda, 1965; *The Transformation of Land Tenure in Buganda since 1896,* Afrika-Studiecentrum (Netherlands), 1969; *Land Policy in Buganda,* Cambridge University Press, 1972; (with O.H.M. Sawyer) *Land Administration: A Bibliography for Developing Countries,* Department of Land Economy, Cambridge University, 1975; (contributor) S. R. Simpson, editor, *Land Law and Registration,* Cambridge University Press, 1976. Author of articles and reviews.

SIDELIGHTS: Henry West's travels include Eastern, Central, and Southern Africa, South and Southeast Asia, the Pacific, the Caribbean, and Latin America.

*   *   *

WEST, Leonard J(ordan)   1921-

PERSONAL: Born April 29, 1921, in New York, N.Y.; married, July 29, 1948; children: three. *Education:* College of the City of New York (now City College of the City University of New York), B.B.A., 1941; Columbia University, M.A., 1947, Ph.D., 1953. *Office:* Department of Education, Bernard M. Baruch College of the City University of New York, New York, N.Y. 10010.

CAREER: Instructor of business subjects in public high schools, and College of the City of New York (now City College of the City University of New York), New York City, 1947-52; Air Force Personnel and Training Research Laboratory, Chanute Air Force Base, Ill., research psychologist, 1953-57; Southern Illinois University at Carbondale, associate professor of business education and psychology, 1957-64; City University of New York, New York City, educational research, 1964-69, professor of educational research, 1969—, professor of education, Bernard M. Baruch College, 1974—. Visiting professor, Columbia University, 1964-70. Consultant to U.S. Air Force, Radio Corporation of America, Royal Typewriter Co., Perceptual Development Laboratories, and McGraw-Hill Book Co., 1957-69; consultant on training to New England Telephone and Telegraph Co., 1969—. *Military service:* U.S. Army, 1942-46. *Member:* American Psychological Association, American Educational Research Association, National Education Association, Delta Pi Epsilon.

WRITINGS: (With Ohmer Milton) *Programmed Instruction: What It Is and How It Works,* Harcourt, 1962; *300 Commas,* McGraw, 1964; *Acquisition of Typewriting Skills,* Pitman, 1969; (contributor) *Seventh Mental Measurements Yearbook,* Gryphon, 1972; *Modern College Typewriting,* Harcourt, 1977. Contributor to *Encyclopedia of Educational Research, Encyclopedia of Education, Second Handbook of Research on Teaching, Yearbook of National Business Education Association, Yearbook of Eastern Business Teachers Association,* and *Journal of Applied Psychology.*

* * *

WESTBROOK, Adele

PERSONAL: Born in New York, N.Y.; daughter of Harold J. and Adele (McLaughlin) Westbrook; married Oscar Ratti (an artist and writer), September 22, 1969. *Education:* Attended Columbia University. *Home:* 270 West 11th St., New York, N.Y. 10014.

CAREER: Batten, Barton, Durstine & Osborn, Inc. (advertising agency), New York City, assistant to vice-president, 1956-71; George Braziller, Inc., New York City, editor and design coordinator of hardcover and paperback art/illustrated books and special projects, 1972—.

WRITINGS—With husband, Oscar Ratti: *Aikido and the Dynamic Sphere,* Tuttle, 1970; *Secrets of the Samurai,* Tuttle, 1973; (editors and translators) Luisa C. Arano, *Medieval Health Handbook: Tacuinum Sanitas,* Braziller, 1976.

WORK IN PROGRESS: Ikaros '70, The Sin, Satire, and Subtleties of M. V. Martialis, a series of illustrated Japanese tales, and an illustrated science fiction saga, all with Oscar Ratti; *Organic Gourmet, Max* (mystery series), and *Who Lives by the Sword,* to be illustrated by Ratti.

AVOCATIONAL INTERESTS: Travel in Europe, cooking, Aikido (black belt rank).

* * *

WESTING, Arthur H(erbert) 1928-

PERSONAL: Born July 18, 1928, in New York, N.Y.; son of S. W. (a physician) and Paula (Riesenfeld) Westing; married Carol A. Eck (a teacher), June 5, 1956; children: Jeanne K., Stephen H. *Education:* Columbia University, A.B.,

1950; Yale University, M.F., 1954, Ph.D., 1959. *Residence:* Amherst, Mass. *Office:* School of Natural Science, Hampshire College, Amherst, Mass. 01002.

CAREER: U.S. Forest Service, Lansing, Mich., research forester, 1954-55; Purdue University, Lafayette, Ind., assistant professor of forestry, 1959-64; University of Massachusetts—Amherst, associate professor of tree physiology, 1964-65; Middlebury College, Middlebury, Vt., associate professor of biology, 1965-66; Windham College, Putney, Vt., associate professor, 1966-71, professor of botany, 1971-76, chairman of department of biology, 1966-75; Stockholm International Peace Research Institute, Stockholm, Sweden, senior research fellow, 1976-78; Hampshire College, Amherst, professor of ecology and dean of School of Natural Science, 1978—. Fellow in forest biology, North Carolina State College of Agriculture and Mechanical Arts (now North Carolina State University at Raleigh), 1960; Charles Bullard fellow, Harvard University, 1963-64. Trustee, Vermont Wild Land Foundation, 1966-75; planning commissioner, Town of Westminster, Vt., 1968-72. *Military service:* U.S. Marine Corps, 1950-52, 1954; became captain.

MEMBER: American Association for the Advancement of Science (fellow; director of herbicide commission, 1970-71), Society of American Foresters, Scientists' Institute of Public Information (fellow), Vermont Academy of Arts and Sciences (trustee, 1967-71), Sigma Xi, Xi Sigma Pi.

WRITINGS: (With J. B. Neilands) *Harvest of Death,* Free Press, 1972; *Ecological Consequences of the Second Indochina War,* Almqvist & Wiksell, 1976; *Weapons of Mass Destruction and the Environment,* Taylor & Francis, 1978; *Warfare in a Fragile World,* Taylor & Francis, in press.

Contributor: *Research Problems in Biology,* Doubleday, 1965, 2nd edition, Oxford University Press, 1976; Barry Weisberg, *Ecocide in Indochina: The Ecology of War,* Canfield Press, 1970; Thomas Whiteside, *The Withering Rain: America's Herbicidal Folly,* Dutton, 1971; *Gravity and the Organism,* University of Chicago Press, 1971; *Understanding Environmental Pollution,* Mosby, 1971; *The Wasted Nations,* Harper, 1972; Jules Janick, *Horticultural Science,* W. H. Freeman, 2nd edition, 1972; *Essays Today,* Harcourt, 1972; Marek Thee, *Armaments and Disarmament in the Nuclear Age,* Almqvist & Wiksell, 1977; F. H. Perring, *Ecological Effects of Pesticides,* Academic Press, 1978. Contributor of over one hundred articles to scientific journals.

* * *

WESTLAKE, Helen Gum 1927-

PERSONAL: Born November 8, 1927, near Elburn, Ill.; daughter of Cecil L. (a farmer) and Helen (McNair) Gum; married Donald G. Westlake (a metallurgist), October 21, 1950; children: Dawn. *Education:* Northern Illinois State Teachers College (now Northern Illinois University), B.S., 1949; Iowa State College of Agriculture and Mechanics Arts (now Iowa State University of Science and Technology), M.S., 1958. *Home:* 611 Plamondon Court, Wheaton, Ill. 60187. *Office:* Department of Home Economics, York High School, Elmhurst, Ill.

CAREER: High school home economics teacher in Hinckley, Ill., 1949-52; Royer & Roger, Edgewood, Md., technical writer, 1952-54; high school home economics teacher in Stanhope, Iowa, 1954-55, and Story City, Iowa, 1955-59; chairman of home economics department in high school in Franklin Park, Ill., 1959-64; part-time instructor in home economics at Chicago State College (now University) and

Triton College, Chicago, Ill., 1966-72; York High School, Elmhurst, Ill., chairman of home economics department, 1972—. Senior writer, Institute for Educational Research; lecturer in the United States and Canada; has conducted college and university workshops.

MEMBER: American Home Economics Association, National Council on Family Relations, American Association of University Women, Illinois Home Economics Association, Illinois Council on Family Relations, Delta Kappa Gamma (president of Iota chapter, 1972-74), Omicron Mu, Delta Kappa Pi, Phi Delta Kappa, Mortar Board.

WRITINGS: Relationships: A Study in Human Behavior, Ginn, 1969, new edition, 1979; *Children: A Study in Individual Behavior,* Ginn, 1973, revised edition, 1977. Contributor to *Illinois Teacher, A. V. A. Journal, Illinois School Board Journal, Illinois Education,* and *Forecast.*

SIDELIGHTS: Helen Gum Westlake was born in the McNair family home, on the farm originally homesteaded by her mother's family in 1840. Westlake told *CA:* "I feel very positive as I work with our youth. I continue to teach in high school because I feel that the adolescents of today predict the adults of tomorrow."

* * *

WHALEY, Barton Stewart 1928-
(S. W. Barton)

PERSONAL: Born May 26, 1928, in San Francisco, Calif.; son of Lloyd Carlisle (an engineer) and Anita (Stewart) Whaley; children: Sandyha. *Education:* University of California, Berkeley, B.A., 1951; School of Oriental and African Studies, London, graduate study, 1954-57; Massachusetts Institute of Technology, Ph.D., 1969. *Religion:* None. *Address:* c/o L. C. Whaley, 1015 Creston Rd., Berkeley, Calif. 94708.

CAREER: American University, Special Operations Research Office, Washington, D.C., senior research scientist and assistant professor in research, 1959-62; Massachusetts Institute of Technology, Center for International Studies, Cambridge, research associate in communications, 1962-68; Tufts University, Fletcher School of Law and Diplomacy, Medford, Mass., associate professor of world politics, 1969-72; Massachusetts Institute of Technology, Center for International Studies, research affiliate, 1969-72; Boston University, School of Public Communication, Boston, Mass., senior research fellow, 1969-72; consultant, RAND Corp., 1973-74; senior consultant, Mathematics, Inc., 1977—. Member of Joint Harvard-MIT Arms Control Seminar, 1967-72. *Military service:* U.S. Army, 1951-52; served in Japan in psychological warfare unit as research librarian. *Member:* Mystery Writers of America.

WRITINGS: Word-of-Mouth Communication in Communist China, U.S. Government Printing Office, 1962; *Stratagem: Deception and Surprise in War,* Center for International Studies, Massachusetts Institute of Technology, 1969; *Codeword Barbarossa,* MIT Press, 1973; (contributor under pseudonym S. W. Barton) *Public Diplomacy and Political Change,* Praeger, 1973; (with Michael Kurland) *The Last President* (novel), Geis, 1979. Contributor of articles and reviews to *Orbis, Christian Science Monitor,* and *Slavic Review.*

WORK IN PROGRESS: Further studies, bibliographies, and dictionaries on deception and surprise; a short story series on a family of magicians-cum-deception planners.

WHARTON, Clifton R(eginald), Jr. 1926-

PERSONAL: Born September 13, 1926, in Boston, Mass.; son of Clifton Reginald (America's first black career diplomat and ambassador) and Harriette (Banks) Wharton; married Dolores Duncan (a writer), 1950; children: Clifton R. III, Bruce D. *Education:* Harvard University, B.A. (cum laude), 1947; Johns Hopkins School of Advanced International Studies, M.A. (international studies), 1948; University of Chicago, M.A. (economics), 1956, Ph.D., 1958. *Home:* South Tower, State University Plaza, Albany, N.Y. 12246. *Office:* Office of the Chancellor, State University of New York, State University Plaza, Albany, N.Y. 12246.

CAREER: American International Association for Economic and Social Development, New York City, executive trainee, 1948-49, program analyst, 1949-51, head of reports and analysis department, 1951-53; University of Chicago, Chicago, Ill., research assistant, 1953-56, research associate in economics, 1956-57; Agricultural Development Council, New York City, executive associate, 1957-58, council associate for Malaysia, Thailand, Vietnam, and Cambodia, 1958-64, director of American universities research program, 1964-67, vice-president, 1967-70; Michigan State University, East Lansing, president, 1970-78; chancellor, State University of New York, 1978—. Visiting professor at University of Malaya, 1958-64, and Stanford University, 1964-65. Member of presidential task force on agriculture in Vietnam, 1966; member of presidential mission to Latin America, 1969; member of advisory panel on East Asian and Pacific affairs, U.S. Department of State, 1966-69, and Southeast Asian Development advisory group of Agency for International Development, 1967-69; member of advisory council, Johns Hopkins School of Advanced International Studies; member of Commission on U.S.-Latin American Relations, 1974—, and Food Panel, Office of Technical Assessment, U.S. Congress, 1974—; chairman of Board for Food and International Agricultural Development Aid, U.S. Department of State, 1976—; member, Presidential Commission on Hunger, 1978—. Member of numerous boards of directors, including Ford Motor Co., Equitable Life Assurance Society, Overseas Development Council, Rockefeller Foundation, Carnegie Foundation, and Agricultural Development Council; former member of numerous boards of directors, including African-American Institute, Agribusiness Council, Educational Development Center, Inc., Burroughs Corp., and Museum of Modern Art. Consultant to Government of Malaysia, Asian Development Bank, and United Nations Economic Commission for Asia and Far East.

MEMBER: International Association for Agricultural Economics, American Economics Association, Association for Asian Studies, Asia Society (former member of board of directors), Council on Foreign Relations, National Academy of Education, American Agricultural Economics Association, Society for International Development. *Awards, honors:* Named Boston Latin School "Man of the Year," 1970; Amistad Award, American Missionary Association, 1970; LL.D. from University of Michigan, Johns Hopkins University, Wayne State University, all 1970, Hahneman Medical School, 1975, Georgetown University, 1976, and City College of the City University of New York, 1978; Doctor of Public Service, Central Michigan University, 1970; Alumni Professional Achievement Award, University of Chicago, 1971; Doctor of Humane Letters, Oakland University, 1971, Northern Michigan University, 1975, Georgetown University, 1976, and Columbia University, 1978; Joseph C. Wilson Award for achievement and promise in international affairs, 1977, for work in Southeast Asia.

WRITINGS: (Contributor) Charles Arnold Anderson and Mary Jean Bowman, editors, *Education and Economic Development*, Aldine, 1965; (editor) *Subsistence Agriculture and Economic Development*, Aldine, 1969; (with Theodore Martin Hesburgh and others) *Patterns for Lifelong Learning*, Jossey-Bass, 1973. Author of numerous monographs on international agriculture and economics. Contributor of articles to *Foreign Affairs* and other journals.

*   *   *

WHEAT, Joe Ben 1916-

PERSONAL: Born April 21, 1916, in Van Horn, Tex.; son of Luther Peers (a merchant) and Elizabeth (Wellborn) Wheat; married Frances Irene Moore (a musician), April 6, 1947. *Education:* University of California, Berkeley, B.A., 1937; University of Arizona, M.A., 1949, Ph.D., 1953. *Politics:* Independent. *Home:* 1515 Baseline Rd., Boulder, Colo. 80302. *Office:* Museum, University of Colorado, Boulder, Colo. 80302.

CAREER: Works Progress Administration, field director of archaeological project at Texas Technological College (now Texas Tech University), Lubbock, 1939-41; Smithsonian Institution, Washington, D.C., archaeologist for river basins survey, 1947; University of Arizona, Tucson, instructor in anthropology, 1948-50, 1952, field foreman in archaeological field school, 1949, 1950, 1951; U.S. National Park Service, Grand Canyon, Ariz., ranger and archaeologist, 1952-53; University of Colorado, Boulder, assistant professor, 1953-57, associate professor, 1957-62, professor of natural history, 1962—, curator of anthropology at university museum, 1953—. Chairman, Plains Anthropological Conference, 1960. Member of project review board, National Science Foundation, 1960—, and National Foundation of Arts and Humanities, 1971. Consultant to McGraw-Hill Publishers, 1966, and Time-Life Publications, 1972—. *Military service:* U.S. Army Air Forces, 1941-45; became master sergeant.

MEMBER: Society for American Archaeology (president, 1966-67), American Anthropological Association (fellow), American Association for the Advancement of Science (fellow), American Ethnological Society, Sigma Xi. *Awards, honors:* Ford Foundation fellowship, 1952-53; National Science Foundation grants, 1961-65, 1968-69; Smithsonian Institution research grants, 1962-63, 1966-67; John Wesley Powell lectureship of American Association for the Advancement of Science, 1969.

WRITINGS: *An Archaeological Survey of Addicks Dam Basin*, U.S. Government Printing Office, 1953; *Crooked Ridge Village*, University of Arizona Press, 1954; *Mogollon Culture Prior to A.D. 1000*, American Anthropological Association and Society for American Archaeology, 1954; (with Sol Tax) *A Preliminary Test of Herskovits' Theory of Cultural Focus*, University of Colorado Studies in Anthropology, 1954; (contributor) Karl K. Hulley, editor, *Prehistoric People of the Northern Southwest*, Grand Canyon Natural History Association, revised edition, 1963; (author of introduction) Roy L. Carlson, *Basket Maker III Sites Near Durango, Colorado*, University of Colorado Press, 1963; (with Henry T. Irwin and Lee F. Irwin) *University of Colorado Investigations of Paleolithic and Epipaleolithic Sites in the Sudan, Africa*, University of Utah Press, 1968; *The Olsen-Chubbuck Site: A Paleo-Indian Bison Kill*, Society for American Archaeology, 1972; (author of text) *Navajo Blankets from the Collection of Anthony Berlant*, Museum of Art, University of Arizona, 1974. Also author of *The Jurgens Site.* Contributor to *Encyclopaedia Britannica;*

contributor to anthropology and archaeology abstracts. Southwest editor of *Abstracts of New World Archaeology*, 1960, 1961.

WORK IN PROGRESS: *The Stevenson Site.*

AVOCATIONAL INTERESTS: Travel, photography, sculpture, woodworking.

*   *   *

WHEELER, Bayard O. 1905-

PERSONAL: Born September 27, 1905, in Modesto, Calif.; son of Baird O. (a contractor) and Lena M. (Laher) Wheeler; married Elsie M. Stone, June 23, 1935 (died, 1963); children: Alfred W. *Education:* Attended Pomona College, 1924; University of California, Berkeley, A.B., 1928, Ph.D., 1942; University of Washington, Seattle, M.A., 1930. *Politics:* Independent. *Office address:* P.O. Box 2485, Reno, Nev. 89505.

CAREER: Oregon State University, Corvallis, assistant professor of business administration, 1936-41; University of Washington, Seattle, associate professor of economics, 1941-42; U.S. Bureau of Labor Statistics, Washington, D.C., price economist, 1942-43; U.S. War Labor Board, Region XII, Seattle, Wash., director of wage stabilization, 1943-44; President's Committee for Congested Areas, Seattle, assistant regional director, 1945-46; U.S. National Housing Agency, Washington, D.C., housing economist, 1946-48; University of Washington, Seattle, professor of business and environment, 1948-72, professor emeritus, 1972—; president, Bayga Ltd., 1974—; real estate appraiser and consultant, 1976—. Visiting professor, University of Nevada, 1976. Director of Housing Market Analysis Studies, Seattle and Vancouver, 1948-59, U.S. Housing Finance Study, 1950-51, and Urban Property Value Study, 1954-56. Member of Seattle Real Estate Research Committee, 1949—, intercensal advisory committee, U.S. Bureau of the Census, 1952-55, sub-committee on housing, Social Science Research Council, 1952-55, National Advisory Committee on Housing Statistics, 1953-58, and educational advisory committee, Society of Real Estate Appraisers, 1965. Price and anti-trust consultant, Ferguson & Burdell, 1958-60; United Nations consultant to Taiwan, 1970-71; consultant to National Chengchi University, Taiwan, 1974.

MEMBER: American Management Association, Society of Real Estate Appraisers, American Economic Association, Business History Conference, American Real Estate and Urban Economics Association, National Historical Society, Academy of Management, Beta Gamma Sigma. *Awards, honors:* Presidential citation, Executive Office of the President, 1945; housing market analysis grant, 1948-50, and housing finance research grant, 1950-51, both from State of Washington; American Securities Industries research grant, 1953; U.S. Highway Research Board fellow, 1955-56; Ford Foundation research grant, 1964; achievement award, National Register of Prominent Americans, 1969; United Nations Industrial Development Organization management and research grant, 1970-71; citation, China Productivity Center, 1971.

WRITINGS: *The Effect of Freeway Access upon Suburban Property Values*, Highway Research Board, 1956; *Business: An Introductory Analysis*, Harper, 1962, 2nd edition, 1968; *Renaissance in Business Theory*, Western Economic Association, 1966; *A Program of Business Research and Educational Training for Taiwan*, China Productivity Center (Taiwan), 1971; (with Thomas J. Adams) *The Business of Business: An Introduction*, Canfield Press, 1973, 2nd edition (by Adams), 1976; *Good News! What's Right with the U.S.,* Exposition Press, 1976. Also author of *Business Systems–An Exploratory Model,* 1965. Contributor of articles to professional journals. Editor of *Real Estate Research Report;* member of editorial board of *Harvard Business History Review,* 1964—.

WORK IN PROGRESS: Research on management in developing countries and urban development; novels.

* * *

WHELAN, Joseph P(aul) 1932-

PERSONAL: Born October 13, 1932, in Boston, Mass.; son of Frank and Anna Whelan. *Education:* Attended Georgetown University, 1952-54; Fordham University, B.A., 1958, M.A., 1960; Woodstock College, Th. L., 1966; University of London, Ph.D., 1969. *Home:* 1419 35th St. N.W., Washington, D.C. 20007. *Office:* Woodstock Theological Center, Georgetown University, Washington, D.C. 20057.

CAREER: Entered Roman Catholic Society of Jesus (Jesuit), 1954; ordained priest, 1965; Woodstock College, New York, N.Y., professor of pastoral theology, 1969-71; Maryland Province of the Society of Jesus, Baltimore, assistant for formation and studies, 1971-78; Georgetown University, Woodstock Theological Center, Washington, D.C., fellow, 1978—.

WRITINGS: The God Experience, Newman, 1971; *The Spirituality of Friedrich von Huegel,* Newman, 1971; *Benjamin: Essays in Prayer,* Newman, 1972. Contributor to *Way, Month, New Catholic World,* and *Dictionnaire de spiritualite.*

* * *

WHISNANT, David E(ugene) 1938-

PERSONAL: Born July 16, 1938, in Asheville, N.C.; son of John K. (an engineer) and Mary (Rudisill) Whisnant; children: Beverly Shannon, Rebecca Suzanne. *Education:* Georgia Institute of Technology, B.S., 1961; Duke University, A.M., 1962, Ph.D., 1965. *Politics:* Democrat. *Home:* 826 Glen Allen Dr., Baltimore, Md. 21229. *Office:* Department of American Studies, University of Maryland, 5401 Wilkens Ave., Baltimore, Md. 21228.

CAREER: University of Illinois at Urbana-Champaign, assistant professor of English, 1965-73; University of Maryland, Baltimore, associate professor of American studies, 1975—. *Member:* American Studies Association, Society for Religion in Higher Education, American Folklore Society, Mid-Atlantic Folklife Association, Phi Beta Kappa. *Awards, honors:* Woodrow Wilson graduate fellowship, 1961-62; Danforth graduate fellowship, 1961-65; Ford Foundation internship in editing, 1964-65; National Endowment for the Humanities Postdoctoral Teaching Residence Award, 1967-68; Danforth Theological Year, 1969-70; Rockefeller Foundation humanities fellowship, 1973-74.

WRITINGS: James Boyd, Twayne, 1972; *Damn Small, Damn Modest: Human Benefits of Planning and Development in Appalachia,* Burt Franklin, 1979. Contributor to *Dictionary of American Biography;* contributor to journals, including *Centennial Review, Soundings, New South, Journal of Higher Education, John Edward's Memorial Foundation Quarterly, Journal of Social History, Nation, South Atlantic Quarterly,* and *Planning for Higher Education.*

WORK IN PROGRESS: Studies of systematic institutional intervention into traditional culture in Appalachia and the southeastern United States; history of public policy formulation in the area of traditional, non-elite culture in the United States.

* * *

WHITE, Florence M(eiman) 1910-

PERSONAL: Born December 26, 1910, in New York, N.Y.; daughter of Morris and Anna (Siegal) Meiman; married Martin White, September, 1933; children: Donald, Lawrence, Judith. *Education:* Hunter College (now Hunter College of the City University of New York), B.A., 1933; graduate study at Columbia University, New York University, and University of California; St. Johns University, Brooklyn, N.Y., LL.B., 1938. *Residence:* Beverly Hills, Calif.

CAREER: Attorney. Has taught in elementary schools in minority neighborhoods of New York, N.Y. and Los Angeles, Calif.; teacher of adults in Los Angeles, Calif., 1950-56; teacher in film industry, 1960—. *Member:* P.E.N., Society of Children's Book Writers, California Writers Guild, Southern California Council on Literature for Children and Young People.

WRITINGS—For children: *My House Is the Nicest Place,* Golden Gate, 1963; *One Boy Lives in My House,* Whitman Publishing, 1965; *Your Friend, the Insect,* Knopf, 1968; *Your Friend, the Tree,* Knopf, 1969; *How to Lose Your Lunch Money,* Ritchie, 1970; *How to Lose Your Best Friend,* Ritchie, 1972; *Cesar Chavez: Man of Courage,* Garrard, 1973; *Hello, Sun,* Rand, 1974; *Malcolm X: Black and Proud,* Garrard, 1975; *Harry Houdini,* Messner, 1979; *Linus Pauling,* Walker, 1979.

Filmscripts: "Biography of Hidalgo," Stephen Bosustow Productions, 1971; "Biography of Juarez," Stephen Bosustow Productions, 1971; "How to Lose Your Lunch Money," BFA Educational Media, 1972. Contributor to *Childcraft, Life and Health,* and *Los Angeles Elementary School Administrators' Journal.*

SIDELIGHTS: "I like to write biographies for young people," Florence M. White told *CA,* "because the people I write about are people with great courage and great conviction. They are the 'movers and shakers' of the world. Without them we would still be in the stone age. They might well inspire a young reader to reach out in new directions." *Avocational interests:* Travel (including East Africa and Eastern Europe).

* * *

WHITE, Owen R(oberts) 1945-

PERSONAL: Born April 28, 1945, in Boston, Mass.; son of James Roberts (a salesman) and Elizabeth (Lewis) White; married Margaret Shaffer (a teacher), August 23, 1969. *Education:* Willamette University, B.A., 1967; University of Oregon, M.A., 1970, Ph.D., 1971. *Office:* Experimental Education Unit, University of Washington, Seattle, Wash. 98105.

CAREER: Fairview Hospital and Training Center, Salem, Ore., assistant psychologist, 1967; University of Oregon, Eugene, associate researcher in Department of Special Education, 1970-73, coordinator of research and evaluation at Regional Resource Center for Handicapped Children, 1970-71, director of research and evaluation, 1971-73, co-director of Special Training for Exceptional Parents Program, 1971-73; University of Washington, Seattle, coordinator of planning and evaluation at Experimental Education Unit,

1973—. Director of seminar in behavioral technology, University of San Francisco, 1969. *Member:* American Educational Research Association.

WRITINGS: (Editor) *A Glossary of Behavioral Terminology,* Research Press, 1971; (contributor) P. L. Browning, editor, *Mental Retardation: Rehabilitation and Counseling,* C. C Thomas, 1974; (with Norris G. Haring) *Exceptional Teaching: A Multimedia Training Package,* C. E. Merrill, 1976; (contributor) Haring and R. L. Schiefelbusch, editors, *Teaching Special Children,* McGraw, 1976. Author of papers on mental retardation, handicapped children, and exceptional parents.†

*   *   *

WHITE, William L(indsay) 1900-1973

June 17, 1900—July 26, 1973; American journalist, editor, and author. Obituaries: *New York Times,* July 27, 1973; *Washington Post,* July 27, 1973; *Time,* August 6, 1973; *Newsweek,* August 6, 1973.

*   *   *

WHITESELL, (James) Edwin 1909-

PERSONAL: Born November 21, 1909, in Buchanan, Va.; son of William James (a minister) and Cora E. (Brubaker) Whitesell; married Virginia Bergdoll (a music teacher), April 27, 1936; children: James Thomas, Carolyn Virginia. *Education:* Randolph-Macon College, B.A., 1930; Harvard University, M.A., 1931, Ph.D., 1935. *Religion:* Methodist. *Home:* 3241 Archdale Rd., Richmond, Va. 23235.

CAREER: Northwestern University, Evanston, Ill., instructor in English, 1935-39; Mary Washington College of the University of Virginia (now Mary Washington College), Fredericksburg, assistant professor of English, 1939-44; University of South Carolina, Columbia, associate professor, 1946-49, professor of English, 1949-66; Virginia Commonwealth University, Richmond, professor of English, 1966-76, dean of School of Arts and Sciences, 1966-72. Director, treasurer, and member of the board of Explicator Literary Foundation, Inc., Richmond. *Military service:* U.S. Naval Reserve, 1944-46; became lieutenant. *Member:* Modern Language Association of America, American Association of University Professors (chapter president of University of South Carolina, 1950-51), College English Association (president of Georgia-South Carolina Conference, 1964-65), National Council of Teachers of English, American Dialect Society, South Atlantic Modern Language Association (member of executive committee, 1965-68), Blue Key, Phi Beta Kappa (chapter president of University of South Carolina, 1959-60), Omicron Delta Kappa, Sigma Upsilon. *Awards, honors:* Danforth Foundation associate, 1952-76.

WRITINGS: (Editor) *The Explicator Cumulative Index 1942-1962,* Vogue Press, 1962; (editor with Charles C. Walcutt) *The Explicator Cyclopedia,* Quadrangle, Volume I: *Modern Poetry,* 1966, Volume II: *Traditional Poetry,* 1968, Volume III: *Prose,* 1968; (editor) *The Explicator Cumulative Index, 1962-1972,* Vogue Press, 1973. *Explicator,* co-founder and co-editor, 1942-54, managing editor, 1954-76.

*   *   *

WHITING, Nathan 1946-

PERSONAL: Born February 24, 1946, in Urbana, Ill.; son of Lester L. (a geologist) and Marguerite (Stiles) Whiting. *Education:* Studied at Oklahoma State University, 1964-65,

and State University of Iowa, 1966-67, *Politics:* "Water Party." *Address:* 101 Lincoln Rd., Brooklyn, N.Y. 11225.

CAREER: Poet and artist.

*WRITINGS—*Poetry: *While Courting the Sergeant's Daughter,* Pym-Randall, 1969; *Buffalo Poem,* Pym-Randall, 1970; *Transitions,* Seven Woods, 1972; *Running,* New Rivers Press, 1975; *London A-Z Poems,* Earthgrip Press, 1976; *This Slave Dreads Her Work as if She Were a Lamb Commanded to Be a Musician,* Hanging Loose Press, 1979.

AVOCATIONAL INTERESTS: Art, music (member of Trash Town Band), science.

*   *   *

WHITLOW, Roger 1940-

PERSONAL: Born January 13, 1940, in Galesburg, Ill.; son of William Robert Whitlow and Lillian (Garrison) Whitlow Sowles; married Miriam Hasselman, October 2, 1960; children: Betha Leanne, Stephen Douglas. *Education:* Illinois State University at Normal (now Illinois State University), B.S., 1962, M.S., 1964; Saint Louis University, Ph.D., 1975. *Religion:* Unitarian. *Home:* 1706 McComb, Charleston, Ill. 61920. *Office:* Department of English, Eastern Illinois University, Charleston, Ill. 61920.

CAREER: High school English teacher in Bloomington, Ill., 1962-65; Eastern Illinois University, Charleston, 1967—, began as assistant professor, currently associate professor of English.

WRITINGS: Black American Literature: A Critical History, Nelson-Hall, 1973; *The Darker Vision,* Gordon Press, 1977. Contributor to *Playboy, Negro American Literature Forum, Illinois English Bulletin, College English, CEA Critic, CEA Forum, CLA Journal, Literary Review, Encounter,* and *New York Culture Review.*

WORK IN PROGRESS: A book, *Cassandra's Daughters: The Women in Hemingway.*

*   *   *

WICK, John W(illiam) 1935-

PERSONAL: Born January 4, 1935, in Mankato, Minn.; son of William T. (an architect) and Ester G. (Gustafson) Wick; married Martha Cogen (a high school teacher), November 30, 1974; children: Patricia, Nancy, Peter, Adam. *Education:* Mankato State College, B.A., 1960; University of Iowa, M.A., 1965, Ph.D., 1967. *Home:* 2305 Pioneer Rd., Evanston, Ill. 60201. *Office:* Research and Evaluation, Chicago Board of Education, 2021 North Burling St., Chicago, Ill. 60614; and School of Education, Northwestern University, Evanston, Ill. 60201.

CAREER: Wick & Stansfield, Architects, Mankato, Minn., architectural draftsman, 1956-61; Northwestern University, Evanston, Ill., assistant professor, 1967-70, associate professor, 1970-74, professor of education, 1974—. Director of department of research and evaluation, Chicago Board of Education, 1974—. *Military service:* U.S. Army, 1953-56. *Member:* American Educational Research Association, National Council for Measurement in Education, American Statistical Association, American Association for the Advancement of Science, Phi Delta Kappa.

WRITINGS: (With Donald L. Beggs) *Evaluation for Decision-Making in the Schools,* Houghton, 1971; *On Measuring Education: Where Are We Going and How Will We Know When We Get There?,* C. E. Merrill, 1973. Also author of test/workbook for "Young Scientist" series, for Harper.

WORK IN PROGRESS: Lead author for comprehensive pre-school to high school testing program, for Scott, Foresman.

* * *

WIENANDT, Elwyn A(rthur)   1917-

PERSONAL: Born July 23, 1917, in Aniwa, Wis.; son of Charles Herman (a retail grocer) and Ida (Loehrl) Wienandt; married Lois Patricia Trachsel (a book editor), July 7, 1950; children: Alan Christopher, Linda, Thomas. *Education:* Lawrence College (now University), B.Mus. (cum laude), 1939; University of Denver, M.Mus., 1948; State University of Iowa, Ph.D., 1951. *Religion:* Episcopalian. *Home:* 1216 Cliffview Dr., Waco, Tex. 76710. *Office:* School of Music, Baylor University, Waco, Tex. 76703.

CAREER: Supervisor of music in public schools of Wisconsin, Montana, and Washington, 1939-49; State University of Iowa, Iowa City, assistant in musicology, 1949-51, visiting lecturer, 1954; New Mexico Highlands University, Las Vegas, N.M., associate professor of music history, 1951-56; Baylor University, Waco, Tex., professor of musicology, 1956—, chairman of graduate studies in music, 1958—, associate dean of School of Music, 1973—. *Military service:* U.S. Naval Reserve, 1943-46. *Member:* American Musicological Society (chairman of Southwest chapter, 1961-63), International Musicological Society, Music Library Association, American Association of University Professors, Lake Waco Country Club. *Awards, honors:* Research grants, Baylor University, 1962, 1965, 1966, 1969, 1972, 1973, 1974, 1975, 1978, 1979.

WRITINGS: Choral Music of the Church, Free Press, 1965; (with Robert H. Young) *The Anthem in England and America,* Free Press, 1970; (editor with Young) *Fifteen Anthems from America,* J. Fischer, 1970; (editor with Young) *Fifteen Anthems from England,* J. Fischer, 1970; *Opinions on Church Music,* Markham, 1974; *The Bicentennial Collection of American Music,* Hope, 1974; (contributor) Carl Schalk, editor, *Key Words in Church Music,* Concordia, 1978. Author of more than one hundred musical compositions and editions. Contributor of articles and music reviews to *Notes, Journal of the American Musicological Society,* and *Grove's Dictionary of Music.*

WORK IN PROGRESS: One hundred forty music entries for *Academic American Encyclopedia,* publication expected in 1980; research on the residual compositions of Johann Pezel.

* * *

WIESNER, William   1899-

PERSONAL: Born April 28, 1899, in Vienna, Austria; naturalized U.S. Citizen; son of Henry and Janette (Presser) Wiesner; married Gertrude Foges, October 17, 1926. *Education:* Attended Technische Hochscule in Vienna, where he received degrees in architecture and engineering. *Residence:* New York, N.Y.; and Woodstock, N.Y.

CAREER: Practicing architect and interior designer in Vienna, Austria, before migrating to France, and then in 1941 to the United States; worked with his wife in textile design, producing designs exhibited at Metropolitan Museum in New York, 1945; also commissioned to paint murals, including works for Hilton hotels in New York, Washington D.C., Boston and Hartford; has continued mural painting, but much of his time since 1960 has been devoted to writing and illustrating children's books. *Awards, honors: More*

Tongue Tanglers, which he illustrated, was an Honor Book in the *New York Herald Tribune'*s Children's Spring Book Festival, 1964.

WRITINGS—Self-illustrated: *Three Good Friends,* Harper, 1946; *Too Many Cooks,* Lippincott, 1961; *Noah's Ark,* Dutton, 1966; (compiler) *A Pocketful of Riddles,* Dutton, 1966, republished as *Plenty of Riddles,* Scholastic Book Services, 1966, abridged edition, Four Winds, 1972; (adapter) *Joco and the Fishbone,* Viking, 1966; (adapter) *Magic Slippers,* Norton, 1967; *Pin, the Reluctant Knight,* Norton, 1968; (adapter) *The Tower of Babel,* Viking, 1968; *Grabbit the Rascal,* Viking, 1969; *Tops,* Viking, 1969; (adapter) *Green Noses,* Four Winds, 1969; *Sillibill,* Four Winds, 1970; (adapter) *Happy-Go-Lucky,* Seabury, 1970; *Funny Questions and Funny Answers,* Follett, 1970; *The Constant Little Mouse,* Four Winds, 1971; *Hansel and Gretel: A Shadow-Puppet Picture Book,* Seabury, 1971; (adapter) *Turnabout,* Seabury, 1972; *Moon Stories,* Seabury, 1973; (compiler) *The Riddle Pot,* Dutton, 1973; (adapter) *Tom Thumb,* Walck, 1974; (compiler) *How Silly Can You Be?,* Seabury, 1974; *Magic Tales and Magic Tricks,* Scribner, 1975.

Illustrator: Hertha Pauli, *The Story of the Christmas Tree,* Houghton, 1944; Phyllis McGinley, *Blunderbus,* Lippincott, 1951; Benjamin Elkin, *Al and His Magic Lamp,* Harper, 1963; C. F. Potter, compiler, *Tongue Tanglers,* World Publishing, 1963; Potter, compiler, *More Tongue Tanglers and a Rigamarole,* World Publishing, 1964; Wilhelmina Harper, compiler, *Ghosts and Goblins,* new edition, Dutton, 1965; *Jack and the Beanstalk,* Scholastic Book Services, 1965; Carl Withers, *A Rocket in the Pocket,* Scholastic Book Services, 1967; Harper, compiler, *The Gunniwolf,* new edition, Dutton, 1967; Christopher B. Wilson, *Hobnob,* Viking, 1968; Gil B. Nagy, *No More Dragons,* Lothrop, 1969; Maria Leach, *Riddle Me, Riddle Me,* Viking, 1970; *Sarah and Her Johnnycake,* Walck, 1975.

SIDELIGHTS: William Wiesner writes: "I wrote my first story at the age of six. Inspired by a particularly ugly oil print of a girl with a St. Bernard dog, I made up a story of about twenty words which produced a paroxysm of laughter in my family—my first success! I like to awaken in children an eagerness to read and try to bring to the child some imaginative element that is sadly lacking in every day life."

BIOGRAPHICAL/CRITICAL SOURCES: Horn Book, December, 1969, April, 1970, December, 1972.

* * *

WIGGINS, Charles W(illiam)   1937-

PERSONAL: Born February 26, 1937, in Clarion, Iowa; son of Arthur Lyle (an electrician) and Mary (Gross) Wiggins; married Mary Jane Burkett, October 24, 1958; children: Angila, Scott, Theodore, Mary Beth. *Education:* University of Iowa, B.A., 1959; Washington University, St. Louis, Mo., M.A., 1963, Ph.D., 1964. *Politics:* Democrat. *Religion:* Protestant. *Home:* 2100 Greeley, Ames, Iowa 50010. *Office:* Department of Political Science, Iowa State University, Ames, Iowa 50011.

CAREER: Iowa State University, Ames, assistant professor, 1964-68, associate professor, 1968-73, professor of political science, 1973—. *Military service:* U.S. Army, 1961-62; became first lieutenant. *Member:* American Political Science Association, Policy Studies Association, Southwest Social Science Association, Southern Political Science Association, Midwest Political Science Association, Iowa Political Science Association (president, 1969-70), Pi Sigma Alpha. *Awards, honors:* State Legislative Service fellow, American Political Science Association, 1967-70.

WRITINGS: *The Legislative Process in Iowa,* Iowa State University Press, 1972; *The Arizona Legislature,* Arizona Legislative Council, 1975. Contributor to *Midwest Journal of Political Science, Western Political Science Quarterly, Journal of Politics, American Journal of Political Science,* and *Policy Studies Journal.*

WORK IN PROGRESS: Research on political reporters, interest groups, governors, and on state legislatures.

*   *   *

WIGGINS, Jack G(illmore)   1926-

PERSONAL: Born January 1, 1926, in Little Rock, Ark.; son of Jack Gillmore (a chartered life underwriter) and Blanche (Miller) Wiggins; married Alice Mae Biggam (a teacher), June 24, 1971; children: Claudia, Elliott, Grant. *Education:* University of Oklahoma, B.A., 1948; Southern Methodist University, M.A., 1951; Purdue University, Ph.D., 1952. *Home:* 7827 Dogwood Lane, Parma, Ohio 44130. *Office:* Psychological Development Center, 7057 West 130th St., Cleveland, Ohio 44130.

CAREER: Cleveland Psychiatric Institute, Cleveland, Ohio, chief psychologist of outpatient clinic, 1952-63; Psychological Development Center, Cleveland, president and clinical psychologist, 1957—. Secretary, Personal Growth Press, Inc., Cleveland, 1967—; partner, Career Development Center, Cleveland, 1970—. Trustee, Education Development Center, 1965—; member of board of directors, Psychological Services, Inc., 1971-78. *Military service:* U.S. Army, 1944-46. *Member:* American Psychological Association (president elect, Division of Psychotherapy, 1978; chairman elect, insurance trust, 1978), Council for the Advancement of Psychological Professions and Sciences (member of executive committee, 1971-78), National Council on Graduate Education in Psychology (member of board of directors, 1969-75), American Psychology and Law Society (member of board of directors, 1971-72), Association for the Advancement of Psychology (member of board of trustees, 1976—, and operations committee, 1977—), Ohio Academy of Consulting Psychologists (president, 1970-72), Ohio Psychological Association, Cleveland Academy of Consulting Psychology, Cleveland Psychological Association (president, 1963-64), Cleveland Mental Health Association, Cleveland Welfare Federation, Sigma Xi, Psi Chi, Phi Delta Theta.

WRITINGS: (Contributor) Robert W. Henderson, editor, *Dealing with Self-Consciousness in Helping Yourself with Applied Psychology,* Parker Publishing, 1967; (with Henderson) *Coping with Personal Depression,* Personal Growth Press, 1968; (with Henderson and Ralph Thompson) *College: This Is the Way It Is,* Personal Growth Press, 1968; (with Henderson and Lynde Steckle) *The Depth Interview,* Personal Growth Press, 1969; (with Henderson and Steckle) *The Depth Interview Guide,* Personal Growth Press, 1969; *Dealing with Temper Tantrums,* Personal Growth Press, 1969; (with Henderson) *Marriage Skills Analysis* (test), Personal Growth Press, 1970; *How to Argue Successfully without Really Trying,* Personal Growth Press, 1971; (contributor) Herbert Dorken, editor, *The Professional Psychologists Today,* Jossey-Bass, 1976. Contributing editor of *Professional Psychologist;* member of editorial board of *Creative Developments in Psychotherapy,* Volume I.

*   *   *

WILBER, Charles G(rady)   1916-

PERSONAL: Born June 18, 1916, in Waukesha, Wis.; son of Charles Bernard (an engineer) and Charlotte Agnes (Grady) Wilber; married Ruth Mary Bodden, July 12, 1944 (died, 1950); married Clare Marie O'Keefe (a musician), June 14, 1952; children: (first marriage) Maureen, Charles Bodden, Michael; (second marriage) Thomas Grady (deceased), Kathleen, Aileen, John Joseph. *Education:* Marquette University, B.Sc., 1938; Johns Hopkins University, M.A., 1941, Ph.D., 1942; also studied at U.S. Air Corps School of Aviation Medicine, 1942. *Politics:* Republican. *Religion:* Roman Catholic. *Home:* 900 Edwards, Fort Collins, Colo. 80524. *Office:* Department of Zoology and Entomology, Colorado State University, Fort Collins, Colo. 80521.

CAREER: St. Louis University, St. Louis, Mo., instructor in zoology, 1942; Fordham University, Bronx, N.Y., assistant professor of physiology, 1945-49; St. Louis University, associate professor of physiology and director of biology laboratories, 1949-52; U.S. Army, Chemical Corps Medical Research Laboratory, Maryland, chief of animal ecology branch, 1952-56, chief of comparative physiology branch, 1959-60; Kent State University, Kent, Ohio, professor of physiology and pharmacology and dean of Graduate School, 1961-64; University of Delaware, Newark, director of marine laboratories, 1964-67; Colorado State University, Fort Collins, professor of zoology and entomology and chairman of department, 1967—, director of Forensic Science Laboratory. Associate professor of physiology and pharmacology, University of Pennsylvania, 1953-61; lecturer in physiology, University of Maryland, Medical School, 1954-61; national lecturer, American Institute of Biological Sciences, 1957-72; professorial lecturer in biological sciences, Loyola College, 1957-61. Regular contributor to radio program "You and Your Life." Consultant to U.S. Public Health Service and to Thorne Ecological Institute. Leader of Arctic expeditions to study biology of northern animals, 1943-44, 1948, 1950, 1951; corporation member of Marine Biological Laboratory (Woods Hole, Mass.), 1947—; member of U.S. Army Panel on Environmental Physiology, 1952-61. Member of board of directors of Ecology Consultants, Inc., and In-Service Institute of Science Teachers, 1958-61. Deputy coroner of Larimer County; special investigator, Fort Collins Police Department. *Military service:* U.S. Army Air Forces, 1942-46; became captain. U.S. Air Force Reserve, 1946-76; final rank, colonel.

MEMBER: American Physiological Society, American Academy of Forensic Sciences (fellow), International Association of Chiefs of Police, New York Academy of Sciences (fellow), Ohio Academy of Sciences (fellow), Cosmos Club (Washington, D.C.), Phi Beta Kappa, Sigma Xi.

WRITINGS—All published by C. C Thomas, except as indicated: *Biological Aspects of Water Pollution,* 1971; (contributor) Wesley E. Brittin, editor, *Air and Water Pollution,* Colorado Associated Universities Press, 1972; *Forensic Biology for the Law Enforcement Officer,* 1974; *Contemporary Violence,* 1975; *Ballistic Science for the Law Enforcement Officer,* 1977; *Medicolegal Investigation of the President John F. Kennedy Murder,* 1978; *Chemical Trauma—Pesticides,* Matthew Bender, 1978. Executive editor, "Adaptation to the Environment," 1964; editor, "American Lecture Series in Environmental Studies," published by C. C Thomas. Contributor to *Harper Encyclopedia* and *Encyclopedia of Chemistry.*

WORK IN PROGRESS: Introduction to Forensic Toxicology; Toxicity of Selenium; Ethics in Forensic Science; a textbook in general zoology for non-science majors.

AVOCATIONAL INTERESTS: Mountain hiking, hunting, competitive target shooting, swimming.

* * *

WILDER, Robert D. 1916-

PERSONAL: Born April 2, 1916, in Gardner, Mass.; son of Solon (a businessman) and Edith (Leavens) Wilder; married Roberta Brackett, July, 1940 (died, 1966); married Ella A. Wales (a university editor at Colgate University), June, 1968; children: Elizabeth L. (Mrs. Robert Peck), Stephen B., Timothy B.; stepchildren: Robert Q. Wales, Christina Wales (Mrs. Thomas Thoburn II). *Education:* Boston University, Mus.B., 1940; Harvard University, A.M., 1942, Ph.D., 1952. *Politics:* Republican. *Religion:* Episcopalian. *Home:* 81 Hamilton St., Hamilton, N.Y. 13346. *Office:* Department of Music, Colgate University, Hamilton, N.Y. 13346.

CAREER: Boston University, Boston, Mass., instructor in music theory, 1946-48; St. Lawrence University, Canton, N.Y., assistant professor of music, 1952-53; Colgate University, Hamilton, N.Y., assistant professor, 1953-56, associate professor, 1956-69, professor of music, 1969-76, professor emeritus, 1976—. Trustee of the Village of Hamilton, N.Y., 1966-70. *Military service:* U.S. Army, 1942-46; became first lieutenant.

WRITINGS: The Masses of Orlando di Lasso, with Emphasis on His Parody Technique, University of Rochester Press, 1959; *Twentieth Century Music,* W. C. Brown, 1969.

WORK IN PROGRESS: Elementary Music Theory.

* * *

WILENSKY, Harold L. 1923-

PERSONAL: Born March 3, 1923, in New Rochelle, N.Y.; son of Joseph and Mary (Wainsten) Wilensky; children: Stephen David, Michael Alan, Daniel Lewis. *Education:* Antioch College, A.B., 1947; University of Chicago, M.A., 1949, Ph.D., 1955. *Home:* 638 Gravatt Dr., Berkeley, Calif. 94705. *Office:* Department of Sociology, University of California, Berkeley, Calif. 94720.

CAREER: University of Chicago, Chicago, Ill., assistant professor of sociology, 1951-53, assistant professor of industrial relations, 1953-54; University of Michigan, Ann Arbor, assistant professor, 1954-57, associate professor, 1957-61, professor of sociology, 1961-62; University of California, Berkeley, professor of sociology and research sociologist at Institute of Industrial Relations, 1963—. Guest professor, University of Lund, Lund, Sweden, fall, 1970. Center for Advanced Study in the Behavioral Sciences, Stanford, Calif., fellow, 1956-57, visiting scholar, 1962-63. Research associate in program on technology and society, Harvard University, 1969. Member of Mental Health Research Career Award committee, National Institute of Mental Health, 1964-67; evaluator of research proposals in sociology, National Science Foundation, 1964—. Member of social policy group of Council of European Studies, 1975—. Member of planning group on intelligence and security of policy council, Democratic National Committee, 1972. Consultant to labor, management, and welfare groups. *Military service:* U.S. Army Air Forces, B-17 pilot, 1943-45.

MEMBER: American Sociological Association (member of executive council, 1969-72; chairman of committee on information technology and privacy, 1970-72), Society for the Study of Social Problems, Sociological Research Association, Industrial Relations Research Association (member of

executive committee, 1965-68), American Association of University Professors, American Civil Liberties Union. *Awards, honors:* Social Science Research Council award for research, 1962; McKensey Foundation book award, 1967, for *Organizational Intelligence;* German Marshall Fund fellowship, 1978-79.

WRITINGS: Industrial Relations: A Guide to Reading and Research, University of Chicago Press, 1954; *Intellectuals in Labor Unions: Organizational Pressures on Professional Roles,* Free Press of Glencoe, 1956; (editor with Conrad Arensberg and others) *Research in Industrial Human Relations,* Harper, 1957; (with C. N. Lebeaux) *Industrial Society and Social Welfare,* Free Press, 1965; (editor with P. F. Lazarsfeld and W. H. Sewell) *The Uses of Sociology,* Basic Books, 1967; *Organizational Intelligence: Knowledge and Policy in Government and Industry,* Basic Books, 1967; (contributor) Richard H. Blum, editor, *Surveillance and Espionage in a Free Society,* Praeger, 1972; (contributor) *The Welfare State and Equality: Structural and Ideological Roots of Public Expenditures,* University of California Press (Berkeley), 1975.

Co-editor, "Modern Society," a series published by Scott, Foresman. Contributor to *American Sociological Review* and other professional journals. Associate editor, *American Sociological Review;* chairman of editorial board, *Social Problems;* member of editorial board, *Industrial Relations;* member of advisory editoral selection committee, "Bobbs-Merrill Reprint Series in the Social Sciences."

WORK IN PROGRESS: Research on the sources, substance, and impact of the welfare state; research on the politics of taxing and spending; studying work, family life cycle, and the quality of life.

* * *

WILKERSON, David R(ay) 1931-

PERSONAL: Born May 19, 1931, in Hammond, Ind.; son of Kenneth (a minister) and Ann (Martin) Wilkerson; married Gwendolyn Carosso, June 4, 1951; children: Debbie Ann, Bonnie Kay, Gary Randall, Gregory Allen. *Education:* Attended Central Bible College, Springfield, Mo. *Office address:* Route 1, Box 80, Lindale, Tex. 75771.

CAREER: Ordained Protestant minister, 1952; minister in Philipsburg, Pa., 1952-58; Teen Challenge, Inc., Brooklyn, N.Y., executive director, 1958—. President, David Wilkerson Youth Crusades, 1965—; president, World Challenge, Inc., 1970—.

WRITINGS: The Cross and the Switchblade, Pyramid Publications, 1962; *Twelve Angels from Hell,* Revell, 1965; *The Little People,* Revell, 1966; *Parents on Trial,* Hawthorn, 1967; *I'm Not Mad at God,* Bethany Fellowship, 1967; *Hey Preach, You're Coming Through,* Revell, 1968; *Purple Violet Squish,* Zondervan, 1969; *Man, Have I Got Problems,* Revell, 1969; *Rebel's Bible,* Revell, 1970; *Get Your Hands Off My Throat,* Zondervan, 1971; (with brother, Don Wilkerson) *The Untapped Generation,* Zondervan, 1971; *Life on the Edge of Time,* Revell, 1972; *Jesus Christ: Solid Rock,* Zondervan, 1973; *David Wilkerson Speaks Out,* Bethany Fellowship, 1973; *The Vision,* Pyramid Publications, 1974; *Beyond the Cross and the Switchblade,* Pillar Books, 1974; *Racing toward Judgment,* Pyramid Publications, 1976; *Suicide,* Revell, 1978; *Sipping Saints,* Revell, 1978.

SIDELIGHTS: David Wilkerson's parish consists of the sidewalks of New York and the slums of big cities across the county. His mission is to teenage gangs and narcotics users wherever they are found. *The Cross and the Switchblade* was made into a movie starring Pat Boone, and released in 1970.

*   *   *

WILKES, Ian (Henry)   1932-

PERSONAL: Born April 15, 1932, in Leigh, Essex, England; son of Henry J. A. (a music engraver) and Winifred (Cowey) Wilkes; married Pamela Jones (a literary agent), March 12, 1956; children: Nicholas, Christopher, Jeremy, Matthew. *Education:* London School of Librarianship, A.L.A., 1953. *Politics:* Independent. *Religion:* Church of England. *Home and office:* 38 Parkstone Ave., Hornchurch, Essex RM11 3LW, England.

CAREER: Affiliated with various libraries and publishers, 1948-63; Tothill Press Ltd., London, England, editor of directories, 1963-68; Library Association, London, manager of publications, 1968-73; White Lion Publishers Ltd., London, projects manager, beginning 1973; Ian Henry Publications, Hornchurch, England, managing director, 1975—. Governor of Gaynes School, 1966-71. *Member:* Library Association, National Union of Journalists.

WRITINGS: British Initials and Abbreviations, Hill, 1963, 3rd edition, 1971. Also contributor to *Three Costume Plays for Women*, Ian Henry Publications. Contributor to *Amateur Stage, Assistant Librarian*, and *Food Industries Weekly*.

WORK IN PROGRESS: A work of fiction and one on local politics.

*   *   *

WILLARD, Beatrice E(lizabeth)   1925-

PERSONAL: Born December 19, 1925, in Palm Springs, Calif.; daughter of Stephen Hallett and Beatrice (Armstrong) Willard. *Education:* Stanford University, B.A., 1947; University of Colorado, M.A., 1960, Ph.D., 1963; also studied at Chico State College (now California State University), University of California, Berkeley, and Yosemite Field School of Natural History. *Politics:* Republican. *Religion:* Protestant. *Home:* 1529 Columbine Ave., Boulder, Colo. 80302. *Agent:* Marie Rodell—Frances Collin Literary Agency, 156 East 52nd St., New York, N.Y. 10022. *Office:* Colorado School of Mines, Golden, Colo. 80401.

CAREER: High school teacher in Salinas, Calif., 1949-50, Oakland, Calif., 1950-52, and Tulelake, Calif., 1952-57; University of Colorado, Boulder, research assistant, Institute for Arctic and Alpine Research, 1958-63, teaching assistant, 1960-63, assistant professor of biology, 1968-69, adjunct professor, 1969—; Southern Oregon College, Ashland, assistant professor of biology, 1963-64; Thorne Ecological Institute, Boulder, executive director, 1965-67, vice-president, 1967-70, president, 1970-72; Executive Office of the President, Washington, D.C., member of Council on Environmental Quality, 1972-77; Colorado School of Mines, Golden, professor of environmental sciences, 1977—. Ecological consultant to government and industry, 1968-72, 1977—. Ranger-naturalist, Lava Beds National Monument, 1952, and Crater Lake National Park, 1953. Founder and director, Rocky Mountain National Park Seminars, 1962-72, and Aspen Seminar on Environmental Arts and Sciences, 1967-72. President, Colorado Open Space Council, 1968-69; secretary, Colorado Air Pollution Control Commission, 1970-71; chairman of Denver Olympic Planning Commis-

sion, 1971-72, and of environmental education subcommittee of Federal Interagency Committee on Education, 1974-77; alternate member, Water Resources Council, 1975-76. Former member of Corps of Engineers, Colorado Citizens Coordinating Committee for Environmental Planning, Wilderness Workshop, Experiment in Ecology, Boulder Creek Flood Control Planning Sub-Committee, and Colorado Advisory Committee on Environmental Education. Trustee of Rocky Mountain Center on Environment, 1970-72, Aspen Center for Environmental Studies, 1970-72, Bolton Institute, 1977—, and Thorne Ecological Institute, 1978—.

MEMBER: Ecological Society of America, American Institute of Biological Sciences, American Association for the Advancement of Science, American Society of Civil Engineers, American Institute of Mining Engineers, Sigma Xi, Phi Sigma. *Awards, honors:* Ford Foundation fellowship to study alpine ecology in Europe, 1954-55; Colorado Conservationist-of-the-Year Award from Colorado Wildlife Federation, 1969; American Motors Award for Professional Conservation, 1970; Outstanding Civilian Service Medal, Department of the Army; Edward Hobbs Award for Rocky Mountain environmental work; Outstanding Evironmental Achievement Award, American Institute of Mining Engineers.

WRITINGS: (With Genny S. Smith, D. Rinehardt, S. Rinehardt, and Eldon Vestal) *A Guide to the Mammoth Lakes Sierra*, Wilderness Press, 1959, revised edition, 1976; (with C. O. Harris) *Alpine Wildflowers of Rocky Mountain National Park*, Rocky Mountain Nature Association, 1963, revised edition, 1975; (with Ann H. Zwinger) *Land above the Trees: A Guide to American Alpine Tundra*, Harper, 1972. Contributor to *Biological Conservation* and other scientific publications.

WORK IN PROGRESS: Phytosociology of Trail Ridge Rocky Mountain National Park, Colorado; research on visitor impact on Alpine tundra on Trail Ridge.

*   *   *

WILLEY, Darrell S.   1925-

PERSONAL: Born May 9, 1925, in Farmington, Utah; son of R. C. (a businessman) and Helen (Barber) Willey; married Velma I. Roush, June 7, 1947 (died May 5, 1971); married Irene Knox Mayfield (a teacher), May 30, 1972; children: (first marriage) Randie (Mrs. Gary L. Boldra), Tricia (Mrs. James Hazelton), Jacqui (Mrs. Timothy Clements). *Education:* University of Denver, A.B., 1948; Utah State University, M.A., 1949; University of Utah, Ed.D., 1953; University of Southern California, postdoctoral study, 1957. *Politics:* Democratic. *Religion:* Latter-day Saints. *Office:* Educational Research Center, Box 3/R, New Mexico State University, Las Cruces, N.M. 88003.

CAREER: Teacher of English and principal in Wendover Schools, Utah, 1949-50; shcool principal in Littleton, Colo., 1952-53; New Mexico State University, Las Cruces, assistant professor, 1953-59, associate professor, 1959-62, professor of educational administration, and head of department, 1962-70, director of Educaional Research Center, 1970—. Director of civil rights program, Equal Educational Opportunity Institute, 1966-67; principal investigator of Educational Resources Information Center-Clearinghouse on Rural Education and Small Schools, 1966—; director of Elementary and Secondary Education Act Title IV research training fellows, 1966—; New Mexico delegate to White House Conference on Children, 1970. *Military service:* U.S. Army Air Forces, 1943-45; became staff sergeant; received

Air medal with clusters. U.S. Air Force Reserve, 1945-56; became second lieutenant. *Member:* American Association for the Advancement of Science, American Association of School Administrators, National Education Association, Comparative Education Society, National Conference of Professors of Educational Administration, American Educational Research Association, Phi Delta Kappa.

WRITINGS: School Personnel Management Game, New Mexico State Press, 1963; (contributor) H. A. Estrin and D. G. Goode, editors, *College and University Teaching,* W. C. Brown, 1964; (with J. D. McComas) *Statewide Study of Vocational and Technical Education in New Mexico,* twenty-three volumes, Governor's Office, New Mexico, 1966; (with H. W. Handy) *Administrator's and Teacher's Guide to Professional Literature,* A. C. McClurg, 1968. Contributor to *International Education, Improving College and University Teaching, Peabody Journal of Education, Journal of Educational Research, Journal of Indian Education, Educational Leadership, Contemporary Education,* and *School Business Affairs.*

WORK IN PROGRESS: Role of Culture in College Student Drinking Habits.

* * *

WILLEY, Richard J(ames) 1934-

PERSONAL: Born April 14, 1934, in Lynn, Mass.; son of Leon H. (a photoengraver) and Margaret (Cochrane) Willey; married Dorothy Ellert (a teacher), September 5, 1959; children: Richard E., Lauren M. *Education:* University of Massachusetts, A.B., 1960; Princeton University, 1960-64, received M.A. and Ph.D. *Office:* Department of Political Science, Vassar College, Poughkeepsie, N.Y. 12601.

CAREER: Vassar College, Poughkeepsie, N.Y., assistant professor, 1964-67, 1968-70, associate professor, 1970-76, professor of political science, 1976—, head of department, 1970-74. Visiting professor, McGill University, 1976-77. Program manager, President's Commission on Postal Organization, Washington, D.C., 1967-68. *Military service:* U.S. Army, 1953-55. *Member:* American Political Science Association, American Association of University Professors, Conference Group on German Politics.

WRITINGS: (Editor with Murray Comarow, William Sullivan, and others, and contributor) *Towards Postal Excellence: Report of the President's Commission on Postal Organization,* U.S. Government, 1968; *Democracy in the West German Trade Unions: A Reappraisal of the "Iron Law,"* Sage Publications, 1971. Contributor to *Proceedings of the Canadian Political Science Association.* Contributor of articles and reviews to *Western Political Quarterly, Public Interest, Gewerkschaftliche Monatshefte, Collier Encyclopedia Yearbook, American Political Science Review, Public Opinion Quarterly,* and *Industrial and Labor Relations Review.*

WORK IN PROGRESS: The German Trade Union Confederation and Politics in the Federal Republic.

* * *

WILLIAMS, (Timothy) Alden 1932-

PERSONAL: Born November 16, 1932, in Charlotte, N.C.; son of John Payne (a professor) and Irena (a poet; maiden name, Foreman) Williams; married Joyce Elaine Schuller (an editor), June 3, 1962; children: Evan Charles, Heather Lee. *Education:* Davidson College, A.B., 1954; University of North Carolina, Ph.D., 1964. *Home:* 1829 Alabama

Lane, Manhattan, Kan. 66502. *Office:* Department of Political Science, Kansas State University, Manhattan, Kan. 66506.

CAREER: United Press International, Chicago, Ill., reporter and editor, 1958-61; Ohio State University, Columbus, associate director, and postdoctoral fellow of Mershon National Security program, 1964-66; Kansas State University, Manhattan, associate professor of political science, 1967—. Visiting professor at Graduate School of International Studies, University of Denver, 1966-67; member of executive council of Inter-University Seminar on Armed Forces and Society; member of editorial board of University Press of Kansas. *Military service:* U.S. Army, Infantry, 1954-58; became first lieutenant. *Member:* Peace Science Society, International Studies Association (chairman of television archives committee; member of governing council).

WRITINGS: (Contributor) Robin Higham, editor, *Bayonets in the Streets,* University Press of Kansas, 1969; (contributor) Edwin Fedder, editor, *NATO in the Seventies,* University of Missouri Press, 1970; (editor with David W. Tarr) *Modules in Security Studies,* University Press of Kansas, 1974; (contributor) M. J. Clark, editor, *Politics in Camera: Film and Television for the Political Scientist and Historian,* Pergamon Press, 1979.

WORK IN PROGRESS: Research on large-scale youthful military officer retirement and comparative civilian-military relations; research on international political communication; coordination of worldwide television archives.

* * *

WILLIAMS, Burton John 1927-

PERSONAL: Born December 24, 1927, in St. Louis, Mo.; son of B. John and Nina (Shoulders) Williams; married Carol Beatty, July 2, 1949; children: Herbert, Laura, Mitchell, Rachel, Gary, William. *Education:* Southern Illinois University, B.A., 1953, M.A., 1959; University of Kansas, Ph.D., 1965. *Home address:* Route 1, Box 1075, Ellensburg, Wash. 98926. *Office:* School of Social and Behavioral Sciences, Central Washington University, Ellensburg, Wash. 98926.

CAREER: U.S. Aeronautical Chart Service, St. Louis, Mo., cartographer, 1948-49; State of Illinois, Division of Highways, Department of Public Works and Buildings, Carbondale, Ill., civil engineer, 1953-56; public school teacher in Indiana, 1957-60; University of Kansas, Lawrence, instructor in history, 1961-63, 1964-65; Baker University, Baldwin, Kan., assistant professor of history, 1963-64; director of Kansas Methodist Historical Archives, 1963-64; University of Cincinnati, Cincinnati, Ohio, assistant professor of history, 1965-67; Chadron State College, Chadron, Neb., professor of history, 1967-69, chairman of Division of Social Sciences, 1967-69; Central Washington University, Ellensburg, professor of history, 1969—, chairman of department, 1969-72, dean of School of Social and Behavioral Sciences, 1972—. *Military service:* U.S. Marines, machinist in engineer maintenance, 1946-48; became sergeant.

MEMBER: Western History Association, Nebraska Historical Society, Kansas Historical Society, Phi Alpha Theta. *Awards, honors:* U.S. Office of Education grant to study history of tree planting in the Great Plains area, 1968.

WRITINGS: Senator John J. Ingalls: Kansas' Iridescent Republican, University Press of Kansas, 1972; (editor) *Essays in American History in Honor of James C. Malin,* Coronado Press, 1973; (editor) *Essays in Kansas History in*

Honor of George L. Anderson, Coronado Press, 1977; (editor) *Washington: Readings in the History of the Evergreen State,* Coronado Press, 1977. Contributor to history journals, including *Methodist History, Midwest Quarterly, Great Plains Journal, Nebraska History, Wesleyan Quarterly Review,* and *Kansas Historical Quarterly.*

WORK IN PROGRESS: Editing the diary of Douglas W. Johnson, who was with Woodrow Wilson at Versailles in 1919; a history of Kansas, completion expected in 1979.

BIOGRAPHICAL/CRITICAL SOURCES: Choice, October, 1972.

* * *

WILLIAMS, Duncan   1927-

PERSONAL: Born October 15, 1927, in Newcastle Emlyn, Wales; son of David Lewis (a naval officer) and Melita (Thomas) Williams; married Joanna Davies, December 1, 1951 (divorced, 1958); married Pamela Anne Lewis, January 5, 1959; children: (second marriage) Dominic, Rosamund, Christopher. *Education:* Attended Magdalen College, Oxford, 1944; Christ Church, Oxford, B.A. (honors), 1951, M.A., 1956. *Religion:* Church of England. *Address:* 4 Park Town, Oxford, England. *Agent:* Curtis Brown Group Ltd., 1 Craven Hill, London W2 3EW, England.

CAREER: Her Majesty's Overseas Civil Service, Tanzania, District Officer, 1951-55; Summer Fields, Oxford, England, assistant master, 1956-63, housemaster, 1960-63; West Virginia Wesleyan College, Buckhannon, assistant professor of English, 1963-66; Marshall University, Huntington, W. Va., associate professor, 1966-69, professor of English, beginning 1969, director of university honors program, 1967-70; Oxford University, Alvescot College, Oxford, professor of English and head of department, 1970-72, dean of College, 1971-72; Farmington Trust, Oxford, director of research, 1972—. Distinguished visiting professor, Rockford College, 1974—. *Military service:* Royal Marines, Royal Welch Fusiliers, 1944-48. *Member:* Modern Language Association of America, Modern Humanities Research Association, American Association of University Professors, Phi Eta Sigma.

WRITINGS: Trousered Apes, Churchill Press, 1971, published with a foreword by Malcolm Muggeridge, Arlington House, 1972; *Education: Threatened Standards,* Churchill Press, 1972; *To Be or Not to Be; a Question of Survival,* Pergamon, 1976. Contributor to *Studia Neophilologica, Philological Papers, Laurel Review,* and newspapers in England and the United States.

SIDELIGHTS: Duncan Williams speaks French, Swahili, and Welsh. *Avocational interests:* Collecting early editions of eighteenth-century authors; finding and cultivating good English pubs.

* * *

WILLIAMS, Irving G(regory)   1915-

PERSONAL: Born March 17, 1915, in Brooklyn, N.Y.; son of Charles Thomas (a State of New York civil servant) and Margaret (Gardner) Williams; married Muriel Kalbacker, October 9, 1942; children: Carol Ann (Mrs. Eugene Kolakowski), Gregory. *Education:* St. John's University, Brooklyn, B.A., 1936, M.A., 1938; New York University, Ph.D., 1953. *Politics:* Democrat. *Religion:* Roman Catholic. *Home:* 54 Sunset Ave., Lynbrook, N.Y. 11563.

CAREER: St. John's Preparatory School, Brooklyn, N.Y., history teacher, 1936-38; St. John's University, Jamaica,

N.Y., instructor, 1938-41, 1946-47, assistant professor, 1947-51, associate professor, 1951-54, professor of history, 1954-77, chairman of department, 1948-58, 1963-66, director of social science, 1960-63, director of historical collections, 1969-71. Historian for CBS-TV series "See It Now," 1955; secretary, vice-president, and president of Southwest Lynbrook Civic Association, 1953—; trustee on Lynbrook Board of Education, 1954-59. *Military service:* U.S. Naval Reserve, 1941-50; executive officer of minesweeper; became commanding officer of V-12 unit in Butte, Montana, 1943-45. *Member:* Manuscript Society, Center for the Study of the Presidency (member of committee of educators), Society of Historians of American Foreign Relations, Faculty Association of St. John's University (member of board of directors, 1971-77). *Awards, honors:* Freedoms Foundation at Valley Forge special award, 1954; Sylvania TV Award, 1955, for best documentary of the year, "The Vice-Presidency: The Great American Lottery"; Best Teacher of the Year Award, St. John's University, 1962; President's Medal, St. John's University, 1972.

WRITINGS: The American Vice-Presidency: New Look, Doubleday, 1954; (contributor) Carl W. Grindel, editor, *Conceit of Freedom,* Regnery, 1955; *The Rise of the Vice-Presidency,* Public Affairs Press, 1956; (contributor) Arpad F. Kovacs, editor, *Thought Patterns,* Volume V, St. John's University, 1957; *Government: Its Structure and Interpretation,* Sadlier, 1965, 2nd edition, 1972. Co-author of "See It Now" TV series script on the vice-presidency, 1955. Contributor to *World Book Encyclopedia, Catholic Youth Encyclopedia, World Scope Encyclopedia,* and *Grolier Encyclopedia.* Contributor to journals.

WORK IN PROGRESS: The New Deal's Vice-Presidents; research on the Tresham family of Northamptonshire, England in the 13th to 17th centuries; *Vice-Presidents from New York.*

* * *

WILLIAMS, J(ames) Earl   1922-

PERSONAL: Born July 16, 1922, in Fonde, Ky.; son of Hobert Lee and Beatrice (Seal) Williams; married Marjorie Marie Hybarger, June 16, 1951. *Education:* Attended Texas Christian University, 1948; Carson-Newman College, B.A., 1949; University of Tennessee, M.A., 1950; University of Wisconsin, Ph.D., 1961. *Home:* 3370 Habersham Rd., Atlanta, Ga. 30305. *Office:* Center for Industrial Relations, College of Business Administration, Georgia State University, Atlanta, Ga. 30303.

CAREER: University of Tennessee, Knoxville, instructor in economics, 1949-50; University of Pennsylvania, Wharton School, Philadelphia, instructor in industry, 1950-51; Socony-Mobil Oil Co., Philadelphia, Pa., marketing representative, 1952-54; Austin Peay State College (now University), Clarksville, Tenn., director of economic program, 1954-56; University of Tennessee, assistant professor, 1958-61, associate professor of economics, 1961-65; University of Houston, Houston, Tex., professor of economics and management, 1966-78, director of Center for Human Resources, beginning 1966; Georgia State University, Atlanta, professor of economics and management, 1978—. Visiting professor of economics, University of Wisconsin, 1963; administrative director of vocational guidance in Houston ghetto high schools for Houston Vocational Guidance Service, 1967-70; administrative director of Negro teenage unemployment study for Manpower Administration of U.S. Department of Labor, 1967-69. Established Labor Research Center for Latin America for International Association of Postal, Telephone and Telegraph Workers in Lima, Peru, for Organization of American States, 1966. Budget analyst, Tennessee Valley Authority, 1951-52; director of Division of Employment Programs, Office of Economic Opportunity, 1965-66. Member of national task force on unemployment insurance and manpower, National Advisory Council on Vocational Education; member of public advisory committee, Texas Employment Commission; member of board of directors, Committee on Southern Progress; member of Job Fair Committee for mayor of Houston; member of Houston-Galveston Coordinated Area Manpower Planning Systems. Consultant to Federal Aviation Administration, Houston Model Cities, U.S. Department of Labor, and U.S. Department of Health, Education, and Welfare. Member of arbitration panel, American Arbitration Association, Federal Mediation and Conciliation Service. *Military Service:* U.S. Marines, 1942-45; became technical sergeant.

MEMBER: Association for Evolutionary Economics, Industrial Relations Research Association (president of Tennessee chapter, 1962-64), American Academy of Political and Social Science, American Association of University Professors, American Vocational Association, National Manpower Training Association. World Future Society, Adult Education Association of the United States of America, Common Cause, Midwestern Association for Latin American Studies, Southwestern Council of Latin American Studies, Texas Association of College Teachers, Houston United Nations Association, University Labor Education Association, L.Q.C. Lamar Society, Phi Kappa Phi, Delta Sigma Pi. *Awards, honors:* Distinguished service award to an outsider from Postal Telephone and Telegraph International, Lima, Peru, 1966.

WRITINGS: (Contributor) Gerald G. Somers, editor, *Retraining the Unemployed,* University of Wisconsin Press, 1968; (editor and contributor) *Retooling Our Human Resources for the Space Age, Papers and Findings: A Conference on Human Resource Development,* Manpower Administration (U.S. Department of Labor) and Center for Human Resources, University of Houston, 1968; (editor and contributor) *Human Resource Development: A Profile of the Houston Employment Process,* Manpower Administration and Center for Human Resources, University of Houston, 1968.

Economics of Southern Politics, Center for Human Resources, University of Houston, 1971; (editor) *Labor Economics,* Center for Human Resources, University of Houston, 1971; (editor) *Manpower Development in Houston: Programs, Agencies and Organizations,* Center for Human Resources, University of Houston, 1971; *The University and Manpower Educational Services: The University of Houston Example,* Manpower Administration and Center for Human Resources, University of Houston, 1971; *Guidelines for the Development of Manpower Educational Services in the University,* Manpower Administration and Center for Human Resources, University of Houston, 1972; *Human Resource Problems: Employment, Poverty, Welfare,* Center for Human Resources, University of Houston, 1972; *Plantation Politics: The Southern Economic Heritage,* Futura, 1972; (with Sam Schulman, Roberto S. Guerra, and others) *Mexican American Youth and Vocational Education in Texas,* with summary and recommendations, Center for Human Resources, University of Houston, 1973.

General editor of labor education textbooks, 1969-71. Contributor to proceedings, conferences, U.S. Senate hearings, yearbooks, reports, and bulletins. Contributor of about thirty-five articles and reviews to professional journals, including *Labor Arbitration Awards, Journal of Human Resources, Monthly Labor Review,* and *Alberta Historical Review.*

WORK IN PROGRESS: Labor Relations in the Telephone Industry.

* * *

WILLIAMS, Jay G(omer) 1932-

PERSONAL: Born December 18, 1932, in Rome, N.Y.; son of Jay Gomer (a minister) and Mary (Craig) Williams; married Hermine Weigel (an organist and choir director), September 6, 1956; children: Jay G., Lynn, Daryl, Ruth. *Education:* Hamilton College, B.A., 1954; Union Theological Seminary, New York, N.Y., B.D., 1957; Columbia University, Ph.D., 1964. *Politics:* Democrat. *Home:* 300 College Hill Rd., Clinton, N.Y. 13323. *Office:* Department of Religion, Hamilton College, Clinton, N.Y. 13323.

CAREER: Clergyman of Presbyterian Church; National Council of Churches, New York, N.Y., associate director, 1958-60; Hamilton College, Clinton, N.Y., associate professor of religion, 1960—. *Member:* American Academy of Religion, American Schools of Oriental Research, Society of Biblical Literature. *Awards, honors:* Presbyterian graduate fellowship, 1964; Ford Humanities grant, 1971.

WRITINGS: Ten Words of Freedom, Fortress, 1971; *Understanding the Old Testament,* Barron's 1972; *Yeshua Buddha,* Quest Books, 1978.

WORK IN PROGRESS: Time, Space, and Power: An Introduction to the Study of Religion; The Way of Adam (a work partly in poetry, partly in prose).

SIDELIGHTS: Jay Williams has travelled in Austria, 1960, France, 1964, in Israel for archaeological excavations, 1967, 1978, in Japan, Korea, and Taiwan to study Chinese religion and its influences, 1971, and in Haiti, Jamaica, and Guyana, 1972, to study Hinduism and other religious beliefs.

* * *

WILLIAMS, Joy 1944-

PERSONAL: Born February 11, 1944, in Chelmsford, Mass.; daughter of Williams Lloyd and Elisabeth (Thomas) Williams; married Rust Hills (a writer and editor); children: Caitlin. *Education:* Marietta College, M.A. (magna cum laude), 1963; State University of Iowa, M.F.A., 1965. *Politics:* Democrat. *Religion:* Protestant. *Home address:* Heron Lagoon, Midnight Pass Rd., Siesta Key, Fla. 33581. *Agent:* Lynn Nesbit, International Creative Management, 40 West 57th St., New York, N.Y. 10019.

CAREER: U.S. Navy, Mate Marine Laboratory, Siesta Key, Fla., researcher and data analyst, 1967-69. Writer. *Member:* Phi Beta Kappa. *Awards, honors:* National Endowment for the Arts grant, 1973; Wallace Stegner fellowship, Stanford University, 1974-75; Guggenheim fellowship, 1974.

WRITINGS: State of Grace (novel), Doubleday, 1973; *The Changeling* (novel), Doubleday, 1978. Work is represented in anthologies, including: *New Campus Writing,* edited by Nolan Miller, McGraw, 1966; *O. Henry Prize Story Collection,* edited by William Abrahams and Richard Poirier, Doubleday, 1966; *Best of the Little Magazines,* edited by C. Johnson, 1969; *Secret Lives of Our Time,* edited by Gordon Lish, Doubleday, 1973; *Bitches and Sad Ladies,* edited by Pat Rotter, Harper Magazine Press, 1974; *All Our Secrets*

Are the Same, edited by Lish, Norton, 1977; *Best American Short Stories 1978*, edited by Theodore Solotaroff, Houghton, 1978; *The Norton Anthology of Short Fiction*, edited by R. V. Cassell, Norton, 1978; *Women on Woman Alone*, Dell, 1978.

Contributor of short stories to *Paris Review, Audience, Esquire, Tri-Quarterly, Antioch Review, Carolina Quarterly, Colorado Quarterly*, and *Transatlantic Review*.

SIDELIGHTS: Joy Williams "is a talented, skillful writer," says Alice Adams in a *New York Times Book Review* critique. "She evokes the feel and smell of certain moments with an eerie precision. . . . Certain characters, too, in her fiction, are entirely original and absolutely credible." *State of Grace* "was a startlingly good novel," writes Anatole Broyard, who adds, "it pains me to have to say that *The Changeling* is a startlingly bad one." Broyard goes on to compare the protagonists of the two books, "While Kate transcends the natural, Pearl falls below it." Adams agrees, calling *The Changeling* "an unconvincing and ultimately unsatisfying novel, instead of the very good one that I believe Joy Williams could write."

BIOGRAPHICAL/CRITICAL SOURCES: New York Times Book Review, April 22, 1973, June 10, 1973, December 2, 1973, July 2, 1978; *Esquire*, July, 1973; *Commentary*, September, 1973; *Carolina Quarterly*, fall, 1973; *Antioch Review*, November, 1973; *New York Times*, November 7, 1973, June 3, 1978.

*   *   *

WILLIAMS, Lee E(rskine) II 1946-

PERSONAL: Born April 2, 1946, in Jackson, Miss.; son of Lee Erskine, Sr. (a college administrator) and Ruth (Harris) Williams. *Education:* Knoxville College, B.A., 1968; East Tennessee State University, M.A., 1970; Mississippi State University, Ph.D., 1975. *Home:* 3800 Sparkman Dr., Huntsville, Ala. 35810. *Office:* Department of History, University of Alabama, Huntsville, Ala. 35807.

CAREER: Middle Tennessee State University, Murfreesboro, instructor in history, 1969-72; University of Alabama, Huntsville, 1972—, began as instructor, currently assistant professor of history. *Member:* American Association of University Professors, Phi Kappa Phi, Phi Alpha Theta, Pi Gamma Mu.

WRITINGS: Anatomy of Four Race Riots, Williams & Williams, 1973.

WORK IN PROGRESS: A revision of his dissertation, for possible publication; articles on blacks in southern history.

SIDELIGHTS: Lee Williams told *CA:* "I hope to do a major study of race riots in the U.S. between 1919-21. I plan to make a study of white racism and the 1960's civil rights movement."

*   *   *

WILLIAMS, Merryn 1944-

PERSONAL: Born July 9, 1944, in Devonshire, England; daughter of Raymond (a writer) and Joyce Mary (Dalling) Williams; married John Hemp (a scientist), April 14, 1973; children: David, Rosalind. *Education:* Cambridge University, B.A., 1966, M.A., 1970, Ph.D., 1970. *Politics:* Socialist. *Religion:* Atheist. *Home:* 5 Henson Close, Wharley End, Cranfield, Bedfordshire, England.

CAREER: Open University, Milton, Keynes, England, lecturer in literature, 1970-71; part-time writer.

WRITINGS: (Editor) *Revolutions 1765-1830*, Penguin, 1971; *Thomas Hardy and Rural England*, Macmillan, 1972; "*Jude the Obscure*," Open University, 1973; "*Germinal*," Open University, 1973; *Literature and the First World War*, Open University, 1973; *Preface to Hardy*, Longman, 1976.

WORK IN PROGRESS: The Squalid Profession, completion expected in 1979.

*   *   *

WILLIAMS, Noel Trevor St. John 1918-

PERSONAL: Born December 26, 1918, in Doncaster, Yorkshire, England; son of Ivor Llewelyn (an army officer) and Edith (Winter) Williams; married Christina McCullagh, February 2, 1943; children: Jacqueline, Noel Alan St. John. *Education:* University of London, B.A., 1940. *Office:* Education Department, County Hall, Chester, Cheshire, England.

CAREER: British Army, Education Corps, career officer, 1940-71, retiring as colonel; Cheshire, England, assistant director of education, 1971—. *Member:* British Institute of Management.

WRITINGS: Looking at Eltham, Eltham Society, 1970; *Tommy Atkin's Children: 1675-1970* (300 years of children's education in the British Army), Her Majesty's Stationery Office, 1971.

WORK IN PROGRESS: Historical research.

*   *   *

WILLIE, Charles V(ert) 1927-

PERSONAL: Born October 8, 1927, in Dallas, Tex.; son of Louis (a former Pullman porter and real estate broker) and Carrie (Sykes) Willie; married Mary Sue Conklin (an organist, singing teacher, and choir director), April 14, 1937; children: Sarah Susannah, Martin Charles, James Theodore. *Education:* Morehouse College, B.A., 1948; Atlanta University, M.A., 1949; Syracuse University, Ph.D., 1957. *Religion:* Episcopalian. *Office:* 457 Gutman Library, Graduate School of Education, Harvard University, Cambridge, Mass. 02138.

CAREER: Syracuse University, Syracuse, N.Y., instructor, 1952-60, assistant professor, 1960-64, associate professor, 1964-68, professor of sociology 1968-74, chairman of department, 1967-71, vice-president of student affairs, 1972-74; Harvard University, Cambridge, Mass., currently professor of education and urban studies. Research sociologist, New York State Mental Health Commission, 1951-52; instructor in sociology at State University of New York Upstate Medical Center, 1955-60; research director of Washington, D.C. Project, President's Committee on Juvenile Delinquency and Youth Crime, 1962-67; lecturer in sociology at the Medical School, Harvard University, 1966-67; vice-president of House of Deputies, Episcopal Church General Convention, 1970-73. *Member:* Social Science Research Council (member of board of directors, 1969-74), Social and Behavioral Sciences Assembly of the National Research Council, American Sociological Society (fellow), Society for the Study of Social Problems, American Public Health Association, Eastern Sociological Society (president, 1974-75), Phi Beta Kappa. *Awards, honors:* Health Information Foundation research grant, 1958-60, State University of New York Upstate Medical Center; National Science Foundation conference grant, Syracuse University, 1967-68; faculty service award from National University Extension Association, 1967; Ford Foundation research grant, 1969-71, for study of black students at white colleges; Falk Medical Fund conference grant, 1970-71; D.H.L., Yale University, 1972; D.D., General Seminary, 1974; M.A., Harvard University, 1974; Distinguished Alumnus Award, Syracuse University, 1974; National Institute of Mental Health grant, 1976-77.

WRITINGS: Church Action in the World, Morehouse, 1969; (editor) *The Family Life of Black People,* C. E. Merrill, 1970; (with Arline McCord) *Black Students at White Colleges,* Praeger, 1972; (with Jerome Beker) *Race Mixing in the Public Schools,* Praeger, 1973; (editor with Bernard Kramer and Betram Brown) *Racism and Mental Health,* University of Pittsburgh Press, 1973; *Oreo: A Perspective on Race and Marginal Men and Women,* Parameter Press, 1975; *A New Look at Black Families,* General Hall, 1976; (editor) *Black–Brown–White Relations: Race Relations in the 1970's,* Transaction Books, 1977; (editor with Ronald R. Edmonds) *Black Colleges in America,* Teachers College Press, 1978; *The Sociology of Urban Education: Desegregation and Integration,* Lexington Books, 1978. Contributor to *Psychology Today, Society, Harvard Magazine, American Sociological Review, American Journal of Sociology, Social Problems, American Journal of Public Health, Journal of Negro Education, Nursing Outlook, Professional Geographer, Dissent,* and *Review of Religious Research.*

* * *

WILLIS, Donald C(halmers) 1947-

PERSONAL: Born September 18, 1947, in Santa Barbara, Calif.; son of Howard Chalmers (an auditor) and Dolores (Medalen) Willis. *Education:* Sacramento City College, A.A., 1967; University of California, Los Angeles, B.A., 1969. *Politics:* Democrat. *Religion:* Lutheran. *Home:* 2410 Dwight Way, No. 3, Berkeley, Calif. 94704.

CAREER: Los Angeles Public Library, Los Angeles, Calif., clerk typist, 1971-75; Berkeley Health Department, Berkeley, Calif., clerk typist, 1976—.

WRITINGS: Horror and Science Fiction Films: A Checklist, Scarecrow, 1972; *The Films of Frank Capra,* Scarecrow, 1974; *The Films of Howard Hawks,* Scarecrow, 1975. Contributor of articles to *Sight and Sound* and *Film Quarterly.*

WORK IN PROGRESS: An article, "Implications of the Modernist Esthetic."

AVOCATIONAL INTERESTS: Reading (Chekhov, James Tolstoy, Dostoevsky, Proust), baseball.

* * *

WILSON, Harold Stacy 1935-

PERSONAL: Born June 22, 1935, in Neva, Tenn.; son of Joseph Hooker (an engineer) and Hazel (Reece) Wilson; married Henrietta Fair, June 21, 1968; children: Katherine, Kyle. *Education:* King College, B.A., 1957; Johns Hopkins University, M.A., 1959; Emory University, Ph.D., 1966. *Politics:* Independent. *Religion:* Protestant. *Office:* Department of History, Old Dominion University, Norfolk, Va. 23508.

CAREER: Emory University, Atlanta, Ga., instructor in history, 1960-62; Wesleyan College, Macon, Ga., assistant professor of history, 1962-66; Old Dominion University, Norfolk, Va., associate professor of history, 1966—. Fulbright professor of history, Tamkang University, 1971-72, University of Singapore, 1977-79. *Member:* American Historical Association, Civil War Historical Society, Organiza-

tion of American Historians, American Civil Liberties Union (member of board of Virginia chapter), Southern Historical Association. *Awards, honors:* Sigma Chi award, 1970, for *"McClure's Magazine" and the Muckrakers,* as one of five best books on journalistic history.

WRITINGS: "McClure's Magazine" and the Muckrakers, Princeton University Press, 1970. Contributor to *Historian, Alabama Review,* and *Georgia Review.*

WORK IN PROGRESS: The Ante-bellum Georgia Textile Industry and *Chicago during the Progressive Era.*†

* * *

WILSON, John A(braham) R(oss) 1911-

PERSONAL: Born August 25, 1911, in Trout Lake, British Columbia, Canada; came to United States in 1951, naturalized in 1956; son of Henry (a minister) and Grace Ellen (Ross) Wilson; married Nora Margaret Mains (a secondary school teacher), June 28, 1940; children: John Richard Meredith, Douglas Gordon. *Education:* University of British Columbia, B.A., 1932, M.A., 1939; Oregon State College (now University), Ed.D., 1951. *Politics:* Independent. *Religion:* United Church of Christ. *Home:* 2519 Chapala St., Santa Barbara, Calif. 93105. *Office:* Department of Education, University of California, Santa Barbara, Calif. 93106.

CAREER: Factory worker, insuranceman, building constructor and manufacturing entrepreneur in British Columbia, 1927-34; teacher and counselor in the schools of British Columbia, 1934-51; University of California, Santa Barbara, assistant professor, 1951-58, associate professor, 1958-68, professor of education, 1968—. Summer professor at University of British Columbia, 1958, Dalhousie University, 1965, 1966, and University of Oregon, 1968. *Member:* American Educational Research Association, American Personnel and Guidance Association, National Vocational Guidance Association, American Association for the Advancement of Science, National Society for the Study of Education, National Education Association, California Educational Research Association (secretary, 1966-67; vice-president, 1967-68; president, 1968-69), California Association for Student Teaching (president, 1960-62), Kappa Delta Pi, Phi Delta Kappa.

WRITINGS: (With Mildred C. Robeck) *Kindergarten Evaluation of Learning Potential,* McGraw, 1967; (with Robeck and William B. Michael) *Psychological Foundations of Learning and Teaching,* with instructor's manual, McGraw, 1969, 2nd edition, 1974; (editor) *Diagnosis of Learning Difficulties,* McGraw, 1971; (with Robeck) *Psychology of Reading,* Wiley, 1973.

WORK IN PROGRESS: A book on the neurology of learning, with Mildred C. Robeck.

* * *

WILSON, Mitchell 1913-1973

July 17, 1913—February 25, 1973; American novelist and science writer. Obituaries: *New York Times,* February 27, 1973; *Publishers Weekly,* April 23, 1973. (See index for CA sketch)

* * *

WILSON, William Ritchie 1911-

PERSONAL: Born January 8, 1911, in Chicago, Ill.; son of William Ritchie and Ethel Maude (Hopkins) Wilson; married Ruby M. Greiling, October 26, 1946. *Education:* U.S.

Naval Academy, B.S., 1932; University of Washington, M.A., 1964, Ph.D., 1967. *Home and office:* 16102 41st Ave. N.E., Seattle, Wash. 98155.

CAREER: U.S. Navy, 1932-63, retiring as captain. Commissioned as ensign, 1932; served on ships, 1932-38; language officer attached to U.S. Embassy, Tokyo, 1938-41; served on U.S.S. Pope, U.S. Asiatic Fleet, 1941-42; prisoner of war in Japan, 1941-45; staff officer attached to Naval Support Group, Japan, 1946-48; served as commander of destroyer-minelayer in Atlantic, 1948-49; intelligence duty in Washington, D.C., 1949-51, 1957-59, Tokyo, 1953-55; served as commander of fleet oiler in Atlantic, 1952-53, and Pacific, 1955-57; intelligence officer, Far East Command, 1953-55, and Naval Forces, Japan, 1959-60; commander of U.S. Fleet Activities, Sasebo, Japan, 1960-63; University of Southern California, Los Angeles, assistant professor of Asian studies, 1967-71. *Member:* Association for Asian Studies, American Oriental Society, U.S. Naval Institute. *Awards, honors*—Military: Legion of Merit with Combat V, plus oak leaf cluster, Bronze Star, Purple Heart, Bronze Cross (Netherlands), Order of the Sacred Treasure, 3rd class (Japan). Civilian: Certificate of Merit (Shojo) from Shuppan Bunka Kokusai Koryukai, 1972, for *Hogen Monogatari.*

WRITINGS: (Translator; author of essay and notes) *Hogen Monogatari* (tale of the Rebellion in Hogen), Sophia University, 1971; (contributor of translations) D. A. Dilworth and T. Rimer, editors, *The Historical Literature of Mori Ogai,* two volumes, University of Hawaii Press, 1977. Contributor to *Monumenta Nipponica* and others.

WORK IN PROGRESS: "Translating *Baishoron (The Plum and Pine Discourse),* a hitherto neglected fourteenth century historical account centered on Ashikaga Takauji."

SIDELIGHTS: "I have been criticized twice for translation style," William Ritchie Wilson told *CA,* "mainly because I am a prisoner of the style of the original. I see some virtue in this. More than content should be translated. When a translator paraphrases a style into what he thinks is an adequate equivalent, he is deceiving the reader. Of course, a precise equivalence of style is impossible, but an attempt should be made and accepted." *Hogen Monogatari* is included in the UNESCO Collection of Representative Works: Japan Series.

BIOGRAPHICAL/CRITICAL SOURCES: Journal of Asian Studies, February, 1972; *Pacific Affairs,* fall, 1972.

*   *   *

WINCHESTER, A(lbert) M(cCombs) 1908-

PERSONAL: Born April 20, 1908, in Waco, Tex.; son of Robert Stevenson and Mamie Katherine (Moore) Winchester; married Josephine Milam Walker, December 23, 1934; children: Betty Jo. *Education:* Baylor University, A.B., 1929; University of Texas, A.M., 1931, Ph.D., 1934; postdoctoral study at University of Chicago, 1940, Harvard University, 1952, University of Michigan, 1959, and University of Munich, 1960. *Office:* College of Arts and Sciences, University of Northern Colorado, Greeley, Colo. 80631.

CAREER: Oklahoma Baptist University, Shawnee, professor of biology, 1937-43, head of department, 1937-43; Baylor University, Waco, Tex., associate professor of biology, 1943-46; Stetson University, DeLand, Fla., professor of biology, 1946-61, head of department, 1946-61; University of Northern Colorado, Greeley, professor of biology, 1962—, dean of College of Arts and Sciences, 1969—.

Member: American Association for the Advancement of Science (fellow), American Society for Human Genetics, Genetics Society of America, Eugenics Society of America, Sigma Xi, Elks, Lions.

WRITINGS—All with photographs and drawings by the author: *Zoology: The Science of Animal Life,* Van Nostrand, 1947, revised edition, 1961; *Biology and Its Relation to Mankind,* Van Nostrand, 1949, 5th edition, 1977; *Genetics: A Survey of the Principles of Heredity,* Houghton, 1951, 5th edition, 1978; *Heredity and Your Life,* Dover, 1957, 3rd edition, 1966; *Genetics Laboratory Manual,* W. C. Brown Co., 1958, 3rd edition, 1978; *Heredity: The Science of Genetics,* Harper, 1962, 3rd edition, 1977; *Modern Biological Principles,* Van Nostrand, 1965, 4th edition, 1971; *Human Development and Inheritance,* C. E. Merrill, 1968; *Los Secretos de la Reproducción y de la herencia,* Ediciones Toray, 1970; *Concepts of Zoology,* Van Nostrand, 1971; *Human Genetics,* C. E. Merrill, 1971; *Human Sex and Reproduction,* C. E. Merrill, 1973; (contributor) *Atlas and Compendium of Human Birth Defects,* National Foundation, 1973; *Heredity, Evolution, and Humankind,* West, 1977. Author of laboratory manuals for W. C. Brown. Contributor to *Encyclopaedia Britannica, World Book Encyclopedia, Van Nostrand's Scientific Encyclopedia, American Peoples Encyclopedia, Young Peoples Science Encyclopedia;* contributor to *Journal of Heredity, Genetics, American Naturalists, American Biology Teacher,* and other professional journals.

SIDELIGHTS: A. M. Winchester told *CA* that the "uniformly dull, pedantic presentations" of older textbooks made him "determined to write textbooks in a syle that was not only understandable and informative, but which stimulated interest by relating the subject to everyday life." His textbooks have appeared in Russian, Spanish, Hebrew, Chinese and Indian translation.

*   *   *

WINDCHY, Eugene G. 1930-

PERSONAL: Born May 5, 1930, in Los Angeles, Calif.; son of O. Eugene (an accountant) and E. Marguerite (Wieda) Windchy; married Hiroko Uchiyama, December 10, 1964. *Education:* University of Illinois at Urbana-Champaign, B.S., 1952; also studied at U.S. Foreign Service Institute, Tokyo, Japan, 1957-59.

CAREER: Employed in the U.S. Information Agency, 1955-67. *Military service:* U.S. Army, 1952-54; became first lieutenant.

WRITINGS: Tonkin Gulf, Doubleday, 1971. Contributor to proceedings of U.S. Naval Institute, and national magazines, including *New Republic, Saturday Review,* and *Nation.*

WORK IN PROGRESS: A book on war prevention.††

*   *   *

WINDOLPH, F(rancis) Lyman 1889-1978

PERSONAL: Born June 10, 1889, in Elizabeth Township, Pa.; son of Jacob Rathvon and Frances (Grugan) Windolph; married Margaret Jane Leader, December 31, 1921. *Education:* Franklin and Marshall College, A.B., 1908. *Home:* 1040 Woods Ave., Lancaster, Pa. 17603. *Office:* Windolph, Burkholder & Stainton, 121 East King St., Lancaster, Pa. 17602.

CAREER: Admitted to Bar of Pennsylvania, 1911, and to Bar of U.S. Supreme Court, 1931; practice of law in Lancaster, Pa., with Windolph, Burkholder & Stainton, 1975-78. Franklin and Marshall College, North Lecturer, 1955, Garvin Lecturer, 1961. Member of procedural rules committee, Supreme Court of Pennsylvania. Trustee, Franklin and Marshall College, 1923-28; Lancaster Free Public Library, director, 1935-49, 1953-69, president of board of directors, 1940-49. *Military service:* U.S. Army, 1918; became first lieutenant.

MEMBER: American Bar Association, American Law Institute, American Judicature Society (member of board of directors, 1939-40), American College of Trial Lawyers (fellow), Selden Society, Pennsylvania Bar Association (regional vice-president, 1936-37), Historical Society of Pennsylvania, Cliosophic Society (Lancaster; president, 1939-42), Lancaster Bar Association, Lancaster Country Club, Hamilton Club (Lancaster), Franklin Inn Club (Philadelphia), Phi Beta Kappa. *Awards, honors:* Litt. D., Franklin and Marshall College, 1937.

WRITINGS: Today and Other Poems, privately printed, 1908; *The Country Lawyer,* University of Pennsylvania Press, 1938, reprinted, Books for Libraries, 1970; *Leviathan and Natural Law,* Princeton University Press, 1951, reprinted, Greenwood Press, 1970; *Reflections of the Law in Literature,* University of Pennsylvania Press, 1956, reprinted, Books for Libraries, 1970; *Last Poems,* privately printed, 1970; *Obiter Scripta,* privately printed, 1971; *Selected Essays,* Franklin and Marshall College, 1972; *Selected Poems,* privately printed, 1972; *Four Portraits from Memory,* privately printed, 1973; *Obiter Postscripta,* privately printed, 1974. Contributor to law journals and to *Atlantic Monthly, Weekly Review, Reformed Church Review, Forum,* and *Pennsylvania Magazine of History and Biography.*†

(Died April 2, 1978)

* * *

WINKELMAN, Donald M.   1934-
(David Moshe)

PERSONAL: Born August 27, 1934, in Detroit, Mich.; son of Herman (a merchant) and Debbe (Greenbaum) Winkelman; married Barbara Bruder (a designer), March 28, 1954; children: Marcie Lynn, Stuart Alan. *Education:* Ohio State University, B.A., 1957, M.A., 1958; Indiana University, graduate study, 1960-62. *Religion:* Jewish. *Home:* 21316 Seasprite Cr., Huntington Beach, Calif. 92646. *Office:* Ostrow, Winkelman & Associates, 1823 East 17th St., Suite 305, Santa Ana, Calif. 92701.

CAREER: Elementary teacher in Gahanna, Ohio, 1956-57; Indiana University at Bloomington, folklore librarian, 1960-62; Purdue University, Lafayette, Ind., instructor in English, 1962-65; Bowling Green State University, Bowling Green, Ohio, instructor in English, 1966-67; New York State Education Department, Albany, associate, 1967-69, supervisor of higher education, 1969-70, coordinator of higher education, 1970-72; Ostrow, Winkelman & Associates, Santa Ana, Calif., vice-president, 1972—. Secretary, New York State College Committee on Educational Opportunity, 1967-72; executive secretary, National Coordinating Council for Education Opportunity, 1970-73. Has given poetry readings at University of Wisconsin—Milwaukee, Hofstra University, Western Michigan University, Purdue University, and elsewhere. *Member:* Modern Language Association of America, Ohio Folklore Society (president, 1966-67).

WRITINGS: (Contributor and editor with Ray B. Browne

and Allen Hayman) *New Voices in American Studies,* Purdue University Studies, 1966; (editor) *Buckeyes and Buckshot,* Ohio Folklore Society, 1971; (editor) *From Out of the Blue,* Union College (Schenectady), 1973; *The Great Hi-Risers,* Bazaar del Mundo, 1977. Also author of short stories, some under pseudonym David Moshe.

Writer of *Folklore of America,* teacher's manual to accompany his educational radio series, "Folklore of America," broadcast for Indiana schools, 1963-64, 1964-65, and distributed nationally by National Association of Educational Broadcasters; other radio series include "Patterns in Folklore," broadcast, 1965-66. Composer of choral arrangement with poems and music, "Sacred Service," performed in Albany, 1972.

Poems have been published in *Laurel Review, Ground Zero, American Bard, Discourse, Haiku Highlights, University Review,* and other literary magazines; contributor of articles and reviews to journals and newspapers, including *Journal of American Folklore, Midwest Folklore, Christian Science Monitor,* and *Sing Out!.* American editor, *YES,* 1960-61; *Quartet,* editor and publisher, 1961-64, contributing editor, 1965—; editor, *Abstracts of Folklore Studies,* 1962-67, and *Educational Opportunity Forum,* 1968—; member of editorial board, *Journal of Popular Culture,* 1968-72; editor and publisher, *California Real Estate Report,* 1976—.

WORK IN PROGRESS: A cookbook of traditional foods; a novel; *The Surviving Spouse,* with David Shacter.

* * *

WINNER, Irene P(ortis)   1923-

PERSONAL: Born April 7, 1923, in Chicago, Ill.; daughter of Henry Roy (a businessman) and Jane (Oransky) Portis; married Thomas G. Winner (a university professor), September 25, 1942; children: Ellen, Lucy Franziska. *Education:* Radcliffe College, B.A., 1943; Columbia University, M.A., 1953; University of North Carolina, Ph.D., 1967. *Home:* 19 Garden St., Cambridge, Mass. 02138. *Office:* Department of Sociology/Anthropology, Emmanuel College, 400 The Fenway, Boston, Mass. 02115.

CAREER: Office of War Information-Office of Strategic Services, Washington, D.C., research analyst, 1943-46; Wayne State University, Detroit, Mich., visiting instructor in anthropology, 1962-63; Brown University, Providence, R.I., research associate in office of provost, 1968-71; Ossabaw Island Project, Ossabaw Island, Ga., fellow, 1971; Tufts University, Medford, Mass., visiting lecturer in anthropology, 1972, 1974, 1975; Brown University, Providence, R.I., research fellow, 1973; Emmanuel College, Boston, Mass., associate professor of anthropology, 1975—. *Member:* American Anthropological Association (fellow), Society for Applied Anthropology (fellow), American Ethnological Society, Current Anthropology (associate), American Association for the Advancement of Slavic Studies, International Association for Semiotic Study, Council on Anthropology and Education, Society for the Anthropology of Visual Communication, American Association for Southeast European Studies, Society for Slovene Studies (member of executive council), Semiotic Society of America, American Association for the Advancement of Science, Northeastern Anthropological Association, Anthropological Society of Washington. *Awards, honors:* Wenner-Gren Foundation fellowship in Yugoslavia, 1964-65; American Council of Learned Societies and Social Science Research Council grant for research in Eastern Europe, 1972-73.

WRITINGS: A Slovenian Village: Zerovnica, Brown University Press, 1971. Contributor to *Central Asian Review, East Central Europe, Canadian-American Slavic Studies, Current Anthropology, American Anthropologist, Sociologija Sela, Semiotica,* and *Etnografia Polska.* Member of editorial board, *East Central Europe* and *Southeastern Europe.*

WORK IN PROGRESS: Editing two books for Peter de Ridder Press in Holland, *East European Peasantry: A Syncretic Approach* and *East European Ethnicity outside of Eastern Europe;* research on semiotics of culture and on Slovene ethnicity in the United States.

* * *

WINOKUR, Joan Gelman 1935-

PERSONAL: Born June 21, 1935, in Philadelphia, Pa.; daughter of Benjamin (a grocer) and Esther (Goldfarb) Gelman; married Emanuel Winokur (a pharmacist), June 24, 1956; children: Bruce, Stephen. *Education:* Temple University, B.Sc., 1957; Beaver College, M.Ed., 1978. *Religion:* Jewish. *Home:* 1008 East Slocum St., Philadelphia, Pa. 19150. *Office:* Masterman Demonstration, 17th and Spring Garden Sts., Philadelphia, Pa. 19103.

CAREER: Oak Lane Day School, Glenside, Pa., kindergarten teacher, 1963-64; Morton Parent Nursery, Philadelphia, Pa., head teacher, 1965-70; St. Peter's Parent Community Cooperative, Philadelphia, head teacher, 1970-78; affiliated with Masterman Demonstration, Philadelphia, 1978—. Member of advisory council, Philadelphia school system, district six; member, board of directors, Temple Sinai. *Member:* Parent Cooperative Preschools International, Benjamin Franklin Institute, Delaware Valley Association of Educators of Young Children (vice president), B'nai Brith Women, Schuylkill Valley Nature Center, Temple Sinai Sisterhood.

WRITINGS: (Adapter) *The Three Pigs,* World Publishing, 1965; (adapter) *The Three Bears,* World Publishing, 1965; *Merrill Phonics Skilltexts, Books A to F* (student's text and teacher's text), C. E. Merrill, 1972. Writer of *Parent Orientation Bulletin* for Philadelphia School District Parent Cooperatives, 1971-72.

WORK IN PROGRESS: Taking and Using Anecdotal Records, a manual for teachers and parents; *Phonics and Other Word Attack Skills,* a reference for complementary and supplementary reading programs; an article on parent involvement.

AVOCATIONAL INTERESTS: Community work, knitting, sewing, reading.

* * *

WINSHIP, Elizabeth 1921-
(Beth)

PERSONAL: Born May 17, 1921, in Pittsfield, Mass.; daughter of A. Sprague (a professor) and Margaret S. (Coit) Coolidge; married Thomas Winship (editor of *Boston Globe*), September 5, 1942; children: Margaret S., Laurence P., Joanna S. (Mrs. Eric Ramstad), Benjamin W. *Education:* Attended Vassar College, 1939-41; Radcliffe College, B.S. (cum laude), 1943. *Politics:* Democrat. *Religion:* Unitarian Universalist. *Home:* Old Concord Rd., Lincoln, Mass. 01773. *Office:* c/o Los Angeles Times Syndicate, Times Mirror Square, Los Angeles, Calif. 90053.

CAREER: Boston Globe, Boston, Mass., book reviewer, 1952-60, children's book editor, 1962-75; author of syndicated column, "Ask Beth," Los Angeles Times Syndicate,

Los Angeles, Calif. Trustee, Putney Schools, 1975—; member of corporation, Walker Home and School, 1975—. Professional advisor, Anorexia Nervosa Aid Society. *Member:* National Book Critics Circle, Women in Communication, National Organization of Women, Women's Rest Tour Association, Drifters Club, Mothers Study Club.

WRITINGS: Ask Beth; You Can't Ask Your Mother, Houghton, 1972; *The Sex Systems* (pamphlet), Los Angeles Times Syndicate, 1976; *Masculinity and Femininity,* Houghton, 1978. Also author of a television program.

WORK IN PROGRESS: A book for adolescents.

SIDELIGHTS: Elizabeth Winship told *CA:* "My work is in the area of today's adolescents and the serious problems facing them. I feel sex education is . . . vital . . . for their welfare." *Avocational interests:* Riding horses, driving, skiing, gardening, travel, and cooking.

* * *

WINSLOW, Dean Hendricks, Jr. 1934-1972
(Pete Winslow)

October 19, 1934—September 17, 1972; American poet, author, and journalist. (See index for *CA* sketch)

* * *

WINSTON, Douglas Garrett

PERSONAL: Born in New York, N.Y. *Education:* New York University, M.A. *Residence:* New York, N.Y.

CAREER: Free-lance writer. *Member:* Writers Guild of America.

WRITINGS: The Screenplay as Literature, Fairleigh Dickinson University Press, 1973.

WORK IN PROGRESS: Two screenplays.

* * *

WINTER, J(erry) Alan 1937-

PERSONAL: Born July 23, 1937, in New York, N.Y.; son of Herman (a dental technician) and Rose (Kavkewitz) Winter; married Gail Dorene Cameron (a reading teacher), June 13, 1964; children: Wendy Yvette, Miriam Rachel. *Education:* New York University, A.B. (cum laude), 1958; University of Michigan, M.A., 1960, Ph.D., 1964. *Religion:* Jewish. *Home:* 43 Beacon Hill Dr., Waterford, Conn. 06385. *Office:* Department of Sociology, Connecticut College, Box 1302, New London, Conn. 06320.

CAREER: University of Michigan, Ann Arbor, lecturer, summer, 1964, instructor in sociology, 1964-65; Rutgers University, New Brunswick, N.J., assistant professor of sociology, 1965-68; Temple University, Philadelphia, Pa., assistant professor of sociology, 1968-70; Connecticut College, New London, associate professor, 1970-77, professor of sociology, 1977—, chairperson of department, 1976—. Director, Ministry Studies Board, 1967-69. *Member:* American Sociological Association, American Association of University Professors, Society for Scientific Study of Religion, Religious Research Association, Alpha Kappa Delta, Phi Beta Kappa, Psi Chi. *Awards, honors:* Rutgers Research Council grant, 1967-68.

WRITINGS: (Editor with J. Rabow and M. Chesler) *Vital Problems for American Society,* Random House, 1968; (with Edgar W. Mills and Polly Hendricks) *Clergy in Action Training,* North American-International Documentation on the Contemporary Church (IDOC), 1971; (editor and author of introduction) *The Poor: A Culture of Poverty, or a Poverty of Culture?*, Eerdmans, 1971; *Continuities in the Sociology of Religion: Creed, Congregation and Community*, Harper, 1977. Contributor to sociological journals. Contributing editor to *Review of Religious Research*, 1973—; book review editor, *Sociological Analysis*, 1973-76.

* * *

WINTON, Harry N(athaniel) M(cQuillian) 1907-

PERSONAL: Born December 10, 1907, in San Francisco, Calif.; son of Ulysses Nathaniel and Alice B. (McQuillian) Winton. *Education:* Stanford University, A.B., 1932, A.M., 1934. *Politics:* Democrat. *Religion:* Presbyterian. *Home:* 221 East 35th St., No. 4E, New York, N.Y. 10016.

CAREER: Stanford University, Stanford, Calif., instructor in history, 1937-40; University of Washington, Seattle, editorial associate of *Pacific Northwest Quarterly*, 1940-42; United Nations, Documents Reference Section, Dag Hammarskjold Library, New York City, chief, 1946-67; UNIPUB, Inc., New York City, bibliographer and editor, 1971-72; R. R. Bowker Co., New York City, managing editor of *International Bibliography, Information, Documentation (IBID)*, 1973-74, consulting editor, 1975—. Consultant on League of Nations and United Nations documentation. *Military service:* U.S. Army, Signal Corps, 1942-46. *Member:* Association of International Libraries, American Society of Indexers. *Awards, honors:* Special fellow, United Nations Institute for Training and Research (UNITAR), 1975-78.

WRITINGS: (Editor) *Sea-bed 1968*, six volumes, Arno, 1970; (editor) *Sea-bed 1969*, eight volumes, Arno, 1971; (editor) *Man and the Environment: A Bibliography of Selected Publications of the United Nations System*, Bowker, 1972; *Publications of the United Nations System: A Reference Guide*, Bowker, 1972. Contributor to *Pacific Northwest Quarterly* and *College and Research Libraries*.

* * *

WIRT, Sherwood Eliot 1911-

PERSONAL: Born March 12, 1911, in Oakland, Calif.; son of Loyal L. and Harriet (Benton) Wirt; married Winola Wells, July 2, 1940; children: Alexander. *Education:* University of California, Berkeley, B.A., 1932; Pacific School of Religion, B.D. (cum laude), 1943; graduate study at Princeton Theological Seminary, 1943, Hartford Theological Seminary, 1944, and University of Zurich, 1950; University of Edinburgh, Ph.D., 1951. *Home:* 14140 Mazatlan Ct., Poway, Calif.

CAREER: Writer for *Martinez Gazette*, Martinez, Calif., *Hilo Tribune Herald*, Hilo, Hawaii, *San Francisco Examiner*, San Francisco, Calif., and *Juneau Daily Press*, Juneau, Alaska; ordained minister of Congregational Church, 1943; minister at church in Collinsville, Conn., 1943-44; received into Presbyterian Church, 1951; minister in Berkeley, Calif., 1951-55, and Oakland, Calif., 1955-59; University of Washington, Seattle, minister to students, 1946-49; Billy Graham Evangelistic Association, Washington, D.C., staff member of *Christianity Today*, 1960, Minneapolis, Minn., editor of *Decision*, 1960-76; Point Loma College, San Diego, Calif., part-time teacher of journalism, 1978-79. *Military service:* U.S. Merchant Marine, 1933-34. U.S. Army Air Forces, chaplain, 1943-45; served in Asiatic-Pacific theater.

WRITINGS: Crusade at the Golden Gate, Harper, 1959; *Open Your Bible*, Revell, 1962; *Magnificent Promise*, Moody, 1964; *Not Me, God*, Harper, 1966; *The Social Con-*

science of the Evangelical, Harper, 1968; *Passport to Life City*, Harper, 1969; (translator) *Love Song* (an adaptation of Augustine's *Confessions*), Harper, 1971; *Jesus Power*, Harper, 1972; *Afterglow*, Zondervan, 1975; *You Can Tell the World: New Directions for Christian Writers*, Augsburg, 1975; (with Ruth McKinney) *Getting into Print*, Nelson, 1977; *Freshness of the Spirit*, Harper, 1978.

* * *

WITHINGTON, William Adriance 1924-

PERSONAL: Born February 17, 1924, in Honolulu, Hawaii; son of Frederic Burnham (a minister) and Margaret (Adriance) Withington; married Anne Tonon, September 1, 1955; children: Robert Adriance, Sally. *Education:* Harvard University, A.B., 1946; Northwestern University, M.A., 1948, Ph.D., 1955. *Office:* Department of Geography, University of Kentucky, Lexington, Ky. 40506.

CAREER: George Washington University, Washington, D.C., instructor, 1948-51, assistant professor of geography, 1951-52; University of Kentucky, Lexington, instructor, 1955-56, assistant professor, 1956-63, associate professor of geography, 1963—. Visiting professor of geography at Nommensen University (Indonesia), 1957-59, California State College at Hayward (now University), summer, 1970; lecturer at University of London, Brussels Center for Southeast Asian Studies, and University of Heidelberg, summer, 1968. Senior planner, Boston City Planning Board, 1955; co-chairman of Lexington-Fayette County Committee on Religion and Human Rights, 1964-65; Lexington-Fayette County Urban League, initial board member, 1965-66; member of Southeast Asia Development Advisory Group, 1968-72; consultant on Southeast Asia to International Development Research Centre, Ottawa, Canada, winter, 1971-72. *Member:* Association of American Geographers, Association for Asian Studies, American Geographical Society, Kentucky Academy of Science, Sigma Xi.

WRITINGS: (With Margaret Fisher Hertel) *Southeast Asia*, Fideler, 1963, revised edition published as *Asia: Man in Southeast Asia*, 1978; (with Hertel) *Asia with Focus on Southeast Asia*, Fideler, 1964, revised edition, 1968; (contributor) Paul Griffin, editor, *Geography of Population*, Fearon, 1969; (contributor) Ashok Dutt, editor, *Southeast Asia: Land of Contrast*, Kendall/Hunt, 1974; *Atlas of Sumatra*, privately printed, 1978; *Gazetteer of Kentucky's Landscape Features*, privately printed, in press. Contributor to *American Peoples' Encyclopedia*, *Encyclopedia Americana*, *Geographical Abstracts*, *Focus*, *Revue de Sud-Est Asiatique et de l'Etreme-Orient*, *Journal of Geography*, *Annals of the Association of American Geographers*, *Tijdschrift voor Economische en Sociale Geographe*, *Pacific Viewpoint*, *Journal of Tropical Geography*, *Communications of the Research Institute*, *Sumatra Planters Association*, *Sumatra Research Bulletin*, *Geographic Review*, and *Kentucky Study Series*. Editor, *Bulletin of the Kentucky Geography Council*, Volumes 1-5, 1964-68; consulting editor, *Asian Forum*, 1968-72.

WORK IN PROGRESS: Geography of Sumatra; research on major cities of Indonesia.

* * *

WOELFEL, James W(arren) 1937-

PERSONAL: Born August 16, 1937, in Galveston, Tex.; son of Warren Charles (a biochemist and teacher) and Mary Frances (Washinka) Woelfel; married Judith Ethelyne Dutton, January 28, 1968; children: Skye Caitlin, Allegra Eve,

Sarah Judith. *Education:* University of Oklahoma, B.A. (with special distinction), 1959; Episcopal Theological School, Cambridge, Mass., M.Div. (with honors), 1962; Yale University, M.A., 1964; University of St. Andrews, Ph.D., 1967. *Home:* 2904 Santa Fe Lane, Lawrence, Kan. 66044. *Office:* 205 Smith Hall, University of Kansas, Lawrence, Kan. 66044.

CAREER: Ordained Episcopal priest, 1963; resigned ministerial functions, 1967. University of Kansas, Lawrence, assistant professor, 1966-71, associate professor, 1971-75, professor of philosophy and religious studies, 1975—. *Member:* Society for Values in Higher Education, American Academy of Religion, International Bonhoeffer Society for Archive and Research, American Association of University Professors, Phi Beta Kappa. *Awards, honors:* Danforth fellowship, 1959-66; Fulbright scholarship, 1962-63; University of Kansas research grants, 1968-72, 1978-79; American Philosophical Society grant, 1972; National Endowment for the Humanities summer stipend, 1973; Institute for Ecumenical and Cultural Research, summer, 1976.

WRITINGS: (Contributor) Martin Marty and Dean Peerman, editors, *New Theology Number 2,* Macmillan, 1965; (contributor to revised translation) Dietrich Bonhoeffer, *Letters and Papers from Prison,* Macmillan, 1967; *Bonhoeffer's Theology: Classical and Revolutionary,* Abingdon, 1970; *Borderland Christianity: Critical Reason and the Christian Vision of Love,* Abingdon, 1973; *Camus: A Theological Perspective,* Abingdon, 1975. Contributor of about thirty-five articles and reviews to *Religion in Life, Christian Century, Journal of Social Philosophy,* and other professional journals.

WORK IN PROGRESS: Augustinian Humanism: Studies in Human Bondage and Earthly Grace (tentative title); co-editing a book of readings, tentatively titled *Philosophical Perspectives on Death and Dying;* "research on providence versus fate, the problem of knowledge (relativism, myth versus reason), a pluralistic theory of religion, the problem of personal survival of death."

AVOCATIONAL INTERESTS: Music (singing and piano).

*　　　*　　　*

WOLF, William C(harles), Jr. 1933-

PERSONAL: Born May 29, 1933, in Allentown, Pa.; son of William C. (a postal employee) and Stella (Marks) Wolf; married; children: Laurian Beth, Alan Champion. *Education:* Kutztown State College, B.S., 1955; Ohio University, M.Ed., 1956; University of Iowa, Ph.D., 1959. *Politics:* Wilkie Republican. *Religion:* Unitarian. *Home:* 33 Pine Grove, Amherst, Mass. 01002. *Office:* School of Education, University of Massachusetts, Amherst, Mass. 01002.

CAREER: Elementary school teacher in Pennsylvania, Ohio, and Iowa, 1954-59; Ohio State University, Columbus, associate professor of education, 1959-63; U.S. Office of Education, Washington, D.C., research administrator, 1963-65; University of Massachusetts—Amherst, professor of education, 1965—. Visiting associate professor, Harvard University, 1963; visiting professor, Smith College, 1972, 1973. Administrative staff member and consultant to Kettering Foundation, 1967-69; consultant and member of advisory board, Far West Laboratory for Research and Development; consultant to federal, state, and local agencies. *Member:* American Educational Research Association (past member of executive board), National Education Association, National Society for the Study of Education, Phi Delta Kappa. *Awards, honors:* American Education Research Association editorial award.

WRITINGS: (With Bradley Loomer) *The Elementary School: A Perspective,* Rand McNally, 1966; (with Frank Laubach) *Building Your Language Power,* Silver Burdette, 1966. Editor of *Educational Researcher,* 1968-71.

WORK IN PROGRESS: Research reports on knowledge communication; satire on the process of education.

*　　　*　　　*

WOLFE, Harry Deane 1901-1975

PERSONAL: Born October 15, 1901, in Lawrence, Mass.; son of Samuel J. (a businessman) and Katherine (Gould) Wolfe; married, 1927; married second wife, Dorothy Nelson, February 1, 1958; children: (first marriage) Isabelle Jean (Mrs. Allan Francis Bacon). *Education:* Attended Massachusetts Institute of Technology, 1919-21; Dartmouth College, B.S., 1924; University of Wisconsin, M.A., 1936, Ph.D., 1938. *Politics:* Republican. *Religion:* Presbyterian. *Home:* 401 New Castle Way, Madison, Wis. 53704.

CAREER: Montgomery Ward & Co., Baltimore, Md., assistant manager, 1924-27; S. Kann Sons Co., Washington, D.C., merchandise manager, 1927-35; Kent State University, Kent, Ohio, associate professor of economics and marketing, 1938-42, director, Bureau of Business Research, 1938-42; War Production Board, Washington, D.C. and New York City, economist, 1942-43; Colgate-Palmolive Co., New York City, director of marketing research, 1943-57; Columbia University, New York City, professor of marketing, 1957-58; University of Wisconsin—Madison, professor of business and journalism, 1958-72, professor emeritus, 1972-75. Director, Bergstrom Paper Co.; and American Family Insurance Co.; member of board of directors, Dane County Cancer Society. *Member:* Market Research Council of New York.

WRITINGS: (With Clark Thompson and James Brown) *Measuring Advertising Results,* National Industrial Conference Board, 1962; (with Thompson and Brown) *Pre-Testing Advertising,* National Industrial Conference Board, 1963; (with Thompson and Brown) *Evaluating Media,* National Industrial Conference Board, 1966; *Business Forecasting Methods,* Holt, 1966; (with Dik Warren Twedt) *Essentials of the Promotional Mix,* Appleton, 1970. Contributor to *Journal of Business.*

WORK IN PROGRESS: The Promotional Process, with R. L. Pinkerton; *Guidelines to Market Segmentation.*†

(Died March 28, 1975)

*　　　*　　　*

WOLFMAN, Bernard 1924-

PERSONAL: Born July 8, 1924, in Philadelphia, Pa.; son of Nathan (a clerk) and Elizabeth (Coff) Wolfman; married Zelda Bernstein, December 25, 1948 (died October, 1973); married Toni Grotta Braemer, June 12, 1977; children: (first marriage) Johathan L., Brian S., Dina A. *Education:* University of Pennsylvania, A.B., 1946, J.D., 1948. *Home:* 229 Brattle St., Cambridge, Mass. 02138. *Office:* Law School, Harvard University, Cambridge, Mass. 02138.

CAREER: Admitted to Pennsylvania Bar, 1948, and Massachusetts Bar, 1976; Wolf, Block, Schorr & Solis-Cohen, Philadelphia, Pa., attorney, 1948-63; University of Pennsylvania, Philadelphia, instructor in political science, 1946-49, lecturer in law, 1959-62, professor of law, 1962-76, Kenneth W. Gemill Professor of Tax Law and Tax Policy, 1973-76, dean of law school, 1970-75, chairman of task force on university governance, 1968-70, chairman of faculty senate,

1969-70; Harvard University, Cambridge, Mass., Fessenden Professor of Law, 1976—. Visiting professor of law at Harvard University, 1964-65, and Stanford University, summer, 1966. Member of National Lawyers Advisory Council of the Earl Warren Legal Training Program; member of advisory group to Commissioner of Internal Revenue, 1966-67; member of steering committee, International Revenue Service Project Administrative Conference, 1974—; member of Philadelphia regional council, Pennsylvania Governor's Justice Commission, 1973-75; member of legal activities policy board, Tax Analysts and Advocates, 1974—; member of executive committee, Federal Tax Institute of New England, 1976—. Consultant on tax policy, U.S. Treasury Department, 1963-68, 1977—; consultant to American Council on Education, 1965-68, Stanford Research Institute, 1970-71, and others; member of editorial board, Law Division, Little, Brown & Co., 1970—. Member of board of directors, Federation of Jewish Agencies of Greater Philadelphia, 1968-74; trustee, Foundation Center (New York, N.Y.), 1970-76; member of advisory committee, Commission on Philanthropy and Public Needs, 1973-75. *Military service:* U.S. Army, 1943-45.

MEMBER: American Bar Association (chairman of committee on taxation and relation to human rights; member of council of section on individual rights and responsibilities), American Law Institute (consultant to federal income tax project, 1974—), American Civil Liberties Union (director of Philadelphia chapter, 1964-76; president of Philadelphia chapter, 1972-75; national director, 1973-75), American Association of University Professors (general counsel, 1966-68; member of council, 1979—), Tax Institute of America (member of advisory council, 1970—), Pennsylvania Bar Association, Philadelphia Bar Association, Philadelphia Defender Association (member of board of directors, 1955-69), Philadelphia Lawyers Committee for Civil Rights Under Law (member of board of directors, 1970-74), Phi Beta Kappa. *Awards, honors:* Order of the Coif, 1948; LL.D., Jewish Theological Seminary of America, 1971; Center for Advanced Study in the Behavioral Sciences fellow, 1975-76.

WRITINGS: Federal Income Taxation of Business Enterprise, Little, Brown, 1971, supplement (with Alan T. Cathcart), 1979; (author of foreword) *The Owen J. Roberts Memorial Lectures, 1957-74,* Scholarly Resources, Inc., 1975; (with Jonathan L. F. Silver and Marjorie A. Silver) *Dissent without Opinion: The Behavior of Justice William O. Douglas in Federal Tax Cases,* University of Pennsylvania Press, 1975. Contributor to proceedings and conferences. Contributor to *Federal Rules Decisions, Journal of Legal Education, Journal of Taxation, Taxes, University of Pennsylvania Law Review,* and other law journals. Member of editorial board, *Journal of Corporate Taxation,* 1973–.

* * *

WONDERS, William C(lare) 1924-

PERSONAL: Born April 22, 1924, in Toronto, Ontario, Canada; son of Clare (an electrical contractor) and Ann (Bell) Wonders; married Lillian Johnson (a cartographer), June 2, 1951; children: Karen E., Jennifer A., Glen W. *Education:* University of Toronto, B.A. (honors), 1946, Ph.D., 1951; Syracuse University, M.A., 1948. *Home:* 6212 128th St., Edmonton, Alberta, Canada. *Office:* Department of Geography, University of Alberta, Edmonton, Alberta, Canada T6G 2H4.

CAREER: University of Toronto, Toronto, Ontario, lecturer in geography, 1948-53; University of Alberta, Edmonton, assistant professor, 1953-55, associate professor, 1955-57, professor of geography, 1957—, head of department, 1957-67. Guest professor at Upsala University, 1962-63; visiting professor at University of Oklahoma, 1965-66. *Member:* Arctic Institute of North America (fellow), Canadian Association of Geographers (president, 1960-61), Royal Canadian Geographical Society, Association of American Geographers, American Geographical Society, Sigma Xi, Gamma Theta Upsilon. *Awards, honors:* Canada Council senior research fellow, 1962-63; National Science Foundation senior foreign scientist fellow at University of Oklahoma, 1965-66; Canada Council leave fellowship and research grant, 1969-71, 1977-78; research fellow at University of Aberdeen, 1970-71, 1978.

WRITINGS: (Contributor) F. H. Underhill, editor, *The Canadian Northwest: Its Potentialities,* University of Toronto Press, 1958; (contributor) L. E. Hamelin, editor, *Melanges geographiques Canadiens,* Presses Universite Laval, 1959; *Looking at Maps,* Longmans, Green, 1960; (contributor) John Warkentin, editor, *Canada,* Methuen, 1967; (coauthor) *Atlas of Alberta,* University of Toronto Press, 1969; (editor and author of introduction) *Canada's Changing North,* McClelland & Stewart, 1971; (editor and contributor) *Canada: The North,* University of Toronto Press, 1972. Contributor to *Canadian Geographer, Canadian Geographical Journal, Arctic,* and *North.*

WORK IN PROGRESS: Research on forestry and settlement in Highland Scotland, recent Scandinavian influences in Shetland and Orkney, Scandinavian settlement in Canada, geographic studies on the settlement in northern North America and Scandinavia, and settlement patterns in western Canada.

* * *

WOODSON, Leslie H(arold) 1929-

PERSONAL: Born January 18, 1929, in Louisville, Ky.; son of Leslie Thomas (a builder) and Sally (Johnston) Woodson; married Gloria May Stephenson, November 7, 1950 (died, 1966); married Betty Lou Eastridge, October 28, 1966; children: (first marriage) Charlotte, Anne, Andrew; (stepchildren) James, Terry, Jerry, David. *Education:* Attended Asbury College, 1946-47; University of Louisville, A.B., 1952; Southern Baptist Seminary, B.D., 1955, M.R.E., 1970; Scarritt College, M.A., 1973. *Residence:* Elizabethtown, Ky.

CAREER: Ordained United Methodist minister, 1952; pastor of churches in Scottsville, Campbellsville, Elizabethtown, and Louisville, Ky.

WRITINGS: The Swinging Church, Vantage, 1970; *Signs in the Sun,* Exposition Press, 1970; *Eight Days of Glory,* Beacon Hill, 1971; *What You Believe and Why,* Zondervan, 1972; *Evangelism for Today's Church,* Zondervan, 1973; *Hell and Salvation,* Revell, 1973; *Population, Pollution, and Prophecy,* Revell, 1973; *A View from the Cornerstone,* Moody, 1973; *The Church: United or Untied,* Zondervan, 1974; *The Beginning: Genesis,* Victor Books, 1974; *Many Signs: One Son,* Moody, 1975; *What the Bible Says about Hell,* Baker, 1976; *Home Study Bible Course on the Entire Bible,* Century House, 1978; *Divorce: Christian Style,* Word Books, 1979. Contributor to *Moody Monthly, Good News, Upper Room, Daily Blessing, Quiet Hour,* and other religious periodicals.

WORK IN PROGRESS: Involved with renewal groups desirous of restoring scriptural Christianity to a church which has grown humanistic and secular; speaking at conferences, camps, and evangelistic meetings; compiling church school curriculum resources; special emphasis on Bible conferences.

* * *

WOODWARD, Carl Raymond 1890-1974

PERSONAL: Born July 20, 1890, in Tennent, N.J.; son of William Henry (a farmer) and Edith (Reid) Woodward; married Lulu Ryno, April 5, 1916; children: Carl Raymond, Jr., Mildred W. (Mrs. James A. Stackhouse, Jr.), William V. N. Education: Rutgers College (now University), B.S., 1914, M.A., 1919; Cornell University, Ph.D., 1926. Politics: Independent Republican. Religion: Congregational. Home: 10 Linden Dr., Kingston, R.I. 02881.

CAREER: Worked on father's farm, 1906-08; teacher in one-room rural school, Monmouth County, N.J., 1908-10; high school science teacher in Madison, N.J., 1914-15; Rutgers University, New Brunswick, N.J., teacher, summer, 1914, editor and librarian in College of Agriculture and New Jersey Agricultural Experiment Station, 1915-16, editor and secretary in College of Agriculture and Agricultural Experiment Station, 1916-27, instructor in English, 1920-26, assistant professor, 1926-27, public relations work (with alumni), 1927-28, assistant to president, 1928-36, director of educational research, 1930-32, secretary of university, 1936-41; University of Rhode Island, Kingston, president, 1941-58, president emeritus, 1958-74. Member of New Jersey State Board of Education, 1936-41, and National Agricultural Bicentenary Committee, 1943-44; lecturer, Franklin Institute, 1940; National Commission on Accrediting, member, 1951-55, member of executive committee, 1954-55. Academic consultant to Barrington College, 1958-60, and Bryant College, 1961-62; consultant to Industrial Research and Development Division, U.S. Department of Commerce, 1947-48; director from Rhode Island, New England Council, 1957-58. President, United Fund of Rhode Island, 1958; Bryant College, trustee, 1962-70, honorary trustee, 1970-74.

MEMBER: Agricultural History Society (president, 1942-43), National Association of State Universities (president, 1955-56), National Association of Land-Grant Colleges and Universities (chairman of committee on federal legislation, 1954-57, and president's council, 1955-56; member of executive committee, 1956-57), Agricultural History Society (president, 1942-43), American Association of Agricultural College Editors (president, 1921-22), Newcomen Society of North America (honorary member), New Jersey Historical Society (trustee, 1940-41), New Jersey Press Association (chairman and secretary of newspaper institute), Rhode Island Historical Society, Patrons of Husbandry, Phi Beta Kappa, Phi Kappa Phi, Phi Delta Kappa, Masons, Providence Art Club, Tavern Hall Club, Barnard Club (president, 1945-46), Little Rest Bird Club.

AWARDS, HONORS: Litt.D., Rutgers University, 1941; D.Sc. from Bryant College, 1943, and Rhode Island College of Pharmacy and Allied Sciences, 1943; LL.D. from Boston University, 1947, University of Maine at Orono, 1948, Providence College, 1950, Brown University, 1955, Northeastern University, 1957, and University of Rhode Island, 1959; Ed.D., Rhode Island College of Education (now Rhode Island College), 1954. Awards from Freedoms Foundation, 1952, 1956, 1964, 4-H Service Committee, 1953, Rutgers Alumni Federation, 1956, and University of Rhode Island Alumni, 1958; certificate of commendation from American Association of State and Local History, 1972, for Plantation in Yankeeland.

WRITINGS: (With Frank App) The Farmer and His Farm, Harcourt, 1924; The Development of Agriculture in New Jersey, New Jersey Agricultural Experiment Station, 1927; (with I. N. Waller) New Jersey's Agricultural Experiment Station, 1880-1930, New Jersey Agricultural Experiment Station, 1932; Ploughs and Politicks: Charles Read of New Jersey and His Notes on Agriculture, Rutgers University Press, 1941, reprinted, Porcupine Press, 1974; From College to University: A Summary Report, 1941-1958, University of Rhode Island, 1960; Plantation in Yankeeland: The Story of Cocumscussoc, Mirror of Colonial Rhode Island, Pequot Press, 1971.

Contributor: Irving S. Kull, editor, New Jersey: A History, American Historical Society, 1930; Meet Dr. Franklin, Franklin Institute, 1943; Alfred Stefferud, editor, The Wonderful World of Books, Houghton, 1953; Aloud to Alma Mater, Rutgers University Press, 1966. Contributor to Dictionary of American Biography, 1928-44, and to other periodicals. Assistant editor, Soil Science, 1916-27.

WORK IN PROGRESS: An autobiographical book on his farm boyhood in New Jersey, tentatively entitled Horse and Buggy Boyhood.

BIOGRAPHICAL/CRITICAL SOURCES: Herman Eschenbacker, The University of Rhode Island: A History of Land-Grant Education in Rhode Island, Meredith, 1967.†

(Died October 2, 1974)

* * *

WOOLLEY, A(lban) E(dward, Jr.) 1926-

PERSONAL: Born September 26, 1926, in El Dorado, Ark.; son of Alban Edward (a printer) and Ira (Sawyer) Woolley; married Dorothy Caroline McInnis, June 6, 1952 (divorced February, 1964); married Dorothy Ellen Riley, November 24, 1964 (divorced April, 1977); children: (first marriage) Wendy, Mike, Jill; (second marriage) Amy, Ben, Daniel. Education: Attended Louisiana State University; Goddard College, B.A., 1969, M.A., 1971. Religion: Methodist. Home: 803 Edgemoor Rd., Cherry Hill, N.J. 08034. Office: Lab World, 401 North Broad St., Philadelphia, Pa. 19108.

CAREER: State University of New York College at New Paltz, New Paltz, associate professor of art and photography, 1958-61; free-lance magazine writer, 1961-67; New York Regional Educational Center, New Paltz, associate director, 1967-68; Pageant (magazine), New York, N.Y., photography editor, 1969-71; Today's Health (magazine), Chicago, Ill., managing editor, 1971-73; currently editorial director, Lab World (magazine), Philadelphia, Pa. Has had twenty one-man photographic exhibitions; other photographs are displayed in permanent collections at Museum of Modern Art, Dartmouth College, State University of New York, Louisiana Art Commission, and Louisiana State University. Democratic candidate for New York State Senate, 1968.

MEMBER: American Society of Magazine Photographers, National Press Photographers Association, Society of Education Photographers, Rotary Club. Awards, honors: Named photographer of the year by Louisiana Art Commission, 1953-54; Jessie H. Neal award for editorial excellence, 1978.

WRITINGS—All self-illustrated: Night Photography, Greenberg, 1955; Photographic Films and Their Uses, Chilton, 1959; Outdoor Four Seasons Photography, Chilton, 1960; Photographic Print Quality, Chilton, 1961; Creative

35mm Techniques, A. S. Barnes, 1962, revised edition, Hastings House, 1970; *Photographic Lighting*, A. S. Barnes, 1963, revised edition, Hastings House, 1970; *Traveling with Your Camera*, A. S. Barnes, 1964, revised edition, Hastings House, 1971; *Camera Journalism*, A. S. Barnes, 1965; *Persia/Iran*, Amphoto, 1965; *35mm Nudes*, Amphoto, 1966; (with John Dyson) *Our Historic Hudson*, James B. Adler, 1968; *Besler Topcon Unirex/Auto 100*, Amphoto, 1972; *Photography: A Practical and Creative Introduction*, McGraw, 1972.

Contributor of stories and articles to major magazines and newspapers, including *Look, Life, Saturday Evening Post, Time, Sports Illustrated, New York Times,* and *Parade.* Editor-at-large, *Contemporary Photographer;* editor, *Journal of International Physicians;* contributing editor, *Photographic Trade News.*

WORK IN PROGRESS: Box Lunch, a photographic essay with a box camera, completion expected in 1979; *Sally and Company,* a novel; *Images of Africa,* for Decker; *The Complete Book of Photography,* for Doubleday.

AVOCATIONAL INTERESTS: Travel, sports, antiques.

* * *

WORONIAK, Alexander   1920-

PERSONAL: Born February 27, 1920, in Lvov, Ukraine, Poland (now Soviet territory); naturalized U.S. citizen; son of Thomas and Eudoxia (Husar) Woroniak; married Zvenyslava Maria Patchovsky (a documentation specialist), April 27, 1943. *Education:* Yoanni Casimiri University, LL.M., 1939; Columbia University, M.S., 1953, further study, 1955-58. *Home:* 1435 Geranium St. N.W., Washington, D.C. 20012. *Office:* Department of Economics and Business Management, Catholic University of America, Washington, D.C. 20017.

CAREER: Yoanni Casimiri University (now Lvov Ivan Franko State University), Lvov, Ukraine, assistant professor of politics, 1939-42; United Nations Relief and Rehabilitation Administration and International Refugee Organization, legal counselor and welfare officer in Germany, 1945-50; accountant and senior accountant in New York, N.Y., with Advance Solvents & Chemical Corp., 1950-51, Gregory V. Collins & Co. (certified public accountants), 1953-54, and Radio Clinic, Inc., 1954-57; Catholic University of America, Washington, D.C., assistant professor, 1958-67, associate professor, 1967-71, professor of economics, 1971—, chairman of department of economics and business management, 1974—, director of accounting program, 1958—. Part-time lecturer in statistics, Howard University, 1962-67; research associate, economics of technological transfer project, U.S. Air Force, 1964-69. Consultant to Commission Nacional del Rio Bermejo and Bermejo International Ltd., Argentina, 1967-69, Institute for Defense Analyses, 1970-71, Stanford Research Institute, 1971—, Federal Energy Administration, 1974-75, and Infodyne, 1974-76.

MEMBER: Philosophy Education Society (member, board of trustees), American Economic Association, American Statistical Association, American Accounting Association, National Association of Accountants, Association for Comparative Economic Studies, American Library Association, American Association of University Professors, Pi Gamma Mu.

WRITINGS: Arbeitsvermittlung und Berufsberatung, Arbeitsverlag, 1942; (with Mykola Pashe-Ozerskii and Evhen Davydyak) *Kodeks Karnoho Spravuvannya* (title means "Code of Criminal Procedure"), Ukrainian Publishing House, 1943; *Berufsbeschreibung und Analyze der Arbeitsvorgaenge,* Berufsausbildung Gesellschaft, 1943; *Integration of Refugees and Displaced Persons into German Economy,* International Refugee Organization, 1949; (editor with Daniel L. Spencer and contributor) *The Transfer of Technology to Developing Countries,* Praeger, 1967; *Ruble/Dollar Conversion Ratio Survey,* Stanford Research Institute, 1972; (with H. T. Ellis and F. W. Dresch) *Feasibility of Obtaining a 1967 Ruble/Dollar Conversion Ratio,* Stanford Research Institute, 1973. Author, with Spencer, of technical reports on technology transfer for Air Force Office of Scientific Research.

Contributor: Edgar Salin and Jacques Stohler, editors, *Notwendigkeit und Gefahr der wirtschaftlichen Konzentration in nationaler und internationaler Sicht,* J.C.B. Mohr/Paul Siebeck, 1969; *Planning for Advanced Skills and Technologies,* United Nations, 1969; Stanislaw Wasowski, editor, *East-West Trade and the Technology Gap: A Political and Economic Appraisal,* Praeger, 1970; *A Comparison of U.S./USSR Gross National Product, National Security Expenditures, and Expenditures for RDT&E,* Stanford Research Institute, 1973; V. N. Bandera and Z. L. Melnyk, editors, *The Soviet Economy in Regional Perspective,* Praeger, 1973.

WORK IN PROGRESS: Economic Analysis of Post Revolutionary Cuba, with Alberto M. Piedra.

SIDELIGHTS: In addition to his native language, Ukrainian, Alexander Woroniak also speaks German, Russian, and Polish, and has a reading knowledge of all Slavic languages, French, Spanish, Latin, and classical Greek. He has traveled extensively in Europe, Latin America, Africa, and Asia.

* * *

WREN, Daniel Alan   1932-

PERSONAL: Born January 8, 1932, in Columbia, Mo.; son of Eulon Leon (a grocer) and Maude (Eubank) Wren; married Karen Tower (a professor), January 27, 1962; children: Jonathan Daniel, Laura Lynn, Lynda Kay. *Education:* University of Missouri—Columbia, B.S., 1954, M.S., 1960; University of Illinois at Urbana-Champaign, Ph.D., 1964. *Home:* 4017 Oxford Way, Norman, Okla. 73069. *Office:* School of Business, University of Oklahoma, Norman, Okla. 73019.

CAREER: Florida State University, Tallahassee, assistant professor, 1963-67, associate professor, 1967-70, professor of management, 1970-73; University of Oklahoma, Norman, professor of management and curator of A. W. Bass Business History Collection, 1973—. *Member:* Society for Advancement of Management, Academy of Management (chairman of public relations, 1971-73), Southern Management Association (vice-president, 1972; president, 1974-75).

WRITINGS: (With Dan Voich, Jr.) *Principles of Management,* Ronald, 1968, 2nd edition, 1976; *The Evolution of Management Thought,* Ronald, 1972, 2nd edition, 1979. Member of editorial board, *Business Perspectives,* 1971-74, *Academy of Management Journal,* 1973-75, and *Academy of Management Review,* 1975-78.

* * *

WRENCH, David F(razer)   1932-

PERSONAL: Born October 10, 1932, in Ann Arbor, Mich.;

son of Harry K. and Ruth (Frazer) Wrench; married Barbara Chris Craw, December 31, 1954; children; Jaime, Paul, Sarah. *Education:* Reed College, B.A., 1954; University of Oregon, M.A., 1958; University of North Carolina, Ph.D., 1961. *Politics:* Democrat. *Residence:* Portland, Ore. *Office:* Department of Psychology, Portland State University, P.O. Box 751, Portland, Ore. 97207.

CAREER: University of Oregon, Eugene, assistant professor of psychology, 1961-65; University of St. Andrews, Queens College, Dundee, Scotland, lecturer, 1965-66; Portland State University, Portland, Ore., assistant professor, 1966-68, associate professor, 1968-73, professor of psychology, 1973—.

WRITINGS: Psychology: A Social Approach, McGraw, 1969, 2nd edition (with wife, Chris Wrench), 1973; (editor) *Readings in Psychology: Foundations and Applications,* McGraw, 1971.

WORK IN PROGRESS: With C. Wrench, *Social Psychology,* for Heath.

* * *

WRIGHT, Harrison M(orris) 1928-

PERSONAL: Born October 6, 1928, in Philadelphia, Pa.; son of Sydney Longstreth (a scientist and administrator) and Catharine (an author and painter; maiden name, Morris) Wright; married Josephine S. Cole, July 20, 1957; children: Rebecca H., J. Rodman, Thomas F., Daniel H., James L. *Education:* Harvard University, B.A., 1950, M.A., 1953, Ph.D., 1957; also attended Brown University, 1950, and University of Otago, 1951. *Home:* 319 Cedar Lane, Swarthmore, Pa. 19081. *Office:* Department of History, Swarthmore College, Swarthmore, Pa. 19081.

CAREER: Swarthmore College, Swarthmore, Pa., instructor, 1957-60, assistant professor, 1960-64, associate professor, 1964-68, professor of history and chairman of department, 1968—. *Member:* American Historical Association, African Studies Society, Conference on British Studies, Newport (R.I.) Historical Society (director, 1973—), Phi Beta Kappa. *Awards, honors:* Fulbright scholarship in New Zealand, 1950-51; Ford Foundation foreign area fellowship to England and Ghana, 1961-62; American Philsophical Society grant to South Africa, 1966-67; Old Dominion fellowship for South Africa, 1971.

WRITINGS: New Zealand, 1769-1840: Early Years of Western Contact, Harvard University Press, 1959; (editor) *The "New Imperialism": Analysis of Late Nineteenth-Century Expansionism,* Heath, 1961, 2nd edition, 1976; (contributor) D. F. McCall, N. R. Bennett, and J. E. Butler, editors, *West African History,* Volume IV, Praeger, 1969; (editor) *James Rose Innes: Selected Correspondence,* Van Riebeeck Society, 1972; *The Burden of the Present: Liberal-Radical Controversy over Southern African History,* Verry, 1977. Contributor to scholarly periodicals.

WORK IN PROGRESS: Research on South African history and on modern imperialism.

* * *

WRIGHT, Lafayette Hart 1917-

PERSONAL: Born December 3, 1917, in Chickasha, Okla.; son of Lafayette Cantrell (a bank president) and Jessie (Hart) Wright; married Phyllis Jeanne Blanchard, July 4, 1938; children: Robin, Jana. *Education:* University of Oklahoma, A.B., 1938, J.D., 1941; University of Michigan, LL.M., 1942. *Politics:* Democrat. *Religion:* None. *Home:*

3079 Exmoor, Ann Arbor, Mich. 48104. *Office:* School of Law, University of Michigan, Ann Arbor, Mich. 48104.

CAREER: University of Michigan, Ann Arbor, assistant professor, 1946-49, associate professor, 1949-53, professor of law, 1953—. Member of advisory group to Commissioner of Internal Revenue, 1960-61. *Military service:* U.S. Army, 1941-46; became major. *Member:* International Fiscal Association, American Bar Association, Michigan State Bar Association. *Awards, honors:* Civilian meritorious service award from U.S. Treasury, 1957.

WRITINGS: Income Tax Law, Internal Revenue Service, 1957; *Corporate Tax Affairs,* Internal Revenue Service, 1960; *International Tax Affairs,* Internal Revenue Service, 1960; (with W. T. Plumb) *Federal Tax Liens,* American Law Institute, 1961, 2nd edition, 1970; (with others) *Comparative Procedures in Taxation,* University of Michigan, 1968; *Needed Changes in IRS Procedures,* American Bar Foundation, 1970.

WORK IN PROGRESS: Research on domestic and foreign tax systems.

* * *

WRIGHT, Monte Duane 1930-

PERSONAL: Born September 9, 1930, in Comanche, Tex.; son of Marvin Troy (a farmer) and Jo Idell (Pannell) Wright; married Joyce Irene Chancellor, March 26, 1952; children: Robin Edward, Julie Ellen, Darcy Ann, Bruce Alan. *Education:* Baylor University, B.A., 1951, M.A. 1953; Duke University, Ph.D., 1970. *Politics:* Republican. *Religion:* Presbyterian. *Home:* 200 St. Lawrence Dr., Silver Spring, Md. 20901. *Office:* History Office, National Aeronautics and Space Administration, Washington, D.C. 20546.

CAREER: U.S. Air Force, 1951-73, retiring as lieutenant colonel; held positions as radar observer (all-weather interceptor), ground control interception director, navigator, and mission analyst and plans officer (wing level), last assignment at U.S. Air Force Academy, Colorado Springs, Colo., as associate professor of history and deputy head of department, 1970-73; National Aeronautics and Space Administration, Washington, D.C., director of history office, 1973—. *Member:* Society for History of Technology. *Awards, honors:* Mellon Foundation award from American Council of Learned Socities, 1973, for *Most Probable Position: A History of Aerial Navigation to 1941.*

WRITINGS: (Editor with Lawrence J. Paszek) *Science, Technology, and Warfare: The Proceedings of the 3rd Military History Symposium,* U.S. Air Force, 1970; *Most Probable Position: A History of Aerial Navigation to 1941,* University Press of Kansas, 1973; (editor with Paszek) *Soldiers and Statesmen: The Proceedings of the 4th Military Symposium,* U.S. Air Force, 1973.

* * *

WRIGHT, William C(ook) 1939-

PERSONAL: Born July 11, 1939, in Jersey City, N.J.; son of Harry C. and Edna (Tompkins) Wright. *Education:* Gettysburg College, B.A., 1961; University of Delaware, M.A., 1965, Ph.D., 1971. *Religion:* Presbyterian. *Home:* 1516 White Pine Cir., Lawrenceville, N.J. 08648. *Office:* Bureau of Archives and History, New Jersey State Library, 185 West State St., Trenton, N.J., 08625.

CAREER: High school history teacher in Salem, N.J., 1961-65; University of Delaware, Newark, instructor in history in Extension Division, 1968-70; New Jersey Historical Commission, Trenton, associate director, 1970-76, head of Bureau of Archives and History, New Jersey State Library, 1976—. *Member:* Society of American Archivists, Organization of American Historians, New Jersey Library Association, New Jersey Historical Society. *Awards, honors:* Citation from New Jersey Civil War Centennial Commission, 1965.

WRITINGS: (Compiler) *Directory of Historical Societies of New Jersey,* League of Historical Societies of New Jersey, 1972; *The Secession Movement in the Middle Atlantic States,* Fairleigh Dickinson University Press, 1973; *The Development of the New Jersey Legislature from Colonial Times to the Present,* New Jersey Historical Commission, 1976; (co-editor) *Directory of New Jersey Newspapers, 1765-1970,* New Jersey Historical Commission, 1977. Editor of New Jersey History Symposium papers, 1972-76. Contributor to *Dictionary of American History, Journal of American History,* and *New Jersey History.*

*　　*　　*

WRIGLEY, Elizabeth S(pringer) 1915-

PERSONAL: Born October 4, 1915, in Pittsburgh, Pa.; daughter of Charles Woodward and Sarah Maria (Roberts) Springer; married O(liver) Kenneth Wrigley, June 16, 1936 (died July 26, 1978). *Education:* University of Pittsburgh, A.B., 1935; Carnegie Institute of Technology (now Carnegie-Mellon University), B.S., 1936. *Home:* 4805 North Pal Mal Ave., Temple City, Calif. 91780. *Office:* 655 North Dartmouth Ave., Claremont, Calif.

CAREER: U.S. Steel Corp., Pittsburgh, Pa., procedure analyst, 1941-43; Francis Bacon Foundation, Inc., Los Angeles, Calif., research assistant, 1944, executive, 1945-50, trustee, 1950—, director of research, 1951-53, president, 1954—, director of library, 1960—. *Member:* Renaissance Society of America, Modern Humanities Research Association, American Library Association, Special Libraries Association, American Cryptogram Association (honorary vice-president, 1972), California Library Association, Order of the Eastern Star, White Shrine, Alpha Delta Pi.

WRITINGS—Published by Francis Bacon Foundation, except as indicated: (Editor) Walter C. Arensberg, *The Skeleton Text of the Shakespeare Folio,* 1952; *Short Title Catalogue Numbers in the Library of the Francis Bacon Foundation,* 1958; *Wing Numbers in the Library of the Francis Bacon Foundation,* 1959; *Supplement to Francis Bacon Library Holdings in the Short Title Catalogue of English Books,* 1967; *The Lee-Bernard Collection in American Political Theory,* 1972; (with D. W. Davies) *A Concordance to the Essays of Francis Bacon,* Gale, 1973. Contributor of articles to journals in the fields of library science, history, and literature.

WORK IN PROGRESS: A concordance to Bacon's *Novum Organum.*

*　　*　　*

WYCKOFF, Peter (Gerritsen) 1914-

PERSONAL: Born October 12, 1914, in New York, N.Y.; son of Clarence Polhemus (a stockbroker) and Margaret (Macdona) Wyckoff; married Mary W. Warner, March 22, 1958; children: Allethy D. (Mrs. John D. Cobb), Adriana W. Burns. *Education:* Attended Yale University, 1934-36, and Columbia University, 1948-49. *Home and office:* Bridgewater, Vt. 05034. *Agent:* Adrian Paradis, Canaan, N.H. 03741.

CAREER: Gude, Winmill & Co., New York City, employed in order room, 1936-38; Delafield & Delafield, New York City, registered representative, 1938-48; Value Line Survey, New York City, securities analyst, 1950-51; *Forbes,* New York City, securities analyst, 1951-53; Hayden, Stone, Inc., New York City, technical analyst, 1953-67; free-lance writer, 1967—. Trustee of Woodstock Learning Clinic, 1971-79. *Military service:* U.S. Naval Reserve, 1943-45.

WRITINGS: Psychology of Stock Market Timing, Prentice-Hall, 1963; (compiler) *Dictionary of Stock Market Terms,* Prentice-Hall, 1964; (contributor) Frank G. Zarb and Gabriel T. Kerekes, editors, *The Stock Market Handbook,* Dow Jones-Irwin, 1970; *Wall Street and the Stock Markets,* Chilton, 1972; *Language of Wall Street,* Hopkinson & Blake, 1973; *The Stock Market: Drawn and Quartered,* Phoenix Financial, 1973. Also author of column for *Financial Weekly Common Stock Reporter,* 1974-77. Editor, *International Stock and Commodity Exchange Directory,* for Phoenix Financial, 1974. Contributor of articles to *Forbes, Saturday Review, Trader's Guide,* and *Financial Analyst's Journal.*

WORK IN PROGRESS: A book on the stock market.

*　　*　　*

WYLIE, Turrell V(erl) 1927-

PERSONAL: Born August 20, 1927, in Durango, Colo.; son of Vernon Glenn (a postman) and Myrtle (Davis) Wylie; married Shirley J. Ernst, August, 1949 (divorced, 1962); married Sharrie L. Stevenson, July 31, 1969. *Education:* University of Washington, Seattle, B.A., 1952, Ph.D., 1958. *Home:* 10666 Exeter N.E., Seattle, Wash. 98125. *Office:* Department of Asian Languages and Literature, Gowen Hall, DO-21, University of Washington, Seattle, Wash. 98195.

CAREER: University of Washington, Seattle, assistant professor, 1958-64, associate professor, 1964-68, professor of Tibetan studies, 1968—. *Military service:* U.S. Army, 1946-47; became sergeant. *Member:* American Oriental Society, Association for Asian Studies, Tibet Society. *Awards, honors:* Ford Foundation fellowship, 1955-57; American Council of Learned Societies fellowship, 1973-74.

WRITINGS: The Geography of Tibet According to the 'Dzam-gling-rgyas-bshad, Serie Orientale Roma, 1962; (editor) Tsepon Shakabpa, *Tibet: A Political History,* Yale University Press, 1967; *A Religious Geography of Nepal,* Serie Orientale Roma, 1971. Contributor to *Encyclopaedia Britannica.*

WORK IN PROGRESS: Research for a book, tentatively entitled *Tibetan Theocracy: Its Rise and Fall.*

*　　*　　*

WYNDHAM, Robert 1906(?)-1973

1906(?)—May 24, 1973; American author, lecturer, and editor. Obituaries: *Publishers Weekly,* June 11, 1973.

*　　*　　*

WYNKOOP, Sally 1944-

PERSONAL: Born April 27, 1944, in Utica, N.Y.; daughter of Ward Albert and Janice (Rathbun) Bohner; married Steven Neil Wynkoop (a journalist), June 17, 1967; children: Brooke Allison. *Education:* State University of New York College at Geneseo, B.A., 1966; University of Denver,

M.A., 1967. *Home:* 3706 North 17th St., Arlington, Va. 22207. *Office:* Grants Management Advisory Service, 2120 L St. N.W., Washington, D.C. 20010.

CAREER: University of Denver, Denver, Colo., reference librarian in charge of periodicals, 1967-69; King Resources Co., Denver, research librarian for publications and public relations department, 1969-70; Libraries Unlimited, Inc., Littleton, Colo., assistant editor of *American Reference Books Annual,* 1971-74; library and editorial consultant, 1976—. *Member:* American Library Association.

WRITINGS—All published by Libraries Unlimited: (With David W. Parish) *Directories of Government Agencies,* 1969; *Government Reference Books: 1968-1969,* 1970; *Subject Guide to Government Reference Books,* 1972; *Government Reference Books: 1970-1971,* 1972; *Government Reference Books: 1972-1973,* 1974.

WORK IN PROGRESS: Continuing research on bibliographical control of government documents, including a second edition of *Subject Guide to Government Reference Books.*

Y

YACOWAR, Maurice 1942-

PERSONAL: Born March 25, 1942, in Prelate, Saskatchewan, Canada. *Education:* University of Calgary, B.A., 1962; University of Alberta, M.A., 1965; University of Birmingham, Ph.D., 1968. *Office:* Department of Drama, Brock University, St. Catharines, Ontario, Canada.

CAREER: University of Lethbridge, Lethbridge, Alberta, lecturer in English, 1964-66; Brock University, St. Catharines, Ontario, assistant professor, 1968-72, associate professor, 1972-78, professor of drama and English, 1978—, chairman of department of drama, 1972-75.

WRITINGS: No Use Shutting the Door (poetry), Fiddlehead, 1971; *Hitchcock's British Films,* Archon, 1976; *Tennessee Williams and Film,* Ungar, 1977; *I Found It at the Movies,* Revisionist Press, 1977.

WORK IN PROGRESS: Research on aesthetics in popular film; a critical study of Woody Allen.

* * *

YANOUZAS, John N(icholas) 1928-

PERSONAL: Born June 2, 1928, in Donora, Pa.; son of Nicholas J. (a steelworker) and Violleta (Loukissa) Yanouzas; married Eleni Nicholas, December 26, 1954; children: Georgette, Niko, Melina. *Education:* Duquesne University, B.S., 1956; Pennsylvania State University, M.S., 1958, Ph.D., 1963. *Politics:* Republican. *Religion:* Greek Orthodox. *Home address:* North Bigelow Rd., Hampton, Conn. 06247. *Office:* Management and Administrative Sciences, University of Connecticut, U-41MAS, Storrs, Conn. 06268.

CAREER: Pennsylvania State University, University Park, 1958-70, began as instructor, became professor of industrial administration; University of Connecticut, Storrs, professor of industrial administration, 1970—, head of department, 1970—. *Military service:* U.S. Army, 1951-52; became sergeant. *Member:* Eastern Academy of Management (member of board of directors).

WRITINGS: (Co-author) *Formal Organization: A Systems Approach,* Irwin, 1967; (co-editor) *Organization Behavior and Management,* Irwin, 1972; *Dynamics of Organization Theory: Gaining a Macro-Perspective,* West Publishing, 1979. Contributor of articles to *Administrative Science Quarterly, Human Organization, Industrial Engineering, Personnel Administration, Studies.*

WORK IN PROGRESS: An empirical study defining the self-perceived role of managers and ideal management roles desired.†

* * *

YATES, Donald A(lfred) 1930-

PERSONAL: Born April 11, 1930, in Ayer, Mass.; son of Alfred Craig (an automobile dealer) and Bessie Mae (Cambridge) Yates; married Mary Ellen Dodd, June 24, 1951 (divorced, 1962); married Lynn Putney (a teacher), March 31, 1962 (divorced, 1975); married Joanne Mueller, March 21, 1977; children: (first marriage) Brian Donald, Juliet Marie; (second marriage) John Allan. *Education:* University of Michigan, B.A., 1951, M.A., 1954, Ph.D., 1961. *Home:* 1219 Daisy Lane, East Lansing, Mich. 48823. *Office:* 537 Wells Hall, Michigan State University, East Lansing, Mich. 48823.

CAREER: Michigan State University, East Lansing, instructor, 1957-60, assistant professor, 1960-64, associate professor, 1964-67, professor of Spanish American literature, 1967—. Fulbright lecturer, University of Buenos Aires and University of La Plata, 1967-68, 1970. *Military service:* U.S. Army, 1951-53.

MEMBER: International Institute of Latin American Literature (president, 1971-73), Associacion Internacional de Hispanistas, International Popular Culture Association, Modern Language Association of America, American Association of Teachers of Spanish and Portuguese (president, Michigan chapter, 1961-62), Latin American Studies Association, American Association of Teachers of Foreign Languages, Mystery Writers of America, Baker Street Irregulars, Midwest Modern Language Association, Michigan Academy of the Arts, Greek Interpreters of East Lansing, Phi Sigma Iota, Sigma Delta Pi. *Awards, honors:* Avery Hopwood creative writing award for drama, University of Michigan, 1954; Fulbright research fellow, Argentina, 1964-65.

WRITINGS: (With John B. Dalbor) *Imaginacion y fantasia: Cuentos de las Americas,* Holt, 1960, 3rd revised edition, 1975; (editor and contributor with David Alexander and John F. Suter) *Tales for a Rainy Night,* Holt, 1961; (editor with James Irby) Jorge Luis Borges, *Labyrinths: Selected Short Stories and Other Writings,* preface by Andre Maurois, New Directions, 1962, revised edition, 1964; (contributor) Angel Flores, editor, *Great Spanish Short Stories*, Dell, 1962; (contributor of translation) Anthony Boucher, editor, *The Best Detective Stories of the Year*, Dutton, 1963; (editor) Marco Denevi, *Rosaura a las diez*, Scribner, 1964; (editor) *Antologia del cuento policial hispanoamericano*, Ediciones de Andrea, 1964; (editor) Marco Denevi, *Ceremonia secreta y otros cuentos*, Macmillan, 1964; (contributor of translation) Willis Knapp Jones, editor, *Spanish American Literature in English Translation since 1888*, Ungar, 1964; (contributor of translation) Gordon Gordon and Mildred Gordon, editors, *A Pride of Felons*, Macmillan, 1964; (translator) Marco Denevi, *Rosa at Ten O' Clock* (novel), Holt, 1964; (editor) Roberto M. Cossa, *Nuestro fin de semana* (play), Macmillan, 1966; (editor with Julian Palley and Joseph Sommers) *Tres cuentistas hispanoamericanos*, Macmillan, 1969.

(Contributor) Ivar Ivask and Lowell Dunham, editors, *The Cardinal Points of Borges*, University of Oklahoma Press, 1971; (editor and translator) *Latin Blood: The Best Crime and Detective Stories of Spanish America*, Herder & Herder, 1972; (translator) Manuel Peyrou, *Thunder of the Roses*, introduction by Jorge Luis Borges, Herder & Herder, 1972; (translator with Gregory Woodruff) Adolfo Bioy-Casares, *Diary of the War of the Pig*, McGraw, 1972; (editor) *Cuentos de las metropoli: Quince narraciones portenas*, Appleton, 1973; (editor) *Otros mundos, otros fuegos: Fantasia y realismo magico en Hispanoamerica*, Latin American Studies Center, Michigan State University, 1975; (coeditor) *Homage to Irving A. Leonard: Essays in Hispanic Art, History, and Literature*, Editorial Mensaje, 1977. General editor, Macmillan's "Modern Spanish American Literature Series." Contributor to literature journals, detective magazines, and popular periodicals, including *Saturday Review* and *Armchair Detective*.

WORK IN PROGRESS: Magical Journey: A Critical Biography of Jorge Luis Borges.

* * *

YEATES, Maurice H. 1938-

PERSONAL: Born May 24, 1938, in England; son of Lewis Yeates; married Marilynn Snelbaker (a lecturer), 1962; children: Maurine, Harry. *Education:* University of Reading, B.A. (honors), 1960; Northwestern University, M.A., 1962, Ph.D., 1963. *Office:* School of Graduate Studies and Research, Queen's University, Kingston, Ontario, Canada.

CAREER: Queen's University, Kingston, Ontario, assistant professor, 1965-68, associate professor, 1968-70, professor of geography, 1970—, head of department, 1973-79, dean of School of Graduate Studies and Research, 1979—. Consultant to Canadian government ministries and departments. *Member:* Canadian Association of Geographers, American Association of Geographers, American Geographical Society, Regional Science Association. *Awards, honors:* American Association of Geographers, 20th International Geographical Congress participation award, 1964; Canada Council leave award, 1971-72, 1978-79; Canadian Association of Geographers travel award, 1976.

WRITINGS: (With E. J. Taaffe and B. J. Garner) *The Peripheral Journey to Work: A Geographic Consideration*, Northwestern University Press, 1963; (with R. S. Thoman and E. C. Conkling) *The Geography of Economic Activity*, McGraw, 1967; *An Introduction to Quantitative Analysis in Economic Geography*, McGraw, 1967; (with P. E. Lloyd) *The Impact of Industrial Incentives*, Queen's Printer, 1970; (with Garner) *The North American City*, Harper, 1971, 2nd

edition, 1975; *An Introduction to Quantitative Analysis in Human Geography*, McGraw, 1973; *Main Street*, Macmillan, 1975; (with Conkling) *Man's Economic Environment*, McGraw, 1976.

WORK IN PROGRESS: Third edition of *The North American City*, with Garner; *Patterns*.

SIDELIGHTS: An Introduction to Quantitative Analysis in Economic Geography has been published in Japanese.

* * *

YELLIN, Jean Fagan 1930-

PERSONAL: Born September 19, 1930, in Lansing, Mich.; daughter of Peter (co-editor of radical labor newspaper) and Sarah (co-editor of radical labor newspaper; maiden name, Robinson) Fagan; married Edward Yellin (a bio-medical engineer in cardio-vascular research), December 17, 1948; children: Peter, Lisa, Michael. *Education:* Attended Michigan State University and University of Michigan; Roosevelt University, B.A., 1951; University of Illinois, M.A., 1963, Ph.D., 1969. *Home:* 38 Lakeside Dr., New Rochelle, N.Y. 10801. *Office:* Department of English, Pace University, New York, N.Y. 10038.

CAREER: Pace University, New York, N.Y., assistant professor, 1968-74, associate professor of English, 1974—. *Member:* Modern Language Association of America, College Language Association, American Studies Association, Association for the Study of Afro-American Life and History, Melville Society, Society for the Study of Multi-Ethnic Literature, Northeast Modern Language Association. *Awards, honors:* American Association of University Women fellow; Pace University scholarly research awards; National Endowment for the Humanities younger humanist fellow and summer fellow; National Humanities Institute fellow; National Collection of Fine Arts-Smithsonian fellow.

WRITINGS: (Author of introduction) William W. Brown, *Clotel*, Arno, 1969; *The Intricate Knot: Black Figures in American Literature, 1776-1863*, New York University Press, 1972; (contributor) Gloria T. Hull and others, editors, *Black Women's Studies*, Feminist Press, 1979; *Afro-American Women Writers, 1800-1910*, G. K. Hall, in Press. Contributor of articles and reviews to *American Quarterly, CLA Journal, Massachusetts Review, Criticism,* and *Freedomways.*

WORK IN PROGRESS: Women and Sisters: The Presence of the Anti-Slavery Feminists in American Culture.

SIDELIGHTS: "What holds this all together," Jean Fagan Yellin comments, "is my ongoing interest in radical criticisms of American culture—especially in art and literature."

* * *

YGLESIAS, Jose 1919-

PERSONAL: Born November 29, 1919, in Tampa, Fla.; son of Jose and Georgia (Milian) Yglesias; married Helen Bassine (a novelist), August 19, 1950; children: Rafael; stepchildren: Lewis Cole, Tamar (Mrs. Richard Lear). *Education:* Attended public schools in Florida; attended Black Mountain College, 1946. *Politics:* "Should like to overthrow capitalism." *Religion:* "What?" *Residence:* North Brooklin, Maine 04661.

CAREER: Held jobs as dishwasher, stock clerk, television assembly line worker, and typist-correspondent, 1937-42; *Daily Worker*, New York, N.Y., movie critic, 1948-50; assistant to vice-president, Merck, Sharp & Dohme International (pharmaceutical concern), 1953-63; free-lance writer, 1963—. Regents Lecturer at University of California, Santa Barbara, winter, 1973. Occasional reader for publishing companies. *Military service:* U.S. Navy, 1942-45; received Naval Citation of Merit. *Member:* P.E.N. *Awards, honors:* Guggenheim fellowship, 1970, 1976; National Endowment for the Humanities award, 1974.

WRITINGS: A Wake in Ybor City (novel), Holt, 1963; *The Goodbye Land* (excerpts first published in *New Yorker*), Pantheon, 1967; *In the Fist of the Revolution: Life in a Cuban Country Town*, Pantheon, 1968; *An Orderly Life* (novel), Pantheon, 1968; *Down There*, World Publishing, 1970; *The Truth about Them* (novel), World Publishing, 1971; *Double Double* (novel), Viking, 1974; *The Kill Price* (novel), Bobbs-Merrill, 1976; *The Franco Years*, Bobbs-Merrill, 1977.

Translator: Juan Goytisolo, *Island of Women*, Knopf, 1962; Xavier Domingo, *Villa Milo*, Braziller, 1962; Juan Goytisolo, *The Party's Over*, Grove, 1966. Contributor of reviews, stories, and articles to *New Yorker, New York Times Magazine, Holiday, Esquire, Nation, New Republic, Venture, New York Review of Books, Massachusetts Review, New York Times Book Review, Book Week,* and other publications.

WORK IN PROGRESS: A nonfiction book about the Havana of 1958, *The Fall of Havana*, for Simon & Schuster.

SIDELIGHTS: A bilingual American of Cuban and Spanish descent, Jose Yglesias traveled to Spain in 1964 to trace the details of his father's birth and death there, and as a result, wrote *The Goodbye Land*. Written, according to Gerald Brenan, in "a deceptively simple style, [it] takes one right into the mysteries of Galician life, as an account by a complete foreigner could never do. . . . The picture it presents of the primitive peasant mind—its warmth and kindness, its reserve and suspicion, its strong family feeling, its obsession about land and money—is the best I have read anywhere."

Avoiding sociological analysis and political moralizing, Yglesias' accounts of life in Cuba and Latin America seek the essence of individual lives, emphasizing personal statements in order to reach the "underlying realities of the revolutionary experience." *In the Fist of the Revolution* was written from material collected in 1967 during a three-month stay in the town of Mayari in Cuba. Juan de Onis writes: "The Cuban Revolution is a strongly emotional experience, and Yglesias does not shield himself from it behind false objectivity. 'I took no tape recorder and no sociological discipline with me,' he says. . . . [He] has a writer's ear for dialogue. He speaks fluent, colloquial Spanish, to the point that many of the Cubans with whom he talked remarked, 'you are more like one of us'. . . . Out of their individual stories emerges a sort of collective memory of the pre-revolutionary past, which is full of contradictions, and a picture of the present which does not hide the tensions and psychological contortions of a turbulent period of transition." Yglesias' narrative study, *Down There*, is written similarly from the personal viewpoints of people in Brazil, Cuba, Chile, and Peru. The book is often cited as being valuable particularly for its disregard of the "official line" on Latin America, and for making available to North Americans a more balanced view of these societies.

Yglesias returned to Spain in 1975 and 1976 and was in Spain when Franco died. *The Franco Years* is, according to John Leonard, "a modest and extremely interesting series of interviews, filtered through a sympathetic intelligence, with Spaniards of various ages, professions and political persua-

sions who managed to survive Franco's dreary rule." Jane Kramer does not find the book entirely satisfactory. She comments: "Yglesias is a fine novelist, and I almost wish that he had tried a novel here, that he had taken a novelist's license with this research of so many years and shaped it into a more expressive narrative than these sketches offer. His discretion as a journalist seems to go against him. . . . He reaches for drama and then abandons it to some absolute standard of fairmindedness that, in the end, flattens what he tries to say instead of underlining it. He is obviously a man of decency and compassion—he has many gifts—but he cannot turn understatement onto its cutting edge, and this book, so deliberately, so decently understated, is often bland where it should be powerful." Leonard is happier with the book, writing: "Mr. Yglesias genuinely likes people, even when . . . they 'have no talent for heroism,' or, like the miners in Asturias, they arouse his 'old impatience with the dogmatism and arrogance and ideological complacency of Communists.' He follows them around—poets, farmers, folklorists, showmen, technocrats, macho waiters, pretty boys on the Madrid homosexual circuit, an old anti-Semite who never leaves home—and he listens. Whether they are going to jail, as most of them have, or starting new political parties, as many of them do, they are allowed their dignity. . . . And always, in a way that I suppose is unintentional and whose manner is impossible to convey, Mr. Yglesias himself comes across as a nice guy. We like him, as much for what he restrains himself from saying—his personal views on property, on rhetoric, on heroism—as for his enthusiasm for the people he meets. He is a kind skeptic."

Yglesias' interest in chronicling the lives of Hispanic people extends to his novels. *An Orderly Life* and *The Truth about Them* deal with the adjustment of working-class Cuban emigre families to American life and seem to reflect Yglesias' intent as a writer. "[I] should like in my work," he told *CA*, "to bring into clear view the moral views and approach to experience of workers, something which seems to me missing from most fiction; [I] should like as well, to do this in the lucid, unpretentious manner of E. M. Forster."

Yglesias continues his study of individual behavior and reaction in *The Kill Price*, which a *Publishers Weekly* reviewer calls "a splendidly written, sometimes deeply probing story of individuals whose concerns reflect a world both immediate and just sufficiently removed to turn its specifics into something approaching universals." However, Dan Wakefield finds the novel's characters to be not believable as people. "An artist may have his characters think or do anything they wish," he writes, "and their behavior does not have to be moral or even likeable, but it does have to be credible. I simply can't believe that this same bunch of college-graduate, liberal Manhattan sophisticates who are so socially and politically with it . . . also sit around in the summer of '73 talking about sex and the sexes like a bunch of refugees from a Sigma Chi beer blast at Ohio State in the first flush of the Eisenhower years." Anatole Broyard feels an aversion for Wolf, the dying protagonist of *The Kill Price*. She comments: "I was glad to see him die. I was tired of his not very witty pontifications, his unimaginative male chauvinism, his egomania, his sexual braggadocio, and his unkindness." But, recognizing Yglesias' craft, she adds: "Mr. Yglesias is an old hand at fiction and he writes well—almost too well for me to believe that the negative impact Wolf had on me was an accident. Perhaps the author wanted to correct the sentimental notion that dying enobles a man, that powerlessness purifies."

AVOCATIONAL INTERESTS: Vegetable gardening.

BIOGRAPHICAL/CRITICAL SOURCES: New Leader, June 3, 1968; *Saturday Review,* June 8, 1968, November 12, 1977; *New York Times Book Review,* July 14, 1968, July 25, 1976, October 30, 1977; *New Republic,* July 20, 1968; *New York Review of Books,* March 9, 1972; *Publishers Weekly,* March 29, 1976, August 22, 1977; *New York Times,* May 28, 1976, October 18, 1977.

*   *   *

YOHN, David Waite 1933-

PERSONAL: Born July 9, 1933, in Sterling, Ill.; son of Wayne Reed and Harriette May (Waite) Yohn; married Nancy Walker, June 13, 1955 (divorced, 1970); married Anna Kolesar (a realtor), October 11, 1971; children: (first marriage) Wayne Reed II, Nancy Kathryn. *Education:* Northwestern University, B.A., 1955; Yale University, M. Div., 1959. *Home and office address:* Box 15, West Barnstable, Mass. 02668.

CAREER: Ordained minister of the United Church of Christ, 1959; pastor in El Paso, Ill., 1959-63, and Hanover, N.H., 1963-70; Massachusetts Institute of Technology, Cambridge, dean for student counseling, 1970-72; West Parish Congregational Church, West Barnstable, Mass., pastor, 1972—.

WRITINGS: The Contemporary Preacher and His Task, Eerdmans, 1969; *The Christian Reader's Guide to the Old Testament,* Eerdmans, 1971; *The Christian Reader's Guide to the New Testament,* Eerdmans, 1973.

WORK IN PROGRESS: Several books on Christian theology; translations of the gospel of Mark and Psalms.††

*   *   *

YOO, Young H(yun) 1927-
(Grace S. Yoo)

PERSONAL: Born July 15, 1927, in Hongsong, Korea; son of Bock Don and Sang S. (Suh) Yoo; married Sun G. Im, October 23, 1958; children: Mi Young (daughter), Tae Young (daughter), Alice, Danny. *Education:* Korea University, LL.B., 1957; George Peabody College for Teachers, M.A.L.S., 1958; Seoul National University, LL.M., 1960; George Washington University, M.C.L., 1977. *Home:* 10204 Bessmer Lane, Fairfax, Va. 22032. *Office:* Processing Department, U.S. Library of Congress, Washington, D.C. 20540.

CAREER: Dongguk University, Seoul, South Korea, chief of Western books section, 1948-59; Yonsei University, Seoul, lecturer in library science, 1958-60; Seoul National University, Seoul, lecturer in library science, 1961-62; Korea University, Seoul, lecturer in civil and criminal law, 1961-62; lecturer in civil and criminal law, National Communications College, 1962-63; U.S. Library of Congress, Washington, D.C., reference librarian in Orientalia Division, 1963-68, subject analyst of Far Eastern studies in processing department, 1968—. Appointed by American Embassy (Korea) to selection committee of library trainees, U.S. Department of State, 1959-61; law librarian, Seoul National University, 1959-63; councillor, Korean Library Association. Consultant, Computerized Bibliographical System, Human Relations Area Files, Yale University, 1967-72.

MEMBER: American Library Association, U.S. Library of Congress Professional Staff Association, Korean Legal Center, Criminal Law Society of Korea, George Wash-

ington Law Association. *Awards, honors:* Grant from International Cooperation Administration, 1957-58.

WRITINGS: (Translator with others) *Toso Sipchin Pullyup'yo* (title means "Dewey Decimal Classification"), Peabody College Advisory Group, Ministry of Education, Republic of Korea and Yonsei University, 1960; (translator) *Tosogwanhak Kgeron* (title means "An Introduction to Library Science"), Yonsei University, 1961; (editor with others) *Glossary of Library Science,* Korean Library Association, 1962; *English-Korean Dictionary Romanized,* Kei-Rim Corp., 1962; *A Glance over the Welfare State—The United States of America,* Pangmun Co., 1962; *On the Bibliographical Control,* Korean Library Association, 1962; *On the Retrieval of Legal Sources,* Pagyongsa, 1963; *Source Materials on Korean Economy,* Korean Research Publication, 1966.

(Under pseudonym Grace S. Yoo) *Two Korean Brothers* (juvenile), Far Eastern Research & Publications Center, 1970; *Wisdom of the Far East: A Dictionary of Proverbs, Maxims, and Famous Classical Phrases of the Chinese, Japanese, and Koreans,* Far Eastern Research & Publications Center, 1972; *Towards World Peace through Legal Controls in the Air and Outer Space,* Far Eastern Research & Publications Center, 1973. Contributor to popular and professional journals. Editor, *Bulletin* of Korean Library Association.

WORK IN PROGRESS: An introduction to the study of proverbs, maxims, and famous classical phrases of the Chinese, Japanese, and Koreans; *Wisdom of the Far East: A Dictionary of Proverbs, Maxims, and Famous Classical Phrases of the Chinese, Japanese, and Koreans,* Volume II; a romanized Chinese-Japanese-Korean-English dictionary; *Constitutional Law of Japan;* a bibliographical survey of air law studies and space exploration of East Asian countries.

*   *   *

YOSHIDA, (Katsumi) Jim 1921-

PERSONAL: Born July 28, 1921, in Seattle, Wash.; son of Ryunosuke (a hotel owner and barber) and Suye (Uyesugi) Yoshida; married Ethel Isobe, February 12, 1949 (divorced June, 1954); married Helen Joy Park; children: (first marriage) Kenneth; (second marriage) Aileen Joy. *Education:* Attended high school in Seattle, Wash. *Politics:* Democrat. *Religion:* Buddhist. *Home and office:* 670 Prospect St., P.H. #1, Honolulu, Hawaii 96813. *Agent:* Paul R. Reynolds, Inc., 12 East 41st St., New York, N.Y. 10017.

CAREER: Worked for British Commonwealth Occupational forces in Japan, 1946-48, for U.S. Army, 24th Division, 1948-50, 1951-53; venetian blind estimator and salesman, 1955-57; president, General Home Products, Inc., a franchised dealer of "Winfield China," 1957-60; general manager, Oahu Plumbing Co., Flexalum Division, 1960-63; president, Dynasty Development Co., real estate developers and contractors, 1963—. Chief instructor, Seido Kan Judo Club, in conjunction with Big Brothers of America. *Military service:* Stranded in Japan at the outbreak of the Second World War, he was conscripted into the Japanese Imperial Army in 1941. Fought in Korea as an unpaid volunteer along with U.S. Army, 24th Division, Military Police, 1950-51. *Member:* Oahu Sumo Association (treasurer and director, 1973-74), Aloha Businessman's Club (YMCA), College Club of Seattle.

WRITINGS: (With William Hosokawa) *The Two Worlds of Jim Yoshida,* Morrow, 1972.

WORK IN PROGRESS: Writing film script for "The Two Worlds of Jim Yoshida."

SIDELIGHTS: As a result of Jim Yoshida's wartime connection with Japan, he lost his United States' citizenship. He later sued for reinstatement and regained citizenship in 1954. Yoshida holds a fourth degree black belt from Kokokan Judo College in Tokyo.

*   *   *

YOUNG, David C(harles)   1937-

PERSONAL: Born December 9, 1937, in Lincoln, Neb.; son of Julius D. (a teacher) and Myrtle (Fallbeck) Young; married Janice Berger, June 18, 1958; children: Patrick, Benedict, Tracy. *Education:* University of Nebraska, B.A., 1959; University of Iowa, M.A., 1960, Ph.D., 1963; University of Minnesota, graduate study, 1960-61. *Home:* 6293 Muirfield Dr., Goleta, Calif. 93817. *Office:* Department of Classics, University of California, Santa Barbara, Calif. 93106.

CAREER: University of California, Santa Barbara, assistant professor, 1963-68, associate professor, 1968-72, professor of classics, 1972—, chairman of department, 1968-72. *Member:* American Philological Association. *Awards, honors:* National Endowment for the Humanities summer fellowship, 1967.

WRITINGS: Three Odes of Pindar, E. J. Brill, 1968; (contributor) William Calder III, editor, *Pindaros und Bakchylides,* Wissenschaftliche Buchgesellschaft, 1970; *Pindar Isthmian 7, Myth and Exempla,* E. J. Brill, 1971.

WORK IN PROGRESS: Research on ancient athletics, Greek lyric poetry, and mythology.

*   *   *

YOUNG, Murat Bernard (Chic)   1901-1973
(Chic Young)

January 9, 1901—March 14, 1973; American syndicated cartoonist, creator of "Blondie." Obituaries: *New York Times,* March 16, 1973; *Washington Post,* March 16, 1973; *Newsweek,* March 26, 1973.

*   *   *

YUNGBLUT, John R(ichard)   1913-

PERSONAL: Born April 29, 1913, in Dayton, Ky.; son of Charles Walter Yungblut; married June J. Johnson, October 28, 1960; children: (earlier marriage; adopted) Marth, John. *Education:* Harvard University, B.A., 1934; Episcopal Theological Seminary, Cambridge, Mass., M.Div., 1939. *Religion:* Quaker. *Residence:* Lincoln, Va.

CAREER: International Student House, Washington, D.C., director, 1968-72; Pendle Hill, Wallingford, Pa., teacher of the contemplative life, 1973—. *Member:* Washington Interchurch Club, Harvard Club.

WRITINGS: Rediscovering Prayers, Seabury, 1972; *Rediscovering the Christ,* Seabury, 1974. Contributor to *Friend.*

WORK IN PROGRESS: Discovering God Within.

AVOCATIONAL INTERESTS: Tennis, bird-study, music.

Z

ZABEEH, Farhang 1919-

PERSONAL: Born March 19, 1919, in Tehran, Persia (now Iran); naturalized U.S. citizen in 1951. Education: University of California, Berkeley, A.B., 1950, M.A., 1952, Ph.D., 1958. Home: 421 Keeney, Evanston, Ill. 60202. Office: Department of Philosophy, Roosevelt University, Chicago, Ill. 60605.

CAREER: University of California, Berkeley, technician at Radiation Laboratory, 1957-58, instructor in philosophy in Extension Division, 1958; University of North Dakota, Grand Forks, assistant professor, 1960-61, associate professor of philosophy, 1961, acting head of department and foreign student adviser, 1960-61; University of Florida, Gainesville, assistant professor, 1961-62, associate professor of philosophy, 1963-65; Roosevelt University, Chicago, Ill., professor of philosophy, 1965—. Awards, honors: Research grants from American Council of Learned Societies, 1959, and Roosevelt University, 1968.

WRITINGS: Hume: Precursor of Modern Empiricism, Nijhoff, 1960; Universals: A New Look at an old Problem, Nijhoff, 1966; What Is in a Name?: An Inquiry into the Semantics and Pragmatics of Proper Names, Nijhoff, 1968; (editor and translator) Avicenna's Treatise on Logic, Nijhoff, 1971; (contributor) E. D. Klemke, editor, Essay on Wittgenstein, University of Illinois Press, 1971; (editor and contributor) Readings in Semantics, University of Illinois Press, 1976.

Also author of Understanding Hume: A New Synthesis; contributor to Hume: A Re-evaluation, edited by Livingstone and King; contributor to proceedings. Contributor of articles and reviews to Philosophy and Phenomenological Research, Ratio, Journal of Philosophy, International Philosophical Quarterly, and to Swedish, Indian, and British professional journals.

* * *

ZAHAROPOULOS, George K. 1933-

PERSONAL: Born March 18, 1933, in Kandalos, Greece; son of Konstantin and Georgia (Bissias) Zaharopoulos; married Katherine Kallergi, July 18, 1965; children: Tina, Mia. Education: San Bernardino Valley College, A.A., 1960; University of California, Riverside, B.A., 1962, M.A., 1964. Home: 718 East Ralston St., San Bernardino, Calif. 92404. Office: San Bernardino Valley College, San Bernardino, Calif. 92403.

CAREER: San Bernardino Valley College, San Bernardino, Calif., instructor, 1964-67, assistant professor, 1967-78, professor of politics, 1978—. Military service: U.S. Army, 1954-56. Member: American Political Science Association, American Association of University Professors. Awards, honors: National Science Foundation fellowship, 1968.

WRITINGS: (Editor with William J. Moore and Aram Sogomonian) American Government and Politics: A Reader, Van Nostrand, 1967, 2nd edition, 1972; (with Jon A. Yinger) United States Government and Politics, Chandler Publishing, 1969, 2nd edition, 1974; (contributor) Richard Clogg and George Yannopoulos, editors, Greece under Military Rule, Basic Books, 1972; (contributor) John T.A. Koumoulides, editor, Greece in Transition, Zeno, 1977.

WORK IN PROGRESS: Research on politics in modern Greece.

* * *

ZAHORCHAK, Michael G(eorge) 1929-

PERSONAL: Born November 13, 1929, in Erie, Pa.; son of Paul and Anna (Macik) Zahorchak; married Lois Catherine Becker, November 27, 1954. Education: University of Pittsburgh, B.S., 1950; City University of New York, M.A., 1963. Politics: Independent. Home: 1230 South Wood Ave., Linden, N.J. 07036. Office: Foundation for the Study of Cycles, 124 South Highland Ave., Pittsburgh, Pa. 15206.

CAREER: General Electric Co., New York City and Cleveland, Ohio, auditor and accountant in Lamp Division, 1953-60; Schenley Industries, New York City, auditor and financial analyst, 1960-61; Merrill Lynch, Pierce, Fenner & Smith, New York City, investment analyst, 1961-63; Macmillan Co., New York City, assistant to controller, 1963-64; American Stock Exchange, New York City, director of listed company liaison, 1964-78; Foundation for the Study of Cycles, Pittsburgh, Pa., executive director, 1978—, publisher of Cycles magazine. Military service: U.S. Army, 1951-53; became sergeant. Member: Society for the Investigation of Recurring Events (secretary, 1968-72, president, 1973-78), Newcomen Society of America, New York Society of Securities Analysts.

WRITINGS: The Art of Low Risk Investing, Van Nostrand, 1972; The Cursed Men of Wall Street, Van Nostrand, 1974, revised edition, 1978.

ZAKARIAN, Richard H(achadoor)   1925-

PERSONAL: Born July 25, 1925, in Lawrence, Mass.; son of Harry and Alice (Lebel) Zakarian; married Roberta Cain, September 3, 1966; children: Stephanie Christina, Jennifer Lynne. *Education:* Bates College, A.B., 1949; Middlebury College, M.A., 1950; Northwestern University, Ph.D., 1960. *Politics:* Democrat. *Religion:* Protestant. *Home:* 8826 Hanna Ave., Canoga Park, Calif. 91304. *Office:* Department of Foreign Languages, California State University, Northridge, Calif. 91324.

CAREER: New York University, New York, N.Y., instructor in French, 1954; University of South Dakota, Vermillion, instructor, 1954-56, assistant professor of French and Spanish, 1957-58; Bates College, Lewiston, Me., assistant professor of French and Spanish, 1958-59; California State University, Northridge, assistant professor, 1961-65, associate professor, 1965-72, professor of foreign languages, 1972—, resident director of California State International Programs, Aix-en-Provence, France, 1968-70. Visiting professor, St. Lawrence University, 1966-67. Participant in National Endowment for the Humanities summer seminars, 1975 and 1978. *Military service:* U.S. Navy, 1943-46. *Member:* Modern Language Association of America, Phi Beta Kappa. *Awards, honors:* Fulbright scholar in Paris, 1956-57; Smith-Mundt fellow in Cambodia, 1960-61.

WRITINGS: Zola's ''Germinal'': A Critical Study of Its Primary Sources, Librairie Droz, 1972. Contributor of articles to *American Notes and Queries, Explicator, Dada-Surrealism,* and *Les Annales de l'Universite d'Aix-Marseille.*

WORK IN PROGRESS: Further Ambiguity and Social Criticism in Abbe Prevost's ''Histoire du Chevalier des Grieux et Manon Lescaut''; Maupassant, a Thematic Obsession; critical studies of Zola's *Les Trois Villages* and Apollinaire's *Metapoetic Bridge.*

*   *   *

ZEBROWSKI, George   1945-

PERSONAL: Surname is pronounced Ze-broff-ski; born December 28, 1945, in Villach, Austria; brought to United States in 1951; son of Anthony and Anna (Popovicz) Zebrowski. *Education:* Attended State University of New York at Binghamton, 1964-69. *Home address:* Box 586, Johnson City, N.Y. 13790. *Agent:* Joseph Elder Agency, 150 West 87th St., New York, N.Y. 10024.

CAREER: Worked as a newspaper copy-editor, publisher's reader, pool operator, and interviewer; State University of New York at Binghamton, lecturer in science fiction, 1971; lecturer for Science Fiction Writers Speakers Bureau, 1971—. *Member:* World Future Society, Science Fiction Writers of America, Science Fiction Writers Speakers Bureau, Authors Guild. *Awards, honors:* Finalist for Nebula Award of Science Fiction Writers of America, 1971, for short story, ''Heathen God.''

WRITINGS: The Omega Point, Ace Books, 1972, revised edition, 1979; (author of introduction) *Horror Tales,* edited by Roger Elwood, Rand McNally, 1974; (author of introduction) H. G. Wells, *Things to Come,* Gregg, 1975; *The Star Web,* Laser Books, 1975; (editor) *Tomorrow Today* (anthology), Unity Press (Santa Cruz), 1975; (editor with Thomas N. Scortia) *Human Machines: An Anthology of Stories about Cyborgs,* Random House, 1975; (editor with Jack Dann) *Faster than Light: An Anthology of Stories about Interstellar Travel,* Harper, 1976; *The Monadic Universe and Other Stories,* introduction by Scortia, Ace Books, 1977; *Ashes and Stars,* Ace Books, 1977; *Macrolife,* Harper, 1979; *Mirror of Minds,* Ace Books, in press; *Free Space* (juvenile), Harper, in press.

Contributor: Roger Elwood, editor, *Strange Gods,* Pocket Books, 1974; Reginald Bretnor, editor, *Science Fiction: Today and Tomorrow,* Harper, 1974; (with Patricia Warrick) Warrick and others, editors, *Science Fiction: Contemporary Mythology,* Harper, 1978. Contributor of more than thirty stories and articles to anthologies, including *Infinity One, Immortal,* edited by Robert Hoskins, Lancer, 1970, *Strange Bedfellows,* edited by Thomas N. Scortia, Random House, 1972, *Saving Worlds,* edited by Elwood and Virginia Kidd, Doubleday, 1973, *Nebula Awards Seven,* edited by Lloyd Biggle, Jr., Harper, 1973, *The Killer Plants and Other Stories,* edited by Elwood, Lerner, 1974, and *Adrift in Space and Other Stories,* edited by Elwood, Lerner, 1974. Contributor of short stories, reviews, and translations to periodicals, including *Amazing, Worlds of IF, Riverside Quarterly, Science Fiction Review, Vector,* and *International Science Fiction, Number 2.* Editor, *Bulletin of the Science Fiction Writers of America,* 1970-75.

WORK IN PROGRESS: A trilogy, for Doubleday; *The Omega Point Trilogy,* for Ace Books.

SIDELIGHTS: Many of George Zebrowski's works have been translated into French, Dutch, Portuguese, and German. His manuscripts, papers, and first editions are being collected by Temple University. *Avocational interests:* Futuristics, chess, classical music, films, tennis, swimming.

*   *   *

ZEDLER, Beatrice H(ope)   1916-

PERSONAL: Born May 14, 1916, in Milwaukee, Wis.; daughter of Edwin (an accountant) and Cecelia M. (Koch) Zedler. *Education:* Marquette University, B.A. (summa cum laude), 1937, M.A., 1938; Fordham University, Ph.D., 1947. *Religion:* Roman Catholic. *Home:* 5305 West Wisconsin Ave., Milwaukee, Wis. 53208. *Office:* Department of Philosophy, Marquette University, Milwaukee, Wis. 53233.

CAREER: Marian College, Fond du Lac, Wis., instructor in English and philosophy, 1939-40; College Misericordia, Dallas, Pa., instructor in English and philosophy, 1941-43; Marquette University, Milwaukee, Wis., instructor, 1946-51, assistant professor, 1951-54, associate professor, 1954-63, professor of philosophy, 1963—, named to Women's Chair of Humanistic Studies, 1967-71. *Member:* American Philosophical Association, American Catholic Philosophical Association, Mediaeval Academy of America, American Association of University Professors.

WRITINGS: (Editor) *Averroes' Destructio Destructionum Philosophiae Algazelis,* Marquette University Press, 1961; (translator and author of annotations) Thomas Aquinas, *On the Unity of the Intellect against the Averroists,* Marquette University Press, 1968; (editor) Gerard Smith, *Christian Philosophy and Its Future,* Marquette University Press, 1971; (editor) Smith, *A Trio of Talks,* Marquette University Press, 1971. Contributor to *New Catholic Encyclopedia* and to *Proceedings* of the American Catholic Philosophical Association; contributor of over forty-five articles and reviews to philosophy journals.

WORK IN PROGRESS: Research on American philosophy, medieval Arabian philosophy and on the history of women philosophers.

SIDELIGHTS: Beatrice Zedler writes: ''Since my primary

career is teaching, most of my time has been spent on tasks directly related to work in the classroom. I see my writing as another mode of teaching: a way of sharing with others the results of my thought and research.''

*   *   *

ZEDLER, Empress Young 1908-

PERSONAL: Born November 9, 1908, in Abilene, Tex.; married Paul Louis Zedler, June 5, 1928; children: one. *Education:* University of Texas, B.A., 1928, M.A., 1950, Ph.D., 1953. *Address:* P.O. Box 465, Luling, Tex. 78648. *Office:* Speech, Hearing and Language Clinic, Southwest Texas State University, San Marcos, Tex. 78666.

CAREER: Southwest Texas State University, San Marcos, instructor, 1948-49, assistant professor, 1949-51, associate professor of speech correction, 1952-56, professor of special education, 1956—, chairman of department, 1962-77, director of Speech, Hearing and Language Clinic, 1977—. Consulting psychologist and speech and language pathologist. Member of committee to study standards for teacher certification in Texas, 1969—; delegate to White House Conference on Children, 1970. *Member:* American Psychological Association, American Speech and Hearing Association (fellow), Academy of Aphasia, American Academy of Cerebral Palsy, American Congress of Rehabilitative Medicine, Association for Children with Learning Disabilities, Texas Psychological Association, Texas Speech and Hearing Association, Daughters of the American Revolution, Phi Beta Kappa, Alpha Delta Pi.

WRITINGS: Listening for Speech Sounds, Harper, 1955; *International Approach to Learning Disabilities of Children and Youth,* Association for Children with Learning Disabilities, 1966; *Research Conference on the Problems of Dyslexia and Related Disorders in Public Schools of the United States,* Southwest Texas State College, 1967; *Educational Programming for Pupils with Neurologically Based Language Disorders,* U.S. Office of Education, 1968; (contributor) Eloise Calkins, editor, *Reading Forum* (monograph), U.S. Department of Health, Education, & Welfare, Public Health Service, 1970; (contributor) John Irwin and Michael Marge, editors, *Principles of Childhood Language Disabilities,* Appleton, 1972. Contributor to education journals.

WORK IN PROGRESS: Methods and Materials for Children with Language Disabilities.

*   *   *

ZEEVELD, W(illiam) Gordon   1902-1975

PERSONAL: Born February 20, 1902, in Rochester, N.Y.; son of William and Laura Alida (Waleson) Zeeveld; married Margaret Ford Jewell, September 9, 1937; children: William Buhr, Martha Maria (Mrs. I. William Jackson), David Gordon, Schuyler Ford. *Education:* University of Rochester, A.B., 1924; Johns Hopkins University, M.A., 1933, Ph.D., 1936. *Politics:* Democrat. *Religion:* Dutch Reformed Church in America. *Home address:* Deep Meadow, Woodbine, Md. 21797.

CAREER: Rice Institute (now Rice University), Houston, Tex., instructor in English, 1929-32; Choate School, Wallingford, Conn., instructor in English, 1934; Northwestern University, Evanston, Ill., instructor in English, 1935-36; University of Maryland, College Park, assistant professor, 1937-48, associate professor, 1949-54, professor of English, 1955-72, professor emeritus, 1972-75. Johns Hopkins University, Evening College, professor of English, beginning

1956. Lecturer, Oxford University, 1961; visiting professor, University of Wisconsin, summer, 1965; lecturer, Institute for Advanced Study in English, 1966. Author and narrator of ''Three Worlds of William Shakespeare,'' WRC-Television. Speaker for documentary films by University of Maryland, 1959, and Folger Shakespeare Library, 1968. Delegate to International Shakespeare Conference, 1964, 1966. Lecturer, World Shakespeare Congress, 1971, and St. Thomas More Symposium, 1971; moderator, Fourth Annual Conference on Contemporary Literary Criticism, 1962; member of national committee, Shakespeare Quartracentennial Celebration, 1964. Member of award committee, Pittsburgh Plate Glass Foundation, beginning 1963. *Member:* Modern Language Association of America, Renaissance Society of America, Conference of British Studies, Royal Historical Society (fellow), Amici Thomae Mori, American Historical Association, Shakespeare Association of America, Shakespeare Society of Washington (honorary member), Cosmos Club (Washington, D.C.), Tudor and Stuart Club.

WRITINGS: Foundations of Tudor Policy, Harvard University Press, 1948, revised edition, Methuen, 1969; (author of introduction) Elizabeth Nugent, editor, *Thought and Culture of the English Renaissance,* Cambridge University Press, 1956; *The Temper of Shakespeare's Thought,* Yale University Press, 1974. Contributor to American, French, and British professional journals. Member of advisory council, *Shakespeare Research Opportunities.*

WORK IN PROGRESS: Edward Hall: Tudor Historian; ''Shakespeare in Two Media: Stage to Page,'' a sixty-minute television series.

BIOGRAPHICAL/CRITICAL SOURCES: Carl Purcell, *Teach Me!: A Photographic Essay on the Joys and Challenges of Teaching and Learning,* National Education Association, 1966.†

(Died July 19, 1975)

*   *   *

ZEGGER, Robert Elie   1932-

PERSONAL: Born April 9, 1932, in New York, N.Y.; son of Bernard and Yvonne (Quidort) Zegger; married Hrisey D. Dimitrakis (a writer), July 3, 1965; children: Anthony Dimitri. *Education:* Columbia University, B.A., 1953, M.A., 1957, Ph.D., 1965. *Home:* 626 Gregory Ave., Wilmette, Ill. 60091. *Office:* Department of History, Northeastern Illinois University, Chicago, Ill. 60625.

CAREER: State University of New York College at New Paltz, assistant professor of history, 1962-66; Northeastern Illinois University, Chicago, assistant professor, 1966-67, associate professor, 1967-70, professor of history, 1970—. *Military service:* U.S. Army, 1954-56. *Member:* American Historical Association, Conference on British Studies, French Historical Society. *Awards, honors:* New York State research grant, 1964-66; Northeastern Illinois University COR grant, 1976-77.

WRITINGS: John Cam Hobhouse: A Political Life, 1819-1852, University of Missouri Press, 1973. Contributor to *Encyclopaedia of English Radicals.* Contributor to *History Today.*

WORK IN PROGRESS: Victorians and Imperial Frenchmen: 1850-1870; Society and Satire; research on philanthropic societies in England and France.

AVOCATIONAL INTERESTS: Travel, music, woodworking.

ZELLNER, Arnold 1927-

PERSONAL: Born January 2, 1927, in New York, N.Y.; son of Israel (a businessman) and Doris (Kleiman) Zellner; married Agnes M. Sumares (a social worker), June 20, 1953; children: David, Philip, Samuel, Daniel, Michael. *Education:* Harvard University, A.B., 1949; University of California, Berkeley, Ph.D., 1957. *Home:* 5628 South Dorchester Ave., Chicago, Ill. 60637. *Office:* Graduate School of Business, University of Chicago, Chicago, Ill. 60637.

CAREER: University of Washington, Seattle, assistant professor, 1955-59, associate professor of economics, 1959-60; University of Wisconsin—Madison, associate professor, 1961-63, professor of economics, 1963-66; University of Chicago, Chicago, Ill., H.G.B. Alexander Professor of Economics and Statistics, 1966—, director of H.G.B. Alexander Research Foundation, 1972—. Fulbright visiting professor at Netherlands School of Economics, Rotterdam, 1960-61. *Military service:* U.S. Army, 1951-53. *Member:* American Statistical Association (fellow), Econometric Society (fellow; member of council), American Economic Association.

WRITINGS: (Editor) *Readings in Economic Statistics and Econometrics,* Little, Brown, 1968; (with H. R. Hamilton, S. E. Goldstone, J. W. Milliman, A. L. Pugh, and E. R. Roberts) *Systems Simulation for Regional Analysis,* Massachusetts Institute of Technology, 1969; *An Introduction to Bayesian Inference in Econometrics,* Wiley, 1971. Co-editor of *Studies in Bayesian Econometrics and Statistics in Honor of L. J. Savage.* Contributor to professional journals. Associate editor, *Econometrica,* 1963-66, *Journal of Economic Literature,* 1971—; co-editor, *Journal of Econometrics,* 1972—.

* * *

ZETTL, Herbert (Lorenz) 1929-

PERSONAL: Born July 15, 1929, in Augsburg, Germany; came to United States in 1950, naturalized citizen in 1963; son of Carl and Anna (Baudrexl) Zettl; married Erika Irene Tronicke (a teacher), July 18, 1953; children: Renee Anabella, Alexander Karlwalter. *Education:* Attended University of Munich, 1952; Stanford University, A.B., 1953, M.A., 1956; University of California, Berkeley, Ph.D., 1966. *Address:* P.O. Box 91, Forest Knolls, Calif. 94933. *Office:* Broadcast Communication Arts Department, San Francisco State University, 1600 Holloway, San Francisco, Calif. 94132.

CAREER: Neue Kaufbeurer Zeitung, Kaufbeuren, Germany, reporter, 1949-50; KOVR-Television, Stockton, Calif., stage manager, 1954; KPIX-Television (affiliate of Columbia Broadcasting System), San Francisco, Calif., producer-director, 1954-59; San Francisco State University, San Francisco, Calif., assistant professor, 1959-63, associate professor, 1963-67, professor of broadcast communication arts, 1967—, television coordinator, 1961-71, director of Center for Production Development and Research in Television, 1967-73.

MEMBER: National Association of Educational Broadcasters, Broadcast Educators of America, Intercontinental Biographical Association. *Awards, honors:* Merit and purchase awards for painting from San Francisco Art Commission, 1956, 1958; distinguished teaching award, California State Legislature, 1966.

WRITINGS: Television Production Handbook, Wadsworth, 1961, 3rd edition, 1976; *Television Production Work-*book, Wadsworth, 1964, 3rd edition, 1977; (graphic adviser) Hans P. Guth and Edgar H. Schuster, *American English Today,* McGraw, 1970; *Sight, Sound, Motion: Applied Media Aesthetics,* Wadsworth, 1973. Contributor to professional journals, including *Journal of Broadcasting, Western Speech, Educational/Instructional Broadcasting, Educational Broadcasting Review, Audio-Visual Instruction,* and *Journal of the University Film Association.*

WORK IN PROGRESS: Research in the areas of vector theory as applied to media aesthetics, new production approaches to educational/instructional television, new television dramaturgy, and multi-screen television.

AVOCATIONAL INTERESTS: International travel, mountain climbing, music (plays violin and viola), painting.

* * *

ZGUSTA, Ladislav 1924-

PERSONAL: Born March 20, 1924, in Czechoslovakia; son of Ladislav (a lawyer) and Sona (Bernasova) Zgusta; married Olga Janouskova, April 10, 1948; children: Monika, Richard. *Education:* University of Prague, Ph.D., 1949; Prague Academy, Dr. Sc., 1964. *Religion:* Roman Catholic. *Home:* 115 West Michigan, Urbana, Ill. 61801. *Office:* Department of Linguistics, University of Illinois, Urbana, Ill. 61801.

CAREER: University of Prague and Prague Academy, Prague, Czechoslovakia, member of faculty, 1949-65; Brno University, Brno, Czechoslovakia, professor of Indo-European comparative linguistics, 1968-70; University of Illinois at Urbana-Champaign, associate of Center for Advanced Study, 1968-70, professor of linguistics and classics, 1971—, member of Center for Advanced Study, 1973—. Academy of Sciences, Oriental Institute, Prague, deputy director, 1954-58, head of department of lexicography, 1959-67, head of section of linguistics, 1959-70. Member of Illinois Place Names Committee, 1971—, and Committee on Application of Computers in Humanities, 1972—. Consultant to Czech Academy of Sciences, 1959-67, and German Academy of Sciences, 1964-70.

MEMBER: Linguistic Society of America, American Name Society (honorary member), Indogermanische Gesellschaft, Societa linguistica Italiana. *Awards, honors:* Research grant, National Science Council, Prague, 1949; prize from Czech Academy of Sciences, 1955, for *Die Personennamen griechischer Staedte;* grants from Czech Academy of Sciences for field research in the Caucasus, 1956, 1963; prize from Czech Academy of Sciences, 1964, for *Kleinasiatische Personennamen;* research grants, Conseil international de la philosophie et des sciences humaines, Paris, 1965, 1969; research grants, Deutsche Forschungsgemeinschaft, Bonn, 1969, 1970, 1971, 1972, 1973; Guggenheim fellowship, 1977.

WRITINGS: Die Personennamen griechischer Staedte der noerdlichen Schwarzemeerkueste (title means "Personal Names in the Greek Cities of the Black Sea"), Academia (Prague), 1955; (contributor) J. Irmscher, editor, *Griechische Staedte und einheimische Voelker des Schwarzmeergebietes* (title means "Greek Cities and the Indigenous Nations of the Black Sea Region"), [Berlin], 1961; *Kleinasiatische Personennamen* (title means "Personal Names of Asia Minor"), Academia, 1964; *Anatolische Personennamensippen* (title means "Groups of Anatolian Personal Names"), Academia, 1964; (contributor) *Lingvisticeskaja tipologija i vostocnyje jazyki* (title means "Linguistic Typology and the Oriental Languages"), [Moscow], 1965; *Neue Beitraege zur kleinasiatischen Anthroponymie* (title means "New Data in the Anthroponymy of Asia Minor"), Academia, 1970; (contributor) K. Riemschneider, editor, *Probleme der Lexikographie* (title means "Problems of Lexicography"), [Berlin], 1970; *Manual of Lexicography*, Mouton, 1971. Also author of *Kleinasiatische Ortsnamen* (title means "Place Names of Asia Minor"), Harrassowitz, and contributor to *Symbolae Kurylowicz* (title means "K.'s Honorary Volume"); contributor to bulletins, annals, and proceedings, and to *Zeitschrift fuer Phonetik, Sprachwiss, und Kommunikationsforschung*. Contributor of about seventy-five articles to professional journals abroad, including *Eastern World*. Executive editor, *Archiv orientalni*, 1955-70; chief editor, *Dissertationes orientales*, 1964-70.

*   *   *

ZIGLER, Edward F(rank) 1930-

PERSONAL: Born March 1, 1930, in Kansas City, Mo.; son of Louis and Gertrude (Gleitman) Zigler; married Bernice Gorelick (a psychologist), August 28, 1955; children: Perrin. *Education:* University of Missouri at Kansas City, B.A., 1954; University of Texas, Ph.D., 1958. *Home:* 177 Ridgewood Ave., Hamden, Conn. *Office address:* P.O. Box 11A, Yale Station, New Haven, Conn. 06520.

CAREER: Missouri State Hospital, St. Joseph, staff psychologist, summers, 1954-55; University of Texas, Main University (now University of Texas at Austin), Texas Child Guidance Clinic, staff psychologist, 1956-57; Worcester State Hospital, Worcester, Mass., psychological intern, 1957-58; University of Missouri—Columbia, assistant professor of psychology and director of Child Diagnostic Center, 1958-59; Yale University, New Haven, Conn., assistant professor, 1959-63, associate professor, 1963-67, professor of psychology, 1967—, Sterling Professor of Psychology, 1976—, chairman of department, 1973-74, director of Child Development Program, 1961-73, director of Bush Center in Child Development and Social Policy, 1977—. Director of Office of Child Development and chief of Children's Bureau, U.S. Department of Health, Education & Welfare, 1970-72. Member of national planning committee of Operation Follow-Through, U.S. Office of Education; member of national steering committee and national research council of Project Head Start, U.S. Office of Economic Opportunity; member of research council and governing council and member of steering committee of task force on psychosocial deprivation, National Institute of Child Health and Human Development; member of national evaluation panel on Program in Psychiatry, Neurology, and Psychology and member of behavioral sciences research evaluation committee, National Veterans Administration; member of national advisory committee, National Laboratory for Early Childhood Education; member of national advisory board, Educational Resources Information Center Clearinghouse on Early Childhood Education; member of board of directors, Day Care and Child Development Council of America, Inc. *Military service:* U.S. Army, 1951-53.

MEMBER: American Psychological Association (fellow), Society for Research in Child Development, American Academy on Mental Retardation, National Association for Retarded Children, Psychonomic Society, American Orthopsychiatric Association (fellow), American Association for the Advancement of Science (fellow), Sigma Xi. *Awards, honors:* Social Science Auxiliary research award, 1962; Gunnar Dybwad Distinguished Scholar Award in the Behavioral Sciences from National Association for Retarded Children, 1964; National Institute of Mental Health grant, 1964-67; National Institute of Child Health and Human Development grant, 1967—; M.A., Yale University, 1967; U.S. Office of Economic Opportunity grant, 1967-68; American Association on Mental Deficiency research award, 1977.

WRITINGS: (With Irvin L. Child) *Socialization and Personality Development*, Addison-Wesley, 1972; (with G. Kimble and N. Garmezy) *Principles of General Psychology*, Ronald, 1974; (editor with J. Valentine) *America's Head Start: A Legacy to the War on Poverty*, Free Press, in press. Also author, with R. Yando and V. Seitz, of *Imitation: A Developmental Perspective*.

Contributor: R. K. Wilcox, editor, *Strategies for Behavioral Research in Mental Retardation*, University of Wisconsin Press, 1961; Melvin Marx, editor, *Psychological Theory*, 2nd edition (Zigler was not associated with earlier edition), Macmillan, 1963; Lewis P. Lipsitt and Davis S. Palermo, editors, *Research Readings in Child Psychology*, Holt, 1963; Melvin Zax and George Stricker, editors, *The Study of Abnormal Behavior*, Macmillan, 1964; Ohmer Milton, editor, *Behavior Disorders: Perspectives and Trends*, Lippincott, 1965; M. L. Hoffman and L. W. Hoffman, editors, *Review of Child Development Research*, Volume II, Russell Sage, 1966; N. R. Ellis, editor, *International Review of Research in Mental Retardation*, Volume I, Academic Press, 1966; J. A. Dyal, editor, *Readings in Psychology: Understanding Human Behavior*, McGraw, 1967; Stella Chess and Alexander Thomas, editors, *Annual Progress in Child Psychiatry and Child Development: Selected Readings*, Robert Brunner, 1968, 1969, 1971; Perry London and David Rosenhan, editors, *Foundations of Abnormal Psychology*, Holt, 1968; Gardner Lindzey and Elliot Aronson, editors, *The Handbook of Social Psychology*, 2nd edition (Zigler was not associated with earlier edition), Addison-Wesley, 1969; D. A. Goslin, editor, *Handbook of Socialization Theory and Research*, Rand McNally, 1969; Jacob Levine, editor, *Motivation in Humor*, Atherton, 1969; H. C. Lindgren, editor, *Contemporary Research in Social Psychology*, Wiley, 1969.

Melvin Marx, editor, *Learning: Interactions*, Macmillan, 1970; Robert Koch and J. C. Dobson, editors, *The Mentally Retarded Child and His Family: A Multidisciplinary Journal*, Academic Press, 1970; H. Carl Haywood, editor, *Social-Cultural Aspects of Mental Retardation*, Appleton, 1970; Freda Rebelsky and Lynn Dorman, editors, *Child Development and Behavior*, Knopf, 1970; Elliott M. McGinnies and C. B. Ferster, editors, *The Reinforcement of Social Behavior: Selected Readings*, Houghton, 1971; E. M. Bower, editor, *Education and Orthopsychiatry*, Wayne State University Press, 1971; R. L. Jones, editor, *Problems and Issues in the Education of Exceptional Children*, Houghton, 1971; H. E. Adams and W. K. Boardman III, editors, *Advances in Experimental Clinical Psychology*, Volume I, Pergamon, 1971; Edward Trapp and Philip Himelstein, editors, *Readings on the Exceptional Child: Research and Theory*, 2nd edition (Zigler was not associated with earlier edition), Appleton, 1972; Celia S. Lavatelli, editor, *Readings in Child Behavior and Development*, 3rd edition (Zigler was not associated with earlier editions), Harcourt, 1972; J. F. Rosenblith, Wesley Allinsmith, and J. P. Williams, editors, *Readings in Educational Psychology: Causes of Behavior*, Allyn & Bacon, 1972.

Contributor to proceedings, reports, and bulletins; contributor to *International Encyclopedia of the Social Sciences*. Contributor of about one hundred articles to psychology, education, and child development journals. Consulting editor, *Journal of Experimental Child Psychology* and *Journal of Experimental Research in Personality;* member of editorial board, *International Review of Research in Mental Retardation.*

* * *

ZIMILES, Martha Rogers 1946-

PERSONAL: Born January 14, 1946, in Portland, Ore.; daughter of Talbot Mercer (an artist and architect) and Janet (Young) Rogers; married Murray Zimiles (an artist and professor), May 23, 1970. *Education:* Sarah Lawrence College, B.A., 1968. *Home:* R.F.D. 1, Millerton, N.Y. 12546.

CAREER: Writer, needlework designer, weaver, and fiber artist. *Member:* International Arthurian Society, Association for Research and Enlightenment, Society for Industrial Archaeology, Society for Preservation of Old Mills, American Crafts Council, Handweavers Guild of America, Embroiderers Guild of America, Fiberarts Guild (founding member).

WRITINGS: (With husband, Murray Zimiles) *Early American Mills,* C. N. Potter, 1973; *A Treasury of Needlework Design,* Van Nostrand, 1976.

WORK IN PROGRESS: *The Complete Book of Design for Needlepoint Canvas.*

SIDELIGHTS: Martha Zimiles has spent a total of three years living in Europe. She is fluent in French and competent in Italian. *Avocational interests:* Gardening, travel, crafts, folklore, extrasensory phenomena, world religions, music, folk medicine, art.

* * *

ZIMILES, Murray 1941-

PERSONAL: Born November 30, 1941, in New York, N.Y.; son of Joseph and Eugenia (Margolis) Zimiles; married Martha Rogers (an author), May 23, 1970. *Education:* University of Illinois, B.F.A., 1963; Cornell University, M.F.A., 1965; also attended Ecole Nationale Superieure des Beaux-Arts, 1965-66. *Home:* R.F.D. 1, Millerton, N.Y. 12546. *Office:* Department of Art, State University of New York College, Purchase, N.Y. 10577.

CAREER: Silvermine College of Art, Silvermine, Conn., assistant professor of art, 1968-71, chairman of department of graphics, 1969-71; State University of New York College at New Paltz, assistant professor of art, 1972-76; State University of New York College at Purchase, associate professor of art, 1976—. Instructor at Pratt Graphics Center, 1968-72; guest lecturer at Herbert H. Lehman College of the City University of New York, 1971-72; director of Silvermine-Lacoste School of Art (Lacoste, Vaucluse, France), 1972—. Work exhibited in one-man and group shows in Paris, London, Santiago, Oslo, and New York, and at Brooklyn Museum, 1970, Zingale Gallery, 1971, Sindin Gallery, 1978, and Vassar College, 1978. *Member:* Society for Industrial Archaeology, Society for Preservation of Old Mills. *Awards, honors:* Harriet Hale Wooley Foundation fellowship, Paris, 1965; Royal Norwegian Government fellowship, Oslo, 1971.

WRITINGS: (With Michael Knigin) *The Technique of Fine Art Lithography,* Van Nostrand, 1970; (with wife, Martha Zimiles) *Early American Mills,* C. N. Potter, 1973. Also author of *Lithography: Lithographic Workshops around the World,* Van Nostrand. Has published folios of his own lithographs, including "Yum Yum Suite" and "Elliot Suite," in 1967, "Avis Librus" and "Bestiary," in 1968.

WORK IN PROGRESS: Boris, a novel.

BIOGRAPHICAL/CRITICAL SOURCES: Artist Proof (annual), 1971.

* * *

ZORNOW, William Frank 1920-

PERSONAL: Surname is pronounced Zor-noh; born August 13, 1920, in Cleveland, Ohio; son of William Frederick Emil (a businessman) and Viola Sophia (Schulz) Zornow. *Education:* Western Reserve University (now Case Western Reserve University), A.B., 1942, M.A., 1944, Ph.D., 1952. *Religion:* Lutheran. *Home:* 7893 Middlesex Rd., Mentor, Ohio 44060. *Office:* 305 Bowman Hall, Kent State University, Kent, Ohio 44242.

CAREER: Deputy clerk of probate court in Cuyahoga County, Ohio, 1941-43; Hickok Electrical Instrument Co., Cleveland, Ohio, production planning engineer, 1943-46; University of Akron, Akron, Ohio, instructor in history, 1946-47; Case Institute of Technology (now Case Western Reserve University), Cleveland, Ohio, instructor in history, 1947-50; Washburn University, Topeka, Kan., instructor in history and political science, 1950-51; Kansas State University, Manhattan, assistant professor of history and general studies, 1951-58; Kent State University, Kent, Ohio, assistant professor, 1958-61, associate professor, 1961-66, professor of history, 1966—. Special lecturer in history, Cleveland College, 1948-49. Vice-president of Glenville Coal & Supply Co., Real Value Coal Corp., and Zornow Coal Co., 1940-45.

MEMBER: American Academy of Political and Social Science, American Association for State and Local History, American Historical Association, Organization of American Historians, Ohio Academy of History, Pi Gamma Mu, Phi Alpha Theta, Phi Delta Kappa. *Awards, honors:* Award of merit from American Association for State and Local History, 1958, for *Kansas: A History of the Jayhawk State.*

WRITINGS: Lincoln and the Party Divided, University of Oklahoma Press, 1954; (contributor) John Bright, editor, *Kansas: The First Century,* four volumes, Lewis Historical Publishing, 1956; *Kansas: A History of the Jayhawk State,* University of Oklahoma Press, 1957; *America at Mid-Century,* Howard Allen, 1959; (contributor) Henry Kranz, editor, *Abraham Lincoln: A New Portrait,* Putnam, 1959. Contributor of more than six hundred abstracts to *America: History and Life* and *Historical Abstracts;* contributor to encyclopedias and to professional journals.

WORK IN PROGRESS: 1933-1972: Years of Depression, War, and Affluence, for Ohio Historical Society; *Harry S Truman: From Political Action to Police Action,* two volumes, for University of Oklahoma Press.

AVOCATIONAL INTERESTS: Collecting books on Lincoln and the Civil War and on oriental art.

* * *

ZUCKERMAN, Arthur J(acob) 1907-

PERSONAL: Born December 16, 1907, in Brooklyn, N.Y.; son of Charles (a garment worker) and Mollie (Hittner) Zuckerman; married Janet Goren; children: (previous marriage) Anne Vivian (Mrs. Shimshon Crystal), Judith (Mrs. Jay D. Bloom), Sharon. *Education:* City College (now City College of the City University of New York), B.A., 1928; Hebrew Union College—Jewish Institute of Religion, Rabbi, 1931; Columbia University, Ph.D., 1963. *Home:* 375 Riverside Dr., New York, N.Y. 10025.

CAREER: Henry Morgenthau, Jr. Scholar at Hebrew University of Jerusalem, Jerusalem, Israel, 1931-33, and University of Vienna, Vienna, Austria, 1933-36; rabbi in Winston-Salem, N.C., 1936-38, and Lansing, Mich., 1938-40; University of Washington, Seattle, founder and director of B'nai B'rith Hillel Foundation, 1940-45; City College of the City University of New York, New York, N.Y., lecturer in history, 1946-68, adjunct associate professor of history, 1968-74, adjunct professor of Jewish studies, 1973-74, director of B'nai B'rith Hillel Foundation, 1945-74; Reconstructionist Rabbinical College, Philadelphia, Pa., professor and director of medieval studies, 1970—. Instructor in Jewish history and religion, Hebrew Union School of Education and Sacred Music, New York, 1952-70; visiting professor, Institut International d'Etudes Hebraiques, Paris, 1956.

MEMBER: American Historical Association, International Association of Hillel Directors, National Association of Hillel Directors (president, 1955-57), Mediaeval Academy of America, National Association for Jewish Studies, Religious Education Association (president of New York City branch, 1959-60), Central Conference of American Rabbis. *Awards, honors:* Henry J. Morgenthau, Jr. traveling fellowship, 1931-36; Lewis Rabinowitz fellowship, 1956, for research in France; D.D., Hebrew Union College—Jewish Institute of Religion, 1957; Jewish Book Council award, 1973, for *A Jewish Princedom in Feudal France, 768-900.*

WRITINGS: *A Jewish Princedom in Feudal France, 768-900,* Columbia University Press, 1972.

Contributor: Joseph L. Blau and others, editors, *Essays on Jewish Life and Thought: Presented in Honor of Salo W. Baron,* Columbia University Press, 1959; S. A. Burrell, editor, *The Role of Religion in Modern European History,* Macmillan, 1964; *Dimensions of Jewish Existence Today,* B'nai B'rith Hillel Foundations, 1964; John R. Sommerfeldt, editor, *Studies in Medieval Culture,* Volume III, Western Michigan University, 1970; Saul Lieberman, Arthur Hyman, and others, *Jubilee Volume for S. W. Baron,* American Academy for Jewish Research, 1975. Member of editorial board, *Reconstructionist,* 1953—.

WORK IN PROGRESS: Research on the impact of social change on woman's status in the medieval Jewish community.

SIDELIGHTS: Arthur Zuckerman has lectured in German, French, and Hebrew, in addition to English. His most extensive research has been conducted in major state archives of Austria and France.

*   *   *

ZURCHER, Louis A(nthony), Jr. 1936-

PERSONAL: Born May 13, 1936, in San Francisco, Calif.; son of Louis Anthony (a grocer) and Kathleen (Walsh) Zurcher; married Susan Lee Shrum (a social worker), September 13, 1964; children: Anthony Walsh, Nora Breen. *Education:* University of San Francisco, B.A. (summa cum laude), 1961; University of Arizona, M.A., 1963, Ph.D., 1965. *Office:* Graduate School, Burruss Hall, Virginia Polytechnic Institute and State University, Blacksburg, Va. 24061.

CAREER: Menninger Foundation, Topeka, Kan., research social psychologist, 1965-68; University of Texas at Austin, assistant professor, 1968-69, associate professor, 1969-73, professor of sociology, 1973-78, chairperson of department, 1974-75, associate graduate dean, 1975-78; Virginia Poly-

technic Institute and State University, Blacksburg, professor of sociology, associate university provost, and dean of graduate school, 1978—. Western Behavioral Sciences Institute, La Jolla, Calif., adjunct research associate, 1969-73, research social psychologist, 1971-73; adjunct professor, Union Graduate School, Antioch College, 1970-78. Consultant to U.S. Office of Economic Opportunity, 1966-69, Hogg Foundation for Mental Health, 1968-72, and other agencies, nonprofit research institutions, and universities. *Military service:* U.S. Navy, 1955-59; became petty officer. U.S. Naval Reserve, 1971—; present rank, lieutenant commander.

MEMBER: American Sociological Association (fellow), American Psychological Association (fellow), Society for the Study of Social Problems (fellow; chairman of section on poverty and human resources, 1968-71), Midwest Sociological Association, Southwestern Sociological Association, Southern Sociological Society, Phi Beta Kappa, Sigma Xi, Alpha Kappa Delta, Psi Chi. *Awards, honors:* Abraham Maslow visiting fellow at Western Behavioral Sciences Insitute, 1971-72; research grants from U.S. Public Health Service, U.S. Office of Economic Opportunity, Menninger Foundation, Hogg Foundation, National Institute of Mental Health, and other agencies.

WRITINGS: *The Leader and the Lost: A Case Study of Indigenous Leadership in a Poverty Program Community Action Committee,* Genetic Psychology Monographs, 1967; (with Alvin E. Green) *From Dependency to Dignity: Some Individual and Social Consequences of a Neighborhood House,* Behavioral Publications, 1969; *Poverty Warriors: The Human Experience of Planned Social Intervention,* University of Texas Press, 1970; (with James B. Taylor and William H. Key) *Tornado: A Community Responds to Disaster,* University of Washington Press, 1970; (editor with Charles M. Bonjean and contributor) *Planned Social Intervention: A Cross-Disciplinary Anthology,* Chandler Publishing, 1970; (with Rosemary J. Erickson and Wayman J. Crow) *Changes in Pockets of Poverty,* Western Behavioral Sciences Institute, 1970; (with others) *The Offender Looks at His Own Needs,* Behavioral Publications, 1973; (with R. George Kirkpatrick) *Citizens for Decency: Anti-Pornography Crusades as Status Defense,* University of Texas Press, 1976; *The Mutable Self: A Self-Concept for Social Change,* Sage Publications, 1977. Also author, with Gwyn Harries, of *Supplementary Military Forces: Reserves, Militias, and Auxiliaries,* 1978. Co-author of four technical reports of the Commission on Obscenity and Pornography, U.S. Government Printing Office, 1971.

Contributor: Milton F. Shore and Fortune B. Mannino, editors, *Community Mental Health: Problems, Programs, and Strategies,* Behavioral Publications, 1969; Robert O'Brien and others, editors, *Readings in General Sociology,* Houghton, 1969. Contributor to about twenty-five other volumes of sociological studies and readings.

Contributor of articles to more than thirty professional journals, including *British Journal of Social Psychiatry.* Consulting editor, *Journal of Applied Behavioral Science,* 1968-71, member of editorial board, 1971-74; advisory editor, *Social Science Quarterly,* 1968-74; advisory editor, *Sociological Symposium,* 1973—; advisory editor, *Sociology of Deviance,* 1978—.

WORK IN PROGRESS: *Collective Behavior: Encounters with Uncertainty and Change,* with David Snow; *Social Problems and Human Responses,* with Louis Schneider, Cookie Stephan, and Sheldon Olson.